Small Business Sourcebook

ISSN 0883-3397

Small Business Sourcebook

The Entrepreneur's Resource

FORTY-SECOND EDITION

Volume 2

Specific Small Business Profiles

(Entries 8086-16529)

Holly M. Selden
Project Editor

Small Business Sourcebook, 42nd edition

Project Editor: Holly M. Selden

Editorial Support Services: Pranav Kokate

Composition and Electronic Prepress:
  Carolyn Roney

Manufacturing: Rita Wimberley

For product information and technology assistance, contact us at
Gale Customer Support, 1-800-877-4253.
For permission to use material from this text or product,
submit all requests online at **www.cengage.com/permissions**.
Further permissions questions can be emailed to
permissionrequest@cengage.com.

Gale, part of Cengage Group
5191 Natorp Blvd.
Mason, OH 45040

978-1-5358-7663-6 (set)
978-1-5358-7664-3 (vol. 1)
978-1-5358-7665-0 (vol. 2)
978-1-5358-7666-7 (vol. 3)
978-1-5358-7667-4 (vol. 4)
978-1-5358-7668-1 (vol. 5)
978-1-5358-7669-8 (vol. 6)

ISSN 0883-3397

This title is also available as an e-book.
978-1-5358-7670-4
Contact your Gale sales representative for ordering information.

Contents

The appeal of small business ownership remains perpetually entrenched in American culture as one of the most viable avenues for achieving the American Dream. To many entrepreneurs, going into business for themselves represents financial independence, an increased sense of identity and self-worth, and the fulfillment of personal goals. Small business owners strive to make their mark in today's competitive marketplace by establishing healthy businesses that can, over time, become legacies handed down from one generation to the next. Entrepreneurs from each generation tackle the obstacles and adversities of the current business and economic climate to test their business savvy and generate opportunities. Today's entrepreneurs face many of the problems of their predecessors, as well as some distinctly new challenges.

With the rightsizing, downsizing, and reorganization of corporate America, many individuals have decided to confront the risks of developing and operating their own businesses. Small business ownership is rapidly becoming a viable alternative to what is perceived as an equally unstable corporate environment. These entrepreneurs, many of whom have firsthand experience with the problems and inefficiencies inherent in today's large corporations, seek to improve upon an archaic business model and to capitalize on their own ingenuity and strengths. Led by their zeal, many would-be entrepreneurs let their desire, drive, and determination overshadow the need for business knowledge and skill. Ironically, aids in obtaining these components of entrepreneurial success are widely available, easily accessible, and often free of charge.

Small Business Sourcebook (*SBS*) is a six-volume annotated guide to nearly 17,000 listings of live and print sources of information designed to facilitate the start-up, development, and growth of specific small businesses, as well as more than 19,500 similar listings on general small business topics. An additional 12,500 state-specific listings and nearly 1,100 U.S. federal government agencies and offices specializing in small business issues, programs, and assistance are also included. *SBS* covers more than 300 specific small business profiles more than 100 general small business topics.

Features of This Edition

This edition of *Small Business Sourcebook* has been revised and updated, incorporating thousands of changes to names, addresses, contacts, and descriptions of listings from the previous edition. We have also added several hundred podcasts that will help users better understand topics on entrepreneurship and small business ownership.

Contents and Arrangement

The geographical scope of *SBS* encompasses the United States and Canada, with expanded coverage for resources pertaining to international trade and for resources that have a U.S. or Canadian distributor or contact. Internet sites that are maintained outside of the U.S. and Canada are also included if they contain relevant information for North American small businesses. Resources that do not relate specifically to small businesses are generally not included.

The information presented in *SBS* is grouped within four sections: Specific Small Business Profiles, General Small Business Topics, State Listings, and Federal Government Assistance. Detailed outlines of these sections may be found in the Users' Guide following this Introduction. Also included is a Master Index to Volumes 1 through 6.

Specific Small Business Profiles This section includes the following types of resources: start-up information, associations and other organizations, educational programs, directories of educational programs, reference works, sources of supply, statistical sources, trade periodicals, videos and podcasts, trade shows and conventions, consultants, franchises, and business opportunities, computerized databases, computer systems/software, Internet databases, libraries, and research centers. All resources are arranged by business type. Entries range from Accounting Service to Word Processing Service, and include such businesses as Cannabis Dispensaries, Computer Consulting, Food Trucks, and Web Site Design.

General Small Business Topics This section offers such resources as associations, books, periodicals, articles, pamphlets, educational programs, directories of educational programs, trade shows and conventions, consultants, computerized databases, Internet databases, software, libraries, and research centers. All resources in this section are arranged alphabetically by business topic.

State Listings Entries include government, academic, and commercial agencies and organizations, as well as select coverage of relevant state-specific publications. Listings are arranged alphabetically by state, territory, and Canadian province. Some examples include small business development consultants, SCORE offices, financing and loan programs, better business bureaus, and chambers of commerce.

Federal Government Assistance Listings Entries include federal organizations and agencies specializing in small business issues, programs, assistance, and policy. Listings are arranged alphabetically by U.S. government agency or office; regional or branch offices are listed alphabetically by state.

Master Index All entries in Volumes 1 through 6 are arranged in one alphabetic index for convenience.

Entries in *SBS* include (as appropriate and available):

- Organization, institution, or product name
- Contact information, including contact name, address and phone, toll-free, and fax numbers
- Author/editor, date(s), and frequency
- Availability, including price
- Brief description of purpose, services, or content
- Company and/or personal E-mail addresses
- Web site addresses

SBS also features the following:

Guide to Publishers—An alphabetic listing of nearly 1,000 companies, associations, institutions, and individuals that publish the periodicals, directories, guidebooks, and other publications noted in the Small Business Profiles and General Topics sections. Users are provided with full contact information, including address, phone, fax, and e-mail and URL when available. The Guide to Publishers facilitates contact with publishers and provides a one-stop resource for valuable information.

Method of Compilation

SBS was compiled by consulting small business experts and entrepreneurs, as well as a variety of resources, including direct contact with the associations, organizations, and agencies through Internet research or materials provided by those listees; government resources; and data obtained from other relevant Gale directories. *SBS* was reviewed by a team of small business advisors, all of whom have numerous years of expertise in small business counseling and identification of small business information resources. The last and perhaps most important resource we utilize is direct contact with our readers, who provide valuable comments and suggestions to improve our publication. *SBS* relies on these comprehensive market contacts to provide today's entrepreneurs with relevant, current, and accurate information on all aspects of small business.

Available in Electronic Formats

Licensing. Small Business Sourcebook is available for licensing. The complete database is provided in a fielded format and is deliverable on various forms of media. For more information, contact Gale's Business Development Group at 1-800-877-GALE, or visit our website at www.gale.com.

Comments and Suggestions Welcome

Associations, agencies, business firms, publishers, and other organizations that provide assistance and information to the small business community are encouraged to submit material about their programs, activities, services, or products. Comments and suggestions from users of this directory are also welcomed and appreciated. Please contact:

Project Editor
Small Business Sourcebook
27555 Executive Dr., Ste. 270
Farmington Hills, MI 48331
Gale, part of Cengage Group
URL: www.gale.com

Small Business Sourcebook (*SBS*) provides information in a variety of forms and presentations for comprehensive coverage and ease of use. The directory contains four parts within six volumes:

- Specific Small Business Profiles
- General Small Business Topics
- State Listings
- Federal Government Assistance

Information on specific businesses is arranged by type of business; the many general topics that are of interest to the owners, operators, or managers of all small businesses are grouped in a separate section for added convenience. Users should consult the various sections to benefit fully from the information *SBS* offers. For example, an entrepreneur with a talent or interest in the culinary arts could peruse a number of specific small business profiles, such as Restaurant, Catering Service, Cooking School, Specialty/ Gourmet Food/Wine Shop, Food Truck, Healthy Restaurant, or Candy/Chocolate Shop. Secondly, the General Small Business Topics section could be consulted for any applicable subjects, such as Service Industry, Retailing, Franchising, and other relevant topics. Then, the appropriate state within the State Listings section would offer area programs and offices providing information and support to small businesses, including venture capital firms and small business development consultants. Finally, the Federal Government Assistance section could supply relevant government offices, such as procurement contacts.

Features Included in Volumes 1 and 2

List of Small Business Profiles. This list provides an alphabetic outline of the small businesses profiled. The page number for the beginning of each profile is indicated.

Standard Industrial Classification (SIC) Codes for Profiled Small Businesses. This section lists four-digit SIC codes and corresponding classification descriptions for the small businesses profiled in this edition. The SIC system, which organizes businesses by type, is a product of the Statistical Policy Division of the U.S. Office of Management and Budget. Statistical data produced by government, public, and private organizations is usually categorized according to SIC codes, thereby facilitating the collection, comparison, and analysis of data as well as providing a uniform method for presenting statistical information. Hence, knowing the SIC code for a particular small business increases access and the use of a variety of statistical data from many sources.

Guide to Publishers. This resource lists alphabetically the companies, associations, institutions, and individuals that publish the periodicals, directories, guidebooks, and other publications noted in the "Small Business Profiles" and "General Topics" sections. Users are provided with full contact information, including address, phone, fax, and e-mail and URL when available. The "Guide" facilitates contact with publishers and provides a one-stop resource for valuable information.

Glossary of Small Business Terms. This glossary defines nearly 400 small business terms, including financial, governmental, insurance, procurement, technical, and general business definitions. Cross-references and acronyms are also provided.

Small Business Profiles A-Z. More than 300 small business profiles are represented in volumes 1 and 2. Profiles are listed alphabetically by business type. Each profile may contain up to sixteen subheadings that correlate to a resource type; entries within are listed alphabetically. These resource types are detailed below:

- *Start-up Information*—Includes periodical articles, books, manuals, book excerpts, kits, and other sources of information. Entries offer title; publisher; address; phone, fax, toll-free numbers; company e-mail and URL addresses; and a description. Bibliographic data is provided for cited periodical articles whenever possible.

- *Associations and Other Organizations*—Includes trade and professional associations whose members gather and disseminate information of interest to small business owners. Entries offer the association's name; address; phone, toll-free and fax numbers; company e-mail address; contact name; purpose and objective; a description of membership; telecommunication services; and a listing of its publications, including publishing frequency.

- **Educational Programs**—Includes university and college programs, schools, training opportunities, association seminars, correspondence courses, and other educational programs. Entries offer name of program or institution, sponsor name, address, phone, toll-free and fax numbers, e-mail and URL addresses; and description of program.

- **Directories of Educational Programs**—Includes directories and other publications that list educational programs. Entries offer name of publication; publisher name, address, and phone, toll-free and fax numbers; editor; frequency or date of publication; price; and description of contents, including directory arrangement and indexes.

- **Reference Works**—Includes handbooks, manuals, textbooks, guides, directories, dictionaries, encyclopedias, and other published reference materials. Entries offer name of publication; publisher name, address, and phone, toll-free and fax numbers; e-mail and URL addresses; and, when available, name of author or editor, publication year or frequency, and price. A brief description is often featured.

- **Sources of Supply**—Includes buyer's guides, directories, special issues of periodicals, and other publications that list sources of equipment, supplies, and services related to the operation of the profiled small business. Entries offer publication name; publisher name, address, and phone, toll-free and fax numbers; e-mail and URL addresses; and, when available, editor's name, frequency or publication year, and price. A brief description of the publication, including directory arrangement and indexes, is often provided.

- **Statistical Sources**—Includes books, reports, pamphlets, and other sources of statistical data of interest to an owner, operator or manager of the profiled small business, such as wage, salary, and compensation data; financial and operating ratios; prices and costs; demographics; and other statistical information. Entries offer publication/data source name; publisher (if applicable); address; phone, toll-free and fax numbers of data source; publication date or frequency; and price. A brief description of the publication/data source is often provided.

- **Trade Periodicals**—Includes trade journals, newsletters, magazines, and other serials that offer information about the management and operation of the profiled small business. Such periodicals often contain industry news; trends and developments; reviews; articles about new equipment and supplies;

and other information related to business operations. Entries offer publication name; publisher name, address, phone, toll-free and fax numbers, and e-mail and URL addresses; editor name; publication frequency; and price. A brief description of the publication's content is also included, when known.

- **Video/Audio Media**—Includes videos, podcasts, and other audiovisual media offering information on the profiled small business. Entries offer program title; creator or distributor name, address, phone, toll-free and fax numbers, and e-mail and URL addresses; description of program; price; and format(s).

- **Trade Shows and Conventions**—Includes tradeshows, exhibitions, expositions, conventions, and other industry meetings that provide prospective and existing business owners with the opportunity to meet and exchange information with their peers, review commercial exhibits, establish business or sales contacts, and attend educational programs. Entries offer event name; sponsor or management company name, address, phone, toll-free and fax numbers, and e-mail and URL addresses; a description of the event, including audience, frequency, principal exhibits, and dates and locations of event for as many years ahead as provided by the event's sponsor.

- **Consultants**—Includes consultants and consulting organizations that provide services specifically related to the profiled small business. Entries offer individual consultant or consulting organization name, address, and phone, toll-free and fax numbers; company and individual e-mail addresses; and a brief description of consulting services. (For e-mail and URL addresses, see the Small Business Development Consultants subheadings in the State Listings section in Volume 2.)

- **Franchises and Business Opportunities**—Includes companies granting franchise licenses for enterprises falling within the scope of the profiled small business, as well as other non-franchised business opportunities that operate within a given network or system. Entries offer franchise name, address, phone, toll-free and fax numbers, and e-mail and URL addresses, as well as a description of the franchise or business opportunity, which has been expanded whenever possible to include the number of existing franchises, the founding date of the franchise, franchise fees, equity capital requirements, royalty fees, any managerial assistance offered, and available training.

- **Computerized Databases**—Includes diskettes, magnetic tapes, CD-ROMs, online systems, and other computer-readable databases. Entries offer database name; producer name, address, phone, toll-free and fax numbers, e-mail and URL addresses; description; and available format(s), including vendor name.

(Many university and public libraries offer online information retrieval services that provide searches of databases, including those listed in this category.)

- **Computer Systems/Software**—Includes software and computerized business systems designed to assist in the operation of the profiled small business. Entries offer name of the software or system; publisher name, address, phone, toll-free and fax numbers; price; and description.

- **Libraries**—Includes libraries and special collections that contain material especially applicable to the profiled small business. Entries offer library or collection name; parent organization (where applicable); address; phone, toll-free and fax numbers; e-mail and URL addresses; contact name and title; scope of collection; and description of holdings, subscriptions, and services.

- **Research Centers**—Includes university-related and independently operated research institutes and information centers that generate, through their research programs, data related to the operation of the profiled small business. Also listed are associations and other business-related organizations that conduct research programs. Entries offer name of organization; address; phone, toll-free and fax numbers; company web site address; contact name and personal e-mail; a description of principal fields of research or services; publications, including title and frequency; and related conferences.

Features Included in Volumes 3 and 4

General Small Business Topics. This section offers chapters on different topics in the operation of any small business, for example, venture capital and other funding, or compensation. Chapters are listed alphabetically by small business topic; entries within each chapter are arranged alphabetically, within up to 14 subheadings, by resource type:

- **Associations and Other Organizations**—Includes trade and professional associations that gather and disseminate information of interest to small business owners. Entries offer the association's name; address; phone, toll-free and fax numbers; organization e-mail and URL addresses; contact name; purpose and objectives; a description of membership; telecommunication services; and a listing of its publications, including publishing frequency.

- **Educational Programs**—Includes university and college programs, schools, training opportunities, association seminars, correspondence courses, and other educational programs. Entries offer name of program or institution, sponsor name, address, phone, toll-free and fax numbers, e-mail and URL addresses, and description of program.

- **Directories of Educational Programs**—Includes directories and other publications that list educational programs. Entries offer name of publication; publisher name, address, phone, toll-free and fax numbers, and e-mail and URL addresses; editor; frequency or date of publication; price; and description of contents, including arrangement and indexes.

- **Reference Works**—Includes articles, handbooks, manuals, textbooks, guides, directories, dictionaries, encyclopedias, and other published reference materials. Entries offer title of article, including bibliographic information; name of publication; publisher name, address, phone, toll-free and fax numbers, and e-mail and URL addresses; and, when available, name of author or editor, publication year or frequency, and price. A brief description is often featured.

- **Sources of Supply**—Includes buyer's guides, directories, special issues of periodicals, and other publications that list sources of equipment, supplies, and services. Entries offer publication name; publisher name, address, phone, toll-free and fax numbers, and e-mail and URL addresses; editor's name, frequency or publication year, price, and a brief description of the publication, when available.

- **Statistical Sources**—Includes books, reports, pamphlets, and other sources of statistical data of interest to an owner, operator, or manager of a small business, such as wage, salary, and compensation data; financial and operating ratios; prices and costs; demographics; and other statistical information. Entries offer publication/data source name; publisher (if applicable); address; phone, toll-free and fax numbers of data source; publication date or frequency; and price. A brief description is often provided.

- **Trade Periodicals**—Includes journals, newsletters, magazines, and other serials. Entries offer name of publication; publisher name, address, phone, toll-free and fax numbers, and e-mail and URL addresses; and name of editor, frequency, and price. A brief description of the periodical's content is included when known.

- **Video/Audio Media**—Includes videos, podcasts, and other audiovisual media. Entries offer program title; distributor name, address, phone, toll-free and fax numbers, and e-mail and URL addresses; price; description of program; and format(s).

- **Trade Shows and Conventions**—Includes tradeshows, exhibitions, expositions, seminars, and conventions. Entries offer event name; sponsor or management company name, address, phone, toll-free and fax numbers, and e-mail and URL addresses; frequency of event; and dates and locations of the event for as many years ahead as known.

- **Consultants**—Includes consultants and consulting organizations. Entries offer individual consultant or consulting organization name, address, and phone, toll-free and fax numbers; company and individual e-mail addresses; and a brief description of consulting services. (See also Consultants in the State Listings section.)

- **Computerized Databases**—Includes diskettes, CD-ROMs, magnetic tape, online systems and other computer-readable databases. Entries offer database name; producer, address, phone, toll-free and fax numbers, and e-mail and URL addresses; description; and available format(s), including vendor name. (Many university and public libraries offer online information retrieval services that provide searches of databases, including those listed in this category.)

- **Computer Systems/Software**—Includes software and computerized business systems. Entries offer name of the software or system; publisher name, address, phone, toll-free and fax numbers, and e-mail and URL addresses; price; and description.

- **Libraries**—Includes libraries and special collections that contain material applicable to the small business topic. Entries offer library or collection name, parent organization (where applicable), address, phone and fax numbers, e-mail and URL addresses, scope of collection, and description of holdings and services.

- **Research Centers**— Includes university-related and independently operated research institutes and information centers that generate, through their research programs, data related to specific small business topics. Entries offer name of organization, address, phone, toll-free and fax numbers, e-mail and URL addresses, a description of principal fields of research or services, and related conferences.

Features Included in Volumes 5 and 6

State Listings. This section lists various sources of information and assistance available within given states, territories, and Canadian provinces; entries include governmental, academic, and commercial agencies, and are arranged alphabetically within up to 15 subheadings by resource type:

- **Small Business Development Center Lead Office**— Includes the lead small business development center (SBDC) for each state.

- **Small Business Development Centers**—Includes any additional small business development centers (SBDC) in the state, territory, or province. SBDCs provide support services to small businesses, including individual counseling, seminars, conferences, and learning center activities.

- **Small Business Assistance Programs**—Includes state small business development offices and other programs offering assistance to small businesses.

- **SCORE Offices**—Includes SCORE office(s) for each state. The Service Corps of Retired Executives Association (SCORE), a volunteer program sponsored by the Small Business Administration, offers counseling, workshops, and seminars across the U.S. for small business entrepreneurs.

- **Better Business Bureaus**—Includes various better business bureaus within each state. By becoming a member of the local Better Business Bureau, a small business owner can increase the prestige and credibility of his or her business within the community, as well as make valuable business contacts.

- **Chambers of Commerce**—Includes various chambers of commerce within each state. Chambers of Commerce are valuable sources of small business advice and information; often, local chambers sponsor SCORE counseling several times per month for a small fee, seminars, conferences, and other workshops to its members. Also, by becoming a member of the local Chamber of Commerce, a small business owner can increase the prestige and credibility of his or her business within the community, as well as make valuable business contacts.

- **Minority Business Assistance Programs**—Includes minority business development centers and other sources of assistance for minority-owned business.

- **Financing and Loan Programs**—Includes venture capital firms, small business investment companies (SBIC), minority enterprise small business investment companies (MESBIC), and other programs that provide funding to qualified small businesses.

- **Procurement Assistance Programs**—Includes state services such as counseling, set-asides, and sheltered-market bidding, which are designed to aid small businesses in bidding on government contracts.

- **Incubators/Research and Technology Parks**— Includes small business incubators, which provide newly established small business owners with work sites, business services, training, and consultation; also includes research and technology parks, which sponsor research and facilitate commercialization of new technologies.

- **Educational Programs**—Includes university and college programs, as well as those sponsored by other organizations that offer degree, nondegree, certificate, and correspondence programs in entrepreneurship and in small business development.

- **Legislative Assistance**—Includes committees, subcommittees, and joint committees of each state's senate and house of representatives that are concerned with small business issues and regulations.

- **Consultants**—Includes consultants and consulting firms offering expertise in small business development.

- **Publications**—Includes publications related to small business operations within the profiled state.

- **Publishers**—Includes publishers operating in or for the small business arena within the profiled state.

- **Early Stage Financing**—Includes organizations offering early-stage capital needed to launch and grow new businesses.

- **Venture Capital Firm**—Includes organizations offering financial support to small, early-stage and emerging firms.

Federal Government Assistance. This section lists federal government agencies and offices, many with additional listings for specific offices, as well as regional or district branches. Main agencies or offices are listed alphabetically; regional, branch, or district offices are listed after each main office or agency.

Master Index. This index provides an alphabetic listing of all entries contained in Volumes 1 through 6. Citations are referenced by their entry numbers. Publication titles are rendered in italics.

List of Small Business Profiles

This list is an outline of the small businesses profiled in this edition of Small Business Sourcebook. The beginning page number of each profile is provided.

Standard Industrial Classification (SIC) Codes for Profiled Small Businesses

Included here are the four-digit SIC codes and corresponding classification descriptions for the businesses profiled in this edition. The SIC system, which organizes businesses by type, is a product of the Statistical Policy Division of the U.S. Office of Management and Budget. Statistical data produced by government, public, and private organizations usually are categorized according to SIC codes, thereby facilitating the collection, comparison, and analysis of data as well as providing a uniform method for presenting statistical information. Hence, knowing the SIC code for a particular small business increases the access to, and the use of, a variety of statistical data from many sources. The following SIC codes were obtained from the 1987 edition of the Standard Industrial Classification Manual, the most recent version available. (The term "nec" stands for "not elsewhere classified.")

Accounting Service

7291	Tax return preparation services
8721	Accounting, auditing, and bookkeeping services

Adult Day Care Center

8322	Individual and family social services (includes adult day care centers)

Advertising Service

7311	Advertising agencies (includes advertising consultants)
7312	Outdoor advertising agencies
7313	Radio, television, and publishers' advertising representatives
7319	Advertising, nec
7331	Direct mail advertising services
8999	Services, nec (includes advertising copywriters)

Airbag Replacement Service Centers

7538	General automotive repair shops
7539	Automotive repair shops, nec

Air Charter Service

4512	Air transportation, scheduled (includes air cargo and passenger carriers)
4513	Air courier services
4522	Air transportation, nonscheduled (includes charter service)

Air-conditioning/Heating and Cooling Contractor

1711	Plumbing, heating, and air-conditioning contractors

Air Purification/Cleaning Service

7699	Repair shops and related services, nec (includes furnace cleaning service)

Ambulance Service

4119	Local passenger transportation, nec (includes ambulance service, road)
4522	Air transportation, nonscheduled (includes ambulance service, air)

Amusement Arcade

7993	Coin-operated amusement devices

Amusement/Water Park

7996	Amusement parks
7999	Amusement and recreation services, nec (includes waterslides and wave pools)

Animal Breeder

0279	Animal specialties, nec (includes kennels, breeding and raising own stock)
0752	Animal specialty services, except veterinary (includes breeding of animals other than farm animals)

Animal Clinic

0742	Veterinary service for animal specialties (includes animal hospitals for pets and other animals)

Antique Shop

5932	Used merchandise stores (includes retail antique stores)

7641	Reupholstery and furniture repair (includes antique furniture repair and restoration)
7699	Repair shops and related services, nec (includes antique repair and restoration, except furniture)

Apartment Locating Service

6531	Real Estate Agents and Managers

Appliance Store

5722	Household appliance stores

Appraisal Service

7389	Business services, nec (includes appraisers, except real estate)
6531	Real estate agents and managers (includes appraisers, real estate)

Aquarium Maintenance/Leasing Service

7359	Equipment rental and leasing, nec
8999	Services, nec

Archery/Target/Shooting Range

7999	Amusement and recreation services, nec (includes archery ranges, shooting galleries, shooting ranges, and trap-shooting facilities, except membership)

Architectural Restoration/Conservation

8712	Architectural Services

Art Gallery

5932	Used merchandise stores (includes retailers of art objects)

| 5999 | Miscellaneous retail stores, nec (includes art dealers) |
| 8412 | Museums and art galleries (includes noncommercial art galleries) |

Art Supplies Store

| 5999 | Miscellaneous retail stores, nec (includes retail artists' supplies and materials stores) |

Assisted Living Facilities

8051	Skilled nursing care facilities (includes extended care facilities and skilled nursing homes)
8052	Intermediate care facilities (includes intermediate care nursing homes)
8059	Nursing and personal care facilities, nec (includes rest homes with health care)

Association Management Service

8611	Business associations
8621	Professional membership organizations
8631	Labor unions and similar labor organizations
8641	Civic, social, and fraternal associations
8699	Membership organizations, nec
8741	Management services (does not include operating staff)

Auctioneer/Broker

5154	Livestock (includes wholesale livestock auctioning)
5999	Miscellaneous retail stores, nec (includes retail general merchandise auction rooms)
7389	Business services, nec (includes auctioneering services)

Auto Supply Store

| 5531 | Auto and home supply stores |

Automobile Detailing/Painting Service

| 7532 | Automotive paint shops |

| 7542 | Carwashes (includes detailing, cleaning and polishing, new autos on a contract or fee basis; washing and polishing, automotive; waxing and polishing, automotive) |

Automobile/Truck Leasing Service

7513	Truck rental and leasing, without drivers
7514	Passenger car rental, without drivers
7515	Passenger car leasing, without drivers

Baby Store

| 5999 | Miscellaneous retail stores, nec (includes retail baby) |

Bagel Shop

| 2051 | Bread and other bakery products, except cookies and crackers (includes bagels) |
| 5461 | Retail bakeries (includes retail bagel stores) |

Bait and Tackle Shop

| 5941 | Sporting goods stores and bicycle shops (includes bait and tackle shops and fishing equipment, retail) |

Bakery/Doughnut Shop

| 5461 | Retail bakeries |

Bar/Nightclub

| 5813 | Drinking places alcoholic beverages (includes bars, cocktail lounges, saloons, tap rooms, taverns, and like establishments) |

Beauty Supply Center

| 5087 | Service establishment equipment and supplies (includes wholesale barber shop and beauty parlor equipment and supplies) |

Bed and Breakfast Operation

| 7011 | Hotels and motels (includes bed and breakfast inns) |

Beekeeping

| 0279 | Animal specialties, nec (includes apiaries and bee farms) |

Beeper/Paging Service

| 4812 | Radiotelephone communications (includes beeper and paging services) |

Bicycle Shop

| 5941 | Sporting goods stores and bicycle shops |
| 7699 | Repair shops and related services, nec (includes bicycle repair shops) |

Billiards Hall

| 7999 | Amusement and recreation services, nec (includes billiard parlors) |

Blacktop Surfacing Business

| 1771 | Concrete work (includes blacktop work: private driveways and private parking areas contractors) |

Blind Cleaning/Installation

| 2431 | Millwork (includes wood blinds and shutters) |
| 2591 | Drapery hardware and window blinds and shades |

Body Care Shop

| 5999 | Miscellaneous retail stores, nec (includes cosmetics stores) |

Book Publishing

| 2731 | Books; publishing or publishing and printing |

Bookbinder

| 2789 | Bookbinding and related work |

Bookkeeping

| 8721 | Accounting, auditing, and bookkeeping services |

Bookstore

| 5932 | Used merchandise stores (includes used book retailers) |
| 5942 | Bookstores |

Bottled Water Service

| 5149 | Groceries and related products, nec (includes natural spring and mineral water bottling and distribution services) |

5499	Miscellaneous food stores (includes mineral water, retail)

Bowling Alley

7933	Bowling centers

Brewpub and Microbrewery

2082	Malt beverages

Bridal Shop/Bridal Consultant

5621	Women's clothing stores (includes retail bridal shops, except custom designers)

Building/Home Inspection Service

7389	Business services, nec (includes safety inspection, except automotive)

Building Maintenance/Custodial Service

7349	Building cleaning and maintenance services, nec (includes interior building cleaning services, contract janitorial services, and like enterprises)

Bulletin Board Service

4822	Telegraph and other message communications (includes electronic mail services)
7379	Computer related services, nec

Business Broker Service

7389	Business services, nec (includes business brokers buying and selling business enterprises)

Business Consulting Service

8748	Business consulting services, nec

Business Services Operation

8744	Facilities support management services (includes base maintenance, providing personnel on continuing basis)

Butcher Shop

5423	Meat and fish (seafood) markets, including freezer provisioners

5499	Miscellaneous food stores (includes retail poultry dealers)

Cable Network

1623	Water, Sewer, Pipeline, and Communications and Power Line Construction (includes cable television line construction-contractors)
1731	Electrical Work (includes cable television hookup-contractors)
4841	Cable and Other Pay Television Services

Calligraphy Service

7389	Business services, nec (includes lettering services)

Camera Shop

5946	Camera and photographic supply stores
7699	Repair shops and related services, nec (includes camera repair shops)

Campground Management

7033	Recreational vehicle parks and campsites

Candy/Chocolate Shop

5441	Candy, nut, and confectionery stores

Car Alarm and Stereo Store

5531	Auto and home supply stores (includes automobile accessory dealers, retail)
5731	Radio, television, and consumer electronics stores (includes automotive stereo equipment, retail)

Car Inspection Service

7549	Automotive services, except repair services and car washes(includes inspection service, automotive)

Car Towing Service

7549	Automotive services, except repair services and car washes (includes automotive towing and wrecker services)

Car Wash

7542	Car washes

Career Counseling

7389	Business services, nec (includes career counseling service)

Carpentry Service

1751	Carpentry work

Catering Service

5812	Eating places (includes caterers)

Cellular Phone/Telephone Business

4812	Radiotelephone communications
5999	Miscellaneous retail stores, nec (includes telephone stores, retail)

Charter Boat Service

4499	Water transportation service, nec (includes boat rental, commercial)

Check Cashing Service

6099	Functions related to depository banking, nec (includes check cashing agencies)

Children's Apparel Shop

5611	Men's and boys' clothing stores
5641	Children's and infants' wear stores
5651	Family clothing stores
5699	Miscellaneous apparel and accessory stores (includes children's wear)
5932	Used merchandise stores (includes retail second hand clothing stores)

Children's Day Care Center

8351	Child day care services

Chimney Sweeping Business

7349	Building cleaning and maintenance services, nec (includes chimney cleaning service)

Christmas Decoration Store

5999	Miscellaneous retail stores, nec

Christmas Tree Farm

0811   Timber tracts (includes Christmas tree growing)

Clipping Service

7389   Business services, nec (includes press clipping service)

Clothing Designer

2311   Men's and boys' suits, coats, and overcoats

2325   Men's and boys' separate trousers and slacks

2329   Men's and boys' clothing, nec

2331   Women's, misses', and juniors' blouses and shirts

2335   Women's, misses', and juniors' dresses

2337   Women's, misses', and juniors' suits, skirts, and coats

2361   Girls', children's, and infants' dresses, blouses, and shirts

Clothing Store

5611   Men's and boys' clothing and accessory stores

5621   Women's clothing stores

5632   Women's accessory and specialty stores

5641   Children's and infants' wear stores

5651   Family clothing stores

5699   Miscellaneous apparel and accessory stores

5932   Used merchandise stores (includes retail secondhand clothing stores)

Coffee Service

5149   Groceries and related products, nec (includes coffee, wholesale)

Coin/Stamp Dealer

5961   Catalog and mail order houses (includes retail mail order coin and stamp businesses)

5999   Miscellaneous retail stores, nec

Comic Book/Collectibles Store

5999   Miscellaneous retail stores, nec

Commercial/Graphic Art Business

7336   Commercial art and graphic design

Commercial Mail Receiving Agency

7389   Business services, nec (includes post office contract stations)

Compact Disc/Record Store

5735   Recorded and prerecorded tape stores

Computer Consulting

7379   Computer related services, nec (includes computer consultants

Computer Data Storage Company

3572   Computer storage devices

Computer Learning/Training Center

8243   Data processing schools

Computer Maintenance and Repair Service

7378   Computer maintenance and repair

Computer Programming and Data Processing Service

7374   Computer processing and data preparation services

Computer Store

5734   Computer and computer software stores

Computer System Integrators

7371   Computer programming services

7373   Computer integrated systems design

7379   Computer related services, nec (includes computer consultants and database developers)

Computerized Billing Service

7374   Computer processing and data preparation and processing services

Computerized Matching Service

7299   Miscellaneous personal services, nec (includes dating services)

7375   Information retrieval services

Concession Stand Business

5812   Eating places (includes concession stands in airports and sports arenas, and refreshment stands)

7999   Amusement and recreation services, nec (concession operators and amusement concessions)

Consignment Shop

5932   Used merchandise stores (includes clothing stores, secondhand retail; furniture stores, secondhand retail; home furnishing stores, secondhand retail)

Construction Company

1521   General contractors—single family houses

1522   General contractors—residential buildings other than single-family

Consumer Electronics Store

5731   Radio, television, and consumer electronics stores

Convenience Store

5411   Grocery stores (includes retail convenience food stores)

Cooking School

8299   Schools and educational services, nec (includes cooking schools)

Copy Shop

7334   Photocopying and duplicating services

Cosmetics Business

2844   Perfumes, cosmetics, and other toilet preparations

5122   Drugs, drug proprietaries, and druggists' sundries (includes cosmetics—wholesale)

5963   Direct selling establishments (includes canvassers, headquarters for retail sale of merchandise, and direct selling organizations—retail)

5999   Miscellaneous retail stores, nec (includes cosmetics-stores—retail)

Costume Shop

7299   Miscellaneous personal services, nec (includes costume rental)

7922   Theatrical producers and miscellaneous theatrical services(includes theatrical costume design)

Craft Artisan

3269   Pottery products, nec (includes art and ornamental ware; pottery; ceramic articles for craft shops; cookware; crockery; china, earthenware and stoneware figures; kitchen articles; coarse earthenware; lamp bases; and vases)

Craft/Hobby Shop

5945   Hobby, toy, and game shops (includes retail hobby stores and craft kit and supply retailers)

5947   Gift, novelty, and souvenir shops pottery; ceramic articles for craft shops; cookware; crockery; china, earthenware and stoneware figures; kitchen articles; coarse earthenware; lamp bases; and vases)

Create Your Own...Store

3269   Pottery Products, nec

5947   Gift, Novelty, and Souvenir Shops

5999   Miscellaneous retail stores, nec

Credit Card Issuing Service

6153   Short-Term Business Credit Institutions, Except Agricultural (includes credit card service, collection by central agency)

7389   Business Services, nec (includes credit card service collection by individual firms)

Credit Repair Service

7299   Miscellaneous personal services, nec (includes debt counseling and adjustment services)

Credit Reporting and Collection Service

7322   Adjustment and collection services

7323   Credit reporting services

Damage Restoration Service

1790   Special trade contractors, nec (includes cleaning building exteriors, damp-proofing buildings, dewatering, fireproofing buildings, steam cleaning of building exteriors, and waterproofing)

Dance School

7911   Dance studios, schools, and halls

Delicatessen/Sandwich Shop

5812   Eating places (includes sandwich bars or shops and submarine sandwich shops)

Desktop Publishing Company

2711   Publishing, or publishing and printing newspapers

2721   Publishing, or publishing and printing periodicals

2731   Publishing, or publishing and printing books

2741   Miscellaneous publishing

Dial-it Services

4813   Telephone communications, except radiotelephone

Disc Jockey Service

8999   Services, nec

Domestic Help/Maid Service

7349   Building cleaning and maintenance services, nec (includes housekeeping and office cleaning services)

8811   Private households (includes private households employing cooks, maids, and other domestic help)

Driving School

8249   Vocational schools, nec (includes truck driving schools)

8299   Schools and educational services, nec (includes automobile driving instruction)

Drug Store/Pharmacy

5912   Drug stores and proprietary stores

Dry Cleaning Service/Coin-Operated Laundry

7215   Coin-operated laundries and dry cleaning services

7216   Dry cleaning plants, except rug cleaning

Editorial/Freelance Writing Business

8999   Services, nec (includes writing and ghostwriting services)

Electrical Contractor

1731   Electrical work (includes trade contractors engaged in on-site electrical work)

Electrical Lighting Supply Store

5719   Miscellaneous home furnishings stores (includes retail lamp and shade shops)

Employee Leasing Service

7363   Help supply services

Employment Agency

361   Employment agencies

Engraving/Monogramming Service

3479   Coating, engraving, and allied services, nec (includes jewelry and silverware engraving)

7389   Business services, nec (includes advertising embroidery services, embossing services, and identification engraving services)

Environmental Consultant

8748   Business consulting services, nec

Environmental Store

5999   Miscellaneous retail stores, nec

Estate Planning

8811   Private Households

Estate Sales Business

6530   Real estate agents and managers

Executive Recruiting Agency

7361   Employment agencies (includes executive placement)

Fashion Accessories/Design Business

3961   Costume jewelry and costume novelties, except precious metal

5137   Women's, children's, and infants' clothing and accessories

5632   Women's accessory and specialty stores

Film and Video Production Operation

7812   Motion picture and videotape production services

Financial Planning Service

282   Investment Advice

Fish and Seafood Store

5421   Meat and fish (seafood) markets, including freezer provisioners

Fish Farm

0273   Animal aquaculture (includes fish farms except hatcheries)

Floor Covering/Restoration Business

5713   Floor covering stores—retail

Florist

5992   Florists

Food Delivery Service

5812   Eating places

5963   Direct selling establishments (includes door-to-door selling organizations and mobile lunch wagons)

5999   Miscellaneous retail stores, nec

Freight Forwarding Service

4731   Arrangement of transportation of freight and cargo (includes freight forwarding services)

Fund-Raising Consultant

7389   Business services, nec (includes fund raising on a contract or fee basis)

Funeral Service

7261   Funeral services and crematories

Fur Farm

0271   Fur-bearing animals and rabbits

Fur Store

5632   Women's accessory and specialty stores (includes fur shops and furriers)

Furniture Restoration Service

7641   Reupholstery and furniture repair

Gambling Organizations/Service

7011   Hotels and Motels (includes casino hotels)

7993   Coin-Operated Amusement Devices

7999   Amusement and Recreation Services, nec (includes gambling establishments not primarily operating coin-operated machines and lotteries, operation of)

9311   Public Finance Taxation, and Monetary Policy (includes gambling control boards-government and lottery control boards-government)

Genealogy Service

7299   Miscellaneous personal services, nec (includes genealogical investigation service)

Gift Basket Service

5961   Catalog and mail-order houses

Gift/Card Shop

5943   Stationery stores

5947   Gift, novelty, and souvenir shops (includes card shops)

Glass Repair and Replacement Service

1751   Carpentry work (includes prefabricated window and door installation)

7536   Automotive glass replacement shops

Golf Shop

5941   Sporting goods stores and bicycle shops (includes retail golf goods and equipment stores)

Gourmet Coffee/Tea House

5499   Miscellaneous food stores (includes coffee stores, retail)

5812   Eating places (includes coffee shops)

Greenhouse/Garden Center/Nursery Business

0181   Ornamental floricultural and nursery products (includes greenhouses for floral products, growing of nursery stock, growing of potted plants)

5261   Retail nurseries, lawn and garden supply stores (includes nursery stock, seeds, and bulbs, retail)

Greeting Card Publishing

2771   Greeting card publishing and printing

8999   Services, nec (includes hand painting of greeting cards)

Grocery Store

5411   Grocery stores

Gunsmith/Gun Shop

5941   Sporting goods stores and bicycle shops (includes firearms, retail)

7699	Repair shops and related services, nec (includes gunsmith shops)

Hair Replacement/Electrolysis Clinic

7299	Miscellaneous personal services, nec (includes depilatory salons, electrolysis, and hair weaving or replacement services)

Hair Salon/Barber Shop

7231	Beauty shops (includes beauty and barber shops combined)
7241	Barber shops

Handwriting Analysis Consultant

7389	Business services, nec (includes handwriting analysis)

Hardware Store

5251	Hardware stores

Hat Store

5611	Men's and boys' clothing and accessory stores (includes retail hat stores)
5621	Women's accessory and specialty stores (includes retail millinery stores)

Hazardous Waste Disposal Business

4953	Refuse systems (includes hazardous waste material disposal sites)

Health Food Store

5499	Miscellaneous food stores (includes health food stores)

Healthy Restaurants

5812	Eating Places

Hearing Aid Testing and Fitting Service

5999	Miscellaneous retail stores, nec (includes hearing aids, retail)
8099	Health and allied services, nec (includes hearing testing service)

Herb Farm

0191	General farms, primarily crop

2833	Medical chemicals and botanical products (includes herb grinding, grading, and milling)
5499	Miscellaneous food stores (includes spice and herb stores)

Home Accessory Store

5714	Drapery, curtain, and upholstery stores
5719	Miscellaneous home furnishings stores

Home Furnishings Store

5712	Furniture stores
5719	Miscellaneous home furnishings stores
5932	Used merchandise stores (including antique and secondhand retail furniture stores)

Home Health Care Service

8082	Home health care services

Horse Riding Academy

752	Animal specialty services, except veterinary (includes boarding and training horses)

Hotel/Motel/Resort Operation

7011	Hotels and motels (includes resort hotels)

Ice Cream/Frozen Yogurt Shop

5451	Dairy products stores (includes retail packaged ice cream stores)
5812	Eating places (includes retail dairy bars)
563	Direct selling establishments (includes ice cream wagons)

Image Consultant

8299	Schools and educational services, nec (includes personal development schools)
8743	Public relations services

Import/Export Service

4731	Arrangement of the transportation of freight and cargo

Incubator

7389	Business services, nec
8748	Business consulting services, nec

Information Broker

7375	Information retrieval services

Insulation Contractor

1742	Plastering, dry wall, acoustical, and insulation work (includes insulation installation contractors)

Insurance Agency

6411	Insurance agents, brokers, and services

Interior Design Service

7389	Business services, nec (includes interior decoration consulting services and interior design services)

Internet/Online Service Provider

4822	Telegraph and other message communications (includes electronic mail services)
7379	Computer related services, nec

Investment/Securities Broker

6211	Security brokers, dealers, and flotation companies

Jewelry Store

5632	Women's accessory and specialty stores (includes costume jewelry stores)
5944	Jewelry stores
7631	Watch, clock, and jewelry repair

Job Training/Retraining

8331	Job training and vocational rehabilitation services (includes job training)

Kiosk/Pushcart/Vendor Business

5812	Eating places (includes box lunch stands, concession stands, food bars, hamburger and hot dog stands, ice cream stands, refreshment stands, and soft drink stands)

Landscaping Service

0781   Landscape counseling and planning services

0782   Lawn and garden services

0783   Ornamental shrub and tree services

Lawn Maintenance Service

0782   Lawn and garden services

0783   Ornamental shrub and tree services

Limousine Service

4119   Local passenger transportation, nec (includes hearse and limousine rental, with drivers)

7514   Passenger car rental (includes limo rental, w/o drivers)

Lingerie Shop

5632   Lingerie stores, retail

Liquor Store

5921   Liquor stores

Literary Agency

7389   Business services, nec (includes agents and brokers for authors and non-performing artists)

Locksmith

7699   Repair shops and related services, nec (includes locksmith shops and made-to order lock parts)

Luggage and Leather Goods Business

5948   Luggage and leather goods stores

Lumberyard

5211   Lumber and other building materials dealers

Machine Shop/Metalworking Shop

3541   Machine tools, metal cutting types

3542   Machine tools, metal forming types

3544   Special dies and tools, die sets, jigs and fixtures, and industrial molds

3545   Cutting tools, machine tool accessories, and machinists' precision measuring devices

3549   Metalworking machinery, nec

Mail Order Business

5961   Catalog and mail order houses

Management Consulting Service

8742   Management consulting services

Manufacturer's Representative

7389   Business services, nec

Marine Shop

5551   Boat dealers (includes retail marine supply dealers)

Market Research and Analysis

8732   Commercial, economic, sociological, and educational research

8742   Management consulting services

Martial Arts Studio

7999   Amusement and recreation services, nec (includes Judo and Karate instruction)

Masonry, Stonework, and Plastering Contractors

1741   Masonry, stone setting, and other stonework

1742   Plastering, dry wall, acoustical, and insulation work

Massage Therapist

7299   Massage parlor

8049   Offices and clinics of health practitioners, nec

Mediation Service

7389   Business services, nec (includes arbitration and conciliation services)

Medical and Dental Instrument Manufacturing

3841   Surgical and medical instruments and apparatus

3843   Dental equipment and supplies

Medical Claims Service

6411   Insurance agents, brokers, and service (includes processing ofmedical claims on a contract or fee basis)

Medical Laboratory Service

8071   Medical laboratories

Medical Supplies Store

5047   Medical, dental, and hospital equipment and supplies

Medical Transcription Service

7374   Computer processing and data preparation and processing services

Messenger/Delivery/Subpoena Service

4215   Courier services, except by air (includes letter, mail, package, and parcel delivery services)

4822   Telegraph and other message communication (includes cablegrams, mailgrams, electronic mail, and other message services)

7389   Business services, nec (includes process serving services)

Miniature Golf Course Operation

7999   Amusement and recreation services, nec (includes miniature golf course operations)

Modeling School/Agency

7363   Help supply services (includes modeling services)

8299   Schools and educational services, nec (includes modeling schools)

Mortgage Broker

6162   Mortgage bankers and loan correspondents (includes mortgage brokers using own money)

6163   Loan brokers (includes mortgage brokers arranging for loans but using money of others)

6211   Security brokers, dealers, and flotation companies (includes buying and selling mortgages)

Motorcycle/Moped Store

5571   Motorcycle dealers

Movie Theatre Operation

7832   Motion picture theatres, except drive-ins

7833   Drive-in motion picture theatres

Moving Service

4212   Local trucking, without storage (includes furniture and other moving services)

4214   Local trucking, with storage (includes furniture and household goods moving services)

Music School

8299   Schools and educational services, nec (includes music schools)

Music Shop

5736   Musical instrument stores

5932   Used merchandise stores (includes retailers of secondhand musical instruments)

7699   Repair shops and related services, nec (includes musical instrument repair shops)

Musical Instrument Repair/Piano Tuning Service

7699   Repair shops and related services, nec (includes musical instrument repair shops and piano tuning and repair)

Nail Salon

7231   Beauty shops (includes manicure and pedicure salons)

Nanny Service

7299   Miscellaneous personal services, nec (includes babysitting bureaus)

New Age Services and Supplies

5999   Miscellaneous retail stores, nec

8999   Services, nec

New and Used Car Dealer

5511   Motor vehicle dealers (new and used)

5521   Motor vehicle dealers (used only)

Newsletter Publishing

2721   Periodicals; publishing or publishing and printing

2741   Miscellaneous publishing (includes business service newsletters publishing and/or printing)

Novelty Items Business

2499   Wood products, nec (includes wood and wood fiber novelties)

2514   Metal household furniture (includes metal novelty furniture)

2679   Converted paper and paperboard products, nec (includes paper novelties)

3199   Leather goods, nec (includes leather novelties)

3229   Pressed and blown glass and glassware, nec (includes novelty glassware made in glassmaking plants)

3231   Glass products, made of purchased glass (includes glass novelties)

3499   Fabricated metal products, nec (includes metal novelties and specialties, except advertising novelties)

3961   Costume jewelry and costume novelties, except precious metal and gems

3999   Manufacturing industries, nec (includes bone, beaded and shell novelties)

Nursing Home/Long-Term Care Center

8051   Skilled nursing care facilities

8052   Intermediate care facilities (includes intermediate care nursing homes)

8059   Nursing and personal care facilities, nec (includes convalescent homes, rest homes, and like facilities)

Nutritional Consultant/Diet Planner

7299   Miscellaneous personal services, nec (includes diet workshops)

Offices and clinics of health practitioners

8049   Offices and clinics of health practitioners, nec (includes offices of nutritionists and offices of dietitians)

Office Design Service

7389   Business services, nec (includes interior decorating and design services)

Office Supply/Equipment Store

5943   Stationery stores (includes retail office forms and supplies stores)

Online/Retail/E-Commerce

5734   Computer and computer software stores

7375   Information retrieval services

Paint/Wall Covering Center

5231   Paint, glass, and wallpaper stores

Painting Contractors

1721   Painting and paperhanging contractors

Party Entertainment Services

7929   Bands, orchestras, actors, and other entertainers and entertainment groups

Party/Reunion Planning Service

7359   Equipment rental and leasing, nec (includes party supplies rental and leasing)

8999   Services, nec

Pawnbroker

5932   Used merchandise stores (includes pawnshops)

Payroll Preparation Service

8721   Accounting, auditing, and bookkeeping services (includes payroll accounting service)

Periodical/Newspaper Publishing

2721   Periodicals; publishing or publishing and printing

Personal Shopping Service

7299   Miscellaneous personal services, nec (includes shopping services for individuals)

Pest Control Service

0851   Forestry services (includes forest pest control)

7342   Disinfecting and pest control services

Pet Boarding/Grooming Service

0279   Animal specialties, nec (includes breeding kennels)

0752   Animal specialty services (includes boarding kennels, dog grooming services, and related services)

Pet Cemetery

0782   Lawn and garden services (includes independent cemetery upkeep services)

6531   Real estate agents and managers (includes cemetery management services)

6553   Cemetery subdividers and developers (includes animal cemetery operations)

Pet Obedience School

0752   Animal specialty services, except veterinary (includes training of pets and other animal specialties)

Pet Shop

5999   Miscellaneous retail stores, nec (includes pet shops)

Pet Sitting Service

0752   Animal specialty services, except veterinary

Photo Finishing Center

7384   Photo finishing laboratories

7819   Services allied to motion picture production (includes motion picture film processing)

Photographer, Commercial

7335   Commercial photography

Photographic Studio

7221   Photographic studios, portrait

Physical Fitness Center

7991   Physical fitness facilities

Physical Therapy Clinic/Practice

8049   Offices and clinics of health practitioners, nec (includes offices of physical therapists)

Pizzeria

5812   Eating places (includes pizza parlors and pizzerias)

Plant Leasing Service

7359   Equipment rental and leasing, nec (includes plants)

Plumbing Service

1711   Plumbing, heating, and air-conditioning contractors

Porcelain Refinishing Service

1799   Special trade contractors, nec

Power Washing Service

1799   Special trade contractors, nec (includes cleaning of building exteriors)

7349   Building cleaning and maintenance services, nec (includes cleaning of building interiors)

7542   Car washes (includes automotive washing and polishing)

Prepaid Phone Card Business

4812   Radiotelephone communications

4813   Telephone communications, except radiotelephone

Print/Frame Shop

7699   Repair shops and related services, nec (includes custom picture framing services)

Printing Business

2752   Commercial printing, lithographic

2754   Commercial printing, gravure

2759   Commercial printing, nec

2761   Manifold business form printers

Private Investigation/Personal Security Service

7381   Detective, guard, and armored car services

Private Label Product Manufacturer/ Retailer

3999   Manufacturing industries, nec

5399   Miscellaneous general merchandise stores

5499   Miscellaneous food stores 5699 Miscellaneous apparel and accessory stores

5999   Miscellaneous retail stores, nec

Professional Organizer

7299   Miscellaneous personal services, nec

7389   Business services, nec

Property Management

6531   Real estate agents and managers

Public Relations Consultant

8743   Public relations services

Public Warehousing/Ministorage Operation

4221   Farm product warehousing and storage

4222   Refrigerated warehousing and storage

4225   General warehousing and storage

4226   Special warehousing and storage, nec (includes fur storage, household goods warehousing and storage, whiskey warehousing, and like enterprises)

Quick Oil Change Service

5541   Gasoline service stations (includes automobile service stations—retail)

7538   General automotive repair shops

Radio Station

4832   Radio broadcasting stations

Radon Testing Service

1799   Special trade contractors, nec

8734   Testing laboratories

Real Estate Agency

6531   Real estate agents and managers

Real Estate Investment Service

6798   Real estate investment trusts

Recording Studio

7399   Business services, nec (includes recording studios operating on a contract or fee basis)

Recreational Vehicle Dealer

5561   Recreational vehicle dealers

Recycling Business

5093   Scrap and waste materials

Rental Service

7299   Miscellaneous personal services, nec (includes clothing rental)

7352   Medical equipment rental and leasing

7353   Heavy construction equipment and leasing

7359   Equipment rental and leasing, nec

7377   Computer rental and leasing

7999   Amusement and recreation services, nec (includes pleasure boat rental, canoe and rowboat rental, bicycle, motorcycle and moped rental, and sporting goods rental)

Restaurant

5812   Eating places (includes sit-down, carry-out, and fast food)

Resume Service

7338   Secretarial and court reporting services (includes resume writing services)

Roofing Contractor

1761   Roofing, siding, and sheet metal work

Satellite Dish Service

4841   Cable and other pay television services (includes direct broadcast satellite services and satellite master antenna systems services)

Screen Printing Business

2261   Finishers of broadwoven fabrics of cotton (includes printing and finishing of cotton broadwoven fabrics)

2262   Finishers of broadwoven fabrics of manmade fiber and silk (includes printing manmade fiber and silk broadwoven fabrics)

2759   Commercial printing, nec (includes screen printing on glass, plastics, paper, and metal, including highway signs)

Security Systems Service

7382   Security systems services

Seminar Planner/Lecturer

8999   Services, nec (including lecturers)

Service Station/Auto Repair and Service Shop

5541   Gasoline service stations

7532   Top, body, and upholstery repair shops and paint shops

7533   Automotive exhaust system repair shops

7534   Tire retreading and repair shops

7536   Automotive glass replacement shops

7537   Automotive transmission repair shops

7538   General automotive repair shops

7539   Automotive repair shops, nec

Sewer and Drain Cleaning Business

7699   Repair shops and related services, nec (includes sewer cleaning and rodding and septic tank cleaning)

Sewing Center

5722   Household appliance stores (includes retail sewing machine stores)

5949   Sewing, needlework, and piece goods stores

7699   Repair shops and related services, nec (includes sewing machine repair shops)

Shoe Repair Shop

7251   Shoe repair shops and shoe-shine parlors

Shoe Store

5661   Shoe stores

Sign Shop

3993   Signs and advertising specialties

7389   Business services, nec (includes sign painting shops)

Silk Plant Shop

5999   Miscellaneous retail stores, nec (includes artificial flowers—retail)

Skating Rink Operation

7999   Amusement and recreation services, nec (includes ice and roller skating rink operations)

Ski Shop

5941   Sporting goods stores and bicycle shops

Software Publishing

7372   Packaged software

Solar Energy Design/Contracting Business

1711   Plumbing, heating, and air-conditioning contractors (includes solar heating apparatus contractors)

1742   Plastering, dry wall, acoustical, and insulation work (includes solar reflecting insulation film contractors)

Specialized Staffing

7361   Employment Agencies

7363   Help Supply Services

Specialty/Gourmet Foods/Wine Shop

5499   Miscellaneous food stores

5921   Liquor stores (includes packaged wine—retail)

Sporting Goods Store

5941   Sporting goods stores and bicycle shops

Sports Promotional Services

7941   Professional Sports Clubs and Promoters

Surveying Service

8713   Surveying services (includes surveying: land, water, and aerial)

Swimming Pool/Hot Tub Business

1799   Special trade contractors, nec (includes swimming pool construction contractors)

5999   Miscellaneous retail stores, nec (includes hot tubs, retail)

7389   Business services, nec (includes swimming pool cleaning and maintenance services)

7999   Amusement and recreation services, nec (includes swimming pool operations)

Tailor Shop

5699   Miscellaneous apparel and accessory stores (includes custom tailor shops) 7219 Laundry and garment services, nec (includes tailor shops, except custom or merchant tailors)

Talent Agency

7922   Theatrical producers and miscellaneous theatrical services (includes agents)

Tanning Parlor/Sauna

7299   Miscellaneous personal services (includes steam baths and tanning salons)

Tattoo Parlor

7299   Miscellaneous personal services, nec (includes tattoo parlors)

Tax Preparation Business

7291   Tax return preparation services

8721   Accounting, auditing, and bookkeeping services

Taxicab/Van Shuttle Service

4121   Taxicabs

Taxidermy Service

7699   Repair shops and related services, nec (includes taxidermy)

Teacher Supply Store

5999   Miscellaneous retail stores, nec

Telemarketing Service

7389   Business services, nec (includes telemarketing services operating on a contract or fee basis)

Telephone Answering Service

7389   Business services, nec (includes answering services)

Television/Radio Repair Service

7622   Radio and television repair shops

Television Station

4833   Television broadcasting stations

Temporary Employment Agency

7363   Help supply services (includes temporary help services

Tennis Court/Racquet Club Operation

7997   Membership sports and recreation clubs (includes racquetball and tennis clubs)

7999   Amusement and recreation services, nec (includes nonmembership racquetball and tennis court operations)

Tire Dealer

5531   Auto and home supply stores (includes retail tire dealers) 7534 Tire retreading and repair shops

Tobacco Shop

5993   Tobacco stores and stands

Tour Guide Operation/Adventure Service

4725   Tour operations

7999   Amusement and recreation services, nec (includes tour guides)

Toy Business

5945   Hobby, toy, and game shops

Trade Show/Conference Management Service

7389   Business services, nec (includes trade show arrangement)

Translating/Interpreting Service

7389   Business services, nec (includes translation service)

Travel Agency

4724   Travel agencies

Trucking Business

4212   Local trucking, without storage services

4213   Trucking, except local

4214   Local trucking, with storage services

Tutoring Service

8299   Schools and educational services, nec (includes tutoring services)

Typesetting Business

2791   Typesetting

Typing/Stenographic Service

7338   Secretarial and court reporting services (includes stenographic and typing services)

Upholstery/Carpet Services

1752   Floor laying and other floor work, nec (includes carpet laying and removing services)

5714   Drapery, curtain, and upholstery stores (includes upholstery materials stores)

7217   Carpet and upholstery cleaning

Vending Machine Merchandising and Service Business

5962   Automatic merchandising machine operators (includes retail sale of products through vending machines)

7359   Equipment rental and leasing services, nec (includes vending machine rental businesses)

Vision Center

5995   Optical goods stores

Voice Mail Service

4813   Telephone communications, except radiotelephone (includes voice telephone communications)

Water Conditioning Service

7389   Business services, nec (includes water softener services)

Web Site Design

7371   Computer programming services (includes custom computer programs or systems software development and computer software systems analysis and design)

Weight Reduction/Control Center

7991   Physical fitness facilities (includes reducing facilities and slenderizing salons)

Welcome Service

7389   Business service, nec (includes welcoming service)

Window Dressing Business

3993   Signs and advertising specialties (includes advertising displays, except printed, and window and lobby cutouts and displays)

7319   Advertising, nec (includes display advertising services, except outdoor)

Word Processing Service

7338   Secretarial and court reporting services (includes word processing services)

START-UP INFORMATION

8086 ■ *"Organic Chain Scouting Cincinatti Sites, Including Kenwood" in Business Courier (Vol. 27, December 3, 2010, No. 31, pp. 1)*

Pub: Business Courier

Ed: Tom Demeropolis. **Description:** Asheville, North Carolina-based Earth Fare has been planning to add a total of six stores in 2011, including the potential opening of more than one store in the Greater Cincinnati area market. Earth Fare has not named specific locations but Kenwood area was reportedly being considered for its first location. Insights on growing trends toward health food stores are also given. **Availability:** Print; Online.

8087 ■ *"Sustainable Advantage" in Inc. (Vol. 36, September 2014, No. 7, pp. 86)*

Pub: Mansueto Ventures L.L.C.

Contact: Stephanie Mehta, Chief Executive Officer

Price: $8.95, hardcopy black and white. **Description:** Four startup companies committed to providing sustainable, eco-friendly products and services while protecting the environment and bettering human health are profiled. Holganix(TM) offers organic lawn care products; Motiv Power Systems electrifies large vehicles; Clean Energy Collective Solar Power builds lareg community solar panel arrays; and Protein Bar offers healthy alternatives to fast food in its chain of restaurants. The company also works with nonprofits focused on wellness and education and has created 167 Learning Gardens nationwide. **Availability:** Print; PDF; Online.

ASSOCIATIONS AND OTHER ORGANIZATIONS

8088 ■ Canadian Health Food Association (CHFA) [Association Canadienne des Aliements de Sante]
235 Yorkland Blvd., Ste. 201
  Toronto, ON, Canada M2J 4Y8
Free: 800-661-4510
Co. E-mail: info@chfa.ca
URL: http://chfa.ca/en
Contact: Aaron Skelton, President
Facebook: www.facebook.com/CAhealthfood
X (Twitter): x.com/cdnhealthfood
Instagram: www.instagram.com/cahealthfood
YouTube: www.youtube.com/user/cdnhealthfood

Description: Seeks to advance the health food industries. Facilitates communication and cooperation among members; represents the commercial and regulatory interests of the health food industries; sponsors educational and promotional programs. **Publications:** *The Natural Voice* (5/year). **Educational Activities:** CHFA West (Annual); CHFA East Tradeshow (Annual). **Geographic Preference:** National.

8089 ■ Holistic Entrepreneur Association (HEA)
Co. E-mail: jessica@holisticentrepreneurassociation.com
URL: http://www.holisticentrepreneurassociation.com
Contact: Rachel Jessica Huxtable, Contact
Facebook: www.facebook.com/HolisticEn trepreneurAssociation

Description: Online organization that provides business support for natural health professionals. Offers strategies for acquiring clients, training for social media and digital marketing, insights from successful practitioners, client resources, and a strategy for establishing and running a successful business.

8090 ■ National Restaurant Association (NRA)
2055 L St. NW, Ste. 700
  Washington, DC 20036
Ph: (202)331-5900
Free: 800-424-5156
Co. E-mail: askus@restaurant.org
URL: http://www.restaurant.org
Contact: Michelle Korsmo, President
Facebook: www.facebook.com/WeRRestaurants
Linkedin: www.linkedin.com/company/22205
X (Twitter): x.com/WeRRestaurants
Instagram: www.instagram.com/werrestaurants
YouTube: www.youtube.com/user/restaurantdotorg

Description: Restaurants, cafeterias, contract foodservice management, drive-ins, caterers, institutional food services and other members of the foodservice industry; represents establishments belonging to nonaffiliated state and local restaurant associations in governmental affairs. Supports foodservice education and research in several educational institutions. Affiliated with the Educational Foundation of the National Restaurant Association to provide training and education for operators, food and equipment manufacturers, distributors and educators. **Founded:** 1919. **Publications:** *Restaurants USA: The Monthly Magazine of the National Restaurant Assn* (Monthly); *Who's Who in the Foodservice Industry*; *Restaurant Information Abstracts* (Biweekly); *Foodservice/ Hospitality College Directory* (Irregular); *National Restaurant Association--Washington Report* (Semimonthly); *Restaurant Operations Report*. **Educational Activities:** National Restaurant Association Restaurant and Hotel-Motel Show (Annual). **Awards:** John L. Hennessy Award (Annual); NRA Restaurant Neighbor Award (Annual). **Geographic Preference:** National.

8091 ■ Restaurants Canada - Library
1155 Queen St. W
  Toronto, ON, Canada M6J 1J4
Ph: (416)923-8416
Free: 800-387-5649
Fax: (416)923-1450
Co. E-mail: info@restaurantscanada.org
URL: http://www.restaurantscanada.org
Contact: Christian Buhagiar, Co-Chief Executive Officer Co-President
Facebook: www.facebook.com/RestaurantsCanada

Linkedin: www.linkedin.com/company/restaurants -canada
X (Twitter): x.com/RestaurantsCA
Instagram: www.instagram.com/RestaurantsCanada
YouTube: www.youtube.com/channel/ UCxVckfCBllSll9LOuflNX8w

Description: Restaurant and food service corporations, hotels, caterers, and food service suppliers and educators, seeks to create a favorable business environment for members. **Scope:** Food service; quantity cooking; legislation; administration; management; statistics; training; customer attitude surveys. **Services:** Copying; open to the public on fee basis. **Founded:** 1944. **Publications:** *CRFA National Hospitality News*; *Canadian Foodservice Industry Operations Report* (Biennial); *Foodservice Facts* (Annual); *Legislation Guide* (Quarterly). **Educational Activities:** Restaurants Canada Show (Annual); ApEx. **Geographic Preference:** National.

REFERENCE WORKS

8092 ■ *"Careers in Organic Food Production" in Occupational Outlook Quarterly (Vol. 54, Fall 2010, No. 3, pp. 3)*

Pub: U.S. Department of Labor Bureau of Labor Statistics
Contact: Amrit Kohli, Director
E-mail: kohli.amrit@bls.gov

Ed: Adam Bibler. **Description:** Organic methods of food production, including methods that combine science with traditional farming practices, are outlined. Facts regarding careers in organic food preparation are presented. **Availability:** Online; PDF.

8093 ■ *"Drink Up!" in (Vol. 92, July 23, 2012, No. 30, pp. 19)*

Pub: Dow Jones & Company Inc.
Contact: Almar Latour, Chief Executive Officer

Ed: Robin Goldwyn Blumenthal. **Description:** Juice bars in the US are expanding as Americans increase the consumption of fresh vegetable and fruit juices. Coffeehouse chain Starbucks entered the market by introducing Evolution Fresh, a seller of coldpressed vegetable and fruit juices. The health benefits of fresh vegetable and fruit juice, however, remain uncertain. **Availability:** Online.

8094 ■ *"Effort Is Growing to Offer Healthier Choices in Vending Machines" in Philadelphia Inquirer (July 29, 2011)*

Ed: Don Sapatkin. **Description:** Since Boston's mayor announced a ban on the sale of all sugar sweetened beverages on city properties, it seems more cities, states, hospitals, businesses, and even park systems are following suit. Thus, vending machines are beginning to offer healthier snacks and drinks to consumers.

8095 ■ *"Garden Bargains: Restaurant Cut Costs With Homegrown Foods" in Washington Business Journal (Vol. 33, August 22, 2014, No. 18, pp. 6)*

Pub: American City Business Journals, Inc.
Contact: Mike Olivieri, Executive Vice President

Released: Weekly. **Price:** $4, introductory 4-week offer(Digital & Print). **Description:** A number of chefs and restaurants in Washington DC are seeing the benefits of growing their own healthy kitchen gardens. The Urbana restaurant is saving $250 monthly in herbs since it started planting them in 2014 and chef, Ethan McKee expects to increase that savings to $75 monthly in 2015. **Availability:** Print; Online.

8096 ■ *"Hain Celestial Acquires Greek Gods Yogurt" in Ice Cream Reporter (Vol. 23, July 20, 2010, No. 8, pp. 1)*
Description: Hain Celestial Group acquired The Greek Gods LLC. Hain Celestial is a natural and organic products company and Greek Gods makes all natural, Greek-style yogurt and ice cream. **Availability:** Print; Online.

8097 ■ *"Healthful, Organic Food is the Name of the Game at Renee's" in AZ Daily Star (May 10, 2012)*
Pub: McClatchy Tribune Information Services
Contact: Patrick J. Talamantes, President

Ed: Kristen Cook. **Description:** Profile of Renee's Organic Oven offer organic and locally grown foods at their restaurant. The eatery is owned by husband and wife team, Steve and Renee Kreager. **Availability:** Online.

8098 ■ *"Healthy Fast Food Acquires Rights to U-Swirl Yogurt" in Ice Cream Reporter (Vol. 21, October 20, 2008, No. 11, pp. 5)*
Description: Healthy Fast Food Inc. will acquire worldwide rights to U-Swirl Frozen Yogurt; the firm will use the new acquisition to create a yogurt superstore in a cafe setting concept for its operations. **Availability:** Print; Online.

8099 ■ *"Healthy Foods Drive Dining Choices" in National Restaurant Association (July 25, 2017)*
URL(s): restaurant.org/Articles/News/Batch2_20190 1/State-of-the-Industry-Healthy-foods-drive-dining-c
Released: July 25, 2017. **Description:** According to the State of the Industry report compiled by the National Restaurant Association, diners want healthier options and this influences where they dine out. Locally sources and environmentally friendly food is also important to diners, especially if they are from the younger generations. **Availability:** Online.

8100 ■ *"In the Raw: Karyn Calabrese Brings Healthy Dining to a New Sophisticated Level" in Black Enterprise (Vol. 41, September 2010)*
Pub: Earl G. Graves Ltd.
Contact: Earl Graves, Jr., President

Ed: Sonia Alleyne. **Description:** Profile of Karyn Calabrese whose businesses are based in Chicago, Illinois. Calabrese has launched a complete line of products (vitamins and beauty items), services (spa, chiropractic, and acupuncture treatments), and restaurants to bring health dining and lifestyles to a better level. **Availability:** Online.

8101 ■ *"Making Healthy Food Affordable for All" in U.S. News & World Report (October 16, 2019)*
URL(s): www.usnews.com/news/healthiest-communi ties/articles/2019-10-16/sam-polk-of-everytable-on -making-healthy-food-affordable-for-all
Ed: Katelyn Newman. **Released:** October 16, 2019. **Description:** The restaurant chain, Everytable, has introduced a new concept for dining: What you pay depends on where you are. Everytable serves up healthy meals, but if you are in pricey LA where the median income is higher than average, expect to pay more for the same meal that is located at the Compton location. This model allows people with less to enjoy and benefit from healthy meals while dining out instead of deterring them with their price. **Availability:** Online.

8102 ■ *"Once Derided As Rabbit Food, Humble Salad Now Fuels Business Plans" in Dallas Business Journal (Vol. 35, August 17, 2012, No. 49, pp. 1)*
Pub: Baltimore Business Journal
Contact: Rhonda Pringle, President

E-mail: rpringle@bizjournals.com
Description: Establishments offering salad concepts are on the rise in Dallas, Texas. The Salad Stop, Greenz, Salata are only some of the restaurants that have ventured into meeting the demand for health food, particularly salads. The market is only getting bigger, urging the restaurants to expand in services and facilities. The beginnings, food choices, and business plans of these restaurants are discussed.

8103 ■ *"Quick Service Restaurants Spring in a New Direction with Focus on Healthy, High Quality Menus" in Forbes (August 8, 2018)*
URL(s): www.forbes.com/sites/garyocchiogrosso/20 18/08/08/new-quick-service-restaurants-sprint-in-a -new-direction-with-on-focus-on-healthy-high-quality -menus/#66b4211226e7
Ed: Gary Occhiogrosso. **Released:** August 08, 2018. **Description:** More consumers are taking a proactive approach to healthy eating, and restaurants and fast food places have taken notice. Referred to as the "Quick Service Restaurant," these eating establishments encompass fast food giants along with smaller, healthier brands. There is often a higher cost associated with healthier fast food, but consumers aren't too particular about price. **Availability:** Online.

8104 ■ *"R&R Launches Upscale Spoony's and Low Fat Dragon's Den" in Ice Cream Reporter (Vol. 23, August 20, 2010, No. 9, pp. 3)*
Description: European ice cream manufacturer R&R has acquired French ice cream maker Rolland and will position itself as an upscale challenger to brands like Ben & Jerry's. **Availability:** Print; Online.

8105 ■ *"Red Mango Set to Grow in Florida" in Ice Cream Reporter (Vol. 23, September 20, 2010, No. 10, pp. 2)*
Description: Red Mango will add 12 new locations throughout Florida. The stores offer healthy, nutritious frozen yogurt, smoothies and parfaits. **Availability:** Print; Online.

8106 ■ *"Sodexo Upgrades Healthy Vending Initiative" in Entertainment Close-Up (September 25, 2011)*
Description: Sodexo launched its Your Health Your Way On-the-Go program for its vending machines across the nation. **Availability:** Online.

8107 ■ *"Yogun Fruz Adds First Location in Southern New York State" in Ice Cream Reporter (Vol. 23, September 20, 2010, No. 10, pp. 2)*
Description: Yogen Fruz signed a master franchise agreement to expand into the southern counties of New York State. The firm offers a healthy and beneficial option to fast food and typical dessert choices. **Availability:** Print; Online.

TRADE PERIODICALS

8108 ■ *Cooking for Profit*
Released: Monthly **Description:** Food service trade publication for owners/operators of food service businesses. Profiles successful operations, offers management tips, recipes with photos and step-by-step instructions, new and improved uses and maintenance of gas equipment. **Availability:** Print; Online.

8109 ■ *Foodservice and Hospitality Magazine*
Pub: Kostuch Publications Ltd.
URL(s): www.kostuchmedia.com/portfolio/foodservice -and-hospitality-magazine
Ed: Rosanna Caira. **Price:** $27.50, Canada for print; $55, U.S. for print; $65, for year outside us & Canada print. **Description:** Magazine for restaurant and hotel operators. **Availability:** Print.

8110 ■ *Restaurant Hospitality*
Pub: Informa USA Inc.
Contact: Gareth Wright, Director
URL(s): www.restaurant-hospitality.com
Facebook: www.facebook.com/RestaurantHospitality
X (Twitter): x.com/RH_restaurant

Released: Monthly **Description:** Dedicated to the success of full service restaurants and edited for chefs and other commercial foodservice professionals. Includes new food and equipment products and trends, menu and recipe ideas, industry news, new technology, food safety, emerging new concepts, consumer attitudes and trends, labor and training, and profiles of successful operations. **Availability:** Online.

8111 ■ *Vegan Journal*
Pub: Vegetarian Resource Group
Contact: Charles Stahler, Contact
URL(s): www.vrg.org/journal/index.php
Ed: Jane Michalek, Keryl Cryer, Carole Hamlin, Charles Stahler. **Released:** Quarterly **Price:** $35, Canada and Mexico; $45, Other countries; $35, U.S. for two years; $25, U.S. for 1 year. **Description:** Focuses on the ethical and nutritional aspects of vegetarianism, as well as health, ecology, animal rights, and world hunger. Recurring features include product reviews, recipes, a calendar of events, and reviews of scientific and informational articles. **Availability:** Print; PDF; Online.

8112 ■ *Vegetarian Journal's Foodservice Update*
Pub: Vegetarian Resource Group
Contact: Charles Stahler, Contact
URL(s): www.vrg.org/fsupdate/index.htm
Released: Quarterly; winter, summer, spring, fall. **Price:** $25, for 1 year membership; $35, for 2 year membership. **Description:** Provides information about serving vegetarian meals in institutions. Includes advice and recipes. **Availability:** PDF.

TRADE SHOWS AND CONVENTIONS

8113 ■ *ApEx*
Restaurants Canada
1155 Queen St. W
Toronto, ON, Canada M6J 1J4
Ph: (416)923-8416
Free: 800-387-5649
Fax: (416)923-1450
Co. E-mail: info@restaurantscanada.org
URL: http://www.restaurantscanada.org
Contact: Christian Buhagiar, Co-Chief Executive Officer Co-President
URL(s): www.apextradeshow.ca
Description: Products and services for the restaurant and hospitality industry, as well as institutions, convenience stores, delis and bakeries. **Audience:** Industry professionals. **Principal Exhibits:** Products and services for the restaurant and hospitality industry, as well as institutions, convenience stores, delis and bakeries. **Telecommunication Services:** chuckn@mediaedge.ca.

8114 ■ *Michigan Restaurant Show*
Michigan Restaurant & Lodging Association (MRLA)
225 W Washtenaw St.
Lansing, MI 48933
Free: 800-968-9668
URL: http://www.mrla.org
Contact: Justin Winslow, President
URL(s): www.mrlashow.org
Frequency: Annual. **Description:** Equipment, supplies, and services for the food service industry. **Audience:** Industry professionals and public. **Principal Exhibits:** Equipment, supplies, and services for the food service industry.

8115 ■ *Western Food Service & Hospitality Expo Los Angeles*
California Restaurant Association (CRA)
621 Capitol Mall, Ste. 2000
Sacramento, CA 95814
Free: 800-765-4842
Fax: (916)200-3453
Co. E-mail: membership@calrest.org
URL: http://www.calrest.org
Contact: Jot Condie, President
E-mail: jcondie@calrest.org
URL(s): www.westernfoodexpo.com

Description: Food, equipment, supplies, and services for food service and lodging industries. **Audience:** Restaurant, food service, hospitality and lodging industry professionals. **Principal Exhibits:** Food, equipment, supplies, and services for food service and lodging industries. **Telecommunication Services:** californiarestaurantshow@xpressreg.net.

8116 ■ WestEx - Colorado Foodservice & Restaurant Conference
Sapporo
  1-1, Odori Nishi, Chuo-ku
  Sapporo, Hokkaido 060-8703, Japan
URL: http://www.nhk.or.jp
URL(s): www.coloradorestaurant.com/education-even
  ts/calendar/61_2015-WestEx:-Colorado-Restauran
  t-&-Foodservice-Conference
Description: Food service and lodging products, equipment, and services. **Audience:** Food service and restaurant industry personnel. **Principal Exhibits:** Food service and lodging products, equipment, and services.

CONSULTANTS

8117 ■ Birchfield Jacobs Foodsystems Inc.
519 N Charles St.
  Baltimore, MD 21201
Contact: John C. Birchfield, Jr., Contact
E-mail: jbirchfield@birchfieldjacobs.com
Description: Firm provides foodservice consulting services.

8118 ■ Linda Lipsky Restaurant Consultants Inc.
216 Foxcroft Rd.
  Broomall, PA 19008
Ph: (610)325-3663
Co. E-mail: lipsky@restaurantconsult.com
URL: http://restaurantconsult.com
Contact: Linda Lipsky, Founder
E-mail: lipsky@restaurantconsult.com
Description: Provider of marketing and survey solutions such as management training, evaluation programs, recipe documentation, cost analysis and bridge management services for restaurants. **Scope:** Provider of marketing and survey solutions such as management training, evaluation programs, recipe documentation, cost analysis and bridge management services for restaurants. **Founded:** 1988. **Training:** Designing Menus for Maximum Sales and Profits; How to Maximize Your Check Average.

FRANCHISES AND BUSINESS OPPORTUNITIES

8119 ■ Evos
609 S Howard Ave.
  Tampa, FL 33606
Ph: (813)258-3867
Free: 877-888-EVOS
Fax: (813)258-9899
Co. E-mail: comments@evos.com
URL: http://evos.com
Facebook: www.facebook.com/evosfeelgreatfood
Instagram: www.instagram.com/evosfeelgreatfood

Description: Chain of fast food restaurants. **Founded:** 1994. **Financial Assistance:** Yes **Training:** Provides 4-6 weeks training at headquarters and ongoing support.

8120 ■ Ho-Lee-Chow
2202 Danforth Ave.
  Toronto, ON, Canada M4C 1K3
Ph: (416)465-3333
Co. E-mail: customercare@holeechow.com
URL: http://holeechow.com
Founded: 1988. **Training:** Offers 4-6 weeks and ongoing support provided.

8121 ■ Subway IP LLC
Roark Capital Group
  325 Sub Way
  Milford, CT 06461
Ph: (404)591-5200
Fax: (404)591-5201
Co. E-mail: contact@roarkcapital.com
URL: http://www.roarkcapital.com
Contact: John Chidsey, Chief Executive Officer
Facebook: www.facebook.com/subway
X (Twitter): twitter.com/subway
Instagram: www.instagram.com/subway
YouTube: www.youtube.com/user/subway
Description: Operates chain of fast food restaurants. **Founded:** 1965. **Training:** Provides training and assistance to franchisees in all areas of business operation.

COMPUTERIZED DATABASES

8122 ■ FDA Food Code
URL(s): www.fda.gov/food/retail-food-protection/fda
  -food-code
Released: Semiannual **Availability:** PDF. **Type:** Full-text.

LIBRARIES

8123 ■ Academy of Nutrition and Dietetics (AND) - Library
120 S Riverside Plz., Ste. 2190
  Chicago, IL 60606-6995
Ph: (312)899-0040
Free: 800-877-1600
URL: http://www.eatright.org
Contact: Kevin L. Sauer, President
X (Twitter): x.com/eatright
YouTube: www.youtube.com/user/EatRightTV
Pinterest: www.pinterest.com/kidseatright
Description: Represents food and nutrition professionals. Promotes nutrition, health and well-being. **Scope:** Food and nutrition. **Services:** Library not open to the public. **Founded:** 1917. **Holdings:** Figures not available. **Publications:** *Weight Loss Matters: Your Weight and Your Health Pamphlet*; *Find a Nutrition Professional Consumer Search*; *Directory of Columbus Registered Dietitians*; *Directory of Registered Dietitians*; *Directory of Dietetics Programs* (Annual); *Directory of Consulting Dietitians in Private Practice*; *Journal of the Academy of Nutrition and Dietetics* (Monthly). **Educational Activities:** Food Nutrition Conference Expo (FNCE) (Annual).

8124 ■ City College of San Francisco (CCSF) - Culinary Arts and Hospitality Studies - Alice Statler Library
50 Frida Kahlo Way
  Statler Wing, Rm. 10
  San Francisco, CA 94112
Ph: (415)239-3460
URL: http://library.ccsf.edu/locations/statler
Scope: Culinary arts and hospitality study; historical menus; notable titles; local chefs, restaurateurs, hoteliers and entrepreneurs in the industry. **Services:** Copying; Wi-Fi; library open to the public for reference use only. **Founded:** 1964. **Holdings:** Books; menus; archives; monographs; periodicals; DVDs.

8125 ■ Geisinger Medical Center (GMC) - Health Sciences Library
100 N Academy Ave.
  Danville, PA 17822
Ph: (570)271-6211
URL: http://www.geisinger.org/patient-care/find-a-loca
  tion/geisinger-medical-center
Description: Community radio station currently operating out of the French Quarter in New Orleans. **Scope:** Medical. **Services:** Library not open to public. **Founded:** 1996. **Holdings:** Figures not available.

8126 ■ Le Cordon Bleu College of Culinary Arts Library
350 Rhode Island St.
  San Francisco, CA 94103
URL: http://www.careered.com/closedschool/loca
  tions
Scope: Culinary arts; nutrition; restaurant and hospitality industry. **Services:** Library open to the public by special appointment only. **Founded:** 1989. **Holdings:** 3,500 books.

8127 ■ Lemmen-Holton Cancer Pavilion Library
145 Michigan St. NE
  Grand Rapids, MI 49503
Ph: (616)486-5700
URL: http://findadoctor.spectrumhealth.org/location/
  profile/7989
Description: Provide a full range of cancer services including, prevention, screening and diagnosis, personalized cancer treatment, integrative therapies, supportive care services, access to clinical trials and leading edge technology. **Scope:** Medicine; literature. **Holdings:** Books.

8128 ■ Voice for Animals, Inc. (VOICE) - Library
PO Box 120095
  San Antonio, TX 78212
Ph: (210)737-3138
Co. E-mail: voice@voiceforanimals.org
URL: http://www.voiceforanimals.org
Contact: Rachel Z. Wolf, Contact
Description: Individuals with an interest in animal rights. Seeks to raise public awareness of animal rights issues. Works to abolish "the systematic abuse of nonhuman animals." Conducts educational programs. **Scope:** Animal rights. **Founded:** 1987. **Holdings:** Figures not available. **Geographic Preference:** National.

ASSOCIATIONS AND OTHER ORGANIZATIONS

8129 ■ Academy of Doctors of Audiology (ADA)
446 E High St., Ste. 10
  Lexington, KY 40507
Free: 866-493-5544
Co. E-mail: info@audiologist.org
URL: http://www.audiologist.org
Contact: Kristin Davis, President
Facebook: www.facebook.com/AcademyOfDoc
  torsOfAudiology
X (Twitter): x.com/AcadDocAud

Description: Individuals with graduate degrees in audiology who dispense hearing aids as part of a rehabilitative practice. Fosters and supports professional dispensing of hearing aids by qualified audiologists; encourages audiology training programs to include pertinent aspects of hearing aid dispensing in their curriculums; conducts seminars on the business aspects of the hearing aid industry. **Founded:** 1977. **Publications:** *ADA Membership Directory; Academy of Doctors of Audiology--Membership Directory* (Annual). **Awards:** Joel Wernick Award (Irregular). **Geographic Preference:** National.

8130 ■ American Auditory Society (AAS)
PO Box 779
  Pennsville, NJ 08070
Free: 877-746-8315
Fax: (650)763-9185
Co. E-mail: amaudsoc@comcast.net
URL: http://www.amauditorysoc.org
Contact: René Gifford, President

Description: Works to increase knowledge and understanding of: the ear, hearing, and balance; disorders of the ear, hearing, and balance; prevention of these disorders; habilitation and rehabilitation of individuals with hearing and balance dysfunction. **Founded:** 1976. **Publications:** *Ear and Hearing* (Bimonthly); *The Bulletin of the American Auditory Society* (Semiannual). **Awards:** Raymond Carhart Memorial Lecture and Award (Annual); AAS Lifetime Achievement Award (Annual). **Geographic Preference:** National.

8131 ■ HEAR Center
301 E Del Mar Blvd.
  Pasadena, CA 91101
Ph: (626)796-2016
Fax: (626)796-2320
Co. E-mail: info@hearcenter.org
URL: http://www.hearcenter.org
Contact: Armida Baylon, President
Facebook: www.facebook.com/hearcenter
Instagram: www.instagram.com/hearcenter1954
YouTube: www.youtube.com/channel/UCX
  2xUyAlGo9RJ4uVHolF4PA

Description: Seeks to develop auditory techniques to aid people who have communication problems due to deafness. **Founded:** 1954. **Publications:** *HEAR Center Proceedings* (Periodic); *The Listener* (8/year). **Geographic Preference:** National.

8132 ■ Hearing Industries Association (HIA)
1301 K St. NW, Ste. 300W
  Washington, DC 20005
Ph: (202)975-0905
Co. E-mail: info@betterhearing.org
URL: http://betterhearing.org
Contact: Kate Carr, President
Facebook: www.facebook.com/betterhearingHIA
X (Twitter): x.com/better_hearing

Description: Companies engaged in the manufacture and/or sale of electronic hearing aids, their component parts, and related products and services on a national basis. Cooperates in and contributes toward efforts to promote the number of hearing aid users; collects trade statistics; conducts market research activities, investigations, and studies in connection with hearing and hearing aids. **Founded:** 1955. **Geographic Preference:** National.

8133 ■ International Hearing Society (IHS)
33900 W 8 Mile Rd., Ste. 101
  Farmington Hills, MI 48335
Ph: (734)522-7200
Fax: (734)522-0200
Co. E-mail: interact@ihsinfo.org
URL: http://www.ihsinfo.org/home
Contact: Patrick Kochanowski, President
Facebook: www.facebook.com/ihsinfo
Linkedin: www.linkedin.com/company/ihsinfo
Instagram: www.instagram.com/ihsinfo

Description: Accredits seminars and workshops for the education of hearing aid specialists. Maintains the International Institute for Hearing Instruments Studies as the educational arm of the society. **Founded:** 1951. **Publications:** *International Hearing Aid Society; International Hearing Society--Directory of Members; The Hearing Professional: Official Journal of the International Hearing Society* (Quarterly). **Geographic Preference:** National.

REFERENCE WORKS

8134 ■ "I Hate My Hearing Aids. What Do I Do?" in Healthy Hearing (November 12, 2019)
URL(s): www.healthyhearing.com/report/53024-I-hate
  -my-hearing-aids

Ed: Debbie Clason. **Released:** November 12, 2019. **Description:** A guide to how to like your new hearing aids. Most people who first receive hearing aids, are not used to them and find them to be uncomfortable. Learning to adjust to these devices is key, because your brain is not used to hearing particular sounds and must relearn them. **Availability:** Online.

8135 ■ "Ten Questions to Ask Your Hearing Health Professional" in Healthy Hearing (October 28, 2019)
URL(s): www.healthyhearing.com/report/52530-10
  -questions-to-ask-your-hearing-healthcare
  -professional

Ed: Debbie Clason. **Released:** October 28, 2019. **Description:** Knowing what to ask your hearing health professional is a key component to receiving excellent care. Included are the ten questions that can be printed out and brought along to the appointment, and each question expands into more information that you may find helpful when dealing with hearing loss. **Availability:** Online.

TRADE PERIODICALS

8136 ■ Volta Voices
Pub: Alexander Graham Bell Association for the
  Deaf & Hard of Hearing
Contact: Emilio Alonso-Mendoza, Chief Executive
  Officer
URL(s): agbell.org/volta-voices

Released: Quarterly **Description:** Magazine providing news and feature articles of interest to the deaf and hearing impaired-child, parent, adult, and professional. **Availability:** Online.

FRANCHISES AND BUSINESS OPPORTUNITIES

8137 ■ Miracle Ear
150 S 5th St., Ste. 2300
  Minneapolis, MN 55402
Free: 800-241-1372
URL: http://www.miracle-ear.com
Contact: Brian J. Hill, Director
Facebook: www.facebook.com/miracleear
YouTube: www.youtube.com/channel/UCgNqKZsU
  5UYEg077oo1CzRg

Description: Manufacturer and retailer of hearing aids. **No. of Franchise Units:** 175. **Founded:** 1948. **Training:** Yes.

LIBRARIES

8138 ■ Atlanta-Fulton Public Library - Learning and Career Center
1 Margaret Mitchell Sq., NW
  Atlanta, GA 30303
Co. E-mail: librarycomments@fultoncountyga.gov
URL: http://www.fulcolibrary.org

Description: Cultural and intellectual center that enriches the community and empowers all residents with essential tools for lifelong learning. **Scope:** Difficult problems and providing intellectual resources. **Services:** Interlibrary loan; copying; free Wi-Fi; library open to the public. **Founded:** 1902. **Holdings:** CD-ROMs.

8139 ■ Central Institute for the Deaf (CID)
825 S Taylor Ave.
  Saint Louis, MO 63110
Ph: (314)977-0132
Free: 877-444-4574
Fax: (314)977-0023
Co. E-mail: cid@cid.edu
URL: http://www.cid.edu
Contact: David J. Schepers, President

Description: Publishes materials to help parents and teachers and test kits to assist in the evaluation and instruction of hearing-impaired children. Reaches market through direct mail. Does not accept unsolicited manuscripts. **Founded:** 1914.

8140 ■ Oregon Health and Science University - Oregon Hearing Research Center (OHRC) - Library
3181 SW Sam Jackson Park Rd., NRC04
  Portland, OR 97239
Ph: (503)494-8032
Fax: (503)494-5656
Co. E-mail: ohrc@ohsu.edu
URL: http://www.ohsu.edu/oregon-hearing-research
  -center
Contact: Dennis R. Trune, Professor
E-mail: truned@ohsu.edu
Description: Integral unit of Oregon Health and Science University. **Scope:** Hearing problems, including clinical studies of ototoxicity, vestibular physiology, noise damage, anatomy of the ear, tinnitus, and interactions between various insults to the ear, through a multiple attack utilizing electrophysiological measures, behavioral measures, histological evaluations, and human psychophysics. **Founded:** 1966. **Holdings:** Figures not available.

RESEARCH CENTERS

8141 ■ The Houston Ear Research Foundation
7737 SW Fwy., Ste. 630
  Houston, TX 77074
Contact: Walter G. McReynolds, Contact
Description: Houston ear research foundation. **Scope:** Provides candidacy testing to determine if adults and children are cochlear implant candidates;

provides initial hook up and follow up reprogramming and testing for cochlear implant recipients; provides aural rehabilitation therapy for cochlear implant recipients. **Founded:** 1983. **Publications:** *HERF Newsletter* (Annual).

8142 ■ University of Michigan - Kresge Hearing Research Institute (KHRI)
4605 Medical Science Unit II
  Ann Arbor, MI 48109-5616
Ph: (734)764-8110
URL: http://www.medicine.umich.edu/dept/kresge
  -hearing-research-institute
Contact: Dr. Gabriel Corfas, Director
E-mail: corfas@umich.edu
Description: Integral unit of University of Michigan Medical School, affiliated with its Department of Otolaryngology at University Medical Center. **Scope:** Auditory physiology and pathology, including studies on the reception, coding and processing of complex speech signals by the auditory system, transduction processes of the inner ear, cochlear blood flow and inner ear metabolism, development of cochlear prostheses and appropriate speech processor schemes, immune mediated hearing loss, the effects of age and environmental stress factors on hearing, biochemistry and motility of hair cells, afferent and efferent transmitters of the inner ear, psychophysics of hearing in normal individuals, immunology and immune systems related to squamous cell carcinoma, mechanisms of sound, localization, molecular biology and genetics of the inner ear, and human genetics (linkage studies). **Founded:** 1960. **Educational Activities:** Hearing, Balance and Chemical Senses Seminar Series (Weekly (Thurs.)).

8143 ■ University of Oklahoma - College of Allied Health Clinics - John W. Keys Speech and Hearing Center
1200 North Stonewall Ave.
  Oklahoma City, OK 73117-1215

Ph: (405)271-2866
Fax: (405)271-3360
URL: http://alliedhealth.ouhsc.edu/Keys-Clinic

Description: Integral unit of College of Allied Health Clinics, University of Oklahoma. **Scope:** Loudness and acoustic reflex, temporal integration and acoustic reflex, critical bands measured with pulsation pattern psychophysical technique, sensory scaling, absolute thresholds for frequency modulated signals, bone conduction vibrator calibration, bone conduction speech audiometry, intelligibility of distorted speech, electrocochleography, brain stem auditory-evoked responses, acoustic correlates of abnormal vocal quality, aerodynamics of voice production, phonemic and morphologic studies of language of the communicatively impaired, assessment of receptive and expressive language abilities, and studies in childhood language disorders in children with attention deficit disorders.

8144 ■ University of Tulsa - Mary K. Chapman Center for Communicative Disorders
800 S Tucker Dr.
  Tulsa, OK 74104
Ph: (918)631-2504
URL: http://healthsciences.utulsa.edu/communication
  -disorders/speech-hearing-clinic

Description: Integral unit of University of Tulsa. Offers speech, language, and clinical hearing assessments. **Scope:** University that deals with communication disorders, including laryngectomy and speech, and language and hearing problems. Also conducts aid tests. **Founded:** 1947. **Educational Activities:** Annual Route 66 Conference (Annual), Communication disorders-related training and educational exhibits.

START-UP INFORMATION

8145 ■ *"Aubry & Kale Walch, Herbivorous Butcher" in Business Journal (Vol. 32, August 29, 2014, No. 14, pp. 6)*

Pub: American City Business Journals, Inc.

Contact: Mike Olivieri, Executive Vice President

Released: August 29, 2014. **Description:** Kale and Aubry Walch, founders of family-owned The Herbivorous Butcher, reveal that the process of formulating recipes for their shop took years. Aubry said that she and her brother used to make fake meats for themselves. Their plan to open a full-scale vegan butcher shop is also discussed. **Availability:** Print; Online.

8146 ■ *"No. 373: Back To the Roots" in Inc. (Vol. 36, September 2014, No. 7, pp. 82)*

Pub: Mansueto Ventures L.L.C.

Contact: Stephanie Mehta, Chief Executive Officer

Released: September 2014. **Description:** AquaFarm uses a technique called aquaponics which combines fish and plant cultivation by using fish waste to fertilize vegetation. The startup company prides itself on being part fish tank, part herb garden and sells a $60 kit for growing mushrooms. **Availability:** Print; Online.

8147 ■ *"Pot Watch: Magic Butter Delivers THC-infused Food Truck" in Puget Sound Business Journal (Vol. 35, May 30, 2014, No. 6, pp. 10)*

Pub: American City Business Journals, Inc.

Contact: Mike Olivieri, Executive Vice President

Description: Magical Butter is a startup in Seattle, Washington that sells a botanical extractor for infusing herbs into food ingredients like the active ingredient in marijuana known as THC into butter or oil. Career chef, Jeremy Cooper, has perfected the peanut butter and jelly sandwich with THC and sells them from the company's food truck business in Denver, Colorado. **Availability:** Online.

ASSOCIATIONS AND OTHER ORGANIZATIONS

8148 ■ American Herb Association (AHA)
PO Box 1673
  Nevada City, CA 95959
URL: http://ahaherb.com/american-herb-association-2
Contact: Kathi Keville, Contact

Description: Enthusiasts and specialists of medicinal herbs and herbal products. Seeks to increase knowledge and provide up-to-date scientific and experiential information on herbs. Offers a network to exchange data and resources among members nationwide. Maintains herb garden. **Founded:** 1981. **Publications:** *Directory of Mail-Order Medicinal Herb Products*; *American Herb Association - Quarterly Newsletter* (Quarterly); *Directory of Mail Order Medicinal Herbs* (Biennial); *Directory of Herbal Education* (Biennial). **Geographic Preference:** National.

8149 ■ American Herbal Products Association (AHPA)
8630 Fenton St., Ste. 918
  Silver Spring, MD 20910
Ph: (301)588-1171
Co. E-mail: ahpa@ahpa.org
URL: http://www.ahpa.org
Contact: Michael McGuffin, President
E-mail: mmcguffin@ahpa.org
Facebook: www.facebook.com/AHPAssociation
Linkedin: www.linkedin.com/company/american-herbal-products-association
X (Twitter): x.com/AHPAssociation
Instagram: www.instagram.com/ahpa1982

Description: Seeks to effectively deal with common interests and industry-related problems by acquiring, affecting and disseminating business and regulatory information. Represents industry to legislators, regulating agencies and media. **Founded:** 1982. **Publications:** *Botanical Safety Handbook*; *Herbs of Commerce*; *St. John's Wart, Ephedra, Echinacea or Saw Palmetto*. **Educational Activities:** Annual AHG Symposium (Annual). **Awards:** AHPA Herbal Hero Award (Annual); AHPA Herbal Industry Leader Award (Annual); Herbal Hero Award (Annual); AHPA Herbal Industry Leader Award (Annual); AHPA Herbal Insight Award (Annual). **Geographic Preference:** Multinational.

8150 ■ Herb Growing and Marketing Network (HGMN)
PO Box 245
  Silver Spring, PA 17575-0245
Ph: (717)368-6360
Fax: (717)393-9261
Co. E-mail: herbworld17@gmail.com
URL: http://www.herbworld.com
Contact: Maureen Rogers, Director
Facebook: www.facebook.com/herbworld
Linkedin: www.linkedin.com/herbworld
X (Twitter): x.com/herbworld

Description: Herb retailers, wholesalers, and growers; manufacturers of related products; serious hobbyists. Provides information on all segments of the herb industry with an emphasis on marketing and locating wholesale sources. **Founded:** 1990. **Publications:** *HerbWorld - Proceedings from 1st Annual Conference* ; *HerbWorld - Conference Proceedings*; *Proceedings from the 2nd Annual Herb Business Winter Getaway Conference*; *Proceedings from the 3rd Annual Herb Business Winter Getaway Conference*; *Starting an Herb Business*; *Herbal Green Pages*. **Geographic Preference:** National.

8151 ■ Herb Research Foundation (HRF) - Library
5589 Arapahoe Ave., Ste. 205
  Boulder, CO 80303
Ph: (303)449-2265
Fax: (303)449-7849
Co. E-mail: rmccaleb@herbs.org
URL: http://www.herbs.org/herbnews
Contact: Rob McCaleb, President
E-mail: rmccaleb@rmccaleb.com

Description: Professionals in the health food industry, plant research scientists, herbal medicine practitioners and their patients, pharmacologists, herbal manufacturers and trade organizations, ethnobotanists, and interested consumers; scientists and students in the fields of pharmacognosy, botany, ethnobotany, and medicine. Encourages research on the chemistry, pharmacology, and use of herbal folk medicines, teas, and other botanical products; provides a forum for discussion and cooperation among herbalists, physicians, health food advocates, and scientists. Works to form a liaison between the U.S. herbal movement and the worldwide scientific community. Disseminates research information on botanicals and serves as a source of information for the public and press on medicinal plants. Provides botanical literature research service. **Scope:** Pharmacognosy, ethnobotany, and toxicology of medicinal plants. **Founded:** 1983. **Holdings:** 300,000 scientific papers. **Publications:** *Herbal Research News* (Quarterly); *Herb Research News* (Quarterly); *Herbs for Health* (Bimonthly); *Information Services Catalog*; *HRF Reports*. **Geographic Preference:** National.

8152 ■ Herb Society of America (HSA) - Library
9019 Kirtland Chardon Rd.
  Kirtland, OH 44094
Ph: (440)256-0514
Co. E-mail: herbs@herbsociety.org
URL: http://www.herbsociety.org
Contact: Amy R. Schiavone, Co-President
Facebook: www.facebook.com/herbsocietyofamerica
X (Twitter): x.com/HerbSociety1933
Instagram: www.instagram.com/herbsocietyofamerica
Pinterest: www.pinterest.com/HerbSocietyAmer

Description: Represents scientists, educators, and others interested in botanical and horticultural research on herbs and the culinary, economic, decorative, fragrant, and historic use of herbs. Maintains herb gardens in arboreta and other public sites. Establishes and maintains gardens for the blind. Planned and funded the National Herb Garden, which was donated to the National Arboretum in Washington, DC. Promotes the knowledge of herbs through educational programs, research, and sharing the experience of its members with the community. **Scope:** Herbs and gardening. **Services:** Interlibrary loan; open to the public by appointment. **Founded:** 1933. **Holdings:** 3,500 volumes; books; periodicals; rare books; photographs; records. **Publications:** *The Herbarist* (Annual); *The Beginners Herb Garden* (Semiannual); *The Herb Society of America - South Texas Unit Newsletter* (Monthly); *Herb Society of America--Business Member Directory*. **Educational Activities:** Annual Meeting of Members and Educational Conference (Annual). **Awards:** Nashville Unit Scholarships (Annual); Pennsylvania Heartland Unit Scholarship (Annual); South Texas Unit Scholarship

(Annual); Horticulture Scholarship of the Western Reserve Herb Society (Annual); Horticulture Scholarship from Frances Sylvia Zverina (Annual); HSA Certificate of Achievement (Annual); HSA Certificate of Appreciation (Annual); Helen de Conway Little Medal of Honor (Annual); Herb Society of America Research Grant (Annual); Nancy Putnam Howard Award for Excellence in Horticulture (Annual). **Geographic Preference:** National.

8153 ■ International Herb Association (IHA)
PO Box 5667
Jacksonville, FL 32247-5667
URL: http://www.iherb.org
Facebook: www.facebook.com/InternationalHerbAssociation

Description: Herb professionals. Works to unite members for growth through promotion and education. Offers help with business concerns such as the packaging and labeling of herbal products, budgets and projections, computerized business problem solving, and retail display and design. Maintains speakers' bureau. **Founded:** 1985. **Publications:** *IHA Newsletter* (Annual); *IHA Membership Directory* (Annual). **Geographic Preference:** National.

REFERENCE WORKS

8154 ■ *Herb Society of America--Business Member Directory*
Pub: Herb Society of America
Contact: Amy R. Schiavone, Co-President
URL(s): www.herbsociety.org/get-involved/hsa-business-member-directory.html

Description: Covers 3,000 scientists, educators, and others interested in botanical and horticultural research on herbs and the culinary, economic, decorative, fragrant, and historic use of herbs. **Entries include:** Name, address, unit or region. **Arrangement:** By unit or region. **Availability:** Print.

8155 ■ *"Planting Success: Nature's Herb Farm President Shares How He Grew His Mother's Business" in San Antonio Express-News (July 8, 2019)*
URL(s): www.expressnews.com/business/business_columnists/texas_power_brokers/article/Planting-success-Nature-s-Herb-Farm-president-14077712.php

Ed: Megan Rodriguez. **Released:** July 08, 2019. **Description:** Profile of Shane Dunford, who took over and grew his mother's business, Nature's Herb Farm, into a successful staple of the community. **Availability:** Online.

8156 ■ *"St. Louis Convention Business 'Fully Recovered'" in St. Louis Business Journal (Vol. 32, July 13, 2012, No. 47, pp. 1)*
Pub: Baltimore Business Journal
Contact: Rhonda Pringle, President
E-mail: rpringle@bizjournals.com

Description: Saint Louis Convention and Visitor Commission (CVC) sales team has booked 479,991 room nights at the America's Center in its fiscal 2012, a 28 percent increased compared with 2011. The CVC also was able to book a major convention with Herbalife for the week when the Saint Loui Rams will travel to London, United Kingdom. **Availability:** Print; Online.

8157 ■ *"Waterdog Herb Farm Sees Sunny Times Ahead" in SF Weekly (October 17, 2019)*
URL(s): www.sfweekly.com/news/chemtales/waterdog-herb-farm/

Ed: Zack Ruskin. **Released:** October 17, 2019. **Description:** Profile of Waterdog Herb Farm, specializing in cannabis, and owner Cyril Guthridge. The farm also uses regenerative agriculture, which helps heal the soil for the plants so that in turn, the plants will also have the best soil to grow in. Solar panels provide power to the farm, and rainwater is collected and used, which also helps keep the farm sustainable. **Availability:** Online.

LIBRARIES

8158 ■ American Herb Association (AHA)
PO Box 1673
Nevada City, CA 95959
URL: http://ahaherb.com/american-herb-association-2
Contact: Kathi Keville, Contact
Description: Enthusiasts and specialists of medicinal herbs and herbal products. Seeks to increase knowledge and provide up-to-date scientific and experiential information on herbs. Offers a network to exchange data and resources among members nationwide. Maintains herb garden. **Founded:** 1981. **Publications:** *Directory of Mail-Order Medicinal Herb Products*; *American Herb Association - Quarterly Newsletter* (Quarterly); *Directory of Mail Order Medicinal Herbs* (Biennial); *Directory of Herbal Education* (Biennial). **Geographic Preference:** National.

8159 ■ Carnegie Mellon University - Hunt Institute for Botanical Documentation Library
4909 Frew St., 5th Fl.
Pittsburgh, PA 15213-3890
URL: http://www.huntbotanical.org/library
Contact: Charlotte A. Tancin, Librarian Principal
E-mail: ctancin@cmu.edu
Scope: Botanical history. **Services:** Interlibrary loan (limited); copying; library open to the public for reference use only. **Founded:** 1961. **Holdings:** 30,000 books; 29,000 portraits; 29,504 watercolors, drawings and prints; 2,000 autograph letters and manuscripts.

8160 ■ Cleveland Botanical Garden - Eleanor Squire Library
11030 E Blvd.
Cleveland, OH 44106
URL: http://holdenfg.org/attractions/cleveland-botanical-garden/elenor-squire-library
Scope: Ecology; urban; general gardening; sustainability; food plants; conservation. **Services:** open to the public; rare book. **Founded:** 1930. **Holdings:** Seed catalog; botanical prints; rare books.

8161 ■ Dittrick Medical History Center (DMHC)
Allen Memorial Medical Library
3rd Fl.11000 Euclid Ave.
Cleveland, OH 44106-1714
Ph: (216)368-3648
Co. E-mail: dittrickmuseum@case.edu
URL: http://artsci.case.edu/dittrick
Contact: Amanda L. Mahoney, Curator
E-mail: curator@case.edu
Facebook: www.facebook.com/DittrickMuseum
X (Twitter): x.com/DittrickMuseum
YouTube: www.youtube.com/user/DittrickMuseum
Description: A museum, archive, and collection of rare books, artifacts, and images, the Dittrick embraces the experience of individuals and society as they grappled with changing conceptions of health and medicine. **Scope:** Medicine - endoscopy; microscopy; contraception; surgery; obstetrics; gynecology and diagnostic instrumentation. **Services:** Archival records are not available online; access to museum collections is by appointment only. **Founded:** 1894. **Holdings:** Papers.

8162 ■ Florida State University - Special Collections
116 Honors Way
Tallahassee, FL 32306-2047
Ph: (850)644-3271
Co. E-mail: lib-specialcollections@fsu.edu
URL: http://www.lib.fsu.edu/special-collections
URL(s): archives.lib.fsu.edu/repositories/10
Scope: Politics. **Services:** Collections open to the public.

8163 ■ The Horticultural Society of New York - Library
148 W 37th St., 13th Fl.
New York, NY 10018
Ph: (212)757-0915

Co. E-mail: info@thehort.org
URL: http://www.thehort.org
Contact: Sara Hobel, Executive Director
E-mail: shobel@thehort.org
Facebook: www.facebook.com/thehortnyc
X (Twitter): x.com/thehort
Instagram: www.instagram.com/thehort
Description: Provides learning gardens for disadvantaged children and horticulture therapy for inmates. **Scope:** Horticulture. **Services:** Library open to the public for reference use only. **Founded:** 1900. **Holdings:** Figures not available. **Geographic Preference:** State.

8164 ■ Kingwood Center Library
50 N Trimble Rd.
Mansfield, OH 44906
Ph: (419)522-0211
URL: http://www.kingwoodcenter.org
Scope: Horticulture, natural history. **Founded:** 1953. **Holdings:** Figures not available.

8165 ■ Miami University - Walter Havighurst Special Collections Library
3rd Fl. King Library 151 S Campus Ave.
Oxford, OH 45056
Ph: (513)529-3323
Co. E-mail: speccoll@miamioh.edu
URL: http://spec.lib.miamioh.edu/home
Contact: William M. Modrow, Head of Legal Department
E-mail: modrowwm@miamioh.edu
Scope: History and culture of the Ohio Valley; art and literature. **Founded:** 1970. **Holdings:** 95,000 volumes, including rare books; manuscripts; 600,000 postcards.

8166 ■ New York Public Library Rare Books Division - Arents Tobacco Collection
Brooke Russell Astor Reading Rm., 3rd Fl., Rm. 328
5th Ave. and 42nd St.
New York, NY 10018-2788
Ph: (212)642-0110
Fax: (212)302-4815
Co. E-mail: rarebook@nypl.org
URL: http://nypl.org/about/divisions/rare-books-division/arents-collection
Scope: History; literature and lore of tobacco. **Services:** Open to qualified researchers by card of admission secured in Special Collections Office. **Founded:** 1944. **Holdings:** 1,200 items; books and manuscripts; cards and pieces of ephemera.

8167 ■ Pennsylvania Horticultural Society (PHS) - McLean Library
100 N 20th St., 5th Fl.
Philadelphia, PA 19103
Ph: (215)988-8800
Co. E-mail: phs-info@pennhort.org
URL: http://phsonline.org
Contact: Matt Rader, President
Facebook: www.facebook.com/PHSgardening
Linkedin: www.linkedin.com/company/pennsylvania-horticultural-society
X (Twitter): x.com/PHSgardening
Instagram: www.instagram.com/phsgardening
YouTube: www.youtube.com/channel/UCK2tCVVaARp9MCLEm0t9TQw
Description: Seeks to use horticulture to advance the health and well-being of the greater Philadelphia region through four pillars: access to fresh food, healthy living environments, deep social connections, and economic opportunities. **Scope:** Gardening; historical; horticultural. **Services:** Library open to the public by appointment; interlibrary loan. **Founded:** 1827. **Holdings:** 15,000 books, DVDs; slides; videos. **Publications:** *PHS News* (6/year); *GROW* (Quarterly). **Educational Activities:** Philadelphia International Flower Show (Annual). **Geographic Preference:** State.

RESEARCH CENTERS

8168 ■ Alberta Agriculture and Rural Development - Crop Diversification Centre South (CDCS)
301 Horticultural Station Rd. E
Brooks, AB, Canada T1R 1E6

URL: http://www.alberta.ca/index.aspx

Description: Integral unit of Alberta Agriculture and Rural Development. Extension for agricultural industries. Offers grower meetings and seminars. **Scope:** Greenhouse crop production, protection and utilization. Field research programs include potato crops emphasizing evaluation of new cultivars, development of production and management techniques suited to a short growing season. Research programs into special crops investigate dry beans and other pulse crops and corn emphasizing cultivar development and development of production and management techniques. The Centre is also home to soil and water management, food science program, plant pathology, weed control, and field crop entomology. **Founded:** 1935.

8169 ■ Herb Research Foundation (HRF) - Library

5589 Arapahoe Ave., Ste. 205
  Boulder, CO 80303
Ph: (303)449-2265
Fax: (303)449-7849
Co. E-mail: rmccaleb@herbs.org
URL: http://www.herbs.org/herbnews
Contact: Rob McCaleb, President
E-mail: rmccaleb@rmccaleb.com

Description: Professionals in the health food industry, plant research scientists, herbal medicine practitioners and their patients, pharmacologists, herbal manufacturers and trade organizations, ethnobotanists, and interested consumers; scientists and students in the fields of pharmacognosy, botany, ethnobotany, and medicine. Encourages research on the chemistry, pharmacology, and use of herbal folk medicines, teas, and other botanical products; provides a forum for discussion and cooperation among herbalists, physicians, health food advocates, and scientists. Works to form a liaison between the U.S. herbal movement and the worldwide scientific community. Disseminates research information on botanicals and serves as a source of information for the public and press on medicinal plants. Provides botanical literature research service. **Scope:** Pharmacognosy, ethnobotany, and toxicology of medicinal plants. **Founded:** 1983. **Holdings:** 300,000 scientific papers. **Publications:** *Herbal Research News* (Quarterly); *Herb Research News* (Quarterly); *Herbs for Health* (Bimonthly); *Information Services Catalog*; *HRF Reports*. **Geographic Preference:** National.

8170 ■ Rodale Institute

611 Siegfriedale Rd.
  Kutztown, PA 19530-9320
Ph: (610)683-1400
Fax: (610)683-8548
Co. E-mail: info@rodaleinstitute.org
URL: http://www.rodaleinstitute.org
Contact: Jeff Moyer, Chief Executive Officer
Facebook: www.facebook.com/rodaleinstitute
Linkedin: www.linkedin.com/company/rodaleinstitute
X (Twitter): twitter.com/rodaleinstitute
Instagram: www.instagram.com/rodaleinstitute
YouTube: www.youtube.com/user/rodaleinstitute

Description: Publishes information for farmers to farm profitably and to manage farm resources better. Reaches market through direct mail. Does not accept unsolicited manuscripts. **Scope:** Organic gardening and farming systems. Specific areas of interest include vegetables, apples, composting, cover crops, soil fertility and soil health, regenerative agriculture, legume screening, interseeding, overseeding, weed control, nitrogen cycling, tillage systems, and perennial grains. **Founded:** 1947. **Publications:** *The New Farm: Magazine of Regenerative Agriculture* (Annual); *How to Make 100,000 Farming 25 Acres*; *Rodale Institute Brochures*; *Rodale Institute Fact sheets*; *Rodale Institute Pamphlets*; *Rodale Institute Technical Reports*. **Educational Activities:** Rodale Institute Field Days (Annual), Offer exemplary teaching and training programs.; Rodale Institute Workshops, Offer exemplary teaching and training programs.

START-UP INFORMATION

8171 ■ *"Etsy: Etsy Business for Beginners! Master Etsy and Build a Profitable Business In No Time"*
Released: December 23, 2014. **Price:** $6.99, regular price is $13.99. **Description:** Craft artisans take note: information is offered to start an online business through Etsy. Whether handmade home accessories, clothing, or knick-knacks, Etsy is the perfect option for artists and crafters to start a home-based, online retail operation. **Availability:** Print; Download.

ASSOCIATIONS AND OTHER ORGANIZATIONS

8172 ■ **The Cookware & Bakeware Alliance (CMA)**
PO Box 297
Bradley Beach, NJ 07720
Ph: (732)361-3710
Co. E-mail: info@cookware.org
URL: http://cookwareandbakeware.org
Contact: Doug Reigle, President
Facebook: www.facebook.com/
CookwareBakewareAlliance
Linkedin: www.linkedin.com/company/cookware
-bakeware-alliance
X (Twitter): x.com/CBAllianceOrg
Instagram: www.instagram.com/
cookwarebakewarealliance
YouTube: www.youtube.com/channel/UCbT0w
5MIoheUKbIRUMmpvMQ

Description: Represents manufacturers of cooking utensils and cooking accessories. Compiles statistics. **Founded:** 1922. **Geographic Preference:** National.

8173 ■ **Home Fashion Products Association (HFPA)**
National Press Bldg., 529 14th St. NW, No. 1280
Washington, DC 20045
Ph: (212)297-2189
URL: http://homefashionproducts.com
Contact: Charles Gaenslen, President
Linkedin: www.linkedin.com/company/home-fashion
-products

Description: Manufacturers of curtains, draperies, bedding, rugs, and related products. Sponsors annual scholarship for students attending accredited schools in home textiles. **Founded:** 1968. **Awards:** HFPA Scholarships. **Geographic Preference:** National.

8174 ■ **International Housewares Association (IHA)**
6400 Shafer Ct., Ste. 650
Rosemont, IL 60018
Ph: (847)292-4200
Fax: (847)292-4211
Co. E-mail: sschatz@housewares.org
URL: http://www.housewares.org
Contact: Derek Miller, Director
E-mail: dmiller@housewares.org

Facebook: www.facebook.com/Interna
tionalHousewaresAssociation
Instagram: www.instagram.com/theinspire
dhomeshow
YouTube: www.youtube.com/housewaresShow
Description: Conducts annual market research survey of the housewares industry. Manages the international housewares show. **Founded:** 1906. **Publications:** *BusinessWatch* (Quarterly); *Housewares MarketWatch* (Quarterly); *IHA Reports* (Monthly); *January Exhibitors Directory* (Annual); *NHMA Reports Newsletter* (Bimonthly); *IHA Membership Directory* (Annual). **Educational Activities:** The Inspired Home Show (Annual); The Inspired Home Show (Annual). **Awards:** IHA Student Design Competition (Annual). **Geographic Preference:** National.

REFERENCE WORKS

8175 ■ *"Bob's Discount Furniture Moving into Harford County, Region"* in *Baltimore Business Journal* (Vol. 27, January 22, 2010, No. 38, pp. 1)
Pub: Baltimore Business Journal
Contact: Rhonda Pringle, President
E-mail: rpringle@bizjournals.com

Ed: Daniel J. Sernovitz. **Description:** Manchester, Connecticut-based Bob's Discount Furniture signed a lease for 672,000 square feet of space in Harford County, Maryland. The site will become the discount furniture retailer's distribution center in mid-Atlantic US. As many as 200 jobs could be generated when the center opens. **Availability:** Print; Online.

8176 ■ *"Entrepreneur Says Spirituality Has Been a Key to Her Success"* in *Business First Columbus* (Vol. 25, October 17, 2008, No. 8, pp. 1)
Description: Profile of Carolyn Williams Francis, CEO of Williams Interior Designs Inc. She outlines her mantra for success in her furniture design business, but emphasizes that faith has taken her business to greater heights.

8177 ■ *"How Are Digital Marketplaces Affecting the Wholesale Model?"* in *Business of Home* (November 5, 2019)
URL(s): businessofhome.com/articles/how-are-digital
-marketplaces-affecting-the-wholesale-model
Ed: Warren Shoulberg. **Released:** November 05, 2019. **Description:** Discusses the B2B wholesale initiative in the gift and home markets industry. Typically, wholesalers sold directly to shops via trade shows, seasonal markets, and buying days, but two digital platforms, Faire and ModMart, are now offering an online alternative. **Availability:** Online.

8178 ■ *"I Brake for Yard Sales: And Flea Markets, Thrift Shops, Auctions, and the Occasional Dumpster"*
Released: April 01, 2012. **Price:** $24.95, Paperback.
Description: Lara Spencer, self-confessed frugalista and new correspondent, shares her passion for shop-

ping at yard sales, consignment shops, and estate sales for decorating her home as well as her friend's homes. She shares her bargain hunting secrets and tells where to shop, what to look for, how to pay for sales, how to restore items, and how to decorate. **Availability:** E-book; Print.

8179 ■ *"New Year's Resolutions: How Three Companies Came Up With Their 2008 Growth Strategies"* in *Inc.* (January 2008, pp. 47-49)
Ed: Martha C. White. **Description:** Three companies share 2008 growth strategies; companies include a candle company, a voice mail and text messaging marketer, and hotel supplier of soap and shampoo. **Availability:** Online.

8180 ■ *"Tuesday Morning's Corporate Clearance Rack"* in *Dallas Business Journal* (Vol. 37, February 28, 2014, No. 25, pp. 4)
Pub: American City Business Journals, Inc.
Contact: Mike Olivieri, Executive Vice President

Released: October 30, 2015. **Description:** Tuesday Morning CEO, Michael Rouleau, has been working to help the company recover from its financial problems. Rouleau has improved the shopping experience from garage sale to discount showroom. The company has also been hiring different executives in the past few years. **Availability:** Print; Online.

8181 ■ *"Uncontained Enthusiasm: Container Store Readies for post IPO Growth"* in *Dallas Business Journal* (Vol. 37, January 10, 2014, No. 18, pp. 4)
Pub: American City Business Journals, Inc.
Contact: Mike Olivieri, Executive Vice President

Released: January 10, 2014. **Price:** $4, introductory 4-week offer(Digital only). **Description:** The Container Store CEO, Kip Tindell, and his team have been balancing the organization and storage retailer's culture of conscious capitalism with executing an aggressive growth plan and returning shareholder value. Tindell could set the stage for large-scale expansion after a successful initial public offering (IPO). Details of Tindells' growth plan are also discussed. **Availability:** Print; Online.

8182 ■ *"Wayfair Unveils New Mobile App Features"* in *Home Accents Today* (November 13, 2019)
URL(s): www.homeaccentstoday.com/e-commerce/
wayfair-unveils-new-mobile-app-features/

Released: November 13, 2019. **Description:** Wanting to make it easier for their customers to discover products and have the ability to design rooms on the go, Wayfair added some new features to its mobile shopping app. Now consumers have access to an augmented reality (AR) tool and a Room Planner 3-D. **Availability:** Online.

8183 ■ *"York Wallcoverings Seals Deal with Lemieux"* in *Home Accents Today* (November 12, 2019)
URL(s): www.homeaccentstoday.com/wall-decor/york
-wallcoverings-seals-deal-with-lemieux/

Released: November 12, 2019. **Description:** York Wallcoverings is partnering with Christiane Lemieux and introducing a new line of wallpaper. Lemieux is an interior and home furnishings designer, and this wallpaper line is expected to be minimalistic, which will help enhance today's modern spaces. **Availability:** Online.

STATISTICAL SOURCES

8184 ■ *Home Decor Retailing: Incl Impact of COVID-19 - US - April 2020*
URL(s): store.mintel.com/report/home-decor-retailing -incl-impact-of-covid-19-us-april-2020

Price: $4,366.35. **Description:** Downloadable report discussing the impact COVID-19 has had on the home decor industry. While consumers desire to save money and only purchase necessities, being at home all day is leading people towards redecorating or adding to their space for a work at home experience. Report includes an executive summary, interactive databook, PowerPoint presentation, infographic overview, report PDF, and previous years data. **Availability:** PDF.

TRADE PERIODICALS

8185 ■ *The duPont Registry: A Buyer's Gallery of Fine Boats*
Pub: duPont Publishing Inc.
Contact: William Chapman, Chief Executive Officer
URL(s): www.dupontregistry.com/about
Facebook: www.facebook.com/dupontregistry
X (Twitter): x.com/duPontREGISTRY
Instagram: www.instagram.com/dupontregistry
YouTube: www.youtube.com/channel/UCSWQ
 -ZuJ9IyHZFGfpoPz8wg
Pinterest: www.pinterest.com/dupontregistry

Released: Monthly **Price:** $89.95, for 12 issues; $149.95, for 24 issues; $189.95, for 36 issues. **Description:** Magazine featuring worldwide luxury homes for sale. **Availability:** Print; Online.

8186 ■ *Gifts & Decorative Accessories*
Pub: Sandow
Contact: Peter Fain, Chief Operating Officer
URL(s): www.giftsanddec.com
Facebook: www.facebook.com/giftsanddecmag
Linkedin: www.linkedin.com/company/gifts-&-decora
 tive-accessories-magazine

X (Twitter): x.com/Gifts_and_Dec
Instagram: www.instagram.com/gifts_and_dec
Released: Monthly **Price:** $55.97, for online 1 Year (11 issues); $68.97, for print and online 1 year (11 issues). **Description:** International magazine for retailers of gifts, greeting cards, decorative accessories, and stationery-related merchandise. **Availability:** Print; Online. **Type:** Full-text; Directory.

8187 ■ *LDB Interior Textiles*
Pub: Pioneer Associates Inc.
URL(s): www.ldbinteriortextiles.com

Released: Monthly **Price:** $165, for 1 year(Elsewhere (Airmail)); $18, for (Elsewhere (Airmail)); $75, U.S. for 1 year; $90, Canada for 1 year; $110, U.S. for 2 year; $7, U.S. for single issue; $12, Canada for single issue. **Description:** Magazine for buyers of home fashions, including bed, bath and table linens, hard and soft window treatments, home fragrances, decorative pillows and home accessories, accent rugs, and decorative fabrics. **Availability:** Print.

VIDEO/AUDIO MEDIA

8188 ■ *Main Street Business Insights: Martha Moore and Ashley Owens, Martha & Ash Custom Drapery*
URL(s): mainstreet.org/resources/knowledge-hub/po dcast/martha-moore-and-ashley-owens-martha-ash -custom-drapery

Ed: Matt Wagner. **Released:** August 30, 2023. **Description:** Podcast features a conversation the mother-daughter owners of a custom drapery shop. Discusses how they transitioned from Etsy to bricks-and-mortar.

TRADE SHOWS AND CONVENTIONS

8189 ■ *Specialty Food Association Winter Fancy Food Show*
Specialty Food Association Inc.
 136 Madison Ave., 12th Fl.
 New York, NY 10016-6788
Ph: (212)482-6440
Fax: (212)482-6459
URL: http://www.specialtyfood.com
Contact: Phil Kafarakis, President
URL(s): www.specialtyfood.com/fancy-food-shows/ winter

Price: $60, Onsite. **Frequency:** Annual. **Description:** Exhibits relating to international specialty food and dessert. **Audience:** Retailers, the educational sector, buyers from various food businesses, manufacturers, the press, and other industry professionals. **Principal Exhibits:** Exhibits relating to international specialty food and dessert. **Dates and Locations:** 2025 Jan 19-21 Las Vegas Convention Center, Las Vegas, NV. **Telecommunication Services:** mboule-frakh@specialtyfood.com.

CONSULTANTS

8190 ■ KV Marketing Inc.
12 Huntsville Rd.
 Katonah, NY 10536-2002
Contact: Katherine L. Vockins, Chief Executive Officer

Description: Provider of international marketing expertise including market research and analysis, new product development, marketing plans and general management assistance to both nonprofits and the commercial sectors. **Scope:** Provider of international marketing expertise including market research and analysis, new product development, marketing plans and general management assistance to both nonprofits and the commercial sectors. **Publications:** "Analysis of US market-opportunities for pygeum," Oct, 2000.

FRANCHISES AND BUSINESS OPPORTUNITIES

8191 ■ Miracle Method Surface Refinishing (MMSR)
4310 Arrowswest Dr.
 Colorado Springs, CO 80907
Ph: (719)594-9196
Free: 800-444-8827
Fax: (719)594-9282
Co. E-mail: sales@miraclemethod.com
URL: http://www.miraclemethod.com
Contact: Charles Pistor, President
Facebook: www.facebook.com/miraclemetho dsurfacerefinishing
YouTube: www.youtube.com/user/MiracleMetho dCom
Pinterest: www.pinterest.com/miraclemethod

Description: Kitchen refinishing company provides repairing and restoring of tubs, ceramic tile and countertops. **Founded:** 1979. **Financial Assistance:** Yes **Training:** Includes 10 days training.

ASSOCIATIONS AND OTHER ORGANIZATIONS

8192 ■ American Home Furnishings Alliance (AHFA)
1912 Eastchester Dr., Ste. 100
  High Point, NC 27265
Ph: (336)884-5000
Co. E-mail: info@ahfa.us
URL: http://www.ahfa.us
Contact: Andy Counts, Chief Executive Officer
E-mail: acounts@ahfa.us
Facebook: www.facebook.com/AHFAToday
X (Twitter): x.com/AHFANews
Description: Furniture manufacturers seeking to provide a unified voice for the furniture industry and to aid in the development of industry personnel. Provides: market research data; industrial relations services; costs and operating statistics; transportation information; general management and information services. Compiles statistics. **Founded:** 1905. **Publications:** *American Home Furnishings Alliance Suppliers Resource Guide* (Annual); *Furniture Executive* (Monthly); *HR Close-Up* (Monthly); *Solutions on Demand* (Quarterly); *AHFA Manufacturer Members Directory* (Annual). **Geographic Preference:** National.

8193 ■ High Point Market Authority (HPMKT)
164 S Main St., Ste. 700
  High Point, NC 27260
Ph: (336)869-1000
Co. E-mail: marketing@highpointmarket.org
URL: http://www.highpointmarket.org
Contact: Tom Conley, President
E-mail: tom@highpointmarket.org
Facebook: www.facebook.com/hpmkt
X (Twitter): x.com/HPMarketNews
Instagram: www.instagram.com/highpointmarket
YouTube: www.youtube.com/channel/
  UCDq7mJLXssH7NAQyLbd1Cow
Pinterest: www.pinterest.com/highpointmarket
Description: Furniture manufacturers and exhibition buildings working to create a cooperative business environment. **Founded:** 1909. **Educational Activities:** High Point Market (Semiannual). **Geographic Preference:** Multinational.

8194 ■ Home Furnishings Association (HFA)
500 Giuseppe Ct., Ste. 6
  Roseville, CA 95678
Free: 800-422-3778
Co. E-mail: info@myhfa.org
URL: http://myhfa.org
Contact: Mark Schumacher, Chief Executive Officer
Facebook: www.facebook.com/myHFA
Linkedin: www.linkedin.com/company/myhfa
X (Twitter): x.com/my_hfa
Instagram: www.instagram.com/my_hfa
Description: Provides business services to help retailers of home furnishings grow their businesses. Provides educational programs for retail sales managers and trainers, for middle management, for

owners and executives, and for family businesses. **Founded:** 1920. **Publications:** *Western Reporter* (Monthly); *WHFA Online Directory*; *Insights Magazine* (Quarterly). **Educational Activities:** Home Furnishings Industry Conference. **Awards:** Retailer of the Year (Annual). **Geographic Preference:** Multinational; National.

8195 ■ International Casual Furnishings Association (ICFA)
1912 Eastchester Dr., Ste. 100
  High Point, NC 27265
Ph: (336)881-1016
Fax: (336)884-5303
Co. E-mail: jackie@icfanet.org
URL: http://www.icfanet.org
Contact: Jackie Hirschhaut, Executive Director
E-mail: jackie@icfanet.org
Facebook: www.facebook.com/ICFA08
X (Twitter): x.com/ICFA08
YouTube: www.youtube.com/user/ICFAVideos/feed
Pinterest: www.pinterest.com/internation0592
Description: A division of American Home Furnishings Alliance. Manufacturers of household summer and casual furniture. Compiles trade statistics; provides legislative, technical, management, and marketing services. Conducts technical and marketing research. **Founded:** 2008. **Geographic Preference:** Multinational.

8196 ■ International Furniture Rental Association (IFRA)
c/o Alston & Bird LLP
  950 F St. NW, 10th Fl.
  Washington, DC 20004
URL: http://www.ifra.org
Description: Companies whose major business is the leasing and rental of home furnishings and accessories; suppliers of products and services to these companies are associate members. Dedicated to upholding ethical standards of the furniture rental industry and providing quality products and service. Conducts industry exposition and statistical surveys. Promotes industry through nationwide consumer education program. Works to safeguard against adverse legislation and regulation. **Founded:** 1967. **Publications:** *IFRA Membership/Referral Directory* (Annual); *Furniture Rental Association of America-- Newsletter* (Quarterly). **Educational Activities:** International Furniture Rental Association Conference (Annual). **Geographic Preference:** National.

8197 ■ International Furniture Transportation and Logistics Council (IFTLC)
282 N Ridge Rd.
  Brooklyn, MI 49230
URL: http://www.iftlc.org
Contact: Erich Price, President
Linkedin: www.linkedin.com/company/iftlc
X (Twitter): twitter.com/IFTLC
Description: Represents and promotes furniture transportation logistics professionals. **Founded:** 1926. **Educational Activities:** International Confer-

ence of Furniture Transportation and Logistics Managers (Annual). **Geographic Preference:** Multi-national.

8198 ■ International Home Furnishings Representatives Association (IHFRA)
209 S Main St.
  High Point, NC 27260
Ph: (336)889-3920
Fax: (336)802-1959
Co. E-mail: ihfra@ihfra.org
URL: http://ihfra.org
Contact: John Pinion, IV, President
E-mail: john@pinionswonderworld.com
Facebook: www.facebook.com/IHFRA
Instagram: www.instagram.com/ihfrasocial
YouTube: www.youtube.com/channel/UC_s0ptN5sG
  5-BjyFQf52gCw
Description: Local affiliated organizations of approximately 2,000 home furnishings representatives. Provides services to affiliates and individual members, including information exchange, listing manufacturers seeking representatives in all territories and representatives seeking manufacturers' lines in specific territories. Conducts certified home furnishings educational program. **Founded:** 1934. **Geographic Preference:** National.

8199 ■ Kitchen Cabinet Manufacturers Association (KCMA)
1768 Business Center Dr., Ste. 390
  Reston, VA 20190
Ph: (703)264-1690
Fax: (703)620-6530
Co. E-mail: info@kcma.org
URL: http://www.kcma.org
Contact: Betsy Natz, Chief Executive Officer
Linkedin: www.linkedin.com/company/kitchen-cabine
  t-manufacturing-association-kcma-
X (Twitter): x.com/KCMAorg
YouTube: www.youtube.com/user/KCMAorg
Description: Serves as a national trade association representing cabinet and countertop manufacturers and suppliers to the industry. Promotes the cabinet manufacturing industry, develops standards for the industry, administers a testing and certification program, conducts education programs and meetings, provides management information and industry data, and engages in activities on behalf of members on legislative and regulatory issues. **Founded:** 1955. **Publications:** *Cabinet News* (Bimonthly); *Directory of Certified Cabinet Manufacturers* (Annual); *Kitchen Cabinet Manufacturers Association Income & Expense Survey* (Annual). **Geographic Preference:** National.

8200 ■ National Kitchen and Bath Association (NKBA) - Professional Resource Library
687 Willow Grove St.
  Hackettstown, NJ 07840
Ph: (908)852-0033
Free: 800-THE-NKBA
Co. E-mail: feedback@nkba.org

URL: http://nkba.org
Contact: Bill Darcy, Chief Executive Officer
Facebook: www.facebook.com/thenkba
Linkedin: www.linkedin.com/company/national-ki
tchen-and-bath-association
X (Twitter): x.com/thenkba
Instagram: www.instagram.com/thenkba

Description: Manufacturers and firms engaged in retail kitchen sales; utilities, publications and other firms supplying products or services to the kitchen and bathroom industry. Protects and promotes the interest and welfare of members by fostering a better business climate in the industry. **Scope:** Kitchen; bath industry. **Founded:** 1963. **Publications:** *National Kitchen & Bath Association--Directory of Accredited Members* (Annual); *Council of Societies--Directory of Certified Kitchen Designers & Certified Bathroom Designers* (Annual). **Educational Activities:** National Design Competition (Annual). **Geographic Preference:** National.

8201 ■ Upholstered Furniture Action Council (UFAC)
1912 Eastchester Dr., Ste. 100
  High Point, NC 27265
Ph: (336)885-5065
Co. E-mail: info@ufac.org
URL: http://ufac.org
Contact: Don Coleman, President

Description: Conducts research and disseminates information regarding the development and adoption of voluntary guidelines for production of more cigarette-resistant upholstered furniture. **Founded:** 1978. **Publications:** *Upholstered Furniture Action Council--Directory of Materials Suppliers* (Annual); *UFAC: Action Guide* (Annual). **Geographic Preference:** National.

REFERENCE WORKS

8202 ■ *"Bob's Discount Furniture Moving into Harford County, Region" in Baltimore Business Journal (Vol. 27, January 22, 2010, No. 38, pp. 1)*
Pub: Baltimore Business Journal
Contact: Rhonda Pringle, President
E-mail: rpringle@bizjournals.com

Ed: Daniel J. Sernovitz. **Description:** Manchester, Connecticut-based Bob's Discount Furniture signed a lease for 672,000 square feet of space in Harford County, Maryland. The site will become the discount furniture retailer's distribution center in mid-Atlantic US. As many as 200 jobs could be generated when the center opens. **Availability:** Print; Online.

8203 ■ *"'Climate Positive Now' a Welcome Message of Sustainability" in Woodworking Network (November 19, 2021)*
URL(s): www.woodworkingnetwork.com/news/woo
dworking-industry-news/climate-positive-now-wel-
come-message-sustainability
Ed: Larry Adams. **Released:** November 19, 2021. **Description:** A positive trend of using sustainable wood materials is being voiced by consumers and designers. Furniture makers are listening and looking for leads on materials that are branded as climate positive.

8204 ■ *"Digging Dallas-Fort Worth: How Top 10 Major Construction Projects Will Change North Texas" in Dallas Business Journal (Vol. 37, May 23, 2014, No. 37, pp. 4)*
Pub: American City Business Journals, Inc.
Contact: Mike Olivieri, Executive Vice President

Price: $4, print. **Description:** A list of the top ten largest construction projects in North Dallas in 2013 and their impact on local economies is presented. Included are the $303 million State Farm Insurance campus in Plano, $138.74 million termination renovation at Dallas-Fort Worth International Airport, and the $133.82 million Nebraska Furniture Mart in the Colony. **Availability:** Print; Online.

8205 ■ *"Entrepreneur Says Spirituality Has Been a Key to Her Success" in Business First Columbus (Vol. 25, October 17, 2008, No. 8, pp. 1)*
Description: Profile of Carolyn Williams Francis, CEO of Williams Interior Designs Inc. She outlines her mantra for success in her furniture design business, but emphasizes that faith has taken her business to greater heights.

8206 ■ *"Forget Your Pants, Calvin Klein Wants Into Your Bedroom" in Globe & Mail (March 31, 2007, pp. B4)*
Ed: Barrie McKenna. **Description:** The plans of Phillips-Van Heusen Corp. to open more Calvin Klein stores for selling the new ranges of clothing, personal care products, luggage and mattresses are discussed. **Availability:** Online.

8207 ■ *"Furniture Making May Come Back--Literally" in Business North Carolina (Vol. 28, March 2008, No. 3, pp. 32)*
Pub: Business North Carolina
Contact: Peggy Knaack, Manager
E-mail: pknaack@businessnc.com

Description: Due to the weak U.S. dollar and the fact that lumber processors never left the country, foreign furniture manufacturers are becoming interested in moving manufacturing plants to the U.S. **Availability:** Online.

8208 ■ *"Furniture Retailers Start to Feel Tariff Pain More Acutely" in The Wall Street Journal (November 11, 2019)*
URL(s): www.wsj.com/articles/furniture-retailers-star
t-to-feel-tariff-pain-more-acutely-11573476321
Ed: Katy Stech Ferek. **Released:** November 11, 2019. **Description:** Caught up in the current administration's tariff wars with China, the furniture industry is feeling the pain. Shares in publicly-traded furniture companies have taken a hit, and furniture stores that import furniture have faced challenges. Some suppliers have agreed to cover the increased costs and some stores work around the tariffs by importing from countries other than China. **Availability:** Online.

8209 ■ *"How Are Digital Marketplaces Affecting the Wholesale Model?" in Business of Home (November 5, 2019)*
URL(s): businessofhome.com/articles/how-are-digital
-marketplaces-affecting-the-wholesale-model
Ed: Warren Shoulberg. **Released:** November 05, 2019. **Description:** Discusses the B2B wholesale initiative in the gift and home markets industry. Typically, wholesalers sold directly to shops via trade shows, seasonal markets, and buying days, but two digital platforms, Faire and ModMart, are now offering an online alternative. **Availability:** Online.

8210 ■ *"IndieCompanyDk Offers Eco-Friendly Furniture That Stands Out" in Ecology, Environment & Conservation Business (September 6, 2014, pp. 39)*
Pub: NewsRX LLC.
Contact: Kalani Rosell, Contact

Description: A new manufacturer of eco-friendly furniture and interiors, IndieCompanyDk, is offering a new concept in sustainable furniture design, using exclusive and affordable smooth designs, which maintain the natural and raw look of quality reclaimed materials. **Availability:** Online.

8211 ■ *Market Resource Guide (Furniture industry)*
Pub: International Home Furnishings Center
URL(s): exhibitor.highpointmarket.org/exhibitor-guide

Released: Semiannual **Description:** Publication includes list of 80,000 manufacturers and distributors in the furniture industry who exhibit at the International Home Furnishings Market. **Entries include:** Company name, address, phone; showroom name and location, president, vice president, dir. of marketing. **Arrangement:** Alphabetical. **Availability:** Diskette; Print; PDF.

8212 ■ *"StyleCraft Consolidates HQ, Distribution Facility" in Memphis Business Journal (Vol. 34, June 1, 2012, No. 7, pp. 1)*
Pub: Baltimore Business Journal
Contact: Rhonda Pringle, President
E-mail: rpringle@bizjournals.com

Ed: Andy Ashby. **Description:** StyleCraft Home Collection Inc. has combined its headquarters and distribution operations into one building in Memphis, Tennessee. The company has leased space at IDI's Airways Distribution Building E. **Availability:** Print; Online.

8213 ■ *Too Good to be Threw: The Complete Operations Manual for Resale & Consignment Shops*
Pub: Katydid Press

Ed: Kate Holmes. **Price:** $76.95. **Description:** Revised edition covers all the information needed to start and run a buy-outright or consignment shop, covering anything from clothing to furniture resale.

STATISTICAL SOURCES

8214 ■ *Bed & Mattress Stores Industry in the US - Market Research Report*
URL(s): www.ibisworld.com/united-states/market-re-
search-reports/bed-mattress-stores-industry/
Price: $925. **Description:** Downloadable report analyzing the current and future trends in the bed and mattress industry. **Availability:** Download.

8215 ■ *Home Decor Retailing: Incl Impact of COVID-19 - US - April 2020*
URL(s): store.mintel.com/report/home-decor-retailing
-incl-impact-of-covid-19-us-april-2020
Price: $4,366.35. **Description:** Downloadable report discussing the impact COVID-19 has had on the home decor industry. While consumers desire to save money and only purchase necessities, being at home all day is leading people towards redecorating or adding to their space for a work at home experience. Report includes an executive summary, interactive databook, PowerPoint presentation, infographic overview, report PDF, and previous years data. **Availability:** PDF.

8216 ■ *RMA Annual Statement Studies*
Pub: Risk Management Association
Contact: Nancy Foster, President

Released: Annual. **Description:** Contains composite balance sheets and income statements for more than 360 industries, including the accounting, auditing, and bookkeeping industries. Also contains five years of comparative historical data for discerning trends. Includes 16 commonly used ratios, computed for most of the size groupings for nearly every industry.

8217 ■ *Standard & Poor's Industry Surveys*
Pub: Standard And Poor's Financial Services LLC.
Contact: Douglas L. Peterson, President

Description: Two-volume book that examines the prospects for specific industries, including trucking. Also provides analyses of trends and problems, statistical tables and charts, and comparative company analyses.

8218 ■ *U.S. Patio and Backyard Living Market Report 2021*
URL(s): store.mintel.com/report/us-patio-and-backyar
d-living-market-report
Price: $4,366.35. **Description:** Downloadable report providing data on the outdoor furniture market. Report includes an executive summary, interactive databook, PowerPoint presentation, infographic overview, report PDF, and previous years data. **Availability:** PDF.

TRADE PERIODICALS

8219 ■ *The duPont Registry: A Buyer's Gallery of Fine Boats*
Pub: duPont Publishing Inc.
Contact: William Chapman, Chief Executive Officer
URL(s): www.dupontregistry.com/about
Facebook: www.facebook.com/dupontregistry
X (Twitter): x.com/duPontREGISTRY

Instagram: www.instagram.com/dupontregistry
YouTube: www.youtube.com/channel/UCSWQ
  -ZuJ9IyHZFGfpoPz8wg
Pinterest: www.pinterest.com/dupontregistry
Released: Monthly **Price:** $89.95, for 12 issues;
$149.95, for 24 issues; $189.95, for 36 issues.
Description: Magazine featuring worldwide luxury
homes for sale. **Availability:** Print; Online.

8220 ▪ Furniture Executive
Pub: American Home Furnishings Alliance
Contact: Andy Counts, Chief Executive Officer
E-mail: acounts@ahfa.us
URL(s): www.ahfa.us/member-resources/furniture
  -executive-newsletter

Released: Monthly **Description:** Reports on the
activities of the American Furniture Manufacturers
Association and on issues impacting the industry.
Availability: Download; Online.

**8221 ▪ Furniture Today: The Weekly
Business Newspaper of the Furniture
Industry**
Contact: Vicky Jarrett, Managing Editor
E-mail: vjarrett@furnituretoday.com
URL(s): www.furnituretoday.com
Facebook: www.facebook.com/FurnitureTodayNews
Linkedin: www.linkedin.com/company-beta/2359473
X (Twitter): twitter.com/FurnitureToday

Ed: Thomas Russell. **Released:** 51/yr. **Price:** $129.
97, for 1 year (print and digital); $103.97, for 1 year
(digital only); $246.97, for 2 year (print and digital);
$197.97, for 2 year (digital only); $356.97, for 3 year
(print and digital); $284.97, for 3 year (digital).
Description: Furniture retailing and manufacturing
magazine (tabloid). **Availability:** Print.

CONSULTANTS

8222 ▪ KV Marketing Inc.
12 Huntsville Rd.
  Katonah, NY 10536-2002
Contact: Katherine L. Vockins, Chief Executive
  Officer
Description: Provider of international marketing
expertise including market research and analysis,
new product development, marketing plans and
general management assistance to both nonprofits
and the commercial sectors. **Scope:** Provider of
international marketing expertise including market
research and analysis, new product development,
marketing plans and general management assistance
to both nonprofits and the commercial sectors.
Publications: "Analysis of US market-opportunities
for pygeum," Oct, 2000.

8223 ▪ Riedel Marketing Group (RMG)
5327 E Pinchot Ave.
  Phoenix, AZ 85018
Contact: Ann Riedel, Member

E-mail: ajr@4rmg.com
Description: The house wares and food service
industry strategic marketing planning experts. Help
manufacturers of house wares and food products
solve marketing problems and identify and exploit
marketing opportunities. Provides a full-range of
strategic marketing planning services including
development of marketing strategy, development of
fact-based sales presentations, category management, definition of market opportunities and new
product development exclusively to the house wares
and food service industries. **Scope:** The house wares
and food service industry strategic marketing planning experts. Help manufacturers of house wares
and food products solve marketing problems and
identify and exploit marketing opportunities. Provides
a full-range of strategic marketing planning services
including development of marketing strategy, development of fact-based sales presentations, category
management, definition of market opportunities and
new product development exclusively to the house
wares and food service industries. **Founded:** 1991.
Publications: "Your Key Consumer: Her Take on the
International Home & Housewares Show," Mar, 2008;
"What's Hot, What's Not: The Consumer Speaks,"
Mar, 2006; "HIPsters SPEAK: What We Love to Buy
and Why," Apr, 2005; "Influentials: Who They Are and
Why You Should Care," Jun, 2004; "The Seven
Secrets to Selling More Housewares," Jan, 2003.
Training: Consumers Speak: What We Love to Buy
and Why, What Do Those Consumers Think; The
Seven Secrets to Selling More House wares. **Special
Services:** Home Trend Influentials Panel.

FRANCHISES AND BUSINESS OPPORTUNITIES

8224 ▪ Bath Saver Inc.
2501 Wabash Ave.
  Springfield, IL 62704
Free: 888-658-0024
URL: http://www.bathfitter.com/us-en
Contact: Glenn Cotton, Founder
Linkedin: www.linkedin.com/company/bath-fitter
X (Twitter): x.com/BathFitter
Instagram: www.instagram.com/bathfitter
YouTube: www.youtube.com/channel/
  UCuESTAuQjUunOjuhdPOrvZw
Pinterest: www.pinterest.ca/bathfitter

Description: Firm offers fabricated plate work.
Founded: 2000.

**8225 ▪ Children's Lighthouse Franchise Co.
(CLFC)**
101 S Jennings Ave., Ste. 209
  Fort Worth, TX 76104
Free: 888-338-4466
Fax: (817)338-2716
Co. E-mail: hello@childrenslighthouse.com

URL: http://childrenslighthouse.com
Contact: Michael Brown, President
Facebook: www.facebook.com/childrenslighthouse
Instagram: www.instagram.com/childrens_lighthouse
YouTube: www.youtube.com/channel/UCODzN
  _cwYIMMuvH9cQXfDvw

Description: School which provides values-based
early childhood education. **Founded:** 1997. **Financial
Assistance:** Yes **Training:** Available at headquarters
for 4 weeks, 4 weeks at franchisee's location,
unlimited training for the first year and unlimited support.

8226 ▪ More Space Place, Inc. (MSP)
1847 Lakewood Ranch Blvd.
  Bradenton, FL 34211
Ph: (941)538-6574
Co. E-mail: marketing@morespaceplace.com
URL: http://www.morespaceplace.com
Facebook: www.facebook.com/morespaceplace
X (Twitter): x.com/morespaceplace
Pinterest: www.pinterest.com/morespaceplace

Description: Manufacturer and wholesaler of equipment for pleasure, sport fishing and sail boats, mega
yachts and commercial vessels. **Founded:** 1987.
Financial Assistance: Yes

8227 ▪ Verlo Mattress Store
301 N Broadway, Ste. 300
  Milwaukee, WI 53202
Free: 866-998-3756
Co. E-mail: support@verlo.com
URL: http://verlo.com
Facebook: www.facebook.com/VerloMattress
Linkedin: www.linkedin.com/company/verlo-mattress

Description: Manufacturer of factory direct mattress.
Founded: 1958. **Training:** Yes.

PUBLICATIONS

**8228 ▪ BedTimes: The Business Journal for
the Sleep Products Industry**
501 Wythe St.
  Alexandria, VA 22314
Ph: (703)683-8371
Co. E-mail: registration@sleepproducts.org
URL: http://sleepproducts.org
Contact: Ryan Trainer, President
URL(s): bedtimesmagazine.com
Facebook: www.facebook.com/ispabe
  dtimesmagazine
Linkedin: www.linkedin.com/company/bedtimes
  -magazine
X (Twitter): x.com/bedtimesmag
YouTube: www.youtube.com/user/Be
  dTimesSleepSavvy

Released: Monthly **Description:** Trade magazine
covering trends and developments in the mattress
bedding industry. **Availability:** Print; PDF; Download;
Online.

VIDEO/AUDIO MEDIA

8229 ■ *The How of Business: Dan Perry - Handyman Business Startup*
URL(s): www.thehowofbusiness.com/300-dan-perry
-handyman-startup
Ed: Henry Lopez. **Released:** November 29, 2021.
Description: Podcast offers an overview of starting a handyman business.

START-UP INFORMATION

8230 ■ "Caring Concern" in Small Business Opportunities (September 2010)
Pub: Harris Publishing, Inc.
Contact: Janet Chase, Contact

Description: Profile of Joshua Hoffman, founder and CEO of HomeWell Senior Care, Inc., provider of non-medical live-in and hourly personal care, companionship and homemaker services for seniors so they can remain in their own homes. **Availability:** Online.

8231 ■ "Home: Where the Money Is!" in Small Business Opportunities (May 1, 2008)
Pub: Harris Publishing, Inc.
Contact: Janet Chase, Contact

Description: Profile of ComForcare, a franchise company that serves the senior population in America; a franchise can be started with one owner and add and build a team as it grows. **Availability:** Print; Online.

8232 ■ "This Biz Is Booming" in Small Business Opportunities (Winter 2010)
Description: Non-medical home care is a $52 billion industry. Advice to start a non-medical home care business is provided, focusing on franchise FirstLight HomeCare, but showing that independent home care agencies are also successful.

ASSOCIATIONS AND OTHER ORGANIZATIONS

8233 ■ American Hospital Association (AHA) - Resource Center
155 N Wacker Dr.
Chicago, IL 60606
Ph: (312)422-3000
Free: 800-424-4301
Co. E-mail: ahahelp@aha.org
URL: http://www.aha.org
Contact: Richard J. Pollack, President
E-mail: rick@aha.org

Description: Represents hospitals and health care provider organizations. Seeks to advance the health of individuals and communities. Leads, represents, and serves health care provider organizations that are accountable to the community and committed to health improvement. **Scope:** Health services information. **Services:** Interlibrary loan; copying. **Founded:** 1898. **Holdings:** Periodicals; books; reference materials; electronic information sources. **Publications:** Hospital Statistics (Annual); Hospital Database (Annual); AHA Healthcare IT Database; AHA Guide® (Annual); AHA Hospital Statistics; AHA Annual Survey Database; Health Services Research (Bimonthly); Directory of Health Care Coalitions in the United States (Annual); Healthcare QuickDisc; Guide to the Health Care Field (Annual); Hospitals & Health Networks (H&HN); American Hospital Association--Ambulatory Outreach; AHA Directory of Health Care Professionals; Directory of Planning and Design Professionals for Health Facilities (Annual); American

Hospital Association--Guide to the Health Care Field (Annual); AHA News Now (Daily); AHA Guide to the Health Care Field (Annual); Coding Clinic for ICD-10-CM Newsletter (Quarterly); AHA Integrated Delivery Network Directory: U.S. Health Care Systems, Networks, and Alliances. **Awards:** Hospital Awards for Volunteer Excellence (HAVE) (Annual); AHA Honorary Life Membership (Annual); AHA Board of Trustees Award (Annual); NHPCO Circle of Life Awards (Annual); AHA Federal Health Care Executive Special Achievement Award (Annual); AHA Award of Honor (Annual); AHA Distinguished Service Award (Annual); Justin Ford Kimball Innovators Award (Irregular). **Geographic Preference:** National.

8234 ■ Association Canadienne de Soins e a Domicile (ACSSD) [Canadian Home Care Association]
2000 Argentia Rd., Plz. 3, Ste. 302
Mississauga, ON, Canada L5N 1W1
Ph: (905)567-7373
Co. E-mail: chca@cdnhomecare.ca
URL: http://cdnhomecare.ca
Contact: Nadine Henningsen, Chief Executive Officer
E-mail: nhenningsen@cdnhomecare.ca
X (Twitter): x.com/cdnhomecare

Description: Providers of home healthcare services. Promotes excellence in the practice of home care. Conducts continuing professional development courses for home care personnel. **Founded:** 1990. **Publications:** Cnez Nous, At Home (Quarterly). **Geographic Preference:** National.

8235 ■ Canadian Association of Nurses in Oncology (CANO) [Association canadienne des infirmieres en oncologie]
1618 Station St.
Vancouver, BC, Canada V6A 1B6
Ph: (604)874-4322
Fax: (604)874-4378
Co. E-mail: info@cano-acio.ca
URL: http://www.cano-acio.ca
Contact: Dr. Lorelei Newton, President
Facebook: www.facebook.com/CADAssocofNursesinOncology
Linkedin: www.linkedin.com/company/cano-acio
X (Twitter): x.com/CANO_ACIO
Instagram: www.instagram.com/cano_acio
YouTube: www.youtube.com/user/CANOACIO

Description: Promotes improved public access to healthcare; seeks to increase the role of nurses in the delivery of healthcare services. Develops business and practice guidelines for members. Conducts educational programs to raise public awareness of nursing and other healthcare services. **Founded:** 1985. **Publications:** Canadian Oncology Nursing Journal (Quarterly). **Geographic Preference:** National.

8236 ■ Canadian Nurses Foundation (CNF)
135 Michael Cowpland Dr., Ste. 105
Kanata, ON, Canada K2M 2E9
Ph: (613)680-0879
Free: 844-204-0124

Co. E-mail: info@cnf-fiic.ca
URL: http://www.cnf-fiic.ca
Contact: Christine R. Buckley, Chief Executive Officer
E-mail: cbuckley@cnf-fiic.ca

Description: Promotes health and patient care in Canada. Fosters excellence in nursing through nursing research grants, scholarships, and specialty certification. **Founded:** 1962. **Publications:** Foundation Focus. **Awards:** AstraZeneca Award (Annual); Canadian Nurses Foundation Scholarships (Annual); Johnson & Johnson Scholarships (Annual); Margaret Munro Award (Annual); Senator Norman Paterson (TBC) (Annual); Sanofi Pasteur Scholarships (Annual); John Vanderlee Award (Annual); Aplastic Anemia and Myelodysplasia Association of Canada Scholarships (Annual); Dr. Ann C. Beckingham Scholarships (Annual); Canadian Nurses Foundation Northern Award (Annual); Extendicare Scholarships in Gerontology (Annual); Dr. Helen Preston Glass Fellowships (Annual); Judy Hill Memorial Scholarships (Annual); Dr. Dorothy J. Kergin Fellowships (Annual); Tecla Lin & Nelia Laroza Memorial Scholarships (Annual); Eleanor Jean Martin Award (Annual); Military Nurses Association Scholarships (Annual); Dr. Helen K. Mussallem Fellowships (Annual); New Brunswick Nurses Association Scholarships (Annual); Sharon Nield Memorial Scholarships (Annual); Sigma Theta Tau International Scholarships (Annual); TD Meloche Monnex Centennial Doctoral Scholarship (Annual). **Geographic Preference:** National.

8237 ■ Canadian Oncology Nursing Journal
1618 Station St.
Vancouver, BC, Canada V6A 1B6
Ph: (604)874-4322
Fax: (604)874-4378
Co. E-mail: info@cano-acio.ca
URL: http://www.cano-acio.ca
Contact: Dr. Lorelei Newton, President
URL(s): www.canadianoncologynursingjournal.com/index.php/conj

Ed: Margaret I. Fitch. **Released:** Quarterly **Availability:** Print; Download; PDF; Online.

8238 ■ Foundation Focus
135 Michael Cowpland Dr., Ste. 105
Kanata, ON, Canada K2M 2E9
Ph: (613)680-0879
Free: 844-204-0124
Co. E-mail: info@cnf-fiic.ca
URL: http://www.cnf-fiic.ca
Contact: Christine R. Buckley, Chief Executive Officer
E-mail: cbuckley@cnf-fiic.ca
URL(s): cnf-fiic.ca/newsletter

Availability: Print; Online.

8239 ■ National Association of Certified Professional Midwives (NACPM)
PO Box 1448
Williston, VT 05495
Ph: (603)358-3322
Co. E-mail: info@nacpm.org

URL: http://www.nacpm.org
Contact: Khailylah Jordan, President
Facebook: www.facebook.com/NACPM
X (Twitter): x.com/NACPM
Instagram: www.instagram.com/nacpmidwives

Description: Strives to ensure that Certified Professional Midwives (CPMs) will achieve their appropriate place in the delivery of maternity care in the United States. Increases women's access to midwives by supporting the work and practice of CPMs. Educates legislators and policy makers about the practice of Certified Professional Midwifery. Works to increase reimbursement for the services of CPMs. **Founded:** 2000. **Geographic Preference:** National.

8240 ■ National Association for Home Care and Hospice (NAHC)

228 7th St. SE
  Washington, DC 20003
Ph: (202)547-7424
Fax: (202)547-3540
URL: http://www.nahc.org
Contact: William A. Dombi, President
Facebook: www.facebook.com/NAHC.org
X (Twitter): x.com/OfficialNAHC

Description: Represents providers of home health care, hospice, and homemaker-home health aide services; interested individuals and organizations. Develops and promotes high standards of patient care in home care services. Seeks to affect legislative and regulatory processes concerning home care services; gathers and disseminates home care industry data; develops public relations strategies. **Publications:** *Homecare News*; *Caring* (Monthly); *NAHC Report* (Quarterly); *NAHC Caring* (Monthly); *Hospice Notes* (Bimonthly); *NAHC Report* (Daily); *NAHC National Home Care and Hospice Directory* (Annual); *Homecare News* (Monthly); *National Home Care and Hospice Directory* (Annual). **Educational Activities:** Home Care and Hospice Conference and Expo (Annual); NAHC's Annual Meeting and Home Care and Hospice Expo (Annual). **Geographic Preference:** National; Multinational.

8241 ■ National Health Council (NHC)

1730 M St. NW, Ste. 500
  Washington, DC 20036-4561
Ph: (202)785-3910
Fax: (202)785-5923
Co. E-mail: info@nhcouncil.org
URL: http://nationalhealthcouncil.org
Facebook: www.facebook.com/nationalhealthcouncil
Linkedin: www.linkedin.com/company/national-health
  -council
X (Twitter): x.com/NHCouncil
YouTube: www.youtube.com/user/nhcouncil

Description: National association of voluntary and professional societies in the health field; national organizations and business groups with strong health interests. Seeks to improve the health of patients, particularly those with chronic diseases, through conferences, publications, policy briefings and special projects. Distributes printed material on health careers and related subjects. Promotes standardization of financial reporting for voluntary health groups. **Founded:** 1920. **Publications:** *Health Groups in Washington: A Directory* (Biennial); *Council Currents* (Bimonthly); *Directory of Health Groups in Washington*; *Guide to America's Voluntary Health Agencies*; *300 Ways to Put Your Talent to Work in the Health Field* (Irregular); *Congress and Health: An Introduction to the Legislative Process and Its Key Participants* (Biennial); *National Health Council--Listing of Member Organizations*. **Geographic Preference:** National.

8242 ■ National League for Nursing (NLN)

2600 Virginia Ave. NW, 8th Fl.
  Washington, DC 20037
Ph: (202)909-2500
Free: 800-669-1656
Co. E-mail: accounting@nln.org
URL: http://www.nln.org
Contact: Beverly Malone, Chief Executive Officer
E-mail: oceo@nln.org

Facebook: www.facebook.com/NationalLeagueforNursing
X (Twitter): x.com/NLN
Instagram: www.instagram.com/nlnursing
YouTube: www.youtube.com/channel/UCs69j
  -7ABCzIBfaM79KAa6A

Description: Champions the pursuit of quality nursing education. A professional association of nursing faculty, education agencies, health care agencies, allied/public agencies, and public members whose mission is to advance quality nursing education that prepares the nursing workforce to meet the needs of diverse populations in an ever-changing health care environment. **Founded:** 1893. **Publications:** *State-Approved Schools of Nursing: R.N.* (Annual); *State-Approved Schools of Nursing: L.P.N./L.V.N.* (Annual); *Scholarships and Loans for Nursing Education* (Annual); *Education for Nursing: The Diploma Way*; *Baccalaureate Education in Nursing: Key to a Professional Career in Nursing*; *Directory of Accredited Nursing Programs*; *Nursing Education Perspectives (NEP)* (Bimonthly); *Professional Development Bulletin* (Semimonthly). **Awards:** NLN Award for Public Policy Advancement (Annual); NLN Mary Adelaide Nutting Award for Outstanding Teaching or Leadership in Nursing Education (Annual). **Geographic Preference:** National.

8243 ■ Société Canadienne des Infirmiè es et Infirmiers en Gastoénterologie et Travailleurs Associés (CSGNA) [Canadian Society of Gastroenterology Nurses and Associates (CSGNA)]

310-4 Cataraqui St.
  Kingston, ON, Canada K7K 1Z7
Ph: (613)507-6130
Co. E-mail: csgna@eventsmgt.com
URL: http://csgna.com
Contact: Cathy Arnold Cormier, President
E-mail: president@csgna.comgna.com
X (Twitter): x.com/CSGNA

Description: Promotes excellence in the teaching and practice of gastroenterological nursing. Facilitates communication among members; produces patient education materials. **Founded:** 1984. **Geographic Preference:** National.

REFERENCE WORKS

8244 ■ "Advancing the Ball" in Inside Healthcare (Vol. 6, December 2010, No. 7, pp. 31)

Description: Profile of Medicalodges an elder-care specialty company that provides both patient care and technology development. President and CEO of the firm believes that hiring good employees is key to growth for any small business. **Availability:** Online.

8245 ■ "Beyond Repair" in Business First Buffalo (Vol. 28, March 23, 2012, No. 27, pp. 1)

Pub: American City Business Journals, Inc.
Contact: Mike Olivieri, Executive Vice President

Released: Weekly. **Price:** $140, one year subscription (Print & Digital); $115, one year subscription (Digital Only). **Description:** Episcopal Church Home and Affiliates once ran a thriving senior care community on a Rhode Island Street property located nearthe Peace Bridge entrance in Buffalo, New York. However, a proposed bridge expansion that would run across the campus has led to the phased shutdown that began seven years ago. Insights on the $14 million liens on the property are also given. **Availability:** Print; Online.

8246 ■ "BRIEF: New In-Home Senior Care Provider Opens In Longmont" in America's Intelligence Wire (September 19, 2012)

Description: HomeWell, provider of live-in and hourly personal care, companionship and homemaker services for seniors, has opened an office in Longmont, Colorado. The firm is fully licensed under the name Home Care Agency in the state and was founded in 1996. **Availability:** Print; Online.

8247 ■ "Corrales Site of New Senior Living/Care Complex" in America's Intelligence Wire (August 13, 2012)

Description: David Dronet, developer of Corrales Senior Living LLC, has chosen Corrales, New Mexico as its newest site to construct a continuum of care for senior citizens. The project entails a $60 million complex of private homes and health care units with amenities like a restaurant, fitness areas, and gardens. **Availability:** Print; Online.

8248 ■ "Elder Care Costs Surge" in National Underwriter Life & Health (Vol. 114, November 8, 2020, No. 21, pp. 25)

Ed: Trevor Thomas. **Description:** Nursing home and assisted living rates rose from 2009 to 2010, according to MetLife Mature Market Institute. Statistical data included. **Availability:** Online.

8249 ■ "Elder Care, Rx Drug Reforms Top Zoeller's Agenda" in Times (December 21, 2010)

Pub: The Times

Ed: Sarah Tompkins. **Description:** Indiana Attorney General Greg Zoeller is hoping to develop a program in the state that will help regulate care for the elderly; freeze medical licenses for doctors involved in criminal investigations; address illegal drug use; and to establish a program to help individuals dispose of old prescription medications easily at pharmacies. **Availability:** Online.

8250 ■ "Elder-Care Seminar to Teach Ways to Avoid Falls" in Virginian-Pilot (November 25, 2010)

Pub: The Virginian-Pilot
Contact: Kevin Goyette, Director
E-mail: kgoyette@dailypress.com

Ed: Amy Jeter. **Description:** ResCare HomeCare, a home health services firm, offers free seminars on helping to make residences safer for seniors prone to falling. **Availability:** Print; Online.

8251 ■ "EVMS Gets Grant to Train Providers for Elder Care" in Virginian-Pilot (October 29, 2010)

Pub: The Virginian-Pilot
Contact: Kevin Goyette, Director
E-mail: kgoyette@dailypress.com

Ed: Elizabeth Simpson. **Description:** Eastern Virginia Medical School received a federal grant to train health providers in elder care. Details of the program are provided. **Availability:** Online.

8252 ■ "Home Elder Care: Buyer, Beware; Scant Background Checks of Aides Often Leave Frail Elderly Vulnerable, Researchers Say" in Consumer Health News (July 12, 2012)

Description: Families must carefully screen applicants when hiring a person or service to care for an aging loved one. Many home aides for the elderly in the US are not required to have training, background checks or drug tests. **Availability:** Online.

8253 ■ "Home Health Franchise Expands Across S. Fla." in South Florida Business Journal (Vol. 34, January 24, 2014, No. 27, pp. 5)

Pub: American City Business Journals, Inc.
Contact: Mike Olivieri, Executive Vice President

Released: Weekly. **Price:** $8, Introductory 4-week offer(Digital & Print). **Description:** Lucy Robellos' Synergy HomeCare franchise in South Florida is experiencing strong growth. The business has 90 active caregiver, and Robellow plans to hire 90 six to ten employees a month for her firm in 2014. She reveals that Synergy aims to keep its clients in the comfort of their own home. **Availability:** Print; Online.

8254 ■ "Home Instead Senior Care Awards National Salute to Senior Service Honoree" in Professional Services Close-Up (June 8, 2012)

Description: Home Instead Senior Care presented Clark Paradise with its Salute to Senior Service award. Paradise is an 85-year old volunteer living in Toms River, New Jersey. He founded a mission for the homeless.

8255 ■ *"Home Instead Senior Care Introduces Post-Discharge Care Initiative; Aims to Reduce Hospital Readmissions Among Seniors"* in Benzinga.com (September 18, 2012)

Pub: Benzinga.com

Contact: Jason Raznick, Founder

Released: September 18, 2012. **Description:** Home Instead Senior Care(R) launched its new, much-needed health program that provides care and support services, mostly for seniors, after being discharged from the hospital. The service is aimed at reducing the number of unnecessary hospital readmissions. **Availability:** Online.

8256 ■ *"Home Instead Senior Care of Seacoast and Southern New Hampshire"* inNew Hampshire Business Review (Vol. 34, April 6, 2012, No. 7, pp. 45)

Description: Portsmouth, New Hampshire-based Home Instead Senior Care of Seacoast and Southern New Hampshire launched a specialized training program for professional and family caregivers designed to help them improve the quality of life for those living with dementia and the families who support them. **Availability:** Online.

8257 ■ *"How Ivanah Thomas Founded a $5 Million Business - While Working Nights"* in Orlando Business Journal (Vol. 30, April 18, 2014, No. 43, pp. 3)

Pub: American City Business Journals, Inc.

Contact: Mike Olivieri, Executive Vice President

Released: Weekly. **Price:** $8, introductory 4-week offer(Digital & Print). **Description:** Caring First Inc. founder, Ivanah Thomas, says her drive to serve people in their home rather than them being institutionalized lead to the establishment of her firm. She added that she ran the home care business by herself during its early years. Thomas also stated her social status posed challenges for the company. **Availability:** Print; Online.

8258 ■ *"Los Angeles Jewish Home to Expand to Westside With New Senior Care Community and In-Home Services"* in PR Newswire (September 12, 2012)

Pub: PR Newswire Association LLC.

Description: Los Angeles Jewish Home plans to develop a senior care community at The Village at Playa Vista on the west side of Los Angeles, California. They will serve residential, healthcare and in-home care for seniors living on the west side of LA. Gonda Healthy Aging Westside Campus, donated by Leslie and Susan Gonda (Goldschmied) Foundation, will be part of the Jewish Home's mission to serve seniors in the area. Statistical data included.

8259 ■ *"Mason Group Seeks $20M for 'Gray' Fund"* in Business Courier Serving Cincinnati-Northern Kentucky (Vol. 29, June 15, 2012, No. 7, pp. 1)

Description: Nonprofit Link-age is seeking to raise $20 millin to fund a new revenue source for its members. The nonprofit is a senior care organization that buys food, medical supplies and medicine for senior members. **Availability:** Print; Online.

8260 ■ *"MMRGlobal Home Health and Senior Care Programs to Be Showcased at Visiting Nurse Associations of America's Annual Meeting"* in Marketwired (April 12, 2012)

Pub: Comtex News Network Inc.

Contact: Kan Devnani, President

Description: MMR Global Inc. will highlight its storage and solutions and electronic document management and imaging systems for healthcare professionals at the Visiting Nurse Associations of America (VNAA) 30th Annual Meeting in Phoenix, Arizona. Personal Health Records (PHRs), MyEsafeDeposit-Box and other programs are profiled. **Availability:** Print; Online.

8261 ■ *"A New Cloud-Based Phone System Is Installed Remotely for North Carolina Senior Care Council"* in Information Technology Business (June 19, 2012)

Description: North Carolina Senior Care Council (NcSCC) has partnered with VoxNet to provide long-term care for Cloud-based PBX to help NcSCC manage their system that assists seniors. **Availability:** Online.

8262 ■ *"Q&A With Devin Ringling: Franchise's Services Go Beyond Elder Care"* in Gazette (October 2, 2010)

Pub: The Gazette

Contact: Vicki Cederholm, Director, Operations

E-mail: vicki.cederholm@gazette.com

Ed: Bill Radford. **Description:** Profile of franchise, Interim HealthCare, in Colorado Springs, Colorado; the company offers home care services that include wound care and specialized feedings to shopping and light housekeeping. It also runs a medical staffing company that provides nurses, therapists and other health care workers to hospitals, prisons, schools and other facilities. **Availability:** Online.

8263 ■ *"Reimbursement Limitations on Home Healthcare Are Being Loosened"* in Modern Healthcare (October 27, 2018)

URL(s): www.modernhealthcare.com/article/201810 27/NEWS/181029949/reimbursement-limitations-on -home-healthcare-are-being-loosened

Ed: Shelby Livingston. **Released:** October 27, 2018. **Description:** Insurers are now focused on keeping patients out of the hospital and letting them be cared for at home, which actually saves money in the long-term. More and more care is being done at home, leading to better patient response and preventing them from returning to the hospital for more care. **Availability:** Online.

8264 ■ *"RF Technologies Celebrates 25th Anniversary of Keeping Patients and Senior Care Residents Safe and Secure"* in PR Newswire (August 1, 2012)

Pub: PR Newswire Association LLC.

Description: RF Technologies has entered into the senior care market by offering wireless wandering managemnt systems and transmitters to help reduce the risk of resident elopements. RF is a leading provider of customized radio frequency identification (RFID) healthcare safety and security solutions for the healthcare sector.

8265 ■ *"Technology: Elder Care Enters the Digital Age: Wireless Companies Devise Ways to Aid Home Health, Let People Stay in Homes"* in Atlanta Journal-Constitution (April 29, 2012, pp. D1)

Description: Mobile phone industry is actually helping families keep aging loved one in their homes. The home healthcare industry is adding technology, telecommunications, smartphone applications and other devices to make it easier for seniors to remain in their homes. Details on this growing industry are included along with statistical data. **Availability:** Online.

8266 ■ *"The Top Trends in Home Care for 2019"* in Home Health Care News (January 6, 2019)

URL(s): homehealthcarenews.com/2019/01/the-top -trends-in-home-care-for-2019%EF%BB%BF/

Ed: Robert Holly. **Released:** January 06, 2019. **Description:** The shift towards allowing some non-skilled in-home care services under the Medicare Advantage program is one of the biggest trends to continue into 2019. More care home care is set to become more clinical and specialized, while recruiting and retaining qualified staff is going to become an even bigger challenge as more of the population ages. **Availability:** Online.

8267 ■ *"VPA to Pay $9.5 Million to Settle Whistle-Blower Lawsuits"* in Crain's Detroit Business (Vol. 26, January 11, 2010, No. 2, pp. 13)

Pub: Crain Communications Inc.

Contact: Barry Asin, President

Ed: Jay Greene. **Description:** According to Terrence Berg, first assistant with the U.S. Attorney's Office in Detroit, Voluntary Physicians Association, a local home health care company, has agreed to pay $9.5 million to settle four whistle-blower lawsuits; the agreement settles allegations that VPA submitted claims to TriCare, the Michigan Medicaid program and Medicare for unnecessary home visits, tests and procedures. **Availability:** Online.

8268 ■ *"Women's Initiative for Self Employment Honors Home Instead Senior Care Owner as 2012 Woman Entrepreneur of the Year"* in Marketwired (September 11, 2012)

Pub: Comtex News Network Inc.

Contact: Kan Devnani, President

Ed: Michelle Rogers. **Description:** Women's Initiative for Self Employment has bestowed its 2012 Woman Entrepreneur of the Year award on Michelle Rogers, owner of Home Instead Senior Care. The Women's Initiative is a nonprofit organization celebrating eight female business owners in the Silicon Valley Region annually. Home Instead Senior Care provides in-home care for seniors in the Bay Area of northern California. **Availability:** Online.

STATISTICAL SOURCES

8269 ■ *Home Health Care And Residential Nursing Care Services Market Covering Nursing Care Facilities; Home Health Care Providers; Retirement Communities; Orphanages & Group Homes; Global Summary 2022*

URL(s): www.marketresearch.com/Business-Re-search-Company-v4006/Home-Health-Care-Resi dential-Nursing-31921953/

Price: $1,500. **Description:** Report covers the home health care and residential nursing care market characteristics, market trends and strategies, growth, market segmentation, regional comparisons, and competitive landscape. **Availability:** Download.

8270 ■ *RMA Annual Statement Studies*

Pub: Risk Management Association

Contact: Nancy Foster, President

Released: Annual. **Description:** Contains composite balance sheets and income statements for more than 360 industries, including the accounting, auditing, and bookkeeping industries. Also contains five years of comparative historical data for discerning trends. Includes 16 commonly used ratios, computed for most of the size groupings for nearly every industry.

TRADE PERIODICALS

8271 ■ *Abbeyfield Houses Society of Canada Newsletter*

Pub: Abbeyfield Houses Society of Canada

Contact: Denis Laframboise, President

URL(s): abbeyfield.ca/start-a-house

Description: Reports on news of Abbeyfield Houses Society of Canada, a provider of care and companion-ship for the elderly. Also features articles related to aging, housing, and lifestyle in Canada and internationally. Recurring features include letters to the editor, and columns titled News of Local Societies and Bits 'n Bites. **Availability:** PDF; Download.

8272 ■ *Home Health Care Management & Practice (HHCMP)*

Pub: SAGE Publications

Contact: Tracey Ozmina, President

URL(s): journals.sagepub.com/home/hhc

Released: Quarterly **Price:** $1,130, Institutions for back file lease, combined plus back file (current volume print & all online content); $976, Institutions for back file lease, e-access plus back file (all online content); $969, Institutions for back file purchase, e-access (content through 1998); $277, Institutions for single print issue; $81, Individuals for single print issue; $1,027, Institutions for print and online; $253, Individuals for print and online; $215, Individuals for online only; $873, Institutions for online only; $1,006, Institutions for print only; $248, Individuals for print only. **Description:** Peer-reviewed journal covering all aspects of home health care practice and management. **Availability:** Print; PDF; Download; Online.

8273 ■ *Home Health Care Services Quarterly*
Pub: Taylor And Francis Group
Contact: Annie Callanan, Chief Executive Officer
URL(s): www.tandfonline.com/journals/whhc20
Ed: Hongdao Meng. **Released:** Quarterly **Price:** $1,767, Institutions for print and online; $257, Individuals for print and online; $1,449, Institutions for online only; $237, Individuals for online only. **Description:** Professional journal. **Availability:** Print; Download; PDF; Online.

8274 ■ *Home Health Line*
Pub: UCG Holdings L.P.
URL(s): homehealthline.decisionhealth.com
Released: Weekly; 48/yr. **Price:** $657, Individuals. **Description:** Reports on Medicare, Medicaid, and other federal and managed care coverage and payment for home health care, including home health agencies, hospice care, home medical equipment, home infusion therapy, and the home care industry as a business. **Availability:** Print; Online.

8275 ■ *Home Healthcare Now*
Pub: Lippincott Williams & Wilkins
URL(s): journals.lww.com/homeheal
thcarenurseonline/pages/default.aspx
Facebook: www.facebook.com/100027792236213
X (Twitter): x.com/HHNonline
Released: 6/year **Price:** $283, Individuals for 1 year print + online international; $88, Individuals for 1 year print + online Canada/Mexico; $283, Individuals for 1 year print + online international; $53, Individuals for 1 year online international; $1,380, Institutions for 1 year print Canada/Mexico; $1,400, Institutions for 1 year print international; $1,400, Institutions for 1 year print UK/Australia; $77, Individuals for one year print online US; $53, Individuals for one year online US; $1,003, Institutions for one year print US. **Description:** Magazine for the practicing professional nurse working in the home health, community health, and public health areas. **Availability:** Print; PDF; Online.

TRADE SHOWS AND CONVENTIONS

8276 ■ NAHC's Annual Meeting and Home Care and Hospice Expo
National Association for Home Care and Hospice (NAHC)
228 7th St. SE
Washington, DC 20003
Ph: (202)547-7424
Fax: (202)547-3540
URL: http://www.nahc.org
Contact: William A. Dombi, President
URL(s): nahc.org/event/2024-home-care-and-hospice
-conference-and-expo
Frequency: Annual. **Description:** General home health products, emergency response systems, computers, uniforms, publications, surgical and medical supplies, pharmaceuticals, durable and home medical equipment. **Audience:** Industry professionals. **Principal Exhibits:** General home health products, emergency response systems, computers, uniforms, publications, surgical and medical supplies, pharmaceuticals, durable and home medical equipment. **Telecommunication Services:** cta@nahc.org.

CONSULTANTS

8277 ■ Linda Berkowitz
1938 Soule Rd.
Clearwater, FL 33759
Contact: Linda Berkowitz, President
Description: Consultant in health care and employee and systems management. **Scope:** Consultant in health care and employee and systems management.

8278 ■ United American Healthcare Corporation (UAHC)
303 E Wacker Dr., Ste. 1040
Chicago, IL 60601
Ph: (313)393-4571
Co. E-mail: relations@uahc.com
URL: http://www.uahc.com

Contact: John M. Fife, President
Description: A contract manufacturing company that offers services to the medical device industry, primarily for the cardiovascular market. Services focus on precision laser-cutting capabilities and the processing of thin-wall tubular metal components, sub-assemblies, and implants. **Founded:** 1985.

FRANCHISES AND BUSINESS OPPORTUNITIES

8279 ■ Accessible Home Health Care (AHHC)
15251 NE 18th Ave., Ste. 9
North Miami Beach, FL 33162
Ph: (305)964-8068
URL: http://www.accessiblehomehealthcare.com
Contact: Ali Mandsaurwala, President
X (Twitter): x.com/accessible_care
Description: Provider of home health care services such as memory loss care, dementia care and other health care services. **Founded:** 2001. **Financial Assistance:** Yes **Training:** Provides 1 week training at headquarters, 2 days at franchise's location and ongoing support.

8280 ■ Affinity Health Canada
60 Columbia Way
Markham, ON, Canada L3R 0C9
Free: 800-565-2273
Co. E-mail: info@retireathomeottawa.com
URL: http://affinityhealth.ca
Contact: Donatein Munyaneza, Manager
Description: Provider of home care services such as home health care, senior care, nursing care, care management services and hospital discharge planning services. **Founded:** 1994. **Training:** Provides 7 days training.

8281 ■ A Better Solution Inc. (ABS)
1515 S Tamiami Trl., Ste. 7
Venice, FL 34285
Ph: (941)906-1881
Free: 866-945-7973
Co. E-mail: info@abs.care
URL: http://www.abs.care
Contact: Donald Cogswell, President
E-mail: dcogswell@abs.care
Facebook: www.facebook.com/abettersolu
tionhomecare
Linkedin: www.linkedin.com/company/a-better-solu
tion-inc
X (Twitter): x.com/ABSHomeHealth
Description: A non-medical solution for our everyday needs. Offer a staff of caring, experienced, dependable caregivers able to assist clients of all ages with non-medical needs. Homemaking, companionship, transportation, meal planning and more. **Founded:** 1998. **Training:** 2 week training and on the job, in your live office location. Your comprehensive FL training class covers marketing and sales, recruitment, operations, scheduling, payroll, and client relations. Full ongoing support includes phone, onsite visits and website support.

8282 ■ BrightStar Healthcare
1125 Tri-State Pky., No. 700
Gurnee, IL 60031
Ph: (847)782-8282
Fax: (847)693-2048
Co. E-mail: info@brightstarcare.com
URL: http://www.brightstarcare.com
Contact: Jaclyn Webster, Director
Facebook: www.facebook.com/BrightStarCare
Description: Firm provides medical, non-medical home care and medical staffing services. **No. of Franchise Units:** 249. **No. of Operating Units:** 280. **Founded:** 2002. **Franchised:** 2005. **Equity Capital Needed:** Net worth of at least $500,000; liquid capital of $100,000. **Royalty Fee:** 5.25% of monthly net billings generated from non-National Accounts; 6.25% of monthly net billings generated from National Accounts. **Financial Assistance:** Yes **Training:** Provides 10 days at headquarters, 10 days onsite with ongoing support.

8283 ■ Comfort Keepers
101 N Fountain Ave.
Springfield, OH 45502
Ph: (937)343-4830
URL: http://www.comfortkeepers.com
Facebook: www.facebook.com/Comfor
tKeepersMiamiValley
YouTube: www.youtube.com/c/comfortkeepers
Description: Provider of in-home senior care services. **No. of Franchise Units:** 927. **Founded:** 1998. **Training:** Franchisee's complete a comprehensive training curriculum with ongoing support.

8284 ■ Comfort Keepers-Canada
245 Fairview Mall Dr., Ste. 401
Toronto, ON, Canada M2J 4T1
Ph: (416)800-2535
Free: 866-363-0072
URL: http://www.comfortkeepers.ca
Contact: Peter Drutz, President
Facebook: www.facebook.com/comfor
tkeeperscanada
Description: Provider of home care, nursing, transportation, end life care services. **Founded:** 1998. **Equity Capital Needed:** $77,550-$109,960. **Franchise Fee:** 45000. **Training:** Offers extensive training.

8285 ■ GEM Health Care Services [Services de Sante GEM]
383 Parkdale Ave., Ste. 304
Ottawa, ON, Canada K1Y 4R4
Ph: (613)761-7474
Free: 877-761-4361
Co. E-mail: services@gemhealthcare.com
URL: http://gemhealthcare.com
Contact: Gaye E. Moffett, President
Facebook: www.facebook.com/GEMHeal
thCareServices
Linkedin: www.linkedin.com/company/gem-health
-care-services
Description: Provider of health care services such as personal health care, staff relief, nursing, home care services and institutional supplemental staffing. **Founded:** 1994. **Training:** Provides 3 weeks training.

8286 ■ Home Helpers
4760 Red Bank Expy., Ste. 300
Cincinnati, OH 45227
Ph: (513)712-0736
Co. E-mail: 57915@homehelpershomecare.com
URL: http://www.homehelpershomecare.com/
cincinnati-nky
Contact: G. Cindy, Director
Facebook: www.facebook.com/
HomeHelpersCincinnatiOH
X (Twitter): x.com/HomeHelpersNATI
Description: Non-medical, in-home companion care for the elderly, new mothers and those recuperating from illness. **Founded:** 2004. **Franchised:** 1997. **Financial Assistance:** Yes **Training:** Yes.

8287 ■ Nurse Next Door Home Care Services
1788 W 5th Ave.
Vancouver, BC, Canada V6J 1P2
Ph: (604)330-9930
Free: 877-588-8609
Co. E-mail: publicrelations@nursenextdoor.com
URL: http://www.nursenextdoor.com
Facebook: www.facebook.com/nursenextdoor
Linkedin: www.linkedin.com/company/nurse-nex
t-door
Description: Provider of home care and nursing services. **Founded:** 2001. **Training:** 1 week training and ongoing support.

8288 ■ Right At Home Inc. (RAH)
6700 Mercy Rd., Ste. 400
Omaha, NE 68106
Free: 877-697-7537
Fax: (402)697-0289
Co. E-mail: info@rightathome.net
URL: http://www.rightathome.net
Contact: Jeff Vavricek, Chief Financial Officer
Facebook: www.facebook.com/RAHSeniorHomeCare

Linkedin: www.linkedin.com/company/right-at-home
-inc
X (Twitter): x.com/rightathomeUS
YouTube: www.youtube.com/RightatHomeCare
Description: Provider of home care services to seniors and disabled adults. **Founded:** 1995. **Franchise Fee:** $48,500. **Financial Assistance:** No **Training:** A comprehensive program of pre-training, 2 week initial training program, and follow up onsite training visit. Full on-going support includes telephone, onsite visits and web site support.

8289 ■ Synergy Homecare
1757 E Baseline Rd., Ste. 124
Gilbert, AZ 85233
Free: 877-432-2692
URL: http://synergyhomecare.com
Facebook: www.facebook.com/synergyhomecare
Linkedin: www.linkedin.com/company/synergy
-homecare
X (Twitter): x.com/SYNERGYHomeCare
Instagram: www.instagram.com/synergyhomecare
YouTube: www.youtube.com/user/
SYNERGYHomeCare
Description: Firm provides home care services. **No. of Franchise Units:** 120. **No. of Operating Units:** 235. **Founded:** 2000. **Equity Capital Needed:** $59,000-$157,000 ; liquid cash of approximately $50,000 is needed. **Franchise Fee:** $24,750-$89,000. **Training:** Yes.

8290 ■ Tender Loving Care (TLC)
Staff Builders, Inc.
394 S Lake Ave., Ste. 610
Duluth, MN 55802
Ph: (516)327-3361
Free: 800-444-4633
Fax: (516)358-3678
Facebook: www.facebook.com/TLCofDuluth
Instagram: www.instagram.com/tlcofduluth
Description: Home health care. **No. of Franchise Units:** 248. **No. of Company-Owned Units:** 32. **Founded:** 2003. **Franchised:** 1987. **Equity Capital Needed:** $125,000-$135,000, includes franchise and working capital. **Franchise Fee:** $$29,500. **Training:** Yes.

8291 ■ TheKey
TheKey
2001 Van Ness
San Francisco, CA 94109
Ph: (415)295-6703
URL: http://thekey.com
Contact: Tad Smith, Chief Executive Officer
E-mail: tsmith@thekey.com
Facebook: www.facebook.com/homecareassistance
Linkedin: www.linkedin.com/company/home-care
-assistance
X (Twitter): x.com/hcassistance

Instagram: www.instagram.com/teamhca
YouTube: www.youtube.com/user/homecareinfo
Description: Firm provides home health care services. **Founded:** 2002. **Financial Assistance:** No

8292 ■ Touching Hearts At Home
7900 W 78th St., Ste. 410
Edina, MN 55439
Free: 877-870-8750
Co. E-mail: contact@touchinghearts.com
URL: http://www.touchinghearts.com
Contact: Renae Peterson, Founder
Facebook: www.facebook.com/touchingheartsinc
Linkedin: www.linkedin.com/company/touching-hear
ts-at-home
X (Twitter): x.com/touchinghearts
Description: Firm provides non-medical in-home care for senior citizens and people with disabilities. **Founded:** 1996. **Training:** Comprehensive 5 day training gives you the knowledge, skills and tools required to run a successful franchise. Outstanding ongoing support is provided through toll free number assistance, email, internal website discussion forum, HQ support staff, and regional and national seminars.

8293 ■ Visiting Angels
937 Haverford Rd., Ste. 200
Bryn Mawr, PA 19010
Free: 800-365-4189
URL: http://www.visitingangels.com
Facebook: www.facebook.com/Visi
tingAngelsCorporate
Linkedin: www.linkedin.com/company/visitingangels
X (Twitter): x.com/_VisitingAngels
Instagram: www.instagram.com/visi
tingangelshomecare
YouTube: www.youtube.com/user/VisitingAngels1
Description: Non-medical senior homecare. **No. of Franchise Units:** 435. **Founded:** 1998. **Franchised:** 1998. **Equity Capital Needed:** $58,285-$95,035. **Franchise Fee:** $31,950-$54,950. **Royalty Fee:** 2-3. 5%. **Financial Assistance:** Yes **Training:** Offers 5.5 days training at headquarters, 5 plus regional refresher meetings per month, monthly webinars, annual conference and ongoing support.

COMPUTERIZED DATABASES

8294 ■ *Health and Medical Care Archive*
University of Michigan Institute for Social Research
Inter-University Consortium for Political and Social
Research
330 Packard St.
Ann Arbor, MI 48104
Ph: (734)615-8400
Co. E-mail: icpsr-help@umich.edu
URL: http://www.icpsr.umich.edu/web/pages/index
.html
Contact: Margaret C. Levenstein, Director

E-mail: maggiel@umich.edu
URL(s): www.icpsr.umich.edu/web/pages/HMCA/in
dex.html
Facebook: www.facebook.com/HMCAdata
Linkedin: www.linkedin.com/company/hmcadata
X (Twitter): x.com/HMCAdata
Instagram: www.instagram.com/hmcadata
Availability: Online. **Type:** Full-text.

LIBRARIES

8295 ■ Boone Hospital Center Medical Library
1600 E Broadway
Columbia, MO 65201
URL: http://boone.health/for-medical-professionals/
resources
Description: Aims to improve the health of the people and communities we serve. **Scope:** Medicine. **Holdings:** Figures not available.

8296 ■ El Camino Hospital - The Health Library & Resource Center
2500 Grant Rd.
Mountain View, CA 94040
Ph: (650)940-7000
URL: http://www.elcaminohealth.org
Contact: Andrew Cope, President
Facebook: www.facebook.com/elcaminohealth
Linkedin: www.linkedin.com/company/el-camino
-health
Instagram: www.instagram.com/el.camino.health
YouTube: www.youtube.com/c/ElCaminoHealth
Scope: Medicine; nursing; healthcare administration. **Services:** Interlibrary loan; copying; library open to the public. **Founded:** 1958. **Holdings:** Books; DVDs, CD-ROMs; journals. **Subscriptions:** 150 journals and other serials. **Geographic Preference:** Local.

8297 ■ Virginia Commonwealth University School of Allied Health Professions - Virginia Center on Aging - Information Resources Center
900 E Leigh St., Ste. 7020
Richmond, VA 23219
Ph: (804)828-1525
Co. E-mail: vcoa@vcu.edu
URL: http://www.sahp.vcu.edu/vcoa/video-library/in
dex.html
Contact: Dr. Edward F. Ansello, Director
E-mail: eansello@vcu.edu
Facebook: www.facebook.com/vcuvcoa
YouTube: www.youtube.com/user/alliedhelp/videos
Scope: Gerontology; mental health; sociology and the politics of aging; geriatrics; family relationships; long-term care; lifelong learning. **Services:** Library open to the public with restrictions (audio/visual materials available to Virginia residents only). **Founded:** 1978. **Holdings:** 1,500 books; 4 archives; 150 videos and DVDs.

START-UP INFORMATION

8298 ■ *Starting & Running Your Own Horse Business*
Pub: Storey Publishing L.L.C.
Contact: Maribeth Casey, Director
E-mail: maribeth.casey@storey.com
Ed: Mary Ashby McDonald. **Released:** Second edition. **Price:** $19.95, trade paper. **Description:** Insight into starting and running a successful equestrian business is given. The book covers safety, tips for operating a riding school or horse camp, strategies for launching a carriage business, along with tax and insurance advice. **Availability:** E-book; Print.

ASSOCIATIONS AND OTHER ORGANIZATIONS

8299 ■ **American Association for Horsemanship Safety (AAHS)**
Co. E-mail: mail@horsemanshipsafety.com
URL: http://www.horsemanshipsafety.com
Contact: Jan Dawson, President
Description: Promotes safe horsemanship skills through training and education. Offers systematic approach to teaching horsemanship safety. Provides information to the general public about safe horsemanship practices. **Founded:** 1995. **Publications:** *Caution: Horses* (Quarterly). **Geographic Preference:** National.

8300 ■ **American Driving Society (ADS)**
PO Box 278
Cross Plains, WI 53528
Ph: (608)237-7382
Fax: (608)237-6468
Co. E-mail: info@americandrivingsociety.org
URL: http://americandrivingsociety.org
Contact: Philip B. Hofmann, President
Facebook: www.facebook.com/american
  drivingsociety
X (Twitter): x.com/adscarriage
YouTube: www.youtube.com/user/AMDrivingSociety
Pinterest: www.Pinterest.com/adscarriage
Description: Promotes horse and pony driving both competitively and for pleasure; creates and maintains public interest in driving events; organizes or facilitates the organization of driving events; establishes a list of qualified judges. **Founded:** 1974. **Publications:** *The Wheelhorse* (8/year); *The Whip Magazine* (Quarterly); *ADS Rulebook*. **Geographic Preference:** National.

8301 ■ **American Horse Council (AHC)**
1616 H St. NW, 7th Fl.
  Washington, DC 20006
Ph: (202)296-4031
Co. E-mail: jbroadway@horsecouncil.org
URL: http://www.horsecouncil.org
Contact: Julie M. Broadway, President
E-mail: jbroadway@horsecouncil.org
Facebook: www.facebook.com/
  AmericanHorseCouncil
X (Twitter): x.com/AmericanHorseCo
Instagram: www.instagram.com/
  americanhorsecouncil
YouTube: www.youtube.com/channel/UCdB
  tNkiAZflDV7Nx92swzg
Description: Represents the horse industry before congress and federal agencies. Promotes equitable taxation and legislation; maintains liaison with government agencies and advises members of current national developments affecting the equine industry. **Founded:** 1969. **Publications:** *AHC Business Quarterly* (Quarterly); *Horse Industry Directory* (Annual). **Geographic Preference:** National.

8302 ■ **American Horse Publications (AHP)**
49 Spinnaker Cir.
  South Daytona, FL 32119
Ph: (386)760-7743
Fax: (386)760-7728
Co. E-mail: ahorsepubs@aol.com
URL: http://www.americanhorsepubs.org
Contact: Chris Brune, Executive Director
E-mail: ahorsepubs@aol.com
Facebook: www.facebook.com/
  AmericanHorsePublications
Linkedin: www.linkedin.com/company/american
  -horse-publications
X (Twitter): x.com/AmerHorsePubs
Description: Members are horse-oriented publications, professionals and businesses. Aims to improve the horse publication field and network within the equine publishing industry. **Founded:** 1970. **Awards:** AHP Champion Award (Annual); Equine Industry Vision Award (Annual). **Geographic Preference:** National.

8303 ■ **American Youth Horse Council (AYHC)**
1 Gainer Rd.
  McDonald, NM 88262
Ph: (817)320-2005
Co. E-mail: info@ayhc.com
URL: http://www.ayhc.com
Contact: Dr. Dean Jousan, President
X (Twitter): x.com/AYHC
Instagram: www.instagram.com/american_youth
  _horse_council
Description: Umbrella organization providing resources and leadership to the youth horse industry. Promotes the youth horse industry and responsible equine management practices. Provides a forum for information exchange. Conducts educational forums for youth leaders. Establishes youth conference guidelines. **Founded:** 1970. **Publications:** *Horse Industry Handbook: A Guide to Equine Care and Management*; *Safety Manual*. **Awards:** AYHC Distinguished Service Award (Annual); AYHC Leader of the Year (Annual); AYHC Student Leader of the Year (Annual); AYHC Grants (Annual). **Geographic Preference:** National.

8304 ■ **Canadian Therapeutic Riding Association (CanTRA) [Association Canadienne d'Equitation Therapeutique]**
5420 Hwy. 6 N RR No. 5
  Guelph, ON, Canada N1H 6J2
Ph: (519)767-0700
Fax: (519)767-0435
Co. E-mail: ctra@golden.net
URL: http://www.cantra.ca/en
Contact: JoAnn Thompson Franklin, President
Facebook: www.facebook.com/CanTRA.ACET
Description: Therapists with an interest in the use of equestrian activities to promote health and fitness. Seeks to advance the practice of therapeutic riding. Serves as a clearinghouse on therapeutic horseback riding. **Founded:** 1980. **Geographic Preference:** National.

8305 ■ **CHA - Certified Horsemanship Association (CHA)**
1795 Alysheba Way, Ste. 7102
  Lexington, KY 40509
Ph: (859)259-3399
Fax: (859)255-0726
Co. E-mail: office@cha.horse
URL: http://cha.horse
Contact: Bob Coleman, President
Facebook: www.facebook.com/CHAinstructors
Linkedin: www.linkedin.com/in/chainstructors
X (Twitter): x.com/chainstructors
Instagram: www.instagram.com/CHAinstructors
YouTube: www.youtube.com/user/chainstructor
Pinterest: www.pinterest.com/chainstructors
Description: Certifies riding instructors and trail guides, accredits equine facilities, maintains an active database of instructors and stables for the general public on the website. **Founded:** 1967. **Publications:** *CHA Composite Horsemanship Manual*; *Riding Instructors Manual*. **Awards:** CHA Partnership in Safety Award (Annual). **Geographic Preference:** National.

8306 ■ **Equine Canada (EC) [Canada Hippique]**
11 Hines Rd., Ste., 201
  Ottawa, ON, Canada K2K 2X1
Ph: (613)287-1515
Free: 866-282-8395
Fax: (613)248-3484
Co. E-mail: inquiries@equestrian.ca
URL: http://www.equestrian.ca
Contact: Chris Sorensen, President
Facebook: www.facebook.com/equestriancan
X (Twitter): x.com/equestrian_can
Instagram: www.instagram.com/equestrian_can
YouTube: www.youtube.com/channel/UCIpQnoBnlnT
  2mxem3Xp4wrw
Description: Participants in equestrian events; admirers of horses. Promotes increased interest and participation in equestrian sports. Sponsors competitions; compiles statistics. **Founded:** 1977. **Geographic Preference:** National.

8307 ■ **Gladstone Equestrian Association (GEA)**
PO Box 469
  Gladstone, NJ 07934
URL: http://gea-nj.org
Contact: James C. Brady, III, Treasurer Secretary

Description: Individuals with an interest in carriage driving and other equestrian events and activities. Seeks to increase interest and participation in carriage driving and related sports. Sponsors competitions. **Founded:** 1985. **Geographic Preference:** National.

8308 ■ Intercollegiate Horse Shows Association (IHSA)
Fairfield, CT
Free: 844-307-4472
URL: http://www.ihsainc.com
Contact: Peter Cashman, Executive Director
E-mail: peter.cashman@usma.edu
Facebook: www.facebook.com/IHSAinc
X (Twitter): x.com/rideihsa

Description: Promotes the education of students in horsemanship and sportsmanship. Provides a basis of competition for intercollegiate riders from beginning through advanced levels. Sponsors clinics, seminars, and other horse-oriented activities. **Founded:** 1967. **Awards:** IHSA Senior Academic Achievement Award (Annual); IHSA Senior Athletic Academic Achievement Essay Award (Annual). **Geographic Preference:** National.

8309 ■ International Gay Rodeo Association (IGRA)
PO Box 460504
Aurora, CO 80046-0504
URL: http://www.igra.com
Contact: Candy Pratt, President
E-mail: igracpratt@rrra-tx.com
Facebook: www.facebook.com/IGRARodeo

Description: Gay rodeo associations in the United States and Canada. Promotes public interest in rodeo events and seeks to increase participation in rodeo by gay people. Facilitates communication and cooperation among members; sponsors competitions. **Founded:** 1985. **Geographic Preference:** National.

8310 ■ National Association of Competitive Mounted Orienteering (NACMO)
c/o Jim Klein, Treasurer/National Pointskeeper
24305 98th St. NW
Zimmerman, MN 55398
Ph: (763)856-6735
Co. E-mail: wendyandjim@sherbtel.net
URL: http://www.nacmo.org
Contact: Jim Klein, Treasurer
E-mail: wendyandjim@sherbtel.net

Description: Promotes horseback riding and fellowship among members. Fosters regulation of the sport through a uniform rules system. **Founded:** 1981. **Publications:** *Meadow Muffin* (Quarterly). **Educational Activities:** National Association of Competitive Mounted Orienteering Banquet. **Awards:** NACMO National High Point Awards (Annual); NACMO Rider Awards (Annual); Horse Awards (Annual); Ride Manager Awards (Annual); State Awards and National Awards (Annual); NACMO Short Course National High Point Male (Annual); NACMO Short Course National High Point Team (Annual); Horse Award (Annual); NACMO National High Point Team (Annual); Ride Manager (Annual); NACMO Male/Female Individual Rider award (Annual). **Geographic Preference:** Multinational.

8311 ■ North American Horsemen's Association (NAHA)
310 Washburne Ave.
Paynesville, MN 56362
Ph: (320)243-7250
Free: 800-328-8894
Fax: (320)243-7224
Co. E-mail: insurance@arkagency.com
URL: http://arkagency.com/north-american
-horsemens-association
Facebook: www.facebook.com/The.Ark.1978
X (Twitter): x.com/arkagencyusa

Description: Represents individual horse owners and clubs. Promotes interests of members. Encourages equine safety. Maintains a reference library of books, periodicals, and clippings on equine law and safety in business issues. Gathers statistics, conducts research, maintains hall of fame, and provides educational programs. **Founded:** 1986. **Publica-**

tions: *Risk Reduction Program Catalog* (Semiannual); *Yearbook of News* (Annual). **Awards:** NAHA Safety Awards (Annual). **Geographic Preference:** National.

8312 ■ United Professional Horsemen's Association (UPHA)
4059 Iron Works Pky., Ste. 2
Lexington, KY 40511
Ph: (859)231-5070
Fax: (859)255-2774
Co. E-mail: info@uphaonline.com
URL: http://www.uphaonline.com
Contact: Cindy Mugnier, President
E-mail: cmugnier@aol.com
Facebook: www.facebook.com/UPHA1968
X (Twitter): x.com/uphaonline

Description: Professional horse trainers involved in the show horse industry; horse owners and breeders. Seeks to educate the public about show horses and improve the industry. Sponsors classics for Three- and Four-Year Olds. Maintains hall of fame. **Founded:** 1968. **Geographic Preference:** National.

8313 ■ United States Dressage Federation (USDF)
4051 Iron Works Pky.
Lexington, KY 40511
Ph: (859)971-2277
Fax: (859)971-7722
Co. E-mail: advertise@usdf.org
URL: http://www.usdf.org
Contact: George Williams, President
E-mail: president@usdf.org
Facebook: www.facebook.com/USDFOfficial
X (Twitter): x.com/USDF
Instagram: www.instagram.com/USDFOfficial
YouTube: www.youtube.com/user/USDFORG

Description: Members of local dressage organizations and other interested individuals. Promotes a high standard of accomplishment in dressage throughout the US., primarily through educational programs, and to improve understanding of dressage through educational clinics, forums, and seminars. (In dressage, a horse is trained to execute intricate and highly refined steps and maneuvers. Ideally, the signals from rider to horse are not visible to the spectator.) Certifies dressage instructors. **Founded:** 1973. **Publications:** *USDF Connection* (6/year); *United States Dressage Federation--Calendar of Competitions* (Annual); *USDF Member Guide* (Annual). **Awards:** USDF Rider Award Medals (Annual); USDF Master's Challenge Awards (Annual); USDF Dressage Seat Equitation Rider Awards (Annual); Adequan/USDF All-Breeds Dressage Sport Horse Breeding Awards (Annual); USDF Junior/Young Rider Awards (Annual); USDF Musical Freestyle Rider Awards (Annual); USDF Rider Performance Award (Annual); USDF Vintage Cup Awards (Annual); USDF/Dover Saddlery Adult Amateur Medal (Annual); Adequan/USDF All-Breeds Awards (Annual). **Geographic Preference:** National.

8314 ■ United States Equestrian Federation (USEF)
4001 Wing Commander Way
Lexington, KY 40511
Ph: (859)258-2472
Fax: (859)231-6662
Co. E-mail: customercare@usef.org
URL: http://www.usef.org
Contact: Murray S. Kessler, President
E-mail: mkessler@usef.org
Facebook: www.facebook.com/USequestrian
X (Twitter): x.com/USEquestrian
Instagram: www.instagram.com/USEquestrian
YouTube: www.youtube.com/usefnetwork

Description: Promotes interest in equestrian sports; establishes and enforces rules governing equestrian competitions; maintains records and sanctions dates for competitions. Administers drugs and medication testing program and research. Provides general and specific assistance on equestrian sports in the U.S. as well as referrals. Conducts educational programs for licensed officials throughout the year. Licenses judges and stewards. National Federation of Eques-

trian Sports for the U.S. National Governing Body for Equestrian Sports. **Founded:** 1917. **Publications:** *American Horse Shows Association--Competition Calendar: Competition Calendar; Equestrian: The Official Magazine of the American Equestrian Sport Since 1937* (5/year). **Educational Activities:** US Equestrian Annual Meeting (Annual). **Awards:** Vaulting Horse Of The Year (Annual). **Geographic Preference:** National.

8315 ■ United States Eventing Association (USEA)
525 Old Waterford Rd. NW
Leesburg, VA 20176
Ph: (703)779-0440
Fax: (703)779-0550
Co. E-mail: info@useventing.com
URL: http://www.useventing.com
Contact: Max Corcoran, President
Facebook: www.facebook.com/USEventing
X (Twitter): x.com/USEventing
Instagram: www.instagram.com/useventing

Description: Formulates, distributes, and explains standards, rules, and regulations for the proper conduct of combined training instruction and equestrian combined training competitions. (A combined training competition is composed of two or all three of the following equestrian activities: dressage, cross-country, and show jumping; when all three activities are included the competition is called a horse trial or event.) Sponsors clinics. Assists to provide training opportunities for potential Olympic games competitors. **Founded:** 1959. **Publications:** *Eventing USA* (Quarterly). **Educational Activities:** USEA Annual Meeting and Convention (Annual). **Awards:** Courtney C. Reeves Memorial Trophy (Irregular). **Geographic Preference:** National.

8316 ■ United States Pony Clubs, Inc. (USPC)
4041 Iron Works Pky.
Lexington, KY 40511
Ph: (859)254-7669
Fax: (859)233-4652
Co. E-mail: mainoffice@ponyclub.org
URL: http://www.ponyclub.org
Contact: Jennifer Sweet, President
E-mail: jennifers@ponyclub.org
Facebook: www.facebook.com/USPonyClubs
Linkedin: www.linkedin.com/company/ponyclub
X (Twitter): x.com/USPonyClub
Instagram: www.instagram.com/unitedsta
tesponyclubs
YouTube: www.youtube.com/user/TheUSPonyClubs

Description: Provides education in riding, mounted sports, horse management, and the care of horses and ponies. Grants certificates of proficiency. **Founded:** 1954. **Publications:** *Pony Club News* (Quarterly); *USPC Handbook and Rules for Eventing Competition.* **Educational Activities:** USPC Festival (Triennial). **Awards:** USPC Founders Award (Annual). **Geographic Preference:** National.

REFERENCE WORKS

8317 ■ "Ambitious Horse Center Is In the Works for Southeastern Idaho" in Idaho Business Review (August 25, 2014)
Pub: BridgeTower Media
Contact: Adam Reinebach, President

Price: $99, Digital & Mobile Only(1 Year); $11.99, Print, Digital & Mobile(1 Month); $149, Print, Digital & Mobile(1 Year); $99, Digital & Mobile Only(For 1 Year); $11.99, Print, Digital & Mobile (For 1 Month Intro Rate); $149, Print, Digital & Mobile (For 1 Year). **Description:** Ernest Bleinberger is planning to develop a 167-acre mixed-use project called Horse Station and will be located in Cache Valley, Idaho. Horse Station will include stables for about 250 horses and an arena, along with medical facilities, a hotel, retail shopping center, and a farmers market. **Availability:** Print; Online.

8318 ■ Horse Industry Directory
Pub: American Horse Council
Contact: Julie M. Broadway, President

E-mail: jbroadway@horsecouncil.org
URL(s): horsecouncil.weblinkconnect.com/atlas/direc
tory/search
Released: Annual **Price:** $25, Nonmembers for one
years both version. **Description:** Covers organizations concerned with all aspects of the horse industry,
including breed registries, racing and showing
organizations, transportation and sales companies,
and rodeo/trail organizations and equine publications.
Includes list of state horse specialists, state veterinarians, and state departments of agriculture. **Entries
include:** Organization name, address, phone, names
and titles of key personnel, e-mail & Internet addresses. **Arrangement:** Classified by service. **Indexes:** Organization name. **Availability:** Online.

**8319 ■ *"Horse Racing Industry Cries Foul
Over Budget Switch" in Philadelphia
Business Journal (Vol. 31, March 23, 2012,
No. 6, pp. 1)***
Pub: Baltimore Business Journal
Contact: Rhonda Pringle, President
E-mail: rpringle@bizjournals.com
Price: Introductory 4-Week Offer(Digital & Print); $4,
Introductory 4-Week Offer(Digital Only). **Description:**
Pennsylvania Governor Tom Corbett's proposal to
slash $72 million from the Horse Racing Develop-
ment Fund is seen to adversely impact the sector.
The plan has been criticized by track operators, train-
ers, owners and horse breeders. **Availability:** Print;
Online.

**8320 ■ *"Horseback Riding on the Beach, in
Brooklyn. Seriously." in The New York Times
(August 14, 2019)***
URL(s): www.nytimes.com/2019/08/14/nyregion/
horseback-riding-brooklyn.html
Ed: Margot Boyer-Dry, Max Falkowitz. **Released:**
August 14, 2019. **Description:** Surprising many New
Yorkers, is the Jamaica Bay Riding Academy in the
southeast corner of Brooklyn. There, 70 horses on
450 acres live and are available for guided rides.
Availability: Online.

**8321 ■ *"Northwest Washington Fair Building
New Horse Arena" in Bellingham Business
Journal (Vol. March 2010, pp. 6)***
Pub: Sound Publishing Inc.
Contact: Josh O'Connor, President
Ed: Isaac Bonnell. **Description:** Northwest Washing-
ton Fair is building a new equestrian arena that will
provide larger show space for the horse community.
The existing arena will function as a warm-up arena
when hosting large shows.

**8322 ■ *"Riding School Teaches Students to
Master Selves While Bonding with Horses" in
The Goshen News (December 27, 2018)***
URL(s): www.goshennews.com/news/local_news/ri
ding-school-teaches-students-to-master-selves
-while-bonding-with/article_7b87b28c-73e0-55a
2-bee5-a5cc2598dbaf.html
Ed: Aimee Ambrose. **Released:** December 27, 2018.
Description: The Savage Riding Academy in Goshen
specializes in riding for children, giving them the
chance to learn to not only ride a horse, but to bond
with the animal. These acts often lead to being able
to face and overcome some of life's difficulties and
gives the children a chance to become more confident. **Availability:** Online.

**8323 ■ *"Talking Tax: The Horse Business" in
Idaho Business Review (September 3, 2014)***
Pub: BridgeTower Media
Contact: Adam Reinebach, President
Description: Tax codes involving a small business
that boards, raises, and sells horses are outlined.

TRADE PERIODICALS

**8324 ■ *Saddle & Bridle: Oldest Name In
Show Horse Magazines***
Pub: Saddle & Bridle Inc.
Contact: Keri Thompson, Business Manager
E-mail: keri@saddleandbridle.com
URL(s): www.saddleandbridle.com/about-us

Facebook: www.facebook.com/saddleandbridle
X (Twitter): x.com/Saddleandbridle
Instagram: www.instagram.com/saddleandbridlemag
Ed: Jeffrey Thompson. **Released:** Monthly **Price:**
$85, Individuals for online 1 year; $100, Individuals
for print 1 year; $150, for online 2 year; $154, for
print 2 year; $170, Individuals for print 1 year out of
us; $175, Individuals for print and online 1 year; $205,
for print 3 year; $217, for print and online 1 year
outside us; $225, for online 3 year; $235, Out of state
for print and online 2 year; $299, for print 2 year out
of us; $349, for print and online 3 year; $399, for
print and online 2 year outside us; $424, for print 3
year out of us; $574, for print and online 3 year
outside us. **Description:** Publication for owners,
trainers, breeders, and horse show managers of
English show horses. **Availability:** Print; Online.

TRADE SHOWS AND CONVENTIONS

**8325 ■ Hoosier Horse Fair and Expo
(HHF&E)**
Indiana Horse Council (IHC)
   7440 Radburn Cir.
   Indianapolis, IN 46214-2634
URL(s): www.indianahorsecouncilfoundation.org/hhh
-application
Description: Horse and equine industry equipment,
supplies, and services. Also includes a fair with 4-H
activities, and a pro-rodeo. **Audience:** Industry
professionals. **Principal Exhibits:** Horse and equine
industry equipment, supplies, and services. Also
includes a fair with 4-H activities, and a pro-rodeo.
Telecommunication Services: ihcfscholarships@
gmail.com.

LIBRARIES

**8326 ■ American Mustang and Burro
Association (AMBA) - Library**
235 Black Stallion Rd.
   Townsend, DE 19734
Ph: (302)653-7005
URL: http://usamba.org
Contact: Debbie Edwards, Secretary
Description: Owners of adopted wild horses and
burros and other interested individuals. Seeks to
promote the cause of wild horses and burros. Con-
ducts educational programs concerning America's
wild equine, such as the Adopt-A-Horse Program.
Promotes social and competitive events. Maintains
speakers' bureau, and wild equine registry. **Scope:**
Wild horses and burros. **Founded:** 1981. **Holdings:**
Figures not available. **Publications:** *American
Mustang and Burro Association Journal* (Quarterly;
3/year). **Awards:** AMBA/USDF All-Breeds Awards
(Annual). **Geographic Preference:** National.

**8327 ■ American Saddlebred Museum -
Library**
4083 Wing Commander Way, Ste. 150
   Lexington, KY 40511
URL: http://www.asbmuseum.org/resources/library
Scope: Saddle bred history; breed standards and
training techniques to historical accounts and personal memoirs. **Services:** Library not open to the
public (museum members only). **Holdings:** 2,400
volumes. **Subscriptions:** 4 journals and other serials.

**8328 ■ American Suffolk Horse Association
(ASHA)**
4170 NE 43rd Ave.
   High Springs, FL 32643-5678
Ph: (386)965-2758
Co. E-mail: americansuffolkhorse@gmail.com
URL: http://www.suffolkpunch.com
Contact: Zelda Gagliardi, Secretary
Description: Owners and breeders of the Suffolk-
Punch horse. Compiles statistics annually on animals
registered and transferred. **Geographic Preference:**
National.

**8329 ■ Arabian Horse Association (AHA) -
Library**
10805 E Bethany Dr.
   Aurora, CO 80014
Ph: (303)696-4500
Fax: (303)696-4599
Co. E-mail: info@arabianhorses.org
URL: http://www.arabianhorses.org
Contact: Caroline Elik, II, Secretary
Facebook: www.facebook.com/ArabianHorseAssocia
tion
Linkedin: www.linkedin.com/company/arabian-horse
-association
X (Twitter): x.com/ahaarabian
Instagram: www.instagram.com/arabianhorseassoc
YouTube: www.youtube.com/user/aha10805
Pinterest: www.pinterest.com/ahaarabian
Description: Maintains purebred Arabian registry.
Scope: Horses. **Founded:** 2003. **Holdings:** Figures
not available. **Publications:** *Arabian Horse Life
(AHL)* (Bimonthly). **Awards:** AHA Volunteer Service
Award (Annual). **Geographic Preference:** National.

**8330 ■ California State Polytechnic
University - W.K. Kellogg Arabian Horse
Library (WKKAHL)**
University Library, Bldg. 15
   3801 W Temple Ave.
   Pomona, CA 91768
Ph: (909)869-3775
Co. E-mail: wkkahl@cpp.edu
URL: http://libguides.library.cpp.edu/wkkahl
Contact: Katie Richardson, Head
E-mail: kjrichardson@cpp.edu
Facebook: www.facebook.com/people/WK-Kellogg
-Arabian-Horse-Library/100067731769099
Scope: Arabian horse. **Services:** Photocopying;
library open to the public for reference use only.
Founded: 1975. **Holdings:** 9,500 books; 760 bound
periodical volumes; 5 VF drawers of club newsletters;
2 VF drawers of farm brochures; 124 videotapes;
photographs; show programs; auction catalogs; films;
negatives; manuscripts; prints; paintings; bronzes.

**8331 ■ Camelot Therapeutic Horsemanship -
Camelot Library**
23623 N Scottsdale Rd., Ste. D-3
   Scottsdale, AZ 85255-3471
Ph: (480)515-1542
Fax: (480)515-1542
Co. E-mail: info@camelotaz.org
URL: http://camelotaz.org
Contact: Mary Hadsall, Executive Director
Facebook: www.facebook.com/CamelotAZ
YouTube: www.youtube.com/user/CamelotScotts
dale/videos
Description: Organization offers horsemanship les-
sons for children and adults with physical disabilities.
Scope: Therapeutic horsemanship; therapeutic use
of animals; nature. **Services:** Open to the public.
Founded: 1985. **Holdings:** Figures not available.

**8332 ■ Harness Racing Museum and Hall of
Fame - The Peter D. Haughton Library**
240 Main St.
   Goshen, NY 10924
Ph: (845)294-6330
Fax: (845)294-3463
Co. E-mail: info@harnessmuseum.com
URL: http://www.harnessmuseum.com
Contact: Joanne Young, Contact
E-mail: development@harnessmuseum.com
Facebook: www.facebook.com/people/Harness-Rac
ing-Museum-Hall-of-Fame/100064824007270
X (Twitter): x.com/harnessmuseum
Description: Harness track owners, Standardbred
farm owners, drivers, persons working in harness
racing, and others interested in the sport. Promotes
the study of the history of the American Standardbred.
Scope: Racing. **Services:** Open to the public by appointment. **Founded:** 1949. **Holdings:** 20,000
photographs; 6,000 ephemera; 2,000 books, bound
periodicals; 2,000 videos; 1,000 trophies; 1,709 fine
art; 400 jackets, caps, helmets; 75 sulkies, carts; 74
items of harness. **Publications:** *Mail Order Catalog*
(Annual); *Museum News* (Quarterly); *Souvenir*

Journal (Annual). **Awards:** Harness Racing Living Hall of Fame (Annual); Harness Racing Living Horse Hall of Fame (Annual). **Geographic Preference:** National.

8333 ■ Keeneland Library
4201 Versailles Rd.
  Lexington, KY 40510
Ph: (859)254-3412
Free: 800-456-3412
Fax: (859)255-2484
Co. E-mail: customerservice@keeneland.com
URL: http://www.keeneland.com
Contact: Shannon Arvin, President
Facebook: www.facebook.com/Keeneland
X (Twitter): x.com/keeneland
Instagram: www.instagram.com/keeneland
YouTube: www.youtube.com/user/keenelandfan

Description: Contains reference materials, journals, books, online materials, and video and audio materials, and historical documents or records. **Scope:** Racing and breeding; history of the horse in culture; racing history. **Services:** Library open to the public for reference use only on limited schedule. **Founded:** 1939. **Holdings:** 20,000 volumes; 1,500 videocassettes; 250,000 photo negatives; 5,000 files containing newspaper clippings; 1,500 videocassettes; pamphlet file. **Subscriptions:** journals and other serials.

8334 ■ Palomino Horse Breeders of America (PHBA)
15253 E Skelly Dr.
  Tulsa, OK 74116
Ph: (918)438-1234
Fax: (918)438-1232
Co. E-mail: yellahrses@palominohba.com
URL: http://www.palominohba.com
Contact: Mimsi Roe Coon, President
X (Twitter): x.com/palominohorseba

Description: Owners, breeders, and exhibitors of purebred Palomino horses. Maintains registry of pedigrees. Maintains hall of fame; compiles statistics. Offers children's services; conducts charitable program. **Founded:** 1941. **Publications:** *Palomino*

Horses. **Educational Activities:** PHBA World Show (Annual). **Awards:** Hall Of Fame Exhibitor Award (Periodic); PHBA Amateur Division Golden Horse (Annual); Youth World Championship Horse Show Open Division Golden Horse Awards (Annual); PHBA Supreme Champion; Hall Of Fame Breeder Award (Irregular). **Geographic Preference:** National.

8335 ■ University of Kentucky (UK) - Gluck Equine Research Center - John A. Morris Memorial Library
Gluck Equine Research Ctr., University of Kentucky
  Lexington, KY 40546-0099
URL: http://vetsci.ca.uky.edu/content/library-and-information-services

Scope: Equine veterinary medicine; horses and horse care. **Services:** Document delivery; SDI; library open to the public for reference use only. **Founded:** 1987. **Holdings:** 300 books; 250 bound periodical volumes; 25 videotapes.

8336 ■ University of Minnesota, Crookston Library
2900 University Ave.
  Crookston, MN 56716
Ph: (218)281-6510
Free: 800-862-6466
Co. E-mail: umcinfo@umn.edu
URL: http://crk.umn.edu
Contact: Mary Holz-Clause, Chancellor
Facebook: www.facebook.com/umncrookston
Linkedin: www.linkedin.com/school/umncrookston
X (Twitter): x.com/umncrookston
Instagram: www.instagram.com/umncrookston
YouTube: www.youtube.com/user/UofMCrookston

Scope: Educational material. **Services:** Interlibrary loan; copying; wireless Internet; scanning; computer access for research; document delivery; library open to public. **Founded:** 1906. **Holdings:** Books; journals; magazines; newspapers; music; videos and DVDs.

RESEARCH CENTERS

8337 ■ Grayson-Jockey Club Research Foundation (GJCRF)
821 Corporate Dr.
  Lexington, KY 40503

Ph: (859)224-2850
Fax: (859)224-2853
Co. E-mail: contactus@grayson-jockeyclub.org
URL: http://www.grayson-jockeyclub.org
Contact: Jamie S. Haydon, President
Facebook: www.facebook.com/GraysonJockeyClub
X (Twitter): x.com/Grayson_JC
Instagram: www.instagram.com/grayson_jockeyclub

Description: Represents organizations and individuals interested in horses and in supporting equine medical research. Funds research projects on horse health and care. **Scope:** Horses, equine medical research, and horse health and care. **Founded:** 1940. **Publications:** *Research Today* (Annual). **Geographic Preference:** National.

8338 ■ Michigan State University (MSU) - Horse Teaching and Research Center
3327 Collins Rd.
  Lansing, MI 48910
Ph: (517)355-7484
URL: http://www.msuarabians.com
Contact: Paula Hitzler, Farm Manager
E-mail: phitzler@msu.edu
URL(s): www.canr.msu.edu/scaf/horse_teaching_and_research_center
Facebook: www.facebook.com/msuarabians

Description: Integral unit of Michigan State University. **Scope:** Equine exercise physiology, nutrition, and management. **Founded:** 1940.

8339 ■ University of Kentucky - College of Agriculture, Food and Environment - Department of Animal and Food Sciences - Horse Unit
900 W P Garrigus Bldg.
  Lexington, KY 40546
URL: http://afs.ca.uky.edu/equine/horse-unit

Description: Integral unit of Department of Animal and Food Sciences, College of Agriculture, Food and Environment at University of Kentucky. **Scope:** Horse nutrition, growth, and exercise physiology. **Founded:** 1967.

ASSOCIATIONS AND OTHER ORGANIZATIONS

8340 ■ American Hotel and Lodging Association (AHLA) - Information Center
1250 Eye St. NW, Ste. 1100
Washington, DC 20005
Ph: (202)289-3100
Co. E-mail: membership@ahla.com
URL: http://www.ahla.com
Contact: Chip Roggers, President
Facebook: www.facebook.com/hotelassociation
Linkedin: www.linkedin.com/company/american-hotel
-&-lodging-association
X (Twitter): x.com/ahla

Description: Represents state lodging associations throughout the U.S. with 13,000 property members worldwide, representing more than 1.7 million guest rooms. Provides members with assistance in operations, education and communications and lobbies on Capitol Hill to provide a business climate in which the industry can continue to prosper. Individual state associations provide representation at the state level and offer many additional cost-saving benefits. **Scope:** Lodging; hospitality; travel; tourism. **Founded:** 1910. **Holdings:** Facts, report, annual survey. **Publications:** *Construction & Modernization Report* (Monthly); *LODGING* (9/year; Monthly); *Who's Who in the Lodging Industry*; *AH&LA Register*; *Green Lodging News* (Weekly (Mon.)). **Educational Activities:** The Hotel Experience (HX) (Annual). **Awards:** AHLA Stars of the Industry Awards (Annual). **Geographic Preference:** National.

8341 ■ American Hotel & Lodging Educational Foundation (AHLEF)
1250 I St. NW, Ste. 1100
Washington, DC 20005
Ph: (202)289-3180
Fax: (202)289-3199
Co. E-mail: ahleffoundation@ahla.com
URL: http://www.ahlafoundation.org
Contact: Anna Blue, President
E-mail: ablue@ahla.com
Facebook: www.facebook.com/AHLAfoundation
Linkedin: www.linkedin.com/company/american-hotel
-&-lodging-educational-foundation
X (Twitter): x.com/AHLAFoundation
Instagram: www.instagram.com/ahlafoundation

Description: Provides financial support that enhances the stability, prosperity, and growth of the lodging industry through educational and research programs. **Founded:** 1953. **Awards:** American Express Professional Development Scholarships (Quarterly); Hyatt Hotels Fund For Minority Lodging Management Students (Annual); Steve Hymans Extended Stay Scholarship Program (Annual); PepsiCo Incoming Freshman Scholarship; Rama Scholarships for the American Dream (Annual); AH&LEF American Express Scholarship (Annual); Arthur J.

Packard Memorial Scholarship (Annual); Ecolab Scholarship (Annual); Rama Scholarship for the American Dream (Annual). **Geographic Preference:** National.

8342 ■ Asian American Hotel Owners Association (AAHOA)
1100 Abernathy Rd., Ste. 1100
Atlanta, GA 30328-6707
Ph: (404)816-5759
Co. E-mail: info@aahoa.com
URL: http://www.aahoa.com
Contact: Hitesh Patel, Director
E-mail: pinal.patel@aahoa.com
Facebook: www.facebook.com/aahoaofficial
Linkedin: www.linkedin.com/company/aahoa
X (Twitter): x.com/AAHOA
YouTube: www.youtube.com/user/AAHOAoffice

Description: Serves as advocacy, educational, and professional development group for Asian-American hotel owners. **Founded:** 1989. **Educational Activities:** The Hotel Experience (HX) (Annual). **Geographic Preference:** National.

8343 ■ Canadian Resort & Travel Association (CVOA)
BC, Canada
Ph: (647)613-5464
Co. E-mail: memberservices@canadianrta.org
URL: http://canadianrta.org
Contact: Gaetan Babin, President
Facebook: www.facebook.com/CRTANews
X (Twitter): x.com/canadianrta

Description: Owners and operators of resorts. Promotes Canada as a vacation destination; seeks to improve the quality of accommodation and service at Canadian resorts. Interacts with provincial and federal governments regarding legislation affecting the resort industries; facilitates exchange of information among members; represents members' interests; conducts research and educational programs. **Founded:** 1980. **Publications:** *Consumers' Guide to Timesharing and Resort Report* (Semiannual); *Resort Report* (Semiannual). **Geographic Preference:** National.

8344 ■ Green Hotels Association (GHA)
1611 Mossy Stone Dr.
Houston, TX 77077-4109
Ph: (713)789-8889
Fax: (713)789-9786
Co. E-mail: green@greenhotels.com
URL: http://greenhotels.com/index.php
Contact: Patricia Griffin, President
X (Twitter): x.com/#!/GreenHotelsAssn

Description: Encourages, promotes and supports ecological consciousness in the hospitality industry. **Founded:** 1993. **Publications:** *Greening Newsletter* (Bimonthly); *Membership Conservation Guidelines and Ideas.* **Geographic Preference:** Multinational.

8345 ■ Hospitality Financial and Technology Professionals (HFTP)
7301 Ranch Rd. 620 N, Ste. 155-193
Austin, TX 78726-4537
Ph: (512)249-5333

Free: 800-646-4387
Fax: (512)249-1533
Co. E-mail: membership@hftp.org
URL: http://www.hftp.org
Contact: Stephanie Anderson, President
Facebook: www.facebook.com/HFTPGlobal
Linkedin: www.linkedin.com/company/hftp
X (Twitter): x.com/hftp
Instagram: www.instagram.com/hftp_hitec
YouTube: www.youtube.com/user/HFTPandHITEC

Description: Conducts education, training, and certification programs; offers placement service. **Founded:** 1952. **Publications:** *The Bottomline* (Quarterly). **Educational Activities:** Hospitality Industry Technology Exposition and Conference (HITEC) (Annual). **Awards:** HFTP Chapter Choice Award (Annual); HFTP International Hospitality Technology Hall of Fame (Annual); HFTP Paragon Award (Annual); HFTP Technology Award of Merit (Quinquennial).

8346 ■ Hospitality Sales and Marketing Association International (HSMAI)
7918 Jones Branch Dr., Ste. 300
McLean, VA 22102
Ph: (703)506-3280
Fax: (703)506-3266
Co. E-mail: info@hsmai.org
URL: http://global.hsmai.org
Contact: Robert A. Gilbert, President
E-mail: bgilbert@hsmai.org

Description: Aims to maintain and improve sound business practices, promote the art and science of hospitality marketing management and cooperate with other organizations that share common interests. Publishes on hospitality sales and marketing. Also publishes quarterly journal. Reaches market through direct mail. Accepts unsolicited manuscripts. **Founded:** 1927. **Publications:** *HSMAI Marketing Review* (Quarterly); *HSMAI Update* (Biweekly). **Educational Activities:** HSMAI's National MEET (Annual). **Awards:** HSMAI Adrian Awards (Annual). **Geographic Preference:** Multinational.

8347 ■ Hotel Brokers International (HBI)
1310 NW Vivion Rd., Ste. 106
Kansas City, MO 64118
Ph: (816)505-4315
Co. E-mail: info@hbihotels.com
URL: http://www.hbihotels.net
Contact: Edward P. Walsh, President
E-mail: ewalsh@alpinerealtycapital.com
Facebook: www.facebook.com/HotelBrokersInternational
Linkedin: www.linkedin.com/company/hotel-brokers
-international
YouTube: www.youtube.com/user/HBIhotels

Description: Provider of trained hotel real estate brokerage services and also a retailer of hotels, motels, resorts and other hospitality properties. **Founded:** 1959. **Publications:** *TransActions Recap* (Annual).

8348 ■ Hotel Electronic Distribution Network Association (HEDNA)
1000 Westgate Dr., Ste. 252
Saint Paul, MN 55114
Ph: (651)290-6291
Fax: (651)290-2266
Co. E-mail: info@hedna.org
URL: http://www.hedna.org
Contact: Sebastien Leitner, President
YouTube: www.youtube.com/c/HEDNATVChannel
Description: Hotel distribution industry. Strives to increase hotel industry revenues and profitability from electronic distribution channels such as the Internet. **Founded:** 1991. **Geographic Preference:** National.

8349 ■ IHG Owners Association (IHGOA)
3 Ravinia Dr., Ste. 100
Atlanta, GA 30346
Ph: (770)604-5555
Co. E-mail: info@owners.org
URL: http://www.owners.org
Contact: John Muehlbauer, Chief Executive Officer
Facebook: www.facebook.com/IHGOwnersAssn
Linkedin: www.linkedin.com/company/ihg-owners -association
X (Twitter): x.com/ihgowners_assn
Instagram: www.instagram.com/ihgownersassocia tion
Description: Holiday Inn hotel owners and franchisees. Serves as liaison among members through owner committees. Sponsors programs in government relations and financial review; reviews corporate programs. Operates employment resume service. **Founded:** 1955. **Geographic Preference:** National.

8350 ■ International Council on Hotel, Restaurant, and Institutional Education (ICHRIE)
3900 Westerre Pky, Ste. 300
Richmond, VA 23233
Ph: (804)346-4800
Fax: (804)346-5009
Co. E-mail: membership@chrie.org
URL: http://www.chrie.org
Contact: Chrystel Masdupuy, President
E-mail: chrystel.masdupuy@institutpaulbocuse.com
Facebook: www.facebook.com/ichrie
Linkedin: www.linkedin.com/company/interna tionalchrie
Description: Provides programs and services to continually improve the quality of global education, research, service and business operations in the hospitality and tourism industry. **Founded:** 1946. **Publications:** *Journal of Hospitality & Tourism Research: The Professional Journal of the International Council on Hotel, Restaurant, and Institutional Education (JHTR)* (8/year); *Council on Hotel, Restaurant and Institutional Education--Member Directory and Resource Guide* (Biennial); *A Guide to College Programs in Hospitality, Tourism, & Culinary Arts; Guide to Hospitality Education* (Semiannual); *Hosteur Magazine* (Biennial); *Journal of Hospitality and Tourism Education (JHTE)* (Quarterly); *Membership Directory and Research Guide* (Annual). **Awards:** Chef Herman Breithaupt Award (Annual); Stevenson W. Fletcher Achievement Award (Annual); ICHRIE Industry Recognition Award; W. Bradford Wiley Memorial Best Research Paper of the Year Award (Annual); Howard B. Meek Award (Annual); ICHRIE Lifetime Research Achievement Award (Annual). **Geographic Preference:** National.

8351 ■ Michigan Restaurant & Lodging Association (MRLA)
225 W Washtenaw St.
Lansing, MI 48933
Free: 800-968-9668
URL: http://www.mrla.org
Contact: Justin Winslow, President
Facebook: www.facebook.com/TheOfficialMRLA
Linkedin: www.linkedin.com/company/michigan-res taurant-association
X (Twitter): x.com/THEOFFICIALMRLA
Instagram: www.instagram.com/theofficialmrla
YouTube: www.youtube.com/user/MichiganRes taurant

Description: Non-profit dedicated to providing services to Michigan's hospitality industry. **Founded:** 1921. **Educational Activities:** Michigan Restaurant Show (Annual). **Geographic Preference:** State.

8352 ■ Resort Hotel Association (RHA)
6641 W Broad St., Ste. G104
Richmond, VA 23230
Ph: (804)525-2020
URL: http://www.rhainsure.com
Contact: Melanie DuPriest, President
Description: Represents resort and hotel owners. Administers products and services customized for the hospitality industry. Offers both liability and property insurance programs. **Founded:** 1987. **Publications:** *Resort Hotel Association Newsletter* (Monthly). **Educational Activities:** RHA Annual Conference (Annual). **Geographic Preference:** National.

8353 ■ Unite Here
275 7th Ave., 16th Fl.
New York, NY 10001-6708
Ph: (212)265-7000
Co. E-mail: communications@unitehere.org
URL: http://unitehere.org
Contact: D. Taylor, President
Facebook: www.facebook.com/UniteHere
X (Twitter): x.com/unitehere
Instagram: www.instagram.com/unitehere
YouTube: www.youtube.com/user/uniteherevideos
Description: AFL-CIO. Helps improve working conditions, wages, and benefits across the U.S. and Canada. Organizes the unorganized in the industry. Works with employers to resolve issues in the workplace and in the relevant industry. **Founded:** 2004. **Publications:** *Catering Industry Employee* (Quarterly); *Unite! Magazine* (Bimonthly). **Geographic Preference:** National.

REFERENCE WORKS

8354 ■ *"Three Ways Proposed New $300M-$400M Megamall, Hotel May Change I-Drive" in Orlando Business Journal (Vol. 30, May 9, 2014, No. 46, pp. 9)*
Pub: American City Business Journals, Inc.
Contact: Mike Olivieri, Executive Vice President
Released: Weekly. **Price:** $8, introductory 4-week offer(Digital only). **Description:** A number of ways in which the new 31-story megamall with hotel may transform the North I-Drive corridor in Orlando, Florida are presented. iSquare Mall & Hotel Development LLC applied for approval to construct the upscale, multistory retail mall with 1,253 hotel rooms in two towers. **Availability:** Print; Online.

8355 ■ *"$100M Complex To Be Built on Purple People Bridge" in Business Courier (Vol. 27, November 12, 2010, No. 28, pp. 1)*
Pub: Business Courier
Ed: Lucy May. **Description:** A development firm closed a deal with the Newport Southbank Bridge Company for a $100M entertainment complex that will be built on top of the Purple People Bridge. The proposed project will cover 150,000 square feet with attractions such as restaurants, a boutique hotel, and pubs. **Availability:** Print; Online.

8356 ■ *"2010 Book of Lists" in Business Courier (Vol. 26, December 26, 2009, No. 36, pp. 1)*
Price: $49.95. **Description:** Rankings of companies and organizations within the business services, education, finance, health care, hospitality and tourism, real estate, and technology industries in the Cincinnati, Ohio-Northern Kentucky area are presented. Rankings are based on sales, business size, or other statistics. **Availability:** PDF; Online.

8357 ■ *"Actian, Data Transformed and Yellowfin BI Mashup Helps Kollaras Group Reap Big Data Rewards" in Computer Business Week (August 28, 2014, pp. 22)*
Pub: NewsRX LLC.
Contact: Kalani Rosell, Contact

Description: Actian announced that Australian liquor, hospitality and property investment company, Kollaras Group can now access real-time analytics; fast, simple and accurate data warehousing; and Yellowfin's Business Intelligence (BI) platform is examined. The BI provides better insights and decision-making across diverse business units. **Availability:** Online.

8358 ■ *"The Alfond Inn: a Small Hotel that Packs a Punch" in Orlando Business Journal (Vol. 30, January 24, 2014, No. 31, pp. 6)*
Pub: American City Business Journals, Inc.
Contact: Mike Olivieri, Executive Vice President
Released: Weekly. **Price:** $8, introductory 4-week offer(Digital & Print). **Description:** The Alfond Inn general manager, Deanne Gabel, says the hotel was named after an alumni of the Alfond Foundation. She also said the hotel's architecture has a Spanish Mediterranean look. Gabel added that familiarity with guests gives the hotel an advantage over larger brands. **Availability:** Print; Online.

8359 ■ *"Alterra Acquiring Sugarbush Resort in Vermont" in Travel Weekly (November 13, 2019)*
URL(s): www.travelweekly.com/Travel-News/Hotel -News/Alterra-acquiring-Sugarbush-Resort-in -Vermont?ct=hotels
Ed: Johanna Jainchill. **Released:** November 13, 2019. **Description:** Continuing its streak of acquiring mountain resorts, Alterra Mountain Co. is poised to take over Sugarbush in central Vermont. **Availability:** Online.

8360 ■ *"Ambitious Horse Center Is In the Works for Southeastern Idaho" in Idaho Business Review (August 25, 2014)*
Pub: BridgeTower Media
Contact: Adam Reinebach, President
Price: $99, Digital & Mobile Only(1 Year); $11.99, Print, Digital & Mobile(1 Month); $149, Print, Digital & Mobile(1 Year); $99, Digital & Mobile Only(For 1 Year); $11.99, Print, Digital & Mobile (For 1 Month Intro Rate); $149, Print, Digital & Mobile (For 1 Year). **Description:** Ernest Bleinberger is planning to develop a 167-acre mixed-use project called Horse Station and will be located in Cache Valley, Idaho. Horse Station will include stables for about 250 horses and an arena, along with medical facilities, a hotel, retail shopping center, and a farmers market. **Availability:** Print; Online.

8361 ■ *"Baltimore Eyeing Tax Breaks for New Arena" in Boston Business Journal (Vol. 29, June 3, 2011, No. 4, pp. 1)*
Pub: Boston Business Journal
Contact: Carolyn M. Jones, President
E-mail: cmjones@bizjournals.com
Ed: Daniel J. Sernovitz. **Description:** Baltimore City is opting to give millions of dollars in tax breaks and construction loans to a group of private investors led by William Hackerman who is proposing to build a new arena and hotel at the Baltimore Convention Center. The project will cost $500 million with the state putting up another $400 million for the center's expansion.

8362 ■ *"Baltimore Restaurants Banking on Andretti Name" in Baltimore Business Journal (Vol. 30, May 18, 2012, No. 2, pp. 1)*
Pub: American City Business Journals, Inc.
Contact: Mike Olivieri, Executive Vice President
Ed: Jack Lambert. **Description:** Former race car driver Michael Andretti is leading the Andretti Sports Marketing to organize the Grand Prix in Baltimore, Maryland for the next five years. Restaurant and hotel owners are banking on Andretti to drive race fans to these establishments. Details of the 2011 event as well as forecasts on the next are discussed. **Availability:** Print; Online.

8363 ■ *"Baltimore's Hilton Convention Headquarters Hotel Still Losing Money" in Baltimore Business Journal (Vol. 28, October 15, 2010, No. 23, pp. 1)*
Pub: Baltimore Business Journal
Contact: Rhonda Pringle, President

E-mail: rpringle@bizjournals.com

Ed: Daniel J. Sernovitz. **Description:** Baltimore, Maryland-owned Hilton Baltimore Convention Center Hotel has been expected by Baltimore Hotel Corporation to wrap up 2010 with a $9.8 million deficit after completing its first year in operation in the red. The forecast would mark the controversial project's third-straight year of losses.

8364 ■ "Bellevue Collection Collects 4 New Towers" in Puget Sound Business Journal (Vol. 35, May 16, 2014, No. 4, pp. 4)
Pub: American City Business Journals, Inc.
Contact: Mike Olivieri, Executive Vice President

Description: A number of real estate development projects planned by Kemper Development Company, as part of the massive expansion of its Bellevue Collection in Washington are presented. Kemper is the builder, owner and operator of the properties that include office space on Lincoln Square, the New Lincoln Square Hotel/Apartments, Bellevue Square Hotel/Apartment Tower and Bellevue Square Apartment Tower. **Availability:** Online.

8365 ■ "Benchmark Makes Granduca Entrance" in Houston Business Journal (Vol. 40, January 8, 2010, No. 35, pp. 2)
Pub: Houston Business Journal
Contact: Bob Charlet, President
E-mail: bcharlet@bizjournals.com

Ed: Jennifer Dawson. **Description:** Houston, Texas-based Interfin Company, owner of the Hotel Granduca, has tapped the services of Benchmark Hospitality International to manage the property. The hiring of Benchmark is part of Interfin's efforts to develop Granduca hotels in other markets. Statistical data included. **Availability:** Print; Online.

8366 ■ "The Best in Business Travel" in Entrepreneur (May 2014)
Pub: Entrepreneur Media Inc.
Contact: Dan Bova, Director
E-mail: dbova@entrepreneur.com

Description: A number of companies have been recognized for making business travel more efficient, comfortable and enjoyable. Kayak CEO Steve Hafner's goal to create the world's best travel Website with the fewest people has made the travel search engine profitable. The subscription model of Surf Air, starting at $1,599 per month for unlimited flights, provides more efficient travel experience for executives. The Club Lounge at the Langham Hotel in Chicago, Illinois combines the efficiency of a working office with a private ambiance.

8367 ■ "Biggest Caribbean Resort Operator Seeks to Get 'IPO Ready'" in Bloomberg (September 3, 2019)
URL(s): www.bloomberg.com/news/articles/2019-09 -03/biggest-caribbean-resort-operator-seeks-to-ge t-ipo-ready

Ed: Ezra Fieser. **Released:** September 30, 2019. **Description:** Alejandro Reynal is poised to lead Apple Leisure Group as its new CEO. The travel conglomerate is potentially going have an initial public offering or a private sale. **Availability:** Online.

8368 ■ "Brought To You By the Letter 'W'" in Washington Business Journal (Vol. 33, August 29, 2014, No. 19, pp. 6)
Pub: American City Business Journals, Inc.
Contact: Mike Olivieri, Executive Vice President

Released: Weekly. **Price:** $4, introductory 4-week offer(Digital & Print). **Description:** W Hotel, Washington DC's food and beverage spaces are undergoing renovations. Hotel guests will see a new roof and a more stylish, upscale restaurant. W Hotel's plan to offer a luxury experience is discussed. **Availability:** Print; Online.

8369 ■ "Brownwood Hotel & Spa to Open in Central Fla." in Travel Weekly (November 13, 2019)
URL(s): www.travelweekly.com/North-America -Travel/Brownwood-Hotel-Spa-to-open-in-Central -Fla?ct=hotels

Ed: Holly V. Kapherr. **Released:** November 13, 2019. **Description:** Slated to open in early 2020, the Brownwood Hotel & Spa is going to make its home in Wildwood, Fl. Wolfgang Puck Kitchen + Bar is set to be the signature dining experience with a "dry" spa offering standard spa services on the premises. **Availability:** Online.

8370 ■ "Building Targeted for Marriott in Violation" in Business Journal-Milwaukee (Vol. 28, December 24, 2010, No. 12, pp. A1)
Pub: The Business Journal
Contact: Heather Ladage, President
E-mail: hladage@bizjournals.com

Ed: Sean Ryan. **Description:** Milwaukee, Wisconsin's Department of Neighborhood Services has ordered structural improvements and safeguards for the Pioneer Building after three violations from structural failures were found. Pioneer was among the five buildings wanted by Jackson Street Management LLC to demolish for the new Marriott Hotel. **Availability:** Print; Online.

8371 ■ "Businesses Encouraged to Imagine the Possibilities With Meeting Planner Package" in Internet Wire (May 23, 2012)
Pub: Comtex News Network Inc.
Contact: Kan Devnani, President

Description: Courtyard Orlando Lake Buena Vista, Florida is featuring an inclusive room rate and Double Event Planning Rewards Points for business planners using the hotel's professional event managers for their future meetings and events. Details of the program are included. **Availability:** Print; Online.

8372 ■ Buying and Running a Guesthouse or Small Hotel
Released: Second edition. **Description:** Teaches how to build and enjoy a lifestyle while running a guesthouse or small hotel.

8373 ■ "Chafee Eyes Tax On Travel Sites" in Providence Business News (Vol. 28, March 24, 2014, No. 51, pp. 1)
Pub: American City Business Journals, Inc.
Contact: Mike Olivieri, Executive Vice President
URL(s): pbn.com/chafee-eyes-tax-on-travel-sites9 5903

Description: Rhode Island Governor, Lincoln D. Chafee's 2015 budget will include new tax rules for travel Websites. State officials claim the new regulations will deal with a loophole that has allowed travel Websites to pay less in taxes. Many hotels enter into partnerships with travel Websites in order to sell rooms in bulk. **Availability:** Online. **Telecommunication Services:** Anderson@pbn.com.

8374 ■ "Chef Revelations - Derek Johnstone" in Caterer & Hotelkeeper (October 28, 2011, No. 288)
Description: Profile of Derek Johnstone, head chef at Greywalls Hotel and Chez Roux and his love for catering. **Availability:** Print; Online.

8375 ■ "Clock Ticks On Columbia Sussex Debt" in Business Courier (Vol. 27, July 30, 2010, No. 13, pp. 1)
Pub: Business Courier

Ed: Dan Monk. **Description:** Cincinnati, Ohio-based Columbia Sussex Corporation has made plans to restructure a $1 billion loan bundle that was scheduled to mature in October 2010. The privately held hotel has strived in a weak hotel market to keep pace with its $3 billion debt load. **Availability:** Print; Online.

8376 ■ "Coca-Cola FEMSA, Family Dollar, Other Dividend Payers On a Roll" in Benzinga.com (June 21, 2012)
Pub: Benzinga.com
Contact: Jason Raznick, Founder

Ed: Nelson Hem. **Description:** Dividend paying companies showing upward price trends are outlined. The firms highlighted include: Agnico-Eagle Mines, Coca-Cola FEMSA, Dean Foods, Expedia, Family Dollar Stores, Ferrellgas Partners, and InterContinental Hotels. **Availability:** Print; Online.

8377 ■ "Commercial Builders Take It on the Chin" in Crain's Chicago Business (Vol. 31, April 28, 2008, No. 17, pp. 16)
Pub: Crain Communications Inc.
Contact: Barry Asin, President

Ed: Alby Gallun. **Description:** Although the health care development sector has seen growth, the rest of Chicago's local commercial building industry has seen steep declines in the first quarter of this year. According to McGraw-Hill Construction, Chicago-area non-residential construction starts totaled $731 million in the quarter, a 60 percent drop from the year-earlier period. Volume in the retail, office and hotel markets fell by nearly 70 percent. **Availability:** Online.

8378 ■ "Convention Ctr. Rehab To Impact Hotels, Eateries" in Silicon Valley/San Jose Business Journal (Vol. 30, May 18, 2012, No. 8, pp. 1)
Pub: Baltimore Business Journal
Contact: Rhonda Pringle, President
E-mail: rpringle@bizjournals.com

Description: The renovation of the San Jose McEnery Convention Center is seen to adversely impact businesses in the area. Contractors have already demolished the former Martin Luther King Jr. Main Library. Business sales in the area are expected to decline owing to the renovation.

8379 ■ "Cooking With Celeb Chef Jet Tila" in Dallas Business Journal (Vol. 37, June 6, 2014, No. 39, pp. 6)
Pub: American City Business Journals, Inc.
Contact: Mike Olivieri, Executive Vice President
Released: June 06, 2014. **Price:** $4, Introductory 4-Week Offer(Digital & Print). **Description:** Celebrity chef, Jet Tila, discloses his plans for the Pakpao restaurant which he co-owns at Dallas Design District in Texas. He hopes to leverage the authentic Thai cuisine offered by the restaurant and bring the concept to airports or hotels. **Availability:** Print; Online.

8380 ■ "Corus Eases Off Ailing Condo Market" in Crain's Chicago Business (April 28, 2008)
Pub: Crain Communications Inc.
Contact: Barry Asin, President

Ed: H. Lee Murphy. **Description:** Corus Bankshares Inc., a specialist in lending for the condominium high-rise construction market, is diversifying its portfolio by making loans to office developers and expects to be investing in hotels through the rest of the year. Corus' $7.57 billion loan portfolio is also discussed in detail as well as the company's earnings and share price. Statistical data included. **Availability:** Online.

8381 ■ "Crystal Hotel Resumes Construction" in Business Journal Portland (Vol. 27, December 31, 2010, No. 44, pp. 1)
Pub: Portland Business Journal
Contact: Andy Giegerich, Managing Editor
E-mail: agiegerich@bizjournals.com

Ed: Wendy Culverwell. **Description:** McMenamins Pubs and Breweries has resumed construction of its Crystal Hotel project. The company has been working to convert a former bath house into a 51-room hotel. The hotel is expected to open in 2011. **Availability:** Print; Online.

8382 ■ "Developers Accommodate Need for Rooms" in Puget Sound Business Journal (Vol. 35, September 19, 2014, No. 22, pp. 8)
Pub: American City Business Journals, Inc.
Contact: Mike Olivieri, Executive Vice President

Description: The number of hotel rooms in Bellevue, Washington has been steadily increasing. Access to capital by investors is seen to contribute to the development. Seven new hotel construction projects are underway in Seattle, Washington. **Availability:** Online.

8383 ■ "DIA Contract Sets a Record for Denver Minority, Woman-Owned Business" in Denver Business Journal (Vol. 65, February 21, 2014, No. 41)
Pub: American City Business Journals, Inc.
Contact: Mike Olivieri, Executive Vice President

Released: Weekly. **Description:** The City of Denver, Colorado has awarded a $39.6 million contract to Burgess Services Inc. to construct a transit and hotel project near the Denver International Airport. Burgess Services is owned by Denise Burgess. This is the largest public contract awarded to a woman0 or minority-owned business in the city's history. **Availability:** Print; Online.

8384 ■ "Discover the Wedding Location of Your Dreams" in Benzinga.com (December 24, 2011)
Description: Ritz Carlton Hotel Company helps couples choose from their 70 wedding locations worldwide with wedding advisors to assist in planning. **Availability:** Online.

8385 ■ "Disguised Age Bias at the Revel Casino?" in Philadelphia Business Journal (Vol. 31, February 17, 2012, No. 1, pp. 1)
Pub: Baltimore Business Journal
Contact: Rhonda Pringle, President
E-mail: rpringle@bizjournals.com
Description: Revel Atlantic City casino hotel's new employment policy is seen to entail age discrimination. The policy places term limits on employees of four, five or six years. The company cited employee burnout at reason for the policy. **Availability:** Print; Online.

8386 ■ "Events, Improved Economy Mean Full Hotels in Silicon Valley" in Silicon Valley/San Jose Business Journal (Vol. 30, September 28, 2012, No. 27, pp. 1)
Pub: Baltimore Business Journal
Contact: Rhonda Pringle, President
E-mail: rpringle@bizjournals.com
Description: The increase in hotel occupancy rates in Silicon Valley was attributed to the improving economy and a wide range of local trade shows and events. The city of Santa Clara, California reached an 82 percent occupancy rate in August 2012, while in downtown San Jose, hotels said they started experiencing increased demand since late 2011. **Availability:** Print; Online.

8387 ■ Every Airbnb Host's Tax Guide
Ed: Stephen Fishman. **Released:** January 26, 2021.
Description: A guide for tracking and paying taxes for those who own Airbnb rentals.

8388 ■ "New Hotels, Offices Eyed Near SJC" in Silicon Valley/San Jose Business Journal (Vol. 30, June 8, 2012, No. 11, pp. 1)
Pub: Baltimore Business Journal
Contact: Rhonda Pringle, President
E-mail: rpringle@bizjournals.com
Description: Developer Hunter/Storm LLC plans to break ground on the first phase of the Coleman Highline mixed-use project in San Jose, California by the first quarter of 2013 to take advantage of the growing mass transit and improved market conditions. The project consists of 1.5 million square feet of office space, two hotels and 50,000 square feet of retail space on Coleman Avenue.

8389 ■ Exceptional Service, Exceptional Profit: The Secrets of Building a Five-Star Customer Service Organization
Pub: HarperCollins Leadership
Contact: Donald Miller, Chief Executive Officer
Ed: Leonardo Inghilleri, Micah Solomon. **Released:** April 14, 2010. **Price:** $19.99, paperback. **Description:** Team of insiders share exclusive knowledge of the loyalty-building techniques pioneered by the world's most successful service leaders, including brick-and-mortar stars such as The Ritz-Carlton and Lexus and online success stories such as Netflix and CD Baby. **Availability:** E-book; Print.

8390 ■ "Expedia Tells Hotels Adding Resort Fees Will Lower Your Listings on Its Pages" in Skift (November 14, 2019)
URL(s): skift.com/2019/11/14/expedia-tells-hotels-adding-resort-fees-will-lower-your-listings-on-its-pages/

Ed: Dennis Schaal. **Released:** November 14, 2019.
Description: Expedia acted upon it's earlier stance that it will send hotel listings lower in its sort order if they add resort fees to the base room rates. This is part of Expedia's effort to be more transparent in their pricing because often, consumers do not understand the resort fee and forget it's there until checkout. **Availability:** Online.

8391 ■ "Fear of the Unknown Muted Impact of Baltimore Grand Prix" in Baltimore Business Journal (Vol. 29, September 9, 2011, No. 18, pp. 3)
Pub: Boston Business Journal
Contact: Carolyn M. Jones, President
E-mail: cmjones@bizjournals.com
Ed: Alexander Jackson. **Description:** Baltimore Grand Prix caught restaurateurs, hoteliers and street vendors in Baltimore, Maryland unprepared for the thousands of race fans who attended the inaugural event over Labor Day weekend. The race popularity is relatively unknown to them and some felt they were not able to make as much money as they had hoped. **Availability:** Online.

8392 ■ "First Look at Downtown's JW Marriott" in Houston Business Journal (Vol. 45, June 27, 2014, No. 7, pp. 10A)
Pub: American City Business Journals, Inc.
Contact: Mike Olivieri, Executive Vice President
Released: Weekly. **Price:** $4, Introductory 4-week offer(Digital & Print). **Description:** The JW Marriott is one of several new hotels being developed for downtown Houston and construction scheduled to be completed in time for the 2017 Super Bowl to be held in the city. The hotel includes two ballrooms, the Picasso and the Monet, a spa with eight treatment rooms, a yoga studio, and an executive lounge for platinum and gold members. **Availability:** Print; Online.

8393 ■ "Florida Fast 100: D&D Construction Services" in South Florida Business Journal (Vol. 35, September 19, 2014, No. 8, pp. 16)
Pub: American City Business Journals, Inc.
Contact: Mike Olivieri, Executive Vice President
Description: Profile of D and D Construction, who reports increased earnings in 2013 totaling $26.5 million. The increase has been attributed to the commercial real estate market's recovery from the economic recession. The company is focusing on offering hospitality (restaurant, hotel) projects. **Availability:** Online.

8394 ■ "Formula One Makes Room(s) for Aspiring Entrepreneur in Austin" in Austin Business Journal (Vol. 31, July 1, 2011, No. 17, pp. 1)
Pub: Austin Business Journal
Contact: Rachel McGrath, Director
E-mail: rmcgrath@bizjournals.com
Ed: Vicky Garza. **Description:** Formula One fan and graphic designer Danielle Crespo cashes in on the June 17, 2012 racing event in Austin, Texas via hosting a Website that allows users to book hotel rooms. She invested less than $100 and long hours on this enterprise which now has 74,000-plus visitors. **Availability:** Print; Online.

8395 ■ "Founding Family Acquires Airport Marriott" in Crain's Cleveland Business (Vol. 28, November 5, 2007, No. 44, pp. 3)
Pub: Crain Communications Inc.
Contact: K. C. Crain, President
Ed: Stan Bullard. **Description:** Big River Real Estate LLC, part of the Marriott family's investment fund, is the new owner of the Cleveland Airport Marriott; renovations estimated at about $11 million will ensure that the hotel meets Marriott's standards. **Availability:** Online.

8396 ■ "From Economy to Luxury, What Matters Most to Hotel Guests; To Win More Repeat Customers, Hotels Must Create a Tailored Guest Experience" in Gallup Business Journal (September 5, 2014)
Pub: Gallup, Inc.
Contact: Jon Clifton, Chief Executive Officer

Description: The most successful hotels know their customers and offer products and services that meet their needs. **Availability:** Print; Online.

8397 ■ "Harrah's Tunica Shutting Down In June" in Memphis Business Journal (No. 35, March 28, 2014, No. 51, pp. 3)
Pub: American City Business Journals, Inc.
Contact: Mike Olivieri, Executive Vice President
Released: Weekly. **Price:** $4, introductory 4-week offer(Digital only). **Description:** Caesars Entertainment Corporation is closing down Harrah's Tunica in June 2014 in an effort to ensure the long-term viability of its remaining operations in Memphis, Tennessee. The company will find positions for the displaced employees and some could be placed at Caesar's Horseshoe Casino & Hotel and Tunica Roadhouse. **Availability:** Print; Online.

8398 ■ "Headington Lures High-End Retailers to Downtown Dallas" in Dallas Business Journal (Vol. 35, July 6, 2012, No. 43, pp. 1)
Pub: Baltimore Business Journal
Contact: Rhonda Pringle, President
E-mail: rpringle@bizjournals.com
Ed: Steven R. Thompson. **Description:** Dallas, Texas-based Headington Companies has leased all of the retail space created with the expansion of The Joule Hotel, to add soft goods retail to downtown Dallas, Texas' revitalization. The company has high-end contemporary brands that include Traffic LA, Tenoversix, and Taschen to fill the retail landscape on Main and Commerce Streets. **Availability:** Print; Online.

8399 ■ "Host Your Dream Wedding at the Minneapolis Marriott Southwest" in Benzinga.com (June 6, 2011)
Description: Minneapolis Marriott Southwest is helping engaged couples plan their wedding destination at their property. Details of wedding reception options are outlined. **Availability:** Online.

8400 ■ "Hostel or Not? Shared Rooms Pop Up in Traditional Hotels" in Skift (November 12, 2019)
URL(s): skift.com/2019/11/12/hostel-or-not-shared-rooms-pop-up-in-traditional-hotels/
Ed: Nancy Trejos. **Released:** November 12, 2019.
Description: Ever since Airbnb launched, travelers have had more choice in accommodations, which have included sharing guest rooms. Traditional hotels are now trying to take back some of the market share by offering shared rooms in order to lure those customers back. Super 8 by Wyndham is rolling out ROOM8, which is a suite of rooms where individual sleeping spaces are available with shared areas for dining and entertaining. **Availability:** Online.

8401 ■ "Hotel Boom Coming to the Palm Beaches" in Travel Weekly (November 14, 2019)
URL(s): www.travelweekly.com/North-America-Travel/Hotel-boom-coming-to-the-Palm-Beaches?ct=hotels
Ed: Holly V. Kapherr. **Released:** November 14, 2019.
Description: The Palm Beaches region in Florida is set to welcome eight new hotel properties by 2021. Also, the Brazilian Court hotel and the Four Seasons Resort Palm Beach revealed some new upgrades. **Availability:** Online.

8402 ■ "Hotel Confidential" in Canadian Business (Vol. 80, Winter 2007, No. 24, pp. 91)
Description: Celebrities such as Jason Priestley, Clint Eastwood, and Francis Ford Coppola have made investment in the hospitality industry. Investing in the hospitality industry has proved to be an excellent long-term investment and the venture also has a vanity aspect to it. **Availability:** Online.

8403 ■ "Hotel Could Move Into Former Movie Studio Site in Allen Park" in Crain's Detroit Business (Vol. 35, September 1, 2014, No. 35, pp. 17)
Pub: Crain Communications Inc.
Contact: Barry Asin, President

Description: The former site of Unity Studios Inc. could become the site for a new hotel. The property was once owned by the former Visteon Corporation on Southfield Road in Allen Park, Michigan. Details of New York City-based Tim Equities Inc. plan for the hotel are included. **Availability:** Online.

8404 ■ "Hotel Expected to Jump Start Downtown Revitalization" in Houston Business Journal (Vol. 44, March 28, 2014, No. 47, pp. 10)
Pub: American City Business Journals, Inc.
Contact: Mike Olivieri, Executive Vice President

Released: Weekly. **Price:** $4, introductory 4-week offer(Digital only). **Description:** Hotel Alessandra has the potential to become the key to revitalize downtown Houston, Texas. Gensler's design principal, Kap Malik, believes the hotel would become a landmark building and together with other projects will bring a lot of excitement and activity to the area. Other hotels that are under construction or planned for downtown are presented. **Availability:** Print; Online.

8405 ■ "Hotel Industry: Getting Better All the Time" in Orlando Business Journal (Vol. 28, May 18, 2012, No. 50, pp. 1)
Pub: Baltimore Business Journal
Contact: Rhonda Pringle, President
E-mail: rpringle@bizjournals.com

Description: Smith Travel Research report has shown Central Florida's hotel industry's average occupancy rate reached 74.5 percent for 2012's first quarter, while daily room rates are up 3.5 percent to reach $105.51. Revenue per room is also up 6.8 percent to hit $75.58, indicating the increasing health of the industry. Insights on Orlando's tourism industry are examined. **Availability:** Print; Online.

8406 ■ "Hotel Pitched by Mortenson Would Be Among First Of Its Kind in U.S." in Business Journal (Vol. 31, February 14, 2014, No. 38, pp. 10)
Pub: American City Business Journals, Inc.
Contact: Mike Olivieri, Executive Vice President

Released: February 14, 2014. **Price:** $4, Introductory 4-week offer(Digital & Print). **Description:** A $63 million, 300-room hotel is proposed by Mortenson Development near the new Minnesota Vikings stadium. The proposed hotel will be co-branded under two Marriott International Inc. brands, AC Hotels and SpringHill Suites. **Availability:** Print; Online.

8407 ■ "Hotel Woes Reflect Area Struggle" in Business Journal Serving Greater Tampa Bay (Vol. 30, December 3, 2010, No. 50, pp. 1)
Pub: Tampa Bay Business Journal
Contact: Ian Anderson, President
E-mail: ianderson@bizjournals.com

Ed: Mark Holan. **Description:** Quality Inn and Suites in East Tampa, Florida has struggled against the sluggish economy but remained open to guests despite facing a foreclosure. The hotel project is the center of East Tampa's redevelopment plans and public officials defend the $650,000 investment in public amenities near the building. **Availability:** Print; Online.

8408 ■ "Hotels Get a Fill-Up: Fee Helps Bring Back Hot Rod Tour, Replace Biz Travel" in Crain's Detroit Business (Vol. 25, June 1, 2009, No. 22, pp. 1)
Pub: Crain Communications Inc.
Contact: Barry Asin, President

Ed: Daniel Duggan. **Description:** Hot Rod Power Tour will have a $1 million economic impact on the area when it arrives in June 2009; the tour will bring 3,500 out-of-state custom vehicles to the event, whose owners will be needing hotel rooms. **Availability:** Print; Online.

8409 ■ "Hotels' Healthy Finish in '07" in Crain's Chicago Business (Vol. 31, March 24, 2008, No. 12, pp. 16)
Pub: Crain Communications Inc.
Contact: Barry Asin, President

Ed: Alby Gallun. **Description:** Chicago's hotel market saw mostly rising occupancies and room rates in the fourth quarter of 2007, reflecting continued strong demand from leisure and business travelers; however, due to the current state of the economy hoteliers face an increasingly uncertain outlook. **Availability:** Online.

8410 ■ "Hotels Make Wallcoverings a Sticking Trend" in Hotel News Now (April 17, 2019)
URL(s): www.hotelnewsnow.com/Articles/294815/Ho tels-make-wallcoverings-a-sticking-trend
Ed: Dana Miller. **Released:** April 17, 2019. **Description:** Wallcoverings, the term used to describe the more durable wallpaper used in hotels, are being used in innovative colors and patterns in hotel settings. Often cheaper than repainting, wallcoverings are a good way to switch up the look of a hotel when it's time to renovate or add a personal touch that is unique to the area the hotel is located. **Availability:** Online.

8411 ■ "Hotels Up the Ante in Bid to Lure Visitors" in Sacramento Business Journal (Vol. 29, June 1, 2012, No. 14, pp. 1)
Pub: Baltimore Business Journal
Contact: Rhonda Pringle, President
E-mail: rpringle@bizjournals.com

Description: Hotel owners in Sacramento, California will spend more on marketing the region to convention planners and tourists. The Sacramento Tourism Marketing District is set to replace a 10-year-old marketing business improvement district on July 1, 2012. It is believed that convention and travel business is an economic driver in the city. **Availability:** Print; Online.

8412 ■ How to Open and Operate a Bed & Breakfast
Ed: Jan Stankus. **Released:** December 20, 2011. **Price:** $21.95, paperback(£14.95); $20.99, e-book(-£13.95); paperback, softback. **Description:** Handbook outlines how to set up and run a bed and breakfast, whether using a spare room of a home or a small inn. **Availability:** E-book; Print.

8413 ■ "How Small, Independent Hotels Are Using Tech to Be More Competitive" in Skift (November 11, 2019)
URL(s): skift.com/2019/11/11/how-small-independen t-hotels-are-using-tech-to-be-more-competitive/
Released: November 11, 2019. **Description:** Consumers are used to using online methods to search for the best deals on hotel prices, which often leaves smaller hotels out of the equation due to them just not having the high-tech systems that big chains can afford. However, online travel agencies like Expedia are trying to bridge the technology gap by offering easy to use solutions for these smaller hotels. **Availability:** Online.

8414 ■ "How South Florida Can Revive a Flagging Sector" in South Florida Business Journal (Vol. 34, April 4, 2014, No. 37, pp. 10)
Pub: American City Business Journals, Inc.
Contact: Mike Olivieri, Executive Vice President

Released: Weekly. **Price:** $8, Introductory 4-week offer(Digital & Print). **Description:** South Florida convention centers are trying to address the sluggish demand for conventions to the area by upgrading its facilities and adding hotels. The ancillary revenue generate by the attendees at hotels, restaurants, and other establishments makes a convention as key economic drivers. The efforts to boost the region's position as convention destinations are also addressed. **Availability:** Print; Online.

8415 ■ "How to... Harness Green Power" in The Caterer (July 20, 2012, No. 325)
Pub: LNRS Data Services Limited
Contact: Mark Vickers Kelsey, Director

Description: Roger and Emma Stevens discuss their success as at winning the Considerate Hoteliers Association's award for Best Green Marketing Initiative. The couple discusses their restaurant and its partnership with tow nearby guesthouses. **Availability:** Online.

8416 ■ "Hyatt Joins Other Big Hotel Chains by Pledging to Eliminate Small Plastic Bottles" in Skift (November 12, 2019)
URL(s): skift.com/2019/11/12/hyatt-joins-other-big-ho tel-chains-by-pledging-to-eliminate-small-plastic-bo ttles/
Ed: Nancy Trejos. **Released:** November 12, 2019. **Description:** While trying to go green and eliminate unnecessary waste, Hyatt is joining Marriott and IHG by not offering single-use plastic bottles of shampoo, conditioner, shower gel, and lotion. **Availability:** Online.

8417 ■ "Ihilani's New Day" in Pacific Business News (Vol. 26, August 22, 2014, No. 26, pp. 14)
Pub: American City Business Journals, Inc.
Contact: Mike Olivieri, Executive Vice President

Description: JW Marriott Ihilani Resort and Spa is likely to be rebranded in 2014 as the Four Seasons Hotels and Resorts, making it the chain's fifth largest property in Hawaii. The implications of the hotel's renovation and rebranding for West Oahu's leisure and business travel sectors are discussed. **Availability:** Online.

8418 ■ "In Ambassador Hotel Debate, Some Dispute Need for Rooms" in Wichita Business Journal (Vol. 27, January 20, 2012, No. 3, pp. 1)
Pub: Baltimore Business Journal
Contact: Rhonda Pringle, President
E-mail: rpringle@bizjournals.com

Ed: John Stearns. **Description:** The city of Wichita, Kansas does not need the additional hotel rooms to be provided by Ambassador Hotel, according to other hotel operators. The proposed hotel will provide an additional 400 new rooms.

8419 ■ "Inland Snaps Up Rival REITs" in Crain's Chicago Business (Vol. 31, November 17, 2008, No. 46, pp. 3)
Pub: Crain Communications Inc.
Contact: Barry Asin, President

Ed: Alby Gallun. **Description:** Discusses Inland American Real Estate Trust Inc., a real estate investment trust that is napping up depressed shares of publicly traded competitors, a possible first step toward taking over these companies; however, with hotel and retail properties accounting for approximately 70 percent of its portfolio, the company could soon face its own difficulties. **Availability:** Online.

8420 ■ INNside Scoop: Everything You Ever Wanted to Know About Bed & Breakfast Inns
Pub: The B&B and Country Inn Marketplace
Contact: Mariette Gagne, Contact
E-mail: mariettehnc@gmail.com

Ed: Maxine Pinson. **Price:** $14.95, Free. **Description:** Guide for running a successful bread and breakfast inn. **Availability:** Print.

8421 ■ "La Cantera Resort Expects to Benefit from Big Transformation" in San Antonio Business Journal (Vol. 28, July 18, 2014, No. 23, pp. 8)
Pub: American City Business Journals, Inc.
Contact: Mike Olivieri, Executive Vice President

Released: Weekly. **Price:** $4, Introductory 4-week offer(Digital & Print). **Description:** La Cantera Hill County Resort in San Antonio, Texas is planning a multimillion dollar major renovation of the property and the addition of a spa. The resort announced the suspension of overnight accommodations and restaurant operations during the major phase of the construction from November 3, 2014 until early April 2015. **Availability:** Print; Online.

8422 ■ "Large Company: With Thomas Dugan, Chief Financial Officer, Westgate Resorts" in Orlando Business Journal (Vol. 31, July 18, 2014, No. 3, pp. 8)
Pub: American City Business Journals, Inc.
Contact: Mike Olivieri, Executive Vice President

Description: Thomas Dugan, CFO, Westgate Resorts, speaks about the new products and services added to their resort properties. **Availability:** Print; Online.

8423 ■ *"Leave It Behind"* in *Crain's Chicago Business (Vol. 31, April 21, 2008, No. 16, pp. 32)*
Pub: Crain Communications Inc.
Contact: Barry Asin, President

Ed: Sarah A. Klein. **Description:** Patrick Brady who investigates possible violations of the Foreign Corrupt Practices Act has a novel approach when traveling to frequent destinations which allows him to travel with only a carry-on piece of luggage: he leaves suits at dry cleaners in the places he visits most often and since he mainly stays at the same hotels, he also leaves sets of workout clothes and running shoes with hotel staff. **Availability:** Online.

8424 ■ *"Local Hotels Brace for Downturn"* in *Crain's Chicago Business (Vol. 31, March 31, 2008, No. 13, pp. 3)*
Pub: Crain Communications Inc.
Contact: Barry Asin, President

Ed: Bob Tita. **Description:** Chicago hotels are seeing a noticeable drop in business-related guests so far this year due to a slumping national economy, tighter corporate expense budgets and higher airfares. **Availability:** Online.

8425 ■ *LODGING*
Pub: American Hotel and Lodging Association
Contact: Chip Roggers, President
URL(s): lodgingmagazine.com
Facebook: www.facebook.com/LodgingMagazine
Linkedin: www.linkedin.com/company/lodging
-magazine-official
X (Twitter): x.com/LodgingMagazine
Instagram: www.instagram.com/lodgingmagazine
YouTube: www.youtube.com/lodgingmagazine

Ed: Kate Hughes. **Released:** 9/year; Monthly **Description:** Publication includes list of about 4,000 suppliers to the hotel industry. **Entries include:** Company name, address, phone, name of principal executive, list of products or services. **Arrangement:** Classified by product or service. **Indexes:** Alphabetical listing, categorical listings. **Availability:** Print; Online.

8426 ■ *"London's Gold-Medal Hotels"* in *Canadian Business (Vol. 85, August 13, 2012, No. 13, pp. 65)*

Ed: Chris Johns. **Description:** Several new hotels in London, England, including Me by Melia, Apex Temple Court Hotel, and Bulgari Hotel London are presented. Prices and tips on how to best maximize the service are provided. **Availability:** Print; Online.

8427 ■ *"Loop Hotel Plan Locks Up Funding"* in *Crain's Chicago Business (Vol. 31, March 24, 2008, No. 12, pp. 2)*
Pub: Crain Communications Inc.
Contact: Barry Asin, President

Ed: Eddie Baeb. **Description:** Signaling further expansion in the downtown hotel market, the secured $395 million in financing will fund a 610-room luxury hotel operated by J.W. Marriott, a more upscale brand in the Marriott line. **Availability:** Online.

8428 ■ *"Madison Partner Eyes Overton: French Quarter Suites May Become Luxury Hotel"* in *Memphis Business Journal (Vol. 34, April 27, 2012, No. 2, pp. 1)*
Pub: Baltimore Business Journal
Contact: Rhonda Pringle, President
E-mail: rpringle@bizjournals.com

Description: Former hotel executive Mohammad Hakimian and a group of investors are planning to purchase and redevelop the French Quarter Suites into a hotel. Loeb Properties Inc. is planning to invest $19.2 million in the project. **Availability:** Print; Online.

8429 ■ *"Marriott Readies for Uptick in Leisure Travel"* in *Dallas Business Journal (Vol. 35, April 13, 2012, No. 31, pp. 1)*
Pub: Baltimore Business Journal
Contact: Rhonda Pringle, President
E-mail: rpringle@bizjournals.com

Description: Dallas Marriott City Center hotel has conducted a $16 million renovation that it hopes will attract leisure travelers visiting the upcoming improvements along Woodall Rodgers Freeway in Dallas. The Dallas Marriott's general manager, Nour Laasri, expects leisure travel and events to gro for the 416-room hotel. **Availability:** Print; Online.

8430 ■ *"Meeting and Banquet Venues"* in *Business Review Albany (Vol. 41, August 8, 2014, No. 20, pp. 6)*
Released: Weekly. **Price:** $25, download. **Description:** The top 25 meeting and banquet venues in Albany, New York in 2013 are ranked by number of banquets hosted. The Desmond Hotel and Conference Center hold the top spot. The Otesega Resort Hotel ranked second. **Availability:** Print; Online.

8431 ■ *"Memphis Marriott Downtown Offers Wedding Reception Discounts to Soon-To-Be Newlyweds"* in *Benzinga.com (June 23, 2011)*
Pub: PR Newswire Association LLC.

Description: Memphis Marriott Downtown in Memphis, Tennessee is offering wedding reception discounts to couples planning their weddings.

8432 ■ *"MGM Resorts Leads U.S. Travel Sector with Job Cuts So Far in 2019"* in *Skift (October 4 2019)*
URL(s): skift.com/2019/10/04/mgm-resorts-leads-u-s
-travel-sector-with-job-cuts-so-far-in-2019/

Ed: Sean O'Neill. **Released:** October 14, 2019. **Description:** The US travel industry is experiencing a trend of job cutbacks, unlike just about every other industry in the nation. The most extensive job cuts were taken at MGM Resorts International, which trimmed 2040 positions, in an effort to cut costs. **Availability:** Online.

8433 ■ *"The Missing Piece"* in *Washington Business Journal (Vol. 33, April 25, 2014, No. 1, pp. 6)*
Pub: American City Business Journals, Inc.
Contact: Mike Olivieri, Executive Vice President

Description: The hospitality industry is looking forward to the additional business that the opening of the $520 million, 1,175-room Marriott Marquis Hotel in Washington DC will bring. The hotel has signed up a number of first time DC corporate events and 15 citywide conventions for 2016. **Availability:** Online.

8434 ■ *"New Holiday Inns Set for Airport Area, Graceland"* in *Memphis Business Journal (Vol. 34, August 17, 2012, No. 18, pp. 1)*
Pub: Baltimore Business Journal
Contact: Rhonda Pringle, President
E-mail: rpringle@bizjournals.com

Description: Two new Holiday Inn hotels are to be constructed in Memphis, Tennessee in the next two years. The plan is in line with the company's celebration of its 60th anniversary. **Availability:** Print; Online.

8435 ■ *"New Year's Resolutions: How Three Companies Came Up With Their 2008 Growth Strategies"* in *Inc. (January 2008, pp. 47-49)*
Ed: Martha C. White. **Description:** Three companies share 2008 growth strategies; companies include a candle company, a voice mail and text messaging marketer, and hotel supplier of soap and shampoo. **Availability:** Online.

8436 ■ *"New York Developer Revives Adams Morgan Hotel Project"* in *Washington Business Journal (Vol. 31, July 6, 2012, No. 11, pp. 1)*
Pub: Baltimore Business Journal
Contact: Rhonda Pringle, President
E-mail: rpringle@bizjournals.com

Description: Real estate developer Brian Friedman brought on Andrew Zobler of Sydell Group LLC as a development partner for the Adams Morgan boutique hotel project. A previous plan for a $100 million property was shelved due to neighborhood opposition. **Availability:** Print; Online.

8437 ■ *"Observers See Different Messages if Voters Reject Ambassador Tax Rebate"* in *Wichita Business Journal (Vol. 27, February 17, 2012, No. 7, pp. 1)*
Pub: Baltimore Business Journal
Contact: Rhonda Pringle, President
E-mail: rpringle@bizjournals.com

Description: Ambassador Hotel's room tax rebate has been put on a referendum in Wichita,Kansas and the rejection is expected to affect future downtown projects. However, the observers differ on the messages of a no vote would send to real estate investors. Insights on the ongoing debate on economic development policy are also given. **Availability:** Print; Online.

8438 ■ *"Offering Service With a :)"* in *Puget Sound Business Journal (Vol. 35, July 11, 2014, No. 12, pp. 12)*
Pub: American City Business Journals, Inc.
Contact: Mike Olivieri, Executive Vice President

Description: Sorrento Hotel's Sorrento Ambassadors of Memories is an entry level job that allows young people to perform menial tasks for hotel guests. Randall Obrecht, Sorrento's general manager, states that the young workers actually serve as personalized butlers or concierges. The program helps hotel staff deal with high occupancy rates. **Availability:** Online.

8439 ■ *"O'Loughlin Cuts $6 Million Deal for Chesterfield Doubletree"* in *Saint Louis Business Journal (Vol. 32, September 2, 2011, No. 1, pp. 1)*
Pub: Saint Louis Business Journal
Contact: Robert Bobroff, President
E-mail: rbobroff@bizjournals.com

Ed: Angela Mueller. **Description:** Lodging Hospitality Management (LHM) acquired the Doubletree Hotel and Conference Center in Chesterfield, Missouri and added it as the 18th hotel in its portfolio. LHM chairman and CEO Bob O'Loughlin plans to invest nearly $15 million in the hotel, including $9 for renovation. **Availability:** Print; Online.

8440 ■ *"On the Green: Sheila Johnson Adds $35 Million Golf Resort To Her Expanding Portfolio"* in *Black Enterprise (January 2008)*
Pub: Earl G. Graves Ltd.
Contact: Earl Graves, Jr., President

Ed: Donna M. Owens. **Description:** Profile of Sheila Johnson, CEO of Salamander Hospitality LLC, made history when she purchased the Innisbrook Resort and Golf Club, making her the first African American woman to own this type of property. The resort includes four championship golf courses, six swimming pools, four restaurants, eleven tennis courts, three conference halls, and a nature preserve. **Availability:** Online.

8441 ■ *"The Owyhee Is Filling Up Faster Than Expected"* in *Idaho Business Review (September 5, 2014)*
Pub: BridgeTower Media
Contact: Adam Reinebach, President

Description: Clay Carley discusses his idea to renovate the 104-year-old Owyhee Hotel into a modern office, residential and commercial center. He transformed the building's rooftop into an event space for weddings and other celebrations. Carley is the developer and part-owner of the property and reported 3,000 people attending its ribbon cutting. Retail and office space are filling faster than expected and the rooftop venue has already celebrated six weddings.

8442 ■ *"Peabody Launching 464-Room Renovation"* in *Memphis Business Journal (Vol. 34, July 13, 2012, No. 13, pp. 1)*
Pub: Baltimore Business Journal
Contact: Rhonda Pringle, President

E-mail: rpringle@bizjournals.com

Ed: Michael Sheffield. **Description:** The Peabody Memphis has announced preparations for a massive renovation that will affect all 464 rooms of the hotel starting in November. Peabody Hotel Group, which manages the hotel fo rBelz Enterprises, has estimated the renovations to cost between $10 million and $20 million. **Availability:** Print; Online.

8443 ■ *"Philadelphia Tourism Push Rising in Fall" in Philadelphia Business Journal (Vol. 30, August 26, 2011, No. 28, pp. 1)*
Pub: Philadelphia Business Journal
Contact: Sierra Quinn, Director
E-mail: squinn@bizjournals.com

Ed: Peter Van Allen. **Description:** Philadelphia is offering events for tourists this fall despite massive cuts for tourism promotion. Governor Tim Corbet slashed $5.5 million in funding for the state's tourism-promotion agencies which received $32 million in 2009. The agencies were forced to cooperate and fend for themselves using the hotel taxes that sustain them. **Availability:** Online.

8444 ■ *"Phoenix Hospitality Plans to Develop Hotel in Live Oak" in San Antonio Business Journal (Vol. 28, May 2, 2014, No. 12, pp. 8)*
Pub: American City Business Journals, Inc.
Contact: Mike Olivieri, Executive Vice President

Released: Weekly. **Price:** $4, introductory 4-week offer(Digital only). **Description:** Phoenix Hospitality Group is developing the Hilton Garden Inn and Live Oak Conference Center in San Antonio, Texas. The hotel will feature 139 guest rooms, along with 14,000-square-feet of meeting, banquet and convention space. **Availability:** Print; Online.

8445 ■ *"Plan Your Next Event at Newport News Marriott at City Center" in Benzinga.com (July 29, 2011)*
Pub: PR Newswire Association LLC.

Description: Newport News Marriott at City Center is promoting itself as the premier venue for business meetings, conventions and weddings.

8446 ■ *"Plan Your Wedding with Cleveland Airport Marriott's Certified Event Planners" in Benzinga.com (February 2, 2011)*

Description: Cleveland's Airport Marriott makes wedding planning easy with its venue spaces and a full team of wedding planners. **Availability:** Print; Online.

8447 ■ *"Plans for $160M Condo Resort in Wisconsin Dells Moves Forward" in Commercial Property News (March 18, 2008)*
Description: Plans for the Grand Cambrian Resort in the Wisconsin Dells is discussed. The luxury condominium resort will include condos, townhomes, and condo-hotel style residences, two water parts, meeting space and indoor entertainment space, as well as a spa, four restaurants and retail offerings. **Availability:** Online.

8448 ■ *"Portland's Hilton For Sale" in Business Journal Portland (Vol. 27, October 22, 2010, No. 34, pp. 1)*
Pub: Portland Business Journal
Contact: Andy Giegerich, Managing Editor
E-mail: agiegerich@bizjournals.com

Ed: Wendy Culverwell. **Description:** Hilton Portland & Executive Tower, Portland's biggest hotel, is being sold by Cornerstone Real Estate Advisers LLC. Cornerstone hopes to close the deal for the 782-room complex by the end of 2010. Cornerstone contracted Jones Lang LaSalle to manage the sale, but terms to the deal are not available. **Availability:** Print; Online.

8449 ■ *"Pre-Certified LEED Hotel Prototype Reduces Energy Use, Conserves Water" in Contractor (Vol. 57, January 2010, No. 1, pp. 3)*
Pub: Informa USA, Inc.
Contact: Stephen A. Carter, Chief Executive Officer

Ed: Candace Roulo. **Released:** January 01, 2010. **Description:** Marriott International Inc.'s LEED pre-certified prototype hotel will reduce a hotel's energy and water consumption by 25 percent and save own-

ers approximately $100,000. Their Courtyard Settler's Ridge in Pittsburgh will be the first hotel built based on the prototype.

8450 ■ *"Radisson Hotel San Jose Airport Headed Into Foreclosure" in Silicon Valley/San Jose Business Journal (Vol. 29, February 3, 2012, No. 45, pp. 1)*
Pub: Baltimore Business Journal
Contact: Rhonda Pringle, President
E-mail: rpringle@bizjournals.com

Description: The Radisson Hotel San Jose Airport is set to be foreclosed. Hotel owner, Silicon Valley Hwang LLC has yet to pay a $15.9 million loan. **Availability:** Print; Online.

8451 ■ *"Receiver's Report Uncovers Trouble in Fashion Mall Redevelopment" in South Florida Business Journal (Vol. 34, July 4, 2014, No. 50, pp. 4)*
Pub: American City Business Journals, Inc.
Contact: Mike Olivieri, Executive Vice President

Released: Weekly. **Price:** $8, introductory 4-week offer(Digital only). **Description:** A report by receiver, Charles Lichtman, reveals possible fraud of fiduciary duty by Wei Chen, who manages the redevelopment of Fashion Mall in Plantation Florida. Chen used funds from the account of Tangshan Ganglu Iron and Steel Company to make a deposit on a purchase contract for the Sheraton Suites Plantation hotel and resort for a company he personally owned. **Availability:** Print; Online.

8452 ■ *"Research and Markets Offers Report on US Business Traveler's Green, New Technology Views" in Airline Industry Information (July 30, 2012)*
Description: The US Business Traveler Expectations of Green and Technology Initiatives in Hotels in 2012 contains comprehensive analysis on US business travelers views on green and technology initiative and socially responsible measures geared towards the business traveler. **Availability:** Print; Online.

8453 ■ *"Ritz Kapalua Sells 93 Suites for $176M to Fund Renovation" in Commercial Property News (March 17, 2008)*
Description: Ritz-Carlton, Kapalua in Lahaina, Hawaii sold ninety-three of its units in order to fund renovations of 463 rooms and suites along with construction of a new spa and fitness center, new and expanded restaurants and pools and an environmental education center for children. **Availability:** Online.

8454 ■ *"Sacramento Businesses Must Cut Water Use 20 Percent" in Sacramento Business Journal (Vol. 30, January 17, 2014, No. 47, pp. 5)*
Pub: American City Business Journals, Inc.
Contact: Mike Olivieri, Executive Vice President

Released: Weekly. **Price:** $4, introductory 4-week offer(Digital & Print). **Description:** The Sacramento, California City, California Council's decision to reduce water use by 20 percent could have a big impact on businesses. Hotels and restaurants are among the biggest commercial users of water, while golf courses generally use well water. The need for businesses to purchase more efficient fixtures is also discussed. **Availability:** Print; Online.

8455 ■ *"Seahawks' Win? A Seattle Windfall" in Puget Sound Business Journal (Vol. 34, January 10, 2014, No. 39, pp. 3)*
Pub: American City Business Journals, Inc.
Contact: Mike Olivieri, Executive Vice President

Released: Weekly. **Price:** $4, introductory 4-week offer(Digital & Print). **Description:** Seattle, Washington is anticipating a windfall from the Seattle Seahawks' ninth game of the season. The sold-out CenturyLink Field can hold 67,000 spectators, who are potential customers outside the stadium at restaurants, bars, hotels and attractions. The economic benefits of hosting a high-profile sports event are explored. **Availability:** Print; Online.

8456 ■ *"Seven Things Great Employers Do (That Others Don't); Unusual, Innovative, and Proven Tactics To Create Productive and Profitable Working Environments" in Gallup Business Journal (April 15, 2014)*
Pub: Gallup, Inc.
Contact: Jon Clifton, Chief Executive Officer

Price: $8.95. **Description:** Seven unusual, innovative, and proven tactics that create productive and profitable working environments are examined through researching 32 companies. These firms represented many industries, including healthcare, financial services, hospitality, manufacturing, and retail throughout the world. **Availability:** Print; PDF; Online.

8457 ■ *"South Florida Lodging Industry Poised for Strong Growth in 2014" in South Florida Business Journal (Vol. 34, January 3, 2014, No. 24, pp. 3)*
Pub: American City Business Journals, Inc.
Contact: Mike Olivieri, Executive Vice President

Released: Weekly. **Price:** $8, Introductory 4-week offer(Digital & Print). **Description:** Demand for the lodging industry in South Florida is expected to grow in 2014. According to hotel consulting and research firm, PKF Hospitality Research LLC, lodging demand in the U.S. would increase by 2.1 percent by the end of 2013 while airport, resort and suburban areas will achieve the biggest gains in revenue per available room in 2014. **Availability:** Print; Online.

8458 ■ *"Survey Says Commercial Real Estate Headed for Turbulence" in Commercial Property News (March 17, 2008)*
Description: Commercial real estate sector is declining due to the sluggish U.S. economy. According to a recent survey, national office, retail and hospitality markets are also on the decline. **Availability:** Online.

8459 ■ *"Then and Now" in Washington Business Journal (Vol. 32, February 21, 2014, No. 45, pp. 6)*
Pub: Conde Nast Publications
Contact: Agnes Chu, President

Released: January 05, 2016. **Description:** The new restaurants and bars at Marriott Marquis Hotel in Washington DC are offering retro lunch-counter items alongside modern offerings. The conference/convention center hotel will open across from the Walter E. Washington Convention Center on May 1, 2014. **Availability:** Print; Online.

8460 ■ *"Travel Tears" in Crain's Chicago Business (Vol. 31, November 17, 2008, No. 46, pp. 3)*
Pub: Crain Communications Inc.
Contact: Barry Asin, President

Ed: Bob Tita. **Description:** Hotels, restaurants and conventions are seeing a decline in profits due to corporate travel cutbacks and the sagging economy. City and state revenues derived from taxes on tourism-related industries are also suffering. **Availability:** Online.

8461 ■ *"Travelodge Intros Program to Streamline Operations, Reduce Waste" in Hotel Business (November 11, 2019)*
URL(s): www.hotelbusiness.com/travelodge-intros-program-to-streamline-operations-reduce-waste/

Released: November 11, 2019. **Description:** Travelodge by Wyndham is introducing a new eco-friendly initiative called Travelodge + GO Green, with the goal of reducing waste and increasing operating efficiencies. **Availability:** Online.

8462 ■ *"Tribes Roll Dice On Ventures as They Push Outside of Casinos" in Business Journal (Vol. 32, May 30, 2014, No. 1, pp. 8)*
Pub: American City Business Journals, Inc.
Contact: Mike Olivieri, Executive Vice President

Released: Weekly. **Price:** $4, introductory 4-week offer(Digital only). **Description:** The growing trend of American Indian tribes in Minnesota diversifying their investments in other sectors beyond gambling is examined. The Shakopee Mdewakanton Sioux Community invested in the 342-room JW Marriott hotel that is being built at the Mall of America. The Mille Lacs Band of Ojibwe also acquired Crowne Plaza St. Paul Riverfront Hotel and the Double Tree in early 2013. **Availability:** Print; Online.

8463 ■ *"Trigate Rebrands Radisson at SMU to Holiday Inn" in Dallas Business Journal (Vol. 35, August 31, 2012, No. 51, pp. 1)*
Pub: Baltimore Business Journal
Contact: Rhonda Pringle, President
E-mail: rpringle@bizjournals.com
Description: Radisson Hotel, located near Southern Methodist University in Dallas, Texas, will soon be known as Holiday Inn Dallas Park Cities. Hotel owner Trigate Capital states that the rebranding is part of the hotel's renovation, which is expected to finish by the end of the year. The new name will take effect in October. **Availability:** Print; Online.

8464 ■ *"Unfilled Hotels Go All Out for Business Meetings" in Crain's Detroit Business (Vol. 25, June 8, 2009, No. 23, pp. 9)*
Pub: Crain Communications Inc.
Contact: Barry Asin, President
Ed: Daniel Duggan. **Description:** Hotels in Michigan are offering discounts to companies holding business meetings at their properties. Details of competition and plans are included. **Availability:** Print; Online.

8465 ■ *"Wagering Opportunities" in Memphis Business Journal (No. 35, April 4, 2014, No. 52, pp. 8)*
Pub: American City Business Journals, Inc.
Contact: Mike Olivieri, Executive Vice President
Released: April 14, 2017. **Description:** Rankings of casino-hotels in the Memphis Metropolitan Area are presented. Rankings were based on the size of gaming space. **Availability:** Print; Online.

8466 ■ *"Washington Hospitality Businesses Eligible for $100 Million Grant Program" in Small Business Trends (March 13, 2023)*
URL(s): smallbiztrends.com/2023/03/100-million-grant-program-washington-hospitality-businesses.html
Ed: Gabrielle Pickard-Whitehead. **Released:** March 13, 2023. **Description:** New grants are available for a total of $100 million. Eligible companies are restricted to the hospitality and lodging industry. **Availability:** Online.

8467 ■ *"Watch Hill Gaining Traction as Luxury Destination" in Providence Business News (Vol. 28, March 24, 2014, No. 51, pp. 1)*
Pub: American City Business Journals, Inc.
Contact: Mike Olivieri, Executive Vice President
Released: March 22, 2014. **Description:** Rhode Island's tourism leaders believe that the increase in the number of leisure tourists visiting Watch Hill can help improve the village's marketability. Mark Brodeur of the Rhode Island Commerce Corporation and Lisa Konicki of the Westerly-Pawcatuck Chamber of Commerce claim that the reopening of the Ocean House Hotel in 2010 led to the village's revival. **Availability:** Print; Online.

8468 ■ *"Web Exclusive: What happens after disaster strikes?" in Hotel Business (October 21, 2021)*
URL(s): www.hotelbusiness.com/web-exclusive-what-happens-after-disaster-strikes
Ed: Abby Elyssa. **Description:** When a disaster strikes a community, hotels are often the first place affected people turn to, but what happens when the hotel is hit by disaster? Tips on choosing restoration partners and what to expect out of the process are explained. **Availability:** Online.

8469 ■ *"Wyndham Program Targeting Women Hotel Owners Signs 30 Franchisees in First Year" in Bizwomen (March 24, 2023)*
URL(s): www.bizjournals.com/bizwomen/news/latest-news/2023/03/wyndham-program-for-women-hotel-owners-signs-30-fr.html
Ed: Anne Stych. **Released:** 24, 2023. **Description:** A program that targets women's advancement in hotel ownership signed on 30 hotel franchises. Noted

in the article that about 50 percent of these hotels are new constructions projects that will now be headed by women. **Availability:** Online.

STATISTICAL SOURCES

8470 ■ *Bed & Breakfast & Hostel Accommodations Industry in the US - Market Research Report*
URL(s): www.ibisworld.com/united-states/market-research-reports/bed-breakfast-hostel-accommodations-industry/
Price: $925. **Description:** Downloadable report analyzing the trends and future outlook for the bed and breakfast and hostel industries. **Availability:** Download.

8471 ■ *Hotels & Motels Industry in the US - Market Research Report*
URL(s): www.ibisworld.com/united-states/market-research-reports/hotels-motels-industry/
Price: $925. **Description:** Downloadable report examining the hotel and motel industry and key aspects and industry outlook. **Availability:** Download.

8472 ■ *RMA Annual Statement Studies*
Pub: Risk Management Association
Contact: Nancy Foster, President
Released: Annual. **Description:** Contains composite balance sheets and income statements for more than 360 industries, including the accounting, auditing, and bookkeeping industries. Also contains five years of comparative historical data for discerning trends. Includes 16 commonly used ratios, computed for most of the size groupings for nearly every industry.

8473 ■ *Standard & Poor's Industry Surveys*
Pub: Standard And Poor's Financial Services LLC.
Contact: Douglas L. Peterson, President
Description: Two-volume book that examines the prospects for specific industries, including trucking. Also provides analyses of trends and problems, statistical tables and charts, and comparative company analyses.

TRADE PERIODICALS

8474 ■ *Cornell Hospitality Quarterly (CHQ)*
Pub: SAGE Publications
Contact: Tracey Ozmina, President
URL(s): us.sagepub.com/en-us/nam/cornell-hospitality-quarterly/journal201681sha.cornell.edu/about/news-and-publications/publications/quarterly; journals.sagepub.com/home/cqx
Ed: Michael Lynn, J. Bruce Tracey. **Released:** Quarterly; February, May, August, November. **Price:** https://us.sagepub.com/en-us/nam/cornell-hospitality-quarterly/journal201681. **Description:** Peer-reviewed, scholarly journal focusing on critical research, practical applied theories, and useful case studies regarding important industry trends and timely topics in lodging, restaurant, and tourism management. Published in association between SAGE and the Cornell University School of Hotel Administration. **Availability:** Print; PDF; Download; Online.

8475 ■ *Hospitality Design*
Contact: Alissa Ponchione, Managing Editor
E-mail: alissa.ponchione@emeraldexpo.com
URL(s): www.hospitalitydesign.com/hospitalitydesign/index.shtml
Facebook: www.facebook.com/HospitalityDesignMagazine
Linkedin: www.linkedin.com/company/hospitality-design
X (Twitter): twitter.com/hdmag
Released: 10/yrs. **Description:** Magazine covering design of restaurants, hotels, facilities, clubs, cruise ships, etc. **Availability:** Print; PDF; Online.

8476 ■ *Hospitality Review*
Pub: Florida International University Chaplin School of Hospitality & Tourism Management
Contact: Dr. Michael Cheng, Dean
URL(s): digitalcommons.fiu.edu/hospitalityreview

Released: Current issue: volume 31, issue 4, 2014. **Price:** $150, Institutions for one year; $50, for electronic back issues (per each issue); $150, Individuals for one year; $10, Individuals for article back issue. **Description:** Trade journal covering hospitality management. **Availability:** Print; PDF.

8477 ■ *Hotel Business*
Pub: ICD Publications
Contact: Dave Palcek, Chief Executive Officer
URL(s): hotelbusiness.com
Linkedin: www.linkedin.com/company/hotel-business
X (Twitter): x.com/hotelbusiness
Ed: Christina Trauthwaein. **Released:** Annual **Price:** $10, for supplements; $17, for regular back issues; $100, for green book (December). **Description:** Trade magazine covering the hotel industry. **Availability:** Print; Online.

8478 ■ *Hotel Management*
Pub: Questex L.L.C.
Contact: Paul Miller, Chief Executive Officer
URL(s): www.hotelmanagement.net
Linkedin: www.linkedin.com/company/hotel-management-magazine
X (Twitter): x.com/HotelMgmtMag
Released: Monthly **Price:** $68, U.S. for annual; $107, U.S. for 2 years; $91, Canada and Mexico for annual; $130, Canada and Mexico for 2 years; $146, for annual (All other countries); $207, for 2 years (All other countries); $6.50, Canada and Mexico for single copies; $12.50, Other countries for single copies; $12, Canada and Mexico for back issues; $24, Other countries for back issues; $5.50, U.S. for single copies; $10, U.S. for back issues. **Description:** Magazine (tabloid) covering the global lodging industry. **Availability:** Print; Online.

8479 ■ *Hotelier*
Pub: Kostuch Publications Ltd.
URL(s): www.hoteliermagazine.com
Facebook: www.facebook.com/HotelierMagazine
Linkedin: www.linkedin.com/company/hotelier-mag
X (Twitter): x.com/hoteliermag
Instagram: www.instagram.com/hoteliermagazine
Ed: Rosanna Caira. **Released:** 8/year **Price:** $30, for 1 year in US; $40, for 1 year in Outside US and Canada; $25, for 1 year in Canada. **Description:** Trade journal covering Canada's hotel industry. **Availability:** Print; Online.

8480 ■ *HOTELS*
Pub: Marketing & Technology Group Inc.
Contact: Mark Lefens, President
URL(s): hotelsmag.commtgmediagroup.com/hotels
Facebook: www.facebook.com/HOTELSmag
Linkedin: www.linkedin.com/company/hotels-magazine
X (Twitter): x.com/HOTELSmagazine
Released: 7/year **Description:** Magazine covering management and operations as well as foodservice and design in the hospitality industry. **Availability:** Print; Download; PDF; Online.

8481 ■ *Journal of Hospitality Marketing & Management*
Pub: Taylor And Francis Group
Contact: Annie Callanan, Chief Executive Officer
URL(s): www.tandfonline.com/journals/whmm20
X (Twitter): x.com/JhmmTfg
Released: 8/year **Price:** $1,767, Institutions for print and online; $390, Individuals for print and online; $1,449, Institutions for online only; $343, Individuals for online only. **Description:** Academic and industry journal dealing with marketing issues in the hospitality and leisure industries. **Availability:** Print; PDF; Download; Online.

8482 ■ *LODGING*
Pub: American Hotel and Lodging Association
Contact: Chip Roggers, President
URL(s): lodgingmagazine.com
Facebook: www.facebook.com/LodgingMagazine
Linkedin: www.linkedin.com/company/lodging-magazine-official
X (Twitter): x.com/LodgingMagazine
Instagram: www.instagram.com/lodgingmagazine

YouTube: www.youtube.com/lodgingmagazine

Ed: Kate Hughes. **Released:** 9/year; Monthly **Description:** Publication includes list of about 4,000 suppliers to the hotel industry. **Entries include:** Company name, address, phone, name of principal executive, list of products or services. **Arrangement:** Classified by product or service. **Indexes:** Alphabetical listing, categorical listings. **Availability:** Print; Online.

VIDEO/AUDIO MEDIA

8483 ■ *Doug Zeif Founder & CEO of Next Hospitality Advisors*

URL(s): restaurantunstoppable.com/doug-zeif-next

Ed: Eric Cacciatore. **Description:** Podcast discusses controlling profit and cost, partners, and accountability in the hospitality industry.

TRADE SHOWS AND CONVENTIONS

8484 ■ AAOHA Convention & Trade Show

URL(s): aahoacon.streampoint.com/upcoming -conventions

Price: $350, Members Early registration.; $450, Members Regular registration.; $500, Members On-site registration. **Frequency:** Annual. **Description:** Provides key topic sessions, education, and networking for Asian American Hotel owners. **Principal Exhibits:** Provides key topic sessions, education, and networking for Asian American Hotel owners.

8485 ■ ApEx

Restaurants Canada
  1155 Queen St. W
  Toronto, ON, Canada M6J 1J4
Ph: (416)923-8416
Free: 800-387-5649
Fax: (416)923-1450
Co. E-mail: info@restaurantscanada.org
URL: http://www.restaurantscanada.org
Contact: Christian Buhagiar, Co-Chief Executive
  Officer Co-President
URL(s): www.apextradeshow.ca

Description: Products and services for the restaurant and hospitality industry, as well as institutions, convenience stores, delis and bakeries. **Audience:** Industry professionals. **Principal Exhibits:** Products and services for the restaurant and hospitality industry, as well as institutions, convenience stores, delis and bakeries. **Telecommunication Services:** chuckn@mediaedge.ca.

8486 ■ Arkansas Hospitality Association Convention & Exhibition

Arkansas Hospitality Association (AHA)
  603 S Pulaski St.
  Little Rock, AR 72201
Ph: (501)376-2323
Co. E-mail: aha@arhospitality.org
URL: http://www.arhospitality.org
Contact: Katie Beck, Chief Executive Officer
URL(s): www.arhospitality.org/convention-2023.html

Frequency: Annual. **Description:** Promotes tourism in the state of Arkansas. **Audience:** Restaurant owners, motel and hotel owners and operators, and resort and recreational attraction trade professionals. **Principal Exhibits:** Promotes tourism in the state of Arkansas. **Telecommunication Services:** aha@arhospitality.org.

8487 ■ Aspiring Lodging Professional Conference

URL(s): www.paii.com/ALP-Industry-Events

Frequency: Annual. **Description:** Provides seminars and talks on how to run a small, private lodging business. **Audience:** Independent lodgers and those who do not yet own a property. **Principal Exhibits:** Provides seminars and talks on how to run a small, private lodging business.

8488 ■ The Hotel Experience (HX)

Guest Supply Inc.
  300 Davidson Ave.
  Somerset, NJ 08873
Ph: (732)868-2200
Free: 800-772-7676
Fax: (800)480-7878
Co. E-mail: info@guestworldwide.com
URL: http://guestsupply.com
URL(s): thehotelexperience.com/show/about-hx/

Frequency: Annual. **Description:** Products and services for lodging and food serving properties, including: technology, uniforms, linens and bedding, tabletop accessories, guest amenities and services, food and beverages, cleaning maintenance, food service equipment and supplies, franchising information, finance and management furnishings and fixtures, fitness equipment, and leisure and entertainment services. **Audience:** Hotel and restaurant professionals. **Principal Exhibits:** Products and services for lodging and food serving properties, including: technology, uniforms, linens and bedding, tabletop accessories, guest amenities and services, food and beverages, cleaning maintenance, food service equipment and supplies, franchising information, finance and management furnishings and fixtures, fitness equipment, and leisure and entertainment services. **Telecommunication Services:** kevin.gaffney@emeraldx.com.

8489 ■ Lodging Professionals Conference and Marketplace

URL(s): www.paii.com/ALP-Industry-Events

Frequency: Annual. **Description:** Provides seminars and talks about owning an independent lodging property plus a marketplace with vendors. **Audience:** Professional small, independent lodging owners. **Principal Exhibits:** Provides seminars and talks about owning an independent lodging property plus a marketplace with vendors.

8490 ■ Miami Hospitality Suppliers Expo

URL(s): www.hotelhospitalityexpo.com

Frequency: Annual. **Description:** A full range of furniture, furnishings, electronics, appliances, textiles and all other products needed to run a hotel, motel, or other hospitality location. **Audience:** Buyers within the hospitality industry. **Principal Exhibits:** A full range of furniture, furnishings, electronics, appliances, textiles and all other products needed to run a hotel, motel, or other hospitality location.

8491 ■ National Restaurant Association Restaurant and Hotel-Motel Show

National Restaurant Association (NRA)
  2055 L St. NW, Ste. 700
  Washington, DC 20036
Ph: (202)331-5900
Free: 800-424-5156
Co. E-mail: askus@restaurant.org
URL: http://www.restaurant.org
Contact: Michelle Korsmo, President
URL(s): www.nationalrestaurantshow.com
Facebook: www.facebook.com/NationalRestaurantShow
X (Twitter): twitter.com/NatlRestShow

Frequency: Annual. **Description:** Food service equipment, supplies, and services and food and beverage products for the hospitality industry. Includes education sessions, and exhibits. **Audience:** Caterers, bakers, chefs, cooks, and restaurant and hotel-motel staff and owners. **Principal Exhibits:** Food service equipment, supplies, and services and food and beverage products for the hospitality industry. Includes education sessions, and exhibits. Dates and Locations: 2025 May 17-20 McCormick Place, Chicago, IL. **Telecommunication Services:** restaurant@maritz.com.

8492 ■ New Lodging Professionals Conference

URL(s): www.paii.com/ALP-Industry-Events

Frequency: Annual. **Description:** Provides seminars and education about running a lodging establishment. **Audience:** New lodging property owners. **Principal Exhibits:** Provides seminars and education about running a lodging establishment.

8493 ■ Ocean City Trade Expo

URL(s): oceancitytradeexpo.com

Frequency: Annual. **Description:** Features new products for the hotel, motel, and restaurant industries. **Principal Exhibits:** Features new products for the hotel, motel, and restaurant industries.

8494 ■ WestEx - Colorado Foodservice & Restaurant Conference

Sapporo
  1-1, Odori Nishi, Chuo-ku
  Sapporo, Hokkaido 060-8703, Japan
URL: http://www.nhk.or.jp
URL(s): www.coloradorestaurant.com/education-events/calendar/61_2015-WestEx:-Colorado-Restaurant-&-Foodservice-Conference

Description: Food service and lodging products, equipment, and services. **Audience:** Food service and restaurant industry personnel. **Principal Exhibits:** Food service and lodging products, equipment, and services.

CONSULTANTS

8495 ■ Cini-Little International Inc.

20251 Century Blvd., Ste. 375
  Germantown, MD 20874
Ph: (301)528-9700
Co. E-mail: kheld@cinilittle.com
URL: http://cinilittle.com
Contact: Kathleen M. Held, Chief Executive Officer
E-mail: kheld@cinilittle.com
Facebook: www.facebook.com/CiniLittle
Linkedin: www.linkedin.com/company/cini-little-international
X (Twitter): x.com/cinilittle
Pinterest: www.pinterest.com/cinilittle

Description: Firm provides planning, operational consulting and designing service. **Founded:** 1968.

8496 ■ Clevenger Associates (CA)

PO Box 811
  Elma, WA 98541
Ph: (253)841-7811
Co. E-mail: info@clevengerassoc.com
URL: http://clevengerassoc.com
Contact: Brent Hall, President
E-mail: brent@clevengerassoc.com
Facebook: www.facebook.com/ClevengerAssociates
Linkedin: www.linkedin.com/company/clevenger -associates
X (Twitter): x.com/ClevengerAssoc

Description: Firm provides consulting and design services such as equipment design, facility master planning, and much more. **Founded:** 1970.

8497 ■ Cornell SC Johnson College of Business - Nestle Library

Cornell SC Johnson College of Business
  Ithaca, NY 14853-6201
URL: http://business.cornell.edu
Linkedin: www.linkedin.com/company/cornell -business
YouTube: www.youtube.com/channel/UC4uNGYE6aV8zzLlOlqL9sdg

Description: Provides hospitality such as food and beverage to real estate and finance, entrepreneurship, labor and employment relations. **Scope:** Provider of reference service for the hospitality industry in the areas such as hotel management, franchising and management contracts, tourism and travel, and food and beverage management. **Services:** Interlibrary loan. **Founded:** 1922. **Subscriptions:** journals newspapers Articles; books; research reports; catalogs; guides. **Publications:** *School of Hotel Administration.*

FRANCHISES AND BUSINESS OPPORTUNITIES

8498 ■ Aloha Hotels and Resorts

PO Box 15341
  Honolulu, HI 96830
Ph: (808)826-6244
Co. E-mail: wb@alohahotels.com

URL: http://www.alohahotels.com
Contact: Walter Bono, Contact
Description: Firm provides independent inn, hotel and resort owners with the ability to obtain new sources of revenue. **Training:** Provides training an support programs. There is one assigned management team member to your property that is available to answer any questions and take you through the steps to become an Aloha Hotel and Resort member. There are many training and support areas that are included in your membership.

8499 ▪ Avis Budget Group, Inc. (ABG)
Avis Budget Group, Inc. (ABG)
  379 Interpace Pkwy.
  Parsippany, NJ 07054
Ph: (973)496-4700
Free: 800-352-7900
URL: http://www.avisbudgetgroup.com
Contact: Joe Ferraro, President
Linkedin: www.linkedin.com/company/avis-budge
  t-group
Description: Provides value-conscious vehicle rental and car sharing services through its domestic brand locations and global licensing arrangements. **Founded:** 1946. **Financial Assistance:** Yes **Managerial Assistance:** To help franchisees develop their skills in getting and retaining customers. Trainers will thoroughly teach how to train staff so your preparers will be up-to-date on the latest tax laws. **Training:** Safety training. **Educational Activities:** Annual Airport Business Diversity Conference (Annual).

8500 ▪ Baymont Inn & Suites
Baymont Franchise Systems, Inc.
  11200 N Rte. 12
  Richmond, IL 60071
URL: http://www.wyndhamhotels.com/en-uk/baymont
Description: Hotel with theater, classroom and banquet hall. **Founded:** 1973. **Financial Assistance:** Yes **Training:** Provides 5 days at headquarters, 2 days at franchisee's location, regional workshops 1-3 days, customized property training with ongoing support.

8501 ▪ Choice Hotels Canada Inc.
Choice Hotels International Inc.
  5015 Spectrum Way
  Mississauga, ON, Canada L4W, CA
Ph: (301)592-5000
Free: 877-424-6423
Fax: (301)294-2201
Co. E-mail: press_inquiry@choicehotels.com
URL: http://www.choicehotels.com
Linkedin: www.linkedin.com/company/choice-hotels
  -canada
X (Twitter): x.com/choicehotels
Instagram: www.instagram.com/choicehotels_canada
YouTube: www.youtube.com/user/Choiceho
  telscanada
Description: Chain of hotels. **Founded:** 1993. **Training:** Yes.

8502 ▪ Choice Hotels International Inc.
Choice Hotels International Inc.
  915 Meeting St., Str. 600
  North Bethesda, MD 20852
Ph: (301)592-5000
Free: 877-424-6423
Fax: (301)294-2201
Co. E-mail: press_inquiry@choicehotels.com
URL: http://www.choicehotels.com
Contact: Patrick Pacious, President
Facebook: www.facebook.com/choicehotels
Linkedin: www.linkedin.com/company/choice-hotels
  -international
X (Twitter): twitter.com/choicehotels
Instagram: www.instagram.com/choicehotels/
YouTube: www.youtube.com/user/Choicehotels
Description: Owns, operates, and franchises hotels and other lodging properties. **Founded:** 1941. **Publications:** *Worldwide Hotel Directory* (Annual). **Financial Assistance:** Yes

8503 ▪ Country Inns and Suites by Carlson
701 Carlson Pky., Ste. 1500
  Minnetonka, MN 55305

Ph: (763)762-2222
Fax: (763)762-2264
Co. E-mail: carlsoncommunications
  @carlsoncompanies.com
URL: http://www.carlson.com
Contact: Geoffrey Gage, President
Description: Firm is engaged in the portfolio of business and travel management. **Founded:** 1987. **Royalty Fee:** 4.5%. **Training:** Provides 1 week training at headquarters, 1 week onsite and ongoing support.

8504 ▪ Days Inns Worldwide Inc.
Wyndham Hotels & Resorts, Inc.
  22 Sylvan Way
  Parsippany, NJ 07054
Ph: (973)753-6000
URL: http://corporate.wyndhamhotels.com
Description: Operator of hotel chain providing lodging and hospitality services. **No. of Franchise Units:** 1,624. **Founded:** 1970. **Franchised:** 1972. **Equity Capital Needed:** $187,370-$6,992,935 total investment. **Franchise Fee:** $36,000-$37,500. **Royalty Fee:** 5.5%. **Financial Assistance:** Yes **Training:** Available 5 days at headquarters, 2 days at franchisee's location, and 1-3 day workshops with ongoing support.

8505 ▪ Howard Johnson International Inc.
Howard Johnson International Inc.
  2904 S Sheridan Way, Ste. 101
  Oakville, ON, Canada L6J 7L7
Ph: (605)679-6699
URL: http://www.wyndhamhotels.com/hojo
Description: Chain of hotels, motels and restaurants. **Founded:** 1972. **Training:** Yes.

8506 ▪ Mainstay Suites
Description: Mid-priced extended-stay hotel. **No. of Franchise Units:** 40. **No. of Company-Owned Units:** 3. **Founded:** 1996. **Franchised:** 1996. **Equity Capital Needed:** $300/room; $30,000 minimum. **Franchise Fee:** 4.5% GRR. **Training:** Yes.

8507 ▪ Microtel Inns and Suites Franchising, Inc.
Wyndham Hotels & Resorts, Inc.
  3159 Rte., 46 E I-287
  Parsippany, NJ 07054
Ph: (973)753-6000
URL: http://corporate.wyndhamhotels.com
YouTube: www.youtube.com/user/MicrotelInnsSuites
Description: Firm provides catering, dining, lodging, accommodations, spa, guest rooms, meeting halls and related services. **Founded:** 1995.

8508 ▪ Motel 6 Operating L.P. [Motel 6; Studio 6]
4001 Intl. Pky.
  Carrollton, TX 75007-1914
Free: 800-899-9841
URL: http://www.motel6.com/en/home.html
Facebook: www.facebook.com/motel6
X (Twitter): x.com/motel6
YouTube: www.youtube.com/user/motel6
Description: Online list of hotels and motels. **Founded:** 2012.

8509 ▪ Ramada International, Inc.
Wyndham Hotels & Resorts, Inc.
  714 S Hwy. 281
  Aberdeen, SD 57401
Ph: (973)753-6000
URL: http://corporate.wyndhamhotels.com
Facebook: www.facebook.com/ramada
X (Twitter): twitter.com/ramadaworldwide
Description: Hotel provides dining, lodging, accommodations, spa, guest rooms, meeting halls and related services. **Founded:** 1954. **Training:** Yes.

8510 ▪ Realstar Hospitality
77 Bloor St. W, Ste. 2000
  Toronto, ON, Canada M5S 1M2
Ph: (416)923-2950
Fax: (416)923-9315
Co. E-mail: info@realstar.ca
URL: http://www.realstargroup.com

Contact: Wayne Squibb, President
Description: Provider of real estate investment and management services. **Founded:** 1974.

8511 ▪ Realstar Management
77 Bloor St. W, Ste. 2000
  Toronto, ON, Canada M5S 1M2
Ph: (416)923-2950
Fax: (416)923-9315
Co. E-mail: info@realstar.ca
URL: http://www.realstargroup.com
Contact: Maryke Wharton, Contact
URL(s): www.realstar.ca
Facebook: www.facebook.com/RealstarManagement
X (Twitter): x.com/realstarmgmt
Pinterest: www.pinterest.com/RealstarMGMT
Description: Provider of property management services for rental homes. **Founded:** 1974. **Franchise Fee:** $40,000. **Training:** Assistance with opening and ongoing support.

8512 ▪ Red Roof Inn
155 W Leffel Ln.
  Springfield, OH 45506
Free: 800-733-7663
Co. E-mail: guestin@redroof.com
URL: http://www.redroof.com
Description: Provider of economy lodging services. **Founded:** 1972. **Training:** Yes.

8513 ▪ Residence Inn by Marriott
5230 Westview Dr.
  Frederick, MD 21703
URL: http://residence-inn.marriott.com
Facebook: www.facebook.com/residenceinn
Instagram: www.instagram.com/residenceinn
Description: Firm that engages in the operation of hotel provides lodging, accommodation, catering service, entertainment facilities, and hospitality services. **Founded:** 1976. **Training:** Yes.

8514 ▪ Rodeway Inn
Choice Hotels International Inc.
  915 Meeting St., Str. 600
  North Bethesda, MD 20852
Ph: (301)592-5000
Free: 877-424-6423
Fax: (301)294-2201
Co. E-mail: press_inquiry@choicehotels.com
URL: http://www.choicehotels.com
Description: Hotels. **No. of Franchise Units:** 146. **Founded:** 1964. **Franchised:** 1964. **Equity Capital Needed:** $125/room; $10,000 minimum. **Franchise Fee:** 3.5% GRR. **Royalty Fee:** $31 per room/month. **Training:** Yes.

8515 ▪ Sleep Inn
2 Research Ct.
  Rockville, MD 20850-3212
URL: http://www.choicehotels.com/en-uk
Description: Motel with state-of-the-art guestrooms. **No. of Franchise Units:** 307. **Franchised:** 1988. **Equity Capital Needed:** $300/room; $40,000 minimum. **Franchise Fee:** 4.5% GRR. **Training:** Yes.

8516 ▪ Studio 6
18405 N 27th Ave.
  Phoenix, AZ 85053
Free: 800-899-9841
URL: http://www.motel6.com/en/home.html
Description: Provider of lodging and rental services. **Founded:** 1998. **Training:** Training and support provided.

8517 ▪ Studio 6 Canada
G6 Hospitality LLC
  60 Britannia Rd., E
  Mississauga, ON, Canada L4Z 3W7
Ph: (972)360-9000
Co. E-mail: info@g6hospitality.com
URL: http://g6hospitality.com
Description: Operator of star hotel and also provides shopping, retail centers, entertainment areas and many restaurants. **Founded:** 2003. **Franchise Fee:** $40,000. **Training:** Yes.

8518 ■ Super 8 Worldwide Inc.
Super 8 Worldwide Inc.
  Asbury Park, NJ
Free: 800-454-3213
URL: http://www.wyndhamhotels.com/en-uk/super-8
Facebook: www.facebook.com/Super8
X (Twitter): x.com/super8
YouTube: www.youtube.com/channel/UCzV4ZG
  -ZPilzb1muEKvTM3w
Description: Operator of motel. **Founded:** 1974.

8519 ■ Travelodge Hotels
Description: Hotels and motels. **No. of Franchise Units:** 433. **Founded:** 1939. **Franchised:** 1966. **Equity Capital Needed:** $186,370-$6,788,300. **Franchise Fee:** $36,000. **Royalty Fee:** 4.5%. **Training:** Available at headquarters for 5 days, 2 days at franchisee's location, regional workshops and customized property training 1-3 days.

8520 ■ WoodSpring Suites
8621 E 21st St. N, Ste. 250
  Wichita, KS 67206
Free: 844-974-6835
URL: http://www.woodspring.com
Description: Hotel provides accommodations and dining room. **Founded:** 2003. **Training:** Yes.

8521 ■ Yogi Bear's Jellystone Park Camp-Resorts
502 TechneCenter Dr., Ste. D
  Milford, OH 45150
URL: http://www.campjellystone.com
Facebook: www.facebook.com/campjellystone
X (Twitter): x.com/campjellystone
Instagram: www.instagram.com/campjellystone
Pinterest: www.pinterest.com/campjellystone
Description: Firm holds an exclusive license to franchise Yogi Bear's resorts in the US and Canada. Presently, there are 70 units in the U.S. and 3 in Canada. **Founded:** 1969. **Franchised:** 1971. **Royalty Fee:** 6% of gross revenues. **Financial Assistance:** Yes **Training:** Franchisee's are required to attend a 5 day training program held at the home office in Cincinnati, OH. Additional onsite training is also conducted for a period of 2-3 days.

PUBLICATIONS

8522 ■ JLL Global Hotels Investment Outlook Report 2021
URL(s): www.us.jll.com/en/trends-and-insights/research/jll-global-hotels-investment-outlook-report-2021
Description: Provides hotel investor trends analysis during the 2020 Covid-19 pandemic and the state of the industry moving forward. **Availability:** Download.

8523 ■ Journal of Hotel and Business Management
2360 Corporate Cir., No. 400
  Henderson, NV 89074
Ph: (650)618-9889
Fax: (650)618-1414
Co. E-mail: contact.omics@omicsonline.org
URL: http://www.omicsonline.org
URL(s): www.longdom.org/hotel-business-management.html
Released: Latest Edition Volume 13, Issue 2, 2024. **Description:** International, peer-reviewed, open access journal covering current research and developments in the hospitality industry and related fields. **Availability:** Print; Online; PDF.

COMPUTER SYSTEMS/ SOFTWARE

8524 ■ Resort Data Processing
Resort Data Processing Inc.
  211 Eagle Rd.
  Avon, CO 81620-3360
Free: 877-779-3717
Co. E-mail: salesinfo@resortdata.com
URL: http://www.resortdata.com
Contact: Barry Biegler, President

URL(s): www.resortdata.com/about
Description: Available for IBM computers and compatibles. System designed for hotels with less than 74 rooms. Options include a package with full accounts payable, general ledger, and financial reporting. **Availability:** Online.

LIBRARIES

8525 ■ American Hotel and Lodging Association (AHLA) - Information Center
1250 Eye St. NW, Ste. 1100
  Washington, DC 20005
Ph: (202)289-3100
Co. E-mail: membership@ahla.com
URL: http://www.ahla.com
Contact: Chip Roggers, President
Facebook: www.facebook.com/hotelassociation
Linkedin: www.linkedin.com/company/american-hotel
  -&-lodging-association
X (Twitter): x.com/ahla
Description: Represents state lodging associations throughout the U.S. with 13,000 property members worldwide, representing more than 1.7 million guest rooms. Provides members with assistance in operations, education and communications and lobbies on Capitol Hill to provide a business climate in which the industry can continue to prosper. Individual state associations provide representation at the state level and offer many additional cost-saving benefits. **Scope:** Lodging; hospitality; travel; tourism. **Founded:** 1910. **Holdings:** Facts, report, annual survey. **Publications:** *Construction & Modernization Report* (Monthly); *LODGING* (9/year; Monthly); *Who's Who in the Lodging Industry*; *AH&LA Register*; *Green Lodging News* (Weekly (Mon.)). **Educational Activities:** The Hotel Experience (HX) (Annual). **Awards:** AHLA Stars of the Industry Awards (Annual). **Geographic Preference:** National.

8526 ■ City College of San Francisco (CCSF) - Culinary Arts and Hospitality Studies - Alice Statler Library
50 Frida Kahlo Way
  Statler Wing, Rm. 10
  San Francisco, CA 94112
Ph: (415)239-3460
URL: http://library.ccsf.edu/locations/statler
Scope: Culinary arts and hospitality study; historical menus; notable titles; local chefs, restaurateurs, hoteliers and entrepreneurs in the industry. **Services:** Copying; Wi-Fi; library open to the public for reference use only. **Founded:** 1964. **Holdings:** Books; menus; archives; monographs; periodicals; DVDs.

8527 ■ Colorado Mountain College - Alpine Campus Library
1275 Crawford Ave.
  Steamboat Springs, CO 80487
Ph: (970)870-4445
Fax: (970)870-4490
URL: http://library.coloradomtn.edu/c.php?g=298848&p=1996026
Contact: Tracey Hughes, Director
E-mail: tshughes@coloradomtn.edu
Scope: Small business; hotel and restaurant management; health and fitness; U.S. history and literature; American music; skiing. **Services:** Interlibrary loan; library open to the public; copying. **Founded:** 1981. **Holdings:** 30,000 books; 580 CDs; maps; state documents; CD-ROMs.

8528 ■ Cornell University - The Nestlé Library
G80 Statler Hall, Cornell University
  Ithaca, NY 14850
Ph: (607)255-3673
Co. E-mail: hotellibrary@cornell.edu
URL: http://hotel.library.cornell.edu
Contact: Ken Bolton, Librarian, Public Services
E-mail: ktb4@cornell.edu
Scope: Hospitality and real estate. **Services:** Interlibrary loan; library open to the public by appointment on a fee basis. **Founded:** 1922. **Holdings:** 28,348 print volumes; 17,551 microforms.

8529 ■ Hospitality Sales and Marketing Association International Research Library (HSMAI)
7918 Jones Branch Dr., Ste. 300
  McLean, VA 22102
Ph: (703)506-3280
Fax: (703)506-3266
Co. E-mail: info@hsmai.org
URL: http://www.hsmai.org
Contact: Agnelo Fernandes, Secretary Treasurer
Scope: Hotels; hospitality; travel and tourism; promotion; merchandising; public relations; marketing; direct mail; publicity; advertising; sales education; revenue management; internet marketing; distribution and channel management; travel and tourism. **Services:** Library open to members by appointment. **Founded:** 1927. **Holdings:** 200 volumes.

8530 ■ Johnson & Wales University-Harborside Culinary Library (JWU)
321 Harborside Blvd.
  Providence, RI 02905
Ph: (401)598-1466
Co. E-mail: ask@jwu-ri.libanswers.com
URL: http://pvd.library.jwu.edu/lticulinary
Contact: Lisa Spicola, Librarian
E-mail: lisa.helwigpayne@jwu.edu
X (Twitter): x.com/jwulibrary
YouTube: www.youtube.com/user/JWULibraryPVD
Scope: Food service; menu planning; nutrition; professional management; catering and banquets; household manuals; canning; preserving and freezing; hotel and motel management. **Services:** Copying; Library open to the public. **Founded:** 1979.

8531 ■ Le Cordon Bleu College of Culinary Arts Library
350 Rhode Island St.
  San Francisco, CA 94103
URL: http://www.careered.com/closedschool/locations
Scope: Culinary arts; nutrition; restaurant and hospitality industry. **Services:** Library open to the public by special appointment only. **Founded:** 1989. **Holdings:** 3,500 books.

8532 ■ Oregon Restaurant & Lodging Association (ORLA) - Resource Library
8565 SW Salish Ln., Ste. 120
  Wilsonville, OR 97070-9633
Ph: (503)682-4422
Free: 800-462-0619
Fax: (503)682-4455
Co. E-mail: info@oregonrla.org
URL: http://www.oregonrla.org
Contact: Jason Brandt, President
E-mail: jbrandt@oregonrla.org
Facebook: www.facebook.com/OregonRLA
Linkedin: www.linkedin.com/company/oregon-restaurant-and-lodging-association
X (Twitter): x.com/oregonrla
YouTube: www.youtube.com/user/ORLAvideos
Description: Hotels, motels, resorts, bed-and-breakfasts, RV parks, and others in the lodging industry interested in promoting and protecting the lodging/tourism industry in the state of OR. Works for favorable legislation; conducts marketing and promotional activities. Negotiates group programs such as insurance and bankcard rates. **Scope:** Marketing; management; operations; security. **Services:** Library open to lodging members. **Founded:** 1946. **Holdings:** 57 books; 86 videocassettes; 300 DVDs; 2,000 bilingual HR and safety policies, training manuals, programs, posters, quizzes, and checklists. **Publications:** *Inn Oregon* (Monthly); *Oregon's Innkeeper's Manual*; *Oregon Trip Planner*. **Awards:** ORLA Innkeeper of the Year (Annual). **Geographic Preference:** State.

8533 ■ Paul Smith's College of Arts & Sciences - Joan Weill Adirondack Library
7777 NY-30
  Paul Smiths, NY 12970
Free: 800-421-2605
Co. E-mail: info@paulsmiths.edu
URL: http://www.paulsmiths.edu

Contact: Matthew Purcell, President

Facebook: www.facebook.com/paulsmithscollege

X (Twitter): x.com/paulsmiths

Instagram: www.instagram.com/paulsmiths

YouTube: www.youtube.com/user/PaulSmi
thsCollege518

Description: Educational institute providing higher education. **Scope:** Hotel and restaurant management; chef training; culinary arts; forestry; urban tree management; environmental science; forest recreation; surveying; ecotourism; natural resources management; fisheries management; business management. **Services:** Interlibrary loan; copying; library open to the public with restrictions. **Founded:** 1946. **Holdings:** 54,000 books; pamphlets.

8534 ■ South College Library
3904 Lonas Dr.
Knoxville, TN 37909

Ph: (865)251-1832

URL: http://library.south.edu/home

Contact: Anya McKinney, Director, Library Services

E-mail: amckinney@south.edu

Scope: Educational material. **Services:** Interlibrary loan; copying; printing; SDI; library open to South College staff and students. **Holdings:** E-books; print and e-journals; other periodicals; CDs; DVDs; streaming videos.

START-UP INFORMATION

8535 ■ *"Lee's Launches With Focus on Liqueur-based Ice Creams" in Ice Cream Reporter (Vol. 23, August 20, 2010, No. 9, pp. 6)*

Description: Lee's Cream Liqueur Ice Cream Parlors launched their grand opening in Old Town Scottsdale in July, featuring premium liqueurs to create adult-only ice creams that can be served on their own or blended into exotic drinks. **Availability:** Print; Online.

8536 ■ *"Sloan's Ice Cream Inks First Franchise Deal In San Diego" in FastCasual.com (September 12, 2014)*

Pub: Networld Media Group
Contact: Kathy Doyle, President
E-mail: publisher@networldmediagroup.com
Description: Sloan's Ice Cream announced that is has awarded the first franchise location outside of South Florida to Ali Hajisattari of San Diego, California. **Availability:** Online.

8537 ■ *"Young Entrepreneur's Business Plan? An Ice Cream Boat? Really Floats: Maine at Work" in Portland Press Herald (August 9, 2010)*

Pub: Portland Press Herald
Contact: Lisa DeSisto, Chief Executive Officer
Ed: Ray Routhier. **Description:** Profile of Jake Viola, founder of and ice cream boat located near Portland, Maine. Viola is a sophomore at Yale University and sells ice cream from his pontoon boat on Little Sebago lake. **Availability:** Print; Online.

ASSOCIATIONS AND OTHER ORGANIZATIONS

8538 ■ **Dairy Management Inc. (DMI)**
10255 W Higgins Rd., Ste. 900
  Rosemont, IL 60018-5616
URL: http://www.usdairy.com
Contact: Barbara O'Brien, President
Description: Operates under the auspices of the United Dairy Industry Association. Milk producers, milk dealers, and manufacturers of butter, cheese, ice cream, dairy equipment, and supplies. Conducts programs of nutrition research and nutrition education in the use of milk and its products. **Founded:** 1915. **Publications:** *Dairy Council Digest* (Bi-monthly). **Educational Activities:** SHAPE America National Convention and Expo (Annual). **Geographic Preference:** National.

8539 ■ **Food Processing Suppliers Association (FPSA)**
1451 Dolley Madison Blvd., Ste. 101
  McLean, VA 22101-3850
Ph: (703)761-2600
URL: http://www.fpsa.org
Contact: David Seckman, President
E-mail: dseckman@fpsa.org
Facebook: www.facebook.com/FPSAorg

Linkedin: www.linkedin.com/company/food-processing-suppliers-association
X (Twitter): x.com/fpsaorg
Description: Manufacturers and distributors of dairy and food processing and packaging equipment, machinery, ingredients, and supplies. Provides marketing and technical services to member firms. Compiles market statistics. **Founded:** 1911. **Publications:** *The Blue Book: Membership Directory and Buyer's Guide*; *Guide to Food & Beverage Industry Publications* (Annual); *Food Processing Machinery and Supplies Association--International Directory*; *Food Processing Machinery and Supplies Association Blue Book--Buyers' Guide and Membership Directory* (Biennial); *IAFIS--Directory of Membership Products and Services* (Biennial); *IAFIS--Reporter* (Monthly); *International Association of Food Industry Suppliers--Directory of Membership, Products and Services* (Annual); *Blue Book Buyer's Guide* (Annual). **Educational Activities:** Process Expo (Biennial); LOGIS-TECH TOKYO (Annual); Worldwide Food Expo; ProFood Tech (Biennial). **Awards:** International Food Engineering Award; Career Development Scholarships (Annual); FPSA Career Development Scholarship (Annual). **Geographic Preference:** National.

8540 ■ **North American Ice Cream Association (NICRA)**
2612 E Ave.
  Wildwood, MO 63040
Ph: (636)778-1822
Free: 866-303-6960
Fax: (636)898-4326
Co. E-mail: info@nicra.org
URL: http://icecreamassociation.org
Contact: Kelly Larson, President
Description: Represents frozen dessert retailers that operate ice cream and frozen yogurt dipping stores or parlors. Provides free and frank exchange of information among members so that all may improve their operations, increase profits and prosper. **Founded:** 1933. **Publications:** *NICRA Bulletin* (Monthly); *NICRA Yearbook* (Annual). **Educational Activities:** National Ice Cream Retailers Association Convention (Annual). **Awards:** Bryce Thomson Scholarship Fund (Annual); Forrest Mock Person of the Year (Annual); NICRA Promotion of the Year (Annual). **Geographic Preference:** National.

REFERENCE WORKS

8541 ■ *"7-Eleven Considers Private Label Ice Cream" in Ice Cream Reporter (Vol. 22, December 20, 2008, No. 1, pp. 1)*

Description: 7-Eleven is considering the introduction of a private label of snack foods, including ice cream desserts. **Availability:** Print; Online.

8542 ■ *"Allied Brands Loses Baskin-Robbins Franchise Down Under" in Ice Cream Reporter (Vol. 23, November 20, 2010, No. 12, pp. 2)*

Description: Dunkin Brands, worldwide franchisor of Baskin-Robbins, terminated the master franchise

agreement for Australia held by the food marketer Allied Brands Services. **Availability:** Print; Online.

8543 ■ *"Baskin-Robbins" in Ice Cream Reporter (Vol. 23, November 20, 2010, No. 12, pp. 7)*

Description: Baskin-Robbins is reintroducing its popular Turkey Ice Cream Cake for the holiday. **Availability:** Online.

8544 ■ *"Baskin-Robbins Expanding in China and U.S." in Ice Cream Reporter (Vol. 21, August 20, 2008, No. 9, pp. 1)*

Description: Baskin-Robbins will open its first store in Shanghai, China along with plans for 100 more shops in that country. They will also be expanding their market in the Dallas/Fort Worth, Texas area as well as Greater Cincinnati/Northern Kentucky regions. **Availability:** Print; Online.

8545 ■ *"Baskin-Robbins: New in U.S., Old in Japan" in Ice Cream Reporter (Vol. 23, August 20, 2010, No. 9, pp. 2)*

Description: Baskin-Robbins is celebrating its first franchise in Japan. **Availability:** Print; Online.

8546 ■ *"Baskin-Robbins Reopens in New Orleans" in Ice Cream Reporter (Vol. 23, September 20, 2010, No. 10, pp. 3)*

Description: Baskin-Robbins will open its first shop in New Orleans, Louisiana after Hurricane Katrina in 2005. The shop stands in the exact location of a Baskin-Robbins shop destroyed by Katrina. **Availability:** Print; Online.

8547 ■ *"Baskin-Robbins Tests New Upscale Concept" in Ice Cream Reporter (Vol. 21, September 20, 2008, No. 10, pp. 1)*

Description: Baskin-Robbins is opening its new upscale store, Cafe 31 in an effort to invigorate its brand. The shop will serve fondues, cakes and other treats prepared by an in-store chef. **Availability:** Print; Online.

8548 ■ *"Ben & Jerry's Changing Some 'All Natural' Labels" in Ice Cream Reporter (Vol. 23, October 20, 2010, No. 11, pp. 1)*

Description: Following criticism from the Center for Science in the Public Interest, Ben & Jerry's will omit the term 'All Natural' from its labeling, however the firm reports it will continue to use the most natural ingredients they can find for its products. **Availability:** Print; Online.

8549 ■ *"Ben & Jerry's Introduces 'Green' Freezer" in Ice Cream Reporter (Vol. 21, October 20, 2008, No. 11, pp. 1)*

Description: Ben & Jerry's describes its latest concept as a cleaner, greener freezer. The hydrocarbon-based freezer provides great environmental benefits by minimizing the freezer's impact on global warming. **Availability:** Print; Online.

8550 ■ "Blue Bell Breaks Ground in South Carolina" in Ice Cream Reporter (Vol. 23, August 20, 2010, No. 9, pp. 3)

Description: Texas-based Blue Bell Creameries will open a new 2,000 square foot transfer facility in North Charleston, South Carolina. The facility will expand Blue Bell's distribution efforts in the state. **Availability:** Print.

8551 ■ "Blue Bell Touts Non-Shrinkage" in Ice Cream Reporter (Vol. 21, July 20, 2008, No. 8, pp. 1)

Description: Blue Bell Ice Cream is promoting its decision to keep their ice cream products in a full half-gallon container rather than downsizing the package. Thirty-second television ads contrast the move by other ice cream makers to offer less for the same money. **Availability:** Online.

8552 ■ "Carvel Offers Franchisee Discount" in Ice Cream Reporter (Vol. 21, August 20, 2008, No. 9, pp. 2)

Description: Carvel Ice Cream is offering new franchise opportunities in Florida, New Jersey, and New York. The company will offer incentive for new franchise owners. **Availability:** Print; Online.

8553 ■ "Celebrating America, Scoop by Frosty Scoop" in The New York Times (July 2, 2019)

URL(s): www.nytimes.com/2019/07/02/dining/ice -cream-shops.html

Ed: Ligaya Mishan. **Released:** July 02, 2019. **Description:** A brief history of ice cream and its popularity in the United States as the "dessert of the people." Contains a dozen profiles of ice cream shops around the nation that are influenced by the owner's culture. **Availability:** Online.

8554 ■ "Cold Stone Creamery Offers New Eight-Layer Ice Cream Cakes" in Ice Cream Reporter (Vol. 23, October 20, 2010, No. 11, pp. 2)

Description: Cold Stone Creamery is introducing a new line of eight-layer ice cream cakes, which are crafted with three layers of ice cream, three layers of cake and two mid-layers of mix-ins and finished with frosting and a creative design. **Availability:** Print; Online.

8555 ■ "Cold Stone in Licensing Agreement with Turin Chocolates" in Ice Cream Reporter (Vol. 22, December 20, 2008, No. 1, pp. 2)

Description: Cold Stone Creamery and Turin Chocolatier are teaming up to offer a new line of chocolate truffles under the Cold Stone label. The treats will feature four the most popular Cold Stone flavors: Coffee Lovers Only, Chocolate Devotion, Our Strawberry Blonde, and Peanut Butter Cup Perfection. **Availability:** Print; Online.

8556 ■ "Dairy Queen Aims to Blitz Blizzberry" in Ice Cream Reporter (Vol. 23, August 20, 2010, No. 9, pp. 1)

Description: International Diary Queens has filed a lawsuit to stop Yogubliz Inc. from using Blizzberry and Blizz Frozen Yogurt as the name of its shops because the name is so close to Dairy Queen's Blizzard frozen dessert. **Availability:** Print; Online.

8557 ■ "Dairy Queen Ends Effort Against Yogubliz" in Ice Cream Reporter (Vol. 23, November 20, 2010, No. 12, pp. 1)

Description: Dairy Queen has stopped demands that Yogubliz Inc. change its Blizzberry and Blizz Frozen Yogurt shops because they sound too much like Dairy Queen's Blizzard frozen dessert treat. Dairy Queen feared consumers would confuse the two brands. **Availability:** Print; Online.

8558 ■ "Dean Foods: Uh Oh. Here Comes Wal-Mart" in Ice Cream Reporter (Vol. 23, September 20, 2010, No. 10, pp. 8)

Description: Dean Foods promoted Joseph Scalzo to President and Chief Operating Officer to oversee the firm's operational turnaround and near-term

strategic initiatives as well as business units. Key functions will include worldwide supply chain and research and development. **Availability:** Online.

8559 ■ "Denali Asks Consumers to Name Next Moose Tracks Flavor" in Ice Cream Reporter (Vol. 23, August 20, 2010, No. 9, pp. 4)

Description: Denali Flavors based in Michigan is inviting consumer to name its newest Moose Tracks version of ice cream flavors. **Availability:** Print; Online.

8560 ■ "Emack & Bolio's Founder Blames Brookline Store Closure on Rising Rents" in Ice Cream Reporter (Vol. 23, October 20, 2010, No. 11, pp. 8)

Released: Weekly. **Description:** Emack & Bolio's is engaging in scent marketing using various odors to help boost sales by attracting consumers with scents appropriate to their products. **Availability:** Print; Online.

8561 ■ "Fieldbrook Foods Acquired By Private Equity Firm" in Ice Cream Reporter (Vol. 23, October 20, 2010, No. 11, pp. 1)

Description: Fieldbrook Foods Corporation, manufacturer of frozen novelty and ice cream products was acquired by Chicago-based private equity firm Arbor Investments. Arbor partnered with Herman 'Bing' Graffunder, a long-term dairy industry partner, in its acquisition of Fieldbrook. **Availability:** Print; Online.

8562 ■ "First Airport Location for Paciugo Gelato" in Ice Cream Reporter (Vol. 23, October 20, 2010, No. 11, pp. 2)

Description: Paciugo Gelato and Caffee has partnered with airport concessions developer Airmail to open a shop in the Cleveland Hopkins International Airport. The firm will create a wide variety of choices for travelers. **Availability:** Print; Online.

8563 ■ "For National Frozen Yogurt Month, Get a Spoonful of These Tasty Franchises" in Entrepreneur (June 9, 2016)

URL(s): www.entrepreneur.com/slideshow/277101

Ed: Lindsay Friedman. **Released:** June 09, 2016. **Description:** The frozen yogurt market is on track towards becoming a $9.3 billion industry and with its popularity soaring, franchises are abundant. Included are profiles of some delicious frozen yogurt places to try. **Availability:** Online.

8564 ■ "Fraser and Neave Acquires King's Creameries" in Ice Cream Reporter (Vol. 23, November 20, 2010, No. 12, pp. 1)

Description: Fraser and Neave Ltd., a Singapore-based consumer products marketer, has entered a conditional agreement to acquire all outstanding shares of King's Creameries, the leading manufacturer and distributor of frozen desserts. **Availability:** Print; Online.

8565 ■ "Friendly Ice Cream Corporation" in Ice Cream Reporter (Vol. 23, August 20, 2010, No. 9, pp. 8)

Description: Friendly Ice Cream Corporation appointed Andrea M. McKenna as vice president of marketing and chief marketing officer. **Availability:** Print; Online.

8566 ■ "Frozen Dessert Year in Review.." in Ice Cream Reporter (Vol. 22, January 20, 2009, No. 2, pp. 1)

Description: Falling economy caused the closing of several ice cream plants across the U.S. in 2008. Top stories of interest to the industry are presented. **Availability:** Print; Online.

8567 ■ "Gifford's Tops in Chocolate" in Ice Cream Reporter (Vol. 21, August 20, 2008, No. 9, pp. 3)

Description: Gifford's Ice Cream was presented with two major awards at the World Dairy Expo: "World's Best Chocolate Ice Cream" and "Worlds Best Vanilla

Ice Cream". Entries are judged on flavor, body and texture, color and appearance, melting quality, and quality assurance. **Availability:** Print; Online.

8568 ■ "Golden Spoon Accelerates Expansion Here and Abroad" in Ice Cream Reporter (Vol. 22, December 20, 2008, No. 1, pp. 2)

Description: Golden Spoon frozen yogurt franchise chain is developing 35 more locations in the Phoenix, Arizona area along with plans to open a store in Japan. **Availability:** Print; Online.

8569 ■ "Haagen-Dazs Recruits Shop Owners through Facebook" in Ice Cream Reporter (Vol. 23, November 20, 2010, No. 12, pp. 1)

Description: Haagen-Dazs Shoppe Company is using Facebook, the leading social media, to recruit new franchises. **Availability:** Print; Online.

8570 ■ "Hain Celestial Acquires Greek Gods Yogurt" in Ice Cream Reporter (Vol. 23, July 20, 2010, No. 8, pp. 1)

Description: Hain Celestial Group acquired The Greek Gods LLC. Hain Celestial is a natural and organic products company and Greek Gods makes all natural, Greek-style yogurt and ice cream. **Availability:** Print; Online.

8571 ■ "The Harris Teeter Grocery Chain Has Started a New Ice Cream Club for Shoppers" in Ice Cream Reporter (Vol. 21, July 20, 2008)

Description: Store loyalty cards are being issued to Harris Teeter customers to purchase any variety of Ben & Jerry's, Haagen-Dazs, Dove, Starbucks, Ciao Bella, Clemmy's, Purely Decadent, So Delicious, Harris Teeter Naturals, HT Traders, Hunter Farms or Denali Ice Cream. One point is earned for every dollar spent, 30 total points earns a $5 electronic coupon towards the next purchase. **Availability:** Print; Online.

8572 ■ "Healthy Fast Food Acquires Rights to U-Swirl Yogurt" in Ice Cream Reporter (Vol. 21, October 20, 2008, No. 11, pp. 5)

Description: Healthy Fast Food Inc. will acquire worldwide rights to U-Swirl Frozen Yogurt; the firm will use the new acquisition to create a yogurt superstore in a cafe setting concept for its operations. **Availability:** Print; Online.

8573 ■ ""I'm Kind of a Vanilla Guy': Steve Herrell Shares Confessions and Memories in His New Book, 'Ice Cream and Me'"" in Masslive.com(January 3, 2022)

URL(s): www.masslive.com/business/2022/01/im-kin d-of-a-vanilla-guy-steve-herrell-shares-confessions -and-memories-in-his-new-book-ice-cream-and-me .html

Ed: Jim Kinney. **Released:** January 03, 2022. **Description:** Profile of Steve Herrell, founder of Herrell's Ice Cream & Sweet Bakery, who self-published a book about running his family business. **Availability:** Online.

8574 ■ "Kosher Ice Cream Features Traditional Jewish Ingredients" in Ice Cream Reporter (Vol. 23, August 20, 2010, No. 9, pp. 5)

Description: Chozen Ice Cream is offering traditional Jewish dessert and snack foods using tradition Jewish ingredients to name items: regelach, coconut-almond macaroon, and chocolate matzo. **Availability:** Print; Online.

8575 ■ "Live and Learn: Penny Chapman" in Canadian Business (Vol. 79, July 17, 2006, No. 14-15, pp. 75)

Pub: Rogers Media Inc.

Contact: Neil Spivak, Chief Executive Officer

Ed: Erin Pooley. **Description:** Interview with Penny Chapman, president of Chapman's Ice Cream, who speaks about her journey from rags to riches. **Availability:** Online.

8576 ■ *"Looking To Hire Young? Be Careful"* in *Boston Business Journal (Vol. 30, November 19, 2010, No. 43, pp. 1)*
Pub: Boston Business Journal
Contact: Carolyn M. Jones, President
E-mail: cmjones@bizjournals.com
Ed: Lisa van der Pool. **Released:** Weekly. **Description:** The Massachusetts Commission Against Discrimination (MCAD) has been using undercover job applicants to expose discrimination. Cabot's Ice Cream and Restaurant has been accused of denying older workers equal employment opportunities. MCAD has discovered unfair hiring practices such as hiring high school and college students. **Availability:** Print; Online.

8577 ■ *"Menchie's Tops Restaurant Business' Future 50 List"* in *Ice Cream Reporter (Vol. 23, August 20, 2010, No. 9, pp. 4)*
Description: Menchie's, frozen yogurt shop, announced it placed first in the Restaurant Business Magazine's Future 50, ranking the franchise the fastest-growing in the food industry. **Availability:** Print; Online.

8578 ■ *"Mini Melts Offers 'Win an Ice Cream Business' Contest"* in *Ice Cream Reporter (Vol. 23, October 20, 2010, No. 11, pp. 3)*
Description: Mini Melts USA launched a promotional program offering contestants the opportunity to win a Mini Melts ice cream business. The business is not a franchise and there are not royalty fees. **Availability:** Print; Online.

8579 ■ *"New Food Concepts Flood Market"* in *Business Journal (Vol. 30, June 8, 2012, No. 2, pp. 1)*
Pub: American City Business Journals, Inc.
Contact: Mike Olivieri, Executive Vice President
Ed: John Vomhof, Jr. **Released:** Weekly. **Price:** $4, introductory 4-week offer(Digital only). **Description:** Twin Cities Metropolitan Area has seen the boom of the frozen yogurt segment over the past few years and the rise of fast casual sandwich shops, which are helping fuel activity in Minnesota's real estate market. However, there are skeptics who doubt whether all of the new concepts can survive. **Availability:** Print; Online.

8580 ■ *"New York's Duane Reade Adds In-Store Yogurt Kiosks"* in *ADWEEK (Vol. 53, February 6, 2012, No. 5, pp. 16)*
Description: Fifty year old chain, Pinkberry, is adding self-serve frozen kiosks to select stores in the New York area. Duane Reade, owner of Pinkberry, is refocusing the business to a health and daily-living destination. **Availability:** Online.

8581 ■ *"New Zealand Natural Co-Branding with Mrs. Fields"* in *Ice Cream Reporter (Vol. 23, November 20, 2010, No. 12, pp. 2)*
Description: Mrs. Fields has partnered with a New Zealand firm to co-brand ice cream and cookies in Australian markets. **Availability:** Print; Online.

8582 ■ *"NexCen Brands Sells Chains and Will Liquidate"* in *Ice Cream Reporter (Vol. 23, August 20, 2010, No. 9, pp. 1)*
Description: NexCen Brands is closing the sale of its franchise businesses, which include the frozen dessert chains MaggieMoo's and Marbel Slab Creamery, to Global Franchise Group. **Availability:** Print; Online.

8583 ■ *"Oberweis Tests Home Ice Cream Delivery"* in *Ice Cream Reporter (Vol. 21, November 20, 2008, No. 12, pp. 1)*
Description: Oberweis Dairy launched its Treat Delivery Program in the Saint Louis area. The program allows customers to order milkshakes, ice cream cones, sundaes and scoops of ice cream and they are delivered to their home or office. Oberweis is a fourth generation family run business. **Availability:** Print; Online.

8584 ■ *"The Ode: CoolBrands (1986 - 2010)"* in *Canadian Business (Vol. 83, September 14, 2010, No. 15, pp. 25)*
Pub: Rogers Media Inc.
Contact: Neil Spivak, Chief Executive Officer
Ed: Joe Castaldo. **Description:** CoolBrands International Inc.'s merger with Swisher International Inc., a US hygiene products and services company, has formally erased the last traces of the former ice cream company. CoolBrands began as a frozen yogurt stand in 1986 and flourished across the world. How the string of acquisitions and poor corporate governance led to its demise are cited. **Availability:** Online.

8585 ■ *"Perry's Goes Organic"* in *Ice Cream Reporter (Vol. 22, December 20, 2008, No. 1, pp. 1)*
Description: Family-owned Perry's Ice Cream is starting a new line of organic ice cream in both vanilla and chocolate flavors. All Perry's products are made with milk and cream from local dairy farmers. **Availability:** Print; Online.

8586 ■ *"Private Label Manufacturers Association"* in *Ice Cream Reporter (Vol. 23, July 20, 2010, No. 8, pp. 7)*
Description: Branded frozen dessert manufacturers sold more frozen desserts in terms of sales volume and revenue and market share in 2009. Statistical details included. **Availability:** Print; Online.

8587 ■ *"Ranch Ice Cream? Brand Collab Figures, Why Not?"* in *Small Business Trends (March 13, 2023)*
URL(s): smallbiztrends.com/2023/03/hidden-valley-ranch-flavored-ice-cream-van-leeuwen.html
Ed: Lisa Price. **Released:** March 13, 2023. **Description:** A new ice cream flavor from Van Leeuwen debuted: Hidden Valley Ranch. This unusual flavor may work, especially if paired with a salty topping. **Availability:** Online.

8588 ■ *"R&R Launches Upscale Spoony's and Low Fat Dragon's Den"* in *Ice Cream Reporter (Vol. 23, August 20, 2010, No. 9, pp. 3)*
Description: European ice cream manufacturer R&R has acquired French ice cream maker Rolland and will position itself as an upscale challenger to brands like Ben & Jerry's. **Availability:** Print; Online.

8589 ■ *"Rebrand, Rebuild, and Recharge Your Business: How This BE 100s CEO Got a New Lease On Life With a Frozen Yogurt Café"* in *Black Enterprise (Vol. 44, March 2014, No. 7, pp. 11)*
Pub: Earl G. Graves Ltd.
Contact: Earl Graves, Jr., President
Description: Profile of Rumia Ambrose-Burbank, chief executive of one of the country's largest minority-owned businesses. Her Troy, Michigan-based firm ranks number 51 on the magazine's 100 Industrial/Service companies and focuses on the maintenance, repair, and operations (MRO) supply side. Ambrose-Burbank opened Sol De Frio, in 2013, a self-serve frozen yogurt dessert shop.

8590 ■ *"Red Mango Set to Grow in Florida"* in *Ice Cream Reporter (Vol. 23, September 20, 2010, No. 10, pp. 2)*
Description: Red Mango will add 12 new locations throughout Florida. The stores offer healthy, nutritious frozen yogurt, smoothies and parfaits. **Availability:** Print; Online.

8591 ■ *"Silver Springs Creamery Opens Retail Store"* in *Bellingham Business Journal (Vol. March 2010, pp. 3)*
Pub: Sound Publishing Inc.
Contact: Josh O'Connor, President
Ed: Isaac Bonnell. **Description:** Eric Sundstrom, owner of Silver Springs Creamery, announced the opening of its on-site retail store that will sell the farm's goat and cow cheese, yogurt, ice cream and flesh milk.

8592 ■ *"Tastee-Freez Celebrates 60th Anniversary"* in *Ice Cream Reporter (Vol. 23, July 20, 2010, No. 8, pp. 2)*
Description: Tastee-Freez founders, Leo Moranz (inventor) and Harry Axene, an inventor partnered to market the soft-serve pump and freezer for serving frozen treats back in 1950. **Availability:** Print; Online.

8593 ■ *"Tasti D-Lite Has Franchise Agreement for Australia"* in *Ice Cream Reporter (Vol. 23, November 20, 2010, No. 12, pp. 3)*
Description: Tasti D-Lite signed an international master franchise agreement with Friezer Australia Pty. Ltd. and will open 30 units throughout Australia over the next five years. **Availability:** Print; Online.

8594 ■ *"Thai Ice Cream Cremo Expanding to Middle East"* in *Ice Cream Reporter (Vol. 23, September 20, 2010, No. 10, pp. 3)*
Description: Thai-based frozen dessert manufacturer Chomthana, maker of Cremo brand ice cream, is expanding into the Middle East. **Availability:** Print; Online.

8595 ■ *"U-Swirl Added to SBA's Franchise Registry"* in *Ice Cream Reporter (Vol. 23, September 20, 2010, No. 10, pp. 1)*
Description: Healthy Fast Food Inc., parent to the U-SWIRL Frozen Yogurt cafe chain announced that the U.S. Small Business Administration listed U-SWIRL Frozen Yogurt on its official franchise registry. This move will allow U-SWIRL the benefits of a streamlined review process for SBA financing. **Availability:** Print; Online.

8596 ■ *"U-Swirl To Open in Salt Lake City Metro Market"* in *Ice Cream Reporter (Vol. 23, November 20, 2010, No. 12, pp. 4)*
Description: Healthy Fast Food Inc., parent company to U-SWIRL International Inc., the owner and franchisor of U-SWIRL Frozen Yogurt cafes signed a franchising area development agreement for the Salt Lake City metropolitan area with Regents Management and will open 5 cafes over a five year period. **Availability:** Print; Online.

8597 ■ *"Unilever Acquiring Danish Operations of Diplom-Is Ice Cream"* in *Ice Cream Reporter (Vol. 23, August 20, 2010, No. 9, pp. 1)*
Description: Unilever will acquire Danish operations of the ice cream company Diplom-Is from Norwegian dairy group Tine. **Availability:** Print; Online.

8598 ■ *"Unilever Acquiring EVGA's Ice Cream Brands in Greece"* in *Ice Cream Reporter (Vol. 23, October 20, 2010, No. 11, pp. 1)*
Description: Unilever will acquire the ice cream brands and distribution network of the Greek frozen dessert manufacturer EVGA. **Availability:** Print; Online.

8599 ■ *"Unilever to Sustainably Source All Paper and Board Packaging"* in *Ice Cream Reporter (Vol. 23, July 20, 2010, No. 8, pp. 1)*
Description: Unilever, a leader in the frozen dessert market, has developed a new sustainable paper and board packaging sourcing policy that will reduce environmental impact by working with suppliers to source 75 percent of paper and board packaging from sustainably managed forests or from recycled material. Unilever is parent company to Breyers, Haagen-Dazs, Klondike, Popsicle and other ice cream brands.

8600 ■ *"Velvet Ice Cream"* in *Ice Cream Reporter (Vol. 21, July 20, 2008, No. 8, pp. 7)*
Description: Velvet Ice Cream is adding a $7 surcharge on deliveries of its products in order to offset rising fuel costs. **Availability:** Online.

8601 ■ *"Wells' Is Title Sponsor for Volleyball Championship"* in *Ice Cream Reporter (Vol. 22, August 20, 2008, No. 9, pp. 4)*
Description: Wells' Dairy was chosen to sponsor the 29th Annual National Association of Intercollegiate Athletics (NAIA) Volleyball National Championship to

be held in Sioux City, Iowa. Blue Bunny will sponsor the 2008 NAIA Women's Volleyball National Championship, also a Wells' brand. **Availability:** Print; Online.

8602 ■ *"Yogun Fruz Adds First Location in Southern New York State" in Ice Cream Reporter (Vol. 23, September 20, 2010, No. 10, pp. 2)*

Description: Yogen Fruz signed a master franchise agreement to expand into the southern counties of New York State. The firm offers a healthy and beneficial option to fast food and typical dessert choices. **Availability:** Print; Online.

8603 ■ *"Yogurtini" in Ice Cream Reporter (Vol. 23, September 20, 2010, No. 10, pp. 7)*

Description: Self-serve frozen yogurt chain, Yogurtini has opened its second store in Kansas City, Missouri. **Availability:** Online.

VIDEO/AUDIO MEDIA

8604 ■ *Marketplace: Persistance Pays Off Agan for L.A. Gelato Maker*

URL(s): www.marketplace.org/2023/08/03/los-angeles-gelato-business

Ed: Richard Cunningham. **Released:** August 03, 2023. **Description:** Podcast tracks the journey of a gelato maker who pivoted from brick-and-mortar stores to e-commerce to grocery supplier.

FRANCHISES AND BUSINESS OPPORTUNITIES

8605 ■ Abbott's Frozen Custard Inc.
4791 Lake Ave.
  Rochester, NY 14612-2154
Ph: (585)865-7400
Fax: (585)865-6034
Co. E-mail: contactus@abbottscustard.com
URL: http://www.abbottscustard.com
Facebook: www.facebook.com/AbbottsFrozenCus
  tard
X (Twitter): x.com/abbottscustard
Instagram: www.instagram.com/abbottsfrozencustard

Description: Frozen custard. **Founded:** 1902. **Franchised:** 1981. **Equity Capital Needed:** $200,000-$300,000. **Royalty Fee:** $2.20/gallon. **Training:** Offers 1 week at headquarters and 1 week at franchisee's location with ongoing support.

8606 ■ All American Specialty Restaurants, Inc.
1201 SW 12th Ave., Ste. 415
  Portland, OR 97205
Ph: (503)224-6199
Free: 800-311-3930
URL: http://www.allamericanrestaurants.com

Description: Chain of restaurants that offers coffee, frozen ice creams, yogurt and much more. **Founded:** 1986. **Equity Capital Needed:** $205,200 - $512,950. **Franchise Fee:** $35,000. **Royalty Fee:** 6.0% of gross sales. **Financial Assistance:** Yes **Training:** Yes.

8607 ■ Applegate Inc.
616 Grove St.
  Upper Montclair, NJ 07043
Ph: (973)744-5900
Co. E-mail: info@applegatefarm.com
URL: http://applegatefarm.com
Contact: Wayne Niles, Contact
Facebook: www.facebook.com/AppleGa
  teFarmIceCream
X (Twitter): x.com/applegatefarm
Instagram: www.instagram.com/applegatefarmic

Description: Producer and distributor of ice creams. **Founded:** 1848. **Training:** Offers 2 weeks training at headquarters, 1 week onsite and ongoing support.

8608 ■ Bahama Buck's Franchise Corp. [Bahama Buck's Original Shaved Ice]
5741 50th St.
  Lubbock, TX 79424
Ph: (806)771-2189

Free: 888-382-8257
Co. E-mail: prsupport@bahamabucks.com
URL: http://bahamabucks.com
Contact: Blake Buchanan, Founder
Facebook: www.facebook.com/bahamabucks
X (Twitter): x.com/bahamabucks
Instagram: www.instagram.com/bahamabucks
YouTube: www.youtube.com/user/BahamaBuck

Description: Producer of shaved ice, snow cones, smoothies, and frozen coffee-flavored drinks. **Founded:** 1990. **Financial Assistance:** Yes

8609 ■ Baskin-Robbins L.L.C.
Inspire Brands, Inc.
  130 Royall St.
  Canton, MA 02021
Ph: (678)514-4100
Co. E-mail: franchising@inspirebrands.com
URL: http://inspirebrands.com
Contact: Scott Murphy, President
Facebook: www.facebook.com/baskinrobbins
X (Twitter): x.com/BaskinRobbins
Instagram: www.instagram.com/baskinrobbins
YouTube: www.youtube.com/user/BaskinRobbinsFan

Description: Chain of ice creams shops offering ice creams, frozen desserts and beverages. **Founded:** 1945. **Training:** Yes.

8610 ■ Ben & Jerry's Homemade, Inc.
Unilever plc
  530 Community Dr., Ste. 1
  South Burlington, VT 05403-6828
Ph: 44 20 782-252-52
Co. E-mail: office.london@unilever.com
URL: http://www.unilever.com
Facebook: www.facebook.com/benandjerrysUS
X (Twitter): x.com/benandjerrys
Instagram: www.instagram.com/benandjerrys

Description: Manufacturer and distributor of a wide variety of ice cream flavors and types. **Founded:** 1978. **Franchised:** 1981. **Equity Capital Needed:** Full-Size Shop $189,600 - $430,800 ; In-Line Scoop Shop $157,600 - $281,800 ; Kiosk $109,485 - $237,850. **Franchise Fee:** Traditional $37,000 ; Special venue $16,000. **Royalty Fee:** 0.03. **Financial Assistance:** No **Training:** Popular Ice-cream franchise.

8611 ■ Bruster's Real Ice Cream Inc.
730 Mulberry St.
  Beaver, PA 15009
Ph: (724)774-4250
Fax: (724)774-0666
Co. E-mail: info@brusters.net
URL: http://brusters.com
Contact: Jim Sahene, Chief Executive Officer
Facebook: www.facebook.com/Brus
  tersRealIceCream
X (Twitter): x.com/BrustersFresh
Instagram: www.instagram.com/brustersfresh
YouTube: www.youtube.com/user/BrustersFresh

Description: "Homemade" ice cream and yogurt shop. **Founded:** 1989. **Training:** Yes.

8612 ■ Carvel Franchisor SPV LLC
GOTO Foods
  5620 Glenridge Dr. NE
  Atlanta, GA 30342
Ph: (404)255-3250
Free: 800-227-8353
URL: http://www.gotofoods.com
Contact: Sarah E. Powell, Contact
Facebook: www.facebook.com/CarvelIceCream
X (Twitter): x.com/CarvelIceCream
Instagram: www.instagram.com/carvelicecream

Description: Firm offers custom ice cream desserts and novelties. **Founded:** 1934. **Training:** 2 week ice cream training school; access to the Carvel Development Network (real estate brokers, architects, lenders, contractors, etc.); Design & construction support & assistance; Grand opening support and toll-free hotline available.

8613 ■ Cold Stone Creamery Inc.
9311 E Via De Ventura
  Scottsdale, AZ 85258
Ph: (480)362-4800

Free: 866-452-4252
Fax: (480)362-4812
Co. E-mail: customerservice@kahalamgmt.com
URL: http://www.coldstonecreamery.com
Facebook: www.facebook.com/coldstonecreamery
X (Twitter): x.com/ColdStone
Instagram: www.instagram.com/coldstone

Description: Producer of ice creams, cakes, smoothies and shakes. **Founded:** 1988. **Training:** 10 day training program at headquarters; ongoing support.

8614 ■ Culvers Frozen Custard
1240 Water St.
  Prairie du Sac, WI 53578
Ph: (608)643-7980
URL: http://www.culvers.com
Facebook: www.facebook.com/culvers
X (Twitter): x.com/culvers
YouTube: www.youtube.com/user/CulversRes
  taurants

Description: Operator of restaurant. **Founded:** 1984. **Training:** Yes.

8615 ■ Dairy Queen Canada (DQ)
International Dairy Queen, Inc. (DQ)
  1111 International Blvd.
  Burlington, ON, Canada L7R 3Y3
Free: 866-793-7582
Co. E-mail: internationaldevelopment2@idq.com
URL: http://www.dairyqueen.com/en-us
Instagram: www.instagram.com/dqcanada

Description: Chain of soft serve ice cream and fast-food restaurants. **Founded:** 1953. **Training:** Yes.

8616 ■ Dippin' Dots Franchising, L.L.C. (DDF)
Dippin' Dots L.L.C.
  5101 Charter Oak Dr.
  Paducah, KY 42001
Ph: (270)443-8994
Fax: (270)443-8997
Co. E-mail: email@dippindots.com
URL: http://www.dippindots.com
Contact: Dan Fachner, Manager
Facebook: www.facebook.com/DippinDots
Linkedin: www.linkedin.com/company/dippindots
X (Twitter): x.com/dippindots
Instagram: www.instagram.com/dippindots
YouTube: www.youtube.com/user/DippinDo
  tsIceCream
Pinterest: www.pinterest.com/dippindots

Description: Chain of ice cream parlors offering candies, yogurts. **Founded:** 1988. **Training:** Ice cream seller and franchiser.

8617 ■ FreshBerry Natural Frozen Yogurt
8801 S Yale, Ste. 400
  Tulsa, OK 74137
Ph: (918)488-9727
Free: 877-99F-RANCHISE
Fax: (918)497-1916
URL: http://thefranchisemall.com/franchises/press/
  12719-1-0-freshberry.htm

Description: Operator of ice cream shop which serves with different flavors. **Founded:** 2008. **Equity Capital Needed:** $170,750 - $392,200. **Franchise Fee:** $25,000. **Royalty Fee:** 6% of total Ssales. **Financial Assistance:** Yes **Training:** Ongoing support focuses on communication with daily email communications from operations and marketing at corporate headquarters, and 7 day a week phone support.

8618 ■ Fuzziwig's Candy Factory, Inc.
1126 Orange Ave.
  Coronado, CA 92118
Ph: (619)437-7290
URL: http://fuzziwigscandyfactory.com

Description: Offers franchise in ice cream, candy and related business. **Founded:** 1995. **Training:** Training provided at one of three locations, choose the one nearest to you. Training covers: merchandising, marketing, customer service, inventory and cost control, record keeping, pre-opening training, ongoing support, regional and national meetings, web site support with current trends in the business.

8619 ■ The Haoagen-Dazs Shoppe Company Inc.

HDIP Inc.
500 S Washington Ave., Ste. 2040
Minneapolis, MN 55415
URL: http://www.icecream.com/us/en/brands/haagen-dazs
X (Twitter): twitter.com/HaagenDazs_US
Instagram: www.instagram.com/haagendazs_us
Pinterest: www.pinterest.com/haagendazs

Description: Operator of ice cream parlor. Also producer of ice cream products. **Founded:** 1960. **Franchised:** 1977. **Equity Capital Needed:** $164,158 -$542,408. **Franchise Fee:** $30,000. **Royalty Fee:** 4%. **Financial Assistance:** Yes **Training:** Sells various ice cream flavours.

8620 ■ Happy & Healthy Products, Inc. (H&H)

1600 S Dixie Hwy., Ste. 100
Boca Raton, FL 33432
Ph: (561)367-0739
Fax: (561)368-5267
Co. E-mail: help@happyandhealthy.com
URL: http://www.happyandhealthy.com
Contact: Linda Kerr Kamm, Founder
Facebook: www.facebook.com/happyandhealthyproducts
Instagram: www.instagram.com/happyandhealthyproducts

Description: 100% natural frozen fruit bars. **Founded:** 1991. **Training:** Yes.

8621 ■ Happy Joe's Pizza and Ice Cream

5239 Grand Ave.
Davenport, IA 52807
Ph: (563)332-8811
Co. E-mail: contact@happyjoes.com
URL: http://happyjoes.com
Contact: Thomas Sacco, Chief Executive Officer
Facebook: www.facebook.com/HappyJoes
Linkedin: www.linkedin.com/company/happy-joes-pizza
X (Twitter): x.com/HappyJoesPizza
Instagram: www.instagram.com/happyjoespizza

Description: Operator of pizza restaurant. **Founded:** 1972. **Equity Capital Needed:** Full Size?/?PIZZA-GRILLE ($310,250 - $1,045,625); Delivery?/?Carry-out Only ($189,00 - $358,000). **Franchise Fee:** $25,000-$30,000. **Royalty Fee:** 4.5%-5% of Sales. **Training:** Yes.

8622 ■ Hogi Yogi

501 E Citrus Ave. D
Redlands, CA 92373
Ph: (909)793-7766
URL: http://www.hogiyogiredlands.com
Facebook: www.facebook.com/people/Hogi-Yogi-of-Redlands/100063764732056

Description: Chain of restaurants serving sandwiches and frozen yogurt. **No. of Operating Units:** 70. **Founded:** 1989. **Franchised:** 1993. **Training:** Fast food industry that sells sandwiches and frozen yogurt.

8623 ■ Juiceblendz International

16700 Creek Bend Dr.
Sugar Land, TX 77478
Contact: Albino R. Sachango, Secretary

Description: Juice. **Founded:** 2005. **Franchised:** 1005. **Training:** Yes.

8624 ■ Kohr Bros. Frozen Custard and Smoothie Station

2151 Richmond Rd., Ste. 200
Charlottesville, VA 22911
Ph: (434)975-1500
URL: http://www.kohrbros.com

Description: Producer of homemade ice creams. **Founded:** 1919. **Equity Capital Needed:** $75,000 in liquid assets and $300,000 net worth. **Training:** Yes.

8625 ■ La Paletera Franchise Systems Inc.

3200 S W Fwy., Ste. 2700
Houston, TX 77027
Contact: Clayton D. Johnson, President

Description: La Paletera is a food centre, which provides ice cream, yogurt, smoothies, fruit bars, candy and beverages. **No. of Franchise Units:** 30. **No. of Company-Owned Units:** 1. **Founded:** 1997. **Franchised:** 2003. **Equity Capital Needed:** $45,000-$60,000. **Franchise Fee:** $28,000. **Financial Assistance:** Yes **Training:** Yes.

8626 ■ La Paloma Gelateria & Cafe

1357 St., Clair Ave., W
Toronto, ON, Canada M6E 1C5
Ph: (416)656-9900
URL: http://lapaloma.ca

Description: Operator of ice cream shop. **Founded:** 1967. **Training:** 2 weeks pre-opening at corporate head office.

8627 ■ Marble Slab Creamery

Calgary, AB, Canada
Free: 888-337-7522
Co. E-mail: customerservice@marbleslab.ca
URL: http://www.marbleslab.ca
Contact: Amarjot Bhatthal, Contact
Facebook: www.facebook.com/MarbleSlabCan
Instagram: www.instagram.com/marbleslabcanada
Pinterest: www.pinterest.com/marbleslabcan

Description: Chain of franchise stores offers ice cream, desserts, cakes, cones and much more. **Founded:** 1983. **Equity Capital Needed:** $12,000-$120,000. **Franchise Fee:** $25,000. **Royalty Fee:** 0.06. **Training:** 11-day extensive interactive training provided.

8628 ■ Marble Slab Creamery Inc.

Global Franchise Group L.L.C. (GFG)
5555 Glenridge Connector, Ste. 850
Atlanta, GA 30342
Ph: (770)514-4500
Free: 800-524-6444
Fax: (770)514-4903
Co. E-mail: franchiseinfo@gfgmanagement.com
URL: http://www.globalfranchise.com
Facebook: www.facebook.com/marbleslabcreameryofficial
X (Twitter): x.com/marbleslab

Description: Marble Slab Creamery is a unique concept where ice cream is actually made fresh daily at each store. Customers can create their own ice cream fantasies by combining any flavor of superpremium ice cream with 'mixins' such as fresh fruit, candy, cookies or nuts. The ice cream & mixins are then folded together on a frozen marble slab & served on a freshly baked waffle cone. Other products include non-fat yogurt, ice cream pies/cakes, specialty coffees & bakery items. **Founded:** 1983. **Equity Capital Needed:** Investment level is $100,000 ; net worth requirement of $250,000. **Franchise Fee:** $30,000. **Financial Assistance:** No Managerial Assistance: Maintains an ongoing business relationship with its franchisees, with assistance available in all phases of store operations. A complete operations manual is provided to all franchisees. Company field personnel visit stores on a regular basis to insure co. **Training:** Marble Slab Creamery offers assistance in site selection, lease negotiation, architectural layout and construction supervision. There is a required 10 day training program in Houston, Texas, store opening assistance, continued field supervision and adver.

8629 ■ Mini Melts Inc.

245 Asylum St.
Norwich, CT 06360
Ph: (860)889-7300
Co. E-mail: info@minimelts.com
URL: http://www.minimelts.com
Contact: Dan Kilcoyne, President
Facebook: www.facebook.com/MiniMelts
Linkedin: www.linkedin.com/company/mini-melts-of-america
X (Twitter): x.com/minimelts
Instagram: www.instagram.com/minimeltsusa

Description: Mini Melts ice cream product. **Founded:** 1999. **Training:** Yes.

8630 ■ Mister Softee Inc.

901 E Clements Bridge Rd.
Runnemede, NJ 08078
Ph: (856)939-4103
Co. E-mail: info@mistersoftee.com
URL: http://mistersoftee.com
Contact: Jim Conway, Jr., Owner
Facebook: www.facebook.com/Mister-Softee-16245239055
Instagram: www.instagram.com/mrsofteetruck

Description: Retails soft ice cream from vehicles. **No. of Franchise Units:** 350. **Founded:** 1958. **Financial Assistance:** Yes **Training:** Yes.

8631 ■ Paciugo Gelato Caffe

1215 Viceroy Dr.
Dallas, TX 75247
Ph: (214)631-2663
Fax: (214)654-9991
Co. E-mail: info@paciugo.com
URL: http://paciugo.com
Contact: Ugo Ginatta, Founder
Facebook: www.facebook.com/Paciugo
X (Twitter): x.com/paciugogelato
Instagram: www.instagram.com/paciugo

Description: Gelato is a traditional Italian ice cream that serves as a sweet, premium alternative to traditional frozen treats. **No. of Operating Units:** 50. **Founded:** 1999. **Franchised:** 2004. **Equity Capital Needed:** $226,300-$442,800; $216,300-$330,800; $100,000-$297,800; $88,500-$141,500. **Franchise Fee:** $30,000. **Royalty Fee:** 4.5% of weekly Gross Sales. **Training:** Yes.

8632 ■ Planet Smoothie

2014 Powers Ferry Rd. SE, Ste. 350
Atlanta, GA 30339
Ph: (770)859-0080
URL: http://www.planetsmoothie.com
Facebook: www.facebook.com/planetsmoothie
X (Twitter): x.com/planetsmoothie
Instagram: www.instagram.com/planetsmoothie

Description: Chain of smoothie stores. **Founded:** 1995. **Training:** Raving Brands University classroom and on-site training provided. From register to food preparation, from hiring staff to accounting procedures, you'll improve your management skills, set-up your back office and develop an airtight sales and marketing plan.

8633 ■ Rita's Italian Ice

3610 Bristol Rd.
Bensalem, PA 19020
Ph: (215)757-5333
URL: http://www.ritasice.com
Contact: Linda Chadwick, President
Facebook: www.facebook.com/RitasItalianIceCompany
X (Twitter): x.com/ritasitalianice

Description: Italian ice, custard, and gelatin. **No. of Franchise Units:** 600. **Founded:** 1984. **Franchised:** 1989. **Equity Capital Needed:** $100,000 liquid; $300,000 net worth. **Franchise Fee:** $25,000. **Financial Assistance:** Yes **Training:** Training is divided into two phases, with 6 days at a corporate training center and 2 days at the franchisee's location for the grand opening. Training covers production, quality control, advertising concepts and strategies and general business practices.

8634 ■ Shake's Frozen Custard Inc.

PO Box 8700
Fayetteville, AR 72703
Ph: (479)444-9777
URL: http://shakesfrozencustard.com
Facebook: www.facebook.com/scoopshakes

Description: Frozen custard. **Founded:** 1991. **Franchised:** 1999. **Training:** 2 weeks at headquarters, 1 week at franchisee's location and ongoing support.

8635 ■ Smoothie King

1412 N Hwy. 190
Covington, LA 70433
Ph: (985)809-9722
Free: 800-577-4200
URL: http://www.smoothieking.com
Facebook: www.facebook.com/SmoothieKing
X (Twitter): x.com/SmoothieKing
Instagram: www.instagram.com/smoothieking

YouTube: www.youtube.com/channel/UCvy
dHFk0PuOLmqekEo18a4A

Pinterest: www.pinterest.com/smoothiekingus

Description: Offers guests the industry's first, original nutritional fruit and function based fresh-blended smoothies. **Founded:** 1989. **Financial Assistance:** Yes **Training:** Provides 1 day pre-opening (orientation), 14 days management training at Corporate store, 8 days store opening (14 days before open & 4 days after opening) onsite. Assistance in real estate, design and construction. **Educational Activities:** Multi-Unit Foodservice Operators Conference (MUFSO) (Annual).

8636 ■ Son's

319 W State St.
Quarryville, PA 17566
Ph: (717)786-5665
URL: http://sonsice.com
Contact: Jason Mencer, Owner
Facebook: www.facebook.com/SonsQuarryville

Description: Provides fruit carvings and chocolate fountains. **Founded:** 2003. **Training:** Yes.

8637 ■ Surf City Squeeze

9311 E Via de Ventura
Scottsdale, AZ 85258
Ph: (480)362-4800
Free: 866-452-4252
Fax: (480)362-4812
URL: http://www.surfcitysqueeze.com
Facebook: www.facebook.com/SurfCitySmoothies
X (Twitter): x.com/surfcitysqueeze

Description: The franchise caters ice cream, yogurt, smoothies, candy and beverages. **Founded:** 1981. **Franchised:** 1981. **Equity Capital Needed:** $77,600-$286,750. **Franchise Fee:** $30,000. **Royalty Fee:** 6% of gross sales. **Financial Assistance:** Yes **Training:** Provides 1 week training at headquarters, 2 weeks at franchisee's location, and ongoing support.

8638 ■ TCBY

2274 S 1300 E
Salt Lake City, UT 84106
Free: 800-348-6311
URL: http://www.tcby.com
Contact: Paul Correale, Director, Development
E-mail: pcorreale@famousbrandsintl.com
Facebook: www.facebook.com/tcby
X (Twitter): x.com/tcby

Description: Chain of yogurt shops that provides yogurt, toppings, shakes and malts. Also provides catering services. **Founded:** 1981. **Franchised:** 1982. **Equity Capital Needed:** net worth of at least $200k with at least $100k being liquid; Single Unit ($100,000 liquid assets, $250,000 net worth); Multi-Unit ($250,000 liquid assets, $500,000 net worth). **Franchise Fee:** $35,000. **Royalty Fee:** 6% of Gross Sales. **Financial Assistance:** No **Training:** Yes.

8639 ■ Tropical Smoothie Cafe, LLC

1117 Perimeter Center W, Ste. W200
Atlanta, GA 30338
Ph: (770)821-1900
URL: http://www.tropicalsmoothiecafe.com
Facebook: www.facebook.com/tropicalsmoothiecafe
Linkedin: www.linkedin.com/company/tropical-smoo
thie-cafe
X (Twitter): x.com/TSmoothieCafe
YouTube: www.youtube.com/channel/UCf6pHZ4g6oY
tjSy3Mjar5BQ
Pinterest: www.pinterest.com/tropicalsmoothiecafe

Description: Restaurant chain offering nutritional smoothies. **Founded:** 1997. **Training:** Comprehensive training on operations, marketing & management of your business.

8640 ■ Wienerschnitzel

Galardi Group Inc.
8950 Montecito Ave.
Atascadero, CA 93422
Contact: John Galardi, Founder
Facebook: www.facebook.com/Wienerschnitzel
X (Twitter): twitter.com/Wienerschnitzel
Instagram: www.instagram.com/wienerschnitzel/
YouTube: www.youtube.com/user/mostwantedwiener/
videos

Description: Fast food, including soft-serve ice cream and desserts. **Founded:** 1950. **Financial Assistance:** Yes **Training:** Consists of 2 weeks at the corporate office - total operation and business training given.

8641 ■ Yogen Fruz (YF)

210 Shields Ct.
Markham, ON, Canada L3R 8V2
Ph: (905)479-8762
Co. E-mail: info@yogenfruz.com
URL: http://yogenfruz.com
Facebook: www.facebook.com/yogenfruz
Instagram: www.instagram.com/yogenfruz
YouTube: www.youtube.com/user/yogenfruz

Description: Producer of frozen yogurt, froyo smoothie. **Founded:** 1986. **Equity Capital Needed:** $150,000-$250,000. **Franchise Fee:** $25,000. **Royalty Fee:** 6%. **Financial Assistance:** Yes **Training:** Offers 1 week at headquarters and 1 week onsite.

INTERNET DATABASES

8642 ■ *We Scream for Ice Cream: An Industry Guide*

Description: Provides links for researching the ice cream industry in the United States. Also includes resources for the dairy industry. **Availability:** Online.

ASSOCIATIONS AND OTHER ORGANIZATIONS

8643 ■ Association of Image Consultants International (AICI)
7794 Grow Dr.
  Pensacola, FL 32514
Ph: (615)290-7468
Fax: (850)484-8762
Co. E-mail: info@aici.org
URL: http://www.aici.org
Contact: Lilian Bustamante, President
E-mail: president@aici.org
Facebook: www.facebook.com/AICIglobalofficial
Linkedin: www.linkedin.com/company/oficialaici
Instagram: www.instagram.com/aiciglobal
YouTube: www.youtube.com/channel/UCXeEOeqDj tP5ih8l_xE8L5w

Description: Promotes quality service for clients; aids in establishing working relations between retail stores and consultants; assists community colleges in offering accredited image consulting programs; maintains standards of professionalism for members in the image consulting industry. Provides continuing education and training. **Scope:** A non profit professional association of men and women specializing in visual appearance and verbal and non-verbal communication. Members counsel both individual and corporate clients on appearance, behavior and communication skills to help achieve their specific goals with authenticity, credibility and confidence. **Founded:** 1990. **Educational Activities:** AICI Global Conference (Biennial). **Awards:** IMMIE Awards - Education (Periodic). **Geographic Preference:** National.

REFERENCE WORKS

8644 ■ "1914 Proved to Be Key Year for Chevy" in Automotive News (Vol. 86, October 31, 2011, No. 6488, pp. S18)
Pub: Crain Communications Inc.
Contact: Barry Asin, President

Ed: Jamie LaReau. **Description:** Chevy Bow Tie emblem was born in 1914, creating the brand's image that has carried through to current days. **Availability:** Print; Online.

8645 ■ "American Airlines Works to Keep Its Brand Aloft" in Dallas Business Journal (Vol. 35, May 18, 2012, No. 36, pp. 1)
Pub: Baltimore Business Journal
Contact: Rhonda Pringle, President
E-mail: rpringle@bizjournals.com

Ed: Matt Joyce. **Description:** As American Airlines is undergoing restructuring, the company is planning to redesign its international aircraft as part of its marketing strategy. But the airline's efforts to improve its brand image present a challenge made difficult by labor relations. Labor unions representing American Airlines employees are fighting the company over their collective bargaining agreements. **Availability:** Print; Online.

8646 ■ "Another California Firm Moving to Austin" in Austin Business Journal (Vol. 31, May 6, 2011, No. 9, pp. 1)
Pub: Austin Business Journal
Contact: Rachel McGrath, Director
E-mail: rmcgrath@bizjournals.com

Ed: Christopher Calnan. **Description:** Main Street Hub Inc. is planning to build a facility in Austin, Texas. The company helps businesses manage their online reputations. Main Street has selected Aquila Commercial LLC as its real estate broker. **Availability:** Print; Online.

8647 ■ "Baseline Metrics CEOs Need for Online Brand Oversight" in South Florida Business Journal (Vol. 34, May 23, 2014, No. 44, pp. 16)
Pub: American City Business Journals, Inc.
Contact: Mike Olivieri, Executive Vice President

Released: Weekly. **Price:** $8, Introductory 4-week offer(Digital & Print). **Description:** Chief executive officers have the option to use metrics that will allow them to monitor their online brands. Social media engagement is an effective customer service metric because it presents a clear assessment of a business social media prowess. Reputation management software, on the other hand, ranks a firm's weekly, hourly, and daily sentiments online. **Availability:** Print; Online.

8648 ■ "The Buck Stops Here" in Canadian Business (Vol. 81, November 10, 2008, No. 19, pp. 25)
Ed: Sarka Halas. **Description:** Reputation strategist Leslie Gaines-Ross says that minimizing the damage followed by the identification of what went wrong are the first steps that companies need to take when trying to salvage their reputation. Gaines-Ross states that it is up to the CEO to ensure the company's speedy recovery and they need to be at the forefront of the process. **Availability:** Online.

8649 ■ "Buckhead Image Consultant Takes Time to Know Clients" in Northside Neighbor (August 4, 2017)
URL(s): www.mdjonline.com/neighbor_newspapers/ northside_sandy_springs/buckhead-image-consul tant-takes-time-to-know-clients/article_34ea82ae-79 39-11e7-a971-5b85e80a8dca.html
Ed: Bill Baldowski. **Released:** August 04, 2017. **Description:** Profile of Beryl Pleasants, owner of Style With Aplomb. She's an image consultant who specializes in wardrobe choices to suit professionals in any industry and circumstance. **Availability:** Online.

8650 ■ "Column: It's Time to Take Full Responsibility" in Harvard Business Review (Vol. 88, October 2010, No. 10, pp. 42)
Pub: Harvard Business Publishing
Contact: Diane Belcher, Managing Director

Ed: Rosabeth Moss Kanter. **Price:** $6, PDF. **Description:** A case for corporate responsibility is cited, focusing on long-term impact and the effects of public accountability. **Availability:** Online; PDF.

8651 ■ "Communication Strategies for Enhancing Perceived Fit in the CSR Sponsorship Context" in International Journal of Advertising (Vol. 31, February 2012, No. 1, pp. 133)
Ed: Yong Seok Sohn, Jin K. Han, Sung-Hack Lee. **Released:** 2012. **Description:** Engaging in corporate social responsibility (CSR) is becoming an increasingly common business practice globally and across industries. By contributing to societal welfare, firms can also enhance their corporate image among its stakeholders, in particular, its customers. For CSR to generate goodwill, consumers generally need to perceive a fit between the sponsoring firm and its CSR. Otherwise, consumers may second-guess the firm's intrinsic CSR motives, which may even evoke a negative reaction. **Availability:** Print; Online.

8652 ■ "Deskside Story: As the Latest Buzzword Suggests, PR Firms Are Happy To Drop By" in Inc. (December 2007, pp. 70, 73)
Ed: Nitasha Tiku. **Description:** Setting up a meeting between a company's CEO and a journalist is known as deskside and is becoming popular again whereby a publicist offers clients deskside visits, briefings and alerts to help promote public relations for a company. **Availability:** Print; Online.

8653 ■ "Empowered" in Harvard Business Review (Vol. 88, July-August 2010, No. 7-8, pp. 94)
Pub: Harvard Business Publishing
Contact: Diane Belcher, Managing Director

Ed: Josh Bernoff, Ted Schadler. **Price:** $8.95, PDF. **Description:** HERO concept (highly empowered and resourceful operative) which builds a connection between employees, managers, and IT is outlined. The resultant additional experience and knowledge gained by employees improves customer relationship management. **Availability:** Online; PDF.

8654 ■ "Enhancing Brand Image Via Sponsorship: Strength of Association Effects" in International Journal of Advertising (Vol. 31, February 2012, No. 1, pp. 113)
Ed: Srdan Zdravkovic, Brian D. Till. **Released:** 2012. **Price:** $42.50. **Description:** Despite the increased usage of sponsorship activities by practitioners, there has been little research on the impact of sponsorship on building brand image. This research examines the influence of sponsorship on associations transfer from sponsored entity to the sponsor. **Availability:** Print; Online.

8655 ■ "Exporting Portlandia: Unconventional Brands Carry a Taste of Portland Across U.S." in Business Journal Portland (Vol. 30, January 17, 2014, No. 46, pp. 4)
Pub: American City Business Journals, Inc.
Contact: Mike Olivieri, Executive Vice President

Description: Some Portland, Oregon-based food companies have been bringing the area's reputation across the U.S. Voodoo Doughnut has opened a branch in Denver, Colorado. Meanwhile, Laughing Planet is opening several West Coast cafes. **Availability:** Print; Online.

8656 ■ "The HBR Interview: "We Had to Own the Mistakes"" in Harvard Business Review (Vol. 88, July-August 2010, No. 7-8, pp. 108)
Pub: Harvard Business Publishing
Contact: Diane Belcher, Managing Director
Ed: Adi Ignatius. **Description:** Interview with Howard Schultz, CEO of Starbucks, covers topics that include investment in retraining, the impact of competition, premium quality, authenticity, customer services, strategy development, work-and-life issues, and international presence. **Availability:** Online.

8657 ■ "Hennelly Aims to Increase Building Work in Great Lakes Region for Ryan Cos." in Crain's Chicago Business (Vol. 34, May 23, 2011, No. 21, pp. 6)
Pub: Crain Communications Inc.
Contact: Barry Asin, President
Ed: Eddie Baeb. **Description:** Profile of Tim Hennelly, who is working to make Ryan Company known as a pure builder rather than a developer-builder. **Availability:** Print; Online.

8658 ■ "Hopkins' Security, Reputation Face Challenges in Wake of Slaying" in Baltimore Business Journal (Vol. 28, August 6, 2010, No. 13)
Pub: Baltimore Business Journal
Contact: Rhonda Pringle, President
E-mail: rpringle@bizjournals.com
Ed: Gary Haber. **Description:** The slaying of Johns Hopkins University researcher Stephen Pitcairn has not tarnished the reputation of the elite school in Baltimore, Maryland among students. Maintaining Hopkins' reputation is important since it is Baltimore's largest employer with nearly 32,000 workers. Insights on the impact of the slaying among the Hopkins' community are also given.

8659 ■ "How Do You Measure Your PR's Return On Investment?" in Puget Sound Business Journal (Vol. 34, March 21, 2014, No. 49, pp. 9)
Pub: American City Business Journals, Inc.
Contact: Mike Olivieri, Executive Vice President
Description: The process of measuring public relations and its return on investment (ROI) is difficult because not all expenditures are directed towards media relations and public image. Public relations covers leadership programs, speaking engagements, and word of mouth campaigns. The possibility of linking PR efforts towards bottom line marketing as a goal is discussed. **Availability:** Online.

8660 ■ "How I Did It: Timberland's CEO On Standing Up to 65,000 Angry Activists" in Harvard Business Review (Vol. 88, September 2010, No. 9, pp. 39)
Pub: Harvard Business Publishing
Contact: Diane Belcher, Managing Director
Ed: Jeff Swartz. **Price:** $8.95, PDF. **Description:** Timberland Company avoided a potential boycott by taking a two-way approach. It addressed a supplier issue that posed a threat to the environment, and launched an email campaign to keep Greenpeace activists informed of the development of a new supplier agreement. **Availability:** Online; PDF.

8661 ■ If You Have to Cry, Go Outside: And Other Things Your Mother Never Told You
Pub: HarperCollins Publishers L.L.C.
Contact: Brian Murray, President
Ed: Kelly Cutrone, Meredith Bryan. **Released:** February 02, 2010. **Price:** $10.99, e-book; $7.24, e-book. **Description:** Women's mentor advices on how to make it in one of the most competitive industries in the world, fashion. She has kicked people out of fashion shows, forced some of reality television's shiny start to fire their friends, and built her own

company which is one of the most powerful public relations firms in the fashion business. **Availability:** E-book; Print.

8662 ■ "Image Consultants" in Entrepreneur (June 2014)
Pub: Entrepreneur Media Inc.
Contact: Dan Bova, Director
E-mail: dbova@entrepreneur.com
Description: The ASAP54 mobile application, created by a company of the same name, uses visual recognition technology to help users determine the name of the designer or retailer of a clothing item using photographs. The company has compiled a database consisting of more than 1 million products from its retail partners. It claims an average of 5 percent commission on purchases completed through the application. Other useful wearable gadgets include Nymi, which authenticates identities based on cardiac rhythms, and Netatmo, a bracelet that measures daily sun exposure. **Availability:** Online.

8663 ■ "The Image Management Function of Sponsorship: A General Theoretical Framework" in International Journal of Advertising (Vol. 31, February 2012, No. 1, pp. 85)
Ed: Kihan Kim, Patricia A. Stout, Yunjae Cheong. **Released:** 2012. **Price:** $42.50. **Description:** A general framework to understand how sponsorship affects the image of the sponsor has been developed from the information-processing perspective. According to this framework, sponsorship information is processed in one of two relatively distinct modes of processing: holistic and analytic, depending on the amount of processing resources available to consumer. Implications of this marketing research is provided. **Availability:** Print; Online.

8664 ■ Media, Organizations and Identity
Pub: Palgrave Macmillan
Released: First edition. **Description:** The mass media, press, and television are essential in the formation of corporate identity and the promotion of business image and reputation. This book offers a new perspective into the interrelationships between media and organizations over three dimensions: media as business, media in business and business in the media.

8665 ■ "Offer Your Own Authentic Truth" in South Florida Business Journal (Vol. 34, July 25, 2014, No. 53, pp. 13)
Pub: American City Business Journals, Inc.
Contact: Mike Olivieri, Executive Vice President
Released: Weekly. **Price:** $8, introductory 4-week offer(Digital only). **Description:** Turkel Brands CEO, Bruce Turkel, was born in Miami Beach, Florida and has a bachelor's degree in design at the University of Florida. Turkel was a respected advertising agency owner and executive creative director before he began blogging on marketing and branding. He shares three tips for building a brand and creating a positive public image. **Availability:** Print; Online.

8666 ■ "Optima Public Relations Gains Partners" in Alaska Business Monthly (Vol. 27, October 2011, No. 10, pp. 10)
Pub: Alaska Business Publishing Company Inc.
Contact: Charles Bell, Vice President, Sales and Marketing
E-mail: cbell@akbizmag.com
Ed: Nancy Pounds. **Description:** Optima Public Relations has partnered with Gogerty Marriott of Seattle and Seattle Design Group. **Availability:** Print; Online.

8667 ■ "Q&A: PSU's Tom Gillpatrick on How Quirkiness Gives Portland Its Edge" in Business Journal Portland (Vol. 30, January 17, 2014, No. 46, pp. 6)
Pub: American City Business Journals, Inc.
Contact: Mike Olivieri, Executive Vice President
Released: Weekly. **Price:** $4, introductory 4-week offer(Digital only). **Description:** Portland State University Food Industry Leadership Center executive director, Tom Gillpatrick, says consumers now

prefer healthier food brands. He also stated the Portland, Oregon's food sector has grown owing to that trend. Gillpatrick added that the state's reputation for being different has also helped the sector. **Availability:** Print; Online.

8668 ■ "Reputation Warfare" in Harvard Business Review (Vol. 88, December 2010, No. 12, pp. 70)
Pub: Harvard Business Publishing
Contact: Diane Belcher, Managing Director
Ed: Leslie Gaines-Ross. **Price:** $8.95, PDF. **Description:** Steps are presented for addressing attacks on corporate public image. These include responding promptly, avoiding disproportionate displays of force, empowering employees to present the firm's position, and stockpiling credentials to bolster credence. **Availability:** Online; PDF.

8669 ■ "Toss the Gum Before You Speak and Other Tips for Presenting to a Potential Principal" in Agency Sales Magazine (Vol. 39, July 2009, No. 7, pp. 34)
Description: When preparing to present to a prospective principal, a salesperson should anticipate the speaking situation and find out in advance the program events that occur around their speech. They should also practice their material in front of a friend or colleague. **Availability:** Online.

8670 ■ "Voice: Rebuilding Trust" in Business Strategy Review (Vol. 21, Summer 2010, No. 2, pp. 79-80)
Ed: David De Cremer. **Released:** June 24, 2010. **Description:** The financial world's attempts to rebuild trust are charted. Three steps to jump-start that process are outlined. **Availability:** Print; PDF; Online.

8671 ■ When the Headline Is You: An Insider's Guide to Handling the Media
Pub: Jossey-Bass
Ed: Jeff Ansell, Jeff Lesson. **Released:** August 01, 2010. **Price:** $29.95, hardcover; $29.95, hardcover. **Description:** How-to guide for executives and other professionals whose high-visibility requires frequent interviews with the media. Tested techniques, tools, and insights for how to respond to all types of media in tough situation are provided. The book also reveals the lessons learned and the pitfalls to avoid by referencing actual news stores from around the world and provides exercises for readers who wish to sharpen their media-handling skills. **Availability:** E-book; Print.

8672 ■ "Why Does Firm Reputation In Human Resource Policies Influence College Students? The Mechanisms Underlying Job Pursuit Intentions" in Human Resource Management (Vol. 51, January-February 2012, No. 1, pp. 121-142)
Pub: John Wiley & Sons, Inc.
Contact: Christina Van Tassell, Executive Vice President Chief Financial Officer
Ed: Julie Holliday Wayne, Wendy J. Casper. **Released:** January 26, 2012. **Description:** The effects of reputational information about human resource practices of companies on college students seeking employment are examined. The reputation of firms in compensation, work-family, and diversity efforts are found to increase intentions to pursue employment in these firms. **Availability:** Print; PDF; Online.

8673 ■ "Why Marketing Slogans Matter" in Canadian Business (Vol. 85, June 11, 2012, No. 10, pp. 18)
Ed: Bruce Philp. **Description:** Slogans earn their meaning in popular culture through dramatic beginnings and repetition over the years so marketers should consider whether the brand can earn it before replacing the tag lines. People in the branding business should not use the tag line exercise as a substitute for creating a strategy. **Availability:** Online.

CONSULTANTS

8674 ■ Bixler Consulting Group
400 Galleria Pky., Ste. 1500
Atlanta, GA 30339

Ph: (404)372-4469
Co. E-mail: info@bixlerconsulting.com
URL: http://bixlerconsulting.com
Contact: Susan Bixler, Chief Executive Officer
Description: Firm provides executive coaching, leadership workshops, and career transitioning programs to enable individuals and organizations to excel in a highly competitive, transforming marketplace, and their target audience are mid-level to senior level leaders, and serves private industries as well as government agencies. **Scope:** Firm provides executive coaching, leadership workshops, and career transitioning programs to enable individuals and organizations to excel in a highly competitive, transforming marketplace, and their target audience are mid-level to senior level leaders, and serves private industries as well as government agencies. **Founded:** 1980. **Publications:** "Professional Presence"; "Take Action!"; "The Professional Image"; "5 Steps to Professional Presence"; "Remaining professional can be more important than the latest fashion"; "Body language can speak volumes during interview," Feb, 2003; "Gift-giving takes careful thought - Don't turn gesture into a faux pas," Dec, 2002; "Role Models," Apr, 2002; "Laugh break can benefit all As seen in The Atlanta Journal-Constitution," Apr, 2002; "E-mail Etiquette," Sep, 2002; "Gaining Co-Workers' Respect," Jan, 2000; "Are You Ignoring Your Rising Stars?". **Training:** Team Building Workshop; Professional Presence Workshop; The Business Case for Leadership Workshops; The 360-Degree Feedback Workshop. **Special Services:** 360-Degree Feedback Report.

8675 ■ The Rothschild Image

13900 Tahiti Way, Ste. 308
  Marina del Rey, CA 90292
Ph: (310)574-6018
Co. E-mail: info@rothschildimage.com
URL: http://www.rothschildimage.com
Contact: Ashley Rothschild, Founder

Description: Provider of VIP consulting, corporate seminars, and training services. **Scope:** Provider of VIP consulting, corporate seminars, and training services. **Publications:** "Is There an O'Neal Family Curse? - ABC News," Feb, 2007; "Can an Image Consultant Help You Dress for Success? - Wall Street Journal," Feb, 2006; "Reality Check - Paris Hilton and Amber Moore," Jan, 2004; "Britney's Mystery Man - Britney Spears," Dec, 2003; "People who need to redo their image," Jun, 2003; "Reshaping an Image," Jun, 2003; "Dress to Impress the World International Business Fashion," Apr, 2003. **Training:** S.T.A.R.POWER: A Professional Image Consultant Training Program; Learn How to Have More Success, Power and Romance in Your Life.

START-UP INFORMATION

8676 ■ *"Savvy Solutions" in Black Enterprise (Vol. 41, December 2010, No. 5, pp. 42)*
Pub: Earl G. Graves Ltd.
Contact: Earl Graves, Jr., President
Ed: Tennille M. Robinson. **Description:** Individual asks for advice in launching a graphic design business, particularly grants available in a slow economy.

ASSOCIATIONS AND OTHER ORGANIZATIONS

8677 ■ American Association of Exporters and Importers (AAEI) - Essential Library
1717 K St. NW, Ste. 1120
Washington, DC 20006
Ph: (202)857-8009
Fax: (202)857-7843
Co. E-mail: hq@aaei.org
URL: http://aaei.org
Contact: Eugene Laney, Jr., President
Facebook: www.facebook.com/AAEITrade
Linkedin: www.linkedin.com/company/american
-association-of-exporters-and-importers
X (Twitter): x.com/aaeitrade
Description: Exporters and importers of goods, products, and raw materials; wholesalers and retailers; customs brokers and forwarders; banks; insurance underwriters; steamship companies; customs attorneys and others engaged directly or indirectly in dealing with exports and imports. **Scope:** Harmonized tariff schedule; international trade references; food & drug industry CFR set; international trade CFR set. **Founded:** 1921. **Holdings:** Figures not available. **Publications:** *International Trade Alert* (Weekly); *American Association of Exporters and Importers-- Membership Directory* (Irregular). **Geographic Preference:** National.

8678 ■ National Association of Export Companies (NEXCO)
396 Broadway, Ste. 603
New York, NY 10013
Description: Established independent international trade firms, bilateral chambers of commerce, banks, law firms, accounting firms, trade associations, insurance companies, and product/service providers; export trading companies; export management companies. Promotes expansion of U.S. trade. Promotes the participation of members in international trade. Conducts educational programs. **Founded:** 1963. **Geographic Preference:** National.

8679 ■ National Foreign Trade Council (NFTC)
1225 New York Ave. NW, Ste. 650B
Washington, DC 20006
Ph: (202)887-0278
Fax: (202)452-8160
Co. E-mail: nftcinformation@nftc.org
URL: http://www.nftc.org/?id=1
Contact: Jake Colvin, President

X (Twitter): x.com/NFTC
Description: Represents U.S. firms by advocating an open rules-based world economy through education, policy leadership, and championing of legislation. **Founded:** 1914. **Awards:** NFTC World Trade Award (Annual). **Geographic Preference:** National.

8680 ■ Small Business Exporters Association of the United States (SBEA)
Washington, DC
Ph: (202)552-2903
Free: 800-345-6728
Co. E-mail: info@sbea.org
URL: http://www.sbea.org
Contact: Jim Morrison, President
Description: Exporters with fewer than 500 employees, banks, insurance underwriters, carriers, custom brokers, trade associations, trade clubs, researchers, students, and individuals employed by federal or state agencies. Promotes interests of small and mid-size export companies. Informs public and governmental agencies of small business concerns and issues. Disseminates information to members on legislation that influences small export companies. Offers information on marketplace opportunities. Conducts educational and research programs. Operates extensive, interactive website. **Founded:** 1937. **Geographic Preference:** National.

8681 ■ U.S.-China Business Council (USCBC)
1818 N St. NW, Ste. 200
Washington, DC 20036
Ph: (202)429-0340
Fax: (202)775-2476
Co. E-mail: info@uschina.org
URL: http://www.uschina.org
Contact: Craig Allen, President
Facebook: www.facebook.com/USChinaBusiness
X (Twitter): x.com/USChinaBusiness
Description: Represents American companies trading with and investing in the People's Republic of China (PRC). Established to facilitate the development of U.S.-China business relations. Provides representation, practical assistance, and up-to-date information to members. Provides business advisory services and sponsors briefings on China trade and investment subjects for member firms. Maintains offices in Washington, DC, in Beijing, and Shanghai. **Founded:** 1973. **Publications:** *The China Business Review; China Market Intelligence* (Weekly); *China Business Review; American Firms Importing from the People's Republic of China.* **Geographic Preference:** National.

8682 ■ United States Council for International Business (USCIB)
1212 Avenue of the Americas
New York, NY 10036
Ph: (212)354-4480
Fax: (212)575-0327
Co. E-mail: info@uscib.org
URL: http://uscib.org
Contact: Whitney Y. Baird, President

E-mail: wbaird@uscib.org
Linkedin: www.linkedin.com/company/uscib-united-s
tates-council-for-international-business
X (Twitter): x.com/USCIB
Description: Serves as the US. National Committee of the International Chamber of Commerce. Enables multinational enterprises to operate effectively by representing their interests to intergovernmental and governmental bodies and by keeping enterprises advised of international developments having a major impact on their operations. **Founded:** 1945. **Publications:** *USCF Occasional Paper.* **Awards:** USCIB International Leadership Award (Annual). **Geographic Preference:** National.

8683 ■ World Trade Centers Association (WTCA)
World Trade Centers Association (WTCA)
115 Broadway, Ste. 1202
New York, NY 10006
Ph: (212)432-2607
Co. E-mail: wtca@wtca.org
URL: http://www.wtca.org
Contact: Mariette Mulaire, President
Facebook: www.facebook.com/wtca.org
X (Twitter): x.com/WTCA
Description: Encourages expansion of world trade and international business relationships. **Founded:** 1970. **Publications:** *World Trade Centers Association--Membership Directory* (Annual); *World Business Directory* (Annual); *WTCA News* (Monthly); *WTCA Services Directory* (Annual). **Geographic Preference:** Multinational.

EDUCATIONAL PROGRAMS

8684 ■ Import/Export Procedures and Documentation (Onsite)
Seminar Information Service Inc. (SIS)
250 El Camino Real., Ste. 112
Tustin, CA 92780
Ph: (714)508-0340
Free: 877-736-4636
Fax: (714)734-8027
Co. E-mail: info@seminarinformation.com
URL: http://www.seminarinformation.com
Contact: Catherine Bellizzi, President
URL(s): www.seminarinformation.com
Description: Obtain the skills necessary to deal with banks, freight forwarders, customs brokers, and foreign customers, as well as how to mark merchandise, use forms, licenses, and insurance documents for profitable and error-free passage. **Audience:** Importer/exporter coordinators, controllers, credit managers and traffic managers. **Principal Exhibits:** Obtain the skills necessary to deal with banks, freight forwarders, customs brokers, and foreign customers, as well as how to mark merchandise, use forms, licenses, and insurance documents for profitable and error-free passage.

DIRECTORIES OF EDUCATIONAL PROGRAMS

8685 ■ *AAPEX Export Interest Directory: 2008*
Contact: Jeremy Denton, Executive Director
E-mail: jdenton@mema.org
URL(s): www.oac-intl.orgwww.mema.org
Released: Latest edition 2008. **Price:** Free to MEMA/OESA members. **Description:** Lists U.S. companies that are interested in overseas markets, and exhibited at AAPEX 2008. **Availability:** Print.

REFERENCE WORKS

8686 ■ *"Africa Rising" in Harvard Business Review (Vol. 86, September 2008, No. 9, pp. 36)*
Pub: Harvard Business Review Press
Contact: Moderna V. Pfizer, Contact
Ed: Vijay Mahajan. **Description:** Review of the book entitled, "Africa Rising: How 900 Million African Consumers Offer More Than You Think" provides advice for marketing to those on the African continent. **Availability:** Print; Online.

8687 ■ *"All About The Benjamins" in Canadian Business (Vol. 81, September 29, 2008, No. 16, pp. 92)*
Description: Discusses real estate developer Royal Indian Raj International Corp., a company that planned to build a $3 billion "smart city" near the Bangalore airport; to this day nothing has ever been built. The company was incorporated in 1999 by Manoj C. Benjamin one investor, Bill Zack, has been sued by the developer for libel due to his website that calls the company a scam. Benjamin has had a previous case of fraud issued against him as well as a string of liabilities and lawsuits. **Availability:** Online.

8688 ■ *"Ampm Focus Has BP Working Overtime" in Crain's Chicago Business (April 28, 2008)*
Pub: Crain Communications Inc.
Contact: Barry Asin, President
Ed: John T. Slania. **Description:** Britian's oil giant BP PLC is opening its ampm convenience stores in the Chicago market and has already begun converting most of its 78 Chicago-area gas stations to ampms. The company has also started to franchise the stores to independent operators. BP is promoting the brand with both traditional and unconventional marketing techniques such s real or simulated 3D snacks embedded in bus shelter ads and an in-store Guitar Hero contest featuring finalists from a recent contest at the House of Blues. **Availability:** Online.

8689 ■ *"Betting On Volatile Materials" in Barron's (Vol. 88, July 14, 2008, No. 28, pp. M11)*
Pub: Dow Jones & Company Inc.
Contact: Almar Latour, Chief Executive Officer
Ed: John Marshall. **Description:** Economic slowdowns in the U.S., Europe and China could cause sharp short-term declines in the materials sector. The S&P Materials sector is vulnerable to shifts in the flow of funds. Statistical data included. **Availability:** Online.

8690 ■ *"Beware this Chinese Export" in Barron's (Vol. 90, August 30, 2010, No. 35, pp. 21)*
Pub: Barron's Editorial & Corporate Headquarters
Ed: Bill Alpert, Leslie P. Norton. **Description:** A look at 158 China reverse-merger stocks in the U.S. reveal that the median underperformed the index of U.S. listed Chinese companies by 75 percent in their first three years. These reverse merger stocks also lagged the Russell 2000 index of small cap stocks by 66 percent. **Availability:** Online.

8691 ■ *"Bottom-Fishing and Speed-Dating in India-How Investors Feel About the Indian Market" in Barron's (Vol. 88, March 24, 2008, No. 12, pp. M12)*
Pub: Dow Jones & Company Inc.
Contact: Almar Latour, Chief Executive Officer

Ed: Elliot Wilson. **Description:** Indian stocks have fallen hard in 2008, with Mumbai's Sensex 30 down 30 percent from its January 2008 peak of 21,000 to 14,995 in March. The India Private Equity Fair 2008 attracted 140 of the world's largest private equity firms and about 24 of India's fastest-growing corporations. Statistical data included. **Availability:** Online.

8692 ■ *"Bountiful Barrels: Where to Find $140 Trillion" in Barron's (Vol. 88, July 14, 2008, No. 28, pp. 40)*
Pub: Dow Jones & Company Inc.
Contact: Almar Latour, Chief Executive Officer
Ed: Andrew Bary. **Description:** Surge in oil prices has caused a large transfer of wealth to oil-producing countries thereby reshaping the global economy. Oil reserves of oil exporting countries are now valued at $140 trillion. Economist Stephen Jen believes that this wealth will be transformed into paper assets as these countries invest in global stocks and bonds. **Availability:** Online.

8693 ■ *"Brazil's New King of Food" in Barron's (Vol. 89, July 13, 2009, No. 28, pp. 28)*
Pub: Dow Jones & Company Inc.
Contact: Almar Latour, Chief Executive Officer
Ed: Kenneth Rapoza. **Description:** Perdigao and Sadia's merger has resulted in the creation of Brasil Foods and the shares of Brasil Foods provides a play on both Brazil's newly energized consumer economy and its role as a major commodities exporter. Brasil Foods shares could climb as much as 36 percent. **Availability:** Online.

8694 ■ *Building Wealth in China: 36 True Stories of Chinese Millionaires and How They Made Their Fortunes*
Released: April 27, 2010. **Price:** $7.99, e-book. **Description:** Thirty-six of China's most successful and innovative entrepreneurs discuss valuable lessons for growing a business in China. **Availability:** E-book.

8695 ■ *"Business Without Borders: All For One, None for All?" in Canadian Business (Vol. 83, October 12, 2010, No. 17, pp. 60)*
Pub: Rogers Media Inc.
Contact: Neil Spivak, Chief Executive Officer
Ed: Michael McCullogh. **Description:** The effect of the growth of Canada's overseas provincial trade offices on Canadian trade is discussed. Economic development commissions in the country have devised a single 'Consider Canada' campaign to pitch foreign investors. It is hoped that large cities will gain from banding together rather than competing against one another. **Availability:** Print; Online.

8696 ■ *"Calendar" in Crain's Detroit Business (Vol. 24, March 10, 2008, No. 10, pp. 21)*
Pub: Crain Communications Inc.
Contact: Barry Asin, President
Description: Listing of events in the Detroit area include conferences addressing entrepreneurialism, economic development, and women business ownership. **Availability:** Print; Online.

8697 ■ *"Canada Joins TPP Free Trade Talks" in Canadian Business (Vol. 85, August 13, 2012, No. 13, pp. 7)*
Ed: Tim Shufelt. **Description:** The decision of the Canadian government to join the Trans-Pacific Partnership (TPP) has potential economic benefits in terms of trading with China and the U.S.Failure of the World Trade Ogranization's Doha Round and the admission of the U.S. to the TPP prompted Canada to join the trade agreement. **Availability:** Print; Online.

8698 ■ *"Canada, Not China, Is Partner In Our Economic Prosperity" in Crain's Chicago Business (Vol. 31, April 14, 2008, No. 15, pp. 14)*
Pub: Crain Communications Inc.
Contact: Barry Asin, President

Ed: Paul O'Connor. **Description:** In 2005 more than $500 billion in two-way trade crossed the friendly border between the Great Lakes states and Canadian provinces and for decades Canada is every Great Lakes State's number one and growing export market. **Availability:** Online.

8699 ■ *"Cemex Paves a Global Road to Solid Growth" in Barron's (Vol. 88, March 10, 2008, No. 10, pp. 24)*
Pub: Dow Jones & Company Inc.
Contact: Almar Latour, Chief Executive Officer
Ed: Sandra Ward. **Description:** Shares of Cemex are expected to perform well with the company's expected strong performance despite fears of a US recession. The company has a diverse geographical reach and benefits from a strong worldwide demand for cement. **Availability:** Online.

8700 ■ *"Charlotte Pipe Launches Satirical Campaign" in Contractor (Vol. 57, January 2010, No. 1, pp. 6)*
Description: Charlotte Pipe and Foundry Co. launched an advertising campaign that uses social media and humor to make a point about how it can be nearly impossible to determine if imported cast iron pipes and fittings meet the same quality standards as what is made in the U.S. The campaign features 'pipe whisperers' and also spoofs pipe sniffing dogs. **Availability:** Print; Online.

8701 ■ *"Cheap Tubing Risk to Local Jobs, Execs Caution" in Pittsburgh Business Times (Vol. 33, May 23, 2014, No. 45, pp. 4)*
Pub: American City Business Journals, Inc.
Contact: Mike Olivieri, Executive Vice President
Released: Weekly. **Price:** $4, introductory 4-week offer(Digital only). **Description:** U.S. Steel Corporation requests the U.S. Department of Commerce to take action against unfairly traded steel imports in the market because thousands of jobs are at risk. At least 26,400 jobs in Pennsylvania may be affected by the unfair trading practices of foreign exporters according to the office of Governor Tom Corbett. **Availability:** Print; Online.

8702 ■ *"Cheese Is Now Idaho's Largest Export" in Idaho Business Review (August 28, 2014)*
Pub: BridgeTower Media
Contact: Adam Reinebach, President
Description: According to the Southern Idaho Economic Development Organization, cheese topped whey and dry milk powders for being the leading export for the state. Statistical details included.

8703 ■ *"China Vs the World: Whose Technology Is It?" in Harvard Business Review (Vol. 88, December 2010, No. 12, pp. 94)*
Pub: Harvard Business Publishing
Contact: Diane Belcher, Managing Director
Ed: Thomas M. Hout, Pankaj Ghemawat. **Price:** $8.95, PDF. **Description:** Examination of the regulation the Chinese government is implementing that require foreign corporations wishing to do business in the country to give up their new technologies. These regulations avoid World Trade Organization technology transfer provisions and complicate the convergence of socialism and capitalism. **Availability:** Online; PDF.

8704 ■ *"Cincinnati Business Committee's Tom Williams: Future is Now" in Business Courier (Vol. 27, August 13, 2010, No. 15, pp. 1)*
Pub: Business Courier
Ed: Lucy May. **Description:** Tom Williams, chairman of the Cincinnati Business Committee (CBC), maintains that politicians and business leaders must cooperate to ensure the competitiveness of the city for the 21st Century. Under Williams' leadership, the CBC has put emphasis on initiatives related to government efficiency, economic development, and public education. Williams' views on a proposed inland port are given. **Availability:** Print; Online.

8705 ■ *"Closed Minds and Open Skies"* in *Barron's (Vol. 88, March 10, 2008, No. 10, pp. 50)*

Pub: Dow Jones & Company Inc.

Contact: Almar Latour, Chief Executive Officer

Ed: Thomas G. Donlan. **Description:** American politicians have closed minds when it comes to fair trade. The American government must not interfere with the country's manufacturing industries or worry about outsourcing defense contracts to European aerospace company Airbus. **Availability:** Online.

8706 ■ *"Coal Train Crush Feared"* in *Puget Sound Business Journal (Vol. 33, July 6, 2012, No. 11, pp. 1)*

Pub: Baltimore Business Journal

Contact: Rhonda Pringle, President

E-mail: rpringle@bizjournals.com

Ed: Steve Wilhelm. **Description:** Coal exports are seen to take up more rail capacity in Washington. The issue was raised in connection with the proposed Gateway Pacific Terminal at Cherry Point. The planned terminal has been opposed by environmental groups. **Availability:** Print; Online.

8707 ■ *"Colorado's Ag Industry Grows Despite Flooding"* in *Denver Business Journal (Vol. 65, January 10, 2014, No. 35, pp. A6)*

Pub: American City Business Journals, Inc.

Contact: Mike Olivieri, Executive Vice President

Description: Colorado's net farm income for 2013 has fallen slightly to $1.6 billion from the record $1.7 billion in 2012 in spite of the damaging floods that affected an estimated 4,500 square miles of land. However, exports of agricultural products from Colorado to other countries are expected to hit $2 billion in 2013. Insights into the flood damage are also offered. **Availability:** Online.

8708 ■ *"Coming: Cheaper Oil and a Stronger Buck"* in *Barron's (Vol. 88, March 24, 2008, No. 12, pp. 53)*

Pub: Dow Jones & Company Inc.

Contact: Almar Latour, Chief Executive Officer

Ed: Lawrence C. Strauss. **Description:** Carl C. Weinberg, the chief economist of High Frequency Economics, forecasts that Chinese economic growth will slow down and that oil prices will drop to $80 a barrel in 2008. He also believes that the US dollar will start rising the moment the Federal Reserve stops cutting interest rates. **Availability:** Online.

8709 ■ *"Compelling Opportunities for Investors in Emerging Markets"* in *Barron's (Vol. 88, March 10, 2008, No. 10, pp. 39)*

Pub: Dow Jones & Company Inc.

Contact: Almar Latour, Chief Executive Officer

Ed: Neil A. Martin. **Description:** Michael L. Reynal, portfolio manager of Principal International Emerging Markets Fund, is bullish on the growth prospects of stocks in emerging markets. He is investing big on energy, steel, and transportation companies. **Availability:** Online.

8710 ■ *"Coping With a Shrinking Planet"* in *Agency Sales Magazine (Vol. 39, December 2009, No. 11, pp. 46)*

Description: China and India are forcing big changes in the world and are posing a huge threat to U.S. manufacturers and their sales representatives. Reps may want to consider expanding into these territories. Helping sell American products out of the country presents an opportunity for economic expansion. **Availability:** Online.

8711 ■ *"Cost Remains Top Factor In Considering Green Technology"* in *Canadian Sailings (June 30, 2008)*

Description: Improving its environmental performance remains a priority in the shipping industry; however, testing new technologies can prove difficult due to the harsh conditions that ships endure as well as installation which usually requires a dry dock. **Availability:** Online.

8712 ■ *"CPR-CN Deal to Ease Vancouver Logjam"* in *Globe & Mail (January 27, 2006, pp. B4)*

Description: In a bid to lessen West coast port grid lock Canadian Pacific Railway Ltd and Canadian National Railway Co. has agreed to share tracks in the Vancouver region. This will allow the trains to operate more efficiently from the Vancouver Port. **Availability:** Print; Online.

8713 ■ *Currency Internationalization: Global Experiences and Implications for the Renminbi*

Pub: Palgrave Macmillan

Released: First edition. **Description:** A collection of academic studies relating to the potential internationalization of China's remninbi. It also discusses the increasing use of China's remninbi currency in international trade and finance.

8714 ■ *"Down the Tracks, a Whistle Is a-Blowin"* in *Barron's (Vol. 89, July 27, 2009, No. 30, pp. 36)*

Pub: Dow Jones & Company Inc.

Contact: Almar Latour, Chief Executive Officer

Ed: Jim McTague. **Description:** Higher numbers of freight-rail carloads are a sign that the economy is improving and it is no stretch to imagine that this is aided by the American Recovery and Reinvestment Act. It is also predicted that 2009 municipal bond issuance will be above $373 billion with at least $55 billion of it made up of Buy America Bonds that are subsidized by the federal government. **Availability:** Online.

8715 ■ *"Europe's Meltdown"* in *Canadian Business (Vol. 83, June 15, 2010, No. 10, pp. 76)*

Description: As European countries such as Greece, Spain, and Portugal struggle with debt problems, it is worth noting that its equities trade at a 30 percent discount to the U.S. and that a 10 percent drop in the Euro translates to a 10 percent rise in profitability for exporters. Investors may also want to focus on business-to-business operations rather than consumer-focused ones. **Availability:** Online.

8716 ■ *"Ex-Im Bank Accepts $105 Million in Financing for Aquarium in Brazil"* in *Travel & Leisure Close-Up (October 8, 2012)*

Description: Export-Import Bank of the United States authorized a $105 million direct loan to the Brazilian state of Ceara to finance the export of American goods and services for the construction of an aquarium in Fortaleza, Brazil. This transaction will support 700 American jobs and at least 90 percent of the export contract value will be provided by U.S. small businesses. **Availability:** Print; Online.

8717 ■ *"Export Opportunity"* in *Business Journal-Portland (Vol. 24, October 12, 2007, No. 33, pp. 1)*

Description: U.S. dollar is weak, hitting an all-time low against the Euro, while the Canadian dollar is also performing well it hit parity for the first time after more than thirty years. The weak U.S. dollar is making companies that sell overseas benefit as it makes their goods cheaper to buy.

8718 ■ *"Furniture Retailers Start to Feel Tariff Pain More Acutely"* in *The Wall Street Journal (November 11, 2019)*

URL(s): www.wsj.com/articles/furniture-retailers-star t-to-feel-tariff-pain-more-acutely-11573476321

Ed: Katy Stech Ferek. **Released:** November 11, 2019. **Description:** Caught up in the current administration's tariff wars with China, the furniture industry is feeling the pain. Shares in publicly-traded furniture companies have taken a hit, and furniture stores that import furniture have faced challenges. Some suppliers have agreed to cover the increased costs and some stores work around the tariffs by importing from countries other than China. **Availability:** Online.

8719 ■ *"Getting Rid of Global Glitches: Choosing Software For Trade Compliance"* in *Black Enterprise (Vol. 41, September 2010, No. 2, pp. 48)*

Pub: Earl G. Graves Ltd.

Contact: Earl Graves, Jr., President

Ed: Marcia Wade Talbert. **Description:** Compliance software for trading with foreign companies must be compatible with the U.S. Census Bureau's Automated Export System (www.aesdirect.gov). It has to be current with regulatory requirements for any country in the world. Whether owners handle their own compliance or hire a logistics company, they need to be familiar with this software in order to access reports and improve transparency and efficiency of theft supply chain. **Availability:** Online.

8720 ■ *"Headwinds From the New Sod Slow Aer Lingus"* in *Barron's (Vol. 88, March 10, 2008, No. 10, pp. M6)*

Pub: Dow Jones & Company Inc.

Contact: Almar Latour, Chief Executive Officer

Ed: Sean Walters, Arindam Nag. **Description:** Aer Lingus faces a drop in its share prices with a falling US market, higher jet fuel prices, and lower long-haul passenger load factors. British media companies Johnston Press and Yell Group are suffering from weaker ad revenue and heavier debt payments due to the credit crunch. **Availability:** Online.

8721 ■ *"Houston Firm To Build World's Largest Plant of Its Kind"* in *Houston Business Journal (Vol. 44, April 25, 2014, No. 51, pp. 4A)*

Pub: American City Business Journals, Inc.

Contact: Mike Olivieri, Executive Vice President

Released: April 25, 2014. **Price:** $4, introductory 4-week offer(Digital only). **Description:** Enterprise Products Partners LP is constructing its largest refrigerate ethane export plant in Houston, Texas and the facility is expected to be operational by the third quarter of 2016. According to CEO, Michael Creel, the facility is designed to process up to 240,000 barrels a day. **Availability:** Print; Online.

8722 ■ *"How Bad Is It?"* in *Hawaii Business (Vol. 54, July 2008, No. 1, pp. 35)*

Pub: PacificBasin Communications

Contact: Chuck Tindle, Director

E-mail: chuckt@pacificbasin.net

Ed: Jolyn Okimoto Rosa. **Description:** Donald G. Horner, chief executive officer of First Hawaiian Bank, says that the current Hawaiian economic situation is a cyclical slowdown. Maurice Kaya, an energy consultant, says the slowdown is due to overdependence on imported fuels. Other local leaders, such as Constance H. Lau, also discuss their view on the current economic situation in Hawaii.

8723 ■ *"How Baltimore's Largest Private Companies Weathered the Recession's Punch; Top Private Companies"* in *Baltimore Business Journal (Vol. 28, August 27, 2010, No. 16, pp. 1)*

Pub: Baltimore Business Journal

Contact: Rhonda Pringle, President

E-mail: rpringle@bizjournals.com

Ed: Gary Haber. **Description:** The combined revenue of the 100 largest private firms in Maryland's Baltimore region dropped from about $22.7 billion in 2008 to $21 billion in 2009, an annual decrease of more than 7 percent. To survive the recession's impact, these firms resorted to strategies such as government contracting and overseas expansion. How these strategies affected the revenue of some firms is described. **Availability:** Print; Online.

8724 ■ *"How Exports Could Save America"* in *Barron's (Vol. 89, July 20, 2009, No. 29, pp. 15)*

Pub: Dow Jones & Company Inc.

Contact: Almar Latour, Chief Executive Officer

Ed: Jonathan R. Laing. **Description:** Increase in US exports should help drive up the nation's economic growth, according to Wells Capital Management strategist Jim Paulsen. He believes US gross domestic product could grow by 3-3.5 percent annually starting in 2010 due to a more favorable trade balance. **Availability:** Online.

8725 ■ "How High Can Soybeans Fly?" in Barron's (Vol. 88, March 10, 2008, No. 10, pp. M14)
Pub: Dow Jones & Company Inc.
Contact: Almar Latour, Chief Executive Officer
Ed: Kenneth Rapoza. **Description:** Prices of soybeans have risen to $14.0875 a bushel, up 8.3 percent for the week. Increased demand, such as in China and in other developing economies, and the investment-driven commodities boom are boosting prices. **Availability:** Online.

8726 ■ "Ill Winds; Cuba's Economy" in The Economist (Vol. 390, January 3, 2009, No. 8612, pp. 20)
Description: Cuba's long-term economic prospects remain poor with the economy forecasted to grow only 4.3 percent for the year, about half of the original forecast, due in part to Hurricane Gustav which caused $10 billion in damage and disrupted the food-supply network and devastated farms across the region; President Raul Castro made raising agricultural production a national priority and the rise in global commodity prices hit the country hard. The only bright spot has been the rise in tourism which is up 9.3 percent over 2007. **Availability:** Online.

8727 ■ Import/Export Kit For Dummies
Pub: John Wiley & Sons, Inc.
Contact: Christina Van Tassell, Executive Vice President Chief Financial Officer
Ed: John J. Capela. **Released:** 3rd Edition. **Price:** $26.99, paperback; $17.99, E-book. **Description:** Provides entrepreneurs and small- to medium-size businesses with information required to start exporting products globally and importing goods to the U.S. Topics covered include the ins and outs of developing or expanding operations to gain market share, with details on the top ten countries in which America trades, from Canada to Germany to China. **Availability:** E-book; Print.

8728 ■ "In China, Railways to Riches" in Barron's (Vol. 88, July 7, 2008, No. 27, pp. M9)
Pub: Dow Jones & Company Inc.
Contact: Almar Latour, Chief Executive Officer
Ed: Assif Shameen. **Description:** Shares of Chinese railway companies look to benefit from multimillion-dollar investments aimed at upgrading the Chinese railway network. Investment in the sector is expected to reach $210 billion for the 2006-2010 period. **Availability:** Online.

8729 ■ "In India, A Gold-Price Threat?" in Barron's (Vol. 88, June 30, 2008, No. 26, pp. M12)
Pub: Dow Jones & Company Inc.
Contact: Almar Latour, Chief Executive Officer
Ed: Melanie Burton. **Description:** Gold purchases in India are falling as record prices take its toll on demand. Gold imports to India fell by 52 percent in May 2008 from the previous year and local prices are higher by one-third from the previous year to 12,540 rupees for 10 grams. **Availability:** Online.

8730 ■ "International Business Law: Interpreting the Term 'Like Products'" in Business Recorder (June 7, 2012)
Ed: Zafar Azeem. **Description:** The term 'like products' needs to be defined for international trade. The battle between the United States and Indonesia regarding this issue is discussed. A technical barrier clause being used by foreign countries is prohibiting imports and hurting competitiveness. **Availability:** Online.

8731 ■ "Is the Sun Setting on Oil Sector's Heydey?" in Globe & Mail (January 25, 2007, pp. B3)
Description: The effects of fuel efficiency management policies of the United States on Canadian petroleum industry are discussed. Canada is the largest exporter of crude oil to America after the Middle East. **Availability:** Online.

8732 ■ "It's Time To Swim" in Canadian Business (Vol. 81, March 3, 2008, No. 3, pp. 37)
Description: Canadian manufacturers should consider Asian markets such as India and the United Arab Emirates as the U.S. economic downturn continues. Canada's shortage in skilled labor is also expected to negatively affect manufacturing industries. Ontario's plans to assist manufacturers are also presented. **Availability:** Print; PDF; Download; Online.

8733 ■ "Keeping Railcars 'Busy At All Times' At TTX" in Crain's Chicago Business (Vol. 31, April 28, 2008, No. 17, pp. 6)
Pub: Crain Communications Inc.
Contact: Barry Asin, President
Ed: Bob Tita. **Description:** Profile of the president of Chicago railcar pool operator TTX Co. and his business plan for the company which includes improving fleet management and car purchasing through better use of data on railroad demand. **Availability:** Online.

8734 ■ Leonard's Guide--International Air Cargo Directory
Pub: G.R. Leonard and Co.
URL(s): www.leonardsguide.com/wla-air-cargo-companies.shtml
Description: Covers companies providing air cargo service from North America to international and domestic destinations. **Availability:** Online.

8735 ■ "Lobster Mania Hits China: They Just Had to Get Used to the Claws" in Canadian Business (Vol. 85, July 16, 2012, No. 11-12, pp. 10)
Ed: Joe Castaldo. **Description:** Canadian lobster exports to China have tripled to almost $30 million annually since 2010 as a result of marketing efforts by Maritimes governments including pitching lobster to cooking shows and organizing training sessions for Chinese chefs. Canadian exporters must decide whether their lobster is a premium product or a commodity product to solidify its image in China. **Availability:** Print; Online.

8736 ■ "Major Advances in Heat Pump Technology - Part Two" in Contractor (Vol. 57, February 2010, No. 2, pp. 22)
Ed: Mark Eatherton. **Description:** Chinese and Japanese companies have come up with refrigerant based heat pump products that are air based which will significantly lower the installed cost of heat pump based systems. Some of these newer models have variable speed, soft start compressors and have the ability to perform high-efficiency heat pump operation on a modulating basis. **Availability:** Print; Online.

8737 ■ Managing Economies, Trade and International Business
Pub: Palgrave Macmillan
Released: 1st edition. **Price:** $89, e-book; $115, Hardcover; $110, softcover. **Description:** An in-depth look at the areas that affect and influence international business, exploring specific issues businesses face in terms of economic development, trade law, and international marketing and management. **Availability:** E-book; Print.

8738 ■ "Market Watch" in Barron's (Vol. 88, March 24, 2008, No. 12, pp. M18)
Ed: Ashraf Laidi, Marc Pado, David Kotok. **Released:** 2018. **Description:** Latest measures implemented by the Federal Reserve to address the credit crisis did not benefit the US dollar, with the Japanese yen and the euro recouping earlier losses against the dollar. Goldman Sachs reported earnings of $3.23 per share, claiming a stronger liquidity position. The US markets bottomed early on 22 January 2007, according to evidence. **Availability:** Print; Online.

8739 ■ "Market Watch: A Sampling of Advisory Opinion US Stock Price Trends, Economic Effects of Global Trade, Chinese Economic Trends" in Barron's (Vol. 92, July 23, 2012, No. 30, pp. M14)
Ed: Richard M. Salsman, Jack Ablin, Francois Sicart. **Description:** US stocks are considered inexpensive due to their low price-earnings ratios compared to

levels before the global financial crisis. The US economy is becoming more dependent on the rest of the worldas a result of global trade. The Chinese economy continues to have strong economic growth despite a slowdown. **Availability:** Online.

8740 ■ "Melamine Analytical Methods Released" in Feedstuffs (Vol. 80, October 6, 2008, No. 41, pp. 2)
Pub: Miller Publishing Company
Description: Romer Labs has released new validations for its AgraQuant Melamine enzyme-linked immunosorbent assay. The test kit screens for melamine in feed and diary products, including pet foods, milk and milk powder. Melamine by itself is nontoxic in low doses, but when combined with cyanuric acid it can cause fatal kidney stones. The Chinese dairy industry is in the midst of a huge melamine crisis; melamine-contaminated dairy and food products from China have been found in more than 20 countries. **Availability:** Print; Online.

8741 ■ "Mission to China" in Canadian Business (Vol. 81, December 8, 2008, No. 21, pp. 28)
Ed: Andrew Wahl. **Released:** October 26, 2016. **Description:** Canada China Business Council and the Council of the Federation visited China for a three-city trade mission. The trade mission aims to re-establish the strong relationship between China and Canada. **Availability:** Online.

8742 ■ "Key Challenges Dog International Banking in South Florida" in South Florida Business Journal (Vol. 35, August 1, 2014, No. 1, pp. 4)
Pub: American City Business Journals, Inc.
Contact: Mike Olivieri, Executive Vice President
Released: Weekly. **Price:** $8, introductory 4-week offer(Digital only). **Description:** Florida International Bankers Association president, Roberto R. Munoz, discusses the challenges and opportunities in the South Florida international banking market. He explains the impact on international banks with the loss of the Export-Import Bank of the United States charter and the Base1 III rules and regulations regarding higher capital requirements. **Availability:** Print; Online.

8743 ■ "Mover and Sheika" in Conde Nast Portfolio (Vol. 2, June 2008, No. 6, pp. 104)
Ed: John Arlidge. **Description:** Profile of Princess Sheika Lubna who is the first female foreign trade minister in the Middle East, the United Arab Emirates biggest business envoy, paving the way for billions in new investment, and also a manufacturer of her own perfume line. **Availability:** Online.

8744 ■ "No Shortage of Challenges for Cross-Border Trade" in Canadian Sailings (June 30, 2008)
Description: Pros and cons of the North American Free Trade Agreement are examined. The agreement between the U.S. and Canada concerning trade was an essential step toward securing economic growth for Canadian citizens. Two-way trade between the counties has tripled since the agreement and accounts for 7.1 million American and 3 million Canadian jobs. **Availability:** Print; Online; PDF.

8745 ■ "On the U.S. Election: Shaky on Free Trade" in Canadian Business (Vol. 81, December 19, 2007, No. 1, pp. 29)
Pub: Rogers Media Inc.
Contact: Neil Spivak, Chief Executive Officer
Ed: Rachel Pulfer. **Description:** Rhetoric at the U.S. presidential elections seems to be pointing toward a weaker free trade consensus, with Democratic candidates being against the renewal of free trade deals, while Republican candidates seem to be for free trade. **Availability:** Online.

8746 ■ "Parent Firm's Global Reach, Stricter Air Quality Rules Have Stock Smiling" in Crain's Cleveland Business (October 15, 2007)
Pub: Crain Communications Inc.
Contact: K. C. Crain, President

Ed: David Bennett. **Description:** Since Stock Equipment Co., a firm that makes industrial pollution control equipment, was acquired by Schenck Process Group, a diversified global manufacturer based in Germany, the company's orders from abroad have been on the rise. The purchase has opened the doors to regions such as Eastern and Central Europe, Latin America and Australia. **Availability:** Online.

8747 ▪ *"Partisan Vote in House for Export-Import Bank Measure"* in U.S. News & World Report (November 15, 2019)
URL(s): www.usnews.com/news/articles/20 19-11-15/partisan-vote-likely-for-export-import-bank
Released: November 15, 2019. **Description:** The Democratic-controlled House passed a measure renewing the charter for the Export-Import Bank. The U.S. agency provides loans to foreign buyers of U.S. exports. However, the White House issued a veto threat and the legislation died when it arrived in the GOP-controlled Senate. **Availability:** Online.

8748 ▪ *"Paying for the Recession: Rebalancing Economic Growth"* in Montana Business Quarterly (Vol. 49, Spring 2011, No. 1, pp. 2)
Pub: University of Montana Bureau of Business and Economic Research
Contact: Patrick Barkey, Director
E-mail: patrick.barkey@business.umt.edu
Ed: Patrick M. Barkey. **Released:** Quarterly. **Description:** Four key issues required to address in order to rebalance economic growth in America are examined. They include: savings rates, global trade imbalances, government budgets and most importantly, housing price correction. **Availability:** Online.

8749 ▪ *"Port Canaveral Plans to Make Big Waves of Business in C. Fla."* in Orlando Business Journal (Vol. 30, June 6, 2014, No. 50, pp. 4)
Pub: American City Business Journals, Inc.
Contact: Mike Olivieri, Executive Vice President
Released: Weekly. **Price:** $8, Introductory 4-week offer(Digital & Print). **Description:** Port Canaveral CEO, John Walsh, has big plans for the expansion of the Port, which include a $500 million cargo and cruise expansion that could net billions of dollars in new economic impact and create more than 15,000 new jobs. Walsh plans to expand cargo capacity, dig deeper harbors for large cruise ships and build a rail transport cargo and, eventually, passengers in and out of the 380-acre Port Canaveral. The Port is the fifth-largest cargo port in Central Florida. **Availability:** Print; Online.

8750 ▪ *"Q&A Interview With Perrin Beatty"* in Canadian Business (Vol. 80, October 8, 2007, No. 20, pp. 13)
Description: Perrin Beatty, president and chief executive officer of the Canadian Chamber of Commerce, talks about his move from the Canadian Manufacturers and Exporters to his current organization. He also discusses the state of Canada's economy, as well as the need for leadership.

8751 ▪ *"Quonset Steering To Import Records"* in Providence Business News (Vol. 29, May 19, 2014, No. 7, pp. 1)
Pub: American City Business Journals, Inc.
Contact: Mike Olivieri, Executive Vice President
Released: May 17, 2014. **Description:** The growing automobile import business at Port of Davisville in North Kingstown, Rhode Island is marked by four consecutive record-breaking years of imports, with 250,000 vehicles expected to arrive by the end of 2014. Quonset Development Corporation managing director, Steven J. King, attributes the success of the auto import business to North Atlantic Distribution Inc. **Availability:** Print; Online.

8752 ▪ *"Refiners, Producers are at Odds in Debate Over U.S. Oil Exports"* in San Antonio Business Journal (Vol. 27, January 17, 2014, No. 50, pp. 4)
Pub: American City Business Journals, Inc.
Contact: Mike Olivieri, Executive Vice President

Released: Weekly. **Price:** $4, Introductory 4-week offer(Digital & Print). **Description:** The American Petroleum Institute has been lobbying for the elimination of the decades-old ban on oil exports to open new markets for U.S. crude. Refiners such as San Antonio-based Valero Energy Corporation and Tesoro Corporation are against lifting the ban because it would drive the price of crude and tighten margins. Insights into the debate over U.S. oil exports are provided. **Availability:** Print; Online.

8753 ▪ *"Religious Revival"* in Canadian Business (Vol. 81, December 8, 2008, No. 21, pp. 57)
Pub: Rogers Media Inc.
Contact: Neil Spivak, Chief Executive Officer
Ed: Paul Webster. **Description:** Canada-based lawyer Cyndee Todgham Cherniak believes that Canadians wishing to do business in China should have professional competence, as well as cultural and spiritual sensitivity. Chinese government officials also acknowledge the role of religion in China's economy. **Availability:** Online.

8754 ▪ *"Riding the Export Wave: How To Find a Good Distributor Overseas"* in Inc. (January 2008, pp. 49)
Ed: Sarah Goldstein. **Description:** Small companies should contact the U.S. embassy in foreign companies in order to connect with the U.S. Commercial Service's Gold Key program that is designed to work with small and midsize exporters. **Availability:** Online.

8755 ▪ *"Rising in the East; Research and Development"* in The Economist (Vol. 390, January 3, 2009, No. 8612, pp. 47)
Description: Impressive growth of the technological research and development in Asian countries is discussed. Statistical data included. **Availability:** Online.

8756 ▪ *"Rough Trade: the Canada-Chile Free Trade Agreement"* in Canadian Business (Vol. 79, September 11, 2006, No. 18, pp. 31)
Pub: Rogers Media Inc.
Contact: Neil Spivak, Chief Executive Officer
Ed: Christina Campbell. **Description:** The divergence between trade policy agreements entered into by Chile and the Canadian government are highlighted. Canada-Chile Free Trade Agreement and the myth around the big benefits to be reaped by bilateral trade policy agreements are discussed. **Availability:** Print; Mailing list; Online.

8757 ▪ *"Russia: Uncle Volodya's Flagging Christmas Spirit"* in The Economist (Vol. 390, January 3, 2009, No. 8612, pp. 22)
Description: Overview of Russia's struggling economy as well as unpopular government decisions such as raising import duties on used foreign vehicles so as to protect Russian carmakers. **Availability:** Print; Online.

8758 ▪ *"Russian Renaissance"* in Chicago Tribune (September 22, 2008)
Pub: Tribune News Service
Contact: Jack Barry, Vice President, Operations
E-mail: jbarry@tribpub.com
Ed: Alex Rodriguez. **Description:** Winemakers from Russia are returning to the craft and quality of wine-making now that they are free from Soviet restraints. **Availability:** Print; Online.

8759 ▪ *"Safety Products Firm Expanding"* in Memphis Business Journal (Vol. 33, March 16, 2012, No. 49, pp. 1)
Pub: Baltimore Business Journal
Contact: Rhonda Pringle, President
E-mail: rpringle@bizjournals.com
Description: Safety products importer and supplier International Sourcing Company Inc., the parent firm of Cordova Safety Products and Cordova Consumer Products, has purchased the 1 million-square-foot Cleo property in southeast Memphis, Tennessee.

Aside from relocating its warehouse and office operations to the facility, the firm will add 20 new jobs as part of its growth initiative. **Availability:** Print; Online.

8760 ▪ *"Sedo Keeps Trucking in Good Times and Bad"* in Crain's Chicago Business (Vol. 31, April 28, 2008, No. 17, pp. 35)
Description: Discusses Seko Worldwide Inc., an Itasca-based freight forwarder, and its complicated road to growth and expansion on a global scale. **Availability:** Print; Online.

8761 ▪ *"Shattering the Myths About U.S. Trade Policy: Stop Blaming China and India. A More Active Trade Policy Can Lead to a Stronger U.S. Economy"* in Harvard Business Review (Vol. 90, March 2012, No. 3, pp. 149)
Pub: Harvard Business Review Press
Contact: Moderna V. Pfizer, Contact
Ed: Robert Z. Lawrence, Lawrence Edwards. **Price:** $8.95, hardcopy black and white. **Description:** Myths debunked include the belief that the US open trade policy has caused job losses, and that living standards are falling due to export market competition. American must leverage China's need for global economic engagement and secure an open domestic market in China. It must also persuade the World Trade Organization to improve market access. **Availability:** Print; PDF; Online.

8762 ▪ *"Slimmed-Down Supplier TI Automotive Relaunches"* in Crain's Detroit Business (Vol. 26, January 11, 2010, No. 2, pp. 14)
Pub: Crain Communications Inc.
Contact: Barry Asin, President
Ed: Robert Sherefkin. **Description:** TI Automotive Ltd., one of the world's largest suppliers of fuel storage and delivery systems, has reorganized the company by splitting it into five global divisions and is relaunching its brand which is now more focused on new technology. **Availability:** Print; Online.

8763 ▪ *"Some Relief Possible Following Painful Week"* in Barron's (Vol. 88, July 14, 2008, No. 28, pp. M3)
Pub: Dow Jones & Company Inc.
Contact: Almar Latour, Chief Executive Officer
Ed: Kopin Tan. **Description:** Dow Chemical is offering a 74 percent premium to acquire Rohm & Haas' coatings and electronics materials operations. Frontline amassed a 5.6 percent stake in rival Overseas Shipholding Group and a merger between the two would create a giant global fleet with pricing power. Highlights of the U.S. stock market during the week that ended in July 11, 2008 are discussed. Statistical data included. **Availability:** Online.

8764 ▪ *"The Superpower Dilemma"* in Canadian Business (Vol. 83, August 17, 2010, No. 13-14, pp. 42)
Description: Canada has been an energy superpower partly because it controls the energy source and the production means, particularly of fossil fuels. However, Canada's status as superpower could diminish if it replaces petroleum exports with renewable technology for using sources of energy available globally. **Availability:** Online.

8765 ▪ *"Tales of the City"* in Canadian Business (Vol. 81, December 8, 2008, No. 21, pp. 37)
Description: Key information on doing business in Hong Kong are shared by an entrepreneur, a consultant, an exporter, and a financier who were from Canada. Hong Kong hosts about 3,900 regional headquarters or offices of international companies. **Availability:** Online.

8766 ▪ *"The Three Amigos"* in Canadian Business (Vol. 81, March 17, 2008, No. 4, pp. 19)
Description: Mexican president Felipe Calderon said that Mexico exported 30 percent more to Europe and 25 percent more to other countries in Latin America in 2006 in light of the downturn in the U.S. economy.

Calderon made this announcement in a speech at Harvard University while protestors marched outside protesting against NAFTA. **Availability:** Online.

8767 ■ _"Timken's Bearings Rolling in China, India"_ in Crain's Cleveland Business (Vol. 28, October 29, 2007, No. 43, pp. 14)
Pub: Crain Communications Inc.
Contact: K. C. Crain, President
Ed: David Bennett. **Description:** Canton-based Timken Co., a manufacturer of bearings and specialty metals, is seeing growing demand for its line of tapered roller bearings, which allow rail users to carry heavy car loads. The company is finding significant growth in China and India due to their rapidly growing rail markets. **Availability:** PDF; Online.

8768 ■ _"To Keep Freight Rolling, Ill. Has to Grease the Hub"_ in Crain's Chicago Business (Vol. 31, April 21, 2008, No. 16, pp. 22)
Pub: Crain Communications Inc.
Contact: Barry Asin, President
Ed: Paul O'Connor. **Description:** Discusses the importance of upgrading Chicago's continental-hub freight rail system which is integral to moving international products as well as domestic ones. Global tonnage is expected to double by 2020 and unless more money is designated to upgrade the infrastructure the local and national economy will suffer. **Availability:** Online.

8769 ■ _"Too Much Precaution About Biotech Corn"_ in Barron's (Vol. 88, March 17, 2008, No. 11, pp. 54)
Pub: Dow Jones & Company Inc.
Contact: Almar Latour, Chief Executive Officer
Ed: Mark I. Schwartz. **Description:** In the U.S., 90 percent of cultivated soybeans are biotech varietals as well as 60 percent of the corn. Farmers have significantly reduced their reliance on pesticides in the growing of biotech corn. Biotech cotton cultivation has brought hundreds of millions of dollars in net financial gains to farmers. The European Union has precluded the cultivation or sale of biotech crops within its border. **Availability:** Online.

8770 ■ _"Trade Winds"_ in Canadian Sailings (June 30, 2008)
Description: Trade between Canada and the United States is discussed as well as legislation concerning foreign trade and the future of this trade relationship. **Availability:** Online.

8771 ■ _"The Transparent Supply Chain"_ in Harvard Business Review (Vol. 88, October 2010, No. 10, pp. 76)
Pub: Harvard Business Publishing
Contact: Diane Belcher, Managing Director
Ed: Steve New. **Price:** $8.95, PDF. **Description:** Examination of the use of new technologies to create a transparent supply chain, such as next-generation 2D bar codes in clothing labels that can provide data on a garment's provenance. **Availability:** Online; PDF.

8772 ■ _"U.S. Import Prices Fall 0.5% in October Amid Steep Drop in Fuel Prices"_ in Nasdaq (November 15, 2019)
URL(s): www.nasdaq.com/articles/u.s.-import-prices -fall-0.5-in-october-amid-steep-drop-in-fuel-prices -2019-11-15
Released: November 15, 2019. **Description:** According to a report released by the Labor Department, import prices in the U.S. fell more than expected. The decrease was driven by lower oil prices, along with falling prices for non-fuel industrial supplies, foods, feeds, beverages, consumer goods, and capital goods. **Availability:** Online.

8773 ■ _"U.S. Primaries: An Amazing Race"_ in Canadian Business (Vol. 81, February 12, 2008, No. 3, pp. 25)
Pub: Rogers Media Inc.
Contact: Neil Spivak, Chief Executive Officer
Ed: Rachel Pulfer. **Description:** U.S. presidential candidates Barack Obama and Hilary Clinton lead the Democratic Part primaries while John McCain is

a frontrunner at the Republican Party. These leading candidates have different plans for the U.S. economy which will affect Canada's own economy particularly concerning trade policies. The presidential candidates' proposals and the impacts of U.S. economic downturn on Canada are examined. **Availability:** Print; Online.

8774 ■ _"Up On The Farm"_ in Canadian Business (Vol. 81, March 31, 2008, No. 5, pp. 23)
Description: Agricultural products have outperformed both energy and metal and even the prospect of a global economic slowdown does not seem to hinder its prospects. The Organization for Economic Cooperation and Development sees prices above historic equilibrium levels during the next ten years given that fuel and fertilizers remain high and greater demand from India and China remain steady. **Availability:** Print; Online.

8775 ■ _"Venture Gap"_ in Canadian Business (Vol. 81, February 26, 2008, No. 4, pp. 82)
Pub: Rogers Media Inc.
Contact: Neil Spivak, Chief Executive Officer
Ed: Joe Castaldo. **Description:** Money raised by Canadian venture capitalist firms has been declining since 2001. A strong venture capital market is important if Canada is to build innovative companies. Fixing Canada's tax policy on foreign investments is a start in reviving the industry. **Availability:** Print; Online.

8776 ■ _"Wegmans Uses Database for Recall"_ in Supermarket News (Vol. 56, September 22, 2008, No. 38)
Pub: Informa USA, Inc.
Contact: Stephen A. Carter, Chief Executive Officer
Ed: Carol Angrisani. **Description:** Wegmans used data obtained through its loyalty card that, in turn, sent automated telephone calls to every customer who had purchased tainted pet food when Mars Petcare recalled dog food products.

8777 ■ _"Why Change?"_ in Canadian Business (Vol. 80, October 8, 2007, No. 20, pp. 9)
Description: The need for economic change in Canada is discussed. Despite the country's economic growth and low unemployment rate, economic reform is needed in order to maximize its economic potential in the future. Other reasons for the need to further develop its economy, such as the rise of manufacturing and service industries in Asia and the emergence of regional trade pacts in South America are also tackled.

8778 ■ _"Why You Aren't Buying Venezuelan Chocolate"_ in Harvard Business Review (Vol. 88, December 2010, No. 12, pp. 25)
Pub: Harvard Business Publishing
Contact: Diane Belcher, Managing Director
Ed: Rohit Deshpande. **Price:** $6, PDF. **Description:** The concept of provenance paradox is defined as the preconceived notions consumers have about the country of origin of a given product, which can pose significant difficulties for emerging markets. Five strategies are presented for combating this problem, including building on historic events that have informed cultural perspectives. **Availability:** Online; PDF.

8779 ■ _"With Whom Do You Trade? Defensive Innovation and the Skill-Bias"_ in Canadian Journal of Electronics (Vol. 43, November 2010)
Pub: Journal of the Canadian Economics Association
Ed: Pushan Dutt, Daniel Traca. **Released:** Vol. 43, No. 4. **Price:** $5. **Description:** Examination into whether increased trade with ineffective protection of intellectual property has contributed to the skill-deepening of the 1980s. An index of effective protection of intellectual property at the country level, combining data on protection of patents and rule of law are presented. An industry-specific version of this index is given using as weights each country's trade share in the total trade of the industry. A decline is

seen in this trade-weighted index, owing to a rise in trade with countries with low effective protection of intellectual property, which explains 29 percent of the rise within-industry skill-intensity. **Availability:** Print; Online; Download.

8780 ■ _"World Watch: Where Michigan Does Business"_ in Crain's Detroit Business (Vol. 30, October 13, 2014, No. 41, pp. 22)
Pub: Crain Communications Inc.
Contact: Barry Asin, President
Description: Canada is Michigan's closest trading partner. Canada's most significant industries include chemicals, minerals, wood/paper products, food products, transportation equipment, petroleum and natural gas. Canada is also the largest energy supplier to the United States, thus helping Canada's petroleum sector grow. Major export partners of Canada include: U.S. (74.5 percent), China (4.3 percent) and the United Kingdom (4.1 percent). Major exports include motor vehicles and parts, aircraft, telecommunication equipment, chemicals, crude petroleum and natural gas. **Availability:** Online.

8781 ■ _Your Guide to Canadian Export Financing: Successful Techniques for Financing Your Exports from Canada_
Pub: Productive Publications
Contact: Iain Williamson, Author Publisher
Ed: Iain Williamson. **Released:** 2022-2023 Edition. **Price:** C$74.95, softcover, Postage/handling $19.95 on first title, Add postage/handling of $3.50 per title thereafter. **Description:** Canadian export financing is covered. **Availability:** Print.

TRADE PERIODICALS

8782 ■ _The Export Practitioner_
Contact: Meridith Gilston, Editor
E-mail: mgilston@comcast.net
URL(s): www.exportprac.com
Ed: Meridith Gilston, Samuel M. Gilston. **Released:** Monthly **Price:** $699, Individuals print only; $799, Individuals print and online; $699, Individuals online only. **Description:** Focuses on regulatory policy and legal trends regarding export of products and services. Covers planning strategies for marketability. **Availability:** Print; PDF; Online.

8783 ■ _ImportCar_
Pub: Babcox Media Inc.
Contact: Bill Babcox, Chief Executive Officer
E-mail: bbabcox@babcox.com
URL(s): www.import-car.combabcox.com/brand/impor tcar
Facebook: www.facebook.com/importcar
LinkedIn: www.linkedin.com/showcase/importcar
X (Twitter): x.com/import_car
Instagram: www.instagram.com/importcarmag
YouTube: www.youtube.com/channel/UCsKl7G 4mLNleqierKaPo05g
Ed: Doug Kaufman. **Released:** Monthly **Price:** $89, for one year Canada; $69, for us one year. **Description:** Magazine focusing on import specialist repair shops that derive more than 50% of revenue from servicing import nameplates. **Availability:** Print; PDF; Download; Online.

CONSULTANTS

8784 ■ International Business Associates
5614 University Ave.
  Cedar Falls, IA 50613
Contact: Barbara J. Hatinger, President
Description: Firm is a international business consultant offers import and export expertise and services. **Scope:** Firm is a international business consultant offers import and export expertise and services.

8785 ■ Polish Business Consultants Group Ltd.
11838 22nd Ave. SW
  Burien, WA 98146
Ph: (206)932-0750
Co. E-mail: alecj@polbiznet.com
URL: http://www.polbiznet.com

Contact: Alexander J. Sitkiewicz, Founder Senior
   Partner
E-mail: alecj@polbiznet.com
Description: Provider of import and export consulting, personal representation, contract negotiation and information about doing business in Poland and their services include direction for couples and individuals interested in adopting Polish children. **Founded:** 1993.

COMPUTERIZED DATABASES

8786 ■ *International Trade Reporter*
Bloomberg Industry Group
   1801 S Bell St.
   Arlington, VA 22202
Ph: (703)341-1818
URL: http://www.bloombergindustry.com
Contact: Josh Eastright, Chief Executive Officer
URL(s): lawcat.berkeley.edu/record/1281051
Released: Daily; Daily. **Availability:** Print; Online.
Type: Full-text.

LIBRARIES

**8787 ■ The Economist Intelligence Unit
Limited (EIU) - Information Center**
The Economist Group Ltd. (TEG)
   750 Third Ave., 5th Fl.
   New York, NY 10017

Ph: 44 20 7576-8000
Co. E-mail: executiveeducation@economist.com
URL: http://www.economistgroup.com
Contact: Shane Naughton, Chief Executive Officer
Description: Provider of country, industry and management analysis. **Scope:** Foreign investment; International trade; economics; finance; forecasting; critical issues monitoring. **Services:** Interlibrary loan; copying. **Founded:** 1946. **Holdings:** Economist Intelligence Unit publications (complete set); corporate directories; databases for the United Nations, the World Bank, and major regional economic organizations. **Publications:** *EIU Investing, Licensing & Trading Conditions Abroad*; *Asia Pacific Business Intelligence Volume I: North Asia & Australasia*; *Asia Pacific Business Intelligence Volume II: Southeast Asia and Indian Subcontinent*; *West European Business Intelligence*; *East European Business Intelligence*; *Latin American Business Intelligence*; *Business China*; *Business Asia*; *Business Eastern Europe*; *Business Middle East*; *Business Russia*; *Business India Intelligence*; *China Business Intelligence on Disc*; *EIU on the Internet*; *EIU Online*; *Investing, Licensing, and Trading*; *The Economist* (Weekly).

RESEARCH CENTERS

**8788 ■ The Heritage Foundation Asian
Studies Center**
214 Massachusetts Ave. NE
   Washington, DC 20002-4999

Co. E-mail: info@heritage.org
URL: http://www.heritage.org/asia
Description: Research activity of Heritage Foundation, an independent nonprofit organization. Offers expert testimony before Congress and party platform committees. **Scope:** International trade and economics, U.S.-Asian relations, U.S. and Western security interests in Asia and the Pacific, U.S. policy towards China and Korea, U.S. interests in the Philippines, U.S. policy regarding the Association of Southeast Asian Nations, and the future of the U.S.-Japan relationship. **Founded:** 1983. **Publications:** *Asian Studies Center Backgrounders*; *Executive Memoranda Series* (Annual); *U.S. and Asia Statistical Handbook*. **Educational Activities:** Heritage Lectures, Offer exemplary teaching programs.; ASC Public diplomacy engagements, Offer exemplary teaching programs.

START-UP INFORMATION

8789 ■ *"Are Accelerators Worth It?"* **in Inc.**
URL(s): www.inc.com/magazine/201407/norm-bro
dsky/are-accelerators-worth-it.html
Description: Discusses the importance of asking
alumni of an accelerator how much time they got to
spend time with mentors as a big value-add for utilizing an accelerator for your business. **Availability:**
Online.

8790 ■ **Evergreen Climate Innovations**
Facebook: www.facebook.com/EvergreenClima
teInnovations
Linkedin: www.linkedin.com/company/evergreen
-climate-innovations
X (Twitter): x.com/evergreen_inno
YouTube: www.youtube.com/channel/UC8t1sHKQ
1iczwggoa93zxgw
Description: Supports startups bringing impactful
climate technologies to market. Makes seed investments and provide hands-on support to entrepreneurs. **Founded:** 2010.

8791 ■ *"How to Pick the Right Accelerator"* **in
Inc.**
URL(s): www.inc.com/magazine/201407/robin-scha
tz/how-to-choose-and-get-accepted-to-an-accelra
tor.html
Ed: Robin Schatz. **Description:** Finding the right
business accelerator is challenging, but when you
choose well, rewards can be great for your business.
Provides information on how to choose the right accelerator for your company. **Availability:** Online.

8792 ■ *"Incubator, Apartment Mix Eyed"* **in
Providence Business News (Vol. 29, April 14,
2014, No. 2, pp. 1)**
Pub: American City Business Journals, Inc.
Contact: Mike Olivieri, Executive Vice President
URL(s): pbn.com/incubator-apartment-mix-eyed9
6427
Description: New York City-based developer, Frank
Manaigo, has been working on plans to develop a
culinary incubator in a vacant mill complex in the
West End at the Armory District in Providence, Rhode
Island. The "Rooms and Works" is a $6.5 million
residential and commercial project that would feature
the "Armory Kitchen". The apartment component of
the project is also discussed. **Telecommunication
Services:** Daddona@pbn.com.

8793 ■ *"Incubators Heat Up Chances of
Small Business Survival"* **in Business News
Daily (Aug. 5, 2022)**
URL(s): www.businessnewsdaily.com/272-incubators
-increase-small-business-success.html
Ed: Ned Smith. **Released:** August 05, 2022. **Descrip-
tion:** Provides information on how an incubator can
nurture a startup and how it differs from other
economic development programs. **Availability:**
Online.

8794 ■ *"Is an Incubator Right for Your
Start-up?"* **in Inc.**
URL(s): www.inc.com/mehdi-maghsoodnia/is-an
-incubator-right-for-your-startup.html
Ed: Mehdi Maghsoodnia. **Description:** A CEO
discusses his beliefs about what to look for in an
incubator to ensure it is right for your start-up. **Availability:** Online.

8795 ■ *"Is Wall Street the Best Start-Up
Incubator?"* **in Inc.**
URL(s): www.inc.com/magazine/201306/darren-dahl/
is-wall-street-the-best-startup-incubator.html
Ed: Darren Dahl. **Description:** Five former invest-
ment bankers explain how their experience at big
banks helped them become better entrepreneurs.
Availability: Online.

8796 ■ *"Kitchen Aid: D.C. Food Incubator
Turns Growth Tactics Inward"* **in Washington
Business Journal (Vol. 32, February 28, 2014,
No. 46, pp. 6)**
Pub: American City Business Journals, Inc.
Contact: Mike Olivieri, Executive Vice President
Released: Weekly. **Price:** $4, introductory 4-week
offer(Digital only). **Description:** The founders of the
14-month-old food business incubator, Union Kitchen,
are considering their own growth strategies as they
open up a second space for small business owners.
The incubator has 55 members that pay monthly fees
from $800 to $1,000, focusing on bar services and
fine dining opportunities. **Availability:** Print; Online.

8797 ■ *"Texas State Seeks Startups"* **in
Austin Business Journal (Vol. 32, April 20,
2012, No. 7, pp. 1)**
Pub: American City Business Journals, Inc.
Contact: Mike Olivieri, Executive Vice President
Ed: Sandra Zaragoza. **Description:** Texas State
University is set to open a new business incubator
for technology startups. The incubator will have
secure wet labs, clean rooms and office space. **Avail-
ability:** Online.

8798 ■ *"What Is a Business Incubator and
How Does It Work?"* **in Draper University
Blog (May 22, 2020)**
URL(s): www.draperuniversity.com/blog/what-is-a
-business-incubator
Released: May 22, 2020. **Description:** Provides
detailed information on what a business incubator is
and what role they play in helping business start-ups.
Availability: Online.

8799 ■ *"Which Accelerator Program Is Right
for Your Company?"* **in Inc.**
URL(s): www.inc.com/magazine/201503/john-bran
don/the-field-guide-to-accelerators.html
Description: Presents data on eight top accelerators
in the U.S. for small businesses looking to enroll.
Availability: Online.

ASSOCIATIONS AND OTHER ORGANIZATIONS

8800 ■ **Imagine H2O**
4 Embarcadero Center, Ste. 1400
  San Francisco, CA 94111
URL: http://www.imagineh2o.org
Contact: Tamin Pechet, Chairman
Linkedin: www.linkedin.com/company/imagine-h2o
X (Twitter): x.com/imagineh2o
Instagram: www.instagram.com/imagineh2o
Description: Works to solve global water challenges
by providing entrepreneurs with reduces to transform
water startups into scalable businesses. **Founded:**
2008.

8801 ■ **International Business Innovation
Association (InBIA)**
PO Box 677279
  Orlando, FL 32867
Ph: (407)965-5553
Co. E-mail: info@inbia.org
URL: http://inbia.org
Contact: Charles Ross, Chief Executive Officer
E-mail: cross@inbia.org
Facebook: www.facebook.com/TheInBIA
Linkedin: www.linkedin.com/company/theinbia
X (Twitter): x.com/TheInBIA
Instagram: www.instagram.com/TheInBIA

Description: Incubator developers and managers;
corporate joint venture partners, venture capital
investors; economic development professionals.
Helps newly formed businesses to succeed. Educates
businesses and investors on incubator benefits; offers
specialized training in incubator formation and
management. Conducts research and referral services; compiles statistics; publishes information
relevant to business incubation and growing companies. **Publications:** *Business Incubators of North
America* (Biennial); *NBIA Insights* (Monthly); *NBIA
Memberabilia* (Semimonthly); *NBIA Review* (Bimonthly); *NBIA Business Incubation Industry Directory* (Annual). **Awards:** NBIA Incubator Innovation
Award (Annual); NBIA Incubator of the Year (Annual);
NBIA Outstanding Incubator Client Award (Annual);
NBIA Outstanding Incubator Graduate Award. **Geographic Preference:** National; Multinational.

8802 ■ **Richi Foundation [Richi Childhood
Cancer Foundation]**
705 Adams St.
  Holliston, MA 01746
Co. E-mail: contact@richifoundation.org
URL: http://www.richifoundation.org
Contact: Ricardo García, President
Facebook: www.facebook.com/RichiFoundation
Linkedin: www.linkedin.com/company/richi-childhoo
  d-cancer-foundation
X (Twitter): x.com/RichiE_RCCF

Description: An initiative whose mission is to boost Life Sciences startups from around the world by connecting them with Boston's unique innovation ecosystem. **Founded:** 2013.

REFERENCE WORKS

8803 ■ *5 Ways Business Incubator Programs Can Help Your Startup Grow*

URL(s): unionriverinnovation.com/5-ways-business -incubator-programs-can-help-your-startup-grow/

Description: Discusses the business resource challenges that startups face and offers five ways business incubators can help your startup grow. **Availability:** Online.

8804 ■ *"7 Ways a Business Incubator Can Benefit Your Online Startup" in Business News Daily (September 10, 2019)*

URL(s): www.businessnewsdaily.com/15279-busi -ness-incubator-benefits-for-online-startups.html

Ed: Skye Schooley. **Released:** September 10, 2019. **Description:** Business incubators can provide more than just startup capital for your online startup. They can provide recruiting, engineering, operations, automated processes, and even technology platforms. These additional resources can help your business become successful quickly and branch away from using an incubator as the company grows. **Availability:** Online.

8805 ■ *"Are Accelerators Worth It?" in Inc.*

URL(s): www.inc.com/magazine/201407/norm-bro dsky/are-accelerators-worth-it.html

Description: Discusses the importance of asking alumni of an accelerator how much time they got to spend time with mentors as a big value-add for utilizing an accelerator for your business. **Availability:** Online.

8806 ■ *"Business Incubator" in HowDo*

URL(s): howdo.com/training/tools/business-incubator/

Description: A detailed, step-by-step training guide to how to build your own business incubator. **Availability:** Online.

8807 ■ *Business Incubator: The Ultimate Step-By-Step Guide*

Ed: Gerardus Blokdyk. **Released:** May 20, 2018. **Price:** $70.24, Paperback; $40.99, E-book. **Description:** A business incubator self-assessment tool, which will also answer many questions regarding the industry. **Availability:** E-book; Print.

8808 ■ *Facilities Management for Business Incubators: Practical Advice and Information for Design, Construction and Management of 21st Century Business Incubation Facilities*

Ed: Mark Long. **Released:** March 13, 2019. **Price:** $59.95, Paperback; $29.95, E-book. **Description:** Ideas, strategies, advice, and tips on various aspects of business incubation. **Availability:** E-book; Print.

8809 ■ *"Funding Drought Stalls Biotech Incubators" in Saint Louis Business Journal (Vol. 31, July 29, 2011, No. 49, pp. 1)*

Pub: Saint Louis Business Journal

Contact: Robert Bobroff, President

E-mail: rbobroff@bizjournals.com

Ed: Angela Mueller. **Description:** Economic slowdown took its toll on cash-strapped startups that fill incubators such as the Bio-Research and Development Growth (BRDG) Park in Creve Coeur, Missouri and the Center for Emerging Technologies in Midtown St. Louis. BRDG put a hold on construction of of its two buildings. **Availability:** Print; Online.

8810 ■ *"Getting Started With Business Incubators" in Entrepreneur*

URL(s): www.entrepreneur.com/money-finance/busi ness-incubators/52802

Description: Presents information on how business incubators work. Includes the upside and downside of using an incubator to jump-start your small business. **Availability:** Online.

8811 ■ *"How to Pick the Right Accelerator" in Inc.*

URL(s): www.inc.com/magazine/201407/robin-scha tz/how-to-choose-and-get-accepted-to-an-accelra tor.html

Ed: Robin Schatz. **Description:** Finding the right business accelerator is challenging, but when you choose well, rewards can be great for your business. Provides information on how to choose the right accelerator for your company. **Availability:** Online.

8812 ■ *"Incubators Heat Up Chances of Small Business Survival" in Business News Daily (Aug. 5, 2022)*

URL(s): www.businessnewsdaily.com/272-incubators -increase-small-business-success.html

Ed: Ned Smith. **Released:** August 05, 2022. **Description:** Provides information on how an incubator can nurture a startup and how it differs from other economic development programs. **Availability:** Online.

8813 ■ *"Innovation Incubators Attract Printers, Designers" in PrintingImpressions October 16, 2019)*

URL(s): www.piworld.com/article/innovation-incuba tors-attract-printers-designers/

Ed: Vince Cahill. **Released:** October 16, 2019. **Description:** Five innovation centers in Brooklyn are examined as they focus on design and print. These centers are part of a bigger plan to mix a variety of industries to drive growth in their respective sectors. Printing studios for a variety of needs such as wallpaper, fabrics, retail, promotion, and others work with graphic designers and other professionals to increase manufacturing growth. **Availability:** Online.

8814 ■ *"Is an Incubator Right for Your Start-up?" in Inc.*

URL(s): www.inc.com/mehdi-maghsoodnia/is-an -incubator-right-for-your-startup.html

Ed: Mehdi Maghsoodnia. **Description:** A CEO discusses his beliefs about what to look for in an incubator to ensure it is right for your start-up. **Availability:** Online.

8815 ■ *"Is Wall Street the Best Start-Up Incubator?" in Inc.*

URL(s): www.inc.com/magazine/201306/darren-dahl/ is-wall-street-the-best-startup-incubator.html

Ed: Darren Dahl. **Description:** Five former jnvestment bankers explain how their experience at big banks helped them become better entrepreneurs. **Availability:** Online.

8816 ■ *"NSU Seeks Private Partners For New $80M Research Building" in South Florida Business Journal (Vol. 34, February 21, 2014, No. 31, pp. 4)*

Pub: American City Business Journals, Inc.

Contact: Mike Olivieri, Executive Vice President

Released: Weekly. **Price:** $8, Introductory 4-week offer(Digital & Print). **Description:** The $80 million Center for Collaborative Research at Nova Southeastern University hopes to become the largest incubator and wet laboratory space in Broward County, Florida. The center had its groundbreaking on February 13, 2014, and will be open for lease to private companies when it is ready in 22 months. **Availability:** Print; Online.

8817 ■ *"What Is a Business Incubator and How Does It Work?" in Draper University Blog (May 22, 2020)*

URL(s): www.draperuniversity.com/blog/what-is-a -business-incubator

Released: May 22, 2020. **Description:** Provides detailed information on what a business incubator is and what role they play in helping business start-ups. **Availability:** Online.

8818 ■ *"When Incubators Go Wrong" in Inc.*

URL(s): www.inc.com/staff-blog/when-incubators-go -wrong.html

Description: Presents information on those considering a business incubator things to be aware of that could go wrong. **Availability:** Online.

8819 ■ *"Which Accelerator Program Is Right for Your Company?" in Inc.*

URL(s): www.inc.com/magazine/201503/john-bran don/the-field-guide-to-accelerators.html

Description: Presents data on eight top accelerators in the U.S. for small businesses looking to enroll. **Availability:** Online.

8820 ■ *"Youngstown's Business Incubator Looks to the Future" in U.S. News & World Report (February 20, 2019)*

URL(s): www.usnews.com/news/cities/articles/2019-0 2-20/youngstown-ohios-business-incubator-l

Ed: John Ettorre. **Released:** February 20, 2019. **Description:** The Youngstown Business Incubator opened in 1995 and used Federal funds to renovate buildings which lead to cheap office space with shared facilities. Today, the incubator supports 75 portfolio companies, attracting millions in investments over the last four years. **Availability:** Online.

TRADE PERIODICALS

8821 ■ *Entrepreneur Magazine*

Pub: Entrepreneur Media Inc.

Contact: Dan Bova, Director

E-mail: dbova@entrepreneur.com

URL(s): www.entrepreneur.com/magazine

Released: 6/year **Price:** $10.99, for print and online 1 year; $9.99, for online or print 1 year. **Description:** Magazine covering small business management and operation. **Availability:** Print; Online.

8822 ■ *Entrepreneurship Theory and Practice (ETP)*

Pub: SAGE Publications

Contact: Tracey Ozmina, President

URL(s): journals.sagepub.com/home/ETP

Facebook: www.facebook.com/En trepreneurshipTheoryPractice

Linkedin: www.linkedin.com/company/etpjournal

X (Twitter): x.com/ETPjournal

Released: Bimonthly **Price:** $218, Institutions for single print issue; $41, Individuals for single print issue; $1,150, Institutions for print and online; $187, Individuals for print and online; $1,332, Institutions for print + online; $1,029, Institutions for online only; $1,187, Institutions for print only; $1,211, Institutions for print only; $2,014, Institutions for online. **Description:** Scholarly journal covering original conceptual and empirical research that contributes to the advancement of entrepreneurship. **Availability:** Print; PDF; Download; Online.

8823 ■ *Minority Business Entrepreneur*

Contact: Barbara Oliver, Editor

E-mail: boliver@mbemag.com

URL(s): www.mbemag.com

Facebook: www.facebook.com/mbemag

X (Twitter): twitter.com/MBEMag

Ed: Barbara Oliver. **Released:** Quarterly **Price:** $28, for 1 year print and online; $20, for 1 year prtint; $14, for 1 year print; $40, for 2 year print and online; $33, for 2 years print; $22, for 2 years online only. **Description:** Business magazine for ethnic minority and women business owners. **Availability:** Print; Online.

VIDEO/AUDIO MEDIA

8824 ■ *Finding a Mentor Who Thinks Holistically with Paul Zelizer*

URL(s): www.awarepreneurs.com/podcast/306-social -entrepreneur-mentor

Ed: Paul Zelizer. **Released:** September 26, 2023. **Description:** Podcast discusses taking a holistic approach to growing a business by finding an accelerator, how investors assess businesses, explains different business models, and offers questions to ask potential mentors. .

8825 ■ *The Strategy Hour: Incubator Client Strategy Breakdown: Bonnie Hit $30K Months & Took a !0-Day Vacay 5 Months into the Incubator Program*

URL(s): bossproject.com/podcast/incubator-client-s trategy-breakdown-bonnie-hit-30k-months-and-took -a-10-day-vacay

Ed: Abagail Pumphrey. **Description:** Podcast explains how an incubator program can help owners understand their business, adjust pricing structures, and transform companies. .

PUBLICATIONS

8826 ■ *"5 Reasons Why Incubators Are So Popular" in Geekers Magazine (August 31, 2021)*

URL(s): www.geekersmagazine.com/5-reasons-why -incubators-are-so-popular

Released: August 31, 2021. **Description:** Defines incubators as it relates to the small business world and gives tips on how to effectively use them.

ASSOCIATIONS AND OTHER ORGANIZATIONS

8827 ■ American Society for Information Science and Technology (ASIS&T)
1625 Prince St.
 Alexandria, VA 22314
Ph: (703)519-6200
Co. E-mail: asis@asisonline.org
URL: http://www.asisonline.org
Contact: Malcolm C. Smith, President
Facebook: www.facebook.com/ASISInternational
Linkedin: www.linkedin.com/company/30614
X (Twitter): x.com/ASIS_Intl
YouTube: www.youtube.com/user/ASISInternational

Description: Information specialists, librarians, administrators, social scientists, and others interested in the use, storage, retrieval, evaluation, and dissemination of recorded specialized information. Seeks to improve the information transfer process through research, development and education. Provides a forum for the discussion and critical analysis of work dealing with the theory, practice and development of elements involved in communication of information. **Founded:** 1937. **Publications:** *Handbook and Directory* (Annual); *Journal of the Association for Information Science and Technology* (Monthly); *American Society for Information Science--Handbook and Directory* (Annual). **Educational Activities:** ASIS&T Annual Meeting (Annual). **Awards:** ASIST Award for Research in Information Science (Annual); ASIS&T Award of Merit (Annual); ASIS&T Best Information Science Book Award (Annual); John Wiley Best JASIST Paper Award (Annual); Chapter Publication of the Year Award (Annual); Pratt Severn Best Student Research Paper Award (Annual); Chapter of the Year Award (Annual); Watson Davis Award (Annual); Clarivate Analytics Outstanding Information Science Teacher Award (Annual); ASIS&T SIG of the Year Award (Annual); Student Chapter of the Year Award (Annual); ASIS&T SIG Publication of the Year Award (Annual); James M. Cretsos Leadership Award (Annual); ASIS&T SIG Member of the Year Award (Annual); Chapter Event of the Year Award (Irregular). **Geographic Preference:** National.

8828 ■ ARMA Canada Region
PO Box 6624
 Calgary, AB, Canada T2P 2E4
URL: http://armacanada.org/arma-canada-chapters
Contact: Joanne McKenzie Hicks, President
Facebook: www.facebook.com/armacalgary
Linkedin: www.linkedin.com/company/arma-calgary
 -chapter
X (Twitter): x.com/armacanada

Description: Information management professionals. Promotes professional advancement of members and seeks to insure adherence to high standards of ethics and practice within the field of information management. Represents members' interests, conducts continuing professional development programs and serves as a clearinghouse on information manage-

ment. **Founded:** 1976. **Awards:** ARMA Canada Member Recognition Award (Annual). **Geographic Preference:** National.

8829 ■ Canadian Association for Information Science (CAIS) [L'Association canadienne des sciences de l'information (ACSI)]
ON, Canada
URL: http://cais-acsi.ca
Contact: Julia Bullard, President

Description: Promotes the advancement of information science in Canada and encourages and facilitates the exchange of information relating to the use, access, retrieval, organization, management, and dissemination of information. Publishes information on library science. Offers a quarterly journal. Accepts unsolicited manuscripts. **Founded:** 1970. **Publications:** *Canadian Journal of Information and Library Science* (Semiannual); *Canadian Association for Information Science / Association Canadienne des Sciences de L'Information (CAIS/ACSI)*. **Geographic Preference:** National.

8830 ■ Canadian Journal of Information and Library Science
5201 Dufferin St.
 Toronto, ON, Canada M3H 5T8
Ph: (416)667-7929
Fax: (416)667-7832
Co. E-mail: journals@utpress.utoronto.ca
URL: http://utpjournals.press
Contact: Antonia Pop, Vice President
E-mail: apop@utpress.utoronto.ca
URL(s): ojs.lib.uwo.ca/index.php/cjils

Ed: Valerie M. Nesset. **Released:** Semiannual **Description:** Journal focusing on research dealing with library and information science. Publishes research findings, both in full-length and in brief format; reviews of books; software and technology; and letters to the editor. Journal of the Canadian Association for Information Science. **Availability:** Print; PDF; Download.

8831 ■ Core: Leadership, Infrastructure, Futures
225 N Michigan Ave., Ste. 1300
 Chicago, IL 60601
Ph: (312)280-2153
Free: 800-545-2433
Co. E-mail: core@ala.org
URL: http://www.ala.org/future
Contact: Julie Reese, Executive Director
E-mail: jreese@ala.org
X (Twitter): x.com/ala_core
Instagram: www.instagram.com/core_ala

Description: Publishes books, journals, and other publications for the field of library leadership and infrastructure. **Founded:** 1966. **Publications:** *Library Leadership & Management (LL&M)* (Quarterly); *Directory of Historical Textbook and Curriculum Collections*; *Book Links* (Quarterly); *Journal of Youth Services in Libraries (JOYS)* (Quarterly); *Library Resources & Technical Services (LRTS)* (Quarterly); *One Hundred and One Software Packages to Use in*

Your Library; *ALA--Online Handbook of Organization* (Annual); *Reference and User Services Quarterly: The Official Journal of the Reference and User Services Association of the American Library Association (RUSQ)* (Quarterly); *0*; *Grapevine*; *The Big Book of Library Grant Money*; *Directory of Ethnic and Multicultural Publishers, Distributors and Resource Organizations*; *Documents to the People (DttP)* (Quarterly); *Booklist/Reference Books Bulletin--Biographical Reference Sources*; *Choice* (Monthly); *Information Technology and Libraries (ITAL)* (Quarterly); *Preservation Education Directory* (Irregular); *Librarian Career Resource Network*; *Genealogical Research and Resources: A Guide for Library Use*; *Technology Electronic Reviews* (Irregular); *American Library Association Guide to Information Access*; *FISCAL Directory of Fee-Based Research & Information Services* (Annual); *Reference Books Bulletin: A Compilation of Evaluations*; *Minorities and Women: A List of Major Organizations in Librarianship* (Annual); *Undergraduate Programs in Library Education*; *ALA Online Handbook of Organization* (Annual); *Guide to Employment Sources in the Library and Information Professions*; *Financial Assistance for Library & Information Studies Directory (FALIS)* (Annual); *Booklist*; *Great Library Promotion Ideas*; *Magazines for Children: A Guide for Parents, Teachers, and Librarians*; *Public Libraries* (Bimonthly); *Booklist Online*; *Choice Magazine: Current Reviews for Academic Libraries* (Monthly); *Directory of Test Collections in Academic, Professional, and Research Libraries*; *Networking CD-ROMs*; *Marketing to Libraries Through Library Associations* (Annual); *Library Technology Reports: Expert Guides to Library Systems and Services* (6/year). **Educational Activities:** ALA Annual Conference (Annual); ALA Midwinter Meeting (Annual); Library and Information Technology Association Meeting (Annual); LITA Forum (Annual). **Awards:** ALA/IIDA Library Interior Design Award (Biennial); Library Hi Tech Award for Outstanding Communication for Continuing Education in Library and Information Science (Annual); Frederick G. Kilgour Award for Research in Library and Information Technology (Annual); Ex Libris Student Writing Award (Annual); Christian Larew Memorial Scholarship in Library and Information Technology (Annual); LITA/Ex Libris Student Writing Award (Annual); Hugh C. Atkinson Memorial Award (Annual); Christian Larew Memorial Scholarship (Annual); LITA/LSSI Minority Scholarship (Annual); LITA / OCLC Spectrum Scholarship in Library and Information Technology (Annual); W.Y. Boyd Literary Award for Excellence in Military Fiction (Annual); ALA Excellence in Library Programming Award (Annual); Elizabeth Futas Catalyst for Change Award (Biennial); Paul Howard Award for Courage (Biennial); Theodor Seuss Geisel Award (Annual).

8832 ■ Special Libraries Association (SLA)
1120 Rte. 73, Ste. 200
 Mount Laurel, NJ 08054
Ph: (703)647-4900
Co. E-mail: membership@sla.org
URL: http://sla.org

Contact: John Digilio, President
E-mail: jdigilio@gmail.com
Facebook: www.facebook.com/
    SpecialLibrariesAssociation
Linkedin: www.linkedin.com/company/sla
X (Twitter): x.com/slahq
Description: International association of information professionals who work in specialized information environments such as business, research, government, universities, newspapers, museums, and institutions. Seeks to advance the leadership role of information professionals through learning, networking and advocacy. Offers consulting services to organizations that wish to establish or expand a library. Conducts strategic learning and development courses, public relations, and government relations programs. Provides employment services. Operates knowledge exchange on topics pertaining to the development and management of special libraries. **Scope:** Libraries. **Founded:** 1909. **Holdings:** Figures not available. **Publications:** *Information Outlook* (Bimonthly); *Business and Finance Division Bulletin* (Quarterly); *Directory of Catalogers in the Special Libraries Association*; *Information Outlook: The Monthly Magazine of the Special Libraries Association* (Bimonthly); *Who's Who in Special Libraries* (Annual); *SLA Annual Salary Survey* (Annual); *SLA Connections* (Continuous); *Physics-Astronomy-Mathematics Division--Membership Directory* (Annual); *SpeciaList* (Monthly); *Insurance and Employee Benefits Literature.* **Educational Activities:** The Library Innovation Conference (Annual). **Awards:** Fellows of SLA (Annual); SLA Hall of Fame (Annual); John Cotton Dana Award (Irregular); H. W. Wilson Company Award (Irregular); SLA Diversity Leadership Development Program Award (Annual); SLA Presidential Citations. **Geographic Preference:** National.

8833 ■ Technation (ITAC) - Library
5090 Explorer Dr., Ste. 510
Mississauga, ON, Canada L4W 4T9
Ph: (905)602-8345
Fax: (905)602-8346
Co. E-mail: memberservices@technationcanada.ca
URL: http://technationcanada.ca/en
Contact: Angela Mondou, President
Facebook: www.facebook.com/TECHNATIONca
X (Twitter): x.com/technationca
Instagram: www.instagram.com/TECHNATIONca
YouTube: www.youtube.com/channel/UCGxLY7
    -bBzlZd2eTiM0ziMA
Description: Corporations producing information technologies and related components. Promotes growth and development in the domestic information technology industry. Represents members' interests; conducts research; maintains advocacy programs. Operates hall of fame; compiles statistics. **Scope:** Information technologies. **Services:** Library open to the public for reference use. **Founded:** 1984. **Holdings:** Books and periodicals. **Educational Activities:** Executive Forum on Microelectronics. **Geographic Preference:** National.

REFERENCE WORKS

8834 ■ "Here Are the Data Brokers Quietly Buying and Selling Your Personal Information" in Fast Company (March 2, 2019)
URL(s): www.fastcompany.com/90310803/here-are
    -the-data-brokers-quietly-buying-and-selling-your
    -personal-information
Ed: Steven Melendez, Alex Pasternack. **Released:** March 02, 2019. **Description:** Vermont recently passed a law requiring companies that buy and sell third-party personal data to register with the Secretary of State. However, the law doesn't require a lot of key information, such as what data they collect, which is frustrating for consumers. Included are the companies that have registered under Vermont's new data broker law with instructions on how to opt out of them collecting your personal data. **Availability:** Online.

8835 ■ International Literary Market Place: The Directory of the International Book Publishing Industry
Pub: Information Today Inc.
Contact: Thomas H. Hogan, President

URL(s): store.infotoday.com/product/literary-marke
    t-place
Released: Latest edition 84th edition, 2024. **Price:** $539.50, for outside North America; $507.50, Single issue; $529.50, Canada and Mexico. **Description:** Covers over 10,500 publishers in over 180 countries outside the United States and Canada, and about 1,499 trade and professional organizations related to publishing abroad; includes major printers, binders, typesetters, book manufacturers, book dealers, libraries, literary agencies, translators, book clubs, reference books and journals, periodicals, prizes, and international reference section. **Entries include:** For publishers--Name, address, phone, fax, telex, names and titles of key personnel, branches, type of publications, subjects, ISBN prefix. Listings for others include similar information but less detail. **Arrangement:** Classified by business activities, then geographical. **Indexes:** Company name, subject, type of publication. **Availability:** Print; Online.

8836 ■ Libraries Canada
Pub: Grey House Publishing Canada Inc.
Contact: Bryon Moore, General Manager
E-mail: bmoore@greyhouse.ca
URL(s): greyhouse.ca/library.htm
Released: Annual; latest edition 37th. **Price:** $399, for price. **Description:** Covers over 6,700 libraries, library associations, library schools and technician programs, archives, periodicals, provincial library agencies, government libraries, regional systems, and library services suppliers (wholesalers, binders, subscription agencies, etc.) in Canada. **Entries include:** Library or firm name, address, phone, fax, TDD, e-mail; names and titles of key personnel and contact, description of collection, services offered to the public; budget range; computers and automated systems in use; publications and url addresses. **Arrangement:** Library schools are geographical; other lists are alphabetical. **Indexes:** Geographical, subject, personal name. **Availability:** CD-ROM; Print; Online.

TRADE PERIODICALS

8837 ■ The Data Base for Advances in Information Systems
Pub: Association for Computing Machinery
Contact: Yannis Ioannidis, President
URL(s): sigmis.org/the-data-base
Released: Quarterly **Description:** Presents articles on practical research relating to business uses of information systems. **Availability:** Online.

8838 ■ The Information Advisor's Guide to Internet Research
Pub: Find/SVP
URL(s): informationadvisor.com
Released: Annual **Price:** $199.95, Individuals; $377, Two years; $578, three years. **Description:** Supplies business data users information on comparing and evaluating competing information sources. Provides comparison charts, reviews, advice on data reliability, and quality for both online and print business information produced in the U.S., Europe, Asia, and Latin America.

8839 ■ Information Standards Quarterly (ISQ)
Pub: National Information Standards Organization
Contact: Todd Carpenter, Executive Director
URL(s): www.niso.org/niso-io/isq
Released: Quarterly; spring, summer, winter, fall. **Description:** NISO's newsletter, Information Standards Quarterly (ISQ), features timely standards-related news, information about implementation of standards, and updates on standards-in-development. The January issue features an annual "State of the Standards" which reports on the status of each standard in NISO's program. **Availability:** Print; PDF; Online.

8840 ■ Information Today (IT)
Pub: Information Today Inc.
Contact: Thomas H. Hogan, President
URL(s): www.infotoday.com/IT/default.asp

Ed: Donovan Griffin. **Released:** Monthly; with combined January/February, July/August and November/December issues. **Description:** User and producer magazine (tabloid) covering electronic and optical information services. **Availability:** Print; Online.

8841 ■ Journal of the Association for Information Science and Technology (JASIST)
Pub: John Wiley & Sons, Inc.
Contact: Christina Van Tassell, Executive Vice President Chief Financial Officer
URL(s): asistdl.onlinelibrary.wiley.com/journal/2330
    1643
Released: Monthly **Price:** $4,132, Institutions for print only US, Canada; $3,962, Institutions for online only US, Canada; $4,450, Institutions for print + online US, Canada; $4,540, Institutions for print only India, Japan; $4,353, Institutions for online only India, Japan; $4,888, Institutions for print and online India, Japan. **Description:** International, peer-reviewed journal covering research in information science. Published by Wiley on behalf of the Association for Information Science and Technology. **Availability:** Print; PDF; Online; Download.

TRADE SHOWS AND CONVENTIONS

8842 ■ Special Libraries Association Information Revolution
URL(s): www.sla.org
Description: Library equipment, supplies, and services, including computers and software, Database information. **Audience:** Industry professionals. **Principal Exhibits:** Library equipment, supplies, and services, including computers and software, Database information.

CONSULTANTS

8843 ■ A. Davis Grant & Co.
295 Pierson Ave.
Edison, NJ 08837-3118
Ph: (732)463-1414
Co. E-mail: info@adg.net
URL: http://www.adg.net
Contact: Allan Grossman, Contact
E-mail: allan@adg.net
Description: Executive search firm dealing exclusively in the field of information systems and technology. **Scope:** Executive search firm dealing exclusively in the field of information systems and technology. **Founded:** 1985.

COMPUTERIZED DATABASES

8844 ■ Library Literature & Information Science Full Text™
EBSCO Information Services
10 Estes St.
Ipswich, MA 01938
Ph: (978)356-6500
Free: 800-653-2726
Co. E-mail: information@ebsco.com
URL: http://www.ebsco.com
Contact: Tim Collins, Chief Executive Officer
URL(s): www.ebsco.com/products/research-da
    tabases/library-literature-information-science-full
    -text
Availability: Online. **Type:** Bibliographic; Full-text; Image.

ASSOCIATIONS AND OTHER ORGANIZATIONS

8845 ■ EIFS Industry Members Association (EIMA)
513 W Broad St., Ste. 210
Falls Church, VA 22046-3257
Ph: (703)538-1616
URL: http://www.eima.com
Contact: Stephen T. Sears, Chief Executive Officer
E-mail: ssears@eima.com
Facebook: www.facebook.com/EIMA.EIFS
Linkedin: www.linkedin.com/company/eifs-industry-members-association-eima
X (Twitter): x.com/EIMA_EIFS
Instagram: www.instagram.com/eima_eifs
YouTube: www.youtube.com/channel/UCeXKB7XhWUdHQOFbExzXBPw
Description: Aims to improve the exterior insulation industry and to widen the use of its products through collective action. Conducts educational and research programs. **Founded:** 1981. **Publications:** *EIFS Briefs*. **Educational Activities:** EIMA Annual Meeting (Annual). **Geographic Preference:** National.

8846 ■ Insulation Contractors Association of America (ICAA)
Alexandria, VA
Ph: (703)739-0356
Co. E-mail: icaa@insulate.org
URL: http://www.insulate.org
Contact: Terry Burnham, President
Description: Residential and commercial insulation contractors; manufacturing and supplier associates. Seeks to develop industry standards; promotes energy conservation in old and new buildings through proper specifications and applications of insulation; represents interests of the industry at all government levels; promotes exchange of information among insulation contractors. Sponsors seminars, field surveys, and research. **Founded:** 1977. **Publications:** *Insulation Industry Buyer's Guide* (Annual); *Insulation Contractors Association of America--Technical Bulletins*; *Insulation Contractors Report* (Quarterly). **Educational Activities:** Annual ICAA Convention & Trade Show (Annual). **Geographic Preference:** National.

8847 ■ National Insulation Association (NIA)
516 Herndon Pky., Ste. D
Herndon, VA 20190
Ph: (703)464-6422
Fax: (703)464-5896
URL: http://www.insulation.org

Contact: Dan Bofinger, Co-President
Facebook: www.facebook.com/NIAinfo
Linkedin: www.linkedin.com/company/niainfo
YouTube: www.youtube.com/niainfo
Description: Insulation contractors, distributors, and manufacturers. **Founded:** 1953. **Publications:** *NIA News* (Quarterly); *Insulation Outlook* (Monthly); *National Commercial & Industrial Insulation Standards Manual*; *Safety Handbook for Insulation Distributors & Fabricators*; *Insulation Outlook: Business Solutions for Expanding or Relocating Companies* (Monthly); *Asbestos Abatement Industry Directory*; *National Insulation Association--Membership Directory and Resource Guide*. **Educational Activities:** NIA Annual Convention (Annual); National Insulation Association Annual Convention (Annual). **Geographic Preference:** National.

8848 ■ North American Insulation Manufacturers Association (NAIMA)
2013 Olde Regent Way, Ste. 150
Leland, NC 28451
Ph: (703)684-0084
Fax: (703)684-0427
URL: http://insulationinstitute.org
Facebook: www.facebook.com/pg/insulationinstitute/community
Linkedin: www.linkedin.com/company/insulation-institute
X (Twitter): x.com/knowinsulation
YouTube: www.youtube.com/user/NAIMAVideo
Description: Manufacturers of fiberglass, rock wool, and slag wool insulation products. Promotes energy efficiency and environmental preservation through the use of fiberglass, rock wool, and slag wool insulation products. Encourages safe production and use of insulation materials. **Founded:** 1933. **Geographic Preference:** National.

REFERENCE WORKS

8849 ■ "6 Core Competencies for Mechanical Insulation Site Foremen" in Insulation Outlook (September 1, 2019)
URL(s): insulation.org/io/articles/6-core-competencies-for-mechanical-insulation-site-foremen/
Ed: Gordon Vierck. **Released:** September 01, 2019.
Description: Discusses the six general responsibilities a project foreman on commercial sites for mechanical insulation needs to prioritize. **Availability:** Online.

8850 ■ National Insulation Association--Membership Directory and Resource Guide
Pub: National Insulation Association
Contact: Dan Bofinger, Co-President

URL(s): insulation.org/membership/membership-directory
Description: Covers about 600 member manufacturers, distributors, and contractors involved in the commercial and industrial insulation and asbestos abatement industries. **Entries include:** Company name, address, phone, names and titles of key personnel, subsidiary and branch names and locations, products and services. **Arrangement:** Alphabetical by company, classified by, product/service. **Indexes:** Product/service, subject, geographical. **Availability:** Print.

TRADE PERIODICALS

8851 ■ Roofing Contractor
Pub: BNP Media
Contact: Harper Henderson, Owner Co-Chief Executive Officer
URL(s): www.roofingcontractor.comeblast.bnpmedia.com/RC/eMag/0623/RC0623-eMag.html
Facebook: www.facebook.com/RoofingContractor
Linkedin: www.linkedin.com/company/roofing-contractor-magazine
X (Twitter): twitter.com/RoofContr
Instagram: www.instagram.com/roofingcontractormedia
YouTube: www.youtube.com/user/RoofingContractorMag
Ed: Art Aisner. **Released:** Monthly **Price:** Free.
Description: Trade magazine on roofing and insulation. **Availability:** Print; Online.

TRADE SHOWS AND CONVENTIONS

8852 ■ National Insulation Association Annual Convention
National Insulation Association (NIA)
516 Herndon Pky., Ste. D
Herndon, VA 20190
Ph: (703)464-6422
Fax: (703)464-5896
URL: http://www.insulation.org
Contact: Dan Bofinger, Co-President
URL(s): insulation.org/convention2024
Frequency: Annual. **Description:** Exhibits relating to insulation. **Audience:** Merit and union contractors, distributors, fabricators, laminators, and manufacturers, Spouses, guests, and children are encouraged. **Principal Exhibits:** Exhibits relating to insulation. **Telecommunication Services:** events@insulation.org.

Insurance Agency

START-UP INFORMATION

8853 ■ *"An Insurer Stretches Out" in Business Journal Portland (Vol. 30, February 21, 2014, No. 51, pp. 4)*
Pub: American City Business Journals, Inc.
Contact: Mike Olivieri, Executive Vice President

Released: Weekly. **Price:** $4, Introductory 4-week offer(Digital & Print). **Description:** The diversification strategy of Cambia Health Solutions has led to investments in several health care startups. The company earned $5.8 billion in revenue from insurance premiums in 2012 and posted a profit margin of about 2 percent for its net income of $173 million. **Availability:** Print; Online.

ASSOCIATIONS AND OTHER ORGANIZATIONS

8854 ■ **American Association of Insurance Management Consultants (AAIMCo) - Library**
2013 Sandy Bank Ln.
 Pearland, TX 77581
URL: http://www.aaimco.com
Contact: Brent Winans, President
E-mail: bwinans@cleararm.com

Description: Consists of individuals who devote a substantial portion of their services to insurance consulting, risk management activities, legal representation relating to insurance issues; as well as education and professional development training, employment consulting, and other technical and management advice to the insurance industry. Advises and assists the insurance industry and seeks to achieve professional recognition for insurance management consultants. Mediates the exchange of ideas; sets standards of service and performance; maintains a code of ethics; offers a referral service and a series of educational conferences and seminars. Operates speakers' bureau; offers placement services; compiles statistics. **Scope:** Business management; insurance management. **Founded:** 1979. **Holdings:** Articles; Books. **Geographic Preference:** National.

8855 ■ **American Association of Insurance Services (AAIS)**
701 Warrenville Rd.
 Lisle, IL 60532
Ph: (630)681-8347
Free: 800-564-AAIS
Fax: (630)681-8356
Co. E-mail: membership@aaisonline.com
URL: http://www.aaisonline.com
Contact: Edmund J. Kelly, President
Facebook: www.facebook.com/AAISconnect
Linkedin: www.linkedin.com/company/1782266
X (Twitter): x.com/AAISConnect
YouTube: www.youtube.com/channel/
 UCmKNcKCNTsG6vSh46SV4ziQ

Description: Property and casualty insurance companies; mutual, stock, and reciprocal companies. Develops loss costs, rules, forms, and statistical services for property and casualty insurance. Licensed in all states, the District of Columbia, and the Commonwealth of Puerto Rico. **Founded:** 1936. **Geographic Preference:** National.

8856 ■ **American Council of Life Insurers (ACLI)**
101 Constitution Ave. NW, Ste. 700
 Washington, DC 20001-2133
Ph: (202)624-2000
Free: 877-674-4659
Co. E-mail: contact@acli.com
URL: http://www.acli.com
Contact: Susan K. Neely, President
Facebook: www.facebook.com/ACLINews
Linkedin: www.linkedin.com/company/acli
X (Twitter): x.com/aclinews

Description: Represents the interests of legal reserve life insurance companies in legislative, regulatory and judicial matters at the federal, state and municipal levels of government and at the NAIC. Member companies hold majority of the life insurance in force in the United States. **Founded:** 1906. **Publications:** *Investment Bulletins* (Quarterly); *Life Insurers Fact Book* (Annual); *Life Insurers Fact Book* (Annual). **Geographic Preference:** National.

8857 ■ **American Property Casualty Insurance Association (APCIA) - Library**
8700 W Bryn Mawr Ave., Ste., 1200S
 Chicago, IL 60631-3512
Ph: (847)297-7800
Fax: (847)297-5064
Co. E-mail: compliance@apci.org
URL: http://www.apci.org
Contact: David A. Sampson, President
E-mail: david.sampson@apci.org
Facebook: www.facebook.com/TeamAPCIA
Linkedin: www.linkedin.com/company/american
 -property-casualty-insurance-association
X (Twitter): x.com/TeamAPCIA

Description: Independent property and casualty insurance companies. Provides advocacy and technical information. **Scope:** Insurance. **Founded:** 2004. **Holdings:** Figures not available. **Publications:** *Individual State Profile* (Annual); *Legislative Reporter* (Biweekly); *State Insurance Department Directory* (Annual); *Policy Kit: A Collection of Sample Insurance Forms*; *Survey of Workers Compensations Laws*. **Educational Activities:** Alliance of American Insurers Meeting (Annual). **Geographic Preference:** National.

8858 ■ **American Risk and Insurance Association (ARIA)**
c/o 716 Providence Rd.
 Malvern, PA 19355-3402
Ph: (610)640-1997
Fax: (610)725-1007
Co. E-mail: aria@theinstitutes.org
URL: http://www.aria.org

Contact: Mary Ann Cook, Executive Director
E-mail: aria@theinstitutes.org
X (Twitter): x.com/ariarisk

Description: Comprises of academics, individual insurance industry representatives, students, and retirees. Works to emphasize research relevant to the operational concerns and functions of insurance professionals. **Founded:** 1932. **Publications:** *Journal of Risk and Insurance (JRI)* (Quarterly); *Risk Management and Insurance Review (RMIR)* (Semiannual). **Educational Activities:** Annual Meeting (Annual). **Awards:** Casualty Actuarial Society Research Award (Annual); ARIA Early Career Scholarly Achievement Award (Annual); ARIA Excellence in Teaching Award (Annual); ARIA/Hagen Family Foundation Travel Award (Annual); Bob Hedges Undergraduate Student Award (Annual); ARIA Presidents' Award (Annual); RMIR Feature Article Award (Annual); RMIR Best Perspectives Article Award (Annual); Kulp-Wright Book Award (Annual); Les B. Strickler Innovation in Instruction Award (Annual); Robert I. Mehr Award (Annual); Robert C. Witt Award (Annual). **Geographic Preference:** National.

8859 ■ **Association Canadienne des Compagnies d'Assurance Mutuelles (ACCAM) [Canadian Association of Mutual Insurance Companies (CAMIC)]**
1000 McGarry Ter., Unit M010
 Ottawa, ON, Canada K2J 7A8
Ph: (613)789-6851
Free: 888-366-7807
Co. E-mail: info@camic.ca
URL: http://camic.ca
Contact: Sangita Kamblé, President
E-mail: skamble@camic.ca
X (Twitter): x.com/camic_accam

Description: Mutual insurance companies. Seeks to advance the insurance industry. Facilitates communication and cooperation among members; represents members' commercial interests before government agencies and the public. **Geographic Preference:** National.

8860 ■ **Canadian Board of Marine Underwriters (CBMU)**
7145 W Credit Ave., Bldg. 2, Ste. 201
 Mississauga, ON, Canada L5N 6J7
Ph: (905)826-4768
Co. E-mail: cbmu@cbmu.com
URL: http://www.cbmu.com
Contact: Danielle Jackson, President
Linkedin: www.linkedin.com/in/the-cbmu-22045159
X (Twitter): x.com/TheCBMU
Instagram: www.instagram.com/the_cbmu

Description: Marine underwriters. Promotes professional development of members; seeks to advance the practice of marine insurance underwriting. Serves as a forum for the exchange of information among members; conducts continuing professional education courses. **Founded:** 1917. **Publications:** *The Log* (Biennial). **Geographic Preference:** National.

8861 ■ Canadian Independent Adjusters Association (CIAA) [L'Association Canadienne des Experts Independants]
Ste. No. 308, 132 Commerce Pk .Dr.
  Barrie, ON, Canada L4N 0Z7
Ph: (416)621-6222
Free: 877-255-5589
Co. E-mail: info@ciaa-adjusters.ca
URL: http://www.ciaa-adjusters.ca
Contact: Jeff Edge, President
E-mail: jeff@leadingedgecs.ca
Linkedin: www.linkedin.com/company/canadian-in
  dependent-adjusters-association
X (Twitter): x.com/CIAAOfficial1
Description: Promotes continuing professional development of members; encourages adherence to high standards of ethics and practice in the industry. Conducts educational programs. **Founded:** 1953. **Publications:** *Claims Manual*; *Canadian Independent Adjusters' Claims Manual* (Annual). **Awards:** Canadian Insurance Claims Education Benevolent Foundation (Annual); CIAA Door Prize (Annual). **Geographic Preference:** National.

8862 ■ Canadian Life and Health Insurance Association Inc. (CLHIA) - Library
79 Wellington St. W, Ste. 2300., TD South Twr
  Toronto, ON, Canada M5K 1G8
Ph: (416)777-2221
Free: 888-295-8112
Co. E-mail: info@clhia.ca
URL: http://www.clhia.ca/web/CLHIA_LP4W_LND
  _Webstation.nsf/index.html?readform
Facebook: www.facebook.com/clhia
Linkedin: www.linkedin.com/company/clhia
X (Twitter): x.com/clhia
Instagram: www.instagram.com/clhia_accap
Description: Seeks to advance the insurance industry; promotes adherence to high standards of ethics and practice among members. Represents the collective interests of the life and health insurance industries. **Scope:** Insurance. **Founded:** 1894. **Holdings:** Figures not available. **Publications:** *Policyholder Tax Manual*. **Geographic Preference:** National.

8863 ■ Conference of Consulting Actuaries (CCA)
21660 W Field Pwy., Ste. 135
  Deer Park, IL 60010
Ph: (847)719-6500
Co. E-mail: conference@ccactuaries.org
URL: http://www.ccactuaries.org
Contact: David Scharf, President
Facebook: www.facebook.com/CCActuaries
Linkedin: www.linkedin.com/company/conference-of
  -consulting-actuaries
YouTube: www.youtube.com/user/ccactuaries
Description: Full-time consulting actuaries or governmental actuaries. Develops and maintains structure and programs to reinforce, enhance, or add to member's knowledge and skills; this includes continuing education, through diverse delivery methods, for all practice areas and for consulting and business skills. **Founded:** 1950. **Publications:** *The Proceedings* (Annual); *Yearbook* (Annual). **Awards:** John Hanson Memorial Prize (Periodic); CCA Lifetime Achievement Award (Annual); CCA Most Valuable Volunteer Award (Annual); Wynn Kent Public Communications Award (Annual). **Geographic Preference:** National.

8864 ■ Consumer Credit Industry Association (CCIA)
1300 Pennsylvania Ave. NW, No. 327
  Washington, DC 20004
Co. E-mail: contact@cciaonline.com
URL: http://cciaonline.com
Contact: Sarah Ferman Baker, President
Description: Insurance companies underwriting consumer credit insurance in areas of life insurance, accident and health insurance, and property insurance. **Founded:** 1951. **Publications:** *Consumer Credit Insurance Association--Annual Meeting Proceedings* (Annual); *Consumer Credit Insurance Association--Digest Bulletin* (Periodic); *Consumer*

Credit Insurance Association--Information Bulletin (Periodic); *Consumer Credit Insurance Association--Legislative Bulletin* (Periodic). **Geographic Preference:** National.

8865 ■ Council of Insurance Agents and Brokers (CIAB)
701 Pennsylvania Ave. NW, Ste. 750
  Washington, DC 20004
Ph: (202)783-4400
Fax: (202)783-4410
Co. E-mail: ciab@ciab.com
URL: http://www.ciab.com
Contact: Ken Crerar, President
E-mail: ken.crerar@ciab.com
Facebook: www.facebook.com/leadersedge
Linkedin: www.linkedin.com/company/the-council-of
  -insurance-agents-&-brokers
X (Twitter): x.com/TheCIAB
YouTube: www.youtube.com/user/TheCouncilDC
Description: Represents the interests of the leading commercial property and casualty insurance agencies and brokerage firms in the U.S. and around the world. **Founded:** 1913. **Publications:** *For Your Benefit* (Monthly); *Leader's Edge* (10/year). **Geographic Preference:** National.

8866 ■ Independent Financial Brokers of Canada (IFB) [Courtiers Indenpendants en Securite Financiere (CISF)]
740-30 Eglinton Ave. W
  Mississauga, ON, Canada L5R 3E7
Ph: (905)279-2727
Free: 888-654-3333
Fax: (905)276-7295
Co. E-mail: general@ifbc.ca
URL: http://www.ifbc.ca
Contact: Sheldon C. Stier, President
Facebook: www.facebook.com/independen
  tfinancialbrokers
X (Twitter): x.com/IFBcanada
Description: Provides tools to help members understand and navigate the regulatory environment and maintain a compliant practice. Conducts exclusive program for succession and continuity planning. **Founded:** 1987. **Publications:** *The Independent* (Quarterly). **Geographic Preference:** National.

8867 ■ Independent Insurance Agents and Brokers of America, Inc. (IIABA)
127 S Peyton St.
  Alexandria, VA 22314
Free: 800-221-7917
Fax: (703)683-7556
Co. E-mail: info@iiaba.net
URL: http://www.independentagent.com/default.aspx
Facebook: www.facebook.com/independentagent
Linkedin: www.linkedin.com/company/independen
  t-insurance-agents-and-brokers-of-america
X (Twitter): x.com/IndAgent
YouTube: www.youtube.com/user/independentagent
Description: Sales agencies handling property, fire, casualty, and surety insurance. Organizes technical and sales courses for new and established agents. Sponsors Independent Insurance Agent Junior Classic Golf Tournament. **Founded:** 1896. **Publications:** *IA Magazine* (Monthly); *Insurance News and Views* (Weekly). **Educational Activities:** Fall Leadership Conference (Annual). **Awards:** Sidney O. Smith Award (Annual); Woodworth Memorial Award (Annual); IIABA Outstanding Young Agents Committee Awards (Annual). **Geographic Preference:** National.

8868 ■ Insurance Brokers Association of Canada (IBAC) [Association des courtiers d'assurances du Canada]
18 King St. E, Ste. 1210
  Toronto, ON, Canada M5C 1C4
Ph: (416)367-1831
Co. E-mail: ibac@ibac.ca
URL: http://www.ibac.ca
Contact: Robyn Young, President
X (Twitter): x.com/ibacanada

Description: Insurance brokers. Promotes advancement of the insurance brokerage industry. Represents members' interests. Conducts educational and training programs for members' staff. **Founded:** 1921. **Geographic Preference:** National.

8869 ■ Insurance Bureau of Canada (IBC) - Library [Bureau d'Assurance du Canada]
777 Bay St., Ste. 2400
  Toronto, ON, Canada M5G 2C8
Ph: (416)362-2031
Free: 844-227-5422
Fax: (416)361-5952
Co. E-mail: memberservices@ibc.ca
URL: http://www.ibc.ca
Contact: Celyeste Power, President
Facebook: www.facebook.com/insurancebureau
Linkedin: www.linkedin.com/company/insurance-bu
  reau-of-canada
X (Twitter): x.com/InsuranceBureau
Instagram: www.instagram.com/insurancebureau
YouTube: www.youtube.com/channel/UChOOs
  6RVUn2WQFVQJgAN0Qw
Description: Works with members to improve communication with the public, government, news media, and other industry associations. **Scope:** Insurance. **Founded:** 1964. **Holdings:** Figures not available. **Publications:** *IBC Between the Lines* (Periodic); *Facts of the General Insurance Industry of Canada* (Periodic); *Perspective: Financial Affairs, Regulatory Affairs* (Quarterly). **Geographic Preference:** National.

8870 ■ Insurance Consumer Affairs Exchange (ICAE)
PO Box 892
  New Hyde Park, NY 11040
Ph: (847)991-8454
URL: http://www.icae.com
Contact: Richard McGee, Executive Director
E-mail: rmcgee@icae.com
Description: Voluntary, professional group of consumer affairs specialists from insurance companies, insurance regulators, and consumer information centers. Provides opportunities to exchange ideas for improving communication between insurers, consumers, and regulators. **Founded:** 1976. **Publications:** *ICAE Catalyst* (Periodic); *ICAE Resource Manual*. **Educational Activities:** Winds of Change: Steering Customer Relations. **Geographic Preference:** National.

8871 ■ Insurance Information Institute (III)
110 William St.
  New York, NY 10038
Ph: (212)346-5500
Co. E-mail: info@iii.org
URL: http://www.iii.org
Contact: Richard P. Creedon, Chairman
URL(s): www.groupunderwriters.com
Facebook: www.facebook.com/iiiorg
Linkedin: www.linkedin.com/company/insurance
  -information-institute
X (Twitter): x.com/iiiorg
YouTube: www.youtube.com/user/iiivideo
Description: Property and casualty insurance companies. Provides information and educational services to mass media, educational institutions, trade associations, businesses, government agencies, and the public. **Publications:** *I.I.I. Data Base Search*; *I.I.I. Insurance Daily*; *Insurance Handbook for Reporters*; *Property-Casualty Insurance Facts*. **Educational Activities:** Property/Casualty Insurance Joint Industry Forum (Annual). **Geographic Preference:** National.

8872 ■ Insurance Marketing & Communications Association (IMCA)
4248 Pk. Glen Rd.
  Minneapolis, MN 55416-4758
Ph: (952)928-4644
Fax: (952)929-1318
Co. E-mail: info@imcanet.com
URL: http://www.imcanet.com
Contact: Hadie Mulvey, Chairperson
Facebook: www.facebook.com/Imcanet

Linkedin: www.linkedin.com/company/insurance
-marketing-&-communications-association
X (Twitter): x.com/IMCAnet

Description: Advertising, marketing, public relations, and sales promotion executives of property and casualty insurance companies. Provides members with a forum for enhancing their knowledge of marketing and communications techniques and strategies, so that they can attain the highest standards of professional excellence in serving the information needs of their policyholders, employees, producers and the general public. **Founded:** 1923. **Awards:** IMCA Innovation Torchbearer Award (Annual); IMCA Best in Show Award (Annual); IMCA Showcase Awards (Annual). **Geographic Preference:** National.

8873 ■ International Association of Insurance Professionals (IAIP)

One Glenlake Pkwy., Ste. 1200
 Atlanta, GA 30328
Ph: (404)789-3153
Free: 800-766-6249
Fax: (404)240-0998
Co. E-mail: membership@iaip-ins.org
URL: http://www.internationalinsuranceprofessionals
 .org/default.aspx
Contact: Tammy Wascher, President
Facebook: www.facebook.com/
 theinsuranceprofessionals
Linkedin: www.linkedin.com/groups/International
 -Association-Insurance-Professionals-IAIP-4067452
X (Twitter): x.com/IAIPInsPros

Description: Insurance industry professionals. Promotes continuing education and networking for the professional advancement of its members. Offers education programs, meetings, services, and leadership opportunities. Provides a forum to learn about other disciplines in the insurance industry. **Founded:** 1940. **Publications:** Today's Insurance Professional (Quarterly). **Educational Activities:** Annual IAIP Convention (Annual). **Geographic Preference:** Multinational.

8874 ■ Medical Professional Liability Association (MPL)

2275 Research Blvd., Ste. 250
 Rockville, MD 20850
Ph: (301)947-9000
Fax: (301)947-9090
Co. E-mail: communications@mplassociation.org
URL: http://www.mplassociation.org
Contact: Brian Atchinson, President
E-mail: batchinson@piaa.us
Facebook: www.facebook.com/MPLassociation
Linkedin: www.linkedin.com/company/mpl-associa
 tion
X (Twitter): x.com/MPLassociation

Description: Physician liability insurance companies, including domestic physician and dental liability insurers, international affiliates, and reinsurers. Seeks to further the best interests of member companies in areas related to physician liability insurance. Focuses on the availability and affordability of professional liability insurance and the effective delivery of quality healthcare. Conducts research and educational programs; monitors and advocates for legislation. **Founded:** 1977. **Publications:** Medical Professional Liability Association--Membership Directory; Inside Medical Liability (Quarterly); PIAA Membership Directory (Annual). **Educational Activities:** MPL Association's workshops. **Awards:** Peter Sweetland Award of Excellence (Annual). **Geographic Preference:** National.

8875 ■ National Association of Health Underwriters (NAHU)

999 E St. NW, Ste. 400
 Washington, DC 20004
Ph: (202)552-5060
Fax: (202)747-6820
Co. E-mail: info@nahu.org
URL: http://nahu.org
Contact: Janet Trautwein, Chief Executive Officer
E-mail: jtrautwein@nahu.org
Facebook: www.facebook.com/nahusocial
Linkedin: www.linkedin.com/company/nahusocial

X (Twitter): x.com/nahusocial
YouTube: www.youtube.com/user/nahunatl

Description: Insurance agents and brokers engaged in the promotion, sale, and administration of disability income and health insurance. Sponsors advanced health insurance underwriting and research seminars. Testifies before federal and state committees on pending health insurance legislation. Sponsors Leading Producers Roundtable Awards for leading salesmen. Maintains a speaker's bureau and a political action committee. Members are engaged in the sale of health and disability insurance. **Publications:** America's Benefit Specialist (10/year). **Educational Activities:** National Association of Health Underwriters Annual Convention (Annual); Capitol Conference (Annual). **Awards:** Harold R. Gordon Memorial Award (Annual); Leading Producer Round Table Awards (LPRT) (Annual). **Geographic Preference:** National.

8876 ■ National Association of Insurance and Financial Advisors - Virginia (NAIFA)

3108 N Parham Rd., Ste. 100-A
 Henrico, VA 23294-4415
Ph: (804)747-6020
Fax: (804)965-0823
Co. E-mail: info@naifa-virginia.org
URL: http://www.naifa-virginia.org
Contact: Timothy D. Westerman, President
Facebook: www.facebook.com/naifanational
Linkedin: www.linkedin.com/company/naifa
X (Twitter): x.com/naifa
YouTube: www.youtube.com/user/naifavideo

Description: Federation of states and local associations representing 75,000 financial planners, life insurance agents, general agents, and managers; associate members are independent insurance agents, general managers of life companies and other life and health insurance professionals. Maintains the highest principles and standards of life and health insurance. Informs the public, render community service, and promotes public goodwill. Sponsors public service programs. **Founded:** 1890. **Publications:** Advisor Today (6/year). **Awards:** John Newton Russell Memorial Award (Annual); NAIFA National Quality Award (Annual). **Geographic Preference:** National; Local.

8877 ■ National Association of Professional Insurance Agents (PIA) - Library

419 North Lee St.
 Alexandria, VA 22314
Ph: (703)836-9340
Fax: (703)836-1279
URL: http://www.pianational.org
Contact: Lauren Pachman, Director
E-mail: lpachman@pianational.org
Facebook: www.facebook.com/PIANational
Linkedin: www.linkedin.com/company/pianational
X (Twitter): x.com/PIANational
Instagram: www.instagram.com/pia_national

Description: Represents independent agents in all fifty states, Puerto Rico and the District of Columbia. Represents members' interests in government and industry; provides educational programs; compiles statistics; conducts research programs; develops products/services unique to independent agencies; provides information and networking opportunities. **Scope:** Advocacy; insurance. **Founded:** 1931. **Holdings:** Figures not available. **Publications:** Consumer Brochures for Your Clients; PIA Connection (10/year); Professional Agent (Monthly). **Awards:** PIA National Company Award of Excellence (Annual); PIA National Company Representative of the Year Award (Annual); PIA National Professional Agent of the Year (Annual); The PIA National Customer Service Representative (CSR) of the Year Award (Annual); Agent of the Year (Annual); Company Representative of the Year (Annual). **Geographic Preference:** National; Regional.

8878 ■ National Association of State Farm Agents (NASFA)

222 S Riverside Plz., Ste. 1870.
 Chicago, IL 60606
Free: 800-789-8609
Fax: (312)795-0749
Co. E-mail: membership@nasfa.com

URL: http://www.nasfa.com
Contact: Nancy Zacheral, President
Facebook: www.facebook.com/nasfanow
Linkedin: www.linkedin.com/company/national
 -association-of-state-farm-agents

Description: Represents individual State Farm contractor agent. Provides information to members. Fosters a spirit of camaraderie and professional fellowship. **Founded:** 1973. **Geographic Preference:** National.

8879 ■ Risk and Insurance Management Society (RIMS)

1407 Broadway, 29th Fl.
 New York, NY 10018
Ph: (212)286-9292
Co. E-mail: cst@rims.org
URL: http://www.rims.org
Contact: Patrick Sterling, President
Facebook: www.facebook.com/RIMSorg
X (Twitter): x.com/rimsorg

Description: Business association serving corporate risk and insurance managers. Dedicated to advancing the practice of risk management, a discipline that protects physical, financial, and human resources. **Publications:** Annual Risk Management Buyers Guide (Annual); Compensation and Benefits Survey; RIMSCANADA; RIMSCOPE; Risk Management; Risk Management Buyer's Guide (Annual); RIMSNET News Bureau; Risk and Insurance Glossary. **Educational Activities:** RISKWORLD (Annual). **Awards:** Arthur Quern Quality Award; Chapter Awards Program (Annual); Harry and Dorothy Goodell Award (Annual); Richard W. Bland Memorial Award (Irregular); Ron Judd "Heart of RIMS" Award (Annual); Fred H. Bossons Award (Annual); The Cristy Award (Periodic). **Geographic Preference:** National.

8880 ■ Society of Chartered Property and Casualty Underwriters (CPCU)

720 Providence Rd.
 Malvern, PA 19355
Free: 800-932-2728
Fax: (610)725-5969
Co. E-mail: memberresources@theinstitutes.org
URL: http://www.cpcusociety.org
Contact: Chris Hampshire, President
Facebook: www.facebook.com/cpcusociety
Linkedin: www.linkedin.com/company/chartere
 d-property-casualty-underwriters-cpcu-society
X (Twitter): x.com/cpcusociety

Description: Serves as a professional society of individuals who have passed national examinations of the American Institute for Chartered Property Casualty Underwriters, have 3 years of work experience, have agreed to be bound by a code of ethics, and have been awarded CPCU designation. Promotes education, research, social responsibility, and professionalism in the field. Holds seminars, symposia, and workshops. **Founded:** 1944. **Publications:** Insights (Quarterly); CPCU News (5/year); CPCU Society Yearbook (Annual); Chartered Property and Casualty Underwriters eJournal (Monthly); CPCU Journal. **Awards:** Circle of Excellence Recognition Program (Annual). **Geographic Preference:** National.

8881 ■ Society of Financial Service Professionals (SFSP)

1000 Wilson Blvd., Ste. 1890
 Arlington, VA 22209
Free: 800-392-6900
URL: http://national.societyoffsp.org
Contact: Tom Cothron, President
Facebook: www.facebook.com/SocietyofFSP

Description: Assists clients to achieve personal and business-related financial goals. Offers educational programs, online professional resources, and networking opportunities. **Founded:** 1928. **Publications:** Society of Financial Service Professionals-- Society Page (Quarterly); Journal of Financial Service Professionals (Bimonthly). **Educational Activities:** Financial Services Professional Forum (Annual). **Awards:** American Business Ethics Award (ABEA) (Annual); Kenneth Black, Jr. Journal Author Awards (Annual). **Geographic Preference:** Multinational.

8882 ■ **Society of Insurance Financial Management (SIFM)**
61 Mountain Ave.
  Caldwell, NJ 07006
Ph: (973)303-6297
Co. E-mail: diane.sifm@verizon.net
URL: http://www.sifm.org
Contact: John Yoon, President

Description: Represents insurance company officers and employees in financial management departments. Provides a timely forum for discussing current insurance industry issues relating to financial accounting and reporting, reinsurance, taxation, regulatory developments and other relevant topics. **Founded:** 1959. **Geographic Preference:** National.

REFERENCE WORKS

8883 ■ **"2010 Book of Lists"** *in Business Courier (Vol. 26, December 26, 2009, No. 36, pp. 1)*
Price: $49.95. **Description:** Rankings of companies and organizations within the business services, education, finance, health care, hospitality and tourism, real estate, and technology industries in the Cincinnati, Ohio-Northern Kentucky area are presented. Rankings are based on sales, business size, or other statistics. **Availability:** PDF; Online.

8884 ■ **"All-Star Advice 2010"** *in Black Enterprise (Vol. 41, October 2010, No. 3, pp. 97)*
Pub: Earl G. Graves Ltd.
Contact: Earl Graves, Jr., President

Ed: Renita Burns, Sheiresa Ngo, Marcia Wade Talbert. **Description:** Financial experts share tips on real estate, investing, taxes, insurance and debt management. **Availability:** Online.

8885 ■ **"The Annual Entitlement Lecture Medicare Elephantiasis"** *in Barron's (March 31, 2008)*
Pub: Dow Jones & Company Inc.
Contact: Almar Latour, Chief Executive Officer

Ed: Thomas G. Donlan. **Description:** Expenditures on Medicare hospital insurance and the revenues available to pay for it have led to a gap of capital valued at $38.6 trillion. Slashing the benefits or raising taxes will not solve the gap which exists unless the government saves the money and invests in it in private markets. **Availability:** Online.

8886 ■ **"Anthem Becomes First to Penalize Small-Business Employees for Smoking"** *in Denver Business Journal (Vol. 64, August 17, 2012, No. 13, pp. 1)*
Pub: Baltimore Business Journal
Contact: Rhonda Pringle, President
E-mail: rpringle@bizjournals.com

Description: Health insurance companies Anthem Blue Cross and Blue Shield of Colorado are first to impose higher premiums on employee smokers who are under their small-group policies. The premiums may increase up to 15 percent starting September, to be paid by the smoking employees or the company. The law aims to help reduce tobacco-related health problems, as well as health care costs.

8887 ■ **"Are Prepaid Legal Services Worthwhile?"** *in Contractor (Vol. 56, December 2009, No. 12, pp. 31)*
Ed: Susan Linden McGreevy. **Description:** Companies' provision of legal insurance as an employee benefit in the United States is discussed. Stoppage of premium payment halts employee coverage. It also does not cover all kinds of personal issues. **Availability:** Print; Online.

8888 ■ **"Are You Overinsured? Some Policies May Not Offer Much Additional Benefit"** *in Black Enterprise (Vol. 38, March 1, 2008, No. 8, pp. 126)*
Pub: Earl G. Graves Ltd.
Contact: Earl Graves, Jr., President

Ed: Tamara E. Holmes. **Description:** Travel insurance, identity-theft insurance, specific disease or health condition insurance policies are described. Advice is given to help determine if you are overinsured. **Availability:** Online.

8889 ■ **"Austin-Based Insuraprise Growing Fast"** *in Austin Business Journal (Vol. 31, April 22, 2011, No. 7, pp. 1)*
Pub: Austin Business Journal
Contact: Rachel McGrath, Director
E-mail: rmcgrath@bizjournals.com

Ed: Sandra Zaragoza. **Description:** Austin, Texas-based Insuraprise Inc. is finalizing the purchase of a 24,000-square-foot office at 12116 Jekel Circle. The firm, with 23 salespeople and sales that are growing nearly 300 percent over the past 18 months, will now have room to grow. Insuraprise plans to hire 35 new salespersons for its call center. **Availability:** Print; Online.

8890 ■ **"Baldwin Connelly Partnership Splits"** *in Business Journal Serving Greater Tampa Bay (Vol. 30, November 19, 2010, No. 48, pp. 1)*
Pub: Tampa Bay Business Journal
Contact: Ian Anderson, President
E-mail: ianderson@bizjournals.com

Description: The fast-growing insurance brokerage Baldwin Connelly is now breaking up after five years. Two different entrepreneurial visions have developed within the organization and founders Lowry Baldwin and John Connell will not take separate tracks. Staffing levels in the firm are expected to remain the same. **Availability:** Print; Online.

8891 ■ **"Bills Raise Blues Debate: An Unfair Edge or Level Playing Field?"** *in Crain's Detroit Business (Vol. 24, January 21, 2008, No. 3)*
Pub: Crain Communications Inc.
Contact: Barry Asin, President

Ed: Sherri Begin. **Description:** Changes in Michigan state law would change the way health insurance can be sold to individuals. Michigan Blue Cross Blue Shield is working to keep its tax-exempt status while staying competitive against for-profit insurers and nonprofit HMOs. **Availability:** Print; Online.

8892 ■ **"Blue Cross to Put Kiosk in Mall"** *in News & Observer (November 9, 2010)*
Pub: News and Observer
Contact: Bill Church, Editor

Ed: Alan M. Wolf. **Description:** Blue Cross and Blue Shield of North Carolina has placed a kiosk in Durham's Streets of Southpoint in order to market its health insurance. **Availability:** Online.

8893 ■ **"Changes Sought to Health Law"** *in Baltimore Business Journal (Vol. 28, July 30, 2010, No. 12, pp. 1)*
Pub: Baltimore Business Journal
Contact: Rhonda Pringle, President
E-mail: rpringle@bizjournals.com

Ed: Kent Hoover. **Description:** Business groups that opposed health care reform are working to undo parts of the new laws even before they go into effect. Business groups are gaining support for one legislative fix, which is repealing the law's provision that requires all businesses to file 1099 forms with the IRS any time they pay more than $600 a year to another business. **Availability:** Print; Online.

8894 ■ **"Cincinnati Hospitals Wage War on 'Bounce-Backs"** *in Business Courier (Vol. 27, July 30, 2010, No. 13, pp. 1)*
Pub: Business Courier

Ed: James Ritchie. **Description:** Health care organizations in Greater Cincinnati area have tried a number of care and follow up programs, primarily focused on congestive heart failure to prevent readmissions to hospitals. Hospital administrators have made the averting of bounce-backs a priority due to new federal government plans on reimbursement. **Availability:** Print; Online.

8895 ■ **"Consulting Firm Goes Shopping"** *in Crain's Chicago Business (Vol. 31, April 28, 2008, No. 17, pp. 45)*
Pub: Crain Communications Inc.
Contact: Barry Asin, President

Ed: Phuong Ly. **Description:** Clark & Wamberg LLC was created last year after the merger of Clark Inc. to a Dutch insurance conglomerate. Clark Inc. was a life insurance and benefits consultancy which had been on a downslide, returning just 5.6 percent a year to shareholders. In contrast Clark & Wamberg posted first-year revenue of $106.8 million, fueled by business from its executive compensation and health care clients. **Availability:** Online.

8896 ■ **"Continuously Monitoring Workers' Comp Can Limit Costs"** *in Crain's Cleveland Business (Vol. 28, October 8, 2007, No. 40, pp. 21)*
Pub: Crain Communications Inc.
Contact: K. C. Crain, President

Ed: Michael Agnoni. **Description:** When operating without a plan for managing its workers' compensation program, a company risks losing money. For most companies workers' compensation insurance premiums are often reduced to an annual budget entry but employers who are actively involved in the management of their programs are more likely to experience reductions in premiums and limit indirect costs associated with claims. **Availability:** Online.

8897 ■ **"Controversial Bill Could Raise Rates for Homeowners"** *in Orlando Business Journal (Vol. 26, January 22, 2010, No. 34, pp. 1)*
Pub: Orlando Business Journal
Contact: Julie Swyers, Director
E-mail: jswyers@bizjournals.com

Ed: Oscar Pedro Musibay, Christopher Boyd. **Description:** Florida Senate Bill 876 and its companion House Bill 447 are pushing for the deregulation of rates in the state's home insurance market. The bill is being opposed by consumer advocates as it could mean higher rates for homeowner insurance policies. **Availability:** Print; Online.

8898 ■ **"Cost of Creating Health Insurance Exchange in Md. 'Largely Unknown"** *in Baltimore Business Journal (Vol. 28, September 3, 2010, No. 17, pp. 1)*
Pub: Baltimore Business Journal
Contact: Rhonda Pringle, President
E-mail: rpringle@bizjournals.com

Ed: Emily Mullin. **Description:** United States health reform is seen to result in increased health insurance prices in Maryland. However, health care reform advocates claim a new marketplace and increased competition will help keep costs down. **Availability:** Print.

8899 ■ **"Crop Insurance Harvest Prices in 2011"** *in Farm Industry News (November 9, 2011)*
Pub: Informa Business Media, Inc.
Contact: Charlie McCurdy, President

Ed: Gary Schnitkey. **Description:** Risk Management Agency (RMA) reported harvest prices for corn and soybean grown in the Midwest with corn at $6.32 per bushel, 31 cents higher than the project $6.01; soybeans were at $12.14 per bushel, down $1.35 from the projected price of $13.49. **Availability:** Print; Online.

8900 ■ **"Cutting Health Care Costs: the 3-Legged Stool"** *in HR Specialist (Vol. 8, September 2010, No. 9, pp. 1)*
Pub: Capitol Information Group Inc.
Contact: Allie Ash, Chief Executive Officer

Description: Employer spending on health insurance benefits to employees is investigated. **Availability:** Print; Online; PDF.

8901 ■ **Dictionary of Real Estate Terms**
Pub: Barron's Educational Series Inc.
Contact: Manuel H. Barron, Contact

Ed: Jack P. Friedman, Jack C. Harris, J. Bruce Lindeman. **Released:** 9th edition. **Price:** $16.99, paperback, plus shipping charges $5.99. **Description:** More than 2,500 real estate terms relating to mortgages and financing, brokerage law, architecture, rentals and leases, property insurance, and more. **Availability:** E-book; Print.

8902 ■ "Digging Dallas-Fort Worth: How Top 10 Major Construction Projects Will Change North Texas" in Dallas Business Journal (Vol. 37, May 23, 2014, No. 37, pp. 4)
Pub: American City Business Journals, Inc.
Contact: Mike Olivieri, Executive Vice President
Price: $4, print. **Description:** A list of the top ten largest construction projects in North Dallas in 2013 and their impact on local economies is presented. Included are the $303 million State Farm Insurance campus in Plano, $138.74 million termination renovation at Dallas-Fort Worth International Airport, and the $133.82 million Nebraska Furniture Mart in the Colony. **Availability:** Print; Online.

8903 ■ "Discovery Communications: Don't Sell, But Don't Buy" in Workforce Management (Vol. 88, December 14, 2009, No. 13, pp. 17)
Pub: Crain Communications Inc.
Contact: Barry Asin, President
Ed: Jeremy Smerd. **Description:** Discovery Communications provides its employees a wealth of free health services via a comprehensive work-site medical clinic that is available to its employees and their dependents. Overview of the company's innovative approach to healthcare is presented. **Availability:** Online.

8904 ■ "Distribution Dilemma: Standard Process of Tariff Revisions Across States Can Make Discoms Viable" in Best's Review (Vol. 113, September 2012, No. 5, pp. 15)
Description: Life insurance companies are addressing the obstacles prohibiting them from increasing sales. **Availability:** Print; Online.

8905 ■ "E-Medical Records Save Money, Time in Ann Arbor" in Crain's Detroit Business (Vol. 24, January 21, 2008, No. 3, pp. 6)
Pub: Crain Communications Inc.
Contact: Barry Asin, President
Ed: Jay Greene. **Description:** Ann Arbor Area Health Information Exchange is improving patient outcomes by sharing clinical and administrative data in electronic medical record systems. **Availability:** Online.

8906 ■ "Elder Care Costs Surge" in National Underwriter Life & Health (Vol. 114, November 8, 2020, No. 21, pp. 25)
Ed: Trevor Thomas. **Description:** Nursing home and assisted living rates rose from 2009 to 2010, according to MetLife Mature Market Institute. Statistical data included. **Availability:** Online.

8907 ■ "Employer Jobless Tax Could Rise" in Sacramento Business Journal (Vol. 28, May 27, 2011, No. 13, pp. 1)
Pub: Sacramento Business Journal
Contact: Stephanie Fretwell, Director
E-mail: sfretwell@bizjournals.com
Ed: Kathy Robertson. **Description:** The government of California is facing an estimated $16 billion deficit in its unemployment insurance fund. Unemployment insurance spending has exceeded employer contributions to the fund. Statistics on unemployment insurance is included. **Availability:** Online.

8908 ■ "FEMA Postpones Switch to New Risk-Based Flood Insurance Rating Until 2021" in Insurance Journal (November 8, 2019)
URL(s): www.insurancejournal.com/news/national/20 19/11/08/548044.htm
Ed: Andrew G. Simpson. **Released:** November 08, 2019. **Description:** Risk Rating 2.0, FEMA's new methodology for calculating its pricing for federal flood insurance is being delayed. More time is

needed to complete a comprehensive analysis of the rating structure and will let NFIP policies switch to the new rating system instead of using a phased approach. **Availability:** Online.

8909 ■ "Firms Sue Doracon to Recoup More Than $1M in Unpaid Bills" in Baltimore Business Journal (Vol. 28, July 9, 2010, No. 9, pp. 1)
Pub: Baltimore Business Journal
Contact: Rhonda Pringle, President
E-mail: rpringle@bizjournals.com
Ed: Scott Dance. **Description:** Concrete supplier Paul J. Rach Inc., Selective Insurance Company, and equipment leasing firm Colonial Pacific Leasing Corporation intend to sue Baltimore, Maryland-based Doracon Contracting Inc. for $1 million in unpaid bills. Doracon owed Colonial Pacific $794,000 and the equipment is still in Doracon's possession. Selective Insurance and Paul J. Rach respectively seek $132,000 and $88,000. **Availability:** Print.

8910 ■ "For 2020, Expect Biggest Commercial Insurance Hikes in Years: Willis Towers Watson" in Insurance Journal (November 15, 2019)
URL(s): www.insurancejournal.com/news/national/20 19/11/15/548582.htm
Released: November 15, 2019. **Description:** According to insurance broker Willis Towers Watson, North American commercial insurance buyers will face sizable price increases starting in 2020. Property, umbrella, and public company directors and officers are expected to to experience the most widespread hikes. **Availability:** Online.

8911 ■ "Geico and the USO of Metropolitan Washington Have Teamed Up to Provide Military Troops with a New 'Home Away From Home'" in Best's Review (Vol. 113, September 2012, No. 5, pp. 13)
Description: Geico and the USO of Metropolitan Washington have partnered to provide military troops and their families an area in the USO airport lounge at Ronald Reagan Washington National Airport with wireless Internet access, seating area with large-screen TV, assistance with travel-related questions, and a snack bar. **Availability:** Online.

8912 ■ "Ground Forces: Insurance Companies Should Help Agents to Build the Skills and Relationships that Translate Into More Business" in Best's Review (Vol. 113, September 2012, No. 5, pp. 25)
Description: The economic challenges of the past few years required insurance agents and financial professionals to better trained. Insurance companies should help their agents build skills and relationships in order to grow. **Availability:** Print; Online.

8913 ■ "Harleysville Eyes Growth After Nationwide Deal" in Philadelphia Business Journal (Vol. 30, October 7, 2011, No. 34, pp. 1)
Pub: Philadelphia Business Journal
Contact: Sierra Quinn, Director
E-mail: squinn@bizjournals.com
Ed: Jeff Blumenthal. **Price:** $4, introductory 4-week offer(Digital & Print). **Description:** Harleysville Group announced growth plans after the company was sold to Columbus, Ohio-based Nationwide Mutual Insurance Company for about $1.63 billion. Nationwide gained an independent agency platform in 32 states with the Harleysville deal. **Availability:** Print; Online.

8914 ■ "Health Care of the Future" in Business Journal Serving Greater Tampa Bay (Vol. 30, November 19, 2010, No. 48, pp. 1)
Pub: Tampa Bay Business Journal
Contact: Ian Anderson, President
E-mail: ianderson@bizjournals.com
Description: Information about accountable care organizations (ACO), which are integrated care systems with doctors and hospitals working closely together to handle patient care, is provided. The

Patient Protection and Affordable Care Act paved the way for ACOs as Medicare demonstration projects. **Availability:** Online.

8915 ■ "Health Centers Plan Expansion: $3M from D.C. Expected; Uninsured a Target" in Crain's Detroit Business (Vol. 25, June 15, 2009, No. 24, pp. 3)
Pub: Crain Communications Inc.
Contact: Barry Asin, President
Ed: Jay Greene. **Description:** Detroit has five federally qualified health centers that plan to receive over $3 million in federal stimulus money that will be used to expand projects that will care for uninsured patients. **Availability:** Print; Online.

8916 ■ "Health IT Regulations Generate Static Among Providers" in Philadelphia Business Journal (Vol. 28, January 29, 2010, No. 50, pp. 1)
Pub: Philadelphia Business Journal
Contact: Sierra Quinn, Director
E-mail: squinn@bizjournals.com
Ed: John George. **Description:** US Centers for Medicaid and Medicare Services and the Office of the National Coordinator for Health Information Technology have proposed rules regarding the meaningful use of electronic health records. The rules must be complied with by hospitals and physicians to qualify for federal stimulus funds. **Availability:** Online.

8917 ■ "Health Reform Could Expand HSA-Based Plans" in Workforce Management (Vol. 88, December 14, 2009, No. 13, pp. 6)
Description: HSA-qualified plans are the cheapest insurance plans on the market as they have a higher deductible but cost less upfront. If health care reform passes, HSA-qualified plans should benefit greatly. **Availability:** Print; Online.

8918 ■ "Health Reform: How to Make it Cheaper" in Business Courier (Vol. 26, December 11, 2009, No. 33, pp. 1)
Description: Greater Cincinnati health care leaders shared views about the health care reform bill. Respondents included the Cincinnati Visiting Nurse's Wallen Falberg, healthcare consultant Hirsch Cohen, Greater Cincinnati Health Council's Coleen O'Toole, Employer Health Care Alliance's Sharron DiMario, Legal Aid Society of Greater Cincinnati's Col Owens, Christ Hospital's Susan Croushore, and Humana of Ohio's Tim Cappel. **Availability:** Online.

8919 ■ "Hospitals Say Medicaid Expansion is Critical" in Dallas Business Journal (Vol. 35, August 3, 2012, No. 47, pp. 1)
Pub: Baltimore Business Journal
Contact: Rhonda Pringle, President
E-mail: rpringle@bizjournals.com
Ed: Bill Hethcock, Matt Joyce. **Description:** Governor Rick Perry's rejection of the Texas expansion of Medicaid is met with disapproval by health organizations such as the Methodist Health System. The federal government has extended $70 billion in financing to help more Texans become eligible for primary health care. Expansion supporters argue that Medicaid is critical in lowering insurance osts for those who need it. **Availability:** Print; Online.

8920 ■ "How to Avoid Leave-Related Lawsuits" in Employee Benefit News (Vol. 25, December 1, 2011, No. 15, pp. 12)
Pub: SourceMedia LLC
Contact: Gemma Postlethwaite, Chief Executive Officer
Ed: John F. Galvin. **Description:** Tips for employers when adding disability and maternity leave benefits to workers are outlined, with focus on ways to avoid leave-related lawsuits.

8921 ■ "How to Maximize Your Investment Income" in Contractor (Vol. 56, December 2009, No. 12, pp. 33)
Ed: Irving L. Blackman. **Description:** Private placement life insurance (PPLI) can minimize taxes and protect assets. PPLI is a form of variable universal

insurance that is offered privately. Risk of insurance company illiquidity is avoided as investments are placed in separate accounts. **Availability:** Online.

8922 ■ "Handling New Health Insurance Regulations" in Baltimore Business Journal (Vol. 31, April 25, 2014, No. 52, pp. 25)
Pub: American City Business Journals, Inc.
Contact: Mike Olivieri, Executive Vice President

Released: March 13, 2014. **Description:** Research and consulting firm, Mercer, surveyed businesses in January 2014 to examine their employer-sponsored health plans following enrollment in the Affordable Care Act-created exchanges. The survey found employers were taking advantage of a delay to a key regulation in the Act on offering insurance to employees who work at least 30 hours a week. **Availability:** Print; Online.

8923 ■ How to Start a Home-Based Senior Care Business
Ed: James L. Ferry. **Released:** 2nd edition. **Price:** Paperback,softback; Electronic Book. **Description:** Information is provided to start a home-based senior care business. **Availability:** E-book; Print.

8924 ■ "Humana Planning Pa. HMO" in Philadelphia Business Journal (Vol. 28, August 10, 2012, No. 26, pp. 1)
Pub: Baltimore Business Journal
Contact: Rhonda Pringle, President
E-mail: rpringle@bizjournals.com

Description: Humana plans to establish an HMO in Philadelphia and other areas of Pennsylvania. Along with this plan is an insurance offering in the Medicare Advantage market focused on senior citizens. The new offering would complement the company's existing preferred provider organization product. **Availability:** Print; Online.

8925 ■ "Humana Seeks Higher Stake in Memphis Market" in Memphis Business Journal (Vol. 33, February 17, 2012, No. 45, pp. 1)
Pub: Baltimore Business Journal
Contact: Rhonda Pringle, President
E-mail: rpringle@bizjournals.com

Ed: Christopher Sheffield. **Description:** Humana of Tennessee has been hoping to get a bigger share of the West Tennessee insurance market through its new three-year contract with Baptist Memorial Health Care Corporation. Louisville, Kentucky-based Humana Inc. has a business relationship with Baptist that stretches back more than two decades. **Availability:** Print; Online.

8926 ■ "Independence Blue Cross Reverses Membership Slide" in Philadelphia Business Journal (Vol. 30, September 23, 2011, No. 32, pp. 1)
Pub: Philadelphia Business Journal
Contact: Sierra Quinn, Director
E-mail: squinn@bizjournals.com

Ed: John George. **Description:** Health insurer Independence Blue Cross (IBC) added more than 40,000 members across all product lines since the start of 2011. It has 2.2 million members in Pennsylvania's Philadelphia region and 3.1 million members across the U.S. Services and other growth-related plans of IBC are covered. **Availability:** Online.

8927 ■ "Insurance Firm Consolidates Offices: Integro Finds the Right Price Downtown" in Crain's New York Business (January 13, 2008)
Pub: Crain Communications, Inc.
Contact: Jessica Botos, Manager, Marketing
E-mail: jessica.botos@crainsnewyork.com

Description: Integro insurance brokers is relocating its headquarters to 1 State Street Plaza, where it will consolidate its operations in March. The firm feels that the upscale design will provide an appropriate setting for entertaining clients and an engaging work environment for employees. **Availability:** Online.

8928 ■ "Insurers No Longer Paying Premium for Advertising" in Brandweek (Vol. 49, April 21, 2008, No. 16, pp. SR3)
Description: Insurance companies are cutting their advertising budgets after years of accelerated double-digit growth in spending due to the economic downturn, five years of record-breaking ad spend and a need to cut expenditures as claims costs rise and a competitive market keeps premiums in place. Statistical data included. **Availability:** Print; Online.

8929 ■ "Internet Marketing 2.0: Closing the Online Chat Gap" in Agent's Sales Journal (November 2009, pp. 14)
Ed: Jeff Denenholz. **Description:** Advice regarding the implementation of an Internet marketing strategy for insurance agencies includes how and why to incorporate a chat feature in which a sales agent can communicate in real-time with potential or existing customers. It is important to understand if appropriate response mechanisms are in place to convert leads into actual sales. **Availability:** Print; Online.

8930 ■ "Is There a Doctor In the House?" in Black Enterprise (Vol. 41, December 2010, No. 5, pp. 42)
Pub: Earl G. Graves Ltd.
Contact: Earl Graves, Jr., President

Ed: Renita Burns. **Description:** Health insurance premiums have increased between 15 percent and 20 percent for small business owners, making it one of the most expensive costs. Ways to evaluate a health plan's costs and effectiveness are examined. **Availability:** Online.

8931 ■ "It's Time for Insurance Carriers To Win More Customers; About One-Third of Insurance Customers are Engaged. This Means the Industry Has a Massive Opportunity to Gain More Business" in Gallup Business Journal (May 28, 2014)
Pub: Gallup, Inc.
Contact: Jon Clifton, Chief Executive Officer

Description: The insurance industry has the opportunity to engage and increase business and profits. Only one-third of insurance customers are engaged. Tips to help engage customers are offered. **Availability:** Print; Online.

8932 ■ "The Keeper of Records" in Black Enterprise (Vol. 41, December 2010, No. 5, pp. 54)
Pub: Earl G. Graves Ltd.
Contact: Earl Graves, Jr., President

Ed: Denise A. Campbell. **Description:** Medical billing and coding, submission of claims to health insurance companies and Medicare or Medicaid for payment is one of the fastest growing disciplines in healthcare. **Availability:** Online.

8933 ■ "Labor Pains" in Canadian Business (Vol. 79, August 14, 2006, No. 16-17, pp. 80)
Description: Canada's employment insurance is analyzed in view of the growing shortage of labor. **Availability:** Print; Online.

8934 ■ "The List: Top Insurance Agencies" in South Florida Business Journal (Vol. 34, May 2, 2014, No. 41, pp. 10)
Pub: American City Business Journals, Inc.
Contact: Mike Olivieri, Executive Vice President

Released: Weekly. **Price:** $8, Introductory 4-week offer(Digital & Print). **Description:** Rankings of insurance agencies in the South Florida area are presented. Rankings were based on the 2013 premium volume. **Availability:** Print; Online.

8935 ■ "Markel American Insurance Company Announces Wedding and Special Event Insurance for Consumers" in Benzinga.com (February 16, 2011)
Pub: Benzinga.com
Contact: Jason Raznick, Founder

Description: Markel American Insurance Company, headquartered in Waukesha, Wisconsin has launched its new special event insurance and wedding insurance to protect both liabilities and cancellations associated with these events. **Availability:** Print; Online.

8936 ■ "Maryland Hospitals Cope with Rare Drop in Patient Admissions" in Baltimore Business Journal (Vol. 29, September 23, 2011, No. 20, pp. 1)
Pub: Boston Business Journal
Contact: Carolyn M. Jones, President
E-mail: cmjones@bizjournals.com

Ed: Scott Dance. **Description:** Admissions to Maryland hospitals have dropped to less than 700,000 in fiscal year 2010 and initial figures for fiscal 2011 show in-patient admissions are now nearing 660,000. The decline can be partly attributed to new ways health insurers are paying hospitals for care and to the financial reward hospitals get for cutting back on admissions. **Availability:** Online.

8937 ■ "The Massachusetts Mess" in Barron's (Vol. 89, July 27, 2009, No. 30, pp. 39)
Pub: Dow Jones & Company Inc.
Contact: Almar Latour, Chief Executive Officer

Ed: Thomas G. Donlan. **Description:** Massachusetts' mandatory health insurance has produced the highest rate of insurance coverage among the states but the state is now unable to afford its dream of universal coverage just three years after they enacted it. This supposed model for federal health-care reform is turning out to be a joke. **Availability:** Online.

8938 ■ "MCM Bulks Up by Merging With Maritime Insurer" in Puget Sound Business Journal (Vol. 33, June 1, 2012, No. 6, pp. 1)
Pub: Baltimore Business Journal
Contact: Rhonda Pringle, President
E-mail: rpringle@bizjournals.com

Ed: Peter Neurath. **Description:** Seattle, Washington-based brokerage and benefits company MCM has formed a merger with Global Insurance Specialists that would strengthen its property-casualty insurance brokerage division. MCM has 2012 premium volume of $794.7 million, a total of 75 employees and provides service in areas such as employee benefits, executive benefits, and retirement plans. **Availability:** Print; Online.

8939 ■ "Md. Faces Daunting Task of Educating Masses About Health Reform Law" in Baltimore Business Journal (Vol. 28, October 15, 2010, No. 23, pp. 1)
Pub: Baltimore Business Journal
Contact: Rhonda Pringle, President
E-mail: rpringle@bizjournals.com

Ed: Emily Mullin. **Description:** The Henry J. Kaiser Family Foundation's survey shows nearly 53 percent of Americans remain confused about health care reform and it was up to the states to educate the people. However, Maryland is still trying to figure out how to conduct the campaign without guidance or funding from the Federal government. **Availability:** Print.

8940 ■ "Meadowbrook To Acquire ProCentury in $272.6 Million Deal" in Crain's Detroit Business (Vol. 24, February 21, 2008, No. 8, pp. 4)
Pub: Crain Communications Inc.
Contact: Barry Asin, President

Ed: Jay Greene. **Description:** Meadowbrook Insurance Group, based in Southfield, Michigan reports its proposed acquisition of ProCentury Corporation based in Columbus, Ohio. Meadowbrook provides risk-management to agencies, professional and trade associations and small-to-midsize businesses. **Availability:** Print; Online.

8941 ■ "Medicaid Insurers See Growth in Small Biz Market" in Boston Business Journal (Vol. 31, July 15, 2011, No. 25, pp. 1)
Pub: Boston Business Journal
Contact: Carolyn M. Jones, President

E-mail: cmjones@bizjournals.com
Ed: Julie M. Donnelly. **Description:** BMC HealthNet Plan announced plans to launch small business products to serve small businesses that are priced out of rising premium rates at large Massachusetts insurers. BMC joined competitors CeltiCare Health Plan and Neighborhood Health Plan in augmenting its core business. **Availability:** Print; Online.

8942 ■ "Medicare Plans Step Up Battle for Subscribers" in Sacramento Business Journal (Vol. 28, October 21, 2011, No. 34, pp. 1)
Pub: Sacramento Business Journal
Contact: Stephanie Fretwell, Director
E-mail: sfretwell@bizjournals.com

Ed: Kathy Robertson. **Description:** California's market for health plans have become increasingly competitive as more than 313,000 seniors try to figure out the best plans to meet their needs for 2012. Health plans are rated on Medicare materials to help consumers distinguish among the Medicare health maintenance organizations (HMOs). **Availability:** Online.

8943 ■ "Michigan Governor: Drivers to See More Savings Under Auto Insurance Reform Law" in Insurance Journal (November 16, 2021)
Released: November 16, 2021. **Description:** Michigan's new auto insurance law went into effect in 2019, which reduced rates for drivers. Now, Michigan drivers will see more savings through another piece of legislation that will allow them to choose their level of medical coverage. **Availability:** Online.

8944 ■ "More Small Businesses in Baltimore Willing to Fund Employees' Health Benefits" in Baltimore Business Journal (Vol. 28, June 18, 2010, No. 6, pp. 1)
Pub: Baltimore Business Journal
Contact: Rhonda Pringle, President
E-mail: rpringle@bizjournals.com

Ed: Scott Graham. **Description:** An increasing number of small businesses in Maryland are tapping into potentially cheaper self-funded health plans instead of providing fully insured benefits to employees through traditional health plans. Self-funded health plans charge employers for health care up to a specified level. Economic implications of self-funded plans to small businesses are discussed.

8945 ■ "The New Janus CEO of Battle-Hardened Money Manager Plots Comeback" in Denver Business Journal (Vol. 64, August 31, 2012, No. 15, pp. 1)
Pub: Baltimore Business Journal
Contact: Rhonda Pringle, President
E-mail: rpringle@bizjournals.com

Description: Richard Well, chief executive officer of Janus Capital Group Inc., discusses the strategic plans of the mutual fund company. He touches on the firm's alliance with Dai-chi Life Insurance Company Ltd., the future of equity markets, and the company's intelligent diversification strategy. **Availability:** Print; Online.

8946 ■ "North American Pet Health Insurance Market Poised for Growth" in Pet Product News (Vol. 64, December 2010, No. 12, pp. 4)
Ed: David Lummis. **Description:** The pet health insurance market is expected to further grow after posting about $350 million in sales in 2009, a gain of more than $40 million. Pet insurance firms have offered strategies such as product humanization in response to this growth forecast. Meanwhile, pet insurance shoppers have been provided more by insurance firms with wider choices. **Availability:** Online.

8947 ■ "Norvax University Health Insurance Sales Training and Online Marketing Conference" in Marketwired (January 27, 2010)
Pub: Comtex News Network Inc.
Contact: Kan Devnani, President

Description: Overview of the Norvax University Marketing and Sales Success Conference Tour which includes insurance sales training seminars, proven and innovative online marketing techniques and a host of additional information and networking opportunities. **Availability:** Print; Online.

8948 ■ "Of Paper Towels and Health Insurance" in Philadelphia Business Journal (Vol. 28, May 11, 2012, No. 13, pp. 1)
Pub: Baltimore Business Journal
Contact: Rhonda Pringle, President
E-mail: rpringle@bizjournals.com

Description: Health insurance companies are using different strategies to take advantage of the demand growth in health coverage in markets such as Philadelphia. Horizon Blue Cross lue Shield of New Jersey, for example, is creating a retail center where customers can get information from specially trained staff about insurance, health and wellness. IBC, on the other hand, has partnered with AAA Mid-Atlantic to market its plan option to AAA members. **Availability:** Print; Online.

8949 ■ "Ohio National to Pay $213,000 to Insurance Agent for Breaching Contract" in Investment News (November 12, 2019)
URL(s): www.investmentnews.com/article/20191112/
FREE/191119979/ohio-national-to-pay-213000-to
-insurance-agent-for-breaching-contract

Ed: Greg Iacurci. **Released:** November 12, 2019. **Description:** After finding out the an insurer breached the recruiting agreements it had in place with agent Elisia Lattimer, a jury awarded her $213,000 in damages. The insurer would not allow Lattimer to recruit insurance agents, causing lost revenue, even through she owned and operated an independent insurance agency. **Availability:** Online.

8950 ■ "Open Enrollment: Staying Healthy During Enrollment Season" in Employee Benefit News (Vol. 25, November 1, 2011, No. 14, pp. 41)
Pub: SourceMedia LLC
Contact: Gemma Postlethwaite, Chief Executive Officer

Ed: Shana Sweeney. **Description:** Tips for staying healthy during your benefit open enrollment period are outlined.

8951 ■ "Patients to Elect to Cut Care" in The Business Journal-Serving Metropolitan Kansas City (Vol. 27, November 21, 2008, No. 11, pp. 1)
Pub: American City Business Journals, Inc.
Contact: Mike Olivieri, Executive Vice President

Ed: Rob Roberts. **Description:** Patients in Kansas City, Missouri are cutting down on health care services due to the economic crisis. A decline in diagnostic procedures has been observed at Northland Cardiology. Elective reconstructive procedures have also been reduced by 25 percent. Additional information and statistics regarding the healthcare sector is included. **Availability:** Online.

8952 ■ "The People Puzzle; Re-Training America's Workers" in The Economist (Vol. 390, January 3, 2009, No. 8612, pp. 32)
Description: With thousands of workers losing their jobs, America is now facing the task of getting them back to work. With an overall unemployment rate of 6.7 percent, the federal government has three main ways for leading workers back to employment: training them for new jobs, providing unemployment insurance in order to replace lost wages during the period of job-hunting; and matching employers who desire a skill with workers who have that skill. Specialized staffing agencies provide employers and potential employees with the help necessary to find a job in some of the more niche markets. **Availability:** Online.

8953 ■ "Planning a Wedding Fit for a Royal? Read This First, Urge Legal & General" in Marketwired (April 21, 2011)
Released: April 21, 2011. **Description:** When planning a wedding, the author suggests checking life insurance to be sure you are covered for any situations that may arise. **Availability:** Print; Online.

8954 ■ "The Price of Citizenship" in Canadian Business (Vol. 79, August 14, 2006, No. 16-17, pp. 13)
Description: Safety and insurance benefits provided by the Canadian government to Canadian passport holders returning from Lebanon, is discussed. **Availability:** Print; Online.

8955 ■ "Private Health-Care Services Growing in Canada" in Canadian Business (Vol. 85, June 11, 2012, No. 10, pp. 10)
Ed: Laura Cameron. **Description:** Some public-private partnerships in Canada include the acquisition of clinics by Centric Health Corporation and the partnership between Westbank First National and Johns Hopkins Hospital. Private healthcare providers have operated by dividing their funding among government contracts, clients not covered by Medicare and patients paying out of pocket and non-insured services. **Availability:** Print; Online.

8956 ■ "Public Health Care Funding and the Montana Economy" in Montana Business Quarterly (Vol. 49, Spring 2011, No. 1, pp. 23)
Pub: University of Montana Bureau of Business and Economic Research
Contact: Patrick Barkey, Director
E-mail: patrick.barkey@business.umt.edu

Ed: Gregg Davis. **Released:** Quarterly. **Description:** Montana has more baby boomers and veterans per capita than any other state in the nation. The role of public health in the state is a crucial part of the state's economy. **Availability:** Online.

8957 ■ "Questions Abound in Voluminous Health Care Reform Law" in Memphis Business Journal (Vol. 34, July 6, 2012, No. 12, pp. 1)
Pub: Baltimore Business Journal
Contact: Rhonda Pringle, President
E-mail: rpringle@bizjournals.com

Ed: Cole Epley. **Description:** US Supreme Court has upheld the health care reform legislation, also known as Obamacare, as thelaw of the land. However, key questions remain and conjecture surrounding which direction states and insurance providers will pursue abounds. Insights on possible impact of health care providers of TennCare are also given. **Availability:** Print; Online.

8958 ■ "Reaching Out: the LIFE Foundation Provides Free Tools and Resources to Help Agents Boost Their Life Insurance Sales" in Best's Review (Vol. 113, September 2012, No. 5, pp. 26)
Description: The LIFE Foundation's LIFE program is profiled. The program offers free tools and resources for life insurance agents. **Availability:** Print; Online.

8959 ■ "Recovery on Tap for 2010?" in Orlando Business Journal (Vol. 26, January 1, 2010, No. 31, pp. 1)
Pub: Orlando Business Journal
Contact: Julie Swyers, Director
E-mail: jswyers@bizjournals.com

Ed: Melanie Stawicki Azam, Richard Bilbao, Christopher Boyd, Anjali Fluker. **Description:** Economic forecasts for Central Florida's leading business sectors in 2010 are presented. These sectors include housing, film and TV, sports business, law, restaurants, aviation, tourism and hospitality, banking and finance, commercial real estate, retail, health care, insurance, higher education, and manufacturing. According to some local executives, Central Florida's economy will slowly recover in 2010. **Availability:** Online.

8960 ■ "Rich or Poor, Hospitals Must Work Together" in Crain's Chicago Business (Vol. 31, April 28, 2008, No. 17, pp. 22)
Pub: Crain Communications Inc.
Contact: Barry Asin, President

Description: Chicago-area safety-net hospitals that serve the poor, uninsured and underinsured are struggling to stay open while wealthier areas compete to build advanced facilities for the expensive surgical procedures their privately insured patients can afford. If these safety-net hospitals close, their patients, many of them in ambulances, will show up at the remaining hospitals resulting in a strain that will test the ability of hospitals across the region to care for all of their patients. Hospitals need to address the threats to the local health care system before it slips into crisis since the current every-hospital-for-itself approach that pays off big for some will eventually make losers of everyone. **Availability:** Online.

8961 ■ *"Rising Above Flood-Insurance Costs"* in *Providence Business News (Vol. 28, February 3, 2014, No. 44, pp. 1)*
Pub: American City Business Journals, Inc.
Contact: Mike Olivieri, Executive Vice President
Released: February 01, 2014. **Description:** Businesses are advised to examine flood insurance costs when rebuilding or expanding their facilities. Some firms choose to elevate their buildings in response to the redrawing of Federal Emergency Management Agency flood maps and regulations. The process for getting a flood-elevation survey is also explored. **Availability:** Print; Online.

8962 ■ *"RPA Preps for Building Radiant Conference, Show"* in *Contractor (Vol. 57, January 2010, No. 1, pp. 5)*
Description: Radiant Panel Association is accepting registrations for its Building Radiant 2010 Conference and Trade Show. The conference will discuss radiant heating as well as insurance and other legal matters for mechanical contractors. **Availability:** Print; Online.

8963 ■ *"A Safety Net in Need of Repair"* in *The Economist (Vol. 390, January 3, 2009, No. 8612, pp. 33)*
Description: America's unemployment-insurance scheme is outdated and skimpy compared to other industrialized countries despite the fact that Americans tend to work harder at returning to the job market; the benefits are lower and available for a smaller amount of time and less unemployed workers are even able to collect these benefits. Statistical data included.

8964 ■ *"Small Biz Owners Are Tapping Into Health Savings Plans"* in *Small Business Opportunities (Fall 2007)*
Description: Health savings accounts were developed by Golden Rule, a United Healthcare company. Today, more than 40 percent of the company's customers are covered by health savings account plans.

8965 ■ *"Small, But Mighty"* in *Employee Benefit News (Vol. 25, November 1, 2011, No. 14, pp. 32)*
Pub: SourceMedia LLC
Contact: Gemma Postlethwaite, Chief Executive Officer
Ed: Andrea Davis. **Description:** Three consulting firms are facing the challenge of helping clients understand the new health care reform in a tight economy. **Availability:** Print; PDF; Online.

8966 ■ *"The Smell of Fear: Is a Bottom Near?"* in *Barron's (Vol. 88, March 17, 2008, No. 11, pp. M3)*
Pub: Dow Jones & Company Inc.
Contact: Almar Latour, Chief Executive Officer
Ed: Kopin Tan. **Description:** Liquidity problems at Bear Stearns frightened investors in markets around the world due to the fear of the prospects of a big bank's failure. Shares of health maintenance organizations got battered led by WellPoint, and Humana but longer-term investors who could weather short-term volatility may find value here. The value of J. Crew shares is also discussed. **Availability:** Online.

8967 ■ *"Spouses, Health Coaching Added to Mix"* in *Pittsburgh Business Times (Vol. 33, June 6, 2014, No. 47, pp. 5)*
Pub: American City Business Journals, Inc.
Contact: Mike Olivieri, Executive Vice President

Released: Weekly. **Price:** $4, introductory 4-week offer (Digital & Print). **Description:** Hospital giant, UPMC, was the Category Winner in the 5,000+ employees group of Healthiest Employers in Western Pennsylvania, for its initiative in expanding its health assessment and wellness programs to the spouses and partners of all its employees, regardless of their health insurance carrier. In addition, UPMC Health Plan expanded its individual health coaching option for members as well as corporate clients. **Availability:** Print; Online.

8968 ■ *"Starting & Running Your Own Horse Business"*
Pub: Storey Publishing L.L.C.
Contact: Maribeth Casey, Director
E-mail: maribeth.casey@storey.com
Ed: Mary Ashby McDonald. **Released:** Second edition. **Price:** $19.95, trade paper. **Description:** Insight into starting and running a successful equestrian business is given. The book covers safety, tips for operating a riding school or horse camp, strategies for launching a carriage business, along with tax and insurance advice. **Availability:** E-book; Print.

8969 ■ *"Steeling for Battle"* in *Crain's Chicago Business (Vol. 31, April 21, 2008, No. 16, pp. 3)*
Pub: Crain Communications Inc.
Contact: Barry Asin, President
Ed: Bob Tita. **Description:** Discusses contract negotiations between the United Steelworkers union and ArcelorMittal USA Inc., the nation's largest steelmaker, and U.S. Steel Corp., the third-largest; the union sees these negotiations as the best chance in two decades to regain lost ground but industry experts predict the companies will try to reduce benefits, demand a separate, lower wage scale for new hires and look for relief from the rising costs for retirees' health insurance coverage. **Availability:** Online.

8970 ■ *"Symbility Solutions Joins Motion Computing Partner Program"* in *Marketwired (May 14, 2007)*
Pub: Comtex News Network Inc.
Contact: Kan Devnani, President
Description: Symbility Solutions Inc., a wholly owned subsidiary of Automated Benefits Corp., announced an agreement with Alliance Partner of Motion Computing, a leader in wireless communications and mobile computing, in which both companies will invest in a sales and marketing strategy that focuses specifically on the insurance market. **Availability:** Print; Online.

8971 ■ *"Taking Full Advantage: What You Need To Know During Open-Enrollment Season"* in *Black Enterprise (Vol. 38, November 2007, No. 4)*
Pub: Earl G. Graves Ltd.
Contact: Earl Graves, Jr., President
Ed: Donald Jay Korn. **Description:** Employees can change or enroll in new insurance benefits during the fall season. It is important to assess each plan offered and to determine your deductible. Statistical data included. **Availability:** Online.

8972 ■ *"Top 50 In Total Revenue"* in *Canadian Business (Vol. 81, Summer 2008, No. 9, pp. 119)*
Description: Table showing the top 50 Canadian companies in terms of total revenue is presented. Manulife Financial Corp. topped the list with revenue of 34.5 billion. The financial services firm is the 6th largest provider of life insurance in the world and the second largest in North America. **Availability:** Print; Online.

8973 ■ *"Tropeano Takes Charge"* in *Philadelphia Business Journal (Vol. 33, August 22, 2014, No. 28, pp. 11)*
Pub: American City Business Journals, Inc.
Contact: Mike Olivieri, Executive Vice President

Released: Weekly. **Price:** $4, introductory 4-week offer(Digital only). **Description:** Dan Tropeano will serve as the new head of United Healthcare of

Pennsylvania, while continuing in his position as executive director of United Healthcare's Pennsylvania and Delaware health plans. Tropeano discusses his new role and notes that the medical insurance market has become increasingly competitive as consumers seek cheaper and more flexible products. **Availability:** Print; Online.

8974 ■ *"Trusted Choice: Mobile App"* in *Best's Review (Vol. 113, September 2012, No. 5, pp. 14)*
Description: Profile of Trusted Choice, the new mobile app launched in March 2012 for use on smartphones and tablet computers. The app helps clients contact their independent insurance agent. Consumers can keep an inventory of insured personal possessions, document a car accident with photos, read insurance tips, communicate with Trusted Choice agent and ask insurance-related questions. **Availability:** Online.

8975 ■ *"U.S. Combined Life and Health Writers--Industry's Reported Admitted Assets of $5.7 Trillion"* in *Best's Review (Vol. 113, September 2012, No. 5, pp. 33)*
Description: U.S. Combined Life and Health Writers--Industry's Reported Admitted Assets of $5.7 Trillion report is presented. Companies/Groups are ranked in 2011 by admitted assets. **Availability:** Print; Online.

8976 ■ *"Virtually Secure"* in *Rough Notes (Vol. 155, February 2012, No. 2, pp. 46)*
Pub: The Rough Notes Company Inc.
Contact: Walter J. Gdowski, President
E-mail: waltg@roughnotes.com
Ed: Nabeel Sayegh. **Availability:** PDF; Online.

8977 ■ *"VPA to Pay $9.5 Million to Settle Whistle-Blower Lawsuits"* in *Crain's Detroit Business (Vol. 26, January 11, 2010, No. 2, pp. 13)*
Pub: Crain Communications Inc.
Contact: Barry Asin, President
Ed: Jay Greene. **Description:** According to Terrence Berg, first assistant with the U.S. Attorney's Office in Detroit, Voluntary Physicians Association, a local home health care company, has agreed to pay $9.5 million to settle four whistle-blower lawsuits; the agreement settles allegations that VPA submitted claims to TriCare, the Michigan Medicaid program and Medicare for unnecessary home visits, tests and procedures. **Availability:** Online.

8978 ■ *"Waukesha Firm Hit for $8.9M for Junk Faxes"* in *Business Journal Milwaukee (Vol. 29, August 3, 2012, No. 45, pp. 1)*
Pub: American City Business Journals, Inc.
Contact: Mike Olivieri, Executive Vice President
Ed: Stacy Vogel Davis. **Released:** Weekly. **Price:** $4, introductory 4-week offer(Digital & Print). **Description:** Waukesha County, Wisconsin-based Easy PC Solutions LLC has been facing an $8.9 million settlement for sending unsolicited faxes to 7,000 health care providers. However, the company won't have to pay since the plaintiffs are expected to go after its insurance company. **Availability:** Print; Online.

8979 ■ *"Week on the Web"* in *Crain's Detroit Business (Vol. 25, June 22, 2009, No. 25, pp. 19)*
Pub: Crain Communications Inc.
Contact: Barry Asin, President
Description: Blue Cross Blue Shield of Michigan, in a class-action lawsuit, will pay about 100 families whose children were either denied coverage for autism treatment or paid for treatment out of pocket. The settlement is worth about $ million. **Availability:** Print; Online.

8980 ■ *"Western & Southern to Trim Rich Retirement Plan"* in *Business Courier (Vol. 27, October 15, 2010, No. 24, pp. 1)*
Pub: Business Courier
Ed: Dan Monk. **Description:** Insurance firm Western & Southern Financial Group announced that it will reduce the pension benefits of its 4,000 associates

by more than 30 percent starting January 1, 2011. The move is expected to reduce annual retirement payments by several thousand dollars per associate. Western is a Fortune 500 company and has $34 billion in total assets. **Availability:** Print; Online.

8981 ■ "What Choice Did I Have?" in Entrepreneur (Vol. 37, October 2009, No. 10, pp. 88)

Pub: Entrepreneur Media Inc.
Contact: Dan Bova, Director
E-mail: dbova@entrepreneur.com
Ed: Craig Matsuda. **Description:** Profile of a worker at a financial services company who acquired first-hand knowledge concerning the relationship between health insurance costs and coverage. The worker's son got severely ill, forcing the worker to spend above what is covered by health insurance. **Availability:** Print; Online.

8982 ■ "What Should Your Insurance Agent Do for You?" in U.S. News & World Report (May 24, 2018)

URL(s): money.usnews.com/money/personal-finance/saving-and-budgeting/articles/2018-05-24/what-should-your-insurance-agent-do-for-you
Ed: Maryalene LaPonsie. **Released:** May 24, 2018. **Description:** Discusses traits that good insurance agents possess, since not all agents and agencies operate the same way. Ones that offer personalized attention and make an effort to check in well after the papers are signed, are two of the most important things an agent to do to go above and beyond. **Availability:** Online.

STATISTICAL SOURCES

8983 ■ Online Insurance Brokers Industry in the US - Market Research Report

URL(s): www.ibisworld.com/united-states/market-research-reports/online-insurance-brokers-industry/
Price: $925. **Description:** Downloadable report analyzing the current and future trends in the online insurance broker industry. **Availability:** Download.

8984 ■ RMA Annual Statement Studies

Pub: Risk Management Association
Contact: Nancy Foster, President
Released: Annual. **Description:** Contains composite balance sheets and income statements for more than 360 industries, including the accounting, auditing, and bookkeeping industries. Also contains five years of comparative historical data for discerning trends. Includes 16 commonly used ratios, computed for most of the size groupings for nearly every industry.

8985 ■ Standard & Poor's Industry Surveys

Pub: Standard And Poor's Financial Services LLC.
Contact: Douglas L. Peterson, President
Description: Two-volume book that examines the prospects for specific industries, including trucking. Also provides analyses of trends and problems, statistical tables and charts, and comparative company analyses.

TRADE PERIODICALS

8986 ■ Best's Review

Pub: A.M. Best Company Inc.
URL(s): bestsreview.ambest.com/default.aspxweb.ambest.com/information-services/sales-information/insurance-news-research/best's-review
Ed: Lynna Goch. **Released:** Monthly **Price:** $42, for print and online; $72, for 1 year; $137, Two years.
Description: Magazine covering issues and trends for the management personnel of life/health insurers, the agents, and brokers who market their products. **Availability:** Print; PDF; Online.

8987 ■ Business Insurance

Pub: Crain Communications Inc.
Contact: Barry Asin, President
URL(s): www.businessinsurance.com
Facebook: www.facebook.com/BusInsMagazine
Linkedin: www.linkedin.com/company/business-insurance

X (Twitter): x.com/BusInsMagazine
Released: Biweekly **Description:** International newsweekly reporting on corporate risk and employee benefit management news. **Availability:** Print; Online. **Type:** Full-text.

8988 ■ The Insurance Journal of the West

Pub: Wells Media Group Inc.
Contact: Josh Carlson, Chief Executive Officer
URL(s): www.insurancejournal.com/magazines/west
Released: Biweekly **Price:** $395, for pint and digital; $99, for digital only; $195, for print only; $195, for print & digital. **Description:** Trade journal covering insurance. **Availability:** Print; PDF; Online.

8989 ■ The John Liner Letter

Pub: Standard Publishing Corp.
Contact: John C. Cross, President
E-mail: j.cross@spcpub.com
URL(s): www.spcpub.com/page.cfm?name=John_Liner_letter&teaser=72
Released: Monthly **Price:** $427.50, for per year for combination print edition and single-user online access; $339, for online edition 12 monthly issue; $339, for print edition 12 monthly issue. **Description:** Provides risk management and technical insurance advice for business firms, such as broadening coverage, cutting costs, and anticipating special insurance problems. **Availability:** Print; Online.

8990 ■ Journal of Insurance Regulation (JIR)

Pub: National Association of Insurance Commissioners
Contact: Dean L. Cameron, President
URL(s): content.naic.org/research/journal-of-insurance-regulation
Ed: Cassandra Cole, Jennifer McAdam. **Released:** latest edition may 2024. **Description:** Forum for research and public policy analysis of topics dealing with the control of insurance companies/markets by regulatory bodies. **Availability:** PDF.

8991 ■ Reinsurance News

Pub: Society of Actuaries
Contact: Greg Heidrich, Executive Director
URL(s): www.soa.org/sections/reinsurance/reinsurance-newsletter
Released: Latest Update June 2024. **Description:** Encourages the professional development of Society members in the field of reinsurance. Recurring features include letters to the editor, news of research, news of educational opportunities, and a calendar of events. **Availability:** Print; PDF; Download; Online.

8992 ■ The Risk Report

Pub: International Risk Management Institute, Inc.
Contact: Jack P. Gibson, President
URL(s): www.irmi.com/categories/risk-management
Released: Monthly **Price:** $71.28, for per month; $27.67, Individuals for per month (annually). **Description:** Deals with risk management and commercial insurance. Monitors trends in loss exposures, insurance pricing, and coverage. Suggests techniques for reducing insurance costs, and provides detailed policy analyses. **Availability:** Print.

8993 ■ Small Talk

Pub: Society of Actuaries
Contact: Greg Heidrich, Executive Director
URL(s): www.soa.org/sections/small-insurance/small-insurance-newsletter
Released: Semiannual; December 2023. **Description:** The purpose of the Smaller Insurance Company newsletter shall be to encourage and facilitate the professional development of its members through activities such as meetings, seminars, and the generation and dissemination of literature pertaining to the unique problems that face actuaries employed by smaller life insurance companies. The Section focuses on methods, techniques and solutions that do not require the more extensive actuarial resources available to large companies, and provides a forum where professionals working in a smaller company environment can discuss their special concerns. The Section newsletter is small talk. **Availability:** Print; Download.

8994 ■ Today's Insurance Professional

Pub: International Association of Insurance Professionals
Contact: Tammy Wascher, President
URL(s): www.internationalinsuranceprofessionals.org/page/tip
Released: Quarterly **Description:** Magazine on insurance and professional development topics for men and women in the risk and insurance field. **Availability:** PDF; Online.

VIDEO/AUDIO MEDIA

8995 ■ The How of Business: LeRoy Wilkerson - Health Insurance Business

URL(s): www.thehowofbusiness.com/epidose-047-leroy-wilkerson
Ed: Henry Lopez. **Released:** October 17, 2016. **Description:** Podcast discusses both staring an insurance agency and offering insurance benefits as a small business,.

TRADE SHOWS AND CONVENTIONS

8996 ■ Annual IAIP Convention

International Association of Insurance Professionals (IAIP)
One Glenlake Pkwy., Ste. 1200
Atlanta, GA 30328
Ph: (404)789-3153
Free: 800-766-6249
Fax: (404)240-0998
Co. E-mail: membership@iaip-ins.org
URL: http://www.internationalinsuranceprofessionals.org/default.aspx
Contact: Tammy Wascher, President
URL(s): iaipconvention.com
Frequency: Annual. **Description:** Learn the hottest industry trends, share best practices and gather fresh ideas. **Audience:** Insurance professionals. **Principal Exhibits:** Learn the hottest industry trends, share best practices and gather fresh ideas. **Telecommunication Services:** ahammerli@iaip-ins.org.

CONSULTANTS

8997 ■ LIMRA International

LIMRA International
300 Day Hill Rd.
Windsor, CT 06095
Ph: (860)285-7789
Co. E-mail: customer.service@limra.com
URL: http://www.limra.com
Contact: David Levenson, President
Facebook: www.facebook.com/LIMRANews
Linkedin: www.linkedin.com/company/limra
X (Twitter): x.com/LIMRA
YouTube: www.youtube.com/user/limraloma

Description: Provides executive and field management development schools and seminars. Offers human resource development consulting services, including needs analysis and program design, evaluation, and implementation. **Scope:** Company research services apply scientific techniques to the areas of performance appraisal, manpower utilization, employee and consumer opinion sampling and market analysis. **Founded:** 1916. **Publications:** "28 Ways to Improve Your Sales Performance"; "Advanced Selection Interview Guide"; "LIMRA's Market Facts"; "Looking Ahead"; "Cross Selling". **Training:** Compensation and Motivation Plans that Deliver Results, Bangkok, Aug, 2009; Sales Compensation Seminar, Simsbury, May, 2009; Growth by Design; Strategic Marketing Review. **Educational Activities:** LIMRA International Conference (Annual). **Geographic Preference:** Multinational. **Special Services:** Career Profile.

8998 ■ Phillips & Associates L.L.C.

15825 Shady Grove Rd., Ste. 40
Rockville, MD 20850
Ph: (301)519-3280
Fax: (301)519-2790

Co. E-mail: contact@pallcfirm.com
URL: http://pallcfirm.com
Contact: Andrew W. Phillips, Contact
E-mail: aphillips@pallcfirm.com
Description: Business and financial planning consultants providing services in mergers and acquisitions, strategic planning and tax planning. Serves insurance agencies and the graphic arts industry. **Scope:** Business and financial planning consultants providing services in mergers and acquisitions, strategic planning and tax planning. Serves insurance agencies and the graphic arts industry. **Founded:** 1982.

FRANCHISES AND BUSINESS OPPORTUNITIES

8999 ■ Paul Davis Systems Canada Ltd.
2233 Argentia Rd Ste.,100
  Mississauga, ON, Canada L5N 2X7
Ph: (416)299-8890
Free: 800-661-5975
Co. E-mail: canada@pauldavis.ca
URL: http://pauldavis.ca
Contact: Rich Wilson, Chief Executive Officer
Facebook: www.facebook.com/pauldaviscanada
Linkedin: www.linkedin.com/company/paul-davis-systems-canada
X (Twitter): x.com/PaulDavisCanada
YouTube: www.youtube.com/user/PaulDavisSystems
Description: Provider of emergency restoration, reconstruction and remodeling services for fire and smoke, extreme weather, water release, flooding and mold growth. **No. of Franchise Units:** 300. **Founded:** 1966. **Training:** Provides 4 weeks training.

COMPUTERIZED DATABASES

9000 ■ *National Underwriter Life & Health*
National Underwriter Co.
  4157 Olympic Blvd., Ste. 225
  Erlanger, KY 41018
Free: 800-543-0874
Co. E-mail: customerservice@nuco.com
URL: http://www.nationalunderwriter.com
URL(s): www.nationalunderwriter.com/insurance/life-and-health.html
Price: $16, for eBook; $20, for print; $22.50, for print and eBook. **Availability:** E-book; Print. **Type:** Fulltext.

9001 ■ *National Underwriter Property & Casualty*
National Underwriter Co.
  4157 Olympic Blvd., Ste. 225
  Erlanger, KY 41018
Free: 800-543-0874
Co. E-mail: customerservice@nuco.com
URL: http://www.nationalunderwriter.com
URL(s): www.nationalunderwriter.com/
  magazineswww.propertycasualty360.com/national-underwriter-property-casualty/issue-gallery/?slreturn=20230621042952
Released: Last Published: June/July 2023. **Availability:** Print; Online. **Type:** Full-text.

9002 ■ *Sage Property & Casualty*
Vertafore Inc.
  300 Deschutes Way SW Ste. 208 MC-CSC1
  Tumwater, WA 98501
URL: http://www.vertafore.com
Contact: Amy Zupon, Governor
URL(s): www.propertyandcasualty.com/doc/sage-0001
Availability: Online. **Type:** Full-text.

LIBRARIES

9003 ■ American Property Casualty Insurance Association (APCIA) - Library
8700 W Bryn Mawr Ave., Ste., 1200S
  Chicago, IL 60631-3512
Ph: (847)297-7800
Fax: (847)297-5064

Co. E-mail: compliance@apci.org
URL: http://www.apci.org
Contact: David A. Sampson, President
E-mail: david.sampson@apci.org
Facebook: www.facebook.com/TeamAPCIA
Linkedin: www.linkedin.com/company/american-property-casualty-insurance-association
X (Twitter): x.com/TeamAPCIA
Description: Independent property and casualty insurance companies. Provides advocacy and technical information. **Scope:** Insurance. **Founded:** 2004. **Holdings:** Figures not available. **Publications:** *Individual State Profile* (Annual); *Legislative Reporter* (Biweekly); *State Insurance Department Directory* (Annual); *Policy Kit: A Collection of Sample Insurance Forms*; *Survey of Workers Compensations Laws*. **Educational Activities:** Alliance of American Insurers Meeting (Annual). **Geographic Preference:** National.

9004 ■ Buset & Partners
1121 Barton St.
  Thunder Bay, ON, Canada P7B 5N3
Ph: (807)623-2500
Free: 866-532-8738
Fax: (807)622-7808
Co. E-mail: info@busetlaw.com
URL: http://busetlaw.com
Contact: Richard J. Buset, Partner Founder
E-mail: rbuset@busetlaw.com
Description: Full-service law firm located in the central part of the City of Thunder Bay. **Founded:** 1980.

9005 ■ Erie Insurance Group Corporate Library
100 Erie Insurance Pl.
  Erie, PA 16530
Free: 800-458-0811
URL: http://erieinsurance.overdrive.com
Facebook: www.facebook.com/erieinsurance
X (Twitter): x.com/erie_insurance
Founded: 1975.

9006 ■ Insurance Information Institute (III)
110 William St.
  New York, NY 10038
Ph: (212)346-5500
Co. E-mail: info@iii.org
URL: http://www.iii.org
Contact: Richard P. Creedon, Chairman
URL(s): www.groupunderwriters.com
Facebook: www.facebook.com/iiiorg
Linkedin: www.linkedin.com/company/insurance-information-institute
X (Twitter): x.com/iiiorg
YouTube: www.youtube.com/user/iiivideo
Description: Property and casualty insurance companies. Provides information and educational services to mass media, educational institutions, trade associations, businesses, government agencies, and the public. **Publications:** *I.I.I. Data Base Search*; *I.I.I. Insurance Daily*; *Insurance Handbook for Reporters*; *Property-Casualty Insurance Facts*. **Educational Activities:** Property/Casualty Insurance Joint Industry Forum (Annual). **Geographic Preference:** National.

9007 ■ Insurance Institute of Ontario Library (IIO)
18 King St. E 16th Fl.
  Toronto, ON, Canada M5C 1C4
Ph: (416)362-8586
Free: 866-362-8585
Fax: (416)362-1126
Co. E-mail: iicmail@insuranceinstitute.ca
URL: http://www.insuranceinstitute.ca
Contact: Dave Smiley, President
Facebook: www.facebook.com/InsuranceinsCA
Linkedin: www.linkedin.com/school/insuranceinstituteofcanada
X (Twitter): x.com/InsuranceInsCA
YouTube: www.youtube.com/channel/UCiGl7S5JVZhBOJqtJBvl_3Q

Description: A source of professional education and career development for the country's property and casualty insurance industry. **Scope:** Property and casualty insurance. **Services:** Library open to members. **Founded:** 1899. **Holdings:** 250 books; 12 serials; 6 other cataloged items.

9008 ■ LIMRA International
LIMRA International
  300 Day Hill Rd.
  Windsor, CT 06095
Ph: (860)285-7789
Co. E-mail: customer.service@limra.com
URL: http://www.limra.com
Contact: David Levenson, President
Facebook: www.facebook.com/LIMRANews
Linkedin: www.linkedin.com/company/limra
X (Twitter): x.com/LIMRA
YouTube: www.youtube.com/user/limraloma
Description: Provides executive and field management development schools and seminars. Offers human resource development consulting services, including needs analysis and program design, evaluation, and implementation. **Scope:** Company research services apply scientific techniques to the areas of performance appraisal, manpower utilization, employee and consumer opinion sampling and market analysis. **Founded:** 1916. **Publications:** "28 Ways to Improve Your Sales Performance"; "Advanced Selection Interview Guide"; "LIMRA's Market Facts"; "Looking Ahead"; "Cross Selling". **Training:** Compensation and Motivation Plans that Deliver Results, Bangkok, Aug, 2009; Sales Compensation Seminar, Simsbury, May, 2009; Growth by Design; Strategic Marketing Review. **Educational Activities:** LIMRA International Conference (Annual). **Geographic Preference:** Multinational. **Special Services:** Career Profile.

9009 ■ MetLife, Inc.
MetLife, Inc.
  200 Park Ave., 12th Fl.
  New York, NY 10166
Ph: (212)578-5500
Free: 800-638-5433
Co. E-mail: customercare@ammetlife.com
URL: http://www.metlife.com
Contact: Michel A. Khalaf, President
Facebook: www.facebook.com/metlife
Linkedin: www.linkedin.com/company/metlife
X (Twitter): twitter.com/metlife
YouTube: www.youtube.com/user/Metlife
Description: A financial services company principally engaged in providing insurance, annuities, employee benefits and asset management services to individuals and institutional customers, globally. **Founded:** 1863. **Educational Activities:** National Agricultural Bankers Conference (Annual).

9010 ■ National Association of Insurance Commissioners (NAIC) - Library
1100 Walnut St., Ste. 1500
  Kansas City, MO 64106-2197
Ph: (816)842-3600
Fax: (816)842-3600
Co. E-mail: help@naic.org
URL: http://content.naic.org
Contact: Dean L. Cameron, President
Facebook: www.facebook.com/NAIC.News
X (Twitter): x.com/NAIC_News
Description: State officials supervising insurance. Promotes uniformity of legislation and regulation affecting insurance to protect interests of policyholders. Conducts educational programs for insurance regulators. Compiles statistics from annual statement of solvency and profit data on all US. insurers of life, health, property, and casualty. **Scope:** Research. **Founded:** 1970. **Holdings:** Figures not available. **Publications:** *NAIC News*; *Journal of Insurance Regulation (JIR)*; *International Insurance Relations*; *NAIC Model Laws, Regulations and Guidelines*; *Retaliation: A Guide to State Retaliatory Taxes, Fees, Deposits and Other Requirements* (Annual); *NAIC Database*. **Awards:** Robert Dineen Award (Annual). **Geographic Preference:** National.

9011 ■ Parker, Smith and Feek Inc. (PSF) - Risk Management Library

2233 112th Ave. NE
 Bellevue, WA 98004
Ph: (425)709-3600
Free: 800-457-0220
Fax: (425)709-7460
Co. E-mail: info@psfinc.com
URL: http://www.psfinc.com
Contact: Dave L. Eckroth, President
Facebook: www.facebook.com/psfinc
Linkedin: www.linkedin.com/company/parker-smith
 -&-feek
X (Twitter): x.com/psfinc
YouTube: www.youtube.com/user/ParkerSmithFeek/
 feed

Description: Provider of insurance and risk management brokerage services. **Scope:** Risk management. **Founded:** 1937. **Holdings:** Safety policies and procedures.

9012 ■ Society of Insurance Research (SIR) - Library

4248 Park Glen Rd.
 Minneapolis, MN 55416
Ph: (952)928-4641
Co. E-mail: info@sirnet.org
URL: http://www.sirnet.org
Contact: Micheal Myers, President
Facebook: www.facebook.com/Society-of-Insurance
 -Research-280465171017
Linkedin: www.linkedin.com/company/society-of
 -insurance-research
X (Twitter): x.com/society_sir
YouTube: www.youtube.com/channel/
 UCCmWcqeXKb_dwswcVjuN69g

Description: Represents individuals or companies interested or actively involved in insurance research and planning. Stimulates insurance research through the interchange of ideas on research methodology and developments in technology. **Scope:** Stimulates insurance research through the interchange of ideas on research methodology. **Founded:** 1970. **Holdings:** Figures not available. **Publications:** *S.I.R. News*; *Society of Insurance Research--Membership Directory*; *SIR News*. **Educational Activities:** Spring Research Workshops (Annual); SIR Annual Conference & Exhibit Fair (Annual); SIR Spring Research Workshops. **Geographic Preference:** National.

RESEARCH CENTERS

9013 ■ Insurance Research Council (IRC)

718 Providence Rd.
 Malvern, PA 19355
Co. E-mail: irc@theinstitutes.org
URL: http://www.insurance-research.org
Contact: Dale Porfilio, President
E-mail: dalep@iii.org

Description: Aims to provide educational programs and professional certification for the property-casualty insurance business. **Scope:** Property-casualty insurance and public policy issues, including studies of insurance fraud, auto insurance reform, catastrophic automobile injuries, compensation for auto injuries, catastrophic losses and damage mitigation, fire following earthquakes, attorney involvement in insurance claims, drinking and driving, and the performance of the auto accident compensation system. Performs research through surveys, computer modeling, and claims data analysis. **Founded:** 1977. **Publications:** *Auto Injury Study* (5/year); *Public Attitude Monitor* (Annual). **Geographic Preference:** National.

9014 ■ Society of Insurance Research (SIR) - Library

4248 Park Glen Rd.
 Minneapolis, MN 55416
Ph: (952)928-4641
Co. E-mail: info@sirnet.org
URL: http://www.sirnet.org
Contact: Micheal Myers, President
Facebook: www.facebook.com/Society-of-Insurance
 -Research-280465171017
Linkedin: www.linkedin.com/company/society-of
 -insurance-research
X (Twitter): x.com/society_sir
YouTube: www.youtube.com/channel/
 UCCmWcqeXKb_dwswcVjuN69g

Description: Represents individuals or companies interested or actively involved in insurance research and planning. Stimulates insurance research through the interchange of ideas on research methodology and developments in technology. **Scope:** Stimulates insurance research through the interchange of ideas on research methodology. **Founded:** 1970. **Holdings:** Figures not available. **Publications:** *S.I.R. News*; *Society of Insurance Research--Membership Directory*; *SIR News*. **Educational Activities:** Spring Research Workshops (Annual); SIR Annual Conference & Exhibit Fair (Annual); SIR Spring Research Workshops. **Geographic Preference:** National.

9015 ■ University of Georgia - Terry College of Business - Center for Insurance Education and Research

600 S Lumpkin St.
 Athens, GA 30602
Contact: David Eckles, Contact
E-mail: deckles@uga.edu

Description: Integral unit of Terry College of Business, University of Georgia. **Scope:** Insurance industry. **Founded:** 1783. **Educational Activities:** Insurance Managers Seminar, Offer exemplary teaching programs.

START-UP INFORMATION

9016 ■ *"Should State Invest in Startups?"* in *Providence Business News (Vol. 28, March 3, 2014, No. 48, pp. 1)*
Pub: American City Business Journals, Inc.
Contact: Mike Olivieri, Executive Vice President
Released: March 01, 2014. **Description:** The U.S. Treasury Department is investigating whether Rhode Island violated Federal rules when it used funds from the State Small Business Credit Initiative (SSBCI) to invest in Betaspring, a startup accelerator program for technology and design entrepreneurs ready to launch their businesses. The Lyon Park audit claims that Rhode Island violated SSBCI rules because a large portion of the money went to the business accelerator's operating expenses and not to the startups themselves. **Availability:** Print; Online.

9017 ■ *"Staking Claim as Hub for Design"* in *Providence Business News (Vol. 28, March 17, 2014, No. 50, pp. 1)*
Pub: American City Business Journals, Inc.
Contact: Mike Olivieri, Executive Vice President
URL(s): pbn.com/staking-claim-as-hub-for-design9 5764
Description: Providence, Rhode Island is expected to have two startup accelerators in 2014, even though the city lacks a large technology and venture capital presence. The Providence Design Forward accelerator is a partnership with Rhode Island School of Design and will focus on architecture and interior design entrepreneurship. It is modeled after Boston's MassChallenge. **Availability:** Online.

ASSOCIATIONS AND OTHER ORGANIZATIONS

9018 ■ **American Society of Interior Designers (ASID) - Material ConneXion Library**
1152 15th St. NW, Ste. 910
  Washington, DC 20005
Ph: (202)546-3480
Fax: (202)546-3240
Co. E-mail: membership@asid.org
URL: http://www.asid.org
Contact: Gary Wheeler, Chief Executive Officer
E-mail: exec@asid.org
Facebook: www.facebook.com/ASID7
Linkedin: www.linkedin.com/company/american-socie ty-of-interior-designers
X (Twitter): x.com/ASID
Instagram: www.instagram.com/asid_hq
YouTube: www.youtube.com/channel/UCiDgXJ0Nav 2fWlXb3m-xc5Q
Description: Represents practicing professional interior designers, students and industry partners. ASID Educational Foundation sponsors scholarship competitions, finances educational research and awards special grants. **Scope:** Healthful environment. **Founded:** 1975. **Holdings:** 300 innovative materials.

Publications: *ASID Resource Guide and Industry Partner Directory* (Annual); *ASID ICON: Success Strategies for Interior Consultants* (Bimonthly). **Awards:** ASID Student Chapter Award (Annual); ASID Foundation Legacy Scholarships for Graduate Students (Annual); Irene Winifred Eno Grant (Annual); ASID Educator of Distinction Award (Annual); ASID Design for Humanity Award (Irregular). **Geographic Preference:** National.

9019 ■ **Association of University Interior Designers (AUID)**
520 S Walnut St.
  Bloomington, IN 47402-2388
Free: 866-860-2843
Co. E-mail: info@auid.org
URL: http://www.auid.org
Contact: Charran James, President
Facebook: www.facebook.com/pg/AUIDdesigners
X (Twitter): x.com/AUIDesigners
Instagram: www.instagram.com/auidesigners
Description: In-house interior designers associated with universities. Serves as an educational forum to share ideas and concerns of interior design relating to universities and colleges. **Founded:** 1979. **Publications:** *Association of University Interior Designers-- Membership Chairperson.* **Awards:** AUID Scholarship Award (Annual). **Geographic Preference:** National.

9020 ■ **Council for Interior Design Accreditation (CIDA)**
206 Cesar E Chavez Ave. SW, Ste. 350
  Grand Rapids, MI 49503-4014
Ph: (616)458-0400
Co. E-mail: info@accredit-id.org
URL: http://www.accredit-id.org
Contact: Holly Mattson, Chief Executive Officer
E-mail: holly@accredit-id.org
Facebook: www.facebook.com/CIDAorg
Linkedin: www.linkedin.com/company/council-for-in terior-design-accreditation
X (Twitter): x.com/cidaorg
Description: Formed by Interior Design Educators Council and American Society of Interior Designers. Administers voluntary plan for the special accreditation of interior design education programs offered at institutions of higher learning throughout the U.S. and its possessions and Canada; emphasizes the use of accreditation procedures to assure that the purposes and accomplishments of programs of interior design education meet the needs of society, students, and the interior design profession; recognized by the Council for Higher Education Accreditation as a national accrediting agency for programs in interior design in schools throughout the country. **Founded:** 1972. **Publications:** *Directory of Interior Design Programs Accredited by FIDER* (Semiannual). **Geographic Preference:** National.

9021 ■ **Home Fashion Products Association (HFPA)**
National Press Bldg., 529 14th St. NW, No. 1280
  Washington, DC 20045

Ph: (212)297-2189
URL: http://homefashionproducts.com
Contact: Charles Gaenslen, President
Linkedin: www.linkedin.com/company/home-fashion -products
Description: Manufacturers of curtains, draperies, bedding, rugs, and related products. Sponsors annual scholarship for students attending accredited schools in home textiles. **Founded:** 1968. **Awards:** HFPA Scholarships. **Geographic Preference:** National.

9022 ■ **Interior Design Society (IDS)**
164 S Main St., Ste. 809
  High Point, NC 27260
Ph: (336)884-4437
Co. E-mail: info@interiordesignsociety.org
URL: http://interiordesignsociety.org
Contact: Mikala Moller, President
E-mail: mikala.moller@rowleycompany.com
Facebook: www.facebook.com/IDSNational
Linkedin: www.linkedin.com/company/interior-design -society
Instagram: www.instagram.com/idsnational
YouTube: www.youtube.com/user/IDSNational
Pinterest: www.pinterest.com/idsnational
Description: Represents independent designers and decorators, retail designers and sales people, design-oriented firms, and manufacturers. Grants accreditation and recognition to qualified residential interior designers and retail home furnishing stores. Conducts educational seminars in design, sales training, and marketing. Offers products and publications for designers and a correspondence course for home furnishing sales people. **Founded:** 1973. **Publications:** *Design for Success* (Monthly); *Portfolio* (Quarterly). **Educational Activities:** IDS Conference (Annual). **Geographic Preference:** National.

9023 ■ **International Association of Lighting Designers (IALD)**
242 N York St., Ste. 514
  Elmhurst, IL 60126
Ph: (312)527-3677
Fax: (312)527-3680
Co. E-mail: iald@iald.org
URL: http://www.iald.org
Contact: Kelly Ashmore, Director
E-mail: kelly@iald.org
Instagram: www.instagram.com/iald
YouTube: www.youtube.com/theiald
Description: Represents professionals, educators, students, and others working in the field of lighting design worldwide. Promotes the benefits of quality lighting design and emphasizes the impact of lighting on architectural design and environmental quality. Furthers professional standards of lighting designers and seeks to increase their function in the interior design industry. **Founded:** 1969. **Publications:** *Reflections* (Monthly); *Why Hire an IALD Lighting Designer; International Association of Lighting Designers--Membership Directory.* **Educational Activities:** LIGHTFAIR International (LFI) (Biennial).

Awards: Thomas M. Lemons Scholarship (Annual); IALD Award (Annual); IALD International Lighting Design Awards (Annual). **Geographic Preference:** National.

9024 ■ International Furnishings and Design Association (IFDA)

610 Freedom Business Ctr., Ste. 110
  King of Prussia, PA 19406
Ph: (610)992-0011
Fax: (610)992-0021
Co. E-mail: info@ifda.com
URL: http://ifda.com
Contact: Dawn Brinson, President
Facebook: www.facebook.com/IFDAssociation
Linkedin: www.linkedin.com/in/ifda-association-9
  4332a32

Description: Represents individuals in design, production, distribution, education, promotion and editorial phases of the interior furnishings industry and related fields. Founded IFDA Educational Foundation in 1968. Conducts charitable programs. **Founded:** 1947. **Publications:** *IFDA Directory* (Annual); *IFDA Network* (Quarterly). **Awards:** IFDA Student Member Scholarship (Annual); International Furnishings and Design Association Part-time Student Scholarship (Annual); IFDA Fellow (Annual); IFDA Honorary Recognition Award (Annual); IFDA Trailblazer Award (Annual). **Geographic Preference:** National.

9025 ■ International Interior Design Association (IIDA)

111 E Wacker Dr., Ste. 222
  Chicago, IL 60601
Ph: (312)467-1950
Free: 888-799-4432
Co. E-mail: iidahq@iida.org
URL: http://iida.org
Contact: Cheryl S. Durst, Chief Executive Officer
Facebook: www.facebook.com/IIDAHQ
Linkedin: www.linkedin.com/company/iida
X (Twitter): x.com/IIDA_HQ
Instagram: www.instagram.com/iida_hq

Description: Represents professional interior designers, including designers of commercial, healthcare, hospitality, government, retail, residential facilities; educators; researchers; representatives of allied manufacturing sources. Conducts research, student programs and continuing education programs for members. Has developed a code of ethics for the professional design membership. **Founded:** 1994. **Publications:** *GRAction.* **Geographic Preference:** Multinational.

9026 ■ National Council for Interior Design Qualification (NCIDQ) - Library

225 Reinekers Ln., Ste. 210
  Alexandria, VA 22314
Ph: (202)721-0220
Co. E-mail: inquiries@cidq.org
URL: http://www.cidq.org
Contact: Erin Jennings, President
Facebook: www.facebook.com/NCIDQexam
Linkedin: www.linkedin.com/company/cidq
Instagram: www.instagram.com/ncidqexam
YouTube: www.youtube.com/channel/UC5j_NrhnfW
  _b4-k3AVGb4iA

Description: Independent organization of state and provincial regulatory bodies. Provides the public with the means to identify those interior designers who have demonstrated the minimum level of competence needed to practice in this profession. Provides a professional examination in interior design. Endeavors to maintain the most advanced examining procedures, and to update continually the examination to reflect expanding professional knowledge and design development techniques to protect the health, safety and welfare of the public. **Scope:** Interior design. **Publications:** *The Mark of a Professional*; *QLetter* (Monthly). **Awards:** Louis S. Tregre Award (Annual). **Geographic Preference:** National.

9027 ■ National Kitchen and Bath Association (NKBA) - Professional Resource Library

687 Willow Grove St.
  Hackettstown, NJ 07840
Ph: (908)852-0033
Free: 800-THE-NKBA
Co. E-mail: feedback@nkba.org
URL: http://nkba.org
Contact: Bill Darcy, Chief Executive Officer
Facebook: www.facebook.com/thenkba
Linkedin: www.linkedin.com/company/national-ki
  tchen-and-bath-association
X (Twitter): x.com/thenkba
Instagram: www.instagram.com/thenkba

Description: Manufacturers and firms engaged in retail kitchen sales; utilities, publications and other firms supplying products or services to the kitchen and bathroom industry. Protects and promotes the interest and welfare of members by fostering a better business climate in the industry. **Scope:** Kitchen; bath industry. **Founded:** 1963. **Publications:** *National Kitchen & Bath Association--Directory of Accredited Members* (Annual); *Council of Societies--Directory of Certified Kitchen Designers & Certified Bathroom Designers* (Annual). **Educational Activities:** National Design Competition (Annual). **Geographic Preference:** National.

9028 ■ Organization of Black Designers (OBD)

300 M St. SW, Ste. N110
  Washington, DC 20024
Ph: (937)837-6319
Co. E-mail: orgblackdesigners@gmail.com
URL: http://obd.org
Contact: Michael Chabbi, President
Facebook: www.facebook.com/groups/Organiza
  tionBlackDesigners

Description: Black designers involved in graphic design, animation, Web design, film/video, illustration, user interface design, or mobile app design. Strives to support black designers through program development, business opportunities, scholarly pursuit, and continuing education. **Founded:** 1968. **Publications:** *DesigNation* (Biennial); *OBData* (Weekly). **Educational Activities:** DesigNation. **Geographic Preference:** National; Multinational.

9029 ■ Paint and Decorating Retailers Association (PDRA)

1401 Triad Ctr. Dr.
  Saint Peters, MO 63376
Free: 800-737-0107
Co. E-mail: info@pdra.org
URL: http://www.pdra.org
Contact: Craig Bond, Chairman of the Board
E-mail: craig@pdra.org
X (Twitter): x.com/PaintDecoRetail
Pinterest: www.pinterest.com/pdra0036

Description: Serves as a trade association of locally-owned paint and decorating stores in the U.S., Canada and around the world. Offers professional advice, personal service and quality products for every paint, wall covering, window treatment and floor covering project. **Founded:** 1947. **Publications:** *PDRA Gold Book* (Annual); *Paint & Decorating Retailer* (Monthly); *Gold Book* (Annual); *Decorating Retailer--Directory of the Wallcoverings Industry Issue* (Annual); *Gold Book: Directory of the Wallcovering Industry* (Annual); *PDRA Decorating Registry.* **Educational Activities:** PDRA Show. **Geographic Preference:** Multinational.

9030 ■ Painting Contractors Association (PCA)

2316 Millpark Dr.
  Maryland Heights, MO 63043
Free: 800-332-7322
Co. E-mail: support@pcapainted.org
URL: http://www.pcapainted.org
Contact: Nigel Costolloe, Executive Director
E-mail: ncostolloe@pcapainted.org
Facebook: www.facebook.com/PCAsocial
Linkedin: www.linkedin.com/company/pcasocial
X (Twitter): x.com/PCAsocial

Instagram: www.instagram.com/pcasocial
YouTube: www.youtube.com/channel/
  UCBTMBYTowqtaZJvPCRL4TtA

Description: Painting and wall covering contractors. Operates educational and charitable programs. Compiles statistics. **Founded:** 1884. **Publications:** *Hazardous Waste Handbook*; *Painting and Wallcovering Contractor*; *PCA Membership Directory*; *Painting and Wallcovering Contractor--PDCA Roster* (Annual). **Awards:** PCA A.E. Robert Friedman Scholarship (Annual); PDCA Picture It Painted Professionally Awards; PDCA Humanitarian Award; Al Quilici Outstanding Member Award; L.E. Travis, Jr. PDCA Craftsman of the Year Award (Annual); PDCA Safety Achievement Awards (Annual). **Geographic Preference:** National.

9031 ■ Window Covering Manufacturers Association (WCMA)

355 Lexington Ave. 15th Flr.
  New York, NY 10017
Ph: (212)297-2122
Co. E-mail: contact@wcmanet.org
URL: http://wcmanet.com

Description: Represents corporations engaged in the manufacture or assembly of Venetian blinds, vertical blinds, pleated shades, or their components. Promotes the use, utility, image, and attractiveness of the products and services offered by the window covering industry. **Founded:** 1950. **Geographic Preference:** National.

REFERENCE WORKS

9032 ■ *"The CEO of Williams-Sonoma on Blending Instinct with Analysis"* in *Harvard Business Review* (Vol. 92, September 2014, No. 9, pp. 41)

Pub: Harvard Business Publishing
Contact: Diane Belcher, Managing Director

Price: $8.95. **Description:** At Williams-Sonoma Inc., analytics are used to provide customers with experiences that best match their preferences, based on browsing history and/or previous purchases. This data is also used to inform designers, vendors, and distributors of supply and demand patterns. **Availability:** Online; PDF.

9033 ■ *"The Disruptive Future of Interior Design Is Here"* in *Inc.* (July 14, 2017)

URL(s): www.inc.com/alex-moazed/is-the-interior
  -design-industry-getting-disrupted.html

Ed: Alex Moazed. **Released:** July 14, 2017. **Description:** Innovative platforms are now starting to take over the interior design industry, replacing traditional in-person client-designer relationships. These startups are addressing the lack of efficiency and convenience that have been the hallmarks of interior design and replacing them with ways to quickly complete projects anywhere in the word.

9034 ■ *"Downtown: Grunnah Trades Homes for a Shot at Warehouse District"* in *Austin Business Journal* (Vol. 34, February 28, 2014, No. 2, pp. 8)

Pub: American City Business Journals, Inc.
Contact: Mike Olivieri, Executive Vice President

Released: Weekly. **Price:** $4, Introductory 4-week offer(Digital only). **Description:** Real estate developer Robert Grunnah is set to open the Highland Club bar in Austin, Texas. Grunnah has invested about $1.5 million on the bar's interior design. **Availability:** Print; Online.

9035 ■ *"Entrepreneur Says Spirituality Has Been a Key to Her Success"* in *Business First Columbus* (Vol. 25, October 17, 2008, No. 8, pp. 1)

Description: Profile of Carolyn Williams Francis, CEO of Williams Interior Designs Inc. She outlines her mantra for success in her furniture design business, but emphasizes that faith has taken her business to greater heights.

9036 ■ *"Finally, New Life For Old IBM Offices"* *in Austin Business Journal (Vol. 34, June 6, 2014, No. 16, pp. A4)*

Pub: American City Business Journals, Inc.

Contact: Mike Olivieri, Executive Vice President

Released: Weekly. **Price:** $4, introductory 4-week offer(Digital only). **Description:** Two nondescript, 1970s-style industrial buildings, occupied in the 1970s by IBM Corporation, were purchased by an Austin-based contracting and construction management company. Burt-Watts Industries, from Powell Austin Properties Ltd., a local family. The company spent $3 million to renovate all the spaces into attractive, contemporary offices. Tommy Burt, co-founder of Burt-Watts was helped in this endeavor by Clay Little, partner in NoackLittle Architecture & Interiors. **Availability:** Print; Online.

9037 ■ *"First, the Merger: Then, The Culture Clash. How To Fix the Little Things That Can Tear a Company Apart"* *in Inc. (January 2008)*

Ed: Elaine Appleton Grant. **Description:** Ways three CEOs handled the culture classes that followed after company mergers; companies profiled include Fuel Outdoor, an outdoor advertising company; Nelson, an interior design and architecture firm; and Beber Silverstein, an ad agency. **Availability:** Online.

9038 ■ *Floor Covering Product Resource Guide*

Pub: FCW

Contact: Mark Flinn, General Manager

E-mail: mflinn@hearst.com

URL(s): www.floorcoveringweekly.com/main/mediakit

Ed: Santiago Montero. **Released:** Annual **Description:** Publication includes lists of manufacturers and importers of carpet, rugs, carpet cushion, fiber, resilient wood, and ceramic floor coverings; separate listing of distributors by state, retail groups and associations. **Entries include:** For manufacturers--Company name, address, phone, regional sales offices, names and titles of key personnel, local distributors, products. For distributors--Company name, address, phone, manufacturers represented. **Arrangement:** Alphabetical. **Indexes:** Geographical by distributor. **Availability:** Print; PDF; Online.

9039 ■ *Heart: Building a Great Brand in the Digital Age*

Pub: CreateSpace

Released: September 29, 2014. **Price:** $3.70, paperback. **Description:** Business leader and consultant who works with designers, contractors and service providers in the green industry helps business owners develop and implement company systems and increase revenue. His is a third-generation horticulturist and small business owner and share the challenges of being an entrepreneur. **Availability:** Print.

9040 ■ *"Hotels Make Wallcoverings a Sticking Trend"* *in Hotel News Now (April 17, 2019)*

URL(s): www.hotelnewsnow.com/Articles/294815/Hotels-make-wallcoverings-a-sticking-trend

Ed: Dana Miller. **Released:** April 17, 2019. **Description:** Wallcoverings, the term used to describe the more durable wallpaper used in hotels, are being used in innovative colors and patterns in hotel settings. Often cheaper than repainting, wallcoverings are a good way to switch up the look of a hotel when it's time to renovate or add a personal touch that is unique to the area the hotel is located. **Availability:** Online.

9041 ■ *"How Does Plant Leasing Work?"* *in Natura (July, 2013)*

URL(s): naturahq.com/2013/07/how-does-plant-leasing-work/

Released: July 2013. **Description:** An introduction to plant leasing and its benefits. Most businesses do not have time to take care of plants, so hiring someone to lease and care for plants in your building

is a solid solution. It also allows an opportunity to change things around each season, add more plants, or thin them out if they are too much. **Availability:** Online.

9042 ■ *"I Brake for Yard Sales: And Flea Markets, Thrift Shops, Auctions, and the Occasional Dumpster"*

Released: April 01, 2012. **Price:** $24.95, Paperback. **Description:** Lara Spencer, self-confessed frugalista and new correspondent, shares her passion for shopping at yard sales, consignment shops, and estate sales for decorating her home as well as her friend's homes. She shares her bargain hunting secrets and tells where to shop, what to look for, how to pay for sales, how to restore items, and how to decorate. **Availability:** E-book; Print.

9043 ■ *"Intel Joins Movement to Turn Cube Farms Into Wide-Open Spaces"* *in Sacramento Business Journal (Vol. 28, May 27, 2011, No. 13, pp. 1)*

Pub: Sacramento Business Journal

Contact: Stephanie Fretwell, Director

E-mail: sfretwell@bizjournals.com

Ed: Melanie Turner. **Description:** Intel Corporation has remodeled its facility in Folsom, California. The renovation has required some workers to give up their cubicles. Comments from executives are included.

9044 ■ *The Interior Design Business Handbook: A Complete Guide to Profitability*

Pub: John Wiley & Sons, Inc.

Contact: Christina Van Tassell, Executive Vice President Chief Financial Officer

URL(s): www.wiley.com/en-us/The+Interior+Design+Business+Handbook%3A+A+Complete+Guide+to+Profitability%2C+5th+Edition-p-9781118139875

Ed: Mary V. Knackstedt. **Released:** 5th edition. **Price:** $83, e-book; $103.95, hardcover. **Description:** A comprehensive resource for interior design business owners. Includes sections on structuring your business, marketing, developing your brand, and networking. Also includes seventy-five sample forms and letters. **Availability:** E-book; Print.

9045 ■ *"Monday Organizer: Clean and De-Clutter in 15 Minutes"* *in Tulsa World (June 13, 2011)*

Pub: The McClatchy Company

Contact: Tony W. Hunter, Chief Executive Officer

Ed: Kim Brown. **Description:** New weekly series highlights practical tips and helpful ideas to simply life by taking 15 minutes to de-clutter your home or office. Paper clutter can be eliminated in 15 minutes by gathering up newspapers and magazines to recycle; sort mail as soon as you receive it and throw away any junk mail at that time. If watching TV, use commercial time to accomplish small tasks. **Availability:** Print; Online.

9046 ■ *New York School of Interior Design: Home: The Foundations of Enduring Spaces*

Ed: Ellen S. Fisher. **Released:** March 27, 2018. **Price:** $32.82, Hardcover; $19.99, E-book. **Description:** Outlines a comprehensive home design and decor education. Built on the Home Study Course from the New York School of Interior Design, this book offers interior designers a definitive reference for their projects. **Availability:** E-book; Print.

9047 ■ *Peggy's Corner: The Art of Staging*

Pub: Eaton-Moghannam Publishing

Ed: Peggy Selinger-Eaton, Gayla Moghannam. **Description:** Techniques to enhance the value of any home are given. Seven principles of staging a home for sale include making a great first impression, maximizing space and eliminating clutter, using lighting for open spacious feeling, de-emphasize flaws, make the home appealing to buyers with varied tastes, creating warmth, and modernizing the home.

9048 ■ *"Staging a Martini-and-GQ Lifestyle"* *in Crain's Chicago Business (April 21, 2008)*

Pub: Crain Communications Inc.

Contact: Barry Asin, President

Ed: Kevin Davis. **Description:** Due to the competition of the slumping housing market, home stagers are becoming more prominent and are using creative ways to make an impression beyond de-cluttering, painting and cleaning by using accents such as casually placed magazines, candles and table settings. **Availability:** Online.

9049 ■ *"These Are the Women Who Really Mean Business"* *in Canadian Business (Vol. 87, October 2014, No. 10, pp. 67)*

Description: A list of the top 100 women entrepreneurs in Canada are ranked, based on sales, three-year revenue growth rate, and profitability of their businesses is presented. Included in the list are Janet Stimpson of White House Design Company, Inc.; builder, Allison Grafton of Rockwood Custom Homes Inc.; and Janet Jing Di Zhang of Vancouver, BC of New Immigrants Information Services Inc. **Availability:** Online.

9050 ■ *"Top Interior Design Firms"* *in Orlando Business Journal (Vol. 30, April 4, 2014, No. 41, pp. 7)*

Pub: American City Business Journals, Inc.

Contact: Mike Olivieri, Executive Vice President

Description: Rankings of interior design firms in the Central Florida region are presented. Rankings are based on the 2013 interior design billings. **Availability:** Print.

9051 ■ *"Wayfair Unveils New Mobile App Features"* *in Home Accents Today (November 13, 2019)*

URL(s): www.homeaccentstoday.com/e-commerce/wayfair-unveils-new-mobile-app-features/

Released: November 13, 2019. **Description:** Wanting to make it easier for their customers to discover products and have the ability to design rooms on the go, Wayfair added some new features to its mobile shopping app. Now consumers have access to an augmented reality (AR) tool and a Room Planner 3-D. **Availability:** Online.

9052 ■ *"What Will the Interior Design Profession Look Like 10 Years in the Future?"* *in Architectural Digest (April 2. 2019)*

URL(s): www.architecturaldigest.com/story/future-interior-design-profession

Ed: Tim McKeough. **Released:** April 02, 2019. **Description:** Contemplates the future of interior design by interviewing experts in digital design services, interior design, social media, retail, and antiques. Many trends and innovations are already here and are set to completely transform the industry and take it in a whole new direction. **Availability:** Online.

9053 ■ *"York Wallcoverings Seals Deal with Lemieux"* *in Home Accents Today (November 12, 2019)*

URL(s): www.homeaccentstoday.com/wall-decor/york-wallcoverings-seals-deal-with-lemieux/

Released: November 12, 2019. **Description:** York Wallcoverings is partnering with Christiane Lemieux and introducing a new line of wallpaper. Lemieux is an interior and home furnishings designer, and this wallpaper line is expected to be minimalistic, which will help enhance today's modern spaces. **Availability:** Online.

STATISTICAL SOURCES

9054 ■ *Interior Designers Industry in the US - Market Research Report*

URL(s): www.ibisworld.com/united-states/market-research-reports/interior-designers-industry/

Price: $925. **Description:** Downloadable report analyzing the current and future trends in the interior design industry. **Availability:** Download.

TRADE PERIODICALS

9055 ■ *Architectural Digest (AD)*

Pub: Conde Nast Publications

Contact: Agnes Chu, President

URL(s): www.architecturaldigest.com
Facebook: www.facebook.com/architecturaldigest
X (Twitter): x.com/archdigest
Instagram: www.instagram.com/archdigestindia
YouTube: www.youtube.com/user/ArchitecturalDigest
Pinterest: www.pinterest.com/archdigest
Ed: Amy Astley. **Released:** Bimonthly **Price:** $2.50, for annual print and online per month; $1, for online per month. **Description:** Magazine on interior design, art, and antiques. **Availability:** Print; Online.

9056 ■ Award Magazine: Architecture, Construction, Interior Design
Pub: Canada Wide Media Ltd.
Contact: Lucy Caithcart, Manager
E-mail: lcaithcart@canadawide.com
URL(s): canadawide.com/award
Ed: Natalie Bruckner-Menchelli. **Released:** Quarterly **Description:** Trade magazine for architects, developers, interior designers, and related professionals. **Availability:** Print; PDF; Online.

9057 ■ Chicago Home and Garden
Pub: Chicago Home & Garden
Ed: Jan Parr. **Description:** Magazine covering home and garden style in the Chicago, IL, area. **Availability:** Online.

9058 ■ Country Sampler
Pub: Country Sampler Group
Contact: Joan Lynch Luckett, Manager
E-mail: jluckett@countrysampler.com
URL(s): www.countrysampler.com
Facebook: www.facebook.com/CountrySamplerMagazine
YouTube: www.youtube.com/CountrySamplerMag
Pinterest: www.pinterest.com/CountrySampler1
Released: 6/year **Price:** $24, for 1 year US, Canada and international; $9.99, for online Download; $10, Canada for 1 year. **Description:** Country arts, crafts, interior design, and lifestyle magazine. **Availability:** Print; Download; Online.

9059 ■ Hospitality Design
Contact: Alissa Ponchione, Managing Editor
E-mail: alissa.ponchione@emeraldexpo.com
URL(s): www.hospitalitydesign.com/hospitalitydesign/index.shtml
Facebook: www.facebook.com/HospitalityDesignMagazine
Linkedin: www.linkedin.com/company/hospitality-design
X (Twitter): twitter.com/hdmag
Released: 10/yrs. **Description:** Magazine covering design of restaurants, hotels, facilities, clubs, cruise ships, etc. **Availability:** Print; PDF; Online.

9060 ■ House Beautiful
Contact: Jeff Bauman, Editor-in-Chief
URL(s): www.hearst.com/magazines/house-beautiful
Facebook: www.facebook.com/HouseBeautiful
X (Twitter): twitter.com/HouseBeautiful
Released: 10/year **Price:** $15, For print only 2 years; $10, For print only 1 year. **Description:** Magazine focusing on architecture, building, interior decorating, gardening, and landscaping. **Availability:** Print; Online.

9061 ■ Interior Design
Pub: Sandow
Contact: Peter Fain, Chief Operating Officer
URL(s): interiordesign.net
Facebook: www.facebook.com/InteriorDesignMagazine
Linkedin: www.linkedin.com/company/interior-design-magazine
X (Twitter): x.com/InteriorDesign
Instagram: www.instagram.com/interiordesignmag
Pinterest: www.pinterest.com/intdesmag
Released: Last edition 2024. **Price:** $12.95, Single issue for print. **Description:** Interior designing and furnishings magazine. **Availability:** Print; Online.

9062 ■ LDB Interior Textiles
Pub: Pioneer Associates Inc.
URL(s): www.ldbinteriortextiles.com

Released: Monthly **Price:** $165, for 1 year(Elsewhere (Airmail); $18, for (Elsewhere (Airmail); $75, U.S. for 1 year; $90, Canada for 1 year; $110, U.S. for 2 year; $7, U.S. for single issue; $12, Canada for single issue. **Description:** Magazine for buyers of home fashions, including bed, bath and table linens, hard and soft window treatments, home fragrances, decorative pillows and home accessories, accent rugs, and decorative fabrics. **Availability:** Print.

9063 ■ Old-House Interiors
Contact: Bill O'Donnell, Publisher
E-mail: bodonnell@oldhouseinteriors.com
Released: Bimonthly **Price:** $29.95, Individuals print and online; $16.99, Individuals digital; $24.95, Individuals print. **Description:** Consumer magazine covering interior design for period homes. **Availability:** Print.

TRADE SHOWS AND CONVENTIONS

9064 ■ Society of Glass and Ceramic Decorated Products Conference
Society of Glass and Ceramic Decorated Products (SGCDpro)
PO Box 2489
Zanesville, OH 43702
Ph: (740)588-9882
Co. E-mail: info@sgcd.org
URL: http://www.sgcd.org
Contact: Todd Barson, President
E-mail: tbarso78@gmail.com
URL(s): www.sgcd.org/Conference_and_Tradeshow
Frequency: Annual. **Description:** Promotes the advancement of the profession of glass and ceramic decorating. **Audience:** Industry professionals. **Principal Exhibits:** Promotes the advancement of the profession of glass and ceramic decorating.

CONSULTANTS

9065 ■ Chambers Ltd.
1800 Washington Blvd., Ste. 111
Baltimore, MD 21230
Ph: (410)727-4535
Fax: (410)727-6982
Co. E-mail: chambers@chambersusa.com
URL: http://www.chambersusa.com
Contact: Jeff Yang, Director
E-mail: jyang@chambersusa.com
Facebook: www.facebook.com/chambers1899
Linkedin: www.linkedin.com/company/the-h--chambers-company
X (Twitter): x.com/chambers1899
Instagram: www.instagram.com/chambers1899
Description: Provider of full-service design solutions. **Founded:** 1899.

9066 ■ Ogden Roemer Wilkerson Architecture (ORW)
29 S Grape St.
Medford, OR 97501
Ph: (541)779-5237
Co. E-mail: office@orwarch.com
URL: http://www.orwarchitecture.com
Contact: Jeffrey Bender, Director
E-mail: jeff@orwarch.com
Facebook: www.facebook.com/ORW-Architecture-181507901962984
Description: Provider of architectural solutions. **Training:** City Of Medford, Mar, 2010.

FRANCHISES AND BUSINESS OPPORTUNITIES

9067 ■ Deck the Walls
5700 Mexico Rd., Ste.6
Saint Peters, MO 63376
Free: 866-719-8200
Co. E-mail: dtwcontact@fcibiz.com
URL: http://deckthewalls.com
Facebook: www.facebook.com/DeckTheWallsCorporate

X (Twitter): x.com/Deck_The_Walls
Instagram: www.instagram.com/deckthewalls
Pinterest: www.pinterest.com/deckthewalls
Description: Firm engages in both custom framing and specialty prints in retail outlets and online. **Founded:** 1979. **Training:** Classroom and in-store training prepare franchisees for all aspects of business, including custom framing.

9068 ■ Decor & You Inc.
464 Heritage Rd., Ste. No 3, 3rd Fl.
Southbury, CT 06488
Ph: (203)264-3500
Co. E-mail: vendor@decorandyou.com
URL: http://www.decorandyou.com
Contact: Karen Powell, Chief Executive Officer
E-mail: kpowell@decorandyou.com
Facebook: www.facebook.com/DecoranDYouFranchiseHeadquarters
Linkedin: www.linkedin.com/company/decor-&-you
X (Twitter): x.com/DecorandYou
Pinterest: www.pinterest.com/decorandyouhq
Description: State of the art computerized sampling and personalized services from professionally trained interior decorators. **Founded:** 1998. **Training:** 4 phase training program for all franchisees. All aspects of the decorating business are covered, including color and design, trends, product knowledge, client development, follow-up skills, advertising and virtual decorating through computer graphics.

COMPUTER SYSTEMS/ SOFTWARE

9069 ■ Design Your Own Home
MCS Investments Inc.
PO Box 22902
Eugene, OR 97402
Ph: (541)431-0592
Fax: (541)349-8694
Co. E-mail: lottasales@theliquidateher.com
URL: http://theliquidateher.com/index.html
URL(s): theliquidateher.com/dyoh3dwalkaround-macintosh.html
Price: $19.99, Individuals. **Description:** Offers several design programs, including Architecture, Interiors, Landscape, and Libraries. Provides methods for determining structural details and drawing floor plans. **Availability:** CD-ROM; Print.

9070 ■ Microspot Interiors
Microspot Interiors Pro
418 S Military Tr.
Deerfield Beach, FL 33441
URL(s): www.microspot.com/products/interiors/upgrade1.htm
Price: $85.99, Individuals sale price; $129, Individuals list price. **Description:** Available for Apple Macintosh and Macintosh Plus computers. System provides an interior design program. Formerly Microspot Interiors. **Availability:** Online.

LIBRARIES

9071 ■ American Intercontinental University Library
2200 E Germann Rd., Ste. 100
Chandler, AZ 85286-1585
URL: http://www.aiuniv.edu/campus-locations/atlanta/student-life
Scope: Education. **Founded:** 1982. **Holdings:** Figures not available.

9072 ■ Bienenstock Furniture Library (BFL)
1009 N Main St.
High Point, NC 27262
Ph: (336)883-4011
Co. E-mail: info@furniturelibrary.com
URL: http://www.furniturelibrary.com
Contact: Christi Spangle, President
Facebook: www.facebook.com/BienenstockFurnitureLibrary
X (Twitter): x.com/FurnLibrary
YouTube: www.youtube.com/channel/UCYD4raFGXFb9DcL6SRsF_Ig

Scope: History and design of furniture; interiors, architecture; textiles; finishes and construction. **Services:** Photographing; library is open to the public. **Founded:** 1970. **Holdings:** 5,000 volumes; bound periodical volumes, including over 100 years of furniture catalogs; Furniture World; trade journals. **Subscriptions:** 10 journals and other serials.

9073 ■ City College of City University of New York - Art Visual Resources Library
c/o Ching-Jung Chen, Librarian
New York, NY 10031
Ph: (212)650-7607
Fax: (212)650-7604
Co. E-mail: cchen@ccny.cuny.edu
URL: http://www.adm.ccny.cuny.edu/v2/directory/dirfind.cfm?urltarget=Library
Contact: Ching-Jung Chen, Librarian
E-mail: cchen@ccny.cuny.edu

Description: New York-Art Visual Resources Library. **Scope:** Arts; education. **Holdings:** Figures not available.

9074 ■ Conde Nast Publications Library and Information Services
1 World Trade Ctr.
New York, NY 10007
Co. E-mail: communications@condenast.com
URL: http://www.condenast.com
Contact: Roger Lynch, Chief Executive Officer
Linkedin: www.linkedin.com/company/conde-nast
X (Twitter): x.com/condenast
Instagram: www.instagram.com/condenast

Description: Produces in-depth research for the world's most celebrated media brands. **Scope:** Fashion; houses; gardens; home furnishings; interior design; health; personalities; photographs. **Services:** Library not open to public. **Founded:** 1935. **Holdings:** 7,000 volumes.

9075 ■ Craigdarroch Castle - Library
1050 Joan Cres.
Victoria, BC, Canada V8S 3L5
Ph: (250)592-5323
Fax: (250)592-1099
Co. E-mail: info@thecastle.ca
URL: http://thecastle.ca
Contact: John Hughes, Executive Director
X (Twitter): x.com/CraigdarrochC
YouTube: www.youtube.com/channel/UCFBwX9p0
5cn9G4_ASc5x6-g

Description: Craigdarroch Castle built between 1887 and 1890. **Scope:** History of craigdarroch castle. **Founded:** 1959. **Holdings:** Figures not available.

9076 ■ HDR Inc. - Library
HDR Inc.
1917 S 67th St.
Omaha, NE 68106-2973
Ph: (402)399-1000
URL: http://www.hdrinc.com
Contact: Eric L. Keen, Chief Executive Officer
Facebook: www.facebook.com/hdrinc
Linkedin: www.linkedin.com/company/hdr
YouTube: www.youtube.com/user/HDRinc

Description: Provider of complete engineering and consulting services for Power Generation, Project Development and Facilities Engineering. **Scope:** Architecture; engineering; graphic arts; interior design. **Services:** Interlibrary loan; copying; SDI; library open to the public for reference use only. **Founded:** 1917. **Holdings:** 2500 books. **Educational Activities:** TechAdvantage Conference & Expo; TechAdvantage Expo (Annual).

9077 ■ Hillwood Estate, Museum & Gardens Art Research Library
4155 Linnean Ave. NW
Washington, DC 20008
Ph: (202)686-5807
URL: http://hillwoodmuseum.org
Contact: Kendall Aughenbaugh, Librarian, Digital Services
E-mail: kaughenbaugh@hillwoodmuseum.org

Description: Hillwood library-holdings reflect the museum's collection of imperial Russian and 18th-century French decorative arts within a broad social context. **Scope:** Art - decorative, French, Russian; Russian imperial history. **Services:** Copying; library open to the public by appointment. **Founded:** 1960. **Holdings:** 38,000 volumes; monographs; serials; annotated; early auction catalogues; and electronic resources; Marjorie Merriweather Post.

9078 ■ Leo A Daly Company
Leo A Daly Company
8600 Indian Hills Dr.
Omaha, NE 68114-4039
Ph: (402)391-8111
Fax: (402)391-8564
Co. E-mail: leoadaly@leoadaly.com
URL: http://www.leoadaly.com
Contact: Jonathan A. Fliege, Director
E-mail: jafliege@leoadaly.com
Facebook: www.facebook.com/leoadaly
Linkedin: www.linkedin.com/company/leo-a-dal
X (Twitter): x.com/LeoADaly
Instagram: www.instagram.com/leoadaly_design

Description: Provides services such as planning, architecture, engineering, interior design. **Services:** Reference services for librarians and qualified

researchers; library not open to the public. **Founded:** 1915. **Subscriptions:** 75 journals and other serials; 6 newspapers.

9079 ■ State University of New York - Fashion Institute of Technology - Gladys Marcus Library
227 W 27th St.
New York, NY 10001-5992
Ph: (212)217-7999
URL: http://www.fitnyc.edu/library/index.php

Description: Library supports the academic and research needs of the institute. **Scope:** Fashion, fashion history, textiles, fashion trend forecasting. **Services:** Interlibrary loan; library open by appointment. **Founded:** 1944. **Holdings:** 300,000 print, non-print, and electronic materials, including sketch collections, clipping files, and fashion show DVDs.

9080 ■ University of Nevada, Las Vegas Architecture Studies Library
4505 S Maryland Pky.
Las Vegas, NV 89154-4049
Ph: (702)895-1959
Co. E-mail: libasl@unlv.edu
URL: http://www.library.unlv.edu/arch
Contact: Richard Saladino, Librarian
E-mail: richard.saladino@unlv.edu

Scope: Architecture. **Services:** Interlibrary loan; Copying. **Founded:** 1997. **Holdings:** Books; journals.

9081 ■ Watkins College of Art, Design, & Film Library
1900 Belmont Blvd.
Nashville, TN 37212
Co. E-mail: librarian@watkins.edu
URL: http://www.watkins.edu

Description: Watkins Library is a comprehensive nerve center of resources for Watkins students, staff, and faculty. **Scope:** Film; fine arts; visual arts; graphic design; photography. **Services:** Interlibrary loan; library open to the public for reference use only. **Holdings:** Books; films.

9082 ■ Woodbury University Library
7500 N Glenoaks Blvd.
Burbank, CA 91510
Ph: (818)252-5200
Co. E-mail: reference@woodbury.edu
URL: http://library.woodbury.edu
Contact: Eric Garcia, Librarian, Reference
E-mail: eric.garcia@woodbury.edu
Facebook: www.facebook.com/wulibrary
X (Twitter): x.com/woodburylib
Instagram: www.instagram.com/woodburyuniversitylibrary

Scope: Education. **Services:** Interlibrary loan (limited). **Founded:** 1884. **Holdings:** Books; journals.

START-UP INFORMATION

9083 ■ *101 Internet Businesses You Can Start from Home: How to Choose and Build Your Own Successful E-Business*
Pub: Maximum Press

Ed: Susan Sweeney. **Released:** Third edition. **Description:** Guide for starting and growing an Internet business; information for developing a business plan, risk levels, and promotional techniques are included.

9084 ■ *"Brand Storytelling Becomes a Booming Business" in Entrepreneur (April 2012)*
Pub: Entrepreneur Media Inc.
Contact: Dan Bova, Director
E-mail: dbova@entrepreneur.com

Ed: Paula Andruss. **Description:** San Francisco-based Story House Creative engages in helping small businesses connect with their audience in communicating their brand identity. Web content, bios and tag lines are some of the marketing materials Story House Creative creates for its clients. The company also does search engine optimization, video, design, and copywriting. The Brandery, another brand-building company, helps startups promote their business. Eight to ten Brandery mentors are assigned to assist each startup client. Meanwhile, Brand Journalists is a Tennessee-based company focusing on corporate storytelling. It offers Web and blog content, human stories reporting and ghostwriting services. **Availability:** Print; Online.

9085 ■ *"Consumer Startup Hub Set for Downtown" in Atlanta Business Chronicle (June 13, 2014, pp. 3A)*
Pub: American City Business Journals, Inc.
Contact: Mike Olivieri, Executive Vice President

Description: Michael Tavani, co-founder of Scoutmob, believes that Atlanta is fast becoming the hub for consumer- and design-focused startups. He is planning to locate his consumer-focused startup, Switchyards, in a 1920s building downtown, which will become a hive for mobile app, media, and ecommerce startups. **Availability:** Print; Online.

9086 ■ *How to Start an Internet Sales Business Without Making the Government Mad*
Pub: Lulu Press Inc.

Ed: Dan Davis. **Released:** October 01, 2011. **Price:** $19.95, paperback; $14.38, PDF; $14.38, e-book. **Description:** Small business guide for launching an Internet sales company. Topics include business structure, licenses, and taxes. **Availability:** E-book; Print; PDF.

ASSOCIATIONS AND OTHER ORGANIZATIONS

9087 ■ **Internet Society**
11710 Plz. America Dr., Ste. 400
Reston, VA 20190

Ph: (703)439-2120
Fax: (703)326-9881
Co. E-mail: isoc@isoc.org
URL: http://www.internetsociety.org
Contact: Dan York, Director
Facebook: www.facebook.com/InternetSociety
Linkedin: www.linkedin.com/company/internet-society
X (Twitter): x.com/internetsociety
Instagram: www.instagram.com/internetsociety
YouTube: www.youtube.com/user/InternetSocietyVideo

Description: Seeks to ensure global cooperation and coordination for the Internet and related internetworking technologies and applications. **Founded:** 1992. **Publications:** *IETF Journal*; *Internet Society Newsletter* (Monthly). **Educational Activities:** Internet Society Conference (Annual); Network and Distributed System Security Symposium (NDSS) (Annual). **Awards:** Internet Society Fellowships to the IETF; Jonathan B. Postel Service Award (Annual). **Geographic Preference:** National.

9088 ■ **World Organization of Webmasters (WOW)**
PO Box 584
Washington, IL 61571-0584
Co. E-mail: membership@webprofessionals.org
URL: http://webprofessionals.org
Contact: Mark DuBois, Executive Director

Description: Individuals who create, manage, market, or maintain websites. Seeks to advance the profession of website creation and management; promotes the online industries. Facilitates communication and cooperation among members. **Founded:** 1996. **Awards:** WOW Web Professionals of the Year Award (Annual). **Geographic Preference:** National.

REFERENCE WORKS

9089 ■ *"2 New Tools for Safeguarding Your Website: Website Backup Made Simple" in Inc. (Vol. 33, September 2011, No. 7, pp. 52)*
Pub: Inc. Magazine

Ed: John Brandon. **Description:** Tools to back up content on a Website are profiled. Vaultpress works only with sites that run on the WordPress publishing platform and CodeGuard works with a variety of publishing platforms and hosting services. **Availability:** Online.

9090 ■ *"13 Ways to Screw over Your Internet Provider" in Tech Crunch (September 2, 2019)*
URL(s): techcrunch.com/2019/09/02/13-ways-to-screw-over-your-internet-provider/

Ed: Devin Coldewey. **Released:** September 02, 2019. **Description:** Discusses thirteen ways consumers can put the squeeze on their internet service provider in order to get better deals and save their bottom line. **Availability:** Online.

9091 ■ *"529.com Wins Outstanding Achievement in Web Development" in Investment Weekly (November 14, 2009, pp. 152)*
Pub: Investment Weekly News

Description: Web Marketing Association's 2009 WebAward for Financial Services Standard of Excellence and Investment Standard of Excellence was won by 529.com, the website from Upromise Investments, Inc., the leading administrator of 529 college savings plans. **Availability:** Online.

9092 ■ *"All About The Benjamins" in Canadian Business (Vol. 81, September 29, 2008, No. 16, pp. 92)*

Description: Discusses real estate developer Royal Indian Raj International Corp., a company that planned to build a $3 billion "smart city" near the Bangalore airport; to this day nothing has ever been built. The company was incorporated in 1999 by Manoj C. Benjamin one investor, Bill Zack, has been sued by the developer for libel due to his website that calls the company a scam. Benjamin has had a previous case of fraud issued against him as well as a string of liabilities and lawsuits. **Availability:** Online.

9093 ■ *"All Those Applications, and Phone Users Just Want to Talk" in Advertising Age (Vol. 79, August 11, 2008, No. 31, pp. 18)*
Pub: Crain Communications, Inc.
Contact: Jessica Botos, Manager, Marketing
E-mail: jessica.botos@crainsnewyork.com

Ed: Mike Vorhaus. **Description:** Although consumers are slowly coming to text messaging and other data applications, a majority of those Americans surveyed stated that they simply want to use their cell phones to talk and do not care about other activities. Statistical data included. **Availability:** Online.

9094 ■ *"Apps For Anybody With an Idea" in Advertising Age (Vol. 79, October 17, 2008, No. 39, pp. 29)*
Pub: Crain Communications, Inc.
Contact: Jessica Botos, Manager, Marketing
E-mail: jessica.botos@crainsnewyork.com

Ed: Beth Snyder Bulik. **Description:** Apple's new online App Store is open to anyone with an idea and the ability to write code and many of these developers are not only finding a sense of community through this venue but are also making money since the sales are split with Apple, 30/70 in the developer's favor. **Availability:** Online.

9095 ■ *"Are Offline Pushes Important to E-Commerce?" in DM News (Vol. 31, September 14, 2009, No. 23, pp. 10)*
Pub: Haymarket Media Inc.
Contact: Kevin Costello, Chief Executive Officer

Description: With the importance of Internet marketing and the popularity of ecommerce increasing experts debate the relevance of more traditional channels of advertising. **Availability:** Online.

9096 ■ *"As Traditional Web Site Adoption Slows, Facebook and Other Social Networks Become Key Platforms for Home-Based Business Promotional and Commercial Activity Online"* in *Marketing Weekly News (June 16, 2012)*

Description: Websites have provided an inexpensive means for businesses to market their products and services. However, home-based businesses are using social networking, email marketing, search engine optimization, search engine marketing, Website optimization for mobile devices, banner advertisements, and the use of ecommerce platforms such as eBay, Craigs list, and Amazon. **Availability:** Print; Online.

9097 ■ *"avVaa World Health Care Products Rolls Out Internet Marketing Program"* in *Health and Beauty Close-Up (September 18, 2009)*

Description: avVaa World Health Care Products, Inc., a biotechnology company, manufacturer and distributor of nationally branded therapeutic, natural health care and skin products, has signed an agreement with Online Performance Marketing to launch of an Internet marketing campaign in order to broaden its presence online. The impact of advertising on the Internet to generate an increase in sales is explored. **Availability:** Online.

9098 ■ *"Bank of America Fights To Keep Top Spot in Mobile Banking"* in *Charlotte Business Journal (Vol. 27, June 15, 2012, No. 13, pp. 1)*

Pub: American City Business Journals, Inc.

Contact: Mike Olivieri, Executive Vice President

Released: Weekly. **Price:** $20, Introductory 12-week offer(Digital & Print). **Description:** Bank of America has been fighting to maintain its lead in mobile banking services. Financial institutions, payment processors and e-commerce firms have started offering mobile banking services. **Availability:** Print; Online.

9099 ■ *"The Bankrate Double Play, Bankrate Is Having Its Best Quarter Yet"* in *Barron's (Vol. 88, March 24, 2008, No. 12, pp. 27)*

Pub: Dow Jones & Company Inc.

Contact: Almar Latour, Chief Executive Officer

Ed: Neil A. Martin. **Description:** Shares of Bankrate may rise as much as 25 percent from their level of $45.08 a share due to a strong cash flow and balance sheet. The company's Internet business remains strong despite weakness in the online advertising industry and is a potential takeover target. **Availability:** Online.

9100 ■ *"BayTSP, NTT Data Corp. Enter Into Reseller Pact to Market Online IP Monitoring"* in *Professional Services Close-Up (Sept. 11, 2009)*

Description: Due to incredible interest from distributors and content owners across Asia, NTT Data Corp. will resell BayTSP's online intellectual property monitoring, enforcement, business intelligence and monetization services in Japan.

9101 ■ *"Be Wary of Legal Advice on Internet, Lawyers Warn"* in *Crain's Detroit Business (Vol. 24, September 22, 2008, No. 38, pp. 16)*

Pub: Crain Communications Inc.

Contact: Barry Asin, President

Ed: Harriet Tramer. **Description:** While some lawyers feel that the proliferation of legal information on the Internet can point people in the right direction, others maintain that it simply results in giving false hope, may bring about confusion or worse yet, it sometimes makes their jobs even harder. **Availability:** Online.

9102 ■ *"Being All a-Twitter"* in *Canadian Business (Vol. 81, December 8, 2008, No. 21, pp. 22)*

Description: Marketing experts suggest that advertising strategies have to change along with new online social media. Companies are advised to find ways to

incorporate social software because workers and customers are expected to continue its use. **Availability:** Print; Online.

9103 ■ *"Beware the Hotspot: How You're Vulnerable"* in *Philadelphia Business Journal (Vol. 33, June 13, 2014, No. 18, pp. 7)*

Pub: American City Business Journals, Inc.

Contact: Mike Olivieri, Executive Vice President

Released: Weekly. **Price:** $4, introductory 4-week offer(Digital only). **Description:** Pete Hazen, technology consultant for Determinant Solutions talks about the dangers of connecting to open public WiFi. He mentions that such connection allows cyber criminals to capture the data like passwords, which then can be used to commit identity fraud, pay for merchandise, or steal money from the user's online accounts. **Availability:** Print; Online.

9104 ■ *"Blog Buzz Heralds Arrival of IPhone 2.0"* in *Advertising Age (Vol. 79, June 9, 2008, No. 40, pp. 8)*

Pub: Crain Communications, Inc.

Contact: Jessica Botos, Manager, Marketing

E-mail: jessica.botos@crainsnewyork.com

Ed: Abbey Klaassen. **Description:** Predictions concerning the next version of the iPhone include a global-positioning-system technology as well as a configuration to run on a faster, 3G network. **Availability:** Online.

9105 ■ *"Boom has Tech Grads Mulling Their Options"* in *Globe & Mail (March 14, 2006, pp. B1)*

Ed: Grant Robertson. **Description:** Internet giant Google Inc. has stepped up its efforts to hire the talented people, in Canada, at Waterloo University in southern Ontario, to expand its operations. The details of the job market and increasing salaries are analyzed. **Availability:** Online.

9106 ■ *"Branding Your Way"* in *Canadian Business (Vol. 80, February 12, 2007, No. 4, pp. 31)*

Description: The trend in involving consumers in brand marketing by seeking their views through contests or inviting them to produce and submit commercials through Internet is discussed. **Availability:** Online.

9107 ■ *"Brite-Strike Tactical Launches New Internet Marketing Initiatives"* in *Marketwired (September 15, 2009)*

Pub: Comtex News Network Inc.

Contact: Kan Devnani, President

Description: Brite-Strike Tactical Illumination Products, Inc. has enlisted the expertise of Internet marketing guru Thomas J. McCarthy to help revamp the company's Internet campaign. An outline of the Internet marketing strategy is provided. **Availability:** Print; Online.

9108 ■ *"BusinessOnLine Launches New Web-Based Search Engine Optimization Tool: First Link Checker for Google"* in *Marketwired (October 19, 2009)*

Pub: Comtex News Network Inc.

Contact: Kan Devnani, President

Description: First Link Checker, a complimentary new search engine optimization tool that helps site owners optimize their on-page links by understanding which of those links are actually being counted in Google's relevancy algorithm, was developed by BusinessOnLine, a rapidly growing Internet marketing agency. This tool will make it easy for the average web master to ensure that their internal link structure is optimized. **Availability:** Print.

9109 ■ *"Buyout Rumors Have Rackspace Back in the News"* in *San Antonio Business Journal (Vol. 28, September 12, 2014, No. 31, pp. 6)*

Pub: American City Business Journals, Inc.

Contact: Mike Olivieri, Executive Vice President

Description: Louisiana-based CenturyLink Inc. has offered to buyout San Antonio, Texas-based Rackspace Hosting in order to boost its Internet and cloud

services. The latest stock market valuation of Rackspace was at $5.33 billion. The potential impact of the CenturyLink and Rackspace merger deal on the managed hosting services market is also analyzed. **Availability:** Online.

9110 ■ *"Campaigner Survey: 46 Percent of Small Businesses Use Email Marketing"* in *Wireless News (November 21, 2009)*

Description: Almost half (46 percent) of small businesses surveyed by Campaigner's 2009 State of Small Business Online Marketing, say that they rely on email marketing to help them find new customers, keep existing ones and grow their businesses. The survey also found that 36 percent of small businesses plan to begin using email marketing over the next year. The trend to utilize Internet marketing tools is allowing small businesses to grow faster and generate higher revenues than those that are not using these mediums. **Availability:** Print; Online.

9111 ■ *"Can People Collaborate Effectively While Working Remotely? Vint Cerf, Co-Creator of the Internet, On How Employees Can Work Together More Productively In An Age When Many Can Work Almost Anywhere"* in *Gallup Business Journal (March 13, 2014)*

Pub: Gallup, Inc.

Contact: Jon Clifton, Chief Executive Officer

Description: Vint Cerf, co-creator of the Internet, discusses ways that employees can work more productively when technology allows them to work from almost anywhere. **Availability:** Online.

9112 ■ *"Charlotte Pipe Launches Satirical Campaign"* in *Contractor (Vol. 57, January 2010, No. 1, pp. 6)*

Description: Charlotte Pipe and Foundry Co. launched an advertising campaign that uses social media and humor to make a point about how it can be nearly impossible to determine if imported cast iron pipes and fittings meet the same quality standards as what is made in the U.S. The campaign features 'pipe whisperers' and also spoofs pipe sniffing dogs. **Availability:** Print; Online.

9113 ■ *"Citadel EFT (CDFT) Contracts With New Search Engine Optimization (SEO) and Banner Ad Web Marketing Companies"* in *Internet Wire (August 8, 2012)*

Pub: Comtex News Network Inc.

Contact: Kan Devnani, President

Description: Citafel EFT Inc. provides credit card terminals, online, mail order and retail credit card processing services. The firm has contracted with two Web marketing companies to increase its awareness on the Internet. **Availability:** Print; Online.

9114 ■ *"ClickFuel Unveils Internet Marketing Tools for Small Businesses"* in *Marketwired (October 19, 2009)*

Pub: Comtex News Network Inc.

Contact: Kan Devnani, President

Description: ClickFuel, a firm that manages, designs and tracks marketing campaigns has unveiled a full software suite of affordable services and technology solutions designed to empower small business owners and help them promote and grow their businesses through targeted Internet marketing campaigns. **Availability:** Online.

9115 ■ *Clicking Through: A Survival Guide for Bringing Your Company Online*

Released: First edition. **Description:** Summary of legal compliance issues faced by small companies doing business on the Internet, including copyright and patent laws.

9116 ■ *"Coca-Cola FEMSA, Family Dollar, Other Dividend Payers On a Roll"* in *Benzinga.com (June 21, 2012)*

Pub: Benzinga.com

Contact: Jason Raznick, Founder

Ed: Nelson Hem. **Description:** Dividend paying companies showing upward price trends are outlined. The firms highlighted include: Agnico-Eagle Mines,

Coca-Cola FEMSA, Dean Foods, Expedia, Family Dollar Stores, Ferrellgas Partners, and InterContinental Hotels. **Availability:** Print; Online.

9117 ■ *"Comcast Launches New Home Security Service, Developed in Portland"* in *The Oregonian (June 7, 2011)*
Pub: McClatchy-Tribune Regional News

Ed: Mike Rogoway. **Description:** Comcast introduced its new high-end home security system that provides 24-hour monitoring and control of homes and utilities, along with Web and mobile access. **Availability:** Print; Online.

9118 ■ *The Complete Guide to Google Adwords: Secrets, Techniques, and Strategies You Can Learn to Make Millions*
Pub: Atlantic Publishing Co.

Contact: Dr. Heather L. Johnson, Contact

Released: 2012. **Description:** Google AdWords, when it launched in 2002 signaled a fundamental shift in what the Internet was for so many individuals and companies. Learning and understanding how Google AdWords operates and how it can be optimized for maximum exposure, boosting click through rates, conversions, placement, and selection of the right keywords, can be the key to a successful online business. **Availability:** Print; Online.

9119 ■ *"Conscious Capitalism: Liberating the Heroic Spirit of Business"*
Released: January 07, 2014. **Price:** $12.47, e-book; $16.79, paperback. **Description:** Conscious Capitalism companies include Whole Foods Market, Southwest Airlines, Costco, Google, Patagonia, The Container Store, UPS and others. These firms under the four specific tenants to success: higher purpose, stakeholder integration, conscious leadership, and conscious culture and management. These companies are able to create value for all stakeholders, including customers, employees, suppliers, investors, society, and the environment. A new preface by the authors is included. **Availability:** E-book; Print.

9120 ■ *"Conversations with Customers"* in *Business Journal Serving Greater Tampa Bay (Vol. 31, December 31, 2010, No. 1, pp. 1)*
Pub: Tampa Bay Business Journal

Contact: Ian Anderson, President

E-mail: ianderson@bizjournals.com

Description: Tampa Bay, Florida-based businesses have been using social media to interact with customers. Forty percent of businesses have been found to have at least one social media platform to reach customers and prospects. **Availability:** Print; Online.

9121 ■ *"Covario Recognized for Second Year in a Row as OMMA Award Finalist for Online Advertising Creativity in Both SEO and SEM"* in *Internet Wire (August 29, 2012)*
Pub: Comtex News Network Inc.

Contact: Kan Devnani, President

Description: Leading independent search marketing agency, Covario, providing search engine optimization (SEO) and search engine marketing (SEM) for companies was chosen as a finalist for the MediaPost Onlien Media, Marketing and Advertising award. This is Covario's second year to be recognized for this award. **Availability:** Print; Online.

9122 ■ *"Cox Opens Norfolk Mall Kiosk; Wireless Service Not Ready"* in *Virginian-Pilot (September 20, 2010)*
Pub: The Virginian-Pilot

Contact: Kevin Goyette, Director

E-mail: kgoyette@dailypress.com

Ed: Carolyn Shapiro. **Description:** Cox Communications opened a kiosk at MacArthur Center that will sell wireless telephone devices and plans. **Availability:** Print; Online.

9123 ■ *"Cross Atlantic Commodities Launches National Internet Marketing Programs"* in *Manufacturing Close-Up (September 8, 2009)*
Description: Profile of the Internet campaign recently launched by Cross Atlantic Commodities, Inc., a manufacturer of specialty beauty and health products. **Availability:** Print; Online.

9124 ■ *"Crossing the Chasm: Marketing and Selling Disruptive Products to Mainstream Customers*
Pub: HarperCollins Publishers L.L.C.

Contact: Brian Murray, President

Ed: Geoffrey A. Moore. **Released:** 3rd edition. **Price:** $21.99, paperback; $11.99, e-book. **Description:** A guide for marketing in high-technology industries, focusing on the Internet. **Availability:** E-book; Print.

9125 ■ *"Cyber Thanksgiving Online Shopping a Growing Tradition"* in *Marketing Weekly News (December 12, 2009, pp. 137)*
Pub: Investment Weekly News

Description: According to e-commerce analysts, Thanksgiving Day is becoming increasingly important to retailers in terms of online sales. Internet marketers are realizing that consumers are already searching for Black Friday sales and if they find deals on the products they are looking for, they are highly likely to make their purchase on Thanksgiving Day instead of waiting. **Availability:** Online.

9126 ■ *"Designing Websites for Every Audience*
Description: Twenty-five case studies targeting six difference audiences are used to help a business design, or make over, a Website. **Availability:** E-book.

9127 ■ *"Designing Women? Apparel Apparatchic at Kmart"* in *Barron's (Vol. 88, March 17, 2008, No. 11, pp. 16)*
Pub: Dow Jones & Company Inc.

Contact: Almar Latour, Chief Executive Officer

Ed: Robin Goldwyn Blumenthal. **Description:** Kmart began a nationwide search for women to represent the company in a national advertising campaign. Contestants need to upload their photos to Kmart's website and winners will be chosen by a panel of celebrity judges. The contest aims to reverse preconceived negative notions about the store's quality and service. **Availability:** Online.

9128 ■ *"Dish's Charlie Ergen Sees Nothing Good in Comcast-Time Warner Merger"* in *Denver Business Journal (Vol. 65, February 21, 2014, No. 41)*
Pub: American City Business Journals, Inc.

Contact: Mike Olivieri, Executive Vice President

Released: Weekly. **Description:** The co-founder and CEO of Dish Network, Charlie Ergen, is against the proposed $45.2 billion merger of Comcast and Time Warner. Ergen feels that his satellite TV company and others in the broadband and TV industries will be put in an unfair situation if the two companies are allowed to combine. **Availability:** Print; Online.

9129 ■ *"Diving Into Internet Marketing"* in *American Agent and Broker (Vol. 81, December 2009, No. 12, pp. 24)*
Ed: Steve Anderson. **Description:** Internet marketing is becoming an essential tool for most businesses; advice is provided regarding the social networking opportunities available for marketing one's product or service on the Internet. **Availability:** Online.

9130 ■ *"Do Coin Shops Have a Future?"* in *Numismatic News (June 1, 2015)*
URL(s): www.numismaticnews.net/article/do-coin -shops-have-a-future

Ed: Pat Heller. **Released:** June 01, 2015. **Description:** Explores the reality of brick-and-mortar coin shops losing out from the advancement of the internet and online sales. However, all is not lost because these stores could potentially extend their markets and products in order to increase their foot traffic. **Availability:** Online.

9131 ■ *"Do-It-Yourself Portfolio Management"* in *Barron's (Vol. 89, July 13, 2009, No. 28, pp. 25)*
Pub: Dow Jones & Company Inc.

Contact: Almar Latour, Chief Executive Officer

Ed: Mike Hogan. **Description:** Services of several portfolio management web sites are presented. These web sites include MarketRiders E.Adviser, TD Ameritrade and E. **Availability:** Online.

9132 ■ *"Don't' Hate the Cable Guy"* in *Saint Louis Business Journal (Vol. 31, August 5, 2011, No. 50, pp. 1)*
Pub: Saint Louis Business Journal

Contact: Robert Bobroff, President

E-mail: rbobroff@bizjournals.com

Ed: Angela Mueller. **Description:** Charter Communications named John Birrer as senior vice president of customer experience. The company experienced problems with its customer services. **Availability:** Print; Online.

9133 ■ *EBay Income: How ANYONE of Any Age, Location, and/or Background Can Build a Highly Profitable Online Business with eBay*
Pub: Atlantic Publishing Co.

Contact: Dr. Heather L. Johnson, Contact

Description: A complete overview of eBay is given and guides any small company through the entire process of creating the auction and auction strategies, photography, writing copy, text and formatting, multiple sales, programming tricks, PayPal, accounting, creating marketing, merchandising, managing email lists, advertising plans, taxes and sales tax, best time to list items and for how long, sniping programs, international customers, opening a storefront, electronic commerce, buy-it now pricing, keywords, Google marketing and eBay secrets.

9134 ■ *Electronic Commerce*
Ed: Gary P. Schneider, Bryant Chrzan, Charles McCormick. **Released:** 12th edition. **Price:** $29.49, e-book. **Description:** E-commerce can open the door to more opportunities than ever before for small business. Packed with real-world examples and cases, the book delivers comprehensive coverage of emerging online technologies and trends and their influence on the electronic marketplace. It details how the landscape of online commerce is evolving, reflecting changes in the economy and how business and society are responding to those changes. Balancing technological issues with the strategic business aspects of successful e-commerce, the new edition includes expanded coverage of international issues, social networking, mobile commerce, Web 2.0 technologies, and updates on spam, phishing, and identity theft. **Availability:** Print.

9135 ■ *"Emerging Business Online: Global Markets and the Power of B2B Internet Marketing*
Pub: FT Press

Ed: Lara Fawzy, Lucas Dworski. **Released:** First edition. **Price:** $39.99, Members, watermarked. **Description:** An introduction into ebocube (emerging business online), a comprehensive proven business model for Internet B2B marketing in emerging markets. **Availability:** E-book; Print; Online; PDF; Electronic publishing.

9136 ■ *"Empowered"* in *Harvard Business Review (Vol. 88, July-August 2010, No. 7-8, pp. 94)*
Pub: Harvard Business Publishing

Contact: Diane Belcher, Managing Director

Ed: Josh Bernoff, Ted Schadler. **Price:** $8.95, PDF. **Description:** HERO concept (highly empowered and resourceful operative) which builds a connection between employees, managers, and IT is outlined. The resultant additional experience and knowledge gained by employees improves customer relationship management. **Availability:** Online; PDF.

9137 ■ *"Endeca Gears Up for Likely IPO Bid"* in *Boston Business Journal (Vol. 31, July 1, 2011, No. 23, pp. 1)*
Pub: Boston Business Journal

Contact: Carolyn M. Jones, President

E-mail: cmjones@bizjournals.com

Ed: Kyle Alspach. **Released:** Weekly. **Price:** $4. **Description:** Endeca Inc. is readying itself for its plans to register as a public company. The search engine technology leader is enjoying continued growth with revenue up by 30 percent in 2010 while its expansion trend makes it an unlikely candidate for an acquisition. **Availability:** Print; Online.

9138 ■ *"Experts Sound Off On Top Legal Trends" in Birmingham Business Journal (Vol. 31, January 17, 2014, No. 3, pp. 4)*
Pub: American City Business Journals, Inc.
Contact: Mike Olivieri, Executive Vice President
Released: Weekly. **Price:** $4, introductory 4-week offer(Digital & Print). **Description:** Lawyers' views on potential legal trends in Birmingham, Alabama for 2014 are presented, with the Affordable Care Act leading the agenda. One attorney addressed the challenges associated with the use of social media. **Availability:** Print; Online.

9139 ■ *The Facebook Effect: The Inside Story of the Company That Is Connecting the World*
Ed: David Kirkpatrick. **Released:** 2011. **Price:** $18, paperback; $13.99, e-book. **Description:** There's never been a Website like Facebook: more than 350 million people have accounts, and if the growth rate continues, by 2013 every Internet user worldwide will have his or her own page. No one's had more access to the inner workings of the phenomenon than Kirkpatrick, a senior tech writer at Fortune magazine. Written with the full cooperation of founder Mark Zuckerberg, the book follows the company from its genesis in a Harvard dorm room through its successes over Friendster and MySpace, the expansion of the user base, and Zuckerberg's refusal to sell. **Availability:** E-book; Print.

9140 ■ *"Facebook, Google, LinkedIn Line Up In Patent Case Before Supreme Court" in San Francisco Business Times (Vol. 28, March 28, 2014, No. 36)*
Pub: American City Business Journals, Inc.
Contact: Mike Olivieri, Executive Vice President
Released: Weekly. **Description:** The U.S. Supreme Court is set to hear a case involving Alice Corporation Pty. Ltd. and CLS Bank International in a dispute over a patented computer-implemented escrow service. The case has larger implications to tech companies concerning whether a business method can be patented if it is made electronic. **Availability:** Print; Online.

9141 ■ *"Facebook IPO Buyers Deserved To Lose" in Canadian Business (Vol. 85, July 16, 2012, No. 11-12, pp. 16)*
Ed: Andrew Hallam. **Description:** Investors buying into an overhyped initial public offering (IPO) like Facebook, which opened with a price/earnings ratio exceeding 100 times earnings, are overpyaing for uncertain promise. Studies found that the most profitable IPO are those unpopular businesses which are not overpriced. **Availability:** Print; Online.

9142 ■ *"The Facebook IPO Hype Meter" in Canadian Business (Vol. 85, June 11, 2012, No. 10, pp. 74)*
Ed: Joe Castaldo. **Description:** Comparison of the Facebook frenzy with other notable initial public offerings (IPO) based on market capitalization divided by profit indicated that an overpriced IPO such as that of Facebook does not equate to poor returns in the short-term. Studies found that IPOs that debut at more reasonable prices get better returns in the long term. **Availability:** Print; Online.

9143 ■ *"ForeSee Finds Satisfaction On Web Sites, Bottom Line" in Crain's Detroit Business (Vol. 24, February 25, 2008, No. 8, pp. 3)*
Pub: Crain Communications Inc.
Contact: Barry Asin, President
Ed: Tom Henderson. **Description:** Ann Arbor-based ForeSee Results Inc. evaluates user satisfaction on Web sites. The company expects to see an increase of 40 percent in revenue for 2008 with plans to expand to London, Germany, Italy and France by the end of 2009.

9144 ■ *"Ga. PMA Launches Online Education Program" in Contractor (Vol. 56, October 2009, No. 10, pp. 8)*
Description: Plumbing & Mechanical Association of Georgia launched an online program that covers technical and business management that will help contractors run their businesses. Future courses will include math for plumbers, graywater systems, and recession-proofing your business. **Availability:** Print; Online.

9145 ■ *"Generation Y Chooses the Mobile Web" in PR Newswire (November 24, 2010)*
Pub: PR Newswire Association LLC.
Description: Generation Y individuals between the ages of 18 - 27 use their mobile phones to browse the Internet more often than a desktop or laptop computer, according to a survey conducted by Opera, a Web browser company. **Availability:** Print; Online.

9146 ■ *"Google 'Drive' May Run Over Some Local Cloud Competitors" in Silicon Valley/San Jose Business Journal (Vol. 29, February 17, 2012, No. 47, pp. 1)*
Pub: Baltimore Business Journal
Contact: Rhonda Pringle, President
E-mail: rpringle@bizjournals.com
Description: Google Inc. has been preparing to roll out a cloud storage service called "Drive" that will allow people to store large files online. However, the move would put Google in competition with companies offering similar services and it could affect other companies looking to enter the space. Insights on reactions of the other companies are also provided. **Availability:** Print; Online.

9147 ■ *"Google Gets Creepy" in Canadian Business (Vol. 85, September 17, 2012, No. 14, pp. 28)*
Ed: Jeff Beer. **Description:** Google's move to integrate its more than 70 different privacy agreements into just one has simplified the privacy deal the search engine company made with its users and improved its ability to obtain information for advertising. Google is addressing concerns about online privacy and allegations of anticompetitive practices in the U.S. and Europe. **Availability:** Online.

9148 ■ *"Google Places a Call to Bargain Hunters" in Advertising Age (Vol. 79, September 29, 2008, No. 36, pp. 13)*
Pub: Crain Communications, Inc.
Contact: Jessica Botos, Manager, Marketing
E-mail: jessica.botos@crainsnewyork.com
Ed: Abbey Klaassen. **Description:** Google highlighted application developers who have created tools for its Android mobile phone in the device's unveiling; applications such as ShopSavvy and CompareEverywhere help shoppers to find bargains by allowing them to compare prices in their local areas and across the web. **Availability:** Online.

9149 ■ *"Google's Next Stop: Below 350?" in Barron's (Vol. 88, March 10, 2008, No. 10, pp. 17)*
Pub: Dow Jones & Company Inc.
Contact: Almar Latour, Chief Executive Officer
Ed: Jacqueline Doherty. **Description:** Share prices of Google Inc. are expected to drop from their level of $433 each to below $350 per share. The company is expected to miss its earnings forecast for the first quarter of 2008, and its continued aggressive spending on non-core areas will eventually bring down earnings. **Availability:** Online.

9150 ■ *"Grey Power: On Target" in Canadian Business (Vol. 81, July 22, 2008, No. 12-13, pp. 45)*
Pub: Rogers Media Inc.
Contact: Neil Spivak, Chief Executive Officer
Ed: Calvin Leung. **Description:** Companies such as LavalifePRIME, a dating website devoted to singles 45 and older, discuss the value of marketing and services aimed at Canada's older consumers. One-

third of Canada's 33 million people are 50-plus, controlling 77 percent of the countries wealth. **Availability:** Print; Online.

9151 ■ *Groundswell: Winning in a World Transformed by Social Technologies*
Pub: Harvard Business Review Press
Contact: Moderna V. Pfizer, Contact
Ed: Charlene Li, Josh Bernoff. **Released:** June 09, 2011. **Price:** $22, paperback/softbound. **Description:** Individuals are using online social technologies such as blogs, social networking sites, YouTube, and podcasts to discuss products and companies, write their own news, and find their own deals. When consumers you've never met are rating your company's products in public forums with which you have no experience or influence, your company is vulnerable. This book teaches the tools and data necessary to turn this treat into an opportunity. **Availability:** E-book; Print.

9152 ■ *"Growth of Free Dailies Dropping" in Globe & Mail (March 24, 2007, pp. B7)*
Ed: Grant Robertson. **Description:** The decrease in the readership of free newspapers in Canada, in view of growing preference for online news, is discussed. **Availability:** Online.

9153 ■ *"Has Microsoft Found a Way to Get at Yahoo?" in Advertising Age (Vol. 79, July 7, 2008, No. 26, pp. 4)*
Pub: Crain Communications, Inc.
Contact: Jessica Botos, Manager, Marketing
E-mail: jessica.botos@crainsnewyork.com
Ed: Abbey Klaassen. **Description:** Microsoft's attempt to acquire Yahoo's search business is discussed as is Yahoo's plans for the future at a time when the company's shares have fallen dangerously low. **Availability:** Print; Online.

9154 ■ *"HBC Enlists IBM to Help Dress Up Its On-Line Shopping" in Globe & Mail (February 7, 2006, pp. B3)*
Description: The details of management contract between Hudson's Bay Co. and International Business Machines Corp. are presented. **Availability:** Print; Online.

9155 ■ *How to Make Money with Social Media: An Insider's Guide to Using New and Emerging Media to Grow Your Business*
Ed: Jamie Turner, Reshma Shah, PhD. **Released:** 2nd edition. **Description:** Marketers, executives, entrepreneurs are shown more effective ways to utilize Internet social media to make money. This guide brings together both practical strategies and proven execution techniques for driving maximum value from social media marketing. **Availability:** E-book; Print.

9156 ■ *"How Marketers Can Tap the Web" in Sales and Marketing Management (November 12, 2009)*
Description: Internet marketing strategies require careful planning and tools in order to track success. Businesses are utilizing this trend to attract new clients as well as keep customers they already have satisfied. Advice on website development and design is provided. **Availability:** Online.

9157 ■ *How to Open and Operate a Financially Successful Bookstore on Amazon and Other Web Sites: With Companion CD-ROM*
Pub: Atlantic Publishing Co.
Contact: Dr. Heather L. Johnson, Contact
Description: This book was written for every used book aficionado and bookstore owner who currently wants to take advantage of the massive collection of online resources available to start and run your own online bookstore business.

9158 ■ *How to Use the Internet to Advertise, Promote, and Market Your Business or Web Site: With Little or No Money*
Pub: Atlantic Publishing Co.
Contact: Dr. Heather L. Johnson, Contact

Ed: Bruce C. Brown. **Released:** Revised third edition. **Description:** Information is given to help build, promote, and make money from your Website or brick and mortar store using the Internet, with minimal costs.

9159 ■ *I'm on LinkedIn - Now What?*
Pub: Happy About
Contact: Ric Vatner, Chief Executive Officer
Ed: Jason Alba. **Released:** Fourth edition. **Price:** $19.95, paperback; $14.95; $9.99. **Description:** Designed to help get the most out of LinkedIn, the popular business networking site and follows the first edition and includes the latest and great approaches using LinkedIn. With over 32 million members there is a lot of potential to find and develop relationships to help in your business and personal life, but many professionals find themselves wondering what to do once they sign up. This book explains the different benefits of the system and recommends best practices (including LinkedIn Groups) so that you get the most out of LinkedIn. **Availability:** E-book; Print; PDF; DVD; Electronic publishing; Download; Online.

9160 ■ *Information Technology for the Small Business: How to Make IT Work For Your Company*
Description: Basics of information technology to help small companies maximize benefits are covered. Topics include pitfalls to avoid, email and Internet use, data backup, recovery and overall IT organization.

9161 ■ *"Ingrian and Channel Management International Sign Distribution Agreement" in Canadian Corporate News (May 16, 2007)*
Description: Channel Management International (CMI), a Canadian channel management and distribution company, and Ingrian Networks, Inc., the leading provider of data privacy solutions, announced a Canadian distribution agreement to resell Ingrian encryption solutions to the Canadian market. **Availability:** Online.

9162 ■ *"Inside Intel's Effectiveness System for Web Marketing" in Advertising Age (Vol. 81, January 25, 2010, No. 4, pp. 4)*
Pub: Crain Communications, Inc.
Contact: Jessica Botos, Manager, Marketing
E-mail: jessica.botos@crainsnewyork.com
Ed: Beth Snyder Bulik. **Description:** Overview of Intel's internally developed program called Value Point System in which the company is using in order to evaluate and measure online marketing effectiveness. **Availability:** Online.

9163 ■ *"The Intel Trinity: How Robert Noyce, Gordon Moore, and Andy Grove Built the World's Most Important Company"*
Pub: Harper Business
Contact: Hollis Heimbouch, Senior Vice President Publisher
Released: July 15, 2014. **Price:** $34.99, hardcover; $11.74, e-book; $4.34, kindle; $19.42, hardcover; $4.30, hardcover(69 used from $4.30); $15.17, hardcover(56 new from $15.17); $19.99, hardcover(1 collectible from $19.99); $31.74, paperback; $22.95, paperback(10 used from $22.95); $19.13, paperback(4 new from $19.13). **Description:** A complete history of Intel Corporation, the essential company of the digital age, is presented. After over four decades Intel remains the most important company in the world, a defining company of the global digital economy. The inventors of the microprocessor that powers nearly every intelligent electronic device worldwide are profiled. These entrepreneurs made the personal computer, Internet, telecommunications, and personal electronics all possible. The challenges and successes of the company and its ability to maintain its dominance, its culture and its legacy are examined. **Availability:** E-book; Print; Online.

9164 ■ *"Internet Marketing 2.0: Closing the Online Chat Gap" in Agent's Sales Journal (November 2009, pp. 14)*
Ed: Jeff Denenholz. **Description:** Advice regarding the implementation of an Internet marketing strategy for insurance agencies includes how and why to

incorporate a chat feature in which a sales agent can communicate in real-time with potential or existing customers. It is important to understand if appropriate response mechanisms are in place to convert leads into actual sales. **Availability:** Print; Online.

9165 ■ *"Internet Providers Look to Cash In on Your Web Habits" in The Wall Street Journal (June 27, 2019)*
URL(s): www.wsj.com/articles/facebook-knows-a-lot-about-you-so-does-your-internet-provider-11561627803
Ed: Sarah Krouse, Patience Haggin. **Released:** June 27, 2019. **Description:** Internet service providers have been mining our web habits for years and are cashing in by selling ads to us based on our habits. There have been some legislation that tried to curb this behavior, but it was overturned recently and individual states, such as Maine, have been trying to pass a law requiring cable providers get customers' explicit consent to use or sell their web-browsing history. **Availability:** Online.

9166 ■ *"Into the Groove: Fine-Tune Your Biz By Getting Into the Good Habit Groove" in Small Business Opportunities (Spring 2008)*
Description: Profile of Ty Freyvogel and his consulting firm Freyvogel Communications. Freyvogel serves the telecommuvications need of Fortune 500 and mid-sized businesses.

9167 ■ *"Into the Light: Making Our Way Through the Economic Tunnel" in Agency Sales Magazine (Vol. 39, August 2009, No. 8, pp. 26)*
Description: Ways in which to avoid business stagnation brought about by the economic downturn is presented. Being different, being a puzzle solver, and knowing the competition are among the things marketing personnel should do in order to wade through the economic downturn. Marketing via direct mail and the Internet also recommended. **Availability:** Online.

9168 ■ *"Intrepid Souls: Meet a Few Who've Made the Big Leap" in Crain's Chicago Business (Vol. 31, November 10, 2008, No. 45, pp. 26)*
Description: Advice is given from entrepreneurs who have launched businesses in the last year despite the economic crisis. Among the types of businesses featured are a cooking school, a child day-care center, a children's clothing store and an Internet-based company. **Availability:** Online.

9169 ■ *"IP Transition Is Unlikely To Make Waves In R.I." in Providence Business News (Vol. 28, January 13, 2014, No. 41, pp. 1)*
Pub: American City Business Journals, Inc.
Contact: Mike Olivieri, Executive Vice President
Released: January 13, 2014. **Description:** The transition from copper and circuit switches to fiber and Internet Protocol is changing the telecommunications landscape across the U.S. The Rhode Island General Assembly passed a bill that deregulates wireless communications systems, which means that the growth of wireless in the area previously held by landlines will not change its status for now. **Availability:** Print; Online.

9170 ■ *"Israeli Spam Law May Have Global Impact" in Information Today (Vol. 26, February 2009, No. 2, pp. 28)*
Pub: Information Today Inc.
Contact: Thomas H. Hogan, President
Ed: David Mirchin. **Description:** Israels new law, called Amendment 40 of the Communications Law, will regulate commercial solicitations including those sent without permission via email, fax, automatic phone dialing systems, or short messaging technologies. **Availability:** PDF; Online.

9171 ■ *"It Was a Very Good Year..To Be Ted Rogers" in Canadian Business (Vol. 80, Winter 2007, No. 24, pp. 121)*
Description: Ted Rogers had a banner year in 2007 as Rogers Communications Inc. (RCI) took in huge profits from its phone and wireless business and his

personal wealth grew sixty-seven percent to $7.6 billion. Rogers has record of betting on technologies that get the best returns relative to the investment in the marketplace such as its use of the GSM network and its cable hybrid fiber coaxial network.

9172 ■ *"Jab, Jab, Jab, Right Hook: How to Tell Your Story in a Noisy Social World"*
Pub: Harper Business
Contact: Hollis Heimbouch, Senior Vice President Publisher
Released: November 26, 2013. **Price:** $23.99, hardcover. **Description:** Author and social media expert shares advice on ways to connect with customers and beat the competition. Social media strategies for marketers and managers need to convert Internet traffic to sales. Communication is the key to online sales that are adapted to high quality social media platforms and mobile devices. **Availability:** E-book; Print.

9173 ■ *"Joining the Fiber" in San Antonio Business Journal (Vol. 28, April 4, 2014, No. 8, pp. 4)*
Pub: American City Business Journals, Inc.
Contact: Mike Olivieri, Executive Vice President
Released: April 4, 2014. **Description:** San Antonio, Texas leaders have been aggressively pursuing the opportunity to install a Google Fiber network that would deliver gigabit-per-second Internet service to the city. San Antonio is included in Google Fiber's list for possible expansion of its broadband network. The potential benefits of Google Fiber choosing San Antonio as the site for their expansion are examined.

9174 ■ *"KCET Takes On Elder-Care With Robust Your Turn To Care Website" in PR Newswire (July 31, 2012)*
Pub: PR Newswire Association LLC.
Description: Your Turn To Care is a new Website created by KCET, the nation's largest independent public television station. The network, serving southern and central California, offers the Website to serve as a resource for families, caregivers and seniors in te US facing the challenges of caring for an ailing or aging loved one. The Website also covers issues involved in aging.

9175 ■ *"Kuno Creative to Present the Three Steps of a Successful B2B Social Media Campaign" in Business Tech & Wireless (August 25, 2011)*
Pub: Close-Up Media Inc.
Contact: Caroline S. Moore, President
E-mail: cms@closeupmedia.com
Released: August 24, 2011. **Description:** Kuno Creative, an inbound marketing agency, will host Three Steps of a Successful B2B Social Media Campaign. The firm is a provider of Website development, branding, marketing strategy, public relations, Internet marketing, and inbound marketing. **Availability:** Print; Online.

9176 ■ *"Lavante, Inc. Joins Intersynthesis, Holistic Internet Marketing Company" in Marketwired (November 5, 2009)*
Pub: Comtex News Network Inc.
Contact: Kan Devnani, President
Description: Lavante, Inc., the leading provider of on-demand vendor information and profit recovery audit solutions for Fortune 1000 companies has chosen Intersynthesis, a new holistic Internet marketing firm, as a provider of pay for performance services. Lavante believes that Intersynthesis' expertise and knowledge combined with their ability to develop integrated strategies, will help them fuel more growth. **Availability:** Print; Online.

9177 ■ *"Leading Ohio Internet Marketing Firm Announces Growth in September" in Marketing Weekly News (September 26, 2009, pp. 24)*
Pub: Investment Weekly News
Description: Despite a poor economy, Webbed Marketing, a leading social media marketing and search engine optimization firm in the Midwest, has added five additional professionals to its fast-growing

team. The company continues to win new business, provide more services and hire talented employees. **Availability:** Online.

9178 ■ *"Legislating the Cloud" in Information Today (Vol. 28, October 2011, No. 9, pp. 1)*

Pub: Information Today Inc.

Contact: Thomas H. Hogan, President

Ed: Kurt Schiller. **Description:** Internet and telecommunications industry leaders are asking for legislation to address the emerging market in cloud computing. Existing communications laws do not adequately govern the modern Internet.

9179 ■ *"Loonies Buy U.S. Cable" in Canadian Business (Vol. 85, September 17, 2012, No. 14, pp. 8)*

Ed: Jeff Beer. **Description:** The move by two Canadian companies to invest in the U.S. cable industry get mixed reactions from analyst and observers. Cogeco Cable purchased Atlantic Broadband for $1.36 billion while the Canada Pension Plan Investment Board announced its partnership with European private equity firm BC Partners to acquire Suddenlink Communications for $6.6 billion. **Availability:** Online.

9180 ■ *"Making It Click: Annual Ranking Of the Best Online Brokers" in Barron's (Vol. 88, March 17, 2008, No. 11, pp. 31)*

Pub: Dow Jones & Company Inc.

Contact: Almar Latour, Chief Executive Officer

Ed: Theresa W. Carey. **Description:** Listing of 23 online brokers that are evaluated based on their trade experience, usability, range of offerings, research amenities, customer service and access, and costs. TradeStation Securities takes the top spot followed by thinkorswim by just a fraction. **Availability:** Online.

9181 ■ *"Managing the Facebookers; Business" in The Economist (Vol. 390, January 3, 2009, No. 8612, pp. 10)*

Pub: Economist Newspaper Ltd.

Contact: Lara Boro, Chief Executive Officer

Description: According to a report from PricewaterhouseCoopers, a business consultancy, workers from Generation Y, also known as the Net Generation, are more difficult to recruit and integrate into companies that practice traditional business acumen. 61 percent of chief executive managers say that they have trouble with younger employees who tend to be more narcissistic and more interested in personal fulfillment with a need for frequent feedback and an over-precise set of objectives on the path to promotion which can be hard for managers who are used to a different relationship with their subordinates. Older bosses should prepare to make some concessions to their younger talent since some of the issues that make them happy include cheaper online ways to communicate and additional coaching, both of which are good for business. **Availability:** Online.

9182 ■ *"Microsoft's Big Gamble" in Canadian Business (Vol. 81, March 3, 2008, No. 3, pp. 13)*

Description: Microsoft Corp. is taking a big risk in buying Yahoo, as it is expected to pay more than $31 a share to finalize the acquisition. The deal would be seven and a half times bigger than any other that Microsoft has entered before, an execution of such deal is also anticipated to become a challenge for Microsoft. Recommendations on how Microsoft should handle the integration of the two businesses are given. **Availability:** Print; Online.

9183 ■ *"More Leading Retailers Using Omniture Conversion Solutions to Boost Sales and Ecommerce Performance" in Marketwired (September 22, 2009)*

Pub: Comtex News Network Inc.

Contact: Kan Devnani, President

Description: Many retailers are utilizing Omniture conversion solutions to improve the performance of their ecommerce businesses; recent enhancements to Omniture Merchandising and Omniture Recommendations help clients drive increased conversion to their Internet ventures.

9184 ■ *"MyWireless.org Commends Arizona Congressman Trent Franks for Committing to Wireless Tax Relief for American Consumers and Businesses" in PR Newswire (September 21, 2012)*

Pub: PR Newswire Association LLC.

Description: MyWireless.org presented Congressman Trent Franks from Arizona with the 2012 Wireless Consumer Hero Award for his work on wireless tax relief for American consumers and businesses. Franks' 'Wireless Tax Fairness Act' (HR 1002) promotes access to wireless networks as a key ingredient of millions of Americans' livelihoods, whether phone, broadband Internet necessary to run a small business. **Availability:** Print; Online.

9185 ■ *"nCircle Launches PCI DSS Compliance Package for Small Businesses" in Health & Beauty Close-Up (May 14, 2012)*

Description: nCircle presents the results of small business security scans from March 30 through April 28, 2012. The provider of information risk and security performance management reportes that eight of the toptne highest risk vulnerabilities detected on small business networks are connected with blank or default passwords. **Availability:** Print; Online.

9186 ■ *"The Neighborhood Watch" in Hawaii Business (Vol. 53, March 2008, No. 9, pp. 36)*

Pub: PacificBasin Communications

Contact: Chuck Tindle, Director

E-mail: chuckt@pacificbasin.net

Ed: David K. Choo. **Description:** OahuRe.com offers information on Hawaii real estate market, with spreadsheets and comparative market analysis page, which shows properties that are active, sold, or in escrow. Other details about OahuRe.com are discussed. A list of other top real estate websites in Hawaii and in the U.S. in general is provided.

9187 ■ *"Net Savings Link Announces SpyderShare Inc. Contract for Development of Search Engine Optimization (S.E.O.) Program" in Internet Wire (February 21, 2012)*

Pub: Comtex News Network Inc.

Contact: Kan Devnani, President

Description: Net Savings Link provides electronically deliverable sales incentives for the business market along with improved Web based savings programs for consumers has partnered with Spyder-Share Inc. to enhance the firm's presence on the Internet. Details of the partnership are included. **Availability:** Print; Online.

9188 ■ *"Networking Web Sites: a Two-Edge Sword" in Contractor (Vol. 56, October 2009, No. 10, pp. 52)*

Ed: H. Kent Craig. **Description:** People need to be careful about the information that they share on social networking Web sites. They should realize that future bosses, coworkers, and those that might want to hire them might read those information. Posting on these sites can cost career opportunities and respect. **Availability:** Print; Online.

9189 ■ *"A New Cloud-Based Phone System Is Installed Remotely for North Carolina Senior Care Council" in Information Technology Business (June 19, 2012)*

Description: North Carolina Senior Care Council (NcSCC) has partnered with VoxNet to provide long-term care for Cloud-based PBX to help NcSCC manage their system that assists seniors. **Availability:** Online.

9190 ■ *"A New Globe - In Print and Online" in Marketing to Women (Vol. 22, August 2009, No. 8, pp. 3)*

Description: Seventeen magazine is unifying its print and Online editions with complementary content, a strategy that seems to be working as every aspect of Seventeen drives the reader to another component. **Availability:** Online.

9191 ■ *"New IPhone Also Brings New Way of Mobile Marketing" in Advertising Age (Vol. 79, June 16, 2008, No. 24, pp. 23)*

Pub: Crain Communications, Inc.

Contact: Jessica Botos, Manager, Marketing

E-mail: jessica.botos@crainsnewyork.com

Ed: Abbey Klaassen. **Description:** Currently there are two kinds of applications for the iPhone and other mobile devices: native applications that allow for richer experiences and take advantage of features that are built into a phone and web applications, those that allow access to the web through specific platforms. Marketers are interested in creating useful experiences for customers and opening up the platforms which will allow them to do this. **Availability:** Online.

9192 ■ *"New Recession-Proof Internet Marketing Package Allows Businesses to Ramp Up Web Traffic and Profits" in PR Newswire (January 25, 2010)*

Pub: PR Newswire Association LLC.

Description: Profile of Reel Web Design, a leading marketing firm in New York City that caters to small to medium sized businesses with smaller budgets that need substantial return on investment; Reel Web Design offers video production and submission, web design and maintenance and press release writing among additional services. **Availability:** Online.

9193 ■ *"New Research and Infographic: Vacation Much More Important than 'Nice to Have'" in PR Newswire (August 26, 2014)*

Pub: Comtex News Network Inc.

Contact: Kan Devnani, President

Description: Search engine optimization is discussed. Tips are offered to help small companies optimize their Web presence.

9194 ■ *"New Sony HD Ads Tout Digital" in Brandweek (Vol. 49, April 21, 2008, No. 16, pp. 5)*

Description: Looking to promote Sony Electronics' digital imaging products, the company has launched another campaign effort known as HDNA, a play on the words high-definition and DNA; originally Sony focused the HDNA campaign on their televisions, the new ads will include still and video cameras as well and marketing efforts will consist of advertising in print, Online, television spots and publicity at various venues across the country. **Availability:** Online.

9195 ■ *"A New Way to Tell When to Fold 'Em" in Barron's (Vol. 88, July 7, 2008, No. 27, pp. 27)*

Pub: Dow Jones & Company Inc.

Contact: Almar Latour, Chief Executive Officer

Ed: Theresa W. Carey. **Description:** Overview of the Online trading company SmartStops, a firm that aims to tell investors when to sell the shares of a particular company. The company's Web site categorizes stocks as moving up, down, or sideways, and calculates exit points for individual stocks based on an overall market trend. **Availability:** Online.

9196 ■ *"'Nobody Knows What To Do' To Make Money on the Web" in Barron's (Vol. 88, March 17, 2008, No. 11, pp. 40)*

Pub: Dow Jones & Company Inc.

Contact: Almar Latour, Chief Executive Officer

Ed: Mark Veverka. **Description:** Attendees of the South by Southwest Interactive conference failed to get an insight on how to make money on the Web from former Walt Disney CEO Michael Eisner when Eisner said there's no proven business model for financing projects. Eisner said he finances his projects with the help of his connections to get product-placement deals. **Availability:** Online.

9197 ■ *"Norvax University Health Insurance Sales Training and Online Marketing Conference" in Marketwired (January 27, 2010)*

Pub: Comtex News Network Inc.

Contact: Kan Devnani, President

Description: Overview of the Norvax University Marketing and Sales Success Conference Tour which includes insurance sales training seminars, proven and innovative online marketing techniques and a host of additional information and networking opportunities. **Availability:** Print; Online.

9198 ■ *"Nowspeed and OneSource to Conduct Webinar: How to Develop Social Media Content That Gets Results" in Marketwired (December 14, 2009)*
Pub: Comtex News Network Inc.
Contact: Kan Devnani, President
Description: OneSource, a leading provider of global business information, and Nowspeed, an Internet marketing agency, will conduct a webinar titled "How to Develop Social Media Content That Gets Results" in order to provide marketers insight into how to develop and optimize effective social media content to get consumer results that translate into purchases and lead generation. **Availability:** Print; Mailing list; Online.

9199 ■ *"On the Horizon" in Advertising Age (Vol. 83, October 1, 2012, No. 35, pp. 5)*
Released: Quarterly. **Description:** Federal Trade Commission is revising rules regarding online marketing aimed at children due to the growth of the Web and innovations like mobile applications. The current Children's Online Privacy Protection Act went into effect in 1998. **Availability:** Print; Online.

9200 ■ *"On Technology: The Web Gets Real" in Canadian Business (Vol. 79, July 17, 2006, No. 14-15, pp. 19)*
Pub: Rogers Media Inc.
Contact: Neil Spivak, Chief Executive Officer
Ed: Andrew Wahl. **Description:** Ron Lake's efforts of bringing the virtual and physical worlds more closely together by using Geographic Markup Language (GML) are presented. **Availability:** Print; PDF; Online.

9201 ■ *"Online Marketing and Promotion of Canadian Films via Social Media Tools: Telefilm Launches New Initiative to Foster Innovative Distribution Strategies" in CNW Group (January 27, 2010)*
Pub: Comtex News Network Inc.
Contact: Kan Devnani, President
Description: Telefilm Canada announced the launch of a pilot initiative aimed at encouraging the integration of online marketing and the use of social media tools into means of distribution ahead of a films' theatrical release. During this pilot phase Web-Cine 360 will target French-language feature films. **Availability:** Online.

9202 ■ *"Partnering for Success" in Art Business News (Vol. 36, October 2009, No. 10, pp. 4)*
Description: In such a volatile economy many savvy artists and gallery owners are turning to out-of-the-box partnerships for continued success; these partnerships are also pervading the Internet, especially with such social media networks as Facebook and Twitter where artists and businesses can develop a loyal following. **Availability:** PDF; Online.

9203 ■ *"Paterson Plots Comeback With Internet IPO" in Globe & Mail (February 20, 2006, pp. B1)*
Ed: Grant Robertson. **Description:** The initial public offering plans of chief executive officer Scott Paterson of JumpTV.com are presented. **Availability:** Online.

9204 ■ *"People; E-Commerce, Online Games, Mobile Apps" in Advertising Age (Vol. 80, October 19, 2009, No. 35, pp. 14)*
Pub: Crain Communications, Inc.
Contact: Jessica Botos, Manager, Marketing
E-mail: jessica.botos@crainsnewyork.com
Ed: Nat Ives. **Description:** Profile of People Magazine and the ways in which the publisher is moving its magazine forward by exploring new concepts in a time of declining newsstand sales and advertising pages; among the strategies are e-commerce such

as the brand People Style Watch in which consumers are able highlight clothing and jewelry and then connect to retailers' sites and a channel on Taxi TV, the network of video-touch screens in New Your City taxis. **Availability:** Online.

9205 ■ *"Philanthropy Good For Business" in Crain's Detroit Business (Vol. 24, February 18, 2008, No. 7, pp. 14)*
Pub: Crain Communications Inc.
Contact: Barry Asin, President
Ed: Sheena Harrison. **Description:** Profile of Burce McCully, founder of Dynamic Edge Inc., and his views on philanthropy as a key to any small company's success. The Ann Arbor, Michigan information technology firm has volunteered and raised funds for many causes since 1999 when the company was founded. **Availability:** Print; Online.

9206 ■ *"The Problem With Passwords" in Canadian Business (Vol. 85, August 13, 2012, No. 13, pp. 61)*
Ed: Richard Warnica. **Description:** A study found that most tips for protecting passwords do nothng to protect against the most common forms of security breaches such as phishing, keystroke logging and looking over shoulders. According to researchers, it is not necessary to switch passwords or make it harder to guess because there is a chance that it will not do any good. **Availability:** Print; Online.

9207 ■ *"Psychological Ownership: A Social Marketing Advertising Message Appeal? Not for Women" in International Journal of Advertising (Vol. 31, May 2012, No. 2, pp. 291)*
Description: An assessment of psychological ownership as a potential persuasive advertising message appeal in the social marketing effort is examined. Psychological ownership is a feeling of possession; it occurs when individuals feel that something is their even though they cannot hold legal tide to it. **Availability:** PDF; Online.

9208 ■ *"Punta Gorda Interested in Wi-Fi Internet" in Charlotte Observer (February 1, 2007)*
Description: Punta Gorda officials are developing plans to provide free wireless Internet services to businesses and residents. **Availability:** Online.

9209 ■ *"Q&A with Google's Patrick Pichette" in Canadian Business (Vol. 81, October 13, 2008, No. 17, pp. 6)*
Description: Patrick Pichette finds challenge in taking over the finances of an Internet company that has a market cap of about $140 billion. He feels, however, that serving as Google's chief financial officer is nothing compared to running Bell Canada Enterprises (BCE). Pichette's other views on Google and BCE are presented. **Availability:** Print; Online.

9210 ■ *"Qorvis Communications Gets Sabre Award for Search Engine Optimization" in Entertainment Close-Up (May 29, 2012)*
Description: Qorvis Communications received the Gold Sabre Award by the Holmes Report for Search Engine Optimization for its work on the Marca Paid Imagen de Mexico on the MexicoToday campaign. MexicoToday.org is a next-generation Website and external branding initiative which focuses on digital and. social media. The site hopes to change the world's perception of Mexico, particularly Europeans and Americans. **Availability:** Print; Online.

9211 ■ *"Quantivo Empowers Online Media Companies to Immediately Expand Audiences and Grow Online Profits" in Marketwired (November 18, 2009)*
Pub: Comtex News Network Inc.
Contact: Kan Devnani, President
Description: Quantivo, the leader in on-demand Behavioral Analytics, has launched a new solution that includes 22 of the most critical Internet audience behavior insights as out-of-the-box reports; Internet marketers need to understand their audience, what

they want and how often to offer it to them in order to gain successful branding and campaigns online. **Availability:** Online.

9212 ■ *"The Quest for Content: How User-Generated Links Can Facilitate Online Exploration" in International Journal of Marketing Research (Vol. 49, August 2012, No. 4, pp. 452)*
Pub: American Marketing Association
Contact: Bennie F. Johnson, Chief Executive Officer
Ed: Jacob Goldenberg, Gal Oestreicher-Singer, Shachar Reichman. **Description:** The role of online dual-network structures in facilitating content exploration is examined. Such structures are created by companies offering social networks and user-generated links alongside the product network. Exposure to dual networks has been found to result in a more effecient exploration process. **Availability:** PDF.

9213 ■ *"Readers' Choice Awards 2019: Internet Service Providers (ISP)" in PC Magazine (May 28, 2019)*
URL(s): www.pcmag.com/news/368489/readers-choice-awards-2019-internet-service-providers-isp
Ed: Ben Z. Gottesman. **Released:** May 28, 2019. **Description:** Based upon the opinions and experiences of PC Magazine readers, the top ISPs are listed. **Availability:** Online.

9214 ■ *"Report Challenges Internet Providers' Advertised Speeds" in U.S. News & World Report (August 31, 2019)*
URL(s): www.usnews.com/best-states/pennsylvania/articles/2019-08-31/report-challenges-internet-providers-advertised-speeds
Ed: Jon O'Connell, Bill Wellock. **Released:** August 31, 2019. **Description:** New research has uncovered that internet service providers aren't being truthful when it comes to disclosing their internet speeds. While boasting about high speeds, the reality is that consumers aren't receiving these high speeds. This has been having detrimental effects on people, especially in rural communities, because it causes a lack of availability to access educational, health care, and commerce tools. **Availability:** Online.

9215 ■ *"Reportlinker.com Adds Report: GeoWeb and Local Internet Markets: 2008 Edition" in Entertainment Close-Up (September 11, 2009)*
Description: Reportlinker.com is adding a new market research report that is available in its catalogue: GeoWeb and Local Internet Markets - 2008 Edition; highlights include the outlook for consumer mapping services and an examination of monetizing services and an analysis the development outlook for geospacial Internet market, also referred to as the Geoweb. **Availability:** Online.

9216 ■ *"Research and Markets Adds Report: Cyprus: Convergence, Broadband and Internet Market" in Wireless News (September 4, 2009)*
Description: Overview of a new report by Research and Markets entitled, "Cyprus Convergence, Broadband and Internet Market - Overview, Statistics and Forecasts." Highlights include information regarding broadband accounts which now account for the majority of household Internet connections. **Availability:** Print; Online.

9217 ■ *"Research and Markets Adds Report: The U.S. Mobile Web Market" in Entertainment Close-Up (December 10, 2009)*
Description: Highlights of the new Research and Markets report "The U.S. Mobile Web Market: Taking Advantage of the iPhone Phenomenon" include: mobile Internet marketing strategies; the growth of mobile web usage; the growth of revenue in the mobile web market; and a look at Internet business communications, social media and networking. **Availability:** Print; Online.

9218 ■ *"The Right Time for REITs"* in *Barron's (Vol. 88, July 14, 2008, No. 28, pp. 32)*

Pub: Dow Jones & Company Inc.

Contact: Almar Latour, Chief Executive Officer

Ed: Mike Hogan. **Description:** Discusses the downturn in U.S. real estate investment trusts so these are worth considering for investment. Several Websites that are useful for learning about real estate investment trusts for investment purposes are presented. **Availability:** Online.

9219 ■ *"Rise Interactive, Internet Marketing Agency, Now Offers Social Media Services"* in *Marketwired (November 4, 2009)*

Pub: Comtex News Network Inc.

Contact: Kan Devnani, President

Description: Profile of Rise Interactive, a full-service Internet marketing agency which has recently added social media to its list of offerings; the agency touts that its newest service gives their clients the power to have ongoing communication with current and potential customers on the sites they are most actively visiting. **Availability:** Print; Online.

9220 ■ *"ROIonline Announces Streaming Video Products"* in *Marketing Weekly News (December 5, 2009, pp. 155)*

Pub: Investment Weekly News

Description: ROIonline LLC, an Internet marketing firm serving business-to-business and the industrial marketplace, has added streaming video options to the Internet solutions it offers its clients; due to the huge increase of broadband connections, videos are now commonplace on the Internet and can often convey a company's message in a must more efficient, concise and effective way that will engage a website's visitor thus delivering a high return on a company's investment. **Availability:** Print; Mailing list; Online.

9221 ■ *"SABER Research Institute's Steve Nivin"* in *San Antonio Business Journal (Vol. 28, April 4, 2014, No. 8, pp. 6)*

Pub: American City Business Journals, Inc.

Contact: Mike Olivieri, Executive Vice President

Released: Weekly. **Price:** $4, Introductory 4-week offer(Digital only). **Description:** SABER Research Institute director and chief economist, Steve Nivin, shares his views on the potential expansion of Google Fiber's broadband Internet network to San Antonio, Texas. Nivin says Google Fiber should encourage entrepreneurs to start businesses in San Antonio. He also says the chances of fast growth companies being created in the city is enhanced with Google Fiber. **Availability:** Print; Online.

9222 ■ *"St. Louis Digital Marketing Agency Publishes Free SEO Audit Tool"* in *Internet Wire (February 16, 2012)*

Pub: Comtex News Network Inc.

Contact: Kan Devnani, President

Description: Evolve Digital Labs has created a document to help with Search Engine Optimization. The Saint Louis digital marketing firm's 'SEO Guide for Beginners' offers comprehensive information on thetopic of search engine operations, on-site component of Web pages, and strategies for improving visibility in search engine result pages (SERPs). **Availability:** Online.

9223 ■ *The Savvy Gal's Guide to Online Networking: Or What Would Jane Austen Do?*

Pub: Booklocker.com Inc.

Ed: Diane K. Danielson, Lindsey Pollak. **Description:** It is a truth universally acknowledged that a woman in search of a fabulous career must be in want of networking opportunities. Or so Jane Austen would say if she were writing, or more likely, blogging today. So begins the must-read guide to networking in the 21st Century. Authors and networking experts share the nuts, bolts and savvy secrets that businesswomen need in order to use technology to build professional relationships. **Availability:** Print; Online; PDF.

9224 ■ *"Say Goodbye to Voicemail, Hello To Ribbit Mobile"* in *Agency Sales Magazine (Vol. 39, November 2009, No. 10, pp. 3)*

Description: Salespeople should think twice before leaving a voicemail. The emerging modern etiquette is to send a text message or to e-mail the customer or client. Communication suggestions for both salespeople and their principals are presented. **Availability:** Print; Online.

9225 ■ *"Search and Discover New Opportunities"* in *DM News (Vol. 31, December 14, 2009, No. 29, pp. 13)*

Pub: Haymarket Media Inc.

Contact: Kevin Costello, Chief Executive Officer

Ed: Chantal Tode. **Description:** Although other digital strategies are gaining traction in Internet marketing, search marketing continues to dominate this advertising forum. Companies like American Greetings, which markets e-card brands online, are utilizing social networking sites and affiliates to generate a higher demand for their products. **Availability:** Print; Online.

9226 ■ *"Search Engine Optimization is Becoming a Must for Businesses, But Unethical Companies Can Hurt Worse than Help"* in *Idaho Business Review (August 3, 2012)*

Ed: Sean Olson. **Description:** Search engine optimization increases presence on the Internet for any small business wishing to market a service or product. It is critical to choose an ethical company that has experience in creating Web sites that will get noticed. **Availability:** Print; Online.

9227 ■ *"Search Engine Optimization Companies Rose From Need and Path of Least Resistance"* in *Idaho Business Review (August 3, 2012)*

Pub: Long Island Business News

Contact: Kathy Lombardo, Manager

E-mail: research@libn.com

Ed: Sean Olson. **Description:** Search engine optimization companies help small businesses gain presence on the Internet by higher placement during online searches. It is suggested that all small firms need to optimize their company's search engine ranking. **Availability:** Print; Online.

9228 ■ *"Search Engines: Image Conscious"* in *Canadian Business (Vol. 81, February 26, 2008, No. 4, pp. 36)*

Pub: Rogers Media Inc.

Contact: Neil Spivak, Chief Executive Officer

Ed: Andrew Wahl. **Description:** Idee Inc. is testing an Internet search engine for images that does not rely on tags but compares its visual data to a database of other images. The company was founded and managed by Leila Boujnane as an off-shoot of their risk-management software firm. Their software has already been used by image companies to track copyrighted images and to find images within their own archives. **Availability:** Online.

9229 ■ *"Securing our Cyber Status"* in *San Antonio Business Journal (Vol. 28, May 16, 2014, No. 14, pp. 4)*

Pub: American City Business Journals, Inc.

Contact: Mike Olivieri, Executive Vice President

Released: Weekly. **Price:** $4, introductory 4-week offer(Digital & Print). **Description:** The San Antonio Chamber of Commerce commissioned Deloitte to conduct a study on the local cyber security sector of San Antonio, Texas. Industry insiders are looking forward to securing the status of San Antonio as a top tier cyber city with the results of the study research. **Availability:** Print; Online.

9230 ■ *"Seen & Noted: A Home's Identity in Black and White"* in *Crain's Chicago Business (Vol. 31, April 21, 2008, No. 16, pp. 35)*

Pub: Crain Communications Inc.

Contact: Barry Asin, President

Ed: Lisa Bertagnoli. **Description:** Real estate agents are finding that showing customers a written floor plan is a trend that is growing since many buyers feel that Online virtual tours distort a room. Although floor plans cost up to $500 to have drawn up, they clearly show potential buyers the exact dimensions of rooms and how they connect. **Availability:** Online.

9231 ■ *The SEO Manifesto: A Practical and Ethical Guide to Internet Marketing and Search Engine Optimization*

Description: Comprehensive guide for each phase of launching an online business; chapters include checklists, process descriptions, and examples.

9232 ■ *"Shellshocked: Dealing With Cyber Insecurity"* in *Philadelphia Business Journal (Vol. 33, June 13, 2014, No. 18, pp. 4)*

Pub: American City Business Journals, Inc.

Contact: Mike Olivieri, Executive Vice President

Description: The threat of cyber theft or data breach is increasing globally as technology becomes advanced and more companies start storing their important data electronically. Therefore, the importance of cyber security has increased. Although big businesses suffer more from data breaches, small companies can also take a beating if data breach happens. A survey found that small businesses were wary of spending money on security issues; good investment in IT and creating a privacy policy will help companies fight cyber threats. **Availability:** Online.

9233 ■ *"Sherwin-Williams Workers Forgo Travel for Virtual Trade Show"* in *Crain's Cleveland Business (Vol. 28, October 15, 2007, No. 41, pp. 4)*

Pub: Crain Communications Inc.

Contact: K. C. Crain, President

Ed: John Booth. **Description:** Overview of CyberCoating 2007, a cutting-edge virtual three-dimensional trade show that exhibitors such as Sherwin-Williams Co.'s Chemical Coatings Division will take part in by chatting verbally or via text messages in order to exchange information and listen to pitches just like they would on an actual trade show floor. **Availability:** Online.

9234 ■ *"Silverpop Recognised for Email Marketing Innovations by Econsultancy"* in *Marketing Weekly News (January 23, 2010, pp. 124)*

Pub: Investment Weekly News

Description: Econsultancy, a respected source of insight and advice on digital marketing and e-commerce, recognized Silverpop, the world's only provider of both marketing automation solutions and email marketing specifically tailored to the unique needs of B2C and B2B marketers at Econsultancy's 2009 Innovation Awards. **Availability:** Online.

9235 ■ *"Social Apps, Business Style: Savvy App Makers Bring Consumer Features to the Enterprise"* in *Silicon Valley/San Jose Business Journal (Vol. 30, September 28, 2012, No. 27, pp. 1)*

Pub: Baltimore Business Journal

Contact: Rhonda Pringle, President

E-mail: rpringle@bizjournals.com

Description: Companies like Good Technology Inc. and Socialtext Inc. are developing mobile apps software for business enterprises with consumer features such as photo sharing and location check-ins. Consumer tendencies have influenced the growth of the enterprise mobiel apps market, which is prediced to reach $11.5 billion by 2004. **Availability:** Print; Online.

9236 ■ *"Social Media, E-Mail Remain Challenging for Employers"* in *Workforce Management (Vol. 88, December 14, 2009, No. 13, pp. 4)*

Pub: Crain Communications Inc.

Contact: Barry Asin, President

Ed: Ed Frauenheim. **Description:** Examining the impact of Internet social networking and the workplace; due to the power of these new technologies, it is important that companies begin to set clear policies regarding Internet use and employee privacy. **Availability:** Online.

9237 ■ "Spinout Success: New Leadership Steps In At UW's C4C" in Puget Sound Business Journal (Vol. 35, June 27, 2014, No. 10, pp. 11)
Pub: American City Business Journals, Inc.
Contact: Mike Olivieri, Executive Vice President

Description: University of Washington's Center for Commercialization vice provost, Vikram Jandhyala, talks about his new position with the school. Jandhyala says he plans to build more synergy between the medical school and engineering and between social sciences and computer science. He also says the medical and software industry need to grow to accommodate the volume of data crossing and stored within the Internet. **Availability:** Online.

9238 ■ "Staying Social Complements Retail Goals" in Pet Product News (Vol. 66, September 2012, No. 9, pp. 34)
Description: Pet supplies retailers can take advantage of social media to brand the store and its products and facilitate dialogue with consumers. As these retail goals are realized, profits can be attained. Strategies that can enable pet supplies retailers to create business networks through social media marketing are also presented. **Availability:** Online.

9239 ■ "Stimulating Fare at the SBA" in Barron's (Vol. 89, July 20, 2009, No. 29, pp. 12)
Pub: Dow Jones & Company Inc.
Contact: Almar Latour, Chief Executive Officer

Ed: Jim McTague. **Description:** Internet access at the Small Business Administration slowed down on 7 July 2009, apparently caused by employees streaming videos of the Michael Jackson tribute. The agency claims that the event did not disrupt its operations. **Availability:** Online.

9240 ■ "Study: New Moms Build A Lot of Brand Buzz" in Brandweek (Vol. 49, April 21, 2008, No. 16, pp. 7)
Description: According to a new survey which sampled 1,721 pregnant women and new moms, this demographic is having 109 word-of-mouth conversations per week concerning products, services and brands. Two-thirds of these conversations directly involve brand recommendations. The Internet is driving these word-of-mouth, or W-O-M, conversations among this segment, beating out magazines, television and other forms of media. **Availability:** Online.

9241 ■ "A Survey of Smart Data Pricing: Past Proposals, Current Plans, and Future Trends" in ACM Computing Surveys (Vol. 46, Summer 2014, No. 2, pp. 15)
Pub: Association for Computing Machinery - University of Wyoming
Contact: Ed Seidel, President
E-mail: uwpres@uwyo.edu

Price: $15, Nonmembers; $42, Students. **Description:** Traditionally, network operators have used simple flat-rate broadband data plans for both wired and wireless network access. But today, with the popularity of mobile devices and exponential growth of apps, videos, and clouds, service providers are gradually moving toward more sophisticated pricing schemes. The benefits and challenges or pricing data are examined. **Availability:** PDF; Online.

9242 ■ "Tale of the Tape: IPhone Vs. G1" in Advertising Age (Vol. 79, October 27, 2008, No. 40, pp. 6)
Pub: Crain Communications, Inc.
Contact: Jessica Botos, Manager, Marketing
E-mail: jessica.botos@crainsnewyork.com

Ed: Rita Chang. **Description:** T-Mobile's G1 has been positioned as the first serious competitor to Apple's iPhone. G1 is the first mobile phone to run on the Google-backed, open-source platform Android.

9243 ■ "Teksapiens, A Leading SEO Company, Offers Free SEO Consulting Services to Dallas Businesses" in Wireless News (March 29, 2012)
Description: Dallas-based Web design firm, Teksapiens, offers free search engine optimization to Dallas businesses signing up at DallasBestSEO.com. The free service provides tips to outperform competition when marketing on the Internet. **Availability:** Print; Online.

9244 ■ "Time for a Little Pruning?" in Barron's (Vol. 89, July 6, 2009, No. 27, pp. 13)
Pub: Dow Jones & Company Inc.
Contact: Almar Latour, Chief Executive Officer

Ed: Dimitra DeFotis. **Description:** Investors are advised to avoid the shares of Whole Foods, American Tower, T. Rowe Price, Iron Mountain, Intuitive Surgical, Salesforce.com, and Juniper Networks due to their high price to earnings ratios. The shares of Amazon.com, Broadcom, and Expeditors International of Washington remain attractive to investors despite their high price to earnings ratios due to their strong growth. **Availability:** Online.

9245 ■ "Time to Tweet: Banks and Fun, Benefits in Social Media" in Philadelphia Business Journal (Vol. 31, February 24, 2012, No. 2, pp. 1)
Pub: Baltimore Business Journal
Contact: Rhonda Pringle, President
E-mail: rpringle@bizjournals.com

Description: Pennsylvania-based banks have benefited from the use of social media to market their services. TD Bank used Twitter to respond to customer complaints. Citizens Bank uses Twitter to provide customers with financial tips. **Availability:** Print.

9246 ■ "The Top Mistakes of Social Media Marketing" in Agency Sales Magazine (Vol. 39, November 2009, No. 9, pp. 42)
Description: One common mistake in social media marketing is having more than one image on the Internet because this ruins a business' credibility. Marketers need to put out messages that are useful to their readers and to keep messages consistent. **Availability:** Online.

9247 ■ "Trust Management of Services in Cloud Environments: Obstacles and Solutions" in ACM Computing Surveys (Vol. 46, Spring 2014, No. 1, pp. 12)
Pub: Association for Computing Machinery - University of Wyoming
Contact: Ed Seidel, President
E-mail: uwpres@uwyo.edu

Description: Trust management is one of the most challenging issues in the emerging cloud computing area. Over the past few years, many studies have proposed different techniques to address trust management issues. However, despite these past efforts, several trust management issues such as identification, privacy, personalization, integration, security, and scalability have been mostly neglected and need to be addressed before cloud computing can be fully embraced. An overview of the cloud service models and a survey of the main techniques and research prototypes that efficiently support trust management services in cloud environments is presented. Open research issues for trust management in cloud environments is also examined. **Availability:** PDF; Online.

9248 ■ "Trusted Choice: Mobile App" in Best's Review (Vol. 113, September 2012, No. 5, pp. 14)
Description: Profile of Trusted Choice, the new mobile app launched in March 2012 for use on smartphones and tablet computers. The app helps clients contact their independent insurance agent. Consumers can keep an inventory of insured personal possessions, document a car accident with photos, read insurance tips, communicate with Trusted Choice agent and ask insurance-related questions. **Availability:** Online.

9249 ■ "Tweet Me, Friend Me, Make Me Buy" in (Vol. 90, July-August 2012, No. 7-8, pp. 88)
Pub: Harvard Business Review Press
Contact: Moderna V. Pfizer, Contact

Ed: Barbara Giamanco, Kent Gregoire. **Price:** $8.95, PDF and hardcover black and white. **Description:** Sales representatives can make the most out of social media through training on communication skills such as tone, etiquette, and consistency. The most valuable aspects of social media are lead qualification, front-end prospecting, and maintaining post-deal relationships. **Availability:** Print; PDF; Online.

9250 ■ "Two Field Service Management Solutions" in Contractor (Vol. 56, November 2009, No. 11, pp. 37)
Ed: William Feldman, Patti Feldman. **Description:** Bella Solutions Field Service Software v. 4.2 is a web based solution for HVAC service contractors that enables scheduling of emergency, one-time, multi-visit or periodically recurring jobs with drag and drop appointments. VaZing is another web based solution that costs $99 per month for contractors. It can handle line-item discounting and invoices aside from scheduling. **Availability:** Print; Online.

9251 ■ "Up To Code? Website Eases Compliance Burden for Entrepreneurs" in Black Enterprise (Vol. 38, March 1, 2008, No. 8, pp. 48)
Pub: Earl G. Graves Ltd.
Contact: Earl Graves, Jr., President

Ed: Robin White-Goode. **Description:** Business.gov is a presidential E-government project created to help small businesses easily find, understand, and comply with laws and regulations pertaining to a particular industry. **Availability:** Online.

9252 ■ "Use Social Media to Enhance Brand, Business" in Contractor (Vol. 56, December 2009, No. 12, pp. 14)
Ed: Elton Rivas. **Description:** Advice on how plumbing contractors should use online social networks to increase sales is presented including such issues as clearly defining goals and target audience. An additional advantage to this medium is that advertisements can easily be shared with other users.

9253 ■ "Verizon's Big Gamble Comes Down to the Wire" in Globe & Mail (February 3, 2007, pp. B1)
Ed: Catherine McLean. **Description:** The launch of a new broadband service by Verizon Communications Inc. based on fiber optic cable technology is discussed. The company has spent $23 billion for introducing the new service. **Availability:** Online.

9254 ■ "Virtually Secure" in Rough Notes (Vol. 155, February 2012, No. 2, pp. 46)
Pub: The Rough Notes Company Inc.
Contact: Walter J. Gdowski, President
E-mail: waltg@roughnotes.com

Ed: Nabeel Sayegh. **Availability:** PDF; Online.

9255 ■ "Virtus.com Wins 'Best of Industry' WebAward for Excellence in Financial Services" in Investment Weekly News (October 24, 2009, pp. 227)
Pub: Investment Weekly News

Description: Web Marketing Association honored Virtus.com, the Website of Virtus Investment Partners, Inc., for Outstanding Achievement in Web Development and Acsys Interactive was awarded the Financial Services Standard of Excellence Award for developing the site. The site was part of a rebranding effort and is a one-stop portal for both financial advisors and their investors. **Availability:** Online.

9256 ■ "Vision Statement: Mapping the Social Internet" in Harvard Business Review (Vol. 88, July-August 2010, No. 7-8, pp. 32)
Pub: Harvard Business Publishing
Contact: Diane Belcher, Managing Director

Ed: Mikolaj Jan Piskorski, Tommy McCall. **Price:** $6, PDF. **Description:** Chart compares and contrasts online social networks in selected countries. **Availability:** Online; PDF.

9257 ■ *"Vistaprint Survey Indicates that Online Marketing Taking Hold Among Small Businesses"* in Marketwired (December 10, 2009)

Pub: Comtex News Network Inc.

Contact: Kan Devnani, President

Description: According to a comprehensive survey from Vistaprint N.V., small businesses are very likely to increase their use of Internet marketing strategies such as paid and organic search, email marketing, social media networking and custom websites over the next year. Trends continue to show that more small businesses are indeed adapting to the changing marketplace and are more willing to diversify their marketing strategies than ever before. **Availability:** Print; Online.

9258 ■ *"Web-Based Marketing Excites, Challenges Small Business Use"* in Colorado Springs Business Journal (January 20, 2010)

Pub: BridgeTower Media

Contact: Adam Reinebach, President

Ed: Becky Hurley. **Description:** Business-to-business and consumer-direct firms alike are using the fast-changing Web technologies to increase sales, leads and track consumer behavior but once a company commits to an Online marketing plan, experts believe, they must be prepared to consistently tweak and overhaul content and distribution vehicles in order to keep up. **Availability:** Online.

9259 ■ *"Web-Based Solutions Streamline Operations"* in Contractor (Vol. 56, December 2009, No. 12, pp. 28)

Ed: William Feldman, Patti Feldman. **Description:** Sage Project Lifecycle Management is a Web-based service platform for plumbing and HVAC contractors. It enables effective workflow and document management. Projectmates, on the other hand, is a Web-based enterprise-wide solution for managing both commercial plumbing and HVAC projects. **Availability:** Print; Online.

9260 ■ *"Web Site Focuses on Helping People Find Jobs, Internships with Area Businesses"* in Crain's Detroit Business (Vol. 26, Jan. 4, 2010)

Pub: Crain Communications Inc.

Contact: Barry Asin, President

Ed: Dustin Walsh. **Description:** DetroitIntern.com, LLC is helping metro Detroit college students and young professionals find career-advancing internships or jobs with local businesses. **Availability:** Print; Online.

9261 ■ *"Website Triples Traffic in Three Weeks Using Press Releases"* in PR Newswire (January 5, 2010)

Pub: PR Newswire Association LLC.

Description: Irbtrax, an Internet marketing firm, concluded a comprehensive study revealing that online press release submission services offer measurable Website traffic-building results. **Availability:** Online.

9262 ■ *"What Online Brokers Are Doing To Keep Their Customers' Accounts Safe"* in Barron's (Vol. 88, March 10, 2008, No. 10, pp. 37)

Pub: Dow Jones & Company Inc.

Contact: Almar Latour, Chief Executive Officer

Ed: Theresa W. Carey. **Description:** Online brokerage firms employ different methods to protect the accounts of their customers from theft. These methods include secure Internet connections, momentary passwords, and proprietary algorithms. **Availability:** Online.

9263 ■ *"What's In Your Toolbox"* in Women In Business (Vol. 61, August-September 2009, No. 4, pp. 7)

Pub: American Business Women's Association

Contact: Rene Street, Executive Director

Ed: Mimi Kopulos. **Description:** Business owners are increasingly turning to using social networking websites, such as Facebook, LinkedIn and Twitter, to

promote their companies. The number of adult social media users has increased from 8 percent in 2005 to 35 percent in 2009. **Availability:** Online.

9264 ■ *"Who Hangs Out Where?"* in Harvard Business Review (Vol. 90, July-August 2012, No. 7-8, pp. 34)

Pub: Harvard Business Review Press

Contact: Moderna V. Pfizer, Contact

Price: $6, PDF. **Description:** A chart breaks down participation in social media gathering places by gender, age group, educational level, and household income. **Availability:** PDF; Online.

9265 ■ *"Wi-Fi Finds Its Way Despite Nixed Plan for Free System"* in Crain's Cleveland Business (Vol. 28, November 12, 2007, No. 45, pp. 3)

Pub: Crain Communications Inc.

Contact: K. C. Crain, President

Ed: Jay Miller. **Description:** Discusses the issues facing Cleveland and Northeast Ohio concerning their proposal to offer citizens wireless Internet services for free or a small fee. **Availability:** Online.

9266 ■ *Wikinomics: How Mass Collaboration Changes Everything*

Pub: Penguin Publishing Group

Ed: Don Tapscott, Anthony D. Williams, Anthony D. Williams. **Released:** September 28, 2010. **Price:** $16.93, paperback; $8.99, e-book; $12.77, audio; $17, paperback; $13.99. **Description:** Research and information about the every changing world of the Internet is provided to help small businesses. **Availability:** E-book; Print; Electronic publishing.

9267 ■ *"Will Mobile's Massive Growth Ever Equal Real Revenue?"* in Advertising Age (Vol. 83, October 1, 2012, No. 35, pp. 18)

Pub: Crain Communications Inc.

Contact: Barry Asin, President

Ed: Jason Del Rey. **Description:** Media companies are concerned over the return on investment when advertising on mobile applications. Firms lament that these ads are worth less to a small business than offline marketing programs. **Availability:** Online.

9268 ■ *"Women Clicking to Earn Virtual Dollars"* in Sales and Marketing Management (November 11, 2009)

Ed: Stacy Straczynski. **Description:** According to a new report from Internet marketing firm Q Interactive, women are increasingly playing social media games where they are able to click on an ad or sign up for a promotion to earn virtual currency. Research is showing that this kind of marketing may be a potent tool, especially for e-commerce and online stores. **Availability:** Print; Online.

9269 ■ *"Words at Work"* in Information Today (Vol. 26, February 2009, No. 2, pp. 25)

Description: Current new buzzwords include the following: digital amnesia, or overload by availability, speed and volume of digital information; maternal profiling, a form a discrimination against women; recipe malpractice, a reminder that just because you can turn on a stove it doesn't make you a chef; ringxiety, the act when everyone reaches for their cell phone when one rings; verbing, the practice of turning good nouns into verbs. **Availability:** Print; Online.

9270 ■ *"WordStream Announces a Pair of Firsts for SEO & PPC Keyword Research Tools"* in Marketwired (November 10, 2009)

Pub: Comtex News Network Inc.

Contact: Kan Devnani, President

Description: WordSteam, Inc., a provider of pay-per-click (PPC) and search engine optimization (SEO) solutions for continuously expanding and optimizing search marketing efforts has released two new features in their flagship Keyword Management solution; these tools will allow marketers to analyze data from paid search, organic search and estimated totals from keyword suggestion tools side-by-side. **Availability:** Print; Online.

9271 ■ *"Xtium Has Its Head in the Clouds"* in Philadelphia Business Journal (Vol. 30, September 23, 2011, No. 32, pp. 1)

Pub: Philadelphia Business Journal

Contact: Sierra Quinn, Director

E-mail: squinn@bizjournals.com

Ed: Peter Key. **Description:** Philadelphia-based cloud computing firm Xtium LLC received an $11.5 million first-round investment from Boston-Massachusetts-based OpenView Venture Partners. Catering to midsize businesses and unit of bigger firms, Xtium offers disaster-recovery, hosting, and managed-information-technology-infrastructure services. **Availability:** Online.

9272 ■ *"The Yahoo Family Tree"* in Conde Nast Portfolio (Vol. 2, June 2008, No. 6, pp. 34)

Pub: Conde Nast Publications

Contact: Agnes Chu, President

Ed: Blaise Zerega. **Description:** Yahoo, founded in 1994 by Stanford students Jerry Yang and David Filo, is still an Internet powerhouse. The company's history is also outlined as well as the reasons in which Microsoft desperately wants to acquire the firm. **Availability:** Print.

9273 ■ *"Your Web Brand Counts"* in Black Enterprise (Vol. 44, June 2014, No. 10, pp. 46)

Pub: Earl G. Graves Ltd.

Contact: Earl Graves, Jr., President

Description: Forty-eight percent of employers use Google or other search engines to find information about job applicants and 25 percent of executives hired were originally identified or contacted through social media, thus the importance of a good Web presence is outlined.

TRADE PERIODICALS

9274 ■ *Green Data Centers and Internet Business*

Pub: Information Gatekeepers Inc.

Contact: Will Ashley, Manager

E-mail: washley@igigroup.com

URL(s): www.igigroup.com/nl/pages/business.html

Ed: Tony Carmona. **Released:** Monthly; 12 issues / year. **Price:** $695, U.S. and Canada for print 1 year; $695, Individuals for pdf - 1 user 1 year; $745, for print overseas 1 year; $2,500, Individuals for pdf - 2 to 10 users; $4,000, Individuals for pdf - 11 to 20 users; $7,500, Individuals for pdf - 21 to 50 users; $10,000, Individuals for pdf - 50+ users. **Description:** Provides marketing and technology information on new developments in the internet telephone industry on a worldwide basis. **Availability:** Print; Online; PDF.

9275 ■ *Information Today (IT)*

Pub: Information Today Inc.

Contact: Thomas H. Hogan, President

URL(s): www.infotoday.com/IT/default.asp

Ed: Donovan Griffin. **Released:** Monthly; with combined January/February, July/August and November/December issues. **Description:** User and producer magazine (tabloid) covering electronic and optical information services. **Availability:** Print; Online.

9276 ■ *Medicine on the Net*

Pub: COR Healthcare Resources

URL(s): www.hcpro.com/services/corhealth/index.cfm

Released: Monthly **Price:** $229, Individuals. **Description:** Spotlights developing issues in the use of the Internet by medical professionals. Recurring features include letters to the editor, interviews, news of research, and book reviews. **Availability:** Print; PDF.

9277 ■ *Online Searcher*

Pub: Information Today Inc.

Contact: Thomas H. Hogan, President

URL(s): www.infotoday.com/OnlineSearcher

Released: Bimonthly; January/February, March/April, May/June, July/August, September/October, and November/December. **Description:** Edited for librarians, Webmasters, site designers, content managers, and others concerned with knowledge/information management. Includes critical reviews of Web sites, software, search engines, and information services. (Formerly published by Online, Inc.). **Availability:** Print; Online.

CONSULTANTS

9278 ■ Argus Business Solutions
PO Box 22
  Willow Grove, PA 19090-0022
Ph: (215)346-6510
Co. E-mail: sales@argusbusinesssolutionsgroup.net
URL: http://argusbusinesssolutionsgroup.net
Contact: Hal Dell, Contact
Linkedin: www.linkedin.com/in/hald9000
Description: Provider of telecommunication solutions that deliver cost and time efficiencies with continued control and assists with transitions and maintains scheduled follow-ups. **Scope:** Provider of telecommunication solutions that deliver cost and time efficiencies with continued control and assists with transitions and maintains scheduled follow-ups. **Training:** Argus Telecommunications Management Program.

9279 ■ Law Offices of Robert J. Keller P.C.
PO Box 33428 - Farragut Sta.
  Washington, DC 20033-3428
Ph: (202)656-8490
Fax: (202)223-2121
Co. E-mail: rjk@telcomlaw.com
URL: http://www.telcomlaw.com
Contact: Robert J. Keller, Contact
E-mail: rjk@telcomlaw.com
Description: Law firm specializes in federal telecommunications law provides legal services for wireless telecommunications, new and emerging technologies. **Founded:** 1994.

FRANCHISES AND BUSINESS OPPORTUNITIES

9280 ■ Pak Mail
2443 S University Blvd.
  Denver, CO 80210
Ph: (303)744-6245
Fax: (303)744-6246
Co. E-mail: us013@pakmail.com
URL: http://www.pakmail.com
Facebook: www.facebook.com/OfficialPakMail
Description: One-stop shop offers the customer a convenient location to send packages, make copies, send or receive a fax or rent a private mailbox. **No. of Operating Units:** 400. **Founded:** 1984. **Equity Capital Needed:** $50,000 cash or liquid assets ; $150,000 net worth. **Franchise Fee:** $29,550. **Financial Assistance:** Yes **Training:** Provides training, education & ongoing support to build your business.

9281 ■ WSI Internet
830 Dixon Rd.
  Etobicoke, ON, Canada M9W 6Y8

Ph: (905)678-7588
Fax: (905)678-7242
Co. E-mail: contact@wsiworld.com
URL: http://www.wsiworld.com
Contact: Valerie Brown-Dufour, President
Facebook: www.facebook.com/WSIWorld
X (Twitter): x.com/wsiworld
YouTube: www.youtube.com/user/WSIWorld
Description: Organization that provides team of digital marketing experts. **Founded:** 1995. **Training:** Yes.

LIBRARIES

9282 ■ Gartner IRC - Research Library
56 Top Gallant Rd.
  Stamford, CT 06902
Ph: (203)964-0096
Co. E-mail: inquiry@gartner.com
URL: http://www.gartner.com/en
Contact: Eugene A. Hall, Chief Executive Officer
Facebook: www.facebook.com/Gartne
Linkedin: www.linkedin.com/company/gartner
X (Twitter): x.com/Gartner_inc
Instagram: www.instagram.com/gartner_inc
YouTube: www.youtube.com/user/Gartnervideo
Description: Research and advisory company. **Scope:** Information technology. **Services:** SDI; center not open to the public (client research only). **Founded:** 1979. **Holdings:** 3,000 items.

9283 ■ International Data Group, Inc. (IDC) - Library
140 Kendrick St., Bldg. B
  Needham, MA 02494
Ph: (508)872-8200
Co. E-mail: leads@idc.com
URL: http://www.idc.com
Contact: Crawford del Prete, President
Linkedin: www.linkedin.com/company/idc
X (Twitter): x.com/IDC
Description: Provides market intelligence, advisory services, and events for the information technology, telecommunications, and consumer technology markets. **Scope:** Information technology; telecommunications; advisory services. **Founded:** 1964. **Holdings:** Figures not available. **Publications:** *Computerworld*; *The Standard*; *Macworld*; *IDG.net*; *WebSolutionsWorld Newsletter Online*; *E-Commerce Newsletter Online*; *Security-Informer Newsletter Online*; *TechInformer Newsletter Online*; *dummies. com*; *cliffsnotes.com*; *Arthur Frommer's Budget Travel Online*; *Network World, Inc.*; *CIO Online*; *Computerworld Online*; *Darwin Magazine Online*; *JavaWorld Online*; *LinuxWorld.com*; *InfoWorld.com*; *NetworkWorld.com*; *SunWorld Magazine Online*; *GamePro. com*; *MacWorld Online* (Monthly); *Publish.com*; *Financial News Channel*; *International News Channel*; *E-Commerce News Channel*; *Enterprise News Channel*; *Personal Computing News Channel*; *How-To & Advice News Channel*; *Multimedia & Leisure News Channel*; *Telecom & Connectivity News Channel*; *Security News Channel*; *Networking &*

Systems News Channel; *Technical Development News Channel*; *IDC Research*; *ExecuTrain Corporation*; *China Network World* (Weekly); *Network World*; *IT Forecaster* (Biweekly).

9284 ■ LexisNexis Technical Library
9443 Springboro Pke.
  Miamisburg, OH 45342
Fax: (937)865-1211
URL: http://www.lexisnexis.com/en-us/gateway.page
Contact: Mike Walsh, Chief Executive Officer
Description: Provides support in data analytics supporting compliance, customer acquisition, fraud detection, health outcomes, identity solutions, investigation, receivables management, risk decisioning and workflow optimization. **Scope:** Online industry. **Services:** Interlibrary loan; library not open to the public. **Founded:** 1992. **Holdings:** Figures not available.

9285 ■ Queens Borough Public Library - Information Services Division
89-11 Merrick Blvd.
  Jamaica, NY 11432
URL: http://www.queenslibrary.org
Facebook: www.facebook.com/QPLNYC
X (Twitter): x.com/QPLNYC
Instagram: www.instagram.com/qplnyc
Description: Serves 2.3 million people from 62 locations plus seven Adult Learning Centers and two Family Literacy Centers. It circulates among the highest numbers of books and other library materials in the country. **Scope:** General. **Services:** Interlibrary loan; copying; email reference; faxing to New York State residents; library open to the public. **Holdings:** 1,000 volumes; partial depository for federal government documents; state and city documents.

RESEARCH CENTERS

9286 ■ Pennsylvania State University Harrisburg - Institute of State and Regional Affairs - Pennsylvania State Data Center (PASDC)
777 West Harrisburg Pke.
  Middletown, PA 17057-4898
Ph: (717)948-6336
Fax: (717)948-6754
Co. E-mail: pasdc@psu.edu
URL: http://pasdc.hbg.psu.edu/Default.aspx
Contact: Jennifer Shultz, Director
E-mail: jjb131@psu.edu
X (Twitter): x.com/PASDC_PSU
Description: Publishes local demographics and policy. Also offers software. **Scope:** Data collection and analysis, including a decennial and economic census, population estimates and projections, migration flows, commutation patterns, housing school district data, geographic information systems, on-line systems, economic impacts of smoking, county to county migration flows, AIDS studies, and health insurance. Conducts regional workshops. Produces county data books, estimates reports, and abstracts. **Founded:** 1981. **Educational Activities:** PASDC User Conference (Annual), Demographics data and related topics.

START-UP INFORMATION

9287 ■ *"Alex Gomez on Leaving Medical School to Launch a Startup" in South Florida Business Journal (Vol. 34, May 9, 2014, No. 42, pp. 19)*
Pub: American City Business Journals, Inc.
Contact: Mike Olivieri, Executive Vice President

Description: New Wave Health Care Ventures managing partners, Alex Gomez, shares his views about leaving medical school to launch his startup. Gomez says he always had the spirit of an entrepreneur and business excites him. He knows what he is looking for in investing at startup companies because of his experience with New Wave Surgical Corporation. **Availability:** Print; Online.

9288 ■ *"Cornerstone Seeks Investors for Hedge Fund" in Baltimore Business Journal (Vol. 32, June 20, 2014, No. 7, pp. 10)*
Pub: American City Business Journals, Inc.
Contact: Mike Olivieri, Executive Vice President

Description: Cornerstone Advisory LLP is looking for investors to create a hedge fund that ties returns to various indices, real estate or commodity prices. Cornerstone hopes to raise between $30 million to $50 million and are planning a fall launch for the fund. They have hired New York law firm Thompson Hine LLP to draft the subscription agreement and NebraskaEs Gimini Fund Services LLC to run as third party administrator. **Availability:** Print; Online.

9289 ■ *"How New Angels Can Get Their Wings" in Business Journal Portland (Vol. 30, February 28, 2014, No. 52, pp. 6)*
Pub: American City Business Journals, Inc.
Contact: Mike Olivieri, Executive Vice President

Released: February 28, 2014. **Price:** $4, Introductory 4-Week Offer(Digital & Print). **Description:** Ferguson Wellman Capital Management executive vice president, Ralph Cole, says few individuals are interested in becoming angel investors. He also stated that investors should determine their motivation for become an angel investor. Cole added that the company helps investors understand the nature of investing. **Availability:** Print; Online.

ASSOCIATIONS AND OTHER ORGANIZATIONS

9290 ■ CFA Institute
915 E High St.
Charlottesville, VA 22902
Ph: (434)951-5499
Co. E-mail: info@cfainstitute.org
URL: http://www.cfainstitute.org
Contact: Margaret Franklin, President
Facebook: www.facebook.com/CFAInstitute
Linkedin: www.linkedin.com/company/cfainstitute
X (Twitter): x.com/cfainstitute

Description: Security and financial analyst association whose members are practicing investment analysts. Includes private, voluntary self-regulation program in which members are enrolled. Known for the Chartered Financial Analyst curriculum and examination program, which has more than 86,000 candidates from 143 countries enrolled. Internationally recognized for its investment performance standards, which investment firms use to document and report investment results, as well as for its Code of Ethics and Standards of Professional Conduct. **Founded:** 1947. **Publications:** *CFA Institute--Membership Directory*; *CFA Institute Journal Review* (Weekly); *AIMR Exchange* (Weekly); *Financial Analysts Journal* (Quarterly). **Awards:** Graham and Dodd Award (Annual); CFA Institute Special Service Award (Periodic); James R. Vertin Award (Annual); CFA Distinguished Service Award (Annual); CFA Outstanding Contribution to Investment Research Award (Periodic); Leadership in Professional Ethics and Standards of Investment Award (Annual); CFA Award for Professional Excellence (Irregular); Outstanding Contribution to CFA Institute Education Programs Award (Annual); Leadership in Global Investment Award (Annual). **Geographic Preference:** Multinational.

9291 ■ CFA Society New York (CFANY)
1540 Broadway, Ste. 1010
New York, NY 10036-2714
Ph: (212)541-4530
Fax: (212)541-4677
Co. E-mail: membership@cfany.org
URL: http://www.cfany.org
Contact: Arun Manansingh, Executive Director
E-mail: amanansingh@cfany.org
Facebook: www.facebook.com/CFASocietyNY
Linkedin: www.linkedin.com/company/cfa-society-new-york
X (Twitter): x.com/CFANewYork
Instagram: www.instagram.com/cfasocietyny

Description: Security analysts and portfolio managers employed primarily in New York by brokerage houses, banks, insurance companies, mutual funds and other financial institutions. Conducts educational forums on topics relating to the securities markets. Maintains placement service. **Founded:** 1937. **Publications:** *Corporate Governance Handbook*; *NYSSA News* (Weekly). **Geographic Preference:** National.

9292 ■ CSI Global Education [Institut Canadien des Valeurs Mobilieres]
200 Wellington St. W, Fl. 15
Toronto, ON, Canada M5V 3C7
Ph: (416)364-9130
Free: 866-866-2601
Fax: (416)359-0486
URL: http://www.csi.ca/en
Contact: Marie Muldowney, President
Facebook: www.facebook.com/csiglobal
Linkedin: www.linkedin.com/company/csi-canada
X (Twitter): x.com/#!/CSIGlobalEd
Instagram: www.instagram.com/csiglobaled

YouTube: www.youtube.com/channel/UC23MJEMDkvUbRXbdFyHxFZQ
Description: Stock exchanges, brokers, and other investment professionals. Promotes increased public understanding of securities investment. Serves as a network linking members; sponsors educational programs. **Founded:** 1970. **Geographic Preference:** National.

9293 ■ Investment Adviser Association (IAA)
818 Connecticut Ave. NW, Ste. 600
Washington, DC 20006
Ph: (202)293-4222
Co. E-mail: iaaservices@investmentadviser.org
URL: http://investmentadviser.org
Contact: Karen L. Barr, President
E-mail: karen.barr@investmentadviser.org
X (Twitter): x.com/IAA_Today
YouTube: www.youtube.com/channel/UCSiGYqDq5SkIDOUbwE-Nsjw

Description: Federally registered investment adviser firms. Represents the interests of the investment management profession before legislative and regulatory bodies. **Founded:** 1937. **Publications:** *Investment Adviser Association-Directory of Member Firms*. **Geographic Preference:** National.

9294 ■ Investments & Wealth Institute
5619 DTC Pky., Ste. 500
Greenwood Village, CO 80111
Ph: (303)770-3377
Fax: (303)770-1812
URL: http://investmentsandwealth.org/home
Contact: Todd Wagenberg, Chairman of the Board
X (Twitter): x.com/iw_inst
YouTube: www.youtube.com/c/InvestmentsWealthInstitute

Description: Consultants, money managers, and others in the investment management consultant business. Seeks to increase public awareness of investment management consultants, provide educational programs to members, and encourage high business standards. Operates consulting industry certification program. Maintains a legislative network with state and federal legislative information affecting the industry. **Founded:** 1985. **Publications:** *Essentials of Investment Consulting*; *The Facts About Investing*; *The Journal of Investment Consulting* (Annual); *The Monitor* (Bimonthly); *Wealth Management Course*. **Educational Activities:** IMCA Annual Conference (Annual); Regional Consultants Conferences. **Awards:** Richard J. Davis Ethics, Legal, Regulatory Insight Award (Annual); Stephen L. Kessler Writing Award (Annual). **Geographic Preference:** Multinational.

9295 ■ National Investment Company Service Association (NICSA)
101 Federal St., Ste. 1900
Boston, MA 02110
Ph: (508)485-1500
Co. E-mail: info@nicsa.org
URL: http://www.nicsa.org/home
Contact: Jim Fitzpatrick, President

E-mail: jfitzpatrick@nicsa.org
Facebook: www.facebook.com/NICSAOnline
Linkedin: www.linkedin.com/company/nicsa
X (Twitter): x.com/NICSAnews

Description: Mutual fund investment managers, distributors, custodians, transfer agents, accounting and legal firms, broker/dealers, and general providers of services and products to the mutual fund industry. Seeks to address future service needs and trends by providing a forum on operational and technological developments. **Founded:** 1962. **Publications:** *NICSA News* (Monthly). **Awards:** NICSA Lifetime Achievement Award (Annual); NICSA/William T. Blackwell Scholarship (Annual); Robert L. Gould Award (Annual); NICSA/William T. Blackwell Scholarship Fund (Annual). **Geographic Preference:** National.

9296 ■ National Investor Relations Institute (NIRI)

225 Reinekers Ln., Ste. 560
  Alexandria, VA 22314
Ph: (703)562-7700
Fax: (703)562-7701
Co. E-mail: niri@niri.org
URL: http://www.niri.org
Contact: Gary A. LaBranche, President
E-mail: glabranche@niri.org
X (Twitter): x.com/NIRI_National
YouTube: www.youtube.com/user/NIRINational

Description: Executives engaged in investor relations. Identifies the role of the investor relations practitioner; protects a free and open market with equity and access to investors of all kinds; improves communication between corporate management and shareholders, present and future. Holds professional development seminars and conducts research programs. Maintains placement service and speakers' bureau; compiles statistics. **Founded:** 1969. **Publications:** *IR Update* (Quarterly); *IR Update Weekly* (Weekly (Tues.)); *Roster* (Annual); *Standards of Practice for Investor Relations* (Periodic). **Educational Activities:** National Investor Relations Institute Conference (Annual). **Geographic Preference:** National.

9297 ■ National Society of Compliance Professionals (NSCP)

PO Box 55
  Cornwall Bridge, CT 06754
Ph: (860)672-0843
Fax: (860)672-3005
Co. E-mail: membership@nscp.org
URL: http://nscp.org
Contact: Lisa Crossley, Executive Director
Linkedin: www.linkedin.com/company/national-society-of-compliance-professionals

Description: Provides a forum for exchange between members. Monitors new state and federal laws and regulations. Offers interpretive and practical assistance in compliance matters. Conducts educational programs. **Founded:** 1986. **Publications:** *NSCP Currents*; *NSCP Hotline Memo* (Monthly). **Educational Activities:** NSCP National Membership Meeting; NSCP National Membership Meeting. **Geographic Preference:** National.

9298 ■ North American Securities Administrators Association (NASAA)

750 1st St. NE, Ste. 990
  Washington, DC 20002
Ph: (202)737-0900
Fax: (202)783-3571
URL: http://www.nasaa.org
Contact: Joseph Brady, Executive Director
Facebook: www.facebook.com/NASAA.org
Linkedin: www.linkedin.com/company/nasaa
X (Twitter): x.com/nasaa

Description: Represents the interests of the state, provincial and territorial securities administrators in the U.S., Canada, Mexico and Puerto Rico. Provides support to its members in government relations and with federal regulators, industry SROs and other groups. **Founded:** 1919. **Publications:** *NASAA*

Insight (Quarterly). **Educational Activities:** NASAA Public Policy Conference (Annual). **Geographic Preference:** National.

9299 ■ Securities Industry and Financial Markets Association (SIFMA)

120 Broadway, 35th Fl.
  New York, NY 10271
Ph: (212)313-1200
Co. E-mail: inquiry@sifma.org
URL: http://www.sifma.org
Contact: Kenneth E. Bentsen, Jr., President
Linkedin: www.linkedin.com/company/sifma
X (Twitter): x.com/sifma

Description: Represents more than 650 member firms of all sizes, in all financial markets in the US. and around the world. Enhances the public's trust and confidence in the markets, delivering an efficient, enhanced member network of access and forward-looking services, as well as premiere educational resources for the professionals in the industry and the investors whom they serve. Maintains offices in New York City and Washington, DC. **Founded:** 1912. **Publications:** *Operation Update* (Quarterly); *Securities Industry DataBank*; *Securities Industry Yearbook* (Annual); *Washington Weekly Update* (Weekly); *Securities Industry Association--Directory and Guide* (Annual); *Securities Industry Association--Foreign Activity Report* (Semiannual); *Securities Industry Association--Yearbook* (Annual); *Securities Industry Trends* (Quarterly); *Securities Industry Databank* (Quarterly). **Educational Activities:** SIFMA C&L Annual Seminar (Annual); Internet Conference; Small Firms Conference. **Geographic Preference:** Multinational.

9300 ■ Security Traders Association (STA)

1115 Broadway, Ste. 1110
  New York, NY 10010
Ph: (646)699-5996
Co. E-mail: sta@securitytraders.org
URL: http://securitytraders.org
Contact: Adm. (Ret.) Jim Toes, President
Facebook: www.facebook.com/Security-Traders-Association-161707260547130
Linkedin: www.linkedin.com/company/security-traders-association
X (Twitter): x.com/STA_National
Instagram: www.Instagram.com/sta_national

Description: Brokers and dealers handling listed and OTC securities, stocks and bonds, and all securities. Conducts educational programs. Promotes the interests of members throughout the global financial markets. Provides representation of these interests in the legislative, regulatory and technological processes. Fosters goodwill and high standards of integrity in accord with the association's founding principle. **Founded:** 1934. **Geographic Preference:** National.

9301 ■ Stable Value Investment Association (SVIA)

1025 Connecticut Ave. NW, Ste. 1000
  Washington, DC 20036
Co. E-mail: info@stablevalue.org
URL: http://www.stablevalue.org
Contact: Gina Mitchell, President
Linkedin: www.linkedin.com/company/stable-value-investment-association
X (Twitter): x.com/stablevalue
YouTube: www.youtube.com/c/StablevalueOrg/featured

Description: Supports pension plan sponsors, investment managers, banks, life insurance companies, and consultants. Promotes retirement savings; educates individuals on the role that stable value funds can play in achieving a financially secure retirement. **Founded:** 1990. **Geographic Preference:** National.

9302 ■ Wealthsimple Investments Inc

Wealthsimple Technologies Inc.
  862 Richmond St, W, Ste. 201
  Toronto, ON, Canada M6J 1C9
URL: http://www.wealthsimple.com/en-ca
Contact: John T. Bart, Founder
Facebook: www.facebook.com/wealthsimple

Description: Firm provides investment services. **Founded:** 1987. **Publications:** *Canadian Shareowner* (Bimonthly); *ShareOwner*. **Geographic Preference:** National.

REFERENCE WORKS

9303 ■ "3Par: Storing Up Value" in Barron's (Vol. 90, August 30, 2010, No. 35, pp. 30)

Pub: Barron's Editorial & Corporate Headquarters
Ed: Mark Veverka. **Description:** Dell and Hewlett Packard are both bidding for data storage company 3Par. The acquisition would help Dell and Hewlett Packard provide customers with a one-stop shop as customers move to a private cloud in the Internet. **Availability:** Online.

9304 ■ "113D Filings: Investors Report to the SEC" in Barron's (Vol. 88, March 24, 2008, No. 12, pp. M13)

Pub: Dow Jones & Company Inc.
Contact: Almar Latour, Chief Executive Officer
Released: April 02, 2016. **Description:** HealthCor Management called as problematic the plan of Magellan Health Services to use its high cash balances for acquisitions. Carlson Capital discussed with Energy Partners possible changes in the latter's board. Investor Carl Icahn suggested that Enzon Pharmaceuticals consider selling itself or divest some of its assets. **Availability:** Print; Online.

9305 ■ "A 16-Year Housing Slump? It Could Happen" in Barron's (Vol. 88, March 17, 2008, No. 11, pp. 27)

Pub: Dow Jones & Company Inc.
Contact: Almar Latour, Chief Executive Officer
Ed: Gene Epstein. **Description:** Housing remains a good protection against inflation but over very long periods. Inflation-adjusted stock prices did even better but have greater volatility. Commodities, on the other hand, underperformed both housing and stocks as inflation hedges. House prices tend to rise faster than the consumer price index is because land is inherently limited. **Availability:** Online.

9306 ■ "401(k) Keys to Stable Value" in Barron's (Vol. 88, March 10, 2008, No. 10, pp. 40)

Pub: Dow Jones & Company Inc.
Contact: Almar Latour, Chief Executive Officer
Ed: Tom Sullivan. **Description:** Stable-value funds offer investors stability in a period of volatility in financial markets, attracting $888 million in funds. The Securities and Exchange Commission approved the launch of actively managed exchange-traded funds. **Availability:** Online.

9307 ■ "529.com Wins Outstanding Achievement in Web Development" in Investment Weekly (November 14, 2009, pp. 152)

Pub: Investment Weekly News
Description: Web Marketing Association's 2009 WebAward for Financial Services Standard of Excellence and Investment Standard of Excellence was won by 529.com, the website from Upromise Investments, Inc., the leading administrator of 529 college savings plans. **Availability:** Online.

9308 ■ "2010 Book of Lists" in Business Courier (Vol. 26, December 26, 2009, No. 36, pp. 1)

Price: $49.95. **Description:** Rankings of companies and organizations within the business services, education, finance, health care, hospitality and tourism, real estate, and technology industries in the Cincinnati, Ohio-Northern Kentucky area are presented. Rankings are based on sales, business size, or other statistics. **Availability:** PDF; Online.

9309 ■ "ACE Agrees to Pay Out $266 Million to Investors" in Globe & Mail (February 17, 2006, pp. B1)

Ed: Brent Jang. **Description:** Canada-based commercial aviation firm ACE Aviation Holdings has agreed to pay 266 million dollars to its investors after filing a bankruptcy one year ago. Complete details of this pay off are discussed. **Availability:** Online.

9310 ■ *"ACE Expands M&A Practice" in Economics & Business Week (March 22, 2014, pp. 2)*

Pub: NewsRX LLC.

Contact: Kalani Rosell, Contact

Description: ACE Group announced an expansion of its mergers and acquisitions practice focusing on insurance solutions for private equity firms, their portfolio companies as well as their M&A transactions. **Availability:** Online.

9311 ■ *"Acquisitions Remain Future Growth Strategy for IMB Partners as Black Firm Achieves $1 Billion Revenue Mark" in Black Enterprise(February 6, 2023)*

URL(s): www.blackenterprise.com/acquisitions-remain-future-growth-strategy-for-imb-partners-ceo-offers-tips-for-entrepreneurs-in-podcast/

Released: February 06, 2023. **Description:** The investment firm, IMB Partners, achieved record growth in 2022 with over $1 billion reported across its investments. CEO Tarrus Richardson explains the company's success and its goals for the future. **Availability:** Online.

9312 ■ *"Addition by Subtraction in Tokyo" in Barron's (Vol. 92, August 25, 2012, No. 38, pp. 20)*

Pub: Dow Jones & Company Inc.

Contact: Almar Latour, Chief Executive Officer

Ed: Kopin Tan. **Description:** Investors in Japan could benefit from the increase in management buyouts, particularly of small capitalization stocks. This increase would shrink the number of Japanese stocks, many of which are trading below book value. **Availability:** Online.

9313 ■ *"Ag Firms Harvest Revenue Growth" in The Business Journal-Serving Metropolitan Kansas City (Vol. 26, July 18, 2008, No. 45, pp. 1)*

Description: Five of the biggest agricultural companies in the Kansas City area, except one, reported multibillion-dollar revenue increases in 2007. The companies, which include Lansing Trade Group, posted a combined $9.5 billion revenue growth. The factors that affected the revenue increase in the area's agricultural companies, such as prices and high demand, are also examined. **Availability:** Print; Online.

9314 ■ *"Air Canada Boss Gains $3.5-Million in Options" in Globe & Mail (January 19, 2007, pp. B5)*

Ed: Brent Jang. **Description:** Air Canada chairman Robert Milton's sale of 200,000 shares in stock options is discussed. **Availability:** Online.

9315 ■ *"Algoma Resolves Hedge Fund Fight" in Globe & Mail (March 8, 2006, pp. B1)*

Ed: Greg Keenan. **Description:** Algoma Steel Inc. has ended a dispute with Paulson and Co., a New York hedge fund, by offering to pay $200 million special dividend, appointing new directors, and continue to go for a sale. **Availability:** Print; Online.

9316 ■ *"All About The Benjamins" in Canadian Business (Vol. 81, September 29, 2008, No. 16, pp. 92)*

Description: Discusses real estate developer Royal Indian Raj International Corp., a company that planned to build a $3 billion "smart city" near the Bangalore airport; to this day nothing has ever been built. The company was incorporated in 1999 by Manoj C. Benjamin one investor, Bill Zack, has been sued by the developer for libel due to his website that calls the company a scam. Benjamin has had a previous case of fraud issued against him as well as a string of liabilities and lawsuits. **Availability:** Online.

9317 ■ *"All Eyes On Iris" in Canadian Business (Vol. 81, July 22, 2008, No. 12-13, pp. 20)*

Description: Provincial governments in Canada are believed to be awaiting Alberta Finance Minister Iris Evans' financial and investment policies as well as Evans' development of a new saving strategy. Alberta is the only Canadian province that is in position to invest in sovereign wealth funds after it eliminated its debt in 2005. **Availability:** Print; Online.

9318 ■ *"All-Star Advice 2010" in Black Enterprise (Vol. 41, October 2010, No. 3, pp. 97)*

Pub: Earl G. Graves Ltd.

Contact: Earl Graves, Jr., President

Ed: Renita Burns, Sheiresa Ngo, Marcia Wade Talbert. **Description:** Financial experts share tips on real estate, investing, taxes, insurance and debt management. **Availability:** Online.

9319 ■ *"America's Top 40 Wealth Management Firms" in Barron's (Vol. 92, September 17, 2012, No. 38, pp. 28)*

Pub: Dow Jones & Company Inc.

Contact: Almar Latour, Chief Executive Officer

Description: The 40 largest wealth managers in the US are ranked according to client assets held in accounts worth $5 million or more as of June 30, 2012. Bank of America Global Wealth and Investment Management remained the largest, with $792 billion in assets under management. **Availability:** Online.

9320 ■ *"American Water's Ed Vallejo Chosen for 2012 Minority Business Leader Awards" in Manufacturing Close-Up (July 30, 2012)*

Description: Ed Vallejo, vice presient of investor relations at American Water, has been awarded the 2012 Minority Business Leader Award from the Philadelphia Business Journal. Vallejo is responsible for developing investor relations strategies for the publicly traded water and wastewater utility firm. He also serves as the company's liaison with financial analyst and investor communities. **Availability:** Online.

9321 ■ *"The Annual Entitlement Lecture Medicare Elephantiasis" in Barron's (March 31, 2008)*

Pub: Dow Jones & Company Inc.

Contact: Almar Latour, Chief Executive Officer

Ed: Thomas G. Donlan. **Description:** Expenditures on Medicare hospital insurance and the revenues available to pay for it have led to a gap of capital valued at $38.6 trillion. Slashing the benefits or raising taxes will not solve the gap which exists unless the government saves the money and invests it in private markets. **Availability:** Online.

9322 ■ *"Apartment Tower in River North Fetches More Than $90 Million" in Crain's Chicago Business (Vol. 34, October 24, 2011, No. 42, pp. 17)*

Pub: Crain Communications Inc.

Contact: Barry Asin, President

Ed: Alby Gallun. **Description:** Apartment tower in River North was sold for over $90 million to a Texas pension fund adviser. Details are included. **Availability:** Online.

9323 ■ *"Are You Ready for Dow 20,000?" in Barron's (Vol. 88, March 24, 2008, No. 12, pp. 26)*

Pub: Dow Jones & Company Inc.

Contact: Almar Latour, Chief Executive Officer

Ed: Jonathan R. Laing. **Description:** Stock strategist James Finucane forecasts that the Dow Jones Industrial Average will rise from its 12,361 level to as high as 20,000 from 2008 to 2009. He believes that stock liquidation and a buildup of cash provide the perfect conditions for a huge rally. **Availability:** Online.

9324 ■ *"Are You Ready To Do It Yourself? Discipline and Self-Study Can Help You Profit From Online Trading" in Black Enterprise (February 1, 2008)*

Pub: Earl G. Graves Ltd.

Contact: Earl Graves, Jr., President

Ed: Steve Garmhausen. **Description:** Steps to help individuals invest in stocks online is given by an expert broker. Discount brokerage houses can save money for online investors. **Availability:** Online.

9325 ■ *"Arena Football League Sees S.A. as Crucial Market" in San Antonio Business Journal (Vol. 28, August 1, 2014, No. 25, pp. 6)*

Pub: American City Business Journals, Inc.

Contact: Mike Olivieri, Executive Vice President

Released: Weekly. **Price:** $4, introductory 4-week offer(Digital only). **Description:** The Arena Football League, which took control of the San Antonio Talons, believes that San Antonio, Texas is a key market. Reports show that football fans continue to support the Talons despite the ownership changes. The league's ability to attract high-profile investors is also examined. **Availability:** Print; Online.

9326 ■ *"As Capital Gains Tax Hike Looms, Baltimore's Merger Activity Percolates" in Baltimore Business Journal (Vol. 28, August 27, 2010, No. 16, pp. 1)*

Pub: Baltimore Business Journal

Contact: Rhonda Pringle, President

E-mail: rpringle@bizjournals.com

Ed: Scott Dance. **Description:** Concerns for higher capital gains taxes in 2011 have been provoking buyers and sellers to engage in mergers and acquisitions activity, which is expected to gain momentum before the end of 2010. Companies that had saved cash during the recession have been taking advantage of the buyer's market. Other trends in local and national mergers and acquisitions activity are presented. **Availability:** Print.

9327 ■ *"As Windows 8 Looms, Tech Investors Hold Their Breath" in Barron's (Vol. 92, July 23, 2012, No. 30, pp. 22)*

Pub: Dow Jones & Company Inc.

Contact: Almar Latour, Chief Executive Officer

Ed: Tiernan Ray. **Description:** Launch of the Microsoft Windows 8 operating system could affect the stock prices of Microsoft and Intel. The effects of the software's introduction on the market share of personal computers remains uncertain. **Availability:** Online.

9328 ■ *"Asia Breathes a Sigh of Relief" in Business Week (September 22, 2008, No. 4100, pp. 32)*

Description: Foreign bankers, such as those in Asia, that had been investing heavily in the United States began to worry as the housing crisis deepened and the impact on Freddie Mac and Fannie Mae became increasingly clear. Due to the government bailout, however, central banks will most likely continue to buy American debt. **Availability:** Print; Online.

9329 ■ *"Au Revoir Or Goodbye?" in Barron's (Vol. 88, July 14, 2008, No. 28, pp. 5)*

Pub: Dow Jones & Company Inc.

Contact: Almar Latour, Chief Executive Officer

Ed: Alan Abelson. **Description:** Former Senator Phil Gramm's opinion that the U.S. is a "nation of whiners" as they moan about recession is another example of the disconnection between Washington and Wall Street on one hand and the real world on the other. It would be a catastrophe for most of the world if Fannie Mae and Freddie Mac were to go under and take their trillions of mortgage debt with them. **Availability:** Online.

9330 ■ *"Avalon Advisors Opens Alamo City Office" in San Antonio Business Journal (Vol. 28, April 18, 2014, No. 10, pp. 7)*

Pub: American City Business Journals, Inc.

Contact: Mike Olivieri, Executive Vice President

Released: Weekly. **Price:** $4, Introductory 4-week offer(Digital only). **Description:** Avalon Advisors LLC opened an office in San Antonio, Texas. The wealth management firm has been serving prominent clients in the city over the past few years. Rob McCaline, director of the company's new office, reveals that the business enjoyed tremendous growth in the city through referrals by existing clients. **Availability:** Print; Online.

9331 ■ *"BABs in Bond Land" in Barron's (Vol. 89, July 6, 2009, No. 27, pp. 14)*
Pub: Dow Jones & Company Inc.
Contact: Almar Latour, Chief Executive Officer
Ed: Jim McTague. **Description:** American Recovery and Reinvestment Act has created taxable Build America Bonds (BAB) to finance new construction projects. The issuance of the two varieties of taxable BABs is expected to benefit the municipal bond market. **Availability:** Online.

9332 ■ *"Back in the Race. New Fund Manager Has Whipped Sentinel International Equity Back into Shape" in Barron's (Vol. 88, March 17, 2008, No. 11, pp. 43)*
Pub: Dow Jones & Company Inc.
Contact: Almar Latour, Chief Executive Officer
Ed: Leslie P. Norton. **Description:** Katherine Schapiro was able to get Sentinel International Equity's Morningstar classification to blended fund from a value fund rating after joining Sentinel from her former jobs at Strong Overseas Fund. Schapiro aims to benefit from the global rebalancing as the U.S.'s share of the world economy shrinks. **Availability:** Online.

9333 ■ *"Back-Tested ETFs Draw Assets, Flub Returns" in Barron's (Vol. 92, July 23, 2012, No. 30, pp. 26)*
Pub: Dow Jones & Company Inc.
Contact: Almar Latour, Chief Executive Officer
Ed: Janet Paskin. **Description:** New exchange-traded funds are attracting investors by using 'back-tested' data offered by the indexes they track. Investors are substituting real performance for these hypothetical returns, which measure past performance of indexes had they been in existence. **Availability:** Online.

9334 ■ *"Bad Loans Start Piling Up" in Crain's New York Business (Vol. 24, January 6, 2008, No. 1, pp. 2)*
Pub: Crain Communications, Inc.
Contact: Jessica Botos, Manager, Marketing
E-mail: jessica.botos@crainsnewyork.com
Ed: Tom Fredrickson. **Description:** Problems in the subprime mortgage industry have extended to other lending activities as evidenced by bank charge-offs on bad commercial and industrial loans which have more than doubled in the third quarter.

9335 ■ *"Bad Paper" in Canadian Business (Vol. 80, November 19, 2007, No. 23, pp. 34)*
Description: The Canadian government froze the market for non-bank asset-backed commercial paper (ABCP) August 2007, which means holders will be unable to withdraw investments. The crisis and value of ABCP are discussed. **Availability:** Print; Online.

9336 ■ *"Baking Up a Bigger Lance" in Charlotte Business Journal (Vol. 25, December 3, 2010, No. 37, pp. 1)*
Pub: Charlotte Business Journal
Contact: Robert Morris, Editor
E-mail: rmorris@bizjournals.com
Ed: Ken Elkins. **Description:** Events that led to the merger between Charlotte, North Carolina-based snack food manufacturer Lance Inc. and Pennsylvania-based pretzel maker Snyder's of Hanover Inc. are discussed. The merger is expected to help Lance in posting a 70 percent increase in revenue, which reached $900 million in 2009. How the merger would affect Snyder's of Hanover is also described. **Availability:** Print; Online.

9337 ■ *"Bank Buys May Heat Up In Birmingham" in Birmingham Business Journal (Vol. 31, May 9, 2014, No. 19, pp. 8)*
Pub: American City Business Journals, Inc.
Contact: Mike Olivieri, Executive Vice President
Released: Weekly. **Price:** $4, introductory 4-week offer(Digital & Print). **Description:** The banking industry in Birmingham, Alabama is poised for more mergers and acquisitions in the next two years as bank failures drop and potential sellers look for protection from increasing regulations. Experts sug-

gest Birmingham is an attractive market for potential buyers because of its rich history as a top financial center and its stable economic environment. **Availability:** Print; Online.

9338 ■ *"The Bankrate Double Play, Bankrate Is Having Its Best Quarter Yet" in Barron's (Vol. 88, March 24, 2008, No. 12, pp. 27)*
Pub: Dow Jones & Company Inc.
Contact: Almar Latour, Chief Executive Officer
Ed: Neil A. Martin. **Description:** Shares of Bankrate may rise as much as 25 percent from their level of $45.08 a share due to a strong cash flow and balance sheet. The company's Internet business remains strong despite weakness in the online advertising industry and is a potential takeover target. **Availability:** Online.

9339 ■ *"Barbarians Set Bar Low With Lowly Canadian Telco" in Globe & Mail (March 31, 2007, pp. B1)*
Ed: Derek DeCloet. **Description:** The efforts of the private equity fund Kohlberg, Kravis, Roberts and Co. to acquire the Canadian telecommunications firm BCE are described. **Availability:** Online.

9340 ■ *"Bargain Hunting In Vietnam" in Barron's (Vol. 88, July 14, 2008, No. 28, pp. M6)*
Pub: Dow Jones & Company Inc.
Contact: Almar Latour, Chief Executive Officer
Ed: Elliot Wilson. **Description:** Vietnam's economy grew by just 6.5 percent for the first half of 2008 and its balance of payments ballooned to $14.4 billion. The falling stock prices in the country is a boon for bargain hunters and investing in the numerous domestic funds is one way of investing in the country. Some shares that investors are taking an interest in are also discussed. **Availability:** Online.

9341 ■ *"Battered U.S. Auto Makers in Grip of Deeper Sales Slump" in Globe & Mail (April 4, 2007, pp. B1)*
Ed: Greg Keenan. **Description:** The fall in Canadian sales and market share of Ford Motor Co., General Motors Corp. and Chrysler Group is discussed. **Availability:** Print; Online.

9342 ■ *"Baupost Group Pours Money into Charlotte Real Estate Projects" in Charlotte Business Journal (Vol. 25, December 3, 2010, No. 37, pp. 1)*
Pub: Charlotte Business Journal
Contact: Robert Morris, Editor
E-mail: rmorris@bizjournals.com
Ed: Will Boye. **Description:** Boston-based hedge fund Baupost Group has been financing real estate project in Charlotte, North Carolina including more than 80 acres just north of uptown. Aside from purchasing the $23.8 million note for the Rosewood Condominiums from Regions Financial Corporation, the Baupost Group is also negotiating with Regions to buy the $93.9 million debt of the EipCentre real estate project. **Availability:** Print; Online.

9343 ■ *"BDC Launches New Online Business Advice Centre" in Marketwired (July 13, 2010)*
Pub: Comtex News Network Inc.
Contact: Kan Devnani, President
Description: The Business Development Bank of Canada (BDC) offers entrepreneurs the chance to use their new online BDC Advice Centre in order to seek advice regarding the challenges of entrepreneurship. Free online business tools and information to help both startups and established firms are also provided. **Availability:** Print; Online.

9344 ■ *"The Bear Stearns-JPMorgan Deal - Rhymes with Steal - Of A Lifetime" in Barron's (Vol. 88, March 24, 2008, No. 12, pp. 24)*
Pub: Dow Jones & Company Inc.
Contact: Almar Latour, Chief Executive Officer
Ed: Andrew Bary. **Description:** JPMorgan Chase's impending acquisition of Bear Stearns for $2.50 a share is a huge steal for the former. JPMorgan is set to acquire a company with a potential annual earn-

ings of $1 billion while the Federal Reserve funds Bear's illiquid assets by providing $30 billion in non-recourse loans. **Availability:** Online.

9345 ■ *"The Bear's Back" in Barron's (Vol. 88, July 7, 2008, No. 27, pp. 17)*
Pub: Dow Jones & Company Inc.
Contact: Almar Latour, Chief Executive Officer
Ed: Randall W. Forsyth, Vito Racanelli. **Description:** US stock markets have formally entered the bear market after the Dow Jones Industrial Average dropped 20 percent from its high as of June 2008. Investors remain uncertain as to how long the bear market will persist, especially with the US economy on the edge of recession. **Availability:** Online.

9346 ■ *"The Beauty of Banking's Big Ugly" in Barron's (Vol. 89, July 27, 2009, No. 30, pp. 31)*
Pub: Dow Jones & Company Inc.
Contact: Almar Latour, Chief Executive Officer
Ed: Andrew Bary. **Description:** Appeal of the shares of Citigroup comes from its sharp discount to its tangible book value and the company's positive attributes include a strong capital position, high loan-loss reserves, and their appealing global-consumer. The shares have the potential to generate nice profits and decent stock gains as the economy turns. **Availability:** Online.

9347 ■ *"Behind the Numbers: When It Comes to Earnings, Look for Quality, Not Just Quantity" in Black Enterprise (Vol. 38, July 2008, pp. 35)*
Pub: Earl G. Graves Ltd.
Contact: Earl Graves, Jr., President
Description: It is important for investors to examine the quality of a company's earnings rather than fixate on the quantity of those earnings. Advice is given regarding issues investors can look at when trying to determine the potential growth of a firm.

9348 ■ *"Bertha's Birth Stirs Juice" in Barron's (Vol. 88, July 14, 2008, No. 28, pp. M11)*
Pub: Dow Jones & Company Inc.
Contact: Almar Latour, Chief Executive Officer
Ed: Tom Sellen. **Description:** Price of frozen concentrated orange juice, which has risen to four-month highs of $1.3620 in July 2008 is due, in part, to the hurricane season that has come earlier than normal in the far eastern Atlantic thereby possibly harming the 2008-2009 Florida orange crop. Future tropical-storm development will affect the prices of this commodity. **Availability:** Online.

9349 ■ *"Best of Breed" in Barron's (Vol. 92, September 17, 2012, No. 38, pp. 24)*
Description: Private banks are offering financial services outside mutual funds to broadn their product portfolio. This move to open architecture has changed traditional corporate culture in Wall Street and has changed the companies' business models. **Availability:** Print.

9350 ■ *"Best Cash Flow Generators" in Canadian Business (Vol. 82, Summer 2009, No. 8, pp. 40)*
Description: Agrium Inc. and FirstService Corporation are in the list of firms that are found to have the potential to be the best cash flow generators in Canada. The list also includes WestJet Airlines Ltd., which accounts for 385 flights each day. More than 80 percent of analysts rate the airline stocks a Buy. **Availability:** Print; Online.

9351 ■ *"The Best Five-Month Run Since 1938" in Barron's (Vol. 89, August 3, 2009, No. 31, pp. M3)*
Pub: Dow Jones & Company Inc.
Contact: Almar Latour, Chief Executive Officer
Ed: Kopin Tan, Andrew Bary. **Description:** US stock markets ended July 2009 registering the highest five-month rise since 1938. The shares of Cablevision could rise as the company simplifies its structure and spins off its Madison Square Garden unit. The shares

of Potash Corp. could fall as the company faces lower earnings due to falling potash purchases. **Availability:** Online.

9352 ■ "Best Turnaround Stocks" in Canadian Business (Vol. 81, Summer 2008, No. 9, pp. 65)
Description: Share prices of Sierra Wireless Inc. and EXFO Electro Optical Engineering Inc. have fallen over the past year but have good chance at a rebound considering that the companies have free cash flow and no long-term debt. One-year stock performance analysis of the two companies is presented. **Availability:** Print; Online.

9353 ■ "Best Value Stocks" in Canadian Business (Vol. 81, Summer 2008, No. 9, pp. 63)
Description: Table showing the one-year performance of bargain or best-value stocks is presented. These stocks are undervalued compared to their North American peers, but it is projected that their five-year average return on equity is greater. **Availability:** Online.

9354 ■ "A Better Way to Tax U.S. Businesses" in (Vol. 90, July-August 2012, No. 7-8, pp. 134)
Pub: Harvard Business Review Press
Contact: Moderna V. Pfizer, Contact
Ed: Mihir A. Desai. **Price:** $8.95, PDF and hardcover black and white. **Description:** Correcting the US corporate tax code will require ending the disconnect between earnings stated to investors and taxable income, implementing rate reductions, eliminating the taxing of overseas income, and securing an agreement by business leaders to acknowledge taxes as a responsibility. **Availability:** Print; PDF; Online.

9355 ■ "Betting Big, Winning Big: Interview With Bruce Berkowitz, CEO of Fairholme Capital Management" in Barron's (Vol. 88, March 17, 2008, No. 11, pp. 49)
Pub: Dow Jones & Company Inc.
Contact: Almar Latour, Chief Executive Officer
Ed: Lawrence C. Strauss. **Description:** Bruce Berkowitz explains that the reason that his portfolio is concentrated is because getting more positions makes the portfolio more average compared to putting the money into your 10th or 20th-best idea. Berkowitz' picks include Berkshire Hathaway, WellCare Health Plus, Sears Holdings, and Mohawk Industries. **Availability:** Online.

9356 ■ "Betting on a Happy Ending" in Barron's (Vol. 88, July 7, 2008, No. 27, pp. 14)
Pub: Dow Jones & Company Inc.
Contact: Almar Latour, Chief Executive Officer
Ed: Dimitra DeFotis. **Description:** Shares of Time Warner, priced at $14.69 each, appear under-priced as financial analysts discount the value of the company. The company should be worth more than $20 a share as the company is spinning off Time Warner Cable. **Availability:** Online.

9357 ■ "Betting On Volatile Materials" in Barron's (Vol. 88, July 14, 2008, No. 28, pp. M11)
Pub: Dow Jones & Company Inc.
Contact: Almar Latour, Chief Executive Officer
Ed: John Marshall. **Description:** Economic slowdowns in the U.S., Europe and China could cause sharp short-term declines in the materials sector. The S&P Materials sector is vulnerable to shifts in the flow of funds. Statistical data included. **Availability:** Online.

9358 ■ "Between the Lines: Intangible Assets" in Canadian Business (Vol. 79, July 17, 2006, No. 14-15, pp. 17)
Pub: Rogers Media Inc.
Contact: Neil Spivak, Chief Executive Officer
Ed: Al Rosen. **Description:** Need for investors to check the actual worth of a company and not to get carried away by the inflated claims made by the company is emphasized.

9359 ■ "Beware this Chinese Export" in Barron's (Vol. 90, August 30, 2010, No. 35, pp. 21)
Pub: Barron's Editorial & Corporate Headquarters
Ed: Bill Alpert, Leslie P. Norton. **Description:** A look at 158 China reverse-merger stocks in the U.S. reveal that the median underperformed the index of U.S. listed Chinese companies by 75 percent in their first three years. These reverse merger stocks also lagged the Russell 2000 index of small cap stocks by 66 percent. **Availability:** Online.

9360 ■ "Beware of Rotting Money" in Barron's (Vol. 89, July 13, 2009, No. 28, pp. 31)
Pub: Dow Jones & Company Inc.
Contact: Almar Latour, Chief Executive Officer
Ed: Thomas G. Donlan. **Description:** Inflation can take hold of a country and do it great harm; it is caused by people, most particularly central bankers in charge of the world's reserve currency. Arrogant economists pushed the belief that the government can engineer the economy and it is argued that there is trouble ahead when the government tries to control the economy. **Availability:** Online.

9361 ■ "Beyond Meat (R) Completes Largest Financing Round to Date" in Ecology, Environment & Conservation Business (August 16, 2014, pp. 4)
Pub: NewsRX LLC.
Contact: Kalani Rosell, Contact
Description: Beyond Meat (R) is the first company to recreate meat from plants and is dedicated to improving human health, positively impacting climate change, conserving natural resources and respecting animal welfare. The firm has completed its Series D financing round, which will also help the company promote consumer awareness and increase capacity at its manufacturing facility to meet demand. **Availability:** Online.

9362 ■ "Beyond Microsoft and Yahoo!: Some M&A Prospects" in Barron's (Vol. 88, March 17, 2008, No. 11, pp. 39)
Pub: Dow Jones & Company Inc.
Contact: Almar Latour, Chief Executive Officer
Ed: Eric J. Savitz. **Description:** Weak quarterly earnings report for Yahoo! could pressure the company's board to cut a deal with Microsoft. Electronic Arts is expected to win its hostile $26-a-share bid for Take-Two Interactive Software. Potential targets and buyers for mergers and acquisitions are mentioned. **Availability:** Online.

9363 ■ "Big Gains Brewing at Anheuser-Busch InBev" in Barron's (Vol. 90, August 30, 2010, No. 35, pp. 34)
Pub: Barron's Editorial & Corporate Headquarters
Ed: Christopher C. Williams. **Description:** Anheuser-Busch InBev is realizing cost synergies and it posted better than expected returns two years after the merger that formed the company. One analyst believes its American depositary receipt could be worth as much as 72 in a year. **Availability:** Online.

9364 ■ "The Big Idea: The Judgment Deficit" in Harvard Business Review (Vol. 88, September 2010, No. 9, pp. 44)
Pub: Harvard Business Publishing
Contact: Diane Belcher, Managing Director
Ed: Amar Bhide. **Price:** $8.95. **Description:** The importance of individual, decentralized initiative and judgment in the capitalist system is outlined. While financial models have their use, they cannot always account appropriately for the inherent uncertainty in economic decision making. **Availability:** Online; PDF.

9365 ■ "Big Oil: Picks and Pans" in Canadian Business (Vol. 79, August 14, 2006, No. 16-17, pp. 67)
Description: A survey on investments in Canadian energy companies and the inflation caused by oil price hike, are discussed. **Availability:** Print; Online.

9366 ■ "Big Trouble at Sony Ericsson" in Barron's (Vol. 88, March 24, 2008, No. 12, pp. M9)
Pub: Dow Jones & Company Inc.
Contact: Almar Latour, Chief Executive Officer
Ed: Angelo Franchini. **Description:** Sony Ericsson is facing trouble as it warned that its sales and net income before taxes will fall by nearly half for the first quarter of 2008. The joint venture of Sony and Ericsson has a global mobile phone market share of nine percent as of 2007, fourth largest in the world. **Availability:** Online.

9367 ■ "Biotech Reels In $120M for 1Q" in Philadelphia Business Journal (Vol. 31, March 30, 2012, No. 7, pp. 1)
Pub: Baltimore Business Journal
Contact: Rhonda Pringle, President
E-mail: rpringle@bizjournals.com
Description: Philadelphia, Pennsylvania-based biotechnology firms have raised over $120 million in 2012 by selling stocks and debts. Discovery Laboratories has accounted for more than a third of the total funding. **Availability:** Print; Online.

9368 ■ "Biotechs Are Using Back Door to Go Public" in Boston Business Journal (Vol. 31, May 27, 2011, No. 18, pp. 1)
Pub: Boston Business Journal
Contact: Carolyn M. Jones, President
E-mail: cmjones@bizjournals.com
Ed: Julie M. Donnelly. **Description:** Members of Massachusetts' biotechnology sector have been engaging in reverse mergers as an alternative to initial public offerings. Reverse mergers provide access to institutional investors and hedge funds. **Availability:** Print; Online.

9369 ■ "Biovail Hits SAC With $4.6 Billion Suit" in Globe & Mail (February 23, 2006, pp. B1)
Ed: Shawn McCarthy. **Description:** The details of Biovail Corp.'s securities fraud case against SAC Management LLC are presented. **Availability:** Online.

9370 ■ "Blackstone Set to Sell Stake" in Globe & Mail (March 17, 2007, pp. B6)
Description: The plan of Blackstone Group to sell 10 percent of its stake to raise $4 billion and its proposal to go for initial public offering is discussed.

9371 ■ "Blackstone's Outlook Still Tough" in Barron's (Vol. 88, March 17, 2008, No. 11, pp. 19)
Pub: Dow Jones & Company Inc.
Contact: Almar Latour, Chief Executive Officer
Ed: Andrew Bary. **Description:** Earnings for the Blackstone Group may not recover soon since the company's specialty in big leveraged buyouts is floundering and may not recover until 2009. The company earns lucrative incentive fees on its funds but those fees went negative in the fourth quarter of 2007 and there could be more fee reversals in the future. **Availability:** Online.

9372 ■ "Bloody Monday for Bear?" in Barron's (Vol. 88, March 17, 2008, No. 11, pp. M14)
Pub: Dow Jones & Company Inc.
Contact: Almar Latour, Chief Executive Officer
Ed: Steven M. Sears. **Description:** Shares of Bear Stearns could slip further at the start of the trading week unless the company is bought out or bolstered by some other development over the weekend. Prices of the company's shares in the options market suggests about a 30 percent chance that the stock falls below $20 before March expirations expire. **Availability:** Online.

9373 ■ "Blue-Collar Broker Ranks in Nation's Elite" in Boston Business Journal (Vol. 31, July 15, 2011, No. 25, pp. 1)
Pub: Boston Business Journal
Contact: Carolyn M. Jones, President
E-mail: cmjones@bizjournals.com

Ed: Tim McLaughlin. **Description:** Richard F. Connolly Jr. was ranked 91st in Barron's latest annual ranking of top financial advisers and his team at Morgan Stanley Smith Barney oversee an estimated $3.7 billion in assets. However, anyone who knew him knows that he's just a blue-collar broker from Woburn who loves golf. **Availability:** Print.

9374 ■ "BMW Revs Up for a Rebound" in Barron's (Vol. 89, July 13, 2009, No. 28, pp. M7)
Pub: Dow Jones & Company Inc.
Contact: Almar Latour, Chief Executive Officer

Ed: Jonathan Buck. **Description:** Investors may like BMW's stocks because the company has maintained its balance sheet strength and has an impressive production line of new models that should boost sales in the next few years. The company's sales are also gaining traction, although their vehicle delivery was down 1.7 percent year on year on June 2009, this was still the best monthly sales figure for 2009. **Availability:** Online.

9375 ■ "Boar Market: Penny-Wise Consumers Favoring Pork" in Crain's Chicago Business (Vol. 31, April 14, 2008, No. 15, pp. 4)
Pub: Crain Communications Inc.
Contact: Barry Asin, President

Ed: Bruce Blythe. **Description:** Interview with Alan Cole who is the president of Cedar Hill Associates Inc. and who discusses ways in which his company is taking advantage of the record highs of oil and natural gas as well as his overall outlook on the market. **Availability:** Online.

9376 ■ "BofA May Part With U.S. Trust" in Boston Business Journal (Vol. 31, May 20, 2011, No. 17, pp. 1)
Pub: Boston Business Journal
Contact: Carolyn M. Jones, President
E-mail: cmjones@bizjournals.com

Ed: Tim McLaughlin. **Description:** Bank of America Corporation is willing to sell its U.S. Trust private banking division to improve its capital ratio. The unit remains to be the corporation's core asset and posted $696 million revenue in the first quarter 2010 in contract with Merrill Lynch Global Wealth Management's $3.5 billion. Analysts say that U.S. Trust would fetch more than $3 billion. **Availability:** Print; Online.

9377 ■ "BofA Will Reach the Top with Countrywide Deal" in Business North Carolina (Vol. 28, March 2008, No. 3, pp. 36)
Description: Bank of America, headquartered in Charlotte, North Carolina, will add Countrywide to its let of credits. Countrywide is the largest U.S. mortgage lender. Statistical data included.

9378 ■ "The Bogleheads' Guide to Investing"
Pub: John Wiley & Sons, Inc.
Contact: Christina Van Tassell, Executive Vice President Chief Financial Officer

Released: Second edition. **Price:** $26.95, hardcover; $17.99, E-Book. **Description:** Advice that provides the first step to successful financial investments includes new information of backdoor Roth IRAs and ETFs as mainstream buy and hold investments, estate taxes and gifting, along with information on the changes in laws regarding Traditional and Roth IRAs and 401k and 403b retirement plans. The author teaches how to craft proven individual investment strategies. **Availability:** E-book; Print.

9379 ■ "Bonds v. Stocks: Who's Right About Recession?" in Barron's (Vol. 90, August 23, 2010, No. 34, pp. M3)
Pub: Barron's Editorial & Corporate Headquarters

Ed: Kopin Tan. **Description:** The future of treasury securities and stocks should the U.S. enter or avoid a recession are discussed. The back to school business climate and BHP Billiton's bid for Potash Corporation of Saskatchewan are also discussed. **Availability:** Online.

9380 ■ "The Book On Indigo" in Canadian Business (Vol. 81, July 22, 2008, No. 12-13, pp. 29)
Description: Indigo Books & Music Inc. reported record sales of $922 million resulting in a record net profit of $52.8 million for the 2008 fiscal year ended March 29, 2008. Earnings per share were $2.13, greater than Standard & Poor's expected $1.70 per share. Additional information concerning Indigo Books is presented.

9381 ■ "Boomers' Spending Hurts Retirement" in Employee Benefit News (Vol. 25, November 1, 2011, No. 14, pp. 18)
Pub: SourceMedia LLC
Contact: Gemma Postlethwaite, Chief Executive Officer

Ed: Ann Marsh. **Description:** Financial planners and employers need to educate clients and employees about retirement planning. Boomers are spending money that should be saved for their retirement.

9382 ■ "Bottom-Fishing and Speed-Dating in India-How Investors Feel About the Indian Market" in Barron's (Vol. 88, March 24, 2008, No. 12, pp. M12)
Pub: Dow Jones & Company Inc.
Contact: Almar Latour, Chief Executive Officer

Ed: Elliot Wilson. **Description:** Indian stocks have fallen hard in 2008, with Mumbai's Sensex 30 down 30 percent from its January 2008 peak of 21,000 to 14,995 in March. The India Private Equity Fair 2008 attracted 140 of the world's largest private equity firms and about 24 of India's fastest-growing corporations. Statistical data included. **Availability:** Online.

9383 ■ "Bountiful Barrels: Where to Find $140 Trillion" in Barron's (Vol. 88, July 14, 2008, No. 28, pp. 40)
Pub: Dow Jones & Company Inc.
Contact: Almar Latour, Chief Executive Officer

Ed: Andrew Bary. **Description:** Surge in oil prices has caused a large transfer of wealth to oil-producing countries thereby reshaping the global economy. Oil reserves of oil exporting countries are now valued at $140 trillion. Economist Stephen Jen believes that this wealth will be transformed into paper assets as these countries invest in global stocks and bonds. **Availability:** Online.

9384 ■ "Bracing for a Bear of a Week" in Barron's (Vol. 88, March 17, 2008, No. 11, pp. 24)
Pub: Dow Jones & Company Inc.
Contact: Almar Latour, Chief Executive Officer

Ed: Jacqueline Doherty. **Description:** JPMorgan Chase and the Federal Reserve Bank of New York's opening of a line of credit to Bear Stearns cut the stock price of Bear Stearns by 47 percent to 30 followed by speculation of an imminent sale. JP Morgan may be the only potential buyer for the firm and some investors say Bears could be sold at $20 to $30. Bears prime assets include its enormous asset base worth $395 billion. **Availability:** Online.

9385 ■ "Brazil's New King of Food" in Barron's (Vol. 89, July 13, 2009, No. 28, pp. 28)
Pub: Dow Jones & Company Inc.
Contact: Almar Latour, Chief Executive Officer

Ed: Kenneth Rapoza. **Description:** Perdigao and Sadia's merger has resulted in the creation of Brasil Foods and the shares of Brasil Foods provides a play on both Brazil's newly energized consumer economy and its role as a major commodities exporter. Brasil Foods shares could climb as much as 36 percent. **Availability:** Online.

9386 ■ "Breaking with Tradition, Foundations Seek Out Diverse Asset Managers" in Crain's Chicago Business (October 15, 2021)
Ed: Steve Hendershot. **Released:** October 15, 2021. **Description:** Within the investment industry, a development to increase diversity in management is taking hold.

9387 ■ "Briefly: Physician Groups Unite" in Crain's Detroit Business (Vol. 25, June 15, 2009, No. 24, pp. 18)
Pub: Crain Communications Inc.
Contact: Barry Asin, President

Ed: Tom Henderson, Jay Greene. **Description:** Details of the merger between Planning Alternatives Ltd. and Oakland Wealth Management are highlighted. The two investment advisory firms will have a combined staff of 12 and will maintain two offices. **Availability:** Online.

9388 ■ "Brookfield Asset Management: A Perfect Predator" in Canadian Business (Vol. 83, July 20, 2010, No. 11-12, pp. 50)
Pub: Rogers Media Inc.
Contact: Neil Spivak, Chief Executive Officer

Ed: Joanna Pachner. **Description:** Brookfield Asset Management CEO Bruce Flatt manages $108 billion worth of real estate and the company has become one of the world's biggest prime real estate owners since he became leader. Flatt says their goal is to earn a 12-15 percent compound annual return per share and that they would shrink in size if it meant reaching that goal. **Availability:** Online.

9389 ■ "Builders Aim to Cut Costs: Pushing Changes to Regain Share of Residential Market; Seek Council's Help" in Crain's New York Business
Pub: Crain Communications, Inc.
Contact: Jessica Botos, Manager, Marketing
E-mail: jessica.botos@crainsnewyork.com

Ed: Erik Engquist. **Description:** Union contractors and workers are worried about a decline in their market share for housing so they intend to ask the City Council to impose new safety and benefit standards on all contractors to avoid being undercut by nonunion competitors. **Availability:** Print; Online.

9390 ■ "Building a Portfolio, BRIC by BRIC" in Barron's (Vol. 92, August 25, 2012, No. 38, pp. M8)
Pub: Dow Jones & Company Inc.
Contact: Almar Latour, Chief Executive Officer

Ed: Reshma Kapadia. **Availability:** Online.

9391 ■ "A Bull Market in Finger-Pointing" in Barron's (Vol. 88, March 10, 2008, No. 10, pp. 9)
Pub: Dow Jones & Company Inc.
Contact: Almar Latour, Chief Executive Officer

Ed: Michael Santoli. **Description:** Discusses who is to blame for the financial crisis brought about by the credit crunch in the United States; the country's financial markets will eventually digest this crisis but will bottom out first before the situation improves. **Availability:** Online.

9392 ■ "Bullish Alert: A Brave Market Call" in Barron's (Vol. 92, July 23, 2012, No. 30, pp. 12)
Pub: Dow Jones & Company Inc.
Contact: Almar Latour, Chief Executive Officer

Ed: Jacqueline Doherty. **Description:** Seth Masters, chief investment officer of Bernstein Global Wealth Management, predicts that the Dow Jones will reach the 20,000 level within five years. He also predicts that the Standard & Poor's 500 index will rise to 2,000 points. **Availability:** Online.

9393 ■ "Business Adventures by John Brooks - A 30-Minute Instaread Summary: Twelve Classic Tales from the World of Wall Street"
Pub: CreateSpace

Released: May 26, 2015. **Price:** $1.74, paperback. **Description:** The concept of the stock market is chronicled. Joseph de la Vega is the stock trader who invented the stock market in Amsterdam in 1611. Insight into the crash in 1962 provides information about the way the market works. **Availability:** Print.

9394 ■ *"Calpine Gets Ready to Light It Up"* in *Barron's (Vol. 92, July 23, 2012, No. 30, pp. 15)*
Pub: Dow Jones & Company Inc.
Contact: Almar Latour, Chief Executive Officer
Ed: Jack Willoughby. **Description:** The stocks of electric power producer Calpine could gain value as natural gas-fired power plants increase their market share. The company's stock prices could rise by 50 percent from $17.50 but the company needs to complete its turnaround to fully realize these gains. **Availability:** Online.

9395 ■ *"Cameco to Supply Reactors With Recycled Nukem Warheads"* in *Canadian Business (Vol. 85, August 13, 2012, No. 13, pp. 10)*
Ed: Richard Warnica. **Description:** Cameco Corporation has acquired Nukem Energy gmbH from private equity firm Advent International for $136 million as part of the Canadian mining company's plan to double annual uranium production to 40 million pounds by 2018. Such agreement gives Cameco access to some of the last of the uranium supply in the Megatons to Megawatt deal between Russia and the U.S. which expires in 2013. **Availability:** Print; Online.

9396 ■ *"Canadian Banks Too Timid in China, Beijing Tells Flaherty"* in *Globe & Mail (January 22, 2007, pp. B1)*
Ed: Steven Chase. **Description:** The article discusses Canadian banks' investments on China according to the views of federal Finance Minister Jim Flaherty. **Availability:** Online.

9397 ■ *"The Canadians Are Coming!"* in *Canadian Business (Vol. 80, October 22, 2007, No. 21, pp. 15)*
Description: Toronto-Dominion Bank declared its acquisition of the New Jersey-based Commerce Bancorp for C$8.5 billion. Royal Bank of Canada has scooped up Trinidad-based Financial Group for C$2.2 billion. Details of the foreign acquisitions, as well as the impact of high Canadian dollars on the mergers are discussed. **Availability:** Online.

9398 ■ *"Candidates Won't Bash Fed; Rate Cuts Bash Savers"* in *Barron's (Vol. 88, March 24, 2008, No. 12, pp. 31)*
Pub: Dow Jones & Company Inc.
Contact: Almar Latour, Chief Executive Officer
Ed: Jim McTague. **Description:** Candidates in the 2008 US presidential election, like the current administration, do not and will not bash the Federal Reserve. The Federal Reserve's aggressive interest rate cuts hurt the incomes of people depending on their savings accounts. **Availability:** Online.

9399 ■ *"Capital Coming Into City, but Local Money Lags"* in *Pittsburgh Business Times (Vol. 33, March 21, 2014, No. 36, pp. 4)*
Pub: American City Business Journals, Inc.
Contact: Mike Olivieri, Executive Vice President
Released: Weekly. **Price:** $4, Introductory 4-week offer(Digital & Print). **Description:** The strong investment market in Pittsburgh, Pennsylvania was fueled by capital from a combination of angel, venture, corporate and other sources, attracting $338 million in capital to finance 148 deals in 2013, but local money is lagging behind. Lynette Horrell of Ernst & Young notes that local money is not keeping up with the growth of technology companies in Pittsburgh. **Availability:** Print; Online.

9400 ■ *"Capital Position: M&I Acquisition Opens the Door for Rivals to Gain Market Share"* in *Business Journal-Milwaukee (Vol. 28, December 24, 2010, No. 12, pp. A1)*
Pub: The Business Journal
Contact: Heather Ladage, President
E-mail: hladage@bizjournals.com
Ed: Rich Kirchen. **Description:** Canada-based BMO Financial Group has purchased Marshall and Isley Corporation (M and I), which dominated lending among Wisconsin businesses for decades. The sale of M and I will enable other banks to recruit M and I's customers but BMO Financial remains a stronger competitor since it possesses a more potent capital position. **Availability:** Print; Online.

9401 ■ *"Capturing Generation Y: Ready, Set, Transform"* in *Credit Union Times (Vol. 21, July 14, 2010, No. 27, pp. 20)*
Ed: Senthil Kumar. **Description:** The financial services sector recognizes that Generation Y will have a definite impact on the way business is conducted in the future. The mindset of Generation Y is social and companies need to use networking tools such as Facebook in order to reach this demographic. **Availability:** Online.

9402 ■ *"The Case of the Deflated IPO"* in *Boston Business Journal (Vol. 29, June 24, 2011, No. 7, pp. 1)*
Pub: Boston Business Journal
Contact: Carolyn M. Jones, President
E-mail: cmjones@bizjournals.com
Ed: Scott Dance. **Description:** IPO market is on the rebound from the recession but for some companies in Maryland, the time is not yet ripe to go public. One of the companies that chooses to wait for better timing is SafeNet Inc. and it is eyeing some possible acquisitions while doing so. **Availability:** Print; Online.

9403 ■ *"Catch the Wind to Hold Investor Update Conference Call on October 18, 2011"* in *CNW Group (October 4, 2011)*
Pub: CNW Group Ltd.
Description: Catch the Wind Ltd., providers of laser-based wind sensor products and technology, held a conference call for analysts and institutional investors. The high-growth technology firm is headquartered in Manassas, Virginia. **Availability:** Print; Online.

9404 ■ *"Cemex Paves a Global Road to Solid Growth"* in *Barron's (Vol. 88, March 10, 2008, No. 10, pp. 24)*
Pub: Dow Jones & Company Inc.
Contact: Almar Latour, Chief Executive Officer
Ed: Sandra Ward. **Description:** Shares of Cemex are expected to perform well with the company's expected strong performance despite fears of a US recession. The company has a diverse geographical reach and benefits from a strong worldwide demand for cement. **Availability:** Online.

9405 ■ *"CEO Pay: The Details"* in *Crain's Detroit Business (Vol. 25, June 22, 2009, No. 25)*
Pub: Crain Communications Inc.
Contact: Barry Asin, President
Description: Total compensation packages for CEOs at area companies our outlined. These packages include salary, bonuses, stock awards, and options. **Availability:** Online.

9406 ■ *"CEOs Gone Wild"* in *Canadian Business (Vol. 79, August 14, 2006, No. 16-17, pp. 15)*
Description: Stock investment decisions of chief executive officers of metal companies in Canada, are discussed. **Availability:** Print; Online.

9407 ■ *CFA Institute--Membership Directory*
Pub: CFA Institute
Contact: Margaret Franklin, President
URL(s): www.cfainstitute.org/en/membership/directory
Description: Covers 38,000 security and financial analysts who are practicing investment analysis. **Availability:** Print.

9408 ■ *"CGB Purchases Illinois Grain-Fertilizer Firm"* in *Farm Industry News (December 2, 2011)*
Pub: Informa Business Media, Inc.
Contact: Charlie McCurdy, President
Description: CGB Enterprises Inc. bought Twomey Company's grain and fertilizer assets. The purchase includes eight locations and a barge loading terminal near Gladstone, Illinois and storage capacity of 51 million bushels and 18,000 tons of liquid fertilizer. **Availability:** Online.

9409 ■ *"Challenges Await Quad in Going Public"* in *Milwaukee Business Journal (Vol. 27, January 29, 2010, No. 18, pp. A1)*
Pub: The Business Journal
Contact: Heather Ladage, President
E-mail: hladage@bizjournals.com
Ed: Rich Rovito. **Description:** Sussex, Wisconsin-based Quad/Graphics Inc.'s impending acquisition of rival Canadian World Color Press Inc. will transform it into a publicly held entity for the first time. Quad has operated as a private company for nearly 40 years and will need to adjust to changes, such as the way management shares information with Quad/Graphics' employees. Details of the merger are included. **Availability:** Print; Online.

9410 ■ *"Chuck's Big Chance"* in *Barron's (Vol. 89, July 13, 2009, No. 28, pp. L3)*
Pub: Dow Jones & Company Inc.
Contact: Almar Latour, Chief Executive Officer
Ed: Leslie P. Norton. **Description:** Charles Schwab is cutting prices and rolling out new products to lure customers and the company is well positioned to benefit from Wall Street's misery. Their shares are trading at just 17 times earnings, which should be at least a multiple of 20. **Availability:** Online.

9411 ■ *"CIBC Spends $1.1 Billion on Caribbean Expansion"* in *Globe & Mail (March 14, 2006, pp. B1)*
Ed: Sinclair Stewart. **Description:** Canadian Imperial Bank of Commerce (CIBC), the fifth-largest bank of Canada, is planning to spend $1.1billion to buy major share of Barbados-based First Caribbean International Bank. The details of the acquisition plan are presented. **Availability:** Print; Online.

9412 ■ *"Citadel Hires Three Lehman Execs"* in *Chicago Tribune (October 2, 2008)*
Description: Citadel Investment Group LLC, Chicago hedge-fund operator, has hired three former senior executives of bankrupt investment banker Lehman Brothers Holding Inc. Citadel believes that the company's hiring spree will help them to further expand the firm's capabilities in the global fixed income business. **Availability:** Online.

9413 ■ *"Citi Ruling Could Chill SEC, Street Legal Pacts"* in *Wall Street Journal Eastern Edition (November 29, 2011, pp. C1)*
Pub: Dow Jones & Company Inc.
Contact: Almar Latour, Chief Executive Officer
Ed: Jean Eaglesham, Chad Bray. **Description:** A $285 million settlement was reached between the Securities and Exchange Commission and Citigroup Inc. over allegations the bank misled investors over a mortgage-bond deal. Now, Judge Jed S. Rakoff has ruled against the settlement, a decision that will affect the future of such attempts to prosecute Wall Street fraud. Rakoff said that the settlement was "neither fair, nor reasonable, nor adequate, nor in the public interest." **Availability:** Online.

9414 ■ *"The Clash of the Cultures: Investment vs. Speculation"*
Pub: John Wiley & Sons, Inc.
Contact: Christina Van Tassell, Executive Vice President Chief Financial Officer
Released: August 05, 2012. **Price:** $29.95, hardcover; $19.99, e-book. **Description:** Founder of Vanguard Group urges a return to the common sense principles of long-term investing. John C. Bogle draws on his sixty-years of experience in the mutual fund industry to discuss his views on the changing culture in mutual fund investing, how speculation has invaded our national retirement system, the failure of institutional money managers to effectively participate in corporate governance, and the need for a federal standard of fiduciary duty. Bogle also discusses the history of the index mutual fund and how he created it. **Availability:** E-book; Print.

9415 ■ *"Clash of the Titans"* **in Canadian Business (Vol. 80, March 12, 2007, No. 6, pp. 27)**

Description: The frequent allegations of Google Inc. and Microsoft Corp. against each other over copyright and other legal issues, with a view to taking away other's market share, is discussed. **Availability:** Print; Online.

9416 ■ *"Climbing the Wall of Worry, Two Steps at a Time"* **in Barron's (Vol. 89, July 13, 2009, No. 28, pp. L16)**

Pub: Dow Jones & Company Inc.

Contact: Almar Latour, Chief Executive Officer

Ed: Brian Blackstone. **Description:** Statistical table that shows the performance of different mutual funds for the second quarter of 2009 is presented. The data shows that on average, the 8,272 diversified equity funds gained 17 percent for this quarter. **Availability:** Online.

9417 ■ *"Cloudy Future for VMware?"* **in Barron's (Vol. 90, September 13, 2010, No. 37, pp. 21)**

Pub: Barron's Editorial & Corporate Headquarters

Ed: Jonathan R. Laing. **Description:** VMWare dominated the virtualization market for years, but it may be ending as it faces more competition from rivals that offer cloud computing services. The company's stocks are also expensive and are vulnerable to the smallest mishap. **Availability:** Online.

9418 ■ *"CMO Nicholson Exits Pepsi as Share Declines"* **in Advertising Age (Vol. 79, July 7, 2008, No. 26, pp. 4)**

Pub: Crain Communications, Inc.

Contact: Jessica Botos, Manager, Marketing

E-mail: jessica.botos@crainsnewyork.com

Ed: Natalie Zmuda. **Description:** Cie Nicholson, the chief marketing officer at Pepsi-Cola UK, is leaving the company at a time when its market share is down; the brand, which was known for its dynamic marketing, has diverted much of its attention from its core brands and shifted attention to the ailing Gatorade brand as well as Sobe Life Water and Amp. **Availability:** Online.

9419 ■ *"Coca-Cola FEMSA, Family Dollar, Other Dividend Payers On a Roll"* **in Benzinga.com (June 21, 2012)**

Pub: Benzinga.com

Contact: Jason Raznick, Founder

Ed: Nelson Hem. **Description:** Dividend paying companies showing upward price trends are outlined. The firms highlighted include: Agnico-Eagle Mines, Coca-Cola FEMSA, Dean Foods, Expedia, Family Dollar Stores, Ferrellgas Partners, and InterContinental Hotels. **Availability:** Print; Online.

9420 ■ *A Colossal Failure of Common Sense: The Inside Story of the Collapse of Lehman Brothers*

Pub: Currency

Contact: Penny Simon, Contact

E-mail: psimon@randomhouse.com

Ed: Lawrence G. McDonald, Patrick Robinson. **Released:** October 12, 2010. **Price:** $17, Paperback; $5.99; $20. **Description:** Former employee of Lehman Brothers details the failure of leadership that led to the demise of the company. **Availability:** E-book; Print; Audio.

9421 ■ *"Columbia's JPB Raising $175M to Acquire Companies, Real Estate"* **in Boston Business Journal (Vol. 29, May 27, 2011, No. 3, pp. 1)**

Pub: Boston Business Journal

Contact: Carolyn M. Jones, President

E-mail: cmjones@bizjournals.com

Ed: Gary Haber. **Description:** JPB Enterprises is preparing to raise $175 million in its goal of acquiring companies and real estate that are major names in America. The $75 million will be raised for a buyout fund that will target wide range of industries while the

$100 million will be used for land investment projects in the Florida Panhandle. Baltimore firms are expected to benefit from this deal. **Availability:** Print; Online.

9422 ■ *"Column: Want People to Save? Force Them"* **in Harvard Business Review (Vol. 88, September 2010, No. 9, pp. 36)**

Pub: Harvard Business Publishing

Contact: Diane Belcher, Managing Director

Ed: Dan Ariely. **Price:** $6, PDF. **Description:** Contrasts in U.S. attitudes towards savings and government regulation with those of Chile, where all employees are required to save 11 percent of their salary in a retirement account, are highlighted. **Availability:** Online; PDF.

9423 ■ *"Coming: Cheaper Oil and a Stronger Buck"* **in Barron's (Vol. 88, March 24, 2008, No. 12, pp. 53)**

Pub: Dow Jones & Company Inc.

Contact: Almar Latour, Chief Executive Officer

Ed: Lawrence C. Strauss. **Description:** Carl C. Weinberg, the chief economist of High Frequency Economics, forecasts that Chinese economic growth will slow down and that oil prices will drop to $80 a barrel in 2008. He also believes that the US dollar will start rising the moment the Federal Reserve stops cutting interest rates. **Availability:** Online.

9424 ■ *"Coming Soon: Bailouts of Fannie and Freddie"* **in Barron's (Vol. 88, July 14, 2008, No. 28, pp. 14)**

Pub: Dow Jones & Company Inc.

Contact: Almar Latour, Chief Executive Officer

Ed: Jonathan R. Laing. **Description:** Assurances from the government that Fannie Mae and Freddie Mac are adequately capitalized and able to carry on their duties as guarantors or owners of over $5 trillion of U.S. home mortgages are designed to keep both entities afloat until they attempt to raise $10 billion in new equity. The government would assume any losses in a bailout and owners of the banks' papers would profit as yields drop. **Availability:** Online.

9425 ■ *"Coming: The End of Fiat Money"* **in Barron's (Vol. 92, July 23, 2012, No. 30, pp. 32)**

Pub: Dow Jones & Company Inc.

Contact: Almar Latour, Chief Executive Officer

Ed: Leslie P. Norton. **Description:** Stephanie Pomboy, founder of MicroMavens, discusses her views on the global financial system. She believes that the global fiat currency system may collapse within five years and be replaced by a gold-backed currency system. **Availability:** Online.

9426 ■ *"Commodity Speculation: Over the Top?"* **in Barron's (Vol. 89, July 13, 2009, No. 28, pp. 22)**

Pub: Dow Jones & Company Inc.

Contact: Almar Latour, Chief Executive Officer

Ed: Gene Epstein. **Description:** Commodity Futures Trading Commission is planning to impose position limits on speculators of oil and other commodities as energy costs rebound from their lows. These regulations make much sense and these position limits would greatly diminish the cash commitment of the commodity index traders if these were imposed on speculators and swaps dealers properly. **Availability:** Online.

9427 ■ *"Compelling Opportunities for Investors in Emerging Markets"* **in Barron's (Vol. 88, March 10, 2008, No. 10, pp. 39)**

Pub: Dow Jones & Company Inc.

Contact: Almar Latour, Chief Executive Officer

Ed: Neil A. Martin. **Description:** Michael L. Reynal, portfolio manager of Principal International Emerging Markets Fund, is bullish on the growth prospects of stocks in emerging markets. He is investing big on energy, steel, and transportation companies. **Availability:** Online.

9428 ■ *"Connect the Thoughts"* **in Canadian Business (Vol. 81, October 27, 2008, No. 18, pp. 8)**

Description: Thomas Homer-Dixon believes the financial crisis that hit Wall Street is a systemic crisis and may result in the reconfiguration of financial markets in ways that people may never understand. He also thinks the U.S. may borrow against its assets, making it a weaker nation. **Availability:** Online.

9429 ■ *"Conscious Capitalism: Liberating the Heroic Spirit of Business"*

Released: January 07, 2014. **Price:** $12.47, e-book; $16.79, paperback. **Description:** Conscious Capitalism companies include Whole Foods Market, Southwest Airlines, Costco, Google, Patagonia, The Container Store, UPS and others. These firms under the four specific tenants to success: higher purpose, stakeholder integration, conscious leadership, and conscious culture and management. These companies are able to create value for all stakeholders, including customers, employees, suppliers, investors, society, and the environment. A new preface by the authors is included. **Availability:** E-book; Print.

9430 ■ *"Consumer Contagion? A Bleak Earnings View"* **in Barron's (Vol. 88, March 10, 2008, No. 10, pp. 15)**

Pub: Dow Jones & Company Inc.

Contact: Almar Latour, Chief Executive Officer

Ed: Robin Goldwyn Blumenthal. **Description:** Analysts expect consumer discretionary profits in the S&P 500 to drop 8.4 percent in the first quarter of 2008. A less confident consumer is expected to pull profits down, putting forecasts of earnings growth in the S&P 500 at risk. Statistical data included. **Availability:** Online.

9431 ■ *"Consumers Turned Off? Not at Best Buy"* **in Barron's (Vol. 88, March 24, 2008, No. 12, pp. 29)**

Pub: Dow Jones & Company Inc.

Contact: Almar Latour, Chief Executive Officer

Ed: Sandra Ward. **Description:** Shares of Best Buy, trading at $42.41 each, are expected to rise to an average of $52 a share due to the company's solid fundamentals. The company's shares have fallen 20 percent from their 52-week high and are attractive given the company's bright prospects in the video game sector and high-definition video. **Availability:** Online.

9432 ■ *"Conversation Starters for the Holiday"* **in Barron's (Vol. 89, July 6, 2009, No. 27, pp. 7)**

Pub: Dow Jones & Company Inc.

Contact: Almar Latour, Chief Executive Officer

Ed: Michael Santoli. **Description:** Investors are concerned that the US will experience high inflation due to low interest rates and improved money supply. US consumer spending has increased to 70 percent of gross domestic product, brought by health-care spending increases, while savings rates have risen to 6.9 percent. **Availability:** Online.

9433 ■ *"A Conversation With: Ron Gantner, Jones Lang LaSalle"* **in Crain's Detroit Business (Vol. 24, October 6, 2008, No. 40, pp. 9)**

Pub: Crain Communications Inc.

Contact: Barry Asin, President

Description: Interview with Ron Gantner who is a corporate real estate adviser with the real estate company Jones Lang LaSalle as well as the company's executive vice president and part of the tenant advisory team; Gantner speaks about the impact that the Wall Street crisis is having on the commercial real estate market in Detroit. **Availability:** Print; Online.

9434 ■ *"Cool on Chicago Office Properties"* **in Crain's Chicago Business (Vol. 31, March 31, 2008, No. 13, pp. 16)**

Pub: Crain Communications Inc.

Contact: Barry Asin, President

Ed: Eddie Baeb. **Description:** Investors predict values on Chicago office buildings to drop 1.3 percent over the next year. **Availability:** Online.

9435 ■ *"Copy Karachi?" in Barron's (Vol. 88, June 30, 2008, No. 26, pp. 5)*
Pub: Dow Jones & Company Inc.
Contact: Almar Latour, Chief Executive Officer
Ed: Randall W. Forsyth. **Description:** Karachi bourse had a historic 8.6 percent one-day gain because the bourse banned short-selling for a month and announced a 30 billion rupee fund to stabilize the market. The shares of General Motors are trading within the same values that it had in 1974. The reasons for this decline are discussed. **Availability:** Online.

9436 ■ *"Corus Eases Off Ailing Condo Market" in Crain's Chicago Business (April 28, 2008)*
Pub: Crain Communications Inc.
Contact: Barry Asin, President
Ed: H. Lee Murphy. **Description:** Corus Bankshares Inc., a specialist in lending for the condominium high-rise construction market, is diversifying its portfolio by making loans to office developers and expects to be investing in hotels through the rest of the year. Corus' $7.57 billion loan portfolio is also discussed in detail as well as the company's earnings and share price. Statistical data included. **Availability:** Online.

9437 ■ *"Cost Cuts Lead Dealers to Record Profits" in Globe & Mail (March 24, 2006, pp. B3)*
Ed: Omar El Akkad. **Description:** The reasons behind posting of $4.3 billion profit by Canadian securities sector, for 2005, are presented. **Availability:** Online.

9438 ■ *"The Coup Is Over, the Execution Begins" in Canadian Business (Vol. 85, June 11, 2012, No. 10, pp. 9)*
Ed: Matthew McClearn. **Description:** U.S. activist investor Bill Ackman of Pershing Square Capital Management faces the challenge of satisfying the high expectations he set when he acquired Canadian Pacific (CP) Railway and all of Pershing's nominees were elected to the CP board. Ackman promises that CP would reach an operating ratio of 65 percent by 2015. **Availability:** Online.

9439 ■ *"CPI, Coal Lead Local Stock Decline" in Saint Louis Business Journal (Vol. 32, October 14, 2011, No. 7, pp. 1)*
Pub: Saint Louis Business Journal
Contact: Robert Bobroff, President
E-mail: rbobroff@bizjournals.com
Ed: Greg Edwards. **Description:** Coal companies and CPI Corporation were among those whose stocks have declined in St. Louis, Missouri. The stocks of local firms have plunged by 28 percent during the first nine months of 2011. **Availability:** Print; Online.

9440 ■ *"CPI Corp. Acquires Assets of Bella Pictures" in Benzinga.com (January 28, 2011)*
Pub: PR Newswire Association LLC.
Description: CPI Corporation acquired assets of Bella Pictures Inc., a leading provider of branded wedding photography services. Details of the acquisition are explained. **Availability:** Online.

9441 ■ *"Crain's Picks Top '08 Stocks" in Crain's New York Business (Vol. 24, January 6, 2008, No. 1, pp. 3)*
Pub: Crain Communications, Inc.
Contact: Jessica Botos, Manager, Marketing
E-mail: jessica.botos@crainsnewyork.com
Ed: Aaron Elstein. **Description:** Listing of five stocks that Crain's believes can deliver solid gains for shareholders. **Availability:** Online.

9442 ■ *"Crash Landing? Serious Signal Flashing" in Barron's (Vol. 88, July 7, 2008, No. 27, pp. 11)*
Pub: Dow Jones & Company Inc.
Contact: Almar Latour, Chief Executive Officer

Description: Discusses the Hindenburg Omen, named after the airship disaster of May 1937, which is considered a predictor of market crashes and has appeared twice in June 2008. There is a 25 percent probability that the US stock market will suffer a crash in the July-October 2008 period. **Availability:** Online.

9443 ■ *Crash Proof 2.0: How to Profit From the Economic Collapse*
Pub: John Wiley & Sons, Inc.
Contact: Christina Van Tassell, Executive Vice President Chief Financial Officer
Ed: Peter D. Schiff, John Downes. **Released:** Second edition. **Price:** $16.95, paperback; $27.95, hardcover; $18.99, e-book; $18.99, E-book. **Description:** Factors that will affect financial stability in the coming years are explained. A three step plan to battle the current economic downturn is also included. **Availability:** E-book; Print.

9444 ■ *"The Credit Crisis Continues to Take Victims" in Barron's (Vol. 88, March 10, 2008, No. 10, pp. M12)*
Pub: Dow Jones & Company Inc.
Contact: Almar Latour, Chief Executive Officer
Ed: Randall W. Forsyth. **Description:** Short-term Treasury yields dropped to new cyclical lows in early March 2008, with the yield for the two-year Treasury note falling to 1.532 percent. Spreads of the mortgage-backed securities of Fannie Mae and Freddie Mac rose on suspicion of collapses in financing. **Availability:** Online.

9445 ■ *"Crime and Punishment" in Canadian Business (Vol. 81, December 24, 2007, No. 1, pp. 21)*
Description: Cmpass Inc.'s survey of 137 Canadian chief executive officers showed that they want tougher imposition of sentences on white-collar criminals, as they believe that the weak enforcement of securities laws gives an impression that Canada is a country where it is easy to get away with fraud. **Availability:** Online.

9446 ■ *"Cummins Is a Engine of Growth" in Barron's (Vol. 88, July 14, 2008, No. 28, pp. 43)*
Pub: Dow Jones & Company Inc.
Contact: Almar Latour, Chief Executive Officer
Ed: Shirley A. Lazo. **Description:** Engine maker Cummins increased its quarterly common dividend by 40 percent to 17.5 cents per share from 12.5 cents. CVS Caremark's dividend saw a hike of 18.4 percent from 9.5 cents to 11.25 cents per share while its competitor Walgreen is continuing its 75th straight year of dividend distribution and its 33rd straight year of dividend hikes. **Availability:** Online.

9447 ■ *Currency Internationalization: Global Experiences and Implications for the Renminbi*
Pub: Palgrave Macmillan
Released: First edition. **Description:** A collection of academic studies relating to the potential internationalization of China's remninbi. It also discusses the increasing use of China's remninbi currency in international trade and finance.

9448 ■ *"Danaher to Acquire Tectronix for $2.8 Billion" in Canadian Electronics (Vol. 22, November-December 2007, No. 7, pp. 1)*
Description: Leading supplier of measurement, test and monitoring equipment Tektronix will be acquired by Danaher Corporation for $2.8 billion. Tektronix products are expected to complement Danaher's test equipment sector. The impacts of the deal on Tektronix shareholders and Danaher's operations are discussed. **Availability:** Print; Online.

9449 ■ *"A Day Late and a Dollar Short" in Indoor Comfort Marketing (Vol. 70, March 2011, No. 3, pp. 30)*
Description: A discussion involving futures options and fuel oil prices is presented. **Availability:** Online.

9450 ■ *"Deal Braces Cramer for Growth Run" in The Business Journal-Serving Metropolitan Kansas City (Vol. 26, July 4, 2008, No. 43, pp. 1)*
Description: Gardner, Kansas-based Cramer Products Inc. bought 100 percent of the stocks of Louisville, Kentucky-based Active Ankle Inc. from 26 private investors increasing its revenue by 20 percent. The latter is the second largest vendor of Cramer. Other details of the merger are presented. **Availability:** Print; Online.

9451 ■ *"Deals Dip In Florida Amid Squabbles Over Price" in South Florida Business Journal (Vol. 34, May 30, 2014, No. 45, pp. 4)*
Pub: American City Business Journals, Inc.
Contact: Mike Olivieri, Executive Vice President
Released: Weekly. **Price:** $8, introductory 4-week offer(Digital only). **Description:** Private equity firm investments in local companies in Florida dropped from 146 in 2012 to 135 in 2013. James Cassel of Cassel, Salpeter and Company, says companies in the information technology and health care sectors have been acquired because of strong multiples of their book value. **Availability:** Print; Online.

9452 ■ *"Death Spiral" in Business Journal Serving Greater Tampa Bay (Vol. 30, October 29, 2010, No. 45, pp. 1)*
Pub: Tampa Bay Business Journal
Contact: Ian Anderson, President
E-mail: ianderson@bizjournals.com
Description: Bay Cities Bank has started working on the loan portfolio of its acquisition, Progress Bank of Florida. Regulators closed Progress Bank in October 2010 after capital collapsed due to charge-offs and increases in the provision for future loan losses. **Availability:** Print; Online.

9453 ■ *"Defendants in Ponzi Case Seek Relief from Court" in Denver Business Journal (Vol. 64, September 7, 2012, No. 16, pp. 1)*
Pub: Baltimore Business Journal
Contact: Rhonda Pringle, President
E-mail: rpringle@bizjournals.com
Price: $4, Introductory 4-Week Offer(Digital Only). **Description:** A US District Court judge has turned down the petition of Ponzi scheme suspects Michael Turnock and William P. Sullivan II to release their assets. The two have been accused of fraud and operating a Ponzi scheme worth $15.7 million. They argued that they are suffering from economic hardship and health issues. **Availability:** Print.

9454 ■ *"Delivering the Milk" in Barron's (Vol. 92, July 23, 2012, No. 30, pp. M7)*
Pub: Dow Jones & Company Inc.
Contact: Almar Latour, Chief Executive Officer
Ed: Kopin Tan. **Description:** The stocks of China Mengniu Dairy could continue losing value in the short term but could gain value in the long term. The company's revenue growth and profit margins face downward pressure due to aggressive pricing after food safety scandals. **Availability:** Online.

9455 ■ *"Despite FDA Approval, Heart Test No Boom for BG Medical" in Boston Business Journal (Vol. 31, June 17, 2011, No. 21, pp. 1)*
Pub: Boston Business Journal
Contact: Carolyn M. Jones, President
E-mail: cmjones@bizjournals.com
Ed: Julie M. Donnelly. **Description:** The Galectin-3 test failed to boost stock prices of its manufacturer, BG Medicine, which has fallen to $6.06/share. The company hopes that its revenue will be boosted by widespread adoption of an automated and faster version of the test, which diagnoses for heart failure. **Availability:** Online.

9456 ■ *"Developers Accommodate Need for Rooms" in Puget Sound Business Journal (Vol. 35, September 19, 2014, No. 22, pp. 8)*
Pub: American City Business Journals, Inc.
Contact: Mike Olivieri, Executive Vice President

Description: The number of hotel rooms in Bellevue, Washington has been steadily increasing. Access to capital by investors is seen to contribute to the development. Seven new hotel construction projects are underway in Seattle, Washington. **Availability:** Online.

9457 ■ Dictionary of Finance, Investment and Banking

Pub: Palgrave Macmillan

Ed: Erik Banks. **Released:** First edition. **Description:** Comprehensive dictionary covering terms used in finance, investment and banking sectors.

9458 ■ "Digging Deep for Gold: David Iben, Manager, Nuveen Tradewinds Value Opportunities Fund" in Barron's (Vol. 88, March 24, 2008, No. 12, pp. 49)

Pub: Dow Jones & Company Inc.

Contact: Almar Latour, Chief Executive Officer

Ed: Suzanne McGee. **Description:** David Iben, manager of the Nuveen Tradewinds Value Opportunities Fund, looks for value in companies and industries where the consensus of analysts is negative. He started investing in gold stocks well before gold prices started to rise. **Availability:** Online.

9459 ■ The Directory of Venture Capital & Private Equity Firms

Pub: Grey House Publishing

Contact: Richard Gottlieb, President

Released: February 01, 2016. **Price:** $250, Softcover. **Description:** Updated and expanded edition that includes new entries offering access to more than 3,500 domestic and international venture capital and private equity firms; detailed contact information and extensive data on investments and funds is included. **Availability:** Print; Online.

9460 ■ "Disappearing Act" in Globe & Mail (April 21, 2007, pp. B1)

Description: The effects of the buyout of BCE Inc. on the trends of stock prices at the Toronto Stock Exchange are described. **Availability:** Online.

9461 ■ "Discount Beers Take Fizz Out Of Molson" in Globe & Mail (February 10, 2006, pp. B3)

Description: The reasons behind the decline in profits by 60 percent for Molson Coors Brewing Co., during fourth quarter 2005, are presented. **Availability:** Online.

9462 ■ "DNERO & Bits of Stock Team Up to Offer Wealth-Building Rewards to Hispanic Market" in Minority Business Entrepreneur (March 7, 2022)

URL(s): mbemag.com/articles/dnero-bits-of-stock -team-up-to-offer-wealth-building-rewards-to-his-panic-market/

Ed: Gaby M. Rojas. **Description:** DNERO and bits of Stock have created a partnership that will allow DNERO users to earn Stock Rewards, which will equal fractional shares of stock. **Availability:** Online.

9463 ■ "Do-It-Yourself Portfolio Management" in Barron's (Vol. 89, July 13, 2009, No. 28, pp. 25)

Pub: Dow Jones & Company Inc.

Contact: Almar Latour, Chief Executive Officer

Ed: Mike Hogan. **Description:** Services of several portfolio management web sites are presented. These web sites include MarketRiders E.Adviser, TD Ameritrade and E. **Availability:** Online.

9464 ■ "Does Diversity Pay Dividends?" in Canadian Business (Vol. 87, October 2014, No. 10, pp. 89)

Description: The growing interest in gender diversity-based investing can be driven in part by a rising number of women investors with progressive ideals. Alex Johnston of Catalyst Canada advocacy group predict the use of a diversity-based approach by institutional investors. **Availability:** Online.

9465 ■ "Dog Days and Stimulus Fatigue" in Barron's (Vol. 92, August 25, 2012, No. 38, pp. M10)

Pub: Dow Jones & Company Inc.

Contact: Almar Latour, Chief Executive Officer

Ed: Michael Aneiro. **Description:** Credit market movements in August 2012 have been influenced by small news and speculation. US Federal Reserve Chairman Ben Bernanke has been more transparent, yet this transparency can also confound investors. **Availability:** Online.

9466 ■ "The Dogs of TSX" in Canadian Business (Vol. 81, Summer 2008, No. 9, pp. 77)

Description: Table showing the one-year stock performance of the ten highest dividend-yielding stocks on the S&P/TSX 60 Composite Index is presented. This technique is similar to the 'Dogs of the Dow' approach. The idea in this investment strategy is to buy equal amounts of stocks from these companies and selling them a year later, and then repeat the process. **Availability:** Online.

9467 ■ "Don't Bet Against The House" in Barron's (Vol. 88, July 14, 2008, No. 28, pp. 20)

Pub: Dow Jones & Company Inc.

Contact: Almar Latour, Chief Executive Officer

Ed: Sandra Ward. **Description:** Shares of Nasdaq OMX have lost more than 50 percent of their value from November 2007 to July 2008 but the value of these shares could climb 50 percent on the strength of world security exchanges. Only 15 percent of the company's revenues come from the U.S. and the shares are trading at 12.5 times the amount expected for 2008. **Availability:** Online.

9468 ■ "Don't Fear the Phone" in Senior Market Advisor (Vol. 13, October 2012, No. 10, pp. 50)

Description: Investment brokers and financial planning advisors must set aside time to make phone calls to clients as well as prospective clients. The article puts this process into perspective for setting appointments. **Availability:** Online.

9469 ■ "Don't Hang Up On FairPoint" in Barron's (Vol. 88, July 7, 2008, No. 27, pp. M5)

Description: Shares of FairPoint Communications, priced at $6.63 each, are undervalued and should be worth over $12 each. The company increased its size by more than five times by acquiring Verizon's local telephone operations in Vermont, New Hampshire, and Maine, but must switch customers in those areas into their system by the end of September 2007. **Availability:** Online.

9470 ■ "Downtown Bank Got High Marks for Irwin Purchase, Is Looking For More" in Business Courier (Vol. 27, September 3, 2010, No. 18, pp. 1)

Pub: Business Courier

Ed: Steve Watkins. **Price:** $4, Introductory 4-Week Offer(Digital & Print). **Description:** First Financial Bancorp is looking to acquire more troubled banks following its purchase of Irwin Union Bank. The bank has reported a $383 million bargain purchase gain during the third quarter of 2009. **Availability:** Print; Online.

9471 ■ "Drilling Deep and Flying High" in Barron's (Vol. 88, June 30, 2008, No. 26, pp. 34)

Pub: Dow Jones & Company Inc.

Contact: Almar Latour, Chief Executive Officer

Ed: Kenneth Rapoza. **Description:** Shares of Petrobras could rise another 25 percent if the three deepwater wells that the company has found proves as lucrative as some expect. Petrobras will become an oil giant if the reserves are proven. **Availability:** Online.

9472 ■ "Drug, Seed Firms Offer Antidote For Inflation" in Crain's Chicago Business (Vol. 31, April 21, 2008, No. 16, pp. 4)

Pub: Crain Communications Inc.

Contact: Barry Asin, President

Ed: Daniel Rome Levine. **Description:** Interview with Jerrold Senser, the CEO of Institutional Capital LLC in Chicago, in which he discusses the ways that the company is adjusting to the economic slowdown and rising inflation, his favorite firms for investment and his prediction of an economic turnaround; he also recommends five companies he feels are worth investing in. **Availability:** Online.

9473 ■ "Drug Trial Halt at YM Sets Stage for Selloff" in Globe & Mail (January 31, 2007, pp. B3)

Description: The decision of YM Biosciences Inc. to stop its trial of cancer drug tesmilifene and stocks following government concern over the safety of the drug is discussed. **Availability:** Online.

9474 ■ "Dynamic Duo: Payouts Rise at General Dynamics, Steel Dynamics" in Barron's (Vol. 88, March 10, 2008, No. 10, pp. 45)

Pub: Dow Jones & Company Inc.

Contact: Almar Latour, Chief Executive Officer

Ed: Shirley A. Lazo. **Description:** General Dynamics, the world's sixth-largest military contractor, raised its dividend payout by 20.7 percent from 29 cents to 35 cents a share. Steel Dynamics, producer of structural steel and steel bar products, declared a 2-for-1 stock split and raised its quarterly dividend by 33 percent to a split-adjusted 10 cents a share. **Availability:** Online.

9475 ■ "Easier Options Orders" in Barron's (Vol. 92, August 25, 2012, No. 35, pp. 28)

Pub: Dow Jones & Company Inc.

Contact: Almar Latour, Chief Executive Officer

Ed: Theresa W. Carey. **Description:** Online brokerage optionsXpress introduced the Walk Limit, a service that allows traders to improve pricing for options and save money. Online brokerage TradeMonster introduced portfolio margining to qualified customers. **Availability:** Online.

9476 ■ "Economic Distance and the Survival of Foreign Direct Investments" in Academy of Management Journal (Vol. 50, No. 5, October 1, 2007, pp. 1156)

Pub: Academy of Management

Contact: Sharon Alvarez, President

Ed: Eric W.K. Tsang, Paul S.L. Yip. **Description:** Study was undertaken to assess the relationship between economic disparities of various countries and foreign direct investments, focusing on Singapore. Results revealed that economic distance has a definite impact on foreign direct investment hazard rates. **Availability:** Electronic publishing; Download; PDF; Online.

9477 ■ "Economic Recovery Prognosis: Four More Years" in Barron's (Vol. 89, July 13, 2009, No. 28, pp. 11)

Pub: Dow Jones & Company Inc.

Contact: Almar Latour, Chief Executive Officer

Ed: Karen Hube. **Description:** Loomis Sayles Bond Fund manager Dan Fuss believes that the economy is bottoming and that recovery will be long and drawn out. Fuss guesses that the next peak in 10-year Treasury yields will be about 6.25% in around 4 and a half or five years ahead of 2009. **Availability:** Online.

9478 ■ "An Educated Play on China" in Barron's (Vol. 88, June 30, 2008, No. 26, pp. M6)

Pub: Dow Jones & Company Inc.

Contact: Almar Latour, Chief Executive Officer

Ed: Mohammed Hadi. **Description:** New Oriental Education & Technology Group sells English-language courses to an increasingly competitive Chinese workforce that values education. The shares in this company have been weighed down by worries on the impact of the Beijing Olympics on enrollment and the Sichuan earthquake. These shares could be a great way to get exposure to the long-term growth in China. **Availability:** Online.

9479 ■ *"The Education of Jack Bogle"* in *Philadelphia Business Journal (Vol. 33, April 4, 2014, No. 8, pp. 4)*
Pub: American City Business Journals, Inc.
Contact: Mike Olivieri, Executive Vice President
Description: Vanguard Group founder and now retired CEO, John C. Bogle, shares his views about life and starting the company. Bogle says Wellington Fund founder, Walter L. Morgan, made all the difference by having confidence in him and basically turned the company over to him when he was 37 years old. Bogle believes Philadelphia's mutual fund industry owes its significant growth to Vanguard. **Availability:** Online.

9480 ■ *"The Effect of Corporate Governance on Firm's Credit Ratings: Further Evidence Using Governance Score in the United States"* in *Accounting and Finance (Vol. 52, June 2012, No. 2, pp. 291)*
Ed: Fatima Alali, Asokan Anandarajan, Wei Jiang. **Released:** January 06, 2012. **Description:** An investigation into whether corporate governance affects a firm's credit ratings and whether improvement in corporate governance standards is associated with improvement in investing grade rating is presented. **Availability:** Print; PDF; Online.

9481 ■ *"Egg Fight: The Yolk's on the Shorts"* in *Barron's (Vol. 88, July 7, 2008, No. 27, pp. 20)*
Pub: Dow Jones & Company Inc.
Contact: Almar Latour, Chief Executive Officer
Ed: Christopher C. Williams. **Description:** Shares of Cal-Maine Foods, the largest egg producer and distributor in the US, are due for a huge rise because of the increase in egg prices. Short sellers, however, continue betting that the stock, priced at $31.84 each, will eventually go down. **Availability:** Online.

9482 ■ *"Election Futures are a Smart Idea"* in *Canadian Business (Vol. 85, June 11, 2012, No. 10, pp. 18)*
Ed: Mike Moffatt. **Description:** The decision of the U.S. Commodity Futures Trading Commission to ban political-event derivatives contracts was criticized along with the idea that such products could cause a systemic financial collapse. Political derivatives can be used as tools to help reduce risk and predict future political events. **Availability:** Print; Online.

9483 ■ *"The Emerging Capital Market for Nonprofits"* in *Harvard Business Review (Vol. 88, October 2010, No. 10, pp. 110)*
Pub: Harvard Business Publishing
Contact: Diane Belcher, Managing Director
Ed: Robert S. Kaplan, Allen S. Grossman. **Price:** $8.95, PDF. **Description:** Demonstration of how nonprofits can use intermediaries to grow their organizational structures, giving them improved scale and impact is offered. Some intermediaries play a mutual-fund role and conduct due diligence, while others act as venture capital funds and implement strategy. **Availability:** Online; PDF.

9484 ■ *"The Emperor Strikes Back"* in *Canadian Business (Vol. 80, March 26, 2007, No. 7, pp. 48)*
Description: The financial performance of Fairfax Financial Holdings Ltd. in 2006 is presented. The efforts of chief executive Prem Watsa to lead the company towards growth track are also presented. **Availability:** Online.

9485 ■ *"EnCana Axes Spending on Gas Wells"* in *Globe & Mail (February 16, 2006, pp. B1)*
Ed: Dave Ebner. **Description:** The reasons behind EnCana Corp.'s cost spending measures by $300 million on natural gas wells are presented. The company projects 2 percent cut in gas and oil sales for 2006. **Availability:** Print; Online.

9486 ■ *"End of the Beginning"* in *Canadian Business (Vol. 81, November 10, 2008, No. 19, pp. 17)*
Ed: David Wolf. **Released:** September 30, 2016. **Description:** The freeze in the money markets and historic decline in equity markets around the world finally forced governments into aggressive coordinated action. The asset price inflation brought on by cheap credit will now work in reverse and the tightening of credit will be difficult economically. Canada is exposed to the fallout everywhere, given that the U.S, the U.K. and Japan buy 30 percent of Canada's output. **Availability:** Print; Online.

9487 ■ *"End of an Era"* in *Barron's (Vol. 88, July 7, 2008, No. 27, pp. 3)*
Ed: Alan Abelson. **Released:** January 01, 2016. **Description:** June 2008 was a very bad month for US stocks, with investors losing as much as 41.9 percent in the first half of 2008 signaling an end to the financial environment that prevailed around the world since the 1980's. The US job market lost 62,000 jobs in June 2008. **Availability:** Print; Online.

9488 ■ *"Endeca Gears Up for Likely IPO Bid"* in *Boston Business Journal (Vol. 31, July 1, 2011, No. 23, pp. 1)*
Pub: Boston Business Journal
Contact: Carolyn M. Jones, President
E-mail: cmjones@bizjournals.com
Ed: Kyle Alspach. **Released:** Weekly. **Price:** $4. **Description:** Endeca Inc. is readying itself for its plans to register as a public company. The search engine technology leader is enjoying continued growth with revenue up by 30 percent in 2010 while its expansion trend makes it an unlikely candidate for an acquisition. **Availability:** Print; Online.

9489 ■ *"Energy Firms Face Stricter Definitions"* in *Globe & Mail (March 26, 2007, pp. B3)*
Ed: David Ebner. **Description:** The Alberta Securities Commission has imposed strict securities regulations on oil and gas industries. Energy industries will have to submit revenue details to stake holders. **Availability:** Online.

9490 ■ *"Energy MPLs: Pipeline to Profits"* in *Barron's (Vol. 89, July 27, 2009, No. 30, pp. 9)*
Pub: Dow Jones & Company Inc.
Contact: Almar Latour, Chief Executive Officer
Ed: Dimitra DeFotis. **Description:** Energy master limited partnership stocks are range-bound in the next few months from July 2009 but there are there are some opportunities that remain. These include Energy Transfer Equity, Enterprise GP holdings, NuStar GP Holdings, and Plains All American Pipeline. **Availability:** Online.

9491 ■ *"Energy Slide Slows 4th-Quarter Profits"* in *Globe & Mail (April 13, 2007, pp. B9)*
Ed: Angela Barnes. **Description:** The decrease in the fourth quarter profits of several companies across various industries in Canada, including mining and manufacturing, due to global decrease in oil prices, is discussed.

9492 ■ *"EPAM May End the IPO Dry Spell"* in *Philadelphia Business Journal (Vol. 31, February 3, 2012, No. 51, pp. 1)*
Pub: Baltimore Business Journal
Contact: Rhonda Pringle, President
E-mail: rpringle@bizjournals.com
Description: EPAM SystemsInc. has launched its initial public offering. The company is the first Philadelphia, Pennsylvania-based firm to go public in more than a year. **Availability:** Print; Online.

9493 ■ *"Equal Weighting's Heavy Allure"* in *Barron's (Vol. 92, July 23, 2012, No. 30, pp. 27)*
Pub: Dow Jones & Company Inc.
Contact: Almar Latour, Chief Executive Officer
Ed: Brendan Conway. **Description:** Equal weight index exchange-traded funds are attracting investors due to their strong returns. This strategy gives inves-

tors a greater exposure to mid-capitalization companies and could provide strong returns over longer stretches. **Availability:** Online.

9494 ■ *"Escape from Iron Mountain"* in *Barron's (Vol. 92, September 17, 2012, No. 38, pp. 23)*
Description: The stocks of Iron Mountain appear fully valued at their most recent price of $33/share. Activist investors Elliott Management and Davis Advisors pushed for the conversion into a real estate investment trust but have since sold their holdings in the company. **Availability:** Online.

9495 ■ *"Essential Releases Record First Quarter Results"* in *Marketwired (May 14, 2007)*
Pub: Comtex News Network Inc.
Contact: Kan Devnani, President
Description: The first quarter of 2007 saw record financial performance despite numerous challenges for Essential Energy Services Trust. Statistical data included. **Availability:** Print; Online.

9496 ■ *"ETF Score Card"* in *Barron's (Vol. 89, July 13, 2009, No. 28, pp. 51)*
Pub: Dow Jones & Company Inc.
Contact: Almar Latour, Chief Executive Officer
Description: Statistical table is presented which shows the net assets of various exchange-traded funds are presented. The table also shows the total return of these funds up to a three-year time period. **Availability:** Online.

9497 ■ *"Europe's Meltdown"* in *Canadian Business (Vol. 83, June 15, 2010, No. 10, pp. 76)*
Description: As European countries such as Greece, Spain, and Portugal struggle with debt problems, it is worth noting that its equities trade at a 30 percent discount to the U.S. and that a 10 percent drop in the Euro translates to a 10 percent rise in profitability for exporters. Investors may also want to focus on business-to-business operations rather than consumer-focused ones. **Availability:** Online.

9498 ■ *"Everyone Out of the Pool"* in *Barron's (Vol. 89, July 20, 2009, No. 29, pp. 18)*
Pub: Dow Jones & Company Inc.
Contact: Almar Latour, Chief Executive Officer
Ed: Sandra Ward. **Description:** Shares of Pool Corp. could drop as continued weakness in the housing market weakens the market for swimming pool equipment. The company's shares are trading at $18.29, about 20 times projected 2009 earnings of $0.91 a share. **Availability:** Online.

9499 ■ *"Executive Summary: How Smart Firms Create Productive Ties"* in *Business Strategy Review (Vol. 23, Spring 2012, No. 1, pp. 83)*
Description: Benjamin L. Hallen and Kathleen M. Eisenhardt wrote, 'Catalyzing Strategies and Efficient Tie Formation: How Entrepreneurial Firms Obtain Investment Ties', May 3, 2011. The report is examined. **Availability:** Online.

9500 ■ *"Facebook IPO Buyers Deserved To Lose"* in *Canadian Business (Vol. 85, July 16, 2012, No. 11-12, pp. 16)*
Ed: Andrew Hallam. **Description:** Investors buying into an overhyped initial public offering (IPO) like Facebook, which opened with a price/earnings ratio exceeding 100 times earnings, are overpaying for uncertain promise. Studies found that the most profitable IPO are those unpopular businesses which are not overpriced. **Availability:** Print; Online.

9501 ■ *"The Facebook IPO Hype Meter"* in *Canadian Business (Vol. 85, June 11, 2012, No. 10, pp. 74)*
Ed: Joe Castaldo. **Description:** Comparison of the Facebook frenzy with other notable initial public offerings (IPO) based on market capitalization divided by profit indicated that an overpriced IPO such as that of Facebook does not equate to poor returns in the

short-term. Studies found that IPOs that debut at more reasonable prices get better returns in the long term. **Availability:** Online.

9502 ■ *"Falling Local Executive Pay Could Suggest a Trend" in Tampa Bay Business Journal (Vol. 30, January 15, 2010, No. 4, pp. 1)*
Pub: Tampa Bay Business Journal
Contact: Ian Anderson, President
E-mail: ianderson@bizjournals.com

Ed: Margie Manning. **Description:** Tampa Bay, Florida-based Raymond James Financial Inc. and MarineMax Inc.'s proxy statements have shown the decreasing compensation of the companies' highest paid executives. The falling trend in executive compensation was a result of intensified shareholder scrutiny and the economy. **Availability:** Print; Online.

9503 ■ *"Falling Markets' Nastiest Habit" in Barron's (Vol. 88, July 7, 2008, No. 27, pp. 7)*
Pub: Dow Jones & Company Inc.
Contact: Almar Latour, Chief Executive Officer

Ed: Michael Santoli. **Description:** US market conditions reflect a bear market, with the S&P 500 index falling 20 percent below its recent high as of June 2008. The bear market is expected to persist in the immediate future, although bear market rallies are likely to occur. **Availability:** Online.

9504 ■ *"Falling Share Prices Will Convince Big Oil Producers to Pay Up to Drill" in Globe & Mail (April 21, 2007, pp. B1)*
Ed: Boyd Erman. **Description:** The effect of the increase in operational costs and the decline in share prices, on the exploration of petroleum deposits in Canada, is described. **Availability:** Online.

9505 ■ *"February Hot for Mutual Fund Sales" in Globe & Mail (March 3, 2006, pp. B10)*
Ed: Keith Damsell. **Description:** The details on Canadian mutual fund sector, which posted $4.7 billion for February 2005, are presented. **Availability:** Print; Online.

9506 ■ *"The Fed Still Has Ammunition" in Barron's (Vol. 90, August 30, 2010, No. 35, pp. M9)*
Pub: Barron's Editorial & Corporate Headquarters

Ed: Randall W. Forsyth. **Description:** Federal Reserve chairman Ben Bernanke said the agency still has tools to combat deflation and a second downturn but these strategies are not needed at this time. The prospects of the Federal Open Market Committee's purchasing of treasuries are also discussed. **Availability:** Online.

9507 ■ *"Fed Tackles Bear of a Crisis" in Barron's (Vol. 88, March 17, 2008, No. 11, pp. M10)*
Pub: Dow Jones & Company Inc.
Contact: Almar Latour, Chief Executive Officer

Ed: Randall W. Forsyth. **Description:** Emergency funding package for Bear Stearns from the Federal Reserve Bank of New York through JPMorgan Chase is one of the steps taken by the central bank shore up bank liquidity. Prior to the emergency funding, the central bank announced the Term Securities Lending Facility to allow dealers to borrow easily saleable Treasuries in exchange for less-liquid issues. **Availability:** Online.

9508 ■ *"Federal Bailout, Three Years Later" in Business Owner (Vol. 35, September-October 2011, No. 5, pp. 6)*
Description: State of the economy and small business sector three years after the government stimulus and bailout programs were instituted. **Availability:** Print; Online.

9509 ■ *"Fees Come Down; Markets Come Down More" in Barron's (Vol. 89, July 13, 2009, No. 28, pp. L8)*
Pub: Dow Jones & Company Inc.
Contact: Almar Latour, Chief Executive Officer

Ed: J.R. Brandstrader. **Description:** Investors spent less on mutual fund fees in 2009 than they did in the last 25 years. These fees include administration, accounting, and legal expense. Despite the popularity of money market funds which has contributed to this decline, the short-term yields of these funds fell in the last year. **Availability:** Online.

9510 ■ *"A Few Points of Contention" in Barron's (Vol. 88, July 14, 2008, No. 28, pp. 3)*
Pub: Dow Jones & Company Inc.
Contact: Almar Latour, Chief Executive Officer

Ed: Michael Santoli. **Description:** Headline inflation tends to revert to the lower core inflation, which excludes food and energy in its calculation over long periods. Prominent private equity figures believe that regulators should allow more than the de facto 10 percent to 25 percent limit of commercial banks to hasten the refunding of the financial sector. **Availability:** Online.

9511 ■ *"Fieldbrook Foods Acquired By Private Equity Firm" in Ice Cream Reporter (Vol. 23, October 20, 2010, No. 11, pp. 1)*
Description: Fieldbrook Foods Corporation, manufacturer of frozen novelty and ice cream products was acquired by Chicago-based private equity firm Arbor Investments. Arbor partnered with Herman 'Bing' Graffunder, a long-term dairy industry partner, in its acquisition of Fieldbrook. **Availability:** Print; Online.

9512 ■ *"Fifth Third Spinoff Eyes More Space" in Business Courier (Vol. 27, July 16, 2010, No. 11, pp. 1)*
Pub: Business Courier

Ed: Dan Monk, Steve Watkins. **Description:** Electronic-funds transfer company Fifth Third Solutions (FTPS), a spinoff of Fifth Third Bancorp, is seeking as much as 200,000 square feet of new office space in Ohio. The bank's sale of 51 percent ownership stake to Boston-based Advent International Corporation has paved the way for the growth of FTPS. How real estate brokers' plans have responded to FTPS' growth mode is discussed. **Availability:** Print; Online.

9513 ■ *"Financial Stability: Fraud, Confidence, and the Wealth of Nations"*
Pub: John Wiley & Sons, Inc.
Contact: Christina Van Tassell, Executive Vice President Chief Financial Officer

Released: September 2014. **Price:** $48.99, e-book; $75, hardcover. **Description:** Instruction is provided to help modern investors and finance professionals to learn from past successes and failures and to gauge future market threats. Insight into today's financial markets and the political economy will help craft a strategy that leads to financial stability. Topics covered include: capital; forecasting; political reaction; and past, present, and future applications within all areas of business. A companion Website offers additional data and research, providing a comprehensive resource for those wishing a better understanding of risk factors in investing. **Availability:** E-book; Print; Online; PDF.

9514 ■ *Financing Your Small Business*
Released: First edition. **Description:** Tips for raising venture capital, dealing with bank officials, and initiating public offerings of stock shares for small business.

9515 ■ *"A Fine Time for Timber" in Barron's (Vol. 92, August 25, 2012, No. 38, pp. 18)*
Pub: Dow Jones & Company Inc.
Contact: Almar Latour, Chief Executive Officer

Ed: Christopher C. Williams. **Description:** The stocks of timber firm and real estate investment trust Weyerhaeuser could have their dividend raised by as much as 50 percent. The company is poised to benefit from a housing sector recovery, which could raise the value of its real estate and timberland holdings. **Availability:** Online.

9516 ■ *"Fine Wine, Poor Returns" in Barron's (Vol. 92, September 17, 2012, No. 38, pp. 11)*
Description: Investing in wines in not considered a good idea due to irrationally high wine prices. Wine collectors buying wines at very high prices are not expected to make money and are charged with a 28 percent 'collectibles' tax. **Availability:** Online.

9517 ■ *"First, the Merger: Then, The Culture Clash. How To Fix the Little Things That Can Tear a Company Apart" in Inc. (January 2008)*
Ed: Elaine Appleton Grant. **Description:** Ways three CEOs handled the culture classes that followed after company mergers; companies profiled include Fuel Outdoor, an outdoor advertising company; Nelson, an interior design and architecture firm; and Beber Silverstein, an ad agency. **Availability:** Online.

9518 ■ *"FIS-Metavante Deal Paying Off for Many" in Business Journal-Milwaukee (Vol. 28, December 17, 2010, No. 11, pp. A1)*
Pub: The Business Journal
Contact: Heather Ladage, President
E-mail: hladage@bizjournals.com

Ed: Rich Kirchen. **Description:** Jacksonville, Florida-based Fidelity National Information Services Inc., also known as FIS, has remained committed to Milwaukee, Wisconsin more than a year after purchasing Metavante Technologies Inc. FIS has transferred several operations into Metropolitan Milwaukee and has continued its contribution to charitable organizations in the area. **Availability:** Print; Online.

9519 ■ *"Fiscal Cliff Notes" in Barron's (Vol. 92, September 15, 2012, No. 38, pp. 27)*
Pub: Dow Jones & Company Inc.
Contact: Almar Latour, Chief Executive Officer

Ed: Mike Hogan. **Description:** Websites and blogs dedicated to providing information on the economic effects of the 'fiscal cliff' are described. These sites discuss possible effects on the US economy, budget, and personal finances. **Availability:** Online.

9520 ■ *"Five Tips for Killer Landing Pages" in Retirement Advisor (Vol. 13, October 2012, No. 10, pp. 27)*
Ed: Amy McIlwain. **Description:** The importance of Web page design is highlighted. Five tips for creating a Webpage that encourages trust and informs users about the financial products and services you offer are are given. **Availability:** Print; Online.

9521 ■ *The Flaw of Averages: Why We Underestimate Risk in the Face of Uncertainty*
Pub: John Wiley & Sons, Inc.
Contact: Christina Van Tassell, Executive Vice President Chief Financial Officer

Ed: Sam L. Savage. **Released:** March 26, 2012. **Price:** $19.95, paperback; $27.95, hardcover; $12.99, E-Book. **Description:** Personal and business plans are based on uncertainties on a daily basis. The common avoidable mistake individuals make in assessing risk in the face of uncertainty is defined. The explains why plans based on average assumptions are wrong, on average, in areas as diverse as finance, healthcare, accounting, the war on terror, and climate change. **Availability:** E-book; Print.

9522 ■ *"A Flawed Yardstick for Banks" in Barron's (Vol. 88, July 14, 2008, No. 28, pp. M6)*
Pub: Dow Jones & Company Inc.
Contact: Almar Latour, Chief Executive Officer

Ed: Arindam Nag. **Description:** Return on equity is no longer the best measure for investors to judge banks by in a post-subprime-crises world. Investors should consider the proportion of a bank's total assets that are considered risky and look out for any write-downs of goodwill when judging a bank's financial health. **Availability:** Online.

9523 ■ *"Florida's Housing Gloom May Add To Woes of National City" in Crain's Cleveland Business (Vol. 28, October 29, 2007, No. 43, pp. 1)*
Pub: Crain Communications Inc.
Contact: K. C. Crain, President

Ed: Shawn A. Turner. **Description:** Already suffering by bad loans in the troubled mortgage market, National City Corp. is attempting to diversify its geographic presence beyond the slow-growth industrial Midwest by acquiring two Florida firms. Analysts worry that the acquisitions may end up making National City vulnerable to a takeover if the housing slump continues and credit quality becomes more of an issue for the bank. **Availability:** Online.

9524 ■ *Fooling Some of the People All of the Time*

Pub: John Wiley & Sons, Inc.

Contact: Christina Van Tassell, Executive Vice President Chief Financial Officer

Ed: David Einhorn. **Released:** January 2011. **Price:** $14.50, Paperback; $10.99, e-book. **Description:** A chronicle of the ongoing saga between author, David Einhorn's hedge fund, Greenlight Capital, and Allied Capital, a leader in the private finance industry. **Availability:** E-book; Print.

9525 ■ *"For Buffett Fans, the Price Is Right"* in Barron's (Vol. 89, July 13, 2009, No. 28, pp. 17)

Pub: Dow Jones & Company Inc.

Contact: Almar Latour, Chief Executive Officer

Ed: Andrew Bary. **Description:** Shares of Warren Buffett's Berkshire Hathaway have fallen to $85,000 and these are cheap since they are trading at just 1.2 times estimated book value and are well below its peak of $149,000. One fan of the stock expects it to top $110,000 in the next year from June 2009. **Availability:** Online.

9526 ■ *"For Gilead, Growth Beyond AIDS"* in Barron's (Vol. 88, June 30, 2008, No. 26, pp. 18)

Pub: Dow Jones & Company Inc.

Contact: Almar Latour, Chief Executive Officer

Ed: Jay Palmer. **Description:** First-quarter 2008 revenue for Gilead Sciences grew by 22 percent and an earnings gain of 19 percent thanks to their HIV-treatment drugs that comprised over two-thirds of the company's sales in 2007. An analyst has a 12-month target from June, 2008 of 65 per share. The factors behind the company's prospects are also discussed. **Availability:** Online.

9527 ■ *"Ford Canada's Edsel of a Year: Revenue Plummets 24 Percent in '05"* in Globe & Mail (February 2, 2006, pp. B1)

Description: Ford Motor Company of Canada Ltd. posted 24% decline in revenues for 2005. The drop in earnings is attributed to plant shutdown in Oaksville, Canada. **Availability:** Online.

9528 ■ *"Ford: Down, Not Out, and Still a Buy"* in Barron's (Vol. 92, July 23, 2012, No. 30, pp. 14)

Pub: Dow Jones & Company Inc.

Contact: Almar Latour, Chief Executive Officer

Ed: Vito J. Racanelli. **Description:** Stocks of Ford Motor Company could gain value as the company continues to improve its finances despite fears of slower global economic growth. The company's stock prices could double from $9.35 per share within three years. **Availability:** Online.

9529 ■ *"The Four Cheapest Plays in Emerging Markets"* in Barron's (Vol. 89, July 27, 2009, No. 30, pp. 34)

Pub: Dow Jones & Company Inc.

Contact: Almar Latour, Chief Executive Officer

Ed: Lawrence C. Strauss. **Description:** Portfolio manager Arjun Divecha of the GMO Emerging Markets III Fund says that the main thing in investing in emerging markets is getting the country right since getting it wrong makes it harder to add value. Divecha says that the four countries that they are positive on are Turkey, Russia, South Korea, and Thailand. **Availability:** Online.

9530 ■ *"Fraser and Neave Acquires King's Creameries"* in Ice Cream Reporter (Vol. 23, November 20, 2010, No. 12, pp. 1)

Description: Fraser and Neave Ltd., a Singapore-based consumer products marketer, has entered a conditional agreement to acquire all outstanding shares of King's Creameries, the leading manufacturer and distributor of frozen desserts. **Availability:** Print; Online.

9531 ■ *"Full-Court Press for Apple"* in Barron's (Vol. 88, March 24, 2008, No. 12, pp. 47)

Pub: Dow Jones & Company Inc.

Contact: Almar Latour, Chief Executive Officer

Ed: Mark Veverka. **Description:** Apple Inc. is facing more intellectual property lawsuits in 2008, with 30 patent lawsuits filed compared to 15 in 2007 and nine in 2006. The lawsuits, which involve products such as the iPod and the iPhone, present some concern for Apple's shareholders. **Availability:** Online.

9532 ■ *"Funds "Friend' Facebook"* in Barron's (Vol. 89, July 27, 2009, No. 30, pp. 30)

Pub: Dow Jones & Company Inc.

Contact: Almar Latour, Chief Executive Officer

Ed: Leslie P. Norton. **Description:** Mutual-fund companies are the latest entrants to the "social media" space and several companies have already set up Facebook and Twitter pages. The use of this technology pose special challenges for compliance and regulators especially since the Financial Industry Regulatory Authority reminds companies that advertising, sales and literature are governed by regulations. **Availability:** Online.

9533 ■ *"Funky Footwear: Walk This Way"* in Barron's (Vol. 90, August 23, 2010, No. 34, pp. 13)

Pub: Barron's Editorial & Corporate Headquarters

Ed: Christopher C. Williams. **Description:** Crocs and Skechers are selling very popular shoes and sales show no signs of winding down. The shares of both companies are attractively prices. **Availability:** Online.

9534 ■ *"The Future of Private Equity"* in Canadian Business (Vol. 80, March 26, 2007, No. 7, pp. 19)

Description: The impact growing Canadian economy and competition in global business on the performance of private equity funds is analyzed. **Availability:** Online; PDF.

9535 ■ *"Future of the Street"* in Barron's (Vol. 88, June 30, 2008, No. 26, pp. 27)

Pub: Dow Jones & Company Inc.

Contact: Almar Latour, Chief Executive Officer

Ed: Michael Santoli. **Description:** Prospects of the securities industry in terms of jobs and profit sources are discussed. Suggestions on what the industry needs with regards to its use of capital are also discussed. **Availability:** Online.

9536 ■ *"Futures Shock for the CME"* in Crain's Chicago Business (Vol. 31, November 10, 2008, No. 45, pp. 8)

Pub: Crain Communications Inc.

Contact: Barry Asin, President

Ed: Ann Saphir. **Description:** Chicago-based CME Group Inc., the largest futures exchange operator in the U.S., is facing a potentially radically altered regulatory landscape as Congress weighs sweeping reform of financial oversight. The possible merger of the CFTC and the Securities and Exchange Commission are among CME's concerns. Other details of possible regulatory measures are provided. **Availability:** Online.

9537 ■ *"Generation Y - An Opportunity for a Fresh Financial Start"* in (September 11, 2010, pp. 241)

Pub: VerticalNews

Description: Eleanor Blayney, the consumer advocate for the Certified Financial Planner Board of Standards, offers a financial strategy for Generation Y individuals starting their financial planning. The first segment of the non-profit's Lifelong Financial Strategies initiative is called 'Starting Out', and focuses on ways Generation Y people can avoid pitfalls of earlier generations by making smart financial decisions. **Availability:** Print; Online.

9538 ■ *"Get Off The Rollercoaster"* in Michigan Vue (Vol. 13, July-August 2008, No. 4, pp. 19)

Description: Benefits of creating and implementing a solid financial plan during these rocky economic times are examined. Things to keep in mind before meeting with a financial planner include risk assessment, investment goals, the length of time required to meet those goals and the amount of money one has available to invest. **Availability:** Print; Online.

9539 ■ *"Getting In on the Ground Floor With World-Class Companies"* in Barron's (Vol. 89, July 27, 2009, No. 30, pp. 32)

Ed: Jacqueline Doherty. **Description:** Shares of AvalonBay Communities have fallen 61 percent in the past two and a half years to July 2009 but at $56, the stock is trading near the asset value. The shares could rise as the economy improves and if the recovery takes longer, investors will be rewarded with a yield of 3.5 percent. **Availability:** Online.

9540 ■ *"Getting More Out of Retirement"* in Agency Sales Magazine (Vol. 39, November 2009, No. 10, pp. 48)

Description: Overview of the Tax Increase Prevention and Reconciliation Act, which lets employees convert to a Roth IRA in 2010. The benefits of conversion depend on age and wealth and it is best to consult a tax advisor to determine the best strategy for retirement planners. **Availability:** Print; Online.

9541 ■ *"Giant Garages Could Rise Up in Downtown Cincinnati"* in Business Courier (Vol. 27, October 22, 2010, No. 25, pp. 1)

Pub: Business Courier

Ed: Dan Monk. **Description:** More than 2,500 new parking spaces could rise up to the eastern edge of downtown Cincinnati, Ohio as public and private investors collect resources for new garage projects. These projects are expected to accommodate almost 1,500 monthly parkers who will lose access at Broadway Commons due to the construction of Harrah's casino. **Availability:** Print; Mailing list; Online.

9542 ■ *"A Gift From Interactive Brokers"* in Barron's (Vol. 92, July 23, 2012, No. 30, pp. M11)

Pub: Dow Jones & Company Inc.

Contact: Almar Latour, Chief Executive Officer

Ed: Steven M. Sears. **Description:** Investors are advised to sell put options of Interactive Brokers stock in anticipation of lower share prices. This trade is also a hedge against a possible takeover but allows investors to buy into a company that pays regular dividends and is managed well. **Availability:** Online.

9543 ■ *"Global Steel Makers Circle Stelco"* in Globe & Mail (April 19, 2007, pp. B3)

Ed: Greg Keenan. **Description:** The details of the take over bids offered to Stelco Inc. are presented. Due to these bids the shares of Stelco Inc rose up to 70 percent. **Availability:** Online.

9544 ■ *"Globus Plans First Phila.-Area Biotech IPO Since 2010"* in Philadelphia Business Journal (Vol. 28, April 20, 2012, No. 10, pp. 1)

Pub: Baltimore Business Journal

Contact: Rhonda Pringle, President

E-mail: rpringle@bizjournals.com

Description: Globus Medical has filed their plans with the SEC regarding an initial public stock offering. The medical device maker hopes to raise $100 million through the IPO. This will be the first IPO from a life science company in the Philadelphia region since 2010. **Availability:** Print; Online.

9545 ■ *"A Good Book Is Worth a Thousand Blogs"* in Barron's (Vol. 88, July 14, 2008, No. 28, pp. 42)

Pub: Dow Jones & Company Inc.

Contact: Almar Latour, Chief Executive Officer

Ed: Gene Epstein. **Description:** Nine summer book suggestions on economics are presented. The list includes 'The Revolution' by Ron Paul, 'The Forgotten Man' by Amity Shales, 'The Commitments of Traders Bible' by Stephen Briese, and 'Economic Facts and Fallacies' by Thomas Sowell. **Availability:** Online.

9546 ■ *"Good Going, Partners"* in Barron's (Vol. 89, July 27, 2009, No. 30, pp. M8)
Pub: Dow Jones & Company Inc.
Contact: Almar Latour, Chief Executive Officer

Ed: Shirley A. Lazo. **Description:** Four master limited partnerships boosted their dividends. Sunoco Logistics raised theirs by 11.2 percent, El Paso Pipeline by 12 percent, Holly Energy upped their dividends by a penny, and Western Gas hiked their dividend to 31 cents per unit. **Availability:** Online.

9547 ■ *"A Good Sign for Commercial Real Estate?"* in Austin Business JournalInc. (Vol. 29, December 18, 2009, No. 41, pp. 1)
Pub: Austin Business Journal
Contact: Rachel McGrath, Director
E-mail: rmcgrath@bizjournals.com

Ed: Kate Harrington. **Description:** Factors that could contribute to the reemergence of the commercial mortgage-backed securities market in Texas are discussed. These securities can potentially boost the commercial real estate market statewide as well as nationwide. Commercial mortgage-backed securities origination in 2009 is worth less that $1 billion, compared with $238 billion in 2008. **Availability:** Online.

9548 ■ *"A Good Step, But There's a Long Way to Go"* in Business Week (September 22, 2008, No. 4100, pp. 10)
Ed: James C. Cooper. **Description:** Despite the historic action by the U.S. government to nationalize the mortgage giants Freddie Mac and Fannie Mae, rising unemployment rates may prove to be an even bigger roadblock to bringing back the economy from its downward spiral. The takeover is meant to restore confidence in the credit markets and help with the mortgage crisis but the rising rate in unemployment may make many households unable to take advantage of any benefits which arise from the bailout. Statistical data included. **Availability:** Online.

9549 ■ *"Goodwill Haunts Local Companies"* in Crain's Chicago Business (Apr. 28, 2008)
Pub: Crain Communications Inc.
Contact: Barry Asin, President

Ed: Ann Saphir. **Description:** Many companies are having to face the reality that they overpaid for acquisitions made in better economic times; investors often dismiss such one-time charges as mere accounting adjustments but writeoffs related to past acquisitions can signal future problems because they mean the expected profits that justified the purchase have not materialized. Writeoffs are particularly worrisome for firms with a lot of debt and whose banks require them to have enough assets to back up their borrowings. **Availability:** Online.

9550 ■ *"Google's Next Stop: Below 350?"* in Barron's (Vol. 88, March 10, 2008, No. 10, pp. 17)
Pub: Dow Jones & Company Inc.
Contact: Almar Latour, Chief Executive Officer

Ed: Jacqueline Doherty. **Description:** Share prices of Google Inc. are expected to drop from their level of $433 each to below $350 per share. The company is expected to miss its earnings forecast for the first quarter of 2008, and its continued aggressive spending on non-core areas will eventually bring down earnings. **Availability:** Online.

9551 ■ *"Graduates to the TSX in 2008"* in Canadian Business (Vol. 81, Summer 2008, No. 9, pp. 79)
Description: Table showing the market capitalization and stock performance of the companies that jumped to the TSX Venture Exchange is presented. The 17

companies that made the leap to the list will have an easier time raising capital, although leeway must be made in investing since they are still new businesses.

9552 ■ *"Graphic Tech Acquires First U.S. :M-Press Tiger with Inline Screen Printing"* in American Printer (Vol. 128, June 1, 2011, No. 6)
Description: Graphic Tech located in California bought M-Press Tiger, the first in North America with an inline screen printing unit. **Availability:** Online.

9553 ■ *"The Great Fall of China"* in Canadian Business (Vol. 85, June 11, 2012, No. 10, pp. 26)
Ed: Michael McCullough. **Description:** China has a growing influence over the future of Canada's economy as emerging economies and commodity prices recover from the recession. Among the problems unique to China which could impact the Canadian economy are the housing market, its demographic risk and the lack of transparency in the corporate and financial sector. **Availability:** Online.

9554 ■ *"The Great Fall: Here Comes The Humpty Dumpty Economy"* in Barron's (Vol. 88, March 10, 2008, No. 10, pp. 5)
Pub: Dow Jones & Company Inc.
Contact: Almar Latour, Chief Executive Officer

Ed: Alan Abelson. **Description:** Discusses the US economy is considered to be in a recession, with the effects of the credit crisis expected to intensify as a result. Inflation is estimated at 4.3 percent in January 2008, while 63,000 jobs were lost in February 2008. **Availability:** Online.

9555 ■ *"The Great Moderation"* in Canadian Business (Vol. 80, February 12, 2007, No. 4, pp. 25)
Description: Caution over the changes to stock inventory levels and their adverse impact on the Canadian economy is discussed. **Availability:** Online.

9556 ■ *"The Green Trap"* in Canadian Business (Vol. 80, April 9, 2007, No. 8, pp. 19)
Description: Expert advice to companies on investing in environmental-friendly measures is presented. **Availability:** Online.

9557 ■ *"Greener Pastures"* in Canadian Business (Vol. 80, February 12, 2007, No. 4, pp. 69)
Description: The effort of venture capitalists, including chief executive officer of Fun Technologies Lorne Abony, in successful running of several ventures in diverse fields is discussed. **Availability:** Print; Online.

9558 ■ *"A Greenish Light for Financial-Sector Funds"* in Barron's (Vol. 88, March 24, 2008, No. 12, pp. 52)
Pub: Dow Jones & Company Inc.
Contact: Almar Latour, Chief Executive Officer

Ed: Tom Sullivan. **Description:** Financial sector funds have lost value in 2008 through 17 March, and investors are advised to reduce investments in the financial sector. Exchange-traded funds present a good way to own financial stocks. **Availability:** Online.

9559 ■ *"A Gripping Read: Bargains & Noble"* in Barron's (Vol. 88, March 17, 2008, No. 11, pp. 20)
Pub: Dow Jones & Company Inc.
Contact: Almar Latour, Chief Executive Officer

Ed: Jonathan R. Laing. **Description:** Barnes & Noble's earnings forecast for the fiscal year ending in January, 2008 to be $1.70 to $1.90 per share which is way lower than the $2.12 analyst consensus. The company also said that sales at stores one-year old or older dropped 0.5 percent in the fourth quarter. However, the shares are now cheap at 4.9 times enterprise value with some analysts putting a price target of 41 per share. **Availability:** Online.

9560 ■ *"Growth Back on CIBC's Agenda"* in Globe & Mail (March 3, 2006, pp. B1)
Ed: Sinclair Stewart. **Description:** The details on business growth of Canadian Imperial Bank of Commerce, which posted $547 million profit for first quarter 2006, are presented. **Availability:** Online.

9561 ■ *"Hain Celestial Acquires Greek Gods Yogurt"* in Ice Cream Reporter (Vol. 23, July 20, 2010, No. 8, pp. 1)
Description: Hain Celestial Group acquired The Greek Gods LLC. Hain Celestial is a natural and organic products company and Greek Gods makes all natural, Greek-style yogurt and ice cream. **Availability:** Print; Online.

9562 ■ *"Half Empty or Half Full"* in Crain's Chicago Business (Vol. 31, March 24, 2008, No. 12, pp. 4)
Pub: Crain Communications Inc.
Contact: Barry Asin, President

Ed: Meghan Streit. **Description:** Lifeway Foods Inc., the health food company which manufactures a yogurt-like drink called kefir, is being negatively affected by the soaring price of milk; however, the fact that probiotics are picking up in the market may mean that Lifeway stands a good chance of bouncing back and the company's lower share price could be an opportunity for long-term investors who have a tolerance for risk. **Availability:** Online.

9563 ■ *"Handleman Liquidation Leaves Questions For Shareholders"* in Crain's Detroit Business (Vol. 24, October 6, 2008, No. 40, pp. 4)
Pub: Crain Communications Inc.
Contact: Barry Asin, President

Ed: Nancy Kaffer. **Description:** Discusses Handleman Co., a Troy-based music distribution company, and their plan of liquidation and dissolution as well as how shareholders will be affected by the company's plan. Handleman filed its plan to liquidate and dissolve assets with the Securities and Exchange Commission in mid-August, following several quarters of dismal earnings. **Availability:** Online.

9564 ■ *"The Hard Thing About Hard Things: Building a Business When There Are No Easy Answers"*
Pub: HarperCollins Publishers L.L.C.
Contact: Brian Murray, President

Released: 2014. **Price:** $29.99, Hardcover; $14.99, E-book; $23.99, Digital Audiobook Unabridged. **Description:** Cofounder of Andreessen Horowitz and well-respected Silicon Valley entrepreneur, offers advice for building and running a startup small business. Horowitz analyzes issues confronting leaders daily and shares insights he gained from managing, selling, buying investing in, and supervising technology firms. **Availability:** E-book; Print; Download.

9565 ■ *"Harleysville Eyes Growth After Nationwide Deal"* in Philadelphia Business Journal (Vol. 30, October 7, 2011, No. 34, pp. 1)
Pub: Philadelphia Business Journal
Contact: Sierra Quinn, Director
E-mail: squinn@bizjournals.com

Ed: Jeff Blumenthal. **Price:** $4, introductory 4-week offer(Digital & Print). **Description:** Harleysville Group announced growth plans after the company was sold to Columbus, Ohio-based Nationwide Mutual Insurance Company for about $1.63 billion. Nationwide gained an independent agency platform in 32 states with the Harleysville deal. **Availability:** Print; Online.

9566 ■ *"Has Microsoft Found a Way to Get at Yahoo?"* in Advertising Age (Vol. 79, July 7, 2008, No. 26, pp. 4)
Pub: Crain Communications, Inc.
Contact: Jessica Botos, Manager, Marketing
E-mail: jessica.botos@crainsnewyork.com

Ed: Abbey Klaassen. **Description:** Microsoft's attempt to acquire Yahoo's search business is discussed as is Yahoo's plans for the future at a time when the company's shares have fallen dangerously low. **Availability:** Print; Online.

9567 ■ *"Headwinds From the New Sod Slow Aer Lingus" in Barron's (Vol. 88, March 10, 2008, No. 10, pp. M6)*
Pub: Dow Jones & Company Inc.
Contact: Almar Latour, Chief Executive Officer
Ed: Sean Walters, Arindam Nag. **Description:** Aer Lingus faces a drop in its share prices with a falling US market, higher jet fuel prices, and lower long-haul passenger load factors. British media companies Johnston Press and Yell Group are suffering from weaker ad revenue and heavier debt payments due to the credit crunch. **Availability:** Online.

9568 ■ *"The Heat Is On" in Crain's Chicago Business (Vol. 31, April 28, 2008, No. 17, pp. 4)*
Pub: Crain Communications Inc.
Contact: Barry Asin, President
Ed: Steve Daniels. **Description:** Discusses Nicor Inc., a natural-gas utility serving 2 million customers in Chicago's suburbs, and its potential acquirers; shares of the company have dropped 17 percent this year making Nicor the second-worst among 31 utilities in an index tracked by Standrd & Poor's. Statistical data included.

9569 ■ *"Hedge Funds for the Average Joe" in Canadian Business (Vol. 85, August 13, 2012, No. 13, pp. 51)*
Ed: Bryan Borzykowski. **Description:** The benefits of the Horizons Morningstar Hedge Fund Index ETF over traditional hedge funds are examined. Retail investors should avoid buying hedge fund exchange-traded funds (ETFs) because they are not actually buying into a hedge fund, the fund is just trying to emulate strategies that popular hedge funds use with derivatives. **Availability:** Print; Online.

9570 ■ *"Hedge Funds Prevail In Merger" in Baltimore Business Journal (Vol. 31, March 21, 2014, No. 47, pp. 8)*
Pub: American City Business Journals, Inc.
Contact: Mike Olivieri, Executive Vice President
Released: Weekly. **Price:** $4, introductory 4-week offer(Digital & Print). **Description:** Contrary to expectations of the retail experts, after five months of internal strife, Jos. A Bank accepted Men's Wearhouse's offer and closed this hot deal. Men's Wearhouse purchased the Jos. A. Bank Clothiers Inc. for $1.8 billion and is planning to continue both brands. However, this will result in the Greater Baltimore area losing one more corporate headquarters. As the two companies combine operations, Jos. A. Banks stores will close, thus cutting more jobs. **Availability:** Print; Online.

9571 ■ *"Her Aim Is True" in Senior Market Advisor (Vol. 13, October 2012, No. 10, pp. 40)*
Description: Profile of Rebecca True, president of True Capital Advisors, discusses her approach to broad marketing plans for her company. True emphasizes on building relationships with women business owners and executives. **Availability:** Print; Online.

9572 ■ *"H.I.G. Capital Announces Acquisition of Next Generation Vending" in Benzinga.com (October 29, 2011)*
Pub: Benzinga.com
Contact: Jason Raznick, Founder
Description: H.I.G. Capital LLC, a leader in global private investments, acquired Next Generation Vending and Food Service Inc. Next Generation is a provider of vending services for corporate and institutional clients in Northeastern United States. **Availability:** Print; PDF; Online.

9573 ■ *"High-Yield Turns Into Road Kill" in Barron's (Vol. 88, July 7, 2008, No. 27, pp. M7)*
Pub: Dow Jones & Company Inc.
Contact: Almar Latour, Chief Executive Officer

Ed: Emily Barrett. **Description:** High-yield bonds have returned to the brink of collapse after profits have recovered from the shock brought about by the collapse of Bear Stearns. The high-yield bond market could decline again due to weakness in the automotive sector, particularly in Ford and General Motors. **Availability:** Online.

9574 ■ *"Higher Freight Rates Keep CPR Rolling in Profit" in Globe & Mail (February 1, 2006, pp. B3)*
Description: Canadian Pacific Railway Ltd. posted $135.4 million in revenues for fourth quarter 2005. The company's earnings projections for 2006 and workforce reduction plans are presented. **Availability:** Print; Online.

9575 ■ *"Higher Payouts Should Be In the Cards" in Barron's (Vol. 92, July 23, 2012, No. 30, pp. 14)*
Pub: Dow Jones & Company Inc.
Contact: Almar Latour, Chief Executive Officer
Ed: Michael Santoli. **Description:** Credit card companies Visa and MasterCard should be more generous to shareholders and pay higher dividends. Both have low dividend yields, with Visa paying $0.88/share a year and MasterCard paying $1.20/share annually. **Availability:** Online.

9576 ■ *"A History of Neglect: Health Care for Blacks and Mill Workers in the Twentieth-Century South" in Canadian Business (Vol. 79, September 11, 2006, No. 18, pp. 21)*
Description: Faulty practices being followed by auditors and regulators of Canada are discussed. The need for appropriate steps to protect investors against these frauds are emphasized. **Availability:** PDF.

9577 ■ *"Hitting Bottom? Several Banks and Brokerages Are Ready to Pop Up for Air" in Barron's (Vol. 88, March 24, 2008, No. 12, pp. 21)*
Pub: Dow Jones & Company Inc.
Contact: Almar Latour, Chief Executive Officer
Ed: Jacqueline Doherty. **Description:** Brokerage houses and banks may stabilize in 2008 as a result of regulatory responses brought about by the near-collapse of Bear Stearns. Some of their shares may rise by as much as 20 percent from 2008 to 2009. **Availability:** Online.

9578 ■ *"Homebuilders Continue to be Our Nemesis" in Contractor (Vol. 56, July 2009, No. 7, pp. 50)*
Ed: Robert P. Mader. **Description:** Homebuilders rank high on the greed scale along with Wall Street brokers. There is this one instance when a builder gave copies of another contractor's quotes that have just been blackened out and another instance when one builder let other bidders visit a site while the current mechanical contractor is working. **Availability:** Print; Online.

9579 ■ *"Hong Kong's Boom in IPOs" in Barron's (Vol. 89, July 13, 2009, No. 28, pp. M7)*
Pub: Dow Jones & Company Inc.
Contact: Almar Latour, Chief Executive Officer
Ed: Nick Lord. **Description:** Hong Kong's IPO (initial public offering) market is booming with 13 Chinese IPOs already on the market for the year as July 2009. One of them is Bawang International which raised $214 million after generating $9 billion in order which makes it 42 times oversubscribed. **Availability:** Online.

9580 ■ *"Hope Grows for a Muscular Dystrophy Drug" in Barron's (Vol. 92, August 25, 2012, No. 35, pp. 35)*
Pub: Dow Jones & Company Inc.
Contact: Almar Latour, Chief Executive Officer
Ed: Andrew Bary. **Description:** The stocks of biotechnology firm Sarepta Therapeutics could gain value if trials for eterpirsen, a drug being developed for Duch-

enne muscular dystrophy, are successful. The company's stock prices could rise from $10/share to as high as $26/share. **Availability:** Online.

9581 ■ *"Hospital Revenue Healthier in 2009" in Orlando Business Journal (Vol. 26, February 5, 2010, No. 36, pp. 1)*
Pub: Orlando Business Journal
Contact: Julie Swyers, Director
E-mail: jswyers@bizjournals.com
Ed: Melanie Stawicki Azam. **Description:** Orlando Health, Health Central and Adventist Health System are Florida-based hospital systems that generated the most profits in 2009. Orlando Health had the highest profit in 2009 at $73.3 million, contrary to about $31 million in losses in 2008. The increased profits are attributed to stock market recovery, cost-cutting initiatives, and rising patient volumes. **Availability:** Print; Online.

9582 ■ *"Hotel Confidential" in Canadian Business (Vol. 80, Winter 2007, No. 24, pp. 91)*
Description: Celebrities such as Jason Priestley, Clint Eastwood, and Francis Ford Coppola have made investment in the hospitality industry. Investing in the hospitality industry has proved to be an excellent long-term investment and the venture also has a vanity aspect to it. **Availability:** Online.

9583 ■ *"How to Avoid the Most Common and Costliest Mistakes in Retirement Portfolio Investing" in Barron's (Vol. 88, March 10, 2008, No. 10, pp. 30)*
Pub: Dow Jones & Company Inc.
Contact: Almar Latour, Chief Executive Officer
Ed: Karen Hube. **Description:** Investors, particularly those having retirement investments, are advised to diversify their investments, refrain from market timing, and minimize payments to maximize investment gains. An investor committing these mistakes could lose as much as $375,000 dollars over ten years. **Availability:** Online.

9584 ■ *"How to Beat the Pros" in Canadian Business (Vol. 81, Summer 2008, No. 9, pp. 59)*
Description: Table showing the results of the Investor 500 beat the S&P/TSX composite index is presented. The average total return, best performing stocks and total return of the 2007 stock screen are provided. **Availability:** Online.

9585 ■ *"How CoolBrands' Thrills Turned to Chills" in Globe & Mail (January 25, 2007, pp. B1)*
Ed: Keith McArthur. **Description:** The key reasons behind the sudden share price fall of ice cream giant CoolBrands International Inc. are discussed. **Availability:** Print; Online.

9586 ■ *"How to Deal" in Canadian Business (Vol. 81, November 10, 2008, No. 19, pp. 36)*
Description: The Great Depression, Japan's Lost Decade, and the Swedish Banking Crisis is compared to the 2008 financial crisis in the U.S. The chances for recession in the U.S. are discussed along with investment strategies to survive.

9587 ■ *"How Foreigners Could Disrupt U.S. Markets" in Barron's (Vol. 90, September 13, 2010, No. 37, pp. 30)*
Pub: Barron's Editorial & Corporate Headquarters
Ed: Jim McTague. **Description:** An informal meeting by the House Homeland Security Panel concluded that U.S. stock exchanges and related trading routes can be the subject of attacks from rogue overseas traders. A drop in funding for the U.S. Department of Defense is discussed. **Availability:** Online.

9588 ■ *"How High Can Soybeans Fly?" in Barron's (Vol. 88, March 10, 2008, No. 10, pp. M14)*
Pub: Dow Jones & Company Inc.
Contact: Almar Latour, Chief Executive Officer

Ed: Kenneth Rapoza. **Description:** Prices of soybeans have risen to $14.0875 a bushel, up 8.3 percent for the week. Increased demand, such as in China and in other developing economies, and the investment-driven commodities boom are boosting prices. **Availability:** Online.

9589 ■ *"How I Became a Serial Entrepreneur"* **in Baltimore Business Journal (Vol. 31, April 18, 2014, No. 51, pp. 26)**
Pub: American City Business Journals, Inc.
Contact: Mike Olivieri, Executive Vice President
Description: Dr. Lisa Beth Ferstenberg, a physician by training, teaches a course at the Maryland Center for Entrepreneurship in Columbia to help CEOs attract prospective investors. Dr. Ferstenberg is also the chief medical officer at Sequella Inc. She reflects on the kind of personality required to become a successful entrepreneur and the mistakes entrepreneurs make in raising capital funding. **Availability:** Print; Online.

9590 ■ *"How Investors React When Women Join Boards"* **in Harvard Business Review (Vol. 88, July-August 2010, No. 7-8, pp. 24)**
Pub: Harvard Business Publishing
Contact: Diane Belcher, Managing Director
Ed: Andrew O'Connell. **Price:** $6, PDF. **Description:** Research reveals a cognitive bias in blockholders regarding the presence of women on boards of directors despite evidence showing that diversity improves results. **Availability:** Online; PDF.

9591 ■ *"How to Maximize Your Investment Income"* **in Contractor (Vol. 56, December 2009, No. 12, pp. 33)**
Ed: Irving L. Blackman. **Description:** Private placement life insurance (PPLI) can minimize taxes and protect assets. PPLI is a form of variable universal insurance that is offered privately. Risk of insurance company illiquidity is avoided as investments are placed in separate accounts. **Availability:** Online.

9592 ■ *"How Not to Raise Bank Capital"* **in Barron's (Vol. 88, June 30, 2008, No. 26, pp. M6)**
Pub: Dow Jones & Company Inc.
Contact: Almar Latour, Chief Executive Officer
Ed: Sean Walters. **Description:** French bank Natixis wants to raise 1 billion euros from cash provided by their two major owners. Natixis will reimburse Banque Populaire and Caisses d'Epargne with hybrid securities so this move will not benefit Natixis' core Tier 1 ratio. This has also given the impression that the company is afraid of a full rights issue which could shake investors' faith in the bank. **Availability:** Online.

9593 ■ *"How Our Picks Beat The Bear"* **in Barron's (Vol. 88, July 14, 2008, No. 28, pp. 18)**
Pub: Dow Jones & Company Inc.
Contact: Almar Latour, Chief Executive Officer
Ed: Andrew Bary. **Description:** Performance of the stocks that Barron's covered in the first half of 2008 is discussed; some of the worst picks and most rewarding pans have been in the financial sector while the best plays were in the energy, materials, and the transportation sectors. **Availability:** Online.

9594 ■ *"How to Play the Tech Mergers"* **in Barron's (Vol. 90, August 30, 2010, No. 35, pp. 18)**
Pub: Barron's Editorial & Corporate Headquarters
Ed: Tiernan Ray. **Description:** The intense bidding by Hewlett-Packard and Dell for 3Par was foreseen in a previous Barron's cover story and 3Par's stock has nearly tripled since reported. Other possible acquisition targets in the tech industry include Brocade Communication Systems, NetApp, Xyratex, and Isilon Systems. **Availability:** Online.

9595 ■ *"How to Prevent Fear, Uncertainty and Doubt from Derailing Your Retirement Plan"* **in Minority Business Entrepreneur (Vol. 39, Fall, 2022, No. 4, pp. 36-37)**
URL(s): digital.mbemag.com/?m=53732&i=769780&p=36&ver=html5

Ed: Barry H. Spencer. **Price:** $7.95. **Description:** Gives advice on reducing fear when investing in your retirement so you can make the best choices for your goals. **Availability:** Print; Online.

9596 ■ *"How to Retire: Do's and Don'ts"* **in Canadian Business (Vol. 79, July 17, 2006, No. 14-15, pp. 29)**
Pub: Rogers Media Inc.
Contact: Neil Spivak, Chief Executive Officer
Ed: Andy Holloway, Erin Pooley, Thomas Watson. **Description:** Strategic tips for planning systematic investments, in order to make life more enjoyable after retirement, are elucidated. **Availability:** Print; Online.

9597 ■ *"How Sweet It Will Be"* **in Barron's (Vol. 89, July 13, 2009, No. 28, pp. M13)**
Pub: Dow Jones & Company Inc.
Contact: Almar Latour, Chief Executive Officer
Ed: Debbie Carlson. **Description:** Raw sugar experienced a rally in the first half of 2009 and the long term outlook for sugar prices is still good. However, there is a likely near-term correction due to the onset of Brazilian harvest that could be 20.7 percent higher for 2009 as compared to the previous year and October contracts could fall to 15.61 cents per pound. **Availability:** Online.

9598 ■ *"How To Win the Fed's New Game"* **in Barron's (Vol. 92, September 17, 2012, No. 38, pp. M10)**
Description: Options trading strategies designed to take advantage of the US Federal Reserve's third quantitative easing program are discussed. Options traders are advised to invest in short-term options to maximize gains. **Availability:** Print; Online.

9599 ■ *"I'll Have What She's Having"* **in Canadian Business (Vol. 85, September 17, 2012, No. 14, pp. 17)**
Ed: Andrew Hallam. **Description:** Studies show that women have the higher tendency to follow responsible investing rules than men, earning more money in the process. Women were also found to perform better in bull markets as well as in the male-dominated hedge fund sector. **Availability:** Online.

9600 ■ *"Ill Winds; Cuba's Economy"* **in The Economist (Vol. 390, January 3, 2009, No. 8612, pp. 20)**
Description: Cuba's long-term economic prospects remain poor with the economy forecasted to grow only 4.3 percent for the year, about half of the original forecast, due in part to Hurricane Gustav which caused $10 billion in damage and disrupted the food-supply network and devastated farms across the region; President Raul Castro made raising agricultural production a national priority and the rise in global commodity prices hit the country hard. The only bright spot has been the rise in tourism which is up 9.3 percent over 2007. **Availability:** Online.

9601 ■ *"The Impact of Acquisitions On the Productivity of Inventors at Semiconductor Firms: A Synthesis of Knowledge-Based and Incentive-Based Perspective"* **in Academy of Management Journal (Vol. 50, No. 5, October 1, 2007, pp. 1133)**
Pub: Academy of Management
Contact: Sharon Alvarez, President
Ed: Rahul Kapoor, Kwanghui Lim. **Description:** Study examined the relation between knowledge-based and incentive-based outlook in explaining the impact of acquisitions on the productivity of inventors at acquired semiconductor firms. Results showed a definite relation between the two perspectives. **Availability:** Electronic publishing; Download; PDF; Online.

9602 ■ *"Imports Frothing Up Beer Market"* **in Globe & Mail (February 16, 2006, pp. B4)**
Ed: Andy Hoffman. **Description:** The reasons behind the rise in market share of beer imports, in Canada, are presented. **Availability:** Online.

9603 ■ *"In China, Railways to Riches"* **in Barron's (Vol. 88, July 7, 2008, No. 27, pp. M9)**
Pub: Dow Jones & Company Inc.
Contact: Almar Latour, Chief Executive Officer
Ed: Assif Shameen. **Description:** Shares of Chinese railway companies look to benefit from multimillion-dollar investments aimed at upgrading the Chinese railway network. Investment in the sector is expected to reach $210 billion for the 2006-2010 period. **Availability:** Online.

9604 ■ *"In the Hot Finance Jobs, Women Are Still Shut Out"* **in Harvard Business Review (Vol. 90, July-August 2012, No. 7-8, pp. 30)**
Pub: Harvard Business Review Press
Contact: Moderna V. Pfizer, Contact
Ed: Nori Gerardo Lietz. **Price:** $6, PDF and hardcover black and white. **Description:** Although women constitute a significant proportion of business school graduates, the percentage of senior investment professionals who are female remain in a single-digit figure. Active effort will be needed to change corporate culture and industry awareness to raise this figure. **Availability:** Print; PDF; Online.

9605 ■ *"In India, A Gold-Price Threat?"* **in Barron's (Vol. 88, June 30, 2008, No. 26, pp. M12)**
Pub: Dow Jones & Company Inc.
Contact: Almar Latour, Chief Executive Officer
Ed: Melanie Burton. **Description:** Gold purchases in India are falling as record prices take its toll on demand. Gold imports to India fell by 52 percent in May 2008 from the previous year and local prices are higher by one-third from the previous year to 12,540 rupees for 10 grams. **Availability:** Online.

9606 ■ *"In the Options Market, Financial-Sector Trading Is Moody and Paranoid"* **in Barron's (Vol. 88, March 10, 2008, No. 10, pp. M14)**
Pub: Dow Jones & Company Inc.
Contact: Almar Latour, Chief Executive Officer
Ed: Steven M. Sears. **Description:** Discusses the options market which remains liquid but is cautious of possible failures, especially for financial companies. Investors are in absolute fear when trading with options involving the financial sector. **Availability:** Online.

9607 ■ *"In Praise of How Not to Invest"* **in Barron's (Vol. 89, July 13, 2009, No. 28, pp. 11)**
Pub: Dow Jones & Company Inc.
Contact: Almar Latour, Chief Executive Officer
Ed: Vito J. Racanelli. **Description:** One research study found that the shares of companies that have growing market shares and expanding asset bases underperform. This is contrary to the widely held premise that stock prices for these companies rise. It is argued that this result is caused by these companies' tendency to sacrifice profitability to grab market share and this is reflected in their stock prices. **Availability:** Online.

9608 ■ *"In Surging Oil Industry, Good Fortune Comes In Stages"* **in Barron's (Vol. 88, July 7, 2008, No. 27, pp. 12)**
Pub: Dow Jones & Company Inc.
Contact: Almar Latour, Chief Executive Officer
Ed: Sandra Ward. **Description:** Shares of US land oil and gas driller Helmerich and Payne, priced at $69 each, are estimated to be at peak levels. The shares are trading at 17 times 2008 earnings and could be in for some profit taking. **Availability:** Online.

9609 ■ *"In the Wake of Pet-Food Crisis, Iams Sales Plummet Nearly 17 Percent"* **in Advertising Age (Vol. 78, May 14, 2007, No. 18, pp. 3)**
Pub: Crain Communications, Inc.
Contact: Jessica Botos, Manager, Marketing
E-mail: jessica.botos@crainsnewyork.com

Ed: Jack Neff. **Description:** Although the massive U.S. pet-food recall impacted more than 100 brands, Procter & Gamble Co.'s Iams lost more sales and market share than any other industry player. According to Information Resources Inc. data, the brand's sales dropped 16.5 percent in the eight-week period ended April 22. Many analysts feel that the company could have handled the crisis in a better manner. **Availability:** Online.

9610 ■ "The Incentive Bubble: Outsourcing Pay Decisions To Financial Markets Has Skewed Compensation and, With It, American Capitalism" in Harvard Business Review (Vol. 90, March 2012, No. 3, pp. 124)
Pub: Harvard Business Review Press
Contact: Moderna V. Pfizer, Contact

Ed: Mihir A. Desai. **Price:** $8.95. **Description:** Basing incentive contracts and executive compensation on financial markets actually rewards luck rather than performance, and can promote dangerous risk taking. This has led to America's two main crises of capitalism: growing income inequality and governance failures. Boards of directors must focus on performance rather than stocks, and endowments and foundations must focus on incentives for long-term growth. **Availability:** Online; PDF.

9611 ■ "Inland Snaps Up Rival REITs" in Crain's Chicago Business (Vol. 31, November 17, 2008, No. 46, pp. 3)
Pub: Crain Communications Inc.
Contact: Barry Asin, President

Ed: Alby Gallun. **Description:** Discusses Inland American Real Estate Trust Inc., a real estate investment trust that is napping up depressed shares of publicly traded competitors, a possible first step toward taking over these companies; however, with hotel and retail properties accounting for approximately 70 percent of its portfolio, the company could soon face its own difficulties. **Availability:** Online.

9612 ■ "Inmet Selling Nunavut Mining Properties" in Globe & Mail (February 15, 2006, pp. B6)
Ed: Allan Robinson. **Description:** The details on Wolfden Resources Inc.'s acquisition of mining assets of Inmet Mining Corp. are presented. **Availability:** Online.

9613 ■ "Insurance Roars Back Into Style" in Barron's (Vol. 92, September 17, 2012, No. 38, pp. 11)
Description: The US Federal Reserve's decision to implement a mortgage-buying policy is seen by the stock market as an insurance policy. The Federal Reserve will buy mortgage-backed securities worth $40 billion each month, a move which could bolster stock prices. **Availability:** Online.

9614 ■ "International ETFs: Your Passport to the World" in Barron's (Vol. 89, July 13, 2009, No. 28, pp. L10)
Pub: Dow Jones & Company Inc.
Contact: Almar Latour, Chief Executive Officer

Ed: John Hintze. **Description:** International exchange traded funds give investors more choices in terms of investment plays and there are 174 U.S. ETF listings worth $141 billion as of July 2009. Suggestions on how to invest in these funds based on one's conviction on how the global economy will unfold are presented. **Availability:** Online.

9615 ■ "Invest Like Harvard" in Barron's (Vol. 92, September 15, 2012, No. 38, pp. 32)
Pub: Dow Jones & Company Inc.
Contact: Almar Latour, Chief Executive Officer

Ed: Andrew Bary. **Description:** Asset management firms are offering endowment-style investment services that allow investors to invest in funds in the same way as foundations and endowments. High-Vista Strategies with $3.6 billion in assets under management, has produced a total return of 43.5 percent after fees from October 2005 to June 2012 using this strategy. **Availability:** Online.

9616 ■ Investing in Cryptocurrency for Dummies
Pub: John Wiley & Sons, Inc.
Contact: Christina Van Tassell, Executive Vice President Chief Financial Officer

Ed: Kiana Danial. **Released:** August 2023. **Price:** $18.99, paperback. **Description:** A guide on how to invest in cryptocurrency. **Availability:** Print.

9617 ■ Investment Adviser Association-Directory of Member Firms
Pub: Investment Adviser Association
Contact: Karen L. Barr, President
E-mail: karen.barr@investmentadviser.org
URL(s): www.investmentadviser.org/membership/
directory-of-member-firms/#/qbeld/Member%
20Directory

Description: Covers over 300 member investment counseling firms. **Entries include:** Name and address of firm; contact, number of clients, assets under management, staff, type of account, minimum account and fee. **Availability:** Online.

9618 ■ "Investment Bank Dinan & Company Launches ConfidentCrowd Exclusive Crowdfunding Portal for FINRA Broker-Dealers" in Investment Weekly (June 9, 2012, pp. 458)
Description: ConfidentCrowd is a newly developed portal created by Dinan & Company to provide exclusive use of FINRA-registered broker-dealers to participate as members in order to screen firms seeking funding. This process will eleviate risk in equity-based crowdfunding. **Availability:** Online.

9619 ■ "Investment Bank Predicts Shakeup in Farm Equipment Industry" in Farm Industry News (November 16, 2011)
Pub: Informa Business Media, Inc.
Contact: Charlie McCurdy, President

Ed: Jodie Wehrspann. **Description:** Farming can expect to see more mergers and acquisitions in the agricultural equipment industry, as it appears to be in the early stages of growth over the next few years. **Availability:** Online.

9620 ■ "Investment Banks" in Black Enterprise (Vol. 44, June 2014, No. 10, pp. 88)
Pub: Earl G. Graves Ltd.
Contact: Earl Graves, Jr., President

Description: A ranking of the top 100 investment banks in the U.S. are presented.

9621 ■ "Investment Firms Unite: Coalition Fights New Tax Law" in Black Enterprise (Vol. 38, December 2007, No. 5, pp. 52)
Description: Minorities working in private equity, real estate and investment management firms have united to form the Access to Capital Coalition to oppose legislation that they feel would adversely affect their ability to attract investments and executives. Details of the group are included. **Availability:** Print; Online.

9622 ■ "Investment Funds: Friends with Money" in Canadian Business (Vol. 81, May 22, 2008, No. 9, pp. 22)
Pub: Rogers Media Inc.
Contact: Neil Spivak, Chief Executive Officer

Ed: Jeff Stanford. **Description:** Two of the most well connected managers in Canadian capital markets Rob Farquharson and Brian Gibson will launch Panoply Capital Asset Management in June. The investment management company aims to raise a billion dollars from institutions and high-net worth individuals. **Availability:** Print; Online.

9623 ■ "Is Fannie Mae the Next Government Bailout?" in Barron's (Vol. 88, March 10, 2008, No. 10, pp. 21)
Pub: Dow Jones & Company Inc.
Contact: Almar Latour, Chief Executive Officer

Ed: Jonathan R. Laing. **Description:** Fannie Mae may need a government bailout as it faces huge hits brought about by the effects of the housing crisis. The shares of the government-sponsored enterprise have dropped 65 percent since the housing crisis began. **Availability:** Online.

9624 ■ "Is the VIX in Denial?" in Barron's (Vol. 88, July 7, 2008, No. 27, pp. M12)
Pub: Dow Jones & Company Inc.
Contact: Almar Latour, Chief Executive Officer

Ed: Lawrence McMillan. **Description:** Volatility Index (VIX) of the Chicago Board Options Exchange did not rise significantly despite the drop in the US stock markets, rising to near 25. This market decline, however, will eventually result in investor panic and the rise of the VIX. **Availability:** Online.

9625 ■ "It Could Be Worse" in Barron's (Vol. 89, July 27, 2009, No. 30, pp. 5)
Pub: Dow Jones & Company Inc.
Contact: Almar Latour, Chief Executive Officer

Ed: Alan Abelson. **Description:** Media sources are being fooled by corporate America who is peddling an economic recovery rather than reality as shown by the report of a rise in existing home sales which boosted the stock market even if it was a seasonal phenomenon. The phrase "things could be worse" sums up the reigning investment philosophy in the U.S. and this has been stirring up the market. **Availability:** Online.

9626 ■ "Ivernia Mine Closing Could Boost Lead" in Globe & Mail (April 4, 2007, pp. B5)
Ed: Andy Hoffman. **Description:** The closing of Ivernia Inc.'s mine in view of government investigation into alleged lead contamination at the port of Esperance is discussed. The likely increase in the price of lead is also discussed. **Availability:** Print; Online.

9627 ■ "Jamieson Eyes $175 Million Trust IPO" in Globe & Mail (March 7, 2006, pp. B1)
Ed: Sinclair Stewart, Leonard Zehr. **Description:** The reasons behind $175 million initial public offering plans of Jamieson Laboratories Ltd. are presented. **Availability:** Print; Online.

9628 ■ "J.C. Penney Head Shops for Shares" in Barron's (Vol. 88, July 7, 2008, No. 27, pp. 29)
Pub: Dow Jones & Company Inc.
Contact: Almar Latour, Chief Executive Officer

Ed: Teresa Rivas. **Description:** Myron Ullman III, chairman and chief executive officer of J.C. Penney, purchased $1 million worth of shares of the company. He now owns 393,140 shares of the company and an additional 1,282 on his 401(k) plan. **Availability:** Online.

9629 ■ "Jet Sales Put Bombardier Back in Black" in Globe & Mail (March 30, 2006, pp. B1)
Ed: Bertrand Marotte. **Description:** The details on Bombardier Inc., which posted 20 percent rise in shares following $86 million profit for fourth quarter 2005, are presented. **Availability:** Online.

9630 ■ "Jim Cramer's Get Rich Carefully"
Pub: Penguin Publishing Group

Released: December 31, 2013 . **Price:** $17, paperback; $11.99, e-book; $20, audiobook download; $14.99. **Description:** Wall Street veteran and host of CNBC's Mad Money, Jim Cramer, provides a guide to high-yield, low-risk investing in a recovering economic market. **Availability:** audiobook; E-book; Print.

9631 ■ "Judge Gives RIM One Last Chance" in Globe & Mail (February 24, 2006, pp. B5)
Ed: Barrie McKenna, Paul Waldie. **Description:** United States District Court Judge James Spencer offers more time for Research In Motion Ltd. (RIM) to settle the patent infringement dispute with NTP Inc. RIM's shares increase by 6.2 percent following the decision. **Availability:** Online.

9632 ■ "Juiced on Energy" in Barron's (Vol. 88, July 14, 2008, No. 28, pp. 33)
Pub: Dow Jones & Company Inc.
Contact: Almar Latour, Chief Executive Officer

Ed: Leslie P. Norton. **Description:** Brad Evans and his team at Heartland Value Plus were able to outperform their peers by significantly under-committing to financials and overexposing themselves with energy stocks. Brad Evans believes that there is a lot of value left in energy stocks such as natural gas. **Availability:** Online.

9633 ■ *"Just Hang Up" in Barron's (Vol. 88, March 10, 2008, No. 10, pp. 45)*
Description: Sprint's shares are expected to continue falling while the company attempts to attract subscribers by cutting prices, cutting earnings in the process. The company faces tougher competition from better-financed AT&T and Verizon Communications.

9634 ■ *"Keeping the Faith in Fuel-Tech" in Barron's (Vol. 88, March 24, 2008, No. 12, pp. 20)*
Pub: Dow Jones & Company Inc.
Contact: Almar Latour, Chief Executive Officer
Ed: Christopher C. Williams. **Description:** Shares of air pollution control company Fuel-Tech remain on track to reach $40 each from their $19 level due to a continued influx of contracts. The stock has suffered from lower-than-expected quarterly earnings and tougher competition but stand to benefit from increased orders. **Availability:** Online.

9635 ■ *"Kineta Helps Grow Start Group of 5 Biotech Partners" in Puget Sound Business Journal (Vol. 35, June 13, 2014, No. 8, pp. 6)*
Pub: American City Business Journals, Inc.
Contact: Mike Olivieri, Executive Vice President
Description: Kineta Inc is seeking new funding through its KPI Therapeutics. Kineta offers investors a return on their investments after three to five years. KPI Therapeutics is a new collaborative initiative between drug development firms and private investors. KPI's vision is to create a better way to develop early- and mid-stage therapies for patients and will act as an investment group and a strategic research hub. **Availability:** Print; Online.

9636 ■ *"The Latin Beat Goes On" in Barron's (Vol. 88, July 7, 2008, No. 27, pp. L5)*
Pub: Dow Jones & Company Inc.
Contact: Almar Latour, Chief Executive Officer
Ed: Tom Sullivan. **Description:** Latin American stocks have outperformed other regional markets due to rising commodities prices and favorable economic climate. Countries such as Brazil, Mexico, Chile, and Peru provide investment opportunities, while Argentina and Venezuela are tougher places to invest. **Availability:** Online.

9637 ■ *"Leaders and Lagards" in Barron's (Vol. 89, July 13, 2009, No. 28, pp. 14)*
Description: Statistical table that shows the returns of different mutual funds in different categories that include U.S. stock funds, sector funds, world equity funds, and mixed equity funds is presented. The data presented is for the second quarter of 2009. **Availability:** Print; Online.

9638 ■ *"Legg Mason Compensation Committee Chair Defends CEO Fetting's Pay" in Baltimore Business Journal (Vol. 29, July 22, 2011, No. 11, pp. 1)*
Pub: Boston Business Journal
Contact: Carolyn M. Jones, President
E-mail: cmjones@bizjournals.com
Ed: Gary Haber. **Description:** Legg Mason Inc. CEO Mark R. Fetting has been awarded $5.9 million pay package and he expects to receive questions regarding it in the coming shareholders meeting. However, Baltimore, Maryland-based RKTL Associates chairman emeritus Harold R. Adams believes Fetting has done a tremendous job in bringing Legg's through a tough market. **Availability:** Print; Online.

9639 ■ *"Less Malaise in Malaysia" in Barron's (Vol. 88, March 17, 2008, No. 11, pp. M12)*
Pub: Dow Jones & Company Inc.
Contact: Almar Latour, Chief Executive Officer
Ed: Assif Shameen. **Description:** Shares of Malaysia's Bursa have been in freefall while the Malaysia government prolongs its pitch to sell a 10 percent stake of the exchange to NYSE Euronext. Asian bourses had produced very good returns for five years and charge some of the highest fees for

exchanges. A key growth driver for Asian bourses could be the derivatives markets and exchange-traded funds. **Availability:** Online.

9640 ■ *Let's Buy a Company: How to Accelerate Growth Through Acquisitions*
Description: Advice for negotiating terms and pricing as well as other aspects of mergers and acquisitions in small companies. **Availability:** Print.

9641 ■ *"Liberty Media Pushes to Close on Sirius XM While Cable Deals Wait" in Denver Business Journal (Vol. 65, February 28, 2014, No. 42)*
Pub: American City Business Journals, Inc.
Contact: Mike Olivieri, Executive Vice President
Released: Weekly. **Description:** Liberty Media Corporation CEO, Greg Maffei, notes that various cable TV mergers are on hold while everyone awaits the decision if Comcast and Time Warner will be allowed to go through with their $45.2 billion merger. Liberty Media had supported Charter Communications plans to buy Time Warner for cash and stock. That deal was pushed aside when Comcast came along with a larger, all-stock offer. **Availability:** Print; Online.

9642 ■ *"Listen Up: There's a Revolution in the Cubicle" in Barron's (Vol. 89, July 27, 2009, No. 30, pp. 18)*
Pub: Dow Jones & Company Inc.
Contact: Almar Latour, Chief Executive Officer
Ed: Jay Palmer. **Description:** Plantronics will be among the first beneficiaries when the unified communications revolution arrives in the office. Plantronics' shares could rise to around 30 in 2009 from the 20s as of July 2009. Unified communications could create a huge new multimillion-dollar market for Plantronics. **Availability:** Online.

9643 ■ *"The Little Biotech that Could" in Barron's (Vol. 89, July 27, 2009, No. 30, pp. 19)*
Pub: Dow Jones & Company Inc.
Contact: Almar Latour, Chief Executive Officer
Ed: Christopher C. Williams. **Description:** OSI Pharmaceuticals' shares is a compelling investment bet among small biotech firms due to its Tarceva anticancer drug which has a 23 percent market share as well as their strong balance sheet. OSI is planning to expand the use of Tarceva which could re-ignite sales and one analyst expects the shares to trade in the 40s one year from July 2009. **Availability:** Online.

9644 ■ *"Live & Learn: François Joly" in Canadian Business (Vol. 79, September 11, 2006, No. 18, pp. 146)*
Pub: Rogers Media Inc.
Contact: Neil Spivak, Chief Executive Officer
Ed: Andy Holloway. **Description:** President and chief operating officer of Desjardins Financial Security, Francois Joly speaks about his interests and emphasizes the need to be passionate about work. **Availability:** Online.

9645 ■ *"Local TV Hits Media Radar Screen" in Business Courier (Vol. 27, July 2, 2010, No. 9, pp. 1)*
Pub: Business Courier
Ed: Dan Monk. **Description:** Fort Wright, Kentucky-based broadcasting company Local TV LLC has acquired 18 television stations since its founding in 2007, potentially boosting its chances of becoming a media empire. In the last twelve months that ended in March 2010, Local TV LLC has posted total revenues of $415 million. How Local TV LLC has entered into cost-sharing deals with other stations is also discussed. **Availability:** Print; Online.

9646 ■ *"Long-Term Bull, Short-Term Bear" in Barron's (Vol. 92, September 17, 2012, No. 38, pp. 24)*
Description: Jason DeSena Trennert, managing partner at Strategas Research Partners, discusses his views on the financial markets and the US economy. He is bullish on the stocks of Merck, McDonalds, IBM and Oracle. **Availability:** Online.

9647 ■ *"Loonie Tunes: When Will the Dollar Rise Again?" in Canadian Business (Vol. 81, November 10, 2008, No. 19, pp. 62)*
Pub: Rogers Media Inc.
Contact: Neil Spivak, Chief Executive Officer
Ed: Joe Castaldo. **Description:** The Canadian dollar has weakened against the U.S. Dollar as the U.S. financial crisis rocked global markets. A currency strategist says that the strength of the U.S. dollar is not based on people's optimism on the U.S. economy but on a structural demand where U.S. non-financial corporations have been repatriating greenbacks from foreign subsidiaries. **Availability:** Print; Online.

9648 ■ *"Loonies Buy U.S. Cable" in Canadian Business (Vol. 85, September 17, 2012, No. 14, pp. 8)*
Ed: Jeff Beer. **Description:** The move by two Canadian companies to invest in the U.S. cable industry get mixed reactions from analyst and observers. Cogeco Cable purchased Atlantic Broadband for $1.36 billion while the Canada Pension Plan Investment Board announced its partnership with European private equity firm BC Partners to acquire Suddenlink Communications for $6.6 billion. **Availability:** Online.

9649 ■ *"Lotus Starts Slowly, Dodges Subprime Woes" in Crain's Detroit Business (Vol. 24, April 14, 2008, No. 15, pp. 3)*
Pub: Crain Communications Inc.
Contact: Barry Asin, President
Ed: Tom Henderson. **Description:** Discusses Lotus Bancorp Inc. and their business plan, which although is not right on target due to the subprime mortgage meltdown, is in a much better position than its competitors due to the quality of their loans. **Availability:** Online.

9650 ■ *"Lower Prices No Shoo-In as Telcos Near Deregulation" in Globe & Mail (March 28, 2007, pp. B1)*
Ed: Catherine McLean. **Description:** The fall in market share and low quality of service among other issues that may disallow telecommunication industries in Canada from setting their phone rates is discussed. **Availability:** Online.

9651 ■ *"Lundin Deal Leaves Nickel Market Thin" in Globe & Mail (April 5, 2007, pp. B4)*
Ed: Andy Hoffman. **Description:** The likely acquisition of Rio Narcea Gold Mines Ltd. by Lundin Mining Corp. and the decreasing number of nickel mining companies on the list of Toronto Stock Exchange are discussed. **Availability:** Online.

9652 ■ *"Lux Coffees, Breads Push Chains to React" In Advertising Age (Vol. 77, June 26, 2006, No. 26, pp. S14)*
Pub: Crain Communications, Inc.
Contact: Jessica Botos, Manager, Marketing
E-mail: jessica.botos@crainsnewyork.com
Ed: Kate MacArthur. **Description:** Fast-food giants such as McDonald's, Burger King, Dunkin' Donuts and Subway have adjusted their menus in order to become more competitive with gourmet coffee shops and bakeries like Panera Bread and Starbucks which have taken a large share in the market. Statistical data included. **Availability:** Online.

9653 ■ *"Magna Banks on Big Cash Hoard" in Globe & Mail (March 1, 2006, pp. B3)*
Ed: Greg Keenan. **Description:** The details on Magna International Inc., which posted decline in profits at $639 million for 2005, are presented. **Availability:** Online.

9654 ■ *"Making It Click: Annual Ranking Of the Best Online Brokers" in Barron's (Vol. 88, March 17, 2008, No. 11, pp. 31)*
Pub: Dow Jones & Company Inc.
Contact: Almar Latour, Chief Executive Officer
Ed: Theresa W. Carey. **Description:** Listing of 23 online brokers that are evaluated based on their trade experience, usability, range of offerings, research amenities, customer service and access, and costs. TradeStation Securities takes the top spot followed by thinkorswim by just a fraction. **Availability:** Online.

9655 ■ *"M&T On the March?" in Baltimore Business Journal (Vol. 28, November 12, 2010, No. 27, pp. 1)*
Pub: Baltimore Business Journal
Contact: Rhonda Pringle, President
E-mail: rpringle@bizjournals.com
Ed: Gary Haber. **Description:** Information on the growth of M&T Bank, as well as its expansion plans are presented. M&T recently acquired Wilmington Trust and took over $500 million in deposits from the failed K Bank. Analysts believe that M&T would continue its expansion through Washington DC and Richmond, Virginia, especially after a bank executive acknowledged that the markets in those areas are attractive. **Availability:** Print; Online.

9656 ■ *"Many Roads Lead to Value Says David J. Williams, Manager of Excelsior Value & Restructuring Fund" in Barron's (Vol. 88, March 10, 2008, No. 10, pp. 46)*
Pub: Dow Jones & Company Inc.
Contact: Almar Latour, Chief Executive Officer
Ed: Lawrence C. Strauss. **Description:** David J. Williams, lead manager of Excelsior Value & Restructuring Fund, invests in struggling companies and those companies whose turnarounds show promise. Morgan Stanley, Lehman Brothers, and Petroleo Brasileiro are some of the companies he holds shares in, while he has unloaded shares of Citigroup, Freddie Mac, and Sallie Mae. **Availability:** Online.

9657 ■ *"Market Watch" in Barron's (Vol. 88, March 24, 2008, No. 12, pp. M18)*
Ed: Ashraf Laidi, Marc Pado, David Kotok. **Released:** 2018. **Description:** Latest measures implemented by the Federal Reserve to address the credit crisis did not benefit the US dollar, with the Japanese yen and the euro recouping earlier losses against the dollar. Goldman Sachs reported earnings of $3.23 per share, claiming a stronger liquidity position. The US markets bottomed early on 22 January 2007, according to evidence. **Availability:** Print; Online.

9658 ■ *"Market Watch: A Sampling of Advisory Opinion" in Barron's (Vol. 88, March 17, 2008, No. 11, pp. M10)*
Pub: Dow Jones & Company Inc.
Contact: Almar Latour, Chief Executive Officer
Ed: Paul Schatz, William Gibson, Michael Darda, Peter Greene, Ian Wyatt, Stephanie Pomboy. **Released:** January 25, 2014. **Description:** S&P 500 bank stocks were down 46 percent from their 2007 peak while the peak to through fall in 1989-1990 was just over 50 percent. This suggests that the bottom on the bank stocks could be near. The Federal Reserve Board announced they will lend up to $200 billion to primary lenders in exchange other securities. **Availability:** Print; Online.

9659 ■ *"Market Watch: A Sampling of Advisory Opinion US Stock Price Trends, Economic Effects of Global Trade, Chinese Economic Trends" in Barron's (Vol. 92, July 23, 2012, No. 30, pp. M14)*
Ed: Richard M. Salsman, Jack Ablin, Francois Sicart. **Description:** US stocks are considered inexpensive due to their low price-earnings ratios compared to levels before the global financial crisis. The US economy is becoming more dependent on the rest of the worldas a result of global trade. The Chinese economy continues to have strong economic growth despite a slowdown. **Availability:** Online.

9660 ■ *"Markets Defy the Doomsayers" in Barron's (Vol. 88, March 24, 2008, No. 12, pp. M5)*
Pub: Dow Jones & Company Inc.
Contact: Almar Latour, Chief Executive Officer
Ed: Leslie P. Norton. **Description:** US stock markets registered strong gains, with the Dow Jones Industrial Average rising 3.43 percent on the week to close at 12,361.32, in a rally that may be seen as short-covering. Shares of Hansen Natural are poised for further drops with a slowdown in the energy drink market. **Availability:** Online.

9661 ■ *"Markets: The Great Deleveraging" in Canadian Business (Vol. 81, October 13, 2008, No. 17, pp. 45)*
Pub: Rogers Media Inc.
Contact: Neil Spivak, Chief Executive Officer
Ed: Jeff Sanford. **Description:** 'Hell Week' of financial crisis on Wall Street is believed to have started with the downgrade of AIG Inc.'s credit rating. AIG is a major player in the credit derivatives market, and its bankruptcy would have affected firms on Wall Street. **Availability:** Online.

9662 ■ *"Mary Kramer: Good Things Happen When We Buy Local" in Crain's Detroit Business (Vol. 24, October 6, 2008, No. 40, pp. 7)*
Pub: Crain Communications Inc.
Contact: Barry Asin, President
Description: Michigan is facing incredibly difficult economic times. One way in which each one of us can help the state and the businesses located here is by purchasing our goods and services from local vendors. The state Agriculture Department projected that if Michigan households earmarked $10 per week in their grocery purchases to made-in-Michigan products, this would generate $30 million a week in economic impact. **Availability:** Online.

9663 ■ *"Massage Heights Chasing Big Expansion Opportunities" in San Antonio Business Journal (Vol. 28, April 25, 2014, No. 11, pp. 6)*
Pub: American City Business Journals, Inc.
Contact: Mike Olivieri, Executive Vice President
Released: Weekly. **Price:** $4, Introductory 4-week offer(Digital only). **Description:** Massage Heights, offering deep tissue massage, hot stone massage and facials, has opened a second corporate-owned facility in Stone Oak, Texas. The company, founded in April 2004, is focusing on expansion plans due to investor interest in the firm's growth. Massage Heights currently has five facilities in Canada. **Availability:** Print; Online.

9664 ■ *The Match King: Ivar Kreuger, the Financial Genius Behind a Century of Wall Street Scandals*
Pub: PublicAffairs
Contact: Jaime Leifer, Director
Ed: Frank Partnoy. **Released:** March 09, 2010. **Price:** $16.99, paperback; $10.99, e-book. **Description:** Ivar Kreuger, the so-called Match King, used a pyramid scheme to become the financier to European leaders. **Availability:** E-book; Print.

9665 ■ *"Maybe We're Exploiting China" in Canadian Business (Vol. 85, September 17, 2012, No. 14, pp. 4)*
Ed: Duncan Hood. **Description:** The proposed deal by China National Offshore Oil Corp. (CNOOC) to acquire Canada's Nexen for $27.50 a share is met with uncertainty by the public. The U.S. is believed to be opposing the deal because it would no longer have quite as much power to set oil prices in Canada. **Availability:** Online.

9666 ■ *"McDonald's Loses Its Sizzle" in Barron's (Vol. 88, March 17, 2008, No. 11, pp. 47)*
Description: McDonald's has promised to return $15 billion to $17 billion to shareholders in 2007-2009 but headwinds are rising for the company. December, 2007 same-store sales were flat and the company's traffic growth in the U.S. is slowing. Its shares are likely to trade in tandem with the market until recession fears recede. **Availability:** Online.

9667 ■ *"Md.'s Boring Bonds Gain Pizzazz as Investors Flock to Debt Issues" in Baltimore Business Journal (Vol. 28, June 11, 2010, No. 5, pp. 1)*
Pub: Baltimore Business Journal
Contact: Rhonda Pringle, President
E-mail: rpringle@bizjournals.com

Ed: Gary Haber. **Description:** Companies and nonprofit organizations have increased the pace of bond offerings in order to take advantage of the bonds' appeal among willing investors. Companies mostly issued corporate bonds to replace existing debt at lower interest rates and save them money from interest payments.

9668 ■ *"Meadowbrook To Acquire ProCentury in $272.6 Million Deal" in Crain's Detroit Business (Vol. 24, February 21, 2008, No. 8, pp. 4)*
Pub: Crain Communications Inc.
Contact: Barry Asin, President
Ed: Jay Greene. **Description:** Meadowbrook Insurance Group, based in Southfield, Michigan reports its proposed acquisition of ProCentury Corporation based in Columbus, Ohio. Meadowbrook provides risk-management to agencies, professional and trade associations and small-to-midsize businesses. **Availability:** Print; Online.

9669 ■ *"Meet Houston's Top Legal Dealmakers" in Austin Business Journal (Vol. 34, June 27, 2014, No. 19, pp. A15)*
Pub: American City Business Journals, Inc.
Contact: Mike Olivieri, Executive Vice President
Description: Austin-based law firm, Vinson & Elkins LLP emerged at the biggest player in Texas in the 12-month period between second quarter 2013 through first quarter 2014 when it comes to mergers and acquisitions. The firm handled 68 deals worth a total of $61.8 billion. **Availability:** Print; Online.

9670 ■ *Mergers and Acquisitions from A to Z*
Pub: HarperCollins Leadership
Contact: Donald Miller, Chief Executive Officer
Released: 2nd edition. **Price:** $19.99, Paperback. **Description:** Guide for the entire process of mergers and acquisitions, including taxes, accounting, laws, and projected financial gain. **Availability:** E-book; Print.

9671 ■ *"Microsoft Goes Macrosoft" in Barron's (Vol. 89, July 27, 2009, No. 30, pp. 25)*
Pub: Dow Jones & Company Inc.
Contact: Almar Latour, Chief Executive Officer
Ed: Mark Veverka. **Description:** Microsoft reported a weak quarter on the heels of a tech rally which suggests the economy has not turned around. Marc Andreesen describes his new venture-capital fund as focused on "classic tech" and that historical reference places him in the annals of the last millennium. **Availability:** Online.

9672 ■ *"Microsoft's Big Gamble" in Canadian Business (Vol. 81, March 3, 2008, No. 3, pp. 13)*
Description: Microsoft Corp. is taking a big risk in buying Yahoo, as it is expected to pay more than $31 a share to finalize the acquisition. The deal would be seven and a half times bigger than any other that Microsoft has entered before, an execution of such deal is also anticipated to become a challenge for Microsoft. Recommendations on how Microsoft should handle the integration of the two businesses are given. **Availability:** Print; Online.

9673 ■ *"Millennial Money: How Young Investors Can Build a Fortune"*
Pub: Palgrave Macmillan
Released: October 14, 2014. **Price:** $26, hardcover. **Description:** Because the millennial generation won't be able to depend on pensions or social security for their retirement security, it is stressed that they save and invest their money wisely. As a generation, though, they are skeptical of advice from their elders, but are committed to passing wealth to future generations. A strategy for wise investments to help overcome shortcomings is included. **Availability:** E-book; Print.

9674 ■ *"Mine Woes Could Rouse Zinc" in Barron's (Vol. 88, July 7, 2008, No. 27, pp. M12)*
Pub: Dow Jones & Company Inc.
Contact: Almar Latour, Chief Executive Officer

Ed: Andrea Hotter. **Description:** Prices of zinc could increase due to supply problems in producing countries such as Australia and China. London Metal Exchange prices for the metal have dropped about 36 percent in 2008. **Availability:** Online.

9675 ■ *"Mining Goldman for Insight"* in *Barron's (Vol. 89, July 20, 2009, No. 29, pp. M8)*
Pub: Dow Jones & Company Inc.
Contact: Almar Latour, Chief Executive Officer

Ed: Steven M. Sears. **Description:** Methods of investing in options for companies with earnings estimates from Goldman Sachs are discussed. These methods take advantage of increased volatility generated by earnings revisions. **Availability:** Online.

9676 ■ *"Minor-League Baseball's Sliders Plan Stock Offering"* in *Crain's Detroit Business (Vol. 25, June 15, 2009, No. 24, pp. 3)*
Pub: Crain Communications Inc.
Contact: Barry Asin, President

Ed: Bill Shea. **Description:** New minor-league baseball team is raising funds to build a new stadium in Waterford Township, Michigan because banks are unwilling to provide loans for the project. Owners of the Midwest Sliders in Ypsilanti, Michigan are waiting for the federal Securities and Exchange Commission to approve a Regulation A public offering. **Availability:** Print; Online.

9677 ■ *"A Mixed-Bag Quarter"* in *Barron's (Vol. 88, July 7, 2008, No. 27, pp. 19)*
Description: Seven component companies of the Dow Jones Industrial Average increased their dividend payouts in the second quarter of 2008 despite the weak performance of the index. Five companies in the Dow Jones Transportation index and three in the Dow Jones Utilities also increased their dividends. **Availability:** Online.

9678 ■ *"Monsanto Acquires Targeted-Pest Control Technology Start-Up; Terms Not Disclosed"* in *Benzinga.com (September 2011)*
Pub: Benzinga.com
Contact: Jason Raznick, Founder

Ed: Eddie Staley. **Description:** Monsanto Company acquired Beelogics, a firm that researches and develops biological tools that control pests and diseases. Research includes a product that will help protect bee health. **Availability:** Online.

9679 ■ *"More Gains in the Pipeline"* in *Barron's (Vol. 89, August 3, 2009, No. 31, pp. M5)*
Description: Shares of El Paso Corp. could recover as the company concludes a deal with a private-equity group to fund pipeline construction. The company's shares are trading at $10.06 and could move up to $12 as bad news has already been priced into the stock. **Availability:** Online.

9680 ■ *"Morgan Keegan Feeds Wunderlich"* in *Memphis Business Journal (Vol. 34, May 18, 2012, No. 5, pp. 1)*
Pub: Baltimore Business Journal
Contact: Rhonda Pringle, President
E-mail: rpringle@bizjournals.com

Ed: Cole Epley. **Description:** Wunderlich Securities Inc. has augmented its equity markets group with a dozen former Morgan Keegan & Company Inc. professionals. Wunderlich assigned ten of the new hires in Memphis, Tennessee while the two joined its institutional sales department in New York. **Availability:** Print; Online.

9681 ■ *"Move Marks KKR's Latest Push into Retail"* in *Globe & Mail (March 13, 2007, pp. B17)*

Ed: Heather Burke. **Description:** Investment giant Kohlberg Kravis Roberts and Co. has finalized a deal to acquire retail store chain Dollar General Corp. for an estimated 6.9 billion dollars. The company will be entering lucrative retail market by this acquisition.

9682 ■ *"Mover and Sheika"* in *Conde Nast Portfolio (Vol. 2, June 2008, No. 6, pp. 104)*
Ed: John Arlidge. **Description:** Profile of Princess Sheika Lubna who is the first female foreign trade minister in the Middle East, the United Arab Emirates biggest business envoy, paving the way for billions in new investment, and also a manufacturer of her own perfume line. **Availability:** Online.

9683 ■ *"Myths of Deleveraging"* in *Barron's (Vol. 90, August 23, 2010, No. 34, pp. M14)*
Pub: Barron's Editorial & Corporate Headquarters

Ed: Gene Epstein. **Description:** The opposite is true against reports about deleveraging or the decrease in credit since inflation-adjusted-investment factories and equipment rose 7.8 percent in the first quarter of 2010. On consumer deleveraging, sales of homes through credit is weak but there is a trend towards more realistic homeownership and consumer spending on durable goods rose 8.8 percent. **Availability:** Online.

9684 ■ *"A Neat SocialTrade"* in *Barron's (Vol. 92, July 23, 2012, No. 30, pp. 23)*
Pub: Dow Jones & Company Inc.
Contact: Almar Latour, Chief Executive Officer

Ed: Theresa W. Carey. **Description:** SocialTrade is a Website that allows users to exchange ideas and data with each other through video. Online broker DittoTrade launched a mobile applications that allows investors to connect to other traders and follow their trades. **Availability:** Online.

9685 ■ *"Needed: A Strategy; Banking In China"* in *The Economist (Vol. 390, January 3, 2009, No. 8612, pp. 54)*
Description: International banks are competing for a role in China but are finding obstacles in their paths such as a reduction in the credit their operations may receive from Chinese banks and the role they can play in the public capital markets which remain limited. **Availability:** Print; Online.

9686 ■ *"Nestle Acquires Waggin' Train Dog Treat Company"* in *Pet Product News (Vol. 64, November 2010, No. 11, pp. 7)*
Description: Vevey, Switzerland-based Nestle has acquired South Carolina-based dog treat firm Waggin' Train LLC from private equity firm VMG Partners in September 2010. Waggin' Train LLC, which will be operated as a wholly owned subsidiary, is expected to fill a gap in Nestle's dog treat product portfolio. **Availability:** Online.

9687 ■ *"New Backers, New Products at Halo"* in *Business Journal (Vol. 32, July 18, 2014, No. 8, pp. 5)*
Pub: American City Business Journals, Inc.
Contact: Mike Olivieri, Executive Vice President

Released: Weekly. **Price:** $4, introductory 4-week offer(Digital only). **Description:** Minnetonka, Minnesota-based Halo Innovations Inc. announced the launch of its first baby bassinet. The product launch follows a recapitalization that allowed new backers, including Balance Point Capital Partners, to buy the stakes of long-time investors. The risk of suffocation in having babies sleep with parents is also discussed. **Availability:** Print; Online.

9688 ■ *"The New Janus CEO of Battle-Hardened Money Manager Plots Comeback"* in *Denver Business Journal (Vol. 64, August 31, 2012, No. 15, pp. 1)*
Pub: Baltimore Business Journal
Contact: Rhonda Pringle, President
E-mail: rpringle@bizjournals.com

Description: Richard Weil, chief executive officer of Janus Capital Group Inc., discusses the strategic plans of the mutual fund company. He touches on the firm's alliance with Dai-chi Life Insurance Company Ltd., the future of equity markets, and the company's intelligent diversification strategy. **Availability:** Print; Online.

9689 ■ *"A New Kid on the Block"* in *Barron's (Vol. 88, March 17, 2008, No. 11, pp. 58)*
Pub: Dow Jones & Company Inc.
Contact: Almar Latour, Chief Executive Officer

Ed: Thomas G. Donlan. **Description:** Discusses the Federal Reserve which has offered to lend $100 billion in cash to banks and $200 billion in Treasuries to Wall Street investment banks that have problems with liquidity. The reluctance of the banks to lend money to meet a margin call on securities that could still depreciate is the reason why the agency is going into the direct loan business. **Availability:** Online.

9690 ■ *"The New Nimble"* in *Barron's (Vol. 90, August 30, 2010, No. 35, pp. S12)*
Pub: Barron's Editorial & Corporate Headquarters

Ed: Suzanne McGee. **Description:** Financial advisors are making investments based on short-lived market trends due to the uncertainty in the long-term market. This strategy can be demanding and advisors should only try it if they are confident about their skill in spotting short-term trends. **Availability:** Online.

9691 ■ *"New No. 1 at Element 8: Angel Group Brings on New Executive Director"* in *Puget Sound Business Journal (Vol. 35, September 19, 2014, No. 22, pp. 6)*
Pub: American City Business Journals, Inc.
Contact: Mike Olivieri, Executive Vice President

Description: Element 8 executive director, Kristi Growdon, says the company continues to find investment opportunities in the Pacific Northwest's clean technology sector. She also said the agricultural sector is a potentially lucrative investment destination. Growdon added that the company bases decisions on clean technology. **Availability:** Online.

9692 ■ *"A New Way to Tell When to Fold 'Em"* in *Barron's (Vol. 88, July 7, 2008, No. 27, pp. 27)*
Pub: Dow Jones & Company Inc.
Contact: Almar Latour, Chief Executive Officer

Ed: Theresa W. Carey. **Description:** Overview of the Online trading company SmartStops, a firm that aims to tell investors when to sell the shares of a particular company. The company's Web site categorizes stocks as moving up, down, or sideways, and calculates exit points for individual stocks based on an overall market trend. **Availability:** Online.

9693 ■ *"Nightmare on Wall Street"* in *Canadian Business (Vol. 80, November 19, 2007, No. 23, pp. 33)*

Ed: Thomas Watson. **Released:** October 29, 2016. **Description:** Merrill Lynch Stanley O'Neal resigned after the company experienced a $2.2 billion loss in third quarter 2007. Citigroup's Charles Prince will also be leaving due to the crisis involving subprime mortgages and collaterized debt obligations. Forecasts for the stock market are supplied. **Availability:** Print; Online.

9694 ■ *"Nightmare on Wall Street"* in *Canadian Business (Vol. 81, October 13, 2008, No. 17, pp. 9)*
Description: Information on events that happened on Wall Street on the week that started September 15, 2008, as well on its effect on financial markets around the world, are presented. Lehman Brothers filed for bankruptcy on September 15, 2008 after negotiations with Barclays Group and Bank of America failed. Details on AIG and Morgan Stanley are also presented. **Availability:** Online.

9695 ■ *"Nonprofit NAIC Acquires Software Developer as For-Profit Arm"* in *Crain's Detroit Business (Vol. 25, June 22, 2009, No. 25, pp. 10)*
Pub: Crain Communications Inc.
Contact: Barry Asin, President

Ed: Sherri Begin Welch. **Description:** Details of National Association of Investors Corporation's acquisition of a Massachusetts investment software developer in order to offer more products to investment clubs and individual investors nationwide. **Availability:** Online.

9696 ■ *"Nortel Outlook Shows Recovery Won't Come Quickly" in Globe & Mail (March 20, 2007, pp. B4)*

Ed: Catherine McLean. **Description:** The forecast about the unlikely recovery of Nortel Networks Corp. from decrease in its share prices is discussed. **Availability:** Online.

9697 ■ *"Nortel Plays Big to Settle Lawsuits" in Globe & Mail (February 9, 2006, pp. B1)*

Description: The details on Nortel Networks Corp.'s settlement of cases with shareholders are presented. **Availability:** Online.

9698 ■ *"Now in Play, Score Keeps Head Up and Stick on Ice" in Globe & Mail (January 20, 2007, pp. B5)*

Ed: Grant Robertson. **Description:** The hike in the shares of Score Media Inc. due to its new services is presented. **Availability:** Online.

9699 ■ *"Now That's Rich" in Canadian Business (Vol. 80, February 12, 2007, No. 4, pp. 92)*

Description: The effort of chief executive officer of Stelco Inc. Rodney Mott in resolving the issue of financial loss of the company by taking up backdating options for share price is discussed. **Availability:** Print; Online.

9700 ■ *"NStar Feels the Heat" in Cape Cod Times (September 30, 2011)*

Pub: Cape Cod Media Group
Contact: Anne Brennan, Executive Editor
E-mail: abrennan@capecodonline.com

Ed: Patrick Cassidy. **Description:** Massachusetts energy officials wish to delay a merger between NStar and Northeast Utilities until it is clear how the partnership would meet the state's green energy goals. Governor Deval Patrick supports the proposed Nantucket Sound wind farm. **Availability:** Online.

9701 ■ *"Nuclear Plans May Stall on Uranium Shortage" in Globe & Mail (March 22, 2007, pp. B4)*

Ed: Shawn McCarthy. **Description:** The poor investments in uranium production and enrichment despite growing demand for it for nuclear energy is discussed. **Availability:** Online.

9702 ■ *"The Numbers Speak For Themselves" in Barron's (Vol. 88, July 14, 2008, No. 28, pp. 16)*

Pub: Dow Jones & Company Inc.
Contact: Almar Latour, Chief Executive Officer

Ed: Bill Alpert. **Description:** Discusses quant fund managers versus traditional long-short equity funds after quants outperformed traditional funds in the year 2000. Causes for the underperformance are outlined and statistical data is included. **Availability:** Online.

9703 ■ *"Nvidia Shares Clobbered After Gloomy Warning" in Barron's (Vol. 88, July 7, 2008, No. 27, pp. 25)*

Pub: Dow Jones & Company Inc.
Contact: Almar Latour, Chief Executive Officer

Ed: Eric J. Savitz. **Description:** Shares of graphics chip manufacturer Nvidia suffered a 30 percent drop in its share price after the company warned that revenue and gross margin forecasts for the quarter ending July 27, 2008 will be below expectations. Stan Glasgow, chief operating officer of Sony Electronics, believes the US economic slowdown will not affect demand for the company's products. Statistical data included. **Availability:** Online.

9704 ■ *"Nvidia's Picture Brighter Than Stock Price Indicates" in Barron's (Vol. 88, March 24, 2008, No. 12, pp. 46)*

Pub: Dow Jones & Company Inc.
Contact: Almar Latour, Chief Executive Officer

Ed: Eric J. Savitz. **Description:** Shares of graphics chip maker Nvidia, priced at $18.52 each, do not indicate the company's strong position in the graphics chip market. The company's shares have dropped due to fears of slower demand for PCs, but the company is not as exposed to broader economic forces. **Availability:** Online.

9705 ■ *"Nymex Dissidents Rattle Sabers" in Crain's Chicago Business (Vol. 31, April 21, 2008, No. 16, pp. 2)*

Pub: Crain Communications Inc.
Contact: Barry Asin, President

Ed: Ann Saphir. **Description:** Two groups of New York Mercantile Exchange members say they have more than enough votes to stop CME Group Inc.'s $10 billion deal to acquire the oil and metals exchange and they are threatening a proxy fight if the Chicago exchange doesn't raise its offer. **Availability:** Online.

9706 ■ *"October 2009: Recovery Plods Along" in Hispanic Business (October 2009, pp. 10-11)*

Description: Economist reports on a possible economic recovery which will not be allowed to rely on a strong domestic demand in order to sustain it. Consumers, looking to counterbalance years of leverage financing based on unrealistic, ever-increasing home and portfolio valuations, are saving rather than spending money.

9707 ■ *"The Ode: CoolBrands (1986 - 2010)" in Canadian Business (Vol. 83, September 14, 2010, No. 15, pp. 25)*

Pub: Rogers Media Inc.
Contact: Neil Spivak, Chief Executive Officer

Ed: Joe Castaldo. **Description:** CoolBrands International Inc.'s merger with Swisher International Inc., a US hygiene products and services company, has formally erased the last traces of the former ice cream company. CoolBrands began as a frozen yogurt stand in 1986 and flourished across the world. How the string of acquisitions and poor corporate governance led to its demise are cited. **Availability:** Online.

9708 ■ *"Oil's Going Down, Down, Down" in Canadian Business (Vol. 79, October 9, 2006, No. 20, pp. 148)*

Description: Strategies for investors to benefit from the fall in global crude oil prices are discussed. **Availability:** Print; Online.

9709 ■ *"The Old Railway is on a Roll" in Globe & Mail (January 26, 2006, pp. B1)*

Description: The reasons behind 5 percent rise in shares for Canadian National Railway Co. are presented. **Availability:** Online.

9710 ■ *"Olympus is Urged to Revise Board" in Wall Street Journal Eastern Edition (November 28, 2011, pp. B3)*

Pub: Dow Jones & Company Inc.
Contact: Almar Latour, Chief Executive Officer

Ed: Phred Dvorak. **Description:** Koji Miyata, once a director on the board of troubled Japanese photographic equipment company, is urging the company to reorganize its board, saying the present group should resign their board seats but keep their management positions. The company has come under scrutiny for its accounting practices and costly acquisitions. **Availability:** Online.

9711 ■ *"One-Time Area Trust Executive Finds Trouble in N.H." in The Business Journal-Serving Metropolitan Kansas City (September 12, 2008)*

Description: About 200 investors, some from Missouri's Kansas City area, claim that they had conducted business with Noble Trust Co. The trust company was placed under New Hampshire Banking Department's conservatorship after $15 million was discovered to be missing from its account. It is alleged that the money was lost in a Colorado Ponzi scheme. **Availability:** Print; Online.

9712 ■ *"Online Forex Broker Tadawul FX Intros Arabic Website" in Services Close-Up (June 23, 2011)*

Pub: Close-Up Media Inc.
Contact: Caroline S. Moore, President
E-mail: cms@closeupmedia.com

Description: Online forex broker, Tadawul FX, launched its Arabic language Website, noting that the Middle East is a key market for the investment firm. **Availability:** Online.

9713 ■ *"Opportunity Now Lies at Short End of the Market" in Barron's (Vol. 88, June 30, 2008, No. 26, pp. M9)*

Pub: Dow Jones & Company Inc.
Contact: Almar Latour, Chief Executive Officer

Ed: Michael S. Derby. **Description:** Renewed credit concerns and the lesser chance of a Federal Reserve interest rate hike boosted the bond market. Some portfolio managers are more bullish on short-dated securities as they expect the market to adjust to a more appropriate outlook. **Availability:** Online.

9714 ■ *"Oracle: No Profit of Doom" in Barron's (Vol. 88, March 31, 2008, No. 13, pp. 40)*

Pub: Dow Jones & Company Inc.
Contact: Almar Latour, Chief Executive Officer

Ed: Mark Veverka. **Description:** Oracle's revenues grew by 21 percent but fell short of expectation and their profits came in at the low-end of expectations. The company's shares dropped 8 percent but investors are advised to pay more attention to the company's earnings expansion rather than revenue growth in a slow economy. Nokia's Rick Simonson points out that their markets in Asia and particularly India is growing so they are not as affected by the U.S. economic conditions. **Availability:** Online.

9715 ■ *"OSC Eyes New Tack on Litigation" in Globe & Mail (April 9, 2007, pp. B1)*

Ed: Janet McFarland. **Description:** The efforts of the Ontario Securities Commission to set up a tribunal for the investigation and control of securities fraud are described. The rate of the conviction of corporate officials in cases heard by the courts is discussed. **Availability:** Online.

9716 ■ *"Outlook 2008 (9 Sectors to Watch): Gold" in Canadian Business (Vol. 81, December 19, 2007, No. 1, pp. 53)*

Pub: Rogers Media Inc.
Contact: Neil Spivak, Chief Executive Officer

Ed: John Gray. **Description:** Turmoil in the financial markets, triggered by the meltdown in subprime mortgages, has pushed the price of gold to more than $840 an ounce in November 2007. Details on investor interest in gold and prediction on price trends in trade are discussed. **Availability:** Online.

9717 ■ *"Over A Barrel" in Canadian Business (Vol. 81, July 21, 2008, No. 11, pp. 13)*

Description: Analysts predict that the skyrocketing price of fuel will cause a crackdown in the market as purported in the peak oil theory. It is forecasted that the price of oil will reach $200 per barrel. Details of the effect of the increasing oil prices on the market are presented.

9718 ■ *"Packaging Firm Wraps Up Remake: Overseas Plants Help Firm Fatten Margins" in Crain's New York Business (January 6, 2008)*

Pub: Crain Communications, Inc.
Contact: Jessica Botos, Manager, Marketing
E-mail: jessica.botos@crainsnewyork.com

Description: Sealed Air Corp., a packaging manufacturer, has seen its share price fall nearly 20 percent over the past two years, making it one of the worst performers in the packaging sector. **Availability:** Online.

9719 ■ *Paper Fortunes: Modern Wall Street: Where It's Been and Where It's Going*

Ed: Roy C. Smith. **Released:** 2010. **Description:** Comprehensive history of Wall Street and lessons learned with insight into ways Wall Street will reinvent itself in this new economy. **Availability:** E-book.

9720 ■ Partnership: Small Business Start-Up Kit

Released: Second edition. **Description:** Guidebook detailing partnership law by state covering the formation and use of partnerships as a business form. Information on filing requirements, property laws, legal liability, standards, and the new Revised Uniform Partnership Act is covered.

9721 ■ "A Parts Maker Primed for Takeoff" in Barron's (Vol. 92, August 25, 2012, No. 35, pp. 39)

Pub: Dow Jones & Company Inc.

Contact: Almar Latour, Chief Executive Officer

Ed: David Englander. **Description:** The stocks of machinery maker Curtiss-Wright could gain value due to the manufacturing company's healthy commercial business. The company's stock prices have fallen to $29.27/share due to concerns about reductions in defense spending, but could be worth $40/share. **Availability:** Online.

9722 ■ "Paterson Plots Comeback With Internet IPO" in Globe & Mail (February 20, 2006, pp. B1)

Ed: Grant Robertson. **Description:** The initial public offering plans of chief executive officer Scott Paterson of JumpTV.com are presented. **Availability:** Online.

9723 ■ "Patience May Pay Off" in Barron's (Vol. 89, July 13, 2009, No. 28, pp. 30)

Description: New CEO Craig Herkert can turn around Supervalu and their shares could double to $30 in three years from June 2009 according to one investment officer. Herkert knows how to run a lean and tight operation since he has worked for Albertsons and Wal-Mart in the past. **Availability:** Online.

9724 ■ "Patience Will Pay Off in Africa" in Barron's (Vol. 92, September 17, 2012, No. 38, pp. M8)

Description: The stocks of African companies present long-term capital appreciation opportunities for investors. This is due to a commodities boom, economic reform and relative political stability in many African countries. **Availability:** Online.

9725 ■ "PC Connection Acquires Cloud Software Provider" in New Hampshire Business Review (Vol. 33, March 25, 2011, No. 6, pp. 8)

Description: Merrimack-based PC Connection Inc. acquired ValCom Technology, a provider of cloud-based IT service management software. Details of the deal are included. **Availability:** Print; Online.

9726 ■ "The Perks of Going Public" in Austin Business Journal (Vol. 31, July 15, 2011, No. 19, pp. A17)

Pub: Austin Business Journal

Contact: Rachel McGrath, Director

E-mail: rmcgrath@bizjournals.com

Ed: Christopher Calnan. **Description:** HomeAway Inc. launched a $216 million initial public offering. Austin Ventures has generated more than $32 million from the IPO. **Availability:** Print; Online.

9727 ■ "Perry Ellis and G-III Apparel--Out of Fashion, but Still in Style" in Barron's (Vol. 88, March 17, 2008, No. 11, pp. 48)

Pub: Dow Jones & Company Inc.

Contact: Almar Latour, Chief Executive Officer

Ed: Robin Goldwyn Blumenthal. **Description:** Shares of Perry Ellis International and G-III Apparel Group have taken some beating in the market despite good growth earnings prospects. Perry Ellis sees earnings growth of 8 to 11 percent for fiscal 2009, while G-III Apparel expects earnings growth of 25 percent. **Availability:** Online.

9728 ■ "Peter Bynoe Trades Up" in Black Enterprise (Vol. 38, July 2008, No. 12, pp. 30)

Pub: Earl G. Graves Ltd.

Contact: Earl Graves, Jr., President

Description: Chicago-based Loop Capital Markets L.L.C. has named Peter Bynoe managing director of corporate finance. Bynoe was previously a senior partner at the law firm DLA Piper U.S. L.L.P., where he worked on stadium deals.

9729 ■ "PetSmart: A Barking Buy" in Barron's (Vol. 89, July 6, 2009, No. 27, pp. 15)

Pub: Dow Jones & Company Inc.

Contact: Almar Latour, Chief Executive Officer

Ed: Jay Palmer. **Description:** Shares of PetSmart could climb from $21.70 to about $28 due to the company's improving profits, cash flow, and product portfolio. The company's shares are trading at 14 times projected 2010 earnings of $1.64 a share. **Availability:** Online.

9730 ■ "Phila. Tax Break Aimed at Luring Investment Funds" in Philadelphia Business Journal (Vol. 28, April 13, 2012, No. 9, pp. 1)

Pub: Baltimore Business Journal

Contact: Rhonda Pringle, President

E-mail: rpringle@bizjournals.com

Description: The City Council of Philadelphia adopted a resolution to attract private investment funds to relocate to the city through tax breaks. Two private-equity firms have already expressed interest to relocate in the city. **Availability:** Print; Online.

9731 ■ "Phillip Frost: 'Technology Is the Future'" in South Florida Business Journal (Vol. 34, June 20, 2014, No. 48, pp. 16)

Pub: American City Business Journals, Inc.

Contact: Mike Olivieri, Executive Vice President

Released: Weekly. **Price:** $8, introductory 4-week offer(Digital only). **Description:** Entrepreneur, Phillip Frost, shares his strategies and perspectives on the business climate of Miami, Florida. He describes investment strategy for the diverse holdings of Opko Health and his criteria for buying companies and licensing technologies. **Availability:** Print; Online.

9732 ■ "Phillips Edison Launches $1.8B Retail REIT" in Business Courier (Vol. 27, October 15, 2010, No. 24, pp. 1)

Pub: Business Courier

Ed: Dan Monk. **Description:** Retail center operator Phillips Edison & Company is organizing a real estate investment trust (REIT) to raise $1.8 billion to finance the planned purchase of 150 grocery-centered shopping centers around the U.S. The offering would be Phillips largest. Phillips Edison employs 174 workers and operates 250 shopping centers nationwide. **Availability:** Print; Online.

9733 ■ "Place Restrictions on Your Stock Shares" in Business Owner (Vol. 35, July-August 2011, No. 4, pp. 14)

Description: It is critical for any small business owner to be certain that the buyer or recipient of any part of the company represents that the stock is being acquired or given for investment purposes only. **Availability:** Online.

9734 ■ "PNC Begins Search for New Baltimore-Area Headquarters" in Baltimore Business Journal (Vol. 28, June 4, 2010, No. 4, pp. 1)

Pub: Baltimore Business Journal

Contact: Rhonda Pringle, President

E-mail: rpringle@bizjournals.com

Ed: Daniel J. Sernovitz. **Description:** PNC Financial Services Group Inc. is searching for a new headquarters building in Greater Baltimore, Maryland. The company is seeking about 150,000 square feet for its regional operations. However, PNC could also end up moving out of Baltimore for space in the surrounding suburbs. **Availability:** Print; Online.

9735 ■ "The Power of Alumni Networks" in Harvard Business Review (Vol. 88, October 2010, No. 10, pp. 34)

Pub: Harvard Business Publishing

Contact: Diane Belcher, Managing Director

Ed: Lauren H. Cohen, Christopher J. Malloy. **Price:** $6, PDF. **Description:** Research indicates that members of alumni associations tend to invest in similar ways; implications for the mutual funds sector are discussed. **Availability:** Online; PDF.

9736 ■ "Power Partnerships" in Business Courier (Vol. 27, October 22, 2010, No. 25, pp. 1)

Description: The $400 million Harrah's casino and the $47 million redevelopment and expansion of Washington Park are project aimed at boosting the economy in downtown Cincinnati, Ohio. These projects will be done in cooperation with the National Association for the Advancement of Colored People. Insights into the role of minority-owned businesses in regional economic development are explored. **Availability:** Print; Online.

9737 ■ PPC's Guide to Choosing Retirement Plans for Small Businesses

Price: $190; $215. **Description:** Guide to evaluate and select retirement plans for small business. **Availability:** Online.

9738 ■ "Pre-Deal Trades More Common in Canada, Study Finds" in Globe & Mail (March 23, 2007, pp. B5)

Ed: John Kipphoff, Joe Schneider. **Description:** The results of the study conducted by Measuredmarkets Inc. to examine the impact of merger activity on insider trading of the companies are presented. **Availability:** Print; Online.

9739 ■ "A Precious Resource: Investing In the Fate of Fresh Water" in Black Enterprise (Vol. 38, February 2008, No. 7, pp. 44)

Pub: Earl G. Graves Ltd.

Contact: Earl Graves, Jr., President

Ed: Charles Keenan. **Description:** Despite rising oil prices, water may become the most precious commodity in years to come because the world's supply of drinkable water is dwindling. **Availability:** Online.

9740 ■ "Private Equity Firm Links First Arizona Deal" in Business Journal-Serving Phoenix and the Valley of the Sun (November 2, 2007)

Description: Pacific Investment Partners and Your Source Financial launched a $10 million fund and signed their first deal. The two companies acquires a minority stake in Dreambrands Inc. for $3 million. Dreambrands is using the capital to market its personal lubricant product Carrageenana.

9741 ■ "Private Equity Firms" in Black Enterprise (Vol. 44, June 2014, No. 10, pp. 89)

Pub: Earl G. Graves Ltd.

Contact: Earl Graves, Jr., President

Description: A ranking of private equity firms in the U.S. is presented. **Availability:** Online.

9742 ■ "Private Equity Firms Focus on Failing Banks" in Baltimore Business Journal (Vol. 28, July 16, 2010, No. 10, pp. 1)

Pub: Baltimore Business Journal

Contact: Rhonda Pringle, President

E-mail: rpringle@bizjournals.com

Ed: Gary Haber. **Description:** Four deals in which assets of failed banks were acquired by private equity firms have been approved by the Federal Deposit Insurance Corporation in the past couple of years. Bay Bank FSK, for example, purchased Bay National Bank's assets in July 2010. Forecasts on more private equity acquisitions in the community banking industry are given. **Availability:** Print; Online.

9743 ■ "Private Pitfalls" in Canadian Business (Vol. 80, October 22, 2007, No. 21, pp. 34)

Description: Guidelines on how minority shareholders can avoid drawbacks at the time of purchase, during ownership, and when selling shares are discussed; contractual protection, sales taxation and share price are also presented. Investment in a private company entails knowing the party you are buying share from. **Availability:** Print; Online.

9744 ■ *"Private TV Industry's Profit Climbs 4 Per Cent"* *in Globe & Mail (March 29, 2006, pp. B6)*

Ed: Simon Tuck. **Description:** The private television industry in Canada is experiencing 4 percent increase in its profits, i.e. $242.2 millions. The revenues of CTV contributed more to this increase in profits. **Availability:** Online.

9745 ■ *"Profits Without Prosperity: Stock Buybacks Manipulate the Market and Leave Most Americans Worse Off"* *in Harvard Business Review (Vol. 92, September 2014, No. 9, pp. 46)*

Pub: Harvard Business Publishing
Contact: Diane Belcher, Managing Director
Price: $8.95. **Description:** While stock prices rise due to stock buybacks, the long-term effects of buybacks are job instability, sluggish growth, and income inequality. Firms should not be permitted to repurchase their shares, and restrictions should be placed on stock-based pay. Profits should be invested in innovation. **Availability:** Online; PDF.

9746 ■ *"The Promise of the Promised Land"* *in San Francisco Business Times (Vol. 28, January 3, 2014, No. 24, pp. 4)*

Pub: American City Business Journals, Inc.
Contact: Mike Olivieri, Executive Vice President
Released: September 15, 2016. **Price:** $4, print. **Description:** San Francisco Bay Area in California has become the site selection for investment, technology and talent. The financing finding its way to Bay Area has led to robust job creation, drawing people and increasing the population by 2.6 percent to 805,000. The impact of the Bay Area's technology boon in rents and home prices are also presented. **Availability:** Print; Online.

9747 ■ *"A Property Rights Analysis of Newly Private Firms"* *Opportunities for Owners to Appropriate Rents and Partition Residual Risks"* *in Business Ethics Quarterly (Vol. 21, July 2011, No. 3, pp. 445)*

Ed: Marguerite Schneider, Alix Valenti. **Description:** A key factor in the decision to convert a publicly owned company to private status is the expectation that value will be create, providing the firm with rent. These rents have implications regarding the property rights of the firm's capital-contributing constituencies. The article identifies and analyzes the types of rent associated with the newly private firm. Compared to public firms, going private allows owners the potential to partition part of the residual risk to bond holders and employees, rendering them to be co-residual risk bearers with owners. **Availability:** Download; PDF; Online.

9748 ■ *"Putting SogoTrade Through Its Paces"* *in Barron's (Vol. 89, July 27, 2009, No. 30, pp. 27)*

Pub: Dow Jones & Company Inc.
Contact: Almar Latour, Chief Executive Officer
Ed: Theresa W. Carey. **Description:** SogoTrade options platform streams options quotes in real time and lets users place a trade in several ways. The site also features notable security tactics and is a reasonable choice for bargain-seekers. OptionsXpress' Xtend platform lets users place trades and get real time quotes. **Availability:** Online.

9749 ■ *"Putting the World at Your Fingertips"* *in Barron's (Vol. 88, July 7, 2008, No. 27, pp. L13)*

Pub: Dow Jones & Company Inc.
Contact: Almar Latour, Chief Executive Officer
Ed: Neil A. Martin. **Description:** Currency-traded exchange funds allow investors to diversify their assets and take advantage of investment opportunities such as speculation and hedging. Investors can use these funds to build positions in favor of or against the US dollar. **Availability:** Online.

9750 ■ *"Q&A: The CAPP's Greg Stringham"* *in Canadian Business (Vol. 81, February 12, 2008, No. 3, pp. 8)*

Pub: Rogers Media Inc.
Contact: Neil Spivak, Chief Executive Officer

Ed: Michelle Magnan. **Description:** Canadian Association of Petroleum Producers' Greg Stringham thinks that the new royalty plan will result in companies pulling out their investments for Alberta's conventional oil and gas sector. Stringham adds that Alberta is losing its competitive advantage and companies must study their cost profiles to retrieve that advantage. The effects of the royalty system on Alberta's economy are examined further. **Availability:** Print; Online.

9751 ■ *"Quality at Bargain Prices"* *in Black Enterprise (Vol. 41, December 2010, No. 5, pp. 30)*

Description: Monica L. Walker, CEO of Holland Capital Management, suggests investors to watch prevailing trends in the financial market and to focus on using bottom-up analysis to identify companies meeting their investment criteria. **Availability:** Online.

9752 ■ *The Quants*

Released: January 25, 2011. **Price:** $22.50, audiobook. **Description:** The story of four rich and powerful men, along with Jim Simons, the founder of the most successful hedge fund in history and how they felt and what they thought in the days and weeks during the crash of Wall Street. **Availability:** E-book; Print; Audio.

9753 ■ *"A Questionable Chemical Romance"* *in Barron's (Vol. 88, July 14, 2008, No. 28, pp. 28)*

Pub: Dow Jones & Company Inc.
Contact: Almar Latour, Chief Executive Officer
Ed: Andrew Bary. **Description:** Dow Chemical paid $78-a-share for the surprise takeover of Rohm & Haas. The acquisition is reducing Dow Chemical's financial flexibility at a time when chemical companies are being affected by high costs and a weak U.S. economy. **Availability:** Online.

9754 ■ *"Quick Earnings Revival Unlikely"* *in Barron's (Vol. 88, June 30, 2008, No. 26, pp. 31)*

Description: Analysts are pushing back their prediction of a U.S. economy turnaround to 2009. A recession in the first half of 2008 may not have happened but unemployment is rising and house prices continue to fall.

9755 ■ *"Ralcorp Investigated for Rejecting ConAgra Bid"* *in Saint Louis Business Journal (Vol. 32, September 16, 2011, No. 3, pp. 1)*

Pub: Saint Louis Business Journal
Contact: Robert Bobroff, President
E-mail: rbobroff@bizjournals.com
Ed: Evan Binns. **Description:** New York-based Levi & Korsinsky started investigating Ralcorp Holidngs Inc. after it rejected ConAgra Foods Inc.'s third and latest takeover bid of $5.17 billion. The investigation would determine whether Ralcorp's directors had acted on behalf of shareholders' best interest. **Availability:** Print; Online.

9756 ■ *"R&R Launches Upscale Spoony's and Low Fat Dragon's Den"* *in Ice Cream Reporter (Vol. 23, August 20, 2010, No. 9, pp. 3)*

Description: European ice cream manufacturer R&R has acquired French ice cream maker Rolland and will position itself as an upscale challenger to brands like Ben & Jerry's. **Availability:** Print; Online.

9757 ■ *"Raptor Opens Austin Office"* *in Austin Business Journal (Vol. 31, July 8, 2011, No. 18, pp. 1)*

Pub: Austin Business Journal
Contact: Rachel McGrath, Director
E-mail: rmcgrath@bizjournals.com
Ed: Christopher Calnan. **Description:** Boston hedge fund operator Raptor Group launched Raptor Accelerator, a consulting business providing sales and advisory services to early-stage companies in Central Texas. Aside from getting involved with the startups in which the Raptor Group invests, Raptor Accelera-

tor will target firms operating in the sports, media, entertainment, and content technology sectors. **Availability:** Print; Online.

9758 ■ *"Raytheon Stock Up, Will Pay New Quarterly Dividend"* *in Barron's (Vol. 88, March 31, 2008, No. 13)*

Pub: Dow Jones & Company Inc.
Contact: Almar Latour, Chief Executive Officer
Ed: Shirley A. Lazo. **Description:** Raytheon hiked their quarterly dividend to 28 cents per share from 25.5 cents. Aircastle slashed their quarterly common dividend by 64 percent for them to retain additional capital that can be used to increase their liquidity position. **Availability:** Online.

9759 ■ *"The RBC Dynasty Continues"* *in Globe & Mail (January 30, 2006, pp. B1)*

Description: The details on business growth of Royal Bank of Canada, under chief executive officer Gordon Nixon, are presented. **Availability:** Print; Online.

9760 ■ *"Ready for a Rally?"* *in The Economist (Vol. 390, January 3, 2009, No. 8612, pp. 54)*

Description: Analysts predict that the recession could end by 2010. The current economic crisis is presented in detail. **Availability:** Print; Online.

9761 ■ *"Real Estate's New Reality"* *in Entrepreneur (Vol. 37, July 2009, No. 7, pp. 32)*

Pub: Entrepreneur Media Inc.
Contact: Dan Bova, Director
E-mail: dbova@entrepreneur.com
Ed: Rosalind Resnick. **Description:** Investing in real estate is still an advisable move, as long as investors are prepared to hold on to the property and there is a rent roll to provide a decent return on investment. Among the key considerations when investing in real estate is the property's expenses and cash flow. Other suggestions for future real estate investors are given. **Availability:** Online.

9762 ■ *"Recovery on Tap for 2010?"* *in Orlando Business Journal (Vol. 26, January 1, 2010, No. 31, pp. 1)*

Pub: Orlando Business Journal
Contact: Julie Swyers, Director
E-mail: jswyers@bizjournals.com
Ed: Melanie Stawicki Azam, Richard Bilbao, Christopher Boyd, Anjali Fluker. **Description:** Economic forecasts for Central Florida's leading business sectors in 2010 are presented. These sectors include housing, film and TV, sports business, law, restaurants, aviation, tourism and hospitality, banking and finance, commercial real estate, retail, health care, insurance, higher education, and manufacturing. According to some local executives, Central Florida's economy will slowly recover in 2010. **Availability:** Online.

9763 ■ *"Regent's Signal, Once Powerful, Fading From Local Scene"* *in Business Courier (Vol. 27, June 4, 2010, No. 5, pp. 1)*

Pub: Business Courier
Ed: Dan Monk. **Description:** Los Angeles, California-based Oaktree Capital Management bought former Regent Communications Inc. from Chapter 11 bankruptcy and transformed it into Townsquare Media Inc., a privately held firm. Regent's corporate presence has faded fast in Cincinnati, Ohio as its operations wind down. Insights on Regent's failed business model are also given. **Availability:** PDF; Online.

9764 ■ *"Regulator Issues Warning On Reverse Mortgage Loans"* *in Retirement Advisor (Vol. 13, October 2012, No. 10, pp. 28)*

Description: Reverse mortgages were first introduced in 1961 and are becoming popular now with aging baby boomers. The new Consumer Financial Protection Bureau warns the public to look closing before entering a reverse mortgage contract. The National Ethics Association encourages financial advisors to use the same caution and offers advise for advisors to help educate their clients about reverse mortgages. **Availability:** Print; Online.

9765 ■ "The REIT Stuff" in Canadian Business (Vol. 80, March 26, 2007, No. 7, pp. 72)

Description: The stock performance of various real estate investment trusts in Canada is analyzed. **Availability:** Online.

9766 ■ "REITs Decry Foreign Limits on Investment" in Globe & Mail (March 29, 2007, pp. B4)

Ed: Elizabeth Church. **Description:** The planned legislation by Canadian government for regulation foreign investments by real estate investment trusts is discussed. **Availability:** Online.

9767 ■ "Reports of Banks' Revival were Greatly Exaggerated" in Barron's (Vol. 88, July 7, 2008, No. 27, pp. L14)

Pub: Dow Jones & Company Inc.

Contact: Almar Latour, Chief Executive Officer

Ed: Jack Willoughby. **Description:** Performance of mutual funds improved for the second quarter of 2008 compared to the previous quarter, registering an average gain of 0.13 percent; funds focusing on natural resources rose the highest, their value rising by an average of 24.50 percent. **Availability:** Online.

9768 ■ "Research Reports" in Barron's (Vol. 88, March 24, 2008, No. 12, pp. M10)

Pub: Dow Jones & Company Inc.

Contact: Almar Latour, Chief Executive Officer

Ed: Anita Peltonen. **Description:** Investors are recommending purchasing shares of Ampco Pittsburgh due to an expected surge in earnings. Deteriorating credit quality presents problems for the shares of BankAtlantic Bancorp, whose price targets have been lowered from $7 to $5 each. Shares of Helicos Biosciences are expected to move sideways from their $6 level. Statistical data included.

9769 ■ "Research Reports" in Barron's (Vol. 90, August 23, 2010, No. 34, pp. M13)

Pub: Barron's Editorial & Corporate Headquarters

Description: Shares of Sirius XM Radio, Target and Deere and Company received an eBuyE rating, while shares of Research in Motion got an eNeutralE rating. **Availability:** Online.

9770 ■ "Research Reports: How Analysts Size Up Companies" in Barron's (Vol. 88, June 30, 2008, No. 26, pp. M11)

Availability: Online.

9771 ■ "Return to Wealth; Bank Strategy" in The Economist (Vol. 390, January 3, 2009, No. 8612, pp. 56)

Description: UBS' strategy to survive these trying economic times is presented. Statistical data included. UBS has a stronger balance-sheet than most of its investment-banking peers and has reduced its portfolio. **Availability:** Print; Online.

9772 ■ Rich Dad, Poor Dad: What the Rich Teach Their Kids About Money-That the Poor and Middle Class Do Not!

Released: October 25, 2016. **Price:** $5.95, hardcover. **Description:** Personal finance expert shares his economic perspective through exposure to a pair of disparate influences: his own highly education but fiscally unstable father and the multimillionaire eighth-grade dropout father of his closest friend. **Availability:** Print.

9773 ■ Rich Dad's Increase Your Financial IQ: Get Smarter with Your Money

Ed: Robert T. Kiyosaki. **Released:** January 07, 2014. **Price:** $14.95, paperback; $12.88, e-book. **Description:** Author describes his five key principles of financial knowledge to help readers build wealth. **Availability:** E-book; Print.

9774 ■ "The Right Time for REITs" in Barron's (Vol. 88, July 14, 2008, No. 28, pp. 32)

Pub: Dow Jones & Company Inc.

Contact: Almar Latour, Chief Executive Officer

Ed: Mike Hogan. **Description:** Discusses the downturn in U.S. real estate investment trusts so these are worth considering for investment. Several Websites that are useful for learning about real estate investment trusts for investment purposes are presented. **Availability:** Online.

9775 ■ "RIM's Options Story Under Fire" in Globe & Mail (March 16, 2007, pp. B1)

Ed: Janet McFarland. **Description:** The investigation of the backdating of options by Research In Motion Ltd. is discussed. The analysis of the backdating of company's options issues by Professor Erik Lie from the University of Iowa is presented. **Availability:** Online.

9776 ■ "Rock of Ages" in Barron's (Vol. 92, September 17, 2012, No. 38, pp. 23)

Description: Financial services firm Rockefeller & Company was hit hard by the global financial crisis of 2008, but managed to thrive despite it. The firm, which offers financial products from other firms aside from its own fund, grew its assets under management by 52 percent to $35 billion for the three-year period that ended June 2012. **Availability:** Online.

9777 ■ "Rogue Caller Infiltrates Cincinnati Firms' Analyst Calls: 'Mr. CEO, Please Do Elaborate On Your Firm's Metrics'" in Business Courier (Vol. 24, February 28, 2008, No. 47, pp. 1)

Pub: American City Business Journals, Inc.

Contact: Mike Olivieri, Executive Vice President

Ed: Jon Newberry. **Description:** Discusses a rogue caller who goes by the name of Joe Herrick, Steven Nissan and Joe Harris has joined in over a dozen conference calls, asking chief executive officers on their plans and commenting on the companies' operations. The mystery caller attempts to pass himself off as a financial analyst. Transcripts of some conference calls, in which the rogue caller is involved, are provided. **Availability:** Online.

9778 ■ "The Role of Leadership In Successful International Mergers and Acquisitions: Why Renault-Nissan Succeeded and DaimlerChrysler-Mitsubishi Failed" in Human Resource Management (Vol. 51,May-June 2012, No. 3, pp. 433-456)

Pub: John Wiley & Sons, Inc.

Contact: Christina Van Tassell, Executive Vice President Chief Financial Officer

Ed: Carol Gill. **Released:** May 25, 2012. **Description:** The effects of national and organizational culture on the performance of Nissan and Mitsubishi after their mergers with Renault and DaimlerChrysler respectively are examined. Japanese national culture was found to influence organizational culture and human resource management practices, while leadership affected the success of their turnaround efforts.

9779 ■ "Ryder's Shock Absorbers Are In Place" in Barron's (Vol. 88, March 24, 2008, No. 12, pp. 19)

Pub: Dow Jones & Company Inc.

Contact: Almar Latour, Chief Executive Officer

Ed: Christopher C. Williams. **Description:** Shares of Ryder System Inc. are expected to continue rising on the back of rising earnings, forecast at $5.20 a share for 2009. The shares of the truck freight company hit a 52-week high of $62.27 each and may reach $70 a share. **Availability:** Online.

9780 ■ "Sacred Success: A Course in Financial Miracles"

Pub: BenBella Books Inc.

Contact: Aida Herrera, Director

E-mail: aida@benbellabooks.com

Released: October 01, 2014. **Price:** $17.46, hardcover; $11.87, paperback; $12.99, e-book(MOBI); $12.99, e-book(PDF), plus shipping charge ; $12.99, E-Book (EPUB) ; $12.99, e-book(electronic publishing). **Description:** A leading expert on women and money helps women to take control of the finances and lose their fear or ambivalence towards it. It is a tutorial for taking charge of a woman's life along with financial investing success. **Availability:** E-book; Print; Electronic publishing; PDF; Online.

9781 ■ Safety Net

Released: February 22, 2011. **Price:** $23, hardcover; $9.99, e-book. **Description:** Ways to build a financial investment strategy that protects you, while ensuring growth in a strong financial future are presented. **Availability:** E-book; Print.

9782 ■ "Sales of Unregistered Securities Are a Growing Problem That's Harming Investors — and the Industry" in Investment News (April 13, 2019)

URL(s): www.investmentnews.com/article/20190413/FREE/190419992/sales-of-unregistered-securities-are-a-growing-problem-thats-harming

Ed: Bruce Kelly. **Released:** April 13, 2019. **Description:** Discusses the negative impacts unregistered securities have on consumers and what is being down to crack down of this type of fraud. **Availability:** Online.

9783 ■ Schaum's Outline of Financial Management

Pub: McGraw-Hill Professional

Ed: Jae K. Shim, Joel G. Siegel. **Released:** Third edition. **Description:** Rules and regulations governing corporate finance, including the Sarbanes-Oxley Act are discussed. **Availability:** E-book; Print; Download.

9784 ■ "Score One for Barron's" in Barron's (Vol. 89, July 13, 2009, No. 28, pp. 14)

Pub: Dow Jones & Company Inc.

Contact: Almar Latour, Chief Executive Officer

Ed: Andrew Bary. **Description:** 57 companies that were bullishly covered on 'Barron's' for the first half of 2009 were up an average of 20.4 percent compared to the 10.2 percent gain in the relevant market indexes. The bearish stock picks by 'Barron's' were down 3.4 percent compared to a 6.4 percent for the benchmarks. **Availability:** Online.

9785 ■ "Scotiabank Targets More Baby Boomers" in Globe & Mail (March 4, 2006, pp. B5)

Ed: Elizabeth Church. **Description:** Bank of Nova Scotia posted $844 million profit for first quarter 2006. The plans of the bank to achieve baby boomer client base are presented. **Availability:** Online.

9786 ■ "Screening for the Best Stock Screens" in Barron's (Vol. 90, September 13, 2010, No. 37, pp. 36)

Pub: Barron's Editorial & Corporate Headquarters

Ed: Mike Hogan. **Description:** Pros and cons of the new and revised stock screening tools from Zack, Finviz.com, and GuruFocus are discussed. FinVix.com is more capable for screening through stocks and the service is free. **Availability:** Online.

9787 ■ "Sears' Lampert Solid in Game of Valuation Chicken" in Globe & Mail (February 25, 2006, pp. B2)

Ed: Eric Reguly. **Description:** The feasibility of share value of Sears Canada Inc., following Sears Holdings Corp.'s acquisition, is discussed. **Availability:** Online.

9788 ■ "S.E.C. Adopts New Broker Rules That Consumer Advocates Say Are Toothless" in The New York Times (June 5, 2019)

URL(s): www.nytimes.com/2019/06/05/your-money/sec-investment-brokers-fiduciary-duty.html

Ed: Tara Siegel Bernard. **Released:** June 05, 2019. **Description:** The SEC voted to pass the Regulation Best Interest, which should help Main Street investors. However, consumer advocates say it does little for its customers. **Availability:** Online.

9789 ■ "SEC Decide if Austin Ventures is VC Firm" in Austin Business Journal (Vol. 31, June 17, 2011, No. 15, pp. 1)

Pub: Austin Business Journal

Contact: Rachel McGrath, Director

E-mail: rmcgrath@bizjournals.com

Ed: Christopher Calnan. **Description:** Investment firm Austin Ventures could lose its classification as a venture capital firm under a new definition of venture capital by the Securities and Exchange Commission. The reclassification could result in additional expenses for Austin Ventures, which has two-thirds of its investments in growth equity transactions. **Availability:** Print; Online.

9790 ▪ *"SEC Report On Rating Agencies Falls Short"* in *Barron's (Vol. 88, July 14, 2008, No. 28, pp. 35)*
Pub: Dow Jones & Company Inc.
Contact: Almar Latour, Chief Executive Officer

Ed: Jack Willoughby. **Description:** The Securities and Exchange Commissions report on credit-rating firms should have drawn attention to the slipshod practices in the offerings of collateralized debt obligations. The report fell short of prescribing correctives for the flawed system of these agencies' relationship with their clients. **Availability:** Online.

9791 ▪ *"Sedentary Shoppers: Point, Click, Buy"* in *Barron's (Vol. 90, September 6, 2010, No. 36, pp. 11)*
Pub: Barron's Editorial & Corporate Headquarters

Ed: Vito J. Racanelli. **Description:** Non-travel online retail sales from January to July 2010 increased nine percent which indicates that online shopping for the coming holidays will be good. Online sales are outpacing traditional shopping, but pricing is still critical. **Availability:** Online.

9792 ▪ *"Selling Michigan; R&D Pushed as Reason For Chinese To Locate In State"* in *Crain's Detroit Business (Vol. 24, January 14, 2008)*
Pub: Crain Communications Inc.
Contact: Barry Asin, President

Ed: Marti Benedetti. **Description:** Southeast Michigan Economic Development organizations are working to develop relationships with Chinese manufacturers so they will locate their automotive research and development operations in the state.

9793 ▪ *"Sense of Discovery"* in *Business Journal Portland (Vol. 27, November 19, 2010, No. 38, pp. 1)*
Pub: Portland Business Journal
Contact: Andy Giegerich, Managing Editor
E-mail: agiegerich@bizjournals.com

Description: Tigard, Oregon-based Exterro Inc. CEO Bobby Balachandran announced plans to go public without the help of an institutional investor. Balachandran believes Exterro could grow to a $100 million legal compliance software company in the span of three years. Insights on Exterro's growth as market leader in the $1 billion legal governance software market are also given. **Availability:** Print; Online.

9794 ▪ *"Sentiment Split on Financials: Is the Worse Over or Still to Come?"* in *Barron's (Vol. 88, March 24, 2008, No. 12, pp. M14)*
Pub: Dow Jones & Company Inc.
Contact: Almar Latour, Chief Executive Officer

Ed: Steven M. Sears. **Description:** Experts in the financial sector are split as to whether or not the worst of the financial crisis brought on by the credit crunch is over. Some options traders are trading on are defensive puts, expecting the worst, while investors buying calls are considered as bullish. **Availability:** Online.

9795 ▪ *"Should the Fed Regulate Wall Street?"* in *Barron's (Vol. 88, March 24, 2008, No. 12, pp. M15)*
Pub: Dow Jones & Company Inc.
Contact: Almar Latour, Chief Executive Officer

Ed: Randall W. Forsyth. **Description:** Greater regulation of the financial sector by the Federal Reserve is essential for it to survive the crisis it is experiencing. The resulting regulation could be in complete contrast with the deregulation the sector previously experienced. **Availability:** Online.

9796 ▪ *"Should I or Shouldn't I?"* in *Indoor Comfort Marketing (Vol. 70, February 2011, No. 2, pp. 30)*

Description: Investment tips are shared for investing in futures options. **Availability:** Print; Online.

9797 ▪ *"A Signaling Theory of Acquisition Premiums: Evidence From IPO Targets"* in *Academy of Management Journal (Vol. 55, June 1, 2012, No. 3, pp. 667)*
Pub: Academy of Management
Contact: Sharon Alvarez, President

Ed: Jeffrey J. Reuer, Tony W. Tong, Cheng-Wei Wu. **Description:** The value of acquisition premiums that newly public targets capture in post-initial public offering (IPO) acquisitions is investigated. Results reveal greater benefits from signals such as interorganizational relationships for IPO targets selling their firms to acquirers from different industries. Associations with prominent alliance partners, venture capitalists and underwriters can also enhance the gains for acquistion targets. **Availability:** Electronic publishing; Download; PDF; Online.

9798 ▪ *"Silver Standard Reports First Quarter 2007 Results"* in *Marketwired (May 14, 2007)*
Pub: Comtex News Network Inc.
Contact: Kan Devnani, President

Description: Silver Standard Resources Inc. reports a first quarter loss of $1.6 million compared with the first quarter of 2006 in which the loss was $1.1 million. Statistical data included. **Availability:** PDF; Online.

9799 ▪ *"A Simple Old Reg that Needs Dusting Off"* in *Barron's (Vol. 88, June 30, 2008, No. 26, pp. 35)*
Pub: Dow Jones & Company Inc.
Contact: Almar Latour, Chief Executive Officer

Ed: Gene Epstein. **Description:** Senator Joe Lieberman has a point when he accused speculators of inflating the prices of food and fuel futures but introducing legislation to address speculation has an alternative. The senator's committee should instead demand that the Commodity Futures Trading Commission enforce position limits on the maximum number of contracts in a given market per speculative entity. **Availability:** Online.

9800 ▪ *"Six Great Stock Funds for the Long Haul"* in *Barron's (Vol. 89, July 13, 2009, No. 28, pp. L5)*
Pub: Dow Jones & Company Inc.
Contact: Almar Latour, Chief Executive Officer

Ed: Lawrence C. Strauss, Tom Sullivan. **Description:** Six mutual funds that have solid long-term performance, transparency, savvy stock picking, and discipline are presented. The managers of these funds are also evaluated. These funds include the T. Rowe Price Emerging Market Stock Fund, Fairholme, and Dodge & Cox Stock. **Availability:** Online.

9801 ▪ *"Skype Ltd. Acquired GroupMe"* in *Information Today (Vol. 28, October 2011, No. 9, pp. 12)*

Description: Skype Ltd. acquired GroupMe, a group messaging company that allows users to form impromptu groups where they can text message, share data, and make conference calls for free and is supported on Android, iPhone, BlackBerry, and Windows phones. **Availability:** Print; Online.

9802 ▪ *"The Skype's the Limit"* in *Canadian Business (Vol. 80, February 12, 2007, No. 4, pp. 70)*

Description: The increase in the market share of Skype Technologies S.A.'s Internet phone service to 171 million users is discussed. **Availability:** Print; Online.

9803 ▪ *"Sleeman Cuts Again as Cheap Suds Bite"* in *Globe & Mail (March 3, 2006, pp. B3)*
Ed: Andy Hoffman. **Description:** The details on 5 percent employee reduction at Sleeman Breweries Ltd., which posted 86 percent decline in profits for fourth quarter 2005, are presented. **Availability:** Online.

9804 ▪ *"A Slice of Danish; Fixing Finance"* in *The Economist (Vol. 390, January 3, 2009, No. 8612, pp. 55)*

Description: Denmark's mortgage-holders and the county's lending system is presented. **Availability:** Print; Online.

9805 ▪ *"Slow Mortgage Market Drags JPMorgan Chase Q1 Earnings Down 18.5 Percent"* in *Boston Business Journal (Vol. 34, April 11, 2014, No. 10)*
Pub: American City Business Journals, Inc.
Contact: Mike Olivieri, Executive Vice President

Released: Weekly. **Description:** JP Morgan Chase reported $5.27 billion in first quarter earnings, down 18.5 percent for the same period last year. Revenue fell slightly to less than $23.9 billion, down from $24.5 billion in 2013. The banking firm has approximately 1,200 employees in Massachusetts and about 60 of them are involved in the private banking sector. This sector saw a 4 percent increase in revenue year-over-year to $1.5 billion for the first quarter 2014. **Availability:** Print; Online.

9806 ▪ *"Slow but Steady into the Future"* in *Barron's (Vol. 88, July 7, 2008, No. 27, pp. M)*
Pub: Dow Jones & Company Inc.
Contact: Almar Latour, Chief Executive Officer

Ed: Mark Veverka. **Description:** Investors are advised to maintain their watch on the shares of business software company NetSuite. The company's chief executive officer, Zach Nelson, claims that the company has a 10-year lead on its competitors with the development of software-as-a service. **Availability:** Online.

9807 ▪ *"Small Firms Punch Ticket for Growth"* in *Houston Business Journal (Vol. 40, January 29, 2010, No. 38, pp. 1)*
Pub: Houston Business Journal
Contact: Bob Charlet, President
E-mail: bcharlet@bizjournals.com

Ed: Allison Wollam. **Description:** Independent ticket agencies anticipate growth as American and Canadian authorities approved a merger between Ticketmaster and concert promoter Live Nation. Expansion of service offerings and acquisition of venues have also been done by independent ticket agencies in light of the merger. Details of the merger are included. **Availability:** Print; Online.

9808 ▪ *"Small Is Bountiful for Intuit"* in *Barron's (Vol. 90, September 13, 2010, No. 37, pp. 22)*
Pub: Barron's Editorial & Corporate Headquarters

Ed: Mark Veverka. **Description:** Finance software maker Intuit wants to tap the underserved small business market. One analyst sees Intuit's shares rising 25 percent to 55 percent in the next 12 months from September 2010. **Availability:** Online.

9809 ▪ *"The Smell of Fear: Is a Bottom Near?"* in *Barron's (Vol. 88, March 17, 2008, No. 11, pp. M3)*
Pub: Dow Jones & Company Inc.
Contact: Almar Latour, Chief Executive Officer

Ed: Kopin Tan. **Description:** Liquidity problems at Bear Stearns frightened investors in markets around the world due to the fear of the prospects of a big bank's failure. Shares of health maintenance organizations got battered led by WellPoint, and Humana but longer-term investors who could weather short-term volatility may find value here. The value of J. Crew shares is also discussed. **Availability:** Online.

9810 ▪ *"A Socko Payout Menu: Rural Phone Carrier Plots to Supercharge Its Shares"* in *Barron's (Vol. 88, June 30, 2008, No. 26, pp. M5)*

Description: CenturyTel boosted its quarterly common payout to 70 cents from 6.75 cents per share die to its strong cash flows and solid balance sheet. Eastman Kodak's plan for a buyback will be partially funded by its $581 million tax refund. CME Group will buyback stocks through 2009 worth $1.1 billion. **Availability:** Online.

9811 ■ *"Software's Last Hurrah"* in *Canadian Business (Vol. 81, December 24, 2007, No. 1, pp. 27)*

Description: Canada's software industry could be facing a challenge with IBM's acquisition of Cognos, which was the country's last major independent business intelligence company and was also IBM's largest acquisition ever. Next in line to Cognos in terms of prominence is Open Text Corporation, which could also be a possible candidate for acquisition, as analysts predict. **Availability:** Print; Online.

9812 ■ *"The Solution Became the Problem"* in *Barron's (Vol. 92, August 25, 2012, No. 35, pp. 45)*

Pub: Dow Jones & Company Inc.

Contact: Almar Latour, Chief Executive Officer

Ed: John Steele Gordon. **Description:** Computers were seen as a solution to technology glitches affecting Wall Street during the 1960s. Telephones and paper proved inadequate in handling rising stock market volumes during the period. **Availability:** Online.

9813 ■ *"Some Relief Possible Following Painful Week"* in *Barron's (Vol. 88, July 14, 2008, No. 28, pp. M3)*

Pub: Dow Jones & Company Inc.

Contact: Almar Latour, Chief Executive Officer

Ed: Kopin Tan. **Description:** Dow Chemical is offering a 74 percent premium to acquire Rohm & Haas' coatings and electronics materials operations. Frontline amassed a 5.6 percent stake in rival Overseas Shipholding Group and a merger between the two would create a giant global fleet with pricing power. Highlights of the U.S. stock market during the week that ended in July 11, 2008 are discussed. Statistical data included. **Availability:** Online.

9814 ■ *"Spectre of Iran War Spooks Oil Markets"* in *Globe & Mail (March 28, 2007, pp. B1)*

Ed: Shawn McCarthy. **Description:** The increase in the price of crude oil by $5 a barrel to reach $68 in the United States following speculation over war against Iran, is discussed. **Availability:** Online.

9815 ■ *"Spin Zone: Where Hawaii's Leaders Face Off, Have High-Tech Tax Credits Helped or Hurt Hawaii?"* in *Hawaii Business (Vol. 53, December 2007, No. 6, pp. 28)*

Pub: PacificBasin Communications

Contact: Chuck Tindle, Director

E-mail: chuckt@pacificbasin.net

Description: Presents the opinons of Channel Capital LLC's Walter R. Roth and Hawaii Venture Capital Association's Bill Spencer concerning the impacts of tax credits. Roth thinks that Act 221 appeals to investors who can earn despite business failure while Spencer thinks that the legislation promotes investments in innovative technology firms. The need to support tax credits is also discussed. **Availability:** Print; Online.

9816 ■ *"Spotlight on Pensions"* in *Business Horizons (Vol. 51, March-April 2008, No. 2, pp. 105)*

Pub: Elsevier Advanced Technology Publications

Ed: Laureen A. Maines. **Description:** Perceptions of pension burden and risk among financial statement users is likely to increase with changes in pension accounting. These perceptions might affect decisions on pension commitments and investments. **Availability:** Online.

9817 ■ *"Spreading Your Wings"* in *Canadian Business (Vol. 81, March 17, 2008, No. 4, pp. 31)*

Ed: Megan Harman. **Released:** February 09, 2017. **Description:** Financing from angel investors is one avenue that should be explored by startups. Angel investors are typically affluent individuals who invest their own money. Angel investors usually want at least 10 times their initial investment within eight years but

they benefit the businesses through their help in decision-making and the industry expertise they provide. **Availability:** Download; Online.

9818 ■ *"Stand-Up Guy: From Bear Stearns to Bear Market"* in *Barron's (Vol. 88, July 7, 2008, No. 27, pp. L11)*

Pub: Dow Jones & Company Inc.

Contact: Almar Latour, Chief Executive Officer

Ed: Suzanne McGee. **Description:** James O'Shaughnessy, a mutual fund manager with O'Shaughnessy Asset Management, is bullish on both financial and energy stocks. He was formerly involved with Bear Stearns until he left the firm in March 2008. **Availability:** Online.

9819 ■ *"Startup Lucena Taking On Wall Street"* in *Atlanta Business Chronicle (May 23, 2014, pp. 1A)*

Pub: American City Business Journals, Inc.

Contact: Mike Olivieri, Executive Vice President

Description: Lucena Research is a predictive analytics startup firm developing software for the financial investment sector. The company's software helps investment professionals identify trading strategies and investing trends to reduce risk and increase returns. **Availability:** Print; Online.

9820 ■ *"State of Play"* in *Canadian Business (Vol. 79, June 19, 2006, No. 13, pp. 25)*

Description: Top 100 information technology companies in Canada are ranked by their market capitalization as of June 1. The statistics that show the revenues of these companies are also presented. **Availability:** Print; Online.

9821 ■ *"Steelhead Makes High-Tech Tanks"* in *Denver Business Journal (Vol. 65, March 28, 2014, No. 46, pp. A7)*

Pub: American City Business Journals, Inc.

Contact: Mike Olivieri, Executive Vice President

Released: Weekly. **Price:** $4, introductory 4-week offer(Digital only). **Description:** Steelhead Composites LLC is known for its high-technology tanks that hold pressurized gases. The company, which was founded in October 2012, aimed to tackle problems associated with long delivery times. Reports show that the firm's supporters have invested more than $5 million into the business. **Availability:** Print; Online.

9822 ■ *"STMicroelectronics"* in *Canadian Electronics (Vol. 23, February 2008, No. 1, pp. 1)*

Description: STMicroelectronics, a semiconductor maker, revealed that it plans to acquire Genesis Microchip Inc. Genesis develops image and video processing systems. It was reported that the acquisition has been approved by Genesis' Board of Directors. It is expected that Genesis will enhance STMicroelectronics' technological capabilities. **Availability:** Online.

9823 ■ *"Stock Car Racing"* in *Canadian Business (Vol. 81, September 15, 2008, No. 14-15, pp. 29)*

Description: Some analysts predict a Chapter 11-style tune-up making GM and Ford a speculative turnaround stock. However, the price of oil could make or break the shares of the Big Three U.S. automobile manufacturers and if oil goes up too high then a speculative stock to watch is an electric car company called Zenn Motor Co. **Availability:** Online.

9824 ■ *"A Stock Worth Trading Down To"* in *Barron's (Vol. 88, July 14, 2008, No. 28, pp. 36)*

Pub: Dow Jones & Company Inc.

Contact: Almar Latour, Chief Executive Officer

Ed: Alexander Eule. **Description:** Shares of Ralcorp Holdings are cheap at around $49.95 after slipping 20 percent prior to their acquisition of Post cereals from Kraft. Some analysts believe its shares could climb over 60 percent to $80 as value-seeking consumers buy more private label products. **Availability:** Print; Online.

9825 ■ *"Stressed Out: 7 St. Louis Banks Rated 'At Risks"* in *Saint Louis Business Journal (Vol. 32, September 16, 2011, No. 3, pp. 1)*

Pub: Saint Louis Business Journal

Contact: Robert Bobroff, President

E-mail: rbobroff@bizjournals.com

Ed: Greg Edwards. **Description:** St. Louis, Missouri has seven banks that are well above the 100 percent level that is considered 'at risk' based on a risk measurement called the Texas ratio. The banks are the Sun Security bank, 1st Advantage Bank, Superior Bank, Truman Bank, Reliance Bank, St. Louis Bank and Meramec Valley Bank. **Availability:** Online.

9826 ■ *"Stretch Your Last Dollar Or Invest It?"* in *Business Owner (Vol. 35, November-December 2011, No. 6, pp. 4)*

Description: Should small business owners cut expenses or invest in a downturned economy? Difficult times can be an opportunity to build a business brad. **Availability:** Print; Online.

9827 ■ *"A Strong, Aligned Board of Directors Is Ideal"* in *South Florida Business Journal (Vol. 35, August 1, 2014, No. 1, pp. 8)*

Pub: American City Business Journals, Inc.

Contact: Mike Olivieri, Executive Vice President

Released: Weekly. **Price:** $8, introductory 4-week offer(Digital only). **Description:** The advantages of an informed and congruent board of directors to a company are described. The board of directors should provide the company with a strategic business perspective, access to prospective investors, and potential strategic business partners to help a firm achieve its vision and goals. **Availability:** Print; Online.

9828 ■ *"A Study in Diversity: What Women Want: There Are Fundamental Differences Between How Men and Women View Retirement Planning"* in *Senior Market Advisor (Vol. 13, October 2012, No. 10, pp. 36)*

Description: An overview of women's attitudes towards finances and retirement planning is provided. Contrasting views are even held by male and female financial advisors. **Availability:** Print; Online.

9829 ■ *"Stymiest's RBC Compensation Triggers Shareholder Outrage"* in *Gl obe & Mail (January 28, 2006, pp. B3)*

Description: The concerns of shareholders over the issue of Royal Bank of Canada's $6.6 million pay package for chief executive officer Barbara Stymiest, in 2004, are presented. **Availability:** Print; Online.

9830 ■ *"Subprime Mess Hits Huntington"* in *Business First-Columbus (November 26, 2007, pp. A1)*

Pub: Business First

Contact: Nick Fortine, President

E-mail: nfortine@bizjournals.com

Ed: Adrian Burns. **Description:** Huntington Bancshares Inc. picked up a $1.5 billion exposure to the country's subprime mortgage mess. It caused the bank to set aside $450 million to cover increases in loan losses. When Huntington acquired Sky Financial, it absorbed a 17-year relationship Sky had with Franklin Credit Corporation, which is a subprime lender and servicer. **Availability:** Print; Online.

9831 ■ *"Sudbury Waits With Future Up in the Air"* in *Globe & Mail (February 22, 2006, pp. B1)*

Ed: Wendy Stueck. **Description:** The takeover of Falconbridge Ltd., by Inco Ltd Sudbury, is in the process with uncertainty. The transaction has been a long overdue. **Availability:** Online.

9832 ■ *"Surprise Package"* in *Business Courier (Vol. 27, June 25, 2010, No. 8, pp. 1)*

Pub: Business Courier

Ed: Dan Monk, Jon Newberry, Steve Watkins. **Description:** More than 60 percent of the chief executive officers (CEOs) in Greater Cincinnati's 35 public companies took a salary cut in 2009, but stock grants resulted in large paper gains for the CEOs. The salary cuts show efforts of boards of directors to observe austerity. Statistics on increased values of stock awards for CEOs, median pay for CEOs, and median shareholder return are also presented. **Availability:** Online.

9833 ■ "Surviving the Storm" in Canadian Business (Vol. 81, July 22, 2008, No. 12-13, pp. 50)

Description: Investment adviser Harry Dent and finance professor Paul Marsh discuss their views and forecasts on the United States' economic condition. Dent believes advisors should concentrate on wealth preservation rather than on returns. Other views regarding U.S. economic conditions are also presented. **Availability:** Print; Online.

9834 ■ "A Swifter, Better Marketplace" in Barron's (Vol. 89, July 13, 2009, No. 28, pp. M13)

Pub: Dow Jones & Company Inc.

Contact: Almar Latour, Chief Executive Officer

Ed: Eric W. Noll. **Description:** Listed-derivatives market is moving towards greater trading through computerized systems with an emphasis on speed and innovation. The market for listed options is also being changed by new techniques from other markets such as algorithmic trading, dark pools, and new-order priority systems. **Availability:** Online.

9835 ■ "Swinging For the Fences: The Effects of Ceo Stock Options on Company Risk Taking and Performance" in Academy of Management Journal (Vol. 50, No. 5, October 1, 2007, pp. 1055)

Pub: Academy of Management

Contact: Sharon Alvarez, President

Ed: Gerard Sanders, Donald C. Hambrick. **Description:** Study examines managerial risk-taking vis-a-vis stock options of the company; results reveal that stock options instigate CEOs to take unwise risks that could bring huge losses to the company. **Availability:** Electronic publishing; PDF; Download; Online.

9836 ■ "Take It to the Bank" in Barron's (Vol. 89, July 13, 2009, No. 28, pp. 20)

Pub: Dow Jones & Company Inc.

Contact: Almar Latour, Chief Executive Officer

Ed: Jim McTague. **Description:** Banks are one of the safest place to put one's principal due to the temporary increase in the Federal Deposit Insurance Corp.'s insurance of bank accounts up to $250,000 and also because of the Cdars (Certificates of Deposit Registry Service) program which spreads the deposit to several banks thereby making the account covered as if it the money was deposited at multiple banks. **Availability:** Online.

9837 ■ "Taking the Over-the-Counter Route to U.S." in Barron's (Vol. 88, July 7, 2008, No. 27, pp. 24)

Pub: Dow Jones & Company Inc.

Contact: Almar Latour, Chief Executive Officer

Ed: Eric Uhlfelder. **Description:** Many multinational companies have left the New York Stock Exchange and allowed their shares to trade over-the-counter. The companies have taken advantage of a 2007 SEC rule allowing publicly listed foreign companies to change trading venues if less than 5 percent of global trading volume in the past 12 months occurred in the US. **Availability:** Online.

9838 ■ "Tao of Downfall: the Failures of High-profile Entrepreneurs in the Chinese Economic Reform" in International Journal of Entrepreneurship and Small Business (Vol. 11, August 31, 2010, No. 2, pp. 121)

Ed: Wenxian Zhang, Ilan Alon. **Description:** Through historical reviews and case studies, this research seeks to understand why some initially successful entrepreneurs failed in the economic boom of past decades. Among various factors contributing to their

downfall are a unique political and business environment, fragile financial systems, traditional cultural influences and personal characteristics. **Availability:** Online.

9839 ■ "The Tech 100" in Canadian Business (Vol. 81, July 21, 2008, No. 11, pp. 48)

Description: Absolute Software Corp. Day4 Energy Inc., Sandvine Corp., Norsat International Inc. and Call Genie Inc. are the five technology firms included in the annual ranking of top companies in Canada by market capitalization. The services and the one-year total return potential of the companies are presented. **Availability:** Online.

9840 ■ "TEDx Talk Puts the Pieces Together" in Philadelphia Business Journal (Vol. 33, April 4, 2014, No. 8, pp. 6)

Pub: American City Business Journals, Inc.

Contact: Mike Olivieri, Executive Vice President

Description: Gabriel Investments managing partner, Richard Vague, shares his views about entrepreneurs wanting to start a company. Vague says they should be relentless because it takes a long time to start and run a business and it is a challenge to recruit customers and grow rapidly. He also states his experience as an entrepreneur enables him to give advice and put things into perspective for the people he mentors. **Availability:** Online.

9841 ■ "That's About It for Quantitative Easing" in Barron's (Vol. 89, July 20, 2009, No. 29, pp. M11)

Pub: Dow Jones & Company Inc.

Contact: Almar Latour, Chief Executive Officer

Ed: Brian Blackstone. **Description:** US Federal Reserve appears to have decided to halt quantitative easing, causing bond prices to drop and yields to rise. The yield for the 1-year Treasury bond rose more than 0.3 percentage point to about 3.65 percent. **Availability:** Online.

9842 ■ "These 10 Black Bankers Are Reshaping Wall Street" in Bloomberg.com(March 16, 2021)

URL(s): www.bloomberg.com/news/articles/2021-0 3-16/these-10-black-bankers-are-reshaping-wall-s treet?leadSource=uverify%20wall

Ed: Lananh Nguyen, Michelle F. Davis. **Released:** March 16, 2021. **Description:** Discusses the top Black bankers involved in Wall Street and their innovations and how they do business.

9843 ■ "They've Fallen, But Can Senior-Housing Stocks Get Up" in Barron's (Vol. 88, March 10, 2008, No. 10, pp. 43)

Pub: Dow Jones & Company Inc.

Contact: Almar Latour, Chief Executive Officer

Ed: Kopin Tan. **Description:** Shares of senior housing companies present buying opportunities to investors because of their low prices. Companies such as Brookdale Senior Living are not as dependent on housing prices but have suffered declines in share prices. **Availability:** Online.

9844 ■ "Three Ways Columbia's Stock Can Keep Rising" in Business Journal Portland (Vol. 30, February 21, 2014, No. 51, pp. 8)

Pub: American City Business Journals, Inc.

Contact: Mike Olivieri, Executive Vice President

Released: Weekly. **Price:** $4, Introductory 4-week offer(Digital & Print). **Description:** The shares of Columbia Sportswear Company reached a record high of $88.25 in February 2014. The company's cold-weather gear, its TurboDown technology and its new joint venture with China are expected to contribute significantly in keeping stock prices high. **Availability:** Print; Online.

9845 ■ "Time For a Change at Canon?" in Barron's (Vol. 92, July 23, 2012, No. 30, pp. 17)

Pub: Dow Jones & Company Inc.

Contact: Almar Latour, Chief Executive Officer

Ed: Neil A. Martin. **Description:** Stocks of Japanese imaging equipment maker Canon could lose value unless the company undergoes changes in opera-

tions and governance. Prices of the company's American Depositary Receipts could fall 20 percent from $37.22 per share within 12 months. **Availability:** Online.

9846 ■ "Time to Leave the Party? Re-Evaluating Commodities" in Barron's (Vol. 88, March 24, 2008, No. 12, pp. M16)

Pub: Dow Jones & Company Inc.

Contact: Almar Latour, Chief Executive Officer

Ed: Andrea Hotter. **Description:** Prices of commodities such as gold, copper, crude oil, sugar, cocoa, and wheat have fallen from their all-time highs set in the middle of March 2008. Analysts, however, caution that this decline in prices may be temporary, and that a banking crisis may trigger new price rises in commodities. **Availability:** Online.

9847 ■ "Time for a Little Pruning?" in Barron's (Vol. 89, July 6, 2009, No. 27, pp. 13)

Pub: Dow Jones & Company Inc.

Contact: Almar Latour, Chief Executive Officer

Ed: Dimitra DeFotis. **Description:** Investors are advised to avoid the shares of Whole Foods, American Tower, T. Rowe Price, Iron Mountain, Intuitive Surgical, Salesforce.com, and Juniper Networks due to their high price to earnings ratios. The shares of Amazon.com, Broadcom, and Expeditors International of Washington remain attractive to investors despite their high price to earnings ratios due to their strong growth. **Availability:** Online.

9848 ■ "To Sell or Not To Sell" in Inc. (December 2007, pp. 80)

Ed: Patrick J. Sauer. **Description:** Owner of a private equity discusses the challenges he faces when deciding to sell his family's business. **Availability:** Online.

9849 ■ "Too Much Precaution About Biotech Corn" in Barron's (Vol. 88, March 17, 2008, No. 11, pp. 54)

Pub: Dow Jones & Company Inc.

Contact: Almar Latour, Chief Executive Officer

Ed: Mark I. Schwartz. **Description:** In the U.S., 90 percent of cultivated soybeans are biotech varietals as well as 60 percent of the corn. Farmers have significantly reduced their reliance on pesticides in the growing of biotech corn. Biotech cotton cultivation has brought hundreds of millions of dollars in net financial gains to farmers. The European Union has precluded the cultivation or sale of biotech crops within its border. **Availability:** Online.

9850 ■ "Tool-o-Rama" in Barron's (Vol. 90, September 6, 2010, No. 36)

Pub: Barron's Editorial & Corporate Headquarters

Ed: Theresa W. Carey. **Description:** New trading tool features from several online brokers are discussed. The new features from Fidelity, ChoiceTrade, JunoTrade and TradeKing are examined. Investors can now screen exchanged traded funds in the same way as stocks with Fidelity, while ChoiceTrade can run in any browser without the need to install additional plug-ins. **Availability:** Online.

9851 ■ "Top 10 Retirement Mistakes and How to Avoid Them" in Canadian Business (Vol. 83, July 20, 2010, No. 11-12, pp. 39)

Pub: Rogers Media Inc.

Contact: Neil Spivak, Chief Executive Officer

Ed: Jacqueline Nelson, Angelina Chapin. **Description:** Some of the top retirement mistakes are relying on selling one's house to find a retirement. Other mistakes are paying too much for investments and planning to work in retirement since no one can be sure that they will be healthy enough to accomplish this. Suggestions to avoid these pitfalls are discussed. **Availability:** Print; Online.

9852 ■ "Top 50 In Total Revenue" in Canadian Business (Vol. 81, Summer 2008, No. 9, pp. 119)

Description: Table showing the top 50 Canadian companies in terms of total revenue is presented. Manulife Financial Corp. topped the list with revenue of 34.5 billion. The financial services firm is the 6th largest provider of life insurance in the world and the second largest in North America. **Availability:** Print; Online.

9853 ■ "Top 100 Indy Advisors" in Barron's (Vol. 92, August 25, 2012, No. 38, pp. S2)
Pub: Dow Jones & Company Inc.
Contact: Almar Latour, Chief Executive Officer

Ed: Suzanne McGee. **Description:** Profiles of five independent financial advisors included the Barron's Top 100 independent financial advisor rankings for 2012 are included. Their investment strategies are also discussed. **Availability:** Online.

9854 ■ "Top Law Firms Join Forces" in Business Journal Portland (Vol. 27, December 3, 2010, No. 40, pp. 1)
Pub: Portland Business Journal
Contact: Andy Giegerich, Managing Editor
E-mail: agiegerich@bizjournals.com

Description: Law Firms Powell PC and Roberts Kaplan LLP will forge a collaboration, whereby 17 Roberts Kaplan attorneys will join the Portland, Oregon-based office of Lane Powell. The partnership is expected to strengthen the law firms' grip on Portland's banking clients. **Availability:** Print; Online.

9855 ■ "Top Pension Fund Sends a Warning" in Barron's (Vol. 92, July 23, 2012, No. 30, pp. M9)
Pub: Dow Jones & Company Inc.
Contact: Almar Latour, Chief Executive Officer

Ed: Michael Aneiro. **Description:** The California Public Employees' Retirement System reported a 1 percent return on investments for the fiscal year ended June 30, 2012. It lost 7.2 percent on stock investments, 11 percent on forest-land holdings and 2 percent on absolute-return assets, negating a 12.7 percent gain on its fixed-income investments. **Availability:** Online.

9856 ■ "Toyota Marks Record Profit Sales" in Globe & Mail (February 7, 2007, pp. B10)
Description: The record quarterly sales and earnings reported by Japanese automaker Toyota Motor Corp. are discussed. The company sold 2.16 million vehicles during the quarter while registering 426.8 billion yen in profits. **Availability:** Print; Online.

9857 ■ "A Trader Gets a Better Deal From the IRS Than an Investor" in Barron's (Vol. 88, March 31, 2008, No. 13, pp. 56)
Pub: Dow Jones & Company Inc.
Contact: Almar Latour, Chief Executive Officer

Ed: Dan McGuire. **Description:** There is a $3,000 a year annual limit to deducting investor's losses and normal investment expenses are purportedly deductible as miscellaneous expenses on Schedule A only to the extent that they exceed two percent of adjusted gross income. Professional gamblers who can use Schedule C are unable deduct a net gaming loss against income from any other sources. **Availability:** Online.

9858 ■ "Transcontinental to Exchange Assets with Quad/Graphics" in American Printer (Vol. 128, August 1, 2011, No. 8)
Description: Transcontinental Inc. and Quad/Graphics Inc. entered into an agreement where Transcontinental will indirectly acquire all shares of Quad Graphics Canada Inc. **Availability:** Print; Online.

9859 ■ "A Trend Is His Friend" in Barron's (Vol. 89, July 27, 2009, No. 30, pp. 28)
Pub: Dow Jones & Company Inc.
Contact: Almar Latour, Chief Executive Officer

Ed: Eric Uhlfelder. **Description:** Global Diversified Program fund under Quality Capital Management is managed through a trading system called the Advanced Resource Allocator which rebalances short-term tactical moves to gather quick profits. CEO Aref Karim's allocations are based on risk and he says their sentiments toward the market conditions are agnostic. **Availability:** Online.

9860 ■ "Trust Buyouts Not My Fault, Flaherty Says" in Globe & Mail (April 3, 2007, pp. B1)
Ed: Tara Perkins, Doug Saunders, Steven Chase. **Description:** The causes of the acquisition of Canadian firms by foreign investors are discussed by the Canadian Finance Minister Jim Flaherty. **Availability:** Online.

9861 ■ "Two Small Broker-Dealers Are Down — and Out" in Investment News (October 10, 2019)
URL(s): www.investmentnews.com/article/20191010/
FREE/191019995/two-small-broker-dealers-are
-down-x2014-and-out
Ed: Bruce Kelly. **Released:** October 10, 2019. **Description:** Taylor Capital Management and Triloma Securities are both closing up shop, both for different reasons. Taylor is suffering from the 1 Global fraud, which has wiped out all of their reps, while Triloma is just not generating enough sales to stay open. **Availability:** Online.

9862 ■ "An Unfair Knock on Nokia" in Barron's (Vol. 88, March 10, 2008, No. 10, pp. 36)
Pub: Dow Jones & Company Inc.
Contact: Almar Latour, Chief Executive Officer

Ed: Mark Veverka. **Description:** Discusses the decision by the brokerage house Exane to recommend a Sell on Nokia shares, presumably due to higher inventories, which is unfounded. The news that the company's inventories are rising is not an indicator of falling demand for its products. The company is also benefiting from solid management and rising market share. **Availability:** Online.

9863 ■ "Unilever Acquiring Danish Operations of Diplom-Is Ice Cream" in Ice Cream Reporter (Vol. 23, August 20, 2010, No. 9, pp. 1)
Description: Unilever will acquire Danish operations of the ice cream company Diplom-Is from Norwegian dairy group Tine. **Availability:** Print; Online.

9864 ■ "Unilever Acquiring EVGA's Ice Cream Brands in Greece" in Ice Cream Reporter (Vol. 23, October 20, 2010, No. 11, pp. 1)
Description: Unilever will acquire the ice cream brands and distribution network of the Greek frozen dessert manufacturer EVGA. **Availability:** Print; Online.

9865 ■ "Unpleasant Surprise - When a Stock Distribution is Taxed as Dividend Income" in Barron's (Vol. 88, March 24, 2008, No. 12, pp. 60)
Pub: Dow Jones & Company Inc.
Contact: Almar Latour, Chief Executive Officer

Ed: Shirley A. Lazo. **Description:** Discusses the $175 million that footwear company Genesco received in a settlement with Finish Line and UBS is considered as a stock distribution and is taxable as dividend income. Railroad company CSX raised its quarterly common payout from 15 cents to 18 cents. **Availability:** Online.

9866 ■ "The Upside of Fear and Loathing" in Barron's (Vol. 88, March 24, 2008, No. 12, pp. 11)
Pub: Dow Jones & Company Inc.
Contact: Almar Latour, Chief Executive Officer

Ed: Michael Santoli. **Description:** Fear and risk aversion prevalent among investors may actually serve to cushion the decline and spark a rally in US stock prices. Surveys of investors indicate rising levels of anxiety and bearishness, indicating a possible positive turnaround. **Availability:** Online.

9867 ■ Using Other People's Money to Get Rich: Secrets, Techniques, and Strategies Investors Use Every Day Using OPM to Make Millions
Pub: Atlantic Publishing Co.
Contact: Dr. Heather L. Johnson, Contact

Ed: Eric J. Leech. **Released:** 2010. **Price:** $22.34. **Description:** Discussion showing individuals how to invest using other people's money. **Availability:** Print; Online.

9868 ■ "Valener Announces that Gaz Metro has Achieved a Key Step in Acquiring CVPS" in CNW Group (September 30, 2011)
Pub: CNW Group Ltd.

Description: Valener Inc., which owns about 29 percent of Gaz Metro Ltd. Partnership, announced that Gaz Metro welcomes the sale of Central Vermont Public Service Corporation (CVPS). Valener owns an indirect interest of 24.5 percent in the wind power projects jointly developed by Beaupre Eole General Partnership and Boralex Inc. on private lands in Quebec. Details of the deal are included. **Availability:** Print; Online.

9869 ■ "Valenti: Roots of Financial Crisis Go Back to 1998" in Crain's Detroit Business (Vol. 24, October 6, 2008, No. 40, pp. 25)
Pub: Crain Communications Inc.
Contact: Barry Asin, President

Ed: Tom Henderson, Nathan Skid. **Description:** Interview with Sam Valenti III who is the chairman and CEO of Valenti Capital L.L.C., a wealth-management firm; Valenti discusses in detail the history that led up to the current economic crisis as well as his prediction for the future of the country. **Availability:** Print; Online.

9870 ■ "Venture Gap" in Canadian Business (Vol. 81, February 26, 2008, No. 4, pp. 82)
Pub: Rogers Media Inc.
Contact: Neil Spivak, Chief Executive Officer

Ed: Joe Castaldo. **Description:** Money raised by Canadian venture capitalist firms has been declining since 2001. A strong venture capital market is important if Canada is to build innovative companies. Fixing Canada's tax policy on foreign investments is a start in reviving the industry. **Availability:** Print; Online.

9871 ■ "Virtue and Vice" in Entrepreneur (September 2014)
Pub: Entrepreneur Media Inc.
Contact: Dan Bova, Director
E-mail: dbova@entrepreneur.com

Description: Socially responsible investments (SRI) are rising in the U.S., but many claim that vice funds offer better returns. Vice fund proponents argue that any profitable company deserves a place in a good investment portfolio. SRI proponents emphasize investments that benefit the society. Analysts note that investors who restrict their investment landscape by selecting only vice funds or only SRI funds may lead to lower returns. Other specialized funds attract activist investors supporting advocacies like gender equality or a positive work environment. **Availability:** PDF; Online.

9872 ■ "Virtus.com Wins 'Best of Industry' WebAward for Excellence in Financial Services" in Investment Weekly News (October 24, 2009, pp. 227)
Pub: Investment Weekly News

Description: Web Marketing Association honored Virtus.com, the Website of Virtus Investment Partners, Inc., for Outstanding Achievement in Web Development and Acsys Interactive was awarded the Financial Services Standard of Excellence Award for developing the site. The site was part of a rebranding effort and is a one-stop portal for both financial advisors and their investors. **Availability:** Online.

9873 ■ "Voice: Rebuilding Trust" in Business Strategy Review (Vol. 21, Summer 2010, No. 2, pp. 79-80)
Ed: David De Cremer. **Released:** June 24, 2010. **Description:** The financial world's attempts to rebuild trust are charted. Three steps to jump-start that process are outlined. **Availability:** Print; PDF; Online.

9874 ■ *"Wabtec Delivering Strategic Plan for Long-term Growth" in Pittsburgh Business Times (Vol. 33, July 11, 2014, No. 52, pp. 10)*

Pub: American City Business Journals, Inc.

Contact: Mike Olivieri, Executive Vice President

Released: July 2014. **Description:** Raymond Betler, new CEO of Wabtec Corporation, the only company with a 13-year streak of annual stock price increase on US exchanges is profiled. Betler attributes the company's growth to four corporate strategies, including to grow internationally, focus on new product development, expand after-market opportunities, and pursue acquisitions. **Availability:** Print; Online.

9875 ■ *"Wall Street Is No Friend to Radical Innovation" in Harvard Business Review (Vol. 88, July-August 2010, No. 7-8, pp. 28)*

Pub: Harvard Business Publishing

Contact: Diane Belcher, Managing Director

Ed: Julia Kirby. **Price:** $6, PDF. **Description:** Research indicates that investors are skittish about backing a business that proposes significant changes to its product or service status quo. **Availability:** Online; PDF.

9876 ■ *"Weather Jitters Boost Coffee" in Barron's (Vol. 92, July 23, 2012, No. 30, pp. M12)*

Pub: Dow Jones & Company Inc.

Contact: Almar Latour, Chief Executive Officer

Ed: Alexandra Wexler. **Description:** Coffee futures prices rose by 20 percent as rains in Brazil sparked concerns about the crop's size and quality. Arabica futures for September 2012 delivery rose to $1.8695/pound and could exceed $2/pound by the end of the summer. **Availability:** Online.

9877 ■ *"A Week of the Worst Kind of Selling" in Barron's (Vol. 88, June 30, 2008, No. 26, pp. M3)*

Pub: Dow Jones & Company Inc.

Contact: Almar Latour, Chief Executive Officer

Ed: Kopin Tan. **Description:** In the week that ended in June 27, 2008 the selloff in the U.S. stock market was brought on by mounting bank losses and the spread of economic slowdown on top of high oil prices. The 31 percent decrease in the share price of Ingersoll-Rand since October 2007 may have factored in most of its risks. The company has completed its acquisition of Trane to morph into a refrigeration-equipment company. **Availability:** Online.

9878 ■ *"Well-Timed Entrance" in Barron's (Vol. 92, July 23, 2012, No. 30, pp. 24)*

Pub: Dow Jones & Company Inc.

Contact: Almar Latour, Chief Executive Officer

Ed: Michael Aneiro. **Description:** Dan Ivascyn, portfolio manager of Pimco Income Fund, discusses the fund's investment bonds. The fund is heavily invested in mortgage-backed securities and is positioned for a low-interest-rate environment well into 2014 or 2015. **Availability:** Online.

9879 ■ *"Wenzel Downhole Tools Ltd. Announces First Quarter Results for 2007" in Marketwired (May 14, 2007)*

Pub: Comtex News Network Inc.

Contact: Kan Devnani, President

Description: Wenzel Downhole Tools Ltd., a manufacturer, renter, and seller of drilling tools used in gas and oil exploration, announced its financial results for the first quarter ended March 31, 2007 which includes achieved revenues of $14.5 million. Statistical data included. **Availability:** Print; Online.

9880 ■ *"Western & Southern to Trim Rich Retirement Plan" in Business Courier (Vol. 27, October 15, 2010, No. 24, pp. 1)*

Pub: Business Courier

Ed: Dan Monk. **Description:** Insurance firm Western & Southern Financial Group announced that it will reduce the pension benefits of its 4,000 associates by more than 30 percent starting January 1, 2011. The move is expected to reduce annual retirement payments by several thousand dollars per associate. Western is a Fortune 500 company and has $34 billion in total assets. **Availability:** Print; Online.

9881 ■ *"Weyerhaeuser's REIT Decision Shouldn't Scare Investors Away" in Barron's (Vol. 88, June 30, 2008, No. 26, pp. 18)*

Pub: Dow Jones & Company Inc.

Contact: Almar Latour, Chief Executive Officer

Ed: Christopher Williams. **Description:** Weyerhaeuser Co.'s management said that a conversion to a real estate investment trust was not likely in 2009 since the move is not tax-efficient as of the moment and would overload its non-timber assets with debt. The company's shares have fallen by 19.5 percent. However, the company remains an asset-rich outfit and its activist shareholder is pushing for change. **Availability:** Online.

9882 ■ *"What Has Sergey Wrought?" in Barron's (Vol. 89, July 13, 2009, No. 28, pp. 8)*

Pub: Dow Jones & Company Inc.

Contact: Almar Latour, Chief Executive Officer

Ed: Alan Abelson. **Description:** Sergey Aleynikov is a computer expert that once worked for Goldman Sachs but he was arrested after he left the company and charged with theft for bringing with him the code for the company's proprietary software for high-frequency trading. The stock market has been down for four straight weeks as of July 13, 2009 which reflects the reality of how the economy is still struggling. **Availability:** Online.

9883 ■ *"What Online Brokers Are Doing To Keep Their Customers' Accounts Safe" in Barron's (Vol. 88, March 10, 2008, No. 10, pp. 37)*

Pub: Dow Jones & Company Inc.

Contact: Almar Latour, Chief Executive Officer

Ed: Theresa W. Carey. **Description:** Online brokerage firms employ different methods to protect the accounts of their customers from theft. These methods include secure Internet connections, momentary passwords, and proprietary algorithms. **Availability:** Online.

9884 ■ *"Whatever Happened to TGIF? How Much Of the Recession Is Priced in Stocks?" in Barron's (Vol. 88, March 10, 2008, No. 10, pp. M3)*

Pub: Dow Jones & Company Inc.

Contact: Almar Latour, Chief Executive Officer

Ed: Kopin Tan. **Description:** US stock markets fell in early March 2008 to their lowest level in 18 months, venturing close to entering a bear market phase. The S&P 500 has dropped an average of 0.78 percent on Fridays for 2008. **Availability:** Online.

9885 ■ *"What's More Important: Stag or Flation?" in Barron's (Vol. 88, July 14, 2008, No. 28, pp. M8)*

Pub: Dow Jones & Company Inc.

Contact: Almar Latour, Chief Executive Officer

Ed: Randall W. Forsyth. **Description:** Economists are divided on which part of stagflation, an economic situation in which inflation and economic stagnation occur simultaneously and remain unchecked for a period of time, is more important. Some economists say that the Federal government is focusing on controlling inflation while others see the central bank as extending its liquidity facilities to the financial sector. **Availability:** Online.

9886 ■ *"When to Roll Over" in Black Enterprise (Vol. 37, November 2006, No. 4, pp. 50)*

Pub: Earl G. Graves Ltd.

Contact: Earl Graves, Jr., President

Ed: Carolyn M. Brown. **Description:** Being proactive and rolling over your funds if you own stock of your former employee will give you more control over your money, especially if the company merges or is sold. **Availability:** Online.

9887 ■ *"Where the Money Is" in Conde Nast Portfolio (Vol. 2, June 2008, No. 6, pp. 113)*

Description: Revenue generated from treatments for common brain disorders that are currently on the market are listed. **Availability:** Online.

9888 ■ *"Where to Stash Your Cash" in Barron's (Vol. 88, March 17, 2008, No. 11, pp. 41)*

Pub: Dow Jones & Company Inc.

Contact: Almar Latour, Chief Executive Officer

Ed: Mike Hogan. **Description:** Investors are putting their money in money-market mutual funds seeking fractionally better yields and a safe haven from the uncertainties that was brought about by subprime lending. These funds, however, are hovering near 3.20 percent which is less than the 4 percent inflation rate. **Availability:** Online.

9889 ■ *"Whistling Past the Graveyard? Higher Quality Stocks Beckon to Investors?" in Barron's (Vol. 88, March 17, 2008, No. 11, pp. 15)*

Pub: Dow Jones & Company Inc.

Contact: Almar Latour, Chief Executive Officer

Ed: Michael Santoli. **Description:** Discusses the Federal Reserve's move to provide $200 billion to the system which can be seen as an effort to avoid the liquidity problems that Bear Stearns suffered. The Federal Reserve's move seems to frighten investors rather than reassure them. **Availability:** Online.

9890 ■ *"Why Asset Allocation Is Important: Don't Only Focus On Your Client's Finances, Start With Their Goals" in Retirement Advisor (Vol. 13, October 2012, No. 10, pp. 20)*

Ed: Lloyd Lofton. **Description:** Asset allocation can help investors, particularly seniors, to manage risk when planning investments. Diversity means spreading assets into three major classes of stocks, bonds and fixed products. These investments should be reviewed annually. **Availability:** Print; Online.

9891 ■ *"Why Intel Should Dump Its Flash-Memory Business" in Barron's (Vol. 88, March 10, 2008, No. 10, pp. 35)*

Pub: Dow Jones & Company Inc.

Contact: Almar Latour, Chief Executive Officer

Ed: Eric J. Savitz. **Description:** Intel Corp. must sell its NAND flash-memory business as soon as it possibly can to the highest bidder to focus on its PC processor business and take advantage of other business opportunities. Apple should consider a buyback of 10 percent of the company's shares to lift its stock. **Availability:** Online.

9892 ■ *"Why Optimism Over Europe Won't Last" in Barron's (Vol. 92, August 25, 2012, No. 38, pp. M6)*

Pub: Dow Jones & Company Inc.

Contact: Almar Latour, Chief Executive Officer

Ed: Jonathan Buck. **Description:** European markets could experience losses in the second half of 2012 as uncertainty over political events could wipe out market gains. Greece has to abide by the terms of ts agreements with creditors to receive bailout funds. The stock prices of BG Group could gain as much as 20 percent in 2013 due to its strong lifquified natural gas business. **Availability:** Online.

9893 ■ *"Why the Rout in Financials Isn't Over" in Barron's (Vol. 88, June 30, 2008, No. 26, pp. 23)*

Pub: Dow Jones & Company Inc.

Contact: Almar Latour, Chief Executive Officer

Ed: Robin Goldwyn Blumenthal. **Description:** Top market technician Louise Yamada warns that the retreat in the shares of financial services is not yet over based on her analysis of stock charts. Yamada's analysis of the charts of Citigroup, Fifth Third Bancorp and Merrill Lynch are discussed together with the graphs for these shares. Statistical data included. **Availability:** Online.

9894 ■ *"Why This Investing Expert Is Bullish On the Energy Sector: William Heard Expects the Changing Landscape to Lead to Greater Opportunities"* in *Black Enterprise* (Vol. 45, July-August 2014, No. 1, pp. 25)

Pub: Earl G. Graves Ltd.

Contact: Earl Graves, Jr., President

Description: Profile of William Heard and his firm Heard Capital, LLC, the Chicago-based investment company that invests in telecommunications, media, technology, financials, industrials, and energy. Heard shares his investment philosophy and current investments.

9895 ■ *"Why WestJet's Culture Guru Chooses to Fly Under the Radar"* in *Globe & Mail* (January 22, 2007, pp. B1)

Ed: Brent Jang. **Description:** The views of cofounder Donald Bell of WestJet Airlines Ltd. on company's shares and services are presented. **Availability:** Online.

9896 ■ *"Wielding a Big Ax"* in *Barron's* (Vol. 89, July 13, 2009, No. 28, pp. 26)

Pub: Dow Jones & Company Inc.

Contact: Almar Latour, Chief Executive Officer

Ed: Shirley A. Lazo. **Description:** Weyerhaeuser cut their quarterly common payout by 80 percent from 25 cents to a nickel a share which they say will help them preserve their long-term value and improve their performance. Paccar also cut their quarterly dividend by half to nine cents a share. Walgreen however, boosted their quarterly dividend by 22.2 percent to 13.75 cents a share. **Availability:** Online.

9897 ■ *"Winners & Losers"* in *Canadian Business* (Vol. 85, July 16, 2012, No. 11-12, pp. 22)

Description: Canadian Pacific Railway's 4,800 locomotive engineers and conductors walked out in protest of the proposed work rules and pension cuts. Shareholders rejected a $25-million bonus and retention payout to Astral Media chief executive officer Ian Greenburg. The Dragon spacecraft of Space Exploration Technologies delivered supplies and experiments to the International Space Station. **Availability:** Print.

9898 ■ *Wisdom From Rich Dad, Poor Dad*

Released: October 25, 2016. **Price:** $5.95, hardcover. **Description:** What the wealthy teach their children about money that others do not. **Availability:** Print.

9899 ■ *"With the Indian Market, You Take Good With the Bad"* in *Globe & Mail* (March 23, 2007, pp. B11)

Ed: David Parkinson. **Description:** The performance of Bombay Stock Exchange in the month of February 2007 is analyzed. The impact of growing economy on the stock market performance is also analyzed. **Availability:** Print; Online.

9900 ■ *"With Mine Approval, Crystallex's Value as Target Seen on Rise"* in *Globe & Mail* (March 28, 2006, pp. B3)

Ed: Wendy Stueck. **Description:** Crystallex International Corp. obtains Venezuelan Ministry of Basic Industry and Mining's authorization on Las Cristinas mining project. The impact of the approval, which posted rise in shares by 21 percent for the company, is discussed.

9901 ■ *"Workplaces: The Human Element"* in *Canadian Business* (Vol. 80, April 23, 2007, No. 9, pp. 78)

Pub: National Association of EMS Educators

Contact: Bryan Ericson, President

Ed: Jeff Sanford. **Description:** The effects of human resource programs on stocks and investor relations are presented. **Availability:** Print; Online.

9902 ■ *"A World of Opportunity: Foreign Markets Offer Diversity to Keen Investors"* in *Canadian Business* (Vol. 81, Summer 2008, No. 9)

Description: International Monetary Fund projected in its 'World Economy Outlook' that there is a 25 percent chance that a global recession will occur in 2008 and 2009. Global growth rate is forecasted at 3.7 percent in 2008. Inflation in Asia emerging markets and forecasts on stock price indexes are presented. **Availability:** Online.

9903 ■ *"World's Best CEOs"* in *Barron's* (Vol. 88, March 24, 2008, No. 12, pp. 33)

Pub: Dow Jones & Company Inc.

Contact: Almar Latour, Chief Executive Officer

Ed: Andrew Bary. **Description:** Listing of the 30 best chief executive officers worldwide which was compiled through interviews with investors and analysts, analysis of financial and stock market performance, and leadership and industry stature.

9904 ■ *"The Worst Lies Ahead for Wall Street: More Losses Certain; More Expensive Capital to Be Needed"* in *Crain's New York Business* (Vol. 24, January 20, 2008, No. 3, pp. 1)

Pub: Crain Communications, Inc.

Contact: Jessica Botos, Manager, Marketing

E-mail: jessica.botos@crainsnewyork.com

Ed: Aaron Elstein. **Description:** Due to the weakening economy, many financial institutions will face further massive losses forcing them to borrow more at higher interest rates and dragging down their earnings for years to come. The effects on commercial real estate and credit card loans are also discussed as well as the trend to investing in Asia and the Middle East. **Availability:** Online.

9905 ■ *"Xstrata's Takeover Bid Comes Up Short in Shareholders' Eyes"* in *Globe & Mail* (March 27, 2007, pp. B16)

Ed: Andy Hoffman. **Description:** The share holders of LionOre Mining International have expressed dissatisfaction over $4.6 billion take over by Xstrata PLC. Share holders are demanding more prices for share value. **Availability:** Online.

9906 ■ *"Year In Review: Houston-Area IPOs Included Nation's Largest"* in *Houston Business Journal* (Vol. 44, January 3, 2014, No. 35, pp. 5)

Pub: American City Business Journals, Inc.

Contact: Mike Olivieri, Executive Vice President

Released: January 03, 2014. **Description:** A list of the initial public offerings (IPOs) held in Houston, Texas, during 2013 is presented. Houston-based Frank's International NV's IPO raised $712 million in August at $22 share price and Cheniere Energy Partners LP Holdings LLC raised $677 million at $20 share price in December. Both companies were included among the nation's largest IPOs. **Availability:** Print; Online.

9907 ■ *"Yield Vanishes, Inflation Lurks"* in *Barron's* (Vol. 92, September 17, 2012, No. 38, pp. M12)

Description: The US Federal Reserve's announcement of a third round of quantitative easing resulted in lower yields for bonds. Investors are becoming concerned with the probability of a rise in inflation after th quantitative easing program expires. **Availability:** Online.

9908 ■ *"You Won't Go Broke Filling Up On The Stock"* in *Barron's* (Vol. 88, July 14, 2008, No. 28, pp. 38)

Pub: Dow Jones & Company Inc.

Contact: Almar Latour, Chief Executive Officer

Ed: Assif Shameen. **Description:** Due to high economic growth, pro-business policies and a consumption boom, the Middle East is a good place to look for equities. The best ways in which to gain exposure to this market include investing in the real estate industry and telecommunications markets as well as large banks that serve corporations and consumers. **Availability:** Online.

9909 ■ *"Young Money"*

Pub: Grand Central Publishing

Contact: Michael Pietsch, Chairman

Released: February 18, 2014. **Price:** $27, hardcover. **Description:** How the financial crisis of 2008 changed a generation and remade Wall Street is discussed. The author spent three years following eight entry-level workers at Goldman Sachs, Bank of America Merrill Lynch and other leading investment firms. These young bankers are exposed to the exhausting workloads, huge bonuses, and recreational drugs that have always characterized Wall Street life, but as they get their education and training, they face questions about ethics, prestige and the value of their work. **Availability:** E-book; Print; Audio.

9910 ■ *"Young People Speak Out On Credit Union Board Involvement"* in *Credit Union Times* (Vol. 21, July 14, 2010, No. 27, pp. 20)

Ed: Myriam DiGiovanni. **Description:** Results of a Credit Union Times survey of Generation Y individuals about serving on Credit Union boards across the country are examined. **Availability:** Online.

9911 ■ *"Your Exposure to Bear Stearns"* in *Barron's* (Vol. 88, March 17, 2008, No. 11, pp. 45)

Pub: Dow Jones & Company Inc.

Contact: Almar Latour, Chief Executive Officer

Ed: Tom Sullivan, Jack Willoughby. **Description:** Bear Stearns makes up 5.5 percent of Pioneer Independence's portfolio, 1.4 percent of Vanguard Windsor II's portfolio, 1.2 percent of Legg Mason Value Trust, about 1 percent of Van Kampen Equity & Income, and 0.79 percent of Putnam Fund for Growth & Income. Ginnie Mae securities are now trading at 1.78 percentage points over treasuries due to the mortgage crises. **Availability:** Online.

9912 ■ *"Zara Eludes the Pain in Spain: Clothing Giant Inditex Sees Its First-Quarter Profits Rise By 30 Percent"* in *Canadian Business* (Vol. 85, September 17, 2012, No. 14, pp. 67)

Ed: Bryan Borzykowski. **Released:** September 17, 2012. **Description:** Clothing retailer Inditex reported a 30 percent increase in profit in the first quarter of 2012 and 15 percent increase in sales year over year. The company's unique business model was attributed to its growth, which also appeals to income investors.

9913 ■ *"Zell Takes a Gamble on Tribune"* in *Globe & Mail* (April 3, 2007, pp. B1)

Ed: Sinclair Stewart. **Description:** The purchase of the majority share in Tribune Co. by Samuel Zell is described. Samuel Zell's plans to keep the company's assets intact are discussed. **Availability:** Online.

9914 ■ *"Zucker's HBC Shakeup Imminent"* in *Globe & Mail* (February 20, 2006, pp. B3)

Ed: Marina Strauss. **Description:** The plans of investor Jerry Zucker to revamp Hudson's Bay Co., upon its acquisition, are presented. **Availability:** Online.

TRADE PERIODICALS

9915 ■ *Barron's*

Pub: Dow Jones & Company Inc.

Contact: Almar Latour, Chief Executive Officer

URL(s): www.dowjones.com/products/barrons

Released: Weekly **Price:** $4, for 2 / 4 weeks 1 year. **Description:** Business and finance magazine. **Availability:** Print; Online.

9916 ■ *Bernie Shaeffer's Option Advisor*

Pub: Schaeffer's Investment Research Inc.

Contact: Bernie Schaeffer, Chief Executive Officer

URL(s): store.schaeffersresearch.com/produc t_pages/option_advisor

Released: Monthly **Price:** $149, for 1 mth autocharge; $395, for 3 month auto-charge; $1,295, for 12 months. **Description:** Makes both aggressive and conservative recommendations on listed stock options for the individual investor. Reports on news pertinent to the options market including new options listings, and suggested brokerage firms. **Remarks:** Subscription includes a telephone hotline service and approximately six special bulletins per year. **Availability:** Print.

9917 ■ *Bollinger Band Letter*
Pub: Bollinger Capital Management Inc.
Contact: John Bollinger, President
URL(s): www.bollingerbands.com/bollinger-band-le
tter
Released: Monthly **Price:** $19, Individuals for first issue; $39, for month. **Description:** Provides investors with specific investment advice on stocks, bonds, precious metals, oil, and the dollar. Contains in-depth analysis, charts, and forecasts, with investment recommendations based on a technically driven Asset Allocation model developed by John Bollinger. **Availability:** Online.

9918 ■ *The Bowser Database*
Pub: The Bowser Report
Contact: Cindy Bowser, Editor
URL(s): simplecirc.com/subscribe/the-bowser-da
tabase
Price: $99, for annual; $39, Single issue. **Description:** Provides extensive information on stocks valued at $3/share or less. **Availability:** Online.

9919 ■ *Global Investment Magazine: The Journal of Money Management, Trading and Global Asset Services*
Pub: Global Investment Technology
Released: Biweekly **Price:** $995, Individuals; $1,075, Other countries. **Description:** Professional journal for the securities and investment industry. **Availability:** Print.

9920 ■ *The Journal of Investing*
Pub: Institutional Investor L.L.C.
Contact: David Antin, Chief Executive Officer
E-mail: dantin@institutionalinvestor.com
URL(s): www.iijournals.com/toc/joi/current
Price: $965, Institutions for 1 year; $1,834, Institutions for 2 year; $2,606, Institutions for 3 year. **Description:** Trade journal covering investing. **Availability:** Print; PDF; Online.

9921 ■ *The KonLin Letter*
Pub: Kon-Lin Research & Analysis Corp.
Contact: Konrad J. Kuhn, Publisher Publisher
URL(s): www.konlin.com
Released: Monthly **Price:** $95, Individuals; $115, Other countries. **Description:** Provides investment advice on stocks under $10, especially Emerging Growth and Special Situations stock poised for Explosive Price Appreciation Potential. Makes specific buy and sell recommendations and monitors a broad range of technical indicators for the best possible market timing advice. **Availability:** Print; PDF; Download; Online.

9922 ■ *MMA Cycles Report*
Pub: Merriman Market Analyst
Contact: Raymond A. Merriman, President
URL(s): www.mmacycles.com/product/mma-monthly
-cycles-report
Released: Monthly **Price:** $35, for a month (one time and automatic); $95, for 3 months (one time and automatic); $325, for a year (one time and automatic). **Description:** Presents summaries and analyses on the stock market, precious metals, T-bonds, currencies, and grains. **Availability:** Electronic publishing; PDF.

9923 ■ *The Moneychanger*
Pub: The Moneychanger
Contact: Franklin Sanders, Owner
URL(s): store.the-moneychanger.com/products/
moneychanger-newsletter
Released: Monthly; except September. **Price:** $149, for one year 12 issue; $94, Single issue; $159, Single issue. **Description:** Makes investment recommendations congruent with the editors' attempts to help Christians prosper with their principles intact in an age of monetary and moral chaos. Focuses on the gold and silver markets. Recurring features include interviews and columns titled Current Market Projections and Unforgettable (quotes and commentary). **Availability:** Online.

9924 ■ *The Option Strategist Newsletter*
Pub: McMillan Analysis Corporation
Contact: Lawrence G. McMillan, President
URL(s): www.optionstrategist.com/advertising
Released: Semimonthly **Price:** $129, Single issue. **Description:** Discusses options on stocks, indices, and futures. Includes investment recommendations and educational articles. **Availability:** Print.

9925 ■ *The Secured Lender*
Pub: Secured Finance Network
Contact: Michele Ocejo, Director, Communications
E-mail: mocejo@sfnet.com
URL(s): www.sfnet.com/home/industry-data-publica
tions/the-secured-lender
Released: 6/year **Price:** $105, Nonmembers for 2 year; $65, Nonmembers for 1 year. **Description:** Bimonthly. Free to members. **Availability:** Print; Online.

9926 ■ *Vickers Weekly Insider Report*
Pub: Vickers Stock Research Corp.
Contact: Joseph Dorsey, Chief Executive Officer
URL(s): www.vickers-stock.com/account/about/winsi
der.asp
Released: Weekly **Description:** Reports on stock insider transactions and maintains portfolios based on insider buy signals-96 up 68%. **Availability:** PDF.

TRADE SHOWS AND CONVENTIONS

9927 ■ Futures and Options Expo
CME Group Inc.
20 S Wacker Dr.
Chicago, IL 60606
Ph: (312)930-1000
Free: 866-716-7274
Co. E-mail: info@cmegroup.com
URL: http://www.cmegroup.com
Contact: Terrence A. Duffy, Chief Executive Officer
URL(s): www.fia.org/fia/events/futures-options-expo
Frequency: Annual. **Description:** Includes keynote speakers, exhibits, and networking opportunities. **Audience:** Leaders and industry stakeholders. **Principal Exhibits:** Includes keynote speakers, exhibits, and networking opportunities. **Telecommunication Services:** tvitalechan@fia.org.

CONSULTANTS

9928 ■ De Bellas & Co.
7700 Irvine Ctr. Dr., Ste. 800
Irvine, CA 92618
URL: http://debellas.com
Contact: Alfred F. De Bellas, Jr., President
E-mail: adebellas@debellas.com
Description: Finance: Investment banking firm. **Scope:** Finance: Investment banking firm. **Founded:** 1983. **Publications:** "Tools to Take Advantage of the Current IT Staffing M and A Market," 2005; "Healthcare Staffing: Buy, Sell or Build," 2005.

9929 ■ Green Rhino Pixelbooks
127 Cherry Valley Ave.
Garden City, NY 11530
Ph: (516)978-6354
URL: http://www.customillustrationslosangeles.com
Description: Publisher of digital books for artists and writers to convey their creativity. **Founded:** 1981.

9930 ■ International Institute of Trading Mastery Inc. (IITM)
102-A Commonwealth Ct.
Cary, NC 27511
Ph: (919)466-0043
Free: 800-385-4486
Fax: (919)415-1877
Co. E-mail: customerservice@vantharp.com
URL: http://www.vantharp.com
Contact: Dr. Van K. Tharp, President
Facebook: www.facebook.com/VanTharpInstitute
Linkedin: www.linkedin.com/company/the-van-tharp
-institute
X (Twitter): x.com/VanTharpInst

YouTube: www.youtube.com/channel/UCIq
1KpIMe0SBnajlaWv89aw
Description: Firm is engaged in trading coaches and provides consulting services in educational products and services for traders and investors. **Founded:** 1982. **Publications:** "New Series Research on New Ways to Manage Your Portfolio," Jun, 2010; "Gold Trend The Pause That Refreshes," Jun, 2010; "At the Half-way Mark: A Project Marathon Update," Jun, 2010; "Traders and Mistakes Part 3 Rule Based Discretionary Traders," Jun, 2010; "What Can You Do When the Markets Go Wild," May, 2010; "While Everyone Was Nervous, One Great Trader Took 100R from the Market Last Week," May, 2010; "Risk Calculation or Profit Factor," Apr, 2010; "Insidious Stress," Mar, 2010; "Should I Change My Figures For My Specific Market," Mar, 2010; "Volatility Highs and Lows," Jan, 2010; "Cause and Effect: Thinking Differently for Traders," Jan, 2010; "The Peak Performance Course for Investors and Traders"; "Trade Your Way to Financial Freedom"; "Financial Freedom Through Electronic Day Trading"; "Safe Strategies for Financial Freedom"; "Another Structural Change in the Market". **Training:** Peak Performance 101 Trading Course, Embassy Suites, Apr, 2007; Blue print for Trading Success, Embassy Suites, Apr, 2007; Highly Effective ETF and Mutual Fund Techniques, Crab tree Marriott, Mar, 2007; Professional E-Mini Futures Tactics, Crab tree Marriott, Mar, 2007; How To Design A Winning Trading System That Fits You; Infinite Wealth Workshop; Simulate Your Trading System and Position Sizing, Stock Market, Options, Electronic Day Trading; How to Develop a Winning Trading System That Fits You.

9931 ■ Kauffman and Drebing Registered Investment Advisors
230 S Broad St., 5th Fl.
Philadelphia, PA 19102
Ph: (215)546-8016
Description: Offers objective personal financial planning. Also conducts seminars on personal financial planning and provides investment management consulting for institutions. **Scope:** Offers objective personal financial planning. Also conducts seminars on personal financial planning and provides investment management consulting for institutions. **Founded:** 1982.

9932 ■ Scan Management Inc.
320 Spangler School Rd.
Gettysburg, PA 17325
Contact: Diana Hallberg, Treasurer
Description: Consultants to the futures and securities industry and provides services to institutions and corporations involved in using the futures market as a risk management tool and conduct compliance audits hedging and reporting audits and due diligence audits on use of derivative products. **Scope:** Consultants to the futures and securities industry and provides services to institutions and corporations involved in using the futures market as a risk management tool and conduct compliance audits hedging and reporting audits and due diligence audits on use of derivative products.

9933 ■ SS&C Technologies Inc.
SS&C Technologies Holdings, Inc.
100 S Wacker Dr. 19th Flr.
Chicago, IL 60606
Ph: (860)298-4500
Free: 800-234-0556
Co. E-mail: solution@sscinc.com
URL: http://www.ssctech.com
Contact: William C. Stone, Chief Executive Officer
Facebook: www.facebook.com/ssctechnologies
X (Twitter): x.com/SSCTechnologies
Instagram: www.instagram.com/ssctechnologies
YouTube: www.youtube.com/c/SsctechInc
Description: Firm provides the global financial services industry with a broad range of highly specialized software, software enabled-services and software as a service solutions for operational excellence. **Founded:** 1986. **Special Services:** Sun

Solaris/MS NT Server Platforms. Software partners with Lotus Notes; Microsoft; Sybase; Ardent (Universe); and others.

9934 ■ Towneley Capital Management, Inc.
23197 La Cadena Dr., Ste. 103
  Laguna Hills, CA 92653
Ph: (949)837-3580
Free: 800-545-4442
Fax: (949)837-3604
Co. E-mail: info@towneley.com
URL: http://www.towneley.com
Contact: Tracy Kuntz, President
Description: Firm provides investment counseling, asset management, financial planning services. **Scope:** Offers investment counseling and mutual fund management services. Industries served: All. **Founded:** 1971. **Publications:** "Stock Market Extremes and Portfolio Performance"; "Keeping Finances Secure".

9935 ■ VRTRADER.com
10632 N Scottsdale Rd., B-426
  Scottsdale, AZ 85254
Ph: (928)282-1275
Fax: (623)243-4174
URL: http://leibovitvrnewsletters.com
Facebook: www.facebook.com/Leibovit-VR-Newsle tters-LLC-452899204806509
X (Twitter): x.com/thevolumeman
YouTube: www.youtube.com/user/VRTrader
Description: Firm offers individual stock selection and overall market timing services, stock pick telephone hotline service and online e-mail services. **Scope:** Firm offers individual stock selection and overall market timing services, stock pick telephone hotline service and online e-mail services. **Founded:** 1979.

FRANCHISES AND BUSINESS OPPORTUNITIES

9936 ■ High Touch - High Tech (HTHT)
PO Box 8495
  Asheville, NC 28814
Ph: (828)684-3192
Free: 800-444-4968
Fax: (828)684-3194
Co. E-mail: info@sciencemadefun.net
URL: http://sciencemadefun.net
Facebook: www.facebook.com/ HighTouchHighTechScienceMadeFun
Linkedin: www.linkedin.com/company/high-touch-high -tech---science-made-fun-
X (Twitter): x.com/hthtrdu
YouTube: www.youtube.com/user/HighTouchCorp
Pinterest: www.pinterest.com/hthtworldwide
Description: Mobile hands-on science experiments for children. **No. of Franchise Units:** 145. **No. of Company-Owned Units:** 14. **Founded:** 1992. **Franchised:** 1993. **Equity Capital Needed:** $59,875-$63,600. **Franchise Fee:** $35,000. **Royalty Fee:** 7%. **Financial Assistance:** Yes **Training:** Provides 5 day training at regional programming office.

PUBLICATIONS

9937 ■ *Investor's Business Daily*
12655 Beatrice St.
  Los Angeles, CA 90066
Ph: (310)448-6600
Free: 800-831-2525
URL: http://www.investors.com
URL(s): get.investors.com
Facebook: www.facebook.com/investorsbusiness daily
Linkedin: www.linkedin.com/company/investors-busi ness-daily
X (Twitter): x.com/IBDinvestors
Instagram: www.instagram.com/investorsbusiness daily
YouTube: www.youtube.com/user/IBDTV
Released: Weekly **Price:** $49.99, for auto-renew at the regular monthly rate; $30, for 2 months (Investor Bundle); $34.95, for regular monthly; $20, for 2

months. **Description:** Business and financial newspaper. Help investors make more money in the stock market. **Availability:** Print; Online.

COMPUTERIZED DATABASES

9938 ■ *Barron's*
Dow Jones & Company Inc.
  1211 Avenue of the Americas
  New York, NY 10036
Free: 800-568-7625
Co. E-mail: support@dowjones.com
URL: http://dowjones.com
Contact: Almar Latour, Chief Executive Officer
URL(s): www.barrons.com
Facebook: www.facebook.com/barrons
Linkedin: www.linkedin.com/company/barrons
X (Twitter): x.com/barronsonline
Instagram: www.instagram.com/Barrons
Released: Daily **Price:** $8.50, Single issue; $1, for online Week/1 Year (digital Bundle print + online); $4, for 4 weeks/1 Year (digital Bundle-print + online); $2, for online 4 weeks/1 year. **Availability:** Print; Online. **Type:** Full-text; Numeric; Statistical.

9939 ■ *Business Wire*
Business Wire, Inc.
  101 California St., 20th Fl.
  San Francisco, CA 94111
Co. E-mail: info@businesswire.com
URL: http://www.businesswire.com
Contact: Geff Scott, Chief Executive Officer
Description: Contains more than 1.4 million records that make up the complete text of press releases from public and private companies and other organizations, such as hospitals and universities. **Availability:** Online. **Type:** Full-text.

9940 ■ *Municipal Market Data-Line®*
Thomson Reuters
  22 Thomson Pl.
  Boston, MA 02210
Ph: (617)856-2000
Free: 800-692-8833
Fax: (800)543-1983
URL: http://www.thomsonreuters.com
Contact: Peter DeBruyne, Director
URL(s): tm3.com
Type: Full-text; Numeric.

9941 ■ *OTC Markets Newsletter*
OTC Markets Group Inc.
  300 Vesey St., 12th Fl.
  New York, NY 10282
Ph: (212)896-4400
Free: 800-547-8682
Co. E-mail: info@otcmarkets.com
URL: http://www.otcmarkets.com
Contact: Cromwell R. Coulson, President
URL(s): www.otcmarkets.com/about/otc-markets -newsletter
Released: Monthly **Availability:** Print. **Type:** Full-text; Numeric.

9942 ■ *U.S. Weekly Statistics*
Haver Analytics
  60 E 42nd St.
  New York, NY 10165
Ph: (212)986-9300
Co. E-mail: sales@haver.com
URL: http://www.haver.com
Contact: Paul L. Kasriel, Contact
URL(s): haverproducts.com/products/market-data/ #top
Released: Weekly **Availability:** Online. **Type:** Statistical; Numeric.

9943 ■ *Value Line DataFile*
Value Line, Inc.
  551 5th Ave., 3rd Fl.
  New York, NY 10176
Ph: (212)907-1500
Co. E-mail: vlcr@valueline.com
URL: http://www.valueline.com
Contact: Howard A. Brecher, Chief Executive Officer
URL(s): www.valuelinepro.com/value-line-data

Released: Weekly **Availability:** Online. **Type:** Numeric.

9944 ■ *Value Line's Fundamental DataFile*
Value Line, Inc.
  551 5th Ave., 3rd Fl.
  New York, NY 10176
Ph: (212)907-1500
Co. E-mail: vlcr@valueline.com
URL: http://www.valueline.com
Contact: Howard A. Brecher, Chief Executive Officer
URL(s): www.valuelinepro.com/fundamental-datafile
Availability: Online. **Type:** Time Series; Numeric.

LIBRARIES

9945 ■ Alberta Securities Commission (ASC)
250-5th St. SW, Ste. 600
  Calgary, AB, Canada T2P 0R4
Ph: (403)297-6454
Free: 877-355-0585
Fax: (403)297-6156
Co. E-mail: inquiries@asc.ca
URL: http://www.asc.ca
Contact: Stan Magidson, Chief Executive Officer
Facebook: www.facebook.com/ASCUpdates
Linkedin: www.linkedin.com/company/alberta-securi ties-commission_2
X (Twitter): x.com/ASCUpdates
Description: Aims to foster a fair and efficient capital market in Alberta. We've made it easy for you to find the information you need. **Founded:** 1955.

9946 ■ AllianceBernstein Holding L.P. - Library
AllianceBernstein Holding L.P.
  501 Commerce St.
  Nashville, TN 37203
Ph: (615)622-0000
Free: 800-251-0539
URL: http://www.alliancebernstein.com
Contact: Seth P. Bernstein, President
Facebook: www.facebook.com/ABinsights
Linkedin: www.linkedin.com/company/abglobal
X (Twitter): twitter.com/ab_insights
Instagram: www.instagram.com/alliancebernstein
YouTube: www.youtube.com/user/AllianceBerns teinLP
Description: Provider of research, diversified investment management, and related services including institutional, retail, and private wealth management services to a broad range of clients such as institutional investors, public and private pension plans, foundations and endowments, insurance companies, central banks, governments, retail clients and private clients with high net-worth individuals and families, trusts, estates and charities. **Scope:** Investments. **Founded:** 2000. **Holdings:** Figures not available.

9947 ■ BMO Nesbitt Burns Inc.
1 First Canadian Pl.
  Toronto, ON, Canada M5X 1H3
Free: 866-391-5897
Co. E-mail: contact@bmonb.com
URL: http://www.bmo.com/nesbittburns
Description: Investment bank that provides financial advisory services including financial planning, estate planning. **Founded:** 1948. **Holdings:** 200 books; 1000 reports; 32 online databases.

9948 ■ Dechert LLP Library
1900 K St. NW
  Washington, DC 20006
Ph: (202)261-3300
Fax: (202)261-3333
URL: http://www.dechert.com
Contact: Douglas P. Dick, Partner
YouTube: www.youtube.com/user/DechertLLP
Scope: Law. **Founded:** 1969.

9949 ■ Fenwick & West LLP Law Library
801 California St.
  Mountain View, CA 94041
Ph: (650)988-8500
URL: http://www.fenwick.com

X (Twitter): x.com/FenwickWest
Description: Practices of law through substantial investments in proprietary technology tools and processes. **Founded:** 1973.

9950 ■ Investment Company Institute (ICI) - Library
1401 H St. NW, Ste. 1200
 Washington, DC 20005
Ph: (202)326-5800
Co. E-mail: memberservices@ici.org
URL: http://www.ici.org
Contact: Eric J. Pan, President
Facebook: www.facebook.com/ici.org
X (Twitter): x.com/ici
YouTube: www.youtube.com/user/ICIVideo
Description: Represents open-end and closed-end investment companies registered under Investment Company Act of 1940; investment advisers to, and underwriters of, such companies; unit investment trust sponsors; interested others. **Scope:** Legislation, taxation, regulation, economic research marketing, small business, public information. **Founded:** 1940. **Holdings:** Figures not available. **Publications:** *The Investment Compant Service Directory* (Annual); *Trends in Mutual Fund Activity* (Monthly); *National Association of Investment Companies--Membership Directory* (Annual); *ICI Membership Directory* (Semi-annual). **Educational Activities:** Annual General Membership Meeting (GMM) (Annual). **Geographic Preference:** National.

9951 ■ Ontario Teachers' Pension Plan Board (OTPP) - Knowledge Centre
Ontario Teachers' Pension Plan Board (OTPP)
 5650 Yonge St.
 Toronto, ON, Canada M2M 4H5
Ph: (416)228-5900
Free: 800-668-0105
Fax: (416)730-5349
Co. E-mail: communications@otpp.com
URL: http://www.otpp.com
Contact: Jo Taylor, President
Facebook: www.facebook.com/myOTPP
Linkedin: www.linkedin.com/company/ontario
 -teachers%E2%80%8B%27-pension-plan
X (Twitter): x.com/OTPPinfo
YouTube: www.youtube.com/user/otppinfo
Description: Engages in administering defined-benefit pensions for teachers. **Scope:** Pension management; investment; economics; finance. **Services:** Library not open to the public. **Founded:** 1989. **Holdings:** Books.

9952 ■ Stearns, Weaver, Miller, Weissler, Alhadeff and Sitterson P.A. - Library
Museum Twr., 150 W Flagler St., Ste. 2200
 Miami, FL 33130
Ph: (305)789-3200
Fax: (305)789-3395
Co. E-mail: info@stearnsweaver.com
URL: http://www.stearnsweaver.com

Contact: Stuart D. Ames, Contact
E-mail: sames@stearnsweaver.com
X (Twitter): x.com/StearnsWeaver
Description: Law firm providing legal solutions. **Scope:** Law. **Founded:** 1950. **Holdings:** Figures not available.

RESEARCH CENTERS

9953 ■ New York University - Leonard N. Stern School of Business - Glucksman Institute
44 West 4th St.
 New York, NY 10012
Ph: (212)998-0700
Fax: (212)995-4220
URL: http://www.stern.nyu.edu/experience-stern/
 about/departments-centers-initiatives/centers-of
 -research/glucksman-institute-for-research-in-securi
 ties-markets
Contact: Mary Jaffier, Contact
E-mail: mjaffier@stern.nyu.edu

Description: Research organization coordinated by Salomon Brother Center for Study of Financial Institutions at New York. **Scope:** Equities, bonds, futures, options, and other financial instruments and the markets in which they are traded. Research topics include implied volatility in options, bank fee structures, and changing character of stock prices.

START-UP INFORMATION

9954 ■ *"E-Commerce Jewelry Startup Gemvara Won't Pursue Retail Store in Boston" in Boston Business Journal (Vol. 34, March 14, 2014, No. 6)*
Pub: American City Business Journals, Inc.
Contact: Mike Olivieri, Executive Vice President
Released: Weekly. **Description:** Janet Holian is CEO of Gemvara, a Boston, Massachusetts-based online jewelry retailer. She ran a pop-up store from November through February and considered opening a traditional brick and mortar store. In the end, Holian decided to focus on the online store. Customers can still make private appointments to Gemvara's One Financial Center location. The company specializes in customizable fine jewelry. **Availability:** Print; Online.

9955 ■ *"Should You Choose a Lump-Sum Pension Payout? Here's How Entrepreneur Ramona Harper Decided" in Black Enterprise (Vol. 44, June 2014, No. 10, pp. 27)*
Pub: Earl G. Graves Ltd.
Contact: Earl Graves, Jr., President
Description: Entrepreneur, Ramona Harper, chose a lump sum payout of her pension in order to start a new business. She used $110,000 to start her accessories boutique and put the remaining money into a small business 401(k), which helped her avoid a large tax. Tips to help individuals decide the best way to collect their pension are provided. **Availability:** Online.

ASSOCIATIONS AND OTHER ORGANIZATIONS

9956 ■ **Accredited Gemologists Association (AGA)**
3315 Juanita St.
San Diego, CA 92105
Free: 844-288-4367
URL: http://accreditedgemologists.org
Contact: Teri Brossmer, President
Description: Gemologists. Promotes the advancement of the science of gemology. Conducts research and educational programs. **Founded:** 1974. **Publications:** *Certified Gemological Lab Directory* (Annual). **Awards:** The AGA Antonio C. Bonanno Award for Excellence in Gemology (Annual). **Geographic Preference:** National.

9957 ■ **American Gem Trade Association (AGTA)**
3030 LBJ Fwy., Ste. 840
Dallas, TX 75234
Ph: (214)742-4367
Free: 800-972-1162
Fax: (214)742-7334
Co. E-mail: info@agta.org
URL: http://agta.org
Contact: John W. Ford, Sr., Chief Executive Officer
E-mail: john@agta.org

Facebook: www.facebook.com/AmericanGemTra deAssociation
X (Twitter): x.com/agta_gems
Instagram: www.instagram.com/agta_gems
YouTube: www.youtube.com/user/agtawebmaster
Description: Seeks to establish closer communication within the industry; works to protect consumers from fraud and to create a greater awareness of natural colored gemstones. Conducts seminars; maintains speaker's bureau. **Founded:** 1981. **Publications:** *Prism* (Weekly); *AGTA Directory.* **Educational Activities:** Conclave (Annual), Jewelry industry, including sales and marketing.; AGTA GemFair (Annual). **Awards:** Spectrum Awards (Annual); Spectrum Awards Design Competition (Annual); Cutting Edge Gemstone Competition (Annual); Cutting Edge Awards (Annual). **Geographic Preference:** National.

9958 ■ **American Hatpin Society (AHS)**
845 Sonoma Dr.
Lake Arrowhead, CA 92352
Co. E-mail: americanhatpinsociety@aol.com
URL: http://www.americanhatpinsociety.com
Contact: Carla Walters, Editor
Description: Collectors of hatpins. Promotes collection, preservation, and restoration of hatpins and related fashion accessories. Serves as a clearinghouse on hatpins and their history; facilitates exchange of information among members; conducts educational programs. **Founded:** 1989. **Publications:** *American Hatpin Society Newsletter* (Quarterly). **Geographic Preference:** Multinational.

9959 ■ **Canadian Gemmological Association (CGA) - Library**
55 Queen St. E, Lower Concourse 105
Toronto, ON, Canada M5C 1R6
Ph: (647)466-2436
Free: 877-242-4366
Co. E-mail: info@canadiangemmological.com
URL: http://canadiangemmological.com
Contact: Donna Hawrelko, President
Facebook: www.facebook.com/Canadian-Gemmo-logical-Association-194830677283253
Linkedin: www.linkedin.com/in/canadian-gemmologi-cal-association
X (Twitter): twitter.com/CanGem3
Instagram: www.instagram.com/canadiangemassoc
Description: Promotes excellence in the practice of gemmology. **Scope:** Gemmology. **Founded:** 1958. **Holdings:** Figures not available. **Publications:** *Canadian Gemmologist* (Quarterly); *Canadian Professional Gemmology Course.* **Geographic Preference:** National.

9960 ■ **Canadian Institute of Gemmology (CIG)**
PO Box 57010
Vancouver, BC, Canada V5K 5G6
Ph: (604)530-8569
Co. E-mail: mail@cigem.ca
URL: http://www.cigem.ca
Contact: J. Wolf Kuehn, Chief Executive Officer

Facebook: www.facebook.com/CanadianInstitu teOfGemmology
X (Twitter): x.com/CIGemNews
Description: Gemologists and others with an interest in gemology and gemology training. Conducts educational programs in gem appreciation, gemology, gem identification, diamond grading and jewelry history and design; gathers and disseminates information to trade bodies and the public. **Founded:** 1983. **Publications:** *Gemmology Canada* (Quarterly). **Geographic Preference:** Multinational.

9961 ■ **Canadian Jewellers Association (CJA)**
27 Queen St. E, Ste. 600
Toronto, ON, Canada M5C 2M6
Ph: (416)368-7616
Free: 800-580-0942
Fax: (416)368-1986
Co. E-mail: info@canadianjewellers.com
URL: http://canadianjewellers.com
X (Twitter): x.com/CanJewellers
Instagram: www.instagram.com/cana dianjewellersassociation
Description: National trade association for the jewelry industry in Canada, with both retail and supply members. Offers educational courses, information on Kimberley Process. **Founded:** 1918. **Publications:** *JW Plus* (Bimonthly); *At a Glance.* **Geographic Preference:** National.

9962 ■ **Diamond Council of America (DCA)**
120 Broadway, Ste. 2820
New York, NY 10271
Ph: (615)385-5301
Free: 877-283-5669
Fax: (615)385-4955
Co. E-mail: info@dcalearning.org
URL: http://dcalearning.org
Contact: Terry Chandler, President
Description: Retail jewelry firms and suppliers of gemstones. Firms operating approximately 4900 retail jewelry stores; associated manufacturers and importers. Offers courses in "gemology" and "diamontology" to employees of member firms; bestows titles of Certified Diamontologist and Guild Gemologist upon those completing courses and examinations. Supplies members with advertising and educational materials. **Founded:** 1944. **Publications:** *Diamond Council of America--Directory.* **Geographic Preference:** National.

9963 ■ **Indian Diamond and Colorstone Association (IDCA)**
580 5th Ave., Ste. No. 625
New York, NY 10036
Ph: (212)921-4488
Co. E-mail: office@idcany.org
URL: http://idcany.org
Contact: Rajeev Pandya, President
Description: Diamond and color stone dealers of Indian descent and others who work with diamonds and gemstones from India. Promotes the growth and awareness of the Indian gem industry in the U.S. **Founded:** 1984. **Publications:** *IDCA By-Laws Direc-*

tory (Annual); *IDCA Pocket Directory* (Periodic). **Awards:** IDCA Retailer of the Year (Annual). **Geographic Preference:** National.

9964 ■ Jewelers of America (JA)
120 Broadway, Ste. 2820
New York, NY 10271
Free: 800-223-0673
Co. E-mail: sposnock@jewelers.org
URL: http://www.jewelers.org
Contact: David J. Bonaparte, President
Facebook: www.facebook.com/JewelersOfAmerica
Linkedin: www.linkedin.com/company/jewelers-of
-america
X (Twitter): x.com/JAjewelryinfo
Instagram: www.instagram.com/jewelersofamerica
Pinterest: www.pinterest.com/JAjewelryinfo
Description: Retailers of jewelry, watches, silver, and allied merchandise. Conducts surveys and compiles statistics. Conducts educational programs. Provides information to consumers. **Founded:** 1957. **Educational Activities:** Conclave (Annual), Jewelry industry, including sales and marketing.; JA New York Show (JANY) (Annual). **Awards:** JA National Retailer Design Competition (Annual). **Geographic Preference:** National.

9965 ■ Jewelers' Security Alliance (JSA)
6 E 45th St.
New York, NY 10017
Free: 800-537-0067
Fax: (212)808-9168
Co. E-mail: jsa2@jewelerssecurity.org
URL: http://jewelerssecurity.org
Contact: John J. Kennedy, President
Linkedin: www.linkedin.com/in/jewelerssecuri
tyalliance
Description: Advocates for crime prevention in the jewelry industry. Provides crime information and assistance to the jewelry industry and law enforcement. **Founded:** 1883. **Publications:** *Annual Report on Crime Against the Jewelry Industry in U.S.* (Annual); *JSA Manual of Jewelry Security.* **Educational Activities:** Security Seminar and Expo for Retail Jewelry Chains (Annual). **Geographic Preference:** National.

9966 ■ Jewelers Vigilance Committee (JVC)
119 W 24th St., No 401
New York, NY 10011
Ph: (212)997-2002
Fax: (212)997-9148
Co. E-mail: info@jvclegal.org
URL: http://www.jvclegal.org
Contact: Tiffany Stevens, President
E-mail: tiffany@jvclegal.org
URL(s): www.jewellersvigilance.ca/html/jvc_re-
sources.htm
X (Twitter): x.com/jvclegal
Description: Represents manufacturers, importers, wholesalers, and retailers. Combats deceptive trade practices and misleading advertising. Aims to develop and maintain high trade standards. Provides advice on markings and assists in prosecution of violations of marking, advertising, and related jewelry industry laws. **Founded:** 1917. **Publications:** *JVC Manufacturers' Legal Handbook.* **Geographic Preference:** National.

9967 ■ Jewellers Vigilance Canada (JVC)
55 Queen St. E, Ste. 205
Toronto, ON, Canada M5C 1R6
Ph: (416)368-4840
Free: 800-580-0942
Fax: (416)368-1986
Co. E-mail: info@jewellerycrimecanada.ca
URL: http://jewellerycrimecanada.ca
Contact: Kelly Ross, Committee Chairman
E-mail: kelly@canadianjewellers.com
Facebook:
JEWELLERSVIGILANCECANADA
Description: Strives to promote ethical practices within the jewelry industry. Offers educational programs and handles complaints from consumers. **Founded:** 1987. **Publications:** *Jewellers Vigilance Canada Action Update.* **Geographic Preference:** National.

9968 ■ Manufacturing Jewelers and Suppliers of America (MJSA)
8 Hayward St.
Attleboro, MA 02703
Ph: (508)316-2132
Free: 800-444-MJSA
Fax: (508)316-1429
Co. E-mail: info@mjsa.org
URL: http://www.mjsa.org
Contact: David W. Cochran, President
E-mail: david.cochran@mjsa.org
Facebook: www.facebook.com/theMJSA
X (Twitter): x.com/MJSAtweets
YouTube: www.youtube.com/mjsavideos
Description: Represents American manufacturers and suppliers within the jewelry industry. Seeks to foster long-term stability and prosperity of the jewelry industry. Provides leadership in government affairs and industry education. **Founded:** 1903. **Publications:** *Buyer's Guide; MJSA Journal* (Monthly); *Manufacturing Jewelers Buyers' Guide; MJSA Benchmark* (Monthly). **Educational Activities:** MJSA Expo (Annual), MJSA Expo Providence (Annual); Jeweler's Bench Conference and Trade Fair (Annual). **Awards:** MJSA Vision Awards (Annual); MJSA Education Foundation Scholarship Award (Annual); MJSA Education Foundation Scholarship (Annual). **Geographic Preference:** National.

9969 ■ National Association of Jewelry Appraisers (NAJP)
PO Box 18
Rego Park, NY 11374-0018
Ph: (718)896-1536
Co. E-mail: office@najaappraisers.com
URL: http://najaappraisers.com
Contact: Gail Brett Levine, Executive Director
Description: Gem and jewelry appraisers, jewelers, importers, brokers, manufacturers, gemological students, and others professionally interested in jewelry appraisal. Seeks to recognize and make available to the public the services of highly qualified, experienced, independent, and reliable jewelry appraisers. **Founded:** 1981. **Publications:** *National Association of Jewelry Appraisers Membership Directory; The Jewelry Appraiser* (Quarterly). **Geographic Preference:** Multinational.

9970 ■ Women's Jewelry Association (WJA)
125 Pk. Ave., 25th Fl.
New York, NY 10017
Ph: (845)473-7324
Fax: (646)355-0219
Co. E-mail: info@womensjewelryassociation.com
URL: http://www.womensjewelryassociation.com
Contact: Susan Chandler, President
Facebook: www.facebook.com/
WomensJewelryAssociation
Linkedin: www.linkedin.com/company/
womensjewelryassociation
X (Twitter): x.com/WomensJewelry
Instagram: www.instagram.com/
womensjewelryassociation
Description: Represents those involved in jewelry design, manufacture, retail, and advertising. Aims to: enhance the status of women in the jewelry industry; make known the contribution of women to the industry; provide a network for women involved with fine jewelry. Maintains hall of fame. **Founded:** 1983. **Publications:** *Jewelry Association Newsletter* (Semiannual); *Women's Jewelry Association--Membership Directory.* **Awards:** WJA Member Grant (Annual); Student Scholarships (Annual); Women's Jewelry Association Member Grants (Annual); WJA Awards for Excellence (Annual). **Geographic Preference:** National.

REFERENCE WORKS

9971 ■ *"3 Tricks Criminals Use to Undermine Jewelry Store Security" in Jewelers of America (November 6, 2019)*
Released: November 06, 2019. **Description:** Useful tips from the Jewelers Mutual Insurance Group are given to help deter criminals from targeting your jewelry business.

9972 ■ *"Big Bling: Signet Acquires Zales Corporation" in Dallas Business Journal (Vol. 37, June 6, 2014, No. 39, pp. 6)*
Pub: American City Business Journals, Inc.
Contact: Mike Olivieri, Executive Vice President
Released: June 06, 2014. **Price:** $4, print. **Description:** Signet Jewelers of Bermuda acquired Zale Corporation in a $1.4 billion deal or $21 per share in cash following the approval by a majority of stockholders of the Irving, Texas-based company. The acquisition will increase Signet's earnings by a high single-digit percentage in the first fiscal year of the merger. **Availability:** Print; Online.

9973 ■ *"Cutting the Power: A New Trend in Jewelry Store Burglaries" in Jewelers of America (July 8, 2019)*
URL(s): www.jewelers.org/ja/careers-education/
business-tips/984-cutting-the-power-a-new-trend-in
-jewelry-store-burglaries
Released: July 08, 2019. **Description:** Burglars have developed a new way to rob jewelry stores which involves cutting the power and seeing if anyone arrives to check on the alarm. Even if the police or owner arrive, there is very little they do at the time to restore power and the alarm, and after leaving the burglar will break into the building. Included are tips to keep your property safe from this new scheme. **Availability:** Online.

9974 ■ *"From New York to Park Avenue: Red Carpet Fashion at a Discount" in Orlando Business Journal (Vol. 30, February 14, 2014, No. 34, pp. 3)*
Pub: American City Business Journals, Inc.
Contact: Mike Olivieri, Executive Vice President
Released: Weekly. **Price:** $8, introductory 4-week offer(Digital & Print). **Description:** Red Carpet Couture & Gems is known for selling high-end discount business attire and accessories. Owner, Caralyce Buford decided to buy from sample sales in New York before opening the store in October 2013. Her retail store caters to women of all sizes. **Availability:** Print; Online.

9975 ■ *"Geo-Location Technology Linking Stores, Shoppers" in Providence Business News (Vol. 29, May 5, 2014, No. 5, pp. 1)*
Pub: American City Business Journals, Inc.
Contact: Mike Olivieri, Executive Vice President
Released: May 03, 2014. **Description:** Jewelry maker, Alex and Ani LLC of Cranston, Rhode Island, outfitted their 40 retail stores in the U.S. with Bluetooth Low Energy systems called iBeacons to communicate directly with customers' mobile phones when they are in or near the store. The company claims that its stores have not received any negative feedback on hyperlocal messaging since the program started in summer 2013. **Availability:** Online.

9976 ■ *"Harvesting the Royal Oak" in Barron's (Vol. 92, September 17, 2012, No. 38, pp. 18)*
Description: The Royal Oak wrist watch made by Audemars Piguet of Switzerland was considered revolutionary during its creation in the 1970s, but enjoys wide popularity 40 years later. The all-steel sports watch pays attention to detail and has enabled its manufacturer to survive. **Availability:** Print; Online.

9977 ■ *"Jewelry and Luxury Goods Sales on Rebound" in Jewelry Industry (November 17, 2021)*
Released: November 17, 2021. **Description:** Discusses the current trends of the global jewelry and luxury brands and it looks like sales are up and rebounding after slumping for the last several years, due to the COVID-19 pandemic.

9978 ■ *"Lincoln Firm Shows Finishing Kick" in Providence Business News (Vol. 29, June 30, 2014, No. 13, pp. 10)*
Pub: American City Business Journals, Inc.
Contact: Mike Olivieri, Executive Vice President

Released: June 28, 2014. **Description:** The advancement of the jewelry plating company, Tanury Industries, has expanded into gold-plating interiors of jets and creating durable finished for eyeglass frames. Tanury's Physical Vapor Deposition (PVD) vacuum chamber is a unique system that applies a thin film of metal to a variety of materials. **Availability:** PDF; Online.

9979 ■ "Modern Bride Unveiled Exclusively at JCPenney" in Benzinga.com (February 3, 2011)
Pub: PR Newswire Association LLC.

Description: JCPenney created its new Modern Bride concept in its bridal find jewelry departments. The new shopping experience is a collaboration between the retailer and Conde Nast catering to the bridal customer. **Availability:** Online.

9980 ■ "RingMaster Ushering in Its 50th Year with a Return to Winston-Salem's Historic Reynolda Village" in Mid-America Jewelry News (October 1, 2019)
URL(s): midamericajewelrynews.com/featured-articles/5205-ringmaster-ushering-in-its-50th-year-with-a-return-to-winston-salem-s-historic-reynolda-village

Released: October 01, 2019. **Description:** Owner Michael Scott is moving longtime community staple, RingMaster's, back to Reynolda Village after having moved out of the area years ago to avoid raising rents. The new location will be renovated and all staff members will be making the move as well. **Availability:** Online.

9981 ■ "Scott Rothstein Ponzi Reveals Ethics Issues in Jewelry Biz" in South Florida Business Journal (Vol. 33, September 14, 2012, No. 7, pp. 1)
Pub: Baltimore Business Journal
Contact: Rhonda Pringle, President
E-mail: rpringle@bizjournals.com

Description: JR Dunn Jewelers of Florida is suing New York jewelry company JB International for an 8.91 carat diamond it claims is tainted because it was allegedly sold offby Ponzi schemer Scott Rothstein or his wife Kimberly. Dunn is being sued for $748,000 in the bankruptcy of Rothstein Rosenfelt Adler, Rothstein's former law firm. **Availability:** Print; Online.

9982 ■ "The Silvery Moon Moves to Larger Location" in Bellingham Business Journal (Vol. March 2010, pp. 5)
Pub: Sound Publishing Inc.
Contact: Josh O'Connor, President

Ed: Isaac Bonnell. **Description:** Jewelry store, the Silvery Moon, moved to a larger location in order to expand its business. The new location was chosen because it offers the firm more visibility. The store offers find silver and gold pieces and specializes in Pacific Northwest native jewelry.

9983 ■ "Six Ways to Make Your Bridal Business More Profitable - Overnight" in Mid-America Jewelry News (October 1, 2019)
URL(s): midamericajewelrynews.com/featured-articles/5203-six-ways-to-make-your-bridal-business-more-profitable-overnight

Released: October 01, 2019. **Description:** Newly engaged, or about to be engaged, couples are very different from the couples of the past. Nowadays, people buying jewelry want gemstones and settings that are not only unique but conflict-free. Included are six ways that jewelry stores can maintain competitive and bring back those customers. **Availability:** Online.

9984 ■ "Sylvie Collection Offers a Feminine Perspective and Voice in Male Dominated Bridal Industry" in Benzinga.com (October 29, 2011)

Description: Bridal jewelry designer Sylvie Levine has created over 1,000 customizable styles of engagement rings and wedding bands and is reaching out to prospective new brides through a new Website, interactive social media campaign and monthly trunk show appearances. **Availability:** Online.

9985 ■ "Transitioning From Hobbyist to Entrepreneur: Teen Designer Creates Custom and Handmade Jewelry for the Everyday Diva" in Black Enterprise (Vol. 44, March 2014, No. 7, pp. 14)
Pub: Earl G. Graves Ltd.
Contact: Earl Graves, Jr., President

Description: Profile of Jaya Kiere Johnson, who states that every one of her jewelry creations represents a generation of black female entrepreneurship in her life, from her mother to her great-grandmother. The young entrepreneur tells how she was inspired while designing and creating handmade jewelry in high school.

STATISTICAL SOURCES

9986 ■ Jewelry Stores Industry in the US - Market Research Report
URL(s): www.ibisworld.com/united-states/market-research-reports/jewelry-stores-industry/

Price: $925. **Description:** Downloadable report analyzing the current and future trends in the jewelry store industry. **Availability:** Online.

9987 ■ RMA Annual Statement Studies
Pub: Risk Management Association
Contact: Nancy Foster, President

Released: Annual. **Description:** Contains composite balance sheets and income statements for more than 360 industries, including the accounting, auditing, and bookkeeping industries. Also contains five years of comparative historical data for discerning trends. Includes 16 commonly used ratios, computed for most of the size groupings for nearly every industry.

9988 ■ US Watches and Jewelry Market Report 2021
URL(s): store.mintel.com/report/us-watches-and-jewelry-market-report

Price: $4,366.35. **Description:** Downloadable report examines the trend of consumers buying expensive watches and jewelry online and how the Covid-19 pandemic affected purchasing attitudes. The report includes an executive summary, interactive databook, PowerPoint presentation, infographic overview, report PDF, and previous years data. **Availability:** PDF.

FRANCHISES AND BUSINESS OPPORTUNITIES

9989 ■ Fast-Fix Jewelry and Watch Repairs
1515 S Federal Hwy., Ste.412
 Boca Raton, FL 33432
Ph: (561)330-6060
Free: 800-359-0407
Fax: (561)431-3231

URL: http://www.fastfix.com
Description: Jewelry and watch repairs. **Founded:** 1984. **Franchised:** 1987. **Training:** Yes.

9990 ■ Hannoush Jewelers, Inc.
1655 Boston Rd., Unit B7
 Springfield, MA 01129-1155
Ph: (413)543-5225
Co. E-mail: customerservice@hannoush.com
URL: http://hannoush.com
Contact: Peter A. Hannoush, President
Facebook: www.facebook.com/HannoushJewelry
Linkedin: www.linkedin.com/company/hannoush-jewelers-inc.
X (Twitter): x.com/HannoushJewelry
Instagram: www.instagram.com/hannoushjewelers

Description: Jewelry store operator. **No. of Franchise Units:** 20. **No. of Company-Owned Units:** 52. **Founded:** 1980. **Franchised:** 1995. **Equity Capital Needed:** $291,000-$717,000. **Franchise Fee:** $20,000. **Royalty Fee:** 4%. **Financial Assistance:** No **Training:** Offers 2 weeks at headquarters, 3 months at franchisee's location as needed with ongoing support.

LIBRARIES

9991 ■ Gemological Institute of America (GIA) - Richard T. Liddicoat Gemological Library and Information Center
The Robert Mouawad Campus
 5345 Armada Dr.
 Carlsbad, CA 92008
Ph: (760)603-4000
Free: 800-421-7250
Co. E-mail: admissions@gia.edu
URL: http://gia.edu
Contact: Susan M. Jacques, President
Facebook: www.facebook.com/GIAEducation
Linkedin: www.linkedin.com/school/gia
X (Twitter): x.com/gianews
YouTube: www.youtube.com/user/officialGIAchannel
Pinterest: www.pinterest.com/giapins

Description: Educational institution teaches about gems and jewelry. **Scope:** Gemstones, including development of gemological equipment and tests for detecting synthetic, imitation, and treated gemstones; gem identification; and diamond quality grading. **Services:** Open to the public by appointments; photocopying. **Founded:** 1931. **Holdings:** 57,000 volumes; 700 international journals and magazine titles; 150,000 images; more than 1,800 videos and DVDs. **Publications:** GIA Alumni Online Directory; The GIA Insider (Monthly); Handbook of GEM Identification; Gemological Institute of America--Alumni Directory (Annual); Gems & Gemology: The Quarterly Journal of the Gemological Institute of America (Quarterly); GIA Jeweler's Manual; GIA Newsletter. **Educational Activities:** Jewellery & Gem WORLD Hong Kong (Annual). **Awards:** Morris Hanauer Scholarship; Richard T. Liddicoat Scholarship (Annual); William Goldberg Scholarship (Annual); Kurt Wayne Scholarship; Eunice Miles Scholarship (Annual); GIA Scholarship - Lab Classes (Annual); North Texas Alumni Scholarship (Annual); CJA Peter Hess Scholarship; Robert B. Westover Scholarships (Annual); Mikimoto Scholarship (Annual); Daniel Swarovski and Company Scholarships; Lone Star GIA Associate and Alumni Scholarships (Annual); ColorMasters Precious Jewelry Scholarship (Annual); GIA Scholarship - Distance Education eLearning; GIA Scholarships - On Campus (Annual). **Geographic Preference:** National.

ASSOCIATIONS AND OTHER ORGANIZATIONS

9992 ■ **National Training and Simulation Association (NTSA)**
2101 Wilson Blvd., Ste. 700
Arlington, VA 22201
Ph: (703)247-9480
Co. E-mail: dlangelier@ndia.org
URL: http://www.ntsa.org
Contact: Shannon Burch, Director, Operations
E-mail: sburch@ntsa.org
Description: Fosters communication between government and industry regarding requirements and procurement issues and policies; promotes responsibility and integrity among members. Compiles statistics; conducts research and educational programs. **Founded:** 1988. **Publications:** *NTSA Training Industry News* (Monthly); *NTSA Training 2012* (Monthly); *NTSA Yearbook* (Annual). **Educational Activities:** Training and Simulation Industry Symposium (Annual). **Awards:** NTSA Modeling & Simulation Awards (Annual). **Geographic Preference:** National.

9993 ■ **Ohio State University College of Education and Human Ecology - Center on Education and Training for Employment (CETE)**
1900 Kenny Rd.
Columbus, OH 43210
Ph: (614)292-6869
Fax: (614)292-3742
Co. E-mail: cete@osu.edu
URL: http://cete.osu.edu
Contact: Beth Crawford, Project Manager
E-mail: crawford.555@osu.edu
Facebook: www.facebook.com/Center-on-Education
-Training-for-Employment-202422833904579
Linkedin: www.linkedin.com/showcase/osu-cete
X (Twitter): x.com/osucete
YouTube: www.youtube.com/channel/UCYoLSALG3B
4olVOnEW_aciw
Description: Aims to increase the ability of diverse agencies, institutions, and organizations to solve educational problems relating to individual career planning, preparation, and progression. Conducts occupational analyses and staff training programs. Evaluates programs and agencies and provides technical assistance. Researches identified problems or needs. Develops databases, information systems, and occupational curricula. **Scope:** Provider of computer searches, document delivery and reference services in the areas of technical and vocational education, adult education, training and related topics. The firms principal clients is the graduate students, government agencies, school districts and state departments. **Founded:** 1963. **Publications:** "Program for Acquiring Competence in Entrepreneurship (PACE) 4th Edition," The Ohio State University. **Training:** Test Construction, Columbus, Jul, 2007; ISO 10015 - Quality of Training Planning To Use The Standard, Columbus, Jun, 2007; SCID Workshop,

Columbus, Apr, 2007; Decreasing the Dropout Rates in the United States. **Educational Activities:** Test Development Workshop; CETE Seminars and workshops; CETE Test Development Workshop, A 3-day seminar to instruct those interested in developing valid, reliable assessments (tests) of job specific knowledge and skills for personnel, certification, and career-technical education purposes. **Geographic Preference:** National.

REFERENCE WORKS

9994 ■ **Career Information Center**
URL(s): www.cengage.com
Released: Biennial; Latest edition 10th; January 2014. **Price:** $946, Individuals. **Description:** Organized into 13 occupational clusters (comprising 13 volumes and an index volume). Each volume includes a section listing accredited occupational educational and vocational institutions. A second section lists more than 700 occupational profiles and over 3,000 organizations with jobs in the field of work with which the volume is concerned. Includes job summary chart; industry snapshots that summarize major developments; photographs; overview of the job market; job hunting information and tips Includes job summary chart; industry snapshots that summarize major developments; photographs; overview of the job market; job hunting information and tips. **Entries include:** For institutions--Name, address, programs and degrees offered. For organizations--Name, address. **Arrangement:** By Career Area/Industry. **Indexes:** Each volume contains a general index, and a master index to the entire series appears in a 13th volume. **Availability:** Print; Electronic publishing.

9995 ■ **"Employee Training and Development Is the Biggest HR Focus Area in 2019"** in **Payscale (January 7. 2019)**
URL(s): www.payscale.com/compensation-today/20
19/01/employee-training-development
Released: January 07, 2019. **Description:** It was revealed in the latest Compensation Best Practices Report that HR professionals plan to heavily invest in employee training and development. Most businesses want to retain the employees they have and therefore want to make sure they have the needed capabilities for future business growth. **Availability:** Online.

9996 ■ **"Is Amazon Training Its Workers or Creating a College Alternative?"** in **Inside Higher Ed (July 17, 2019)**
URL(s): www.insidehighered.com/digital-learning/ar
ticle/2019/07/17/perspectives-field-amazons-big
-dollar-entry-training-workers
Ed: Doug Lederman. **Released:** July 17, 2019. **Description:** Amazon is making a huge investment in its employees by spending $700 million on their training. In the past, most companies would outsource the training but Amazon is taking care of this in-house and educating their employees themselves. **Availability:** Online.

9997 ■ **Learning While Working: Structuring Your On-the-Job Training**
Ed: Paul Smith. **Released:** July 10, 2018. **Price:** $42. 95, Paperback; $42.95, E-book. **Description:** A guide to providing the focus and structure your employees need to receive on-the-job training that develop top-tier talent for your business. **Availability:** E-book; Print.

9998 ■ **"A Man of Courage: Leon Sullivan, First Black Corporate Director Who Fought against Inequality and Apartheid"** in **Black Enterprise(February 25, 2023)**
URL(s): www.blackenterprise.com/a-man-of-courage
-leon-sullivan-first-black-corporate-director-who
-fought-against-inequality-and-apartheid/
Ed: Atiya Jordan. **Released:** February 25, 2023. **Description:** Profile of Rev. Leon Sullivan, the first Black corporate director appointed to General Motors' board in 1971. **Availability:** Online.

9999 ■ **The Sales Manager's Guide to Greatness: Ten Essential Strategies for Leading Your Team to the Top**
Ed: Kevin F. Davis. **Released:** March 28, 2017. **Price:** $17.55, Hardcover; $8.69, E-book. **Description:** A business leadership book that will guide sales managers towards achieving high results with your team. **Availability:** E-book; Print.

10000 ■ **"Smart Locks, Home Surveillance Change Locksmith Trade"** in **U.S. News & World Report (June 22, 2019)**
URL(s): www.usnews.com/news/best-states/pennsyl-
vania/articles/2019-06-22/smart-locks-home-surveil-
lance-change-locksmith-trade
Ed: Andrew Kulp. **Released:** June 22, 2019. **Description:** The locksmith trade isn't all about just locks and keys. Electronics and new technology play a large role in home security industry, and locksmiths have had to retrain and learn new techniques. Chip keys for cars led the way down this new path and locksmiths had to adjust their trade and nowadays, they need to be savvy in the field of smart locks for homes and businesses. **Availability:** Online.

10001 ■ **"Warning: You Need to Reinvest in Job Training"** in **U.S. News & World Report (October 19, 2018)**
URL(s): money.usnews.com/money/blogs/outside
-voices-careers/articles/2018-10-19/warning-you
-need-to-reinvest-in-job-training
Ed: Hannah Morgan. **Released:** October 19, 2018. **Description:** With the fastest-growing occupations having a technical component, workers will need to seek out additional job training to keep skills up to par and satisfy demand. Trends in various industries are always updating, so it's best to keep an eye on anything new and try to keep up. Micro-degrees or various certifications apply and are often the type of retraining employers are looking for with their employees. **Availability:** Online.

10002 ■ "When Is On-the-Job Training the Right Solution?" in Training Industry (May 2, 2019)
URL(s): trainingindustry.com/articles/conten t-development/when-is-on-the-job-training-the-righ t-solution/

Ed: Brian Blecke, Kelly Smith. **Released:** May 02, 2019. **Description:** Discusses when on-the-job training is beneficial to the business and five elements that the training should contain so you and your employees maximize the benefits. **Availability:** Online.

STATISTICAL SOURCES

10003 ■ Job Training and Career Counseling - 2022 U.S. Market Research Report with Updated Forecasts
URL(s): www.marketresearch.com/Kentley-Insights-v 4035/Job-Training-Career-Counseling-Research -32203844/

Price: $295. **Description:** Comprehensive and in-depth assessments of the job training and career counseling industry in the United States with over 100 data sets covering 2013-2026. The report includes historical and forecasted market size, product lines, profitability, financial ratios, BCG matrix, statistics by state, operating expense details, organizational breakdown, consolidation analysis, employee productivity, price inflation, pay bands for the top 20 industry jobs, trend analysis and forecasts on companies, locations, employees, and payroll. **Availability:** Download.

10004 ■ Job Training & Career Counseling in the US - Industry Market Research Report
URL(s): www.marketresearch.com/IBISWorld-v2487/ Job-Training-Career-Counseling-Research-3217 5372/

Price: $1,020. **Description:** Report covering the scope, size, disposition and growth of the job training and career counseling industry including the key sensitivities and success factors. Also included are five-year industry forecasts, growth rates and an analysis of the industry key players and their market shares. **Availability:** Download.

TRADE PERIODICALS

10005 ■ TD Magazine
Pub: Association for Talent Development
Contact: Tony Bingham, President
URL(s): www.td.org/td-magazine

Ed: Patty Gaul, Paula Ketter. **Released:** Monthly **Price:** $19.50, Members for paperback non member; $169, Members for 2 years; $240, Nonmembers for 2 years; $180, Nonmembers for 1 year; $99, Members for 1 year; $19.50, Nonmembers for pdf. **Description:** Magazine on training and development. **Availability:** Print; PDF; Download.

RESEARCH CENTERS

10006 ■ Brandeis University - Center for Youth and Communities (CYC) - Library
415 South St. 35
 Waltham, MA 02453

Ph: (781)736-4835
URL: http://heller.brandeis.edu/cyc
Contact: Susan P. Curnan, Executive Director
E-mail: curnan@brandeis.edu

Description: Integral unit of the Heller School for Social Policy and Management, Brandeis University. **Scope:** Youth development policy and programs, including education, workforce, family and community connections, management and leadership in nonprofit organizations. **Founded:** 1983. **Holdings:** Figures not available. **Publications:** *Anthology*; *CYD Journal* (Occasionally); *CYC Reports*.

10007 ■ FHI 360
359 Blackwell St., Ste. 200
 Durham, NC 27701
Ph: (919)544-7040
Fax: (919)544-7261
Co. E-mail: careercentersupport@fhi360.org
URL: http://www.fhi360.org
Contact: Tessie San Martin, Chief Executive Officer
Facebook: www.facebook.com/fhi360
Linkedin: www.linkedin.com/company/fhi-360
X (Twitter): x.com/FHI360
Instagram: www.instagram.com/fhi360
YouTube: www.youtube.com/@FHIVideo

Description: Works to increase the availability, safety, effectiveness, acceptability, and ease of using family planning methods and primary health care services, while reducing the spread of HIV/AIDS, sexually transmitted diseases (STIs), tuberculosis (TB), malaria, Ebola, neglected endemic tropical diseases, and emerging pandemic threats from zoonotic diseases. **Founded:** 1971. **Publications:** *Connections*; *Bridging the Gap: A National Directory of Services for Women and Girls with Disabilities* (Periodic); *Building Community: A Manual Exploring Issues of Women and Disability*; *Playtime Is Science*; *Quit It! A Teacher's Guide on Teasing and Bullying for Use with Students in Grades K-3*; *What Will Happen If: Young Children and the Scientific Method*; *Policy papers*; *NIWL Reports*; *A Place to Grow: Evaluation of the New York City Beacons Final Report*; *Environmental Education and Communication for a Sustainable World: Handbook for International Practitioners*; *Handbook for Excellence in Focus Group Research*; *Handbook for HIV Prevention Communication Planning*. **Educational Activities:** Peace Corps Connect (Annual). **Geographic Preference:** Multinational; National.

10008 ■ Human Resources Research Organization (HumRRO) - Library
Human Resources Research Organization (HumRRO)
 66 Canal Center Plz., Ste. 700
 Alexandria, VA 22314
Ph: (703)549-3611
Fax: (703)548-2860
URL: http://www.humrro.org/corpsite
Contact: Dr. Suzanne Tsacoumis, President
Facebook: www.facebook.com/HumRRO
Linkedin: www.linkedin.com/company/humrro
X (Twitter): x.com/HumRROorg
YouTube: www.youtube.com/user/humrro

Description: Behavioral and social science researchers seeking to improve human performance, particularly in organizational settings, through behavioral and social science research, development, consulta-tion and instruction. Promotes research and development to solve specific problems in: training and education; development, refinement, and instruction in the technology of training and education; measurement and evaluation of human performance under varying circumstances; organizational development studies, including performance counseling, group decision-making, and factors that affect organizational competence; development of manpower information systems and the application of management science on personnel systems. Encourages use of high technology for instructional purposes by means of computer assisted instruction, interactive video, and computer literacy. Offers technical publication services including data analysis and editorial, word processing, production, and printing services. **Scope:** An independent, nonprofit corporation which strives to improve human performance (primarily in organizational settings) through behavioral and social science research, product development, consultation, and instruction. Active in the fields of education and training, testing and assessment, survey research, program evaluation, and human factors engineering. **Founded:** 1951. **Holdings:** Figures not available. **Training:** An examination of the properties of local dependence measures when applied to adaptive data, Computing and communicating test accuracy for high-stakes decisions, Development of cross-cultural perspective taking skills, Developing, implementing, and scoring valid job simulations, Executive and senior leader development: A best practices review, Integrating reliability and validity based perspectives on error in performance ratings, Job incumbent perceptions of faking on noncognitive inventories, Modeling the psychometric properties of multisource ratings: CFA vs. GLMM, Performance level descriptions: Similarities and differences among select states, Reducing bias through propensity scoring: A study of SAT coaching, Retaining personality measures after failure: Changes in scores and strategies, Review of information and communication technology literacy measures, Self-presentation on personality measures: A meta-analysis, Using cases as a proxy for experience in leadership development, Using patterns to understand the dynamics of leader behavior, Verification testing in unproctored internet testing programs, A cross-cultural look at items of logic-based reasoning, An overlooked problem with standard practices for analyzing ratings data from ill-structured measurement designs, Context effects in internet testing: A literature review, Differentiating in the Upper Tail: Selecting Among High-Scoring Applicants, Gaining insight into situational judgment test functioning via spline regression, Ill-Structured measurement designs and reliability: The tale of a HumRRO IR&D project, Influence of subject matter expert (SME) personality on job analysis ratings, Modeling intraindividual change in soldiers attitudes and values during the first term of enlistment SES and admissions test validity: Within race analyses, The Feasibility of using O NET to study skill changes, Validation of a person organization personality hybrid measure, Validating psychological screening examinations and background investigations for applicant screening. **Awards:** Meredith Crawford Fellowship for Industrial and Organizational Psychology (Annual), Scholarship to graduate students in Industrial and Organizational Psychology for completing dissertations; Meredith P. Crawford Fellowship in I-O Psychology (Annual). **Geographic Preference:** National.

START-UP INFORMATION

10009 ■ *"So You Want To Be a Food Truck Vendor?" in Philadelphia Business Journal (Vol. 33, August 15, 2014, No. 27, pp. 7)*
Pub: American City Business Journals, Inc.
Contact: Mike Olivieri, Executive Vice President

Released: Weekly. **Price:** $4, introductory 4-week offer(Digital only). **Description:** Food truck vendors assert that the most challenging part of starting a food truck business is acquiring a license as well as the price and number of licenses and permits required. Other costs include additional fees to vend in prime locations, maintenance, and inventory. **Availability:** Print; Online.

REFERENCE WORKS

10010 ■ *"Amazon Hits Back at Bloomberg Report About Small Suppliers Purge" in Fast Company (May 28, 2019)*
URL(s): www.fastcompany.com/90355900/amazon-is-about-to-halt-orders-from-small-suppliers-report#:~:targetText=A%20purge%20is%20on%20the,selling%20platform%2C%20according%20to%20Bloomberg.

Ed: Cale Guthrie Weissman. **Released:** May 28, 2019. **Description:** Bloomberg reported that Amazon would be purging small wholesalers in favor of large suppliers in order to maintain a competitive edge. However, Amazon is claiming that report is false and there will be no large-scale purge, even if they do review their vendors and make periodic changes as needed. **Availability:** Online.

10011 ■ *"Amazon Is Poised to Unleash a Long-Feared Purge of Small Suppliers" in Bloomberg (May 28, 2019)*
URL(s): www.bloomberg.com/news/articles/2019-05-28/amazon-is-poised-to-unleash-long-feared-purge-of-small-suppliers

Ed: Spencer Soper. **Released:** May 28, 2019. **Description:** Online giant Amazon is planning a permanent purge of thousands of small wholesale vendors in favor of larger suppliers. **Availability:** Online.

10012 ■ *"Annapolis Seeks City Market Vendors" in Boston Business Journal (Vol. 29, June 10, 2011, No. 5, pp. 3)*
Pub: Boston Business Journal
Contact: Carolyn M. Jones, President
E-mail: cmjones@bizjournals.com

Ed: Daniel J. Sernovitz. **Price:** $350. **Description:** The city of Annapolis, Maryland is planning to revive the historical landmark Market House and it is now accepting bids from vendors until June 10, 2011. The city hopes to reopen the facility by July 2011 for a six-month period after which it will undergo renovations. **Availability:** Print; Online.

10013 ■ *"Automated Kiosks Ease Downtown Parking Pain" in America's Intelligence Wire (September 19, 2012)*
Pub: McClatchy-Tribune Regional News

Description: City of Tampa, Florida rid the city of its parking meters downtown in favor of computerized kiosks that accept credit cards. Businesses in the area requested the change because customers were being ticketed because the meters allowed only 20 minute parking. **Availability:** Print; Online.

10014 ■ *"Bike Company Sharing More Than Pedal Power: Long Beach To Get Some of Bike Nation's Profits; L.A. Might, Too" in Los Angeles Business Journal (Vol. 34, September 3, 2012, No. 36, pp. 12)*
Pub: CBJ L.P.
Contact: Terri Cunningham, Contact

Ed: James Rufus Koren. **Description:** Bike Nation USA plans to have up to 250 kiosks so customers can pay to borrow specially equipped bikes for rides in town. They hope to eventually have 400 kiosks installed in the Los Angeles, California area. Details of the plans are outlined. **Availability:** Online.

10015 ■ *"Bloomington Police to Buy 24-Hour Electronic Kiosk With Federal Grant" in Herald-Times (September 5, 2012)*
Ed: Abby Tonsing. **Description:** Bloomington, Indiana police department will purchase two electronic kiosks with money from a federal grant. The kiosks will operate 24 hours a day and provide the public with the ability to communicate with the police, obtain forms and permits, as well as other police-related activities. **Availability:** Print; Online.

10016 ■ *"Blue Cross to Put Kiosk in Mall" in News & Observer (November 9, 2010)*
Pub: News and Observer
Contact: Bill Church, Editor

Ed: Alan M. Wolf. **Description:** Blue Cross and Blue Shield of North Carolina has placed a kiosk in Durham's Streets of Southpoint in order to market its health insurance. **Availability:** Online.

10017 ■ *"Border Boletin: UA to Take Lie-Detector Kiosk to Poland" in Arizona Daily Star (September 14, 2010)*
Pub: Arizona Daily Star
Contact: John D'Orlando, President
E-mail: jdorlando@tucson.com

Ed: Brady McCombs. **Description:** University of Arizona's National Center for Border Security and Immigration Research will send a team to Warsaw, Poland to show border guards from 27 European Union countries the center's Avatar Kiosk. The Avatar technology is designed for use at border ports and airports to assist Customs officers detect individuals who are lying. **Availability:** Print; Online.

10018 ■ *"Cabela's Plans Outpost Strategy for Smaller Markets" in Pet Product News (Vol. 66, April 2012, No. 4, pp. 21)*
Description: Sidney, Nebraska-based outdoor gear retailer Cabela's Inc. plans to launch its first Cabelas Outpost Store, a retail initiative aimed at markets

with fewer than 250,000 people. The initial 40,000-square-foot Cabela's Outpost Store is scheduled for a fall 2012 opening in Union Gap, Washington. Online order kiosks are among the features of the new store. **Availability:** Print; Online.

10019 ■ *"Cash for Kiosks: EcoATM Pulls in Series B Funding" in San Diego Business Journal (Vol. 33, May 7, 2012, No. 19, pp. 10)*
Pub: CBJ L.P.
Contact: Terri Cunningham, Contact

Ed: Brad Graves. **Description:** EcoATM received $17 million in Series B venture funds as well as a $1 million grant from the National Science Foundation. The Series B funds will be used to install mall kiosks that offer cash for used cellphones and other small electronic devices. **Availability:** Online.

10020 ■ *"Coinstar, Inc. and Seattle's Best Coffee Sign Exclusive Agreement to Roll Out Thousands of the New Rubi Kiosks in Grocery, Drug and Mass Channels" in Marketing Weekly News (June 23 2012, pp. 77)*
Pub: PR Newswire Association LLC.

Description: Seattles' Best Coffee, a firm of Starbucks Corporation, has partnered with Coinstar Inc. to install coffee kiosks in grocery, drug and mass merchant retailers featuring Seattle's Best coffee drinks. Rubi kiosk is the third automated kiosk owned by Coinstar. Details of the deal are included.

10021 ■ *"Cox Opens Norfolk Mall Kiosk; Wireless Service Not Ready" in Virginian-Pilot (September 20, 2010)*
Pub: The Virginian-Pilot
Contact: Kevin Goyette, Director
E-mail: kgoyette@dailypress.com

Ed: Carolyn Shapiro. **Description:** Cox Communications opened a kiosk at MacArthur Center that will sell wireless telephone devices and plans. **Availability:** Print; Online.

10022 ■ *"Encore on Cue: Migratory Hopes More Venues, Artists Take Note of Its Kiosks That Offer Concert Recordings to Fans Immediately After Shows" in Los Angeles Business Journal (Vol. 34, May 28, 2012, No. 22, pp. 5)*
Pub: CBJ L.P.
Contact: Laura Garrett, Vice President Publisher
E-mail: garrett@ocbj.com

Description: Album quality recordings of concerts are now available using Culver City startup Migratory Music's technology. The firm installed 15 kiosks where consumers can purchase concert recordings performed at the Greek Theatre. Details of this service are included. **Availability:** Online.

10023 ■ *"Fear of the Unknown Muted Impact of Baltimore Grand Prix" in Baltimore Business Journal (Vol. 29, September 9, 2011, No. 18, pp. 3)*
Pub: Boston Business Journal
Contact: Carolyn M. Jones, President

E-mail: cmjones@bizjournals.com

Ed: Alexander Jackson. **Description:** Baltimore Grand Prix caught restaurateurs, hoteliers and street vendors in Baltimore, Maryland unprepared for the thousands of race fans who attended the inaugural event over Labor Day weekend. The race popularity is relatively unknown to them and some felt they were not able to make as much money as they had hoped. **Availability:** Online.

10024 ■ *"Floral-Design Kiosk Business Blossoming" in Colorado Springs Business Journal (September 24, 2010)*
Pub: Dolan Media Newswires

Ed: Monica Mendoza. **Description:** Profile of Shellie Greto and her mother Jackie Martin who started a wholesale flower business in their garage. The do-it-yourself floral arrangement firm started a kiosk business in supermarkets called Complete Design. **Availability:** Online.

10025 ■ *"Hanson's to Widen Marketing Window; Company Plans Mall Kiosks, to Attend Events" in Crain's Detroit Business (Vol. 28, May 28, 2012, No. 22, pp. 3)*
Pub: Crain Communications Inc.
Contact: Barry Asin, President

Ed: Sherri Welch. **Description:** Hanson's Window and Construction Company is expanding its presence through the use of kiosks installed at malls as well as attending local events in order to increase awareness of their firm. Las year Hanson spent nearly $9.2 million on marketing their vinyl replacement windows, siding and roofing for homes. **Availability:** Print; Online.

10026 ■ *"Healthy Start for Medical Kiosks; Lions Kick in $20K" in Crain's Detroit Business" (Vol. 28, June 11, 2012, No. 24, pp. 18)*
Pub: Crain Communications Inc.
Contact: Barry Asin, President

Ed: Jay Greene. **Description:** Detroit Lions Charities has given Henry Ford Health System's school-based and community health program money to purchase nine interactive health kiosks. These kiosks will be provided by Medical Imagineering LLC, a spinoff of Henry Ford's Innovation Institute and installed in elementary and middle schools in Detroit. **Availability:** Print; Online.

10027 ■ *"IJ Challenges Atlanta's Vending Monopoly" in Benzinga.com (July 28, 2011)*
Pub: Benzinga.com
Contact: Jason Raznick, Founder

Description: A lawsuit was filed by The Institute for Justice to challenge Atlanta's unconstitutional vending monopoly on behalf of two Atlanta street vendors. **Availability:** Print; Online.

10028 ■ *"Kiosk Outfit ecoATM Now Recycling Video Games" in San Diego Union-Tribune (October 7, 2010)*
Pub: The San Diego Union-Tribune
Contact: Phyllis Pfeiffer, President
E-mail: ppfeiffer@lajollalight.com
URL(s): www.sandiegouniontribune.com/sdut-kiosk -outfit-ecoatm-now-recycling-video-games-2010oc t07-story.html

Ed: Mike Freeman. **Description:** ecoATM makes automated kiosks to buy back cell phones,it will now include video games as part of their recycling center for consumer electronics. **Availability:** Print; Online.

10029 ■ *"Kroger Family of Pharmacies to Offer Health Assessment Kiosks at Locations Nationwide" in Entertainment Close-Up (August 22, 2012)*
Pub: Close-Up Media Inc.
Contact: Caroline S. Moore, President
E-mail: cms@closeupmedia.com

Description: Kroger HealthCENTER kiosks will be placed in Kroger Company Family of Pharmacies in 1,950 locations across the country. The kiosks are provided by Styhealthy, a wellness solutions firm and will offer self-use health screening to customers. **Availability:** Online.

10030 ■ *"Lancaster Offers Kiosks to Downtown Businesses: InSite Development is Planning to Lease Up to 20 Retail Units Along Lancaster Boulevard" in San Fernando Valley Business Journal (Vol. 17, June 25, 2012, No. 13, pp. 4)*
Pub: CBJ L.P.
Contact: Terri Cunningham, Contact

Ed: Mark Madler. **Description:** At least 20 low-cost kiosks will be installed in downtown Lancaster, California to offer customers a means in which to purchase items from retailers wanting to sell downtown, but cannot handle the overhead of a new store. **Availability:** PDF; Online.

10031 ■ *"LCB Puts a Cork in Kiosk Wine Sales" in Times Leader (December 22, 2010)*
Ed: Andrew M. Seder. **Description:** The Pennsylvania Liquor Control Board closed down thirty Pronto Wine Kiosks located in supermarkets throughout the state. The Board cited mechanical and technological issues such as products not dispensing. **Availability:** Online.

10032 ■ *"Lindbergh Receives Kiosks to Expedite Travel Through Customs: Vetting Process 'Pre-Screens' Low-Risk Travelers" in San Diego Business Journal (Vol. 33, August 20, 2012, No. 34, pp. 8)*
Pub: CBJ L.P.
Contact: Terri Cunningham, Contact

Ed: Mike Allen. **Description:** Lindbergh Field airport in California installed two automated kiosks to help international travelers pass through customs in minutes. Global Entry verifies identification and allows declaration of items and is used for low risk passsengers. **Availability:** Online.

10033 ■ *"McDonald's Finds a Flaw in Ordering Kiosks: No Cash Accepted" in Bloomberg (November 13, 2019)*
URL(s): www.bloomberg.com/news/articles/2019 -11-13/mcdonald-s-finds-a-flaw-in-its-ordering-ki osks-no-cash-accepted

Ed: Leslie Patton. **Released:** November 13, 2019. **Description:** Since touchscreen ordering is increasing worldwide, McDonald's has been investing in kiosks as part of their effort to attract more on-the-go customers. However, the kiosks they invested in have a major flaw: they do not accept cash. Many households do not have access to debit or credit cards making these kiosks unusable to them. Adding to the frustration is that many franchises have invested their own money into the cost of the renovations featuring these kiosks. **Availability:** Online.

10034 ■ *"Minnesota State Fair Vendors Accept Big Risks for Big Rewards" in Business Journal (Vol. 32, August 22, 2014, No. 13, pp. 10)*
Pub: American City Business Journals, Inc.
Contact: Mike Olivieri, Executive Vice President
Released: Weekly. **Price:** $4, introductory 4-week offer(Digital & Print). **Description:** Food and beverage concessionaires compete for booths at the Minnesota State Fair and there are many vendors that wait for years to get one, especially a large booth with room for tables and a beer garden. The State Fair has been a good business opportunity and a family bonding experience for most of the vendors. **Availability:** Video; Print; Online.

10035 ■ *"New York's Duane Reade Adds In-Store Yogurt Kiosks" in ADWEEK (Vol. 53, February 6, 2012, No. 5, pp. 16)*
Description: Fifty year old chain, Pinkberry, is adding self-serve frozen kiosks to select stores in the New York area. Duane Reade, owner of Pinkberry, is refocusing the business to a health and daily-living destination. **Availability:** Online.

10036 ■ *"Place Your Bets: Horse, Dog Racing Kiosks Bring the Track to Local Bars" in Dickinson Press (March 28, 2012)*
Pub: McClatchy Tribune Information Services
Contact: Patrick J. Talamantes, President

Description: MTPBets USA Inc., headquartered in Wilmington, Delaware, installed self-betting kiosks in businesses located in southwest North Dakota. The kiosks will feature live horse and dog races. **Availability:** Online.

10037 ■ *"The Rise of Digital Currencies and Atlanta's Key Role" in Atlanta Business Chronicle (July 4, 2014, pp. 25A)*
Pub: American City Business Journals, Inc.
Contact: Mike Olivieri, Executive Vice President

Released: Weekly. **Price:** $4, introductory 4-week offer(Digital only). **Description:** Virtual currency bitcoin, which is an Internet protocol that defines a decentralized online payment system is discussed. A description of how bitcoin and other virtual currencies are used and concerns over its future use are examined. A short profile of Atlanta-based startup BitPay, which provides software solutions to help businesses accept bitcoin payments without risking operating cash flow is included. BitPay also enables rapid currency conversion through bitcoin ATMs or kiosks. **Availability:** Print; Online.

10038 ■ *"Self-Order Kiosks Are Finally Having a Moment in the Fast Food Space" in Forbes (July 30, 2019)*
URL(s): www.forbes.com/sites/aliciakelso/2019/07/ 30/self-order-kiosks-are-finally-having-a-moment-in -the-fast-food-space/#730429f24275

Ed: Alicia Kelso. **Released:** July 30, 2019. **Description:** Self-ordering kiosks are becoming more popular in the fast food industry. Not only do they promote speed and convenience for the consumer, but with add-ons, it also provides more revenue for the company. **Availability:** Online.

10039 ■ *"Titan to Become New York's Largest Provider of Phone Kiosk Advertising" in Marketing Weekly News (September 11, 2010, pp. 150)*
Pub: VerticalNews

Description: Titan will acquire from Verizon 1,900 payphones at 1,300 phone kiosk locations in New York City, New York. This transaction will triple the firm's inventory of New York Phone Kiosk media to over 5,000 advertising faces. Details are included. **Availability:** Print; Online.

10040 ■ *"Wal-Mart Is Testing Mobile Checkout: App Would Let Shoppers Scan Items, Pay at Kiosks; Giant Saves $12 Million a Year for Every Second It Can Cut" in Wall Street Journal. Europe (September 4, 2012, pp. A19)*
Ed: Shelly Banjo. **Description:** Wal-Mart Stores Inc. is testing a new checkout system at some of its US stores that would allow customers to scan items as they browse through stores and pay at self-service kiosks. Wal-Mart estimates savigs of $12 million for every second it cuts from the checkout process. **Availability:** Online.

FRANCHISES AND BUSINESS OPPORTUNITIES

10041 ■ **Mr. Pickle's Sandwich Shop**
445 Grass Valley Hwy., (Hwy. 49)
Auburn, CA 95603
Ph: (530)823-3359
Free: 855-677-4255
Co. E-mail: corp@mrpickles.com

URL: http://www.mrpickles.com
Facebook: www.facebook.com/Mr.PicklesSan
  dwichShops
X (Twitter): x.com/MrPicklesShops
Instagram: www.instagram.com/mrpicklessan
  dwichshops
Description: Owner and operator of sandwich shop franchise. It offers menus such as sandwiches, salads, deli meats and cheeses. **Founded:** 1995.

Training: 2 weeks training included at franchisee's location and ongoing support.

10042 ■ Printwell Management Inc.
1200 St. Laurent Blvd., Store Ste. 120
  Ottawa, ON, Canada K1K 3B8
Ph: (613)744-2001
Fax: (613)744-6555
Co. E-mail: sales@printwell.ca

URL: http://printwell.ca
Facebook: www.facebook.com/printwellcanada
Linkedin: www.linkedin.com/company/printwell-o
  ttawa
X (Twitter): x.com/printwellcanada
Instagram: www.instagram.com/printwellcanada
Founded: 2002. **Training:** Provides 3 weeks training.

Landscape Equipment and Supplies

START-UP INFORMATION

10043 ■ *"Sustainable Advantage"* in *Inc.* (Vol. 36, September 2014, No. 7, pp. 86)
Pub: Mansueto Ventures L.L.C.
Contact: Stephanie Mehta, Chief Executive Officer
Price: $8.95, hardcopy black and white. **Description:** Four startup companies committed to providing sustainable, eco-friendly products and services while protecting the environment and bettering human health are profiled. Holganix(TM) offers organic lawn care products; Motiv Power Systems electrifies large vehicles; Clean Energy Collective Solar Power builds lareg community solar panel arrays; and Protein Bar offers healthy alternatives to fast food in its chain of restaurants. The company also works with nonprofits focused on wellness and education and has created 167 Learning Gardens nationwide. **Availability:** Print; PDF; Online.

ASSOCIATIONS AND OTHER ORGANIZATIONS

10044 ■ **American Seed Trade Association (ASTA)**
1701 Duke St., Ste. 275
 Alexandria, VA 22314
Ph: (703)837-8140
Free: 888-890-7333
Fax: (703)837-9365
Co. E-mail: info@betterseed.org
URL: http://www.betterseed.org
Contact: Andrew W. LaVigne, President
Linkedin: www.linkedin.com/company/american-seed-trade-assn
X (Twitter): x.com/Better_Seed
Instagram: www.instagram.com/better_seed
YouTube: www.youtube.com/channel/UCeN dXgUMZy8a8_u0ZD_yrZQ
Description: Breeders, growers, assemblers, conditioners, wholesalers, and retailers of grain, grass, vegetable, flower, and other seed for planting purposes. **Founded:** 1883. **Publications:** *Corn and Sorghum Proceedings* (Annual); *Soybean Seed Proceedings* (Annual). **Geographic Preference:** National.

10045 ■ **AmericanHort**
525 9th St NW Ste. 800
 Washington, DC 20004
Ph: (202)789-2900
Co. E-mail: hello@americanhort.org
URL: http://www.americanhort.org
Contact: Ken Fisher, President
Facebook: www.facebook.com/AmericanHort
Linkedin: www.linkedin.com/company/americanhort
X (Twitter): x.com/American_Hort
Description: Vertical organization of wholesale growers; landscape firms; garden centers; mail order nurseries; suppliers. Promotes the industry and its products. Offers management and consulting services and public relations programs. Provides government representation and bank card plan for members. Maintains hall of fame. **Founded:** 1876. **Publications:** *American Nursery & Landscape Association-- Member Directory: Who's Who in the Nursery Industry* (Annual); *Directory of Forest Tree Nurseries in the United States* (Irregular). **Educational Activities:** Farwest Show (Annual). **Geographic Preference:** National.

10046 ■ **Association of Professional Landscape Designers (APLD)**
2207 Forest Hills Dr.
 Harrisburg, PA 17112
Ph: (717)238-9780
Fax: (717)238-9985
URL: http://www.apld.org
Contact: Eric Gilbey, President
E-mail: egilbey@vectorworks.net
Facebook: www.facebook.com/pages/Association-of -Professional-Landscape-Designers/121318833307
X (Twitter): x.com/APLD
Pinterest: www.pinterest.com/theapld
Description: Works to improve status and establish professional credentials for landscape designers. International and regional continuing education opportunities. Offers certification programs. **Founded:** 1989. **Awards:** APLD International Landscape Design Awards (Annual); APLD Award of Distinction (Annual); Harry Schuster Service Award (Annual). **Geographic Preference:** Multinational.

10047 ■ **Farm Equipment Manufacturers Association (FEMA)**
1000 Executive Pky., Ste. 100
 Saint Louis, MO 63141-6369
Ph: (314)878-2304
Fax: (314)732-1480
Co. E-mail: info@farmequip.org
URL: http://www.farmequip.org
Contact: Tim Burenga, President
Facebook: www.facebook.com/shortliner
X (Twitter): x.com/Shortliner
YouTube: www.youtube.com/channel/UC5-F 6hzJhCCOUIBBI7ASE8Q
Description: Comprised of manufacturers of "shortlines" (specialized farm equipment). **Founded:** 1950. **Publications:** *Shortliner*; *Informa Economics Daily Policy Report*; *Farm Equipment Manufacturers Association--Membership Directory* (Continuous). **Educational Activities:** Farm Equipment Manufacturers Association Marketing & Distribution Convention (Annual). **Awards:** Harold B. Halter Memorial Scholarship (Annual). **Geographic Preference:** National.

10048 ■ **Independent Turf and Ornamental Distributors Association (ITODA)**
174 Crestview Dr.
 Bellefonte, PA 16823
Ph: (814)357-9197
Co. E-mail: info@itoda.org
URL: http://www.itoda.org
Contact: Craig Mylor, President
E-mail: craig.tenbargeseeds@gmail.com
Facebook: www.facebook.com/turfindependent
X (Twitter): x.com/turfindependent
Description: Wholesale suppliers of lawn and turf chemicals, fertilizers, and equipment. Represents members' interests. Conducts educational programs. Provides consulting services. Maintains speakers' bureau; compiles statistics. **Founded:** 1990. **Geographic Preference:** National.

10049 ■ **New York State Turf and Landscape Association (NYSTLA)**
1 Prospect Ave.
 White Plains, NY 10607
Ph: (914)993-9455
Co. E-mail: nystlassoc@gmail.com
URL: http://www.nystla.com
Contact: Michael Iorio, President
X (Twitter): x.com/NYSTLA1
Instagram: www.instagram.com/nys_tla
Description: Landscaping and grounds keeping professionals. Promotes the landscaping industry. **Publications:** *Installation*; *Irrigation*; *Mantenimiento* (Monthly). **Educational Activities:** Professional Turf & Landscape Conference & Trade Show (Annual). **Awards:** Frank Rossi Horticultural Scholarship Award (Annual); NYSTLA Scholarship. **Geographic Preference:** National.

REFERENCE WORKS

10050 ■ *"All the Trimmings"* in *Green Industry Pro* (Vol. 23, March 2011, No. 3, pp. 29)
Ed: Gregg Wartgow. **Description:** When choosing lawn mowing equipment, it is advised to purchase commercial-grade 21-inch walk mowers rather than less expensive consumer-grade mowers. John Deere is reentering the commercial 21-inch walk behind mower market after a five-year hiatus. **Availability:** Online.

10051 ■ *"Hey, You Can't Do That"* in *Green Industry Pro* (Vol. 23, September 2011)
Ed: Rod Dickens. **Description:** Manufacturers of landscape equipment are making better use of energy resources, such as the use of fuel-injection systems instead of carburetors, lightweight materials, better lubricants, advanced battery technology, and innovative engine designs. **Availability:** Online.

10052 ■ *"Joystick Operated Zero-Turn Mower Marks 30 Years"* in *Turf Magazine* (November 11, 2019)
URL(s): www.turfmagazine.com/manufacturersupplier -updates/joystick-operated-zero-turn-mower-marks -30-years/
Ed: Christine Menapace. **Released:** November 11, 2019. **Description:** County Clipper is celebrating the 30 year anniversary of manufacturing the joystick controlled zero-turn mower. Debuted in 1989, this mower was first manufactured under the Snapper brand name, and today Country Clipper offers 20 various joystick models. **Availability:** Online.

10053 ■ "The Landscape of Landscaping Is Changing" in Lawn & Landscape (July 19, 2018)

URL(s): www.lawnandlandscape.com/article/ll-0718 18-landscape-market-growth-potential/

Ed: Ken Gibson. **Released:** July 19, 2018. **Description:** Due to home improvement projects increasing, landscaping has also enjoyed a comeback. The single-family home market is growing and with that, comes a need for more landscape services. Also added to the effect is the growing number of older Americans who need assistance with their lawns. **Availability:** Online.

10054 ■ "Morbark Launches New Equipment" in Lawn & Landscape (November 14, 2019)

URL(s): www.lawnandlandscape.com/article/morbark -new-equipment-tci-expo/

Ed: Lauren Rathmell. **Released:** November 14, 2019. **Description:** Morbark debuted two new pieces of landscape equipment at the TCI Expo in Pittsburgh. Shown were the Rayco 1800AWL Articulated Wheel Loader and the RG165T-R Stump Cutter. **Availability:** Online.

10055 ■ "New to the Class" in Lawn & Landscape (November 14, 2019)

URL(s): www.lawnandlandscape.com/article/new-to -the-class-caterpillar-products/

Ed: Lauren Rathmell. **Released:** November 14, 2019. **Description:** Caterpillar opened its training facility in Cary, NC to the media in order to introduce their latest equipment. The highlight was the 6-ton mini excavator, which is Caterpillar's first entry into the 6-ton class offering. **Availability:** Online.

10056 ■ "New Earth Poised to Expand as Organic Recycling Grows" in San Antonio Business Journal (Vol. 28, May 23, 2014, No. 15, pp. 12)

Pub: American City Business Journals, Inc.

Contact: Mike Olivieri, Executive Vice President

Released: Weekly. **Price:** $4, introductory 4-week offer(Digital & Print). **Description:** New Earth Soils & Compost is expected to benefit from San Antonio, Texas' efforts to bring organic recycling to more homes. The company will invest $1 million into new facilities in order to facilitate growth. New Earth recycles manure, paper, food and wood in San Antonio and Conroe, Texas. **Availability:** Print; Online.

10057 ■ "Precision Crop Control with Valley Irrigation/CropMetrics Partnership" in Farm Industry News (January 6, 2011)

Pub: Informa Business Media, Inc.

Contact: Charlie McCurdy, President

Ed: Karen McMahon. **Description:** Irrigation systems have become a precision farming tool since partnering with agronomic software systems to apply products across the field by prescription. Valley Irrigation and CropMetrics have partnered in order to variably control water, fertilizer and other crop management products through a center pivot irrigation system. **Availability:** Print; Online.

10058 ■ "Toro Launches Z Master 7500" in Lawn & Landscape (November 6, 2019)

URL(s): www.lawnandlandscape.com/article/toro-z -master-7500-mower/

Ed: Lauren Rathmell. **Released:** November 06, 2019. **Description:** Toro introduced its new product, the Z master 7500-G, which is a 96 inch gas mower for commercial grass cutting crews. **Availability:** Online.

STATISTICAL SOURCES

10059 ■ Landscaping Services Industry in the US - Market Research Report

URL(s): www.ibisworld.com/united-states/market-re-search-reports/landscaping-services-industry/

Price: $925. **Description:** Downloadable report analyzing current and future trends in the landscaping services industry. **Availability:** Download.

TRADE PERIODICALS

10060 ■ Landscape Trades: Canada's Premier Horticultural Trade Publication

Pub: Landscape Ontario Horticultural Trades Association

Contact: Joe Salemi, Director, Operations Deputy Director

E-mail: jsalemi@landscapeontario.com

URL(s): landscapetrades.com

Facebook: www.facebook.com/Landscape.Trades

X (Twitter): x.com/landscapetrades

Instagram: www.instagram.com/landscapetrades

Ed: Lee Ann Knudsen. **Released:** 6/year; February, March, may, August, October and December. **Price:** $84.74, Two years; $118.64, for 3 year; $46.90, for 1 year. **Description:** Landscape/nursery magazine. **Availability:** Print; Online.

TRADE SHOWS AND CONVENTIONS

10061 ■ Landscape New Jersey Trade Show and Conference

Frequency: Annual. **Description:** Education and product show featuring new products, equipment, and machinery for the landscape industry. **Principal Exhibits:** Education and product show featuring new products, equipment, and machinery for the landscape industry.

10062 ■ National LICA Winter Convention

Land Improvement Contractors of America (LICA)
3080 Ogden Ave., Ste. 300
Lisle, IL 60532
Ph: (630)548-1984
Co. E-mail: anational.lica@gmail.com
URL: http://www.licanational.com
Contact: Chris Wagner, President

URL(s): www.licanational.com/event-posts/2025-na tional-winter-convention

Frequency: Annual. **Description:** Exhibits related to construction and building equipment, supplies, and services. **Audience:** Land contractors and industry professionals. **Principal Exhibits:** Exhibits related to construction and building equipment, supplies, and services. Dates and Locations: 2025 Feb 11-15 Marriott Jacksonville Downtown, Jacksonville, FL; 2026 Mar 03-07 Las Vegas Convention Center, Las Vegas, NV; 2027. **Telecommunication Services:** anational. lica@gmail.com.

10063 ■ Norcal Landscape and Nursery Show

URL(s): norcaltradeshow.org

Frequency: Annual. **Description:** Tradeshow and exhibition of landscape and gardening products. **Principal Exhibits:** Tradeshow and exhibition of landscape and gardening products.

10064 ■ Northeast Texas Nursery Growers Association Trade Show

URL(s): www.ntnga.org

Frequency: Annual. **Description:** Nursery and landscaper tradeshow featuring product vendors, educational opportunities, and networking. **Principal Exhibits:** Nursery and landscaper tradeshow featuring product vendors, educational opportunities, and networking.

10065 ■ SC Green Conference and Trade Show

URL(s): scgreen.org

Frequency: Annual. **Description:** Provides classes, vendors, and networking for landscapers. **Audience:** Landscape professionals. **Principal Exhibits:** Provides classes, vendors, and networking for landscapers.

FRANCHISES AND BUSINESS OPPORTUNITIES

10066 ■ Outdoor Lighting Perspectives Franchise Inc. (OLP)

Empower Brands
Richmond, VA
Ph: (804)353-6999
URL: http://empowerfranchising.com
Contact: Scott Zide, President

Description: Firm provides outdoor lighting system services. **Founded:** 1995. **Equity Capital Needed:** 40000. **Franchise Fee:** $39,500 . **Training:** 5 days of training at corporate location and 3 days within ninety days of start-up in that city. Product & technical training at manufacturing plant shortly after start-up.

Landscaping Service

START-UP INFORMATION

10067 ■ *How to Open & Operate a Financially Successful Landscaping, Nursery, or Lawn Service Business: With Companion CD-ROM*
Pub: Atlantic Publishing Co.
Contact: Dr. Heather L. Johnson, Contact

Ed: Lynn Wasnak. **Released:** 2010. **Description:** Guide provides understanding of the basic concepts of starting and running a service business, focusing on the operation of a small nursery, landscaping, or lawn service or combining the three operations. It also offers tips for running the business from the home. **Availability:** CD-ROM; Print; Online.

10068 ■ *How to Start a Home-Based Landscaping Business*
Ed: Owen E. Dell. **Released:** 7th edition. **Price:** $21.95, paperback(£14.95); $9.99, e-book(£6.95); $18.95; Electronic Book. **Description:** Guide to starting and running a home-based landscaping business. **Availability:** E-book; Print.

10069 ■ *Start Your Own Lawn Care or Landscaping Business: Your Step-by-Step Guide to Success*
Pub: Entrepreneur Media Inc.
Contact: Dan Bova, Director
E-mail: dbova@entrepreneur.com

Ed: Ciree Linsenman. **Released:** Fourth edition. **Description:** Steps for starting and running a lawn care service.

ASSOCIATIONS AND OTHER ORGANIZATIONS

10070 ■ **American Society of Consulting Arborists (ASCA)**
2331 Rock Spring Rd.
Forest Hill, MD 21050
Ph: (443)640-1084
Fax: (443)640-1031
Co. E-mail: asca@asca-consultants.org
URL: http://www.asca-consultants.org
Contact: Kristen Philips, Executive Director
E-mail: kristen@asca-consultants.org
Facebook: www.facebook.com/ASCAConsultingArborists
X (Twitter): x.com/ConsulArborists

Description: Arboriculture professionals who possess extensive technical knowledge and experience including skills in the areas of written and oral communications, consulting ethics, expert witness activities, and practice management. Allows members to provide independent diagnoses, opinions, appraisal of value, and condition evaluation on trees for clients in the legal, insurance, and development communities as well as the general public. **Founded:** 1967. **Publications:** *Arboriculture Consultant*; *American Society of Consulting Arborists--Membership Direc-*

tory (Annual). **Educational Activities:** ASCA Annual Conference (Annual). **Awards:** Chadwick Scholarship Fund (Annual). **Geographic Preference:** National.

10071 ■ **American Society of Landscape Architects (ASLA) - Professional Practice Library**
636 Eye St. NW
Washington, DC 20001-3736
Ph: (202)898-2444
Free: 888-999-2752
Fax: (202)898-1185
Co. E-mail: info@asla.org
URL: http://www.asla.org
Contact: Torey Carter-Conneen, Chief Executive Officer
Facebook: www.facebook.com/NationalASLA
X (Twitter): x.com/NationalASLA
Instagram: www.instagram.com/nationalasla
Pinterest: www.pinterest.com/NationalASLA

Description: Professional society of landscape architects. Promotes the advancement of education in the art of landscape architecture as an instrument in service to the public welfare. Seeks to strengthen existing and proposed university programs. Offers counsel to new and emerging programs; encourages state registration of landscape architects. Offers placement service; conducts specialized education and research. **Scope:** Landscape architecture. **Services:** Interlibrary loan not available; library open to the public by appointment. **Founded:** 1899. **Holdings:** Membership directories; articles; catalogs; books; guides for archiving. **Subscriptions:** 130 journals and other serials. **Publications:** *ASLA Members Handbook* (Annual; Monthly); *Guide to Educational Programs in Landscape Architecture* (Biennial); *Landscape Architecture Magazine: The Magazine of the American Society of Landscape Architects (LAM)* (Monthly); *Landscape Architecture Accredited Programs* (Annual); *American Society of Landscape Architects--Members' Handbook* (Annual); *LAND*; *Landscape Architecture News Digest - LAND Online*. **Educational Activities:** Conference on Landscape Architecture (Annual). **Awards:** ASLA Council of Fellows Scholarships (Annual); Peridian International, Inc./Rae L. Price, FASLA Scholarship; Bradford Williams Medal (Annual); Jot D. Carpenter Teaching Medal (Annual); The Landscape Architecture Medal of Excellence (Annual); Olmsted Medal (Annual); ASLA President's Medal (Annual); ASLA Honorary Membership (Annual); ASLA Professional Awards (Annual); Frederick Law Olmsted Medal (Annual); The LaGasse Medals (Annual); The ASLA Design Medal (Annual); ASLA Landscape Architecture Firm Award (Annual); ASLA Community Service Award (Annual); ASLA Landmark Award (Annual); The Landscape Architecture Medal Of Excellence (Annual). **Geographic Preference:** National.

10072 ■ **Association of Professional Landscape Designers (APLD)**
2207 Forest Hills Dr.
Harrisburg, PA 17112

Ph: (717)238-9780
Fax: (717)238-9985
URL: http://www.apld.org
Contact: Eric Gilbey, President
E-mail: egilbey@vectorworks.net
Facebook: www.facebook.com/pages/Association-of-Professional-Landscape-Designers/121318833307
X (Twitter): x.com/APLD
Pinterest: www.pinterest.com/theapld

Description: Works to improve status and establish professional credentials for landscape designers. International and regional continuing education opportunities. Offers certification programs. **Founded:** 1989. **Awards:** APLD International Landscape Design Awards (Annual); APLD Award of Distinction (Annual); Harry Schuster Service Award (Annual). **Geographic Preference:** Multinational.

10073 ■ **Canadian Nursery Landscape Association (CNLA) [Association Candienne des Pepinieristes et des Paysagistes]**
7856 5th Line S
Milton, ON, Canada L9T 2X8
Fax: (905)875-1840
Co. E-mail: info@cnla-acpp.ca
URL: http://cnla.ca
Contact: Anthony O'Neill, President
E-mail: aoneillnl@gmail.com
Facebook: www.facebook.com/canadanursery
X (Twitter): x.com/CNLA_ACPP

Description: Devises standards and develops and administers tests to ensure competence in nursery production, garden supply retailing, landscape contracting, and construction and maintenance. **Publications:** *CNLA Newsbrief* (Quarterly). **Awards:** CNLA Honorary Life Member (Periodic); CNLA President's Award (Periodic). **Geographic Preference:** National.

10074 ■ **Canadian Society of Landscape Architects (CSLA) [L'Association des architects paysagistes du Canada (AAPC)]**
12 Forillon Cres.
Ottawa, ON, Canada K2M 2W5
Ph: (613)668-4775
URL: http://www.csla-aapc.ca/csla-aapc
Contact: Michelle Legault, Executive Director
E-mail: executive-director@csla-aapc.ca
Facebook: www.facebook.com/CSLA.AAPC
Linkedin: www.linkedin.com/company/canadian-society-of-landscape-architects
Instagram: www.instagram.com/csla_aapc

Description: Represents and promotes members' interests at national and international levels; develops and supports national activities and programs implemented by members. Maintains accreditation program; makes available professional liability insurance program. **Founded:** 1934. **Publications:** *Landscapes/Paysages* (Quarterly). **Awards:** CSLA Awards of Excellence (Annual); Schwabenbauer President's Award (Annual); CSLA Community Service Award (Annual); CSLA Lifetime Achievement Award (Annual); CSLA President's Award (Annual); Student Award of Excellence (Annual); CSLA Teaching Award (Annual). **Geographic Preference:** National.

10075 ■ CNLA Newsbrief
7856 5th Line S
  Milton, ON, Canada L9T 2X8
Fax: (905)875-1840
Co. E-mail: info@cnla-acpp.ca
URL: http://cnla.ca
Contact: Anthony O'Neill, President
E-mail: aoneillnl@gmail.com
URL(s): cnla.ca/become-a-member
Released: Quarterly **Description:** Provides news and information of the association. **Availability:** Print.

10076 ■ Independent Turf and Ornamental Distributors Association (ITODA)
174 Crestview Dr.
  Bellefonte, PA 16823
Ph: (814)357-9197
Co. E-mail: info@itoda.org
URL: http://www.itoda.org
Contact: Craig Mylor, President
E-mail: craig.tenbargeseeds@gmail.com
Facebook: www.facebook.com/turfindependent
X (Twitter): x.com/turfindependent
Description: Wholesale suppliers of lawn and turf chemicals, fertilizers, and equipment. Represents members' interests. Conducts educational programs. Provides consulting services. Maintains speakers' bureau; compiles statistics. **Founded:** 1990. **Geographic Preference:** National.

10077 ■ International Society of Arboriculture (ISA)
Champaign, IL 61821
Co. E-mail: isa@isa-arbor.com
URL: http://www.isa-arbor.com
Contact: Chris Walsh, President
Facebook: www.facebook.com/InternationalSocie tyofArboriculture
Linkedin: www.linkedin.com/company/interna tionalsocietyofarboriculture
X (Twitter): x.com/ISArboriculture
YouTube: www.youtube.com/user/ISAAdmin
Description: Disseminates information on the care and preservation of shade and ornamental trees. Supports research projects at educational institutions. **Founded:** 1924. **Publications:** *Arborist News* (Bimonthly); *Arboriculture & Urban Forestry (AUF)* (Bimonthly). **Educational Activities:** ISA Annual International Conference & Trade Show (Annual). **Awards:** Harry J. Banker Gold Leaf Award (Annual); Alex L. Shigo Award for Excellence in Arboricultural Education (Annual). **Geographic Preference:** National.

10078 ■ Landscape Architecture Foundation (LAF)
1200 17th St. NW Ste. 210
  Washington, DC 20036
Ph: (202)331-7070
Fax: (202)331-7079
Co. E-mail: rbooher@lafoundation.org
URL: http://www.lafoundation.org
Contact: Barbara Deutsch, Chief Executive Officer
E-mail: bdeutsch@lafoundation.org
Facebook: www.facebook.com/lafoundation.org
Linkedin: www.linkedin.com/company/landscape -architecture-foundation
X (Twitter): x.com/lafoundation
Instagram: www.instagram.com/lafoundation
Description: Serves as an education and research vehicle for the landscape architecture profession in the United States. Combines the capabilities of landscape architects, interests of environmentalists, and needs of agencies and resource foundations. Provides for the preparation and dissemination of educational and scientific information through publications, exhibits, lectures, and seminars. Solicits and expends gifts, legacies, and grants. Established an endowment fund for professorships at colleges and universities. Sponsors California Landscape Architectural Student Scholarship Fund. Conducts a study of the profession to establish goals in terms of education, research needs, practice, and formulation of

public policy. **Scope:** Landscape planning, land use planning and design, environmental planning, landscape change, landscape intervention, place-based land use planning, public participation processes. **Founded:** 1966. **Publications:** *American Landscape Report* (Quarterly). **Awards:** ASLA Council of Fellows Scholarships (Annual); Courtland P. Paul Scholarships (Annual); Steven G. King Play Environments Scholarship (Annual); Landscape Forms Scholarship in Memory of Peter Lindsay Schaudt, FASLA (Annual); Peridian International, Inc./Rae L. Price, FASLA Scholarships (Annual); Rain Bird Intelligent Use of Water Scholarship (Annual); Hawaii Chapter/David T. Woolsey Scholarship (Annual). **Geographic Preference:** National.

10079 ■ Michigan Green Industry Association (MGIA)
30600 Telegraph Rd., Ste. 3360
  Bingham Farms, MI 48025
Ph: (248)646-4992
Fax: (248)646-4994
Co. E-mail: facebook@landscape.org
URL: http://www.landscape.org
Contact: Michelle Atkinson, Executive Director
E-mail: michelle@landscape.org
Facebook: www.facebook.com/michigangreenindus tryassociation
Description: Represents landscape, lawn maintenance, irrigation, snow removal and tree care workers. **Founded:** 1960. **Publications:** *The Landsculptor* (Monthly). **Educational Activities:** Michigan Green Industry Association Trade Show (Annual). **Geographic Preference:** State.

10080 ■ National Association of Landscape Professionals (NALP)
12500 Fair Lakes Cir., Ste. 200
  Fairfax, VA 22033
Ph: (703)736-9666
Free: 800-395-2522
Fax: (703)322-2066
Co. E-mail: info@landscapeprofessionals.org
URL: http://www.landscapeprofessionals.org
Contact: Britt Wood, Chief Executive Officer
Facebook: www.facebook.com/thenalp
Linkedin: www.linkedin.com/company/professional -landcare-network-planet
X (Twitter): x.com/the_nalp
Instagram: www.instagram.com/landscape_assoc
YouTube: www.youtube.com/user/landcarenetwork
Description: Landscape contractors. Works to represent, lead, and unify the interior and exterior landscape industry by working together on a national basis; addressing environmental and legislative issues; and creating increased opportunities in business. Provides forum to encourage member's profitability, personal growth, and professional advancement. **Founded:** 2005. **Publications:** *PLANET News*; *Who's Who in Landscape Contracting* (Annual); *Landscape Contractor News* (Monthly). **Educational Activities:** Landscapes (Annual); Leaders Forum (Annual); ELEVATE The National Conference & Expo (Annual). **Awards:** National Association of Landscape Professionals Safety Recognition Awards (Annual); National Association of Landscape Professionals Awards of Excellence (Annual). **Geographic Preference:** National.

10081 ■ New York State Turf and Landscape Association (NYSTLA)
1 Prospect Ave.
  White Plains, NY 10607
Ph: (914)993-9455
Co. E-mail: nystlassoc@gmail.com
URL: http://www.nystla.com
Contact: Michael Iorio, President
X (Twitter): x.com/NYSTLA1
Instagram: www.instagram.com/nys_tla
Description: Landscaping and grounds keeping professionals. Promotes the landscaping industry. **Publications:** *Installation*; *Irrigation*; *Mantenimiento* (Monthly). **Educational Activities:** Professional Turf & Landscape Conference & Trade Show (Annual).

Awards: Frank Rossi Horticultural Scholarship Award (Annual); NYSTLA Scholarship. **Geographic Preference:** National.

10082 ■ Outdoor Power Equipment Institute (OPEI)
1605 King St.
  Alexandria, VA 22314
Ph: (703)549-7600
Co. E-mail: info@opei.org
URL: http://www.opei.org
Contact: Kris Kiser, President
E-mail: kkiser@opei.org
Facebook: www.facebook.com/OPEInstitute
X (Twitter): x.com/OPEInstitute
Instagram: www.instagram.com/weareopei
Description: Manufacturers of lawn mowers, garden tractors, snow throwers, utility vehicles, chainsaws, motor tillers, shredder/grinders, edger/trimmers, leaf vacuums, log splitters, stump cutters, chippers and sprayers, and major components. **Founded:** 1952. **Publications:** *Contractor Connections*. **Educational Activities:** GIE+EXPO (Annual). **Geographic Preference:** National.

10083 ■ Turf and Ornamental Communicators Association (TOCA)
126 W Main St.
  New Prague, MN 56071
Ph: (952)758-6340
URL: http://www.toca.org
Contact: Mark LaFleur, President
Facebook: www.facebook.com/TOCAorg
X (Twitter): x.com/TOCAorg
Description: Editors, writers, photographers, public relations and advertising practitioners involved in green industry communications (turf and ornamental). Promotes communications excellence within trade and consumer media. Maintains speaker's bureau. **Founded:** 1990. **Publications:** *Turf and Ornamental Communicators Association--Membership Directory*. **Awards:** TOCA Communication Awards Contest - Design (Annual); TOCA Environmental Communicator of the Year (Annual); TOCA Communication Awards Contest (Annual); TOCA Scholarship (Annual); TOCA Communication Awards Contest - Writing (Annual); Turf and Ornamental Communicators Association Scholarship Program (Annual). **Geographic Preference:** National.

REFERENCE WORKS

10084 ■ "5 Marketing Practices Most Landscaping Contractors Get Wrong" in Lawn & Landscape (March 2, 2017)
Ed: Joy Gendusa. **Released:** March 02, 2017. **Description:** In a competitive industry like landscaping, marketing your business is critical. To keep a steady flow of customers calling, making marketing as routine as maintaining your equipment is key. This article provides five of the most common marketing mistakes lawn care businesses make and how to fix them. **Availability:** Online.

10085 ■ 8 Ideas on How to Get Landscaping Customers
Description: Provides techniques to utilize to gain landscaping customers to help you build a profitable landscape business. **Availability:** Online.

10086 ■ 25 Dead Simple Landscape Marketing Ideas to Increase New Lawn Care Customers and Sales
Ed: Joy Gendusa. **Released:** August 03, 2020. **Description:** From lawn care flyers to social media landscape advertising, there are dozens of landscaping marketing strategies. This article provides a list of 25 proven landscape advertising ideas that you can use to promote your small business. **Availability:** Online.

10087 ■ "All the Trimmings" in Green Industry Pro (Vol. 23, March 2011, No. 3, pp. 29)
Ed: Gregg Wartgow. **Description:** When choosing lawn mowing equipment, it is advised to purchase commercial-grade 21-inch walk mowers rather than

less expensive consumer-grade mowers. John Deere is reentering the commercial 21-inch walk behind mower market after a five-year hiatus. **Availability:** Online.

10088 ■ "Cincinnati's Minority Business Accelerator Welcomes First Hispanic Firms" in Business Courier (Vol. 27, August 13, 2010, No. 15, pp. 1)
Pub: Business Courier

Ed: Lucy May. **Description:** The Minority Business Accelerator (MBA) initiative of the Cincinnati USA Regional Chamber in Ohio has included Hispanic-owned firms Best Upon Request and Vivian Llambi and Associates Inc. to its portfolio. Vivian Llambi and Associates is a design, landscape architecture and civil engineering specialist. Prior to these firms' membership, MBA was limited to black-owned companies. **Availability:** Print; Online.

10089 ■ "Corrales Site of New Senior Living/ Care Complex" in America's Intelligence Wire (August 13, 2012)
Description: David Dronet, developer of Corrales Senior Living LLC, has chosen Corrales, New Mexico as its newest site to construct a continuum of care for senior citizens. The project entails a $60 million complex of private homes and health care units with amenities like a restaurant, fitness areas, and gardens. **Availability:** Print; Online.

10090 ■ "Customer Retention is Proportionate to Employee Retention" in Green Industry Pro (Vol. 23, September 2011)
Description: Presented in a question-answer format, information is provided to help retain customers as well as keeping workers happy. **Availability:** Online.

10091 ■ "Customized Before Custom Was Cool" in Green Industry Pro (July 2011)
Ed: Gregg Wartgow. **Description:** Profile of Turf Care Enterprises and owner Kevin Vogeler, who discusses his desire to use more natural programs using little or no chemicals in 1986. At that time, that sector represented 20 percent of his business, today it shares 80 percent. **Availability:** Online.

10092 ■ "Deep in the Heart of Drought" in Green Industry Pro (Vol. 23, October 2011)
Ed: Gregg Wartgow. **Description:** Challenges faced by landscape contractors during the recent drought in Texas are explored. Despite these challenges, opportunity for contractors providing irrigation services has risen. **Availability:** Online.

10093 ■ "Dozens 'Come Alive' in Downtown Chicago" in Green Industry Pro (July 2011)
Ed: Gregg Wartgow. **Description:** Highlights from the Come Alive Outside training event held in Chicago, Illinois July 14-15, 2011 are shared. Nearly 80 people representing 38 landscape companies attended the event that helps contractors review their services and find ways to sell them in new and various ways. **Availability:** Online.

10094 ■ "Finding a Way to Continue Growing" in Green Industry Pro (Vol. 23, March 2011, No. 3, pp. 31)
Ed: Gregg Wartgow. **Description:** Profile of Brett Lemcke, VP of R.M. Landscape located in Rochester, New York. Lemcke tells how his Landscape Industry Certified credentials helped him to grow his business and beat out his competition. **Availability:** Online.

10095 ■ "Five Distinct Divisions, One Collective Focus" in Green Industry Pro (Vol. 23, October 2011)
Ed: Gregg Wartgow. **Description:** Profile of ACLS Inc., an amalgamation of All Commercial Landscape Service (commercial maintenance), All Custom Landscape Service (design/build), Fresno Tree Service, Certified Water Consulting (irrigation), and Tractor Service (disking and flailing services on everything from one-acre lots to hundreds of acres of open land). The firm discusses its rebranding effort in order to increase sales. **Availability:** Online.

10096 ■ "Forward Motion" in Green Industry Pro (July 2011)
Ed: Gregg Wartgow. **Description:** Several landscape contractors have joined this publication's Working Smarter Training Challenge over the last year. This process is helping them develop ways to improve work processes, boost morale, drive out waste, reduce costs, improve customer service, and be more competitive. **Availability:** Print; Online.

10097 ■ "Gain the 'Come Alive Outside' Selling Edge" in Green Industry Pro (July 2011)
Ed: Jim Paluch. **Description:** Marketing the 'Come Alive Outside' slogan can help landscapers to increase their market share by identifying and applying these elements to each customer as well as their workers. **Availability:** Online.

10098 ■ "The Green Industry Jobs Gap" in Green Industry Pro (Vol. 23, October 2011)
Ed: Gregg Wartgow. **Description:** According to the U.S. Bureau of Labor Statistics, the landscaping industry employs over 829,000 workers. According to another private study, the industry would employ more if they were able to find more people interested in performing the required work. **Availability:** Online.

10099 ■ "Hey, You Can't Do That" in Green Industry Pro (Vol. 23, September 2011)
Ed: Rod Dickens. **Description:** Manufacturers of landscape equipment are making better use of energy resources, such as the use of fuel-injection systems instead of carburetors, lightweight materials, better lubricants, advanced battery technology, and innovative engine designs. **Availability:** Online.

10100 ■ "How to Create a Landscaping Business Website" in GoDaddy (May 19, 2020)
Ed: Jayson DeMers. **Released:** March 19, 2020. **Description:** Discusses why having a website for your landscaping business is important from visibility and information to lead generation. Includes information on what to include on your website, characteristics of a successful website, and how to create your website. **Availability:** Online.

10101 ■ "How to Develop an Active Sales Program" in Green Industry Pro (Vol. 23, September 2011)
Ed: Gregg Wartgow. **Description:** Craig den Hartog, owner of Emerald Magic Lawn Care located in Holtsville, New York, describes the various marketing tactics he has developed to increase sales in the current economic environment. Statistical data included. **Availability:** Online.

10102 ■ "How to Dominate in Residential Maintenance" in Green Industry Pro (Vol. 23, October 2011)
Ed: Gregg Wartgow. **Description:** Lawn care services were ranked among the most expendable consumer expenditures, according to the National Retail Federation data accumulated in early 2011. This makes it critical for any landscape firm to target sales efforts toward higher-income households and higher-value homes. **Availability:** Online.

10103 ■ "How to Start a Landscaping or Lawn Care Business" in JustBusiness (October 22, 2020)
Ed: Eric Goldschein. **Released:** October 22, 2020. **Description:** Details a five step process to begin your own landscaping business including deciding what services you want to offer, business insurance and licenses, insurance, marketing, and financials. **Availability:** Online.

10104 ■ "Is Your Lawn Care Business Legal?" in Service Autopilot Blog (May 28, 2019)
Ed: Wendy Komancheck. **Released:** May 28, 2019. **Description:** Provides information about how to ensure that you are legally operating your lawn care company. Includes details on finding the right name

and making it official, getting an employer identification number, making your business an LLC, getting the right insurance, and tax information. **Availability:** Online.

10105 ■ "Joystick Operated Zero-Turn Mower Marks 30 Years" in Turf Magazine (November 11, 2019)
URL(s): www.turfmagazine.com/manufacturersupplier -updates/joystick-operated-zero-turn-mower-marks -30-years/
Ed: Christine Menapace. **Released:** November 11, 2019. **Description:** County Clipper is celebrating the 30 year anniversary of manufacturing the joystick controlled zero-turn mower. Debuted in 1989, this mower was first manufactured under the Snapper brand name, and today Country Clipper offers 20 various joystick models. **Availability:** Online.

10106 ■ "Labor of Love" in Green Industry Pro (Vol. 23, March 2011, No. 3, pp. 14)
Ed: Gregg Wartgow. **Description:** Profile of CLS Landscape Management in Chino, California and its owner who started the company when he was 21 years old. Kevin Davis built his landscape firm into a $20 million a year business without using any dedicated salesperson. **Availability:** Online.

10107 ■ "The Landscape of Landscaping Is Changing" in Lawn & Landscape (July 19, 2018)
URL(s): www.lawnandlandscape.com/article/ll-0718 18-landscape-market-growth-potential/
Ed: Ken Gibson. **Released:** July 19, 2018. **Description:** Due to home improvement projects increasing, landscaping has also enjoyed a comeback. The single-family home market is growing and with that, comes a need for more landscape services. Also added to the effect is the growing number of older Americans who need assistance with their lawns. **Availability:** Online.

10108 ■ "Landscaping Insurance: Definition, Cost & Providers" in Fit Small Business (August 26, 2020)
Ed: Virginia Hamill. **Released:** August 26, 2020. **Description:** Describes how landscaping insurance works, who needs landscaping insurance, how much insurance costs for your small business, providers of insurance, and the importance of having insurance coverage for your small business. **Availability:** Online.

10109 ■ "New to the Class" in Lawn & Landscape (November 14, 2019)
URL(s): www.lawnandlandscape.com/article/new-to -the-class-caterpillar-products/
Ed: Lauren Rathmell. **Released:** November 14, 2019. **Description:** Caterpillar opened its training facility in Cary, NC to the media in order to introduce their latest equipment. The highlight was the 6-ton mini excavator, which is Caterpillar's first entry into the 6-ton class offering. **Availability:** Online.

10110 ■ "Problem Solving Requires Total Team Approach" in Green Industry Pro (Vol. 23, September 2011)
Ed: Bob Coulter. **Description:** Working Smarter Training Challenge teaches that leaders are able to carry out solutions directly into their organization, develop skills and drive business results in key areas by creating a culture of energized workers who are able to take ownership of their performance as well as the performance of the company as a whole. **Availability:** Online.

10111 ■ "Pros & Cons of Starting a Lawn Business" in The Balance Small Business (September 10, 2019)
Ed: Mindy Lilyquist. **Released:** September 10, 2019. **Description:** Lawn service companies have the ability of offering customized services to fit your specific desires and needs. This article offers pros and cons of starting your own lawn care business, estimated start-up costs, earning potential, and marketing. **Availability:** Online.

10112 ■ "Reagan HQ In Limbo" in Austin Business Journal (Vol. 32, April 6, 2012, No. 5, pp. A1)
Pub: American City Business Journals, Inc.
Contact: Mike Olivieri, Executive Vice President
Ed: Vicky Garza. **Description:** Reagan National Advertising has been awaiting the Austin City Council decision on whether it would be allowed to build a new headquarters that was on the drawing board for more than five years. However, approval of Reagan's plan would cut down several trees and that would violate the Heritage tree ordinance. **Availability:** Online.

10113 ■ "Savatree Acquires Pauley Tree and Lawn Care" in Landscape Business (November 17, 2019)
URL(s): landscape-business.com/savatree-acquires -pauley-tree-and-lawn-care/
Released: November 17, 2019. **Description:** SavA-Tree acquired Pauley Tree and Lawn Care of New Canaan, Connecticut. This will add to SavATree's ability to provide quality tree, shrub, and lawn care services to their customers. **Availability:** Online.

10114 ■ "Take Control of Your Company's Finances" in Green Industry Pro (Vol. 23, March 2011, No. 3, pp. 24)
Ed: Gregg Wartgow. **Description:** Understanding that when certain leading indicators that affect the outcome of certain lagging indicators are aligned, companies will be able to take control of their firm's finances. Ways to improve the processes that drive financial performance for landscape firms are outlined. **Availability:** Online.

10115 ■ "Take This Job and Love It" in Green Industry Pro (Vol. 23, October 2011)
Ed: Gregg Wartgow. **Description:** Details of the lawsuit filed by the Professional Landcare Network (PLANET) against the U.S. Department of Labor are explained. Challenges faced by landscape firms because of employment costs are outlined. Statistical data included. **Availability:** PDF; Online.

10116 ■ "Toro Launches Z Master 7500" in Lawn & Landscape (November 6, 2019)
URL(s): www.lawnandlandscape.com/article/toro-z -master-7500-mower/
Ed: Lauren Rathmell. **Released:** November 06, 2019. **Description:** Toro introduced its new product, the Z master 7500-G, which is a 96 inch gas mower for commercial grass cutting crews. **Availability:** Online.

10117 ■ "Way More Than Mowing" in Green Industry Pro (Vol. 23, September 2011)
Ed: Rod Dickens. **Description:** Shipp Shape Lawn Services located in Sylvester, Georgia now offers aeration, fertilizing and weed control, mulching, yard renovation, flowerbed maintenance, landscaping, as well as irrigation repairs and installation in order to diversify the business and stay competitive. **Availability:** Online.

10118 ■ "Why Landscape Businesses Fail...and How to Keep Yours From Being One of Them" in Irrigation & Green Industry (September 6, 2018)
Ed: Mary Elizabeth Williams-Villano. **Released:** September 06, 2018. **Description:** While a landscape business may be one of the easiest types of small businesses to start, sustaining it is another matter. This article provides reasons why landscape businesses fail including poor business management, pricing that doesn't work for customers, and accounting errors. **Availability:** Online.

STATISTICAL SOURCES

10119 ■ RMA Annual Statement Studies
Pub: Risk Management Association
Contact: Nancy Foster, President
Released: Annual. **Description:** Contains composite balance sheets and income statements for more than 360 industries, including the accounting, auditing, and bookkeeping industries. Also contains five years

of comparative historical data for discerning trends. Includes 16 commonly used ratios, computed for most of the size groupings for nearly every industry.

TRADE PERIODICALS

10120 ■ Fuchsia Flash
Pub: Northwest Fuchsia Society
Contact: Lyn Kortlever, President
E-mail: shoestringvalley@tds.net
URL(s): www.nwfuchsiasociety.com/flash.htm
Released: Quarterly; February, May, August, November. **Price:** $20, Individuals for Canada and other countries. http://www.nwfuchsiasociety.com/flash.htm; $12, Individuals for United States, per year. http:// www.nwfuchsiasociety.com/flash.htm. **Description:** Provides information for individuals who cultivate fuchsia flowers worldwide. **Availability:** Print.

10121 ■ LAND
Pub: American Society of Landscape Architects
Contact: Torey Carter-Conneen, Chief Executive Officer
URL(s): www.asla.org/Land/LandNewsletter.aspx
Description: Carries news and monitors developments in landscape architecture, environmental design, and related fields. Focuses on public policy, education, and other areas affecting landscape architecture. **Availability:** Print; Online.

10122 ■ Landscape Architect and Specifier News
Pub: Landscape Communications Inc.
URL(s): landscapearchitect.com/LandscapeProducts/ magazine.php
Facebook: www.facebook.com/LASNMagazine
Linkedin: www.linkedin.com/showcase/landscape -architect-and-specifier-news
Instagram: www.instagram.com/landscapeasn
Released: Monthly **Price:** $34.95, Canada for continental us, Alaska, Hawaii 12 issues; $55, Canada for continental us, Alaska, Hawaii 24 issues; $65, for Mexico 12 issues per year. **Description:** Trade magazine covering landscape architecture and planning for professionals. **Availability:** Print; Download; Online.

10123 ■ Landscape Architecture Magazine: The Magazine of the American Society of Landscape Architects (LAM)
Pub: American Society of Landscape Architects
Contact: Torey Carter-Conneen, Chief Executive Officer
URL(s): landscapearchitecturemagazine.orgwww .asla.org/publications.aspx
Facebook: www.facebook.com/landscapearchitec turemagazine
Linkedin: www.linkedin.com/company/landscape -architecture-magazine
X (Twitter): x.com/landarchmag
Instagram: www.instagram.com/landarchmag
Released: Monthly **Price:** $79, for print 1 year; $68, for online 1 year; $125, for print and online 1 year; $129, Institutions for library print 1 year; $110, Institutions for library online 1 year; $203, Institutions for library print and online 1 year; $119, for print 1 year international; $68, for online 1 year international; $187, for print and online 1 year international; $178, Institutions for library print 1 year international; $110, Institutions for library online 1 year international; $272, Institutions for library print and online 1 year international; $14, Members; $16, Nonmembers; $16, Institutions for library; $10, Single issue for online. **Description:** Professional magazine covering land planning and design. **Availability:** Print; Online.

10124 ■ Landscape Journal (LJ)
Pub: Council of Educators in Landscape Architecture
Contact: Galen D. Newman, President
E-mail: gnewman@arch.tamu.edu
URL(s): lj.uwpress.orgthecela.org/landscape-journal
Facebook: www.facebook.com/landscapejournal
Ed: Brian D. Lee, Arnold Alanen, James F. Palmer, Robert B. Riley, David Pitt. **Released:** Semiannual; Spring, Fall. **Price:** $116, Individuals for print and online 1 year; $333, Institutions for print and online 1

year; $106, Individuals for online only 1 year; $294, Institutions for online 1 year. **Description:** Contains editorial columns, correspondence section and reviews. **Availability:** Print; PDF; Online.

10125 ■ Landscape Management
Pub: North Coast Media
URL(s): www.landscapemanagement.net
Facebook: www.facebook.com/Lan dscapeManagement
Linkedin: www.linkedin.com/company-beta/3160776
X (Twitter): x.com/landscapemgmt
Instagram: www.instagram.com/landscapemgmt
YouTube: www.youtube.com/channel/UCdIO7 -QYFWHUI4KR5D4bKDA
Released: Monthly **Price:** $55, U.S. For 1 year; $76, U.S. For 2 year; $87, Canada and Mexico For 1 year; $127, Canada and Mexico For 2 year; $165, Other countries For 1 year; $246, Other countries For 2 year. **Description:** Magazine for professionals in landscape, grounds management and lawn care, construction, and maintenance. **Availability:** Print; Online.

10126 ■ Landscape Trades: Canada's Premier Horticultural Trade Publication
Pub: Landscape Ontario Horticultural Trades Association
Contact: Joe Salemi, Director, Operations Deputy Director
E-mail: jsalemi@landscapeontario.com
URL(s): landscapetrades.com
Facebook: www.facebook.com/Landscape.Trades
X (Twitter): x.com/landscapetrades
Instagram: www.instagram.com/landscapetrades
Ed: Lee Ann Knudsen. **Released:** 6/year; February, March, may, August, October and December. **Price:** $84.74, Two years; $118.64, for 3 year; $46.90, for 1 year. **Description:** Landscape/nursery magazine. **Availability:** Print; Online.

10127 ■ Lawn & Landscape
Pub: GIE Media Inc.
Contact: Chris Foster, President
URL(s): www.lawnandlandscape.com
Linkedin: www.linkedin.com/company/lawn-lan dscape-magazine
X (Twitter): twitter.com/lawnlandscape
Instagram: www.instagram.com/lawnlandscape
Ed: Brian Horn, Chuck Bowen. **Released:** Monthly **Price:** $5, Single issue; $30, U.S. for one year; $35, Canada for one year; $98, Other countries for one year; $218, for foreign airmail; $42, for two year. **Description:** Business management magazine for lawn and landscape contracting professionals. **Availability:** Print; PDF; Online.

10128 ■ Tree City U.S.A. Bulletin
Pub: Arbor Day Foundation
Contact: Dan Lambe, President
E-mail: dlambe@arborday.org
URL(s): www.arborday.org/trees/bulletins
Ed: James R. Fazio. **Released:** Bimonthly **Price:** $3, Single issue; $7.95, for 3-ring binder. **Description:** Features information on pruning, caring for storm-damaged trees, watering and fertilizing, and wise tree selection. **Availability:** Print; PDF; Download; Online.

VIDEO/AUDIO MEDIA

10129 ■ The Roots of Success: Transforming Landscapes and Lives with Steve Griggs
URL(s): www.eofire.com/podcast/steveriggs
Ed: Jon Lee Dumas. **Released:** December 04, 2023. **Description:** Podcast discusses landscape architecture and entrepreneurship.

TRADE SHOWS AND CONVENTIONS

10130 ■ Conference on Landscape Architecture
PlayCore Inc.
544 Chestnut St.
Chattanooga, TN 37402

Ph: (423)265-7529
Free: 877-762-7563
Fax: (423)425-3124
Co. E-mail: info@playcore.com
URL: http://www.playcore.com
Contact: Roger Posacki, President
URL(s): www.aslaconference.com

Frequency: Annual. **Description:** Education sessions, and professional awards presentation. **Audience:** Landscape architects, landscape designers, architects, educators, researchers, allied professionals, developers, students, product suppliers, manufacturers, and service providers. **Principal Exhibits:** Education sessions, and professional awards presentation. **Telecommunication Services:** conferences@asla.org.

10131 ■ ISA Annual International Conference & Trade Show
International Society of Arboriculture (ISA)
Champaign, IL 61821
Co. E-mail: isa@isa-arbor.com
URL: http://www.isa-arbor.com
Contact: Chris Walsh, President
URL(s): www.isa-arbor.com/Events/Annual
-Conference/2024-Annual-Conference

Frequency: Annual. **Description:** Chippers, bucket trucks, chain saws, hand tools, computer software and hardware, consulting services, and tree and lawn care products. **Audience:** Arboricultural professionals, researchers, and educators. **Principal Exhibits:** Chippers, bucket trucks, chain saws, hand tools, computer software and hardware, consulting services, and tree and lawn care products. Dates and Locations: 2025 Oct Christchurch. **Telecommunication Services:** adoty@isa-arbor.com.

10132 ■ TPI Summer Convention & Field Days
Turfgrass Producers International (TPI)
444 E Roosevelt Rd., Ste. 346
Lombard, IL 60148
Ph: (847)649-5555
Free: 800-405-8873
Fax: (847)649-5678
Co. E-mail: info@turfgrasssod.org
URL: http://www.turfgrasssod.org
Contact: Dr. Casey Reynolds, Executive Director
E-mail: creynolds@turfgrasssod.org
URL(s): www.turfgrasssod.org/events/conference
2023

Frequency: Annual. **Description:** Exhibits relating to the turfgrass sod industry equipment, supplies and services. **Audience:** Industry professionals. **Principal Exhibits:** Exhibits relating to the turfgrass sod industry equipment, supplies and services. **Telecommunication Services:** kcooper@turfgrasssod.org.

CONSULTANTS

10133 ■ Jobs In Horticulture Inc.
PO Box 521731
Longwood, FL 32752-1731
Free: 800-428-2474
Fax: (800)884-5198
Co. E-mail: info@hortjobs.com
URL: http://www.hortjobs.com
Contact: Armand Pichardo, Manager
X (Twitter): x.com/hortjobs

Description: Firm provides staffing and recruitment services. **Scope:** Firm provides staffing and recruitment services. **Founded:** 1993.

10134 ■ Western Arborists Inc.
147 Underhill Dr.
Glendora, CA 91741
Contact: Kathleen Walker, Contact

Description: Provides tree care services. The company provides tree trimming, stump grinding, and clean-up services. It also offers consultation on tree disease and insect infestation, as well as damage appraisal services.

FRANCHISES AND BUSINESS OPPORTUNITIES

10135 ■ Clintar Groundskeeping Services
200 Cachet Woods Ct., Unit 119
Markham, ON, Canada L6C 0Z8
Free: 800-361-3542
Co. E-mail: info@clintar.com
URL: http://www.clintar.com
Contact: Rob Gannett, Chief Executive Officer
Description: Firm provides commercial landscape services such as parking lot maintenance, water management. **No. of Franchise Units:** 23. **Founded:** 1973. **Equity Capital Needed:** Approximately $100,000-$150,000 to start. **Royalty Fee:** 8%. **Training:** Yes.

10136 ■ The Gardener Inc.
7030 Woodbine Ave., Unit 101
Markham, ON, Canada L3R 6G2
Free: 800-970-6947
Co. E-mail: corporate@hirethegardener.com
URL: http://www.hirethegardener.com
Facebook: www.facebook.com/hirethegardener
X (Twitter): x.com/TheGardenerLM
YouTube: www.youtube.com/user/HireGardener
Description: The company franchises residential landscape maintenance and snow removal services. **Founded:** 1994. **Training:** 1 week in class, 1 week in field and ongoing support.

10137 ■ Grass!365, Inc
394 7th St. NE
Atlanta, GA 30308
Ph: (404)392-2783
Co. E-mail: bonds@grass365.com
URL: http://atlanta.grass365.com
Contact: Kent Bonds, Contact
E-mail: bonds@grass365.com
Linkedin: www.linkedin.com/company/grass365
YouTube: www.youtube.com/user/intelliturf
Description: Firm designs and installs custom, synthetic golf surfaces that look, play and feel like natural grass, the applications include swimming pools, outdoor courts, croquet fields, soccer fields, and indoor putting surfaces. **Founded:** 1998. **Franchised:** 2008. **Training:** Offers initial training at corporate headquarters in Atlanta and at franchisee's location.

10138 ■ The Grounds Guys
Orangeville, ON, Canada L9W 5C7
Free: 888-942-5787
URL: http://www.groundsguys.ca
Facebook: www.facebook.com/thegroundsguyscanada
X (Twitter): x.com/groundsguysus
Instagram: www.instagram.com/thegroundsguys
YouTube: www.youtube.com/user/GroundsGuys
Pinterest: www.pinterest.com/groundsguys
Description: Provider of landscaping and lawn care services for residential and commercial clients. **Founded:** 1987. **Training:** Provides 1 week initial training and ongoing.

10139 ■ Professional Polish Inc. (PPE)
5308 Sun Valley Dr.
Fort Worth, TX 76119
Ph: (817)572-7353
Co. E-mail: janitorial@professionalpolish.com
URL: http://professionalpolish.com
Contact: Carren Lee Cavanaugh, President
Description: Janitorial, lawn, landscape and light building maintenance service at the local level. **Founded:** 1983. **Financial Assistance:** Yes **Training:** Yes.

LIBRARIES

10140 ■ American Horticultural Society (AHS) - Library
7931 East Blvd. Dr.
Alexandria, VA 22308
Ph: (703)768-5700
Fax: (703)768-8700

URL: http://ahsgardening.org
Contact: Marcia Zech, Chairman of the Board
Facebook: www.facebook.com/americanhorticulturalsociety
Linkedin: www.linkedin.com/company/the-american
-horticultural-society
X (Twitter): x.com/ahs_gardening
Instagram: www.instagram.com/ahs_gardening
YouTube: www.youtube.com/channel/UCXUu
4FafeTTqC8S-VnnhPrg
Pinterest: www.pinterest.com/amhortsociety

Description: Represents amateur and professional gardeners. Aims to educate and inspire people of all ages to become successful and environmentally responsible gardeners by advancing the art and science of horticulture. **Scope:** Horticulture. **Founded:** 1922. **Holdings:** Figures not available. **Publications:** *North American Horticulture: A Reference Guide* (Irregular); *The American Gardener: The Magazine of the American Horticultural Society* (Bimonthly). **Awards:** Liberty Hyde Bailey Award (Irregular); Paul Ecke Jr. Commercial Award (Annual); G. B. Gunlogson Award (Annual); B.Y. Morrison Communication Award (Annual); AHS Horticultural Therapy Award (Irregular); AHS Landscape Design Award (Irregular); AHS Meritorious Service Award (Annual); Frances Jones Poetker Award (Irregular); AHS Professional Award (Irregular); H. Marc Cathey Award (Biennial); Catherine H. Sweeney Award (Periodic); AHS Teaching Award (Irregular); Community Greening Award (Annual); Horticultural Innovation Award (Biennial); Jane L. Taylor Award (Annual); American Horticultural Society Professional Award (Annual). **Geographic Preference:** National.

10141 ■ American Society of Landscape Architects (ASLA) - Professional Practice Library
636 Eye St. NW
Washington, DC 20001-3736
Ph: (202)898-2444
Free: 888-999-2752
Fax: (202)898-1185
Co. E-mail: info@asla.org
URL: http://www.asla.org
Contact: Torey Carter-Conneen, Chief Executive Officer
Facebook: www.facebook.com/NationalASLA
X (Twitter): x.com/NationalASLA
Instagram: www.instagram.com/nationalasla
Pinterest: www.pinterest.com/NationalASLA

Description: Professional society of landscape architects. Promotes the advancement of education in the art of landscape architecture as an instrument in service to the public welfare. Seeks to strengthen existing and proposed university programs. Offers counsel to new and emerging programs; encourages state registration of landscape architects. Offers placement service; conducts specialized education and research. **Scope:** Landscape architecture. **Services:** Interlibrary loan not available; library open to the public by appointment. **Founded:** 1899. **Holdings:** Membership directories; articles; catalogs; books; guides for archiving. **Subscriptions:** 130 journals and other serials. **Publications:** *ASLA Members Handbook* (Annual; Monthly); *Guide to Educational Programs in Landscape Architecture* (Biennial); *Landscape Architecture Magazine: The Magazine of the American Society of Landscape Architects (LAM)* (Monthly); *Landscape Architecture Accredited Programs* (Annual); *American Society of Landscape Architects--Members' Handbook* (Annual); *LAND*; *Landscape Architecture News Digest - LAND Online*. **Educational Activities:** Conference on Landscape Architecture (Annual). **Awards:** ASLA Council of Fellows Scholarships (Annual); Peridian International, Inc./Rae L. Price, FASLA Scholarship; Bradford Williams Medal (Annual); Jot D. Carpenter Teaching Medal (Annual); The Landscape Architecture Medal of Excellence (Annual); Olmsted Medal (Annual); ASLA President's Medal (Annual); ASLA Honorary Membership (Annual); ASLA Professional Awards (Annual); Frederick Law Olmsted Medal (Annual); The LaGasse Medals (Annual); The ASLA Design Medal (Annual); ASLA Landscape Architecture Firm Award (Annual); ASLA Community Service

Award (Annual); ASLA Landmark Award (Annual); The Landscape Architecture Medal Of Excellence (Annual). **Geographic Preference:** National.

10142 ■ The Arboretum at Flagstaff - Transition Zone Horticultural Institute Library

4001 S Woody Mountain Rd.
Flagstaff, AZ 86005
Ph: (928)774-1442
Co. E-mail: info@thearb.org
URL: http://thearb.org
Contact: Erin Creekmur, President

Scope: Horticulture studies. **Services:** Library open to arboretum members and researchers by appointment for reference use only. **Founded:** 1981. **Holdings:** Figures not available.

10143 ■ Birmingham Botanical Gardens Library

2612 Ln. Pk. Rd.
Birmingham, AL 35223
Ph: (205)414-3950
URL: http://bbgardens.org/programs/library
Contact: Hope Long, Director, Library Services
E-mail: hlong@bbgardens.org
Facebook: www.facebook.com/BirminghamBo
tanicalGardens
Instagram: www.instagram.com/bbgardens

Scope: Gardening; horticulture. **Services:** Copying; printing (black and white, color); free wifi and internet access; library open to the public. **Holdings:** 14,000 books; DVDs; audiobooks; magazines; 65 magazines.

10144 ■ Cleveland Botanical Garden - Eleanor Squire Library

11030 E Blvd.
Cleveland, OH 44106
URL: http://holdenfg.org/attractions/cleveland-bo
tanical-garden/elenor-squire-library

Scope: Ecology; urban; general gardening; sustainability; food plants; conservation. **Services:** open to the public; rare book. **Founded:** 1930. **Holdings:** Seed catalog; botanical prints; rare books.

10145 ■ Garfield Park Conservatory Alliance - Garfield Park Conservatory - Library

300 N Central Pk. Ave.
Chicago, IL 60624
Ph: (773)638-1766
Co. E-mail: membership@garfieldpark.org
URL: http://garfieldconservatory.org
Contact: Jennifer Van Valkenburg, President
E-mail: jvanvalkenburg@garfieldpark.org
Facebook: www.facebook.com/GarfieldParkConserva
tory
Linkedin: www.linkedin.com/company/garfield-park
-conservatory-alliance/about
X (Twitter): x.com/gpconservatory
Instagram: www.instagram.com/gpconservatory
YouTube: www.youtube.com/channel/
UCn70zMRoK9xueMgdlP9PuIA

Scope: Horticulture. **Services:** Library not open to the public. **Founded:** 1908. **Holdings:** Books.

10146 ■ The Horticultural Society of New York - Library

148 W 37th St., 13th Fl.
New York, NY 10018
Ph: (212)757-0915
Co. E-mail: info@thehort.org
URL: http://www.thehort.org
Contact: Sara Hobel, Executive Director
E-mail: shobel@thehort.org
Facebook: www.facebook.com/thehortnyc
X (Twitter): x.com/thehort
Instagram: www.instagram.com/thehort

Description: Provides learning gardens for disadvantaged children and horticulture therapy for inmates. **Scope:** Horticulture. **Services:** Library open to the public for reference use only. **Founded:** 1900. **Holdings:** Figures not available. **Geographic Preference:** State.

10147 ■ Morton Arboretum - Sterling Morton Library

4100 Illinois, Rte. 53
Lisle, IL 60532
Ph: (630)968-0074
Co. E-mail: trees@mortonarb.org
URL: http://mortonarb.org
Facebook: www.facebook.com/MortonArboretum
X (Twitter): twitter.com/MortonArboretum
YouTube: www.youtube.com/user/MortonArboretum
Pinterest: www.pinterest.com/mortonarboretum

Description: Non-profit educational and research museum. Offers a plant clinic as a free public service; answers inquiries about plant selection and care. **Scope:** Arboriculture and horticulture, including woodland plants, urban vegetation, natural area preservation, rare plant conservation, root and soil research studies, and urban tree breeding and selection. **Services:** Interlibrary loan; circulation; copying; library open to the public. **Founded:** 1922. **Holdings:** 5,000 volumes; Books; journals; artwork; correspondence; papers; maps; video and audio recordings; images; nursery catalogs. **Subscriptions:** 9000 journals. **Publications:** *Plant Health Care Reports* (Weekly); *Tree and Shrub Handbook.* **Educational Activities:** Education Programs, Includes classes for adults and children, dedicated to broader understanding of plants and nature.

10148 ■ Ontario Association of Landscape Architects Library (OALA)

3 Church St., Ste. 506
Toronto, ON, Canada M5E 1M2
Ph: (416)231-4181
Fax: (416)231-2679
Co. E-mail: oala@oala.ca
URL: http://www.oala.ca
Contact: Steve Barnhart, President
Facebook: www.facebook.com/Ontario-Association
-of-Landscape-Architects-109687249113317
Linkedin: www.linkedin.com/company/ontario-associa
tion-of-landscape-architects
X (Twitter): x.com/oala_on
Instagram: www.instagram.com/oala_on
YouTube: www.youtube.com/channel/UCzuvb
_TMzQm1bORbXsvNFsw

Scope: Landscape architecture. **Services:** Library open to OALA members and interns only. **Founded:** 1968. **Holdings:** Books.

10149 ■ U.S. National Park Service - Blue Ridge Parkway Archives

199 Hemphill Knob Rd.
Asheville, NC 28803-8686
Ph: (828)298-0398
Co. E-mail: blri_public_affairs@nps.gov
URL: http://www.nps.gov/blri/index.htm
Contact: Moses Cone, Contact
Facebook: www.facebook.com/BlueRidgeNPS
X (Twitter): x.com/BlueRidgeNPS
Instagram: www.instagram.com/BlueRidgeNPS
YouTube: www.youtube.com/user/BlueRi
dgeParkwayNPS

Scope: Blue ridge parkway – history. **Services:** Archives open to researchers by appointment only. **Founded:** 1990. **Holdings:** 350,000 archives.

10150 ■ University of Alberta - Botanic Garden - Library

c/o University of Alberta Central Receiving
116 St. & 85 Ave.
Edmonton, AB, Canada T6G 2R3
Ph: (780)492-3050
Co. E-mail: uabg.info@ualberta.ca
URL: http://www.ualberta.ca/botanic-garden/visit/
hours-location.html
Contact: Carl Charest, Director
E-mail: charest@ualberta.ca
Facebook: www.facebook.com/UABotanicGarden
X (Twitter): twitter.com/UABotanicGarden
Instagram: www.instagram.com/uabotanicgarden
Pinterest: www.pinterest.ca/UABotanicGarden

Description: Integral unit of University of Alberta. **Scope:** Biodiversity and floristics bryophytes; taxonomy of microfungi. **Founded:** 1959. **Holdings:** Figures not available. **Publications:** *Kinnikinnick* (Quarterly).

10151 ■ University of Georgia - State Botanical Garden of Georgia

2450 S Milledge Ave.
Athens, GA 30605
Ph: (706)542-1244
Co. E-mail: garden@uga.edu
URL: http://botgarden.uga.edu
Contact: Jennifer Cruse-Sanders, Director
E-mail: crusesanders@uga.edu
Facebook: www.facebook.com/botgarden
X (Twitter): twitter.com/botgardenGA
Instagram: www.instagram.com/botanicalgarden_ga

Description: Integral unit of University of Georgia, guided by its own advisory board. **Scope:** 313-acre site maintaining plant collections for research by scientists and students, including documented collections of native and cultivated plants, a plant evaluation site for woody ornamental plants in the Southeast, theme gardens and display collections of bulbs, annuals, perennials and woody plants, both native and exotic. **Services:** Library open to the public for reference use only. **Founded:** 1968. **Holdings:** 2,000 books; 85 videotapes; CD-ROMs; archives; manuscripts. **Subscriptions:** 14 journals and other serials. **Publications:** *Garden News Quarterly.*

10152 ■ University of Nevada, Las Vegas Architecture Studies Library

4505 S Maryland Pky.
Las Vegas, NV 89154-4049
Ph: (702)895-1959
Co. E-mail: libasl@unlv.edu
URL: http://www.library.unlv.edu/arch
Contact: Richard Saladino, Librarian
E-mail: richard.saladino@unlv.edu

Scope: Architecture. **Services:** Interlibrary loan; Copying. **Founded:** 1997. **Holdings:** Books; journals.

RESEARCH CENTERS

10153 ■ Landscape Architecture Foundation (LAF)

1200 17th St. NW Ste. 210
Washington, DC 20036
Ph: (202)331-7070
Fax: (202)331-7079
Co. E-mail: rbooher@lafoundation.org
URL: http://www.lafoundation.org
Contact: Barbara Deutsch, Chief Executive Officer
E-mail: bdeutsch@lafoundation.org
Facebook: www.facebook.com/lafoundation.org
Linkedin: www.linkedin.com/company/landscape
-architecture-foundation
X (Twitter): x.com/lafoundation
Instagram: www.instagram.com/lafoundation

Description: Serves as an education and research vehicle for the landscape architecture profession in the United States. Combines the capabilities of landscape architects, interests of environmentalists, and needs of agencies and resource foundations. Provides for the preparation and dissemination of educational and scientific information through publications, exhibits, lectures, and seminars. Solicits and expends gifts, legacies, and grants. Established an endowment fund for professorships at colleges and universities. Sponsors California Landscape Architectural Student Scholarship Fund. Conducts a study of the profession to establish goals in terms of education, research needs, practice, and formulation of public policy. **Scope:** Landscape planning, land use planning and design, environmental planning, landscape change, landscape intervention, place-based land use planning, public participation processes. **Founded:** 1966. **Publications:** *American Landscape Report* (Quarterly). **Awards:** ASLA Council of Fellows Scholarships (Annual); Courtland P. Paul Scholarships (Annual); Steven G. King Play Environments Scholarship (Annual); Landscape Forms Scholarship in Memory of Peter Lindsay Schaudt, FASLA (Annual); Peridian International, Inc./Rae L. Price, FASLA

Scholarships (Annual); Rain Bird Intelligent Use of Water Scholarship (Annual); Hawaii Chapter/David T. Woolsey Scholarship (Annual). **Geographic Preference:** National.

10154 ■ Nature Conservancy in Maine
14 Maine St. Ste. 401
  Brunswick, ME 04011
Ph: (207)729-5181
Co. E-mail: naturemaine@tnc.org
URL: http://www.nature.org/en-us/about-us/where-we
  -work/united-states/maine
Contact: Jeremy Bell, Program Director
E-mail: jbell@tnc.org
Facebook: www.facebook.com/TNCmaine
X (Twitter): x.com/TNCmaine
Instagram: www.instagram.com/TNCmaine
Description: State chapter of The Nature Conservancy, an international, nonprofit organization. **Scope:** Impact of threats on natural communities with intention of abating threats and adapting to climate changes; identifies rare plants and animals and the lands where they live; works with private and public landowners who voluntarily protect terrestrial, freshwater and marine resources; acquires conservation easements or management agreements which protect habitats, and purchases lands; manages and conserves privately-owned nature preserves; applies market-based solutions and encourages collaborative problem-solving. **Founded:** 1956. **Geographic Preference:** State.

10155 ■ University of Guelph - Arboretum
College Ave. E
  Guelph, ON, Canada N1G 2W1
Ph: (519)824-4120
Co. E-mail: arbor@uoguelph.ca
URL: http://arboretum.uoguelph.ca
Contact: Justine Richardson, Director
E-mail: justine.richardson@uoguelph.ca
Facebook: www.facebook.com/uogarboretum
X (Twitter): twitter.com/uogarboretum
Instagram: www.instagram.com/uogarboretum
YouTube: www.youtube.com/channel/UCFg
  6-3XPBFETE7Wm6ijhrnw/videos
Description: Educational, recreational, and research unit of University of Guelph. Offers annual one day plant sale and nature interpretation programs, living collections of native and exotic woody plants, a computerized database, herbarium, and the Ontario Tree Atlas. **Scope:** Botany, fine arts, horticulture, landscape architecture, nature interpretation, ecology, and zoology. **Founded:** 1970. **Publications:** *The Green Web*; *A Life Zone Approach to School Yard Naturalization*; *Ontario Tree Atlas*; *Seasonal Program*. **Educational Activities:** Arboretum Horticultural and zoological adult programs, To develop specialized gardens, botanical collections, and gene conservation programs.; Arboretum Special events and conservation-related symposia, To develop specialized gardens, botanical collections, and gene conservation programs.

10156 ■ University of Pennsylvania - Morris Arboretum - Archives
100 E Northwestern Ave.
  Philadelphia, PA 19118
Ph: (215)247-5777
Fax: (215)247-8128
Co. E-mail: info@morrisarboretum.org
URL: http://www.morrisarboretum.org
Contact: William Cullina, Executive Director
Facebook: www.facebook.com/morrisarboretum/
X (Twitter): twitter.com/morrisarboretum
Instagram: www.instagram.com/morrisarboretum/
YouTube: www.youtube.com/user/morrisarboretum
Description: Integral unit of University of Pennsylvania, but under its own advisory board of managers. Offers plant clinic. **Scope:** Taxonomy, pests and diseases of woody plants, history of landscape architecture, and flora of Pennsylvania, including exploration and introduction of plants from Asia, integrated pest management for ornamental plants, field studies of rare and endangered species. **Services:** Interlibrary loan; copying; reference services; library open to the public. **Founded:** 1933. **Holdings:** Documents; letters; maps; blueprints; drawings; ledgers; diaries; lantern slides; photos; negatives; books; newspapers; research material; reports. **Publications:** *Morris Arboretum Impact Report* (Annual); *Morris Arboretum Newsletter- Seasons*. **Educational Activities:** Morris Arboretum Development Courses, For arborists.; Morris Arboretum Workshops.

START-UP INFORMATION

10157 ■ *"Cost to Open a Laundromat" in ZenBusiness*
URL(s): www.zenbusiness.com/startup-costs-laundromat/
Description: Takes a look at initial expenses and costs to start a laundromat, including equipment. **Availability:** Online.

10158 ■ *"How to Calculate Start Up Costs for a Laundromat" in Chron (March 19, 2019)*
URL(s): smallbusiness.chron.com/calculate-start-up-costs-laundromat-44480.html
Ed: John Csiszar. **Released:** March 19, 2019. **Description:** Provides information on startup costs for a laundromat and how you can finance your new venture. **Availability:** Online.

10159 ■ *"How Much Does It Cost to Open a Laundromat?" in NerdWallet (Oct. 18, 2020)*
URL(s): www.nerdwallet.com/article/small-business/how-much-does-it-cost-to-open-a-laundromat
Ed: Marianne Hayes. **Released:** October 18, 2020. **Description:** Opening a laundromat requires startup costs and the ability to cover recurring expenses month after month. This article discusses what to expect to spend money on as you start up your laundry business. **Availability:** Online.

10160 ■ *How to Start a $24K/Month Laundromat Business*
URL(s): www.upflip.com/blog/how-to-start-a-laundromat
Ed: Donna Arceneaux. **Description:** A guide to how to start a laundromat from scratch with information from two different laundromat business owners. **Availability:** Online.

10161 ■ *How to Start a Laundromat*
URL(s): howtostartanllc.com/business-ideas/laundromat
Released: October 08, 2022. **Description:** A ten-step guide to starting your laundromat. Following these steps will ensure that your new business is well planned out, registered properly, and legally compliant. **Availability:** Online.

10162 ■ *How to Start a Laundromat. A Simple Step-by-Step Guide*
URL(s): oppbusinessloans.com/how-to-start-a-laundromat-a-simple-step-by-step-guide/
Released: April 30, 2021. **Description:** A guide covering the steps involved in starting your own laundromat. Includes information on writing a business plan, startup capital, equipment needed, and how to start generating revenue right away. **Availability:** Online.

10163 ■ *How to Start a Laundromat Business With Little to No Money*
URL(s): www.newfoundr.com/how-to/start-laundromat-business

Released: July 12, 2022. **Description:** There are three main types of laundromats: coin-op, card-op, and drop-off/pick-up. This article guides entrepreneurs on which type they may wish to open and provides eleven steps to help you get started. **Availability:** Online.

10164 ■ *Tips for Starting a Laundromat*
URL(s): www.laundrysolutionscompany.com/tips-for-starting-a-laundromat/
Released: September 29, 2022. **Description:** Provides tips for entrepreneurs looking into the laundromat business. Topics covered include business plan, type of services offered, location, equipment, and marketing. **Availability:** Online.

REFERENCE WORKS

10165 ■ *8 DIY Laundromat Marketing Ideas that Work*
URL(s): www.worldwidelaundry.com/laundromat-marketing-ideas/

Released: May 19, 2022. **Description:** Proper marketing is crucial to attracting customers for a successful laundromat business. This article describes numerous easy and affordable ways to promote your business yourself. **Availability:** Online.

10166 ■ *"8 Marketing Tactics to Boost Your Laundromat Business" in Safi Laundry Blog (June 24, 2022)*
URL(s): www.safilaundry.com/post/8-marketing-tactics-to-boost-your-laundromat-business
Ed: Anita Kibunguchy-Grant. **Released:** June 24, 2022. **Description:** Discusses the importance of utilizing the right marketing tactics for your laundry business. Provides eight essential tactics to explore for your business. **Availability:** Online.

10167 ■ *16 Pros & Cons of Owning a Laundromat New Investors Need to Know*
URL(s): martinray.com/n-41-16-pros-cons-of-owning-a-laundromat-new-investors-need-to-know.html
Description: Laundromats can be highly profitable, recession-resistant, and flexible businesses, making them highly attractive for entrepreneurs. This article discusses pros and cons to consider before opening a laundromat. **Availability:** Online.

10168 ■ *"Digital Marketing 101" in PlanetLaundry (Nov. 2, 2021)*
URL(s): planetlaundry.com/digital-marketing-101/
Ed: Kim Foxcroft. **Released:** November 02, 2021. **Description:** Provides information on digital marketing and how to utilize it to reach your target market and promote your laundromat business. **Availability:** Online.

10169 ■ *The Finer Points of a Laundromat Business Plan*
URL(s): huebsch.com/news/the-finer-points-of-a-laundromat-business-plan/

Released: July 12, 2021. **Description:** If you're thinking of opening a laundromat, starting with a well-written business plan is a must. This article provides information on how to write a business plan for your laundromat. **Availability:** Online.

10170 ■ *"How to Get Laundry Equipment Financing in 24 Hours or Less" in Laundrylux Blog*
URL(s): laundrylux.com/blog/how-to-get-laundry-equipment-financing-in-24-hours-or-less/
Description: Provides information on laundry equipment financing solutions to help you achieve your business goals and gain a competitive edge. **Availability:** Online.

10171 ■ *"How to Purchase a Laundromat Franchise" in Chron (Apr. 5, 2019)*
URL(s): smallbusiness.chron.com/purchase-laundromat-franchise-74089.html
Ed: Patrick Gleeson. **Released:** April 05, 2019. **Description:** Presents information on what to expect when purchasing a laundromat franchise. **Availability:** Online.

10172 ■ *"Laundromat Franchise: 10 Steps to Buying Into a Franchise" in Mulberrys Berry Blog (Aug. 31, 2022)*
URL(s): www.mulberryscleaners.com/blog/laundromat-franchise-10-steps-to-buying-into-a-franchise/
Released: August 31, 2022. **Description:** Outlines ten steps to buying a laundromat franchise. **Availability:** Online.

10173 ■ *Laundromat Marketing Strategies to Promote Your Business*
URL(s): www.trycents.com/our-2-cents/laundromat-marketing-strategies
Ed: Jordan Berry. **Released:** October 18, 2022. **Description:** With so many platforms and strategies to choose from, it can be hard to know where to start with marketing your laundry business. This article provides information on the most important marketing strategies to help promote your business. **Availability:** Online.

10174 ■ *Laundromat Marketing Tips to Promote Your Business Online*
URL(s): laundrylux.com/blog/laundromat-marketing-tips-promote-business-online/
Description: Pairing online and offline efforts will make for the best marketing strategy and set your business up for long-term success. This article provides tips to help you market your laundromat business online. **Availability:** Online.

10175 ■ *"Marketing a Laundromat" in Chron*
URL(s): smallbusiness.chron.com/marketing-laundromat-23116.html
Ed: Elizabeth Smith. **Description:** Because laundromats rely on foot traffic for business, marketing is a crucial part of getting customers in the door. This article describes how to develop a promotional campaign and target it to a specific audience. **Availability:** Online.

10176 ■ *"Pros and Cons of Owning a Laundromat for a New Business Owner" in Laundrylux Blog*
URL(s): laundrylux.com/blog/pros-cons-owning-a-laundromat-new-business-owner/
Description: Laundromats are considered to be recession-proof businesses. This article states the importance of understanding startup and operational costs as well as the demands on owners to provide customer service, maintenance, and more. See full list of pros and cons in the article. **Availability:** Online.

10177 ■ *Start a Profitable Laundromat: Let's Crunch Some Numbers*
URL(s): www.projectionhub.com/post/start-a-profitable-laundromat-lets-crunch-some-numbers
Ed: Adam Hoeksema. **Released:** September 12, 2022. **Description:** Presents information on the numbers behind the laundromat business, the different business models you can choose from, and how to put together a financial projection model that will help you secure a business loan to launch your own laundromat. **Availability:** Online.

10178 ■ *"Starting a Laundromat Business: Expectations vs. Reality" in Laundrylux*
URL(s): laundrylux.com/blog/starting-a-laundromat-business-expectations-vs-reality/
Description: Explores four common expectations related to startup costs, experience, time required to manage the business, and the profitability of a laundromat business as a whole. **Availability:** Online.

10179 ■ *Using Technology and Data to Build Marketing for Your Laundromat*
URL(s): huebsch.com/news/using-technology-and-data-to-build-marketing-for-your-laundromat/
Released: December 08, 2020. **Description:** Discusses marketing activities that are data-driven and how to utilize these activities to your advantage as you market your laundry business. **Availability:** Online.

10180 ■ *Why a Laundromat Is the Best Recession-Proof Business*
URL(s): martinray.com/n-96-why-a-laundromat-is-the-best-recession-proof-business.html
Description: Explains why investing in a laundromat business is a great, recession-proof choice. **Availability:** Online.

STATISTICAL SOURCES

10181 ■ *Automated Laundromat Services Market Forecasts to 2028*
URL(s): www.marketresearch.com/Stratistics-Market-Research-Consulting-v4058/Automated-Laundromat-Services-Forecasts-Global-30738837/
Price: $4,150. **Description:** Provides global analysis of automated laundromat services by service type (washing, drying, heat roll and folding), clothing type, generation, operation (card-operated, coin-operated, hybrid), and by geography. **Availability:** PDF.

10182 ■ *Global Laundromat Payment System Market 2022 by Company, Regions, Type and Application, Forecast to 2028*
URL(s): www.marketresearch.com/GlobalInfoResearch-v4117/Global-Laundromat-Payment-System-Company-32259193/
Price: $3,480. **Description:** A detailed and comprehensive analysis for global Laundromat Payment System market. Both quantitative and qualitative analyses are presented by company, by region & country, by type and by application. **Availability:** PDF.

10183 ■ *Global Laundromat Payment System Market Growth (Status and Outlook) 2022-2028*
URL(s): www.marketresearch.com/LP-Information-Inc-v4134/Global-Laundromat-Payment-System-Growth-32225714/

Price: $3,660. **Description:** This report aims to provide a comprehensive picture of the global Laundromat Payment System market, with both quantitative and qualitative data, to help readers understand how the Laundromat Payment System market scenario changed across the globe during the pandemic and Russia-Ukraine War. **Availability:** PDF.

10184 ■ *Laundromat Franchises Industry in the US - Market Research Report*
URL(s): www.ibisworld.com/united-states/market-research-reports/laundromat-franchises-industry/
Price: $545. **Description:** On demand report that analyzes current and future trends in the laundromat franchise industry. **Availability:** On Demand.

10185 ■ *Laundromats - 2022 U.S. Market Research Report with Updated COVID-19 Forecasts*
URL(s): www.marketresearch.com/Kentley-Insights-v4035/Laundromats-Research-Updated-COVID-Forecasts-31716902/
Price: $295. **Description:** Comprehensive, in-depth assessment of the laundromat industry in the United States. Includes over 100 data sets covering 2013-2026. **Availability:** Online.

10186 ■ *Laundromats in the US*
URL(s): www.marketresearch.com/IBISWorld-v2487/Laundromats-Research-32383241/
Price: $1,020. **Description:** Report covering the scope, size, disposition and growth of the laundromat industry including the key sensitivities and success factors. Also included are five-year industry forecasts, growth rates and an analysis of the industry key players and their market shares. **Availability:** Download.

TRADE PERIODICALS

10187 ■ *American Laundry News*
Pub: Crain Associated Enterprises Inc. - American Trade Magazines
Contact: K. C. Crain, President
URL(s): americanlaundrynews.com
Facebook: www.facebook.com/americanlaundrynews
Linkedin: www.linkedin.com/company/american-laundry-news
X (Twitter): x.com/laundryNews
Description: Institutional laundry magazine. **Availability:** Print; Online.

VIDEO/AUDIO MEDIA

10188 ■ *The How of Business: Daniel Feliciano - Transforming the Laundry Industry*
URL(s): www.thehowofbusiness.com/521-daniel-feliciano-transforming-laundry
Ed: Henry Lopez. **Released:** June 10, 2024. **Description:** Podcast discusses an outsourced laundry business.

10189 ■ *The How of Business: Laundromats with Keith Leimbach*
URL(s): www.thehowofbusiness.com/episode-321-keith-leimbach
Ed: Henry Lopez. **Released:** July 13, 2020. **Description:** Podcast discusses starting a laundromat.

CONSULTANTS

10190 ■ *ADL Consulting Services*
PO Box 1656
Boca Raton, FL 33429
Ph: (954)270-6936
URL(s): http://adlconsulting.com
Contact: Arthur Lapon, Founder
Facebook: www.facebook.com/profile.php?id=100065683771472
Description: Provides the expertise necessary for clients to become successful commercial laundry business owners. Offers services in all facets of their business from self-service to drop-off laundry and dry cleaning.

10191 ■ Beverly Kay Laundry Consulting and Training Services [Fluff & Fold 101]
Los Angeles, CA
Ph: (818)455-9105
Co. E-mail: info@fluffandfold101.com
URL: http://fluffandfold101.com
Contact: Beverly Kay, Consultant
Description: Offers consulting and training to help laundromat owners and new investors succeed in the laundry business.

10192 ■ Coin-O-Matic
3900 W 127th St.
Alsip, IL 60803
Ph: (708)232-3566
Co. E-mail: info@coinomatic.com
URL: http://www.coinomatic.com
Facebook: www.facebook.com/CoinOMatic
Description: Helps owners of coin laundromats succeed. Provides site location services, real estate assistance, site feasibility studies, laundromat design, laundromat construction, and ongoing business consulting services.

10193 ■ Laundromat Resource LLC [Laundromat Consulting and Coaching]
7801 San Pedro St.
Los Angeles, CA 90003
Ph: (714)869-7595
Co. E-mail: info@laundromatresource.com
URL: http://www.laundromatresource.com
Contact: Andrew Cunningham, Consultant
Facebook: www.facebook.com/TheLaundromatResource
Linkedin: www.linkedin.com/company/laundromat-resource
X (Twitter): x.com/LaundryResource
Instagram: www.instagram.com/laundromatresource
YouTube: www.youtube.com/laundromatresource
Description: Dedicated to helping clients find financial freedom through laundromat ownership. **Founded:** 2017.

10194 ■ Laundry One
60 Elm St.
Canal Winchester, OH 43110
Free: 800-800-0322
Co. E-mail: info@laundryone.com
URL: http://www.laundryone.com
Contact: Daniel Duckworth, President
Description: Distributor and servicer of commercial laundry equipment. Offers consulting services as well as pre-approved financing.

10195 ■ Laundry Solutions Group
472 N Sugar Grove Pky., Ste. F 126
Sugar Grove, IL 60554
Ph: (630)999-8610
Co. E-mail: jim@laundrysolutionsgroup.com
URL: http://laundrysolutionsgroup.com
Contact: Jim Winkelman, President
Facebook: www.facebook.com/LaundrySolutionsGroup
Description: Provides energy-efficient laundry consultation, brokerage, remodeling, new store development, financing, and service for vended laundry businesses.

10196 ■ Laundrylux
461 Doughty Blvd.
Inwood, NY 11096
Free: 800-645-2204
URL: http://laundrylux.com
Contact: Cody Milch, President
X (Twitter): x.com/laundryluxusa
YouTube: www.youtube.com/channel/UCelIdz4t1cFdUpKES4vYkiA
Description: Supplier of Electrolux Professional and Wascomat commercial laundry equipment for laundromats. Offers support services including in-house equipment financing, laundry management software, laundromat marketing, and real estate services.

10197 ■ National Laundry Equipment
2909 Armory Dr.
Nashville, TN 37204
Ph: (615)885-1115

URL: http://www.nationallaundryequipment.com
Facebook: www.facebook.com/nationallaundryequipment
X (Twitter): x.com/LaundryEquipmen

Description: Provides equipment, parts, service, and consultation for commercial laundry. Also serves the coin-operated laundry and laundromat community as well.

10198 ■ PBI Laundry Consulting
PO Box 790
Lake Forest, CA 92609
Ph: (657)333-6165
Co. E-mail: info@pbilaundry.com
URL: http://pbilaundry.com
X (Twitter): x.com/PBILaundry
YouTube: www.youtube.com/channel/UCz2mmUQP9jIQSNXImU5m99A/videos

Description: Consultants experienced in the vended laundry business, specializing in assisting those building, re-tooling, selling, or buying coin-operated laundries. **Founded:** 1985.

10199 ■ Wash Broker Ltd.
2472 State Rte., 30, Ste. B103-115
Oswego, IL 60543
URL: http://www.washbroker.com
Contact: Joe Hollendonner, Co-Founder
E-mail: joe@washbroker.com
Facebook: www.facebook.com/WashBroker

Description: Consultants help navigate the pitfalls of buying and selling a laundry business. Works to create win-win scenarios for both buyers and sellers.

FRANCHISES AND BUSINESS OPPORTUNITIES

10200 ■ The Eco Laundry Co.
249 W 18th St.
New York, NY 10011
Ph: (646)649-3806
Co. E-mail: info@ecolaundrycompany.com
URL: http://www.ecolaundrycompany.com
Contact: Jean Calleja, Contact
Facebook: www.facebook.com/ecolaundry

Description: A New York based, queer-owned, majority immigrant small business. Provides eco-friendly and non-toxic laundry and dry cleaning services. **Founded:** 2012.

10201 ■ LaundroLab LLC
4444 S Blvd., Ste.300
Charlotte, NC 28209
Ph: (704)251-9620
Free: 844-633-9274
Co. E-mail: info@laundrolabusa.com
URL: http://www.laundrolabfranchise.com
Contact: Alex Smereczniak, Co-Founder Co-Chief Executive Officer
Facebook: www.facebook.com/laundrolab
Linkedin: www.linkedin.com/company/laundrolabfranchise

Description: A re-imagined laundromat franchise with customer-first approach providing a one-stop-shop for all laundry needs. **Founded:** 2020.

10202 ■ Maytag Commercial Laundry
400 Klock Rd.
Benton Harbor, MI 49022
URL: http://www.maytagcommerciallaundry.com/mclstorefront
Linkedin: www.linkedin.com/showcase/maytagcommerciallaundry
YouTube: www.youtube.com/channel/UChRHet_FgpbKg-zDu246oVw

Description: Delivers Maytag laundry machines to laundromat owners, route operators, and on-premises laundry operations. Focused on producing durable commercial washers and dryers that run without distractions so that you can focus on running your business. **Founded:** 1959.

10203 ■ Speed Queen Laundry
221 Shepard St.
Ripon, WI 54971
URL: http://speedqueenlaundry.com
URL(s): franchise.speedqueen.com

Description: Global laundry brand franchise operating laundromats worldwide.

10204 ■ Spin Doctor Laundromat
1070 Whitehorse-Mercerville Rd.
Hamilton, NJ 08610
Ph: (609)981-7746
URL: http://www.spindoctorlaundromat.com
Facebook: www.facebook.com/profile.php?id=100063749611156

Description: A modern, coinless, full-service laundry featuring high-performance washers and dryers.

10205 ■ SuperSuds Management, LLC
5 Leway Dr., Ste. 101
Fredericksburg, VA 22405
Contact: John F. McManus, Contact

Description: Provider of self-service laundry, drop-off/curbside laundry, and commercial laundry services.

10206 ■ WaveMAX Laundry
929 McDuff Ave. S, Ste. 107
Jacksonville, FL 32205
Ph: (904)388-1717
URL: http://www.wavemaxlaundry.com
Contact: Sheila Roberts, Chief Financial Officer
Facebook: www.facebook.com/wavemaxlaundry

Description: National laundry franchise that has focused its business model on developing the prototypical market and store. **Founded:** 2012.

10207 ■ Zoom Express Laundry
8201 Preston Rd., Ste. 700
Dallas, TX 75225
Ph: (972)707-9555
Co. E-mail: letsgo@zoomexpresslaundry.com
URL: http://zoomexpresslaundry.com
Contact: Tony Ramji, President

Description: A modern laundromat that exists to help customers get their laundry done efficiently in a safe and clean environment. Offers pick-up and delivery, wash/dry/fold, and dry cleaning services.

PUBLICATIONS

10208 ■ How to Start a Laundromat Business
Ed: John Russel. **Released:** March 07, 2022. **Price:** $14.97. **Description:** A self-made millionaire reveals how to start, run, and scale a successful laundromat business. **Availability:** Print.

10209 ■ Laundromat Business Startup for Beginners 2022
Ed: Brian Reeves. **Released:** June 28, 2022. **Price:** $10.65. **Description:** A guide to how to start and grow your laundromat business. **Availability:** Print.

10210 ■ Laundromat Ownership Step-by-Step: A Realistic Guide to Operating and Growing Laundromats
Ed: Joseph Haywood. **Released:** August 31, 2017. **Price:** $18.49. **Description:** Written for laundromat owners and those interested in buying a laundromat. Explains day-to-day laundromat operations as well as how to evaluate, buy, and grow a laundry business. **Availability:** Print.

10211 ■ PlanetLaundry
17w635 Butterfield Rd., Ste. 145
Oakbrook Terrace, IL 60181
Free: 800-570-5629
Fax: (630)953-7925
Co. E-mail: marketing@coinlaundry.org
URL: http://www.coinlaundry.org
Contact: Brian Wallace, President
URL(s): planetlaundry.com
Facebook: www.facebook.com/PlanetLaundry
X (Twitter): x.com/planetlaundry

Released: Monthly; Delivers once a month. **Price:** $3, U.S. for single copy one year; $36, U.S. for one year; $40, Canada and Mexico for one year. **Description:** Includes legislative alerts, owner/store profiles and industry forum. **Availability:** Print; PDF; Download; Online.

10212 ■ Success in the Laundry Business
Ed: William Arthur. **Released:** April 09, 2022. **Price:** $9.99. **Description:** A practical guide to help you through the purchase and operation of your first laundromat. **Availability:** Print.

10213 ■ Today's Laundromat: Coin Laundry Association's Official Guide to Getting Started in the Laundry Business
Released: August 26, 2020. **Price:** $49. **Description:** Covering everything from inspecting an existing laundry to closing the deal, this book will guide you through basics of starting a self-service laundry. **Availability:** Print.

ASSOCIATIONS AND OTHER ORGANIZATIONS

10214 ■ Federal Bar Association (FBA)
4075 Wilson Blvd., 8th fl.
  Arlington, VA 22203
Ph: (571)481-9100
Fax: (571)481-9090
Co. E-mail: fba@fedbar.org
URL: http://www.fedbar.org
Contact: Jonathan O. Hafen, President
Facebook: www.facebook.com/FederalBar
Linkedin: www.linkedin.com/company/federal-bar
  -association
X (Twitter): x.com/federalbar
Description: Promotes the interests and professional development of attorneys involved in federal law. **Founded:** 1920. **Publications:** *The Federal Lawyer* (6/year). **Educational Activities:** Federal Bar Association Annual Meeting and Convention (Annual). **Awards:** Earl W. Kintner Award for Distinguished Service (Annual); FBA Chapter Activity Awards (Annual); FBA Younger Federal Lawyer Awards (Annual); Elaine R. "Boots" Fisher Award (Annual). **Geographic Preference:** National.

10215 ■ Hispanic Lawyers Association of Illinois (HLAI)
27 N Wacker Dr., Ste. No. 462
  Chicago, IL 60606
Ph: (312)620-5303
Co. E-mail: communications@hlai.org
URL: http://hlai.org
Contact: Andrea Belard, Contact
Facebook: www.facebook.com/hispaniclawyersIllinois
Linkedin: www.linkedin.com/company/hispanic
  -lawyers-association-of-illinois
X (Twitter): x.com/hlaitweets
Instagram: www.instagram.com/
  hispaniclawyersillinois
Description: Aims to promote high standards of competence, professionalism, and integrity with and among Hispanic attorneys and the Hispanic communities within the state of Illinois. **Founded:** 1995. **Awards:** Kaplan Scholarships. **Geographic Preference:** National.

10216 ■ Houston Intellectual Property Law Association (HIPLA)
1611 Lamar
  Houston, TX 77010
URL: http://www.hipla.org
Contact: Lee Eubanks, President
E-mail: leubanks@eubanksip.com
Facebook: www.facebook.com/Houston-Intellectual
  -Property-Law-Association-HIPLA-39945488719
  5461
Linkedin: www.linkedin.com/company/houston-in
  tellectual-property-law-association-hipla
Description: Law firm provides legal services. **Awards:** HIPLA Fellowship (Biennial); HIPLA Scholarships for University of Houston Law Center Students (Annual). **Geographic Preference:** State.

REFERENCE WORKS

10217 ■ "As Talent War Escalates, Law Firms Fear Business Pros Getting Poached" in The American Lawyer (November 23, 2021)
Ed: Andrew Maloney. **Released:** November 23, 2021. **Description:** It takes more than just lawyers to make up a law firm. Other professionals, such as secretaries and financial analysts, are also needed. With a worker shortage, law firms are keeping track of their talent and doing what they can to retain these critical workers.

10218 ■ "Can Online Legal Services Really Help Your Business?" in Business News Daily (February 21, 2021)
URL(s): www.businessnewsdaily.com/10243-online
  -legal-services-pros-cons.html
Ed: Adam Uzialko. **Released:** February 21, 2023. **Description:** Online legal services are an option for small businesses when they need this type of help. This article discusses what they can and cannot do and how they are different from established brick-and-mortar firms. **Availability:** Online.

10219 ■ "You're Being Sued: A Guide to Handling a Business Lawsuit" in Business News Daily (February 21, 2023)
URL(s): www.businessnewsdaily.com/8724-small
  -business-lawsuit-tips.html
Ed: Jennifer Post. **Released:** February 21, 2023. **Description:** Discusses what to do if your small business is getting sued. **Availability:** Online.

STATISTICAL SOURCES

10220 ■ Law Firms Industry in the US - Market Research Report
URL(s): www.ibisworld.com/united-states/market-re
  search-reports/law-firms-industry/
Price: $925. **Description:** Downloadable report analyzing the current and future trends in the law firm industry. **Availability:** Download.

TRADE SHOWS AND CONVENTIONS

10221 ■ Florida Bar Convention
URL(s): www.floridabar.org
Frequency: Annual. **Description:** Networking conference for lawyers in Florida. **Principal Exhibits:** Networking conference for lawyers in Florida.

PUBLICATIONS

10222 ■ Advising the Small Business
Ed: Jean L. Batman. **Released:** 2019. **Description:** A guide for lawyers to consult when advising small businesses. Includes forms and documents. **Availability:** Print.

START-UP INFORMATION

10223 ■ *How to Open & Operate a Financially Successful Landscaping, Nursery, or Lawn Service Business: With Companion CD-ROM*

Pub: Atlantic Publishing Co.

Contact: Dr. Heather L. Johnson, Contact

Ed: Lynn Wasnak. **Released:** 2010. **Description:** Guide provides understanding of the basic concepts of starting and running a service business, focusing on the operation of a small nursery, landscaping, or lawn service or combining the three operations. It also offers tips for running the business from the home. **Availability:** CD-ROM; Print; Online.

ASSOCIATIONS AND OTHER ORGANIZATIONS

10224 ■ **Outdoor Power Equipment Institute (OPEI)**

1605 King St.

Alexandria, VA 22314

Ph: (703)549-7600

Co. E-mail: info@opei.org

URL: http://www.opei.org

Contact: Kris Kiser, President

E-mail: kkiser@opei.org

Facebook: www.facebook.com/OPEInstitute

X (Twitter): x.com/OPEInstitute

Instagram: www.instagram.com/weareopei

Description: Manufacturers of lawn mowers, garden tractors, snow throwers, utility vehicles, chainsaws, motor tillers, shredder/grinders, edger/trimmers, leaf vacuums, log splitters, stump cutters, chippers and sprayers, and major components. **Founded:** 1952. **Publications:** *Contractor Connections.* **Educational Activities:** GIE+EXPO (Annual). **Geographic Preference:** National.

REFERENCE WORKS

10225 ■ *"All the Trimmings"* in *Green Industry Pro* (Vol. 23, March 2011, No. 3, pp. 29)

Ed: Gregg Wartgow. **Description:** When choosing lawn mowing equipment, it is advised to purchase commercial-grade 21-inch walk mowers rather than less expensive consumer-grade mowers. John Deere is reentering the commercial 21-inch walk behind mower market after a five-year hiatus. **Availability:** Online.

10226 ■ *"Customer Retention is Proportionate to Employee Retention"* in *Green Industry Pro* (Vol. 23, September 2011)

Description: Presented in a question-answer format, information is provided to help retain customers as well as keeping workers happy. **Availability:** Online.

10227 ■ *"Customized Before Custom Was Cool"* in *Green Industry Pro* (July 2011)

Ed: Gregg Wartgow. **Description:** Profile of Turf Care Enterprises and owner Kevin Vogeler, who discusses his desire to use more natural programs using little or no chemicals in 1986. At that time, that sector represented 20 percent of his business, today it shares 80 percent. **Availability:** Online.

10228 ■ *"Deep in the Heart of Drought"* in *Green Industry Pro* (Vol. 23, October 2011)

Ed: Gregg Wartgow. **Description:** Challenges faced by landscape contractors during the recent drought in Texas are explored. Despite these challenges, opportunity for contractors providing irrigation services has risen. **Availability:** Online.

10229 ■ *"Dozens 'Come Alive' in Downtown Chicago"* in *Green Industry Pro* (July 2011)

Ed: Gregg Wartgow. **Description:** Highlights from the Come Alive Outside training event held in Chicago, Illinois July 14-15, 2011 are shared. Nearly 80 people representing 38 landscape companies attended the event that helps contractors review their services and find ways to sell them in new and various ways. **Availability:** Online.

10230 ■ *"Finding a Way to Continue Growing"* in *Green Industry Pro* (Vol. 23, March 2011, No. 3, pp. 31)

Ed: Gregg Wartgow. **Description:** Profile of Brett Lemcke, VP of R.M. Landscape located in Rochester, New York. Lemcke tells how his Landscape Industry Certified credentials helped him to grow his business and beat out his competition. **Availability:** Online.

10231 ■ *"Five Distinct Divisions, One Collective Focus"* in *Green Industry Pro* (Vol. 23, October 2011)

Ed: Gregg Wartgow. **Description:** Profile of ACLS Inc., an amalgamation of All Commercial Landscape Service (commercial maintenance), All Custom Landscape Service (design/build), Fresno Tree Service, Certified Water Consulting (irrigation), and Tractor Service (disking and flailing services on everything from one-acre lots to hundreds of acres of open land). The firm discusses its rebranding effort in order to increase sales. **Availability:** Online.

10232 ■ *"Forward Motion"* in *Green Industry Pro* (July 2011)

Ed: Gregg Wartgow. **Description:** Several landscape contractors have joined this publication's Working Smarter Training Challenge over the last year. This process is helping them develop ways to improve work processes, boost morale, drive out waste, reduce costs, improve customer service, and be more competitive. **Availability:** Print; Online.

10233 ■ *"Gain the 'Come Alive Outside' Selling Edge"* in *Green Industry Pro* (July 2011)

Ed: Jim Paluch. **Description:** Marketing the 'Come Alive Outside' slogan can help landscapers to increase their market share by identifying and applying these elements to each customer as well as their workers. **Availability:** Online.

10234 ■ *"The Green Industry Jobs Gap"* in *Green Industry Pro* (Vol. 23, October 2011)

Ed: Gregg Wartgow. **Description:** According to the U.S. Bureau of Labor Statistics, the landscaping industry employs over 829,000 workers. According to another private study, the industry would employ more if they were able to find more people interested in performing the required work. **Availability:** Online.

10235 ■ *"Hey, You Can't Do That"* in *Green Industry Pro* (Vol. 23, September 2011)

Ed: Rod Dickens. **Description:** Manufacturers of landscape equipment are making better use of energy resources, such as the use of fuel-injection systems instead of carburetors, lightweight materials, better lubricants, advanced battery technology, and innovative engine designs. **Availability:** Online.

10236 ■ *"How to Develop an Active Sales Program"* in *Green Industry Pro* (Vol. 23, September 2011)

Ed: Gregg Wartgow. **Description:** Craig den Hartog, owner of Emerald Magic Lawn Care located in Holtsville, New York, describes the various marketing tactics he has developed to increase sales in the current economic environment. Statistical data included. **Availability:** Online.

10237 ■ *"How to Dominate in Residential Maintenance"* in *Green Industry Pro* (Vol. 23, October 2011)

Ed: Gregg Wartgow. **Description:** Lawn care services were ranked among the most expendable consumer expenditures, according to the National Retail Federation data accumulated in early 2011. This makes it critical for any landscape firm to target sales efforts toward higher-income households and higher-value homes. **Availability:** Online.

10238 ■ *"Joystick Operated Zero-Turn Mower Marks 30 Years"* in *Turf Magazine* (November 11, 2019)

URL(s): www.turfmagazine.com/manufacturersupplier-updates/joystick-operated-zero-turn-mower-marks-30-years/

Ed: Christine Menapace. **Released:** November 11, 2019. **Description:** County Clipper is celebrating the 30 year anniversary of manufacturing the joystick controlled zero-turn mower. Debuted in 1989, this mower was first manufactured under the Snapper brand name, and today Country Clipper offers 20 various joystick models. **Availability:** Online.

10239 ■ *"Labor of Love"* in *Green Industry Pro* (Vol. 23, March 2011, No. 3, pp. 14)

Ed: Gregg Wartgow. **Description:** Profile of CLS Landscape Management in Chino, California and its owner who started the company when he was 21 years old. Kevin Davis built his landscape firm into a $20 million a year business without using any dedicated salesperson. **Availability:** Online.

10240 ■ *"The Landscape of Landscaping Is Changing"* in *Lawn & Landscape* (July 19, 2018)

URL(s): www.lawnandlandscape.com/article/ll-0718 18-landscape-market-growth-potential/

Ed: Ken Gibson. **Released:** July 19, 2018. **Description:** Due to home improvement projects increasing, landscaping has also enjoyed a comeback. The single-family home market is growing and with that, comes a need for more landscape services. Also added to the effect is the growing number of older Americans who need assistance with their lawns. **Availability:** Online.

10241 ■ "New to the Class" in Lawn & Landscape (November 14, 2019)
URL(s): www.lawnandlandscape.com/article/new-to-the-class-caterpillar-products/
Ed: Lauren Rathmell. **Released:** November 14, 2019. **Description:** Caterpillar opened its training facility in Cary, NC to the media in order to introduce their latest equipment. The highlight was the 6-ton mini excavator, which is Caterpillar's first entry into the 6-ton class offering. **Availability:** Online.

10242 ■ "Planning to Start a Landscaping Business? Here Are Some Services You Should Offer" in Home Business (April 21, 2020)
Released: April 21, 2020. **Description:** Offers information to landscaping small businesses on the variety of services that clients commonly request that you should consider offering. **Availability:** Online.

10243 ■ "Problem Solving Requires Total Team Approach" in Green Industry Pro (Vol. 23, September 2011)
Ed: Bob Coulter. **Description:** Working Smarter Training Challenge teaches that leaders are able to carry out solutions directly into their organization, develop skills and drive business results in key areas by creating a culture of energized workers who are able to take ownership of their performance as well as the performance of the company as a whole. **Availability:** Online.

10244 ■ "Pros & Cons of Starting a Lawn Business" in The Balance Small Business (September 10, 2019)
Ed: Mindy Lilyquist. **Released:** September 10, 2019. **Description:** Lawn service companies have the ability of offering customized services to fit your specific desires and needs. This article offers pros and cons of starting your own lawn care business, estimated start-up costs, earning potential, and marketing. **Availability:** Online.

10245 ■ "Savatree Acquires Pauley Tree and Lawn Care" in Landscape Business (November 17, 2019)
URL(s): landscape-business.com/savatree-acquires-pauley-tree-and-lawn-care/
Released: November 17, 2019. **Description:** SavA-Tree acquired Pauley Tree and Lawn Care of New Canaan, Connecticut. This will add to SavATree's ability to provide quality tree, shrub, and lawn care services to their customers. **Availability:** Online.

10246 ■ "Take Control of Your Company's Finances" in Green Industry Pro (Vol. 23, March 2011, No. 3, pp. 24)
Ed: Gregg Wartgow. **Description:** Understanding that when certain leading indicators that affect the outcome of certain lagging indicators are aligned, companies will be able to take control of their firm's finances. Ways to improve the processes that drive financial performance for landscape firms are outlined. **Availability:** Online.

10247 ■ "Take This Job and Love It" in Green Industry Pro (Vol. 23, October 2011)
Ed: Gregg Wartgow. **Description:** Details of the lawsuit filed by the Professional Landcare Network (PLANET) against the U.S. Department of Labor are explained. Challenges faced by landscape firms because of employment costs are outlined. Statistical data included. **Availability:** PDF; Online.

10248 ■ "Toro Launches Z Master 7500" in Lawn & Landscape (November 6, 2019)
URL(s): www.lawnandlandscape.com/article/toro-z-master-7500-mower/

Ed: Lauren Rathmell. **Released:** November 06, 2019. **Description:** Toro introduced its new product, the Z master 7500-G, which is a 96 inch gas mower for commercial grass cutting crews. **Availability:** Online.

10249 ■ "Way More Than Mowing" in Green Industry Pro (Vol. 23, September 2011)
Ed: Rod Dickens. **Description:** Shipp Shape Lawn Services located in Sylvester, Georgia now offers aeration, fertilizing and weed control, mulching, yard renovation, flowerbed maintenance, landscaping, as well as irrigation repairs and installation in order to diversify the business and stay competitive. **Availability:** Online.

SOURCES OF SUPPLY

10250 ■ Green Industry Pros
URL(s): www.greenindustrypros.com
Released: Irregular **Description:** Publication includes lists of about 33,000 dealers, retailers, and distributors of lawn and garden power equipment. **Entries include:** Product name, description and photograph, name and address of distributor or manufacturer. **Arrangement:** Classified by type of product. **Availability:** Print; Online.

STATISTICAL SOURCES

10251 ■ Maids, Nannies & Gardeners Industry in the US - Market Research Report
URL(s): www.ibisworld.com/united-states/market-research-reports/maids-nannies-gardeners-industry/
Price: $925. **Description:** Downloadable report analyzing current and future trends in the domestic help industries. **Availability:** Download.

10252 ■ US Lawn and Garden Products Market Report 2020
URL(s): store.mintel.com/report/us-lawn-and-garden-products-market-report
Price: $4,366.35. **Description:** Downloadable report containing data on lawn and garden products and the impact COVID-19 has had on the industry. Report includes an executive summary, interactive databook, PowerPoint presentation, infographic overview, report PDF, and previous years data. **Availability:** PDF.

TRADE PERIODICALS

10253 ■ Landscape Management
Pub: North Coast Media
URL(s): www.landscapemanagement.net
Facebook: www.facebook.com/LandscapeManagement
Linkedin: www.linkedin.com/company-beta/3160776
X (Twitter): x.com/landscapemgmt
Instagram: www.instagram.com/landscapemgmt
YouTube: www.youtube.com/channel/UCdlO7-QYFWHUI4KR5D4bKDA
Released: Monthly **Price:** $55, U.S. For 1 year; $76, U.S. For 2 year; $87, Canada and Mexico For 1 year; $127, Canada and Mexico For 2 year; $165, Other countries For 1 year; $246, Other countries For 2 year. **Description:** Magazine for professionals in landscape, grounds management and lawn care, construction, and maintenance. **Availability:** Print; Online.

10254 ■ Lawn & Landscape
Pub: GIE Media Inc.
Contact: Chris Foster, President
URL(s): www.lawnandlandscape.com
Linkedin: www.linkedin.com/company/lawn-landscape-magazine
X (Twitter): twitter.com/lawnlandscape
Instagram: www.instagram.com/lawnlandscape
Ed: Brian Horn, Chuck Bowen. **Released:** Monthly **Price:** $5, Single issue; $30, U.S. for one year; $35, Canada for one year; $98, Other countries for one year; $218, for foreign airmail; $42, for two year. **Description:** Business management magazine for lawn and landscape contracting professionals. **Availability:** Print; PDF; Online.

VIDEO/AUDIO MEDIA

10255 ■ The How of Business: Growing a Lawncare Business with Bryan Clayton
URL(s): www.thehowofbusiness.com/episode-343-bryan-clayton
Ed: Henry Lopez. **Released:** December 07, 2020. **Description:** Podcast discusses different varieties of lawn care businesses.

TRADE SHOWS AND CONVENTIONS

10256 ■ Landscapes
National Association of Landscape Professionals (NALP)
12500 Fair Lakes Cir., Ste. 200
Fairfax, VA 22033
Ph: (703)736-9666
Free: 800-395-2522
Fax: (703)322-2066
Co. E-mail: info@landscapeprofessionals.org
URL: http://www.landscapeprofessionals.org
Contact: Britt Wood, Chief Executive Officer
URL(s): www.landscapeprofessionals.org/ELEVATE
Frequency: Annual. **Description:** Lawn care equipment, supplies, and services, including fertilizers, weed control materials, insurance information, and outdoor power equipment. **Audience:** Lawn Care Professionals. **Principal Exhibits:** Lawn care equipment, supplies, and services, including fertilizers, weed control materials, insurance information, and outdoor power equipment. Dates and Locations: 2025 Nov 02-05 Phoenix Convention Center, Phoenix, AZ; 2026 Nov 08-11 Tampa Convention Center, Tampa, FL; 2027 Nov 07-10 Anaheim Convention Center, Anaheim, CA. **Telecommunication Services:** elevate@landscapeprofessionals.org.

10257 ■ St. Louis Builders Home & Garden Show
American Family Insurance Group
6000 American Pky.
Madison, WI 53783
Free: 800-692-6326
Co. E-mail: cfrsalessupport@amfam.com
URL: http://www.amfam.com
Contact: Bill Westrate, President
URL(s): www.stlhba.com/STLHBA/STLHBA/Events/Event_Display.aspx?EventKey=03_HG23
Frequency: Annual. **Description:** Exhibits relating to homes, pools, kitchen, baths, interior design, lawns, and gardens. **Audience:** General public and trade professionals. **Principal Exhibits:** Exhibits relating to homes, pools, kitchen, baths, interior design, lawns, and gardens. **Telecommunication Services:** ridgleyt@hbastl.com.

CONSULTANTS

10258 ■ Forest City Tree Protection Company Inc.
731 Beta Dr., Ste. E
Mayfield Village, OH 44143
Ph: (440)421-9589
Fax: (440)421-9593
Co. E-mail: info@forestcitytree.com
URL: http://www.forestcitytree.com
Contact: Lauren S. Lanphear, Jr., President
Facebook: www.facebook.com/forestcitytree
Description: Provider of complete tree care and arboricultural services to home owners and commercial establishments. **Scope:** Provider of complete tree care and arboricultural services to home owners and commercial establishments. **Founded:** 1910. **Training:** Evaluating Trees and Damage to Trees, 1987; Tree Fertilization, 1987; Knots, Ropes and Rigging, 1987; Tree Appraisal, 1985; Trees, People and the Law, 1985. **Special Services:** Offers tree maintenance, tree trimming, pruning, and tree removal services.

10259 ■ Fred J. Robinson & Associates Inc.
7191 Auburn Rd.
Concord Township, OH 44077-9559
Contact: Fred J. Robinson, Contact
Description: Provider of information concerning trees health, appraised value, pest management and both care and preservation. Consults with architects, landscape architects, attorneys, insurance adjusters, government agencies and engineers in addition to tree owners. **Scope:** Provider of information concerning trees health, appraised value, pest management and both care and preservation. Consults with architects, landscape architects, attorneys, insurance adjusters, government agencies and engineers in addition to tree owners.

10260 ■ LandCare
5295 Westview Dr., Ste. 100
Frederick, MD 21703
Ph: (301)874-3300
Free: 877-526-3227
Co. E-mail: landcare.authority@gmail.com
URL: http://landcare.com
Contact: Mike Bogan, Chief Executive Officer
E-mail: mike.bogan@landcare.com
Facebook: www.facebook.com/LandCareLLC
Linkedin: www.linkedin.com/company/landcare-lc
X (Twitter): x.com/landcare_
Instagram: www.instagram.com/landcare
Description: Landscape management company providing full-service grounds care programs and provides consulting services to clients, landscape architects, building and property managers and developers on contract and specification development. **Scope:** Landscape management company providing full-service grounds care programs and provides consulting services to clients, landscape architects, building and property managers and developers on contract and specification development.

10261 ■ North Haven Gardens Inc. (NHG)
7700 Northaven Rd.
Dallas, TX 75230
Ph: (214)363-5316
Co. E-mail: feedback@nhg.com
URL: http://nhg.com
Contact: Keith Green, Manager
Facebook: www.facebook.com/NorthHavenGardens
X (Twitter): x.com/nhgdallas
Instagram: www.instagram.com/northhavengardens
YouTube: www.youtube.com/channel/UCL9IopWlyjHKUgqmFJxB6NQ
Pinterest: www.pinterest.com/nhgdallas
Description: Garden center and art gallery specializing in garden education and quality plant selections. **Scope:** Garden center and art gallery specializing in garden education and quality plant selections. **Founded:** 1951. **Training:** Gardening 101, Jan, 2008.

10262 ■ Plantscape Inc.
3101 Liberty Ave.
Pittsburgh, PA 15201
Ph: (412)281-6352
Free: 800-303-1380
Fax: (412)281-4775
Co. E-mail: plants@plantscape.com
URL: http://www.plantscape.com
Contact: Jim Consoli, Manager
E-mail: jconsoli@plantscape.com
Facebook: www.facebook.com/PlantscapePittsburgh
Description: Provider of interior and exterior landscape services to the Pittsburgh business commercial market. **Scope:** Provider of interior and exterior landscape services to the Pittsburgh business commercial market. **Founded:** 1973.

10263 ■ Western Arborists Inc.
147 Underhill Dr.
Glendora, CA 91741
Contact: Kathleen Walker, Contact
Description: Provides tree care services. The company provides tree trimming, stump grinding, and clean-up services. It also offers consultation on tree disease and insect infestation, as well as damage appraisal services.

FRANCHISES AND BUSINESS OPPORTUNITIES

10264 ■ Clintar Groundskeeping Services
200 Cachet Woods Ct., Unit 119
Markham, ON, Canada L6C 0Z8
Free: 800-361-3542
Co. E-mail: info@clintar.com
URL: http://www.clintar.com
Contact: Rob Gannett, Chief Executive Officer
Description: Firm provides commercial landscape services such as parking lot maintenance, water management. **No. of Franchise Units:** 23. **Founded:** 1973. **Equity Capital Needed:** Approximately $100,000-$150,000 to start. **Royalty Fee:** 8%. **Training:** Yes.

10265 ■ The Environmental Factor Inc. (EFI)
85 Chambers Dr., Ste. 8
Ajax, ON, Canada L1Z 1E2
Ph: (905)686-9909
Fax: (905)686-0357
Co. E-mail: sales@environmentalfactor.com
URL: http://www.environmentalfactor.com
Facebook: www.facebook.com/environmentalfactor
Linkedin: www.linkedin.com/company/the-environmental-factor-inc
X (Twitter): x.com/envirofactor
Instagram: www.instagram.com/environmentalfactor
YouTube: www.youtube.com/channel/UCvFRfLdltO7UxyzkXIG8L7Q
Description: Manufacturer and distributor of organic lawn and garden products. **Founded:** 1991. **Training:** Initial and ongoing one on one training.

10266 ■ Jim's Mowing Canada Inc.
Vancouver, BC, Canada
Ph: (604)310-5467
URL: http://jimsmowing.ca
Contact: Jim Penman, Founder
Description: Provider of professional gardening and lawn mowing services including lawn maintenance, pruning, aeration and more. **No. of Franchise Units:** 1800. **Founded:** 1997. **Training:** Training and ongoing support provided.

10267 ■ Lawn Doctor Inc.
142 State Rte. 34
Holmdel, NJ 07733
Free: 800-845-0580
Co. E-mail: customerservice@lawndoctor.com
URL: http://www.lawndoctor.com
Contact: Russell J. Frith, President
Facebook: www.facebook.com/LawnDoctorFans
X (Twitter): x.com/LawnDoctor
Instagram: www.instagram.com/lawndoctorinc
YouTube: www.youtube.com/user/LawnDoctor
Description: Firm provides lawn care services. **Founded:** 1967. **Training:** Field and classroom intensive training program.

10268 ■ NaturaLawn of America, Inc.
1 E Church St.
Frederick, MD 21701
Ph: (301)694-5440
Free: 800-989-5444
Fax: (301)846-0320
Co. E-mail: info@naturalawn.com
URL: http://naturalawn.com
Contact: Autumn Moore, Contact
Facebook: www.facebook.com/NaturaLawn
Linkedin: www.linkedin.com/company/naturalawn-of-america
YouTube: www.youtube.com/user/NaturaLawn
Description: Franchises organic-based lawn care services. **Founded:** 1987. **Training:** No.

10269 ■ NiteLites Outdoor Lighting Franchise
6107 Market Ave.
Franklin, OH 45005
Free: 866-648-3548
Co. E-mail: info@nitelites.com
URL: http://www.nitelites.com
Contact: Dustin Huling, Contact

Facebook: www.facebook.com/CincinnatiOutdoorLighting
Description: Designer, installer and maintainer of commercial and home outdoor lights. **No. of Franchise Units:** 17. **No. of Company-Owned Units:** 4. **Founded:** 1992. **Franchised:** 2004. **Equity Capital Needed:** $65,585-$105,295. **Franchise Fee:** $65,585-$105,295. **Financial Assistance:** Yes **Training:** Yes.

10270 ■ Nutri-Lawn
2390 Haines Rd.
Unit No. 16
Mississauga, ON, Canada L4Y 1Y6
Ph: (905)272-5296
Co. E-mail: mississauga@nutrilawn.com
URL: http://www.nutrilawn.com
Contact: Cam Hansuld, Owner General Manager
Facebook: www.facebook.com/Nutrilawn
X (Twitter): x.com/nutrilawn
YouTube: www.youtube.com/user/nutrilawn
Description: Provides the best lawn care and weed control services across Canada for over 25 years. **Founded:** 1986. **Training:** Provides 1 week initial training, onsite for 1 week and ongoing support.

10271 ■ Spring-Green Lawn Care Corp.
11909 Spaulding School Dr.
Plainfield, IL 60585
Free: 800-777-8608
Co. E-mail: service@spring-green.com
URL: http://www.spring-green.com
Contact: Ted Hofer, Chief Executive Officer
X (Twitter): x.com/springgreenlawn
YouTube: www.youtube.com/springgreenlawncare
Description: National network of lawn and tree care businesses. **Founded:** 1977. **Training:** Initial training at headquarters covering areas of marketing, operations and computer system Besides, on-going training is offered through field visits, regional meetings, professional development programs, intranet, website, telephone and newsletters.

10272 ■ Weed Man USA
B3-1129 Wentworth St. W
Oshawa, ON, Canada L1J 8P7
Ph: (416)269-8333
Free: 888-321-9333
Co. E-mail: social@weedmanusa.com
URL: http://weedman.com/en-us
URL(s): scarborough.weedman.com; weedmanfranchise.com
Facebook: www.facebook.com/weedmanusa
Linkedin: www.linkedin.com/company/weed-man-usa
X (Twitter): x.com/WeedManLawnCare
Instagram: www.instagram.com/weedman_lawncare
YouTube: www.youtube.com/user/weedmanusalawncare
Description: Residential lawn care services. **No. of Franchise Units:** 399. **Founded:** 1970. **Franchised:** 1976. **Equity Capital Needed:** $65,980-$82,940. **Franchise Fee:** $20,000-$34,000. **Financial Assistance:** Yes **Training:** Yes.

RESEARCH CENTERS

10273 ■ Kansas State University - John C. Pair Center
1901 E 95th St. S
Haysville, KS 67060-8351
Ph: (316)788-0492
Fax: (316)788-3844
URL: http://www.k-state.edu/jcp
Contact: Dr. Bob Weaber, Department Head
E-mail: bweaber@ksu.edu
Description: Off-campus research activity of Department of Horticulture at Kansas State University. **Scope:** Ornamental trees and shrubs, vegetable crops, and turfgrass. **Founded:** 1970. **Publications:** *Horticultural Center Newsletter* (Semiannual). **Educational Activities:** John C. Pair Horticultural Center Group tours, Offer exemplary teaching and training programs.; John C. Pair Horticultural Center Open House, Offer exemplary teaching and training programs.; John C. Pair Horticultural Center Ornamental Field Day, Offer exemplary teaching and training

programs.; John C. Pair Horticultural Center Vegetable Twilight Tour, Offer exemplary teaching and training programs.

10274 ■ North Carolina Department of Agriculture and Consumer Services - Sandhills Research Station (SRS)

c/o Jeremy Martin, Station Superintendent
2148 Windblow Rd.
Jackson Springs, NC 27281-9505
Ph: (910)974-4673
Co. E-mail: sandhills.resst@ncagr.gov
URL: http://cals.ncsu.edu/research/research-stations/
sandhills-research-station
Contact: Jeremy Martin, Superintendent
E-mail: sandhills.resst@ncagr.gov
Description: Integral unit of North Carolina Department of Agriculture and Consumer Services, operated in cooperation with North Carolina State University. **Scope:** Peaches, nectarines, plums, blueberries, peanuts, peppers, soybeans, brambles, strawberries, and turf, including ground covers, soil fertility, plant breeding, and weed, insect, disease, and nematode control. **Founded:** 1951. **Educational Activities:** Peach Field Day; Small Fruits Field Day (Annual), Focuses on research related to strawberries,

brambles and blueberries.; Turfgrass Field Day (Biennial), To promote turfgrass management.

10275 ■ University of Arizona - Karsten Turfgrass Research Facility (KTRF)

2101 E Roger Rd.
Tucson, AZ 85719
Ph: (520)318-7142
Fax: (520)621-7186
Co. E-mail: dkopec@cals.arizona.edu
URL: http://turf.arizona.edu/karsten.htm
Description: Integral unit of University of Arizona. Offers troubleshooting and consulting; televised courses and colloquia. **Scope:** Turfgrass management focusing on water conservation and irrigation management, wastewater research, nitrogen fate, turfgrass development and evaluation, and herbicide efficacy. **Founded:** 1991. **Publications:** *Annual Turfgrass and Ornamentals Research Summary* (Annual).

10276 ■ University of Guelph - Guelph Turfgrass Institute (GTI) - G. M. Frost Research and Information Centre

The Guelph Turfgrass Institute
G.M. Frost Research & Information Centre
364 College Ave., E
Guelph, ON, Canada N1G 3B9

Ph: (226)971-1563
Co. E-mail: gti@uoguelph.ca
URL: http://www.guelphturfgrass.ca
Contact: Dr. Eric Lyons, Director
E-mail: elyons@uoguelph.ca
Facebook: www.facebook.com/GuelphTurf
X (Twitter): twitter.com/GuelphTurf
Instagram: www.instagram.com/guelphturf

Description: Integral unit of University of Guelph. Offers consulting through the Institute and through Ontario Ministry of Agriculture and Food; independent study correspondence courses, short courses, workshops, and seminars. **Scope:** Turfgrass production and management, including soil science, growth regulation, toxicology, environmental research, disease etiology and management, insect control, weed control, and turfgrass physiology, seed production, and nutrition. **Founded:** 1987. **Holdings:** Figures not available. **Publications:** *Annual Research Report* (Annual); *GTI advisor* (Biweekly). **Educational Activities:** GTI Research Field Day, To conduct quality research and providing accurate and timely information and education services in turfgrass science with a special emphasis on environmental sustainability and enhancement.; Ontario Turfgrass Symposium (Annual), For research and development.

ASSOCIATIONS AND OTHER ORGANIZATIONS

10277 ■ National Limousine Association (NLA)
1002 Lincoln Dr. W, Ste. C
Marlton, NJ 08053
Ph: (856)596-3344
Free: 800-652-7007
Fax: (856)596-2145
Co. E-mail: info@limo.org
URL: http://www.limo.org
Contact: Robert Alexander, President
Facebook: www.facebook.com/NLA1985
Linkedin: www.linkedin.com/company/national
-limousine-association---nla
X (Twitter): x.com/NLA4

Description: Limousine owners and operators; limousine manufacturers and suppliers to the industry. Seeks to: promote and advance industry professionalism and the common interests of members; increase use of chauffeured transportation in both business and public sectors. Monitors legislation and organizes lobbying activities. Sponsors seminars on safety/regulatory issues and management techniques. **Founded:** 1985. **Geographic Preference:** National.

REFERENCE WORKS

10278 ■ "ALLSTAR Chauffeured Services Celebrates 25 Years of Growth" in Chauffeur Driven (November 12, 2019)
URL(s): www.chauffeurdriven.com/news-features/in
dustry-news/2343-allstar-chauffeured-services
-celebrates-25-years-of-growth.html

Released: November 12, 2019. **Description:** ALL-STAR Chauffeured Services is celebrating its 25th anniversary in Troy, Michigan. After growing his business from one limousine, owner Bob Beutel is attributing his company's success on his staff of dedicated team members. **Availability:** Online.

10279 ■ "Capital Metro May Soon Seek Contractor" in Austin Business Journal (Vol. 31, June 10, 2011, No. 14, pp. 1)
Pub: Austin Business Journal
Contact: Rachel McGrath, Director
E-mail: rmcgrath@bizjournals.com

Ed: Vicky Garza. **Description:** Capital Metropolitan Transportation Authority may be forced to contract out its bus services provided by StarTran Inc. as early as September 2012 following legislation approved by the Texas legislature. The bill originates in a report by the Sunset Advisory Commission. Details are included. **Availability:** Print; Online.

10280 ■ "Full Speed Ahead?" in San Antonio Business Journal (Vol. 28, May 9, 2014, No. 13, pp. 4)
Pub: American City Business Journals, Inc.
Contact: Mike Olivieri, Executive Vice President

Released: May 09, 2014. **Price:** $4, Introductory 4-Week Offer(Digital & Print). **Description:** Lyft and Uber Technologies Inc. have launched ride-sharing services in San Antonio, Texas without the city's permission and the objections of taxi and limousine industries. The ride-sharing service issues were brought into court and to the City Council, while the San Antonio Police Department issued a cease-and-desist order to the ride-sharing companies. The complaints against Lyft and Uber are outlined. **Availability:** Print; Online.

10281 ■ How to Start a Home-Based Senior Care Business
Ed: James L. Ferry. **Released:** 2nd edition. **Price:** Paperback,softback; Electronic Book. **Description:** Information is provided to start a home-based senior care business. **Availability:** E-book; Print.

10282 ■ "Limo University Launches First North American Tour" in Chauffeur Driven (November 12, 2019)
URL(s): www.chauffeurdriven.com/news-features/in
dustry-news/2344-limo-university-launches-first-nor
th-american-tour.html

Released: November 12, 2019. **Description:** Limo University is offering their first-ever North American Boot Camp Tour. This unique event will provide one day of intensive sales and marketing training for 9 hours for operators. **Availability:** Online.

10283 ■ "Marine-Services Firm Eyes Expansion" in Providence Business News (Vol. 29, August 25, 2014, No. 21, pp. 8)
Pub: American City Business Journals, Inc.
Contact: Mike Olivieri, Executive Vice President

Released: August 23, 2014. **Description:** Jamestown, Rhode Island-based Conanicut Marine Services Inc. is looking to expand the business with a bigger marina, the addition of a third boat to his ferry fleet, and a climate-controlled storage shed. Owner, Bill Munger, discusses his efforts to overcome the challenges of sustaining the business during the economic recession. **Availability:** Print; Online.

10284 ■ "Professional Help: Cross That Off Your To-Do List" in Inc. (November 2007, pp. 89-90, 92)
Ed: Alison Stein Wellner. **Description:** Small business owners are finding that it pays to hire someone to takeover the personal tasks of daily living, including hiring a personal assistant, chauffeur, chef, stylist, pet caregiver, or concierge service. **Availability:** Online.

10285 ■ "Ride Apps Uber, Lyft, Sidecar Hit Speed Bumps" in San Francisco Business Times (Vol. 28, January 24, 2014, No. 27, pp. 4)
Pub: American City Business Journals, Inc.
Contact: Mike Olivieri, Executive Vice President

Released: Weekly. **Price:** $4, Introductory 4-week offer(Digital & Print). **Description:** California's Public Utilities Commission (PUC) has reversed its earlier prohibition and allowed mobile app ride services, while imposing insurance and safety regulations on these alternatives to taxicabs and limousine services. However, the PUC did not take action when the issue of liability and insurance were raised due to the death of Sofia Liu, who was hit by an Uber driver. The lawsuits against Uber are discussed. **Availability:** Print; Online.

10286 ■ "Ride-Share Field Has New Player" in Providence Business News (Vol. 29, April 21, 2014, No. 3, pp. 1)
Pub: American City Business Journals, Inc.
Contact: Mike Olivieri, Executive Vice President
URL(s): pbn.com/ride-share-field-has-new-player9
6580

Description: Lyft is Providence, Rhode Island's newest ride-sharing service. State officials continue to look for ways to regulate Internet vehicle services, taxis and limousines. Nearly all of Lyft's drivers are part-time employees using their own personal vehicles.

10287 ■ "Ride-Share Programs Seem to Fit San Antonio's Future" in San Antonio Business Journal (Vol. 28, May 9, 2014, No. 13, pp. 6)
Pub: American City Business Journals, Inc.
Contact: Mike Olivieri, Executive Vice President

Price: $4, Introductory 4-Week Offer(Digital & Print). **Description:** San Antonio, Texas Mayor Julian Castro has been promoting the SA2020 plan that calls for an increase in downtown living and expanded public transit options. Castro made positive comments regarding the ride sharing services, even if they include a few disqualifications. The potential benefits of the ride sharing services into the city's plan are examined. **Availability:** Print; Online.

10288 ■ "Ride Sharing Market Size Worth Around US$344.4 Bn by 2030" in GlobeNewswire (September 28, 2021)
Released: September 28, 2021. **Description:** The global value in ride sharing was valued at US$73.5 billion for 2020 but is expected to rise dramatically within the next ten years. Discusses the factors that are driving market growth in this industry. **Availability:** Online.

10289 ■ "Taxis Are Set to Go Hybrid" in Philadelphia Business Journal (Vol. 30, September 16, 2011, No. 31, pp. 1)
Pub: Philadelphia Business Journal
Contact: Sierra Quinn, Director
E-mail: squinn@bizjournals.com

Ed: Natalie Kostelni. **Description:** Taxis are going hybrid in several major states such as New York, California and Maryland where it is mandated, but it is yet to happen in Philadelphia, Pennsylvania with the exception of one taxi company. Freedom Taxi is awaiting Philadelphia Parking Authority's sign off. **Availability:** Online.

STATISTICAL SOURCES

10290 ■ *RMA Annual Statement Studies*
Pub: Risk Management Association
Contact: Nancy Foster, President
Released: Annual. **Description:** Contains composite balance sheets and income statements for more than 360 industries, including the accounting, auditing, and bookkeeping industries. Also contains five years of comparative historical data for discerning trends. Includes 16 commonly used ratios, computed for most of the size groupings for nearly every industry.

10291 ■ *Taxi & Limousine Services Industry in the US - Market Research Report*
URL(s): www.ibisworld.com/united-states/market-research-reports/taxi-limousine-services-industry/
Price: $925. **Description:** Downloadable report analyzing current and future trends in the taxi and limousine services industry. **Availability:** Download.

LIBRARIES

10292 ■ Alabama Department of Transportation (ALDOT)
PO Box 303050
  Montgomery, AL 36130-3050
Ph: (334)353-6554
Co. E-mail: aldotinfo@dot.state.al.us
URL: http://www.dot.state.al.us
Contact: John Cooper, Director
E-mail: cooperjr@dot.state.al.us
Scope: Transportation. **Services:** Interlibrary loan; library not open to the public. **Founded:** 1953. **Holdings:** 1,000 books; 5,000 reports.

10293 ■ California State Department of Motor Vehicles - Licensing Operations Division - Research and Development Branch - Traffic Safety Research Library
1120 N St., Rm. 1430
  Sacramento, CA 95814
Ph: (914)654-4601
Co. E-mail: library@dot.ca.gov
URL: http://dot.ca.gov/programs/transportation-library
Scope: Automobile transportation. **Services:** Copying; library not open to the public. **Holdings:** 500 books; 10,000 bound periodical volumes; reports; manuscripts. **Subscriptions:** 20 journals and other serials.

10294 ■ Kansas Department of Transportation (KDOT) - Library
Dwight D. Eisenhower State Office Building 700 SW
  Harrison St.
  Topeka, KS 66603-3745

Ph: (785)296-3566
Fax: (785)368-7415
Co. E-mail: kdot#publicinfo@ks.gov
URL: http://www.ksdot.gov
Contact: Bob Brock, Director
Facebook: www.facebook.com/KSDOTHQ
X (Twitter): x.com/KDOTHQ
YouTube: www.youtube.com/user/kansastransportation
Pinterest: www.pinterest.com/kdothq
Description: Transportation: Local and suburban transit. **Scope:** Transportation. **Founded:** 1868. **Holdings:** Figures not available.

10295 ■ Missouri Department of Transportation-Division of Materials Library
Rm. 200 600 W Main St.
  Jefferson City, MO 65101
URL: http://www.modot.org
Scope: Transportation. **Services:** Library not open to the public. **Holdings:** Figures not available.

10296 ■ Montana Department of Transportation (MDT)
2701 Prospect Ave.
  Helena, MT 59601
Ph: (406)444-6200
Co. E-mail: mdtcommteam@mt.gov
Facebook: www.facebook.com/montanadot
Linkedin: www.linkedin.com/company/montana-department-of-transportation
Instagram: www.instagram.com/mtdot
YouTube: www.youtube.com/user/MontanaDOT
Description: Mission is to serve the public by providing a transportation system and services that emphasize quality, safety, cost effectiveness, economic vitality, and sensitivity to the environment. **Scope:** Transportation. **Services:** Interlibrary loan; copying. **Founded:** 1913. **Holdings:** 20,000 titles.

10297 ■ New Jersey Department of Transportation Research Library (NJDOT)
c/o David J. Goldberg Transportation Complex
  1035 Pky., Ave.
  Trenton, NJ 08625
Ph: (609)963-1982
URL: http://www.nj.gov/transportation/business/research/library
Contact: David J. Goldberg, Contact
Scope: Transportation. **Services:** Interlibrary loan; copying; library open to the public by appointment. **Founded:** 1962. **Holdings:** 300 books; 11,000 reports.

10298 ■ North Dakota Department of Transportation - Materials and Research Division - Library
608 East Blvd. Ave.
  Bismarck, ND 58505-0700
URL: http://www.dot.nd.gov/divisions/materials/materials.htm
Facebook: www.facebook.com/nddot
X (Twitter): x.com/NorthDakotaDOT
YouTube: www.youtube.com/user/NDDOTOnline
Description: Integral unit of North Dakota Department of Transportation. **Scope:** Transportation. **Services:** Library not open to the public. **Founded:** 1970. **Holdings:** 6,600 reports.

10299 ■ South Carolina Department of Transportation (SCDOT) - Library
955 Pk. St.
  Columbia, SC 29201-3959
Ph: (803)737-1200
Free: 855-467-2368
URL: http://www.scdot.org
Facebook: www.facebook.com/SCDOT
X (Twitter): x.com/SCDOTPress
YouTube: www.youtube.com/user/SCDOTconnectoronline
Scope: Transportation. **Founded:** 1998. **Holdings:** Figures not available.

10300 ■ University of Kentucky College of Engineering - Kentucky Transportation Center (KTC) - Library
176 Oliver H Raymond Bldg.
  Lexington, KY 40506
Ph: (859)257-4513
URL: http://ktc.uky.edu
URL(s): www.engr.uky.edu/research-faculty/departments/civil-engineering/kentucky-transportation-center
Facebook: www.facebook.com/KYTRANSPORTATION
Linkedin: www.linkedin.com/company/ktc-uky
X (Twitter): x.com/kytransport
YouTube: www.youtube.com/channel/UCCkzZxbfj-2ZzMKYgH6Jn5Q
Description: Integral unit of College of Engineering, University of Kentucky, operating under its own board of control. Offers technology transfer program, including transportation workshops, audiovisual and library materials, mail lists, and technical assistance. **Scope:** Highways; bridges; the environment; geotechnology; Intelligent Transportation Systems (ITS); pavements; traffic and safety; structures; construction management; transportation policy, planning, and finance. **Services:** Interlibrary loan; copying; library open to the public. **Founded:** 1981. **Holdings:** Books; Reports; Videotapes. **Subscriptions:** 300 journals and other serials. **Publications:** *The Link Technology Transfer Newsletter.* **Educational Activities:** Annual Transportation Forum, Cosponsored with the Advanced Institute for Transportation Systems Science.

ASSOCIATIONS AND OTHER ORGANIZATIONS

10301 ■ American Apparel and Footwear Association (AAFA)
740 6th St., NW
  Washington, DC 20001
Ph: (202)853-9080
Co. E-mail: membership@aafaglobal.org
URL: http://www.aafaglobal.org
Contact: Stephen Lamar, President
E-mail: slamar@apparelandfootwear.org
Facebook: www.facebook.com/apparelandfootwear
Linkedin: www.linkedin.com/company/aafa
X (Twitter): x.com/apparelfootwear
Instagram: www.instagram.com/apparelandfootwear
YouTube: www.youtube.com/user/apparelandfoo
  twear

Description: Manufacturers of infants', children's, boys', girls', juniors', men's, and women's wearing apparel; associate members are suppliers of fabrics, equipment, accessories, and services to the apparel industry. Operates the Apparel Foundation; offers placement service through newsletter. **Founded:** 2000. **Publications:** *AAFA Directory of Members and Associate Members* (Annual); *Technical Advisory Committee Bulletin* (Periodic); *SoleSource: The Footwear Industry Directory* (Annual); *SoleSource: The footwear industry reservice directory* (Annual). **Geographic Preference:** National.

REFERENCE WORKS

10302 ■ "The Bottom Line" in Retail Merchandiser (Vol. 51, July-August 2011, No. 4, pp. 60)
Description: Hanky Panky believes that comfort and style don't have to be mutually exclusive when designing their line of intimate apparel for women. The lingerie retailer was launched in 1977. **Availability:** Print; PDF; Online.

10303 ■ "Empreinte Enters the Activewear Market with IN-PULSE" in The Lingerie Journal (November 5, 2019)
URL(s): thelingeriejournal.com/empreinte-enters-the
-activewear-market-with-in-pulse/
Ed: Estelle Puleston. **Released:** November 05, 2019.
Description: French lingerie brand Empreinte launched its first activewear line, IN-PULSE to meet demand of women who want function and fashion in the undergarments. **Availability:** Online.

10304 ■ "Pink Label: Victoria's Sales Secret" in Advertising Age (Vol. 79, July 7, 2008, No. 26, pp. 4)
Pub: Crain Communications, Inc.
Contact: Jessica Botos, Manager, Marketing
E-mail: jessica.botos@crainsnewyork.com
Ed: Natalie Zmuda. **Description:** Victoria Secret's Pink label accounted for roughly 17 percent of the retailer's total sales last year. The company is launching a Collegiate Collection which will be promoted by a campus tour program. **Availability:** Print; Online.

10305 ■ "The Rise, Fall, and Comeback of Victoria's Secret, America's Biggest Lingerie Retailer" in Business Insider (June 17, 2021)
Ed: Mary Hanbury. **Released:** June 17, 2021.
Description: Details the rise of Victoria's Secret in the 1990s and how the company lost relevance over the decades. The company is poised to make a comeback, but it may not be easy with so many other companies taking up market share. **Availability:** Online.

10306 ■ "This Local Lingerie Shop Donated Thousands of Bras to Harvey Victims" in Houstonia (December 25, 2017)
URL(s): www.houstoniamag.com/articles/2017/12/25/
top-drawer-harvey
Ed: Brittanie Shey. **Released:** December 25, 2017.
Description: Top Drawer Lingerie donated more than $200,000 worth of new bras to more than 5,000 people in need after the devastation of Hurriacane Harvey. Owner Dow Hickman had been stockpiling undergarments to donate to Dress for Success, but saw the immediate need after the hurricane hit the area and partnered with I Support the Girls to get these donations to those who needed it. **Availability:** Online.

SOURCES OF SUPPLY

10307 ■ Canadian Apparel Directory
Canadian Apparel Federation
Contact: Flora Kodl, Contact
URL(s): www.apparel.ca/directories.html
Description: Publication includes lists of Canadian industry suppliers, and manufacturers of apparel. **Entries include:** Company name, address, phone, fax, names and titles of key personnel, name and title of contact, product/service, description of company business activities. **Arrangement:** Alphabetical. **Indexes:** Trade name, product/service, geographical. **Availability:** Print; Online.

STATISTICAL SOURCES

10308 ■ Lingerie, Swimwear & Bridal Stores Industry in the US - Market Research Report
URL(s): www.ibisworld.com/united-states/market-re-
search-reports/lingerie-swimwear-bridal-stores-in
dustry/
Price: $925. **Description:** Downloadable report analyzing the current and future trends in the lingerie, swimwear, and bridal store industries. **Availability:** Download.

TRADE SHOWS AND CONVENTIONS

10309 ■ Trendz Show
Florida Fashion Focus, Inc.
URL(s): www.trendzshow.com/show-dates
Frequency: Irregular. **Description:** Ladies ready-to-wear clothing, handbags, jewelry, and accessories. Order-writing for future delivery. **Audience:** Industry professionals. **Principal Exhibits:** Ladies ready-to-wear clothing, handbags, jewelry, and accessories. Order-writing for future delivery. Dates and Locations: Palm Beach County Convention Center, Palm Beach, FL.

ASSOCIATIONS AND OTHER ORGANIZATIONS

10310 ■ American Beverage Licensees (ABL)
5101 River Rd., Ste. 108
 Bethesda, MD 20816-1560
Ph: (301)656-1494
Fax: (301)656-7539
Co. E-mail: info@ablusa.org
URL: http://ablusa.org
Contact: John D. Bodnovich, Executive Director
E-mail: bodnovich@ablusa.org
Facebook: www.facebook.com/ABLUSA
X (Twitter): x.com/ablusa
Description: Federation of associations of alcohol beverage retailers. **Publications:** *ABL Leader* (Monthly); *Alcohol Beverage Legislative Council Bulletin* (Periodic); *National Licensed Beverage Association--Members Directory; NLBA News.* **Educational Activities:** American Beverage Licensees Conference (Annual). **Awards:** ABL Top Shelf Award. **Geographic Preference:** National.

10311 ■ National Association of Beverage Importers Inc. (NABI)
National Press Bldg.
 529 14th St. NW, Ste. 1300
 Washington, DC 20045
Ph: (202)393-6224
URL: http://www.bevimporters.org
Contact: Robert M. Tobiassen, President
Facebook: www.facebook.com/National-Association
 -Of-Beverage-Importers-Inc-528207333909022
Linkedin: www.linkedin.com/company/national
 -association-of-beverage-importers-inc-
X (Twitter): x.com/bevimporters
Description: Represents importers of alcoholic beverages. Compiles and reports statistics from Bureau of Census and Internal Revenue sources. **Founded:** 1999. **Publications:** *Statistics and Member Letter* (Periodic). **Geographic Preference:** National.

10312 ■ National Beer Wholesalers Association (NBWA)
1101 King St., Ste. 600
 Alexandria, VA 22314-2944
Ph: (703)683-4300
Free: 800-300-6417
Fax: (703)683-8965
Co. E-mail: info@nbwa.org
URL: http://www.nbwa.org
Contact: Craig Purser, President
Facebook: www.facebook.com/NBWABeer
Linkedin: www.linkedin.com/company/national-beer
 -wholesalers-association
X (Twitter): x.com/NBWA
Instagram: www.instagram.com/followyourbeer
YouTube: www.youtube.com/user/NBWABeer
Description: Independent wholesalers of malt beverages and affiliates of the malt beverage industry. Conducts specialized education programs. **Founded:** 1938. **Publications:** *NBWA Beer Perspectives*

(Biweekly). **Educational Activities:** SPE Middle East Oil & Gas Show & Conference (MEOS) (Annual); NBWA Annual Convention & Trade show. **Geographic Preference:** National.

10313 ■ Wine and Spirits Wholesalers of America (WSWA)
805 15th St. NW, Ste. 1120
 Washington, DC 20005
Ph: (202)371-9792
Fax: (202)789-2405
Co. E-mail: info@wswa.org
URL: http://www.wswa.org
Contact: Michelle L. Korsmo, President
Facebook: www.facebook.com/wswa
Linkedin: www.linkedin.com/company/wine-&-spirits
 -wholesalers-of-america
X (Twitter): x.com/wswamedia
YouTube: www.youtube.com/user/
 wswaannualconvention
Description: Represents wholesale distributors of domestic and imported wine and distilled spirits. **Founded:** 1943. **Publications:** *Wine and Spirits Wholesalers of America--Membership Roster and Industry Directory; Upfront* (Monthly); *WSWA Member Roster and Industry Directory.* **Educational Activities:** WSWA Annual Convention & Exposition (Annual). **Geographic Preference:** National.

REFERENCE WORKS

10314 ■ "Actian, Data Transformed and Yellowfin BI Mashup Helps Kollaras Group Reap Big Data Rewards" in Computer Business Week (August 28, 2014, pp. 22)
Pub: NewsRX LLC.
Contact: Kalani Rosell, Contact
Description: Actian announced that Australian liquor, hospitality and property investment company, Kollaras Group can now access real-time analytics; fast, simple and accurate data warehousing; and Yellowfin's Business Intelligence (BI) platform is examined. The BI provides better insights and decision-making across diverse business units. **Availability:** Online.

10315 ■ "Amazon's Booze Business in Jeopardy with Investigation into Fake LA Liquor Store" in Vinepair (August 20, 2019)
URL(s): vinepair.com/booze-news/amazons-fake-la
 -liquor-store/
Ed: Tim McKirdy. **Released:** August 20, 2019.
Description: The California Department of Alcoholic Beverage Control has opened an investigation into Amazon for not maintaining a physical liquor store in the state, thus violating its liquor license requirements. **Availability:** Online.

10316 ■ "Canadian Wine to Ship Across Provincial Borders: Let the Wine Flow Freely. Feds To Allow Shipments Inside Canada" in Canadian Business (Vol. 85, August 13, 2012, No. 13, pp. 8)
Ed: Sarah Barmak. **Description:** The passage of federal Bill C-311 is anticipated to remove restriction on interprovincial wine trade imposed under the

Importation of Intoxicating Liquors Act of 1928. There are claims that legalizing direct-to-consumer selling will not affect liquor store sales. **Availability:** Print; Online.

10317 ■ "Day-Care Center Owner to Argue Against Liquor Store Opening Nearby" in Chicago Tribune (March 13, 2008)
Pub: Tribune News Service
Contact: Jack Barry, Vice President, Operations
E-mail: jbarry@tribpub.com
Ed: Matthew Walberg. **Description:** NDLC's owner feels that Greenwood Liquors should not be granted its liquor license due to the claim that the NDLC is not only a day-care center but also a school that employs state-certified teachers. **Availability:** Print; Online.

10318 ■ "Discount Beers Take Fizz Out Of Molson" in Globe & Mail (February 10, 2006, pp. B3)
Description: The reasons behind the decline in profits by 60 percent for Molson Coors Brewing Co., during fourth quarter 2005, are presented. **Availability:** Online.

10319 ■ "Executive Decision: Damn the Profit Margins, Sleeman Declares War on Buck-a-Beer Foes" in Globe & Mail (January 28, 2006, pp. B3)
Description: The cost savings plans of chief executive officer John Sleeman of Sleeman Breweries Ltd. are presented. **Availability:** Online.

10320 ■ "Family Dollar Plans to Sell Alcohol at 1,000 Stores" in The New York Times (June 1, 2019)
URL(s): www.nytimes.com/2019/06/01/business/fam
 ily-dollar-tree-alcohol.html
Ed: Derrick Bryson Taylor. **Released:** June 01, 2019.
Description: Dollar Tree, the owner of Family Dollar, announced it will sell alcohol in 1,000 select stores across the nation. This is after a test run of 45 stores was completed and found to be successful. **Availability:** Online.

10321 ■ "First Venture Reports Proprietary Yeasts Further Reduce Ethyl Carbamate in Sake" in Canadian Corporate News (May 16, 2007)
Description: First Ventures Technologies Corp., a biotechnology company that develops and commercializes advanced yeast products, confirmed that two of their proprietary yeasts used in the making of sake have yielded reductions in ethyl carbamate compared to previous sake brewing trials.

10322 ■ "Hike in Md.'s Alcohol Tax May Be Hard For Lawmakers to Swallow" in Baltimore Business Journal (Vol. 28, November 19, 2010, No. 28)
Pub: Baltimore Business Journal
Contact: Rhonda Pringle, President
E-mail: rpringle@bizjournals.com

Ed: Emily Mullin. **Description:** Maryland's General Assembly has been reluctant to support a dime-per-drink increase in alcohol tax that was drafted in the 2009 bill if the tax revenue goes into a separate fund. The alcohol tax increase is considered unnecessary by some lawmakers and business leaders due to impending federal spending boosts. **Availability:** Print; Online.

10323 ■ *"Homes, Not Bars, Stay Well Tended" in Advertising Age (Vol. 79, January 28, 2008, No. 4, pp. 8)*
Pub: Crain Communications, Inc.
Contact: Jessica Botos, Manager, Marketing
E-mail: jessica.botos@crainsnewyork.com
Ed: Jeremy Mullman. **Description:** Due to the downturn in the economy, consumers are drinking less at bars and restaurants; however, according to the Distilled Spirits Council of the United States, they are still purchasing expensive liquor to keep in their homes. **Availability:** Online.

10324 ■ *"Imports Frothing Up Beer Market" in Globe & Mail (February 16, 2006, pp. B4)*
Ed: Andy Hoffman. **Description:** The reasons behind the rise in market share of beer imports, in Canada, are presented. **Availability:** Online.

10325 ■ *"Labatt to Swallow Lakeport" in Globe & Mail (February 2, 2007, pp. B1)*
Ed: Keith McArthur. **Description:** The decision of Labatt Brewing Company Ltd. to acquire Lakeport Brewing Income Fund for $201.4 million is discussed. **Availability:** Print; Online.

10326 ■ *"Law Firms Cash In On Alcohol" in Business Journal Portland (Vol. 27, November 19, 2010, No. 38, pp. 1)*
Pub: Portland Business Journal
Contact: Andy Giegerich, Managing Editor
E-mail: agiegerich@bizjournals.com
Ed: Andy Giegerich. **Description:** Oregon-based law firms have continued to corner big business on the state's growing alcohol industry as demand for their services increased. Lawyers, who represent wine, beer and liquor distillery interests, have seen their workload increased by 20 to 30 percent in 2009. **Availability:** Print; Online.

10327 ■ *"Liquor-Sales Issue in Kansas Creates Strange Bedfellows" in Wichita Business Journal (Vol. 27, February 10, 2012, No. 6, pp. 1)*
Pub: Baltimore Business Journal
Contact: Rhonda Pringle, President
E-mail: rpringle@bizjournals.com
Description: How the business community in Kansas has reacted to House Bill 2532, a legislation that would alter the way liquor is sold in the state, is presented. Under the legislation, groceries and convenience stores would be allowed to get licenses to sell liquor, wine and full-strength beer. On the other hand, liquor stores would be permitted to sell other products on the premises. **Availability:** Print; Online.

10328 ■ *"Liquor Stores Feeling Financial Impact Six Months after Grocery Stores Allowed to Sell Wine on Sundays" in wsmv.com (June 26, 2019)*
URL(s): www.wsmv.com/news/liquor-stores-feeling -financial-impact-six-months-after-grocery-stores/ar ticle_89c13f36-987f-11e9-bb72-8f7b70b01ee4.html
Ed: Cameron Taylor. **Released:** June 26, 2019. **Description:** Six months after a new Tennessee law went info effect allowing grocery stores to sell liquor on Sundays, local liquor stores noticed they are losing profits. Since it's easier to pick up alcohol while doing grocery shopping, there is no longer an incentive to visit the liquor store and make a purchase. **Availability:** Online.

10329 ■ *"Liquor Stores Sips on Growth Cocktail" in Globe & Mail (February 6, 2006, pp. B5)*
Description: The business growth plans of Liquor Stores Income Fund are presented. **Availability:** Online.

10330 ■ *"Little Cheer in Holiday Forecast for Champagne" in Advertising Age (Vol. 88, November 17, 2008, No. 43, pp. 6)*
Pub: Crain Communications, Inc.
Contact: Jessica Botos, Manager, Marketing
E-mail: jessica.botos@crainsnewyork.com
Ed: Jeremy Mullman. **Description:** Due to a weak economy that has forced consumers to trade down from the most expensive alcoholic beverages as well as a weak U.S. dollar that has driven already lofty Champagne prices higher, makers of the French sparkling wine are anticipating a brutally slow holiday season. **Availability:** Online.

10331 ■ *"Mazel Tov: L'Chaim Gets a Deal to Expand with Southern Wine" in South Florida Business Journal (Vol. 33, September 7, 2012, No. 6, pp. 1)*
Pub: Baltimore Business Journal
Contact: Rhonda Pringle, President
E-mail: rpringle@bizjournals.com
Description: L'Chaim Kosher Vodka could triple its sales in 2012. The company won a deal to expand with Southern Wine and Spirits, which is the largest distributor of wine and spirits in the United States. The Distilled Spirits Council of the United States reported that vodka drives 31 percent of all spirit sales.

10332 ■ *"MillerCoors Needs the Quickie Mart" in Crain's Chicago Business (Vol. 32, November 16, 2009, No. 46, pp. 2)*
Pub: Crain Communications Inc.
Contact: Barry Asin, President
Ed: David Sterrett. **Description:** Power Marts convenience store owner Sam Odeh says that Chicago-based MillerCoors LLC has done a poor job at promoting its brand, keeping its signs up to date and stocking the shelves at his stores. He complains that the company's service has been awful and the marketing pathetic. Convenience stores accounted for more than $14 billion in beer sales in the past year. **Availability:** Online.

10333 ■ *"Online Alcohol Purchasing Comes of Age" in Supermarket News (September 16, 2021)*
Ed: Amber Roberts. **Released:** September 16, 2021. **Description:** The demand for online alcohol sales increases during the COVID-19 pandemic, so more traditional brick-and-mortar stores are beginning to add online sales. However, regulations are often strict, which has led to online delivery platform companies dominating the industry.

10334 ■ *"Strange Brew" in Canadian Business (Vol. 85, June 11, 2012, No. 10, pp. 52)*
Ed: Paul Brent. **Description:** Molson Coors is launching the Coors Light Iced T beer in summer 2012 as part of its effort to improve weak sales in North America. The new product is aimed at female drinkers and is part of an effort to win back sales from wine and spirits. **Availability:** Print; Online.

10335 ■ *"Texas Legislature Green-Lights Bigger Liquor Chains, but Still Excludes the Biggest Retailer, Walmart" in Dallas News (May 28, 2019)*
URL(s): www.dallasnews.com/business/retail/2019/0 5/28/texas-legislature-green-lights-bigger-liquor -chains-but-still-excludes-the-biggest-retailer -walmart/

Ed: Maria Halkias. **Released:** May 28, 2019. **Description:** A new bill in Texas is closing some liquor law loopholes, but is still denying publicly traded companies like Walmart, Costco, Walgreens, and Kroger from selling liquor in Texas. **Availability:** Online.

10336 ■ *"Utah Liquor Stores to Pour Cases of Beer Down the Drain" in U.S. News & World Report (October 24, 2019)*
URL(s): www.usnews.com/news/best-states/utah/ar ticles/2019-10-24/utah-liquor-stores-to-pour-cases -of-beer-down-the-drain
Released: October 24, 2019. **Description:** Due to a new law in Utah where beer must be 4% alcohol by volume (ABV) or less, liquor stores announced plans to pour any beer higher than that down the drain if they don't sell by October 31. **Availability:** Online.

STATISTICAL SOURCES

10337 ■ *Online Beer, Wine & Liquor Sales Industry in the US - Market Research Report*
URL(s): www.ibisworld.com/united-states/market-re search-reports/online-beer-wine-liquor-sales-indus try/
Price: $925. **Description:** Downloadable report analyzing the online beer, wine, and liquor retail industry. **Availability:** Online.

10338 ■ *RMA Annual Statement Studies*
Pub: Risk Management Association
Contact: Nancy Foster, President
Released: Annual. **Description:** Contains composite balance sheets and income statements for more than 360 industries, including the accounting, auditing, and bookkeeping industries. Also contains five years of comparative historical data for discerning trends. Includes 16 commonly used ratios, computed for most of the size groupings for nearly every industry.

10339 ■ *US Alcoholic Beverages Online Market Report 2021*
URL(s): store.mintel.com/report/us-alcoholic-bever ages-online-market-report
Price: $4,366.35. **Description:** When the Covid-19 pandemic hit, online alcoholic beverage sales went up, due to people not wanting to shop instore. This downloadable report covers the reasons online sources are used to purchase alcohol, barriers to doing so, and consumer behavior trends. Included are an executive summary, interactive databook, PowerPoint presentation, infographic overview, report PDF, and previous years data. **Availability:** PDF.

TRADE PERIODICALS

10340 ■ *Modern Brewery Age*
Contact: Peter V.K. Reid, Publisher
E-mail: pete@breweryage.com
Released: Bimonthly **Price:** $95, U.S. and other countries 52 PDF weekly tabloids via email & delivery of quarterly magazine. **Description:** Magazine for the wholesale and brewing industry. **Availability:** Print; Online.

FRANCHISES AND BUSINESS OPPORTUNITIES

10341 ■ **Sculpture Hospitality**
601-505 Consumers Rd.
Toronto, ON, Canada M2J 4V8
Ph: (512)572-6123
Free: 888-238-4626
Co. E-mail: info@sculpturehospitality.com
URL: http://www.sculpturehospitality.com
Contact: Vanessa De Caria, President
Facebook: www.facebook.com/sculpturehospitality
Linkedin: www.linkedin.com/company/sculpturehospi tality

X (Twitter): x.com/sculptureHQ

Instagram: www.instagram.com/sculpture.hospitality

YouTube: www.youtube.com/channel/UCMzz
  -FD7WmK2W4FGI41O-BQ

Description: Firm provides technology solutions and services to bar and restaurant operators. **Founded:** 1987. **Financial Assistance:** Yes **Training:** 7 days corporate training in Toronto, 5-10 days regional training with state master franchise.

INTERNET DATABASES

10342 ■ *Alcoholic Beverage Industry*

URL(s): guides.loc.gov/alcoholic-beverage-industry

Description: A guide on the various alcoholic beverages made and sold in the United States. Contains market information and trade literature. Also includes a section on the Temperance Movement and Prohibition. **Availability:** Online.

LIBRARIES

10343 ■ Distilled Spirits Council of the United States (DISCUS)

101 Constitution Ave., NW, Ste. 350 W
  Washington, DC 20001

Ph: (202)628-3544

Co. E-mail: membership@distilledspirits.org

URL: http://www.distilledspirits.org

Contact: Chris R. Swonger, President

Facebook: www.facebook.com/DistilledSpiri
  tsCouncilUS

X (Twitter): x.com/DistilledSpirit

Description: Producers and marketers of distilled spirits sold in the U.S. Provides statistical and legal data for industry and the public and serves as public information source; conducts educational programs. **Founded:** 1973. **Publications:** *Distilled Spirit, Wine and Beer Directories* (Biennial); *Summary of State Laws and Regulations Relating to Distilled Spirits.* **Geographic Preference:** National.

ASSOCIATIONS AND OTHER ORGANIZATIONS

10344 ■ The Association of American Literary Agents (AAR)
50 Broad St., Ste. 1609
New York, NY 10004
Co. E-mail: administrator@aaronline.org
URL: http://aalitagents.org
Contact: Regina Brooks, President
X (Twitter): x.com/aalitagents

Description: Association of professional literary and dramatic agents. **Founded:** 1991. **Publications:** *The Literary Agent.* **Geographic Preference:** National.

10345 ■ Association of Talent Agents (ATA)
3019 Ocean Pk. Blvd., Ste. 344
Santa Monica, CA 90405
Ph: (310)274-0628
URL: http://www.agentassociation.com
Contact: Rita Vennari, President

Description: Employs legal counsel to prepare opinions upon request and to file briefs in arbitrations and labor commission hearings. Maintains liaison with labor commission representatives in San Francisco and Los Angeles, CA, and intervenes on behalf of individual members having special problems. Conducts seminars and symposia. **Founded:** 1937. **Publications:** *Employment Law.* **Geographic Preference:** National.

10346 ■ National Association of Independent Publishers Representatives (NAIPR)
450 Seventh Ave.
New York, NY 10123
Contact: Steven M. Sack, Contact

Description: Promotes the welfare and interests of its members. Educates publishers to the advantages of independent sales representation. Fosters closer relationships among publishers, wholesalers, sales representatives and booksellers. Exchanges information, ideas, plans and programs helpful to the members. Educates the publishing community at large about sales issues and practices related to field sales promotion and independent bookselling. **Founded:** 1989. **Geographic Preference:** National.

REFERENCE WORKS

10347 ■ *"$400M Fiction Giant Wattpad Wants to Be Your Literary Agent" in Forbes (September 24, 2018)*
URL(s): www.forbes.com/sites/hayleycuccinello/20
18/09/24/400m-fiction-giant-wattpad-wants-to-be
-your-literary-agent/#4d0e3752aaeb

Ed: Hayley C. Cuccinello. **Released:** September 24, 2018. **Description:** Writing platform Wattpad allows writers to post their stories for their 65 million active readers, and now its branching out by brokering deals with its writers to mainstream publishers. The mobile app is very popular with consumers seeking online reading and writing and by acting as an intermediary, they can increase profits by charging a standard literary agent fee. **Availability:** Online.

10348 ■ *International Literary Market Place: The Directory of the International Book Publishing Industry*
Pub: Information Today Inc.
Contact: Thomas H. Hogan, President
URL(s): store.infotoday.com/product/literary-marke
t-place

Released: Latest edition 84th edition, 2024. **Price:** $539.50, for outside North America; $507.50, Single issue; $529.50, Canada and Mexico. **Description:** Covers over 10,500 publishers in over 180 countries outside the United States and Canada, and about 1,499 trade and professional organizations related to publishing abroad; includes major printers, binders, typesetters, book manufacturers, book dealers, libraries, literary agencies, translators, book clubs, reference books and journals, periodicals, prizes, and international reference section. **Entries include:** For publishers--Name, address, phone, fax, telex, names and titles of key personnel, branches, type of publications, subjects, ISBN prefix. Listings for others include similar information but less detail. **Arrangement:** Classified by business activities, then geographical. **Indexes:** Company name, subject, type of publication. **Availability:** Print; Online.

TRADE PERIODICALS

10349 ■ *Publishers Weekly: The International voice for Book Publishing and Bookselling*
Pub: Publishers Weekly
Contact: George Slowik, Jr., President
URL(s): www.publishersweekly.com/pw/corp/aboutus
.html
Facebook: www.facebook.com/pubweekly
Linkedin: www.linkedin.com/company/publishers
-weekly
X (Twitter): x.com/PublishersWkly
Instagram: www.instagram.com/pwpics

Ed: Michael Coffey. **Released:** Weekly **Price:** $199, for print and online; $169, for online and digital; $9.99, for back issues; $15, for online and digital monthly; $20, for print and online monthly. **Description:** Magazine for publishers. **Availability:** Print; Online.

ASSOCIATIONS AND OTHER ORGANIZATIONS

10350 ■ ALOA Security Professionals Association, Inc. (ALOA) - Video Library
1408 N Riverfront Blvd., Ste. 303
  Dallas, TX 75207
Ph: (214)819-9733
Free: 800-532-2562
Fax: (214)819-9736
Co. E-mail: education@aloa.org
URL: http://www.aloa.org
Contact: Bill Mandelbaum, President
Facebook: www.facebook.com/ALOA.org
Description: Retail locksmiths; manufacturers and distributors of locks, keys, safes, and burglar alarms. Provides current information to individuals in the physical security industry. Maintains information and referral services for members; offers insurance and bonding programs. **Scope:** Locksmiths; Security and technical standards. **Founded:** 1955. **Holdings:** Videotapes. **Publications:** *Keynotes* (Monthly); *Associated Locksmiths of America--Membership Directory.* **Educational Activities:** ALOA Convention and Security Expo; ALOA Security Expo; Associated Locksmiths of America Convention (Annual). **Awards:** ALOA Scholarship Foundation (Annual). **Geographic Preference:** National; Local.

10351 ■ Institutional Locksmiths' Association (ILA)
PO Box 84
  Butler, MD 21023
URL: http://www.ilanational.org
Contact: John Hubel, Chairman
Description: Promotes the goals of its member. Sponsors educational programs. **Founded:** 1983. **Geographic Preference:** National.

10352 ■ Lock Museum of America (LMA) - Lock Museum of America
230 Main St.
  Terryville, CT 06786
Ph: (860)480-4408
Co. E-mail: tlockmuseum@gmail.com
URL: http://www.lockmuseumofamerica.org
Description: Locksmiths, lock collectors, lock and key manufacturers, and builders. Seeks to preserve and exhibit the colonial American craft of lock, key, and security device making. Maintains hall of fame and museum. **Scope:** Locks, keys, ornate hardware. **Founded:** 1972. **Holdings:** 1,000 locks, keys; safe locks, door locks, padlocks, handcuffs. **Publications:** *Newsletter and Historical Research Series* (Quarterly). **Educational Activities:** Antique Lock Collectors Show (Annual). **Geographic Preference:** National.

10353 ■ Security Hardware Distributors Association (SHDA)
National Press Blg., 529 14th St. NW, Ste. 1280
  Washington, DC 20045
Ph: (410)940-6346
Co. E-mail: info@shda.org
URL: http://www.shda.org/aws/SHDA/pt/sp/home_page
Contact: Robert Justen, President
Facebook: www.facebook.com/shda.org
Linkedin: www.linkedin.com/company/shda
YouTube: www.youtube.com/channel/UCxXvKbeihh7RdtJ4dmpupNw
Description: Wholesalers of locksmith supplies; associate members are manufacturers of locks and locksmith supplies. **Founded:** 1970. **Publications:** *SHDA Unlocked.* **Educational Activities:** University of Innovative Distribution (Annual); Security Hardware Distributors Association Conference. **Geographic Preference:** National.

REFERENCE WORKS

10354 ■ "Eye in the Sky: A Look at Security Tech from All Angles" in Bellingtham Business Journal (October 2008, pp. 23)
Ed: Lance Henderson. **Description:** High tech solutions to security issues in any company are not the only things to be considered; a low-tech evaluation of a building and its security fixtures, such as door knobs, locks, doors and windows as well as lighting are important aspects to security any office. **Availability:** Print; Online.

10355 ■ "Smart Locks, Home Surveillance Change Locksmith Trade" in U.S. News & World Report (June 22, 2019)
URL(s): www.usnews.com/news/best-states/pennsylvania/articles/2019-06-22/smart-locks-home-surveillance-change-locksmith-trade
Ed: Andrew Kulp. **Released:** June 22, 2019. **Description:** The locksmith trade isn't all about just locks and keys. Electronics and new technology play a large role in home security industry, and locksmiths have had to retrain and learn new techniques. Chip keys for cars led the way down this new path and locksmiths had to adjust their trade and nowadays, they need to be savvy in the field of smart locks for homes and businesses. **Availability:** Online.

10356 ■ "Vandal-Resistant Mortise Locks" in Building Design and Construction (Vol. 49, September 1, 2008, No. 12, pp. 78)
Description: Stanley Security Solutions offers mortise locks with a vandal-resistant feature that includes a clutch mechanism designed to break away when excessive force is applied either by kicking or standing on the lever. Once the mortise lock breaks away it can be easily reset to its original position without sustaining damage. **Availability:** Print; Online.

TRADE PERIODICALS

10357 ■ American Lock Collectors Association
Pub: American Lock Collectors Association
Contact: Robert Dix, President
E-mail: dixlock@aol.com
URL(s): alca.name/menu.htm
Description: Provides information on the collecting, history, buying, selling, and trading of antique and unusual locks, keys, handcuffs, and locking devices. Carries announcements and reports of collector shows. **Availability:** Print.

10358 ■ Keynotes
Pub: ALOA Security Professionals Association, Inc.
Contact: Bill Mandelbaum, President
URL(s): member.aloa.org/membersonly/keynotes/archives/archive.htm
Released: Monthly; except for combined January/February and July/August. **Price:** $25, Members. **Description:** Trade magazine for locksmiths and other security specialists. Provides technical information, management insights, educational resources, calendar of events in the industry, legislative reports, and association news. **Availability:** Print; PDF; Online; Download.

10359 ■ The National Locksmith
Contact: Greg Mango, Editor
URL(s): www.thenationallocksmith.com
Facebook: www.facebook.com/tnlmag
Ed: Greg Mango. **Released:** Monthly; 13/year. **Description:** Magazine focusing on physical security and locksmithing. **Availability:** Print; PDF; Online.

TRADE SHOWS AND CONVENTIONS

10360 ■ ALOA Security Expo
ALOA Security Professionals Association, Inc. (ALOA)
1408 N Riverfront Blvd., Ste. 303
  Dallas, TX 75207
Ph: (214)819-9733
Free: 800-532-2562
Fax: (214)819-9736
Co. E-mail: education@aloa.org
URL: http://www.aloa.org
Contact: Bill Mandelbaum, President
URL(s): aloa.org/convention/convention-aloa.html
Description: Physical security products, including: locks, safes, door hardware, alarms and related products and services. **Audience:** Retailers, wholesalers, manufacturers and locksmith/security professionals. **Principal Exhibits:** Physical security products, including: locks, safes, door hardware, alarms and related products and services.

FRANCHISES AND BUSINESS OPPORTUNITIES

10361 ■ Pop-A-Lock Franchise System
Lafayette, LA
Free: 800-767-2562
URL: http://www.popalock.com
Contact: Tony McKeon, President
Facebook: www.facebook.com/popalock

Linkedin: www.linkedin.com/company/pop-a-lock
X (Twitter): x.com/popalock
Description: Mobile locksmith/car unlocking service. There is no build-out required with quick to market/revenue generation. Your employees provide our mobile tech services to commercial and residential customers and national accounts. **Founded:** 1991. **Training:** Offers new franchisee business training, employee advanced technical training including state-of-the-art dispatch service. Provides ongoing technical updates, public relations and marketing, business analysis, and National Accounts Support-mentor program.

LIBRARIES

10362 ■ Lock Museum of America (LMA) - Lock Museum of America
230 Main St.
  Terryville, CT 06786
Ph: (860)480-4408
Co. E-mail: tlockmuseum@gmail.com
URL: http://www.lockmuseumofamerica.org
Description: Locksmiths, lock collectors, lock and key manufacturers, and builders. Seeks to preserve and exhibit the colonial American craft of lock, key, and security device making. Maintains hall of fame and museum. **Scope:** Locks, keys, ornate hardware. **Founded:** 1972. **Holdings:** 1,000 locks, keys; safe locks, door locks, padlocks, handcuffs. **Publications:** *Newsletter and Historical Research Series* (Quarterly). **Educational Activities:** Antique Lock Collectors Show (Annual). **Geographic Preference:** National.

ASSOCIATIONS AND OTHER ORGANIZATIONS

10363 ■ National Luggage Dealers Association (NLDA) [NLDA Associates Inc.]
1817 Elmdale Ave.
 Glenview, IL 60026
Ph: (847)998-6869
Fax: (847)998-6884
Co. E-mail: inquiry@nlda.com
URL: http://www.luggagedealers.com
Description: Represents retailers of luggage, leather goods, gifts, and handbags. Buying group producing promotional materials. **Founded:** 1925. **Educational Activities:** Annual Summer Luggage, Gift and Travel Goods Show (Annual). **Geographic Preference:** National.

REFERENCE WORKS

10364 ■ "Fur Centre Stakes Former Byron Cade Spot in Clayton" in St. Louis Business Journal (Vol. 33, August 10, 2012, No. 51, pp. 1)
Pub: Baltimore Business Journal
Contact: Rhonda Pringle, President
E-mail: rpringle@bizjournals.com
Description: The Fur & Leather Centre is relocating from 601 S. Lindbergh Blvd. to the Byron Cade Building at 7901 Clayton Road in Saint Louis, Missouri. The store purchased the building for an undisclosed price, while its current lease is set to expire in March 2013. **Availability:** Print; Online.

10365 ■ "Handbag Revenues Climbing Back to Pre-pandemic Times" in WWD (October 6, 2021)
Ed: Misty White Sidell. **Released:** October 06, 2021. **Description:** As the COVID-19 pandemic has made consumers purchase only the necessities, after a few years people are starting to shop like their pre-pandemic selves. This includes treating themselves to luxury handbags and preparing for special occasions again.

10366 ■ "Is This the Suitcase of the Summer?" in The New York Times (August 28, 2018)
URL(s): www.nytimes.com/2018/08/28/style/away-sui tcases.html

Ed: Sheila Marikar. **Released:** August 28, 2018. **Description:** New, sleek, and colorful suitcases by Away are taking over the luggage industry. These cases have a hard-shell and built-in chargers, which celebrities have taken to. This is a fresh departure from the standard black and navy options, which consumers have embraced and are now enjoying a cult-like following. **Availability:** Online.

10367 ■ "Packing Chic" in Black Enterprise (Vol. 38, February 2008, No. 7, pp. 154)
Pub: Earl G. Graves Ltd.
Contact: Earl Graves, Jr., President

Ed: Sonia Alleyne. **Description:** Profile of Angela Theodora's leather overnight bags that offer a variety of smart compartments for the business traveler.

STATISTICAL SOURCES

10368 ■ Handbag, Luggage & Accessory Stores Industry in the US - Market Research Report
URL(s): www.ibisworld.com/united-states/market-re search-reports/handbag-luggage-accessory-stores -industry/
Price: $925. **Description:** Downloadable report analyzing the current and future trends in the handbag, luggage and accessory industry. **Availability:** Download.

10369 ■ RMA Annual Statement Studies
Pub: Risk Management Association
Contact: Nancy Foster, President

Released: Annual. **Description:** Contains composite balance sheets and income statements for more than 360 industries, including the accounting, auditing, and bookkeeping industries. Also contains five years of comparative historical data for discerning trends. Includes 16 commonly used ratios, computed for most of the size groupings for nearly every industry.

TRADE PERIODICALS

10370 ■ Travel Goods Showcase: Products & Trends for Travelers
Pub: Travel Goods Association
Contact: Robert Williams, President
URL(s): travelgoods.show/pages/magazine-options

Released: Quarterly **Description:** Magazine featuring domestic luggage, leather goods, and handbags. **Availability:** Print; Online; PDF.

TRADE SHOWS AND CONVENTIONS

10371 ■ The Travel Goods Show
Travel Goods Association (TGA)
 259 Nassau St., Ste.119
 Princeton, NJ 08542
Free: 877-842-1938
Fax: (877)842-1938
Co. E-mail: hello@travel-goods.org
URL: http://travel-goods.org
Contact: Robert Williams, President
URL(s): travelgoods.show

Frequency: Annual. **Description:** Exhibits relating to luggage and other travel goods. **Audience:** General public and trade professionals. **Principal Exhibits:** Exhibits relating to luggage and other travel goods. Dates and Locations: 2025 Mar 25-27 Las Vegas Convention Center, Las Vegas, NV. **Telecommunication Services:** hello@travel-goods.org.

FRANCHISES AND BUSINESS OPPORTUNITIES

10372 ■ Leather Medic
12901 Metro Pky.
 Fort Myers, FL 33966
Ph: (239)482-2027
Fax: (239)277-5715
Co. E-mail: support@leathermedic.com
URL: http://leathermedic.com
Contact: Chade Life, Founder
Facebook: www.facebook.com/LeatherMedic/timeline
X (Twitter): x.com/Leather_Medic
YouTube: www.youtube.com/user/LeatherMedicHQ

Description: Firm engages in automotive leather and vinyl repair, leather furniture repair and refinishing. **No. of Franchise Units:** 22. **Founded:** 1988. **Franchise Fee:** $49,500. **Financial Assistance:** Yes **Training:** Offers 2 weeks of one-on-one training.

ASSOCIATIONS AND OTHER ORGANIZATIONS

10373 ■ American Lumber Standard Committee, Incorporated (ALSC)
7470 New Technology Way, Ste. F
  Frederick, MD 21703
Ph: (301)972-1700
Fax: (301)540-8004
Co. E-mail: alsc@alsc.org
URL: http://www.alsc.org
Contact: D. E. Kretschmann, President
Description: Represents producers, consumers, and specifiers of softwood lumber. Establishes and maintains standards for size, grade, and other matters; elects an independent board of review to approve softwood lumber grading rules and accredits agencies that audit treating plants and agencies that audit pallet, box, and crate manufacturers for international trade. **Founded:** 1922. **Geographic Preference:** Multinational.

10374 ■ American Walnut Manufacturers Association (AWMA)
505 E State St.
  Jefferson City, MO 65101
Ph: (573)635-7877
Fax: (573)636-2591
URL: http://walnutassociation.org
Contact: Brian Brookshire, Executive Director
E-mail: brian@walnutassociation.org
Description: Manufacturers of hardwood veneer and lumber, especially American black walnut. Seeks to improve the sale of products made from hardwoods through advertising, promotion, sales education and product improvement; also promotes good forest management. **Founded:** 1912. **Geographic Preference:** National.

10375 ■ APA: The Engineered Wood Association - Resource Library
7011 S 19th St.
  Tacoma, WA 98466-5333
Ph: (253)565-6600
Fax: (253)565-7265
Co. E-mail: help@apawood.org
URL: http://www.apawood.org
Contact: Mark Tibbetts, President
Facebook: www.facebook.com/APAEngineeredWood
Linkedin: www.linkedin.com/company/apa---the-engineered-wood-association
X (Twitter): x.com/APAwood
YouTube: www.youtube.com/channel/UCWTANfghnStQCubPxXAFdkQ
Description: Manufacturers of structural panel products, oriented strand board and composites. Conducts trade promotion through advertising, publicity, merchandising, and field promotion. Maintains quality supervision in accordance with US. product standards, APA performance standards, and APA trademarking. **Scope:** Architects and building related technical studies. **Services:** Open to the public. **Founded:** 1933. **Holdings:** Videos; images; PDF files; webinars; photography. **Publications:** *Engineered Wood Journal* (Semiannual); *Management Report* (Monthly); *APA--Membership and Product Directory: Structural Panels and Engineered Wood Products*; *APA--The Engineered Wood Association-- Management Journal*. **Educational Activities:** Info Fair (Annual). **Awards:** APA Safety and Health Award (Annual). **Geographic Preference:** National.

10376 ■ Decorative Hardware Association (DHA) - Library
42777 Trade West Dr.
  Sterling, VA 20166
Ph: (703)435-2900
Fax: (703)435-2537
Co. E-mail: resources@decorativehardwoods.org
URL: http://www.decorativehardwoods.org
Contact: Keith Christman, President
E-mail: kchristman@decorativehardwoods.org
Facebook: www.facebook.com/DecorativeHardwoods
Linkedin: www.linkedin.com/company/decorativehardwoods
X (Twitter): x.com/DecHardwoods
Description: Manufacturers and finishers of hardwood plywood; manufacturers and sales agents of veneer; suppliers of glue, machinery, and other products related to the industry; stocking distributors. Conducts laboratory testing of plywood, adhesives, finishes, flame spread, formaldehyde emissions, structural, and smoke density. **Scope:** Manufacture and structure of hardwood plywood, veneer, glue bond, flame spread, finishes, and adhesives. Reviews federal and military specifications and foreign standards affecting hardwood plywood and laminated hardwood flooring. Provides in-plant inspection and verification. **Founded:** 1921. **Subscriptions:** 50 journals and other serials; 32 newspapers. **Publications:** *Directory of Veneer Manufacturers, Veneer Sales Representatives, Veneer Importers in the United States and Canada* (Annual); *Directory of Manufacturers of Marine Hardwood Plywood* (Annual); *Hardwood Plywood & E-News* (Semimonthly); *HPMA Testing and Inspection and Listed Products Manual* (Annual); *Where to Buy Hardwood Plywood and Veneer Directory* (Annual); *Veneer Manufacturers in the United States and Canada* (Annual); *Where to Buy Hardwood Plywood, Veneer, and Engineered Hardwood Flooring Buyers' Guide* (Annual); *Hardwood Plywood*; *Hardwood Plywood and Veneer News* (Monthly); *Where to Buy Hardwood Plywood, Veneer, and Engineered Hardwood Flooring Membership Directory* (Annual); *Associations and Organizations of Interest to Hardwood Plywood & Veneer Manufacturers* (Annual); *Magazines & Publications of Interest to Hardwood Plywood & Veneer Manufacturers* (Irregular); *Hardwood Plywood Manufacturers Association--Face Veneer Manufacturers List*. **Educational Activities:** Decorative Hardwoods Association (Annual); Grading Workshop (Daily). **Geographic Preference:** National.

10377 ■ Hardwood Distributor's Association (HDA)
PO Box 427
  High Point, NC 27261
Ph: (336)821-2933
Fax: (336)886-8865
Co. E-mail: info@hardwooddistributors.org
URL: http://www.hardwooddistributors.org
Facebook: www.facebook.com/HardwoodDistributors
Instagram: www.instagram.com/hardwooddistributors 2019
Pinterest: www.pinterest.com/hardwooddist
Description: Promotes the interests of Hardwood distributors. **Founded:** 1933. **Publications:** *The Yardstick* (3/year). **Geographic Preference:** National.

10378 ■ Hardwood Manufacturers Association (HMA)
1 Williamsburg Pl., Ste. 108
  Warrendale, PA 15086
Ph: (412)244-0440
Co. E-mail: info@hardwood.org
URL: http://www.hmamembers.org
Facebook: www.facebook.com/HardwoodManufacturersAssociation
Description: Represents manufacturers of hardwood lumber and hardwood products. Conducts national consumer promotion program. **Publications:** *HMA Link* (Monthly); *Hardwood Manufacturers Association--Membership Directory*; *Hardwood Manufacturers Association Buyers Guide*. **Educational Activities:** HMA National Conference & Expo (Annual). **Awards:** Robert B. Hendricks Memorial / Hardwood Manufacturers Association Scholarship (Annual). **Geographic Preference:** National.

10379 ■ International Wood Products Association (IWPA)
4214 King St.
  Alexandria, VA 22302
Ph: (703)820-6696
Fax: (703)820-8550
Co. E-mail: info@iwpawood.org
URL: http://www.iwpawood.org
Contact: Jordan McIlvain, President
Facebook: www.facebook.com/International-Wood-Products-Association-98537846310
Linkedin: www.linkedin.com/company/international-wood-products-association
X (Twitter): x.com/iwpawood
Description: Promotes acceptance and use of imported wood products; develops product standards; compiles statistics; supports good forestry management. **Founded:** 1956. **Publications:** *International Wood* (Annual); *International Wood Products Association--Membership Directory*. **Educational Activities:** World of Wood Convention (Annual). **Awards:** IWPA Aesthetic Excellence (Annual); IWPA Environmental Excellence (Annual); IWPA Innovative Excellence (Annual).

10380 ■ National Hardwood Lumber Association (NHLA) - Library
6830 Raleigh Lagrange Rd.
  Memphis, TN 38184
Ph: (901)377-1818
Fax: (901)382-6419
Co. E-mail: info@nhla.com

URL: http://www.nhla.com

Contact: Renee Hornsby, Director, Communications
Director, Marketing

E-mail: r.hornsby@nhla.com

Facebook: www.facebook.com/NHLAOfficial

X (Twitter): x.com/NHLA_Official

YouTube: www.youtube.com/channel/UCMt-KICGI-IM
tie22LqRDfQ

Description: Maintains inspection training school.
Conducts management and marketing seminars for
the hardwood industry. Promotes research in hard-
wood timber management and utilization. **Scope:**
Hardwood. **Holdings:** Figures not available. **Publica-
tions:** *NHLA Newsletter* (Monthly); *National Hard-
wood Lumber Association Membership Directory;
Hardwood Matters: The Voice of the Hardwood
Industry* (11/year). **Educational Activities:** NHLA
Annual Convention & Exhibit Showcase (Annual).

10381 ■ National Lumber and Building Material Dealers Association (NLBMDA)

2001 K St. NW, 3rd Fl., N
Washington, DC 20006

Ph: (202)367-1169

Co. E-mail: info@dealer.org

URL: http://www.dealer.org

Contact: Jonathan M. Paine, President

E-mail: jonathon@dealer.org

Facebook: www.facebook.com/nlbmda

Linkedin: www.linkedin.com/company/national-lumber
-&-building-material-dealers-association-nlbmda-

X (Twitter): x.com/NLBMDA

Description: Represents more than 8,000 lumber
and building material companies with over 400,000
employees, 20 state and regional associations and
the industry's leading manufacturers and service
providers. **Founded:** 1917. **Publications:** *Building
Material Dealer; Cost of Doing Business (CODB)* (An-
nual); *Forklift and You; NLBMDA Advocate* (Monthly);
Nuts & Bolts; ProSales (Monthly); *Risk Management
Best Practices; Your National Perspective* (Quarterly).
Educational Activities: ProDealer Industry Summit
(Annual); Annual Spring Meeting & Legislative
Conference (Annual). **Awards:** NLBMDA Grassroots
Dealer of the Year (Annual). **Geographic Prefer-
ence:** National.

10382 ■ North American Wholesale Lumber Association (NAWLA)

330 N Wabash, Ste. 2000
Chicago, IL 60611

Ph: (312)321-5133

Free: 800-527-8258

Co. E-mail: info@nawla.org

URL: http://nawla.org

Contact: Scott Parker, Executive Director

E-mail: sparker@nawla.org

Facebook: www.facebook.com/NAWLA1893

Linkedin: www.linkedin.com/company/nawla

X (Twitter): x.com/NAWLA1893

Description: Wholesale distributors of lumber, wood
products, and complementary products. Aids members with procedure for settling trade disputes.
Provides weeklong course for wholesale lumber traders. Compiles statistics. Provides networking opportunities at regional and annual meetings, trade
show, and NAWLA Traders Market. **Founded:** 1893.
Publications: *North American Wholesale Lumber
Association--Membership Bulletin* (Monthly); *North
American Wholesale Lumber Association--Distribution
Directory* (Annual). **Educational Activities:** University of Innovative Distribution (Annual); NAWLA Trad-
ers Market (Annual). **Geographic Preference:**
National.

10383 ■ Northeastern Lumber Manufacturers Association (NELMA)

272 Tuttle Rd.
Cumberland Center, ME 04021

Ph: (207)829-6901

Fax: (207)829-4293

Co. E-mail: info@nelma.org

URL: http://www.nelma.org

Contact: George F. Burns, Officer

Facebook: www.facebook.com/Northeas
ternLumberMfg

X (Twitter): x.com/iNELMA

YouTube: www.youtube.com/user/NelmaTV

Description: Promotes the interests of the northeastern lumber manufacturing industry. Encourages
uniformity, efficiency, and economy in the manufacture, gradation, distribution, and use of lumber and
timber products. **Founded:** 1933. **Publications:**
*Northeastern Lumber Manufacturers Association--
Buyers Guide and Membership Directory; Dimen-
sional Lumber; Eastern White Pine; Standard Grading Rules for Northeastern Lumber; Membership
Directory; Ask NELMA Newsletter* (Monthly). **Geographic Preference:** National.

10384 ■ Northeastern Retail Lumber Association (NRLA)

585 N Greenbush Rd.
Rensselaer, NY 12144

Ph: (518)286-1010

Free: 800-292-6752

Fax: (518)286-1755

URL: http://www.nrla.org

Contact: Rita Ferris, CAE, President

E-mail: rferris@nrla.org

Facebook: www.facebook.com/VisitNRLA

Linkedin: www.linkedin.com/company/northeastern-re
tail-lumber-association

X (Twitter): x.com/TheNRLA

YouTube: www.youtube.com/channel/UCtWpcs
3LwRM4CB75ZjvPnqA

Description: Retail lumber and building material
dealers in the Northeast. Conducts educational,
legislative, and government affairs programs.
Founded: 1894. **Publications:** *The Source: Buyers'
Guide & Dealer Directory* (Annual); *The Lumber Co-
Operator: The Official Publication of the Northeastern
Retail Lumber Association; The Source.* **Educational
Activities:** LBM Expo (Annual). **Geographic Prefer-
ence:** National.

10385 ■ Northwestern Lumber Association (NLA)

701 Decatur Ave. N, Ste. 105
Golden Valley, MN 55427

Ph: (763)544-6822

Free: 888-544-6822

Fax: (763)595-4060

Co. E-mail: info@nlassn.org

URL: http://www.nlassn.org

Contact: Cody Nuernberg, President

E-mail: cnuernberg@nlassn.org

Linkedin: www.linkedin.com/company/bldconnection

X (Twitter): x.com/nlassn

Description: Building materials dealers in Iowa, Minnesota, North Dakota, South Dakota and Wisconsin;
associate members are distributors, manufacturers,
and allied industries. **Founded:** 1890. **Publications:**
Building Products Connection (Bimonthly); *Dealer
Reference Manual and Buyer's Guide* (Annual); *Scene...in a Flash* (Monthly); *Dealer Reference Manual
and Buyers' Guide (DRM)* (Annual). **Educational
Activities:** Northwestern Building Products Expo (Annual); Iowa Lumber Convention (Annual); Nebraska Lumber
Dealers Convention (Annual); Nebraska Lumber
Dealers Convention; Nebraska Lumber Dealers
Convention; Northwestern Building Products Expo
(Annual). **Geographic Preference:** Regional; Re-
gional.

10386 ■ Southeastern Lumber Manufacturers Association (SLMA)

PO Box 3630
Peachtree City, GA 30269

Ph: (770)631-6701

URL: http://www.slma.org

Contact: Bryan Smalley, President

Facebook: www.facebook.com/Southeastern-Lumber
-Manufacturers-Association-94236541457

X (Twitter): x.com/SLMAchoosewood

Description: Independent southeastern lumber
manufacturers. Represents and coordinates efforts of
membership to alleviate local, regional, and national
problems that affect independent southeastern
lumber manufacturing industry. Conducts marketing
and promotional activities. **Founded:** 1962. **Geographic Preference:** National.

10387 ■ Western Building Material Association (WBMA)

1018 Capitol Way S, Ste. 206
Olympia, WA 98501

Ph: (360)943-3054

Fax: (360)943-1219

Co. E-mail: wbma@wbma.org

URL: http://www.wbma.org

Contact: Casey Voorhees, Executive Director

E-mail: casey@wbma.org

Facebook: www.facebook.com/Western-Building-Ma
terial-Association-285818461476246

X (Twitter): x.com/WBMA_

Description: Retail lumber and building material
dealers in states of Alaska, Hawaii, Idaho, Montana,
Oregon, and Washington. Seeks to further and
protect the interests of retail lumber dealers. Services
include: classes, workshops, and seminars; group
insurance and pension; printing of business forms;
government and legislative action; information
clearinghouse; training courses for personnel. Maintains a learning resource center. Conducts educational programs. **Founded:** 1903. **Publications:**
*Western Building Material Association--Management
Guide* (Monthly); *Western Building Material
Association--Newsletter; Western News* (Monthly).
Educational Activities: Western Building Material
Association Annual Convention (Annual); Building
Products Showcase. **Awards:** WBMA Distinguished
Dealer of the Year (Annual). **Geographic Prefer-
ence:** National.

10388 ■ Western Red Cedar Lumber Association (WRCLA)

Ste. 415 4-32465 S Fraser Way
Abbotsford, BC, Canada V2T 0C7

Ph: (604)891-1262

Free: 866-778-9096

URL: http://www.realcedar.com

YouTube: www.youtube.com/user/WRCLA

Description: Aims to help consumers understand
cedar's long-term benefits and special features.
Provides information on how to use cedar properly.
Founded: 1954. **Publications:** *Where to Buy West-
ern Red Cedar* (Annual). **Educational Activities:**
Western Red Cedar Lumber Association Meeting (An-
nual); WRCLA Cedar School (Annual). **Geographic
Preference:** National.

10389 ■ Western Wood Products Association (WWPA)

2 Centerpointe Dr., Ste. 360
Lake Oswego, OR 97035

Ph: (503)224-3930

Fax: (503)224-3935

Co. E-mail: info@wwpa.org

URL: http://www.wwpa.org

Contact: Dyanne Martin, Contact

Facebook: www.facebook.com/WWPALSV

Description: Represents lumber manufacturers in 12
Western states and Alaska. Delivers lumber grade
inspection and quality control, technical support,
product/market support and statistical services to
Western sawmills. **Founded:** 1933. **Publications:**
*Western Lumber Buyers Guide; Western Lumber
Facts* (Monthly); *Western Wood Products
Association--Buyers Manual* (Annual); *Export Report*
(Monthly); *Injury and Illness Incidence* (Quarterly);
*Monthly F.O.B. Price Summary, Past Sales--Coast
Mills* (Monthly); *Monthly F.O.B. Price Summary, Past
Sales--Inland Mills* (Monthly). **Geographic Prefer-
ence:** National.

REFERENCE WORKS

10390 ■ "ABC Supply Company Finally Finds Idaho" in Idaho Business Review (September 17, 2014)

Pub: BridgeTower Media

Contact: Adam Reinebach, President

Description: The nation's largest wholesale distributor, ABC Supply Company, has entered a store in
Idaho. The roofing supply firm has now has stores in
48 states. Franklin Lumber Supply, a home supply
chain will be ABCs its major competitor in the area.

10391 ■ *"City Buys Aspen Mini Storage, Expanding Lumberyard Property" in Aspen Daily News (October 9, 2019)*
URL(s): www.aspendailynews.com/news/city-buys -aspen-mini-storage-expanding-lumberyard-proper ty/article_24013aa4-ea3a-11e9-be64-df6a7b677af 5.html
Ed: Alycin Bektesh. **Released:** October 09, 2019. **Description:** The Aspen City Council agreed to purchase $11 million worth of land that is set to enhance a future affordable housing development, which is adjacent to the city-owned lumberyard. **Availability:** Online.

10392 ■ *"A Fine Time for Timber" in Barron's (Vol. 92, August 25, 2012, No. 38, pp. 18)*
Pub: Dow Jones & Company Inc.
Contact: Almar Latour, Chief Executive Officer
Ed: Christopher C. Williams. **Description:** The stocks of timber firm and real estate investment trust Weyerhaeuser could have their dividend raised by as much as 50 percent. The company is poised to benefit from a housing sector recovery, which could raise the value of its real estate and timberland holdings. **Availability:** Online.

10393 ■ *"Furniture Making May Come Back--Literally" in Business North Carolina (Vol. 28, March 2008, No. 3, pp. 32)*
Pub: Business North Carolina
Contact: Peggy Knaack, Manager
E-mail: pknaack@businessnc.com
Description: Due to the weak U.S. dollar and the fact that lumber processors never left the country, foreign furniture manufacturers are becoming interested in moving manufacturing plants to the U.S. **Availability:** Online.

10394 ■ *"Goldbelt Inc.: Targeting Shareholder Development" in Alaska Business Monthly (Vol. 27, October 2011, No. 10, pp. 108)*
Pub: Alaska Business Publishing Company Inc.
Contact: Charles Bell, Vice President, Sales and Marketing
E-mail: cbell@akbizmag.com
Ed: Tracy Kalytiak. **Description:** Profile of Goldbelt Inc., the company that has changed its original focus of timber to real estate to tourism and then to government contracting opportunities. **Availability:** Print; Online.

10395 ■ *International Wood Products Association--Membership Directory*
Pub: International Wood Products Association
Contact: Jordan McIlvain, President
URL(s): www.iwpawood.org/page/Resources#
Description: Covers includes 220 U.S. importers, overseas suppliers, and service providers to the imported wood products industry. **Entries include:** Company name, address, phone, names of executives, list of products or services, fax, e-mail addresses, URL. **Arrangement:** Classified by type of membership. **Availability:** Print.

10396 ■ *"Montana's Manufacturing Industry" in Montana Business Quarterly (Vol. 49, Spring 2011, No. 1, pp. 29)*
Pub: University of Montana Bureau of Business and Economic Research
Contact: Patrick Barkey, Director
E-mail: patrick.barkey@business.umt.edu
Ed: Todd A. Morgan, Charles E. Keegan, III, Colin B. Sorenson. **Released:** Quarterly. **Description:** Manufacturing remains a vital part of Montana's economy despite the recession and decline in the production of wood products. Statistical data included. **Availability:** Online.

10397 ■ *North American Building Material Distribution Association--Membership Directory (Internet only)*
Pub: North American Building Material Distribution Association
Contact: Scott Narug, Manager, Sales
URL(s): my.nbmda.org/account/login.aspx

Description: Covers about 200 wholesale distributors of building products who are members, and 150 manufacturers in that field who are associate members and over 800 of their locations. **Entries include:** Company name, address, phone, fax, name of principal executive, products offered. **Arrangement:** Geographical. **Indexes:** Alphabetical. **Availability:** Print.

10398 ■ *"Wood Increasingly Used in School Construction" in Arkansas Business (Vol. 29, July 23, 2012, No. 30, pp. 11)*
Pub: Arkansas Business Publishing Group
Contact: Mitch Bettis, President
Ed: Jan Cottingham. **Description:** Arkansas state guidelines have increased the use of wood in school building construction. Wood is believed to provide strength and durability along with cost effectiveness and environmental benefits. **Availability:** Online.

STATISTICAL SOURCES

10399 ■ *RMA Annual Statement Studies*
Pub: Risk Management Association
Contact: Nancy Foster, President
Released: Annual. **Description:** Contains composite balance sheets and income statements for more than 360 industries, including the accounting, auditing, and bookkeeping industries. Also contains five years of comparative historical data for discerning trends. Includes 16 commonly used ratios, computed for most of the size groupings for nearly every industry.

10400 ■ *Standard & Poor's Industry Surveys*
Pub: Standard And Poor's Financial Services LLC.
Contact: Douglas L. Peterson, President
Description: Two-volume book that examines the prospects for specific industries, including trucking. Also provides analyses of trends and problems, statistical tables and charts, and comparative company analyses.

TRADE PERIODICALS

10401 ■ *Ask NELMA Newsletter*
Pub: Northeastern Lumber Manufacturers Association
Contact: George F. Burns, Officer
URL(s): www.nelma.org/asknelma-newsletter
Released: Monthly **Description:** Discusses the growth, harvesting, production, and marketing of Northeastern lumber. Includes news of federal and state activities and of business of the Association. **Availability:** Online.

10402 ■ *Panel World*
Pub: Hatton-Brown Publishers Inc.
Contact: Cindy Segrest, Director
URL(s): www.panelworldmag.com
Facebook: www.facebook.com/panelworld
Linkedin: www.linkedin.com/showcase/panel-world
X (Twitter): x.com/panelworldmag
YouTube: www.youtube.com/channel/UClWVW3xA d7T9kjxAv-nnj1g
Released: 6/year **Description:** Business magazine serving the worldwide veneer, plywood, and panel board industry. **Availability:** Print; Online.

10403 ■ *Random Lengths Weekly Report*
Pub: Random Lengths Publications Inc.
URL(s): www.rlmyprint.com/About/FeaturesBenefits .aspx
Released: Weekly **Description:** Covers the North American softwood markets, including lumber, plywood, oriented strand board, and related products. Includes price guides. Recurring features include a calendar of events and notices of publications available. **Availability:** Print.

TRADE SHOWS AND CONVENTIONS

10404 ■ *Iowa Lumber Convention*
Northwestern Lumber Association (NLA)
701 Decatur Ave. N, Ste. 105
Golden Valley, MN 55427

Ph: (763)544-6822
Free: 888-544-6822
Fax: (763)595-4060
Co. E-mail: info@nlassn.org
URL: http://www.nlassn.org
Contact: Cody Nuernberg, President
E-mail: cnuernberg@nlassn.org
URL(s): https://cdn.ymaws.com/www.nlassn.org/re source/collection/717FC00A-6A7D-430C-8019-7C 59767A6E5A/1-29-20_EXPO_SOUTH_-_AN _EVENT_YOU_WONT_WANT_TO_MISS.pdf
Description: Exhibits related to lumber industry equipment, supplies and services. **Audience:** Lumber and building material professionals. **Principal Exhibits:** Exhibits related to lumber industry equipment, supplies and services.

10405 ■ *LAT Convention & Buying Show*
Lumbermen's Association of Texas & Louisiana
2630 Exposition Blvd., Ste. G-06
Austin, TX 78703
Ph: (512)472-1194
Co. E-mail: mireya@lat.org
URL: http://www.lat.org
Contact: Kate Woodson Borroni, President
URL(s): www.lat.org/annual-conference.html
Frequency: Annual. **Description:** Lumber, building materials, hardware, and related products. **Audience:** Industry professionals. **Principal Exhibits:** Lumber, building materials, hardware, and related products. **Telecommunication Services:** michelle.milner@ conferencedirect.com.

10406 ■ *LBM Expo*
Northeastern Retail Lumber Association (NRLA)
585 N Greenbush Rd.
Rensselaer, NY 12144
Ph: (518)286-1010
Free: 800-292-6752
Fax: (518)286-1755
URL: http://www.nrla.org
Contact: Rita Ferris, CAE, President
E-mail: rferris@nrla.org
URL(s): lbmexpo.net
Frequency: Annual. **Audience:** Lumber and building material suppliers and associated professionals. **Telecommunication Services:** lbmexpo@nrla.org.

10407 ■ *Mississippi Lumber Manufacturers Association Convention and Trade Show*
Mississippi Lumber Manufacturers Association (MLMA)
c/o Ellery Jones, Executive Director
PO Box 5241
Jackson, MS 39296
Ph: (601)672-7362
Co. E-mail: ellery@mlmalumber.com
URL: http://www.mlmalumber.com
Contact: Ellery Jones, Executive Director
E-mail: ellery@mlmalumber.com
URL(s): www.mlmalumber.com/events/2024-conven tion-and-trade-show
Frequency: Annual. **Description:** Lumber manufacturing equipment, supplies, and services. **Audience:** Mill members, lumber and mill producers, business-related firms, wholesalers and producers. **Principal Exhibits:** Lumber manufacturing equipment, supplies, and services. **Telecommunication Services:** ellery@mlmalumber.com.

10408 ■ *NHLA Annual Convention & Exhibit Showcase*
National Hardwood Lumber Association (NHLA)
6830 Raleigh Lagrange Rd.
Memphis, TN 38184
Ph: (901)377-1818
Fax: (901)382-6419
Co. E-mail: info@nhla.com
URL: http://www.nhla.com
Contact: Renee Hornsby, Director, Communications Director, Marketing
E-mail: r.hornsby@nhla.com
URL(s): nhla.com/convention/nhla-annual-convention
Frequency: Annual. **Description:** Exhibits relating to management and marketing of the hardwood lumber industry and technology. **Audience:** Industry profes-

sionals. **Principal Exhibits:** Exhibits relating to management and marketing of the hardwood lumber industry and technology. **Telecommunication Services:** registration@nhla.com.

10409 ■ Northwestern Building Products Expo

Northwestern Lumber Association (NLA)
  701 Decatur Ave. N, Ste. 105
  Golden Valley, MN 55427
Ph: (763)544-6822
Free: 888-544-6822
Fax: (763)595-4060
Co. E-mail: info@nlassn.org
URL: http://www.nlassn.org
Contact: Cody Nuernberg, President
E-mail: cnuernberg@nlassn.org
URL(s): www.nlassn.org/page/Expos
Frequency: Annual. **Description:** Any product or service that is ultimately sold or used by retail lumber and building material dealers. **Audience:** Industry professionals. **Principal Exhibits:** Any product or service that is ultimately sold or used by retail lumber and building material dealers.

10410 ■ World of Wood Convention

International Wood Products Association (IWPA)
  4214 King St.
  Alexandria, VA 22302
Ph: (703)820-6696
Fax: (703)820-8550
Co. E-mail: info@iwpawood.org
URL: http://www.iwpawood.org
Contact: Jordan McIlvain, President
URL(s): www.iwpawood.org/page/2025savethedate
Frequency: Annual. **Description:** Imported wood products industry, new laws and regulations. **Audience:** Manufacturers, exporters, wholesalers, offshore suppliers and service providers of wood products. **Principal Exhibits:** Imported wood products industry, new laws and regulations. Dates and Locations: 2025 Mar 26-28 New Orleans, LA. **Telecommunication Services:** baron@iwpawood.org.

CONSULTANTS

10411 ■ Lee Resources International Inc.

445 Bypass 72NW
  Greenwood, SC 29649
Ph: (864)229-0600
Free: 800-277-7888
URL: http://leeresources.com
Contact: Bob Erwin, Chief Executive Officer
X (Twitter): x.com/Lee_Resources

Description: Provides business training, recruitment and publishing services. **Founded:** 1987. **Publications:** "The Artichoke Factor"; "Customer Care"; "The Impact Selling System"; "Time Out"; "You Can Sell More Professionally"; "You Can Build a Better You"; "You Can Prospect More Creatively"; "You Can Manage and Motivate"; "The Secrets of Power Negotiating"; "Take Charge of Your Life"; "Swim with the Sharks Without Being Eaten Alive"; "The Psychology of Winning"; "The Psychology of Selling"; "The Management Advantage"; "The 7 Habits of Highly

Effective People"; "Even Further Up the Organization"; "Defrosting Telephone Cold Calls"; "Guide to Everyday Negotiating". **Training:** Developing Your Sales Process; I Dare You; Relationship Selling; Time Management; Customer Service; Protecting Your Margins; Business Development.

LIBRARIES

10412 ■ International Society of Wood Science and Technology (SWST) - Library

PO Box 6155
  Monona, WI 53716-6155
Ph: (608)577-1342
Fax: (608)254-2769
Co. E-mail: vicki@swst.org
URL: http://www.swst.org/wp
Contact: Jeffrey Morrell, President
E-mail: jeff.morrell@oregonstate.edu
Facebook: www.facebook.com/SocietyWood
Linkedin: www.linkedin.com/company/society-of-wood-science-and-technology
X (Twitter): x.com/SocietyWood

Description: Wood scientists and technologists in the forest products industry, research, or education; student members are college juniors, seniors, or graduate students in wood science and technology curricula. Sponsors Visiting Scientist Program for colleges offering wood science and technology courses. **Scope:** Wood science. **Founded:** 1958. **Holdings:** Figures not available. **Publications:** *Directory of Schools*; *Wood & Fiber Science* (Quarterly); *SWST Newsletter*. **Awards:** SWT Award for Distinguished Service to the Profession of Wood Science and Technology (Irregular); George Marra Award (Annual); Fellow Award (Annual); SWST Student Poster Competition (Annual); SWST Fellow Award (Annual); SWST International Visiting Scientist Award (Annual). **Geographic Preference:** National.

10413 ■ National Hardwood Lumber Association (NHLA) - Library

6830 Raleigh Lagrange Rd.
  Memphis, TN 38184
Ph: (901)377-1818
Fax: (901)382-6419
Co. E-mail: info@nhla.com
URL: http://www.nhla.com
Contact: Renee Hornsby, Director, Communications Director, Marketing
E-mail: r.hornsby@nhla.com
Facebook: www.facebook.com/NHLAOfficial
X (Twitter): x.com/NHLA_Official
YouTube: www.youtube.com/channel/UCMt-KICGI-IMtie22LqRDfQ

Description: Maintains inspection training school. Conducts management and marketing seminars for the hardwood industry. Promotes research in hardwood timber management and utilization. **Scope:** Hardwood. **Holdings:** Figures not available. **Publications:** *NHLA Newsletter* (Monthly); *National Hardwood Lumber Association Membership Directory*; *Hardwood Matters: The Voice of the Hardwood Industry* (11/year). **Educational Activities:** NHLA Annual Convention & Exhibit Showcase (Annual).

10414 ■ U.S.D.A. Forest Service (FPL Library) - Forest Products Laboratory Library

One Gifford Pinchot Dr.
  Madison, WI 53726
Ph: (608)231-9200
Fax: (608)231-9592
Co. E-mail: sm.fs.mailroomfpl@usda.gov
URL: http://research.fs.usda.gov/fpl
Scope: Forestry; forest products and wood utilization. **Services:** Interlibrary loan; copying (limited); library open to the public. **Founded:** 1910. **Holdings:** Books. **Subscriptions:** journals.

RESEARCH CENTERS

10415 ■ Decorative Hardware Association (DHA) - Library

42777 Trade West Dr.
  Sterling, VA 20166
Ph: (703)435-2900
Fax: (703)435-2537
Co. E-mail: resources@decorativehardwoods.org
URL: http://www.decorativehardwoods.org
Contact: Keith Christman, President
E-mail: kchristman@decorativehardwoods.org
Facebook: www.facebook.com/DecorativeHardwoods
Linkedin: www.linkedin.com/company/decorativehardwoods
X (Twitter): x.com/DecHardwoods

Description: Manufacturers and finishers of hardwood plywood; manufacturers and sales agents of veneer; suppliers of glue, machinery, and other products related to the industry; stocking distributors. Conducts laboratory testing of plywood, adhesives, finishes, flame spread, formaldehyde emissions, structural, and smoke density. **Scope:** Manufacture and structure of hardwood plywood, veneer, glue bond, flame spread, finishes, and adhesives. Reviews federal and military specifications and foreign standards affecting hardwood plywood and laminated hardwood flooring. Provides in-plant inspection and verification. **Founded:** 1921. **Subscriptions:** 50 journals and other serials; 32 newspapers. **Publications:** *Directory of Veneer Manufacturers, Veneer Sales Representatives, Veneer Importers in the United States and Canada* (Annual); *Directory of Manufacturers of Marine Hardwood Plywood* (Annual); *Hardwood Plywood & E-News* (Semimonthly); *HPMA Testing and Inspection and Listed Products Manual* (Annual); *Where to Buy Hardwood Plywood and Veneer Directory* (Annual); *Veneer Manufacturers in the United States and Canada* (Annual); *Where to Buy Hardwood Plywood, Veneer, and Engineered Hardwood Flooring Buyers' Guide* (Annual); *Hardwood Plywood*; *Hardwood Plywood and Veneer News* (Monthly); *Where to Buy Hardwood Plywood, Veneer, and Engineered Hardwood Flooring Membership Directory* (Annual); *Associations and Organizations of Interest to Hardwood Plywood & Veneer Manufacturers* (Annual); *Magazines & Publications of Interest to Hardwood Plywood & Veneer Manufacturers* (Irregular); *Hardwood Plywood Manufacturers Association--Face Veneer Manufacturers List*. **Educational Activities:** Decorative Hardwoods Association (Annual); Grading Workshop (Daily). **Geographic Preference:** National.

ASSOCIATIONS AND OTHER ORGANIZATIONS

10416 ■ Aluminum Extruders Council (AEC)

Aluminum Extruders Council (AEC)
1000 N Rand Rd., Ste. 214
Wauconda, IL 60084
Ph: (847)526-2010
Fax: (847)526-3993
Co. E-mail: mail@aec.org
URL: http://www.aec.org
Contact: Jeff Henderson, President
E-mail: jhenderson@tso.net
Facebook: www.facebook.com/AluminumExtru
dersCouncilAEC
YouTube: www.youtube.com/user/AECorg

Description: Manufacturers of extruded aluminum shapes and their suppliers. Compiles statistics; provides technical assistance and develops markets. Conducts workshops. **Founded:** 1950. **Publications:** *Buyer's Guide*; *Aluminum Extrusion*; *Executive Report* (Bimonthly); *Publications Catalog*. **Educational Activities:** Management Conference (Annual). **Geographic Preference:** Multinational.

10417 ■ Association des Fonderies Canadiennes (AFC) [Canadian Foundry Association (CFA)]

33 Prince Charles Dr.
Welland, ON, Canada L3B 5P4
Co. E-mail: info@foundryassociation.ca
URL: http://www.foundryassociation.ca
Contact: Grant Stuempfle, President
Linkedin: www.linkedin.com/company/canadian-foun
dry-association
X (Twitter): x.com/CanadianFoundry

Description: Foundries. Seeks to advance the metals and forging industries. Serves as a forum for the exchange of information among members; represents members' interests before labor and industrial organizations, government agencies, and the public. **Founded:** 1975. **Geographic Preference:** National.

10418 ■ Canadian Welding Bureau (CWB) [Le Bureau Canadien de Soudage; CWB Group]

8260 Parkhill Dr.
Milton, ON, Canada L9T 5V7
Free: 800-844-6790
Fax: (905)542-1318
Co. E-mail: info@cwbgroup.org
URL: http://www.cwbgroup.org
Contact: Doug Luciani, President
Facebook: www.facebook.com/cwbgroupwelding
Linkedin: www.linkedin.com/company/cwb-group
X (Twitter): x.com/cwbgroupwelding
YouTube: www.youtube.com/user/cwbgroup

Description: Seeks to ensure maintenance of high standards of practice and compliance to accepted workmanship standards in the welding profession. Provides welding certification for fabricating and

manufacturing companies and manufacturers of steel building systems. **Founded:** 1947. **Publications:** *CWB NET* (Periodic). **Geographic Preference:** National.

10419 ■ Fabricators and Manufacturers Association, International (FMA) - Library

2135 Point Blvd.
Elgin, IL 60123
Ph: (815)399-8700
Free: 888-394-4362
Co. E-mail: info@fmanet.org
URL: http://www.fmanet.org
Contact: Carlos Mendizabal-Perez, Chairman
Facebook: www.facebook.com/FabricatorsAn
dManufacturers
Linkedin: www.linkedin.com/company/fabricators
-&-manufacturers-association-int'l-fma-
X (Twitter): x.com/fmamembership
YouTube: www.youtube.com/FMAnetorg

Description: People involved in the metal forming and fabricating industry. Disseminates technological information on the fabrication of sheet, coil, tube, pipe, plate, and structural metal shapes. Conducts continuing education conferences. Maintains technical information center. **Scope:** Metal fabrication; manufacturing. **Holdings:** Figures not available. **Publications:** *Who's Who in Metal Forming & Fabricating* (Annual); *The FABRICATOR's Literature Directory* (Semiannual); *TPJ--The Tube & Pipe Journal (TPJ)* (6/year); *The WELDER* (Bimonthly); *Member Connections*; *Member Connections* (Bimonthly); *Stamping Journal* (Bimonthly); *Stamping Journal's Literature Directory* (Annual); *The Fabricator* (Monthly); *American Tube Association--FMA Member Resource Directory* (Annual). **Educational Activities:** FABTECH. **Geographic Preference:** Multinational.

10420 ■ Precision Metalforming Association (PMA)

6363 Oak Tree Blvd.
Independence, OH 44131
Ph: (216)901-8800
URL: http://www.pma.org/home
Contact: David Klotz, President
Facebook: www.facebook.com/PrecisionMe
talformingAssociation
Linkedin: www.linkedin.com/company/precision-me
talforming-association
X (Twitter): x.com/PMATalk
Instagram: www.instagram.com/metalformingmatters
YouTube: www.youtube.com/user/PrecisionMetalform

Description: Represents the metalforming industry of North America; the industry that creates precision metal products using stamping, fabricating and other value-added processes. Its member companies include metal stampers, fabricators, spinners, slide formers and roll formers, as well as suppliers of equipment, materials and services to the industry. **Founded:** 1942. **Publications:** *PMA Pulse* (Weekly); *Sources* (Annual); *Metalforming: Serving the Precision Metalforming Industry* (Monthly). **Educational Activities:** METALFORM Mexico (Annual);

FABTECH; METALFORM Exhibition; American Welding Society International Welding & Fabricating Exposition & Convention (Annual); MAX International, co-locating AWS International Welding & Fabricating Expo/American Welding Society & METALFORM. **Geographic Preference:** Multinational; Regional.

10421 ■ Society of Manufacturing Engineers (SME)

1000 Town Ctr., Ste. 1910
Southfield, MI 48075
Ph: (313)425-3000
Free: 800-733-4763
Fax: (313)425-3400
Co. E-mail: advertising@sme.org
URL: http://www.sme.org
Facebook: www.facebook.com/SMEmfg
Linkedin: www.linkedin.com/company/sme
X (Twitter): x.com/SME_MFG
YouTube: www.youtube.com/user/SMEEvents

Description: Professional society of manufacturing engineers, practitioners and management executives concerned with manufacturing technologies for improved productivity. Seeks to advance the science of manufacturing through the continuing education of manufacturing engineers, practitioners and management. Conducts expositions, international seminars and clinics. **Founded:** 1932. **Publications:** *Manufacturing Engineering New Manufacturing Equipment Buyers Guide* (Annual); *Machine Vision and Robotics Industry Directory* (Biennial); *INTIME Manufacturing Data Bank*; *TMEH Knowledge Base*; *Vision--Show Directory Issue*; *Directory of Manufacturing Education Programs in Colleges, Universities, and Technical Institutes* (Updated continuously; printed on request); *Forming & Fabricating* (9/year); *Manufacturing Engineering*; *Plastics Insights* (Quarterly); *Composites in Manufacturing*; *Electronics Manufacturing: SME's Quarterly on Electronics Manufacturing Technology* (Quarterly); *Finishing Line: AFP/SME's Quarterly on Finishing and Coatings Technology* (Quarterly); *Journal of Manufacturing Systems (JMSY)* (6/year); *Vision: SME's Quarterly on Vision Technology* (Quarterly); *Directory of Composites Manufacturers, Suppliers, Consultants, and Research Organizations* (Biennial). **Educational Activities:** South-tec (Annual); Westec (Biennial); SME Automotive Finishing Conference and Exposition; EASTEC - Advanced Productivity Exposition (Biennial); Micro-Manufacturing Conference & Exhibits; Midwest Machine Tool Show (Annual); NanoManufacturing Conference & Exhibits; Twin Cities APEX - Advanced Productivity Exposition/Twin Cities. **Awards:** SME Award of Merit (Annual); Donald C. Burnham Manufacturing Management Award (Annual); SME Honorary Membership (Irregular); SME Outstanding Young Manufacturing Engineer Award (Annual); SME Albert M. Sargent Progress Award (Annual); Joseph A. Siegel Service Award (Annual); SME Education Award (Annual); SME Frederick W. Taylor Research Medal (Annual); SME Gold Medal (Annual); Eli Whitney Productivity Award (Annual); J.H. "Jud" Hall Composites Manufacturing Award (Annual). **Geographic Preference:** National; Multinational.

10422 ■ Specialty Tools and Fasteners Distributors Association (STAFDA) - Library
500 Elm Grove Rd., Ste. 210
  Elm Grove, WI 53122
Ph: (262)784-4774
Free: 800-352-2981
Fax: (262)784-5059
Co. E-mail: info@stafda.org
URL: http://www.stafda.org
Contact: Georgia Foley, Chief Executive Officer
E-mail: ghfoley@stafda.org
Facebook: www.facebook.com/STAFDAHQ
X (Twitter): x.com/STAFDAHQ
Instagram: www.instagram.com/stafda
Description: Distributors and suppliers of power tools, power-actuated tools, anchors, fastening systems, diamond drilling, and related construction equipment. Encourages legal, ethical, and friendly business relations within the industry. Collects and disseminates information pertinent to the industry; develops more effective, economical, and profitable distribution. **Scope:** Business and industry. **Founded:** 1976. **Holdings:** Books; CD-ROMs; DVD. **Publications:** *Specialty Tools & Fasteners Distributors Association--Membership Directory* (Annual). **Educational Activities:** University of Innovative Distribution (Annual); STAFDA Annual Convention & Trade Show (Annual). **Geographic Preference:** National.

10423 ■ Tooling, Manufacturing and Technologies Association (TMTA)
28237 Orchard Lake Rd., Ste. 101
  Farmington Hills, MI 48334
Ph: (248)488-0300
Fax: (248)488-0500
URL: http://thetmta.com
Contact: Lucas Wright, Secretary
Description: Manufacturers of dies, jigs, fixtures, molds, gages, tools, special machinery, and related products; suppliers of die tryout, machining, and experimental and designing service. **Founded:** 1933. **Publications:** *TMTA Talk.* **Geographic Preference:** National.

10424 ■ United States Cutting Tool Institute (USCTI)
1300 Sumner Ave.
  Cleveland, OH 44115-2851
Ph: (216)241-7333
Fax: (216)241-0105
Co. E-mail: uscti@uscti.com
URL: http://www.uscti.com
Contact: Jeff Major, President
Description: Manufacturers of rotary metal cutting tools. Objectives are to: promote the manufacture and sale of rotary metal cutting tools in the U.S. and in foreign markets; promote the standardization of sizes, dimensions, and tolerances in cooperation with the American National Standards Institute, American Society of Mechanical Engineers, and other engineering organizations; increase the use of metal cutting tools and allied products. **Founded:** 1988. **Publications:** *Drilled Holes for Tapping; Standards and Dimensions for Ground Thread Taps.* **Geographic Preference:** National.

REFERENCE WORKS

10425 ■ AMT--Member Product Directory
Pub: Association for Manufacturing Technology
Contact: Douglas K. Woods, President
URL(s): www.amtonline.org/membership
Description: Covers machine tools and related products built by members of the Association for Manufacturing Technology. **Entries include:** Company name, address, phone, telex, fax, e-mail, website, and product specifications. **Arrangement:** Product type; company name. **Indexes:** Product type (in English, French, Spanish, German, Japanese, Italian, Portuguese, Chinese). **Availability:** Print.

10426 ■ "Banks Looking to Lend, Compete to Make Small-Business Loans" in Puget Sound Business Journal (Vol. 33, August 17, 2012, No. 17, pp. 1)
Pub: Baltimore Business Journal
Contact: Rhonda Pringle, President

E-mail: rpringle@bizjournals.com
Ed: Greg Lamm. **Description:** Mobile Tool Management has grown from four employees to 30 during the past five years, and its expansion was completed after owner Mike woogerd applied for a loan from Chase. Figures show that Chase lent $132 million in the second quarter of 2012 to businesses. A report by the Federal Reserve shows that large banks are owering their standatrds for lending to large and medium-sized companies. **Availability:** Print; Online.

10427 ■ "Cogs in R.I. Manufacturing Machine" in Providence Business News (Vol. 28, January 27, 2014, No. 43, pp. 1)
Pub: American City Business Journals, Inc.
Contact: Mike Olivieri, Executive Vice President
URL(s): pbn.com/cogs-in-ri-manufacturing-machine9
  4640
Description: Machine shops are capable of fixing or designing unique parts for manufacturing equipment and serve as a critical link in a company's production and distribution. Rhode Island has at least 50 machine shops capable of fabricating parts for companies. The Rhode Island Manufacturers Association's efforts to close the skills gap in machining are examined. **Availability:** Online.

10428 ■ "The Consequences of Tardiness" in Modern Machine Shop (Vol. 84, August 2011, No. 3, pp. 34)
Description: Five point addressing motivating factors behind employees who are tardy and those who choose to be on time in the workplace are shared. **Availability:** Online.

10429 ■ "Evaluate Your Process and Do It Better" in Modern Machine Shop (Vol. 84, October 2011, No. 5, pp. 34)
Pub: Gardner Business Media Inc.
Contact: Rick Kline, Jr., President
E-mail: rkline2@gardnerweb.com
Ed: Wayne Chaneski. **Released:** September 15, 2011. **Description:** In order to be more competitive, many machine shops owners are continually looking at their processes and procedures in order to be more competitive. **Availability:** Print; Online.

10430 ■ "Fabricator's Toolroom Becomes Captive CNC Machine Shop" in Modern Machine Shop (November 3, 2019)
URL(s): www.mmsonline.com/blog/post/fabricators
  -toolroom-becomes-captive-cnc-machine-shop
Ed: Matt Danford. **Released:** November 03, 2019. **Description:** Profile of Ace Stamping & Machine Co.'s transformation from just an ordinary toolroom to CNC machine shop. **Availability:** Online.

10431 ■ "From Chelsea Machine Shop to Nobel Prize" in Crain's Detroit Business (Vol. 30, October 13, 2014, No. 41, pp. 35)
Pub: Crain Communications Inc.
Contact: Barry Asin, President
Description: Profile of Eric Betzig, one of three scientists recognized with the Nobel Prize in Chemistry for devising ways for microscopes to look into the molecular hearts of living cells. Betzig is an Ann Arbor, Michigan native who performs research in Virginia for the Howard Hughes Medical Institute. **Availability:** Print; Online.

10432 ■ "Getting the Word Out" in Modern Machine Shop (Vol. 84, September 2011, No. 4, pp. 16)
Pub: Gardner Business Media Inc.
Contact: Rick Kline, Jr., President
E-mail: rkline2@gardnerweb.com
Ed: Derek Korn. **Description:** Many times machine shops create devices to streamline their own machining processes and find these devices can be used by other shops, thus developing a marketable product. Tips for this process are outlined. **Availability:** Print; Online.

10433 ■ "Got Skills? Think Manufacturing" in Occupational Outlook Quarterly (Vol. 58, Summer 2014, No. 2, pp. 28)
Pub: Government Publishing Office
Contact: Hugh Nathanial Halpern, Director
Released: June 22, 2014. **Description:** According to the U.S. Bureau of Labor Statistics, 264,000 job openings in manufacturing were reported in March 2014. Employers are finding it difficult to fill jobs for machinists and maintenance technicians, among other skilled trades. Manufacturers are also looking for welders, but also for workers outside of production, including biomedical engineers, dispatchers, and truck drivers. An overview of current manufacturing issues and statistics is included. **Availability:** Print; Online.

10434 ■ "Lampton Welding Launches Work on New Compressed-Gas Facility" in Wichita Business Journal (Vol. 27, February 3, 2012, No. 5, pp. 1)
Pub: Baltimore Business Journal
Contact: Rhonda Pringle, President
E-mail: rpringle@bizjournals.com
Description: Lampton Welding Supply has announced plans to open its new filling and mixing plant for cylinders containing industrial, medical and specialty gases in June. The site includes a state-of-the-art compressed-gas facility that co-owner David Lampton believed will attrac industry representatives to Wichita, Kansas. Insights on Lampton Welding's other facilities are also given.

10435 ■ Machine Tool Reference Guide
Pub: Machinery Dealers National Association
Contact: Craig L. Ward, President
URL(s): www.mdna.org/buyers-guide--serial-number
  -reference-book.html
Price: $39.95, Nonmembers for CD-ROM; $29.95, Individuals for CD-ROM. **Description:** Covers nearly 1,000 metalworking machine tool manufacturers; international coverage. Includes information on mergers and sources of parts. **Entries include:** Company name, address, phone, fax, product/service provided. **Arrangement:** Alphabetical. **Indexes:** Company name, type of equipment. **Availability:** CD-ROM.

10436 ■ "A Model Machine for Titanium" in Modern Machine Shop (Vol. 84, October 2011, No. 5, pp. 84)
Pub: Gardner Business Media Inc.
Contact: Rick Kline, Jr., President
E-mail: rkline2@gardnerweb.com
Released: September 15, 2011. **Description:** Researchers have developed a machine tool that controls vibration in order to mill titanium more productively. In-depth information on the machine tool as well as understanding the processes involved in milling titanium is covered. **Availability:** Online.

10437 ■ "A Parts Maker Primed for Takeoff" in Barron's (Vol. 92, August 25, 2012, No. 35, pp. 39)
Pub: Dow Jones & Company Inc.
Contact: Almar Latour, Chief Executive Officer
Ed: David Englander. **Description:** The stocks of machinery maker Curtiss-Wright could gain value due to the manufacturing company's healthy commercial business. The company's stock prices have fallen to $29.27/share due to concerns about reductions in defense spending, but could be worth $40/share. **Availability:** Online.

10438 ■ "Parts, Tooling Manufacturer Machinists Inc. Opts to Expand in South Park" in Puget Sound Business Journal (Vol. 34, February 21, 2014, No. 45, pp. 6)
Pub: American City Business Journals, Inc.
Contact: Mike Olivieri, Executive Vice President
Description: Seattle, Washington-based Machinists Inc. announced an expansion with a seventh building in South Park. The new 20,000-square-foot building will increase the company's footprint to 115,000-

square-feet when fully outfitted. The machine manufacturer shares insight into its decision to stay in Seattle rather than relocate is offered. **Availability:** Online.

10439 ■ *"Pedal to the Medal" in Small Business Opportunities (Summer 2010)*
Description: Profile of Darlene Miller who became and partner and eventually took over Permac Industries, a firm that specializes in precision machine products. **Availability:** Print; Online.

10440 ■ *"San Antonio's Alamo Iron Works Is On the Prowl for Acquisitions" in San Antonio Business Journal (Vol. 26, August 3, 2012, No. 27, pp. 1)*
Pub: Baltimore Business Journal
Contact: Rhonda Pringle, President
E-mail: rpringle@bizjournals.com
Description: Alamo Iron Works is preparing for acquisitions two years after emerging from Chapter 11 bankruptc reorganization. The company is in talks to purchase other firms to strengthen its share in the Texas steel market and serve the state's energy industry.

10441 ■ *"Sheet Metal Union Locals Join Forces: Could Help Local Contractors Compete for Bay Area Jobs" in Sacramento Business Journal (Vol. 29, June 29, 2012, No. 18, pp. 1)*
Pub: Baltimore Business Journal
Contact: Rhonda Pringle, President
E-mail: rpringle@bizjournals.com
Description: The Sacramento Local 162 and Local 104 of Sheet Metal Workers International Association in California's Bay Area have merged, leading to an action that is expected to help local contractors compete for jobs in the area. Aside from improving efficiency in operations, the merger could also prevent duplication of services. Other potential benefits of the merger are discussed. **Availability:** Print; Online.

10442 ■ *"Tempering Urgency Within Your Shop" in Modern Machine Shop (Vol. 84, October 2011, No. 5, pp. 16)*
Pub: Gardner Business Media Inc.
Contact: Rick Kline, Jr., President
E-mail: rkline2@gardnerweb.com
Ed: Derek Korn. **Released:** September 20, 2011. **Description:** Because machine shops operate under an environment of urgency, patience can commingle with the pressure to produce products efficiently and timely. **Availability:** Print; Online.

10443 ■ *"To Be or Not To Be an S Corporation" in Modern Machine Shop (Vol. 84, September 2011, No. 4, pp. 38)*
Pub: Gardner Business Media Inc.
Contact: Rick Kline, Jr., President
E-mail: rkline2@gardnerweb.com
Ed: Irving L. Blackman. **Description:** The definitions of both C corporations and S corporations are defined to help any machine shop discover which best suits the owner's business plan. **Availability:** Online.

10444 ■ *"Tooling Firm Thinks Being In U.P. Gives It Upper Hand" in Crain's Detroit Business (Vol. 30, October 13, 2014, No. 41, pp. 21)*
Pub: Crain Communications Inc.
Contact: Barry Asin, President
Description: Extreme Tool & Engineering is located in a remote region of Michigan's Upper Peninsula. The firm's employees average age is 28 and owner, Mike Zacharias, believes that combination contributes to the mold maker's success. He believes in the power of youth and reinvesting in training. Despite the economic challenges of the area, he employs nearly 80 workers. **Availability:** Online.

10445 ■ *"Upsurge" in Puget Sound Business Journal (Vol. 33, July 13, 2012, No. 12, pp. 1)*
Description: Kent, Washington-based Flow International Corporation posted a record of $254 million in annual sales for fiscal 2012 and it is expected to

reach about $300 million by 2014. Flow is being lifted by a global manufacturing revival and by its machines' ability to handle the carbon-fiber composites used in aerospace. Insights on Flow's water jet cutting tools are also given.

10446 ■ *Used Machinery Buyer's Guide*
Pub: Machinery Dealers National Association
Contact: Craig L. Ward, President
URL(s): www.mdna.org/mdna-member-benefits.h
tmlweb.mdna.org/search
Description: Covers 450 member dealers in used capital equipment. **Entries include:** Company name, address, phone, names of executives, telex number, telefax. **Arrangement:** Geographical, Alphabetical, specialty. **Indexes:** Company name, types of equipment. **Availability:** Print.

10447 ■ *"What Do Your ISO Procedures Say?" in Modern Machine Shop (Vol. 84, September 2011, No. 4, pp. 34)*
Pub: Gardner Business Media Inc.
Contact: Rick Kline, Jr., President
E-mail: rkline2@gardnerweb.com
Ed: Wayne Chaneski. **Released:** August 24, 2011. **Description:** ISO 9000 certification can be time-consuming and costly, but it is a necessary step in developing a quality management system that meets both current and potential customer needs. **Availability:** Print; Online.

10448 ■ *"What Is In Your Company Library?" in Modern Machine Shop (Vol. 84, October 2011, No. 5, pp. 60)*
Pub: Gardner Business Media Inc.
Contact: Rick Kline, Jr., President
E-mail: rkline2@gardnerweb.com
Ed: Mike Lynch. **Released:** September 15, 2011. **Description:** A good company library in any machine shop can help keep employees productive. Safety as well as information are critical to complete any task in a shop. **Availability:** Print; Online.

STATISTICAL SOURCES

10449 ■ *RMA Annual Statement Studies*
Pub: Risk Management Association
Contact: Nancy Foster, President
Released: Annual. **Description:** Contains composite balance sheets and income statements for more than 360 industries, including the accounting, auditing, and bookkeeping industries. Also contains five years of comparative historical data for discerning trends. Includes 16 commonly used ratios, computed for most of the size groupings for nearly every industry.

TRADE PERIODICALS

10450 ■ *Die Casting Engineer (DCE)*
Pub: North American Die Casting Association
Contact: Stephen Udvardy, President
E-mail: udvardy@diecasting.org
URL(s): www.diecasting.org/Web/Resources/Die
_Casting_Engineer/Web/Resources/DCE.aspx
Ed: Andy Ryzner. **Released:** 6/year; January, March, May, July, September and November. **Price:** $150, Canada and Mexico; $35, Single issue; $100, for annual in north America; $200, for 2 year north American; $170, for international annual; $340, for 2 year international; $15, for single copy. **Description:** Trade magazine serving the die casting industry. **Availability:** Print; Online.

10451 ■ *The Fabricator*
Pub: Fabricators and Manufacturers Association, International
Contact: Carlos Mendizabal-Perez, Chairman
URL(s): www.thefabricator.com
Facebook: www.facebook.com/thefabricator
Linkedin: www.linkedin.com/company/the-fabricator
-magazine
X (Twitter): x.com/fabricating
Instagram: www.instagram.com/thefabricator_maga
zine

Ed: Dan Davis. **Released:** Monthly **Description:** Trade journal covering the metal-forming and fabricating industry. Reports on state-of-the-art technology. Includes association and industry news, new product information, recently published literature, and reviews. **Availability:** Print; Online.

10452 ■ *Global Casting Magazine*
Pub: American Foundry Society
Contact: Doug Kurkul, Chief Executive Officer
URL(s): www.foundry-planet.com/home/globalcas
tingmagazine
Released: Quarterly **Description:** Magazine on metal casting plants and pattern shops. **Availability:** Print; Download; PDF; Online.

10453 ■ *Machining Science and Technology*
Pub: Taylor & Francis Group (Journals)
Contact: Annie Callanan, Chief Executive Officer
URL(s): www.tandfonline.com/journals/lmst20
Released: 6/year **Price:** $2,355, Institutions for print + online; $1,931, Institutions for online only; $610, Individuals for print only. **Availability:** Print; Download; PDF; Online.

10454 ■ *Metalforming: Serving the Precision Metalforming Industry*
Pub: Precision Metalforming Association
Contact: David Klotz, President
URL(s): www.metalformingmagazine.com
Facebook: www.facebook.com/Me
talFormingMagazine
Linkedin: www.linkedin.com/company/metalforming
-magazine
X (Twitter): x.com/MetalForming
YouTube: www.youtube.com/channel/UChsI-EQJ
3m773dP7vYGAPew
Released: Monthly **Price:** $40, for annual North America; $225, for annual North America international. **Description:** Covers materials and equipment, electronics in metal forming and assembly, taxes, legal issues, and management. **Availability:** Print; Online.

10455 ■ *Tooling & Production: Providing Solutions for Metalworking Manufacturers*
Pub: Nelson Publishing Inc.
Contact: Arnold L. V. Nelson, President
URL(s): www.toolingandproduction.com/web/adver
tise.php
Released: Bimonthly; 24 issue. **Description:** Magazine concerning metalworking. **Availability:** Print.

10456 ■ *The WELDER*
Pub: Fabricators and Manufacturers Association, International
Contact: Carlos Mendizabal-Perez, Chairman
URL(s): www.thefabricator.com/thewelder
Ed: Amanda Carlson. **Released:** Bimonthly **Description:** Covers instructional and educational information on welding. **Availability:** Print; Online.

TRADE SHOWS AND CONVENTIONS

10457 ■ *Metalcon*
Practice Management Associations Ltd.
10 Midland Ave.
Newton, MA 02458-1001
URL: http://NA
Contact: Gregory Hart, President
URL(s): metalcon.com
Facebook: www.facebook.com/PSMJMETALCON
Linkedin: www.linkedin.com/company/metalcon-in
ternational
X (Twitter): twitter.com/metalcon
Frequency: Annual. **Description:** Building systems components supplies, accessories, technologies, and services for the metal construction industry. **Audience:** Industry professionals. **Principal Exhibits:** Building systems components supplies, accessories, technologies, and services for the metal construction industry. Dates and Locations: 2025 Oct 21-23 Las Vegas Convention Center, Las Vegas, NV. **Telecommunication Services:** info@metalcon.com.

10458 ■ METALfab
National Ornamental & Miscellaneous Metals
  Association (NOMMA)
  3751 Main St., Ste. 600, No. 373
  The Colony, TX 75056
Free: 888-516-8585
Fax: (314)480-7118
Co. E-mail: info@nomma.org
URL: http://www.nomma.org
Contact: Peter Zadrozinski, President
URL(s): www.nomma.org/page/metalfab
Frequency: Annual. **Description:** Premier metal-
working event with exhibitors, education seminars,
and special activities. **Audience:** Metal industry
professionals. **Principal Exhibits:** Premier metal-
working event with exhibitors, education seminars,
and special activities. **Telecommunication Services:**
metalfab@nomma.org.

10459 ■ METALFORM Mexico
Precision Metalforming Association (PMA)
  6363 Oak Tree Blvd.
  Independence, OH 44131
Ph: (216)901-8800
URL: http://www.pma.org/home

Contact: David Klotz, President
URL(s): www.metalformingmagazine.com/article/?/
  management/consulting-and-training/metalform
  -mexico-set-for-monterrey

Frequency: Annual. **Description:** Presses and
stamping equipment, tooling and fabricating machines, management aids, and related materials.
Audience: Metal stampers and industry professionals. **Principal Exhibits:** Presses and stamping equipment, tooling and fabricating machines, management
aids, and related materials.

START-UP INFORMATION

10460 ■ *How to Start a Home-Based Mail Order Business*

Ed: Georganne Fiumara. **Released:** June 01, 2011. **Price:** Paperback. **Description:** Step-by-step guide for starting and growing a home-based mail order business. Information about equipment, pricing, online marketing, are included along with worksheets and checklists for planning. **Availability:** Print; Online.

REFERENCE WORKS

10461 ■ *"Citadel EFT (CDFT) Contracts With New Search Engine Optimization (SEO) and Banner Ad Web Marketing Companies" in Internet Wire (August 8, 2012)*

Pub: Comtex News Network Inc.

Contact: Kan Devnani, President

Description: Citafel EFT Inc. provides credit card terminals, online, mail order and retail credit card processing services. The firm has contracted with two Web marketing companies to increase its awareness on the Internet. **Availability:** Print; Online.

10462 ■ *The Directory of Mail Order Catalogs*

Pub: Grey House Publishing

Contact: Richard Gottlieb, President

URL(s): www.greyhouse.com/Directory-of-mail-order -catalogs

Released: Annual; latest edition 34th, 2020. **Price:** $250, Single issue for price. **Description:** Covers over 13,000 mail order firms and the catalogs they offer. **Entries include:** Company, address and phone for catalog orders, fax, description of merchandise offered; names of buyers, company president, marketing and production manager; size of catalog, price and frequency of catalog, availability of mailing list, number of employees, sales volume. **Arrangement:** Type of catalog or merchandise offered. **Indexes:** Company name, product, online. **Availability:** Print; Online; PDF; Download.

10463 ■ *"Extreme Temperatures May Pose Risks to Some Mail-Order Meds" in NPR (January 7, 2019)*

URL(s): www.npr.org/sections/health-shots/2019/01/ 07/673806506/extreme-temperatures-may-pose -risks-to-some-mail-order-meds

Ed: Alex Smith. **Released:** January 07, 2019. **Description:** With most medications instructing to store at room temperature, what happens when a mail delivery service leaves your meds in extreme weather conditions? Many prescriptions are filled online and home delivered, with packages being left in either extreme cold or heat, depending on the season and the location. A push is being made to go back to retail pharmacy services unless the mail-order services can prove that the drugs are being delivered at the right temperatures. **Availability:** Online.

10464 ■ *"In 'Unprecedented' Case, Maine Suspends Mail-Order Pharmacy Whose Drugs Killed Two Racehorses" in Bangor Daily News (October 7, 2019)*

URL(s): bangordailynews.com/2019/10/07/news/sta te/in-unprecedented-case-maine-suspends-mail-or der-pharmacy-whose-drugs-killed-two-racehorses/

Ed: Caitlin Andrews. **Released:** October 07, 2019. **Description:** Rapid Equine Pharmacy LLC was suspended by Maine regulators after two racehorses died after receiving the drugs without a prescription. **Availability:** Online.

10465 ■ *"The Retail Revolution: How Mail Order Changed Middle-Class Life" in BBC (May 8, 2019)*

URL(s): www.bbc.com/news/business-47954905

Ed: Tim Harford. **Released:** May 08, 2019. **Description:** History of the mail-order business, exploring Montgomery Ward's business model. **Availability:** Online.

10466 ■ *SRDS Direct Marketing List Source*

Pub: SRDS

URL(s): srds.com/direct-marketing-lists

Description: Covers over 38,000 mailing lists composed of business persons and firms, general consumers, and rural and farm consumers, plus cooperative mailings, card decks, and package insert programs. Includes separate sections for new listings, mailing list brokers, compilers, managers; and suppliers of products and services to the direct mail industry (e.g., lettershops, etc.); and an international counterpart to all of the above. **Entries include:** For mailing lists--Title of list; name, address, phone of owner, manager, or broker, and name of contact; description of list, and its arrangement, maintenance, quantity, etc.; specific identification of source of list; addressing selections, method of delivery, schedules; mailing services offered; restrictions on use of list; price. For brokers and compilers--Firm name, address, phone, names of principal personnel, types of lists handled, fees and deposit mailing services offered, association memberships. **Arrangement:** Lists arranged by market classification (safety, literature and book buyers, etc.), by list name within classifications; managers, compilers, and brokers are alphabetical; suppliers classified by service. **Indexes:** Subject/market classification, list title/list owner. **Availability:** Print.

10467 ■ *"Three Emerging Trends in Consumer Digital Mail-Order Health Products" in Mobi Health News (April 15, 2019)*

URL(s): www.mobihealthnews.com/content/three -emerging-trends-consumer-digital-mail-order-heal th-products

Ed: Laura Lovett. **Released:** April 15, 2019. **Description:** Online pharmacies are booming thanks to sites such as Amazon-owned Pillpack, and a startup called Capsule. Mail-order test kits are also gaining in popularity due to its ease of use for patients because they can get it all delivered to the homes without having to make an appointment at a doctor's office. **Availability:** Online.

STATISTICAL SOURCES

10468 ■ *Mail Order Industry in the US - Market Research Report*

URL(s): www.ibisworld.com/united-states/market-re search-reports/mail-order-industry/

Price: $925. **Description:** Downloadable report analyzing the current and future trends of the mail order industry. **Availability:** Online.

10469 ■ *RMA Annual Statement Studies*

Pub: Risk Management Association

Contact: Nancy Foster, President

Released: Annual. **Description:** Contains composite balance sheets and income statements for more than 360 industries, including the accounting, auditing, and bookkeeping industries. Also contains five years of comparative historical data for discerning trends. Includes 16 commonly used ratios, computed for most of the size groupings for nearly every industry.

10470 ■ *Standard & Poor's Industry Surveys*

Pub: Standard And Poor's Financial Services LLC.

Contact: Douglas L. Peterson, President

Description: Two-volume book that examines the prospects for specific industries, including trucking. Also provides analyses of trends and problems, statistical tables and charts, and comparative company analyses.

TRADE SHOWS AND CONVENTIONS

10471 ■ **Direct Marketing Association Annual Conference & Exhibition**

URL(s): www.thedma.org

Frequency: Annual. **Description:** Printers, list brokers, envelope manufacturers, telephone marketing companies, computers and other equipment, supplies, and services for direct marketing. **Audience:** Trade professionals and members. **Principal Exhibits:** Printers, list brokers, envelope manufacturers, telephone marketing companies, computers and other equipment, supplies, and services for direct marketing.

CONSULTANTS

10472 ■ **Jeffrey Lant Associates, Inc. (JLA)**

50 Follen St., No. 507
  Cambridge, MA 02138

Ph: (617)547-6372

Co. E-mail: drlant@drjeffreylant.com

URL: http://www.drjeffreylant.com

Description: Publishes technical assistance books for nonprofit organizations, consultants, independent professionals and small and home-based businesses. Offers audio cassettes, workshops and consultation services. Also publish twice the monthly Worlgram newsletter. Reaches market through commission representatives, direct mail, telephone sales and the Internet. Accept unsolicited manuscripts. **Founded:** 1997. **Publications:** "E-mail El Dorado," JLA Publications, 1998; "Web Wealth: How to Turn the World Wide Web Into a Cash Hose for Your Business. Whatever You're Selling," 1997; "Multi-Level Money,"

JLA Publications, 1994; "No More Cold Calls," JLA Publications, 1997; "Cash Copy"; "How to make at least $100000 a year"; "E-Money". **Training:** Business and personal development, including Establishing and Operating Your Successful Consulting Business; Successfully Promoting Your Small Business and Professional Practice; Succeeding in Your Mail Order Business; Successfully Raising Money for Your

Nonprofit Organization from Foundations, Corporations and Individuals; Money Making Marketing: Finding the People Who Need What You're Selling and Making Sure They Buy It; Getting Corporations, Foundations, and Individuals to Give You the Money Your Nonprofit Organization Needs.

START-UP INFORMATION

10473 ■ *How to Start a Home-Based Consulting Business: Define Your Specialty Build a Client Base Make Yourself Indispensable*

Ed: Bert Holtje. **Released:** January 06, 2010. **Price:** Paperback. **Description:** Everything needed for starting and running a successful consulting business from home. **Availability:** Print.

ASSOCIATIONS AND OTHER ORGANIZATIONS

10474 ■ **American Management Association (AMA)**

American Management Association (AMA)
 1601 Broadway
 New York, NY 10019
Ph: (212)586-8100
Free: 800-262-9699
Fax: (212)903-8168
Co. E-mail: customerservice@amanet.org
URL: http://www.amanet.org
Contact: Manny Avramidis, President
Facebook: www.facebook.com/AmericanManagemen
 tAssn
Linkedin: www.linkedin.com/company/american
 -management-association
X (Twitter): x.com/amanet
Instagram: www.instagram.com/
 americanmanagementassociation
YouTube: www.youtube.com/user/
 AmericanManagement

Description: Provides educational forums worldwide where members and their colleagues learn superior, practical business skills and explore best practices of world-class organizations through interaction with each other and expert faculty practitioners. Maintains a publishing program providing tools individuals use to extend learning beyond the classroom in a process of lifelong professional growth and development through education. **Holdings:** 15,000 multilingual learning objects. **Publications:** *Small Business Reports: For Decision Makers in America's Small and Mid-Size Companies* (Monthly); *AMA's Directory of Human Resource Products and Services*; *Management Review* (Monthly); *The Take-Charge Assistant* (Monthly); *Organizational Dynamics: A Quarterly Review of Organizational Behavior for Management Executives*; *HR Focus* (Monthly). **Educational Activities:** Negotiating to Win (Continuous); Writing for the Web; AMA Management Skills for Administrative Professionals (Continuous); AMA Project Management for Administrative Professionals (Onsite); AMA Managing Chaos: Dynamic Time Management, Recall, Reading, and Stress Management Skills for Administrative Professionals (Onsite); AMA The Voice of Leadership: How Leaders Inspire, Influence, and Achieve Results (Onsite); AMA Making the Transition to Management (Onsite); AMA Making the Transition from Staff Member to Supervisor (Onsite); AMA

Principles of Professional Selling (Continuous); AMA Technical Project Management (Onsite); AMA Leading Virtual Teams (Continuous); AMA Successful Product Management (Onsite); AMA's Course on Mergers and Acquisitions (Onsite); AMA Improving Your Project Management Skills: The Basics for Success (Continuous); AMA Partnering with Your Boss: Strategic Skills for Administrative Professionals (Continuous); AMA Effective Technical Writing (Onsite); AMA Strategies for Developing Effective Presentation Skills (Onsite); AMA Developing Your Personal Brand and Professional Image (Continuous); AMA Customer Service Excellence: How to Win and Keep Customers (Continuous); AMA Fundamentals of Cost Accounting (Onsite); AMA Recruiting, Interviewing and Selecting Employees (Onsite); AMA Managing Emotions in the Workplace: Strategies for Success (Onsite); AMA Responding to Conflict: Strategies for Improved Communication (Continuous); Assertiveness Training for Women in Business (Continuous); Leadership and Team Development for Managerial Success (Onsite); AMA's Leading with Emotional Intelligence (Onsite); AMA's 5-Day MBA Workshop (Continuous); Taking on Greater Responsibility: Step-up Skills for Nonmanagers (Onsite) (Irregular); Successfully Managing People (Continuous); Managing Chaos: How to set Priorities and Make Decisions Under Pressure (Continuous); Moving Ahead: Breaking Behavior Patterns That Hold You Back (Onsite); The Effective Facilitator: Maximizing Involvement and Results (Continuous); Conquering Your Management Challenges: Advanced Management Skills for Supervisors (Onsite); Coaching and Counseling for Outstanding Job Performance (Continuous); Advanced Critical Thinking Applications Workshop (Onsite); AMA's Advanced Course in Strategic Marketing (Onsite); AMA's Advanced Executive Leadership Program (Onsite); AMA's Comprehensive Budgeting Workshop (Continuous); AMA's Comprehensive Project Management Workshop (Onsite) (Continuous); AMA's Advanced Financial Forecasting and Modeling Workshop (Onsite) (Continuous); AMA's PMP Exam Prep Express (Onsite); Building Better Work Relationships: New Techniques for Results-oriented Communication (Continuous); Assertiveness Training for Managers (Onsite); Managing Chaos: Tools to Set Priorities and Make Decisions Under Pressure (Onsite) (Continuous); Developing Your Analytical Skills: How to Research and Present Information (Onsite); AMA's 2-Day Business Writing Workshop (Live Online) (Continuous); Business Writing for the Multilingual Professional; Effective Executive Speaking (Onsite) (Continuous); Communication and Interpersonal Skills: A Seminar for IT and Technical Professionals (Onsite) (Continuous); Communicating with Confidence (Onsite) (Continuous); Developing Effective Business Conversation Skills (Onsite); Interpersonal Skills for Managers (Onsite); How to Present Online: A Skills-Based Workshop; Succession Planning: Developing Talent from Within (Onsite); Collaborative Leadership Skills (Onsite) (Continuous); Fundamentals of Marketing: Your Action Plan for Success (Continuous); Information Technology Project Management (Continuous); Best Practices for the Multi-project Manager (Continuous);

Fundamentals of Purchasing for the New Buyer (Onsite); Selling to Major Accounts: A Strategic Approach (Onsite); Strategic Sales Negotiations (Onsite) (Continuous); Advanced Sales Management (Onsite); Effective Technical Writing (Onsite) (Continuous); Essentials of Project Management for the Nonproject Manager (Continuous). **Geographic Preference:** Multinational; National.

10475 ■ **Institute of Management Consultants USA (IMC USA)**
2598 E Sunrise Blvd., Ste. 2104
 Fort Lauderdale, FL 33304
Free: 800-793-4992
Co. E-mail: info@imcusa.org
URL: http://www.imcusa.org
Contact: Gregory Brooks, Executive Director
E-mail: greg@imcusa.org
Facebook: www.facebook.com/imcusa.org
Linkedin: www.linkedin.com/company/imcusa
X (Twitter): x.com/imcusa
Instagram: www.instagram.com/imc.usa
YouTube: www.youtube.com/channel/UCJ0K0FwRx
 3rWyrzlPmTk2uw/about
Pinterest: www.pinterest.com/IMCUSAconsultants

Description: Individual management consultants who work privately or in consulting firms. Sets standards of professionalism and ethics for the management consulting profession. **Scope:** Promotes excellence and ethics in management consulting through certification, education and professional resources. **Founded:** 1968. **Publications:** *Management Consultants Resource Guide* (Annual). **Educational Activities:** IMC USA Consulting Conference (Annual); IMC USA Management Consulting. **Awards:** Fellow of the Institute of Management Consultants (FIMC) (Irregular). **Geographic Preference:** National.

10476 ■ **International Association for Time Use Research (IATUR)**
Brussels, Belgium
URL: http://www.iatur.org
Contact: Theun Pieter van Tienoven, Treasurer
E-mail: t.p.van.tienoven@vub.be

Description: Facilitates exchange of ideas, methodology, and data collection techniques among researchers and compilers of official statistics on the patterns of daily activities and changes in people's behaviours over time. **Founded:** 1970. **Publications:** *The Journal of Time Use Research (eIJTUR)* (Annual); *Fifteenth Reunion of the International Association for Time Use Research Amsterdam* (Periodic); *Time Use Methodology: Towards Consensus*. **Geographic Preference:** Multinational.

10477 ■ *The Journal of Time Use Research (eIJTUR)*
Brussels, Belgium
URL: http://www.iatur.org
Contact: Theun Pieter van Tienoven, Treasurer
E-mail: t.p.van.tienoven@vub.be
URL(s): jtur.iatur.org
X (Twitter): x.com/journaltur

Ed: Prof. Jonathan Gershuny, Prof. Andrew S. Harvey. **Released:** Annual **Availability:** Print; Download; Online.

10478 ■ Professional and Technical Consultants Association (PATCA)

PO Box 2261
Santa Clara, CA 95055
Free: 800-747-2822
Fax: (866)746-1053
Co. E-mail: admin@patca.org
URL: http://patca.org
Contact: Chris Hansen, President
Facebook: www.facebook.com/pages/PATCA/48258
307732
X (Twitter): x.com/PATCA_SV
YouTube: www.youtube.com/channel/UCL
6gesDzEPk3NPdi1g8qFJA

Description: Represents Independent consultants active in the support of business, industry, and government. Serves as a referral service to aid independent consultants in marketing their services as well as to assist those seeking their services. **Publications:** *Professional and Technical Consultants Association--Member Directory* (Annual); *PATCA Survey of Rates and Business Practices*; *PATCA News and Events.* **Geographic Preference:** National.

10479 ■ Turnaround Management Association (TMA)

150 N Wacker Dr., Ste. 1900
Chicago, IL 60606
Ph: (312)578-6900
Fax: (312)578-8336
Co. E-mail: info@turnaround.org
URL: http://www.turnaround.org
Contact: Scott Y. Stuart, Chief Executive Officer
E-mail: sstuart@turnaround.org
Facebook: www.facebook.com/Turnaroun
dManagementAssociation
Linkedin: www.linkedin.com/company/868513
X (Twitter): x.com/TMAGlobal
Instagram: www.instagram.com/tmaglobal

Description: Works with companies to improve performance, manage disruption, restructure, work through insolvency, preserve equity, and drive significantly improved results. It seeks to strengthen the global economy by working to save distressed businesses, assist management to navigate off-plan events, and help healthy companies avoid similar pitfalls. **Founded:** 1988. **Publications:** *Professional Fees in Bankruptcy Handbook.* **Educational Activities:** Turnaround Management Association Spring Leadership Meeting (Annual). **Awards:** TMA Turnaround of the Year (Annual). **Geographic Preference:** National.

REFERENCE WORKS

10480 ■ *"Benchmark Makes Granduca Entrance" in Houston Business Journal (Vol. 40, January 8, 2010, No. 35, pp. 2)*

Pub: Houston Business Journal
Contact: Bob Charlet, President
E-mail: bcharlet@bizjournals.com

Ed: Jennifer Dawson. **Description:** Houston, Texas-based Interfin Company, owner of the Hotel Granduca, has tapped the services of Benchmark Hospitality International to manage the property. The hiring of Benchmark is part of Interfin's efforts to develop Granduca hotels in other markets. Statistical data included. **Availability:** Print; Online.

10481 ■ *Case Master: Thoughtful Cases for Competitive Future Consultants*

Ed: Valentin Nugmanov, Ron Clouse. **Released:** November 12, 2018. **Price:** $22.75, Paperback; $9.99, E-book. **Description:** A collection of practice cases for consultants to study in order to gain a competitive edge when interviewing for a potential project. **Availability:** Print; Online.

10482 ■ *"CFOs Walk a Tightrope When Picking Consultants" in The Wall Street Journal (July 26, 2016)*

URL(s): blogs.wsj.com/cfo/2016/07/26/cfos-walk-a
-tightrope-when-picking-consultants/
Ed: Tatyana Shumsky. **Released:** July 26, 2016.
Description: Choosing a business consultant is often tricky and picking someone who isn't a good fit for the company can waste funds and time. CFOs often bring in outside help and they need to do their due diligence to make sure this person will get the job done. That includes contacting references and making sure the consultant has actually done this type of work in the past. Giving them a small project to start is often advised, and then moving them onto bigger projects once the scope of their knowledge and skill set are known. **Availability:** Online.

10483 ■ *Consultants & Consulting Organizations Directory (CCOD)*

Pub: Gale, part of Cengage Group
Contact: Paul Gazzolo, General Manager Senior Vice President
URL(s): www.gale.com/ebooks/9780028668062/con-
sultants--consulting-organizations-directory
Released: Latest 46th Edition. **Description:** Covers over 26,000 firms, individuals, and organizations active in consulting. **Entries include:** Individual or organization name, address, phone, fax, e-mail, URL, specialties, founding date, branch offices, names and titles of key personnel, number of employees, financial data, publications, seminars and workshops. **Arrangement:** By broad subject categories. **Indexes:** Subject, geographical, organization name. **Availability:** E-book; Download. **Type:** Directory.

10484 ■ *Consulting Success: The Proven Guide to Start, Run and Grow a Successful Consulting Business*

Ed: Michael Zipursky. **Released:** October 18, 2018. **Price:** $14.99, Paperback; $9.99, E-book. **Description:** A guide to the time-tested principles, strategies, tactics, and best-practices successful consultants engage in. **Availability:** Online.

10485 ■ *"The Couch in the Corner Office: Surveying the Landscape of the CEO Psyche" in Inc. (January 2008, pp. 33-34)*

Description: Profile of Leslie G. Mayer, founder of the Leadership Group, a firm that provides assistance to CEOs of firms by offering a deep understanding of the relationships, insecurities, and blind spots that can weaken strong leadership. **Availability:** Online.

10486 ■ *The Mirror Test: Is Your Business Really Breathing?*

Pub: Grand Central Publishing
Contact: Michael Pietsch, Chairman
Ed: Jeffrey W. Hayzlett. **Released:** May 05, 2010. **Price:** $9.99, e-book. **Description:** Consultant and author, Jeffrey Hayzlett, explains why a business is not doing well and asks the questions that most business managers are afraid to ask. **Availability:** E-book; Print.

10487 ■ *Professional and Technical Consultants Association--Member Directory (Internet only)*

Pub: Professional and Technical Consultants Association
Contact: Chris Hansen, President
URL(s): patca.org/join/benefits-of-membership
Released: Annual **Description:** Covers more than 350 consultants involved in computer technology, management, marketing, manufacturing, engineering, etc. **Entries include:** Individual or firm name, address, phone, specialties, degrees held. **Arrangement:** Alphabetical. **Indexes:** Specialty, geographical. **Availability:** Online.

10488 ■ *"Sleeping with Your Smartphone: How to Break the 24/7 Habit and Change the Way You Work"*

Pub: Harvard Business Review Press
Contact: Moderna V. Pfizer, Contact

Released: May 29, 2012. **Price:** $30, Hardcover/Hardcopy. **Description:** Harvard Business School professor, Leslie Perlow, reveals ways to become more productive after disconnecting from your smartphone. A six-person team was used in an experiment at The Boston Consulting Group, an elite management consulting firm, where teams changed the way they worked and became more efficient and effective by disconnecting. The team was better able to perform and recruit new talent. A step-by-step guide is offered to change your team. **Availability:** E-book; Print.

STATISTICAL SOURCES

10489 ■ *RMA Annual Statement Studies*

Pub: Risk Management Association
Contact: Nancy Foster, President

Released: Annual. **Description:** Contains composite balance sheets and income statements for more than 360 industries, including the accounting, auditing, and bookkeeping industries. Also contains five years of comparative historical data for discerning trends. Includes 16 commonly used ratios, computed for most of the size groupings for nearly every industry.

TRADE PERIODICALS

10490 ■ *Productivity Software*

Pub: Worldwide Videotex
URL(s): wvpubs.com/publications

Released: Annual **Price:** $200, Individuals for hard copy; $185, Individuals for hard copy; $165, Other countries for e-file (PDF or DOC). **Description:** Provides information on computer software. **Availability:** Print; Online; PDF.

VIDEO/AUDIO MEDIA

10491 ■ *Rewiring Organziations for a Successful Digital Transformation*

URL(s): ducttapemarketing.com/rewiring-organiza
tions-for-a-successful-digital-transformation

Ed: John Jantsch. **Released:** June 20, 2023. **Description:** Offers insights on digital transformation as an ongoing journey, along with the importance of up-skilling and reskilling talent. Features Rodney Zemmel, the co-leader of McKinsey Digital Practice.

CONSULTANTS

10492 ■ Advisory Management Services Inc.

9600 E 129th St.
Kansas City, MO 64149
Contact: William H. Wood, President

Description: A management consulting and training firm specializing in employee relations, management and staff training, organizational development, strategic planning and continuous quality improvement. **Scope:** A management consulting and training firm specializing in employee relations, management and staff training, organizational development, strategic planning and continuous quality improvement. **Founded:** 1979.

10493 ■ Agiletic Law Group

17085 Via Del Campo
San Diego, CA 92127
URL: http://agiletic.com
Contact: James Cartoni, Principal
E-mail: jim@agiletic.com

Description: A small firm of highly experienced attorneys providing advisory services to entrepreneurs, private companies and public companies. Helps with business startup, raising financing, business growth, and business transactions. **Scope:** A small firm of highly experienced attorneys providing advisory services to entrepreneurs, private companies and public companies. Helps with business startup, raising financing, business growth, and business transactions.

10494 ■ The Alliance Management Group Inc.

38 Old Chester Rd., Ste. 300
Gladstone, NJ 07934
Ph: (908)234-2344
Fax: (908)234-0638
URL: http://www.strategicalliance.com
Contact: Dr. Gene Slowinski, Director

Description: Firm is engaged in business management consultant such as integration, technology management and related services. **Scope:** Firm is engaged in business management consultant such as integration, technology management and related services. **Publications:** "Effective Practices For Sourcing Innovation," Jan-Feb, 2009; "Intellectual Property Issues in Collaborative Research Agreements," Nov-Dec, 2008; "Building University Relationships in China," Sep-Oct, 2008; "Reinventing Corporate Growth: Implementing the Transformational Growth Model"; "The Strongest Link"; "Allocating Patent Rights in Collaborative Research Agreements"; "Protecting Know-how and Trade Secrets in Collaborative Research Agreements," Aug, 2006; "Sourcing External Technology for Innovation," Jun, 2006. **Special Services:** "Want, Find, Get, Manage" Model®; "Want, Find, Get, Manage" Framework®; WFGM Framework®; The Alliance Implementation Program®; WFGM Paradigm®; WFGM Model®; "Want, Find, Get, Manage" Paradigm®, Transformational Growth®; T-growth®.

10495 ■ Alliance Management International Ltd.

6200 Rockside Rd.
Cleveland, OH 44131
Contact: Carolyn K. Matheson, Contact

Description: A consulting company that helps to form national and international strategic alliances. Handles alliances between companies forming joint ventures. Staff specialized in small company-large company alliance, alliance assessment and analysis and alliance strategic planning. **Scope:** A consulting company that helps to form national and international strategic alliances. Handles alliances between companies forming joint ventures. Staff specialized in small company-large company alliance, alliance assessment and analysis and alliance strategic planning. **Training:** Joint Business Planning; Developing a Shared Vision; Current and New/Prospective Partner Assessment; Customer Service; Sales Training; Leader and Management Skills.

10496 ■ American Business Advisors Inc. (ABA)

6635 S Dayton St., Ste. 200
Greenwood Village, CO 80111
Ph: (303)335-4218
Co. E-mail: info@abadvisors.com
URL: http://abadvisors.com
Contact: Dennis R. Guse, President
Facebook: www.facebook.com/AmericanBusinessAdvisors
Linkedin: www.linkedin.com/company/ab_advisors
X (Twitter): x.com/AB_Advisors

Description: Firm provides business management solutions and consulting services, strategic solutions such as managing finance, increasing market shares, and much more. **Scope:** Firm provides business management solutions and consulting services, strategic solutions such as managing finance, increasing market shares, and much more. **Founded:** 1984. **Publications:** "To Market or Not to Market in a Recession," 2008; "The Wheels on the Bus Go Round and Round," 2008; "It Takes A Team," 2008; "Dos and Don'ts of Email Communication," 2007; "The Power of Purpose," 2007. **Training:** Building Cash Cow; Improving Quality of Life; Effective Personal Productivity; Strategic Exit. **Special Services:** Emerging Track Companies™, Fast Track Companies™, RightTrack Companies™, On Track Companies™, Exit TrackCompanies™, The Strategic Edge™, The ABAInsider™, American Business Advisors®, Building Cash Cow®, Improving Quality of Life®.

10497 ■ Amplio Strategies (AS)

9880 rue Clark, Ste. 215
Montreal, QC, Canada H3L 2R3
Free: 866-983-6837
Co. E-mail: info@ampliostrategies.com
URL: http://ampliostrategies.com
Contact: Philippe Richard-Bertrand, President
E-mail: prbertrand@ampliostrategies.com
Facebook: www.facebook.com/AmplioStrategies
Instagram: www.instagram.com/ampliostrategies

Description: An agile consulting firm working to support managers and teams of SMEs and large companies as they work to grow and transform. **Scope:** An agile consulting firm working to support managers and teams of SMEs and large companies as they work to grow and transform. **Founded:** 2016.

10498 ■ Amusement Consultants Ltd.

56 Harrison St.
New Rochelle, NY 10801
Ph: (914)576-7800
Fax: (914)576-3620
Co. E-mail: info@amusementconsultants.com
URL: http://www.amusementconsultants.com
Contact: Melvin Getlan, President

Description: Owns and operates amusement centers, and provides a variety of business development and management services to other independent operators. **Scope:** Owns and operates amusement centers, and provides a variety of business development and management services to other independent operators. **Founded:** 1952.

10499 ■ Andrade Business Consultants L.L.C.

9901 W Interstate 10 Ste. 800
San Antonio, TX 78230-2292
Contact: Dr. Gloria Merrell, Member
E-mail: gloria@andradebc.com

Description: Bilingual management consulting firm integrates hands-on training programs to assist developing and growing companies, their services extend from a global marketing to accounting procedures, but include management, business and financial plans, import feasibility analysis, project management, market research, global sourcing, and marketing strategy. **Training:** Time management; Conflict resolution; Project management; Harassment in the workplace; Cross-Cultural Management; Team-building.

10500 ■ Apex Innovations Inc.

19951 W 162nd St.
Olathe, KS 66062
Ph: (913)254-0250
Fax: (913)254-0320
URL: http://www.apex-innovations.com

Description: Developer of software for dynamically sharing information and processes between organizations. **Scope:** Developer of software for dynamically sharing information and processes between organizations. **Founded:** 2002. **Special Services:** i-INFO. EPR™; i-INFO.WORKS™; i-INFO Classes™.

10501 ■ Arnold S. Goldin & Associates Inc.

PO Box 276158
Boca Raton, FL 33427
Ph: (561)994-5810
Fax: (561)431-3102
URL: http://www.arnoldgoldin.com

Description: An accounting and management consulting firm. Serves clients worldwide. Provides management services. Handles monthly write-ups and tax returns. **Scope:** An accounting and management consulting firm. Serves clients worldwide. Provides management services. Handles monthly write-ups and tax returns.

10502 ■ Aspire Business Development Inc.

10955 Lowell Ave., Ste. 400
Overland Park, KS 66210
Ph: (913)660-9400
Co. E-mail: info@aspirekc.com
URL: http://aspirekc.com
Contact: Shawn Kinkade, President
E-mail: skinkade@aspirekc.com

Description: Firm provides business management consulting services, business aspirations models, business effectiveness analysis, and much more services. **Scope:** Firm provides business management consulting services, business aspirations models, business effectiveness analysis, and much more services.

10503 ■ Associated Enterprises, Ltd.

Unilever plc
183 Pauls Ln.
Bailey, CO 80421
Ph: 44 20 782-252-52
Co. E-mail: office.london@unilever.com
URL: http://www.unilever.com
Contact: Lawrence J. Rouse, Contact

Description: General management consulting in all disciplines plus specialty in franchise and franchisee development programs. Additional specialties include economic research, analysis and forecasting, financial management, business planning and financing packaging, involving equity, debt, SBA 7A loans, 501 or 504 program development and federal, state and local program packages. **Scope:** General management consulting in all disciplines plus specialty in franchise and franchisee development programs. Additional specialties include economic research, analysis and forecasting, financial management, business planning and financing packaging, involving equity, debt, SBA 7A loans, 501 or 504 program development and federal, state and local program packages. **Founded:** 1968.

10504 ■ Associated Management Services, Inc. (AMSI)

8701 Georgia Ave., Ste. 705
Silver Spring, MD 20910-3713
Ph: (301)588-9694
Co. E-mail: info@amsihq.com
URL: http://www.amsihq.com
Contact: Robert Mckinney, Chief Operating Officer
E-mail: robertmckinney@msn.com

Description: Firm provides management and technical services such as warehouse and distribution services, building maintenance, and much more. **Scope:** Firm provides management and technical services such as warehouse and distribution services, building maintenance, and much more. **Founded:** 1984.

10505 ■ Aurora Management Partners Inc.

1201 Peachtree St., Ste. 1570
Atlanta, GA 30361
Ph: (704)377-6010
Co. E-mail: info@auroramp.com
URL: http://www.auroramp.com
Contact: David Baker, CTP, Managing Partner
Linkedin: www.linkedin.com/company/aurora-management-partners/about

Description: Specializes in turnaround management and reorganization consulting, the company develops strategic initiatives, organize and analyze solutions, deal with creditor issues, review organizational structures and develop time frames for decision making. **Founded:** 2000. **Publications:** "TMA Turnaround of the Year Award, Small Company, Honorable Mention," Nov, 2005; "Back From The Brink - Bland Farms," Progressive Farmer, Oct, 2004; "New Breed of Turnaround Managers," Catalyst Magazine, Aug, 2004; "Key Performance Drivers - Bland Farms," The Produce News, Apr, 2004; "Corporate Governance: Averting Crisis's Before They Happen," ABJ journal, Feb, 2004.

10506 ■ Bahr International Inc.

12221 Merit Dr., Ste. 1305
Dallas, TX 75251
Contact: C. Charles Bahr, III, President

Description: Firm provides full-service turnaround management services and its operating solutions. **Scope:** Firm provides full-service turnaround management services and its operating solutions.

10507 ■ Beacon Management-Management Consultants

Pompano Beach, FL 33069
Co. E-mail: md@beaconmgmt.com

URL: http://www.beaconmgmt.com
Contact: Michael J. Donnelly, Consultant Managing Director Principal
Description: Provider of management consulting services such as strategic and business planning, market intelligence, decision support services, corporate finance, and much more. **Scope:** Provider of management consulting services such as strategic and business planning, market intelligence, decision support services, corporate finance, and much more. **Founded:** 1985. **Publications:** "Sun-Sentinel Article," Oct, 2012.

10508 ■ BioSciCon, Inc. [Biomedical Science Consulting Company, Inc.]
14905 Forest Landing Cir.
 Rockville, MD 20850
Ph: (301)610-9130
Fax: (301)610-7662
Co. E-mail: info@bioscicon.com
URL: http://www.bioscicon.com
Contact: Dr. Nenad Markovic, President
Description: Provider of biomedical science consulting and also a developer of biotechnology products. **Scope:** Provider of biomedical science consulting and also a developer of biotechnology products. **Founded:** 1996. **Publications:** "Cervical Acid Phosphates: A Biomarker of Cervical Dysplasia and Potential Surrogate Endpoint for Colposcopy," 2004; "Enhancing Pap test with a new biological marker of cervical dysplasia," 2004; "A cytoplasmic biomarker for liquid-based Pap," The FACEB Journal Experimental Biology, 2004; "Pap test and new biomarker-based technology for enhancing visibility of abnormal cells," 2004. **Special Services:** MarkPap®; PreservCyt®.

10509 ■ Blankinship & Associates Inc.
1615 5th St., Ste. A
 Davis, CA 95616
Ph: (530)757-0941
URL: http://www.h2osci.com
Contact: Michael Blankinship, President
Description: Provider of consulting services to support water resources, agriculture and risk evaluation and communication, water resources management and regulatory. **Scope:** Provider of consulting services to support water resources, agriculture and risk evaluation and communication, water resources management and regulatory. **Founded:** 2000. **Publications:** "Air Blast Sprayer Calibration and Chlorpyrifos Irrigation Study," Oct, 2007; "How Green is your golf course," Prosper Magazine, 2007. **Training:** CDFG Wildlands IPM Seminar, Oct, 2009.

10510 ■ Business Development International Inc. (BDII)
5100 Cinnabar Dr., Ste. 100
 Johns Creek, GA 30022
Ph: (770)740-9979
Co. E-mail: info@bdii.net
URL: http://www.bdii.net
Contact: Russell H. Schoper, II, President
Description: Management consulting firm provides consulting services worldwide and works with clients in Europe, Asia, China, Australia, Latin America, South Africa, Canada and the United States, their primary focus is on business development strategy, card sales support, co-branding, affinity programs, merchant sales support, card processing, electronic commerce, credit and debit cards and retail banking. **Scope:** Management consulting firm provides consulting services worldwide and works with clients in Europe, Asia, China, Australia, Latin America, South Africa, Canada and the United States, their primary focus is on business development strategy, card sales support, co-branding, affinity programs, merchant sales support, card processing, electronic commerce, credit and debit cards and retail banking.

10511 ■ Business Engineering
412 Woodview Dr.
 Prospect Heights, IL 60070
Ph: (847)824-0809
Co. E-mail: info@bus-eng.com
URL: http://www.bus-eng.com

Description: Provider of management consulting committed to obtaining financial benefits for its clients by improving efficiencies, optimizing resources, and reducing costs. **Scope:** Provider of management consulting committed to obtaining financial benefits for its clients by improving efficiencies, optimizing resources, and reducing costs. **Publications:** "Preventing Tantrums in Two Year Old Teams"; "Easy and Affordable Warehouse Fixes to Handle Volume Without Extra Help"; "Don't Let a WMS Derail Your Incentive Plan Concept"; "If You Want to Make Enemies, Try to Change Something"; "Maintaining Your Sanity During a Facility Change"; "Plant Facilities Provide Key Production Resources"; "Facilities - the Least Managed Asset"; "Lawson Doubles Pick Rates"; "Manufacturer Gains Insight with Simulation Study"; "Want to Cut Inventory? Forget Your Abc's "; "Are Profits Buried in Your Warehouse?"; "How a Continuous Improvement Process Can Help Your Business"; "Common Sense Logistics"; "Mapping Distribution"; "Hours of Stock, a New Concept in Scheduling"; "What They Don't Tell You About Warehouse Management Systems(Wms)"; "The Customer Relation Equation"; "A New Concept in Manufacturing Scheduling: Hours of Stock"; "Breaking the Bottlenecks"; "Lean Thinking"; "The Sweet Spot".

10512 ■ Business Improvement Architects (BIA)
633 Lakelands Ave.
 Innisfil, ON, Canada L9S 4E5
Co. E-mail: info@bia.ca
URL: http://bia.ca
Contact: Rowena Lamy, Consultant
E-mail: rlamy@bia.ca
Facebook: www.facebook.com/BusinessImprovementArchitects
Linkedin: www.linkedin.com/company/business-improvement-architects
Description: Provider of the following services, strategic planning, leadership development, innovation and project and quality management. Specialize in strategic planning, change management, leadership assessment and development of skills. **Scope:** Provider of the following services, strategic planning, leadership development, innovation and project and quality management. Specialize in strategic planning, change management, leadership assessment and development of skills. **Founded:** 1989. **Publications:** "Avoiding Pit falls to Innovation"; "Create a New Dimension of Performance with Innovation"; "The Power of Appreciation in Leadership"; "Why It Makes Sense To Have a Strategic Enterprise Office"; "Burning Rubber at the Start of Your Project"; "Accounting for Quality"; "How Pareto Charts Can Help You Improve the Quality of Business Processes"; "Managing Resistance to Change". **Training:** The Innovation Process From Vision to Reality, San Diego, Oct, 2007; Critical Thinking, Kuala Lump or, Sep, 2007; Critical Thinking, Brunei, Sep, 2007; Delivering Project Assurance, Auckland, Jun, 2007; From Crisis to Control: A New Era in Strategic Project Management, Prague, May, 2007; What Project Leaders Need to Know to Help Them Sleep Better At Night, London, May, 2007; Innovation Process. From Vision To Reality, Orlando, Apr, 2007. **Special Services:** Project Planning Tool™.

10513 ■ Business Management Consultants
1502 Augusta Dr., Ste. 315, Ste. D
 Houston, TX 77057
Co. E-mail: info@bmc-global.com
URL: http://www.bmc-global.com
Linkedin: www.linkedin.com/company/business-management-consultants
X (Twitter): x.com/Merguerian
YouTube: www.youtube.com/user/GlobalBMCVideo
Description: International management consulting firm specializes in global project management training and consulting, their consultants conduct organizational development, management training, and consulting in project management. **Scope:** International management consulting firm specializes in global project management training and consulting, their consultants conduct organizational develop-

ment, management training, and consulting in project management. **Founded:** 1985. **Publications:** "How The Art of Project Management improved the performance of pharmaceutical clinical trials in a Major Global Pharmaceutical Company," May, 2007. **Training:** Senior Project Management, Singapore, Oct, 2007; Fundamentals of Project Management I: Tools and Techniques, Houston, Jun, 2007; Fundamentals of Project Management II: Project Leadership and Communication, Houston, Jun, 2007; Project Management for Administrators, Singapore, Jun, 2007; Project Management for IT/IS I - Tools and Techniques, Singapore, Jun, 2007.

10514 ■ Business Performance Improvement Consorium L.L.C. (BPI)
225 S 6th St., Ste. 3900
 Minneapolis, MN 55402
Co. E-mail: consultants@bpi-consortium.com
URL: http://www.bpi-consortium.com
Contact: Rod Hagedorn, Senior Partner General Manager
E-mail: rod.hagedorn@bpi-consortium.com
Description: Firm provides management consulting services including organizational research and business performance improvement consulting. **Scope:** Firm provides management consulting services including organizational research and business performance improvement consulting. **Founded:** 1993.

10515 ■ Business Performance Improvement Consortium L.L.C.
225 S 6th St., Ste. 3900
 Minneapolis, MN 55402
Co. E-mail: consultants@bpi-consortium.com
URL: http://www.bpi-consortium.com
Contact: Rod Hagedorn, Senior Partner General Manager
E-mail: rod.hagedorn@bpi-consortium.com
Description: Consulting firm engages in diagnosing problematic areas, recommending solutions and determining operating efficiencies. **Scope:** Consulting firm engages in diagnosing problematic areas, recommending solutions and determining operating efficiencies. **Founded:** 1993. **Training:** What is Operational Marketing; Who is CMS Solutions; Call System Services; eNewsletter Campaigns; eDrip Campaigns; Database Services; Sales Support Services; Sales Services; Consulting Services. **Special Services:** Power of NO 2 Call System™.

10516 ■ ByrneMRG Corp.
5459 Rinker Cir.
 Doylestown, PA 18902
Ph: (215)630-7411
Co. E-mail: info@byrnemrg.com
URL: http://www.byrnemrg.com
Contact: Patrick Boyle, Founder Consultant
E-mail: pjboyle@byrnemrg.com
Description: Services: Management consulting. **Scope:** Services: Management consulting. **Founded:** 1972. **Publications:** "Implementing Solutions to Everyday Issues".

10517 ■ CBIZ, Inc.
CBIZ, Inc.
 5959 Rockside Woods Blvd. N, Ste. 600
 Independence, OH 44131
Ph: (216)447-9000
Fax: (216)447-9007
Co. E-mail: cbizwomensadvantage@cbiz.com
URL: http://www.cbiz.com
Contact: Jerome P. Grisko, Jr., President
Facebook: facebook.com/cbizmhmcareers
Linkedin: www.linkedin.com/company/cbiz
X (Twitter): twitter.com/cbz
YouTube: www.youtube.com/user/CBIZSolutions
Description: Diversified services company is engaged in providing an array of professional business services which include accounting and tax, healthcare and health benefits consulting, financial advisory, valuation, risk and advisory services, payroll, property and casualty insurance, retirement planning, managed networking and hardware services primarily to small and medium-sized businesses, as well as individuals, government agencies, and not-for-profit

enterprises. **Founded:** 1996. **Training:** Health Care - What the Future Holds; Consumer Driven Health Plans; Executive Plans; Health Savings Accounts; Healthy Wealthy and Wise; Legislative Update; Medicare Part D; Retirement Plans.

10518 ■ The Center for Organizational Excellence, Inc. (COE)
15204 Omega Dr., Ste. 300
  Rockville, MD 20850
Contact: Stephen P. Goodrich, Contact
E-mail: sgoodrich@center4oe.com

Description: Firm provides consulting services such as designing and delivering consulting solutions in the areas of organizational effectiveness, human capital, information technology, and data management. **Scope:** Firm provides consulting services such as designing and delivering consulting solutions in the areas of organizational effectiveness, human capital, information technology, and data management. **Founded:** 1984.

10519 ■ Chartered Management Co.
100 Saunders Rd., Ste. 150
  Lake Forest, IL 60045
Contact: William B. Avellone, President

Description: Operations improvement consultants. Specializes in strategic planning, feasibility studies, management audits and reports, profit enhancement, start-up businesses, mergers and acquisitions, joint ventures, divestitures, interim management, crisis management, turnarounds, business process re-engineering, venture capital and due diligence. **Scope:** Operations improvement consultants. Specializes in strategic planning, feasibility studies, management audits and reports, profit enhancement, start-up businesses, mergers and acquisitions, joint ventures, divestitures, interim management, crisis management, turnarounds, business process re-engineering, venture capital and due diligence. **Founded:** 1985.

10520 ■ Cicco & Associates Inc.
221 Rainprint Sq.
  Murrysville, PA 15668
Contact: John A. Cicco, Jr., President

Description: Provider of marketing and management consulting services to smaller businesses and marketing and research consulting to larger corporations wishing to market to the U.S. small-business market. **Scope:** Provider of marketing and management consulting services to smaller businesses and marketing and research consulting to larger corporations wishing to market to the U.S. small-business market. **Training:** Corporate Executive Briefing on Marketing to Small Business; The Simple Secret to Marketing Success; Japanese Management: Made in the USA.

10521 ■ Clubnet Solutions Inc.
77 City Centre Dr., East Twr., Ste. 501
  Mississauga, ON, Canada L5B 1M5
Ph: (416)992-0909
Co. E-mail: info@clubnet.ca
URL: http://clubnet.ca
Contact: Iliana Rocha, Leader
Facebook: www.facebook.com/clubnetsolutions
Linkedin: www.linkedin.com/company/clubnet-solu
  tions-inc
X (Twitter): x.com/clubnet_inc
Instagram: www.instagram.com/clubnetsolutions

Description: Works as a partner to business leaders looking to transform and scale their businesses profitably. **Scope:** Works as a partner to business leaders looking to transform and scale their businesses profitably. **Founded:** 2019.

10522 ■ Confidante Consulting
W 103rd St.
  New York, NY 10025
Ph: (332)208-2448
URL: http://consultconfidante.com

Description: Management consulting services with a focus toward assisting private equity investors in procuring the best deals, assisting dreamers and startups in finding their way toward success, and talent development. **Scope:** Management consulting

services with a focus toward assisting private equity investors in procuring the best deals, assisting dreamers and startups in finding their way toward success, and talent development.

10523 ■ Consulting & Conciliation Service (CCS)
Sacramento, CA
Ph: (916)396-0480
URL: http://conciliation.org
Contact: Jane McCluskey, Contact
E-mail: jane@conciliation.org

Description: Firm offers consulting and conciliation services, they provide pre-mediation counseling, training and research on preparing for a peaceful society, mediation and facilitation, preparation for shifts in structure, policy, and personnel, it offers sliding scale business rates and free individual consultation. **Scope:** Firm offers consulting and conciliation services, they provide pre-mediation counseling, training and research on preparing for a peaceful society, mediation and facilitation, preparation for shifts in structure, policy, and personnel, it offers sliding scale business rates and free individual consultation. **Publications:** "Native America and Tracking Shifts in US Policy"; "Biogenesis: A Discussion of Basic Social Needs and the Significance of Hope". **Training:** Positive Approaches to Violence Prevention: Peace building in Schools and Communities.

10524 ■ Corporate Consulting, Inc.
100 Fillmore St.
  Denver, CO 80206
Contact: Devereux C. Josephs, Contact

Description: Engaged in feasibility studies, organizational development, small business management, mergers and acquisitions, joint ventures, divestitures, interim management, crisis management, turnarounds, financing, appraisals valuations and due diligence studies. **Scope:** Engaged in feasibility studies, organizational development, small business management, mergers and acquisitions, joint ventures, divestitures, interim management, crisis management, turnarounds, financing, appraisals valuations and due diligence studies.

10525 ■ COTC Technologies Inc.
PO Box 17413
  Denver, CO 80217
Contact: Thomas I. Renz, Contact

Description: Firm provides software consulting services to organizations that require assistance with their HP3000 computer system. Firm provides systems analysis, programming, operations support and system management. Also provides PC software and hardware support and consulting. Additionally provides various training for the HP3000 computer system. **Scope:** Firm provides software consulting services to organizations that require assistance with their HP3000 computer system. Firm provides systems analysis, programming, operations support and system management. Also provides PC software and hardware support and consulting. Additionally provides various training for the HP3000 computer system.

10526 ■ David G. Schantz
29 Wood Run Cir.
  Rochester, NY 14612-2271
Ph: (716)723-0760
Fax: (716)723-8724
Co. E-mail: daveschantz@yahoo.com
URL: http://daveschantz.freeservers.com

Description: Provider of industrial engineering services for photo finishing labs, including amateur-wholesale, professional, commercial, school and package. **Scope:** Provider of industrial engineering services for photo finishing labs, including amateur-wholesale, professional, commercial, school and package.

10527 ■ DRI Consulting Inc. (DRIC)
Two Otter Ln.
  Saint Paul, MN 55127
Ph: (651)415-1400
Co. E-mail: dric@dric.com
URL: http://www.dric.com

Contact: Dr. John Fennig, Director

Description: Provides high-quality, research-based services and training in leadership, team processes, supervision, and management, and organizational development, clients with direct and substantial impact on individual and team performance and on organizational success through proven processes for selecting, developing and deploying leaders. **Scope:** Provides high-quality, research-based services and training in leadership, team processes, supervision, and management, and organizational development, clients with direct and substantial impact on individual and team performance and on organizational success through proven processes for selecting, developing and deploying leaders. **Founded:** 1991.

10528 ■ Family Business Institute Inc. (FBI)
3520 Ridge View Ct.
  Marietta, GA 30068
Ph: (770)952-4085
URL: http://www.family-business-experts.com
Contact: Don A. Schwerzler, Founder

Description: Firm engages in business consulting and professional services. **Scope:** Assists families in business to achieve personal, family and organizational goals. **Founded:** 1995. **Publications:** "Professional Intervention in the Family Owned Business"; "Building Consensus in a Family Business"; "Professionalizing Family Business Management".

10529 ■ First Strike Management Consulting Inc. (FSMC)
PO Box 1188
  Little River, SC 29566-1188
Ph: (843)385-6338
Co. E-mail: info@fsmc.com
URL: http://www.fsmc.com

Description: Offers proposal management and program management services. Specializes in enterprise systems, management systems, and staff augmentation. Serves the following industries: Nuclear/Fossil Power, Petro-Chemical, Aerospace and Defense, Telecommunications, Engineering and Construction, Information Technology, Golf Course Construction/Management, Utility Engineering/Construction, Civil Works, and Housing Development. **Scope:** Offers proposal management and program management services. Specializes in enterprise systems, management systems, and staff augmentation. Serves the following industries: Nuclear/Fossil Power, Petro-Chemical, Aerospace and Defense, Telecommunications, Engineering and Construction, Information Technology, Golf Course Construction/Management, Utility Engineering/Construction, Civil Works, and Housing Development. **Founded:** 1991. **Publications:** "Project Management for Executives"; "Project Risk Management"; "Project Communications Management"; "Winning Proposals, Four Computer Based Training (CBT) courses"; "Principles of Program Management". **Training:** Preparing Winning Proposals in Response to Government RFPs.

10530 ■ FocalPoint Business Coaching
130 Tobey Garden St.
  Duxbury, MA 02332
Contact: Marc R. Cote, Manager
Instagram: www.instagram.com/focalpointcoaching
YouTube: www.youtube.com/c/FocalPoin
  tBusinessCoachingwww.youtube.com/c/FocalPoin
  tBusinessCoachingwww.youtube.com/c/FocalPoin
  tBusinessCoachingwww.youtube.com/c/Fwww.you
  tube.com/c/FocalPointBusinessCoachingwww.you
  tube.com/c/FocalPointBusinessCoachingocalPoin
  tBusinessCoaching

Description: Firm provides coaching, training, and development of individuals and organizations. **Scope:** Firm provides coaching, training, and development of individuals and organizations. **Founded:** 2004.

10531 ■ Freese & Associates Inc. (F&A)
16105 Lucky Bell Ln.
  Newbury, OH 44065
Ph: (440)487-4509
URL: http://www.freeseinc.com
Contact: Thomas L. Freese, Principal
E-mail: tfreese@freeseinc.com

Description: Provider of supply chain management and logistics consulting services such as customer service, material management, transportation, and much more. **Scope:** Provider of supply chain management and logistics consulting services such as customer service, material management, transportation, and much more. **Founded:** 1987. **Publications:** "Building Relationships is Key to Motivation," Distribution Center Management, Apr, 2006; "Getting Maximum Results from Performance Reviews," WERC Sheet, Oct, 2003; "SCM: Making the Vision a Reality," Supply Chain Management Review, Oct, 2003; "Contents Under Pressure," DC Velocity, Aug, 2003; "When Considering Outsourcing, It's Really a Financial Decision," Inventory Management Report, Mar, 2003. **Training:** WERC/CAWS Warehousing in China Conference, Sep, 2008; CSCMP Annual Conference, Denver, Oct, 2008; Keys to Retaining and Motivating Your Associates, Dallas, Mar, 2006; The Value and Challenges of Supply Chain Management, Dubai, Feb, 2006; Best Practices in Logistics in China, Jun, 2005; Keys to Motivating Associates, Dallas, May, 2005; The Goal and the Way of International Cooperation in Logistics, Jenobuk, Apr, 2005.

10532 ■ Global Technology Transfer L.L.C.
1500 Dixie Hwy.
 Park Hills, KY 41011
Contact: Anthony R. Zembrodt, Sr., Member

Description: Firm specializes in product development, quality assurance, new product development, and total quality management focusing on household chemical specialties, especially air fresheners. Utilizes latest technology from global resources. Specializes in enhancement products for home and automobile. **Scope:** Firm specializes in product development, quality assurance, new product development, and total quality management focusing on household chemical specialties, especially air fresheners. Utilizes latest technology from global resources. Specializes in enhancement products for home and automobile.

10533 ■ Goldenwest Business Advisory Services
2655 Hoskins Rd.
 North Vancouver, BC, Canada 875 326
Ph: (604)987-9143
Fax: (604)987-9902
Co. E-mail: info@goldenwestcapital.com
URL: http://www.goldenwestcapital.com
Contact: Ron M. Woywitka, President
E-mail: info@goldenwestcapital.com

Description: Provider of strategic, managerial and financial advisory services. **Scope:** Provider of strategic, managerial and financial advisory services.

10534 ■ Harvey A. Meier Co. (HAM)
410 W Nevada St.
 Ashland, OR 97520-1043
Ph: (509)458-3210
Fax: (541)488-7905
Co. E-mail: harvey@harveymeier.com
URL: http://www.harveymeier.com
Contact: Dr. Harvey A. Meier, President
E-mail: harvey@harveymeier.com

Description: Services: Management consulting. **Scope:** Services: Management consulting. **Publications:** "The D'Artagnan Way".

10535 ■ Hewitt Development Enterprises (HDE)
1717 N Bayshore Dr., Ste. 2154
 Miami, FL 33132
Ph: (305)372-0941
Fax: (305)372-0941
Co. E-mail: info@hewittdevelopment.com
URL: http://www.hewittdevelopment.com
Contact: Robert G. Hewitt, Contact
E-mail: bob@hewittdevelopment.com

Description: Firm specializes in strategic planning, profit enhancement, startup businesses, interim and crisis management, turnarounds, production planning, just-in-time inventory and project management, serves senior management and acquirers of distressed businesses. **Scope:** Firm specializes in strategic planning, profit enhancement, startup busi-

nesses, interim and crisis management, turnarounds, production planning, just-in-time inventory and project management, serves senior management and acquirers of distressed businesses. **Founded:** 1985.

10536 ■ Human Resource Specialties, Inc. (HRS)
DCI Consulting Group Inc.
 PO Box 1995
 Missoula, MT 59806
Ph: (202)828-6900
URL: http://www.dciconsult.com
Contact: Sandy L. Henderson, President

Description: Provider of human resources assistance to organizations. Offers preparation of affirmative action plans, support documents, and adverse impact studies of personnel activities. Also offers customized consultations in small business services, diversity and discrimination, and investigations, complaints and grievances. Provides investigations, including allegations of unfair treatment, equal employment opportunity (EEO) and racial or sexual harassment. Offers customized web-based training (webinars) on a variety of HR, EEO and AAP-related topics. **Scope:** Provider of human resources assistance to organizations. Offers preparation of affirmative action plans, support documents, and adverse impact studies of personnel activities. Also offers customized consultations in small business services, diversity and discrimination, and investigations, complaints and grievances. Provides investigations, including allegations of unfair treatment, equal employment opportunity (EEO) and racial or sexual harassment. Offers customized web-based training (webinars) on a variety of HR, EEO and AAP-related topics. **Founded:** 1984.

10537 ■ Institute for Management Excellence
Trabuco Canyon, CA 92679
Ph: (949)667-1012
URL: http://www.itstime.com
Contact: Barbara Taylor, Executive Director

Description: Consulting firm and training focuses on improving productivity, using practices and creative techniques. **Scope:** Consulting firm and training focuses on improving productivity, using practices and creative techniques. **Founded:** 1995. **Publications:** "Income Without a Job," 2008; "The Other Side of Midnight, 2000: An Executive Guide to the Year 2000 Problem"; "Concordance to the Michael Teachings"; "Handbook of Small Business Advertising"; "The Personality Game"; "How to Market Yourself for Success". **Training:** The Personality Game; Power Path Seminars; Productivity Plus; Sexual Harassment and Discrimination Prevention; Worker's Comp Cost Reduction; Americans with Disabilities Act; In Search of Identify: Clarifying Corporate Culture.

10538 ■ Interminds & Federer Resources Inc.
PO Box 438
 Pasadena, CA 91102
Ph: (512)261-0761
Co. E-mail: yesyoucan@interminds.com
URL: http://www.interminds.com

Description: Firm specializes in feasibility studies, startup businesses, small business management, mergers and acquisitions, joint ventures, divestitures, interim and crisis management, turnarounds, production planning, team building, appraisals, and valuations. **Scope:** Firm specializes in feasibility studies, startup businesses, small business management, mergers and acquisitions, joint ventures, divestitures, interim and crisis management, turnarounds, production planning, team building, appraisals, and valuations. **Founded:** 1985. **Publications:** "Yes You Can: How To Be A Success No Matter Who You Are Or Where You're From".

10539 ■ John C. Randall & Associates Inc.
PO Box 2800
 Mechanicsville, VA 23116
Ph: (804)746-4450
Co. E-mail: john@johncrandall.com
URL: http://www.johncrandall.com
Contact: John C. Randall, Contact
E-mail: john@johncrandall.com

Description: Provider of results-oriented management, business, and technical assistance, as well as general management, consulting and emphasis on ventures, business, and marketing plans and cost and profit improvement and diversified services to reduce costs, improve profits, optimize cash flow, evaluate capital programs, provide business systems, develop technical programs and effect strategic planning. **Scope:** Provider of results-oriented management, business, and technical assistance, as well as general management, consulting and emphasis on ventures, business, and marketing plans and cost and profit improvement and diversified services to reduce costs, improve profits, optimize cash flow, evaluate capital programs, provide business systems, develop technical programs and effect strategic planning. **Founded:** 1981. **Publications:** "How to Save Time and Worry Less"; "So You Want to Be an Entrepreneur: Do You Really Want to Go Into Business for Yourself," Innsbrook Today; "Marketing Insights for Entrepreneurs," Innsbrook Today; "Mastering Your Marketing"; "How to Save Time and Worry Less; First Things First". **Training:** Lead Self - or Be Led; Master Minder System for Self-Leadership.

10540 ■ Johnston Co.
78 Bedford St.
 Lexington, MA 02420
Ph: (781)862-7595
Fax: (781)862-9066
Co. E-mail: info@johnstoncompany.com
URL: http://johnstoncompany.com
Contact: Jim Johnston, Chief Executive Officer
E-mail: jimj@johnstoncompany.com

Description: Firm provides consulting on environmental and workplace services such as LSRP service, property acquisition and redevelopment, engineering and site remediation. **Scope:** Firm provides consulting on environmental and workplace services such as LSRP service, property acquisition and redevelopment, engineering and site remediation. **Publications:** "Why are board meetings such a waste of time," Boston Business Journal, Apr, 2004.

10541 ■ Keecha Harris and Associates
217 Country Club Pk., Ste. 423
 Birmingham, AL 35213
Ph: (205)538-7433
URL: http://khandassociates.com
Contact: Keecha Harris, President
Linkedin: www.linkedin.com/company/keecha-harris-and-associates
X (Twitter): x.com/KHandAssociates

Description: Consultancy specializing in research and evaluation, organizational development, and project management for philanthropy, government, corporations, and nongovernmental organizations. **Scope:** Consultancy specializing in research and evaluation, organizational development, and project management for philanthropy, government, corporations, and nongovernmental organizations.

10542 ■ Kelly Business Advisors L.L.C.
3071 Voyager Dr., Ste. E
 Green Bay, WI 54311
Ph: (920)737-2579
URL: http://kellybusinessadvisors.com
Facebook: www.facebook.com/kellybusinessadvisors
Linkedin: www.linkedin.com/in/bizcoachkelly

Description: Provider of coaching, consulting and training services. **Scope:** Provider of coaching, consulting and training services.

10543 ■ McShane Group L.L.C.
2119 E Franklin St.
 Richmond, VA 23223
URL: http://www.mcshanegroup.com
Contact: Jim L. Huitt, Jr., Principal
E-mail: jhuitt@mcshanegroup.com

Description: Firm provides diligence services, interim management, strategic business realignments, marketing, and much more. **Scope:** Firm provides diligence services, interim management, strategic business realignments, marketing, and much more. **Founded:** 1987.

10544 ■ Medical Imaging Consultants Inc. (MIC)

1037 US Hwy. 46, Ste. G-2
 Clifton, NJ 07013-2445
Ph: (973)574-8000
Free: 800-589-5685
Fax: (973)574-8001
Co. E-mail: info@micinfo.com
URL: http://www.micinfo.com
Contact: Philip A. Femano, President

Description: Provider of professional support services in radiology management and comprehensive continuing education programs for radiologic technologists such as professional educators, life scientists, biomedical engineers, and much more. **Scope:** Provider of professional support services in radiology management and comprehensive continuing education programs for radiologic technologists such as professional educators, life scientists, biomedical engineers, and much more. **Founded:** 1991. **Training:** Sectional Anatomy and Imaging Strategies; CT Cross-Trainer; CT Registry Review Program; MR Cross Trainer; MRI Registry Review Program; Digital Mammography Essentials for Technologists; Radiology Trends for Technologists.

10545 ■ Medical Outcomes Management Inc. (MOM)

15 S Main St., Ste. 208
 Sharon, MA 02067
Ph: (781)806-0275
URL: http://www.mom-inc.us
Contact: Dr. Alan Kaul, Chief Executive Officer
E-mail: alan@mom-inc.us
Facebook: www.facebook.com/akaul2019
Linkedin: www.linkedin.com/company/medical-ou
 tcomes-management

Description: Management and technology consulting firm providing a specially focused group of services such as disease management programs and pharmacoeconomic studies. Services include clinical and educational projects, medical writing and editing, marketing and sales projects, disease registries, educational seminars, strategic planning projects, managed care organizations and pharmaceutical and biotechnology companies. **Scope:** Management and technology consulting firm providing a specially focused group of services such as disease management programs and pharmacoeconomic studies. Services include clinical and educational projects, medical writing and editing, marketing and sales projects, disease registries, educational seminars, strategic planning projects, managed care organizations and pharmaceutical and biotechnology companies. **Founded:** 1991. **Publications:** "Treatment of acute exacerbation's of chronic bronchitis in patients with chronic obstructive pulmonary disease: A retrospective cohort analysis logarithmically extended release vs. Azithromycin," 2003; "A retrospective analysis of cyclooxygenase-II inhibitor response patterns," 2002; "DUE criteria for use of regional urokinase infusion for deep vein thrombosis,"2002; "The formulary management system and decision-making process at Horizon Blue Cross Blue Shield of New Jersey," Pharmaco therapy, 2001. **Training:** Economic Modeling as a Disease Management Tool, Academy of Managed Care Pharmacy, Apr, 2005; Integrating Disease State Management and Economics, Academy of Managed Care Pharmacy, Oct, 2004; Clinical and economic outcomes in the treatment of peripheral occlusive diseases, Mar, 2003.

10546 ■ Mefford, Knutson & Associates Inc. (MKA)

6437 Lyndale Ave. S
 Richfield, MN 55423
Co. E-mail: info@mkcconsulting.com
URL: http://mkaconsulting.com
Contact: Jeanette Mefford, Co-Founder

Description: Provider of consulting services to home health and related sectors. **Scope:** Provider of consulting services to home health and related sectors. **Founded:** 1990.

10547 ■ Midwest Computer Group L.L.C. (MCG)

6060 Franks Rd.
 House Springs, MO 63051
Contact: Leon Sanford, Jr., Contact

Description: Specializes in helping businesses create accounting, marketing and business information systems, software development and database design and management. **Scope:** Specializes in helping businesses create accounting, marketing and business information systems, software development and database design and management.

10548 ■ Miller, Leiby & Associates P.C.

32 Broadway, 13th Fl.
 New York, NY 10004
Ph: (212)227-4200
Fax: (212)504-8369
URL: http://www.millerleiby.com
Contact: Doron Leiby, Partner
Facebook: www.facebook.com/MillerLeibyAssocia
 tesPc
Linkedin: www.linkedin.com/company/1269719
Instagram: www.instagram.com/millerleiby

Description: Firm is engaged in legal counsel for individuals and businesses. **Scope:** Firm is engaged in legal counsel for individuals and businesses. **Training:** Objectives and standards/recruiting for boards of directors.

10549 ■ Murray Dropkin & Associates

390 George St.
 New Brunswick, NJ 08901
URL: http://dropkin.com
Contact: Murray Dropkin, Contact

Description: Firm specializes in feasibility studies, business management, business process reengineering, team building, healthcare, and housing. **Scope:** Firm specializes in feasibility studies, business management, business process reengineering, team building, healthcare, and housing. **Publications:** "Bookkeeping for Nonprofits," Jossey Bass, 2005; "Guide to Audits of Nonprofit Organizations," PPC; "The Nonprofit Report," Warren, Gorham & Lamont; "The Budget Building Book for Nonprofits," Jossey-Bass; "The Cash Flow Management Book for Nonprofits," Jossey-Bass.

10550 ■ Nathan Associates Inc. - Library

1777 N Kent St., Ste. 1400.
 Arlington, VA 22209
Ph: (703)516-7700
Fax: (703)351-6162
URL: http://www.nathaninc.com
Contact: Susan B. Chodakewitz, Chief Executive
 Officer
Facebook: www.facebook.com/NathanAssociatesInc
Linkedin: www.linkedin.com/company/nathan
 -associates
X (Twitter): x.com/Nathan_Inc

Description: Planning, evaluation and cost-benefit analysis of economic policies and investment projects; expert testimony on litigation-related liability and damages in antitrust, financial markets and other issues; analysis of economic and financial impacts and costs and benefits of business decisions and economic and public policy choices and analysis and testimony for economic issues in regulatory proceedings. **Scope:** Planning, evaluation and cost-benefit analysis of economic policies and investment projects; expert testimony on litigation-related liability and damages in antitrust, financial markets and other issues; analysis of economic and financial impacts and costs and benefits of business decisions and economic and public policy choices and analysis and testimony for economic issues in regulatory proceedings. **Founded:** 1967. **Holdings:** Figures not available. **Publications:** "Anticorruption Interventions: Lessons for Future Projects"; "Anticorruption Studies: Bangladesh and Ukraine"; "Informal Remittance Systems and Afghanistan"; "Islamic Banking and its Potential"; "Islamic Finance and International Donor Policy: The Example of Indonesia"; "The Second Coming of Agricultural Credit"; "Poverty and Profits: CK Prahalad's The Fortune at the Bottom of the Pyramid"; "Reaching the Limits of Laws, Markets, and Games: Dixit's Lawlessness and Economics and McMillan's Reinventing the Bazaar"; "Saving Capitalism from its Losers: Rajan and Zingales on Financial Markets, Wealth, and Opportunity"; "Scratches on the Sands of Time: Prospective Economic Studies of Indian Villages"; "Competitiveness Strategy for Sri Lanka's ICT Industry"; "Intellectual Property and Developing Countries"; "Intellectual Property: Principles and Practice"; "The Economic Dimensions of Intellectual Property"; "Developing Country Labor Market Adjustments to Trade Reform". **Training:** Investment Opportunities for United States Business; World Trade Organization; Regional Trade Agreements; Port Sector Reform.

10551 ■ Nightingale Associates

7445 Setting Sun Way
 Columbia, MD 21046
Ph: (410)381-4280
URL: http://www.nightingaleassociates.net
Contact: Frederick C. Nightingale, Managing Director
E-mail: fredericknightingale@nightingaleassociates
 .net
X (Twitter): x.com/FCNightingale

Description: Management training and consulting firm offering the following skills productivity and accomplishment, leadership skills for the experienced manager, management skills for the new manager, leadership and teambuilding, supervisory development, creative problem solving, real strategic planning. **Scope:** Management training and consulting firm offering the following skills productivity and accomplishment, leadership skills for the experienced manager, management skills for the new manager, leadership and teambuilding, supervisory development, creative problem solving, real strategic planning. **Founded:** 1984. **Training:** Productivity and Accomplishment Management Skills for the New Manager; Leadership and Team building; Advanced Management; Business Process Re engineering; Strategic Thinking; Creative Problem Solving; Customer Service; International Purchasing and Materials Management; Fundamentals of Purchasing; Negotiation Skills Development; Providing superior customer service; Leadership skills for the experienced manager.

10552 ■ Performance Consultants Group, Inc. (PCG)

1 Innovation Way., Ste. 400
 Newark, DE 19711
Ph: (302)738-7532
Free: 888-724-3578
URL: http://www.pcgius.com

Description: Firm provides consulting services in the areas of strategic planning, profit enhancement, product development, and production planning. **Scope:** Firm provides consulting services in the areas of strategic planning, profit enhancement, product development, and production planning. **Founded:** 1988.

10553 ■ Performance Consulting Associates, Inc. (PCA)

3700 Crestwood Pky., Ste. 100
 Duluth, GA 30096
Ph: (770)717-2737
Co. E-mail: info@pcaconsulting.com
URL: http://pcaconsulting.com
Contact: Richard deFazio, President
Linkedin: www.linkedin.com/company/pcaconsulting

Description: Firm provides asset management solutions, business process optimization, and much more. **Scope:** Firm provides asset management solutions, business process optimization, and much more. **Founded:** 1976. **Publications:** "Does Planning Pay," Plant Services, Nov, 2000; "Asset Reliability Coordinator," Maintenance Technology, Oct, 2000; "Know What it is You Have to Maintain," Maintenance Technology, May, 2000; "Does Maintenance Planning Pay," Maintenance Technology, Nov, 2000.; "What is Asset Management?"; "Implementing Best Business Practices".

10554 ■ Professional Business Management, Inc.

8401 Corporate Dr., Ste. 160
Landover, MD 20785
Ph: (301)459-8811
Fax: (301)459-8818
URL: http://www.pbmservicesinc.com
Contact: Larry M. Weissman, Principal
E-mail: lweissmanpbm@verizon.net

Description: Firm provides consulting services in accounting, practice and tax management, retirement plans, payroll services, financial planning, and much more. **Scope:** Firm provides consulting services in accounting, practice and tax management, retirement plans, payroll services, financial planning, and much more.

10555 ■ Rolston & Associates

7232 Mastin St.
Merriam, KS 66203

Description: Management consultants working with small businesses to improve their profits. Practice is directed towards problem identification and solution, market plan development and improving management techniques. Serves both manufacturing concerns and retail organizations. **Scope:** Management consultants working with small businesses to improve their profits. Practice is directed towards problem identification and solution, market plan development and improving management techniques. Serves both manufacturing concerns and retail organizations. **Founded:** 1981. **Publications:** "Time Management Techniques: Essential Skills to Juggle Priorities and Eliminate Distractions," Nov, 2008; "Time Management is an Oxymoron," Leathers Publishing, Nov, 2001. **Training:** How to Handle Paper work Effectively.

10556 ■ Rose & Crangle Ltd.

102 E Lincoln Ave.
Lincoln, KS 67455
Contact: S. Jeanne Crangle, Contact

Description: Provider of evaluation, planning and policy analyzes for universities, associations, foundations, governmental agencies and private companies engaged in scientific, technological or educational activities. Special expertise in the development of new institutions. Special skills in providing planning and related group facilitation workshops. **Scope:** Provider of evaluation, planning and policy analyzes for universities, associations, foundations, governmental agencies and private companies engaged in scientific, technological or educational activities. Special expertise in the development of new institutions. Special skills in providing planning and related group facilitation workshops. **Publications:** "Preface to Bulgarian Integration Into Europe and NATO: Issues of Science Policy And research Evaluation Practice," Ios Press, 2006; "Allocating Limited National Resources for Fundamental Research," 2005.

10557 ■ RSC Business Group Inc.

12130 Millennium Dr., Ste. 02-198
Los Angeles, CA 90094
Ph: (310)709-5188
Co. E-mail: inquiry@rscbusinessgroup.com
URL: http://rscbusinessgroup.com
Contact: Robert S. Chun, Chief Executive Officer
Facebook: www.facebook.com/RSCBusinessGroup

Description: A full-service business coaching, consulting, and service provider. **Scope:** A full-service business coaching, consulting, and service provider.

10558 ■ Schneider Consulting Group Inc.

2801 E 4th Ave.
Denver, CO 80206
Contact: Frank S. Schneider, Contact

Description: Firm assists family-owned and privately-held business transition to the next generation and or to a more professionally managed company, turn around consulting for small and medium-sized companies. **Scope:** Firm assists family-owned and privately-held business transition to the next generation and or to a more professionally managed company, turn around consulting for small and

medium-sized companies. **Founded:** 1987. **Training:** Family Business Council; Impact of the Energy Renaissance.

10559 ■ Tornado Business Solutions

PO Box 1857
Suffolk, VA 23439
Ph: (757)951-7368
Co. E-mail: info@tornadobusinesssolutions.com
URL: http://www.tornadobusinesssolutions.com

Description: Firm that provides management consulting services. **Scope:** Firm that provides management consulting services.

10560 ■ Transpective Business Consulting Inc.

12 River Rd.
Newfields, NH 03856
Contact: Robert Richard Elliott, President

Description: Firm provides management consulting, leadership development, executive coaching and large scale change initiatives. **Scope:** Firm provides management consulting, leadership development, executive coaching and large scale change initiatives. **Publications:** "The Coping and Stress Profile," Inscape Publishing; "The Dimensions of Leadership Profile," Inscape Publishing; "Everything DiSC 363 For Leaders Research Report," Inscape Publishing; "Everything DiSC 363 Validation Report," Inscape Publishing; "A Comparison of Work Expectations Profile and the DISC Dimensions," Inscape Publishing. **Special Services:** Stress Navigator™.

10561 ■ Trendzitions Inc.

25691 Atlantic Ocean, Dr. No. B13
Lake Forest, CA 92630
Ph: (949)727-9100
URL: http://www.trendzitions.com
Contact: Chris Tooker, President
E-mail: ctooker@trendzitions.com
X (Twitter): x.com/trendzitions
Instagram: www.instagram.com/trendzitions

Description: Provider of services in the areas of communications consulting, project management, construction management, and furniture procurement. Offers information on spatial uses, building codes, ADA compliance and city ordinances. Also offers budget projections. **Scope:** Provider of services in the areas of communications consulting, project management, construction management, and furniture procurement. Offers information on spatial uses, building codes, ADA compliance and city ordinances. Also offers budget projections. **Founded:** 1986.

10562 ■ Zuckerman Consulting Group Inc.

2400 Balmoral Dr.
Akron, OH 44333
Contact: Laurie B. Zuckerman, Contact

Description: Consulting firm provides strategic planning, leadership development, executive coaching and team building services. **Scope:** Consulting firm provides strategic planning, leadership development, executive coaching and team building services. **Founded:** 1987. **Publications:** "Beyond the Wall of Resistance"; "Leadership Models: Been There, Done That"; "Do We Really Need A Strategic Plan?"; "On Your Own: A Woman's Guide To Building A Business".

FRANCHISES AND BUSINESS OPPORTUNITIES

10563 ■ Belron Canada Inc. (BCI)

8288 Blvd. PIE-IX
Montreal, QC, Canada H1Z 3T6
Ph: (514)593-7000
Free: 800-363-7131
URL: http://www.belroncanada.com
Contact: Michel Savard, President
Linkedin: www.linkedin.com/company/belron-canada-inc

Description: Provider of automotive glass replacement, repair services and also glass distribution. **Founded:** 1965.

10564 ■ Clean First Time Inc.

7362 Futures Dr., Ste. 5
Orlando, FL 32819
Ph: (407)352-1441
Free: 866-390-2532
URL: http://www.cleanfirsttime.com
Contact: Dan Gunkel, Officer

Description: Firm offers commercial, residential and construction cleaning services. **Founded:** 2003. **Royalty Fee:** 7%. **Training:** Includes 3-5 days training at headquarters, 3-5 days at franchisee's location and ongoing support.

10565 ■ Cleaning Consultant Services Inc. (CCS)

PO Box 98757
Seattle, WA 98198
URL: http://www.cleaningbusiness.com
Contact: Bill Griffin, Founder

Description: Firm provides engineering and consulting services and deals with claim and dispute resolution, program and material development and cleaning services and also offers business solutions and support services for cleaning professionals, and publishes books on various areas of the cleaning industry. **Scope:** Firm provides engineering and consulting services and deals with claim and dispute resolution, program and material development and cleaning services and also offers business solutions and support services for cleaning professionals, and publishes books on various areas of the cleaning industry. **Founded:** 1973. **Publications:** "Raising the Bar with Science, Training and Upward Mobility," Jan, 2010; "Technology Revolutionizes the Cleaning Process "Cleaning for Health" is the New Mantra," Distribution Sales and Management Magazine, May, 2003; "Bill Griffin's Crystal Balls-Cleaning Trends in the Usa 2001," Floor Care is Hot in 2001," Mar, 2001; "Inclean Magazine (Australia), Feb, 2001; "Maintaining Swimming Pools, Spas, Whirlpool Tubs and Saunas," Executive House keeping, Feb, 2001; "Whats New with Floor Care," 2001. **Training:** Publisher of books and magazines.

10566 ■ Sandler Systems Inc.

300 Red Brook Blvd., Ste. 400
Owings Mills, MD 21117
Ph: (410)653-1993
Co. E-mail: info@sandler.com
URL: http://www.sandler.com
Contact: Dave Mattson, President
X (Twitter): x.com/SandlerTraining
Instagram: www.instagram.com/sandlertraining
YouTube: www.youtube.com/user/SandlerWorldwide

Description: No. 1 Rated Management Training Franchise by Entrepreneur Magazine 2001. The franchise offered consists of the right to operate a Sandler Sales Institute business devoted to a distinctive style of training persons in the fields of sales and sales management, management consulting, human relations, leadership development, and methods of teaching such subjects through ongoing training, seminars and workshops. **No. of Operating Units:** 250. **Founded:** 1967. **Equity Capital Needed:** Net worth of $200,000-$400,000. **Franchise Fee:** $73,000. **Royalty Fee:** Flat monthly fee based on tenure. **Financial Assistance:** No **Training:** Toll-free hotline for training support, frequent initial training schools, quarterly training conferences, training and operating manuals, newsletter, promotional materials, lead generation, leader's guides.

10567 ■ Turbo Leadership Systems Ltd. (TLS)

36280 NE Willsonville Rd.
Newberg, OR 97132
Free: 800-574-4373
Fax: (503)625-2699
Co. E-mail: turbo@turbols.com
URL: http://turboleadershipsystems.com
Contact: Larry W. Dennis, President
E-mail: larry@turbols.com

Description: Management training and team building training. **Scope:** Provider of improvement programs that creates synergistic teamwork, impacts culture, and much more. **Founded:** 1985. **Publications:**

"Empowering Leadership"; "How to Turbo Charge You"; "Repeat Business"; "Making Moments Matter, Information"; "The Turbo Charger"; "15 Leadership Principles and Ronald Reagan"; "Motorcycle Meditations"; "Repeat Business"; "Empowering Leadership"; "Communication For Results"; "The Great Baseball Cap". **Training:** Yes.

LIBRARIES

10568 ■ Association for Talent Development (ATD) - Library
1640 King St.
 Alexandria, VA 22313-1443
Ph: (703)683-8100
Free: 800-628-2783
Fax: (703)683-1523
Co. E-mail: customercare@td.org
URL: http://www.td.org
Contact: Tony Bingham, President
Facebook: www.facebook.com/ATD
Linkedin: www.linkedin.com/company/15989
X (Twitter): x.com/ATD
Instagram: www.instagram.com/atdnational
Pinterest: www.pinterest.com/ATDofficial

Description: Supports the talent development profession by providing trusted content in the form of research, books, webcasts, events, and education programs. **Scope:** Management; leadership. **Services:** Library open to members only. **Founded:** 1943. **Holdings:** 170 monographs; 100 books; 100 newspapers. **Publications:** *American Society Training and Development Buyer's Guide and Consultant Directory* (Annual); *Technical Training Basics*; *ASTD Buyer's Guide & Consultant Directory* (Annual); *TD at Work* (Monthly); *Learning Circuits* (Monthly); *TD Magazine* (Monthly); *Member Information Exchange (MIX)*; *TRAINET*; *ATD Buyer's Guide*; *ATD Buyer's Guide*; *American Society for Training and Development--Training Video Directory*; *Who's Who in Training and Development* (Annual). **Educational Activities:** ATD International Conference and Exposition (Annual); ATD TechKnowledge Conference (Annual); TechKnowledge Conference and Exposition (Annual). **Awards:** ATD BEST Award (Annual); Awards in the Advancing Workplace Learning and Performance; ATD Excellence in Practice Awards (Annual); Gordon M. Bliss Memorial Award (Annual); ATD Dissertation Award (Annual); ASTD Talent Development Thought Leader Award (Annual); ATD Torch Award (Annual). **Geographic Preference:** Multinational.

10569 ■ Right Management Inc. - Library
Right Management Inc.
 100 Manpower Pl.
 Milwaukee, WI 53212
Free: 800-237-4448
Co. E-mail: contactus@right.com
URL: http://www.right.com
Contact: Caroline Pfeiffer, Senior Vice President
Facebook: www.facebook.com/rightmanagement
Linkedin: www.linkedin.com/company/righ t-management
X (Twitter): twitter.com/rightmanagement

Description: Provides consulting in career transition and human resources management. **Scope:** Workforce. **Founded:** 1980. **Holdings:** Figures not available. **Publications:** "Seven Days to Online Networking: Make Connections to Advance Your Career and Business Quickly"; "Networking for Job Search and Career Success," Jist Publishing, Jun, 2004; "The Unofficial Guide to Landing a Job"; "Re Inventing Hr Changing Roles to Create the High Performance Organization"; "Corporate Mvps Managing Your Companys Most Valuable Performers"; "Help Wanted: A Complete Guide to Human Resources for Canadian Entrepreneurs"; "Flexible Leadership Creating Value By Balancing Multiple Challenges and Choices," Pfe-iffer, May, 2004; "On the Fly Executing Strategy in a Changing World," John Wiley and Sons, Jan, 2004; "Global Leaders: Why they succeed and fail," Leadership Excellence, Aug, 2011; "Navigating Change Together," Talent Management, Feb, 2011; "Coaching: Navigating the Emerging Trends in Financial Services," The International Journal of Coaching in Organizations, 2009.

10570 ■ Strategic Account Management Association (SAMA) - Library
200 W Madison St.
 Ste. 1040
 Chicago, IL 60606
Ph: (312)251-3131
Fax: (312)251-3132
Co. E-mail: info@strategicaccounts.org
URL: http://www.strategicaccounts.org/en
Contact: Denise Freier, President
X (Twitter): x.com/samatweet

Description: Corporation sales executives concerned with strategic account sales. Holds seminars on strategic account management. Serves as an information provider on strategic customer-supplier relationship resources. **Scope:** Account management. **Founded:** 1964. **Holdings:** Figures not available. **Publications:** *Focus: Account Manager* (Semiannual); *Velocity* (Quarterly). **Educational Activities:** SAMA Annual Conference (Annual). **Geographic Preference:** Multinational.

10571 ■ University of Kentucky - Business & Economics Information Center
105 Main Bldg.
 Lexington, KY 40506-0132
URL: http://gatton.uky.edu
Description: Center that provides various programs involving business strategies and ideas about the economy. **Scope:** Business, economics, business management, marketing, finance, accounting. **Services:** Library open to the public for reference use only. **Founded:** 1993.

ASSOCIATIONS AND OTHER ORGANIZATIONS

10572 ■ **Manufacturers' Agents Association for the Foodservice Industry (MAFSI)**
1199 Euclid Ave.
 Atlanta, GA 30307
Ph: (404)214-9474
Fax: (888)254-0033
Co. E-mail: info@mafsi.org
URL: http://www.mafsi.org
Contact: Tom Mitchel, President
Facebook: www.facebook.com/MAFSIAssoc
Linkedin: www.linkedin.com/company/mafsi
X (Twitter): x.com/MAFSIAssoc
Instagram: www.instagram.com/mafsi_foodservice
YouTube: www.youtube.com/channel/
 UCEmIOiWOKEYzek3-oM8BX0g
Description: Independent manufacturers' representative firms selling equipment, furnishings, and supplies to dealers and users. Sponsors annual mini manufacturer sales meetings. Conducts specialized education programs. **Founded:** 1949. **Publications:** *MAFSI Agent Member Directory*; *MAFSI Messenger* (Monthly). **Educational Activities:** MAFSI Conference (Biennial). **Awards:** MAFSI Pacesetter Award (Periodic); MAFSI Special Recognition Award (Biennial). **Geographic Preference:** National; Local.

10573 ■ **Manufacturers' Agents N.A. (MANA)**
6321 W Dempster St., Ste. 110
 Morton Grove, IL 60053
Ph: (949)859-4040
Free: 877-626-2776
Fax: (949)855-2973
Co. E-mail: mana@manaonline.org
URL: http://www.manaonline.org
Contact: Charles Cohon, President
E-mail: ccohon@manaonline.org
Facebook: www.facebook.com/MANAonline.org
X (Twitter): x.com/MANA_Online
YouTube: www.youtube.com/user/MANAspeaks
Description: Manufacturers' agents representing two or more manufacturers on a commission basis, associate members are manufacturers and others interested in improving the agent-principal relationship. Maintains code of ethics and rules of business and professional conduct, issues model standard form of agreement. **Founded:** 1947. **Publications:** *MANA Matters* (Monthly); *Manufacturers' Agents National Association - Directory of Manufacturers' Sales Agencies*; *Manufacturers' Agents National Association--Directory of Manufacturers' Sales Agencies*; *Agency Sales: The Marketing Magazine for Manufacturers' Agencies and Their Principals* (Monthly); *Agency Sales Magazine* (Monthly); *Rep-Letter*; *MANA Online Directory of Manufacturers' Sales Agencies*. **Geographic Preference:** National; Regional.

10574 ■ **Manufacturers Representatives of America (MRA)**
c/o Pamela L. Battle, Executive Director
 28316 183rd Ave., SE
 Kent, WA 98042
Ph: (817)690-4308
Co. E-mail: pbattle@mrareps.com
URL: http://mrareps.com
Contact: Pamela L. Battle, Executive Director
E-mail: pbattle@mrareps.com
Facebook: www.facebook.com/mrareps
Linkedin: www.linkedin.com/in/mrareps
X (Twitter): x.com/MRAreps
Description: Independent manufacturers' representatives handling paper and plastic disposable products and sanitary supplies. Aims to improve agent sales skills, market coverage and customer service and to establish more effective agent/principal communications. **Founded:** 1978. **Geographic Preference:** National.

10575 ■ **Manufacturers' Representatives Educational Research Foundation (MRERF) - Library**
601 16th Street Ste. C-453
 Golden, CO 80401
Ph: (303)463-1801
Co. E-mail: certify@mrerf.org
URL: http://mrerf.org
Contact: David Coleman, President
Description: Sponsored by 35 national and state associations of manufacturers' representatives, distributors and manufacturers. Promotes the profession of outsourced field sales through academic research and publication; disseminates research findings on the role of manufacturers' representatives to academic institutions; provides a forum for the exchange of information. **Scope:** Role and profession of outsourced sales. **Founded:** 1984. **Holdings:** Figures not available. **Publications:** *MRERF Annual report* (Annual). **Educational Activities:** MRERF Professional Sales Certification, Sharpened skills to augment new tools for improved sales success.; Certified Professional Manufacturers' Representatives (CPMR); Managing Your Manufacturer's Representative Network. **Awards:** George Hayward CPMR Champion Award (Annual); George Hayward CPMR Champion Trophy. **Geographic Preference:** National.

10576 ■ **National Association of General Merchandise Representatives (NAGMR)**
1305 Thorndale Ave.
 Elk Grove Village, IL 60007
Free: 877-377-8322
URL: http://nagmr.com
Description: Consumer products brokers specializing in selling drug, health, beauty aids, and nonfood products to food chains and the same products and grocery items to the nonfood market. **Founded:** 1948. **Educational Activities:** NAGMR Convention; National Association of General Merchandise Representatives Annual Convention. **Geographic Preference:** National.

DIRECTORIES OF EDUCATIONAL PROGRAMS

10577 ■ *Scott's Directories: National Manufacturers*
Pub: Scott's Directories
URL(s): www.scottsdirectories.com/canadian-business-database/national-manufacturers-all-employees-directory
Ed: Barbara Peard. **Released:** Annual **Description:** Covers 58,000 manufacturers throughout Canada. **Entries include:** Company name, address, phone, fax, telex, names and titles of key personnel, number of employees, parent or subsidiary companies, North American Standard Industrial (NAICS) code, product, export interest, and year established. **Availability:** Online.

REFERENCE WORKS

10578 ■ *"Bodovino Is a World Leader in Self-Service Wine Tasting"* in Idaho Business Review (September 8, 2014)*
Pub: BridgeTower Media
Contact: Adam Reinebach, President
Description: Bodovino's wine bar and retail shop offers self-service wine tasting for its customers. It is the largest outlet globally for the Italian wine dispenser manufacturer WineEmotion. Visitors to the shop can choose from 144 wines set up in the dispensing machines.

10579 ■ *"Cogs in R.I. Manufacturing Machine"* in Providence Business News (Vol. 28, January 27, 2014, No. 43, pp. 1)*
Pub: American City Business Journals, Inc.
Contact: Mike Olivieri, Executive Vice President
URL(s): pbn.com/cogs-in-ri-manufacturing-machine9 4640
Description: Machine shops are capable of fixing or designing unique parts for manufacturing equipment and serve as a critical link in a company's production and distribution. Rhode Island has at least 50 machine shops capable of fabricating parts for companies. The Rhode Island Manufacturers Association's efforts to close the skills gap in machining are examined. **Availability:** Online.

10580 ■ *"PCH Solutions Named New Sales Representative for Nor-Lake"* in ACHR News (July 19, 2019)*
URL(s): www.achrnews.com/articles/141613-pch-solutions-named-new-sales-representatives-for-nor-lake
Released: July 19, 2019. **Description:** Nor-Lake Inc. announced that PCH Solutions is its newest sales and marketing representatives, working in the MAFSI 24 region. **Availability:** Online.

TRADE PERIODICALS

10581 ■ *Agency Sales Magazine*
Pub: Manufacturers' Agents N.A.
Contact: Charles Cohon, President

E-mail: ccohon@manaonline.org
URL(s): www.manaonline.org/agency-sales
-magazine

Ed: Jack Foster. **Released:** Monthly **Description:** Magazine for manufacturers' agents and manufacturers. Includes tax developments and tips, management aids for manufacturers and agents, legal bulletins, trend-identifying market data, classified ads. **Availability:** Print; Online.

10582 ■ *UAMR Confidential Bulletin*

Pub: United Association Manufacturers' Representatives

Contact: Karen Mazzola, Executive Director
URL(s): www.uamr.com/services.html

Released: Monthly; 12 times a year. **Price:** $65, for one year; $110, for two years; $150, for three years; $10, Single issue. **Description:** Covers product lines offered for representation in all fields. Provides details of the company and product, type of accounts to be serviced, and the areas open for representation. Subscription includes bulletin of lines for representatives, articles on rep business, and trade show listings. **Availability:** Print.

TRADE SHOWS AND CONVENTIONS

10583 ■ National Association of General Merchandise Representatives Annual Convention

National Association of General Merchandise Representatives (NAGMR)
1305 Thorndale Ave.
Elk Grove Village, IL 60007
Free: 877-377-8322
URL: http://nagmr.com
URL(s): www.nagmr.com

Description: Health and beauty aids that are sold in drug stores. **Audience:** Food industry brokers and manufacturers. **Principal Exhibits:** Health and beauty aids that are sold in drug stores.

RESEARCH CENTERS

10584 ■ Manufacturers' Representatives Educational Research Foundation (MRERF) - Library

601 16th Street Ste. C-453
Golden, CO 80401

Ph: (303)463-1801
Co. E-mail: certify@mrerf.org
URL: http://mrerf.org
Contact: David Coleman, President

Description: Sponsored by 35 national and state associations of manufacturers' representatives, distributors and manufacturers. Promotes the profession of outsourced field sales through academic research and publication; disseminates research findings on the role of manufacturers' representatives to academic institutions; provides a forum for the exchange of information. **Scope:** Role and profession of outsourced sales. **Founded:** 1984. **Holdings:** Figures not available. **Publications:** *MRERF Annual report* (Annual). **Educational Activities:** MRERF Professional Sales Certification, Sharpened skills to augment new tools for improved sales success.; Certified Professional Manufacturers' Representatives (CPMR); Managing Your Manufacturer's Representative Network. **Awards:** George Hayward CPMR Champion Award (Annual); George Hayward CPMR Champion Trophy. **Geographic Preference:** National.

ASSOCIATIONS AND OTHER ORGANIZATIONS

10585 ■ American Boat Builders & Repairers Association (ABBRA)
50 Water St.
Warren, RI 02885
Ph: (401)236-2466
Co. E-mail: info@abbra.org
URL: http://abbra.org
Contact: Chad Morse, President
Facebook: www.facebook.com/abbramarine
Description: Boat yards, marinas, and sailmakers. Seeks to: develop and encourage high standards of service and conduct within the industry; foster and promote the common business and professional interests of members; provide a forum for the discussion of problems and the exchange of experiences and ideas. **Founded:** 1943. **Publications:** *Capstan* (Quarterly). **Awards:** Dennis Snow President's Award (Annual). **Geographic Preference:** National.

10586 ■ American Boat & Yacht Council (ABYC) - Library
613 Third St., Ste. 10
Annapolis, MD 21403
Ph: (410)990-4460
Fax: (410)990-4466
Co. E-mail: info@abycinc.org
URL: http://abycinc.org
Contact: John Adey, President
E-mail: jadey@abycinc.org
Facebook: www.facebook.com/abycinc
Linkedin: www.linkedin.com/company/abyc
X (Twitter): x.com/ABYC_BoatSafety
Instagram: www.instagram.com/ABYC_BoatSafety
YouTube: www.youtube.com/user/ABYCAnnapolis
Description: Consists of boatbuilders, boat owners, boat yards, dealerships, educational institutions, equipment and accessory manufacturers, government agencies, insurance companies, law firms, marinas, marine retailers, service technicians, surveyors and trade associations. Develops the consensus-based safety standards for the design, construction, equipage, maintenance and repair of small craft and their systems through 18 project technical committees. **Founded:** 1954. **Holdings:** Figures not available. **Publications:** *American Boat and Yacht Council* (Monthly); *Boating Information: A Bibliography and Source List* (Irregular); *American Boat and Yacht Council--Membership Directory.* **Awards:** ABYC Service Award (Annual). **Geographic Preference:** National.

10587 ■ Boat Owners Association of the United States [BoatUS]
5323 Port Royal Rd.
Springfield, VA 22151
Free: 800-937-3300
URL: http://www.boatus.com
Contact: Tammy Moore, President
Facebook: www.facebook.com/BoatUS
Linkedin: www.linkedin.com/company/boatus

X (Twitter): x.com/boatus
Instagram: www.instagram.com/boatus
YouTube: www.youtube.com/boatus
Description: Represents owners or prospective owners of recreational boats. Independent, consumer service organization offering representation, benefits, and programs for boat owners. **Founded:** 1966. **Publications:** *BOAT U.S. Magazine* (5/year); *Boat U.S. Trailering Magazine* (Bimonthly); *Equipment Catalog* (Annual); *Seaworthy*; *Boater's Source Directory* (Semiannual). **Geographic Preference:** National.

10588 ■ Inland Seas Education Association (ISEA)
100 Dame St., No. 218
Suttons Bay, MI 49682
Ph: (231)271-3077
Fax: (231)271-3088
Co. E-mail: isea@schoolship.org
URL: http://schoolship.org
Contact: John Seefeld, President
Facebook: www.facebook.com/iseaschoolship
X (Twitter): x.com/inlandseas
Instagram: www.instagram.com/inland_seas_education_assoc
YouTube: www.youtube.com/channel/UCynuTHpo1de7n9p6p3KK9uQ
Description: Develops leadership and commitment needed for long-term stewardship of the Great Lakes. Provides shipboard educational programs where people of all ages can gain first-hand training and experience in the Great Lakes ecosystem. Offers aquatic science, environmental awareness, and sail training classes. **Founded:** 1989. **Publications:** *Schoolship Log* (Quarterly). **Geographic Preference:** National.

10589 ■ International Shipmasters Association (ISMA)
MI
Co. E-mail: info@shipmaster.org
URL: http://www.shipmaster.org
Facebook: www.facebook.com/InternationalShipMastersAssociation
Instagram: www.instagram.com/shipmasters
Description: Represents licensed marine officers operating on the Great Lakes. Promotes legislation to increase greater safety, health, and welfare of Great Lakes transportation and navigation. **Founded:** 1886. **Awards:** ISMA Cadet Scholarship Award (Annual); ISMA Hawsepipe Scholarship Award (Annual). **Geographic Preference:** National.

10590 ■ Marine Retailers Association of Americas (MRAA)
8401 73rd Ave. N, Ste. 71
Minneapolis, MN 55428
Ph: (763)315-8043
Co. E-mail: marketing@mraa.com
URL: http://mraa.com
Contact: Matt Gruhn, President
E-mail: matt@mraa.com
Facebook: www.facebook.com/MRAAonline

Linkedin: www.linkedin.com/ompany/3055608
X (Twitter): x.com/marineretailers
Instagram: www.instagram.com/marineretailers
YouTube: www.youtube.com/c/MraaOnline
Description: Marine retail dealers, marine manufacturers and accessory distributors, and marine services. Disseminates information and promotes activities and programs for the betterment of recreational boating. Co-sponsors dealer management seminars to improve professional management skills. Maintains speakers' bureau; compiles statistics. **Founded:** 1972. **Publications:** *Bearings* (Semimonthly). **Educational Activities:** Charleston In-Water Boat Show. **Geographic Preference:** National.

10591 ■ National Marine Distributors Association (NMDA)
c/o Nancy Cueroni, Executive Director
10421 Hickory Path Way, Ste. 103
Knoxville, TN 37922
Ph: (865)518-6257
Fax: (865)518-6197
Co. E-mail: info@nmdaonline.com
URL: http://www.nmdaonline.com
Contact: Nancy Cueroni, Executive Director
Description: Wholesale distributors of marine accessories and hardware to the Pleasure Boating Industry. **Founded:** 1965. **Educational Activities:** University of Innovative Distribution (Annual). **Geographic Preference:** National.

10592 ■ National Marine Electronics Association (NMEA)
846 Ritchie Hwy., Ste. L4
Severna Park, MD 21146
Ph: (410)975-9425
Co. E-mail: info@nmea.org
URL: http://www.nmea.org
Contact: Mark Reedenauer, President
E-mail: mreedenauer@nmea.org
Facebook: www.facebook.com/people/National-Marine-Electronics-Association-NMEA/100081624424023
X (Twitter): x.com/NMEA_org
Instagram: www.instagram.com/nmea_org
Description: Manufacturers, retail service dealers, distributors, educational institutions, and organizations associated with sales and service of marine electronics. Promotes the education and advancement of the marine electronics industry and the market which it serves. **Founded:** 1957. **Publications:** *Marine Electronics Journal* (Bimonthly). **Awards:** NMEA Product Awards (Annual). **Geographic Preference:** National.

10593 ■ National Marine Lenders Association (NMLA)
100 Severn Ave., Ste. 101
Annapolis, MD 21403
Ph: (410)980-1401
Co. E-mail: info@marinelenders.org
URL: http://marinelenders.org
Contact: Noelle Norvell, President

Facebook: www.facebook.com/people/National-Marine-Lenders-Association/100064453338864
X (Twitter): x.com/NMLAssociation
Description: Banks, savings institutions, and financial service firms that extend credit to consumers, retailers, and manufacturers of recreational boating equipment. Provides a forum in which lenders can exchange information on developing recreational boating loan programs. **Founded:** 1979. **Publications:** *Business of Pleasure Boats* (Quarterly); *Lender's Boating Handbook*; *Summary of Annual Marine Lending Survey* (Annual). **Educational Activities:** Marine Lending Workshop (Annual); National Marine Bankers Association Annual Conference (Annual). **Awards:** William B. Otto III Marine Industry Service Award (Annual). **Geographic Preference:** National.

10594 ■ National Marine Manufacturers Association (NMMA)
231 S LaSalle St., Ste. 2050
Chicago, IL 60604
Ph: (312)946-6200
URL: http://www.nmma.org
Contact: Frank Hugelmeyer, President
E-mail: fhugelmeyer@nmma.org
Facebook: www.facebook.com/thenmma
Linkedin: www.linkedin.com/company/nmma
X (Twitter): x.com/therealnmma
YouTube: www.youtube.com/thenmma
Description: Manufacturers of pleasure boats, marine engines, outboard motors, and boating products. Advocates for and promotes marine manufacturing and the boating lifestyle. Compiles statistics and provides specialized training for designers of yachts. **Founded:** 1979. **Publications:** *Recreational Boating Facilities Directory of Architects, Engineers, and Consultants* (Biennial); *Inter/Port* (Monthly); *NMMA Currents* (Daily). **Educational Activities:** DesignBUILD (Annual); belektro Berlin: Specialist Electrical Engineering Fair (Biennial); Kansas Agri Business Expo (Annual); Northwest Sportshow (Annual); Atlantic City Boat Show (Annual); The International Boatbuilders Exhibition & Conference (IBEX) (Annual); Marine Equipment Trade Show (METS) (Annual); Nashville Boat Sports Show (Annual); Progressive Tampa Boat Show (Annual); New Orleans Boat Show; Atlanta Boat Show (Annual); Miami International Boat Show (Annual); Toronto International Boat Show (Annual); St. Louis Boat Sports Show (Annual); Kansas City Boat Sportshow (Annual); Minneapolis Boat Show (Annual); Annual Los Angeles Boat Show (Annual); Progressive Insurance Strictly Sail Long Beach; National Marine Manufacturers Association Conference (Annual). **Geographic Preference:** National.

10595 ■ Northwest Marine Trade Association (NMTA)
1900 N Northlake Way, No. 233
Seattle, WA 98103
Ph: (206)634-0911
Fax: (206)632-0078
URL: http://www.nmta.net
Contact: George Harris, President
E-mail: george@nmta.net
Facebook: www.facebook.com/GrowBoating
X (Twitter): x.com/nmta
Description: Sole proprietorships, firms, partnerships, or corporations engaged in the sales, service, distribution, and construction of boats, engines, and accessories; allied businesses. Seeks to further the interests of members; to promote public interest in boating; to cooperate with similar organizations; to develop local and state legislation beneficial to the industry and the boating public. Produces and sponsors boat shows; serves as legislative consultant and watchdog for the industry; conducts seminars and management and sales workshops; maintains advertising and public relations programs for the industry; commissions special studies and reports; conducts social activities. **Founded:** 1947. **Publications:** *Northwest Marine Trade Association--Membership Directory* (Annual); *Water Life* (Biweekly). **Educational Activities:** Seattle Boat Show (Annual). **Geographic Preference:** National.

10596 ■ Personal Watercraft Industry Association (PWIA)
c/o David Dickerson, Vice President, State Government Relations
650 Massachusetts Ave. NW, Ste. 520
Washington, DC 20001
Ph: (202)737-9761
Co. E-mail: ddickerson@nmma.org
URL: http://www.pwia.org
Contact: David Dickerson, Vice President, Government Relations
E-mail: ddickerson@nmma.org
Description: Represents the four U.S. personal watercraft manufacturers. Works to ensure that personal watercraft (PWC) and personal watercraft users are treated fairly when local, state, and federal government officials consider boating regulations; supports and actively advocates for reasonable regulations, strong enforcement of boating and navigation laws, and mandatory boating safety education for all PWC operators. **Founded:** 1987. **Publications:** *An Environmental Guide for Personal Watercraft Operators*; *Riding Rules for Personal Watercraft*. **Geographic Preference:** National.

REFERENCE WORKS

10597 ■ American Boat and Yacht Council--Membership Directory (Internet only)
Pub: American Boat & Yacht Council
Contact: John Adey, President
E-mail: jadey@abycinc.org
URL(s): abycinc.org/membership/member-directory
Description: Covers over 4,000 marine engineers, marine underwriters, naval architects, marine surveyors, manufacturers and designers of small boats and related equipment, attorneys, boat owners, and Coast Guard, Navy, and state government personnel. **Entries include:** Name, address, phone, fax, email. **Arrangement:** Alphabetical. **Availability:** Online.

10598 ■ *"Bellingham Boatbuilder Norstar Yachts Maintains Family Tradition"* in Bellingham Business Journal (Vol. February 2010, pp. 12)
Description: Profile of Norstar Yachts and brothers Gary and Steve Nordtvedt who started the company in 1994. The company recently moved its operations to a 12,000 square foot space in the Fairhaven Marine Industrial Park. **Availability:** Print; Online.

10599 ■ *"Boat Sales Sputter as Cash-Strapped Buyers Drift Away"* in Puget Sound Business Journal (Vol. 29, August 15, 2008, No. 17, pp. 1)
Description: Boat sales in Washington fell by 44 percent in the second quarter of 2008. The decline is attributed to the soft economy, which has given customers second thoughts on purchasing recreational water vehicles. **Availability:** Print; Online.

10600 ■ *"Boatyard Expansion 8-Year Odyssey"* in Providence Business News (Vol. 28, March 31, 2014, No. 52, p. 1)
Pub: American City Business Journals, Inc.
Contact: Mike Olivieri, Executive Vice President
Released: March 29, 2014. **Description:** Bristol Marine owner, Andy Tyska, has found it challenging to operate and improve the boatyard due to lack of available coastal land and restrictive environmental regulations. Tyska made a large investment in plans for expanding the property he purchased in 1998. Tyska discusses the challenges faced while trying to improve his boatyard. **Availability:** Print; Online.

10601 ■ *BUC Used Boat Price Guide*
Pub: BUC International Corp.
URL(s): www.buc.com/index.cfm?fuseaction=books
Released: Semiannual; 127rd 2024 summer edition. **Price:** $211.95, Individuals. **Description:** Covers current market price for about 3,500 manufacturers of outboard, inboard, outdrives, sailboats, houseboats, and custom boats as well as approximately 20 manufacturers of boat trailers. In three volumes--Volume 1 covers 1994-2003; volume 2 covers 1982-1993; volume 3 covers 1905-1981. **Entries include:**

Listings for manufacturers still in business include company name, city and state, and Coast Guard identification code; defunct manufacturer listings show city in which last operated. All listings show boat and engine manufacturer's complete specifications. **Arrangement:** Alphabetical by manufacturer name. **Indexes:** Company, trade name. **Availability:** Online.

10602 ■ *"General Dynamics Secures U.S. Navy Contract"* in Travel & Leisure Close-Up (October 8, 2012)
Description: General Dynamics Electric Boat was awarded a $100.4 million contract modification by the U.S. Navy. Electric Boat will provide lead-yard services for Virginia-class nuclear-powered attack submarines. Details of the government procured contract are included. **Availability:** Online.

10603 ■ *"Half a World Away"* in Tampa Bay Business Journal (Vol. 30, December 4, 2009, No. 50, pp. 1)
Description: Enterprise Florida has offered four trade grants for Florida's marine industry businesses to give them a chance to tap into the Middle East market at the Dubai International Boat Show on March 9 to 13, 2010. The grants pay for 50 percent of the exhibition costs for the qualifying business. **Availability:** Online.

10604 ■ *"Longtime Seattle Company Wards Cove Selling Last Seattle Properties"* in Puget Sound Business Journal (Vol. 34, February 21, 2014, No. 45, pp. 4)
Pub: American City Business Journals, Inc.
Contact: Mike Olivieri, Executive Vice President
Description: Seattle, Washington-based Wards Cove Company is selling two renovated office buildings and a marina on Lake Union as the 86-year-old real estate investment firm winds down its operations. The company is also selling an industrial property on the lake's north side. Wards Cove history is profiled. **Availability:** Online.

10605 ■ *"Marine-Services Firm Eyes Expansion"* in Providence Business News (Vol. 29, August 25, 2014, No. 21, pp. 8)
Pub: American City Business Journals, Inc.
Contact: Mike Olivieri, Executive Vice President
Released: August 23, 2014. **Description:** Jamestown, Rhode Island-based Conanicut Marine Services Inc. is looking to expand the business with a bigger marina, the addition of a third boat to his ferry fleet, and a climate-controlled storage shed. Owner, Bill Munger, discusses his efforts to overcome the challenges of sustaining the business during the economic recession. **Availability:** Print; Online.

10606 ■ National Marine Representatives Association--Membership Directory (Internet only)
Pub: National Marine Representatives Association
Contact: Aaron Freeman, President
E-mail: aaron@tidelinemarketing.com
URL(s): nmraonline.org/rep-groups-join-here
Description: Covers independent sales representatives of pleasure boats and boating accessories. Provides territories covered and the primary customers. **Entries include:** Name, address, phone, fax, e-mail, manufacturers represented, territories covered, customer classifications. **Arrangement:** Alphabetical. **Indexes:** Geographical. **Availability:** Print.

10607 ■ *Pacific Boating Almanac*
Pub: ProStar Publications Inc.
URL(s): www.prostarpublications.com/b1/index.php?cPath=34_28
Ed: Peter L. Griffes. **Released:** Annual; Latest edition 2006. **Price:** $24.95, Single issue. **Description:** Covers over 3,000 marine facilities serving recreational boating in California, Oregon, Washington, British Columbia, Alaska, and Mexico's Baja area. **Entries include:** Name of facility, address, phone, name of owner, list of services. **Arrangement:** Geographical in four volumes: Volume 1, Pacific Northwest; volume

2, Pacific Northwest and Alaska; volume 3, Northern California the Delta; volume 4, Southern California and Baja. **Availability:** Print.

10608 ■ *"Pentagon Awards $17.6B Contract for EB-Built Subs Through 2018" in Providence Business News (Vol. 29, April 28, 2014, No. 4)*
Pub: American City Business Journals, Inc.
Contact: Mike Olivieri, Executive Vice President
URL(s): pbn.com/pentagon-awards-176b-contract-for-eb-built-subs-through-20189678
Description: The U.S. Navy has signed a $17.6 billion contract with Newport News Shipbuilding and General Dynamics Corporation for construction of 10 new naval submarines. The deal will help employment at General Dynamics' Quonset Business Park Electric Boat production site. The submarines are scheduled to be built between 2014-2018. Electric Boat expects to hire 650 additional workers.

10609 ■ *"Plenty of Jobs, Will Workers Follow?" in Providence Business News (Vol. 28, January 27, 2014, No. 43, pp. 1)*
Pub: American City Business Journals, Inc.
Contact: Mike Olivieri, Executive Vice President
URL(s): pbn.com/plenty-of-jobs-will-workers-follow94642
Description: Electric Boat announced a plan to hire 650 employees in 2014 for its facility at Quonset Business Park in North Kingstown, Rhode Island. However, meeting the hiring goals will be a challenge because of smaller educational pipeline for welders, electricians, shipfitters, and pipefitters. Rhode Island's internship programs to fill the skills gap are also discussed. **Availability:** Online.

10610 ■ *"Ready for Our Ships to Come In" in Philadelphia Business Journal (Vol. 33, April 11, 2014, No. 9, pp. 4)*
Pub: American City Business Journals, Inc.
Contact: Mike Olivieri, Executive Vice President
Description: Philadelphia Regional Port Authority planned the construction of the Southport Marine Terminal in South Philadelphia at a cost of $300 million to capitalize on changes in the shipping industry. The Tioga Marine Terminal in Port Richmond is also being improved using a mix of public and private money. The growing competition among the East Coast ports is also discussed. **Availability:** Online.

STATISTICAL SOURCES

10611 ■ *RMA Annual Statement Studies*
Pub: Risk Management Association
Contact: Nancy Foster, President
Released: Annual. **Description:** Contains composite balance sheets and income statements for more than 360 industries, including the accounting, auditing, and bookkeeping industries. Also contains five years of comparative historical data for discerning trends. Includes 16 commonly used ratios, computed for most of the size groupings for nearly every industry.

TRADE PERIODICALS

10612 ■ *Boating Magazine*
Contact: John McEver, Publisher
E-mail: john.mcever@bonniercorp.com
URL(s): www.boatingmag.com
Facebook: www.facebook.com/boatingmag?loc=footer&lnk=fb
X (Twitter): twitter.com/boatingmagazine?loc=footer&lnk=tw
Released: 10/year **Price:** $12, for 10 issue 1 year.
Description: Magazine reporting on boat tests, new gear, electronics, and sport fishing for pleasure power boaters. **Availability:** Handheld; Print; Online.

10613 ■ *The duPont Registry: A Buyer's Gallery of Fine Homes*
Pub: duPont Publishing Inc.
Contact: William Chapman, Chief Executive Officer
URL(s): www.dupontregistry.com/about

Released: Monthly **Price:** $149.95, U.S. for 24 issues; $89.95, U.S. for 12 issues; $119.95, Canada for 12 issues no auto renew; $279.95, Canada for 36 issues; $209.95, Canada for 24 issues; $189.95, U.S. for 36 issues; $429.95, for 36 issues international; $169.95, for 12 issues international; $309.95, for 24 issues international. **Description:** Magazine featuring worldwide luxury sail and sport boats for sale. **Availability:** Print; Online.

10614 ■ *Power and Motoryacht*
Pub: Active Interest Media
Contact: Andrew W. Clurman, President
E-mail: aclurman@aimmedia.com
URL(s): www.powerandmotoryacht.com
Facebook: www.facebook.com/powerandmotoryacht
X (Twitter): x.com/pmyacht
Instagram: www.instagram.com/powerandmotoryacht
Ed: Dan Harding. **Released:** Monthly **Price:** $15, for print 1 year; $13, for digital; $20, for print + online; $13, Canada for digital only international. **Description:** Magazine for owners of large powerboats. **Availability:** Print; PDF; Online.

10615 ■ *Soundings Trade Only: Daily News for Marine Industry Professionals*
Pub: Soundings Publications L.L.C.
Contact: Paul Smith, Director
E-mail: psmith@aimmedia.com
URL(s): www.tradeonlytoday.com
Facebook: www.facebook.com/TradeOnlyToday
Linkedin: www.linkedin.com/company/soundings-trade-only
X (Twitter): twitter.com/tradeonlytoday
YouTube: www.youtube.com/user/SoundingsTradeOnly
Released: Monthly **Description:** Trade magazine for the recreational boating industry. **Availability:** Print; Online.

10616 ■ *Yachting: The Best of Today's Boats & Gear*
Pub: Bonnier LLC
Contact: David Ritchie, Co-Chief Executive Officer
URL(s): www.yachtingmagazine.com
Facebook: www.facebook.com/yachtingmagazine
X (Twitter): x.com/YachtingMag
Instagram: www.instagram.com/yachtingmagazine
YouTube: www.youtube.com/user/YachtingMagazine
Pinterest: www.pinterest.com/yachtingmag
Released: Monthly **Price:** $89, for print + online 2 year international; $59, for print+ online 1 year international; $54, for print + online Canada 1 year; $84, for print + online 2 year Canada; $26, for online 1 year international; $39, for print + online 1 year US; $69, for print + online 2 year US; $26, for online 1 year Canada; $26, for online US. **Description:** Yachting magazine for affluent, experienced sail and power yachtsmen. **Availability:** Print; Online.

TRADE SHOWS AND CONVENTIONS

10617 ■ *Atlanta Boat Show*
Thai Gem and Jewelry Traders Association (TGJTA)
919/119, 919/615-621 Jewelry Trade Center Bld., 52nd Fl., Silom Rd.
Bangkok 10500, Thailand
Ph: 66 2 6301390
Co. E-mail: info@thaigemjewelry.org
URL: http://www.thaigemjewelry.or.th
Contact: Porntiva Niparin, President
URL(s): www.atlantaboatshow.com
Frequency: Annual. **Description:** Powerboats, sailboats, fishing boats, water ski boats, pontoon boats, houseboats, personal watercraft, inflatable and more. Exhibits also include marine accessories, services and a showcase on outdoor travel section featuring lodges, marinas and boating resorts. **Audience:** General public and professionals. **Principal Exhibits:** Powerboats, sailboats, fishing boats, water ski boats, pontoon boats, houseboats, personal watercraft, inflatable and more. Exhibits also include marine accessories, services and a showcase on

outdoor travel section featuring lodges, marinas and boating resorts. **Telecommunication Services:** info@atlantaboatshow.com.

10618 ■ *Atlantic City Boat Show*
National Marine Manufacturers Association (NMMA)
231 S LaSalle St., Ste. 2050
Chicago, IL 60604
Ph: (312)946-6200
URL: http://www.nmma.org
Contact: Frank Hugelmeyer, President
E-mail: fhugelmeyer@nmma.org
URL(s): www.acboatshow.com
Frequency: Annual. **Description:** Exhibits relating to motor and express yachts, sports fishing boats, cruisers, and sport boats. **Audience:** General public and trade professionals. **Principal Exhibits:** Exhibits relating to motor and express yachts, sports fishing boats, cruisers, and sport boats. Dates and Locations: 2025 Feb 26-Mar 02 Atlantic City Convention Center, Atlantic City, NJ. **Telecommunication Services:** info@acboatshow.com.

10619 ■ *Detroit Boat Show*
Michigan Boating Industries Association (MBIA)
8625 Richardson Rd.
Commerce Township, MI 48390
Ph: (734)261-0123
Fax: (734)261-0880
Co. E-mail: boatmichigan@mbia.org
URL: http://www.mbia.org
Contact: Nicki Polan, Executive Director
E-mail: npolan@mbia.org
URL(s): boatmichigan.org/detroit-boat-show/#detroit-exhibitor-list
Facebook: www.facebook.com/DetroitBoatShow
Price: $12, adults. **Frequency:** Annual. **Description:** Boats, fishing equipment, boat-related accessories, charter rentals, nautical attire, trailer and outboard motors, and personal watercraft. **Audience:** Boat enthusiasts and manufacturers. **Principal Exhibits:** Boats, fishing equipment, boat-related accessories, charter rentals, nautical attire, trailer and outboard motors, and personal watercraft. Dates and Locations: 2025 Jan Huntington Place, Detroit, MI. **Telecommunication Services:** boatmichigan@mbia.org.

10620 ■ *Fort Lauderdale International Boat Show*
Fort Lauderdale International Boat Show (FLIBS)
801 Seabreeze Blvd.
Fort Lauderdale, FL 33316
Ph: (954)463-6762
URL: http://www.flibs.com/en/home.html
URL(s): www.flibs.com/en/attend/show_overview.html
Frequency: Annual. **Description:** Boats and marine equipment, supplies, and services. **Audience:** Trade professionals, marine manufacturers and shipyards, and general public. **Principal Exhibits:** Boats and marine equipment, supplies, and services. Dates and Locations: Broward County Convention Center, Fort Lauderdale, FL. **Telecommunication Services:** boatshows@onpeak.com.

10621 ■ *The International Boatbuilders Exhibition & Conference (IBEX)*
Gardner Business Media Inc. (GBMI)
6915 Valley Ave.
Cincinnati, OH 45244-3029
Ph: (513)527-8800
Fax: (513)527-8801
URL: http://www.gardnerweb.com
Contact: Rick Kline, Jr., President
E-mail: rkline2@gardnerweb.com
URL(s): www.ibexshow.com
Facebook: www.facebook.com/IBEXShow
X (Twitter): twitter.com/IBEXShow
Frequency: Annual. **Description:** Exhibits related to new models of boats and other marine equipment. **Audience:** Trade professionals, including boat builders, designers, repairers, surveyors, boatyard and marina operators, purchasing agents, military engineers, marine wholesalers and distributors, fabricators and laminators, yacht captains, and the marine

press. **Principal Exhibits:** Exhibits related to new models of boats and other marine equipment. **Telecommunication Services:** ibexshow@xpressreg.net.

10622 ■ Miami International Boat Show
National Marine Manufacturers Association (NMMA)
    231 S LaSalle St., Ste. 2050
    Chicago, IL 60604
Ph: (312)946-6200
URL: http://www.nmma.org
Contact: Frank Hugelmeyer, President
E-mail: fhugelmeyer@nmma.org
URL(s): www.miamiboatshow.com/en/home.html
Price: $20, regular adult admission; free for children ages 15 and under. **Frequency:** Annual. **Description:** Boats (power and sail), engines and accessories, fishing and water sport accessories. **Audience:** General public. **Principal Exhibits:** Boats (power and sail), engines and accessories, fishing and water sport accessories. Dates and Locations: 2025 Feb 12-16 Miami Beach Convention Center, Miami Beach, FL; 2025 Feb 12-16 The Progressive Boat Show Experience at Pride Park, Miami Beach, FL; 2025 Feb 12-16 Herald Plaza, Miami Beach, FL; 2025 Feb 12-16 Venetian Marina, Miami Beach, FL; 2025 Feb 12-16 Museum Park Marina, Miami Beach, FL; 2025 Feb 12-16 SuperYacht Miami at Yacht Haven Grande Miami, Miami Beach, FL. **Telecommunication Services:** cxteam@informa.com.

10623 ■ Miami Yacht Show
Fort Lauderdale International Boat Show (FLIBS)
    801 Seabreeze Blvd.
    Fort Lauderdale, FL 33316
Ph: (954)463-6762
URL: http://www.flibs.com/en/home.html
URL(s): iyba.org/past-event/discover-boating-miami-international-boat-show
Frequency: Annual. **Description:** Yachts and the industry's leading yacht brokerage firms. **Audience:** Trade professionals and general public. **Principal Exhibits:** Yachts and the industry's leading yacht brokerage firms.

10624 ■ St. Louis Boat Sports Show
National Marine Manufacturers Association (NMMA)
    231 S LaSalle St., Ste. 2050
    Chicago, IL 60604
Ph: (312)946-6200
URL: http://www.nmma.org
Contact: Frank Hugelmeyer, President
E-mail: fhugelmeyer@nmma.org
URL(s): www.stlouisboatshow.com/about
Price: $12, for adults; free for youth ages 15 and younger. **Frequency:** Annual. **Description:** Fishing tackle, vacation travel resorts, boats, motors, and boating accessories. **Audience:** Outdoor enthusiasts. **Principal Exhibits:** Fishing tackle, vacation travel resorts, boats, motors, and boating accessories. Dates and Locations: 2025 Feb St. Louis, MO. **Telecommunication Services:** denvall@nmma.org.

10625 ■ Seattle Boat Show
Northwest Marine Trade Association (NMTA)
    1900 N Northlake Way, No. 233
    Seattle, WA 98103
Ph: (206)634-0911
Fax: (206)632-0078
URL: http://www.nmta.net
Contact: George Harris, President
E-mail: george@nmta.net
URL(s): seattleboatshow.com
Facebook: www.facebook.com/SeattleBoatShow
X (Twitter): twitter.com/SeattleBoatShow
Frequency: Annual. **Description:** An in-water display of powerboats, sailboats, motors, trailers, engines, new and used accessories, and related services.

Audience: General public and media. **Principal Exhibits:** An in-water display of powerboats, sailboats, motors, trailers, engines, new and used accessories, and related services. Dates and Locations: 2025 Jan 31-Feb 08. **Telecommunication Services:** ticketing@seattleboatshow.com.

CONSULTANTS

10626 ■ J-U-B Engineers Inc.
2760 W Excursion Ln., Ste. 400
    Meridian, ID 83642
Ph: (208)376-7330
URL: http://web.jub.com
Contact: Lisa Bachman, Manager
Facebook: www.facebook.com/jubengineers
Linkedin: www.linkedin.com/company/jub-engineers-inc
Instagram: www.instagram.com/jubengineers
YouTube: www.youtube.com/channel/UCVSRHWeemCPoZMwQSSzDMpg
Description: Firm provides problem solvers, trusted advisors and professionals who services in planning, funding, designing, and construction. **Scope:** Firm provides problem solvers, trusted advisors and professionals who services in planning, funding, designing, and construction. **Founded:** 1954. **Publications:** "Idaho Engineering Firm of the Year," McGraw-Hill Companies, 2005.

LIBRARIES

10627 ■ Alaska Marine Safety Education Association (AMSEA) - Library
2924 Halibut Point Rd.
    Sitka, AK 99835
Ph: (907)747-3287
Fax: (907)531-1756
URL: http://www.amsea.org
Contact: Jerry Dzugan, Executive Director
E-mail: director@amsea.org
Facebook: www.facebook.com/alaskamarinesafety
X (Twitter): x.com/akmarinesafety
Instagram: www.instagram.com/amsea.training
YouTube: www.youtube.com/channel/UC9jClGoMAk76VkuTdojmjlg
Description: Promotes cold water safety education. Sponsors marine and cold water safety instructor network and curriculum development. Provides and disseminates educational materials. **Scope:** Cold water safety education. **Founded:** 1985. **Holdings:** Figures not available. **Publications:** *Marine Safety Update* (Quarterly). **Geographic Preference:** Regional.

10628 ■ Chesapeake Bay Maritime Museum - Howard I. Chapelle Memorial Library
213 N Talbot St.
    Saint Michaels, MD 21663
URL: http://cbmm.org/donate
Contact: H. Norman, Contact
Description: Contains reference materials, journals, books, online materials, and video and audio materials on historical studies. **Scope:** State and local history; water fowling; marine engineering; navigation, seamanship; boat design and construction; yachting; recreational boating; maritime material culture and folklife. **Services:** Library open to the public with restrictions. **Founded:** 1968. **Holdings:** 10,000 volumes; 117 periodicals; 110 manuscripts; 210 lin.ft. of archives; 890 taped oral histories; 45,000 historic and contemporary photographs.

10629 ■ Deer Isle-Stonington Historical Society (DISHS) - Library
416 Sunset Rd., Rte. 15A
    Deer Isle, ME 04627

Ph: (207)348-6400
Co. E-mail: dishs.info@gmail.com
URL: http://www.deerisle.com/2010/deer-isle-stonington-historical-society/276
URL(s): www.dis-historicalsociety.org
Description: Seeks to collecting and preserving 'historical facts, records, and relics pertaining to Deer Isle, Stonington, and adjoining communities and islands of East Penobscot Bay in the State of Maine'. **Scope:** Local history; genealogy. **Services:** Open to members. **Founded:** 1959. **Holdings:** 100 photographs; book.

10630 ■ The Library at the Mariners' Museum
100 Museum Dr.
    Newport News, VA 23606
Ph: (757)596-2222
Co. E-mail: library@marinersmuseum.org
URL: http://www.marinersmuseum.org/learn/research-services/library-archives
Contact: Howard H. Hoege, III, President
E-mail: hhoege@marinersmuseum.org
Facebook: www.facebook.com/marinersmuseum
Linkedin: www.linkedin.com/company/the-mariners-museum
X (Twitter): x.com/marinersmuseum
Instagram: www.instagram.com/marinersmuseum
YouTube: www.youtube.com/c/themarinersmuseum
Scope: Maritime history; merchant marine. **Services:** Copying; library open to the public. **Founded:** 1930. **Holdings:** 4,000 volumes of books; postcards; 600,000 photographs; 5,000 charts and maps; 60 microfilms; journals. **Subscriptions:** 1500 magazines journals newsletters.

10631 ■ Maine Maritime Academy - Nutting Memorial Library
Pleasant St.
    Castine, ME 04420
Ph: (207)326-2263
Co. E-mail: library@mma.edu
URL: http://mainemaritime.edu/nutting-memorial-library
Contact: Lauren Starbird, Director
E-mail: lauren.starbird@mma.edu
Facebook: www.facebook.com/NuttingMemorialLibrary
X (Twitter): x.com/NuttingMemorial
Scope: Educational materials. **Services:** Interlibrary loan; copying; library open to the public. **Founded:** 1941. **Holdings:** 100,000 academic eBooks; 70,000 books; 5,300 maps; 2,000 videos;audiovisual ; periodicals; journals; newspapers.

10632 ■ Mystic Seaport - G.W. Blunt White Library
75 Greenmanville Ave.
    Mystic, CT 06355-0990
Ph: (860)572-0711
Co. E-mail: info@mysticseaport.org
URL: http://www.mysticseaport.org
Contact: Peter J. Armstrong, President
Facebook: www.facebook.com/mysticseaport
X (Twitter): x.com/mysticseaport
Instagram: www.instagram.com/mysticseaportmuseum
YouTube: www.youtube.com/user/MysticSeaportVideos
Pinterest: www.pinterest.com/mysticseaportmuseum
Description: Museum provides history, maritime history, art, maritime preservation, education, sailing, marina, and much more. **Scope:** Maritime; genealogy. **Services:** Open to the public by appointment; Copying. **Founded:** 1929. **Holdings:** 1,000,000 manuscript; 75,000 books; 200,000 sheets; 2,000 logbooks; 10,000 charts and maps; periodicals; journal; audio and videotapes. **Educational Activities:** Maritime History Symposium; Small Craft Workshop (Annual). **Geographic Preference:** National.

Market Research and Analysis

ASSOCIATIONS AND OTHER ORGANIZATIONS

10633 ■ **American Marketing Association (AMA)**
American Marketing Association (AMA)
130 E Randolph St., 22nd Fl.
Chicago, IL 60601
Ph: (312)542-9000
Free: 800-262-1150
Co. E-mail: customersupport@ama.org
URL: http://www.ama.org
Contact: Bennie F. Johnson, Chief Executive Officer
Facebook: www.facebook.com/AmericanMarketing
Linkedin: www.linkedin.com/company/american
  -marketing-association
X (Twitter): x.com/ama_marketing
Description: Serves as a professional society of marketing and market research executives, sales and promotion managers, advertising specialists, academics, and others interested in marketing. Fosters research; sponsors seminars, conferences, and student marketing clubs; provides educational placement service and doctoral consortium. **Founded:** 1937. **Publications:** *Journal of International Marketing (JIM)* (Quarterly); *Journal of Public Policy & Marketing (JPP&M)* (Quarterly); *Marketing Health Services* (Quarterly); *Journal of Marketing Research (JMR)* (Bimonthly); *Marketing News: Reporting on the Marketing Profession* (Monthly); *AMA Conference Proceedings*; *Marketing Academics at AMA* (Bimonthly); *Marketing Matters* (Biweekly); *Journal of Marketing* (Bimonthly); *Marketing Management* (Bimonthly); *Marketing Executive Report* (Monthly); *Services Marketing Today* (Bimonthly); *Marketing News--Directory of Professional Courses for Marketing Issue*; *American Marketing Association--The M Guide Services Directory* (Annual); *International Membership Directory and Marketing Services Guide* (Annual); *Marketing News--Software Directory* (Annual); *Marketing Insights* (Quarterly). **Educational Activities:** AMA International Collegiate Conference (Annual); AMA Research and Strategy Summit; AMA Summer Academic Conference (Annual); Winter Academic Conference (Annual). **Awards:** AMA Explor Award (Annual); AMA/Irwin/McGraw-Hill Distinguished Marketing Educator Award (Annual); Shelby D. Hunt/Harold H. Maynard Award (Annual); Weitz-Winer-O'Dell Award (Annual); Charles Coolidge Parlin Marketing Research Award (Annual); AMA/Marketing Science Institute/H. Paul Root Award (Annual). **Geographic Preference:** National; Local.

10634 ■ **Association of Marketing and Communication Professionals (AMCP)**
127 Pittsburg St.
Dallas, TX 75207
Ph: (214)377-3524
Co. E-mail: info@amcpros.com
URL: http://www.amcpros.com
Facebook: www.facebook.com/amcpros
Linkedin: www.linkedin.com/company/association-of
  -marketing-&-communication-professionals
X (Twitter): x.com/AMCP_Awards
Description: Administers and judges international competitions for marketing and communication professionals involved in the concept, writing, and design of marketing and communication programs as well as print, visual, and audio materials. **Founded:** 1995. **Awards:** AMCP MarCom Awards (Annual); AMCP Hermes Creative Awards (Annual); AMCP AVA Digital Awards (Annual).

LEGISLATIVE ASSISTANCE

10635 ■ **Office of the Governor - Economic Development and Tourism Division - Economic Information Clearinghouse**
1100 San Jacinto Blvd.
Austin, TX 78711-2428
Co. E-mail: egrants@gov.texas.gov
URL: http://egrants.gov.texas.gov/Default.aspx
Description: Program attempts to ensure that each state agency awards 10 percent of all purchases of articles, supplies, commodities, materials, or services to small businesses.

REFERENCE WORKS

10636 ■ *"The AHA Moment' in Hispanic Business (December 2010)*
Description: An interview with Gisela Girard on how competitive market conditions push buttons. Girard stepped down from her 18-month position as chairwoman the Association of Hispanic Advertising Agencies. She has more than 20 years of experience in advertising and research marketing. **Availability:** Print; Online.

10637 ■ *"And Now, Goodbye: Consumer Response To Sponsor Exit' in International Journal of Advertising (Vol. 31, February 2012, No. 1, pp. 39)*
Ed: Julie A. Ruth, Yuliya Strizhakova. **Description:** While most sponsorship research focuses on the initiation and maintenance of properties and the brands that sponsor them, little is known about how brands fare when they terminate sponsorship relationships. **Availability:** Download; PDF; Online.

10638 ■ *"Are Nutrient-Content Claims Always Effective? Match-Up Effects Between Product Type and Claim Type in Food Advertising" in International Journal of Advertising (Vol. 31, May 2012, No. 2, pp. 421)*
Ed: Hojoon Choi, Hye-Jin Paek, Karen Whitehill King. **Released:** 2012. **Description:** Research examines the extent to which recently prevalent nutrient-content claims in food advertising are effective and how the level of effectiveness might differ between food products perceived as healthy and unhealthy. **Availability:** Online.

10639 ■ *"Because Kids Need To Be Heard: Tina Wells: Buzz Marketing Group: Voorhees, New Jersey" in Inc. (Volume 32, December 2010)*
Pub: Mansueto Ventures L.L.C.
Contact: Stephanie Mehta, Chief Executive Officer

Ed: Tamara Schweitzer. **Released:** December 01, 2010. **Description:** Profile of Tina Wells, founder and CEO of Buzz Marketing Group, who writes a tween book series called Mackenzie Blue to reach young girls. **Availability:** Online.

10640 ■ *Bradford's International Directory of Marketing Research Agencies*
Pub: Business Research Services, Inc.
URL(s): www.sba8a.com/brs.htm
Description: Covers over 2,300 marketing research agencies worldwide. Includes domestic and international demographic data and professional association contacts. **Entries include:** Company name, address, phone, name and title of contact, date founded, number of employees, description of products or services, e-mail, URL. **Arrangement:** Geographical. **Indexes:** Alphabetical by company. **Availability:** Print. **Type:** Directory.

10641 ■ *Business-to-Business Marketing 2023*
Released: 6th edition. **Description:** Delves into the world of business-to-business marketing by presenting and examining tactics, surveys, and trends of the industry. **Availability:** Online.

10642 ■ *"Communication Strategies for Enhancing Perceived Fit in the CSR Sponsorship Context' in International Journal of Advertising (Vol. 31, February 2012, No. 1, pp. 133)*
Ed: Yong Seok Sohn, Jin K. Han, Sung-Hack Lee. **Released:** 2012. **Description:** Engaging in corporate social responsibility (CSR) is becoming an increasingly common business practice globally and across industries. By contributing to societal welfare, firms can also enhance their corporate image among its stakeholders, in particular, its customers. For CSR to generate goodwill, consumers generally need to perceive a fit between the sponsoring firm and its CSR. Otherwise, consumers may second-guess the firm's intrinsic CSR motives, which may even evoke a negative reaction. **Availability:** Print; Online.

10643 ■ *"Cosmetics Are a Case Study for Embracing Diversity in Marketing" in Forbes (October 17, 2019)*
URL(s): www.forbes.com/sites/kylewong/2019/10/17/
  cosmetics-are-a-case-study-for-embracing-diversity
  -in-marketing/#5437c6c2144d
Ed: Kyle Wong. **Released:** October 17, 2019. **Availability:** Online.

10644 ■ *"Decoding Demand Opportunities" in Business Strategy Review (Vol. 21, Spring 2010, No. 1, pp. 64)*
Ed: Erich Joachimsthaler, Markus Pfeiffer. **Released:** February 09, 2010. **Description:** Classic marketing techniques, such as the use of focus groups or ethnographies, miss the enormous opportunities that can be leveraged once companies commit to understanding consumers in the context of life experiences. **Availability:** Print; PDF; Online.

10645 ■ *"Eclectic Reading" in Business Strategy Review (Vol. 23, Spring 2012, No. 1, pp. 68)*

Released: March 06, 2012. **Description:** If ever a field of study was both science and art, marketing seems to fit the bill. Which may be why Nader Tavassoli has a keen interest in diverse subjects: branding, consumer cognition, communication effectiveness, consumer behavior across culturesand several others. What keeps his mind open to a constant flow of new possibilities? As you'll see by his suggested top ten list of books to read, Tavassoli believes strongly in delving into the arts and sciences. **Availability:** Print; PDF; Online.

10646 ■ *"The Effect of 3-D Product Visualization on the Strength of Brand Attitude" in International Journal of Advertising (Vol. 31, May 2012, No. 2, pp. 377)*

Description: Research investigates the effect of 3-D product visualization on attitude accessibility and attitude confidence in advertising, two non-evaluative dimensions of attitudes that have not been studied in previous research. The experiment analyzed two versions of a Website (3-D vs 2-D), in which the capacity to interact with the product has been manipulated. **Availability:** PDF; Online.

10647 ■ *"The Effectiveness of Advertising That Leverages Sponsorship and Cause-Related Marketing: A Contingency Model" in International Journal of Advertising (Vol. 31, May 2012, No. 2, pp. 317)*

Description: Consumers are more likely to have ambivalent attitudes towards cause-related marketing (CRM) than sponsorship. Wherease consumers share similar positive perceptions of CRM and sponsorship, and attribute the motives behind them to altruism, their negative perceptions and attributions of CRM are more accessible than those of sponsorship. **Availability:** Print; Online.

10648 ■ *"Enhancing Brand Image Via Sponsorship: Strength of Association Effects" in International Journal of Advertising (Vol. 31, February 2012, No. 1, pp. 113)*

Ed: Srdan Zdravkovic, Brian D. Till. **Released:** 2012. **Price:** $42.50. **Description:** Despite the increased usage of sponsorship activities by practitioners, there has been little research on the impact of sponsorship on building brand image. This research examines the influence of sponsorship on associations transfer from sponsored entity to the sponsor. **Availability:** Print; Online.

10649 ■ *Entrepreneurial Marketing: How to Develop Customer Demand*

Ed: E.J. Nijssen. **Released:** 2022. **Description:** For entrepreneurs who are developing new products and are having trouble with marketing that product since data doesn't exist for it. The author discusses key issues and helps with creating marketing plans. **Availability:** Print.

10650 ■ *"Environment Consulting Service Market Incredible Possibilities, Growth Analysis and Forecast to 2024" in Tech Mag (October 28, 2019)*

URL(s): technologymagazine.org/environment-consul ting-service-market-incredible-possibilities-growth -analysis-forecast-2024/

Ed: Partha Ray. **Released:** October 28, 2019. **Description:** An overview of the Environment Consulting Service Market study, which includes profitability prospects, growth dynamics, market size, market share forecast, and revenue estimation. **Availability:** Online.

10651 ■ *"The Evolution of Self-Regulation in Food Advertising: an Analysis of CARU Cases from 2000-2012" in International Journal of Advertising (Vol. 31, May 2012, No. 2, pp. 257)*

Price: $42.50. **Description:** The FTC envisions the Children's Advertising Review Unit (CARU) and the Children's Food and Beverage Advertising Initiative playing lead roles in self-regulatory efforts to address advertising's contribution to childhood obesity. Peeler (2009) notes that CARU's decisions provide comprehensive guidance to advertisers. Limited research has investigated those decisions. This study examines CARU case reports from 2000 to 2010 involving food marketers from a longitudinal perspective. **Availability:** Print; Online.

10652 ■ *"Fair and Lovely: Building an Integrated Model to Examine How Peer Influence Mediates the Effects of Skin-Lightening Advertisements On College Women In Singapore" in International Journal of Advertising (Vol. 31, February 2012, No. 1, pp. 189)*

Ed: Stella C. Chia, Yuen Ting Chay, Poh Kwan Cheong. **Released:** January 02, 2012. **Description:** Research uses an integrated model with which suggested that perceptions of peers and interpersonal communication with peers each mediate the influence of skin-lightening advertisements on college women in the South Asian country, Singapore. The model is build based on the influence-of-presumed-influence model. The study found that college women in Singapore tended to infer their peers' advertising exposure and the corresponding advertising influence on peers based on the own advertising exposure. Their exposure to the skin-lightening advertisements also induced their discussions about fair-skinned appearance with peers, resulting in favorable attitudes towards fair-skinned appearance. **Availability:** Online.

10653 ■ *"For Tax Preparation Agencies, Inbound Consumer Calls Trend Higher in January than April" in Marketing Weekly News (May 5, 2012)*

Pub: NewsRX LLC.

Contact: Kalani Rosell, Contact

Description: According to Marchex Institute, caller activity is highest in January, no April when tax deadlines loom. Online advertising campaigns for tax preparers should be optimized at the beginning of the year when peak calls occurred during the week of January 9, 2012. **Availability:** Online.

10654 ■ *"Global Organic Food" in Investment Weekly News (January 21, 2012, pp. 272)*

Description: Research and Markets has added 'Global Organic Food' to its reporting of industry profiles. The report will offer top-line qualitative and quantitative summary information including, market size, description of leading players with key financial metrics and analysis of competitive pressures within the market covering the global organic food market. Market size and segmentation data, textual and graphical analysis of market growth trends, leading companies and macroeconomic information will be provided. **Availability:** Online.

10655 ■ *"How to Conduct a Market Analysis for Your Business" in Business News Daily (February 21, 2023)*

URL(s): www.businessnewsdaily.com/15751-conduc t-market-analysis.html

Ed: Max Freedman. **Released:** February 21, 2023. **Description:** If you are wondering how to conduct a market analysis for your small business, this article will explain the steps you need to take to complete this task. **Availability:** Online.

10656 ■ *"How to (Realistically) Start an Online Ecommerce Busines That Actually Grows in 2019" in Big Commerce*

URL(s): www.bigcommerce.com/blog/how-to-create -online-store/#learn-how-to-create-your-own-online -store

Ed: Tracey Wallace. **Description:** A 9-chapter guide on everything you need to know to start an online business. Topics include how to find niche products to sell; how to evaluate the market; online market research; conducting a competitive analysis; business laws; how to analyze your target market; how to source and manufacture products; and how to create, setup, and launch an online store. **Availability:** PDF; Online.

10657 ■ *"I Hear You're Interested In A..." in Inc. (January 2008, pp. 40-43)*

Ed: Leah Hoffmann. **Description:** Four tips to help any small business generate sales leads online are examined. **Availability:** Online.

10658 ■ *"Ideas at Work: Sparkling Innovation" in Business Strategy Review (Vol. 21, Summer 2010, No. 2, pp. 07)*

Ed: Julian Birkinshaw, Peter Robbins. **Released:** June 24, 2010. **Description:** GlaxoSmithKline faced a situation common to large global organizations: how to allocate marketing resources to smaller, regional brands. The company's approach to worldwide marketing that led to the development of a unique and productive network is outlined. **Availability:** Print; PDF; Online.

10659 ■ *"The Image Management Function of Sponsorship: A General Theoretical Framework" in International Journal of Advertising (Vol. 31, February 2012, No. 1, pp. 85)*

Ed: Kihan Kim, Patricia A. Stout, Yunjae Cheong. **Released:** 2012. **Price:** $42.50. **Description:** A general framework to understand how sponsorship affects the image of the sponsor has been developed from the information-processing perspective. According to this framework, sponsorship information is processed in one of two relatively distinct modes of processing: holistic and analytic, depending on the amount of processing resources available to consumer. Implications of this marketing research is provided. **Availability:** Print; Online.

10660 ■ *"Kroger Recasts Its Brand" in Supermarket News (November 6, 2019)*

URL(s): www.supermarketnews.com/retail-financial/ kroger-recasts-its-brand

Ed: Russell Redman. **Released:** November 06, 2019. **Description:** The Kroger Co. has unveiled a new logo and a new brand identity that emphasizes "food first." Their new slogan is "Fresh for Everyone" while still maintaining an updated version of its classic Kroger logo. **Availability:** Online.

10661 ■ *"Kubient Audience Cloud Launched" in ResearchLive (November 18, 2019)*

URL(s): www.research-live.com/article/news/kubien t-audience-cloud-launched/id/5061662

Released: November 18, 2019. **Description:** Kubient Audience Cloud was launched by Kubient. The platform acts as a single point of entry for buyers and sellers to execute and monetize media campaigns. **Availability:** Online.

10662 ■ *"Managing a Sponsored Brand: The Importance of Sponsorship Portfolio Congruence" in International Journal of Advertising (Vol. 31, February 2012, No. 1, pp. 63)*

Ed: Mark D. Groza, Joe Cobbs, Tobias Schaefers. **Description:** The congruence of fit between a sponsored brand and sponsoring firm is a central tenet of sponsorship research. The influence of such congruence on the sponsored brand however, has received little attention. This research is important because the strength of a sponsored organization's brand equity is the basis for many sponsorship alliances. **Availability:** PDF; Online; Download.

10663 ■ *Marketing for Entrepreneurs*

Pub: FT Press

Ed: Jurgen Wolff. **Released:** 1st edition. **Description:** This text identifies marketing as the entire process of researching, creating, distributing and selling a product or service. It isn't about theory and metrics, rather it is a practical guide that starts with the basics of all marketing aspects. **Availability:** Print.

10664 ■ *"Mars Advertising's Orbit Grows as Other Ad Segments Fall" in Crain's Detroit Business (Vol. 25, June 1, 2009, No. 22, pp. 10)*

Pub: Crain Communications Inc.

Contact: Barry Asin, President

Ed: Bill Shea. **Description:** An electrical fire burned at Mars Advertising's headquarters in Southfield, Michigan. The company talks about its plans for regrouping and rebuilding. The family firm specializes in in-store marketing that targets consumers already in the buying mode. **Availability:** Print; Online.

10665 ■ *"Miller's Crossroad" in Canadian Business (Vol. 83, September 14, 2010, No. 15, pp. 58)*
Ed: Joe Castaldo. **Released:** September 14, 2010. **Description:** Future Electronics founder and billionaire Robert Miller shares the secret of Future's unique operating model, which is based on inventory and market research. Miller attributes much of the company's success to its privately held status that enables quick movement against competitors. **Availability:** Print; Online.

10666 ■ *"Missing Ingredients In Cause-Related Advertising: The Right Formula of Execution Style and Cause Framing" in International Journal of Advertising (Vol. 31, May 2012, No. 2, pp. 231)*
Description: In traditional cause-related marketing (CRM) campaigns, marketers focus on a promoted product and ads containing CRM messesage only in small print at the bottom. Some recent marketers have choses to highlight the cause, with the product taking a lesser role in the advertising copy. The purpose of this research is to compare these two execution styles. **Availability:** Download; PDF; Online.

10667 ■ *"A Multicategory Model of Consumers' Purchase Incidence, Quantity, and Brand Choice Decisions: Methodological Issues and Implications On Promotional Decisions" in Journal of Marketing Research (Vol. 49, August 2012, No. 4, pp. 435)*
Pub: American Marketing Association
Contact: Bennie F. Johnson, Chief Executive Officer
Ed: Nitin Mehta, Yu Ma. **Description:** A multicategory model of consumers' purchase incidence, quantity, and brand choice decisions is presented. The research model allows for cross-category promotion effects in incidence and quantity decisions. Retailers are seen to be better off promoting brands across categories. **Availability:** PDF.

10668 ■ *"Private Label Is More Influential Than Ever in Determining Store Choice, Report Says" in Grocery Dive (November 8, 2019)*
URL(s): www.grocerydive.com/news/private-label-is
-more-influential-than-ever-in-determining-store
-choice-re/566939/
Ed: Krishna Thakker. **Released:** November 08, 2019. **Description:** Grocers are seeing more sales from their own private label lines recently, mostly because they are no longer just copying national brands but using those labels to create innovative products. This has been noticed by consumers who welcome the brands and develop a loyalty to them. **Availability:** Online.

10669 ■ *"Promotional Marketing: How to Create, Implement & Integrate Campaigns That Really Work"*
Pub: Kogan Page
Released: Sixth edition. **Description:** Promotional marketing helps companies stay ahead of competition to gain new customers and keep existing ones. The guide includes new developments in the field of marketing, examining the use of digital media such as mobile devices and phones, interactive television, and Web-based advertising, as well as ways to research and evaluate promotional marketing campaigns. **Availability:** Online; PDF.

10670 ■ *"Psychological Ownership: A Social Marketing Advertising Message Appeal? Not for Women" in International Journal of Advertising (Vol. 31, May 2012, No. 2, pp. 291)*
Description: An assessment of psychological ownership as a potential persuasive advertising message appeal in the social marketing effort is examined.

Psychological ownership is a feeling of possession; it occurs when individuals feel that something is their even though they cannot hold legal tide to it. **Availability:** PDF; Online.

10671 ■ *"The Quest for Content: How User-Generated Links Can Facilitate Online Exploration" in International Journal of Marketing Research (Vol. 49, August 2012, No. 4, pp. 452)*
Pub: American Marketing Association
Contact: Bennie F. Johnson, Chief Executive Officer
Ed: Jacob Goldenberg, Gal Oestreicher-Singer, Shachar Reichman. **Description:** The role of online dual-network structures in facilitating content exploration is examined. Such structures are created by companies offering social networks and user-generated links alongside the product network. Exposure to dual networks has been found to result in a more effecient exploration process. **Availability:** PDF.

10672 ■ *"The Rise of Pompei" in Retail Merchandiser (Vol. 51, September-October 2011, No. 5, pp. 13)*
Description: Soho creative consulting group follows its C3 philosophy to create an invigorated brand experience that transforms customers from consumers to empowered buyers. Pompei AD is a leading creative consultancy that specializes in design and branding for retail, museum, hospitality, and other sectors. **Availability:** Print; Online.

10673 ■ *"The Role of Advertising in Consumer Emotion Management" in International Journal of Advertising (Vol. 31, May 2012, No. 2, pp. 339)*
Description: Consumer research has demonstrated that emotions play an important role in the decision-making process. Individuals may use consumption or purchasing as a way to manage their emotions. This research develops a model to help explain the process by which individuals engage in consumption to manage their emotions, and examines the efficacy of an advertisement for a hedonic product that uses affect-laden language in marketing to stimulate such a process. **Availability:** Print; Online; Download.

10674 ■ *"Scepticism Towards DTC Advertising: A Comparative Study of Korean and Caucasian Americans" in International Journal of Advertising (Vol. 31, February 2012, No. 1, pp. 147)*
Ed: Jisu Huh, Denise E. DeLorme, Leonard N. Reid. **Description:** Studies of cultural and subcultural differences among consumers are important for advancing knowledge on direct-to-consumer prescription drug advertising (DTCA). This study investigates and compares scepticism towards DTCA between Korean and Caucasian Americans and the relationship of cultural values (collectivism vs individualism) and acculturation to DTCA secpticism. The results of the research is provided.

10675 ■ *"Signs Point To Improving CRE Market" in Birmingham Business Journal (Vol. 31, May 2, 2014, No. 18, pp. 7)*
Pub: American City Business Journals, Inc.
Contact: Mike Olivieri, Executive Vice President
Released: Weekly. **Price:** $4, introductory 4-week offer(Digital only). **Description:** Xceligent real estate research firm's data shows collective improvement in Birmingham, Alabama's retail, office and industrial markets over the first three months of 2014. The office market has a less than 10 percent vacancy rate for Class A office space. Vacancy rates for both retail and industrial markets are also provided. **Availability:** Print; Online.

10676 ■ *"Trader Joe's Secret Sauce? An Army of Influencers" in Grocery Dive (November 8, 2019)*
URL(s): www.grocerydive.com/news/trader-joes
-secret-sauce-an-army-of-influencers/566912/
Ed: Jennifer Sweeney. **Released:** November 08, 2019. **Description:** Influencer marketing is giving Trader Joe's a boost on Instagram thanks to several

social media accounts from fans of the company. Featuring products and recipes, these digital influencers have inadvertently created a whole marketing campaign for the grocer. **Availability:** Online.

10677 ■ *"The View From the Front Row" in Philadelphia Business Journal (Vol. 32, January 31, 2014, No. 51, pp. 6)*
Pub: American City Business Journals, Inc.
Contact: Mike Olivieri, Executive Vice President
Released: Weekly. **Price:** $4, introductory 4-week offer(Digital & Print). **Description:** Eric Smallwood, senior vice president of Front Row Analytics, reveals that the company conducts full-season sponsorship marketing analysis for the Seattle Seahawks. He mentions that a 30-second Super Bowl commercial could cost $4 million. Information about his favorite Super Bowl commercials is revealed. **Availability:** Print; Online.

10678 ■ *"Why Messaging Is the Future of Market Research" in Entrepreneur (July 2, 2019)*
URL(s): www.entrepreneur.com/article/332354
Ed: Andrew Reid. **Released:** July 02, 2019. **Availability:** Online.

10679 ■ *"Why You Need a New-Media 'Ringmaster" in Harvard Business Review (Vol. 88, December 2010, No. 12, pp. 78)*
Pub: Harvard Business Publishing
Contact: Diane Belcher, Managing Director
Ed: Patrick Spenner. **Price:** $8.95, PDF. **Description:** The concept of ringmaster is applied to brand marketing. This concept includes integrative thinking, lean collaboration skills, and high-speed decision cycles. **Availability:** Online; PDF.

STATISTICAL SOURCES

10680 ■ *Hispanics: Digital Trends & Impact of COVID-19 One Year Later - US - April 2021*
URL(s): store.mintel.com/report/hispanics-digital-tren
ds-impact-of-covid-19-one-year-later-us-april-2021
Price: $4,366.35. **Description:** Downloadable report discussing the impact the COVID-19 pandemic has had on the Hispanic community and their shopping habits. Provides data on Hispanics' approach to technology and attitudes about digital products. Report includes an executive summary, interactive databook, PowerPoint presentation, infographic overview, report PDF, and previous years data. **Availability:** PDF.

TRADE PERIODICALS

10681 ■ *Alert!*
URL(s): insightsassociation.org/stay-informed/aler
t-magazine
Released: Quarterly **Price:** Included in membership. **Description:** Provides information about marketing industry events, trends in marketing research, management techniques, association events, and legislative activities affecting the marketing industry. Recurring features include news of research, a calendar of events, reports of meetings, news of educational opportunities, job listings, notices of publications available, business opportunities, and facilities for sale. **Availability:** Print; Online.

10682 ■ *Journal of Marketing Research (JMR)*
Pub: SAGE Publications
Contact: Tracey Ozmina, President
URL(s): journals.sagepub.com/home/MRJ
Linkedin: www.linkedin.com/company/journal-of
-marketing-research
Ed: Sachin Gupta. **Released:** Bimonthly; February, April, June, August, October, December. **Price:** $222, Individuals for print only; $686, Institutions for print only; $770, Institutions for print and online (backfile lease, combined plus backfile); $665, Institutions for online (backfile lease, e-access plus backfile); $1,770, Institutions for backfile purchase, e-access; $126, Institutions for single print issue; $48, Individu-

als for single print issue; $227, Individuals for print and online; $700, Institutions for print and online; $193, Individuals for online only; $595, Institutions for online only. **Description:** Scholarly, professional, peer-reviewed journal focused on research in marketing and marketing research practice. Published in association between SAGE and the American Marketing Association. **Availability:** Print; PDF; Download; Online.

10683 ■ *SRIC-BI News*

Pub: Business Intelligence Program
URL(s): www.sric-bi.com.
Released: Monthly. **Price:** free. **Description:** Reports research being performed in technical, market, and management areas. Analyzes early signs of potential social, political, economic, and technological change, and, relating these developments to one another, suggests possible implications for BIP's clients.

TRADE SHOWS AND CONVENTIONS

10684 ■ Document Strategy Forum

URL(s): www.documentstrategyforum.com
Frequency: Annual. **Description:** Presents key topics on creating and managing content, communications, and strategies for marketing and operations departments. **Principal Exhibits:** Presents key topics on creating and managing content, communications, and strategies for marketing and operations departments.

10685 ■ Email Innovations Summit

URL(s): emailinnovationssummit.com
Frequency: Annual. **Description:** Workshops and talks about new email marketing trends and developments. **Principal Exhibits:** Workshops and talks about new email marketing trends and developments.

10686 ■ Experiential Marketing Summit

URL(s): emsummit.eventmarketer.com
Frequency: Annual. **Description:** Provides sessions and professional speakers for the experiential marketing industry. **Principal Exhibits:** Provides sessions and professional speakers for the experiential marketing industry.

10687 ■ LeadsCon

URL(s): www.leadscon.com
Facebook: www.facebook.com/leadscon
Linkedin: www.linkedin.com/groups/1810842
X (Twitter): twitter.com/leadscon
Description: Talks and workshops focused on generating leads and market strategies for small businesses. **Principal Exhibits:** Talks and workshops focused on generating leads and market strategies for small businesses.

CONSULTANTS

10688 ■ Brink & Associates Inc.

3100 Clarendon Blvd., Ste. 200
  Arlington, VA 22201
Ph: (202)550-2451
URL: http://www.brinkassociates.net
Contact: Deborah S. Brink, President
Description: A full-service healthcare consulting company. Provides services in clinical operations, research, hospital administration, marketing and communications. **Scope:** A full-service healthcare consulting company. Provides services in clinical operations, research, hospital administration, marketing and communications.

10689 ■ Business Research Services, Inc. (BRS)

7720 Wisconsin Ave., Ste. 213
  Bethesda, MD 20814
Ph: (301)229-5561
Free: 800-845-8420
Fax: (301)229-6133
Co. E-mail: brspubs@sba8a.com
URL: http://www.sba8a.com

Description: Publishes business directories and newsletters. Also offers software and publications in electronic formats. Does not accept unsolicited manuscripts. Reaches market through telephone sales. **Founded:** 1984. **Publications:** *National Directory of Woman-Owned Business Firms*; *Regional Directory of Minority & Woman-Owned Business Firms* (Biennial); *Minority-Owned High Technology Business Directory*; *Bradford's International Directory of Marketing Research Agencies*; *National Directory of Minority-Owned Business Firms*.

10690 ■ The Chatham Group Inc. (CG)

PO Box 780
  Chatham, MA 02633
Ph: (617)965-5233
Fax: (617)965-5243
Co. E-mail: info@chathamgroup.com
URL: http://www.chathamgroup.com
Contact: Frederick T. Miller, President
E-mail: miller@chathamgroup.com
Description: Management consulting firm specializing in the areas of strategy, competitive positioning, governance and organizational effectiveness, the philosophy of the company is based on three tenets information-driven strategy, multi-discipline teams to assure requisite expertise and state-of-the-art applications of knowledge and technology. **Scope:** Management consulting firm specializing in the areas of strategy, competitive positioning, governance and organizational effectiveness, the philosophy of the company is based on three tenets information-driven strategy, multi-discipline teams to assure requisite expertise and state-of-the-art applications of knowledge and technology. **Founded:** 1984. **Training:** Board development, planning, and management.

10691 ■ The Coxe Group Inc.

7221 Soundview Dr., Apt. 310
  Gig Harbor, WA 98335-1982
Contact: Hugh M. Hochberg, Governor
E-mail: hhochberg@coxegroup.com
Description: Provider of organization management, financial management, marketing, personnel management and human resource services. **Publications:** "Being a Real Architect Means Being a Conscientious Practitioner, Spring," 2008; "Those Without Courage Step Aside, Summer," 2008; "So You're Starting a Practice," 2007; "Practice Made Simple," 2006; "Observations From Prague," 2005; "Tips for Anticipating and Strategizing for the Next Ten Years," 2005; "Cultural Understanding the First Step to Successful Offshoring Strategy," 2005; "Sell, Acquire, Merge: Another Perspective," 2005; "Architects Advised to Get Smart About Design Competitions," 2004; "Architect's Essentials of Ownership Transition," John Wiley And Qmp; Sons Inc, 2002; "Architect's Essentials of Starting a Design Firm," John Wiley and Sons Inc, 2002; "So You're Starting a Practice". **Training:** Marketing Coordinators Clinic; Leadership Development Programs; Clinic for Marketing Professionals; Advanced Marketing Workshop; Effective Negotiations; Marketing Workshop; Project Management Workshop; Project Process Workshop; Selling Skills Clinic.

10692 ■ Customer Perspectives

875-A Island Dr.
  Alameda, CA 94502
Free: 800-339-2861
Co. E-mail: info@customerperspectives.com
URL: http://www.customerperspectives.com
Contact: Judi Hess, Founder
Facebook: www.facebook.com/CustomerPerspectivesMysteryShopping
Linkedin: www.linkedin.com/company/customer-perspectives
X (Twitter): x.com/JancynShops
Description: Firm provides mystery and secret shopping, customer service telephone evaluations, customer experience measurement, call center evaluations, training need and manager assessments, and competitor comparisons. **Scope:** A market research consultancy specializing in mystery shopping. **Founded:** 1983. **Special Services:** Customer Perspectives™.

10693 ■ Goldhaber Research Associates L.L.C. (GRA)

1525 Amherst Manor Dr., Ste. 907
  Williamsville, NY 14221
Ph: (716)689-3311
URL: http://www.goldhaber.com
Contact: Dr. Gerald Goldhaber, President
E-mail: geraldgoldhaber@yahoo.com
Description: Firm is engaged in legal and market research and specializes in litigation and warning label research and design, product and warning label testing, custom-designed market studies, and much more. **Publications:** "Organizational Communication". **Training:** Design and Development of a Product Warning System.

10694 ■ Harold L. Kestenbaum P.C. (HLK)

3401 Merrick Rd., Ste. 4
  Wantagh, NY 11793
Ph: (215)544-2972
Co. E-mail: hkestenbaum@spadealaw.com
Contact: Harold L. Kestenbaum, Contact
E-mail: hkestenbaum@spadealaw.com
Facebook: www.facebook.com/haroldlkestenbaum
Linkedin: www.linkedin.com/in/hkestenbaum
X (Twitter): x.com/Kestenbaum_Law
Description: Provider of consulting services for startup and existing franchisors, their services include feasibility studies, determination of franchise format, business plan development, capital resources, manual preparation and legal services, and practices franchise law and offers marketing services, and serves all types of industries. **Scope:** Provider of consulting services for startup and existing franchisors, their services include feasibility studies, determination of franchise format, business plan development, capital resources, manual preparation and legal services, and practices franchise law and offers marketing services, and serves all types of industries. **Publications:** "Four tips to starting a successful franchise".

10695 ■ Ilium Associates Inc.

10900 NE 8th St., Ste. 1495
  Bellevue, WA 98004
Ph: (425)646-6525
Free: 800-874-6525
Fax: (425)646-6522
Co. E-mail: ilium@ilium.com
URL: http://www.ilium.com
Contact: Carolyn Andersen, President
Description: Firm provides communication and marketing consulting services and graphic designs.

10696 ■ Irwin Broh & Associates Inc.

1011 E Touhy Ave., Ste. 450
  Des Plaines, IL 60018
Ph: (847)297-7515
Fax: (847)297-7847
Co. E-mail: info@irwinbroh.com
URL: http://www.irwinbroh.com
Contact: Melissa Deluca, President
Description: Firm provides market research services. **Founded:** 1971.

10697 ■ Maritz Inc.

1375 N Hwy. Dr.
  Fenton, MO 63099
Free: 877-462-7489
Co. E-mail: info@maritz.com
URL: http://www.maritz.com
Contact: David Peckinpaugh, President
Facebook: www.facebook.com/corporatemaritz
Linkedin: www.linkedin.com/company/maritz
X (Twitter): x.com/maritz
YouTube: www.youtube.com/user/MaritzCorpComm
Description: Firm provides sales incentives and performance travel programs, employee recognition solutions, business meetings and events, customer experience research and technology, customer loyalty solutions, rewards and fulfillment and much more. **Scope:** Firm provides sales incentives and performance travel programs, employee recognition solutions, business meetings and events, customer experience research and technology, customer loyalty solutions, rewards and fulfillment and much more.

Founded: 1894. **Training:** Creating a Successful Health and Productivity Strategy, Mar, 2009; Coaching Your Sales Team to Higher Levels of Performance, Nov, 2005.

10698 ■ Musicals Tonight Inc.
150 W 79th St., No. 9A
New York, NY 10024
Ph: (212)362-5620
Facebook: www.facebook.com/MusicalsTonight
Description: A not-for-profit theatre company involved in theatrical productions for the revival of neglected musicals in a manner affordable to most audience members. **Scope:** A not-for-profit theatre company involved in theatrical productions for the revival of neglected musicals in a manner affordable to most audience members.

10699 ■ Paul A. Warner Associates Inc.
4521 PGA Blvd., Ste. 122
Palm Beach Gardens, FL 33418
Ph: (404)401-2002
Co. E-mail: paul@pwarner.com
URL: http://www.pwarner.com
Contact: Paul Warner, Contact
E-mail: paul@pwarner.com
Description: Full-service market research and consulting firm, the companies capabilities include quantitative research study design, focus group moderation, data gather and information analysis that provides consumer insights and is target market relevant. **Founded:** 1980.

10700 ■ Research USA, Inc.
2364 Essington Rd., No. 149
Joliet, IL 60435
Ph: (815)730-1662
Fax: (815)730-1668
Co. E-mail: info@researchusainc.com
URL: http://www.researchusainc.com/index2.htm?
Description: Full-service marketing and media research firm specializes in conducting customized primary research services for associations, magazines, and other media advertisers, businesses, and government agencies, it conducts mail, telephone, internet, electronic mail, fax and personal interview surveys, and custom designs for each project to meet the specific needs of the client. **Founded:** 1972.

10701 ■ The Spectrem Group Inc.
920 S Waukegan Rd., Ste. 310
Lake Forest, IL 60045
Ph: (224)544-5353
Co. E-mail: info@spectrem.com
URL: http://www.spectrem.com
Contact: George Walper, President
X (Twitter): twitter.com/SpectremGroup
Description: Finance: Wealth and asset management and brokerage. **Scope:** Finance: Wealth and asset management and brokerage. **Founded:** 1990. **Publications:** "Affluent Market Insights," 2009; "Ultra Rich Invest Far More Aggressively Than Other Wealthy Individuals," Nov, 2007.

10702 ■ Technology Management Associates Inc. (TMA)
1699 Wall St., Ste. 635
Mount Prospect, IL 60056
URL: http://techmanage.com
Contact: Joanne F. Gucwa, President
E-mail: jogucwa@techmanage.com
Description: Firm is engaged in providing business research and consulting services, the company offers data analysis and a variety of services regarding business management, marketing and technology, including strategy, planning and much more. **Publications:** "Three Indisputable Truths About Business Intelligence and The Internet"; "Beyond Customer Satisfaction"; "Keys to Creating Successful New Products"; "Increased Profitability By Building Customer Loyalty"; "Global-scale partnering and business alliances"; "10 Keys to Collecting Information"; "The Thinking Manager's Toolbox: Effective Processes for Problem Solving and Decision Making"; "My Say"; "Successful Project Management"; "Thinking Through the Privatization Option"; "Your Marketing Mindset"; "Intellectual Capital: The New Wealth of Organizations"; "Lean

and Meaningful"; "Nuts!: Southwest Airlines' Crazy Recipe for Business and Personal Success"; "If Aristotle Ran General Motors: The New Soul of Business"; "Real Time: Preparing for the Age of the Never Satisfied Customer"; "Webonomics: Nine Essential Principles for Growing your Business on the World Wide Web"; "Asia Rising"; "Customer Centered Growth: Five Proven Strategies for Building Competitive Advantage"; "Cybercorp: The New Business Revolution"; "Net Gain: Expanding Markets Through Virtual Communities"; "Strategic Cost Management"; "Three Indisputable Truths About Business Intelligence and the Internet"; "Leveraging Technology To Build Customer Loyalty"; "Practical and Effective Customer Satisfaction Studies".

10703 ■ Vertex Consultants Inc.
555 Balliol St.
Toronto, ON, Canada M4S 1E1
Ph: (416)550-1838
URL: http://www.vertexconsultants.com
Contact: Marc Beaulieu, President
E-mail: marcrbeaulieu@gmail.com
Description: Management consultancy whose practice focus is on the intersection between strategy and implementation, they are committed to help clients identify and implement profitable change, their services include assisting insetting and evolving effective strategy, assisting in the implementation of strategy throughout the organization and research. **Scope:** Management consultancy whose practice focus is on the intersection between strategy and implementation, they are committed to help clients identify and implement profitable change, their services include assisting insetting and evolving effective strategy, assisting in the implementation of strategy throughout the organization and research. **Founded:** 2013.

10704 ■ Young & Associates Inc. (YA)
131 E Main St.
Kent, OH 44240
Ph: (330)678-0524
Free: 800-525-9775
Fax: (330)678-6219
URL: http://www.younginc.com
Contact: Jerry Sutherin, President
Linkedin: www.linkedin.com/company/young-&-associates-inc
Description: Offers a wide array of management consulting and outsourcing products and services, including risk management, capital planning, strategic planning, mergers and acquisitions, internal audit, branching and expansion, loan review, information technology, human resources, marketing, and regulatory compliance. **Founded:** 1978. **Publications:** "An Avalanche of New Compliance Regulations," Oct, 2009; "Fair Lending Risk Assessment," May, 2009. **Special Services:** The Compliance Monitoring System™; Compliance Monitoring Update Service™; The Compliance Review Program™; Compliance Review Program Update Service™.

FRANCHISES AND BUSINESS OPPORTUNITIES

10705 ■ Fransurvey.com
PO Box 6385
Lincoln, NE 68506
Ph: (402)489-5205
URL: http://franchiseresearchinstitute.com
Contact: Jeff Johnson, Chief Executive Officer
E-mail: jeff@fransurvey.com
Facebook: www.facebook.com/WorldClassFranchise
Linkedin: www.linkedin.com/company/franchise-research-institute
Description: Complete market research services. **Founded:** 2002.

PUBLICATIONS

10706 ■ *Journal of Marketing Analytics*
4 Crinan St.
London N1 9XW, United Kingdom
Ph: 44 20 78334000

Co. E-mail: palgrave@macmillan.com.au
URL: http://www.palgrave.com
Contact: Beth Farrow, Editor
E-mail: beth.farrow@palgrave.com
URL(s): www.palgrave.com/gp/journal/41270link.springer.com/journal/41270/volumes-and-issues
Ed: Anjala Krishen. **Released:** Quarterly **Description:** Journal covering the themes of customer management, including multichannel marketing, customer loyalty and experience, call-centre operations, e-business, and account management; and marketing strategy, with analysis of results-based CRM, data sourcing, warehousing, lifestyle and psychographic data, database building, and software and hardware selection. **Availability:** Print; PDF; Download; Online.

LIBRARIES

10707 ■ The Advertising Research Foundation (ARF) - Library
432 Park Ave. S 4th Fl.
New York, NY 10016
Ph: (212)751-5656
Fax: (212)689-1859
Co. E-mail: membership@thearf.org
URL: http://thearf.org
Contact: Scott McDonald, Executive
Facebook: www.facebook.com/ARF
Linkedin: www.linkedin.com/company/advertising-research-foundation
X (Twitter): x.com/The_ARF
YouTube: www.youtube.com/user/TheARFvideos
Description: Advertisers, advertising agencies, research organizations, associations, and the media are regular members of the foundation; colleges and universities are associate members. Objectives are to: further scientific practices and promote greater effectiveness of advertising and marketing by means of objective and impartial research. **Scope:** Advertising. **Founded:** 1936. **Holdings:** Figures not available. **Publications:** *Journal of Advertising Research (JAR)* (Quarterly). **Awards:** David Ogilvy Awards (Annual); ARF Rising Star Award (Annual); ARF Innovation Award (Annual); ARF Member Recognition Award (Annual). **Geographic Preference:** National.

10708 ■ Escalent Inc. - Library
17430 College Pky.
Livonia, MI 48152
Ph: (734)542-7600
Fax: (734)542-7620
Co. E-mail: info@escalent.co
URL: http://escalent.co
Contact: Chris Barnes, President
E-mail: chris.barnes@escalent.co
Facebook: www.facebook.com/ThinkEscalent
Linkedin: www.linkedin.com/company/thinkescalent
X (Twitter): x.com/ThinkEscalent
YouTube: www.youtube.com/c/EscalentThinking
Description: A market research and consulting company specializing in market definition and segmentation, product design and marketing, brand and image positioning, pricing and marketing strategy. Expertise in external and internal customer satisfaction, quality measurements and Customer Relationship Management (CRM). Industries served: Automotive, consumer products, financial services, health care, retail, and technology. **Scope:** Marketing; branding; business. **Founded:** 1989. **Holdings:** Figures not available. **Publications:** "Using ANCOVA to gauge the impact of demographic differences on satisfaction," QUIRK S MARKETING RESEARCH REVIEW MAGAZINE, Aug, 2007; "Change priorities: Tech convergence forces MR to re-evaluate function," MARKETING NEWS MAGAZINE, Jun, 2006. **Financial Assistance:** Yes **Training:** Collage Building; Story Telling; Elicitation Exercises; Word Association. **Special Services:** Morpace eCommunities?.

10709 ■ General Mills, Inc.
General Mills, Inc.
1 General Mills Blvd.
Minneapolis, MN 55426
Ph: (763)764-7600
Free: 800-248-7310

Fax: (763)764-2268
Co. E-mail: corporate.response@generalmills.com
URL: http://www.generalmills.com
Contact: Jeffrey L. Harmening, Chief Executive
  Officer
Facebook: www.facebook.com/GeneralMills
Linkedin: www.linkedin.com/company/general-mills
X (Twitter): twitter.com/generalmills
Instagram: www.instagram.com/generalmills/
YouTube: www.youtube.com/user/generalmills
Description: Producer and distributor of branded
consumer foods sold through retail stores. **Founded:**

1866. **Educational Activities:** GSF West; Natural
Products Expo East (Annual); Natural Products Expo
West (Annual). **Awards:** Pillsbury Bake-Off® Contest
(Annual).

RESEARCH CENTERS

**10710 ■ University of Alabama - Capstone
International Center (CIC)**
135 BB Comer Hall
  Tuscaloosa, AL 35487-0134
Ph: (205)348-5256

Co. E-mail: cic@ua.edu
URL: http://international.ua.edu
Contact: Dr. Carolina Robinson, Director
E-mail: carolir@ua.edu

Description: Integral unit of University of Alabama.
Scope: Developments in Latin America, Asia, and
Mediterranean Europe through projects conducted by
faculty members of the University and supported by
international opportunity program travel grants. Also
conducts market studies for small businesses in
Alabama. **Founded:** 1966. **Publications:** *Capstone
International Newsletter.*

ASSOCIATIONS AND OTHER ORGANIZATIONS

10711 ■ American Amateur Karate Federation (AAKF)
1948 Mancha Way
Monterey Park, CA 91755
Contact: Richard Kageyama, Contact
Description: Seeks to improve the physical and mental health of the public through the practice of karate; promotes public understanding of karate. **Founded:** 1979. **Publications:** *Times Newsletter* (Monthly). **Geographic Preference:** National.

10712 ■ American Kenpo Karate International (AKKI)
800 Uinta St.
Evanston, WY 82930
URL: http://akki.com
Contact: Paul Mills, Contact
Facebook: www.facebook.com/akkikenpo
Description: Seeks to honor, and elevate Kenpo Karate. Sponsors competitions. Maintains educational, charitable, and research programs, children's services, and a speakers' bureau. **Founded:** 1997. **Publications:** *1st Level Club Manual; 1st Level Knife Manual; Kenpo Karate-Works.* **Geographic Preference:** Multinational.

10713 ■ Canadian Kendo Federation (CKF)
35 Mayfair Ave.
Dundas, BC, Canada L9H 3K7
Co. E-mail: support@kendo-canada.com
URL: http://kendo-canada.com
Contact: Hyun-June Choi, President
E-mail: hjchoi@kendo-canada.com
Facebook: www.facebook.com/KendoCanada
Linkedin: www.linkedin.com/company/canadian-kendo-federation
Instagram: www.instagram.com/kendocanada
Description: Promotes increased interest and participation in Kendo, a Japanese form of swordsmanship. Facilitates creation of Kendo clubs; conducts educational programs; sponsors competitions. **Founded:** 1962. **Publications:** *Kendo Referee Handbook.* **Geographic Preference:** National.

10714 ■ International Traditional Karate Federation (ITKF)
1930 Wilshire Blvd., Ste. 503
Los Angeles, CA 90057
URL: http://www.itkf.org
Facebook: www.facebook.com/International-Traditional-Karate-Federation-ITKF-202086400613594
Description: Represents national karate federations. Provides international rules, regulations, and competition standards for traditional karate; sanctions international competitions and seminars. **Founded:** 1974. **Geographic Preference:** National.

10715 ■ Tomiki Aikido of the Americas (TAA)
1124 E Pacific Coast Hwy., No. 1120
Long Beach, CA 90806-5102
URL: http://tomiki.org

Contact: Greg Linden, Treasurer
Description: Fosters international amateur sports competition. Seeks to introduce and promote the Japanese martial art Aikido by organizing training camps, exhibitions, and tournaments around the world. Promotes international and intercultural exchange, education, and understanding. **Founded:** 1990. **Publications:** *The Aikido Times* (Quarterly). **Educational Activities:** TAA International Aikido Festival and Tournament; TAA National Tournaments. **Geographic Preference:** National.

10716 ■ United States Judo Association (USJA)
2059 Merrick Rd., No. 313
Merrick, NY 11566
Ph: (516)366-3311
Fax: (844)892-6608
URL: http://www.usja.net
Facebook: www.facebook.com/USJudoAssoc
Description: Amateur judo athletes and coaches. Promotes the recreational and physical benefits of judo; advocates practice of the sport to develop sportsmanship, good citizenship, and mental well-being. Encourages public interest and participation in Judo. Seeks the advancement of amateur judo competition in the U.S. and worldwide. Maintains National Judo Hall of Fame. Sanctions local, state, and regional tournaments. Offers training and certification program for coaches and referees. **Founded:** 1954. **Publications:** *American Judo Magazine* (Monthly). **Educational Activities:** Junior National Tournament. **Geographic Preference:** National.

10717 ■ U.S. Taekwondo (USTU)
30 Cimino Dr.
Colorado Springs, CO 80903
Ph: (719)374-5745
Co. E-mail: info@usa-taekwondo.us
URL: http://www.usatkd.org
Contact: Steve McNally, Chief Executive Officer
E-mail: smcnally@usatkd.org
Facebook: www.facebook.com/USATaekwondo
X (Twitter): x.com/USA_Taekwondo
Instagram: www.instagram.com/usatkd.official
YouTube: www.youtube.com/channel/UC-wubY7hGyE-KZz_9XBR1Og
Description: A member of the United States Olympic Committee and the national governing body for the sport of Taekwondo. Amateur Taekwondo athletes and instructors. **Founded:** 1974. **Publications:** *USAT Referee Seminar; U.S. Taekwondo Journal* (Annual); *USTU Club Newsletter* (Bimonthly). **Educational Activities:** National Championships (Annual); U.S. Jr. Olympic Taekwondo Championship (Annual). **Geographic Preference:** National.

10718 ■ U.S.A. Karate Federation (USAKF)
1550 Ritchie Rd., Stow
Stow, OH 44224
URL: http://www.usankf.org/about-us/affiliated-organizations
Contact: Adm. (Ret.) Patrick M. Hickey, Director

Description: Individuals, corporations, sports organizations, and karate clubs. Serves as a national federation for karate in the U.S. Seeks to promote karate as a sport and to advance karate performance and instruction; certifies karate instructors. Organizes competitions, selects U.S. a national karate team. Conducts classes for karate students and masters. Conducts research; compiles statistics; maintains hall of fame and speakers' bureau. **Founded:** 1986. **Geographic Preference:** National.

10719 ■ World Martial Arts Association (WMAA)
8101 Ridge Blvd.
Brooklyn, NY 11209
Co. E-mail: worldmartialartsassoc@gmail.com
URL: http://wmaa.com
Contact: Michael T. Dealy, Contact
Facebook: www.facebook.com/WorldMartialArtsAssociation
Description: Purpose is to teach, promote, and grade the technical aspects of martial arts such as judo, karate, tae kwon do, kung fu, jujitsu, and aikido. **Geographic Preference:** National.

10720 ■ Zen-Do Kai Martial Arts International (ZDK)
490 N Perry St.
Johnstown, NY 12095
Ph: (518)762-4723
Co. E-mail: zdk.fenton@americanzendokai.com
URL: http://www.zendokaius.com
Contact: Adm. (Ret.) Michael Campos, Contact
Description: Firm is a martial arts club that conducts demonstrations of the martial arts, organizes martial arts sports production and conducts instructor training programs. **Founded:** 1969. **Publications:** *The Warrior; The Warrior* (Quarterly). **Educational Activities:** Awards Banquet Weekend (Annual). **Geographic Preference:** National.

REFERENCE WORKS

10721 ■ "Bruce Lee's Martial Arts Studio Has Reopened in Chinatown" in Los Angeles Magazine (October 22, 2019)
URL(s): www.lamag.com/culturefiles/bruce-lee-chinatown/
Ed: Chris Nichols. **Released:** October 22, 2019. **Description:** The famed studio where beloved martial arts expert Bruce Lee taught is once again open and being let by the protege of one of Lee's apprentices. **Availability:** Online.

TRADE PERIODICALS

10722 ■ T'ai Chi
Pub: Wayfarer Publications
URL(s): taichi-daily.com/tai-chi-magazine
Ed: Marvin Smalheiser. **Released:** Bimonthly **Description:** A magazine for practitioners of T'ai Chi and related martial arts, health and fitness disciplines. **Availability:** Print.

ASSOCIATIONS AND OTHER ORGANIZATIONS

10723 ■ Architectural Engineering Institute of ASCE (AEI) - Library
c/o American Society of Civil Engineers
1801 Alexander Bell Dr.
Reston, VA 20191
Co. E-mail: aei@asce.org
URL: http://www.asce.org/communities/institutes-an d-technical-groups/architectural-engineering-insti tute
Contact: Christopher H. Raebel, President
Description: Seeks to advance the state-of-the-art and state-of-the-practice of the building industry worldwide by facilitating effective and timely technology transfer. **Scope:** Civil engineering. **Services:** Interlibrary loan; copying. **Founded:** 1998. **Holdings:** 355 books; 38 journals; magazine; 572 proceedings paper. **Publications:** *Journal of Hydrologic Engineering* (Bimonthly); *Natural Hazards Review* (Quarterly); *Journal of Hazardous, Toxic, and Radioactive Waste* (Quarterly); *Civil Engineering Database (CEDB)*; *Journal of Water Resources Planning and Management* (Monthly); *Civil Engineering Database (CEDB)*; *Leadership and Management in Engineering* (Quarterly); *ASCE Publications Information* (Bimonthly); *Civil Engineering* (Monthly); *Emerging Technology* (Bimonthly); *Manuals and Reports on Engineering Practice*; *Worldwide Projects* (Quarterly); *Civil Engineering--Buyers' Guide Issue*; *Journal of Aerospace Engineering* (Bimonthly); *Journal of Cold Regions Engineering* (Quarterly); *Journal of Computing in Civil Engineering* (Bimonthly); *Journal of Construction Engineering and Management* (Monthly); *Journal of Energy Engineering* (Bimonthly); *Transactions of the American Society of Civil Engineers*; *Journal of Composites for Construction* (Bimonthly); *Leadership and Management in Engineering* (Quarterly); *Journal of Infrastructure Systems* (Quarterly); *Journal of Architectural Engineering* (Quarterly); *Journal of Bridge Engineering* (Monthly); *Waterpower '99: Hydro's Future: Technology, Markets, and Policy*; *Engineering Approaches to Ecosystem Restoration*; *Natural Hazards Review* (Quarterly); *Minimum Design Loads for Buildings and Other Structures, ASCE/SEI 7-05*; *Civil Engineering-ASCE* (Monthly); *ASCE Library*; *Journal of Engineering Mechanics* (Monthly); *Journal of Environmental Engineering* (Monthly); *Journal of Geotechnical and Geoenvironmental Engineering* (Monthly); *Journal of Hydraulic Engineering* (Monthly); *Journal of Irrigation and Drainage Engineering* (Bimonthly); *Journal of Management in Engineering* (Bimonthly); *Journal of Materials in Civil Engineering* (Monthly); *Journal of Performance of Constructed Facilities* (Bimonthly); *Journal of Civil Engineering Education* (Quarterly); *Journal of Structural Engineering* (Monthly); *Journal of Surveying Engineering* (Quarterly); *Journal of Transportation Engineering* (Monthly); *Journal of Urban Planning and Development* (Quarterly); *Journal of Waterway, Port, Coastal, and Ocean Engineering* (Bimonthly); *ASCE News* (Weekly); *Practice Periodi-cal on Structural Design and Construction*; *Journal of Structural Engineering*; *Journal of Infrastructure Systems*; *Journal of Waterway, Port, Coastal, and Ocean Engineering*; *Journal of Hazardous, Toxic, and Radioactive Waste*; *Journal of Computing in Civil Engineering*; *Journal of Urban Planning and Development*; *Journal of Professional Issues in Engineering Education & Practice* (Quarterly); *Journal of Energy Engineering: The International Journal* (Quarterly). **Educational Activities:** Geotechnical and Structural Engineering Congress; Structures Congress (Annual). **Awards:** EWRI Lifetime Achievement Award (Annual); Arthur Casagrande Professional Development Award (Annual); ASCE Civil Engineering History and Heritage Award (Annual); Collingwood Prize (Annual); ASCE Construction Management Award (Annual); J. James R. Croes Medal (Annual); Hans Albert Einstein Award (Annual); ASCE Freeman Fellowship (Annual); Simon W. Freese Environmental Engineering Award and Lecture (Annual); Alfred M. Freudenthal Medal (Biennial); Edmund Friedman Professional Recognition Award (Annual); Edmund Friedman Young Engineer Award for Professional Achievement (Annual); ASCE Government Civil Engineer of the Year Award (Annual); Samuel Arnold Greeley Award (Annual); Shortridge Hardesty Award (Annual); Rudolph Hering Medal (Annual); Karl Emil Hilgard Hydraulic Prize (Annual); Julian Hinds Award (Annual); Phillip R. Hoffman Award (Annual); ASCE Distinguished Membership (Annual); Wesley W. Horner Award (Annual); Robert Horonjeff Award (Annual); Ernest E. Howard Award (Annual); Walter L. Huber Civil Engineering Research Prizes (Annual); ASCE Hydraulic Structures Medal (Annual); Innovation in Sustainable Engineering Award (Annual); ASCE International Coastal Engineering Award (Annual); Martin S. Kapp Foundation Engineering Award (Annual); James Laurie Prize (Annual); T. Y. Lin Award (Annual); Frank M. Masters Transportation Engineering Award (Annual); Daniel W. Mead Prize for Younger Members (Annual); Thomas A. Middlebrooks Award (Annual); John G. Moffat-Frank E. Nichol Harbor and Coastal Engineering Award (Annual); Moisseiff Award (Annual); Nathan M. Newmark Medal (Annual); Alfred Noble Prize (Annual); Norman Medal (Annual); ASCE Outstanding Civil Engineering Achievement Award (Annual); John I. Parcel-Leif J. Sverdrup Civil Engineering Management Award (Annual); Peurifoy Construction Research Award (Annual); Harold R. Peyton Award for Cold Regions Engineering (Annual); Raymond C. Reese Research Prize (Annual); Rickey Medal (Irregular); Robert Ridgway Student Chapter Award (Annual); Roebling Award (Annual); Hunter Rouse Hydraulic Engineering Award (Annual); Thomas Fitch Rowland Prize (Annual); Wilbur S. Smith Award (Annual); J. Waldo Smith Hydraulic Fellowship (Annual); J. C. Stevens Award (Irregular); ASCE Surveying and Mapping Award (Annual); Royce J. Tipton Award (Annual); Richard R. Torrens Award (Irregular); Francis C. Turner Award (Annual); Theodore von Karman Medal (Annual); Arthur M. Wellington Prize (Annual); William H. Wisely Award (Annual); ASCE Young Government Civil Engineer of the Year Award (Annual); ASCE Younger Member Group Award (Annual); Charles Martin Duke Lifeline Earthquake Engineering Award (Annual); George Winter Award (Annual); Ven Te Chow Award (Annual); ASCE Excellence in Journalism Award (Annual); Maurice A. Biot Medal (Annual); Jack E. Cermak Medal (Annual); ASCE Henry L. Michel Award for Industry Advancement of Research (Annual); ASCE Citizen Engineer Award (Annual); ASCE Computing in Civil Engineering Award (Annual); ASCE Professional Practice Ethics and Leadership Award (Annual); Walter LeFevre Award (Annual); Raymond D. Mindlin Award (Annual); Walter P. Moore Jr. Award (Annual); ASCE Outstanding Projects and Leaders Awards (OPAL) (Annual); Ralph B. Peck Award (Annual); Robert H. Scanlan Medal (Annual); Harry Schnabel Jr. Award (Annual); H. Bolton Seed Medal (Annual); Dennis L. Tewksbury Award (Annual); Karl Terzaghi Award (Biennial); ASCE Journal of Architectural Engineering Best Paper Award (Annual); Arid Lands Hydraulic Engineering Award (Annual); ASCE Presidents' Medal (Annual); ASCE State-of-the-Art of Civil Engineering Award (Annual); ASCE Award of Excellence of the Pipeline Division (Annual); Harland Bartholomew Award (Annual); Stephen D. Bechtel Pipeline Engineering Award (Annual); John O. Bickel Award (Annual); Can-Am Civil Engineering Amity Award (Annual). **Geographic Preference:** Multinational; National.

10724 ■ Association of the Wall and Ceiling Industry (AWCI)
513 W Broad St., Ste. 210
Falls Church, VA 22046
Ph: (703)538-1600
Fax: (703)534-8307
URL: http://www.awci.org
Contact: Travis Vap, President
Facebook: www.facebook.com/AWCIwall
Linkedin: www.linkedin.com/company/association-of -the-wall-and-ceiling-industry
X (Twitter): x.com/awci_info
Instagram: www.instagram.com/awci_fwci
YouTube: www.youtube.com/user/AWCImedia

Description: Acoustical tile, drywall, demountable partitions, lathing and plastering, fireproofing, light-gauge steel framing, stucco and exterior insulation finish systems contractors, suppliers and manufacturers. **Founded:** 1918. **Publications:** *Buyer's Guide for the Wall and Ceiling Industry* (Annual); *Association of the Wall and Ceiling Industries International--Buyer's Guide* (Annual); *Who's Who in the Wall and Ceiling Industry* (Annual); *Construction Dimensions Magazine* (Monthly); *Information Resources*. **Educational Activities:** AWCI Annual Convention (Annual). **Awards:** AWCI Excellence in Construction Safety Award (Annual); AWCI Pinnacle Award (Annual). **Geographic Preference:** Multinational.

10725 ■ Brick Industry Association (BIA) - Library
12007 Sunrise Valley Dr., Ste. 430
Reston, VA 20191
Ph: (703)620-0010
Fax: (703)620-3928
Co. E-mail: socialmedia@bia.org

URL: http://www.gobrick.com
Contact: Ray Leonhard, President
E-mail: ceo@bia.org
Facebook: www.facebook.com/brickindustry
Linkedin: www.linkedin.com/groups/1931504/profile
X (Twitter): x.com/BrickIndustry
Instagram: www.instagram.com/brickindustry
YouTube: www.youtube.com/user/BrickIndustry
Pinterest: www.pinterest.com/brickindustry
Description: Manufacturers and distributors of clay brick. Promotes clay brick with the goal of increasing its market share. **Scope:** Clay brick. **Founded:** 1934. **Holdings:** Figures not available. **Publications:** *Brick in Architecture* (Annual); *Annual Sales and Marketing Report* (Monthly); *Directory of Manufacturers*; *BIA News* (Monthly); *Brick Industry Association--Membership Directory.* **Awards:** Brick in Architecture Awards (Annual). **Geographic Preference:** National.

10726 ■ Ceilings and Interior Systems Construction Association (CISCA)
1010 Jorie Blvd., Ste. 30
 Oak Brook, IL 60523
Ph: (630)584-1919
Fax: (866)560-8537
Co. E-mail: cisca@cisca.org
URL: http://www.cisca.org/i4a/pages/index.cfm
Contact: Shirley Wodynski, Executive Director
E-mail: shirley.wodynski@cisca.org
Facebook: www.facebook.com/ciscaassociation
X (Twitter): x.com/ciscassociation
Description: International trade association for the advancement of the interior commercial construction industry. Provides quality education, resources and a forum for communication among its members. **Founded:** 1949. **Publications:** *Ceilings & Interior Systems Construction Association--Industry Resource Guide* (Annual); *Acoustical Interior Construction* (Quarterly); *Ceiling Systems.* **Educational Activities:** CISCA Convention (Annual). **Awards:** CISCA Construction Excellence Award. **Geographic Preference:** Multinational.

10727 ■ Indiana Limestone Institute of America, Inc. (ILIA)
1001 E 10th St., Ste. 6028
 Bloomington, IN 47405
Ph: (812)275-4426
URL: http://iliai.com
Contact: Todd Schnatzmeyer, Executive Director
E-mail: todd@iliai.com
Facebook: www.facebook.com/Indiana-Limestone
 -Institute-of-America-Inc-191270307575081
Linkedin: www.linkedin.com/company/indiana-limes
tone-institute-of-america-inc.
Description: Conducts promotional and technical services for the Indiana limestone industry; sponsors research; establishes standards; offers technical service in product use to architects, builders, and owners. Maintains speakers' bureau; conducts specialized education. **Founded:** 1928. **Geographic Preference:** National.

10728 ■ International Masonry Institute (IMI)
17101 Science Dr.
 Bowie, MD 20715
Free: 800-464-0988
Co. E-mail: masonryquestions@imiweb.org
URL: http://www.imiweb.org
Contact: Caryn Halifax, President
E-mail: chalifax@imiweb.org
Facebook: www.facebook.com/Interna
 tionalMasonryInstitute
X (Twitter): x.com/imiweb
YouTube: www.youtube.com/channel/UCRP7
 teSaUSNtO5agB06QQzg/featured
Description: Joint labor/management trust fund of the International Union of Bricklayers and Allied Craftworkers and union masonry contractors. Advances quality masonry construction through national and regional training, advertising and labor management relations programs in the U.S. and Canada. Provides support and materials for local/regional masonry promotion groups in the U.S. and Canada, and cooperates with national groups and organizations promoting the industry. Sponsors craft training and

research programs. Maintains museum. **Founded:** 1970. **Publications:** *IMI Today* (Bimonthly). **Educational Activities:** Masonry Day Educational Conference and Tradeshow. **Geographic Preference:** National.

10729 ■ Mason Contractors Association of America (MCAA)
1481 Merchant Dr.
 Algonquin, IL 60102
Ph: (224)678-9709
Free: 800-536-2225
Fax: (224)678-9714
URL: http://www.masoncontractors.org
Contact: Paul Oldham, Chairman of the Board
Facebook: www.facebook.com/masoncontractors
Linkedin: www.linkedin.com/in/masoncontractors
X (Twitter): x.com/mcaa
Instagram: www.instagram.com/masoncontractors
YouTube: www.youtube.com/user/masoncontrac
 torsassn
Pinterest: www.pinterest.com/masoncontractor
Description: Masonry construction firms. Conducts specialized education and research programs. Compiles statistics. **Founded:** 1950. **Publications:** *Masonry Buyer's Guide.* **Educational Activities:** MCAA Convention (Annual). **Awards:** Tribute to Exemplary Achievements in Masonry Awards (TEAM) (Annual); MCAA Masonry Skills Challenge (Annual). **Geographic Preference:** National.

10730 ■ The Masonry Society (TMS)
105 S Sunset St., Ste. Q
 Longmont, CO 80501-6172
Ph: (303)939-9700
Fax: (303)541-9215
Co. E-mail: info@masonrysociety.org
URL: http://masonrysociety.org
Contact: Christine Subasic, President
Description: Serves as professional, technical, and educational association dedicated to the advancement and knowledge of masonry. Gathers and disseminates technical information. **Founded:** 1977. **Publications:** *The Masonry Society Journal* (Annual); *TMS Journal* (Annual). **Educational Activities:** TMS Annual Meeting (Annual); North American Masonry Conference (Quadrennial). **Awards:** TMS Outstanding Student Thesis Awards (Annual); The Masonry Society Honorary Members (Annual); TMS President's Award (Annual); TMS Service Award (Annual); The Masonry Society Fellow Member Award (Annual); Clayford T. Grimm, P.E. Student Scholarship (Annual); James L. Noland Student Fellowship (Quadrennial); John B. Scalzi Research Award (Annual); Outstanding TMS Journal Paper Award (Annual); North American Masonry Conference Outstanding Paper Awards (Quadrennial); Paul Haller Structural Design Award (Annual). **Geographic Preference:** Multinational.

10731 ■ National Concrete Masonry Association (NCMA) - Technical Library
13750 Sunrise Valley Dr.
 Herndon, VA 20171
Ph: (703)713-1900
Fax: (703)713-1910
Co. E-mail: info@ncma.org
URL: http://ncma.org
Contact: Robert D. Thomas, President
E-mail: rthomas@ncma.org
Facebook: www.facebook.com/NationalConcre
 teMasonryAssociation
Linkedin: www.linkedin.com/company/national-concre
 te-masonry-association
X (Twitter): x.com/ConcreteMasonry
YouTube: www.youtube.com/channel/UCU9BEyXp
 6di6jvpaR7lpmiA
Description: Manufacturers of concrete masonry units (concrete blocks), segmental retaining wall units and paving block; associate members are machinery, cement and aggregate manufacturers. Conducts testing and research on masonry units and masonry assemblies. **Founded:** 1918. **Holdings:** Notes; manuals; guides. **Publications:** *CM News*; *CM News* (Monthly); *NCMA Buyer's Guide/Associate Member Directory*; *C/M News--Directory of Products and*

Services for the Block Industry Issue; *Engineering Bulletins* (Bimonthly). **Educational Activities:** ICONXchange. **Awards:** NCMA/ICPI Design Awards of Excellence (Biennial). **Geographic Preference:** National.

10732 ■ Natural Stone Institute
380 E Lorain St.
 Oberlin, OH 44074
Ph: (440)250-9222
Fax: (440)774-9222
Co. E-mail: info@naturalstoneinstitute.org
URL: http://www.naturalstoneinstitute.org
Contact: James A. Hieb, Chief Executive Officer
E-mail: jim@naturalstoneinstitute.org
Facebook: www.facebook.com/naturalstoneinstitute
Linkedin: www.linkedin.com/company/naturalstoneins
 titute
X (Twitter): x.com/marbleinstitute
YouTube: www.youtube.com/c/NaturalStoneInstitute
Description: Trade association representing every aspect of the natural stone industry. **Founded:** 1907. **Publications:** *Building Stone Magazine* (Semiannual); *Stone Information Manual*; *Who's Who in the Stone Business* (Annual); *Care and Cleaning Brochure for Natural Stone Surfaces*; *Cutting Edge* (Monthly); *Dimension Stone - Design Manual, Version VI*; *Marble Institute of America--Membership Products and Services Directory* (Semiannual). **Educational Activities:** The International Surface Event (TISE) (Annual); StonExpo (Annual). **Awards:** Tucker Design Award (Biennial); Advertising Awards (Annual); Tucker Architectural Awards Competition; Migliore Award for Lifetime Achievement (Annual); MIA Pinnacle Awards (Annual). **Geographic Preference:** Multinational; National.

10733 ■ Precast/Prestressed Concrete Institute (PCI)
8770 W Bryn Mawr Ave., Ste. 1150
 Chicago, IL 60631
Ph: (312)786-0300
Co. E-mail: info@pci.org
URL: http://www.pci.org
Contact: Robert J. Risser, President
Facebook: www.facebook.com/pciprecast
Linkedin: www.linkedin.com/company/pciprecast
X (Twitter): x.com/PCIprecast
Instagram: www.instagram.com/pciprecast
YouTube: www.youtube.com/c/pciprecast
Description: Manufacturers, suppliers, educators, engineers, technicians and others interested in the design and construction of prestressed concrete. Compiles statistics. Maintains 17 committees, including marketing, technical and research committees. **Founded:** 1954. **Publications:** *PCI Journal* (Bimonthly). **Educational Activities:** World of Concrete (WOC) (Annual); PCI Convention (Annual). **Awards:** Harry H. Edwards Industry Advancement Award (Periodic); Martin P. Korn Award; Robert J. Lyman Award (Annual); Charles C. Zollman Award (Annual); PCI Fellow Award (Annual). **Geographic Preference:** National.

10734 ■ Tile Council of North America (TCNA)
100 Clemson Research Blvd.
 Anderson, SC 29625
Ph: (864)646-8453
Fax: (864)646-2821
URL: http://www.tcnatile.com
Contact: Eric Astrachan, Executive Director
E-mail: eastrachan@tcnatile.com
Description: Manufacturers of domestic ceramic tile for floors, walls, and related products. Promotes increase in the marketability of ceramic tile. Conducts testing program on tile and tile installation materials. Supervises international licensing program with 16 licensees. Compiles statistics. **Founded:** 1945. **Publications:** *Directory of Manufacturers of Ceramic Tile and Related Products* (Annual); *Handbook for Ceramic, Glass, and Stone Tile Installation* (Annual); *TileFlash* (Monthly). **Educational Activities:** Coverings (Annual). **Geographic Preference:** National.

REFERENCE WORKS

10735 ■ *Brick Industry Association--Membership Directory (Internet only)*
Pub: Brick Industry Association
Contact: Ray Leonhard, President
E-mail: ceo@bia.org
URL(s): www.gobrick.com/about-bia/member-direc tory
Description: Covers brick distributors, brick manufacturers, and related service providers throughout the U.S. and Canada. **Entries include:** Company name, address, phone, name of principal executives, list of products or services. **Arrangement:** Alphabetical by personnel. **Availability:** Print.

10736 ■ *"Firms Sue Doracon to Recoup More Than $1M in Unpaid Bills" in Baltimore Business Journal (Vol. 28, July 9, 2010, No. 9, pp. 1)*
Pub: Baltimore Business Journal
Contact: Rhonda Pringle, President
E-mail: rpringle@bizjournals.com
Ed: Scott Dance. **Description:** Concrete supplier Paul J. Rach Inc., Selective Insurance Company, and equipment leasing firm Colonial Pacific Leasing Corporation intend to sue Baltimore, Maryland-based Doracon Contracting Inc. for $1 million in unpaid bills. Doracon owed Colonial Pacific $794,000 and the equipment is still in Doracon's possession. Selective Insurance and Paul J. Rach respectively seek $132,000 and $88,000. **Availability:** Print.

10737 ■ *"Housing Slide Picks Up Speed" in Crain's Chicago Business (Vol. 31, April 19, 2008, No. 16, pp. 2)*
Pub: Crain Communications Inc.
Contact: Barry Asin, President
Ed: Eddie Baeb. **Description:** According to Tracy Cross & Associates Inc., a real estate consultancy, sales of new homes in the Chicago area dropped 61 percent from the year-earlier period which is more bad news for homebuilders, contractors and real estate agents who are eager for an indication that market conditions are improving. **Availability:** Online.

10738 ■ *"U.S. House Approves Concrete Masonry Products Promotion Act" in Masonry Magazine (November 15, 2016)*
URL(s): www.masonrymagazine.com/blog/2016/11/ 15/u-s-house-approves-concrete-masonry-products -promotion-act/
Released: November 15, 2016. **Description:** The U.S. House of Representatives approved HR 985, otherwise known as the Concrete Masonry Products, Research, Education, and Promotion Act of 2015. It will provide authorization for the concrete masonry industry to create an industry-wide commodity check-off program. **Availability:** Online.

STATISTICAL SOURCES

10739 ■ *RMA Annual Statement Studies*
Pub: Risk Management Association
Contact: Nancy Foster, President
Released: Annual. **Description:** Contains composite balance sheets and income statements for more than 360 industries, including the accounting, auditing, and bookkeeping industries. Also contains five years of comparative historical data for discerning trends. Includes 16 commonly used ratios, computed for most of the size groupings for nearly every industry.

TRADE PERIODICALS

10740 ■ *TMS Journal*
Pub: The Masonry Society
Contact: Christine Subasic, President
URL(s): masonrysociety.org/product-category/tms -journals
Released: Annual; December / January. **Price:** $150, Other countries for print; $125, U.S. for print; $75, for technical papers. **Description:** Presents news of the activities of this Society, devoted to the use of

masonry. Contains information on codes and standards, testing, research and development, education and training, inspection, quality control, construction, and public relations. **Availability:** Print; Online.

10741 ■ *Walls & Ceilings*
Pub: BNP Media
Contact: Harper Henderson, Owner Co-Chief Executive Officer
URL(s): www.wconline.com
Facebook: www.facebook.com/WallsnCeilings
Linkedin: www.linkedin.com/company/walls-ceilings -magazine
X (Twitter): twitter.com/WallsnCeilings
Instagram: www.instagram.com/wallsnceilings
YouTube: www.youtube.com/user/WallsCeilingsMag
Ed: John Wyatt. **Released:** Monthly **Description:** Trade magazine for contractors, suppliers, and distributors of drywall, plaster, stucco, EIFS, acoustics, metal framing, and ceilings. **Availability:** Online.

TRADE SHOWS AND CONVENTIONS

10742 ■ International Cement Seminar
URL(s): www.internationalcementseminar.com
Description: Focuses on concrete and cement producers. **Principal Exhibits:** Focuses on concrete and cement producers.

10743 ■ MCAA Convention
Mason Contractors Association of America (MCAA)
  1481 Merchant Dr.
  Algonquin, IL 60102
Ph: (224)678-9709
Free: 800-536-2225
Fax: (224)678-9714
URL: http://www.masoncontractors.org
Contact: Paul Oldham, Chairman of the Board
URL(s): masoncontractors.azurewebsites.net/Defaul t?pageID=114
Frequency: Annual. **Description:** Masonry equipment, supplies, and services. **Audience:** Mason contractors, industry suppliers, manufacturers, and distributors. **Principal Exhibits:** Masonry equipment, supplies, and services. Dates and Locations: 2025 Las Vegas, NV.

FRANCHISES AND BUSINESS OPPORTUNITIES

10744 ■ A-1 Concrete Leveling Inc.
388 S Main St., Ste. 402b
  Akron, OH 44311
Free: 888-675-3835
URL: http://www.a1concrete.com
Contact: James W. Creed, President
YouTube: www.youtube.com/user/A1Concre teCorporate
Description: Provider of commercial and residential concrete leveling and foundation repair services. **No. of Franchise Units:** 50.0. **Founded:** 1992. **Financial Assistance:** Yes **Training:** Provides 1 week at headquarters, 2 weeks of onsite and ongoing support including newsletter, meetings toll-free phone line, Internet, security/safety procedures, and field operations/evaluations.

10745 ■ Case Handyman and Remodeling Services LLC
3601 W Hundred Rd., Ste. 10
  Chester, VA 23831
Ph: (804)748-8500
Fax: (804)748-2808
Co. E-mail: casechester@gmail.com
URL: http://www.casechester.com
Contact: Fred Case, Chief Executive Officer
Facebook: www.facebook.com/casehan dymanservices
Pinterest: www.pinterest.com/casechester
Description: Handyman services. **No. of Franchise Units:** 57. **No. of Company-Owned Units:** 4. **Founded:** 1992. **Franchised:** 1997. **Equity Capital Needed:** $105,000-$150,000. **Franchise Fee:**

$25,000. **Royalty Fee:** 4-6%. **Training:** Includes 3 weeks training at headquarters, 2 days at franchisee's location and ongoing support.

10746 ■ Concrete Raising of America, Inc.
2855 S 166th St.
  New Berlin, WI 53151
Ph: (262)827-5000
Fax: (262)827-5005
Co. E-mail: info@crc1.com
URL: http://www.crc1.com
Facebook: www.facebook.com/CRC262.827.5000
Linkedin: www.linkedin.com/in/crc-concrete-raising -7b5a8b30
X (Twitter): x.com/RaiseConcreteWI
Instagram: www.instagram.com/crcconcreteraisingw
YouTube: www.youtube.com/channel/UC6TknacJa -mnRUz4le6qRWw
Description: Firm provides concrete services for residential, commercial, industrial and municipal sectors. **Founded:** 1995. **Financial Assistance:** Yes **Training:** Yes.

10747 ■ Precision Concrete Cutting (PCC)
3191 N Canyon Rd.
  Provo, UT 84604
Ph: (801)224-0025
Free: 877-224-0025
URL: http://safesidewalks.com
Linkedin: www.linkedin.com/company/precision -concrete-cutting---www-safesidewalks-com
X (Twitter): x.com/safesidewalk
Description: Firm provides trip hazard repair services for uneven sidewalks and other concrete walkways across North America. **Founded:** 1992. **Equity Capital Needed:** $135,000. **Franchise Fee:** $63,000. **Royalty Fee:** 0.09. **Financial Assistance:** Yes **Training:** Offers 1 week at headquarters and 1 week at franchisee's location with ongoing support.

LIBRARIES

10748 ■ Brick Industry Association (BIA) - Library
12007 Sunrise Valley Dr., Ste. 430
  Reston, VA 20191
Ph: (703)620-0010
Fax: (703)620-3928
Co. E-mail: socialmedia@bia.org
URL: http://www.gobrick.com
Contact: Ray Leonhard, President
E-mail: ceo@bia.org
Facebook: www.facebook.com/brickindustry
Linkedin: www.linkedin.com/groups/1931504/profile
X (Twitter): x.com/BrickIndustry
Instagram: www.instagram.com/brickindustry
YouTube: www.youtube.com/user/BrickIndustry
Pinterest: www.pinterest.com/brickindustry
Description: Manufacturers and distributors of clay brick. Promotes clay brick with the goal of increasing its market share. **Scope:** Clay brick. **Founded:** 1934. **Holdings:** Figures not available. **Publications:** *Brick in Architecture* (Annual); *Annual Sales and Marketing Report* (Monthly); *Directory of Manufacturers*; *BIA News* (Monthly); *Brick Industry Association-- Membership Directory*. **Awards:** Brick in Architecture Awards (Annual). **Geographic Preference:** National.

10749 ■ Foundation of the Wall and Ceiling Industry (FWCI) - John H. Hampshire Memorial Library
513 W Broad St., Ste. 210
  Falls Church, VA 22046
Ph: (703)538-1600
Co. E-mail: selvitelli@awci.org
URL: http://www.awci.org/foundation
Contact: Adm. (Ret.) Johnny Barnes, President
Facebook: www.facebook.com/AWCIwall
Linkedin: www.linkedin.com/company/association-of -the-wall-and-ceiling-industry
X (Twitter): x.com/awci_info
Instagram: www.instagram.com/awci_fwci
YouTube: www.youtube.com/user/AWCImedia
Description: National and local contractors, manufacturers of construction products, architects, specifiers, and distributors/suppliers of wall and ceiling

products. Supports the wall and ceiling industry's educational and research activities. Operates information clearinghouse. **Scope:** Industry specifications; historical reference materials. **Services:** Open to members for research only. **Founded:** 1918. **Holdings:** 10,000 valuable and historical reference materials. **Publications:** *Standard Practice for the Testing and Inspections of Field Applied Sprayed Fire-Resistive Materials: An Annotated Guide.* **Geographic Preference:** National.

10750 ■ National Concrete Masonry Association (NCMA) - Technical Library
13750 Sunrise Valley Dr.
 Herndon, VA 20171
Ph: (703)713-1900
Fax: (703)713-1910
Co. E-mail: info@ncma.org
URL: http://ncma.org
Contact: Robert D. Thomas, President
E-mail: rthomas@ncma.org
Facebook: www.facebook.com/NationalConcre
 teMasonryAssociation
Linkedin: www.linkedin.com/company/national-concre
 te-masonry-association
X (Twitter): x.com/ConcreteMasonry
YouTube: www.youtube.com/channel/UCU9BEyXp
 6di6jvpaR7lpmiA
Description: Manufacturers of concrete masonry units (concrete blocks), segmental retaining wall units and paving block; associate members are machinery, cement and aggregate manufacturers. Conducts testing and research on masonry units and masonry as-

semblies. **Founded:** 1918. **Holdings:** Notes; manuals; guides. **Publications:** *CM News; CM News* (Monthly); *NCMA Buyer's Guide/Associate Member Directory; C/M News--Directory of Products and Services for the Block Industry Issue; Engineering Bulletins* (Bimonthly). **Educational Activities:** ICON-Xchange. **Awards:** NCMA/ICPI Design Awards of Excellence (Biennial). **Geographic Preference:** National.

RESEARCH CENTERS

10751 ■ National Concrete Masonry Association (NCMA) - Technical Library
13750 Sunrise Valley Dr.
 Herndon, VA 20171
Ph: (703)713-1900
Fax: (703)713-1910
Co. E-mail: info@ncma.org
URL: http://ncma.org
Contact: Robert D. Thomas, President
E-mail: rthomas@ncma.org
Facebook: www.facebook.com/NationalConcre
 teMasonryAssociation
Linkedin: www.linkedin.com/company/national-concre
 te-masonry-association
X (Twitter): x.com/ConcreteMasonry
YouTube: www.youtube.com/channel/UCU9BEyXp
 6di6jvpaR7lpmiA
Description: Manufacturers of concrete masonry units (concrete blocks), segmental retaining wall units and paving block; associate members are machinery,

cement and aggregate manufacturers. Conducts testing and research on masonry units and masonry assemblies. **Founded:** 1918. **Holdings:** Notes; manuals; guides. **Publications:** *CM News; CM News* (Monthly); *NCMA Buyer's Guide/Associate Member Directory; C/M News--Directory of Products and Services for the Block Industry Issue; Engineering Bulletins* (Bimonthly). **Educational Activities:** ICON-Xchange. **Awards:** NCMA/ICPI Design Awards of Excellence (Biennial). **Geographic Preference:** National.

10752 ■ University of Manitoba - W.R. McQuade Laboratory
Room E1-368A Engineering, 15 Gillson St.
 University of Manitoba
 Winnipeg, MB, Canada R3T 5V6
URL: http://umanitoba.ca/faculties/engineering/depar
 tments/civil/154.html
Description: Integral unit of Department of Civil Engineering at University of Manitoba. **Scope:** Large scale static and dynamic testing of steel, concrete, masonry, timber and fiber reinforced polymer (FRP) structures and components; structural health monitoring of infrastructure; civionics testing; fiber optic sensors; field testing of structures. Projects include testing of full scale steel free bridge decks; glass fiber reinforced polymer (GFRP) utility poles and towers; FRP strengthened timber beams in controlled environmental conditions; and durability of concrete subject to chemical attack. **Founded:** 1995. **Publications:** *Design manuals; Innovator Newsletter* (Biennial). **Educational Activities:** W.R. McQuade Laboratory Conference; W.R. McQuade Laboratory Workshops, seminars.

ASSOCIATIONS AND OTHER ORGANIZATIONS

10753 ■ American Massage Therapy Association (AMTA)
500 Davis St., Ste. 900
Evanston, IL 60201
Free: 877-905-2700
Co. E-mail: info@amtamassage.org
URL: http://www.amtamassage.org
Contact: Steve Albertson, President
Facebook: www.facebook.com/AMTAmassage
Linkedin: www.linkedin.com/company/american-massage-therapy-association
X (Twitter): x.com/AMTAmassage
Instagram: www.instagram.com/amtamassage
YouTube: www.youtube.com/amtamassage

Description: Massage therapists and massage schools. Promotes standards for the profession and supports chapter efforts for state regulation of massage. Sponsors National Massage Therapy Awareness Week to promote public education on the benefits of massage. Offers educational literature. Supports research on the efficacy of massage. Offers locator service to help consumers and healthcare professionals find qualified, professional massage therapists. **Founded:** 1943. **Publications:** *Massage Therapy*; *AMTA's Find a Massage Therapist*; *Massage Therapy Journal (MTJ)* (Quarterly); *Sports Massage*; *Stress*. **Geographic Preference:** National.

10754 ■ American Organization for Bodywork Therapies of Asia (AOBTA)
391 Wilmington Pke., Ste. 3
Glen Mills, PA 19342
Ph: (484)841-6023
Co. E-mail: office@aobta.org
URL: http://aobta.org
Contact: Karen Elisa Broyles, President
E-mail: president@aobta.org
Facebook: www.facebook.com/AOBTA
X (Twitter): x.com/AOBTANational

Description: Identifies qualified practitioners; serves as a legal entity representing members when dealing with the government, especially in terms of establishing professional status. **Founded:** 1989. **Publications:** *AOBTA Directory*. **Geographic Preference:** National.

10755 ■ American Society of Hand Therapists (ASHT)
1120 Rte. 73, Ste. 200
Mount Laurel, NJ 08054
Ph: (856)380-6856
Fax: (856)439-0525
Co. E-mail: asht@asht.org
URL: http://asht.org
Contact: Gene S. Terry, Executive Director
E-mail: gterry@asht.org
Facebook: www.facebook.com/HandTherapyASHT
X (Twitter): x.com/HandTherapyASHT
Instagram: www.instagram.com/handtherapyasht
YouTube: www.youtube.com/user/HandTherapyASHT
Pinterest: www.pinterest.com/handtherapyasht

Description: Registered and licensed occupational and physical therapists specializing in hand therapy and committed to excellence and professionalism in hand rehabilitation. Works to promote research, publish information, improve treatment techniques, and standardize hand evaluation and care. Fosters education and communication between therapists in the US. and abroad. Compiles statistics; conducts research and education programs and continuing education seminars. **Founded:** 1977. **Publications:** *ASHT Times* (Quarterly); *Journal of Hand Therapy* (Quarterly). **Educational Activities:** American Society of Hand Therapists Annual Meeting (Annual). **Geographic Preference:** National.

10756 ■ Associated Bodywork & Massage Professionals (ABMP)
25188 Genesee Trl. Rd., Ste. 200
Golden, CO 80401
Ph: (303)674-8478
Free: 800-667-8260
Co. E-mail: expectmore@abmp.com
URL: http://www.abmp.com
Contact: Les Sweeney, President
X (Twitter): x.com/ABMPmassage

Description: Seeks to promote a positive image of massage therapy and bodywork, and to educate the public about its benefits. **Founded:** 1987. **Publications:** *Massage & Bodywork: Nurturing Mind, Body & Spirit* (6/year); *ABMP Massage Marketplace* (Annual); *ABMP Successful Business Handbook*; *ABMP Touch Resource Guide*; *Different Strokes*; *The Massage Educator* (Quarterly); *Skin Deep*; *Body Sense* (Quarterly). **Educational Activities:** School Issues Forum (Annual). **Geographic Preference:** National.

10757 ■ International Association of Infant Massage (IAIM) [Infant Massage WINC - World Institute for Nurturing Communication]
35 W Main St., Ste. B No. 392
Ventura, CA 93001
Ph: (805)644-8524
Fax: (805)299-4563
Co. E-mail: wincs@me.com
URL: http://www.infantmassagewinc.com/home.html
Contact: Susan Campbell, Contact
Facebook: www.facebook.com/infantmassagewinc

Description: Parents, caregivers. Works to promote nurturing touch, positive interactive contact, and communication through massage. Trains and certifies individuals to teach parents and caregivers to massage their babies. **Founded:** 1986. **Geographic Preference:** Multinational.

REFERENCE WORKS

10758 ■ *"The 5 Keys to Successful Marketing"* in Massage Magazine (January 10, 2019)
Ed: Savanna Bell. **Released:** January 10, 2019. **Description:** Provides an overview of how to market your massage therapy business, providing five keys to successful marketing. **Availability:** Online.

10759 ■ *"50 Best Spa & Massage Small Business Ideas for 2021"* in Profitable Venture Magazine
Ed: Ajaero Tony Martins. **Description:** The benefits of massage are a wonderful part of health and well-being. This article offers fifty profitable niche ideas that small business entrepreneurs can pursue in the spa and massage industry. **Availability:** Online.

10760 ■ *Building a Wellness Business That Lasts: How to Make a Great Living Doing What You Love*
URL(s): www.wiley.com/en-us/Building+a+Wellness+Business+That+Lasts%3A+How+to+Make+a+Great+Living+Doing+What+You+Love-p-9781119679066
Ed: Rick Stollmeyer. **Released:** October 2020. **Price:** $17, e-book; $28, hardcover. **Description:** There are a lot of business opportunities to bring wellness into the community, through gyms, spas, salons, etc. This book will help guide you on starting your own wellness small business. **Availability:** E-book; Print.

10761 ■ *Choosing the Best Massage Business Structure*
Description: One of the most important decisions you will make for the legal and financial health of your new massage therapy business is deciding what kind of business structure you will use. This article explains the different types of business structures, including sole proprietorship, LLC, S-Corporation, Cooperative, and Partnership, and discusses the differences between each type. **Availability:** Online.

10762 ■ *The Complete Guide to Modern Massage: Step-by-Step Massage Basics and Techniques from Around the World*
Ed: Ryan Jay Hoyme. **Released:** December 11, 2018. **Price:** $12.43, Paperback; $9.99, E-book. **Description:** An updated reference to massage techniques from classic styles such as Swedish or Shiatsu to new practices such as Ayurvedic and Thai. **Availability:** E-book; Print.

10763 ■ *"How to Cover Unexpected Costs for a New Massage Business"* in Awebtoknow.com (August 26, 2019)
Ed: Adley Reed. **Released:** August 26, 2019. **Description:** Apart from the startup costs for your massage business, you should also consider the unexpected costs of operating your new business. Becoming aware of these unexpected expenses allows you to plan ahead and find ways to overcome potential financial challenges and understand exactly what it takes to be successful in this endeavor. This article provides suggestions that will help you navigate the challenging side of running your massage business. **Availability:** Online.

10764 ■ *"How Do I Get New Massage Clients?"* in Massage Business Blueprint Blog (July 23, 2020)
Ed: Allissa Haines. **Released:** July 23, 2020. **Description:** While there is no single tactic that will get

new and long-term clients, marketing your business is key to bringing in and maintaining clients. This article provides information on different marketing avenues and how to best utilize each one. **Availability:** Online.

10765 ■ *"How I Did It: Jack Ma, Alibaba.com"* *in Inc. (January 2008, pp. 94-102)*
Ed: Rebecca Fannin. **Description:** Profile of Jack Ma, who started as a guide and interpreter for Western tourists in Hangzhou. Ma used the Internet to build Alibaba.com, China's largest business-to-business site and one of the hottest IPOs in years. **Availability:** Online.

10766 ■ *"How to Start Your Own Massage Therapy Business"* *in Chron (March 4, 2019)*
Ed: David Weedmark. **Released:** March 04, 2019. **Description:** Opening your own massage therapy business is a great way to be self-employed while helping others. Before starting, it's important to research the requirements for running a massage business in your region. This article provides an overview of resources and startup requirements for massage therapy small businesses. **Availability:** Online.

10767 ■ *"Launching Your Massage Therapy Business"* *in American Massage Therapy Association (November 14, 2017)*
Ed: Matt Alderton. **Released:** November 14, 2017. **Description:** For those opening their own massage therapy practice, this article asks three of the most important questions you'll need to answer in order to be successful. **Availability:** Online.

10768 ■ *Managing a Massage Business*
Description: This article discusses a variety of factors to consider before starting your own massage therapy business including licensing, taxes, choosing a business name, signing a lease, insurance, business type, hiring, marketing, and advertising. **Availability:** Online.

10769 ■ *"Massage Heights Chasing Big Expansion Opportunities"* *in San Antonio Business Journal (Vol. 28, April 25, 2014, No. 11, pp. 6)*
Pub: American City Business Journals, Inc.
Contact: Mike Olivieri, Executive Vice President
Released: Weekly. **Price:** $4, Introductory 4-week offer(Digital only). **Description:** Massage Heights, offering deep tissue massage, hot stone massage and facials, has opened a second corporate-owned facility in Stone Oak, Texas. The company, founded in April 2004, is focusing on expansion plans due to investor interest in the firm's growth. Massage Heights currently has five facilities in Canada. **Availability:** Print; Online.

10770 ■ *"Massage Therapy Field on the Rise, According to AMTA Survey"* *in Well Spa 360*
URL(s): www.wellspa360.com/news/industry-news/news/21821301/american-massage-therapy-asso-e ditorial-massage-therapy-field-on-the-rise
Released: November 19, 2021. **Description:** With COVID safety protocols in place, many massage therapists are returning to in-house work while more and more people are turning to massage to deal with physical pain and to add to their health and wellness routines. **Availability:** Online.

10771 ■ *"Massage Therapy Practice Marketing Tips"* *in Click4Time Blog*
Description: Provides tips for massage therapy businesses to successful market their services to increase the bottom line. **Availability:** Online.

10772 ■ *Mosby's Pathology for Massage Therapists*
Ed: Susan G. Salvo. **Released:** October 16, 2017. **Price:** $50.60, Paperback; $51.16, E-book. **Description:** A textbook of massage pathology, written by a massage therapist. Shows how to tailor treatment and contains over 500 full-color photographs. **Availability:** E-book; Print.

10773 ■ *"Relax! 5 Marketing Ideas for Massage Therapists"* *in Outbound Engine (January 13, 2020)*
Ed: Taylor Landis. **Released:** January 13, 2020. **Description:** As stress levels increase with our face-paced lives, services such as massage therapy are needed more than ever. Coming up with marketing ideas and thinking creatively to ensure your business stands out. This article provides 5 marketing ideas to improve your visibility. **Availability:** Online.

10774 ■ *"What Is the Cost to Start a Massage Business?"* *in Chron (April 9, 2019)*
Ed: Shanika Chapman. **Released:** April 09, 2019. **Description:** With training, licensing, supplies, equipment, advertising and start-up costs, starting a massage therapy business may cost you as little as $6,000. This article details startup tasks and costs associated with them. **Availability:** Online.

10775 ■ *"What Supplies Do I Need to Start My Massage Business?"* *in Chron*
Ed: Miranda Brookins. **Description:** Whether you work in a spa or salon, or opt to start your massage therapy business at home, you will need certain supplies to get your business off the ground. This article details those supplies and also discusses marketing supplies to ensure you attract clients. **Availability:** Online.

10776 ■ *"Whether You Are Opening Up Now or Later, You Must Understand the Business of Planning for Your Massage Practice"* *in Massage Magazine (June 18, 2020)*
Ed: Lozelle Mathai. **Released:** June 18, 2020. **Description:** The process of writing a business plan for your massage business should follow a predefined format, allowing you to explore the financial risks, benefits and alternatives that are present and projected as you plan your new business. This article discusses why you need a business plan, what your business plan should include, and how to implement your plan. **Availability:** Online.

10777 ■ *"You Shouldn't Start a Massage Practice Without These 3 Items"* *in Massage Magazine (October 2, 2017)*
Ed: Christina DeBusk. **Released:** October 02, 2017. **Description:** Discusses important factors in setting up your massage therapy business. Identifies three key items to have as you launch your practice: massage equipment, a variety of lubricants, and marketing materials. **Availability:** Online.

STATISTICAL SOURCES

10778 ■ *Massage Services Industry in the US - Market Research Report*
URL(s): www.ibisworld.com/united-states/market-research-reports/massage-services-industry/
Price: $925. **Description:** Downloadable report analyzing the current and future trends in the massage industry. **Availability:** Download.

TRADE SHOWS AND CONVENTIONS

10779 ■ American Massage Therapy Association National Convention
URL(s): www.amtamassage.org/continuing-educa tion/national-convention
Frequency: Annual. **Description:** Education and networking for massage therapists. **Principal Exhibits:** Education and networking for massage therapists.

10780 ■ World Massage Festival
URL(s): worldmassagefestival.com
Description: Workshops, demonstrations, and classes for massage therapists. **Principal Exhibits:** Workshops, demonstrations, and classes for massage therapists. **Telecommunication Services:** festival@worldmassagefestival.com.

FRANCHISES AND BUSINESS OPPORTUNITIES

10781 ■ Elements Therapeutic Massage L.L.C. [Elements Massage]
4004 Red Cedar Dr., C-3
 Highlands Ranch, CO 80126
Ph: (720)642-7478
Co. E-mail: sugarland@elementsmassage.com
URL: http://elementsmassage.com
Contact: Anthony Delvecchio, Manager
Linkedin: www.linkedin.com/company/elements -massage-inc
X (Twitter): x.com/ElementsMassage
Instagram: www.instagram.com/elementsmassage
YouTube: www.youtube.com/channel/ UCXLHkAYMgmA6_MJ8DSEZm-A/videos
Description: Firm provides therapeutic massage services. **Founded:** 2000. **Equity Capital Needed:** $192,150-$391,050. **Franchise Fee:** $49,500. **Royalty Fee:** 6%. **Financial Assistance:** Yes **Training:** Yes.

10782 ■ Hand and Stone Massage and Facial Spa
630 Marketplace Blvd.
 Hamilton, NJ 08691
Ph: (609)585-2250
Co. E-mail: spa@handandstone.com
URL: http://handandstone.com
Contact: Todd Leff, Contact
Facebook: www.facebook.com/handandstoneusa
Linkedin: www.linkedin.com/in/handandstone
Instagram: www.instagram.com/handandstoneusa
YouTube: www.youtube.com/user/HandAndStone
Description: Provider of professional massage, facial and hair removal services. **Founded:** 2005. **Financial Assistance:** Yes **Training:** Offers 3 weeks at headquarters, 1 week onsite with ongoing support.

10783 ■ Massage Envy Franchising L.L.C.
14350 N 87th St., Ste. 200
 Scottsdale, AZ 85260
Ph: (480)366-4100
URL: http://www.massageenvy.com
Contact: Beth Stiller, Chief Executive Officer
Facebook: www.facebook.com/MassageEnvy
X (Twitter): x.com/MassageEnvy
Instagram: www.instagram.com/massageenvy
Description: Therapeutic massage services. **Founded:** 2002. **Financial Assistance:** Yes **Training:** Offers 5 days at headquarters, 5 days on-site and ongoing training and support as requested.

ASSOCIATIONS AND OTHER ORGANIZATIONS

10784 ■ ADR Institute of Canada, Inc. (ADRIC) [Institut d'arbitrage et de Médiation du Canada Inc. (IAMC)]
234 Eglinton Ave. E, Ste. 407
Toronto, ON, Canada M4P 1K5
Ph: (416)487-4733
Free: 877-475-4353
Fax: (416)901-4736
Co. E-mail: admin@adric.ca
URL: http://adric.ca
Contact: Elton Simoes, President
Facebook: www.facebook.com/ADRIC.IAMC
Linkedin: www.linkedin.com/company/adr-institute-of
-canada
X (Twitter): x.com/ADRIC_IAMC
YouTube: www.youtube.com/channel/UCeiI0F
d7Ylx0yFPGwQcu_ug
Description: Professionals providing arbitration and mediation services. Promotes the professional advancement of members; seeks to raise awareness of arbitration and services. Makes available arbitration and mediation rules and services to parties wishing to resolve disputes; works with regional affiliate institutes to set standards. **Founded:** 1974. **Geographic Preference:** National.

10785 ■ American Arbitration Association (AAA)
120 Broadway, 21st Fl.
New York, NY 10271
Ph: (212)716-5800
Free: 800-778-7879
Fax: (646)663-3074
Co. E-mail: mediationservices@adr.org
URL: http://www.adr.org
Contact: Eric P. Tuchmann, General Counsel
Linkedin: www.linkedin.com/company/american-arbi
tration-association
X (Twitter): x.com/adrorg
YouTube: www.youtube.com/channel/UCs9Y1btc
_lh7m2xGoM6Yhzg
Description: Works to achieve the resolution of disputes through the use of mediation, arbitration, democratic elections, and other voluntary methods. Provides administrative services for arbitrating, mediating, or negotiating disputes and impartial administration of elections. Maintains National Roster of Arbitrators and Mediators for referrals to parties involved in disputes. **Founded:** 1926. **Publications:** *Labor Arbitration in Government*; *The Punch List* (Quarterly); *Summary of Labor Arbitration Awards*; *New York No-Fault Arbitration Reports*; *Dispute Resolution Journal (DRJ)*. **Educational Activities:** LERA Annual Meeting. **Geographic Preference:** Multinational; Regional.

10786 ■ Association for Conflict Resolution (ACR)
PO Box 5
Eagle, NE 68347-0005
Ph: (614)262-2724
Co. E-mail: membership@acrnet.org
URL: http://acrnet.org
Facebook: www.facebook.com/AssociationforConflic
tResolution
X (Twitter): x.com/ACRgroup
Description: Professional organization dedicated in enhancing the practice and public understanding of conflict resolution. **Founded:** 2001. **Publications:** *ACResolution* (Quarterly). **Geographic Preference:** Multinational; Regional.

10787 ■ Institute for Mediation and Conflict Resolution (IMCR)
369 E 148th St., Lower Level
Bronx, NY 10455
Ph: (718)585-1190
Co. E-mail: trich@imcr.org
URL: http://www.imcr.org
Contact: Dr. Arthur Lerman, Chairperson
Facebook: www.facebook.com/IMCRBronx
Description: Agency, supported by foundation grants and contracts, to which community disputants can turn for assistance in resolving differences on a voluntary basis. Seeks to: mediate community conflicts; train people in mediation techniques and conflict resolution skills; design dispute settlement systems. Facilitates discussion on current trends in dispute resolution. **Founded:** 1969. **Publications:** *F.Y.I., Institute for Mediation and Conflict Resolution* (Quarterly). **Geographic Preference:** National.

10788 ■ International Ombudsman Institute (IOI) - Library [Institut International de l'Ombudsman; Instituto Internacional del Ombudsman]
c/o Austrian Ombudsman Board
Singerstrasse 17
A-1015 Vienna, Austria
Ph: 43 1 512-9388
Fax: 43 1 512 93 88-200
Co. E-mail: ioi@volksanw.gv.at
URL: http://www.theioi.org
Contact: Hannah Suntinger, Executive Director
E-mail: hannah.suntinger@volksanwaltschaft.gv.at
X (Twitter): x.com/the_ioi
Description: Ombudsman offices, complaint handling organizations, institutions, libraries, and individuals in 74 countries. Promotes concept of ombudsmanship and supports research and educational efforts in the field. Disseminates information about ombudsmanship; participates in seminars concerning the ombudsman concept. **Scope:** Ombudsman. **Founded:** 1978. **Holdings:** Figures not available. **Publications:** *International Ombudsman Institute--Directory* (Annual). **Geographic Preference:** Multinational.

10789 ■ National Academy of Arbitrators (NAA)
NAA Operations Ctr.
1 N Main St., Ste. 412
Cortland, NY 13045
Ph: (607)756-8363
Fax: (607)756-8365
Co. E-mail: naa@naarb.org
URL: http://naarb.org
Contact: Homer C. La Rue, President
E-mail: homer@laruedisputeresolution.com
Description: Labor-management arbitrators. Works to improve general understanding of the nature and use of arbitration as a means of settling labor disputes. Conducts research and educational programs. **Founded:** 1947. **Publications:** *National Academy of Arbitrators--Membership Directory*. **Geographic Preference:** National.

10790 ■ National Association of Certified Mediators (NACM)
244 5th Ave., Ste. T-205
New York, NY 10001
Free: 877-850-0052
Co. E-mail: support@mediatorcertification.org
URL: http://www.mediatorcertification.org
Facebook: www.facebook.com/nationalassocia
tioncertifiedmediators
YouTube: www.youtube.com/channel/UCQBBdV
3Gam2lYHE3iyEycKQ
Description: Seeks to provide certification examinations, training, continuing education, and initiatives to improve communication with the mediation field. **Founded:** 1999.

10791 ■ Peace Education Foundation - Library
11300 NE 2nd Ave.
Miami, FL 33161
Ph: (305)576-5075
Free: 800-749-8838
Fax: (305)576-3106
URL: http://www.peaceeducation.org
Contact: Lloyd Van Bylevett, President
E-mail: lloyd@peace-ed.org
Description: Teachers, counselors, and school administrators; clergy and laypersons. Works to educate students, parents, and teachers on creative and nonviolent methods of resolving conflict. Develops and disseminates grade-specific curricula on nonviolent conflict resolution and mediation for preschool through high school students. Maintains the Training Institute for Conflict Resolution, Mediation, and Peacemaking. **Scope:** Peace movement; conflict resolution; mediation. **Services:** Library open to the public on a fee basis. **Founded:** 1980. **Holdings:** 1,000 articles; books; periodicals. **Publications:** *Prepared for Action: Responding Effectively to Crisis in Your School*. **Educational Activities:** Peacemakers Conference to Stop the Violence. **Geographic Preference:** National.

REFERENCE WORKS

10792 ■ "3 Business Situations That Are Ripe for Mediation" in Small Business Trends (January 21, 2020)
Ed: Barbara Weltman. **Released:** January 21, 2020. **Description:** As a business owner, you know how expensive legal fees can be, so the sooner you can

settle disputes, the less costly it is. Mediation is a dispute resolution process in which parties agree to work out a legal matter themselves with the help of a third party. This article details three situations where you may want to consider using mediation before proceeding to litigation,. **Availability:** Online.

10793 ■ Conflict Resolution for the Helping Professions: Negotiation, Mediation, Advocacy, Facilitation, and Restorative Justice

Ed: Allan Barsky. **Released:** January 24, 2017. **Price:** $48.94, Paperback. **Description:** A comprehensive guide to dealing with conflict in the workplace. **Availability:** Print.

10794 ■ How to Dissolve a Business Partnership Through Mediation

Ed: Marie Huntington. **Description:** Mediation is a process used as a tool for conflict management. This article discusses how to dissolve a business partnership through the use of mediation. **Availability:** Online.

10795 ■ "How Does the Process of Mediation Work?" in The Balance Small Business (June 24, 2019)

Ed: Jean Murray. **Released:** June 24, 2019. **Description:** Mediation is an informal dispute settlement process run by a trained third party, called a mediator. This article discusses how mediation works, the difference between mediation and arbitration, small business mediation, and online mediation. **Availability:** Online.

10796 ■ "How to Resolve Business Disputes with Arbitration or Mediation" in The Balance Small Business (February 28, 2020)

Ed: Jean Murray. **Released:** February 28, 2020. **Description:** The processes of mediation and arbitration are often confused. They are two different processes, alternative ways to resolve conflicts between individuals, families, groups, and businesses. This article discusses how each works and how they are different. **Availability:** Online.

10797 ■ How Small Businesses Should Approach Mediation

Ed: Ben Lobel. **Released:** October 20, 2017. **Description:** Disputes can be messy, time-consuming and expensive for smaller businesses without the necessary resources and experience required to navigate them efficiently and effectively. This article discusses how utilizing the problem-solving approach of mediation is an attractive option for small businesses. **Availability:** Online.

10798 ■ "Mediation Can Help Small Businesses Solve Conflicts and Protect Relationships" in Bloomberg Businessweek (July 10, 2020)

Ed: Nick Leiber. **Released:** July 10, 2020. **Description:** This article discusses why hiring a neutral third party to resolve small business disputes is often more effective than going to court. **Availability:** Online.

10799 ■ Mediation for Small Businesses

Ed: Emily Doskow. **Description:** Small businesses may benefit tremendously from using mediation, rather than litigation, to resolve conflicts. This article discusses the advantages of using mediation, costs of mediation, finding a mediator, and results that may result from using mediation. **Availability:** Online.

10800 ■ "Mediation vs. Arbitration vs. Litigation: The Differences You Need to Know about in Business" in Mediate.com (November, 2019)

URL(s): www.mediate.com/articles/costello-ADR -differences.cfm

Ed: Jaimie Costello. **Released:** November 2019. **Description:** In case of possible legal issues arising, business owners should be familiar with the differences between mediation, arbitration, and litigation. Here, all three processes are defined along with what constitutes a successful vs. unsuccessful outcome in each instance. **Availability:** Online.

10801 ■ Starting an Arbitration & Mediation Service

Description: This article assembles useful information on how to go about opening an arbitration and mediation service. **Availability:** Online.

10802 ■ Starting Your Own Mediation Business

Description: A guide to how to start your own mediation business for recent law school graduates and for seasoned mediators alike. **Availability:** Online.

10803 ■ Using Mediation for Resolving Disputes

Released: November 13, 2020. **Description:** This is a case study demonstrating how mediation can be more beneficial to a business relationship than other dispute resolution mechanisms. **Availability:** Online.

TRADE PERIODICALS

10804 ■ Ohio State Journal on Dispute Resolution

Pub: Ohio State University Michael E. Moritz College of Law

Contact: Alan C. Michaels, Chairman

E-mail: michaels.23@osu.edu

URL(s): moritzlaw.osu.edu/study/journals/osjdr-ohio-s tate-journal-dispute-resolution

Released: Quarterly; three to five times a year. **Price:** $50, Libraries for other institutional; $60, Individuals for international; $15, Single issue for domestics; $50, Individuals for domestic; $15, Single issue for foreign. **Description:** Professional legal journal covering alternative dispute resolution. **Availability:** Online.

CONSULTANTS

10805 ■ Consulting & Conciliation Service (CCS)

Sacramento, CA

Ph: (916)396-0480

URL: http://conciliation.org

Contact: Jane McCluskey, Contact

E-mail: jane@conciliation.org

Description: Firm offers consulting and conciliation services, they provide pre-mediation counseling, training and research on preparing for a peaceful society, mediation and facilitation, preparation for shifts in structure, policy, and personnel, it offers sliding scale business rates and free individual consultation. **Scope:** Firm offers consulting and conciliation services, they provide pre-mediation counseling, training and research on preparing for a peaceful society, mediation and facilitation, preparation for shifts in structure, policy, and personnel, it offers sliding scale business rates and free individual consultation. **Publications:** "Native America and Tracking Shifts in US Policy"; "Biogenesis: A Discussion of Basic Social Needs and the Significance of Hope". **Training:** Positive Approaches to Violence Prevention: Peace building in Schools and Communities.

LIBRARIES

10806 ■ Peace Center - Library & Resource Center

102 W Maple Ave.

Langhorne, PA 19047-2820

Ph: (215)750-7220

Co. E-mail: mediation@thepeacecenter.org

URL: http://www.thepeacecenter.org

Contact: Stephen Moyer, President

X (Twitter): x.com/peace_center

Description: Provides education in violence prevention, conflict resolution and anger management. Conducts education programs in schools. **Scope:** Conflict resolution; peace resources. **Services:** Library open to the public. **Founded:** 1982. **Holdings:** Books. **Geographic Preference:** Local.

10807 ■ York University - Centre for Research on Work and Society (CRWS)

York Research Twr., 6th Fl., 4700 Keele St.

Toronto, ON, Canada M3J 1P3

Ph: (416)736-5612

Fax: (416)736-5916

Co. E-mail: crws@yorku.ca

URL: http://www.yorku.ca/crws

Contact: Stephanie Ross, Director

E-mail: stephr@yorku.ca

Description: Research activity at York University. Offers consulting for government agencies; research for unions and community organizations. **Scope:** Changes in Canadian economic life and work, including global economic integration, industrial relations, health and safety, union structures, corporate practices, changes in daily work life, women and international economic restructuring, young workers, and internationally comparative research in union strategy linking Canada to Eastern and Western Europe, Australia, and South Africa. **Services:** Library open to students, faculty and staff; open by appointment only from May to August. **Holdings:** 500 books; journals; primary and secondary documents and sources. **Publications:** CRWS Conference Papers; CRWS News (Quarterly); Working Paper Series. **Educational Activities:** CRWS Intellectual Forums and Discussions, Focusing on work and the political economy of labor.; CRWS Visiting Scholars Program. **Awards:** CRWS Apprenticeships.

RESEARCH CENTERS

10808 ■ Center for Policy Research (CPR)

1570 Emerson St.

Denver, CO 80218

Ph: (303)837-1555

URL: http://centerforpolicyresearch.org

Contact: Dr. Jessica Pearson, Director

E-mail: jspearson@centerforpolicyresearch.org

Linkedin: www.linkedin.com/company/center-for -policy-research

YouTube: www.youtube.com/channel/UC-NCA2g7Us -37m42WvfVdMg

Description: Independent, nonprofit organization. **Scope:** Problems in legal, social, and human services, including studies on mediation, alternatives to litigation, child abuse, legal needs of the poor, child support, welfare, and education reform. **Founded:** 1981. **Publications:** Reports, papers, articles.

10809 ■ Harvard University - Harvard Negotiation Project (HNP)

501 Pound Hall

1563 Massachusetts Ave.

Cambridge, MA 02138

URL: http://www.pon.harvard.edu/research_projects/ harvard-negotiation-project/hnp

Contact: James K. Sebenius, Director

Description: Integral unit of Harvard Law School at Harvard University. **Scope:** Seeks to improve the theory and practice of negotiation, mediation, and conflict resolution in the contexts of business, labor disputes, and international conflicts. Conducts seminars. **Founded:** 1979.

10810 ■ Northwestern University - Dispute Resolution Research Center (DRRC)

2211 Campus Dr.

Evanston, IL 60208

URL: http://www.kellogg.northwestern.edu/research/ dispute-resolution-research-center.aspx

Contact: Cynthia Wang, Executive Director

Description: Integral unit of Kellogg School of Management at Northwestern University. **Scope:** Dispute resolution, including the causes of disputes, negotiation processes, fair settlements, and the role of third parties. Conducts interdisciplinary studies in game theory, procedural justice, behavioral decision theory, and dispute systems design. Projects focus on judgment, group negotiation, tactics in negotiation, alternative dispute resolution, environmental dispute resolution, ethics, and cross-cultural negotiations. **Founded:** 1986. **Publications:** Teaching Materials; Working Paper Series. **Educational Activities:** DRRC Negotiation teaching workshops;

Research Seminar Series (Monthly); DRRC Seminars, Exhibit relating to managers and lawyers. **Awards:** Northwestern University DRRC Grants Program.

10811 ■ Pennsylvania State University - Smeal College of Business - Center for Research in Conflict and Negotiation (CRCN)
485B Business Bldg.
  University Park, PA 16802
Ph: (814)865-3822
Fax: (814)865-0123
URL: http://directory.smeal.psu.edu/contact/crcn
Description: Multidisciplinary center at Smeal College of Business, Pennsylvania State University. Offers consulting and mediation programs. **Scope:** Conflict and dispute resolution, emphasizing international joint venture negotiations; multi-party disputes; game theoretic models of negotiating; bargaining experiments, arbitration, and mediation; organizational conflicts and teambuilding; environmental conflict; the effect of individual cognitions, emotions, and language patterns on negotiations; cross-cultural negotiations; and management of diversity. **Founded:** 1988. **Publications:** *CRCN Newsletter; Working*

Paper Series. **Educational Activities:** CRCN Negotiations training for organizations, Provides team building workshops and negotiations training and training on collaborative problem solving, and collaborative leadership for public, private and NGO organizations.; CRCN Practitioners' Conferences; CRCN Seminar series.

10812 ■ Syracuse University - Maxwell School of Citizenship & Public Affairs - Program for the Advancement of Research on Conflict and Collaboration (PARCC)
400 Eggers Hall
  Syracuse, NY 13244
Ph: (315)443-2367
Co. E-mail: parccadm@syr.edu
URL: http://www.maxwell.syr.edu/research/program
  -for-the-advancement-research-on-conflic
  t-collaboration
Contact: Catherine M. Gerard, Director, Research
  Administrator
E-mail: cgerard@syr.edu
Description: Anthropologists. Fosters research on the social and cultural dynamics of peace and war. Provides curricular services; operates speakers'

bureau and placement service; compiles statistics. Sponsors seminars and professional workshops. **Scope:** Conflict and conflict resolution, including peacekeeping, negotiation, mediation, studies on family violence, alternative dispute resolution methods, computational modeling, mediation training programs, community organizing efforts, prevention of disputes through increased public participation in environmental issues, nonviolent means of protest, geopolitical ideologies, foreign policy decision making during crises, de-escalation achievements in U.S.-Soviet and Arab-Israeli relations, cognitive mapping for international negotiations, ethnic and culture conflicts, and gender problems, including the empowerment of women using dispute resolution services. **Founded:** 1986. **Publications:** *PARC News* (Semi-annual); *25-Hour Meditation Manual; PARC Articles; PARC Newsletter; Occasional papers; Reprint series; Working Paper Series; Directory of Anthropologists Working on Topics of Peace, Conflict Resolution, and International Security* (Periodic). **Educational Activities:** PARC Conferences; PARCC Summer Institute on Creative Conflict Resolution. **Geographic Preference:** National.

START-UP INFORMATION

10813 ■ *"Alex Gomez on Leaving Medical School to Launch a Startup" in South Florida Business Journal (Vol. 34, May 9, 2014, No. 42, pp. 19)*

Pub: American City Business Journals, Inc.
Contact: Mike Olivieri, Executive Vice President

Description: New Wave Health Care Ventures managing partners, Alex Gomez, shares his views about leaving medical school to launch his startup. Gomez says he always had the spirit of an entrepreneur and business excites him. He knows what he is looking for in investing at startup companies because of his experience with New Wave Surgical Corporation. **Availability:** Print; Online.

10814 ■ *"Crowdfunding Becomes Relevant for Medical Start-Ups as TCB Medical Launches Campaign On Idiegogo to Bring Life-Saving Epinephrine Key to Market" in PR Newswire (July 31, 2012)*

Pub: PR Newswire Association LLC.
Ed: Hilton Head. **Description:** Startup company, TCB Medical Devices, is hoping to raise money through crowdfunding to launch its life-saving Epinephrine Key to the marketplace. According to allergist, Thomas C. Beller, MD, epinephrine provides safe and effective relief to allergy sufferers. **Availability:** Online.

10815 ■ *"StartX Med Prescribed for Innovation" in Silicon Valley/San Jose Business Journal (Vol. 30, June 8, 2012, No. 11, pp. 1)*

Pub: Baltimore Business Journal
Contact: Rhonda Pringle, President
E-mail: rpringle@bizjournals.com

Description: StartX Med is a program started by entrepreneur Divya Nag along with Stanford student-led nonprofit StartX to help medical startups. Under the program, entrepreneurs will have access to wet and dry laboratory space, animal testing and information related to US Food and Drug Adminstration regulations. **Availability:** Print; Online.

10816 ■ *"Wheel Genius" in Entrepreneur (June 2014)*

Pub: Entrepreneur Media Inc.
Contact: Dan Bova, Director
E-mail: dbova@entrepreneur.com

Description: Electric car startup, Kenguru, has developed a hatchback that aims to improve mobility for wheelchair users, who enter the vehicle using a rear-opening tailgate and automatic ramp. The Kenguru, which is Hungarian for kangaroo, uses motorcycle-style handlebars instead of steering wheels. The 1,000-pound car has an estimated range of 60 miles and can travel up to 35 miles per hour. The Kenguru could sell for about $25,000. Founder Stacy Zoern partnered with Budapest, Hungary-based Istvan Kissaroslaki in developing the new car. **Availability:** Print; Online.

ASSOCIATIONS AND OTHER ORGANIZATIONS

10817 ■ **Advanced Medical Technology Association (AdvaMed) - Library**
1301 Pennsylvania Ave. NW, Ste. 400
 Washington, DC 20004
Ph: (202)783-8700
Fax: (202)783-8750
URL: http://www.advamed.org
Contact: Scott Whitaker, President
Facebook: www.facebook.com/AdvaMed
X (Twitter): x.com/advamedupdate
Instagram: www.instagram.com/advamed
YouTube: www.youtube.com/user/AdvaMedUpdate

Description: Represents domestic (including U.S. territories and possessions) manufacturers of medical devices, diagnostic products, and healthcare information systems. Develops programs and activities on economic, technical, medical, and scientific matters affecting the industry. **Scope:** Medicine. **Founded:** 1974. **Holdings:** Books. **Publications:** *In Brief* (Monthly); *Advanced Medical Technology Association--Directory*; *Smart Brief*. **Geographic Preference:** National.

10818 ■ **Association for the Advancement of Medical Instrumentation (AAMI)**
901 N Glebe Rd., Ste. 300
 Arlington, VA 22203
Ph: (703)525-4890
Fax: (703)276-0793
Co. E-mail: customerservice@aami.org
URL: http://www.aami.org
Contact: Robert Jensen, President
Facebook: www.facebook.com/aamiconnect
X (Twitter): x.com/aami_connect
Instagram: www.instagram.com/aamiconnect
YouTube: www.youtube.com/user/aamiconnect

Description: Works to improve the quality of medical care through the application, development, and management of technology. **Founded:** 1967. **Publications:** *Biomedical Instrumentation & Technology (BI&T)* (6/year); *Association for the Advancement of Medical Instrumentation--Membership Directory*; *AAMI News* (Weekly); *AAMI News Extra* (Monthly); *AAMI News* (Weekly). **Educational Activities:** AAMI Conference & Expo (Annual). **Awards:** AAMI Foundation's Laufman-Greatbatch Award (Annual); AAMI & Becton Dickinson's Patient Safety Award (Annual); AAMI BI&T Outstanding Articles (Annual); AAMI HTM Leadership Award (Annual); AAMI & GE Healthcare BMET of the Year Award (Annual); AAMI Foundation & ACCE Robert L. Morris Humanitarian Award (Annual). **Geographic Preference:** Multinational.

10819 ■ **Dental Trade Alliance (DTA)**
4350 N Fairfax Dr., Ste. 650
 Arlington, VA 22203
Ph: (703)379-7755
URL: http://dentaltradealliance.org
Contact: Tim E. Rogan, Chairman of the Board

Description: Represents dental manufacturers, dental dealers, dental laboratories, dental market service providers and dental publications. **Founded:** 2004. **Publications:** *Dental Trade Newsletter* (Bi-monthly); *Large Equipment Sales Report* (Monthly; Quarterly). **Geographic Preference:** National; Local.

10820 ■ **Health Industry Distributors Association (HIDA)**
310 Montgomery St.
 Alexandria, VA 22314
Ph: (703)549-4432
Co. E-mail: hida@hida.org
URL: http://www.hida.org
Contact: Doug Bryant, President
Facebook: www.facebook.com/hida
Linkedin: www.linkedin.com/company/hidaorg
X (Twitter): x.com/HIDAorg

Description: Represents distributors of medical, laboratory, surgical, and other health care equipment and supplies to hospitals, physicians, nursing homes, and industrial medical departments. Conducts sales training, management seminars, and research through the HIDA Educational Foundation. **Founded:** 1902. **Publications:** *HIDA--Membership Directory and Buyer's Guide*. **Educational Activities:** HIDA Executive Conference (Annual); HIDA Streamlining Healthcare Expo and Business Exchange (Annual). **Awards:** John F. Sasen Leadership Award (Annual). **Geographic Preference:** National.

10821 ■ **Hearing Industries Association (HIA)**
1301 K St. NW, Ste. 300W
 Washington, DC 20005
Ph: (202)975-0905
Co. E-mail: info@betterhearing.org
URL: http://betterhearing.org
Contact: Kate Carr, President
Facebook: www.facebook.com/betterhearingHIA
X (Twitter): x.com/better_hearing

Description: Companies engaged in the manufacture and/or sale of electronic hearing aids, their component parts, and related products and services on a national basis. Cooperates in and contributes toward efforts to promote the number of hearing aid users; collects trade statistics; conducts market research activities, investigations, and studies in connection with hearing and hearing aids. **Founded:** 1955. **Geographic Preference:** National.

10822 ■ **Independent Medical Specialty Dealers Association (IMDA)**
PO Box 886
 White House, TN 37188
Ph: (615)859-2337
Fax: (615)859-2997
Co. E-mail: imda@imda.org
URL: http://imda.org
Contact: Bill Carmouche, President

Description: Represents sales, marketing and distribution organizations focused on bringing innovative medical technologies to market. Employs salespeople who are technically sophisticated, and who enjoy long-standing relationships with clinicians in their territories. **Founded:** 1978. **Publications:** *IMDA Directory*; *IMDA--Update*; *Independent Medical Distributors Association--Membership Directory*. **Geographic Preference:** National.

REFERENCE WORKS

10823 ■ *"Breast Surgery Breakthrough Propels Palo Alto Startup AirXpanders"* in *Silicon Valley/San Jose Business Journal (Vol. 30, June 22, 2012, No. 13, pp. 1)*
Pub: Baltimore Business Journal
Contact: Rhonda Pringle, President
E-mail: rpringle@bizjournals.com

Description: Palo Alto, California-based AirXpanders Inc. has designed and started the testing of the Aero-Form tissue expander, a medical device to help women undergoing reconstructive surgery. The device helps in expanding tissue to accommodate reconstruction of a woman's breast following a mastectomy. The extent to which this device would succeed in the market is discussed. **Availability:** Print; Online.

10824 ■ *"Despite FDA Approval, Heart Test No Boom for BG Medical"* in *Boston Business Journal (Vol. 31, June 17, 2011, No. 21, pp. 1)*
Pub: Boston Business Journal
Contact: Carolyn M. Jones, President
E-mail: cmjones@bizjournals.com

Ed: Julie M. Donnelly. **Description:** The Galectin-3 test failed to boost stock prices of its manufacturer, BG Medicine, which has fallen to $6.06/share. The company hopes that its revenue will be boosted by widespread adoption of an automated and faster version of the test, which diagnoses for heart failure. **Availability:** Online.

10825 ■ *"Doctor: J & J Alerted in '06 to Procedure Risks"* in *Pittsburgh Business Times (Vol. 33, June 6, 2014, No. 47, pp. 4)*
Pub: American City Business Journals, Inc.
Contact: Mike Olivieri, Executive Vice President

Released: Weekly. **Price:** $4, introductory 4-week offer(Digital & Print). **Description:** Dr. Robert Lamparter, then pathologist at Lewisburg's Evangelical Community Hospital, states that he had alerted Johnson and Johnson (J and J) in 2006 of the potential risk of spreading undetected cancer following the use of its power morcellator during hysterectomy procedures. J and J suspended worldwide sales of the device in April 2014 after the laboratory warning, and days after a US Food and Drug Administration advisory discouraging doctors from using it, but doctors are still divided over the morcellation procedure. **Availability:** Print; Online.

10826 ■ *"Early-Stage Biomed Firm Seeks Funds for First Device"* in *San Antonio Business Journal (Vol. 28, March 7, 2014, No. 4, pp. 6)*
Pub: American City Business Journals, Inc.
Contact: Mike Olivieri, Executive Vice President

Released: Weekly. **Price:** $4, Introductory 4-week offer(Digital & Print). **Description:** Leto Solutions, an early stage medical device company, wants to raise $2 million in seed funding for the Aquilonix Prosthesis Cooling System. The thermoelectric temperature management is used to cool the prosthesis. A working prototype of the Aquilonix system has already been developed by the company. **Availability:** Print; Online.

10827 ■ *"From Chelsea Machine Shop to Nobel Prize"* in *Crain's Detroit Business (Vol. 30, October 13, 2014, No. 41, pp. 35)*
Pub: Crain Communications Inc.
Contact: Barry Asin, President

Description: Profile of Eric Betzig, one of three scientists recognized with the Nobel Prize in Chemistry for devising ways for microscopes to look into the molecular hearts of living cells. Betzig is an Ann Arbor, Michigan native who performs research in Virginia for the Howard Hughes Medical Institute. **Availability:** Print; Online.

10828 ■ *"The Game of Operation"* in *Crain's Chicago Business (Vol. 31, April 28, 2008, No. 17, pp. 26)*
Pub: Crain Communications Inc.
Contact: Barry Asin, President

Ed: Samantha Stainburn. **Description:** Revenue at Medline Industries Inc., a manufacturer of medical products, has risen 12 percent a year since 1976, reaching $2.81 billion last year. Growth at the company is due to new and increasingly sophisticated operations by surgeons which brings about the need for more specialized tools. **Availability:** Online.

10829 ■ *"Globus Plans First Phila.-Area Biotech IPO Since 2010"* in *Philadelphia Business Journal (Vol. 28, April 20, 2012, No. 10, pp. 1)*
Pub: Baltimore Business Journal
Contact: Rhonda Pringle, President
E-mail: rpringle@bizjournals.com

Description: Globus Medical has filed their plans with the SEC regarding an initial public stock offering. The medical device maker hopes to raise $100 million through the IPO. This will be the first IPO from a life science company in the Philadelphia region since 2010. **Availability:** Print; Online.

10830 ■ *"Health Care Briefs: Survey Says Most Approve of Donating Used Pacemakers to Medically Underserved"* in *Crain's Detroit Business (Vol. 25, June 1, 2009)*
Pub: Crain Communications Inc.
Contact: Barry Asin, President

Description: According to a survey conducted by University of Michigan Cardiovascular Center, 87 percent of those with pacemakers and 71 percent of the general population would donate the device to patients in underserved nations.

10831 ■ *"Heart Hospitals Ranked for Mortality Rates"* in *Philadelphia Business Journal (Vol. 30, September 2, 2011, No. 29, pp. 1)*
Pub: Philadelphia Business Journal
Contact: Sierra Quinn, Director
E-mail: squinn@bizjournals.com

Ed: John George. **Description:** Centers for Medicare and Medicaid Services (CMS) released updated data on mortality rates for heart attack patients as hospitals in Pennsylvania. Doylestown Hospital posted the lowest mortality rates with 10.9 percent, tying the fourth best in the entire nation. Other details on the CMS data are presented. **Availability:** Online.

10832 ■ *"Hospitals Try to Buy Smarter"* in *Crain's Detroit Business (Vol. 25, June 1, 2009, No. 22, pp. M025)*
Pub: Crain Communications Inc.
Contact: Barry Asin, President

Ed: Jay Greene. **Description:** Hospitals in southeast Michigan are using bulk discount purchasing of medical and non-medical supplies through group purchasing organizations in order to cut costs. **Availability:** Online.

10833 ■ *"Hospitals Waste Billions of Dollars in Medical Supplies"* in *U.S. News & World Report (March 9, 2017)*
URL(s): www.usnews.com/news/healthcare-of
-tomorrow/articles/2017-03-09/hospitals-are-was
ting-billions-of-dollars-worth-of-medical-equipment

Ed: Anzish Mirza. **Released:** March 09, 2017. **Description:** A surprising amount of perfect, usable medical supplies are thrown out to the tune of $765 billion a year. This cost is passed onto healthcare consumers, which has resulted in higher health care costs all around. Often, supplies are tossed in the trash when new versions are released, even though nothing is wrong with the older versions. Also, if an item is placed in a patient's room it must be disposed of, even if it was never opened. Some efforts are being made to reduce this waste through incentives, but not much else can be done at this time. **Availability:** Online.

10834 ■ *"How to Conduct a Functional Magnetic Resonance (fMRI) Study in Social Science Research"* in *MIS Quarterly (Vol. 36, September 2012, No. 3, pp. 811)*
Pub: University of Minnesota Carlson School of Management Management Information Systems Research Center

Ed: Angelika Dimoka. **Description:** A set of guidelines for conducting functional magnetic resonance imaging studies in social sciences and information systems research is provided. **Availability:** PDF; Online.

10835 ■ *"Image Consultants"* in *Entrepreneur (June 2014)*
Pub: Entrepreneur Media Inc.
Contact: Dan Bova, Director
E-mail: dbova@entrepreneur.com

Description: The ASAP54 mobile application, created by a company of the same name, uses visual recognition technology to help users determine the name of the designer or retailer of a clothing item using photographs. The company has compiled a database consisting of more than 1 million products from its retail partners. It claims an average of 5 percent commission on purchases completed through the application. Other useful wearable gadgets include Nymi, which authenticates identities based on cardiac rhythms, and Netatmo, a bracelet that measures daily sun exposure. **Availability:** Online.

10836 ■ *"Infusion Device Gets $1.47 Million Army Grant"* in *Memphis Business Journal (Vol. 33, January 20, 2012, No. 41, pp. 1)*
Pub: Baltimore Business Journal
Contact: Rhonda Pringle, President
E-mail: rpringle@bizjournals.com

Ed: Michael Sheffield. **Description:** Infusense has procured a $1.47 million grant from the US Army to develop an automated delivery system for the anesthesia Propofol. The drug is used in more than 70 million surgeries and procedures in the country. The medical device would allow for the administration of the anesthesia to wounded soldiers by medics in the field. **Availability:** Print; Online.

10837 ■ *"Inventive Doctor New Venture Partner"* in *Houston Business Journal (Vol. 40, January 29, 2010, No. 38, pp. A2)*
Pub: Houston Business Journal
Contact: Bob Charlet, President
E-mail: bcharlet@bizjournals.com

Ed: Ford Gunter. **Description:** Dr. Billy Cohn, a surgeon from Houston, Texas has been named as venture partner for venture firm Sante Ventures LLC of Austin, Texas. Cohn will be responsible for seeing marketable developing technologies in the medical industry. The motivation for Cohn's naming as venture partner is his development of a minimally invasive therapy for end-stage renal disease. **Availability:** Print; Online.

10838 ■ *"Med-Tech Vet's Trip From Heart to Sleeve"* in *Business Journal (Vol. 31, February 14, 2014, No. 38, pp. 8)*
Pub: American City Business Journals, Inc.
Contact: Mike Olivieri, Executive Vice President

Released: February 14, 2014. **Price:** $4, Introductory 4-week offer(Digital & Print). **Description:** Conventus Orthopaedics CEO, Paul Buckman, describes the device which repairs wrist fractures. Buckman reveals plans to use the $17 million venture capital to continue research and development and to conduct clinical studies to justify use of the technology. **Availability:** Print; Online.

10839 ■ *"Medical-Device Firm Targets a Heart-Valve Market in Flux"* in *Philadelphia Business Journal (Vol. 33, May 9, 2014, No. 13, pp. 9)*
Pub: American City Business Journals, Inc.
Contact: Mike Olivieri, Executive Vice President

Released: May 09, 2014. **Price:** $4, Introductory 4-week offer(Digital only). **Description:** Montgomery County-based medical products company, Thubrikar Aortic Valve Inc., is developing the Optimum TAV, a next-generation transcatheter aortic valve implantation (TAVI) device to treat heart patients with aortic stenosis. The company is raising funds to start clinical testing for the Optimum TAV in 2014, aiming to provide a more durable and efficient transcatheter aortic valve for lower-risk patients. **Availability:** Print; Online.

10840 ■ *"Medical Device Makers Brace for Excise Tax" in Memphis Business Journal (Vol. 34, July 20, 2012, No. 14, pp. 1)*
Pub: Baltimore Business Journal
Contact: Rhonda Pringle, President
E-mail: rpringle@bizjournals.com

Ed: Michael Sheffield. **Description:** The US Government's plan to increase excise tax is seen to impact medical device manufacturers. The tax is expected to raise as much as $60 billion over the next 10 years. **Availability:** Print; Online.

10841 ■ *Medical Device Manufacturing Industry in the US - Market Research Report*
URL(s): www.ibisworld.com/united-states/market-research-reports/medical-device-manufacturing-industry/

Price: $925. **Description:** Downloadable report analyzing the current and future trends in the medical device manufacturing industry. **Availability:** Download.

10842 ■ *"Medical Supplies Market Size to Hit USD 186 Billion by 2030" in Globe Newswire (November 24, 2021)*
Released: November 24, 2021. **Description:** The medical supply industry is primed to increase, especially for chronic disease diagnostic supplies and surgery supplies.

10843 ■ *"Medtronic Heading to Foreign Markets" in Memphis Business Journal (Vol. 34, September 28, 2012, No. 24, pp. 1)*
Pub: Baltimore Business Journal
Contact: Rhonda Pringle, President
E-mail: rpringle@bizjournals.com

Description: Medtronics Inc.'s Spinal and Biologics Division will launch a new spinal surgery system in 2012. The spinal fusion procedure has not yet been approved by international surgical governing bodies, but the company is already rolling it out in different countries. The new service uses the company's various surgical systems and implants. **Availability:** Print; Online.

10844 ■ *"Newton Robotics Company Bets on Rehab Robots for Growth" in Boston Business Journal (Vol. 34, April 4, 2014, No. 9, pp. 6)*
Pub: American City Business Journals, Inc.
Contact: Mike Olivieri, Executive Vice President

Description: Robotics firm Barrett Technology is transforming into a health care company by developing rehabilitation robots. The business is expected to generate 80 percent of its revenue from its health care clients over the next five years. The possibility of hiring new employees is also discussed. **Availability:** Print; Online.

10845 ■ *"On the Use of Neurophysiological Tools In IS Research: Developing a Research Agenda for NeuroIS" in MIS Quarterly (Vol. 36, September 2012, No. 3, pp. 679)*
Pub: University of Minnesota Carlson School of Management Management Information Systems Research Center

Ed: Angelika Dimoka. **Price:** $15. **Description:** The role of neurophysiological tools and neuroimaging tools in information systems research is discussed. Promising application areas and research questions regarding the use of neurophysiological data to benefit information systems researchers are identified. **Availability:** PDF.

10846 ■ *"OrthoPediatrics Launches PediFood System" in Mass Device (November 18, 2019)*
URL(s): www.massdevice.com/orthopediatrics-launches-pedifoot-system/

Ed: Sean Whooley. **Released:** November 18, 2019. **Description:** OrthoPediatrics announced the launch of its PediFoot deformity correction system for feet. Utilizing plates and screws, the device addresses cavus foot, flatfoot, clubfoot, and hallux valgus foot deformities. **Availability:** Online.

10847 ■ *"Patient Monitoring Tool Nears Testing Phase" in Pittsburgh Business Times (Vol. 33, February 7, 2014, No. 30, pp. 5)*
Pub: American City Business Journals, Inc.
Contact: Mike Olivieri, Executive Vice President

Description: Aided with a $500,000 investment, Wellbridge Health Inc. and its partner, Philadelphia-based Biotelemetry Inc., will launch an interactive and easy to use patient monitoring tool. Wellbridge CEO, Mary Del Brady, reports that this device will allow for a real-time monitoring of a patient's condition. **Availability:** Online.

10848 ■ *"Preceptis Gets Gopher Angels' Biggest-Ever Investment" in Business Journal (Vol. 31, January 31, 2014, No. 36, pp. 8)*
Pub: American City Business Journals, Inc.
Contact: Mike Olivieri, Executive Vice President

Description: Preceptis Medical Inc. has secured $1.2 million in funding from Gopher Angels. The funding will help Preceptis to finance ongoing clinical studies and general operating expenses. The company develops surgical tools for pediatric ear-tube surgery. **Availability:** Print; Online.

10849 ■ *"San Antonio Luring Biotech Firms With Venture Capital" in San Antonio Business Journal (Vol. 28, August 8, 2014, No. 26, pp. 6)*
Pub: American City Business Journals, Inc.
Contact: Mike Olivieri, Executive Vice President

Description: Bluegrass Vascular Technologies Inc. has secured $4.5 million in funding from Targeted Technology Fund II. Under the deal, the company will be required to relocate to San Antonio, Texas. A portion of the funding will be used on regulatory approval submissions for the company's Surfacer Inside-Out Catheter System. **Availability:** Print; Online.

10850 ■ *"San Antonio Researchers Develop New Laser-Based Imaging System" in San Antonio Business Journal (Vol. 26, August 24, 2012, No. 30, pp. 1)*
Pub: Baltimore Business Journal
Contact: Rhonda Pringle, President
E-mail: rpringle@bizjournals.com

Description: Researchers at the University of Texas Health Science Center at San Antonio in Texas have developed an optical sensor-dependent medical imaging system, which is ready for commercialization. The laser-based imaging system is expected to improve non-invasive imaging for medical diagnostics. **Availability:** Print; Online.

10851 ■ *Scott's Canadian Dental Directory*
Pub: Scott's Directories
URL(s): www.scottsdirectories.com/canadian-business-database/canadian-dental-directory

Price: $3,299, for unlimited; $2,199, for standard; $1,199, for version. **Description:** Covers approximately 18,000 dentists, dental suppliers, and dental laboratories and associations in Canada. **Entries include:** Name, address, phone, names and titles of key personnel, biographical data (for dentists), geographical area served. **Arrangement:** For dentists--Same information available in geographical and alphabetical sections. For others--Classified by line of business, then alphabetical. **Availability:** Online.

10852 ■ *"Sterotaxis Needs $10 Million in 60 Days" in Saint Louis Business Journal (Vol. 32, October 7, 2011, No. 6, pp. 1)*
Pub: Saint Louis Business Journal
Contact: Robert Bobroff, President
E-mail: rbobroff@bizjournals.com

Ed: E.B. Solomont. **Description:** Medical device firm Stereotaxis signed a loan modification deal with Silicon Valley Bank. The company suffered massive losses during second quarter 2011. Under the deal,

the company waived the minimum tangible net work covenant of the original loan in exchange for reduction in its credit line. **Availability:** Print; Online.

10853 ■ *"Theranos Growing Close to Home in Palo Alto" in Silicon Valley/San Jose Business Journal (Vol. 30, June 29, 2012, No. 14, pp. 1)*
Pub: Baltimore Business Journal
Contact: Rhonda Pringle, President
E-mail: rpringle@bizjournals.com

Description: Theranos Inc. will move its headquarters near Facebook Inc.'s former building in Palo Alto, California. The company will then relocate into a building on Page Mill Road near Hillview Avenue. The medical-advice maker is currently growing, and it is also said to be taking space across the San Francisco Bay. **Availability:** Print; Online.

10854 ■ *"These Trends Have Made Medical Device Manufacturing What It Is Today" in Mass Device (February 16, 2018)*
URL(s): www.massdevice.com/trends-medical-device-manufacturing/

Ed: Heather Thompson. **Released:** February 16, 2018. **Description:** The medical device industry has grown over the last several decades by meeting new clinical demands and responding to ever-changing economic realities. A historical look at trends over the years is discussed. **Availability:** Online.

10855 ■ *"Tony Armand, Shock Doctor CEO" in Business Journal (Vol. 31, March 21, 2014, No. 43, pp. 6)*
Pub: American City Business Journals, Inc.
Contact: Mike Olivieri, Executive Vice President

Released: March 21, 2014. **Price:** $4, print. **Description:** Tony Armand, CEO of Shock Doctor Inc., discusses the company's acquisition by private equity firm Bregal Partners. Armand believes the deal will give the sports protective equipment manufacturer a strong financial partner that will help with the executive strategy. **Availability:** Print; Online.

10856 ■ *"UIC Medical Ethicist Faces Life-and-Death Decisions Daily" in Crain's Chicago Business (Vol. 34, October 24, 2011, No. 42, pp. 31)*
Pub: Crain Communications Inc.
Contact: Barry Asin, President

Ed: Lisa Bertagnoli. **Description:** Technology has enabled doctors to provide more and better methods for helping patients, however end of life issues faced by medical ethicists are discussed. **Availability:** Print.

STATISTICAL SOURCES

10857 ■ *The Market for Minimally Invasive Medical Devices*
Pub: MarketResearch.com
Contact: Russell Eustice, Specialist
E-mail: reustice@marketresearch.com

Released: September 2019. **Price:** $5,500, online download, plus $25 for shipping to united states, $35 for shipping to Canada, $75 for shipping to other nations. **Availability:** Print; PDF; Download.

10858 ■ *RMA Annual Statement Studies*
Pub: Risk Management Association
Contact: Nancy Foster, President

Released: Annual. **Description:** Contains composite balance sheets and income statements for more than 360 industries, including the accounting, auditing, and bookkeeping industries. Also contains five years of comparative historical data for discerning trends. Includes 16 commonly used ratios, computed for most of the size groupings for nearly every industry.

10859 ■ *Standard & Poor's Industry Surveys*
Pub: Standard And Poor's Financial Services LLC.
Contact: Douglas L. Peterson, President

Description: Two-volume book that examines the prospects for specific industries, including trucking. Also provides analyses of trends and problems, statistical tables and charts, and comparative company analyses.

TRADE PERIODICALS

10860 ■ AAMI News
Pub: Association for the Advancement of Medical Instrumentation
Contact: Robert Jensen, President
URL(s): array.aami.org/newswww.aami.org/news-resources/publications/newsletters

Released: Weekly **Description:** Covers Association programs, policies, and meetings. Reports on AAMI standards program and publications in the Standards Monitor section as well as regulatory and legislative proposals or actions. Recurring features include news of educational opportunities and a calendar of events. **Availability:** Print; PDF.

10861 ■ Biomedical Instrumentation & Technology (BI&T)
Pub: Association for the Advancement of Medical Instrumentation
Contact: Robert Jensen, President
URL(s): array.aami.org/journal/bmit

Released: 6/year **Description:** Peer-reviewed journal for clinical engineers, biomedical equipment technicians, and other medical technology professionals. Includes advertisers and annual subject indexes, book reviews, statistics, association news, information on medical instrumentation. **Availability:** Print; Download; PDF; Online.

10862 ■ FDAnews Device Daily Bulletin
URL(s): www.fdanews.com/newsletters/7-fdanews-device-daily-bulletin

Description: Seeks to provide executives in the industry with information on regulatory developments regarding medical devices and in vitro diagnostic products. Reports on the Food and Drug Administration (FDA), the Health Care Financing Administration, and Congress. Discusses a variety of issues, including manufacturing practices, compliance and inspection programs, defect reporting, labeling and testing rules, and performance standards. Recurring features include news of research and reports of meetings. **Availability:** Print; Online.

10863 ■ Medical Devices, Diagnostics & Instrumentation Reports - The Gray Sheet
Contact: Mary Houghton, Editor
URL(s): www.medtech.pharmaintelligence.informa.com

Ed: Mary Houghton. **Released:** Weekly **Price:** $3,090, Individuals online only. **Description:** Covers the medical device and diagnostics field, including FDA regulations; policies and congressional reform initiatives concerning pre-market approvals and 501(k) exemptions; new products; business start-ups and financial deals; international developments; and technology reimbursement. Recurring features include columns titled In Brief, Financings In Brief, Device Approvals, Recalls & FDA Seizures, and MDDI Stock Index. **Availability:** Print; Online.

10864 ■ Medical Imaging: News, Issues, and Trends in Health Technology Management
Released: Monthly **Description:** Trade magazine covering medical imaging technology for healthcare professionals. **Availability:** Print; Online.

10865 ■ Wednesday in Washington
URL(s): aahomecare.org/news/member-alerts-and/newsletters

Price: Included in membership. **Description:** Informs members of developments in government agencies, state legislatures, and on Capitol Hill, as well as any other pertinent information that affects the home medical equipment services and homecare industries. **Remarks:** Available in print, e-mail, or fax format. **Availability:** Print; Online.

VIDEO/AUDIO MEDIA

10866 ■ A Medical Device-to-Market Journey
URL(s): www.startuphustlepodcast.com/a-medical-device-to-market-journey

Ed: Lauren Conaway. **Released:** December 27, 2023. **Description:** Podcast discusses the device-to-market journey. Also addresses mitigating the opioid crisis, inherent challenges in launching wearable devices, and customer engagement.

10867 ■ Saving Lives with Medical Device Startups
URL(s): www.startuphustlepodcast.com/saving-lives-with-medical-device-startups

Ed: Matt Watson. **Released:** January 04, 2024. **Description:** Discusses the challenges of developing medical devices, the dynamics of family collaboration, the intricacies of the EMS sector, and the importance of patents.

TRADE SHOWS AND CONVENTIONS

10868 ■ AAMI Conference & Expo
Koninklijke Philips N.V.
 Breitner Center
 Amstelplein 2
 1096 BC Amsterdam, Netherlands
Ph: 31 20 597-7230
URL: http://www.philips.com/global
Contact: Roy Jakobs, Chief Executive Officer
URL(s): www.aami.org/events/exchange24

Frequency: Annual. **Description:** The latest innovations, upgrades, and advances in healthcare technology. **Audience:** Industry professionals. **Principal Exhibits:** The latest innovations, upgrades, and advances in healthcare technology. Dates and Locations: 2025 Jun 19-23 New Orleans, LA; 2026 May 29-Jun 01 Denver, CO. **Telecommunication Services:** exchange@aami.org.

10869 ■ American Academy of Implant Dentistry Annual Meeting
URL(s): www.aaid.com/Annual_Conference/index.html

Frequency: Annual. **Audience:** General dentists, oral and maxillofacial surgeons, periodontists, and prosthodontists. **Telecommunication Services:** aaid@aaid-implant.org.

10870 ■ American Dental Association Annual Session & Technical Exhibition
URL(s): www.ada.org/en/meeting/attendee-information/future-meetings

Frequency: Annual. **Description:** Exhibits related to dental equipment, instruments, materials, therapeutics, and services. **Audience:** Dentists, dental hygienists, assistants, dealers, manufacturers, and lab technicians. **Principal Exhibits:** Exhibits related to dental equipment, instruments, materials, therapeutics, and services.

10871 ■ American Dental Hygienists' Association Convention
URL(s): www.adha.org/annual-session

Frequency: Annual. **Description:** Exhibits related to dental hygiene products and services. **Audience:** Dental hygienists and members. **Principal Exhibits:** Exhibits related to dental hygiene products and services. **Telecommunication Services:** mail@adha.net.

10872 ■ AMIA Fall Symposium
American Medical Informatics Association (AMIA)
 6218 Georgia Ave., NW Ste., No. 1
 Washington, DC 20011
Ph: (301)657-1291
Co. E-mail: mail@amia.org
URL: http://www.amia.org
Contact: Dr. Genevieve Melton-Meaux, President
URL(s): www.amia.org/education-events/amia-2024-annual-symposium

Frequency: Annual; held in November. **Description:** Commercial and scientific medical informatics hardware and software, supplies, and services. **Audience:** Industry Professionals. **Principal Exhibits:** Commercial and scientific medical informatics hardware and software, supplies, and services. Dates and Locations: 2025 Nov 01-05 Atlanta, GA; 2026 Nov 07-11 Dallas, TX; 2027 Nov 06-10 San Diego, CA. **Telecommunication Services:** dsantucci@amia.org.

10873 ■ Annual Session of the American Dental Society of Anesthesiology
American Dental Society of Anesthesiology (ADSA)
 211 E Chicago Ave., No. 1720
 Chicago, IL 60611
Ph: (312)664-8270
Co. E-mail: adsa@adsahome.org
URL: http://www.adsahome.org
Contact: David L. Rothman, President
URL(s): www.adsahome.org/annual-session

Frequency: Annual. **Description:** Anesthetics and anesthesia monitoring equipment. **Audience:** Dentists, oral surgeons, and dental anesthesiologists. **Principal Exhibits:** Anesthetics and anesthesia monitoring equipment. Dates and Locations: 2025 Apr 03-05 San Juan; 2026 Apr 23-25 HI.

10874 ■ APHON Conference & Exhibit
Association of Rehabilitation Nurses (ARN)
 8735 W Higgins Rd., Ste. 300
 Chicago, IL 60631-2738
Free: 800-229-7530
Co. E-mail: info@rehabnurse.org
URL: http://rehabnurse.org
Contact: Jill Rye, President
URL(s): aphon.org/meetings/future-conferences

Frequency: Annual; Held in the fall each year . **Description:** Exhibits related to pediatric oncology nursing equipment, supplies, and services. **Audience:** Pediatric hematology/oncology nurses and pediatric hematology/oncology healthcare professionals. **Principal Exhibits:** Exhibits related to pediatric oncology nursing equipment, supplies, and services.

10875 ■ CAS Annual Meeting
Merck & Co., Inc.
 126 E Lincoln Ave.
 Rahway, NJ 07065
Ph: (908)740-4000
Free: 800-444-2080
URL: http://www.merck.com
Contact: Robert M. Davis, President
URL(s): www.cas.ca/en/annual-meeting/cas-annual-meeting/cas-annual-meeting

Frequency: Annual. **Description:** Anaesthesia equipment manufacturers, medical manufacturers, pharmaceutical companies and suppliers, and medical publishers. **Audience:** Anesthesiologists and allied health professionals. **Principal Exhibits:** Anaesthesia equipment manufacturers, medical manufacturers, pharmaceutical companies and suppliers, and medical publishers. Dates and Locations: 2025 Jun 20-23 St. John's Convention Center, St. John's, NL; 2026. **Telecommunication Services:** info@casmeeting.com.

10876 ■ FAH Public Policy Conference and Business Exposition
Abbott Laboratories Limited
 Abbot House, Vanwall Business Pk., Vanwall Rd.
 Maidenhead SL6 4XE, United Kingdom
Ph: 44 1 62-877-3355
URL: http://www.abbott.co.uk
URL(s): www.fah.org/2025-conference-business-expo

Frequency: Annual. **Description:** Conference representing hospital management companies and health systems, Group Purchasing Organizations (GPOs), Integrated Delivery Networks (IDNs), and health care supplier companies. **Audience:** Business professionals, hospital management companies and health systems, Group Purchasing Organizations (GPOs), Integrated Delivery Networks (IDNs), and health care supplier companies. **Principal Exhibits:** Conference representing hospital management companies and health systems, Group Purchasing Organizations

(GPOs), Integrated Delivery Networks (IDNs), and health care supplier companies. **Dates and Locations:** 2025 Mar 05-07 Washington Hilton, Washington, DC. **Telecommunication Services:** kprice@fah.org.

10877 ■ KYDA The Kentucky Meeting
Elevance Health, Inc.
  220 Virginia Ave.
  Indianapolis, IN 46204
Free: 833-401-1577
Co. E-mail: anthemppi@anthem.com
URL: http://www.elevancehealth.com
Contact: Gail K. Boudreaux, President
URL(s): www.kyda.org/the-kentucky-meeting.html
Frequency: Annual. **Description:** Dental, pharmaceutical, and healthcare supplies and services. **Audience:** Dentists, dental hygienists, dental assistants, and laboratory technicians. **Principal Exhibits:** Dental, pharmaceutical, and healthcare supplies and services. **Telecommunication Services:** kevinwalldmd@gmail.com.

10878 ■ Medical Association of the State of Alabama Annual Meeting
Medical Association of the State of Alabama (MASA)
  19 S Jackson St.
  Montgomery, AL 36104
Ph: (334)954-2500
Free: 800-239-6272
Fax: (334)269-5200
Co. E-mail: staff@alamedical.org
URL: http://www.alamedical.org
Contact: Mark Jackson, Executive Director
E-mail: mjackson@alamedical.org
URL(s): www.alamedical.org/CM/Nav_Items/Education_Events/Annual_Session/Annual_Conference
.aspx?WebsiteKey=dc3f7bf1-749b-444d-986f-187
6aef66618&hkey=6b8725ac-c977-4f9d-91ec-bb4db
3a1eef1&New_ContentCollec
tionOrganizerCommon=1#New_ContentCollec
tionOrganizerCommon
Frequency: Annual. **Description:** Pharmaceuticals, business services, and office equipment and supplies. **Audience:** Medical professionals, physicians, and patients. **Principal Exhibits:** Pharmaceuticals, business services, and office equipment and supplies.

10879 ■ Medical Dental Hospital Business Associates Annual Convention
Medical Dental Hospital Business Associates (MDHBA)
  350 Poplar Ave.
  Elmhurst, IL 60126
Ph: (630)359-4273
Fax: (630)359-4274
Co. E-mail: info@mdhba.org
URL: http://www.mdhba.org
Contact: Kathy Shambre, President
Frequency: Annual. **Description:** Exhibits relating to medical, dental, and hospital services. **Audience:** Medical and hospital business professionals. **Principal Exhibits:** Exhibits relating to medical, dental, and hospital services. **Telecommunication Services:** info@mdhba.org.

10880 ■ Medical Society of Virginia Annual Meeting
Medical Society of Virginia (MSV)
  2924 Emerywood Pky., Ste. 300
  Richmond, VA 23294
Free: 800-746-6768
Fax: (804)355-6189
Co. E-mail: memberservice@msv.org
URL: http://www.msv.org
Contact: Mohit Nanda, President
URL(s): www.msv.org/msv-annual-meeting

Frequency: Annual. **Description:** Opportunities to exchange knowledge, learn the latest scientific and medical advances, and listen to engaging and provocative discussions. **Audience:** Physicians and members. **Principal Exhibits:** Opportunities to exchange knowledge, learn the latest scientific and medical advances, and listen to engaging and provocative discussions.

10881 ■ Rocky Mountain Dental Convention
Metropolitan Denver Dental Society (MDDS)
  925 Lincoln St., Unit B
  Denver, CO 80203
Ph: (303)488-9700
Free: 800-810-0140
Fax: (303)488-0177
URL: http://www.mddsdentist.com
Contact: Shelly Fava, Executive Director
E-mail: director@mddsdentist.com
URL(s): rmdconline.com/about
Facebook: www.facebook.com/RMDConline
X (Twitter): twitter.com/RMDConline
Frequency: Annual. **Audience:** Dental professionals. **Dates and Locations:** 2025 Jan 23-25 Colorado Convention Center, Denver, CO; 2026 Jan 22-24 Colorado Convention Center, Denver, CO; 2027 Jan 21-23 Colorado Convention Center, Denver, CO. **Telecommunication Services:** mdds@mddsdentist.com.

10882 ■ SCAI Scientific Sessions
Society for Cardiovascular Angiography and Interventions (SCAI)
  1100 17th St. NW, Ste. 400
  Washington, DC 20036
Ph: (202)741-9854
Free: 800-992-7224
Fax: (800)863-5202
Co. E-mail: info@scai.org
URL: http://www.scai.org
Contact: Timothy D. Henry, President
URL(s): scai.org/scai-2024-scientific-sessions
Frequency: Annual. **Description:** Cardiology-related products and supplies. **Audience:** Invasive and interventional cardiologists, physicians. **Principal Exhibits:** Cardiology-related products and supplies. **Dates and Locations:** 2025 May 01-03 WALTER E. WASHINGTON CONVENTION CENTER, WASHINGTON, DC; 2026 Apr 23-25 PALAIS DES CONGRES DE MONTREAL, Montreal, QC. **Telecommunication Services:** shung@scai.org.

10883 ■ South Dakota Dental Association Annual Session
South Dakota Dental Association (SDDA)
  804 N Euclid Ave., Ste. 103
  Pierre, SD 57501
Ph: (605)224-9133
Fax: (605)224-9168
URL: http://www.sddental.org
Contact: Paul Knecht, Executive Director
E-mail: paul.knecht@sddental.org
URL(s): www.sddental.org/meetings-events/sdda
-annual-session
Frequency: Annual. **Description:** Dental equipment and supplies. **Audience:** Dentists, hygienists, and assistants, front office staff, and oral health professionals. **Principal Exhibits:** Dental equipment and supplies. **Dates and Locations:** 2025 May 15-17 The Monument, Rapid City, SD. **Telecommunication Services:** melissa@sddental.org.

FRANCHISES AND BUSINESS OPPORTUNITIES

10884 ■ BioPed Footcare Centres
2150 Winston Park Dr., Unit 27
  Oakville, ON, Canada L6H 5V1

Ph: (905)829-0505
Free: 866-424-6733
Fax: (905)829-5199
Co. E-mail: contactus@bioped.com
URL: http://www.bioped.com
Contact: Peter Scully, President
Facebook: www.facebook.com/biopedfootcare
Description: Retailer of shoes. **Founded:** 1981. **Training:** Yes.

PUBLICATIONS

10885 ■ HME News: The Business Newspaper for Home Medical Equipment Providers
106 Lafayette St.
  Yarmouth, ME 04096
Ph: (207)846-0600
Fax: (207)846-0657
Co. E-mail: unitedpublications@theygsgroup.com
URL: http://www.hmenews.com
Contact: Sarah Flanagan, President
E-mail: sflanagan@hmenews.com
URL(s): www.hmenews.com
Facebook: www.facebook.com/people/HME-News/
  100024792432227
Linkedin: www.linkedin.com/company/hme-news
X (Twitter): x.com/hme_news
Ed: Elizabeth Beaulieu. **Released:** Monthly **Price:** $65, U.S. and Canada for annually; $150, Other countries; $7, for back issues within the past 12 months; $12, for each prior to the past 12 months. **Description:** Business newspaper for home medical equipment providers. Editorial coverage focuses on industry news, mergers and acquisitions, governmental and regulatory impact on the HME industry, as well as product reviews and industry trend coverage. **Availability:** Print; PDF; Download; Online.

RESEARCH CENTERS

10886 ■ ECRI Institute - Library
5200 Butler Pke.
  Plymouth Meeting, PA 19462
Ph: (610)825-6000
Co. E-mail: info@ecri.org
URL: http://www.ecri.org
Contact: Marcus Schabacker, President
Facebook: www.facebook.com/ECRIOrg
Linkedin: www.linkedin.com/company/ecri-org
X (Twitter): x.com/ECRI_Org
YouTube: www.youtube.com/user/ECRIInstitute
Description: Improves the safety, performance and cost effectiveness of health care technology. Provides technical consulting, accident investigation and educational programs. **Scope:** Offers expertise in medical technology assessment, medical equipment acquisition and medical equipment purchasing. **Founded:** 1968. **Holdings:** Figures not available. **Publications:** "Health Devices Source book". **Training:** Top Ten Health Technology Hazards, Vancouver, Mar, 2010; Biomedical Engineering; State of the infusion technology market; Role of smarter infusion pumps in the field of medication safety technologies; Pump evaluation and selection factors; Implementation challenges and successes; How to assess your facilities readiness and infrastructure requirements for implementation; Clinical implications and work flow impact; Maintenance of libraries and log analysis; Successful wireless implementation; Hands-on interaction with the latest devices, guided by on-site pump trainers is offered; Infection Control Risk Assessment (ICRA) for Construction Activities; Take Control: Hazard and Recall Management Strategies, Royal Oak, MI, Sep, 2006. **Educational Activities:** ECRI Institute Annual conference (Annual). **Geographic Preference:** Multinational.

ASSOCIATIONS AND OTHER ORGANIZATIONS

10887 ■ American Health Information Management Association (AHIMA) - Library
233 N Michigan Ave., 21st Fl.
  Chicago, IL 60601-5809
Ph: (312)233-1100
Free: 800-335-5535
Fax: (312)233-1500
Co. E-mail: info@ahima.org
URL: http://www.ahima.org
Contact: Wylecia Wiggs Harris, Chief Executive Officer
Facebook: www.facebook.com/AHIMAOfficial
X (Twitter): x.com/AHIMAResources
YouTube: www.youtube.com/AHIMAonDemand
Description: Health information management professionals; registered record administrators; accredited record technicians with expertise in health information management, biostatistics, classification systems, and systems analysis. Sponsors Independent Study Programs in Medical Record Technology and coding. Conducts annual qualification examinations to credential medical record personnel as Registered Record Administrators, Accredited Record Technicians and Certified Coding Specialists. Maintains Foundation of Research and Education Library, Scholarships and loans. Dedicated to the effective management of personal health information required to deliver quality healthcare to the public. **Scope:** Health. **Founded:** 1928. **Holdings:** Figures not available. **Publications:** *From the Couch: Official Newsletter of the Mental Health Record Section of the American Medical Record Association* (Quarterly); *Volunteer* (Quarterly); *Certification Connection* (Quarterly); *Spectrum* (Quarterly); *Journal of AHIMA* (Monthly); *Accredited Educational Programs in Health Information Technology and Health Information Administration.* **Educational Activities:** American Health Information Management Association National Convention & Exhibit (Annual). **Geographic Preference:** National.

10888 ■ International Claim Association (ICA)
1800 M St., NW 400 S
  Washington, DC 20036
Ph: (202)452-0143
Fax: (202)530-0659
Co. E-mail: memberservices@claim.org
URL: http://www.claim.org
Contact: Kimberly Tomaselli, President
Linkedin: www.linkedin.com/company/claim-org
Instagram: www.instagram.com/claim_org
Description: Claim executives and administrators representing companies writing life, health, or accident insurance. Promotes efficiency, effectiveness and high standards of performance in claim administration by member companies. Provides a forum for research, education and the exchange of ideas relating to various aspects of claim administration. **Founded:** 1909. **Publications:** *ICA News* (Quarterly); *International Claim Association--Annual Report* (Annual). **Educational Activities:** International Claim Association Annual Education Conference (Annual). **Geographic Preference:** National.

REFERENCE WORKS

10889 ■ "1 in 3 Americans Frustrated with Patient Billing, Collections" in RevCycle Intelligence (October 18, 2019)
URL(s): revcycleintelligence.com/news/1-in-3-americans-frustrated-with-patient-billing-collections
Ed: Samantha McGrail. **Released:** October 18, 2019. **Description:** A recent survey of over 1,000 people revealed that half of healthcare consumers are frustrated with their health insurance provider's patient billing and collections process. It was also revealed that this is the reason many do not pay medical bills. More than a third of healthcare consumers have had a medical bill go to collections, with many not even realizing the bill was owed. **Availability:** Online.

10890 ■ "Hospital Communication Goes Mobile" in Providence Business News (Vol. 29, July 7, 2014, No. 14, pp. 12)
Pub: American City Business Journals, Inc.
Contact: Mike Olivieri, Executive Vice President
Released: July 05, 2014. **Description:** Software company, Care Thread, has designed a mobile health records application that allows providers to share patient e-medical records over a secure network. Care Thread signed a contract for the system with Eastern Connecticut Health Network and Boston's Brigham and Women's Hospital as well as a deal with health care management firm Beacon Partners Inc. to sell and implement the app across the U.S. **Availability:** Print; Online.

10891 ■ "Hospitals Waste Billions of Dollars in Medical Supplies" in U.S. News & World Report (March 9, 2017)
URL(s): www.usnews.com/news/healthcare-of-tomorrow/articles/2017-03-09/hospitals-are-wasting-billions-of-dollars-worth-of-medical-equipment
Ed: Anzish Mirza. **Released:** March 09, 2017. **Description:** A surprising amount of perfect, usable medical supplies are thrown out to the tune of $765 billion a year. This cost is passed onto healthcare consumers, which has resulted in higher health care costs all around. Often, supplies are tossed in the trash when new versions are released, even though nothing is wrong with the older versions. Also, if an item is placed in a patient's room it must be disposed of, even if it was never opened. Some efforts are being made to reduce this waste through incentives, but not much else can be done at this time. **Availability:** Online.

10892 ■ Medical Claims Processing Services Industry in the US - Market Research Report
URL(s): www.ibisworld.com/united-states/market-research-reports/medical-claims-processing-services-industry/
Price: $925. **Description:** Downloadable report analyzing the current and future trends in the medical billing services industry. **Availability:** Download.

10893 ■ "OmniSYS Plans Big Richardson Expansion" in Dallas Business Journal (Vol. 35, June 8, 2012, No. 39, pp. 1)
Pub: Baltimore Business Journal
Contact: Rhonda Pringle, President
E-mail: rpringle@bizjournals.com
Ed: Bill Hethcock. **Description:** OmniSYS LLC will hire about 250 more people in the next two years and open a 50,000-square-foot office in Richardson, Texas in October 2012. The Medicare claims processing company posted revenue growth of more than 30 percent in 2011 primarily in the Medicare audit and compliance area. **Availability:** Print; Online.

10894 ■ "Physicians Hail New York's Surprise Billing Law as a Success" in RevCycle Intelligence (September 30, 2019)
URL(s): revcycleintelligence.com/news/physicians-hail-new-yorks-surprise-billing-law-as-a-success
Ed: Jacqueline LaPointe. **Released:** September 30, 2019. **Description:** A surprise billing law that was passed several years ago has been deemed a success according to New York's Department of Financial Services. In total, it's saved over $400 million from 2015 to 2018 for healthcare consumers and relieving the burden of a surprise bill. **Availability:** Online.

10895 ■ "Spinout Success: New Leadership Steps In At UW's C4C" in Puget Sound Business Journal (Vol. 35, June 27, 2014, No. 10, pp. 11)
Pub: American City Business Journals, Inc.
Contact: Mike Olivieri, Executive Vice President
Description: University of Washington's Center for Commercialization vice provost, Vikram Jandhyala, talks about his new position with the school. Jandhyala says he plans to build more synergy between the medical school and engineering and between social sciences and computer science. He also says the medical and software industry need to grow to accommodate the volume of data crossing and stored within the Internet. **Availability:** Online.

10896 ■ "UPMC Aims to Profit From Billing Angst" in Pittsburgh Business Times (Vol. 33, Jun3 27, 2014, No. 50, pp. 8)
Pub: American City Business Journals, Inc.
Contact: Mike Olivieri, Executive Vice President

Released: Weekly. **Price:** $4, introductory 4-week offer(Digital only). **Description:** Hospital network UPMC has created a wholly owned, for-profit subsidiary named Ovation Revenue Cycle Solutions that helps medical providers with the complex new Medicare billing codes that take effect October 2015. The service provides revenue-cycle tools designed to help medical groups enhance efficiency, cut rejection rates and reduce time between billing and payment. **Availability:** Print; Online.

RESEARCH CENTERS

10897 ■ American University - College of Arts and Sciences - School of Education - National Center for Health Fitness (NCHF) - Reference Collection
4400 Massachusetts Ave., NW
  Washington, DC 20016
URL: http://www.american.edu/cas/faculty/rkarch.cfm
Contact: Dr. Robert Karch, Founder

E-mail: rkarch@american.edu

Description: Integral unit of School of Education, Teaching, and Health, College of Arts and Sciences, American University. Offers consulting services. **Scope:** Worksite health promotion programs, focusing on costs, benefits, and cost-effectiveness, and including international health promotion and special populations. **Holdings:** Figures not available.

START-UP INFORMATION

10898 ■ *"StartX Med Prescribed for Innovation" in Silicon Valley/San Jose Business Journal (Vol. 30, June 8, 2012, No. 11, pp. 1)*
Pub: Baltimore Business Journal
Contact: Rhonda Pringle, President
E-mail: rpringle@bizjournals.com
Description: StartX Med is a program started by entrepreneur Divya Nag along with Stanford student-led nonprofit StartX to help medical startups. Under the program, entrepreneurs will have access to wet and dry laboratory space, animal testing and information related to US Food and Drug Adminstration regulations. **Availability:** Print; Online.

ASSOCIATIONS AND OTHER ORGANIZATIONS

10899 ■ **American Association of Bioanalysts (AAB)**
906 Olive St., Ste. 1200
Saint Louis, MO 63101-1448
Ph: (314)241-1445
Fax: (314)241-1449
Co. E-mail: aab@aab.org
URL: http://www.aab.org/aab/default.asp
Contact: Mark Birenbaum, Contact
Facebook: www.facebook.com/AAB.MT
Linkedin: www.linkedin.com/company/american
-assoication-of-bioanalysts
X (Twitter): x.com/AABioanalysts
Description: Directors, owners, managers, supervisors, technologists and technicians of bio analytical clinical laboratories devoting their efforts to clinical laboratory procedure and testing. Sponsors Proficiency Testing Service open to individuals engaged in the clinical laboratory field. Provides specialized education and representation before federal and state legislatures and regulatory agencies. **Founded:** 1956. **Publications:** *AAB Bulletin*; *AAB Update* (Periodic). **Educational Activities:** Meeting and Educational Conference (Annual). **Geographic Preference:** National.

10900 ■ **American Association for Laboratory Accreditation (A2LA)**
5202 President's Ct., Ste. 220
Frederick, MD 21703
Ph: (301)644-3248
Co. E-mail: info@a2la.org
URL: http://a2la.org
Contact: Lonnie Spires, President
Facebook: www.facebook.com/A2LAAccreditation
Linkedin: www.linkedin.com/company/american
-association-for-laboratory-accreditation-a2la-
X (Twitter): x.com/A2LA_
Instagram: www.instagram.com/a2la_accreditation
Description: Represents individuals, associations, corporations, universities, laboratories, research institutes and government agencies interested in improving the quality of laboratories. Accredits testing laboratories, certifies laboratory reference materials and registers quality systems. **Founded:** 1978. **Publications:** *A2LA Directory*; *American Association for Laboratory Accreditation Directory of Accredited Laboratories* (Annual; Weekly); *American Association for Laboratory Accreditation Annual Report* (Annual); *A2LA Today*. **Geographic Preference:** National.

10901 ■ **American Board of Bioanalysis (ABB)**
906 Olive St., Ste. 1200
Saint Louis, MO 63101-1448
Ph: (314)241-1445
Fax: (314)241-1449
Co. E-mail: aab@aab.org
URL: http://www.aab.org/aab/default.asp
Contact: Mark Birenbaum, Executive Director
E-mail: birenbaumm@birenbaum.org
Facebook: www.facebook.com/AAB.MT
Linkedin: www.linkedin.com/company/american-boar
d-of-bioanalysis
X (Twitter): x.com/AABioanalysts
Description: Certifying agency consisting of scientists, educators, and authorities in the clinical laboratory field. Certifies clinical laboratory directors at two levels depending on qualifications, including High Complexity or Moderate Complexity Clinical Laboratory Director. Also certifies Technical Consultants, two levels of supervisor (Technical and General), and Bioanalyst Laboratory Manager (BLM). **Founded:** 1968. **Geographic Preference:** National.

10902 ■ **American Clinical Laboratory Association (ACLA)**
1201 Pennsylvania Ave. NW, Ste. 810
Washington, DC 20004
Ph: (202)637-9466
Co. E-mail: info@acla.com
URL: http://www.acla.com
Contact: Susan Van Meter, President
Facebook: www.facebook.com/ACLAlabs
Linkedin: www.linkedin.com/company/american-clini-
cal-laboratory-association
X (Twitter): x.com/ACLAlabs
Description: Promotes the development of uniformly high quality laboratory testing; eliminates the present inequalities in the standards applied to different segments of the clinical laboratory market. **Founded:** 1971. **Publications:** *Results* (Monthly). **Geographic Preference:** National.

10903 ■ **American Medical Technologists (AMT)**
10700 W Higgins Rd., Ste. 150
Rosemont, IL 60018
Ph: (847)823-5169
Co. E-mail: mail@americanmedtech.org
URL: http://www.americanmedtech.org
Contact: Jeannie Hobson, President
Facebook: www.facebook.com/americanmedtech
Linkedin: www.linkedin.com/company/american-me
dical-technologists
X (Twitter): x.com/americanmedtech
YouTube: www.youtube.com/c/americanmedical
technologists
Description: Represents medical technologists, medical laboratory technicians, medical assistants, medical administrative specialists, dental assistants, office laboratory technicians, phlebotomy technicians, laboratory consultants, and allied health instructors. Provides allied health professionals with professional certification services and membership programs to enhance their professional and personal growth. Aims to issue certification credentials to medical and dental assistants, clinical laboratory personnel, laboratory consultants, and allied health instructors. **Founded:** 1939. **Publications:** *AMT Events* (3/year); *AMT Events and Continuing Education Supplement* (6/year); *Journal of Continuing Education Topics & Issues*. **Educational Activities:** Educational Program and National Meeting (Annual); Joint Educational Program and Convention. **Awards:** AMT President's Award (Annual); The Becky Award (Annual); AMT Distinguished Achievement (Annual); RMA Medallion of Merit (Annual); AMT Exceptional Merit Awards (Annual); AMT Technical Writing Award (Annual); AMT Order of the Golden Microscope (Annual); AMT Outstanding Student Award (Annual); The Silver Service Award (Irregular); AMT Pillar Award (Irregular). **Geographic Preference:** National.

10904 ■ **American Society for Clinical Laboratory Science (ASCLS)**
1861 International Dr., Ste. 200
McLean, VA 22102
Ph: (571)748-3770
Co. E-mail: ascls@ascls.org
URL: http://ascls.org
Contact: Claude Rector, President
Facebook: www.facebook.com/ASCLS
X (Twitter): x.com/ascls
YouTube: www.youtube.com/channel/UC5EA
2gaOOHQzrMjWaUtyncQ
Description: Primarily clinical laboratory personnel who have an associate or baccalaureate degree and clinical training and specialists who hold at least a master's degree in one of the major fields of clinical laboratory science such as bacteriology, mycology, or biochemistry; also includes technicians, specialists, and educators with limited certificates and students enrolled in approved programs of clinical laboratory studies and military medical technology schools. Promotes and maintains high standards in clinical laboratory methods and research and advances standards of education and training of personnel. Conducts educational program of seminars and workshops. Approves programs of continuing education and maintains records on participation in continuing education programs for members. **Founded:** 1933. **Publications:** *ASCLS TODAY Newsletter* (6/year); *Clinical Laboratory Science* (Quarterly). **Awards:** Gloria F. "Mike" Gilbert Memorial Trustee Award (Annual); Joseph J. Kleiner Memorial Awards (Annual); Robin H. Mendelson Memorial Awards (Annual); AMTF Graduate Scholarships (Annual); Alpha Mu Tau Fraternity (AMTF) Undergraduate Scholarships (Annual); ASCLS Education and Research

Fund (E and R) Scholarship Program (Annual); AS-CLS Education Scientific Assembly Student Paper Award (Annual); ASCLS Member of the Year (Annual); Dorothy Morrison Undergraduate Scholarships (Annual). **Geographic Preference:** Multinational.

10905 ■ American Society for Clinical Pathology (ASCP)
33 West Monroe St., Ste. 1600
Chicago, IL 60603
Ph: (312)541-4999
Fax: (312)541-4998
Co. E-mail: pdinfo@ascp.org
URL: http://www.ascp.org/content#
Facebook: www.facebook.com/ASCP.Chicago
X (Twitter): x.com/ASCP_Chicago
Description: Works to promote public health and safety by the appropriate application of pathology and laboratory medicine. Provides educational programs for pathologists and laboratory professionals throughout the year, certification for laboratory professionals, and publishes scientific journals and reference textbooks. **Founded:** 1922. **Publications:** *Critical Values* (Continuous); *American Journal of Clinical Pathology (AJCP)* (Monthly); *ASCP Member Newsletter* (Quarterly); *Laboratory Medicine* (Bimonthly); *Pathology Today* (Bimonthly). **Awards:** Siemens-ASCP Scholarship (Annual); ASCP Foundation Garza & Becan McBride Endowed Scholarship (Annual); Ward Burdick Award for Distinguished Service to Pathology (Annual); Philip Levine Award for Outstanding Research (Annual); H.P. Smith Award for Distinguished Pathology Educator (Annual); ASCP Member Lifetime Achievement Award (Annual). **Geographic Preference:** National.

10906 ■ *Canadian Journal of Medical Laboratory Science (CJLMS)*
33 Wellington St. N
Hamilton, ON, Canada L8R 1M7
Ph: (905)528-8642
Free: 800-263-8277
Fax: (905)528-4968
Co. E-mail: info@csmls.org
URL: http://www.csmls.org
Contact: Christine Nielsen, Chief Executive Officer
URL(s): csmls.org/About-Us/Publications/Canadian-Journal-of-Medical-Laboratory-Science-(CJ.aspx
Released: Quarterly **Price:** $95, Other countries; $46, Canada; $60, U.S. **Description:** Magazine presenting updates on current medical and laboratory issues. **Availability:** Print; PDF; Online.

10907 ■ Canadian Society for Medical Laboratory Science (CSMLS) - Library
33 Wellington St. N
Hamilton, ON, Canada L8R 1M7
Ph: (905)528-8642
Free: 800-263-8277
Fax: (905)528-4968
Co. E-mail: info@csmls.org
URL: http://www.csmls.org
Contact: Christine Nielsen, Chief Executive Officer
Facebook: www.facebook.com/csmls
X (Twitter): x.com/csmls
YouTube: www.youtube.com/user/csmls
Description: Promotes the interests of medical laboratory technologists. Emphasizes the importance of continuing education; sponsors courses. **Scope:** Medical laboratory technology. **Services:** Interlibrary loan. **Founded:** 1937. **Holdings:** Books. **Publications:** *Canadian Clinical Laboratory* (Bimonthly); *Annual Roster* (Annual); *Canadian Journal of Medical Laboratory Science* (Quarterly); *Catalogs of Continuing Education*; *Laboratory Safety Guidelines*. **Educational Activities:** LABCON: National Conference of Medical Laboratory Science (Annual). **Awards:** CSMLS Student Scholarship (Annual). **Geographic Preference:** National.

10908 ■ Clinical Laboratory Management Association (CLMA)
33 W Monroe St., Ste. 1600
Chicago, IL 60603
Free: 800-267-2727
Co. E-mail: info@clma.org
URL: http://www.clma.org

Contact: Christina Nickel, President
E-mail: christina.nickel@bryanhealth.org
Facebook: www.facebook.com/ClinicalLaboratoryManagementAssn
Linkedin: www.linkedin.com/company/clma
X (Twitter): twitter.com/CLMAorg
YouTube: www.youtube.com/user/CLMAHeadquarters
Description: Individuals holding managerial or supervisory positions with clinical laboratories; persons engaged in education of such individuals; manufacturers or distributors of equipment or services to clinical laboratories. Objectives are: to enhance management skills and promote more efficient and productive department operations; to further exchange of professional knowledge, new technology, and colleague experience; to encourage cooperation among those engaged in management or supervisory functions. Activities include: workshops, seminars, and expositions; dissemination of information about legislation and other topics. **Founded:** 1976. **Publications:** *Clinical Leadership and Management Review (CLMR)* (Bimonthly); *Clinical Leadership & Management Review (CLMR)* (Annual); *Clinical Laboratory Management Association--Membership Directory.* **Educational Activities:** CLMA KnowledgeLab (Annual). **Awards:** CLMA Chapter of the Year (Annual). **Geographic Preference:** National.

10909 ■ Clinical and Laboratory Standards Institute (CLSI)
1055 Westlakes Dr., Ste. 300
Berwyn, PA 19312
Ph: (610)688-0100
Free: 877-447-1888
Fax: (610)688-0700
Co. E-mail: customerservice@clsi.org
URL: http://clsi.org
Contact: James H. Nichols, President
Facebook: www.facebook.com/clsilabnews
Linkedin: www.linkedin.com/company/clsilabnews
X (Twitter): x.com/CLSI_LabNews
YouTube: www.youtube.com/channel/UCfvQrLzswA20IWnTy_VqOBA
Pinterest: www.pinterest.com/clsi_labnews
Description: Purposes are to promote the development of national and international standards for medical testing and to provide a consensus mechanism for defining and resolving problems that influence the quality and cost of healthcare work performed. **Founded:** 1968. **Publications:** *Clinical and Laboratory Standards Institute - eNews*; *Member/Volunteer Directory.* **Awards:** Russell J. Eilers Memorial Award (Annual). **Geographic Preference:** Multinational.

10910 ■ *Laboratory Safety Guidelines*
33 Wellington St. N
Hamilton, ON, Canada L8R 1M7
Ph: (905)528-8642
Free: 800-263-8277
Fax: (905)528-4968
Co. E-mail: info@csmls.org
URL: http://www.csmls.org
Contact: Christine Nielsen, Chief Executive Officer
URL(s): www.csmls.org/About-Us/Publications/Laboratory-Safety-Guidelines.aspx
Released: Latest Edition 9th. **Price:** $30, for more than 10 copies; $35, for plus gst charges applicable. **Availability:** PDF.

10911 ■ National Accrediting Agency for Clinical Laboratory Sciences (NAACLS)
5600 N River Rd., Ste. 720
Rosemont, IL 60018-5119
Ph: (773)714-8880
Fax: (773)714-8886
Co. E-mail: info@naacls.org
URL: http://www.naacls.org
Contact: Maribeth L. Flaw, President
Description: Independently accredits academic programs in hospitals, colleges, and universities. **Founded:** 1973. **Publications:** *National Accrediting Agency for Clinical Laboratory Sciences--Annual Report* (Annual); *NAACLS News.* **Geographic Preference:** National.

REFERENCE WORKS

10912 ■ *"Biotech Reels In $120M for 1Q"* in Philadelphia Business Journal (Vol. 31, March 30, 2012, No. 7, pp. 1)
Pub: Baltimore Business Journal
Contact: Rhonda Pringle, President
E-mail: rpringle@bizjournals.com
Description: Philadelphia, Pennsylvania-based biotechnology firms have raised over $120 million in 2012 by selling stocks and debts. Discovery Laboratories has accounted for more than a third of the total funding. **Availability:** Print; Online.

10913 ■ *"Brown Lab Image of R.I. Innovation"* in Providence Business News (Vol. 28, February 24, 2014, No. 47, pp. 1)
Pub: American City Business Journals, Inc.
Contact: Mike Olivieri, Executive Vice President
Released: February 22, 2014. **Description:** The Advanced Baby Imaging Lab at Brown University in Rhode Island is studying infant brain development using magnetic resonance imaging (MRI). The lab is attracting attention from researchers from Europe and California who see potential in Sean C. Deoni's technique to take an MRI of an infant without using sedation. **Availability:** Print; Online.

10914 ■ *"Compassion Fatigue in the Time of COVID-19"* in AACC (November 1, 2021)
Ed: James H. Berry, DO. **Released:** November 01, 2021. **Description:** Discusses the signs of compassion fatigue and how it affects those working in healthcare, including diagnostic laboratories. **Availability:** Online.

10915 ■ *Diagnostic & Medical Laboratories Industry in the US - Market Research Report*
URL(s): www.ibisworld.com/united-states/market-research-reports/diagnostic-medical-laboratories-industry/
Price: $925. **Description:** Downloadable report analyzing the current and future trends in the diagnostic and medical lab industry. **Availability:** Download.

10916 ■ *Directory of International and Regional Organizations Conducting Standards-Related Activities*
Pub: U.S. Department of Commerce
Contact: Ron Jarmin, Director
URL(s): gpo.gov
Ed: Breitenberg Maureen. **Description:** Covers 338 international and regional organizations which conduct standardization, certification, laboratory accreditation, and other standards-related activities. **Entries include:** Description, scope of each organization, national affiliations of members, U.S. Participants, restrictions on membership, availability of any standards in English. **Availability:** Microfiche; Print.

10917 ■ *"Doctor: J & J Alerted in '06 to Procedure Risks"* in Pittsburgh Business Times (Vol. 33, June 6, 2014, No. 47, pp. 4)
Pub: American City Business Journals, Inc.
Contact: Mike Olivieri, Executive Vice President
Released: Weekly. **Price:** $4, introductory 4-week offer(Digital & Print). **Description:** Dr. Robert Lamparter, then pathologist at Lewisburg's Evangelical Community Hospital, states that he had alerted Johnson and Johnson (J and J) in 2006 of the potential risk of spreading undetected cancer following the use of its power morcellator during hysterectomy procedures. J and J suspended worldwide sales of the device in April 2014 after the laboratory warning, and days after a US Food and Drug Administration advisory discouraging doctors from using it, but doctors are still divided over the morcellation procedure. **Availability:** Print; Online.

10918 ■ *"GeneTree.com Unveils New Family Consultation Service in Interpreting Genealogical DNA Data"* in Benzinga.com (February 2, 2012)
Description: Family Consultation Services has been launched by GeneTree.com. The service will provide an in-depth examination of genealogical and DNA

information to help genealogist help families identify ancestors in specific family lines. The new DNA test called Y-19 will be used by the service. **Availability:** Print; Online.

10919 ■ *"The Heart of Health Village: Innovation Is Key, and to Get It, Florida Hospital Is Wooing Disruptors, Millenials"* in *Orlando Business Journal (Vol. 30, May 16, 2014, No. 47, pp. 4)*
Pub: American City Business Journals, Inc.
Contact: Mike Olivieri, Executive Vice President
Released: May 16, 2014. **Description:** The economic impact of Florida Hospital's planned Health Village in downtown Orlando is explored. The 172-acre development aims to bring together business people, scientists for research, and early and mid-stage companies to combine co-working activities in its Medical Innovation Laboratory. **Availability:** Print; Online.

10920 ■ *"How To Spark Up a Medical Marijuana Firm in Florida - and Not Get Burned in the Process"* in *Orlando Business Journal (Vol. 30, March 21, 2014, No. 39, pp. 6)*
Pub: American City Business Journals, Inc.
Contact: Mike Olivieri, Executive Vice President
Released: Weekly. **Price:** $8, introductory 4-week offer(Digital & Print). **Description:** Colorado business owners and experts offer tips on starting a medical marijuana business in Florida. Andy Williams recalls that he was filled with fear he would wake up in Federal prison and not see his family again when he started Medicine Man. Jerald Bovine of GreenZipp.com advises those interested in entering the medical marijuana field to know the details of regulation of facilities and labs. **Availability:** Print; Online.

10921 ■ *"Innovation: A Blood Test on a Chip"* in *Inc. (Vol. 33, November 2011, No. 9, pp. 42)*
Pub: Inc. Magazine
Ed: Christine Chafkin-Lagorio. **Description:** Harvard University researchers have developed a device called the mChip that produces accurate blood tests in about 10 minutes. Plans to apply for FDA approval for the mChip in the US should happen in 2012. **Availability:** Online.

10922 ■ *"The List: Top South Florida Diagnostic Centers"* in *South Florida Business Journal (Vol. 34, April 18, 2014, No. 39, pp. 12)*
Pub: American City Business Journals, Inc.
Contact: Mike Olivieri, Executive Vice President
Released: Weekly. **Description:** Rankings of medical diagnostic centers in South Florida are presented. Rankings were based on the number of patients each laboratory or medical facility saw in 2013. **Availability:** Print; Online.

10923 ■ *"Locals Eager for $785M Medical Marijuana Business"* in *Orlando Business Journal (Vol. 30, March 21, 2014, No. 39, pp. 4)*
Pub: American City Business Journals, Inc.
Contact: Mike Olivieri, Executive Vice President
Released: Weekly. **Price:** $8, introductory 4-week offer(Digital & Print). **Description:** A number of local companies in Central Florida are preparing for a ballot initiative to legalize medical marijuana in November 2014. The National Cannabis Association estimates the medical marijuana market in Florida at $785 million, with about 260,000 patients, while Orlando's share is estimated at $89.1 million, with 29,518 potential patients. **Availability:** Print; Online.

10924 ■ *"NSU Seeks Private Partners For New $80M Research Building"* in *South Florida Business Journal (Vol. 34, February 21, 2014, No. 31, pp. 4)*
Pub: American City Business Journals, Inc.
Contact: Mike Olivieri, Executive Vice President
Released: Weekly. **Price:** $8, introductory 4-week offer(Digital & Print). **Description:** The $80 million Center for Collaborative Research at Nova Southeast-

ern University hopes to become the largest incubator and wet laboratory space in Broward County, Florida. The center had its groundbreaking on February 13, 2014, and will be open for lease to private companies when it is ready in 22 months. **Availability:** Print; Online.

10925 ■ *"Pathology Firm Building New HQ: Poplar Healthcare Facility Will Be Near FedEx Corp."* in *Memphis Business Journal (Vol. 34, June 29, 2012, No. 11, pp. 1)*
Pub: Baltimore Business Journal
Contact: Rhonda Pringle, President
E-mail: rpringle@bizjournals.com
Ed: Andy Ashby. **Description:** Poplar Healthcare Management LLC is building a new 113,000 square foot coporate headquarters in Southeast Memphis, Tennessee. The laboratory services company purchased the 18.6 acre property for $1.2 million and filed an $11.5 million construction permit for the office building. **Availability:** Print; Online.

10926 ■ *"Putting Down Roots"* in *Entrepreneur (August 2014)*
Released: October 28, 2016. **Description:** Entrepreneur Justin Hartfield and partner Doug Francis created Weedmaps.com, an online portal for marijuana dispensaries, after California legalized the sale of medical marijuana. Hartfield is looking forward to a billion-dollar business once the federal prohibition of marijuana is ended. Local dispensaries pay a monthly subscription of $420 to appear on the site while doctors pay $295 to be featured on the site. Harfield is seeking partnerships with laboratories that will provide marijuana testing and other services. **Availability:** Online.

10927 ■ *"Renal Solutions Move Not a Sign of the Times"* in *Pittsburgh Business Times (Vol. 33, February 14, 2014, No. 31, pp. 5)*
Pub: American City Business Journals, Inc.
Contact: Mike Olivieri, Executive Vice President
Released: Weekly. **Price:** $4, Introductory 4-week offer(Digital only). **Description:** Renal Solutions, a Pittsburgh, Pennsylvania-based company, has decided to relocate to California. Company founder, Pete DeComo, believes that the firm's move should not be a cause for concern within the city's business community. Renal Solutions was acquired by Fresenius Medical Care North America in 2007. **Availability:** Print; Online.

STATISTICAL SOURCES

10928 ■ *RMA Annual Statement Studies*
Pub: Risk Management Association
Contact: Nancy Foster, President
Released: Annual. **Description:** Contains composite balance sheets and income statements for more than 360 industries, including the accounting, auditing, and bookkeeping industries. Also contains five years of comparative historical data for discerning trends. Includes 16 commonly used ratios, computed for most of the size groupings for nearly every industry.

TRADE PERIODICALS

10929 ■ *AAB Bulletin*
Pub: American Association of Bioanalysts
Contact: Mark Birenbaum, Contact
URL(s): www.aab.org/aab/Bulletins.asp
Description: Addresses legislative and regulatory issues and scientific developments. Contains commentary, news from other laboratory professionals, regional activities, and continuing education programs. Recurring features include interviews, news of research, a calendar of events, reports of meetings, news of educational opportunities, and job listings. **Availability:** Online.

10930 ■ *AIDS Research and Human Retroviruses*
Pub: Mary Ann Liebert Inc. Publishers
Contact: Mary Ann Liebert, Founder
URL(s): home.liebertpub.com/publications/aids-research-and-human-retroviruses/2

Released: Monthly **Description:** Peer-reviewed, multidisciplinary journal covering HIV and retrovirus-related research. **Availability:** Print; Online.

10931 ■ *Laboratory Medicine*
Pub: American Society for Clinical Pathology
URL(s): academic.oup.com/labmed
Ed: Roger L. Bertholf, PhD. **Released:** Bimonthly **Price:** $192, Institutions for online only US; $258, Institutions for print and online US; $160, Individuals for online only US; $216, Individuals for print only US; $76, Institutions for print single issue UK; $34, Individuals for print single issue UK. **Description:** Provides continuing education, career development and new technologies to laboratory professionals. **Availability:** Print; Online.

10932 ■ *NAACLS News*
Pub: National Accrediting Agency for Clinical Laboratory Sciences
Contact: Maribeth L. Flaw, President
URL(s): naaclsnews.org
Description: Provides news of the activities of the Agency as well as issues related to laboratory scientists. **Availability:** Online.

10933 ■ *Translational Research: The Journal of Laboratory and Clinical Medicine*
Pub: Elsevier Inc.
URL(s): www.translationalres.com
Released: Monthly **Price:** $346, Individuals for print and online, us annual; $622.80, Individuals for print and online, us 2 year; $882.30, Individuals for print and online, us 3 year; $446, Individuals for print and online, Canada annual; $802.80, Individuals for print and online, Canada 2 year; $1,137.30, Individuals for print and online, Canada 3 year; $442, Individuals for print and online, India France up annual; $795.60, Individuals for print and online, India France up 2 year; $1,127.10, Individuals for print and online, India France up 3 year; $1,626, Institutions for print annual us; $1,877, Institutions for print annual Canada India France up; $311, Individuals for online only us Canada international. **Description:** Interdisciplinary journal covering original research in the broad fields of laboratory, clinical, and public health research. **Availability:** Print; Download; PDF; Online.

TRADE SHOWS AND CONVENTIONS

10934 ■ **American Association for Laboratory Animal Science Conference & Exhibits**
URL(s): www.aalas.org/national-meeting/general-information/future-meetings#.VopIEbZ94dV
Frequency: Annual. **Description:** Exhibits related to pharmaceuticals and laboratory animal facility equipment and supplies. **Audience:** Professionals concerned with the production, care, and use of laboratory animals. **Principal Exhibits:** Exhibits related to pharmaceuticals and laboratory animal facility equipment and supplies. **Telecommunication Services:** info@aalas.org.

10935 ■ **American Medical Technologists Convention**
URL(s): www.americanmedtech.org/BeInvolved/AMTAnnualMeeting.aspx
Frequency: Annual. **Description:** Clinical laboratory books, equipment, supplies, and services. **Audience:** Allied health professionals and medical technologists. **Principal Exhibits:** Clinical laboratory books, equipment, supplies, and services.

10936 ■ **CLMA KnowledgeLab**
Clinical Laboratory Management Association (CLMA)
33 W Monroe St., Ste. 1600
Chicago, IL 60603
Free: 800-267-2727
Co. E-mail: info@clma.org
URL: http://www.clma.org
Contact: Christina Nickel, President
E-mail: christina.nickel@bryanhealth.org
URL(s): www.clma.org/page/knowledgelab-2021

Frequency: Annual. **Description:** Laboratory devices manufacturers, laboratory information systems, coagulation homeostasis, publishers, autoimmune disease testing, bacteriology, allergy testing, chemistry systems. **Audience:** Industry professionals. **Principal Exhibits:** Laboratory devices manufacturers, laboratory information systems, coagulation homeostasis, publishers, autoimmune disease testing, bacteriology, allergy testing, chemistry systems. **Telecommunication Services:** exhibit@ascp.org.

COMPUTERIZED DATABASES

10937 ■ *American Hospital Directory*
American Hospital Directory Inc.
166 Thierman Ln.
Louisville, KY 40207
Free: 800-894-8418
Fax: (502)899-7738
Co. E-mail: inbox@ahd.com
URL: http://www.ahd.com
Contact: Kenton Shoemaker, President
URL(s): www.ahd.com
Price: $445, for single user license; $400, for 2-5 users; $355, for 6-10 users; $320, for 11-20 users; $310, for 21-35 users. **Description:** Database covers comparative data on hospitals in the U.S. **Entries include:** Hospital name, address, phone, fax, characteristics, financial statistics, services, accreditation status, utilization statistics, hospital web page. **Availability:** PDF; Download; Online. **Type:** Directory.

10938 ■ *Smoking and Tobacco Use Data and Statistics*
U.S. Centers for Disease Control and Prevention
1600 Clifton Rd.
Atlanta, GA 30329
Free: 800-232-4636
Co. E-mail: hrcs@cdc.gov
URL: http://www.cdc.gov
Contact: Dr. Mandy K. Cohen, Director
URL(s): www.cdc.gov/ophdst/data-research/index.html
Availability: Online. **Type:** Bibliographic.

LIBRARIES

10939 ■ Canadian Society for Medical Laboratory Science (CSMLS) - Library
33 Wellington St. N
Hamilton, ON, Canada L8R 1M7
Ph: (905)528-8642
Free: 800-263-8277
Fax: (905)528-4968
Co. E-mail: info@csmls.org
URL: http://www.csmls.org
Contact: Christine Nielsen, Chief Executive Officer
Facebook: www.facebook.com/csmls

X (Twitter): x.com/csmls
YouTube: www.youtube.com/user/csmls
Description: Promotes the interests of medical laboratory technologists. Emphasizes the importance of continuing education; sponsors courses. **Scope:** Medical laboratory technology. **Services:** Interlibrary loan. **Founded:** 1937. **Holdings:** Books. **Publications:** *Canadian Clinical Laboratory* (Bimonthly); *Annual Roster* (Annual); *Canadian Journal of Medical Laboratory Science* (Quarterly); *Catalogs of Continuing Education*; *Laboratory Safety Guidelines*. **Educational Activities:** LABCON: National Conference of Medical Laboratory Science (Annual). **Awards:** CSMLS Student Scholarship (Annual). **Geographic Preference:** National.

RESEARCH CENTERS

10940 ■ American Federation for Medical Research (AFMR)
500 Cummings Ctr., Ste. 4400
Beverly, MA 01915
Ph: (978)927-8330
Fax: (978)524-0498
Co. E-mail: admin@afmr.org
URL: http://afmr.org
Contact: Samrat U. Das, President
Facebook: www.facebook.com/AFMResearch1940
X (Twitter): x.com/AFMResearch

Description: Provides a forum for young clinical scientists (under 43); promotes and encourages original research in clinical and laboratory medicine. Offers specialized education program; maintains information services on membership status, files, and National Abstracting Processing. Annual scientific program presents sections on: Cardiovascular; Dermatology; Endocrinology; Gastroenterology; Genetics; Hematology; Immunology and Connective Tissue; Infectious Disease; Metabolism; Neoplastic Disease; Patient Care; Pulmonary; Renal and Electrolytes. **Scope:** Cardiovascular medicine, dermatology, endocrinology, gastroenterology, genetics, hematology, immunology, connective tissue disease, infectious disease, metabolism, neoplastic disease, patient care, pulmonary medicine. **Founded:** 1940. **Publications:** *Journal of Investigative Medicine (JIM)* (8/year). **Awards:** AFMR Research Day Awards (Annual); Henry Christian Awards (Annual); AFMR Junior Physician-Investigator Awards (Irregular); AFMR Outstanding Investigator Awards (Annual). **Geographic Preference:** National.

10941 ■ Indiana University-Purdue University Indianapolis - Indiana Alzheimer Disease Center (IADC)
340 West 10th St. Fairbanks Hall, Ste. 6200
Indianapolis, IN 46202-3082
Ph: (317)963-5500

URL: http://medicine.iu.edu/research-centers/alzheimers
Contact: Eric Bailey, Manager
E-mail: baileye@iu.edu
Description: One of the National Institute on Aging-funded Alzheimer's Disease Centers, located at Indiana University-Purdue University Indianapolis. Offers clinical services. **Scope:** Causes, diagnosis, treatment, and genetics of Alzheimer's Disease. **Founded:** 1983. **Educational Activities:** IADC Conferences.

10942 ■ Public Health Institute (PHI)
555 12th St., Ste. 600
Oakland, CA 94607
Ph: (510)285-5500
Fax: (510)285-5501
Co. E-mail: communications@phi.org
URL: http://www.phi.org
Contact: Dr. Mary A. Pittman, President
E-mail: mpittman@phi.org
Facebook: www.facebook.com/PublicHealthInstitute
Linkedin: www.linkedin.com/company/public-health-institute
X (Twitter): x.com/phidotorg
Description: Focuses on the ideas, programs and individuals positioned to transform health. **Scope:** Dedicated to improving health and wellness by discovering new research, strengthening key partnerships and programs, and advancing sound health policies. **Founded:** 1964. **Educational Activities:** California Association of Regional Cancer Registries Conference. **Geographic Preference:** Regional.

10943 ■ University of California, San Francisco - Center for AIDS Prevention Studies (CAPS)
550 16th St., 3rd Fl.
San Francisco, CA 94158
Ph: (415)476-6288
URL: http://prevention.ucsf.edu
Contact: Susan Kegeles, Professor
E-mail: susan.kegeles@ucsf.edu
Facebook: www.facebook.com/CAPS.UCSF
X (Twitter): x.com/UCSFCAPS
YouTube: www.youtube.com/channel/UCFNYJXAgUTCStmoTm_GFsPg
Description: Integral unit of University of California, San Francisco. **Scope:** Methods to change AIDS high risk behavior. Activities include developing and testing AIDS prevention strategies for at-risk populations, promoting multidisciplinary research on the prevention of HIV disease, funding pilot studies on minority issues in AIDS, and operating the CAPS International Visiting Scholars Program, which brings scholars from Africa, Asia, Eastern Europe, and Latin America to work with CAPS scientists in developing AIDS prevention research protocols. **Founded:** 1986. **Publications:** *Prevention Fact Sheets*. **Educational Activities:** CAPS conference. **Awards:** Traineeships in AIDS Prevention Studies (Annual).

ASSOCIATIONS AND OTHER ORGANIZATIONS

10944 ■ **Advanced Medical Technology Association (AdvaMed) - Library**
1301 Pennsylvania Ave. NW, Ste. 400
Washington, DC 20004
Ph: (202)783-8700
Fax: (202)783-8750
URL: http://www.advamed.org
Contact: Scott Whitaker, President
Facebook: www.facebook.com/AdvaMed
X (Twitter): x.com/advamedupdate
Instagram: www.instagram.com/advamed
YouTube: www.youtube.com/user/AdvaMedUpdate

Description: Represents domestic (including U.S. territories and possessions) manufacturers of medical devices, diagnostic products, and healthcare information systems. Develops programs and activities on economic, technical, medical, and scientific matters affecting the industry. **Scope:** Medicine. **Founded:** 1974. **Holdings:** Books. **Publications:** *In Brief* (Monthly); *Advanced Medical Technology Association--Directory*; *Smart Brief*. **Geographic Preference:** National.

REFERENCE WORKS

10945 ■ *"Amazon Makes Inroads Selling Medical Supplies to the Sick" in The Wall Street Journal (November 29, 2018)*
URL(s): www.wsj.com/articles/amazon-makes-inroa ds-selling-medical-supplies-to-the-sick-1543487401

Ed: Melanie Evans. **Released:** November 29, 2018. **Description:** A new app is allowing doctors to direct patients towards medical supplies that can be purchased on Amazon.com, raising some privacy concerns. However, doctors are saying its the same as handing over a handwritten note which are often lost or sparing patients from having to spend time trying to track down the needed supplies. **Availability:** Online.

10946 ■ *"Beaumont Outsources Purchasing as Route to Supply Cost Savings" in Crain's Detroit Business (Vol. 25, June 1, 2009, No. 22)*
Pub: Crain Communications Inc.
Contact: Barry Asin, President

Ed: Jay Greene. **Description:** William Beaumont Hospitals in Royal Oak have begun outsourcing the purchasing of supplies in order to cut costs. So far, Beaumont is the only hospital in southeast Michigan to outsource its purchasing department. Other hospitals employ their own purchasing supply workers. **Availability:** Online.

10947 ■ *Emergency Medical Services Magazine--Buyers Guide Issue: The Journal of Emergency Care, Rescue and Transportation*
URL(s): www.emsresponder.com

Released: Annual **Description:** Publication includes lists of about 1,000 manufacturers, suppliers, and distributors of equipment and other products used in emergency medical services; coverage includes Canada. Also covers 50 emergency medical service associations, state agencies, and meetings, workshops, and other conferences of interest. **Entries include:** For companies--Company name, address, phone, fax, toll-free, E-mail address, name of principal executive, product/service. For associations--Name, address, phone, name of director, number of members, description of membership, publications, meeting time. **Arrangement:** Alphabetical. **Indexes:** Product/service. **Availability:** Print.

10948 ■ *"Extreme Temperatures May Pose Risks to Some Mail-Order Meds" in NPR (January 7, 2019)*
URL(s): www.npr.org/sections/health-shots/2019/01/ 07/673806506/extreme-temperatures-may-pose -risks-to-some-mail-order-meds

Ed: Alex Smith. **Released:** January 07, 2019. **Description:** With most medications instructing to store at room temperature, what happens when a mail delivery service leaves your meds in extreme weather conditions? Many prescriptions are filled online and home delivered, with packages being left in either extreme cold or heat, depending on the season and the location. A push is being made to go back to retail pharmacy services unless the mail-order services can prove that the drugs are being delivered at the right temperatures. **Availability:** Online.

10949 ■ *"Green Peak Innovations to Open First of Planned 30 Marijuana Stores This Week in Bay City" in Crain's Detroit Business(July 8, 2019)*
Pub: Crain Communications Inc.
Contact: Barry Asin, President
URL(s): www.crainsdetroit.com/marijuana/green-peak -innovations-open-first-planned-30-marijuana-stores -week-bay-city

Ed: Anisa Jibrell. **Description:** Green Peak Innovations, LLC, a medical cannabis manufacturer based in Michigan, is opening a retail outlet in Bay City, the first of 30 retail centers it aims to open by the end of 2020. **Availability:** Online.

10950 ■ *"Health Care Briefs: Survey Says Most Approve of Donating Used Pacemakers to Medically Underserved" in Crain's Detroit Business (Vol. 25, June 1, 2009)*
Pub: Crain Communications Inc.
Contact: Barry Asin, President

Description: According to a survey conducted by University of Michigan Cardiovascular Center, 87 percent of those with pacemakers and 71 percent of the general population would donate the device to patients in underserved nations.

10951 ■ *"Hospitals Try to Buy Smarter" in Crain's Detroit Business (Vol. 25, June 1, 2009, No. 22, pp. M025)*
Pub: Crain Communications Inc.
Contact: Barry Asin, President

Ed: Jay Greene. **Description:** Hospitals in southeast Michigan are using bulk discount purchasing of medical and non-medical supplies through group purchasing organizations in order to cut costs. **Availability:** Online.

10952 ■ *"Hospitals Waste Billions of Dollars in Medical Supplies" in U.S. News & World Report (March 9, 2017)*
URL(s): www.usnews.com/news/healthcare-of -tomorrow/articles/2017-03-09/hospitals-are-was ting-billions-of-dollars-worth-of-medical-equipment

Ed: Anzish Mirza. **Released:** March 09, 2017. **Description:** A surprising amount of perfect, usable medical supplies are thrown out to the tune of $765 billion a year. This cost is passed onto healthcare consumers, which has resulted in higher health care costs all around. Often, supplies are tossed in the trash when new versions are released, even though nothing is wrong with the older versions. Also, if an item is placed in a patient's room it must be disposed of, even if it was never opened. Some efforts are being made to reduce this waste through incentives, but not much else can be done at this time. **Availability:** Online.

10953 ■ *"Lampton Welding Launches Work on New Compressed-Gas Facility" in Wichita Business Journal (Vol. 27, February 3, 2012, No. 5, pp. 1)*
Pub: Baltimore Business Journal
Contact: Rhonda Pringle, President
E-mail: rpringle@bizjournals.com

Description: Lampton Welding Supply has announced plans to open its new filling and mixing plant for cylinders containing industrial, medical and specialty gases in June. The site includes a state-of-the-art compressed-gas facility that co-owner David Lampton believed will attrac industry representatives to Wichita, Kansas. Insights on Lampton Welding's other facilities are also given.

10954 ■ *"Medical-Device Firm Targets a Heart-Valve Market in Flux" in Philadelphia Business Journal (Vol. 33, May 9, 2014, No. 13, pp. 9)*
Pub: American City Business Journals, Inc.
Contact: Mike Olivieri, Executive Vice President

Released: May 09, 2014. **Price:** $4, Introductory 4-week offer(Digital only). **Description:** Montgomery County-based medical products company, Thubrikar Aortic Valve Inc., is developing the Optimum TAV, a next-generation transcatheter aortic valve implantation (TAVI) device to treat heart patients with aortic stenosis. The company is raising funds to start clinical testing for the Optimum TAV in 2014, aiming to provide a more durable and efficient transcatheter aortic valve for lower-risk patients. **Availability:** Print; Online.

10955 ■ *"Medical Supplies Market Size to Hit USD 186 Billion by 2030" in Globe Newswire (November 24, 2021)*
Released: November 24, 2021. **Description:** The medical supply industry is primed to increase,

especially for chronic disease diagnostic supplies and surgery supplies.

10956 ■ *"Newton Robotics Company Bets on Rehab Robots for Growth" in Boston Business Journal (Vol. 34, April 4, 2014, No. 9, pp. 6)*

Pub: American City Business Journals, Inc.

Contact: Mike Olivieri, Executive Vice President

Description: Robotics firm Barrett Technology is transforming into a health care company by developing rehabilitation robots. The business is expected to generate 80 percent of its revenue from its health care clients over the next five years. The possibility of hiring new employees is also discussed. **Availability:** Print; Online.

STATISTICAL SOURCES

10957 ■ *Medical Supplies Wholesaling Industry in the US - Market Research Report*

URL(s): www.ibisworld.com/united-states/market-research-reports/medical-supplies-wholesaling-industry/

Price: $925. **Description:** Downloadable report analyzing the current and future trends in the medical supplies wholesaling industry. **Availability:** Download.

TRADE PERIODICALS

10958 ■ *OrthoKinetic Review*

URL(s): www.laspineinstitute.com/OrthoKineticReview.htm

Description: Magazine featuring new products and services available in the podiatric field. **Availability:** Print; Online.

TRADE SHOWS AND CONVENTIONS

10959 ■ **American Academy of Implant Dentistry Annual Meeting**

URL(s): www.aaid.com/Annual_Conference/index.html

Frequency: Annual. **Audience:** General dentists, oral and maxillofacial surgeons, periodontists, and prosthodontists. **Telecommunication Services:** aaid@aaid-implant.org.

10960 ■ **North Carolina Medical Society Annual Meeting**

North Carolina Medical Society (NCMS)
 222 N Person St.
 Raleigh, NC 27601
Ph: (919)833-3836
Free: 800-722-1350
Fax: (919)833-2023
Co. E-mail: ncms@ncmedsoc.org
URL: http://www.ncmedsoc.org
Contact: Dr. Michael J. Utecht, President
URL(s): www.ncmedsoc.org/events/ncms-annual-meeting

Frequency: Annual. **Description:** Medical equipment, supplies, and services. **Audience:** Physicians and health care professionals. **Principal Exhibits:** Medical equipment, supplies, and services.

10961 ■ **Southern Medical Association Annual Scientific Assembly**

Southern Medical Association (SMA)
 3500 Blue Lake Dr., Ste. 360
 Birmingham, AL 35243
Ph: (205)945-1840
Free: 800-423-4992
Fax: (205)945-1830
Co. E-mail: customerservice@sma.org
URL: http://sma.org
Contact: Randall E. Glick, Executive Director
URL(s): web.cvent.com/event/b45f0906-611e-4ae7-8
5eb-1e35613918bf/summary?Refid=ASA
24Summary&locale=en-US

Frequency: Annual. **Description:** Medical equipment and pharmaceutical products. **Audience:** Doctors, students, residents, and medical professionals. **Principal Exhibits:** Medical equipment and pharmaceutical products. **Telecommunication Services:** education@sma.org.

FRANCHISES AND BUSINESS OPPORTUNITIES

10962 ■ **Relax The Back Corp. (RTB)**

4600 E Conant St.
 Long Beach, CA 90808
Ph: (901)683-8385
Free: 800-222-5728
Co. E-mail: customerservice@relaxtheback.com
URL: http://relaxtheback.com
Facebook: www.facebook.com/RelaxTheBack
Instagram: www.instagram.com/RelaxTheBack
Pinterest: www.pinterest.com/relaxtheback

Description: Ergonomic and back care retailers. **No. of Franchise Units:** 90. **Founded:** 1984. **Franchised:** 1989. **Equity Capital Needed:** $221,000-$371,200 total investment; $500,000 net worth; $100,000 liquid. **Franchise Fee:** 29500. **Royalty Fee:** 2%-5%. **Financial Assistance:** Yes **Training:** Pain relief center.

COMPUTERIZED DATABASES

10963 ■ *American Hospital Directory*

American Hospital Directory Inc.
 166 Thierman Ln.
 Louisville, KY 40207
Free: 800-894-8418
Fax: (502)899-7738
Co. E-mail: inbox@ahd.com
URL: http://www.ahd.com
Contact: Kenton Shoemaker, President
URL(s): www.ahd.com

Price: $445, for single user license; $400, for 2-5 users; $355, for 6-10 users; $320, for 11-20 users; $310, for 21-35 users. **Description:** Database covers comparative data on hospitals in the U.S. **Entries include:** Hospital name, address, phone, fax, characteristics, financial statistics, services, accreditation status, utilization statistics, hospital web page. **Availability:** PDF; Download; Online. **Type:** Directory.

LIBRARIES

10964 ■ **ECRI Institute - Library**

5200 Butler Pke.
 Plymouth Meeting, PA 19462
Ph: (610)825-6000

Co. E-mail: info@ecri.org
URL: http://www.ecri.org
Contact: Marcus Schabacker, President
Facebook: www.facebook.com/ECRIOrg
Linkedin: www.linkedin.com/company/ecri-org
X (Twitter): x.com/ECRI_Org
YouTube: www.youtube.com/user/ECRIInstitute

Description: Improves the safety, performance and cost effectiveness of health care technology. Provides technical consulting, accident investigation and educational programs. **Scope:** Offers expertise in medical technology assessment, medical equipment acquisition and medical equipment purchasing. **Founded:** 1968. **Holdings:** Figures not available. **Publications:** "Health Devices Source book". **Training:** Top Ten Health Technology Hazards, Vancouver, Mar, 2010; Biomedical Engineering; State of the infusion technology market; Role of smarter infusion pumps in the field of medication safety technologies; Pump evaluation and selection factors; Implementation challenges and successes; How to assess your facilities readiness and infrastructure requirements for implementation; Clinical implications and work flow impact; Maintenance of libraries and log analysis; Successful wireless implementation; Hands-on interaction with the latest devices, guided by on-site pump trainers is offered; Infection Control Risk Assessment (ICRA) for Construction Activities; Take Control: Hazard and Recall Management Strategies, Royal Oak, MI, Sep, 2006. **Educational Activities:** ECRI Institute Annual conference (Annual). **Geographic Preference:** Multinational.

10965 ■ **Harvard University - School of Medicine - Massachusetts Eye and Ear Library**

243 Charles St.
 Boston, MA 02114
Ph: (617)573-3664
URL: http://masseyeandear.org/education/library-resources
Contact: Louise Collins, Director
E-mail: louise_collins@meei.harvard.edu

Scope: Ophthalmology; otolaryngology; plastic surgery; neurology; general medicine. **Services:** Interlibrary loan; copying; library blog; library open to the public for reference use only. **Founded:** 1876. **Holdings:** 1,000 volumes; e-books; e-journals.

10966 ■ **U.S. Food & Drug Administration - Center for Devices & Radiological Health Library HFZ-46**

10903 New Hampshire Ave.
 Silver Spring, MD 20993
Free: 888-463-6332
URL: http://www.fda.gov
Contact: Brian Krueger, Vice President
Facebook: www.facebook.com/FDA
X (Twitter): x.com/US_FDA
YouTube: www.youtube.com/user/USFoodandDrugAdmin

Description: Includes laboratory and field research in the areas of physical, life, and engineering sciences as well as epidemiological research in post-market device safety. **Scope:** Medical devices; artificial organs; biomedical engineering; biomaterials; radiology; radiobiology; radiation; nuclear medicine; radiological health; radiation protection; radiation hazards; emission; microwaves; ultrasonics; lasers. **Services:** Interlibrary loan; library open to the public for reference use only. **Founded:** 1976. **Holdings:** 7000 books; periodical titles (bound and microfilm).

ASSOCIATIONS AND OTHER ORGANIZATIONS

10967 ■ Association for Healthcare Documentation Integrity (AHDI)
3430 Tully Rd., Ste. 20 No. 112
  Modesto, CA 95350
Ph: (209)527-9620
Free: 800-982-2182
Fax: (209)527-9633
Co. E-mail: ahdi@ahdionline.org
URL: http://www.ahdionline.org
Contact: Patricia King, President
Facebook: www.facebook.com/AHDI.FB
X (Twitter): x.com/AHDI_Tweets

Description: Medical transcriptionists, their supervisors, teachers and students of medical transcription, owners and managers of medical transcription services, and other interested health personnel. Provides information about the profession of medical transcription and gives continuing education for medical transcriptionists. Advocates professional recognition of medical transcriptionists in county, state, and national medical societies and in health care facilities nationwide. Sponsors voluntary certification/ credentialing program. Offers updates on developments in medicine and curricula, and on new transcription methods and equipment; sponsors and encourages research in the field. Establishes guidelines for education of medical transcriptionists. **Founded:** 1978. **Publications:** *Health Data Matrix* (Bimonthly); *Vitals* (Weekly). **Awards:** Employer of the Year Award (Annual); Rising Star Award (Annual). **Geographic Preference:** National.

REFERENCE WORKS

10968 ■ *"Dox Choice Joins Growing Medical Records Industry"* in Memphis Business Journal (Vol. 34, April 13, 2012, No. 53, pp. 1)
Pub: Baltimore Business Journal
Contact: Rhonda Pringle, President
E-mail: rpringle@bizjournals.com

Description: A profile of electronic health records provider Dox Choice LLC is presented. The company has received an incentive from the Center for Medicare and Medicaid Services. **Availability:** Print; Online.

10969 ■ *"Help Wanted: 100 Hospital IT Workers"* in Business Courier (Vol. 27, October 8, 2010, No. 23, pp. 1)
Pub: Business Courier

Ed: James Ritchie. **Description:** Hospitals in the Greater Cincinnati area are expected to hire more than 100 information technology (IT) workers to help digitize medical records. Financial incentives from the health care reform bill encouraged investments in electronic medical record systems, increasing the demand for IT workers that would help make information exchange across the healthcare system easier. **Availability:** Print; Online.

10970 ■ *"Hospitals Up the Ante for Medical Transcription Tools as Vendors Modernize with Automation, Voice Recognition"* in Healthcare IT News (July 17, 2018)
URL(s): www.healthcareitnews.com/news/hospitals-ante-medical-transcription-tools-vendors-modernize-automation-voice-recognition
Ed: Jeff Lagasse. **Released:** July 17, 2018. **Description:** New technology and products are becoming available for those needing medical transcription services, and hospitals are willing to invest in these devices. Voice recognition is being adopted and quickly replacing analog devices. Hospitals are also outsourcing more medical transcription services to third-parties, which the new technology will help make even easier. **Availability:** Online.

10971 ■ *"Providers Ride First Wave of eHealth Dollars"* in Boston Business Journal (Vol. 31, June 10, 2011, No. 20, pp. 1)
Pub: Boston Business Journal
Contact: Carolyn M. Jones, President
E-mail: cmjones@bizjournals.com
Ed: Julie M. Donnelly. **Released:** Weekly. **Description:** Health care providers in Massachusetts implementing electronic medical records technology started receiving federal stimulus funds. Beth Israel Deaconess Medical Center was the first hospital to qualify for the funds. **Availability:** Print.

10972 ■ *"Spinout Success: New Leadership Steps In At UW's C4C"* in Puget Sound Business Journal (Vol. 35, June 27, 2014, No. 10, pp. 11)
Pub: American City Business Journals, Inc.
Contact: Mike Olivieri, Executive Vice President
Description: University of Washington's Center for Commercialization vice provost, Vikram Jandhyala, talks about his new position with the school. Jandhyala says he plans to build more synergy between the medical school and engineering and between social sciences and computer science. He also says the medical and software industry need to grow to accommodate the volume of data crossing and stored within the Internet. **Availability:** Online.

LIBRARIES

10973 ■ American Health Information Management Association (AHIMA) - Library
233 N Michigan Ave., 21st Fl.
  Chicago, IL 60601-5809
Ph: (312)233-1100
Free: 800-335-5535
Fax: (312)233-1500
Co. E-mail: info@ahima.org
URL: http://www.ahima.org
Contact: Wylecia Wiggs Harris, Chief Executive Officer
Facebook: www.facebook.com/AHIMAOfficial
X (Twitter): x.com/AHIMAResources
YouTube: www.youtube.com/AHIMAonDemand
Description: Health information management professionals; registered record administrators; accredited record technicians with expertise in health information management, biostatistics, classification systems, and systems analysis. Sponsors Independent Study Programs in Medical Record Technology and coding. Conducts annual qualification examinations to credential medical record personnel as Registered Record Administrators, Accredited Record Technicians and Certified Coding Specialists. Maintains Foundation of Research and Education Library, Scholarships and loans. Dedicated to the effective management of personal health information required to deliver quality healthcare to the public. **Scope:** Health. **Founded:** 1928. **Holdings:** Figures not available. **Publications:** *From the Couch: Official Newsletter of the Mental Health Record Section of the American Medical Record Association* (Quarterly); *Volunteer* (Quarterly); *Certification Connection* (Quarterly); *Spectrum* (Quarterly); *Journal of AHIMA* (Monthly); *Accredited Educational Programs in Health Information Technology and Health Information Administration.* **Educational Activities:** American Health Information Management Association National Convention & Exhibit (Annual). **Geographic Preference:** National.

10974 ■ Davenport University - Thomas F. Reed, Jr. Memorial Library
6767 W O Ave.
  Kalamazoo, MI 49003
Ph: (269)552-3328
Fax: (269)353-2723
Co. E-mail: info@davenport.edu
URL: http://www.davenport.edu
Contact: Richard J. Pappas, President
Facebook: www.facebook.com/DavenportU
X (Twitter): x.com/davenportu
Instagram: www.instagram.com/davenportuniversity
YouTube: www.youtube.com/channel/UCaxSQhSboBlHxBkPJOpCvTQ

Description: A quiet corner for studying and fast access to a wealth of information, the Library Information Commons is home to many students looking to study or down time between classes. **Scope:** Education. **Services:** Interlibrary loan; copying; faxing. **Founded:** 1981. **Holdings:** Figures not available.

10975 ■ Florida A&M University (FAMU) - Frederick S. Humphries Science Research Center Library
309 W Pershing St., Ste. 401
  Tallahassee, FL 32301
Ph: (850)599-3393
URL: http://library.famu.edu/index/src

Description: Coleman Library was built in 1948, renovated in 1972, expanded in 1990 and again in 2004. The 88,964 square foot facility includes group study rooms, a student study lounge and cafe, graduate/faculty study carrels, teleconference rooms, and a state of the art information literacy classroom. **Scope:** Pharmacy and pharmaceutical sciences; nursing and allied health science; environmental science; physics; computer science and other related disciplines. **Services:** Library open to the public. **Founded:** 1957. **Holdings:** Monographs; periodicals; print and online journals; indexes; books.

ASSOCIATIONS AND OTHER ORGANIZATIONS

10976 ■ **Customized Logistics and Delivery Association (CLDA)**
529 14th St. NW, Ste. 750
  Washington, DC 20045
Ph: (202)591-2460
Co. E-mail: info@clda.org
URL: http://clda.org
Contact: Matt Mantione, Executive Director
Facebook: www.facebook.com/theclda
Linkedin: www.linkedin.com/company/customize
  d-logistics-and-delivery-association
X (Twitter): x.com/TheCLDA

Description: Provides training, discount purchasing programs, and legislative and regulatory issue monitoring. Conducts educational and research programs; compiles statistics. **Founded:** 1987. **Publications:** *Who's Who in the Messenger Courier Industry* (Annual); *Customized Logistics and Delivery Association--Membership Directory* (Annual). **Educational Activities:** CLDA Annual Meeting & Exposition (Annual). **Geographic Preference:** National.

10977 ■ **National Association of Professional Process Servers (NAPPS)**
PO Box 4547
  Portland, OR 97208-4547
Ph: (503)222-4180
Free: 800-477-8211
Fax: (503)222-3950
Co. E-mail: administrator@napps.org
URL: http://www.napps.org
Contact: Lance Randall, President
Facebook: www.facebook.com/NAPPS.Professionals
Linkedin: www.linkedin.com/company/napps
X (Twitter): x.com/napps82
Instagram: www.instagram.com/napps82
YouTube: www.youtube.com/channel/UCkgfx9w
  -QgYC1K2rgS3mrCQ

Description: Individuals and companies who serve summonses, complaints, subpoenas, and other legal documents. Goals are to: promote and upgrade the process-serving industry; establish high moral and ethical standards for the industry; monitor legislation at the state and federal level; assist in the formation and continuation of state associations representing the industry. Seeks to improve relations between process servers and members of the legal community such as attorneys, judges, clerks, and court officers. **Founded:** 1982. **Publications:** *The Docket Sheet*; *Membership Directory and Civil Rules Guide* (Semi-annual); *NAPPS Membership Directory*. **Awards:** Donald C. MacDonald Award (Irregular). **Geographic Preference:** National.

REFERENCE WORKS

10978 ■ **"Americans Spend Billions on Takeout. But Food Delivery Apps Are Still a Terrible Business" in Barron's (November 15, 2019)**
URL(s): www.barrons.com/articles/food-delivery
  -grubhub-doordash-and-uber-eats-51573859107
Ed: Eric J. Savitz. **Released:** November 15, 2019.
Description: Discusses the negative issues with food-delivery apps. **Availability:** Online.

10979 ■ **"Business for Sale: Pocket Change?" in Inc. (Vol. 30, December 2008, No. 12, pp. 28)**
Pub: Mansueto Ventures L.L.C.
Contact: Stephanie Mehta, Chief Executive Officer
Ed: Ryan McCarthy. **Description:** Owner of a chain of nine retail billiard showrooms grew his business by starting to deliver pool tables for Sears. The company, consisting of seven retail locations and two warehouses, is now for sale. Details are included. **Availability:** Online.

10980 ■ **"Survey: People Willing to Pay More for Food Delivery" in U.S. News & World Report (July 30, 2019)**
URL(s): www.usnews.com/news/national-news/ar
  ticles/2019-07-30/survey-people-willing-to-pay-more
  -for-food-delivery

Ed: Alexa Lardieri. **Released:** July 30, 2019. **Description:** With consumers using food delivery apps more and more, a new survey from U.S. Foods concluded that Uber Eats is the most popular app followed by GrubHug, DoorDash, and Postmates. People are also unwilling to wait for more than 40 minutes for their delivery and there are caps on the amount of money they will spend on fees and tips. **Availability:** Online.

FRANCHISES AND BUSINESS OPPORTUNITIES

10981 ■ **AIM Mail Centers**
Annex Brands, Inc.
  6300 Grelot Rd., Ste. G
  Mobile, AL 36609-3602
Ph: (619)563-4800
Free: 800-456-1525
Fax: (619)563-9850
URL: http://www.annexbrands.com
Facebook: www.facebook.com/AIMMailCenters

Description: Business service center. **No. of Franchise Units:** 58. **Founded:** 1985. **Franchised:** 1989. **Equity Capital Needed:** $138,800-$199,050l. **Franchise Fee:** $29,950. **Royalty Fee:** 5%. **Training:** Provides 10 days training at headquarters, 3 days at franchisees location, regional meetings, annual convention, and ongoing support.

10982 ■ **Parcel Plus**
13121 Louetta Rd.
  Cypress, TX 77429
Ph: (281)376-0054
Fax: (281)376-0056
Co. E-mail: pp146@parcelplus.com
URL: http://www.parcelplus.com

Description: Offer packaging, freight, cargo, crating and international shipping in a retail setting. **No. of Operating Units:** 450. **Founded:** 1986. **Financial Assistance:** Yes **Training:** Owners attend 4 days classroom training and visit existing locations.

ASSOCIATIONS AND OTHER ORGANIZATIONS

10983 ■ National Golf Foundation (NGF)
501 N Hwy. A1A
Jupiter, FL 33477-4577
Ph: (561)744-6006
Free: 888-275-4643
Fax: (561)744-6107
Co. E-mail: general@ngf.org
URL: http://www.ngf.org
Contact: Joe Beditz, Executive Chairman of the Board
Facebook: www.facebook.com/NationalGolfFoundation
Linkedin: www.linkedin.com/company/national-golf-foundation
X (Twitter): x.com/ngf_golfbizinfo

Description: Golf-oriented businesses including: equipment and apparel companies; golf facilities; golf publications; golf course architects, developers and builders; companies offering specialized services to the golf industry; golf associations; teachers, coaches and instructors and other interested individuals. Serves as a market research and strategic planning organization for the golf industry. **Scope:** Golf consumers, golf courses, range operations and maintenance, industry sales, and golf facility development. **Founded:** 1936. **Publications:** *The Graffis Report* (Annual); *Profile of Golf Practice Facility Operations 2003*; *Golf Course Directory* (Annual); *NGF Membership Directory* (Quarterly); *The NGF's Directory of Golf Retailers: Off-Course Golf Retail Stores in the U.S.*; *The NGF's Executive and Par-3 Golf Course Directory: A Viable Enterprise*; *The NGF's Golf Course Directory*; *The NGF's Golf Course Directory and Range Directory*; *The NGF's Golf Practice Range and Learning Center Directory*; *The NGF's Media Directory*; *Directory of Golf: The People and Businesses in Golf* (Annual). **Educational Activities:** NGF Golf course management schools. **Geographic Preference:** National.

10984 ■ Professional Putters Association (PPA)
Augusta, GA
URL: http://www.proputters.org
Contact: Adm. (Ret.) Jerry Pinotti, Contact

Description: Seeks to recognize, develop, and reward the skills and abilities of America's putters. Sponsors competitions; compiles statistics; presents awards national, regional and local titles and cash prizes. **Founded:** 1959. **Publications:** *Putt Putt World* (Biennial). **Awards:** PPA Hall of Fame Award (Irregular). **Geographic Preference:** National.

10985 ■ United States Golf Association (USGA) - Library
PO Box 708
Far Hills, NJ 07931
Ph: (908)234-2300
URL: http://www.usga.org
Contact: J. Stuart Francis, President
Facebook: www.facebook.com/USGA
Linkedin: www.linkedin.com/company/united-states-golf-association
X (Twitter): x.com/usga
Instagram: www.instagram.com/usga
YouTube: www.youtube.com/user/TheUSGA

Description: Serves as governing body for golf in the U.S. Turfgrass Visiting Service promotes scientific work in turf management. Provides data on rules, handicapping, amateur status, tournament procedure, turf maintenance, and golf balls and implements. **Scope:** Golf. **Founded:** 1894. **Holdings:** Figures not available. **Publications:** *Golf Journal: Official Publication of the United States Golf Association*; *Golf Journal* (9/year); *The Rules of Golf*; *Building a USGA Green*. **Awards:** Curtis Cup (Biennial); Walker Cup (Biennial); USGA Green Section Award (Annual); Bob Jones Award (Annual); Joe Dey Award (Annual); USGA U.S. Women's Open (Annual); USGA U.S. Senior Open (Annual); USGA U.S. Amateur Championship (Annual); USGA U.S. Women's Amateur (Annual); USGA/Chevron STEM Scholarship Program. **Geographic Preference:** National; Local.

REFERENCE WORKS

10986 ■ "Phoenix History: How Miniature Golf Made Its Way from California to the Valley" in azcentral (July 11, 2019)
URL(s): www.azcentral.com/story/news/local/phoenix-history/2019/07/11/miniature-golf-courses-phoenix-here-how-they-spread/1687711001/

Ed: Donna Reiner. **Released:** July 11, 2019. **Description:** A history of how the iconic game of miniature golf first came to Arizona. **Availability:** Online.

10987 ■ "Psychology Professor Puts Sweet Mini Golf Course on the Roof of her Vacation Home" in Golf Digest (January 18, 2018)
URL(s): www.golfdigest.com/story/psychology-professor-puts-sweet-mini-golf-course-on-the-roof-of-her-vacation-home
Ed: Alex Myers. **Released:** January 18, 2018. **Description:** Psychology professor Jean Rhodes installed a nine-hole mini golf course on the roof of her vacation home. **Availability:** Online.

VIDEO/AUDIO MEDIA

10988 ■ The How of Business: Matt Grech-Smith - Swingers Crazy Golf
URL(s): www.thehowofbusiness.com/459-matt-grech-smith-swingers-crazy-golf
Ed: Henry Lopez. **Released:** February 13, 2023. **Description:** Podcast discusses the opening of Crazy Swingers, where mini golf meets cocktails.

FRANCHISES AND BUSINESS OPPORTUNITIES

10989 ■ Monster Mini Golf (MMG)
3695 Chama Ave.
Las Vegas, NV 89121
Ph: (401)454-8100
Co. E-mail: franchise@monsterminigolf.com
URL: http://monsterminigolf.com
Contact: Christina Vitagliano, Chief Executive Officer
Facebook: www.facebook.com/MonsterMiniGolf
X (Twitter): twitter.com/monsterminigolf
Instagram: www.instagram.com/monsterminigolf
Description: Firm offers miniature golf course. **Founded:** 2004. **Financial Assistance:** Yes **Training:** Offers 2-4 weeks at headquarters, 2 weeks onsite with ongoing support.

10990 ■ Topgolf International, Inc.
8750 N Central Expy., Ste. 1200
Dallas, TX 75231
URL: http://topgolf.com/us
Contact: Artie Starrs, Chief Executive Officer
URL(s): www.topgolfinternational.com
Description: Golf entertainment complex with worldwide locations.

ASSOCIATIONS AND OTHER ORGANIZATIONS

10991 ■ Modeling Association of America International (MAAI)
New York, NY
URL: http://maai.org
X (Twitter): x.com/ModelingAssoc
Instagram: www.instagram.com/maaiorg
Description: Supports the professional development of aspiring models and actors around the world, and promotes high standards and ethics within the industry. Organizes an annual Convention and Showcase. **Founded:** 1960.

REFERENCE WORKS

10992 ■ *"Fashionistas Weigh in on the Super-Thin" in Charlotte Observer (February 7, 2007)*
Description: Council of Fashion Designers of America held a panel discussion regarding the weight and ages of models used to highlight clothing. **Availability:** Online.

10993 ■ *"How Instagram's Influencers Changed the Model Industry" in BBC News (April 3, 2021)*
URL(s): www.bbc.com/news/technology-56592913
Ed: Cristina Criddle. **Released:** April 03, 2021. **Description:** When the COVID-19 pandemic hit, many models turned to Instragram to create their own content since in-face production was shut down. Now, there is a demand for models who are capable of shooting their own content, which has caused a shift in the traditional modeling agency industry. **Availability:** Download.

10994 ■ *"New Under-18 Model Bans Are Changing How Agencies Recruit and Sign Talent" in Fashionista (June 13, 2019)*
URL(s): fashionista.com/2019/06/under-18-model-bans-agencies
Ed: Erin Cunningham. **Released:** June 13, 2019. **Description:** Most luxury brands are taking the initiative by not hiring models under the age of 18, in an effort to protect vulnerable young women from the dangers of working in the industry. This changes how agencies operate and opens up discussions with the models and their parents on how best to handle a career in modeling. **Availability:** Online.

STATISTICAL SOURCES

10995 ■ *Model Agencies Industry in the US - Market Research Report*
URL(s): www.ibisworld.com/united-states/market-research-reports/model-agencies-industry/
Price: $925. **Description:** Downloadable report analyzing the current and future trends in the model agency industry. **Availability:** Download.

START-UP INFORMATION

10996 ■ "No. 64: Scaling the Business Meant Rebuilding a Bridge" in Inc. (Vol. 36, September 2014, No. 7, pp. 48)
Pub: Mansueto Ventures L.L.C.
Contact: Stephanie Mehta, Chief Executive Officer
Released: September 2014. **Description:** Profile of Susan Meitner, mortgage industry veteran who founded Centennial Lending Group, a mortgage lending institution. Meitner and her family helped raise the needed $2.5 million to launch the firm in order to provide loans to new customers. **Availability:** Print; Online.

ASSOCIATIONS AND OTHER ORGANIZATIONS

10997 ■ Association of Independent Mortgage Experts (AIME)
2001 Market St., Ste. 505
Philadelphia, PA 19103
Ph: (215)720-1794
Co. E-mail: info@aimegroup.com
URL: http://aimegroup.com
Contact: Marc Summers, Secretary
Facebook: www.facebook.com/AIMEnational
Linkedin: www.linkedin.com/company/aimenational
X (Twitter): x.com/AIMEnational
YouTube: www.youtube.com/channel/UCryM
2yQYZhpme0FnTTGC8TA

Description: A nonprofit, national trade membership association for independent mortgage brokers. Provides exclusive technology and access to member-only partnerships, business development resources, and networking opportunities with industry experts. **Founded:** 2018.

10998 ■ Mortgage Bankers Association (MBA)
1919 M St. NW, 5th Fl.
Washington, DC 20036
Ph: (202)557-2700
Free: 800-793-6222
Co. E-mail: education@mba.org
URL: http://www.mba.org
Contact: Susan Stewart, Chairman
Facebook: www.facebook.com/mbamortgage
Linkedin: www.linkedin.com/company/mortgage
-bankers-association
X (Twitter): x.com/mbamortgage
Instagram: www.instagram.com/mortgage_bankers
_association

Description: Principal lending and investor interests in the mortgage finance field, including mortgage banking firms, commercial banks, life insurance companies, title companies, and savings and loan associations. **Founded:** 1913. **Holdings:** Figures not available. **Publications:** *MBA Directory of Members*; *Mortgage Banking Magazine: The Magazine of Real Estate Finance* (Monthly); *State and Local MBA Directory* (Semiannual); *Mortgage Banking Source-book*; *Real Estate Finance Today* (Weekly); *Mortgage Banking: The Magazine of Real Estate Finance Managers and Employees*; *Mortgage Bankers Performance Study* (Quarterly); *Mortgage Banking: The Magazine of Real Estate Finance* (Monthly); *National Delinquency Survey (NDS)* (Quarterly). **Educational Activities:** MBA's Commercial Real Estate Finance/ Multi-Family Housing Convention Expo (Annual). **Geographic Preference:** National.

10999 ■ The National Association of Mortgage Brokers (NAMB)
601 Pennsylvania Ave., NW S Bldg., Ste. 900
Washington, DC 20004
Ph: (202)434-8250
Fax: (530)484-2906
Co. E-mail: membership@namb.org
URL: http://namb.org
Contact: Linda McCoy, President
E-mail: linda.mccoy@namb.org
Facebook: www.facebook.com/NAMB-Association-of
-Mortgage-Professionals-134445796889
Linkedin: www.linkedin.com/company/national
-association-of-mortgage-brokers
X (Twitter): x.com/NAMBpros
Instagram: www.instagram.com/namb_stagram
YouTube: www.youtube.com/channel/UCLhQJjk
_QjOK_jJcP1Qgz9g/featured

Description: Mortgage brokers seeking to increase professionalism and to foster business relationships among members. Offers three levels of professional certification. Focuses on education and government affairs. **Founded:** 1973. **Publications:** *NAMB Certification Applicant Handbooks*. **Educational Activities:** National Association of Mortgage Brokers Convention and Trade Show. **Awards:** NAMB Broker of the Year (Annual). **Geographic Preference:** National.

11000 ■ National Association of Professional Mortgage Women (NAPMW)
c/o Cris Poole 1903 NE 85th St., No.,305
Seattle, WA 98115
Ph: (206)499-7735
Co. E-mail: napmw1@napmw.org
URL: http://www.napmw.org
Contact: Cris Poole, Contact
URL(s): www.napmw.org/?page=localBakersfield
Facebook: www.facebook.com/NAPMW
Linkedin: www.linkedin.com/company/national
-napmw
X (Twitter): x.com/napmw1

Description: Supports professional and personal development for individuals in the mortgage lending industry. Aims to maintain high standards of professional conduct and to encourage the educational advancement of women in the industry. Believes in equal recognition and professional opportunities for women. Offers professional designations through the Institute of Mortgage Lending. **Founded:** 1964. **Educational Activities:** National Association of Professional Mortgage Women Annual Convention (Annual). **Geographic Preference:** National; Local.

11001 ■ National Association of Real Estate Brokers (NAREB) - Willis E. Carson Library
9831 Greenbelt Rd.
Lanham, MD 20706
Ph: (301)552-9340
Fax: (301)552-9216
Co. E-mail: nareb@nareb.com
URL: http://www.nareb.com
Contact: Lawrence Bastiste, Chairman
Facebook: www.facebook.com/realtistnareb
X (Twitter): x.com/realtist_nareb
YouTube: www.youtube.com/user/RealtistUSA/videos

Description: Research, educational and certification programs include: Real Estate Management Brokers Institute; National Society of Real Estate Appraisers; Real Estate Brokerage Institute; United Developers Council. Encourages unity among those who are engaged in real estate. Promotes and maintains high standards of conduct. Protects the public against unethical, improper, or fraudulent practices connected with the real estate business. Conducts research; compiles statistics on productivity, marketing and development. **Scope:** Real estate. **Founded:** 1947. **Holdings:** Figures not available. **Publications:** *Realtist Membership Directory* (Annual). **Geographic Preference:** National.

11002 ■ National Association of Review Appraisers and Mortgage Underwriters (NARA/MU)
PO Box 879
Palm Springs, CA 92263
Free: 877-743-6805
Fax: (760)327-5631
Co. E-mail: info@naramu.org
URL: http://www.naramu.org
Contact: Brent Felstead, Associate Manager

Description: Real estate professionals and mortgage underwriters who aid in determining value of property. Acts as umbrella group for real estate appraisers. Conducts educational seminars; maintains speakers' bureau; operates placement service. **Founded:** 1975. **Educational Activities:** National Association of Review Appraisers and Mortgage Underwriters Convention - National Conference & Expo. **Geographic Preference:** National.

11003 ■ New York Association of Mortgage Brokers (NYAMB)
610 Wood St.
Mamaroneck, NY 10543
Ph: (914)315-6644
Fax: (888)900-1602
Co. E-mail: etella@teammgmtsvs.com
URL: http://www.nyamb.org
Contact: Mark Favaloro, President
E-mail: mfavaloro@aamtrust.com
Facebook: www.facebook.com/NYAMP
Linkedin: www.linkedin.com/in/new-york-association
-of-mortgage-brokers-95863268
X (Twitter): x.com/NYAMB1
Instagram: www.instagram.com/nyambrokers
YouTube: www.youtube.com/user/thenyamb

Description: Represents the mortgage broker industry in the United States. **Founded:** 1985. **Publications:** *The Mortgage Press* (Monthly). **Geographic Preference:** State.

11004 ■ Pennsylvania Association of Mortgage Brokers (PAMB)
330 Mount Corner Dr., No. 181
Freehold, NJ 07728
Ph: (732)596-1619
URL: http://www.pamb.org
Contact: Rose Stancato, President
E-mail: rose@firstmortgagehomeloans.com
Description: Promotes the mortgage broker industry through education, programs, professional certification and government affairs representation. Seeks to increase professionalism and to foster business relationships among members. **Founded:** 1987. **Geographic Preference:** State.

11005 ■ Real Estate Business Institute (REBI)
430 N Michigan Ave.
Chicago, IL 60611
Ph: (312)321-4437
Free: 800-621-8738
Fax: (312)329-8882
Co. E-mail: info@rebinstitute.com
URL: http://www.rebinstitute.com
Contact: Sue Miller, President
Facebook: www.facebook.com/rebusinessinstitute
Linkedin: www.linkedin.com/company/real-estate
-business-institute
X (Twitter): x.com/rebinstitute
Instagram: www.instagram.com/rebinstitute
Description: Exemplifies professional achievement and recognition in real estate brokerage management. Bestows CRB (Certified Real Estate Brokerage Manager) designation on members who have completed courses conducted by REBMC. **Founded:** 1968. **Publications:** *e-Connections Newsletter* (Monthly); *Real Estate Business Magazine (REB)* (Bimonthly). **Awards:** CRB Hall of Leaders Award (Annual). **Geographic Preference:** Multinational.

11006 ■ Wisconsin Association of Mortgage Brokers
16 N Carroll St., No. 900
Madison, WI 53703
Ph: (608)259-9262
Fax: (608)251-8192
Co. E-mail: info@wambrokers.com
URL: http://www.wambrokers.com/index_htm.html
Contact: Patrick Essie, Director
Description: Promotes the mortgage broker industry through education, programs, professional certification and government affairs representation. Seeks to increase professionalism and to foster business relationships among members. **Geographic Preference:** State.

FINANCING AND LOAN PROGRAMS

11007 ■ American Express Kabbage Inc.
American Express Company
925B Peachtree St. NE, Ste. 1688
Atlanta, GA 30309
Ph: (212)640-2000
Free: 800-528-4800
URL: http://www.americanexpress.com
Contact: Laquisha Milner, Chief Executive Officer
Description: Provider of small business financing. **Founded:** 2009.

REFERENCE WORKS

11008 ■ "2015 Marketing Calendar for Real Estate Pros: Own It"
Pub: CreateSpace
Released: October 14, 2014. **Price:** $9.56, paperback. **Description:** Real estate agents, mortgage loan agents, and new home builders and site and listing agents are shown how to use low-cost, high yield, proven marketing techniques to create digital real estate listings, find more customers, and sell more homes. Advice for building a brand and public relations; attracting renters and buyers; developing a good Website; and a digital marketing plan are explained. **Availability:** Print.

11009 ■ "Asia Breathes a Sigh of Relief" in Business Week (September 22, 2008, No. 4100, pp. 32)
Description: Foreign bankers, such as those in Asia, that had been investing heavily in the United States began to worry as the housing crisis deepened and the impact on Freddie Mac and Fannie Mae became increasingly clear. Due to the government bailout, however, central banks will most likely continue to buy American debt. **Availability:** Print; Online.

11010 ■ "Au Revoir Or Goodbye?" in Barron's (Vol. 88, July 14, 2008, No. 28, pp. 5)
Pub: Dow Jones & Company Inc.
Contact: Almar Latour, Chief Executive Officer
Ed: Alan Abelson. **Description:** Former Senator Phil Gramm's opinion that the U.S. is a "nation of whiners" as they moan about recession is another example of the disconnection between Washington and Wall Street on one hand and the real world on the other. It would be a catastrophe for most of the world if Fannie Mae and Freddie Mac were to go under and take their trillions of mortgage debt with them. **Availability:** Online.

11011 ■ "Bad Loans Start Piling Up" in Crain's New York Business (Vol. 24, January 6, 2008, No. 1, pp. 2)
Pub: Crain Communications, Inc.
Contact: Jessica Botos, Manager, Marketing
E-mail: jessica.botos@crainsnewyork.com
Ed: Tom Fredrickson. **Description:** Problems in the subprime mortgage industry have extended to other lending activities as evidenced by bank charge-offs on bad commercial and industrial loans which have more than doubled in the third quarter.

11012 ■ "Baltimore Commercial Real Estate Foreclosures Continue to Rise" in Baltimore Business Journal (Vol. 28, October 1, 2010, No. 21, pp. 1)
Pub: Baltimore Business Journal
Contact: Rhonda Pringle, President
E-mail: rpringle@bizjournals.com
Ed: Daniel J. Sernovitz. **Description:** Foreclosures of commercial real estate across the Greater Baltimore area have continued to rise. The region is now host to about $2 billion worth of commercial properties that carry a maturing debt or have been foreclosed. Commercial real estate owners are unable to finance their debts because banks have become stricter in passing out loans. **Availability:** Print; Online.

11013 ■ "Bills Would Regulate Mortgage Loan Officers" in Crain's Detroit Business (Vol. 24, February 25, 2008, No. 8, pp. 9)
Pub: Crain Communications Inc.
Contact: Barry Asin, President
Ed: Amy Lane. **Description:** New legislation in Michigan, if passed, would create a registration process for mortgage loan officers in the state in order to address the mortgage loan crisis. **Availability:** Print; Online.

11014 ■ "BofA Will Reach the Top with Countrywide Deal" in Business North Carolina (Vol. 28, March 2008, No. 3, pp. 36)
Description: Bank of America, headquartered in Charlotte, North Carolina, will add Countrywide to its let of credits. Countrywide is the largest U.S. mortgage lender. Statistical data included.

11015 ■ "Bottom's Up: This Real-Estate Rout May Be Short-Lived" in Barron's (Vol. 88, July 14, 2008, No. 28, pp. 25)
Pub: Dow Jones & Company Inc.
Contact: Almar Latour, Chief Executive Officer
Ed: Jonathan R. Laing. **Description:** Economist Chip Case believes that home prices are nearing a bottom based on his analysis of the history of the housing market; surprisingly, in the past the housing market has rebounded after a quarter from a massive housing start drop. The drop in early stage delinquencies is another sign of the housing market's recovery. **Availability:** Online.

11016 ■ "A Bull Market in Finger-Pointing" in Barron's (Vol. 88, March 10, 2008, No. 10, pp. 9)
Pub: Dow Jones & Company Inc.
Contact: Almar Latour, Chief Executive Officer
Ed: Michael Santoli. **Description:** Discusses who is to blame for the financial crisis brought about by the credit crunch in the United States; the country's financial markets will eventually digest this crisis but will bottom out first before the situation improves. **Availability:** Online.

11017 ■ "Buying a Short Sale Property: A Guide to Understanding the Short Sale Process and How to Profit From Short Sale"
Released: September 26, 2014. **Price:** $6.09, Paperback. **Description:** A short sale is the process where a house is sold for less than the amount of money actually owed on it in order to avoid foreclosure. This trend is becoming more prevalent so it is important to understand the requirements and processes involved in purchasing a foreclosed home or property. **Availability:** Print.

11018 ■ "Cash Deals Are King, But Don't Reign Supreme In Birmingham" in Birmingham Business Journal (Vol. 31, May 16, 2014, No. 20, pp. 6)
Pub: American City Business Journals, Inc.
Contact: Mike Olivieri, Executive Vice President
Released: Weekly; 16 May 14. **Price:** $4, introductory 4-week offer(Digital & Print). **Description:** Data from market research firm, RealtyTrac found that all-cash transactions in Birmingham, Alabama accounted for less than 31 percent of home sales in the first quarter of 2014, compared with a stronger all-cash transactions recorded by Southern metropolitan areas like Atlanta, Memphis and Charlotte. Ben Chenault of MortgageBanc sees a trend among average homebuyers who prefer cash over finance. **Availability:** Print; Online.

11019 ■ "Citi Ruling Could Chill SEC, Street Legal Pacts" in Wall Street Journal Eastern Edition (November 29, 2011, pp. C1)
Pub: Dow Jones & Company Inc.
Contact: Almar Latour, Chief Executive Officer
Ed: Jean Eaglesham, Chad Bray. **Description:** A $285 million settlement was reached between the Securities and Exchange Commission and Citigroup Inc. over allegations the bank misled investors over a mortgage-bond deal. Now, Judge Jed S. Rakoff has ruled against the settlement, a decision that will affect the future of such attempts to prosecute Wall Street fraud. Rakoff said that the settlement was "neither fair, nor reasonable, nor adequate, nor in the public interest." **Availability:** Online.

11020 ■ "CitiMortgage to Hire Hundreds in Dallas-Fort Worth" in Dallas Business Journal (Vol. 35, April 20, 2012, No. 32, pp. 1)
Pub: Baltimore Business Journal
Contact: Rhonda Pringle, President
E-mail: rpringle@bizjournals.com
Ed: Jeff Bounds. **Description:** Citibank NA mortgage lending and servicing arm of CitMortgage is hiring at least 750 employees to work with borrowers in relation to a $2.2 billion settlement of alleged questionable foreclosure practices. Most of the staff will work in Dallas-Fort Worth, Texas in areas such as default servicing, refinancing an single points of contact as required under the settlement. **Availability:** Print; Online.

11021 ■ "Coming Soon: Bailouts of Fannie and Freddie" in Barron's (Vol. 88, July 14, 2008, No. 28, pp. 14)
Pub: Dow Jones & Company Inc.
Contact: Almar Latour, Chief Executive Officer
Ed: Jonathan R. Laing. **Description:** Assurances from the government that Fannie Mae and Freddie Mac are adequately capitalized and able to carry on

their duties as guarantors or owners of over $5 trillion of U.S. home mortgages are designed to keep both entities afloat until they attempt to raise $10 billion in new equity. The government would assume any losses in a bailout and owners of the banks' papers would profit as yields drop. **Availability:** Online.

11022 ■ *"Commercial Loans Ready for Refinance: High Number of Mortgages Creates Buying Opportunities"* in *Memphis Business Journal (Vol. 34, June 22, 2012, No. 10, pp. 1)*
Pub: Baltimore Business Journal
Contact: Rhonda Pringle, President
E-mail: rpringle@bizjournals.com

Ed: Cole Epley. **Description:** Commercial mortgage lending in Memphis, Tennessee improves as area volume loan increased from 2010 to 2011. The industry is projecting $600 billion in commercial mortgages held by banks coming to term over the next four to eight quarters.

11023 ■ *"Condos Becoming FHA No-Lending Zones"* in *Providence Business News (Vol. 29, June 2, 2014, No. 9, pp. 7)*
Pub: American City Business Journals, Inc.
Contact: Mike Olivieri, Executive Vice President

Description: Federal policy changes and decisions by condominium boards of directors have made the condominium development ineligible for Federal Housing Administration (FHA) loans, making several communities prohibited lending zones. As a result, the number of condo developments approved for FHA funding has fallen by more than half, presenting a growing problem for first-time buyers, those with modest down payment cash, and senior citizens using a reverse mortgage. **Availability:** Online.

11024 ■ *"Contingent Offers: Weighing the Risk"* in *Crain's Chicago Business (Vol. 31, April 21, 2008, No. 16, pp. 48)*
Pub: Crain Communications Inc.
Contact: Barry Asin, President

Ed: Darci Smith. **Description:** Interview with Greer Haseman, the broker-owner of Town Square Associates, who discusses contingent offers in a challenging housing market. **Availability:** Online.

11025 ■ *"The Credit Crisis Continues to Take Victims"* in *Barron's (Vol. 88, March 10, 2008, No. 10, pp. M12)*
Pub: Dow Jones & Company Inc.
Contact: Almar Latour, Chief Executive Officer

Ed: Randall W. Forsyth. **Description:** Short-term Treasury yields dropped to new cyclical lows in early March 2008, with the yield for the two-year Treasury note falling to 1.532 percent. Spreads of the mortgage-backed securities of Fannie Mae and Freddie Mac rose on suspicion of collapses in financing. **Availability:** Online.

11026 ■ *"Detroit Residential Market Slows; Bright Spots Emerge"* in *Crain's Detroit Business (Vol. 24, October 6, 2008, No. 40, pp. 11)*
Pub: Crain Communications Inc.
Contact: Barry Asin, President

Ed: Daniel Duggan. **Description:** Discusses the state of the residential real estate market in Detroit; although condominium projects receive the most attention, deals for single-family homes are taking place in greater numbers due to financing issues. Buyers can purchase a single family home with a 3.5 percent down payment compared to 20 percent for some condo deals because of the number of first-time homebuyer programs under the Federal Housing Administration.

11027 ■ *Dictionary of Real Estate Terms*
Pub: Barron's Educational Series Inc.
Contact: Manuel H. Barron, Contact

Ed: Jack P. Friedman, Jack C. Harris, J. Bruce Lindeman. **Released:** 9th edition. **Price:** $16.99, paperback, plus shipping charges $5.99. **Description:** More than 2,500 real estate terms relating to mort-

gages and financing, brokerage law, architecture, rentals and leases, property insurance, and more. **Availability:** E-book; Print.

11028 ■ *"Docs Might Hold Cure for Baltimore-Area Real Estate, Banks"* in *Baltimore Business Journal (Vol. 28, November 5, 2010, No. 26, pp. 1)*
Pub: Baltimore Business Journal
Contact: Rhonda Pringle, President
E-mail: rpringle@bizjournals.com

Ed: Gary Haber. **Description:** Health care providers, including physicians are purchasing their office space instead of renting it as banks lower interest rates to 6 percent on mortgages for medical offices. The rise in demand offers relief to the commercial real estate market. It has also resulted in a boom in building new medical offices. **Availability:** Print; Online.

11029 ■ *"Dream Town Launches Organic Food Delivery for Its Employees"* in *Internet Wire (June 28, 2012)*
Pub: Comtex News Network Inc.
Contact: Kan Devnani, President

Description: Local organics were spotlighted by Chicago real estate online firm, Dream Team, who held a special event for its employees and special guests at the Landmark Century Cinema. Robert Kenner's Food Inc. presented Irv and Shelly's Fresh Picks. Dream Team is committed to helping first time home buyers. **Availability:** Print; Online.

11030 ■ *"East-Side Real Estate Forum Detours To Grand Rapids"* in *Crain's Detroit Business (Vol. 24, October 6, 2008, No. 40, pp. 17)*
Pub: Crain Communications Inc.
Contact: Barry Asin, President

Ed: Daniel Duggan. **Description:** Tom Wackerman was elected chairman of the University of Michigan-Urban Land Institute Real Estate Forum and proposed that the annual conference be held in Grand Rapids due to the brisk economic activity he was finding there; although the idea was initially met with resistance, the plan to introduce East-siders to the West side began receiving more enthusiasm due to the revitalization of the area, which was once considered to have a bleak outlook. Many are hoping to learn the lessons of those who were able to change a negative economic climate into a positive one in which the cooperation of private business and government can work together to accomplish goals. **Availability:** Print; Online.

11031 ■ *"Ex-MetLife Lenders Align With Illinois Mortgage Group"* in *Wichita Business Journal (Vol. 27, January 27, 2012, No. 4, pp. 1)*
Pub: Baltimore Business Journal
Contact: Rhonda Pringle, President
E-mail: rpringle@bizjournals.com

Description: Former MetLife mortgage loan officers Jeff Rathbun, Aaron Vierthatler and Tyler Kobler have joined with Chicago-based Inland Home Morgage Company LLC's first residential lending offices in Wichita, Kansas. Inland believes the trio will help it diversify beyond Illinois' market volatility and sees Wichita as much more stable. Profiles of the three lenders are provided. **Availability:** Print; Online.

11032 ■ *"A Flawed Yardstick for Banks"* in *Barron's (Vol. 88, July 14, 2008, No. 28, pp. M6)*
Pub: Dow Jones & Company Inc.
Contact: Almar Latour, Chief Executive Officer

Ed: Arindam Nag. **Description:** Return on equity is no longer the best measure for investors to judge banks by in a post-subprime-crises world. Investors should consider the proportion of a bank's total assets that are considered risky and look out for any write-downs of goodwill when judging a bank's financial health. **Availability:** Online.

11033 ■ *The Foreclosure of America: Life Inside Countrywide Home Loans and the Selling of the American Dream*
Pub: Berkley Trade/Penguin Group USA Inc.

Ed: Adam Michaelson. **Released:** January 06, 2009. **Price:** $6.99, E-book; Paperback. **Description:** An inside look at Countrywide Home Loans and the mortgage crisis. **Availability:** E-book; Print.

11034 ■ *"Fresh Off its IPO, HomeStreet Bank is Now the No. 2 Mortgage Lender in King County"* in *Puget Sound Business Journal (Vol. 33, June 15, 2012, No. 8, pp. 3)*
Pub: Baltimore Business Journal
Contact: Rhonda Pringle, President
E-mail: rpringle@bizjournals.com

Ed: Greg Lamm. **Description:** HomeStreet Bank has hired 300 new workers to work in its mortgage lending business and plans to open 13 new loan centers. Such moves has positioned the bank as King County's top two mortgage lenders. Federal regulators ordered HomeStreet Banki three years ago to raise additional capital of tens of millions.

11035 ■ *"GM's Mortgage Unit Deal Brings in $9 Billion"* in *Globe & Mail (March 24, 2006, pp. B3)*
Ed: Shawn McCarthy. **Description:** General Motors Corp. sells General Motors Acceptance Corp.'s commercial real estate division to Kohlberg Kravis Roberts & Co. Five Mile Capital Partners LLC and Goldman Sachs Capital Partners. The reasons behind the deal are presented. **Availability:** Print; Online.

11036 ■ *"A Good Sign for Commercial Real Estate?"* in *Austin Business JournalInc. (Vol. 29, December 18, 2009, No. 41, pp. 1)*
Pub: Austin Business Journal
Contact: Rachel McGrath, Director
E-mail: rmcgrath@bizjournals.com

Ed: Kate Harrington. **Description:** Factors that could contribute to the reemergence of the commercial mortgage-backed securities market in Texas are discussed. These securities can potentially boost the commercial real estate market statewide as well as nationwide. Commercial mortgage-backed securities origination in 2009 is worth less that $1 billion, compared with $238 billion in 2008. **Availability:** Online.

11037 ■ *"A Good Step, But There's a Long Way to Go"* in *Business Week (September 22, 2008, No. 4100, pp. 10)*
Ed: James C. Cooper. **Description:** Despite the historic action by the U.S. government to nationalize the mortgage giants Freddie Mac and Fannie Mae, rising unemployment rates may prove to be an even bigger roadblock to bringing back the economy from its downward spiral. The takeover is meant to restore confidence in the credit markets and help with the mortgage crisis but the rising rate in unemployment may make many households unable to take advantage of any benefits which arise from the bailout. Statistical data included. **Availability:** Online.

11038 ■ *"Hollander 95 Business Park Project Getting Bigger"* in *Baltimore Business Journal (Vol. 29, September 23, 2011, No. 20, pp. 1)*
Pub: Boston Business Journal
Contact: Carolyn M. Jones, President
E-mail: cmjones@bizjournals.com

Ed: Gary Haber. **Description:** Hollander 95 Business Park is in for a huge change as its new owners plan a $50 million expansion which calls for building as many as eight more buildings or a total of more than 500,000 square feed. FRP Development bought the site for $4.35 million at a foreclosure sale in July 2010 and is now seeking city approval for an Industrial Planned Unit Development designation. **Availability:** Online.

11039 ■ *"Home Price Trends from a Financial Perspective"* in *Real Estate Review (Vol. 41, Spring 2012, No. 1, pp. 5)*
Description: Factors responsible for home price volatility are examined. Home prices have increased by four percent annually in the past quarter century. The availability of credit and underwriting standards are seen to account for home price variations.

Meanwhile, home builders and mortgage lenders are also seen to contribute to home price volatility. **Availability:** Print; Online.

11040 ■ *"Home Prices Sag" in Crain's Chicago Business (Vol. 31, April 28, 2008, No. 17, pp. 3)*
Pub: Crain Communications Inc.
Contact: Barry Asin, President
Ed: Alby Gallun. **Description:** Since the slump in the housing market is continuing with no sign of recovery, Chicago-area home prices are poised for an even steeper drop this year. In 2007, the region's home prices fell nearly 5 percent and according to a forecast by Fiserv Inc., they will decline 8.1 percent this year and another 2.2 percent in 2009. Statistical data included. **Availability:** Online.

11041 ■ *"Hotel Woes Reflect Area Struggle" in Business Journal Serving Greater Tampa Bay (Vol. 30, December 3, 2010, No. 50, pp. 1)*
Pub: Tampa Bay Business Journal
Contact: Ian Anderson, President
E-mail: ianderson@bizjournals.com
Ed: Mark Holan. **Description:** Quality Inn and Suites in East Tampa, Florida has struggled against the sluggish economy but remained open to guests despite facing a foreclosure. The hotel project is the center of East Tampa's redevelopment plans and public officials defend the $650,000 investment in public amenities near the building. **Availability:** Print; Online.

11042 ■ *"Housing Agency Says Lending on Rise" in Providence Business News (Vol. 29, June 30, 2014, No. 13, pp. 5)*
Pub: American City Business Journals, Inc.
Contact: Mike Olivieri, Executive Vice President
Released: June 28, 2014. **Description:** The steep rise of more than 45 percent in the value of home mortgages closed by Rhode Island Housing, which works with a number of approved lenders statewide, including Coastway Community Bank, Homestar Mortgage and Washington Trust. The major factor in the jump in closing is related to Rhode Island Housing's broadening of mortgage options. **Availability:** Print; Online.

11043 ■ *"Housing Slide Picks Up Speed" in Crain's Chicago Business (Vol. 31, April 19, 2008, No. 16, pp. 2)*
Pub: Crain Communications Inc.
Contact: Barry Asin, President
Ed: Eddie Baeb. **Description:** According to Tracy Cross & Associates Inc., a real estate consultancy, sales of new homes in the Chicago area dropped 61 percent from the year-earlier period which is more bad news for homebuilders, contractors and real estate agents who are eager for an indication that market conditions are improving. **Availability:** Online.

11044 ■ *"Housing Stats Contradicting" in Memphis Business Journal (Vol. 34, July 20, 2012, No. 14, pp. 1)*
Pub: Baltimore Business Journal
Contact: Rhonda Pringle, President
E-mail: rpringle@bizjournals.com
Ed: Cole Epley. **Description:** Home mortgage foreclosures in Memphis, Tennessee have increased despite the decrease in the number of homeowners missing out on payments, Reis Inc. has reported. Rental vacancies have also decreased. **Availability:** Print; Online.

11045 ■ *"How the Mortgage Market Is Opening Up to Brokers" in Entrepreneur (October 9, 2019)*
URL(s): www.entrepreneur.com/article/340541
Ed: Eric Weisbrot. **Released:** October 09, 2019. **Description:** With today's complex mortgage market, working with a mortgage broker could help ease the process. They often know about all of the resources needed to get the best deal, including working with the right loan providers. **Availability:** Online.

11046 ■ *"How to Start, Operate and Market a Freelance Notary Signing Agent Business*
Released: Revised second edition. **Description:** Due to the changes in the 2001 Uniform Commercial Code allowing notary public agents to serve as a witness to mortgage loan closings (eliminating the 2-witness requirement under the old code), notaries are working directly for mortgage, title and signing companies as mobile notaries.

11047 ■ *"Identity Theft Can Have Long-Lasting Impact" in Providence Business News (Vol. 28, February 10, 2014, No. 45, pp. 7)*
Pub: American City Business Journals, Inc.
Contact: Mike Olivieri, Executive Vice President
URL(s): pbn.com/identity-theft-can-have-long-lasting-impact94959
Description: According to mortgage credit experts, recently reported massive data breaches at Nieman Marcus, Target, and other merchants could have negative impacts on several real estate deals scheduled for the upcoming months. Although victims are not liable for the unlawful debts, their credit reports and scores can be damaged for months, thus endangering loan applications for mortgages on home sale transactions. **Availability:** Online.

11048 ■ *"In Control: Tips For Navigating a Buyer's Market" in Black Enterprise (Vol. 38, December 2007, No. 5, pp. 64)*
Pub: Earl G. Graves Ltd.
Contact: Earl Graves, Jr., President
Ed: Erinn R. Johnson. **Description:** Tips are given to help would-be home buyers. The importance of finding a good real estate agent is stressed.

11049 ■ *"Is Fannie Mae the Next Government Bailout?" in Barron's (Vol. 88, March 10, 2008, No. 10, pp. 21)*
Pub: Dow Jones & Company Inc.
Contact: Almar Latour, Chief Executive Officer
Ed: Jonathan R. Laing. **Description:** Fannie Mae may need a government bailout as it faces huge hits brought about by the effects of the housing crisis. The shares of the government-sponsored enterprise have dropped 65 percent since the housing crisis began. **Availability:** Online.

11050 ■ *"It Could Be Worse" in Barron's (Vol. 89, July 27, 2009, No. 30, pp. 5)*
Pub: Dow Jones & Company Inc.
Contact: Almar Latour, Chief Executive Officer
Ed: Alan Abelson. **Description:** Media sources are being fooled by corporate America who is peddling an economic recovery rather than reality as shown by the report of a rise in existing home sales which boosted the stock market even if it was a seasonal phenomenon. The phrase "things could be worse" sums up the reigning investment philosophy in the U.S. and this has been stirring up the market. **Availability:** Online.

11051 ■ *"Law Firms See Improvement in Financing Climate" in Sacramento Business Journal (Vol. 28, October 14, 2011, No. 33, pp. 1)*
Pub: Sacramento Business Journal
Contact: Stephanie Fretwell, Director
E-mail: sfretwell@bizjournals.com
Ed: Kathy Robertson. **Description:** Sacramento, California-based Weintraub Genshlea Chediak Law Corporation has helped close 26 financing deals worth more than $1.6 billion in 2010, providing indication of improvement in Sacramento's economy. Lawyers have taken advantage of low interest rates to make refinancing agreements and help clients get new funds. **Availability:** Online.

11052 ■ *"Leaning Tower" in Business Courier (Vol. 27, June 4, 2010, No. 5, pp. 1)*
Pub: Business Courier
Ed: Jon Newberry. **Description:** New York-based developer Armand Lasky, owner of Tower Place Mall in downtown Cincinnati, Ohio has sued Birmingham, Alabama-based Regions Bank to prevent the bank's foreclosure on the property. Regions Bank claims Lasky was in default on an $18 million loan agreement. Details on the mall's leasing plan are also discussed. **Availability:** Online.

11053 ■ *"Lenders Get Boost from Low Rates" in Saint Louis Business Journal (Vol. 32, September 9, 2011, No. 2, pp. 1)*
Pub: Saint Louis Business Journal
Contact: Robert Bobroff, President
E-mail: rbobroff@bizjournals.com
Ed: Greg Edwards. **Description:** St. Louis, Missouri-based lenders have benefitted from record low mortgage interest rates. Housing loan applications have increased in view of the development. **Availability:** Print; Online.

11054 ■ *"Lotus Starts Slowly, Dodges Subprime Woes" in Crain's Detroit Business (Vol. 24, April 14, 2008, No. 15, pp. 3)*
Pub: Crain Communications Inc.
Contact: Barry Asin, President
Ed: Tom Henderson. **Description:** Discusses Lotus Bancorp Inc. and their business plan, which although is not right on target due to the subprime mortgage meltdown, is in a much better position than its competitors due to the quality of their loans. **Availability:** Online.

11055 ■ *"Making Money on Foreclosures" in Memphis Business Journal (Vol. 33, March 9, 2012, No. 48, pp. 1)*
Pub: Baltimore Business Journal
Contact: Rhonda Pringle, President
E-mail: rpringle@bizjournals.com
Ed: Cole Epley. **Description:** Investors and residential rental property buyers have benefited from home foreclosures in the US. Mortgage foreclosures have resulted in decreased home prices. **Availability:** Print; Online.

11056 ■ *"A Matter of Perspective" in Business Journal-Portland (Vol. 24, November 2, 2007, No. 35, pp. 1)*
Pub: Portland Business Journal
Contact: Andy Giegerich, Managing Editor
E-mail: agiegerich@bizjournals.com
Ed: Andy Giegerich. **Description:** Oregon Governor Ted Kulongoski assembled the Mortgage Lending Work Group, made up of members of the mortgage industry and consumer groups, to recommend possible bills for the Oregon Senate and House to consider. How its members try to balance philosophical differences in mortgage lending rules is discussed. **Availability:** Online.

11057 ■ *"Md. Housing Leaders Race to Stem Rising Tide of Foreclosures: Neighborhood Watch" in Baltimore Business Journal (Vol. 28, July 23, 2010, No. 11, pp. 1)*
Pub: Baltimore Business Journal
Contact: Rhonda Pringle, President
E-mail: rpringle@bizjournals.com
Ed: Daniel J. Sernovitz. **Description:** Maryland government and housing leaders are set to spend $100 million in federal funding to stem the increase in foreclosures in the area. The federal funding is seen as inadequate to resolve the problem of foreclosures. **Availability:** Print.

11058 ■ *"Mortgage Companies are Adding Staff" in Sacramento Business Journal (Vol. 29, September 14, 2012, No. 29, pp. 1)*
Pub: Baltimore Business Journal
Contact: Rhonda Pringle, President
E-mail: rpringle@bizjournals.com
Ed: Sanford Nax. **Description:** Mortgage companies have been increasing their hiring as a result of persistently low interest rates and tough new government regulations. The mortgage industry has gained 1,335 jobs in the second quarter nationally, while the number of applications to receive a mortgage loan originator license is rising in California. **Availability:** Print; Online.

11059 ■ *"The Mortgage Red Flags that Bankers See"* in *Providence Business News (Vol. 29, August 4, 2014, No. 18, pp. 9)*
Pub: American City Business Journals, Inc.
Contact: Mike Olivieri, Executive Vice President
URL(s): pbn.com/the-mortgage-red-flags-tha
t-bankers-see98980

Description: A survey of credit-score company FICO reveals that an excessive debt-to-income (DTI) ratio is the biggest reason why credit-risk managers reject potential new home buyers when applying for mortgages. Other factors that affect mortgage applications include new buyers credit scores and numerous recent credit applications.

11060 ■ *"Mortgage Servicer Wingspan Portfolio Advisors Makes Mark in Frisco"* in *Dallas Business Journal (Vol. 35, September 7, 2012, No. 52, pp. 1)*
Pub: Baltimore Business Journal
Contact: Rhonda Pringle, President
E-mail: rpringle@bizjournals.com

Ed: Candace Carlisle. **Description:** Carrollton, Texas-based Wingspan Portfolio Advisors LLC has seen rapid growth in its business and the company plans to hire another 500 employees. Wingspan has subleased a 125,000-square-foot building in Firsco, Texa to accommodate the expansion and making it the company's third site in North Texas.

11061 ■ *"Myths of Deleveraging"* in *Barron's (Vol. 90, August 23, 2010, No. 34, pp. M14)*
Pub: Barron's Editorial & Corporate Headquarters

Ed: Gene Epstein. **Description:** The opposite is true against reports about deleveraging or the decrease in credit since inflation-adjusted-investment factories and equipment rose 7.8 percent in the first quarter of 2010. On consumer deleveraging, sales of homes through credit is weak but there is a trend towards more realistic homeownership and consumer spending on durable goods rose 8.8 percent. **Availability:** Online.

11062 ■ *"New PHH Building Still Going Up In Amherst Despite Job Cuts"* in *Business First of Buffalo (Vol. 30, February 28, 2014, No. 24, pp. 5)*
Pub: American City Business Journals, Inc.
Contact: Mike Olivieri, Executive Vice President

Released: Weekly. **Price:** $140, Digital & Print; $115, Digital only. **Description:** New Jersey-based PHH Mortgage Company has maintained the construction of its $34 million back-office complex in Amherst, New York despite eliminating 135 employees. PHH confirms that lower industry-wide demand in the mortgage business has caused the job cuts. The Erie County Industrial Development Agency's adoption of a recapture policy is also examined. **Availability:** Print; Online.

11063 ■ *"New Rule Rankles In Jersey"* in *Philadelphia Business Journal (Vol. 30, September 16, 2011, No. 31, pp. 1)*
Pub: Philadelphia Business Journal
Contact: Sierra Quinn, Director
E-mail: squinn@bizjournals.com

Ed: Jeff Blumenthal. **Description:** A new rule in New Jersey which taxes out-of-state companies that conduct business in the state earned the ire of several banks, mortgage lenders and credit card companies and prompted opponents to threaten to file lawsuits. The new rule is an amendment to New Jersey Division of Taxation's corporate business tax regulation and is retroactive to 2002. Details are given. **Availability:** Online.

11064 ■ *"Nightmare on Wall Street"* in *Canadian Business (Vol. 80, November 19, 2007, No. 23, pp. 33)*
Ed: Thomas Watson. **Released:** October 29, 2016. **Description:** Merrill Lynch Stanley O'Neal resigned after the company experienced a $2.2 billion loss in third quarter 2007. Citigroup's Charles Prince will

also be leaving due to the crisis involving subprime mortgages and collaterized debt obligations. Forecasts for the stock market are supplied. **Availability:** Print; Online.

11065 ■ *"October 2009: Recovery Plods Along"* in *Hispanic Business (October 2009, pp. 10-11)*
Description: Economist reports on a possible economic recovery which will not be allowed to rely on a strong domestic demand in order to sustain it. Consumers, looking to counterbalance years of leverage financing based on unrealistic, ever-increasing home and portfolio valuations, are saving rather than spending money.

11066 ■ *"OK, Bring in the Lawyers"* in *Crain's Chicago Business (Vol. 31, November 17, 2008, No. 46, pp. 26)*
Pub: Crain Communications Inc.
Contact: Barry Asin, President

Ed: Daniel Rome Levine. **Description:** Bankruptcy attorneys are finding the economic and credit crisis a benefit for their businesses due to the high number of business owners and mortgage holders that are need of their services. One Chicago firm is handling ten times the number of cases they did the previous year and of that about 80 percent of their new clients are related to the real estate sector. **Availability:** Online.

11067 ■ *"Older, But Not Wiser"* in *Canadian Business (Vol. 85, July 16, 2012, No. 11-12, pp. 54)*
Ed: Matthew McClearn, Michael McCullough. **Description:** Data from Statistics Canada revealed that two-thirds of workers aged 55 and above have some form of debt from mortgage to credit card balance while its one-third among the retired. Some factors contributing to the trend are the decline in borrowing costs, real estate, and older Canadians' car purchasing behavior. **Availability:** Print; Online.

11068 ■ *"Outlook 2008 (9 Sectors to Watch): Gold"* in *Canadian Business (Vol. 81, December 19, 2007, No. 1, pp. 53)*
Pub: Rogers Media Inc.
Contact: Neil Spivak, Chief Executive Officer

Ed: John Gray. **Description:** Turmoil in the financial markets, triggered by the meltdown in subprime mortgages, has pushed the price of gold to more than $840 an ounce in November 2007. Details on investor interest in gold and prediction on price trends in trade are discussed. **Availability:** Online.

11069 ■ *"Past Due: $289 Million in Loans - University Club Tower, Sheraton St. Louis City Center in Default"* in *Saint Louis Business Journal (Vol. 32, September 23, 2011, No. 4, pp. 1)*
Pub: Saint Louis Business Journal
Contact: Robert Bobroff, President
E-mail: rbobroff@bizjournals.com

Ed: Evan Binns. **Description:** New York-based Trepp LLC research found about $289 million in local commercial mortgage-backed securities loans on 20 properties delinquent in payments by 30 days or more as of August 31, 2011. The report also placed the delinquency rate for St. Louis at that time at 9.64 percent. **Availability:** Online.

11070 ■ *"Paying for the Recession: Rebalancing Economic Growth"* in *Montana Business Quarterly (Vol. 49, Spring 2011, No. 1, pp. 2)*
Pub: University of Montana Bureau of Business and Economic Research
Contact: Patrick Barkey, Director
E-mail: patrick.barkey@business.umt.edu

Ed: Patrick M. Barkey. **Released:** Quarterly. **Description:** Four key issues required to address in order to rebalance economic growth in America are examined. They include: savings rates, global trade imbalances, government budgets and most importantly, housing price correction. **Availability:** Online.

11071 ■ *"Phila.-Area Foreclosures Rising"* in *Philadelphia Business Journal (Vol. 28, May 18, 2012, No. 14, pp. 1)*
Pub: Baltimore Business Journal
Contact: Rhonda Pringle, President
E-mail: rpringle@bizjournals.com

Description: California-based RealtyTrac has reported residential mortgage foreclosures increased in Pennsylvania's Philadelphia region by 36 percent in first quarter from 2011's fourth quarter. Experts believe the numbers will continue to rise up to the end of the year and will negatively affect home values and the broader regional economy. Insights on bank robo-signing practices are also explained. **Availability:** Print; Online.

11072 ■ *"Race, Not Income, Played Role in Subprime Loans"* in *Black Enterprise (Vol. 40, July 2010, No. 12, pp. 26)*
Pub: Earl G. Graves Ltd.
Contact: Earl Graves, Jr., President

Ed: Deborah Creighton Skinner. **Description:** African Americans were 80 percent more likely than whites to receive a subprime loan and were almost 20 percent more likely to go into foreclosure, according to a study done by the National Community Reinvestment Coalition. Statistical data included.

11073 ■ *"Ready for a Rally?"* in *The Economist (Vol. 390, January 3, 2009, No. 8612, pp. 54)*
Description: Analysts predict that the recession could end by 2010. The current economic crisis is presented in detail. **Availability:** Print; Online.

11074 ■ *"Refinance: To Do Or Not To Do?"* in *Real Estate Review (Vol. 41, Spring 2012, No. 1, pp. 91)*
Description: An author's experiences in home mortgage refinancing are presented. The author's encounter with home appraisers is mentioned. Special or streamlined loans can be secured by parties with existing conforming loans. **Availability:** Print; Online.

11075 ■ *"Regulator Issues Warning On Reverse Mortgage Loans"* in *Retirement Advisor (Vol. 13, October 2012, No. 10, pp. 28)*
Description: Reverse mortgages were first introduced in 1961 and are becoming popular now with aging baby boomers. The new Consumer Financial Protection Bureau warns the public to look closing before entering a reverse mortgage contract. The National Ethics Association encourages financial advisors to use the same caution and offers advise for advisors to help educate their clients about reverse mortgages. **Availability:** Print; Online.

11076 ■ *"Santander 'Redlining' Suit is a Crass and Opportunistic Shakedown"* in *Boston Business Journal (Vol. 34, June 6, 2014, No. 18, pp. 7)*
Pub: American City Business Journals, Inc.
Contact: Mike Olivieri, Executive Vice President

Released: Weekly. **Description:** Santander Bank's residential mortgage lending to minorities in Providence, Massachusetts has declined by 34 percent in recent years. The development is a violation of the US Fair Housing Act and the Equal Credit Opportunity Act. The city has sued Santander over the issue. **Availability:** Print; Online.

11077 ■ *"Scoring Boost Should be Coming for Renters' Credit"* in *Providence Business News (Vol. 29, July 14, 2014, No. 15, pp. 7)*
Pub: American City Business Journals, Inc.
Contact: Mike Olivieri, Executive Vice President

Released: July 12, 2014. **Description:** National credit bureaus, Experian and TransUnion, are working with online rental payment service RentTrack to include verified rental payment data into credit files so that it may be included in calculating consumer scores during mortgage applications. In addition, a study by TransUnion finds that consumer scores increase when their rental data is included in bureau records and when they move from renter status to homeowner. **Availability:** Print; Online.

11078 ■ *"A Slice of Danish; Fixing Finance"* *in The Economist (Vol. 390, January 3, 2009, No. 8612, pp. 55)*

Description: Denmark's mortgage-holders and the county's lending system is presented. **Availability:** Print; Online.

11079 ■ *"Slow Mortgage Market Drags JPMorgan Chase Q1 Earnings Down 18.5 Percent" in Boston Business Journal (Vol. 34, April 11, 2014, No. 10)*

Pub: American City Business Journals, Inc.
Contact: Mike Olivieri, Executive Vice President

Released: Weekly. **Description:** JP Morgan Chase reported $5.27 billion in first quarter earnings, down 18.5 percent for the same period last year. Revenue fell slightly to less than $23.9 billion, down from $24.5 billion in 2013. The banking firm has approximately 1,200 employees in Massachusetts and about 60 of them are involved in the private banking sector. This sector saw a 4 percent increase in revenue year-over-year to $1.5 billion for the first quarter 2014. **Availability:** Print; Online.

11080 ■ *"Some Homeowners Caught in Tax-Code Limbo" in Providence Business News (Vol. 29, June 23, 2014, No. 12, pp. 9)*

Pub: American City Business Journals, Inc.
Contact: Mike Olivieri, Executive Vice President

Released: June 22, 2014. **Description:** The Mortgage Forgiveness Debt Relief Act expired on December 31, 2013 and Congress delayed reauthorizing the tax code, thus impacting homeowners looking for short sales in 2014. Short sellers are unsure whether they will avoid taxation on their forgiven mortgage debt or if the lack of reauthorization by Congress, retroactive to January 1, will lead to large income tax payouts in 2015. **Availability:** Print; Online.

11081 ■ *"South Jersey Office Space in Doldrums" in Philadelphia Business Journal (Vol. 31, March 16, 2012, No. 5, pp. 1)*

Pub: Baltimore Business Journal
Contact: Rhonda Pringle, President
E-mail: rpringle@bizjournals.com

Description: Morgage lenders have been trying to boost office building occupancies in preparation of eventual sales. They are also selling loans at discounted prices. **Availability:** Print; Online.

11082 ■ *"Stuck With Two Mortgages" in Crain's Chicago Business (Vol. 31, April 21, 2008, No. 16)*

Pub: Crain Communications Inc.
Contact: Barry Asin, President

Ed: Darci Smith. **Description:** Discusses the problem a number of people are facing due to the slump in the housing market: being stuck with two mortgages when they move because their former homes have not sold. Many thought they could afford to move to a larger home, anticipating significant equity appreciation that did not occur; now they are left with lowering their price and competing with the host of new developments. **Availability:** Online.

11083 ■ *"Subprime Mess Hits Huntington" in Business First-Columbus (November 26, 2007, pp. A1)*

Pub: Business First
Contact: Nick Fortine, President
E-mail: nfortine@bizjournals.com

Ed: Adrian Burns. **Description:** Huntington Bancshares Inc. picked up a $1.5 billion exposure to the country's subprime mortgage mess. It caused the bank to set aside $450 million to cover increases in loan losses. When Huntington acquired Sky Financial, it absorbed a 17-year relationship Sky had with Franklin Credit Corporation, which is a subprime lender and servicer. **Availability:** Print; Online.

11084 ■ *"Suit: Bank Bypassing Minorities" in Providence Business News (Vol. 29, June 9, 2014, No. 10, pp. 1)*

Pub: American City Business Journals, Inc.
Contact: Mike Olivieri, Executive Vice President
URL(s): pbn.com/suit-bank-bypassing-minori ties97644

Description: The City of Providence, Rhode Island filed a lawsuit against the U.S. operations of Santander Bank for purposely bypassing minority neighborhoods in prime mortgage lending. The lawsuit alleges the Madrid, Spain-based bank of violating the Fair Housing Act by not lending into the minority communities of the city.

11085 ■ *"Unions Pony Up $1 Million for McBride Stimulus" in Saint Louis Business Journal (Vol. 31, July 29, 2011, No. 49, pp. 1)*

Pub: Saint Louis Business Journal
Contact: Robert Bobroff, President
E-mail: rbobroff@bizjournals.com

Ed: Evan Binns. **Description:** Carpenters District Council of Greater St. Louis and International Brotherhood of Electrical Workers Local 1 were among the nine unions that agreed to split the cost of nearly $1 million in incentives for homebuyers who purchase homes in McBride communities. McBride & Son has spent over $100,000 to promote the incentive program. **Availability:** Print; Online.

11086 ■ *"Valenti: Roots of Financial Crisis Go Back to 1998" in Crain's Detroit Business (Vol. 24, October 6, 2008, No. 40, pp. 25)*

Pub: Crain Communications Inc.
Contact: Barry Asin, President

Ed: Tom Henderson, Nathan Skid. **Description:** Interview with Sam Valenti III who is the chairman and CEO of Valenti Capital L.L.C., a wealth-management firm; Valenti discusses in detail the history that led up to the current economic crisis as well as his prediction for the future of the country. **Availability:** Print; Online.

11087 ■ *"Well-Timed Entrance" in Barron's (Vol. 92, July 23, 2012, No. 30, pp. 24)*

Pub: Dow Jones & Company Inc.
Contact: Almar Latour, Chief Executive Officer

Ed: Michael Aneiro. **Description:** Dan Ivascyn, portfolio manager of Pimco Income Fund, discusses the fund's investment bonds. The fund is heavily invested in mortgage-backed securities and is positioned for a low-interest-rate environment well into 2014 or 2015. **Availability:** Online.

11088 ■ *"Wells Fargo and NeighborWorks America Offer Down Payment Assistance: Low- to Middle-Income Consumers Get the Help They Need" in Black Enterprise (Vol. 44, June 2014, No. 10, pp. 34)*

Pub: Earl G. Graves Ltd.
Contact: Earl Graves, Jr., President

Description: A new homeownership program, called NeighborhoodLIFT, helps low to middle income earners obtain mortgages. Currently, the program is present in 25 markets throughout the U.S. and has committed $195 million to those markets. **Availability:** Online.

11089 ■ *"What's Ahead for Fannie and Fred?" in Barron's (Vol. 90, August 30, 2010, No. 35, pp. 26)*

Pub: Barron's Editorial & Corporate Headquarters

Ed: Jonathan R. Laing. **Description:** A meeting presided by Treasury Secretary Timothy Geithner discussed the future of Fannie Mae and Freddie Mac. The two government sponsored enterprises were mismanaged and reforming these two agencies is critical. **Availability:** Online.

11090 ■ *"Where to Stash Your Cash" in Barron's (Vol. 88, March 17, 2008, No. 11, pp. 41)*

Pub: Dow Jones & Company Inc.
Contact: Almar Latour, Chief Executive Officer

Ed: Mike Hogan. **Description:** Investors are putting their money in money-market mutual funds seeking fractionally better yields and a safe haven from the uncertainties that was brought about by subprime lending. These funds, however, are hovering near 3.20 percent which is less than the 4 percent inflation rate. **Availability:** Online.

11091 ■ *"The Worst Lies Ahead for Wall Street: More Losses Certain; More Expensive Capital to Be Needed" in Crain's New York Business (Vol. 24, January 20, 2008, No. 3, pp. 1)*

Pub: Crain Communications, Inc.
Contact: Jessica Botos, Manager, Marketing
E-mail: jessica.botos@crainsnewyork.com

Ed: Aaron Elstein. **Description:** Due to the weakening economy, many financial institutions will face further massive losses forcing them to borrow more at higher interest rates and dragging down their earnings for years to come. The effects on commercial real estate and credit card loans are also discussed as well as the trend to investing in Asia and the Middle East. **Availability:** Online.

11092 ■ *"You Better Shop Around: Four Steps to Getting the Best Deal on a Home Loan" in Black Enterprise (Vol. 40, July 2010, No. 12, pp. 78)*

Pub: Earl G. Graves Ltd.
Contact: Earl Graves, Jr., President

Ed: Tara-Nicholle Nelson. **Description:** Four steps to help anyone seeking a mortgage for a home purchase are listed. **Availability:** Online.

11093 ■ *"Your Exposure to Bear Stearns" in Barron's (Vol. 88, March 17, 2008, No. 11, pp. 45)*

Pub: Dow Jones & Company Inc.
Contact: Almar Latour, Chief Executive Officer

Ed: Tom Sullivan, Jack Willoughby. **Description:** Bear Stearns makes up 5.5 percent of Pioneer Independence's portfolio, 1.4 percent of Vanguard Windsor II's portfolio, 1.2 percent of Legg Mason Value Trust, about 1 percent of Van Kampen Equity & Income, and 0.79 percent of Putnam Fund for Growth & Income. Ginnie Mae securities are now trading at 1.78 percentage points over treasuries due to the mortgage crises. **Availability:** Online.

TRADE PERIODICALS

11094 ■ *Inside MBS & ABS*
Pub: Inside Mortgage Finance Publications Inc.
Contact: Bryan Cecala, Chief Executive Officer
E-mail: bcecala@imfpubs.com
URL(s): www.insidemortgagefinance.com/newsle tters/21-inside-mbs-abs

Released: Weekly; 48 times per year. **Price:** $2,367, U.S. for 1 year.; $525, Single issue; $1,275, for 6 months. https://www.insidemortgagefinance.com/ products/297810-inside-mbs-abs-6-mos. **Description:** Covers the mortgage-related securities market and secondary mortgage market, including regulatory and market developments. Also covers ABS and CMBS markets. Recurring features include interviews, news of research, and exclusive market statistics. **Availability:** Print.

11095 ■ *Mortgage Banking Magazine: The Magazine of Real Estate Finance*
Pub: Mortgage Bankers Association
Contact: Susan Stewart, Chairman
URL(s): nationalmortgageprofessional.com/ magazine/mortgage-banker-magazine

Ed: Lesley Hall. **Released:** Monthly **Description:** Magazine of the real estate finance industry. **Availability:** Print; Online.

11096 ■ *National Mortgage News*
Pub: SourceMedia LLC
Contact: Gemma Postlethwaite, Chief Executive Officer
URL(s): www.nationalmortgagenews.com
Facebook: www.facebook.com/NationalMor tgageNews

Linkedin: www.linkedin.com/company/nationalmor
tgagenews

X (Twitter): x.com/NatMortgageNews

Released: 8/year **Description:** Magazine covering technological trends and developments within the mortgage industry. **Availability:** Print; Online.

TRADE SHOWS AND CONVENTIONS

11097 ■ National Association of Review Appraisers and Mortgage Underwriters Convention - National Conference & Expo
National Association of Review Appraisers and
  Mortgage Underwriters (NARA/MU)
  PO Box 879
  Palm Springs, CA 92263
Free: 877-743-6805
Fax: (760)327-5631
Co. E-mail: info@naramu.org
URL: http://www.naramu.org
Contact: Brent Felstead, Associate Manager
URL(s): www.naramu.org

Description: Real estate-related information and services. **Audience:** Real estate appraisers, consultants, and professionals . **Principal Exhibits:** Real estate-related information and services. **Telecommunication Services:** info@naramu.org.

CONSULTANTS

11098 ■ HilBren Computing Services LLC. (HCS)
287 Valencia Dr.
  Monroe Township, NJ 08831
Ph: (732)545-7913
Co. E-mail: info@hilbren.com
URL: http://www.hilbren.com
Contact: Gary L. Tinkel, President

Description: Firm provides computer consulting services such as expert witness, litigation support, commercial banking applications, and much more. **Scope:** Firm provides computer consulting services such as expert witness, litigation support, commercial banking applications, and much more. **Founded:** 1983.

11099 ■ James Quinn Agency Inc.
513 W Park Ave.
  Greenwood, MS 38930-2945

Description: Firm offers a wide range of real estate appraisal and brokerage services involving residential, commercial, industrial and agricultural properties and also provides investment analysis and feasibility studies and serves attorneys, accountants, banks, mortgage lenders, trustees for estates and individual investors on land development, financing, and valuation matters and available for expert witness testimony. **Scope:** Firm offers a wide range of real estate appraisal and brokerage services involving residential, commercial, industrial and agricultural properties and also provides investment analysis and feasibility studies and serves attorneys, accountants, banks, mortgage lenders, trustees for estates and individual investors on land development, financing, and valuation matters and available for expert witness testimony.

FRANCHISES AND BUSINESS OPPORTUNITIES

11100 ■ Centum Financial Group Inc.
The Charlwood Pacific Group (CPG)
  1285 W Pender St. No 500
  Vancouver, BC, Canada V6E 4B1
Ph: (604)718-2612
Fax: (604)718-2638
URL: http://www.charlwoodpacificgroup.com
Contact: Chris Turcotte, President
Facebook: www.facebook.com/CentumCanada
Linkedin: www.linkedin.com/company/centum
X (Twitter): x.com/centumcanada
Instagram: www.instagram.com/centumcanada

Description: Provider of financial services such as mortgages, financing, real estate, loans, franchising and entrepreneurs. **Founded:** 2002. **Training:** Yes.

COMPUTERIZED DATABASES

11101 ■ *American Banker: Charting the Future of Financial Services (AB)*
SourceMedia LLC
  1 State St., Plz.
  New York, NY 10004
Ph: (212)803-8200
Co. E-mail: help@arizent.com
URL: http://www.arizent.com
Contact: Gemma Postlethwaite, Chief Executive
  Officer
URL(s): www.americanbanker.com/magazine

Description: Magazine serving the financial services industry. **Availability:** Print; Online. **Type:** Full-text.

11102 ■ *Barron's*
Dow Jones & Company Inc.
  1211 Avenue of the Americas
  New York, NY 10036
Free: 800-568-7625
Co. E-mail: support@dowjones.com

URL: http://dowjones.com
Contact: Almar Latour, Chief Executive Officer
URL(s): www.barrons.com
Facebook: www.facebook.com/barrons
Linkedin: www.linkedin.com/company/barrons
X (Twitter): x.com/barronsonline
Instagram: www.instagram.com/Barrons

Released: Daily **Price:** $8.50, Single issue; $1, for online Week/1 Year (digital Bundle print + online); $4, for 4 weeks/1 Year (digital Bundle-print + online); $2, for online 4 weeks/1 year. **Availability:** Print; Online. **Type:** Full-text; Numeric; Statistical.

11103 ■ *Business Wire*
Business Wire, Inc.
  101 California St., 20th Fl.
  San Francisco, CA 94111
Co. E-mail: info@businesswire.com
URL: http://www.businesswire.com
Contact: Geff Scott, Chief Executive Officer

Description: Contains more than 1.4 million records that make up the complete text of press releases from public and private companies and other organizations, such as hospitals and universities. **Availability:** Online. **Type:** Full-text.

11104 ■ *U.S. Weekly Statistics*
Haver Analytics
  60 E 42nd St.
  New York, NY 10165
Ph: (212)986-9300
Co. E-mail: sales@haver.com
URL: http://www.haver.com
Contact: Paul L. Kasriel, Contact
URL(s): haverproducts.com/products/market-data/
  #top

Released: Weekly **Availability:** Online. **Type:** Statistical; Numeric.

EARLY STAGE FINANCING

11105 ■ Business Development Bank of Canada (BDC)
5 Place Ville Marie, Ground Fl.
  Montreal, QC, Canada H3B 5E7
Free: 877-232-2269
Fax: (877)329-9232
Co. E-mail: info@bdc.ca
URL: http://www.bdc.ca
Contact: Isabelle Hudon, President
Facebook: www.facebook.com/BDC.ca
Linkedin: www.linkedin.com/company/bdc
X (Twitter): x.com/bdc_ca
Instagram: www.instagram.com/bdc_ca
YouTube: www.youtube.com/user/BDCBanx

Description: Firm offers loans, financing solutions and non-financing advisory services. **Founded:** 1944.

ASSOCIATIONS AND OTHER ORGANIZATIONS

11106 ■ American Motorcyclist Association (AMA)
13515 Yarmouth Dr.
Pickerington, OH 43147
Ph: (614)856-1900
Free: 800-262-5646
Fax: (614)856-1924
Co. E-mail: membershipmailbox@ama-cycle.org
URL: http://americanmotorcyclist.com
Contact: Rob Dingman, President
Facebook: www.facebook.com/AmericanMotorcyclist
YouTube: www.youtube.com/user/AmericanMo
torcyclist

Description: Represents motorcycle enthusiasts. Acts as a rulemaking body for motorcycle competition. Promotes highway safety. Maintains museum and hall of fame. **Founded:** 1924. **Publications:** *American Motorcyclist: Journal of the American Motorcyclist Assn* (Monthly); *American Motorcyclist Association*; *Cycle Connection: Motorcyclings' Yellow Pages* (Annual). **Awards:** Daytona 200 AMA (Irregular); AMA Hazel Kolb Brighter Image Award (Annual). **Geographic Preference:** National.

11107 ■ Motorcycle Industry Council (MIC)
2 Jenner St., Ste. 150
Irvine, CA 92618
Ph: (949)727-4211
Fax: (949)727-3313
Co. E-mail: memberservices@mic.org
URL: http://www.mic.org
Contact: Erik Pritchard, President

Description: Manufacturers and distributors of motorcycles and allied industries. Maintains liaison with state and federal governments. Operates collection of research documents, federal and state government documents, and trade publications. Compiles statistics. **Founded:** 1914. **Publications:** *MIC Statistical Annual* (Annual). **Educational Activities:** Dealernews International Powersports Dealer Expo (Annual). **Geographic Preference:** National.

REFERENCE WORKS

11108 ■ "Ditch the Rental Car: A New Way to Arrive in Style" in Inc. (Vol. 33, September 2011, No. 7, pp. 54)
Pub: Inc. Magazine

Ed: Matt Rist. **Description:** EagleRider is a franchise offering various two-wheeled rentals, including BMWs and Harley-Davidsons at more than 100 locations worldwide. **Availability:** Online.

11109 ■ "Ducati Returns to Production: "We Are Ready to Go" - Domenicali' in Ultimate Motorcycling (April 28. 2020)
Ed: Don Williams. **Released:** April 28, 2020. **Description:** The Ducati factory is once again up and running producing the famed motorcycles, after the Italian government declared it an essential business.

11110 ■ "For Janus Motorcycles, Building Bikes by Hand Is the Only Way" in Gear Patrol (November 11, 2019)
URL(s): gearpatrol.com/2019/11/11/janus-mo
torcycles-handmade-250-cc-bikes-amish-made-in
diana/
Ed: Will Sabel Courtney. **Released:** November 11, 2019. **Description:** Profile of Janus Motorcycles, which grew out of a custom moped business. **Availability:** Online.

STATISTICAL SOURCES

11111 ■ Motorcycle Dealership and Repair Industry in the US - Market Research Report
URL(s): www.ibisworld.com/united-states/market-re
search-reports/motorcycle-dealership-repair-indus
try/
Price: $925. **Description:** Downloadable report analyzing the current and future trends in the motorcycle dealership and repair industry. **Availability:** Download.

11112 ■ RMA Annual Statement Studies
Pub: Risk Management Association
Contact: Nancy Foster, President

Released: Annual. **Description:** Contains composite balance sheets and income statements for more than 360 industries, including the accounting, auditing, and bookkeeping industries. Also contains five years of comparative historical data for discerning trends. Includes 16 commonly used ratios, computed for most of the size groupings for nearly every industry.

TRADE PERIODICALS

11113 ■ cycle news
Pub: Cycle News
URL(s): www.cyclenews.com
Facebook: www.facebook.com/CycleNews
X (Twitter): x.com/cyclenews
Instagram: www.instagram.com/cyclenews
YouTube: www.youtube.com/user/CycleNews
Ed: Kit Palmer. **Released:** Weekly (Mon.); 50 times per year. **Description:** Newspaper (tabloid) for motorcycle enthusiasts. **Availability:** Print; Online.

TRADE SHOWS AND CONVENTIONS

11114 ■ Blue Knights International Law Enforcement Motorcycle Club Convention
Blue Knights International Law Enforcement
Motorcycle Club (BKLEMC)
38 Alden St.
Bangor, ME 04401
Ph: (207)947-4600
Free: 877-254-5362
Co. E-mail: renewals@blueknights.org
URL: http://www.blueknights.org
Contact: D. J. Alvarez, President
E-mail: president@blueknights.org
URL(s): www.bki2024international.com

Frequency: Annual. **Description:** Deputy sheriffs, game wardens, local police, parole officers, state troopers, and other law enforcement personnel participating in recreational motorcycling. **Audience:** Industry professionals. **Principal Exhibits:** Deputy sheriffs, game wardens, local police, parole officers, state troopers, and other law enforcement personnel participating in recreational motorcycling. **Telecommunication Services:** treasurer@blueknights.org.

11115 ■ Springfield Motorcycle Show
Vernon Promotions
MA
Ph: (978)777-4439
URL: http://www.bostoninwaterboatshow.com
URL(s): www.boatma.com/springfield.html
Description: Motorcycles and related equipment, supplies, and services. **Audience:** Manufacturers, retailers, and motorcycle enthusiasts. **Principal Exhibits:** Motorcycles and related equipment, supplies, and services.

11116 ■ Women On Wheels International Ride-In
Women on Wheels Motorcycle Association
4940 O St. No.1007
Lincoln, NE 68510
Ph: (402)326-9736
Co. E-mail: membership1@womenonwheels.org
URL: http://womenonwheels.org
Contact: Carol Skala, President
URL(s): womenonwheels.org/ride-in
Frequency: Annual. **Description:** Women motorcyclists. **Audience:** General public. **Principal Exhibits:** Women motorcyclists.

LIBRARIES

11117 ■ Antique Automobile Club of America (AACA) - The Chris & Kathleen Koch AACA Library & Research Center
800 W Hersheypark Dr.
Hershey, PA 17033
Ph: (717)534-1910
Co. E-mail: general@aaca.org
URL: http://www.aaca.org
Contact: Steve Moskowitz, Chief Executive Officer
E-mail: aaca1@aaca.org
Facebook: www.facebook.com/AntiqueAu
tomobileClubOfAmerica
Instagram: www.instagram.com/antiqueau
tomobileclubofamerica
YouTube: www.youtube.com/channel/
UCS8evFEQZMkGvOEmzJ-LuLQ
Description: Collectors, hobbyists, and others interested in the preservation, maintenance, and restoration of automobiles and in automotive history. Encourages historical research. **Scope:** History of automobiles, commercial vehicles, and motorcycles in the U.S. and abroad. **Services:** Open to the public. **Founded:** 1935. **Holdings:** 2,000,000 sales literature pieces; 60,000 periodicals; 40,000 advertisements; photographs; owners manuals and clippings; 6,500 reference books; 3,500 shop manuals; 230 periodicals; blueprints; wiring diagrams; annual reports. **Publications:** *Antique Automobile* (Bimonthly). **Geographic Preference:** National.

ASSOCIATIONS AND OTHER ORGANIZATIONS

11118 ■ Independent Film & Television Alliance (IFTA)
10850 Wilshire Blvd., 9th Fl.
  Los Angeles, CA 90024-4311
Ph: (310)446-1000
Fax: (310)446-1600
Co. E-mail: info@ifta-online.org
URL: http://ifta-online.org
Contact: Jean M. Prewitt, President
Facebook: www.facebook.com/IndependentFilman
  dTelevisionAlliance
Linkedin: www.linkedin.com/company/independen
  t-film-&-television-alliance
X (Twitter): x.com/ifta_official
YouTube: www.youtube.com/user/IFTAOFFICIAL

Description: Trade association for the worldwide independent film and television industry. Contributes to negotiations with foreign producer associations; develops standardized theatrical, TV, and video contracts for international distribution. Establishes and maintains the IFTA International Arbitration Tribunal, a system through which prominent entertainment attorneys throughout the world assist members and consenting clients in reaching equitable and binding agreements. Produces the American Film Market (AFM), the largest international motion picture trade event in the world. **Founded:** 1980. **Educational Activities:** American Film Market (AFM) (Annual). **Geographic Preference:** Multinational.

11119 ■ Motion Picture Association of America, Inc. (MPAA)
1600 I St. NW
  Washington, DC 20006
Ph: (202)293-1966
Fax: (202)785-3026
Co. E-mail: contactus@mpaa.org
URL: http://www.motionpictures.org
Contact: Charles H. Rivkin, Chief Executive Officer
Facebook: www.facebook.com/MotionPictureAssocia
  tionAmerica
Linkedin: www.linkedin.com/company/motionpic
  tureassociation

Description: Represents principal producers and distributors of motion pictures in the U.S. Serves as an advocate of the American motion picture, home video, and television industries; activities also include preserving and protecting the rights of copyright owners; fighting censorship and restrictive attacks on First Amendment rights of motion picture, television, and home video producers; and directing anti-piracy programs to protect U.S. films, television programming, and home video throughout the U.S. **Founded:** 1922. **Geographic Preference:** National.

11120 ■ National Association of Theatre Owners (NATO)
1705 N St. NW
  Washington, DC 20036
Ph: (202)962-0054
Co. E-mail: nato@natodc.com
URL: http://www.natoonline.org
Contact: John Fithian, President

Description: Provides services to assist theater owners in successfully operating their theaters including monitoring legislative and technological advancements; compiles statistics. **Publications:** *Encyclopedia of Exhibition* (Semiannual); *National Association of Theatre Owners--Encyclopedia of Exhibition* (Semiannual). **Educational Activities:** ShowEast (Annual); Show West. **Geographic Preference:** Multinational.

11121 ■ United Drive-in Theatre Owners Association, Inc. (UDITOA)
PO Box 24771
  Middle River, MD 21220
Ph: (443)490-1250
Co. E-mail: info@uditoa.org
URL: http://uditoa.wildapricot.org
Contact: John Vincent, Jr., President

Description: Serves drive-in theatre owners. Promotes commercial motion picture exhibition at drive-in theatres worldwide. Ensures that drive-in theatres remain a viable and competitive part of the motion picture industry. Forms a strong membership of drive-in owners who can help one another with problems, assists others in getting into the business, and educates the public, the media, and association members. Produces a benchmark to the industry. **Founded:** 1999. **Geographic Preference:** Multinational.

REFERENCE WORKS

11122 ■ *Film Journal International--Equipment, Concessions & Services Guide (Internet only)*
Contact: Kevin Lally, Executive Editor
E-mail: kevin.lally@nielsen.com

Ed: Robert Sunshine. **Released:** Annual; Latest edition 2008. **Description:** Publication includes lists of about 300 manufacturers and suppliers of equipment, products, and services for the theatrical motion picture and concession industries; more than 20 film processors, and over 200 dealers and distributors of equipment and supplies. **Entries include:** Company name, address, phone, names and titles of key personnel, products or services. **Arrangement:** Separate alphabetical sections for manufacturers and processors; dealers are geographical. **Indexes:** Product/service. **Availability:** Print.

11123 ■ *"Here's How Movie Theaters Will Survive the Next 10 Years: Exhibitors Speak Out" in IndieWire (June 28, 2019)*
Ed: Eric Kohn. **Released:** June 28, 2019. **Description:** As giant multiplex movie theaters face a decline in attendance, moviegoers are exploring their local independent theaters and finding them to be more valuable. **Availability:** Online.

11124 ■ *"Inside Indie Movie Theaters' Battle to Survive" in Variety*
URL(s): variety.com/2019/film/features/small-theaters
  -exhibitors-movie-business-1203170700/
Ed: Brent Lang. **Released:** 2019. **Description:** Explores the challenges facing small movie theaters as they compete against larger chains with all the amenities, streaming devices that consumers use at home, and aging audiences. High rent and inconsistent revenues are also hurdles many of these theaters have to overcome. **Availability:** Online.

11125 ■ *Motion Picture TV and Theatre Directory*
Pub: Motion Picture Enterprises Publications Inc.
Contact: Neal R. Pilzer, Publisher

Released: Semiannual; published each Spring and Fall. **Price:** $22.64, for within new York; $20.79, for outside of new York. **Description:** Covers companies providing products and services to the motion picture and television industries. All listings are paid. **Entries include:** Company name, address, phone. **Arrangement:** Classified by product or service. **Indexes:** Alphabetical. **Availability:** Print; Online.

11126 ■ *"Sneak Preview: Alamo Revamp" in Austin Business JournalInc. (Vol. 28, December 12, 2008, No. 39, pp. 1)*
Description: Austin, Texas-based Alamo Drafthouse Cinemas is planning to build a new Circle C Ranch. The new theater will showcase digital projectors and the latest sound systems to show 3-D movies. The company is in lease negotiations with developer Stratus Properties Inc. **Availability:** Print; Online.

11127 ■ *"StubHub Launches in the UK" in Entertainment Close-Up (March 25, 2012)*
Description: StubHub, an eBay company, is expanding to the United Kingdom. The firm sells tickets, third party, to music, sport, and entertainment events by connecting buyers and sellers. Details of the service and expansion are explored. **Availability:** Online.

STATISTICAL SOURCES

11128 ■ *RMA Annual Statement Studies*
Pub: Risk Management Association
Contact: Nancy Foster, President

Released: Annual. **Description:** Contains composite balance sheets and income statements for more than 360 industries, including the accounting, auditing, and bookkeeping industries. Also contains five years of comparative historical data for discerning trends. Includes 16 commonly used ratios, computed for most of the size groupings for nearly every industry.

11129 ■ *US Movie Theaters Industry Report 2020*
URL(s): store.mintel.com/report/us-movie-theaters
  -market-report
Price: $4,366.35. **Description:** Downloadable report detailing the US movie theater industry. Includes analysis of how COVID-19 impacted theaters. Report

includes an executive summary, interactive databook, PowerPoint presentation, infographic overview, report PDF, and previous years data. **Availability:** PDF.

TRADE PERIODICALS

11130 ■ *Film Comment*
Pub: Film Society of Lincoln Center
Contact: Lesli Klainberg, President
URL(s): www.filmcomment.com
Facebook: www.facebook.com/filmcommentmagazine
X (Twitter): x.com/filmcomment
Ed: Nicolas Rapold, Gavin Smith. **Released:** 6/year; last edition May-June 2020. **Description:** Motion picture magazine. **Availability:** Print; Online.

VIDEO/AUDIO MEDIA

11131 ■ *How I Built This: Alamo Drafthouse Cinema: Tim and Karrie League*
URL(s): wondery.com/shows/how-i-built-this/episode/10386-alama-drafthouse-cinema-tim-and-karrie-league
Ed: Guy Raz. **Released:** May 22, 2023. **Description:** Podcast how the purchase of an abandoned movie theater on the wrong side of the tracks evolved into a national chain--despite a failed first theater, a lawsuit with business partners, and a pandemic.

CONSULTANTS

11132 ■ Stage Equipment and Lighting Inc.
1717 Diplomacy Row
  Orlando, FL 32809
URL: http://seal-fla.com
Linkedin: www.linkedin.com/company/stage-equipment-and-lighting-inc
Description: Offers creative services for presentations, staging, and lighting, including systems designs, installation supervision, seminars for personnel, theatrical equipment maintenance and lighting for all forms of presentations and presentation facilities, theaters, television, film, audiovisuals, meetings, and product presentations. **Founded:** 1967. **Publications:** "Lighting&Sound America".

FRANCHISES AND BUSINESS OPPORTUNITIES

11133 ■ The Actor's Garage
152 RYDER Rd.
  Manhasset, NY 11030
Ph: (516)375-5417
Co. E-mail: actorsgarage2004@gmail.com
URL: http://www.theactorsgarage.com
Contact: Ann Graf, Contact

Description: Education institution offers children acting. **Founded:** 2004. **Training:** Provides 5 days at headquarters with ongoing support.

11134 ■ Kidstage Wisconsin
Appleton, WI
URL: http://www.kidstage.net/wisconsin
Contact: Karen Cain, Co-Founder
Description: Drama classes and performance opportunities. **No. of Franchise Units:** 14. **No. of Company-Owned Units:** 3. **Founded:** 1996. **Franchised:** 2003. **Equity Capital Needed:** $14,000. **Franchise Fee:** $12,500. **Financial Assistance:** Yes **Training:** Yes.

LIBRARIES

11135 ■ American Film Institute (AFI) - Louis B. Mayer Library
2021 N W Ave.
  Los Angeles, CA 90027-1657
Ph: (323)856-7600
Fax: (323)467-4578
Co. E-mail: information@afi.com
URL: http://www.afi.com
Contact: Bob Gazzale, President
X (Twitter): x.com/americanfilm
YouTube: www.youtube.com/AFI
Description: Preserves the nation's artistic and cultural resources in film and video. Catalogs and preserves America's film heritage. Acts as a bridge between learning a craft and practicing a profession, through an intensive two-year course in filmmaking and film theory. Promotes the study of film as an art form with its own aesthetics, history, and techniques, through seminars for film teachers and special materials. Brings outstanding classic and contemporary films to public attention at a national film theater through The American Film Institute Theatre in the Kennedy Center in Washington, DC. **Scope:** Filmmaking; movie history; theory and criticism. **Services:** Open to the public by appointment; Scanning; Printing. **Founded:** 1967. **Holdings:** Books; DVDs; films; documentary; photography; scripts. **Publications:** *Catalog of Feature Films*; *Catalog of Motion Pictures Produced in the United States*; *National Moving Image Database (NAMID)*. **Awards:** AFI Movies of the Year (Annual); AFI TV Programs of the Year (Annual); AFI Life Achievement Award (Annual). **Geographic Preference:** National.

11136 ■ John E. Allen Inc. - Motion Picture Archives
PO Box 452
  Newfoundland, PA 18445
URL: http://www.allenarchive.com
Scope: Motion pictures, 1896-1980s; history. **Services:** Copying; archives open to the public by appointment on fee basis. **Founded:** 1896. **Holdings:** 25 million feet of 35mm and 16mm film.

11137 ■ University of Southern California - Cinematic Arts Library
3550 Trousdale Pky.
  Los Angeles, CA 90089
Ph: (213)740-4357
Co. E-mail: ctlibarc@usc.edu
URL: http://libraries.usc.edu/locations/cinematic-arts-library
Contact: Sona Basmadjian, Curator
E-mail: sonab@usc.edu
Description: Contains reference materials, journals, books, online materials, and video and audio materials on cinematic arts studies. **Scope:** History of the film industry; motion pictures; television. **Services:** Interlibrary loan; copy; open to the public. **Founded:** 1964. **Holdings:** 200,000 books; 450 journals.

RESEARCH CENTERS

11138 ■ Theatre Historical Society of America (THSA) - Archives
1221 Penn Ave.
  Pittsburgh, PA 15222
Ph: (315)789-6158
Co. E-mail: office@historictheatres.org
URL: http://historictheatres.org
Contact: Gary Lee Parks, President
Facebook: www.facebook.com/TheatreHistoricalSociety
X (Twitter): x.com/ThrHistSociety
YouTube: www.youtube.com/user/THSAmerica
Description: Individual hobbyists, college and public libraries, historical societies, and architects. Aims: to preserve the history of popular theatre in the US.; to make available information relating to American theatres; to encourage study in this field; to promote preservation of important theatre buildings. Emphasizes on theater architecture, management, advertising, and publicity and includes movie houses and legitimate, vaudeville, and stock company houses. **Scope:** American theater, including all buildings designed or regularly used for exhibition of stage or motion picture presentations and theater equipment and personnel. Acts as a clearinghouse for theater research. **Founded:** 1969. **Holdings:** Photographic prints; operational records; blueprints; photo negatives and slides; programs; books; artifacts; newspaper clippings; artwork; magazines. **Publications:** *Marquee* (Semiannual); *Marquee: The Quarterly Journal of the Theatre Historical Society of America* (Quarterly). **Educational Activities:** THS Annual convention and theater tour. **Awards:** Theatre Historical Society of America President's Award (Annual); THS Outstanding Book of the Year Award (Annual); THS Member of the Year Award; THS Honorary Member of the Year Award (Annual); Jeffery Weiss Literary Award Competition (Annual). **Geographic Preference:** National.

REFERENCE WORKS

11139 ■ *7 Mistakes Hurting Your Moving Company's Local SEO Ranking*

Description: When people search for "nearby moving companies", the result will include a few local results right at the top of the search results page. This article explains the importance of rising to the top of search engine results and how to ensure your company does so. **Availability:** Online.

11140 ■ *9 Ways to Improve Cash Flow for Your Moving Company*

Description: This article recommends cost saving ideas as well as ideas on managing day-to-day operations to improve the cash flow for your moving business. **Availability:** Online.

11141 ■ *10 Unconventional Ways to Get More Moving Leads*

Ed: Jason Rothman. **Released:** August 09, 2017. **Description:** This article looks at unconventional moving ideas can bring in tons of leads and moving clients to your business. **Availability:** Online.

11142 ■ *"For His Bigness of Heart: Larry O'Toole: Gentle Giant Moving, Somerville, Massachusetts" in Inc. (Volume 32, December 2010)*

Pub: Mansueto Ventures L.L.C.

Contact: Stephanie Mehta, Chief Executive Officer

Ed: Leigh Buchanan. **Released:** December 01, 2010. **Description:** Profile of Larry O'Toole, owners of Gentle Giant Moving Company, where his company charges more, but in return consumers receive a higher quality service. **Availability:** Online.

11143 ■ *"Hire Interstate Movers Without Getting Scammed" in The New York Times (May 8, 2018)*

URL(s): www.nytimes.com/2018/05/08/smarter-living/hire-interstate-movers-without-getting-scammed.html

Ed: Ayn-Monique Klahre. **Released:** May 08, 2018. **Description:** Tips and guidelines for moving across state lines with the help of a moving company. Not all companies are honest and many work against the consumer, which is why it is important to research various moving companies and further vet them to make sure you getting what you need. **Availability:** Online.

11144 ■ *"How Do I Get a License for a Moving Company?" in Chron (March 4, 2019)*

Ed: Kimberlee Leonard. **Released:** March 04, 2019. **Description:** A moving company license requires meeting the Department of Transportation (DOT) and Federal Motor Carrier Safety Administration (FMCSA) standards and regulations. This article details how to get the proper licensing and permits for your small business moving company. **Availability:** Online.

11145 ■ *How to Start a Moving Company*

Description: Moving companies are businesses that will always be in demand. This article provides detailed information on who is this business right for and nine steps to take to start your moving company. **Availability:** Online.

11146 ■ *"How to Start a Moving Company Business" in Chron (April 24, 2019)*

Ed: Shanika Chapman. **Released:** April 24, 2019. **Description:** Discusses steps to consider before starting your own moving company business including developing a business plan, getting industry training, finding space for your business, buying trucks, obtaining insurance, applying for licenses and permits, marketing, and equipment you'll need. **Availability:** Online.

11147 ■ *How to Start a Moving Company Without Alot of Money*

Description: This article discusses how you can start a small weekend moving company to supplement your income and how you can grow that company over time. **Availability:** Online.

11148 ■ *"How to Start a Successful Moving Company Business" in MyMovingReviews.com (June 3, 2020)*

Ed: Vasilka Atanasova. **Released:** June 03, 2020. **Description:** This article provides moving company startup tips, business ideas, steps, and requirements. **Availability:** Online.

11149 ■ *"KXAN Seeks Larger Studio, Office Space in Austin" in Austin Business Journal (Vol. 31, May 27, 2011, No. 12, pp. A1)*

Pub: Austin Business Journal

Contact: Rachel McGrath, Director

E-mail: rmcgrath@bizjournals.com

Ed: Cody Lyon. **Description:** Austin NBC affiliate KXAN Television is opting to sell its property north of downtown and relocate to another site. The station is now inspecting possible sites to house its broadcasting facility and employees totaling as many as 200 people. Estimated cost of the construction of the studios and offices is $13 million plus another million in moving the equipment. **Availability:** Print; Online.

11150 ■ *"Moving Company Accused of Holding Customers' Belongings Hostage" in CBSnews (January 28, 2019)*

URL(s): www.cbsnews.com/news/spartan-van-lines-moving-scams-florida-crackdown-attorney-general/

Released: January 28, 2019. **Description:** The state of Florida is taking action against multiple moving companies that have been defrauding consumers around the country. Fourteen companies have been named and they face allegations ranging from damaging property to extortion. **Availability:** Online.

11151 ■ *The Three Types of Moving Companies*

Ed: Jason Rothman. **Released:** April 07, 2016. **Description:** Some of the keys to profitably running a moving business are to know your company,

understand your market, and figure out where you fit in. This article discusses three types of moving companies and how to determine which type you want to run. **Availability:** Online.

11152 ■ *"Use These Unique Resources to Start a Moving Business" in A Touch of Business (June 23, 2020)*

Released: June 23, 2020. **Description:** A thorough guide to several issues to consider before deciding to start a moving business. **Availability:** Online.

11153 ■ *"Yes, You're Paying About 15% More to Move This Year. Here's Why." in Forbes (August 3, 2021)*

Ed: Samantha Allen. **Released:** August 03, 2021. **Description:** Discusses the labor shortage throughout the US and how it's impacting the moving industry, which is driving up costs for those moving house. **Availability:** Online.

STATISTICAL SOURCES

11154 ■ *Moving Services Industry in the US - Market Research Report*

URL(s): www.ibisworld.com/united-states/market-research-reports/moving-services-industry/

Price: $925. **Description:** Downloadable report analyzing the current and future trends in the moving services industry. **Availability:** Download.

11155 ■ *RMA Annual Statement Studies*

Pub: Risk Management Association

Contact: Nancy Foster, President

Released: Annual. **Description:** Contains composite balance sheets and income statements for more than 360 industries, including the accounting, auditing, and bookkeeping industries. Also contains five years of comparative historical data for discerning trends. Includes 16 commonly used ratios, computed for most of the size groupings for nearly every industry.

VIDEO/AUDIO MEDIA

11156 ■ *The How of Business: Scott Krone - Self-Storage Business*

URL(s): www.thehowofbusiness.com/477-scott-krone-self-storage-business

Ed: Henry Lopez. **Released:** June 19, 2023. **Description:** Podcast discusses starting a self-storage business.

11157 ■ *The How of Business: Wade Swikle - Starting a Moving Business*

URL(s): www.thehowofbusiness.com/486-wade-swikle-moving-business

Ed: Henry Lopez. **Released:** August 21, 2023. **Description:** Podcast discusses starting a small moving business.

FRANCHISES AND BUSINESS OPPORTUNITIES

11158 ■ **Craters & Freighters**
Craters & Freighters Franchise Co.
331 Corporate Cir., Ste. J
Golden, CO 80401

Free: 866-254-7376
URL: http://www.cratersandfreighters.com
Contact: Matthew Schmitz, President
Facebook: www.facebook.com/CFNTL
Linkedin: www.linkedin.com/company/craters-&-freigh
  ters-national
X (Twitter): x.com/CF_National

Description: Serves an up-scale market on art galleries, museums, estate liquidators, interior decorators and a host of other clients to fulfill their specialized needs in moving a multitude of large, delicate and valuable freight shipments. **No. of Franchise Units:** 65. **Founded:** 1990. **Franchised:** 1991. **Equity Capital Needed:** $183,600-$252,500. **Franchise Fee:** $35,000. **Royalty Fee:** 5%. **Training:** Offers training at headquarters 10 days, 2-3 days at franchisee's location, 2 days annual convention with ongoing support.

11159 ■ Moving Solutions Franchise L.L.C.
115 W Eagle Rd.
  Havertown, PA 19083
Description: Move management and relocation services. **Founded:** 1996. **Training:** Available at headquarters for 10 days and ongoing support.

11160 ■ Two Men and A Truck International Inc.
3400 Belle Chase Way
  Lansing, MI 48911
Free: 800-345-1070
URL: http://twomenandatruck.com
Contact: Randy Shacka, President
X (Twitter): x.com/TwoMenAndATruck
YouTube: www.youtube.com/user/twomenandatruck
Description: Provider of local trucking services including home moving, business moving, packing, customer services. **Founded:** 1985.

11161 ■ Two Men and a Truck Canada
245 Yorkland Blvd., Ste. 100
  Toronto, ON, Canada M2J 4W9
Free: 866-684-6448
Co. E-mail: customer.service@twomen.ca
URL: http://twomenandatruck.ca
Contact: John Prittie, President
Facebook: www.facebook.com/TwoMenCanada
Linkedin: www.linkedin.com/company/two-men-and-a
  -truck-canada
X (Twitter): x.com/twomencanada
Instagram: www.instagram.com/twomencanada
YouTube: www.youtube.com/user/TwoMenCanada

Description: Provider of moving services such as home moving in Michigan. **Founded:** 2005. **Equity Capital Needed:** $171,000-$320,500; A minimum net worth of $500,000. **Franchise Fee:** $50,000-$85,000. **Training:** Provides 3 weeks training.

ASSOCIATIONS AND OTHER ORGANIZATIONS

11162 ■ American String Teachers Association (ASTA)
4155 Chain Bridge Rd.
 Fairfax, VA 22030
Ph: (703)279-2113
Fax: (703)279-2114
Co. E-mail: asta@astaweb.com
URL: http://www.astastrings.org
Contact: Kristen Pellegrino, President
Facebook: www.facebook.com/American-String
 -Teachers-Association-104343234646
Instagram: www.instagram.com/astastrings

Description: Promotes excellence in string and orchestra teaching and playing, together with the National School Orchestra Association. Pursues its mission through: an open sharing of ideas; benefits, services, and activities responsive to the needs of all members; development of strong state leadership and chapters; enhancing the image and visibility of string teaching and study; advocacy for string education; and an inclusive community of string teachers and players. **Founded:** 1946. **Publications:** *American String Teacher (AST)* (Quarterly); *ASTA e-newsletter* (Weekly). **Awards:** ASTA Artist-Teacher Award (Annual); Elizabeth A. H. Green School Educator Award (Annual). **Geographic Preference:** National.

11163 ■ Association for Technology in Music Instruction (ATMI)
312 East Pine St.
 Missoula, MT 59802
Contact: Brendan McConville, Contact

Description: Seeks to increase public awareness of computer-based music systems. Provides a forum for publishing research; facilitates the exchange of information among users of computers in music instruction; aids music teachers in implementing computer-based systems in music education. Serves as a research clearinghouse in the field. **Founded:** 1975. **Publications:** *ATMI International Newsletter* (Quarterly); *ATMI Music Technology Directory*; *Technology Directory* (Annual). **Geographic Preference:** National.

11164 ■ Canadian Federation of Music Teachers' Associations (CFMTA) [Federation Canadienne des Professeurs de Musique (FCAPM)]
PO Box 814
 Summerland, BC, Canada V0H 1Z0
Ph: (250)328-2198
Co. E-mail: admin@cfmta.org
URL: http://www.cfmta.org/en
Contact: Laura Gray, President
E-mail: president@cfmta.org
YouTube: www.youtube.com/channel/UCCHayVosTa
 5Cvp31jfoJbyA

Description: Private music teachers that promote music education in Canada. The company organizes performances and competitions, and sponsors music appreciation programs. **Founded:** 1935. **Publications:** *The Canadian Music Teacher* (3/year); *The Canadian Music Teacher: Canada Music Week Edition* (3/year). **Educational Activities:** CFMTA /FCAPM National Conference (Biennial). **Awards:** William Andrews Award (Annual); Memorial Pedagogy Award (Annual). **Geographic Preference:** National.

11165 ■ *The Canadian Music Teacher*
PO Box 814
 Summerland, BC, Canada V0H 1Z0
Ph: (250)328-2198
Co. E-mail: admin@cfmta.org
URL: http://www.cfmta.org/en
Contact: Laura Gray, President
E-mail: president@cfmta.org
Released: 3/year; Winter, Spring, Fall. **Price:** $35, Members for Canadian residents; $45, Nonmembers for non Canadian residents; $35, Members for 3 issues; $10, Members for 1 issue; $45, Nonmembers for 3 issues. **Availability:** Print; Download; PDF.

11166 ■ *The Canadian Music Teacher: Canada Music Week Edition*
PO Box 814
 Summerland, BC, Canada V0H 1Z0
Ph: (250)328-2198
Co. E-mail: admin@cfmta.org
URL: http://www.cfmta.org/en
Contact: Laura Gray, President
E-mail: president@cfmta.org
URL(s): www.cfmta.org/en/canadian-music-teacher
 -magazine
Released: 3/year **Price:** $35, Members for Canadian resident; $45, Nonmembers for non Canadian resident; $10, Members for 1 issue. **Availability:** Print; Online; PDF.

11167 ■ International Computer Music Association (ICMA) - Library
1819 Polk St., Ste. 330
 San Francisco, CA 94109
Co. E-mail: icma@umich.edu
URL: http://www.computermusic.org
Contact: Kerry L. Hagan, President
E-mail: kerry.hagan@ul.ie
Description: Works to advance individuals and institutions involved in the technical, creative and performance aspects of computer music. Provides networking opportunities; sponsors research and projects; holds competitions. **Scope:** Music; technology. **Founded:** 1974. **Holdings:** Figures not available. **Awards:** ICMC Best Presentation Award (Annual); ICMA International Computer Music Commission Awards (Annual). **Geographic Preference:** Multinational.

11168 ■ *Intersections*
c/o DAN School of Drama & Music
 39 Bader Ln.
 Harrison LeCaine Hall
 Kingston, ON, Canada K7L 3N6

Co. E-mail: office@muscan.org
URL: http://muscan.org
Contact: Laura Gray, President
URL(s): muscan.org/intersectionswww.erudit.org/en/
 journals/is
Ed: Robin Elliott. **Released:** Semiannual **Availability:** Print; PDF; Online.

11169 ■ Music Publishers' Association of the United States (MPA)
442 5th Ave., No. 1137
 New York, NY 10018
Co. E-mail: admin@mpa.org
URL: http://www.mpa.org
Contact: Steven Lankenau, President
Facebook: www.facebook.com/MPAoftheUSA
X (Twitter): x.com/MusicPublishers

Description: Publishers of music intended for educational and concert purposes. Promotes trade and commerce; encourages understanding of and compliance with copyright laws to protect musical works against piracy and infringement. **Founded:** 1895. **Awards:** Paul Revere Awards for Graphic Excellence (Annual). **Geographic Preference:** National.

11170 ■ Music Teachers National Association (MTNA)
600 Vine St., Ste. 1710
 Cincinnati, OH 45202
Ph: (513)421-1420
Free: 888-512-5278
Co. E-mail: mtnanet@mtna.org
URL: http://www.mtna.org/MTNA/Home/MTNA/
 Default.aspx?hkey=91963004-fbe4-4711-a192-b
 6293aedc31c
Contact: Gary L. Ingle, Chief Executive Officer
E-mail: gingle@mtna.org
Facebook: www.facebook.com/mtnapage
Linkedin: www.linkedin.com/company/music-teachers
 -national-association
X (Twitter): x.com/MTNA1
Instagram: www.instagram.com/mtnaorg
YouTube: www.youtube.com/channel/UCdzWx
 _UxrOZz9HoeXsZxWig
Pinterest: www.pinterest.com/musicteache0952

Description: Professional society of independent and collegiate music teachers committed to furthering the art of music through programs that encourage and support teaching, performance, composition, and scholarly research. **Founded:** 1876. **Publications:** *Directory of Nationally Certified Teachers of Music* (Annual); *American Music Teacher (AMT)* (6/year); *American Music Teacher* (6/year). **Educational Activities:** MTNA National Conference (Annual). **Awards:** Piano Technicians Guild Scholarship (Irregular); Shepherd Distinguished Composer of the Year Award (Annual); MTNA Junior Performance Competition (Annual); MTNA Student Composition Competition (Annual); MTNA Senior Performance Competitions (Annual); MTNA Chamber Music Performance Competition (Annual); MTNA Distinguished Composer of the Year (Annual). **Geographic Preference:** National.

11171 ■ National Association for Music Education (NAFME)
585 Grove St., Ste. 145 No. 711
  Herndon, VA 20170
Ph: (703)860-4000
Free: 800-336-3768
Co. E-mail: nafme@nafme.org
URL: http://nafme.org
Contact: Deb Confredo, President
Facebook: www.facebook.com/NAfME
Linkedin: www.linkedin.com/company/national
  -association-for-music-education-nafme
X (Twitter): x.com/NAfME
Instagram: www.instagram.com/nafme
Pinterest: www.pinterest.com/nafme
Description: Comprised of music educators, administrators, supervisors, consultants, and music education majors in colleges. Publishes materials for music educators, presents conferences, compiles statistics. **Founded:** 1907. **Publications:** *Teaching Music* (Quarterly); *Journal of Research in Music Education* (Quarterly); *Journal of General Music Education (JGME)* (3/year); *Update: Applications of Research in Music Education* (3/year); *Music Educators Journal (MEJ)* (Quarterly); *Journal of Music Teacher Education (JMTE)* (3/year); *Tri-M News* (Semiannual); *TRI-M News* (Semiannual). **Educational Activities:** MENC National Conference (Biennial); National In-Service Conference; NAfME National In-Service Conference (Annual). **Awards:** Tri-M Leadership (Annual); Tri-M Master Musician (Annual); Tri-M Outstanding Service (Annual); Master Musician Award (Annual); Leadership Award (Annual); Outstanding Service Award; National Chapter of the Year (Annual); Chapter of the Year Award (Annual). **Geographic Preference:** National.

11172 ■ National Association of Music Merchants (NAMM)
5790 Armada Dr.
  Carlsbad, CA 92008
Ph: (760)438-8001
Free: 800-767-6266
Fax: (760)438-7327
Co. E-mail: info@namm.org
URL: http://www.namm.org
Contact: Joe Lamond, President
Facebook: www.facebook.com/nammorg
X (Twitter): x.com/NAMM
Instagram: www.instagram.com/thenammshow
YouTube: www.youtube.com/user/nammorg
Description: Retailers of musical instruments and allied products, manufacturers, distributors, jobbers, wholesalers and publishers of print music. Holds several professional development seminars in various locations around the country and two major trade shows. **Founded:** 1901. **Publications:** *Playback* (Semiannual). **Educational Activities:** The NAMM Show (Annual); Summer NAMM (Annual). **Awards:** William R. Gard Memorial Scholarship (Annual); William R. Gard Memorial Scholarships (Annual). **Geographic Preference:** Multinational; Local.

11173 ■ National Association of School Music Dealers, Inc. (NASMD)
14070 Proton Rd., Ste. 100
  Dallas, TX 75244
Ph: (972)233-9107
Fax: (972)490-4219
Co. E-mail: office@nasmd.com
URL: http://www.nasmd.com
Contact: Whitney Brown Grisaffi, Contact
Facebook: www.facebook.com/nasmd
Description: Retail music stores and companies engaged in sales, service and repair of band and orchestra instruments to elementary and secondary schools and colleges. **Founded:** 1962. **Publications:** *NASMD Newsletter* (Quarterly). **Geographic Preference:** National.

11174 ■ National Association of Schools of Music (NASM)
11250 Roger Bacon Dr., Ste. 21
  Reston, VA 20190-5248
Ph: (703)437-0700
Fax: (703)437-6312

Co. E-mail: info@arts-accredit.org
URL: http://nasm.arts-accredit.org
Contact: Dan Dressen, President
Description: Serves as an accrediting agency for music educational programs. Compiles statistics. **Founded:** 1924. **Publications:** *National Association of Schools of Music--Directory Lists*. **Geographic Preference:** National.

11175 ■ National Association for the Study and Performance of African-American Music (NASPAAM)
c/o Martha C. Brown, Treasurer
  809 E Gladwick St.
  Carson, CA 90746
URL: http://naspaa.hostcentric.com/index.html
Contact: Dr. Marsha Kindall-Smith, President
Description: Provides a forum for the discussion of concerns. Coordinates and disseminates materials concerning black-derived music in order to assist music teachers in teaching black music and students. **Founded:** 1972. **Publications:** *Con Brio* (Quarterly). **Educational Activities:** National Association for the Study and Performance of African-American Music Conference. **Geographic Preference:** National.

11176 ■ National Association of Teachers of Singing (NATS)
9957 Moorings Dr., Ste. 401
  Jacksonville, FL 32257
Ph: (904)992-9101
Fax: (904)262-2587
Co. E-mail: info@nats.org
URL: http://www.nats.org
Contact: Carole Blankenship, President
E-mail: president@nats.org
Facebook: www.facebook.com/OfficialNATS
Linkedin: www.linkedin.com/company/nat%27l-assoc
  .-of-teachers-of-singing-nats
X (Twitter): x.com/OfficialNATS
YouTube: www.youtube.com/user/OfficialNATS
Pinterest: www.pinterest.com/officialnats
Description: Serves as a professional society of teachers of singing. Encourages the highest standards of the vocal art and of ethical principles in the teaching of singing. Promotes vocal education and research at all levels, both for the enrichment of the general public and for the professional advancement of the talented. **Founded:** 1944. **Publications:** *National Association of Teachers of Singing--Membership Directory*; *Journal of Singing* (5/year). **Awards:** NATS Art Song Composition Award (Annual); NATS Artist Awards (NATSAA) (Biennial). **Geographic Preference:** National.

11177 ■ Organization of American Kodaly Educators (OAKE)
650 NE Holladay St., Ste. 1600
  Portland, OR 97232
Ph: (310)441-3555
Fax: (310)441-3577
Co. E-mail: info@oake.org
URL: http://www.oake.org
Contact: Kevin Pearson, President
Facebook: www.facebook.com/oakeorg
X (Twitter): x.com/OAKENational
Instagram: www.instagram.com/oakenational
Description: Music educators, students, organizations, schools, and libraries interested in the Kodaly concept of music education. Zoltan Kodaly (1882-1967), Hungarian composer and educator, originated a concept of music education that seeks to develop the sensibilities, intellectual facilities, and skills of children, with the intention of creating a musically educated public. Objectives are: to encourage communication and cooperation among Kodaly educators; to encourage musical and human growth; to recognize, identify, and convey the multicultural musical heritage of American society; to contribute to and encourage the aesthetic education of the child. **Founded:** 1975. **Publications:** *Kodaly Concept of Music Education*; *Kodaly Envoy* (Quarterly). **Educational Activities:** Annual OAKE National Conference (Annual). **Geographic Preference:** National.

11178 ■ Societe de Musique des Universites Canadiennes (SMUC) [Canadian University Music Society (CUMS)]
c/o DAN School of Drama & Music
  39 Bader Ln.
  Harrison LeCaine Hall
  Kingston, ON, Canada K7L 3N6
Co. E-mail: office@muscan.org
URL: http://muscan.org
Contact: Laura Gray, President
Facebook: www.facebook.com/MusCanSoc
Description: Represents university music schools and professors, graduate students, and independent scholars. **Founded:** 1964. **Publications:** *Intersections* (Semiannual). **Awards:** SOCAN Foundation/ George Proctor Prize (Annual). **Geographic Preference:** National.

REFERENCE WORKS

11179 ■ *"Music Students Do Better in School Than Non-Musical Peers"* in ScienceDaily (June 24, 2019)
URL(s): www.sciencedaily.com/releases/2019/06/190
  624111504.htm
Released: June 24, 2019. **Description:** A new study shows that high school students who engage in music classes have higher scores in math, science, and English. **Availability:** Online.

11180 ■ *National Association of Schools of Music--Directory Lists*
Pub: National Association of Schools of Music
Contact: Dan Dressen, President
URL(s): nasm.arts-accredit.org/directory-lists
Description: Covers approximately 630 college and university departments of music and music conservatories accredited by the association. **Entries include:** School name, address, type of membership, description of music program, name of chief administrator, phone, degree or other study programs offered in music. **Arrangement:** Alphabetical. **Availability:** Print; Online.

11181 ■ *National Opera Association--Membership Directory*
Pub: National Opera Association
Contact: Benjamin Brecher, President
E-mail: president@noa.org
URL(s): www.noa.org/about/membership.html
Description: Covers about 675 music and singing teachers, singers, directors, and about 300 schools, colleges, and organizations interested in opera; international coverage. **Entries include:** Name, address, phone, activity or occupation. **Arrangement:** Alphabetical within membership divisions. **Indexes:** Geographical. **Availability:** Print.

11182 ■ *"One of the Last Music Stores in San Francisco Is Closing"* in San Francisco Chronicle (September 14, 2019)
URL(s): www.sfchronicle.com/business/article/One-of
  -the-last-music-stores-in-San-Francisco-is-1443920
  3.php
Ed: Shwanika Narayan. **Released:** September 14, 2019. **Description:** Independent music store Haight Ashbury Music Center is closing its doors for the final time after almost half a century in the business. **Availability:** Online.

11183 ■ *"Performing Leadership"* in Business Strategy Review (Vol. 23, Spring 2012, No. 1, pp. 56)
Description: Can you create a great performance in three days? Orchestra conductors do so time and time again. Bernhard Kerres investigates how they do it and what we can learn from them. Profile of Kerres in included. **Availability:** PDF; Online.

11184 ■ *"Should All Schools Offer Music Programs?"* in The New York Times (May 17, 2018)
URL(s): www.nytimes.com/2018/05/17/learning/shoul
  d-all-schools-offer-music-programs.html

Ed: Natalie Proulx. **Released:** May 17, 2019. **Description:** Making the case to include music classes in all NYC schools, not just private schools or schools in higher socioeconomic areas. **Availability:** Online.

SOURCES OF SUPPLY

11185 ■ *Music Trades--The Purchaser's Guide to the Music Industries*
Music Trades Corp.
Contact: Brian T. Majeski, Editor
E-mail: brian@musictrades.com
URL(s): www.musictrades.com/guide.html
Ed: Brian T. Majeski. **Released:** Annual; latest edition, 2020. **Price:** $20, Individuals for one year. **Description:** Publication includes list of 3,000 musical instrument manufacturers and wholesalers, publishers of sheet music, and manufacturers of musical accessories; international coverage. **Entries include:** Company name, address, phone, names of executives, trade and brand names, products or services. **Arrangement:** Alphabetical. **Availability:** Print; Online.

TRADE PERIODICALS

11186 ■ *Acoustic Guitar Magazine*
Pub: Acoustic Guitar
URL(s): store.acousticguitar.com/collections/back -issues
Facebook: www.facebook.com/AcousticGui tarMagazine
Released: Monthly **Price:** $35.99, for online one year; $90.99, for online 3 year; $66.99, for 2 year; $35.99, for print and online 1 year; $66.99, for print and online 2 year; $90.99, for print and online 3 year. **Description:** Magazine for professional and amateur acoustic guitar enthusiasts offering advice on choosing, maintaining, and playing acoustic guitar. **Availability:** Print; Download; Online.

11187 ■ *Alla Breve*
Pub: Kodály Society of Canada
Contact: Laurel Forshaw, Treasurer
URL(s): www.kodalysocietyofcanada.ca/alla-breve
Released: Last Edition Vol. 47 May 2023. **Description:** Trade journal covering music education. **Availability:** Print; Online; Download; PDF.

11188 ■ *American Music Teacher*
Pub: Music Teachers National Association
Contact: Gary L. Ingle, Chief Executive Officer
E-mail: gingle@mtna.org
URL(s): www.mtna.org/MTNA/Stay_Informed/Ameri-can_Music_Teacher/American_Music_Teacher.aspx
Released: 6/year **Price:** $128, for three year international; $48, for one year international; $88, for two year international; $6, Single issue for back issues; $96, for three year; $36, Nonmembers for one year; $66, for two year. **Description:** Magazine provides articles, reviews and regular columns that inform, educate and challenge music teachers and foster excellence in the music teaching profession. **Availability:** Online.

11189 ■ *American Suzuki Journal (ASJ)*
Pub: Suzuki Association of the Americas
Contact: Pam Brasch, Chief Executive Officer
URL(s): suzukiassociation.org/news/journal
Released: Quarterly **Description:** Music education journal. **Availability:** Print; Online.

11190 ■ *British Journal of Music Education*
Pub: Cambridge University Press
Contact: Peter Phillips, Chief Executive Officer
URL(s): www.cambridge.org/core/journals/british -journal-of-music-education
X (Twitter): x.com/BJMEMusic
Ed: Martin Fautley, Regina Murphy. **Released:** 3/year **Price:** $639, Institutions for bundle print & online; $430, Institutions for online. **Description:** Peer-reviewed journal focusing on current issues in music education. **Availability:** Print; Download; PDF; Online.

11191 ■ *Down Beat: Jazz, Blues & Beyond*
Pub: Maher Publications
URL(s): downbeat.com/magazine
Facebook: www.facebook.com/downbeatmagazine
X (Twitter): x.com/DownBeatMag
Released: Monthly **Price:** $31.99, for print & digital 1 year; $58.99, for print & digital 2 year; $80.99, for print & digital 3 year; $23.99, for digital 1 year; $47.99, for digital 2 year; $71.99, for digital 3 year; $8, Single issue. **Description:** Magazine edited for the learning musician. **Availability:** Print; Online.

11192 ■ *Journal of Music Teacher Education (JMTE)*
Pub: SAGE Publications
Contact: Tracey Ozmina, President
URL(s): journals.sagepub.com/home/jmt
Ed: Colleen Conway. **Released:** 3/year **Price:** $164, Institutions for online only; us.sagepub.com/en-us/nam/journal/journal-music-teacher-education; $133, Institutions for purchase, e-access (content through 1998); $149, Institutions for e-access. **Description:** Peer-reviewed, online only journal covering issues related to music teacher education. Published in association between SAGE and the National Association for Music Education on behalf of the Society for Music Teacher Education. **Availability:** Print; PDF; Online; Download.

11193 ■ *Journal of Research in Music Education*
Pub: SAGE Publications
Contact: Tracey Ozmina, President
URL(s): journals.sagepub.com/home/JRM
Ed: Peter Miksza. **Released:** Quarterly **Price:** $466, Institutions for subscription & backfile lease, combined plus backfile (current volume print & all online content); $402, Institutions for subscription & backfile lease, e-access plus backfile (all online content); $1,412, Institutions for backfile purchase, e-access; $114, Institutions for single issue print; $424, Institutions for print & online; $416, Institutions for print only; $360, Institutions for online. **Description:** Peer-reviewed journal covering original research related to music teaching and learning. Published in association between SAGE and the National Association for Music Education. **Availability:** Print; PDF; Online.

11194 ■ *Kodaly Envoy*
Pub: Organization of American Kodaly Educators
Contact: Kevin Pearson, President
URL(s): www.oake.org/kodaly-envoy-info
Released: Quarterly **Price:** $5, Members for back issue; $5, Nonmembers for back issue. **Description:** Promotes the use of Kodaly music education, a teaching approach founded by Hungarian composer, teacher, and ethnomusicologist, Zoltan Kodaly (1882-1967). The Kodaly approach is for general and choral music education. Recurring features include book reviews, news of members, a calendar of events, news of research, and feature articles. **Availability:** Print; Online.

11195 ■ *Music Educators Journal (MEJ)*
Pub: SAGE Publications
Contact: Tracey Ozmina, President
URL(s): journals.sagepub.com/home/mejc
Ed: Ella Wilcox. **Released:** Quarterly **Price:** $440, Institutions for backfile lease, e-access plus backfile (all online content); $2,806, Institutions for backfile purchase, e-access (content through 1998); $125, Institutions for single print issue; $463, Institutions for print and online; $394, Institutions for online only; $454, Institutions for print only; $509, Institutions for backfile lease, combined plus backfile (current volume print & all online content). **Description:** Peer-reviewed, scholarly journal covering music teaching approaches and philosophies, instructional techniques, current trends and issues in music education, and the latest in products and services. Published in association between SAGE and the National Association for Music Education. **Availability:** Print; PDF; Online.

11196 ■ *Music Trades*
Pub: Music Trades Corp.
Contact: Brian T. Majeski, Editor

E-mail: brian@musictrades.com
URL(s): www.musictrades.com/about.html
Facebook: www.facebook.com/people/Music-Trades -Magazine/100067015846955
Ed: Brian T. Majeski. **Released:** Monthly **Price:** $299, Individuals. **Description:** Music trade magazine. **Availability:** Print; PDF; Online.

TRADE SHOWS AND CONVENTIONS

11197 ■ **American Choral Directors Association National Conference**
American Choral Directors Association (ACDA)
  545 Couch Dr.
  Oklahoma City, OK 73102-2207
Ph: (405)232-8161
Fax: (405)232-8162
Co. E-mail: membership@acda.org
URL: http://acda.org
Contact: Dr. Tim Sharp, Executive Director
E-mail: sharp@acda.org
URL(s): acda.org/archives/events/2025-national -conference
Frequency: Biennial. **Audience:** Choral directors. Dates and Locations: 2025 Mar 19-22 Dallas, TX. **Telecommunication Services:** shail@acda.org.

11198 ■ **American Harp Society National Conference**
American Harp Society (AHS)
  PO Box 260
  Bellingham, MA 02019-0260
Ph: (805)410-4277
Fax: (508)803-8383
Co. E-mail: membership@harpsociety.org
URL: http://www.harpsociety.org
Contact: Kathryn McManus, Executive Director
URL(s): www.harpsociety.org/national-conference
Frequency: Annual. **Description:** Dynamic concerts and workshops, and to enjoy true southern hospitality with friends old and new. **Audience:** Harpists and harp enthusiasts. **Principal Exhibits:** Dynamic concerts and workshops, and to enjoy true southern hospitality with friends old and new. **Telecommunication Services:** execdirector@harpsociety.org.

11199 ■ **College Music Society National Conference**
College Music Society (CMS)
  312 E Pine St.
  Missoula, MT 59802
Ph: (406)721-9616
Co. E-mail: cms@music.org
URL: http://www.music.org
Contact: William L. Pelto, Executive Director
E-mail: executivedirector@music.org
URL(s): www.music.org/2024-natl-overview.html
Frequency: Annual; held each fall. **Description:** Music publishers, instrument manufacturers, music retailers, music careers, composition, ethnomusicology, higher education, music technology, music theory, performance, and mentoring. **Audience:** Faculty, administrators, graduate students, independent scholars, composers, publishers, and music business personnel. **Principal Exhibits:** Music publishers, instrument manufacturers, music retailers, music careers, composition, ethnomusicology, higher education, music technology, music theory, performance, and mentoring. Dates and Locations: 2025 Oct 30-Nov 01 The Davenport Grand Hotel, Spokane, WA; 2026 Nov 12-14 Amway Grand Plaza, Grand Rapids, MI. **Telecommunication Services:** conferenceplanner@music.org.

11200 ■ **NAfME National In-Service Conference**
National Association for Music Education (NAFME)
  585 Grove St., Ste. 145 No. 711
  Herndon, VA 20170
Ph: (703)860-4000
Free: 800-336-3768
Co. E-mail: nafme@nafme.org
URL: http://nafme.org
Contact: Deb Confredo, President

URL(s): us-tdm-tso-15eb63ff4c6-1626e-1680662e
555.force.com/s/lt-event?id=a1Y2H000009
tRsOUAU&site=a0d1U000001qiZcQAI#Home
Frequency: Annual. **Description:** Music education
equipment, supplies, and services. Includes keynote
speakers, and plenary sessions. **Audience:** Professional music educators. **Principal Exhibits:** Music
education equipment, supplies, and services. Includes keynote speakers, and plenary sessions.

11201 ■ New York State School Music Association Winter Conference

New York State School Music Association
(NYSSMA)
718 The Plain Rd.
Westbury, NY 11590-5931
Ph: (516)997-7200
Fax: (516)997-1700
Co. E-mail: info@nyssma.org
URL: http://www.nyssma.org
Contact: Edmund Chiarello, President
URL(s): www.nyssma.org/event/new-york-state
-summer-music-conference
Frequency: Annual. **Description:** Music publishers,
musical instruments, fund-raising materials, and
educational materials. **Audience:** New York state
school music association members and students.
Principal Exhibits: Music publishers, musical instru-
ments, fund-raising materials, and educational materials. **Telecommunication Services:** conference@
nyssma.org.

11202 ■ TMEA Convention

Texas Music Educators Association (TMEA)
7900 Centre Pk. Dr.
Austin, TX 78754
Ph: (512)452-0710
Free: 888-318-8632
URL: http://www.tmea.org
Contact: Dr. Robert Floyd, Executive Director
E-mail: rfloyd@tmea.org
URL(s): www.tmea.org/convention
Frequency: Annual. **Description:** Music publishers,
uniform/gowns, recruitment, photographers, software.
Audience: Music educators, college students, family
attendees, high school and middle school students,
non-music educators, and performing group mem-
bers/chaperones. **Principal Exhibits:** Music publish-
ers, uniform/gowns, recruitment, photographers,
software. Dates and Locations: 2025 Feb 12-15; 2026
Feb 11-14; 2027 Feb 10-13; 2028 Feb 09-12; 2029
Feb 07-10; 2030 Feb 13-16. Henry B. González
Convention Center, San Antonio, TX. **Telecommunication Services:** susand@tmea.org.

CONSULTANTS

11203 ■ Music Business Solutions (MBS)

PO Box 230266
Boston, MA 02123
Ph: (978)887-8041
URL: http://www.mbsolutions.com
Description: Provider of consulting service for the
music career and business development. **Scope:**
Provider of consulting service for the music career
and business development. **Founded:** 1991. **Publi-
cations:** "Indie Business Power: A Step-By-Step
Guide for 21st Century Music Entrepreneurs New!";
"The Self-Promoting Musician: Strategies for Indepen-
dent Music Success"; "Indie Marketing Power," MBS
Business Media Publication, 2006; "Indie Power,"
MBS Business Media publication, Apr, 2003; "The
Musician's Internet," Berklee Press/Hal Leonard
publication, 2002. **Training:** How to Succeed in Music
Without Overpaying Your Dues; Be Sharp or Be Flat:
Making It in the Music Industry; Unfolding Artists:
Helping Musical Artists Reach Their Full Creative
Potential; How to Start and Grow Your Own Record
Label or Music Production Company.

FRANCHISES AND BUSINESS OPPORTUNITIES

11204 ■ Arcadia Academy of Music

205 Marycroft Ave., Unit 6
Woodbridge, ON, Canada L4L 5X8

Ph: (905)851-8631
Co. E-mail: woodbridge@arcadiamusicacademy.com
URL: http://arcadiaacademyofmusic.com
Contact: Carmine Di Rauso, Sr., Founder
Facebook: www.facebook.com/arcadiamusicaca
demy
X (Twitter): x.com/ArcadiaAcademy
Instagram: www.instagram.com/arcadiaaca
demyofmusic
Description: Music school. **No. of Franchise Units:**
9. **No. of Company-Owned Units:** 1. **Founded:**
1984. **Franchised:** 1998. **Equity Capital Needed:**
$60,000 and up leasehold/equipment. **Franchise
Fee:** $20,000. **Training:** Yes.

LIBRARIES

11205 ■ American Conservatory of Music - Robert R. McCormick Memorial Library

4607 Magoun Ave.
East Chicago, IN 46312
URL: http://www.americanconservatory.edu/library
.html
Scope: Music. **Services:** Copying; library not open
to the public. **Founded:** 1886. **Holdings:** 1,600
volumes of books.

11206 ■ Andy Warhol Museum Archives Study Center

117 Sandusky St.
Pittsburgh, PA 15212
URL: http://www.warhol.org/research/archives-study
-center/archives-collection-research-request-form
Description: Library of archiever collections. **Scope:**
Museums collections. **Founded:** 1994. **Holdings:**
Figures not available.

11207 ■ Bagaduce Music Lending Library (BMLL)

49 S St.
Blue Hill, ME 04614
Ph: (207)374-5454
Co. E-mail: library@bagaducemusic.org
URL: http://www.bagaducemusic.org
Contact: Richard Howe, President
Facebook: www.facebook.com/bagaducemusic
Instagram: www.instagram.com/bagaducemusic
YouTube: www.youtube.com/channel/UC_Bvrr-gs4Nx
2bm-mu53jjg
Scope: Music studies. **Founded:** 1983.

11208 ■ Baylor University - Crouch Fine Arts Library (CFAL)

1 Bear Pl., No. 97148
Waco, TX 76798-7148
URL: http://library.web.baylor.edu/visit/institute-oral
-history/history-ioh-faqs
Scope: Music; art. **Services:** Interlibrary loan; library
open to the public. **Founded:** 1929. **Holdings:**
50,000 books; 75,000 audio and video recordings;
95,000 music scores; audiovisual materials; audiobooks; videos; DVDs.

11209 ■ Berklee College of Music - Stan Getz Library

150 Massachusetts Ave.
Boston, MA 02115
Ph: (617)747-2258
Co. E-mail: library@berklee.edu
URL: http://library.berklee.edu
Contact: Pablo Vargas, Dean
Scope: Music. **Services:** Interlibrary loan; library
open to the public with restrictions. **Founded:** 1945.
Holdings: 24,837 books; 19,573 scores; 27,500
sound recordings; 3,315 videos.

11210 ■ Brown University - Orwig Music Library

Orwig Music Bldg.
1 Young Orchard Ave.
Providence, RI 02912
Ph: (401)863-3759
Co. E-mail: orwig@brown.edu
URL: http://library.brown.edu/about/orwig
Contact: Nancy Jakubowski, Officer
E-mail: nancy_jakubowski@brown.edu

Scope: Music. **Services:** Interlibrary loan; library
open to persons affiliated with Brown University.
Founded: 1988. **Holdings:** 21,000 books; 43,000
sound recordings; 24,000 scores; 1,100 videos; 150
music periodicals; microforms.

11211 ■ California University of Pennsylvania - Louis L. Manderino Library - Special Collections

250 University Ave., Rm. 435
California, PA 15419
Ph: (724)938-5767
Co. E-mail: libraryarchives@calu.edu
URL: http://www.calu.edu/catalog/current/undergra
duate/about/library.aspx
Contact: Daniel T. Zyglowicz, Library Technician
E-mail: zyglowicz@calu.edu
Facebook: www.facebook.com/PennWCalifornia
X (Twitter): twitter.com/i/flow/login?redirect_after
_login=%2FPennWCalifornia
Instagram: www.instagram.com/PennWCalifornia/
YouTube: www.youtube.com/user/CalUofPA
Scope: History; the Civil War. **Services:** Interlibrary
loan; library open to the public by appointment.
Founded: 1852. **Holdings:** Journals; books; e-books;
audiovisual materials.

11212 ■ Cambridge Public Library - Audio-Visual Department

449 Broadway
Cambridge, MA 02138
URL: http://www.cambridgema.gov/cpl/Services/
Collections/AudioVisual.aspx
Scope: Music- rock, pop, classical, jazz, folk, blues,
world music, and soundtracks. **Services:** Interlibrary
loan; Wi-Fi; library open to the public. **Holdings:**
5,000 books, 8,000 music CDs, and 12,000 DVDs.

11213 ■ Catholic University of America - Music Library

620 Michigan Ave., NE
Washington, DC 20064
URL: http://www.catholic.edu/about-us/a-z-index/in
dex.html
Description: Provides library services on music.
Scope: Music. **Services:** Interlibrary loan; copying;
library open to the public with restrictions. **Founded:**
1952. **Holdings:** Figures not available.

11214 ■ Chapman University - Albert Schweitzer Institute - Library

One University Dr.
Orange, CA 92866
Ph: (714)997-6636
URL: http://www.chapman.edu/research/institutes-an
d-centers/schweitzer-institute
Description: Integral unit of Chapman University.
Speakers for service clubs, churches, and schools.
Scope: Life and work of Albert Schweitzer (1875-
1965), author and 1952 Nobel Peace Prize Winner,
and his relevance today. **Services:** Interlibrary loan.
Founded: 1985. **Holdings:** Books. **Publications:**
*Albert Schweitzer and Alice Ehlers: A Friendship in
Letters*; *Albert Schweitzer Memoirs of Childhood and
Youth*; *Albert Schweitzer Institute Bulletins* (Occasion-
ally); *Reverence for Life: The Ethics of Albert
Schweitzer for the Twenty-First Century*.

11215 ■ Chicago Public Library - Visual & Performing Arts Division - Music Information Center

400 S State St.
Chicago, IL 60605
URL: http://www.chipublic.org/archival_subject/
theater
Contact: Deanie Adams, Director
E-mail: dadams@chipublib.org
Scope: History and theory of music, biographies of
musicians and composers, music education, opera,
musical comedy, sacred music, popular music,
discography, music business, musical instruments,
vocal and instrumental pedagogy, music therapy, folk
music, composition and orchestration, arranging.
Services: Interlibrary loan; copying; listening/viewing
center; practice rooms; music chamber; center open
to the public. **Founded:** 1915. **Holdings:** 49,800
books; 8,025 bound periodical volumes; 67,000

bound volumes of music; 30,000 pieces of music; 15 VF drawers of pamphlets and clippings; 6,102 microfiche of music; 2,220 reels of microfilm of periodicals; 169,000 phonograph records, compact discs, audiocassettes; 3,900 music videos; 334 laserdiscs; 4,250 photographs; 51,957 uncatalogued scores.

11216 ■ Cleveland Institute of Music (CIM) - Robinson Music Library
11021 E Blvd.
  Cleveland, OH 44106
Ph: (216)791-5000
Co. E-mail: admission@cim.edu
URL: http://www.cim.edu
Contact: Paul W. Hogle, President
E-mail: paul.hogle@cim.edu
Facebook: www.facebook.com/ClevelandInstitu teofMusic
Linkedin: www.linkedin.com/school/cleveland-institute -of-music
X (Twitter): x.com/cim_edu
Instagram: www.instagram.com/cimedu
YouTube: www.youtube.com/user/ClevelandIns tOfMusic

Description: Music institution, promotes and educates music to its students. **Scope:** Foster music. **Services:** Interlibrary loan (limited); coping. **Founded:** 1920. **Holdings:** 12,000 volumes of books; 16,000 CDs; 1,000 DVDs; photographs. **Awards:** CIM Cleveland International Piano Competition (Annual).

11217 ■ Concord Free Public Library Music Collection
129 Main St.
  Concord, MA 01742
Ph: (978)318-3300
Fax: (978)318-3344
Co. E-mail: concord@minlib.net
URL: http://www.concordlibrary.org
Contact: Emily Smith, Director
Facebook: www.facebook.com/concordlibrary
X (Twitter): x.com/cfpl_updates
Instagram: www.instagram.com/p/_KLutFinCJ
YouTube: www.youtube.com/channel/UCot3xpZf dwbcmPkpKNu67Ng
Pinterest: www.pinterest.com/concordlibrary

Scope: Printed books; archival; manuscript materials; pamphlets; ephemera; broadsides; maps; photographic and pictorial holdings; municipal records; printed town reports; street directories; vital records; genealogical volumes; historic building files; works of. **Services:** Interlibrary loan; Wi-Fi; library open to the public for reference use only. **Founded:** 1873. **Holdings:** 1,500 books and bound periodical volumes; 375 music scores; 4,450 sound recordings.

11218 ■ Conservatoire de Musique de Quebec Bibliotheque
270 rue St. Jacques-Parizeau
  Quebec, QC, Canada G1R 5G1
Ph: (418)643-2190
URL: http://biblio.cmadq.gouv.qc.ca/in/faces/ homeInBook.xhtml

Scope: Classical music; orchestral music. **Services:** Library open to the public for reference use only. **Founded:** 1944. **Holdings:** 65,000 books; manuscripts; periodicals. **Subscriptions:** 33 journals and other serials; newspapers.

11219 ■ Curtis Institute of Music (CIM) - Milton L. Rock Resource Center
1726 Locust St.
  Philadelphia, PA 19103
URL: http://www.curtis.edu/apply/student-life/rock -resource-center

Description: Contains reference materials, journals, books, online materials, and video and audio materials on musical studies. **Scope:** Music. **Services:** Interlibrary loan. **Founded:** 1925. **Holdings:** Figures not available.

11220 ■ Edinboro University - Baron-Forness Library Special Collections
200 Tartan Dr.
  Edinboro, PA 16444

URL: http://www.edinboro.edu/offices-services/library/ index.php

Scope: Pennsylvania history; education. **Services:** Interlibrary loan;Tutoring. **Holdings:** 300,000 volumes;680,000 microform units;100 full-text journal databases; Reserve materials; software; equipment.

11221 ■ Grinnell College - Burling Library Media Room
1115 8th Ave.
  Grinnell, IA 50112
URL: http://www.grinnell.edu/academics/libraries/stu dents/using-burling-kistle-libraries/media-recording
Contact: Randye Jones, Contact

Scope: Educational material. **Services:** Library open to the public with restrictions (public may use items in-house, unless space is needed by students or faculty).Interlibrary loan. **Founded:** 1846. **Holdings:** Figures not available.

11222 ■ Hardin-Simmons University - Smith Music Library
2200 Hickory St.
  Abilene, TX 79698
URL: http://www.hsutx.edu/about-hsu/w-hines-sims

Scope: Music. **Services:** Interlibrary loan. **Founded:** 1891. **Holdings:** Scores; various composers' collected works; recordings; music books; 48,000 periodicals; 375,000 items and 1,800,000 volumes.

11223 ■ Interlochen Center for the Arts (ICA) - Frederick and Elizabeth Ludwig Fennell Music Library
4000 Hwy. M-137
  Interlochen, MI 49643
Ph: (231)276-7200
Co. E-mail: admission@interlochen.org
URL: http://www.interlochen.org
Contact: Trey Devey, President
Facebook: www.facebook.com/interlochencenterfor thearts
X (Twitter): x.com/InterlochenArts
Instagram: www.instagram.com/interlochenarts
YouTube: www.youtube.com/interlochenarts

Description: Educational center offering two separate programs: the Interlochen Arts Camp and the Interlochen Arts Academy. **Scope:** Music. **Founded:** 1928. **Holdings:** 114,000 items; CDs; records. **Publications:** Crescendo; IAA Catalog (Annual); IAC Catalog (Annual); Performance Programs (Weekly). **Geographic Preference:** Multinational.

11224 ■ John Brown University - Music Library
2000 W University St.
  Siloam Springs, AR 72761
Ph: (479)524-9500
Co. E-mail: jbuinfo@jbu.edu
URL: http://www.jbu.edu/academics/music
Facebook: www.facebook.com/JohnBrownUniversity
X (Twitter): x.com/johnbrownuniv
Instagram: www.instagram.com/johnbrownuniversity
YouTube: www.youtube.com/user/ JohnBrownUniversity

Scope: Music. **Services:** Interlibary Loan; Library open to the public. **Founded:** 1997. **Holdings:** Figures not available.

11225 ■ Lawrence University - Seeley G. Mudd Library Music Collections
113 S Lawe St.
  Appleton, WI 54911
URL: http://www.lawrence.edu/library/library-collec tions

Description: Library serves the students and faculties of Lawrence University. **Scope:** Music studies. **Services:** Interlibrary loan. **Founded:** 1847. **Holdings:** 350,000 books and periodicals; 23,000 musical scores; 14,000 audio recordings; 11,000 video recordings.

11226 ■ Lenox Library Association - Music Department
18 Main St.
  Lenox, MA 01240
URL: http://lenoxlib.org/category/blog/music
Contact: Edward S. Richter, President

Scope: Music. **Services:** Interlibrary loan; copying; library open to the public. **Founded:** 1940. **Holdings:** 1,600 books; 5,000 compact discs; 1,800 music scores; 500 LPs; 400 videos; 300 cassettes.

11227 ■ Longy School of Music - Bakalar Music Library
27 Garden St.
  Cambridge, MA 02138
Co. E-mail: library@longy.edu
URL: http://longy.edu/study/library/policies
Contact: Jay Colbert, Director
E-mail: jcolbert@longy.edu

Scope: Music. **Services:** Interlibrary loan; copying; library open to the public for reference use only with letter from a music librarian. **Founded:** 1992. **Holdings:** 4,300 books; 11,000 music scores; 9,000 sound recordings; 150 videos and DVDs.

11228 ■ Manhattan School of Music - Peter Jay Sharp Library
130 Claremont Ave.
  New York, NY 10027
Ph: (917)493-4512
Co. E-mail: library@msmnyc.edu
URL: http://msmnyc.libguides.com/homepage
Contact: Peter Caleb, Director
E-mail: pcaleb@msmnyc.edu
Facebook: www.facebook.com/PJSharpMSM

Scope: Music; community; fostering academic and artistic development. **Services:** Interlibrary loan; library open to the public by appointment or via METRO card. **Founded:** 1925. **Holdings:** Figures not available.

11229 ■ Mannes College The New School for Music - Harry Scherman Music Library
150 W 85th St.
  New York, NY 10024
URL: http://library.newschool.edu
URL(s): www.newschool.edu/mannes

Description: Provides access to collections, services and spaces sufficient in quality, depth, diversity, format and currency to support the research and teaching missions of The New School. Together, these collections, services and spaces support The New School's interdisciplinary approach to education and offer an excellent starting place for research. **Scope:** Music. **Services:** Interlibrary loan. **Founded:** 1954. **Holdings:** 8,529 books; 31,298 scores; 9,000 phonograph records; 2,000 compact discs; 152 videocassettes; 300 video recordings.

11230 ■ Mount Holyoke College Music and Dance Library
50 College St.
  South Hadley, MA 01075
URL: http://guides.mtholyoke.edu/c.php?g=102111&p =6435266
Contact: Pratt Hall, Contact

Scope: DVDs, journals, CDs, music scores, photographs. **Services:** Interlibrary loan; copying; library open to the public for reference use only. **Holdings:** 4,600 books and bound periodical volumes; 6,948 music scores.

11231 ■ Naval School of Music Reference Library
1420 Gator Blvd.
  Virginia Beach, VA 23459-2617
URL: http://www.netc.navy.mil/Commands/Center-for -Service-Support/Naval-School-of-Music/History

Scope: Music. **Founded:** 1942. **Holdings:** 1,000 books; materials.

11232 ■ New England Conservatory of Music (NEC) - Harriet M. Spaulding Library
290 Huntington Ave.
  Boston, MA 02115-5018
Co. E-mail: library@necmusic.edu
URL: http://necmusic.edu/library/history
Contact: Hannah Ferello, Librarian
E-mail: hannah.ferello@necmusic.edu

Scope: Music and arts. **Services:** Interlibrary loan; Library open to the public for reference use only. **Founded:** 1867. **Holdings:** 85,000 Volumes of music and books; 290 journals; Newsletters and Newspapers.

11233 ■ Ohio Wesleyan University - Kinnison Music Library
61 S Sandusky St.
Delaware, OH 43015
Ph: (740)368-3314
Free: 800-922-8953
Co. E-mail: musicd@owu.edu
URL: http://www.owu.edu
Contact: John Milligan, Chairman
Facebook: www.facebook.com/
OhioWesleyanUniversity
Linkedin: www.linkedin.com/school/ohio-wesleyan
-university
X (Twitter): x.com/OhioWesleyan
Instagram: www.instagram.com/ohiowesleyan
YouTube: www.youtube.com/user/OhioWesleyanU

Scope: Music. **Services:** Interlibrary loan; copying; library open to the public. **Holdings:** Figures not available.

11234 ■ Orchestras Canada (OC) - Library [Orchestres Canada]
c/o Peterborough Business Hub
398 McDonnel St., Unit No. 4
Peterborough, ON, Canada K9H 2X4
Ph: (416)366-8834
Free: 877-809-7288
Co. E-mail: info@oc.ca
URL: http://oc.ca/en
Contact: Roberta Smith, President
Facebook: www.facebook.com/orchestrascanada
Linkedin: www.linkedin.com/company/orches
trascanada
X (Twitter): x.com/OrchCanada
Instagram: www.instagram.com/orchestrascanada
YouTube: www.youtube.com/channel/UC0vEh7o
_IQCLMPOOxdGz38w

Description: Represents professional, semi-professional, and community symphony orchestras in Canada. Promotes orchestral music by providing artistic and administrative support to members. Works to enhance the financial health and security of musicians. Conducts educational programs; compiles statistics. **Scope:** Orchestra. **Founded:** 1997. **Holdings:** Figures not available. **Publications:** *Orchestras Canada--Membership Directory*; *Orchestras Canada Newsletter* (Monthly). **Educational Activities:** National Orchestras Meeting (Annual). **Geographic Preference:** National.

11235 ■ Percussive Arts Society (PAS) - Resource Library
110 W Washington St., Ste. A
Indianapolis, IN 46204
Ph: (317)974-4488
Fax: (317)974-4499
Co. E-mail: percarts@pas.org
URL: http://www.pas.org
Contact: Michael Burritt, President
Facebook: www.facebook.com/PercussiveArts
X (Twitter): x.com/PercussiveArts
Instagram: www.instagram.com/percussivearts
YouTube: www.youtube.com/user/PercArts

Description: Promotes percussion education, research, performance and appreciation worldwide. Accomplishes goals through publications, a worldwide network of chapters, website, workshops, museum, and convention. **Scope:** Music. **Founded:** 1961. **Holdings:** Recordings; videos; publications; articles; research databases; documents. **Publications:** *Percussive Notes* (6/year); *Rhythm! Scene* (Bimonthly). **Educational Activities:** Percussive Arts Society Conference; Percussive Arts Society International Convention (PASIC) (Annual). **Awards:** Fred Sanford Award (Annual); PAS Hall of Fame Award (Annual); PAS Lifetime Achievement in Education Award (Annual); Outstanding PAS Supporter Award (Annual). **Geographic Preference:** Multinational.

11236 ■ Portland Public Library Art/ Audiovisual Department (PPL)
5 Monument Sq.
Portland, ME 04101
Ph: (207)871-1700
Fax: (207)871-1703
Co. E-mail: reference@portlandpubliclibrary.org
URL: http://www.portlandlibrary.com
Contact: Peter F. Richardson, President
Facebook: www.facebook.com/portlandpubliclibrary
X (Twitter): x.com/PortPublicLibME

Scope: Music. **Services:** Interlibrary loan; copying; library open to the public. **Holdings:** 2,500 books and bound periodical volumes; 7 file drawers of sheet music; 9,500 sound recordings; 3,600 videocassettes.

11237 ■ St. Norbert Arts Centre Archives (SNAC)
100 rue des Ruines du Monastere
Winnipeg, MB, Canada R3V 1L6
Ph: (204)269-0564
Co. E-mail: snac@snac.mb.ca
URL: http://www.snac.mb.ca
Contact: Naomi Gerrard, Chairman of the Board
Facebook: www.facebook.com/StNorbertArtsCentre
YouTube: www.youtube.com/channel/UC2yIUh
tsPQPin4LkfA86pqQ

Founded: 1991. **Holdings:** Figures not available.

11238 ■ San Francisco Conservatory of Music Library (SFCM)
50 Oak St.
San Francisco, CA 94102
Ph: (415)503-6213
Co. E-mail: library@sfcm.edu
URL: http://sfcm.edu/discover/student-resources/li
brary

Description: Focus on educating the whole person, with an interconnected curriculum that breaks down barriers between the intellectual, artistic, professional, and individual. **Scope:** Music; encompasses the arts; humanities; social sciences and sciences. **Services:** Interlibrary loan; library open to students, faculty and staff. **Founded:** 1917. **Holdings:** 38,000 scores and parts; 15,000 audio-visual material; 12,500 books; 60,000 items; 77 periodical titles.

11239 ■ San Francisco Public Library - Bernard Osher Foundation Art, Music & Recreation Center
100 Larkin St.
San Francisco, CA 94102
Ph: (415)557-4525
Co. E-mail: artmusicrec@sfpl.org
URL: http://sfpl.org/locations/main-library/art-music

Scope: Visual arts; performing arts; music; sports and recreation. **Services:** Center open to the public. **Holdings:** Books; serials; scores; CD-ROMs; DVDs.

11240 ■ State University of New York at Buffalo - Music Library
112 Baird Hall, N Campus
Buffalo, NY 14260-4750
Ph: (716)645-2923
Co. E-mail: dtc3@buffalo.edu
URL: http://library.buffalo.edu/music

Scope: History of music. **Services:** Interlibrary loan; copying; library open to the public. **Founded:** 1970. **Holdings:** 50,000 volumes of literature; 24,000 bound periodical volumes; 100,000 scores and parts; 47,000 sound recordings; 8000 microforms; 2000 slides; 5000 photographs; 1600 videos.

11241 ■ Toronto Reference Library - Arts Centre
789 Yonge St.
Toronto, ON, Canada M4W 2G8
URL: http://www.torontopubliclibrary.ca/books-video
-music/specialized-collections/performing-arts-cen
tre.jsp

Scope: Music; dance; film; theatre; television. **Services:** Library open to the public; photocopy. **Founded:** 1915. **Holdings:** Books; periodicals; music scores; sound recordings; archival materials.

11242 ■ University of California, Los Angeles - Music Library
1102 Schoenberg Music Bldg.
Los Angeles, CA 90095
Ph: (310)825-4882
Co. E-mail: music-ref@library.ucla.edu
URL: http://www.library.ucla.edu/visit/locations/music
-library
Contact: Allison R. Benedetti, Director
E-mail: abenedetti@library.ucla.edu
Facebook: www.facebook.com/UCLA.Music.Library

Description: Contains reference materials, journals, books, online materials, and video and audio materials on musical studies. **Scope:** Music; musicology; ethnomusicology; music education. **Services:** Interlibrary loan; copying; library open to the public. **Founded:** 1942. **Holdings:** 400,000 items; 80,000 books; 115,000 scores; 100 journals; 200,000 sound recordings; visual media; facsimiles of music scores.

11243 ■ University of Cincinnati College Conservatory of Music - Albino Gorno Memorial Music Library
600 Blegen Library, 2602 University Cir.
Cincinnati, OH 45221
URL: http://libraries.uc.edu/libraries/ccm.html

Description: Serves the research and instructional needs of the students and faculty of the UC College-Conservatory of Music (CCM). **Scope:** Music; musical theatre; dance; theatre and drama. **Services:** Interlibrary loan; copying; library open to the public for reference use only. **Founded:** 1949. **Holdings:** 4,650,472 Volumes; 1895,398, e-books; 2,682,693 Articles.

11244 ■ University of Nevada, Las Vegas Music Library (UNLV)
4505 S Maryland Pky.
Las Vegas, NV 89154-7002
Ph: (702)895-2541
Co. E-mail: music.library@unlv.edu
URL: http://www.library.unlv.edu/music
Contact: Deanna Stefanelli, Contact
Facebook: www.facebook.com/unlvlib
X (Twitter): x.com/unlvlibraries
Instagram: www.instagram.com/unlvlibraries
YouTube: www.youtube.com/user/unlvlibraries

Description: To inspire discovery, appreciation, and respect for animals and nature. **Scope:** Music. **Services:** Interlibrary loan (limited); open to faculty, students, and the las vegas music community. **Founded:** 2001. **Holdings:** 35,000 scores; 15,500 recordings; 3,000 DVDs; audiovisual materials; manuscripts.

11245 ■ University of North Carolina at Greensboro - Martha Blakeney Hodges Special Collections & University Archives - Cello Music Collections (CMC)
Walter Clinton Jackson Library
320 College Ave.
Greensboro, NC 27412-0001
URL: http://library.uncg.edu/info/depts/scua/collec
tions/cello/index.aspx
Contact: Martha Blakeney Hodges, Contact

Scope: Music; research and learning. **Services:** Interlibrary Loan ; Copying (limited); collection open to the public for research. **Holdings:** 300 books, including 20 bound periodical volumes and 80 bound volumes of chamber music; 240 boxes of manuscripts and printed scores, representing 4,300 indexed items; 100 boxes of archival materials, including photographs, teaching notes, and correspondence.

11246 ■ University of North Carolina School of the Arts - Semans Library
1533 S Main St.
Winston Salem, NC 27127-2738
Ph: (336)770-3399
URL: http://www.uncsa.edu/faculty-staff-hub/aroun
d-campus/facilities-maintenance/design-and-cons
truction-projects/semans-renovation.aspx

Description: Library collects, organizes, describes and preserves access to records of permanent administrative, legal, fiscal and historical value.

Scope: Art and design. **Services:** Interlibrary loan; library open to the public; copying; printing; scanning. **Founded:** 1965. **Holdings:** Books; periodicals; music and media.

11247 ■ University of Redlands - Armacost Library Special Collections
1200 E Colton Ave.
 Redlands, CA 92373
URL: http://library.redlands.edu/specialcollections

Scope: Barney child's; harry pottle. **Services:** Interlibrary loan; copying; library open to the public with restrictions. **Founded:** 1907. **Holdings:** 208,503 books; 314,219 microforms; 168,228 documents.

11248 ■ VanderCook College of Music - Harry Ruppel Memorial Library
3140 S Federal St.
 Chicago, IL 60616
Ph: (312)225-6288
Fax: (312)225-5211
URL: http://www.vandercook.edu/about-vandercook/
 campus/the-harry-ruppel-library
Contact: Rob DeLand, Head Librarian
E-mail: rdeland@vandercook.edu

Scope: Music education; general music; general education; psychology. **Services:** Interlibrary loan; listening facilities; library open to alumni and associates of Vandercook College and one neighboring institution (Illinois Institute of Technology identification necessary). **Founded:** 1967. **Holdings:** Figures not available.

11249 ■ Weill-Lenya Research Center (WLRC) - Library
7 E 20th St.
 New York, NY 10003
Ph: (212)505-5240
Fax: (212)353-9663
Co. E-mail: wlrc@kwf.org
URL: http://www.kwf.org/research-center

Description: Research unit of the Kurt Weill Foundation for Music, Inc., a private, non-profit foundation. Offers information referral. **Scope:** Life and works of Kurt Julian Weill (1900-1950), German-born American composer, and Lotte Lenya (1898-1981), Austrian actress-singer and Weill's widow. Also studies music in the Weimar Republic and the American musical theater. **Services:** Copying at staff discretion; lending photos for reprinting; library open to the public by appointment. **Founded:** 1983. **Holdings:** Books; printed music; music manuscripts; scripts; correspondence; audio and video recordings; films; programs; photographs; posters; press clippings; business records; personal papers. **Publications:** *Guide to the Weill-Lenya Research Center; Kurt Weill Newsletter* (Semiannual). **Awards:** Kurt Weill Foundation Grant Program- Professional Performance (Annual).

11250 ■ Western Connecticut State University (WCSU) - Ruth A. Haas Library
181 White St.
 Danbury, CT 06810
Ph: (203)837-9100
URL: http://www.wcsu.edu/faculty-handbook/library
 -information-and-procedures

Scope: Management; marketing; local history. **Services:** Interlibrary loan; library open to the public for reference use only. **Founded:** 1903. **Holdings:** 175,000 volumes; 359 bound periodical volumes; 4,712 music scores; 3,084 sound recordings; 8 reels of microfilm; 8,700 media titles.

11251 ■ Westminster Choir College - Rider University - Talbott Library
2083 Lawrenceville Rd.
 Lawrenceville, NJ 08648
Ph: (609)921-7100
Co. E-mail: library@rider.edu
URL: http://guides.rider.edu/talbottlibrary

Description: Collections comprises of over 85,000 volumes of music books and scores, over 7,200 choral music titles in performance quantities, a choral music reference collection over 80,000 titles, and over 28,000 sound and video recordings. **Scope:** Music. **Services:** Interlibrary loan (fee); copying; scanning; open to the public with fee for circulation for area residents. **Founded:** 1982. **Holdings:** Books; manuscripts; documents; music; journals.

RESEARCH CENTERS

11252 ■ American Institute of Musical Studies (AIMS)
28 East 69th St.
 Kansas City, MO 64113
Ph: (816)268-3657
Co. E-mail: aimsadminkc@gmail.com
URL: http://aimsgraz.com
Contact: Brian Bridges, Director, Operations
Facebook: www.facebook.com/AIMSinGraz

Description: Launches advanced young singers, pianists and instrumentalists on a professional career by providing experience and emphasizing audition training. Faculty, comprised of over 60 internationally known professional musicians, conducts hands-on training programs. **Scope:** Music and music studies, focusing on advancing young singers, pianists, and instrumentalists toward a professional career. **Founded:** 1969. **Publications:** *The AIMSer Newsletter.* **Awards:** The Meistersinger Competition (Annual). **Geographic Preference:** National.

11253 ■ Council for Research in Music Education (CRME)
University of Illinois Press
 1325 S Oak St.
 Champaign, IL 61820-6903
Ph: (217)244-0626

Free: 866-244-0626
Fax: (217)244-9910
Co. E-mail: journals@uillinois.edu
URL: http://bcrme.press.uillinois.edu
Contact: Dr. Janet Barrett, IX, Editor
E-mail: janetbar@illinois.edu

Description: International organization of authors who contribute articles to the Bulletin of the Council for Research in Music Education. Aims to promote scholarly research in music education. **Scope:** Aims to promote scholarly research in music education. **Founded:** 1963. **Publications:** *Bulletin of the Council for Research in Music Education* (Quarterly). **Awards:** CRME Outstanding Dissertation Award (Annual). **Geographic Preference:** Multinational.

11254 ■ Florida State University College of Music - Center for Music Research (CMR)
122 N Copeland St.
 Tallahassee, FL 32306-1180
URL: http://music.fsu.edu/music-research-centers/
 center-for-music-research

Description: Aims to bring together the already strong research component of the College of Music with its newly created computer facilities. **Scope:** Music, music education, music therapy development through scholarly inquiry. Provides space and facilities to develop applications of research to music performance, teaching, therapy, and analysis. Develops new technology and applications in teaching and research. **Founded:** 1980. **Educational Activities:** CMR Seminars; CMR Workshops (Occasionally).

11255 ■ Rutgers University - Institute of Jazz Studies (IJS) - John Cotton Dana Library
185 University Ave.
 Newark, NJ 07102
Ph: (973)353-5595
Co. E-mail: ask_ijs@libraries.rutgers.edu
URL: http://www.libraries.rutgers.edu/newark/visit-stu
 dy/institute-jazz-studies
Contact: Wayne Winborne, Executive Director
E-mail: wayne.winborne@rutgers.edu

Description: Integral unit of John Cotton Dana Library at Rutgers University, with its own advisory board. **Scope:** Jazz and related music, oral history, ethnomusicology, African American history, and sound documentation. **Services:** Copying; institute open to the public by appointment; library on facebook and twitter(www.facebook.com/pages/John-Cotton-Dana-Library-at-Rutgers-Newark/263494630345773; twitter.com/runewark_dana). **Founded:** 1952. **Holdings:** 600,000 volumes; approximately 300,000 books, 100,000 bound periodicals, and 200,000 federal and state publications; 600,000 pieces of microform; 15,000 audiovisual items. **Subscriptions:** 30,000 e-journals. **Publications:** *Journal of Jazz Studies (JJS)* (Periodic); *Studies in Jazz Monograph Series.* **Educational Activities:** IJS Conferences; IJS Research Roundtable (Irregular); IJS Seminars. **Awards:** The Morroe Berger - Edward Berger - Benny Carter Jazz Research Fund (Annual).

ASSOCIATIONS AND OTHER ORGANIZATIONS

11256 ■ **American School Band Directors Association (ASBDA)**
2280 W High St.
Lima, OH 45805
Ph: (419)996-9667
URL: http://www.asbdaband.org
Contact: Travis Coakley, President
E-mail: travis.coakley@asbdaband.org
Facebook: www.facebook.com/ASBDAband
X (Twitter): x.com/asbdaband
Instagram: www.instagram.com/asbdaband
YouTube: www.youtube.com/channel/UCsaBrM0ji
5ZArDDeFxW706A
Description: Persons actively engaged in teaching instrumental music at the elementary, junior high or senior high school level; affiliates are persons no longer engaged in active teaching; associates are commercial firms dealing in products used by members. Seeks to improve instruction of instrumental music in the schools, the equipment used in instrumental music, music materials and methods, audiovisual aids, and acoustics of musical instruments used in school instructional programs. **Founded:** 1987. **Publications:** *ASBDA Directory and Handbook* (Annual). **Awards:** Austin Harding Award (Biennial); Edwin Franko Goldman Award (Periodic); ASBDA Outstanding State Chair Award (Annual). **Geographic Preference:** National.

11257 ■ **Early Music America (EMA)**
801 Vinial St., Ste. 300
Pittsburgh, PA 15212
Ph: (412)642-2778
Co. E-mail: info@earlymusicamerica.org
URL: http://www.earlymusicamerica.org
Contact: Derek Tam, President
E-mail: derek.saiho.tam@gmail.com
Facebook: www.facebook.com/earlymusicamerica
YouTube: www.youtube.com/user/
EMAEarlyMusicAmerica
Description: Serves and strengthens the early music community in North America. Compiles statistics. Conducts educational programs. **Founded:** 1985. **Publications:** *Early Music America* magazine (3/year); *Early Music America* (3/year); *EMA Electronic Bulletin* (Quarterly); *Early Music America--Directory of Members.* **Educational Activities:** Early Music America Conference and Exhibition. **Awards:** Laurette Goldberg Award (Annual); Howard Mayer Brown Award (Annual); Thomas Binkley Award (Annual); Barbara Thornton Memorial Scholarship (Biennial); Laurette Goldberg Early Music Outreach Award (Annual). **Geographic Preference:** National.

11258 ■ **National Association of School Music Dealers, Inc. (NASMD)**
14070 Proton Rd., Ste. 100
Dallas, TX 75244
Ph: (972)233-9107
Fax: (972)490-4219
Co. E-mail: office@nasmd.com
URL: http://www.nasmd.com
Contact: Whitney Brown Grisaffi, Contact
Facebook: www.facebook.com/nasmd
Description: Retail music stores and companies engaged in sales, service and repair of band and orchestra instruments to elementary and secondary schools and colleges. **Founded:** 1962. **Publications:** *NASMD Newsletter* (Quarterly). **Geographic Preference:** National.

REFERENCE WORKS

11259 ■ *"Attention Songwriters: Protect Your Valuable Assets with a Copyright"* in *Legal Zoom* (March 24, 2023)
URL(s): www.legalzoom.com/articles/attention
-songwriters-protect-your-valuable-assets-with-a
-copyright
Ed: Peter Smith. **Released:** March 24, 2023. **Description:** A discussion of copyrighting songs and why it's important to do so. **Availability:** Online.

11260 ■ *The Big Payback: The History of the Business of Hip-Hop*
Ed: Dan Charnas. **Released:** November 01, 2011. **Price:** $17, paperback; $13.99. **Description:** The complete history of hip-hop music is presented, by following the money and the relationship between artist and merchant. In its promise of economic security and creative control for black artist-entrepreneurs, it is the culmination of dreams of black nationalists and civil rights leaders. **Availability:** E-book; Print.

11261 ■ *"The Book On Indigo"* in *Canadian Business* (Vol. 81, July 22, 2008, No. 12-13, pp. 29)
Description: Indigo Books & Music Inc. reported record sales of $922 million resulting in a record net profit of $52.8 million for the 2008 fiscal year ended March 29, 2008. Earnings per share were $2.13, greater than Standard & Poor's expected $1.70 per share. Additional information concerning Indigo Books is presented.

11262 ■ *"Eagle River's Only Music Store Is Closing up Shop"* in *U.S. News & World Report* (June 15, 2019)
URL(s): www.usnews.com/news/best-states/alaska/
articles/2019-06-15/eagle-rivers-only-music-store-is
-closing-up-shop
Released: June 15, 2019. **Description:** In Eagle River, Alaska, Mike's Music is closing up shop after 25 years in business. A 7.1 earthquake caused major damage to the building, which led to a big disruption to the business. **Availability:** Online.

11263 ■ *"Encore on Cue: Migratory Hopes More Venues, Artists Take Note of Its Kiosks That Offer Concert Recordings to Fans Immediately After Shows"* in *Los Angeles Business Journal* (Vol. 34, May 28, 2012, No. 22, pp. 5)
Pub: CBJ L.P.
Contact: Laura Garrett, Vice President Publisher
E-mail: garrett@ocbj.com
Description: Album quality recordings of concerts are now available using Culver City startup Migratory Music's technology. The firm installed 15 kiosks where consumers can purchase concert recordings performed at the Greek Theatre. Details of this service are included. **Availability:** Online.

11264 ■ *"Handleman Liquidation Leaves Questions For Shareholders"* in *Crain's Detroit Business* (Vol. 24, October 6, 2008, No. 40, pp. 4)
Pub: Crain Communications Inc.
Contact: Barry Asin, President
Ed: Nancy Kaffer. **Description:** Discusses Handleman Co., a Troy-based music distribution company, and their plan of liquidation and dissolution as well as how shareholders will be affected by the company's plan. Handleman filed its plan to liquidate and dissolve assets with the Securities and Exchange Commission in mid-August, following several quarters of dismal earnings. **Availability:** Online.

11265 ■ *"How Sharing Sent Record Sales Soaring"* in *Business Strategy Review* (Vol. 25, Summer 2014, No. 2, pp. 7)
Released: June 02, 2014. **Description:** Removing copy protection from songs actually increased music sales. **Availability:** Print; PDF; Online.

11266 ■ *Music Trades--The Purchaser's Guide to the Music Industries*
Pub: Music Trades Corp.
Contact: Brian T. Majeski, Editor
E-mail: brian@musictrades.com
URL(s): www.musictrades.com/guide.html
Ed: Brian T. Majeski. **Released:** Annual; latest edition, 2020. **Price:** $20, Individuals for one year. **Description:** Publication includes list of 3,000 musical instrument manufacturers and wholesalers, publishers of sheet music, and manufacturers of musical accessories; international coverage. **Entries include:** Company name, address, phone, names of executives, trade and brand names, products or services. **Arrangement:** Alphabetical. **Availability:** Print; Online.

11267 ■ *"Welcome to Babesland"* in *Women In Business* (Vol. 62, June 2010, No. 2, pp. 33)
Description: Music group, Four Bitchin' Babes will be performing at the 2010 American Business Women's Association's National Women's Leadership Conference. The group has been in the industry for 20 years and has released nine albums. The Four Bitchin' Babes consist of Sally Fingerett, Nancy Moran, Deirdre Flint, and Debi Smith. **Availability:** Online.

STATISTICAL SOURCES

11268 ■ *Guitar Stores Industry in the US - Market Research Report*
URL(s): www.ibisworld.com/united-states/market-re-
search-reports/guitar-stores-industry/

Price: $925. **Description:** Downloadable report analyzing current and future trends in the guitar store industry. **Availability:** Download.

11269 ■ Record Stores Industry in the US - Market Research Report

URL(s): www.ibisworld.com/united-states/market-research-reports/record-stores-industry/

Price: $925. **Description:** Downloadable report analyzing the current and future trends in the record store industry. **Availability:** Online.

11270 ■ RMA Annual Statement Studies

Pub: Risk Management Association
Contact: Nancy Foster, President

Released: Annual. **Description:** Contains composite balance sheets and income statements for more than 360 industries, including the accounting, auditing, and bookkeeping industries. Also contains five years of comparative historical data for discerning trends. Includes 16 commonly used ratios, computed for most of the size groupings for nearly every industry.

11271 ■ Standard & Poor's Industry Surveys

Pub: Standard And Poor's Financial Services LLC.
Contact: Douglas L. Peterson, President

Description: Two-volume book that examines the prospects for specific industries, including trucking. Also provides analyses of trends and problems, statistical tables and charts, and comparative company analyses.

TRADE PERIODICALS

11272 ■ Acoustic Guitar Magazine

Pub: Acoustic Guitar
URL(s): store.acousticguitar.com/collections/back-issues
Facebook: www.facebook.com/AcousticGuitarMagazine

Released: Monthly **Price:** $35.99, for online one year; $90.99, for online 3 year; $66.99, for 2 year; $35.99, for print and online 1 year; $66.99, for print and online 2 year; $90.99, for print and online 3 year. **Description:** Magazine for professional and amateur acoustic guitar enthusiasts offering advice on choosing, maintaining, and playing acoustic guitar. **Availability:** Print; Download; Online.

11273 ■ American Music

Pub: University of Illinois Press
Contact: Laurie Matheson, Director
E-mail: lmatheso@uillinois.edu
URL(s): www.press.uillinois.edu/journals/?id=am

Ed: Gayle Sherwood Magee. **Released:** Quarterly; Spring, Summer, Fall, and Winter. **Price:** $30, Individuals for students online US; $47, Individuals for 1 year, both print and online US; $47, Individuals for 1 year, online only US; $52, Individuals for print only US; $171, Institutions for print and online; $52, Individuals for print and online; $178, Institutions for print & online; $150, Institutions for print only US; $159, Institutions for online 1 year; $47, Individuals for 1 year online; $22, Institutions for back issue; $153, Institutions for online; $144, Institutions for print. **Description:** Scholarly journal devoted to American music. **Availability:** Print; PDF; Online.

11274 ■ Down Beat: Jazz, Blues & Beyond

Pub: Maher Publications
URL(s): downbeat.com/magazine
Facebook: www.facebook.com/downbeatmagazine
X (Twitter): x.com/DownBeatMag

Released: Monthly **Price:** $31.99, for print & digital 1 year; $58.99, for print & digital 2 year; $80.99, for print & digital 3 year; $23.99, for digital 1 year; $47.99, for digital 2 year; $71.99, for digital 3 year; $8, Single issue. **Description:** Magazine edited for the learning musician. **Availability:** Print; Online.

11275 ■ Harmonica Happenings

Pub: Society for the Preservation and Advancement of the Harmonica
Contact: Michael D'Eath, President
URL(s): www.spah.org/content.asp?contentid=21

Ed: J. P. Pagan. **Released:** Quarterly; Winter, Spring, Summer, Fall. **Description:** Promotes appreciation for harmonica music. Contains material of interest to harmonica players, with profiles of and interviews with musicians, instructional material, and news notes. Recurring features include letters to the editor, editorials on professional harmonicists. **Availability:** Print; PDF; Download.

11276 ■ ITG Journal

Pub: International Trumpet Guild
Contact: Grant Peters, President
E-mail: president@trumpetguild.org
URL(s): trumpetguild.org/journal

Released: Quarterly **Price:** $11, for back issue. **Description:** Carries news of interest to trumpet players, teachers, and students. Contains book reviews, record reviews, and listings of new publications and recordings, and occassionally includes sheet music and CD recordings. Also carries articles on trumpet pedagogy, players of note, musical analysis, and historical instruments. **Availability:** Print; Electronic publishing; Download; PDF; DVD; Online.

11277 ■ Music Inc.

Pub: Maher Publications
URL(s): www.musicincmag.com
Facebook: www.facebook.com/MusicIncMagazine
Linkedin: www.linkedin.com/company/music-inc-magazine
X (Twitter): x.com/musicincmag
Instagram: www.instagram.com/musicincmagazine

Released: Monthly; except May. **Description:** Magazine serving retailers of music and sound products. **Availability:** Print; PDF; Online.

11278 ■ Music Trades

Pub: Music Trades Corp.
Contact: Brian T. Majeski, Editor
E-mail: brian@musictrades.com
URL(s): www.musictrades.com/about.html
Facebook: www.facebook.com/people/Music-Trades-Magazine/100067015846955

Ed: Brian T. Majeski. **Released:** Monthly **Price:** $299, Individuals. **Description:** Music trade magazine. **Availability:** Print; PDF; Online.

11279 ■ Premiere Guitar

Pub: Gearhead Communications L.L.C.
Contact: Amy D. Plummer, Contact
URL(s): www.premierguitar.com
Facebook: www.facebook.com/premierguitar
X (Twitter): x.com/premierguitar
Instagram: www.instagram.com/premierguitar
YouTube: www.youtube.com/premierguitar

Released: Monthly **Price:** $12.99, for 1 year; $39.95, Two years for US print; $115, for print one year international; $119.90, Two years for Canada print; $230, Two years for international print; $55.95, Canada for print one year; $24.95, U.S. for print one year; $0.99, Single issue for digital; $12.95, Canada for 5 months; $4.95, U.S. for 5 months; $2.50, for back issues. **Description:** Consumer magazine covering equipment, services, and supplies for professional, performing musicians. **Availability:** Print; Download; Online.

VIDEO/AUDIO MEDIA

11280 ■ Marketplace: Mississippi Record Store Owner Hopes "Greatest Hits" Compilations Sound Good to Collectors

URL(s): www.marketplace.org/2021/09/13/jackson-reocrd-store-onwer-summer-retail

Ed: Sean McHenry. **Released:** September 13, 2023. **Description:** Podcast discusses vinyl with the owner of a record store.

TRADE SHOWS AND CONVENTIONS

11281 ■ American Choral Directors Association National Conference

American Choral Directors Association (ACDA)
545 Couch Dr.
Oklahoma City, OK 73102-2207
Ph: (405)232-8161
Fax: (405)232-8162
Co. E-mail: membership@acda.org
URL: http://acda.org
Contact: Dr. Tim Sharp, Executive Director
E-mail: sharp@acda.org
URL(s): acda.org/archives/events/2025-national-conference

Frequency: Biennial. **Audience:** Choral directors. Dates and Locations: 2025 Mar 19-22 Dallas, TX. **Telecommunication Services:** shail@acda.org.

11282 ■ College Music Society National Conference

College Music Society (CMS)
312 E Pine St.
Missoula, MT 59802
Ph: (406)721-9616
Co. E-mail: cms@music.org
URL: http://www.music.org
Contact: William L. Pelto, Executive Director
E-mail: executivedirector@music.org
URL(s): www.music.org/2024-natl-overview.html

Frequency: Annual; held each fall. **Description:** Music publishers, instrument manufacturers, music retailers, music careers, composition, ethnomusicology, higher education, music technology, music theory, performance, and mentoring. **Audience:** Faculty, administrators, graduate students, independent scholars, composers, publishers, and music business personnel. **Principal Exhibits:** Music publishers, instrument manufacturers, music retailers, music careers, composition, ethnomusicology, higher education, music technology, music theory, performance, and mentoring. Dates and Locations: 2025 Oct 30-Nov 01 The Davenport Grand Hotel, Spokane, WA; 2026 Nov 12-14 Amway Grand Plaza, Grand Rapids, MI. **Telecommunication Services:** conferenceplanner@music.org.

11283 ■ IBMA Business Conference

International Bluegrass Music Association (IBMA)
4206 Gallatin Pk.
Nashville, TN 37216
Ph: (615)256-3222
Free: 888-438-4262
Fax: (615)256-0450
Co. E-mail: info@ibma.org
URL: http://ibma.org
Contact: Pat Morris, Executive Director
URL(s): orldofbluegrass.org/conference/

Frequency: Annual; usually September and October. **Description:** Share and discover the latest tools, strategies, technology and sounds. **Audience:** Bluegrass music professionals. **Principal Exhibits:** Share and discover the latest tools, strategies, technology and sounds. Dates and Locations: 2025 Sep 16-20 Chattanooga, TN. **Telecommunication Services:** anna@ibma.org.

11284 ■ NAfME National In-Service Conference

National Association for Music Education (NAFME)
585 Grove St., Ste. 145 No. 711
Herndon, VA 20170
Ph: (703)860-4000
Free: 800-336-3768
Co. E-mail: nafme@nafme.org
URL: http://nafme.org
Contact: Deb Confredo, President
URL(s): us-tdm-tso-15eb63ff4c6-1626e-1680662e 555.force.com/s/lt-event?id=a1Y2H000009 tRsOUAU&site=a0d1U000001qiZcQAI#Home

Frequency: Annual. **Description:** Music education equipment, supplies, and services. Includes keynote speakers, and plenary sessions. **Audience:** Professional music educators. **Principal Exhibits:** Music education equipment, supplies, and services. Includes keynote speakers, and plenary sessions.

11285 ■ The NAMM Show

National Association of Music Merchants (NAMM)
5790 Armada Dr.
Carlsbad, CA 92008
Ph: (760)438-8001
Free: 800-767-6266
Fax: (760)438-7327

Co. E-mail: info@namm.org
URL: http://www.namm.org
Contact: Joe Lamond, President
URL(s): registration.namm.org

Frequency: Annual. **Description:** Platform for the music, sound and event technology communities to promote music products. **Audience:** Music retailers, corporate buyers, manufacturer representatives, global distributors, artists, music educators, and sound contractors. **Principal Exhibits:** Platform for the music, sound and event technology communities to promote music products. Dates and Locations: 2025 Jan 21-25 Anaheim Convention Center, Anaheim, CA. **Telecommunication Services:** trade-showsales@namm.org.

11286 ■ New York State School Music Association Winter Conference
New York State School Music Association (NYSSMA)
718 The Plain Rd.
Westbury, NY 11590-5931
Ph: (516)997-7200
Fax: (516)997-1700
Co. E-mail: info@nyssma.org
URL: http://www.nyssma.org
Contact: Edmund Chiarello, President
URL(s): www.nyssma.org/event/new-york-state
-summer-music-conference

Frequency: Annual. **Description:** Music publishers, musical instruments, fund-raising materials, and educational materials. **Audience:** New York state school music association members and students. **Principal Exhibits:** Music publishers, musical instruments, fund-raising materials, and educational materials. **Telecommunication Services:** conference@nyssma.org.

11287 ■ TMEA Convention
Texas Music Educators Association (TMEA)
7900 Centre Pk. Dr.
Austin, TX 78754
Ph: (512)452-0710
Free: 888-318-8632
URL: http://www.tmea.org
Contact: Dr. Robert Floyd, Executive Director
E-mail: rfloyd@tmea.org
URL(s): www.tmea.org/convention

Frequency: Annual. **Description:** Music publishers, uniform/gowns, recruitment, photographers, software. **Audience:** Music educators, college students, family attendees, high school and middle school students, non-music educators, and performing group members/chaperones. **Principal Exhibits:** Music publishers, uniform/gowns, recruitment, photographers, software. Dates and Locations: 2025 Feb 12-15; 2026 Feb 11-14; 2027 Feb 10-13; 2028 Feb 09-12; 2029 Feb 07-10; 2030 Feb 13-16. Henry B. González Convention Center, San Antonio, TX. **Telecommunication Services:** susand@tmea.org.

CONSULTANTS

11288 ■ Jess Barker, Document Research/Retrieval L.L.C.
209 A S Macoupin St.
Gillespie, IL 62033
Contact: Barbara Barker, Manager

Description: Provides property title search for banks, lenders and real-estate investors.

FRANCHISES AND BUSINESS OPPORTUNITIES

11289 ■ Music Go Round (MGR)
1705 Weir Dr., Ste.1
Woodbury, MN 55125
Ph: (651)714-1460
Co. E-mail: sales@mgrwood.com
URL: http://www.musicgoround.com/locations/woodbury-mn
Facebook: www.facebook.com/MGRWoodbury
Instagram: www.instagram.com/musicgoroundwoodburymn

Description: Retailer of musical instruments and gear. **Founded:** 1986. **Training:** Training program includes product acquisition, inventory management, retail store operations, employee management, and ongoing support.

LIBRARIES

11290 ■ Alberta Band Association Music Lending Library (ABA)
5708 72 St. NW
Edmonton, AB, Canada T6B 3J4
Ph: (780)800-0482
Free: 877-687-4239
Co. E-mail: library@albertabandassociation.com
URL: http://www.albertabands.com/lending-library
.html
Contact: Sarah Rossi, Library Assistant

Description: A non-profit provincial service organization whose mission is to promote and develop the musical, educational and cultural value of bands and band music in Alberta. **Scope:** Music. **Services:** Library not open to the public. **Holdings:** Concert band titles, scores, methods, and recordings.

11291 ■ Andy Warhol Museum Archives Study Center
117 Sandusky St.
Pittsburgh, PA 15212
URL: http://www.warhol.org/research/archives-study
-center/archives-collection-research-request-form

Description: Library of archiever collections. **Scope:** Museums collections. **Founded:** 1994. **Holdings:** Figures not available.

11292 ■ Bagaduce Music Lending Library (BMLL)
49 S St.
Blue Hill, ME 04614
Ph: (207)374-5454
Co. E-mail: library@bagaducemusic.org
URL: http://www.bagaducemusic.org
Contact: Richard Howe, President
Facebook: www.facebook.com/bagaducemusic
Instagram: www.instagram.com/bagaducemusic
YouTube: www.youtube.com/channel/UC_Bvrr-gs4Nx
2bm-mu53jjg

Scope: Music studies. **Founded:** 1983.

11293 ■ California University of Pennsylvania - Louis L. Manderino Library - Special Collections
250 University Ave., Rm. 435
California, PA 15419
Ph: (724)938-5767
Co. E-mail: libraryarchives@calu.edu
URL: http://www.calu.edu/catalog/current/undergra
duate/about/library.aspx
Contact: Daniel T. Zyglowicz, Library Technician
E-mail: zyglowicz@calu.edu
Facebook: www.facebook.com/PennWCalifornia
X (Twitter): twitter.com/i/flow/login?redirect_after
_login=%2FPennWCalifornia
Instagram: www.instagram.com/PennWCalifornia/
YouTube: www.youtube.com/user/CalUofPA

Scope: History; the Civil War. **Services:** Interlibrary loan; library open to the public by appointment. **Founded:** 1852. **Holdings:** Journals; books; e-books; audiovisual materials.

11294 ■ Chicago Public Library - Visual & Performing Arts Division - Music Information Center
400 S State St.
Chicago, IL 60605
URL: http://www.chipublib.org/archival_subject/
theater
Contact: Deanie Adams, Director
E-mail: dadams@chipublib.org

Scope: History and theory of music, biographies of musicians and composers, music education, opera, musical comedy, sacred music, popular music, discography, music business, musical instruments, vocal and instrumental pedagogy, music therapy, folk music, composition and orchestration, arranging. **Services:** Interlibrary loan; copying; listening/viewing

center; practice rooms; music chamber; center open to the public. **Founded:** 1915. **Holdings:** 49,800 books; 8,025 bound periodical volumes; 67,000 bound volumes of music; 30,000 pieces of music; 15 VF drawers of pamphlets and clippings; 6,102 microfiche of music; 2,220 reels of microfilm of periodicals; 169,000 phonograph records, compact discs, audiocassettes; 3,900 music videos; 334 laserdiscs; 4,250 photographs; 51,957 uncatalogued scores.

11295 ■ Conservatoire de Musique de Quebec Bibliotheque
270 rue St. Jacques-Parizeau
Quebec, QC, Canada G1R 5G1
Ph: (418)643-2190
URL: http://biblio.cmadq.gouv.qc.ca/in/faces/
homeInBook.xhtml

Scope: Classical music; orchestral music. **Services:** Library open to the public for reference use only. **Founded:** 1944. **Holdings:** 65,000 books; manuscripts; periodicals. **Subscriptions:** 33 journals and other serials; newspapers.

11296 ■ Edinboro University - Baron-Forness Library Special Collections
200 Tartan Dr.
Edinboro, PA 16444
URL: http://www.edinboro.edu/offices-services/library/
index.php

Scope: Pennsylvania history; education. **Services:** Interlibrary loan;Tutoring. **Holdings:** 300,000 volumes;680,000 microform units;100 full-text journal databases; Reserve materials; software; equipment.

11297 ■ Grinnell College - Burling Library Media Room
1115 8th Ave.
Grinnell, IA 50112
URL: http://www.grinnell.edu/academics/libraries/stu
dents/using-burling-kistle-libraries/media-recording
Contact: Randye Jones, Contact

Scope: Educational material. **Services:** Library open to the public with restrictions (public may use items in-house, unless space is needed by students or faculty).Interlibrary loan. **Founded:** 1846. **Holdings:** Figures not available.

11298 ■ Hardin-Simmons University - Smith Music Library
2200 Hickory St.
Abilene, TX 79698
URL: http://www.hsutx.edu/about-hsu/w-hines-sims

Scope: Music. **Services:** Interlibrary loan. **Founded:** 1891. **Holdings:** Scores; various composers' collected works; recordings; music books; 48,000 periodicals; 375,000 items and 1,800,000 volumes.

11299 ■ John Brown University - Music Library
2000 W University St.
Siloam Springs, AR 72761
Ph: (479)524-9500
Co. E-mail: jbuinfo@jbu.edu
URL: http://www.jbu.edu/academics/music
Facebook: www.facebook.com/JohnBrownUniversity
X (Twitter): x.com/johnbrownuniv
Instagram: www.instagram.com/johnbrownuniversity
YouTube: www.youtube.com/user/
JohnBrownUniversity

Scope: Music. **Services:** Interlibary Loan; Library open to the public. **Founded:** 1997. **Holdings:** Figures not available.

11300 ■ Lawrence University - Seeley G. Mudd Library Music Collections
113 S Lawe St.
Appleton, WI 54911
URL: http://www.lawrence.edu/library/library-collec
tions

Description: Library serves the students and faculties of Lawrence University. **Scope:** Music studies. **Services:** Interlibrary loan. **Founded:** 1847. **Holdings:** 350,000 books and periodicals; 23,000 musical scores; 14,000 audio recordings; 11,000 video recordings.

11301 ■ Ohio Wesleyan University - Kinnison Music Library
61 S Sandusky St.
  Delaware, OH 43015
Ph: (740)368-3314
Free: 800-922-8953
Co. E-mail: musicd@owu.edu
URL: http://www.owu.edu
Contact: John Milligan, Chairman
Facebook: www.facebook.com/
  OhioWesleyanUniversity
Linkedin: www.linkedin.com/school/ohio-wesleyan
  -university
X (Twitter): x.com/OhioWesleyan
Instagram: www.instagram.com/ohiowesleyan
YouTube: www.youtube.com/user/OhioWesleyanU
Scope: Music. **Services:** Interlibrary loan; copying; library open to the public. **Holdings:** Figures not available.

11302 ■ St. Norbert Arts Centre Archives (SNAC)
100 rue des Ruines du Monastere
  Winnipeg, MB, Canada R3V 1L6
Ph: (204)269-0564
Co. E-mail: snac@snac.mb.ca
URL: http://www.snac.mb.ca
Contact: Naomi Gerrard, Chairman of the Board
Facebook: www.facebook.com/StNorbertArtsCentre
YouTube: www.youtube.com/channel/UC2yIUh
  tsPQPin4LkfA86pqQ
Founded: 1991. **Holdings:** Figures not available.

11303 ■ San Francisco Public Library - Bernard Osher Foundation Art, Music & Recreation Center
100 Larkin St.
  San Francisco, CA 94102
Ph: (415)557-4525
Co. E-mail: artmusicrec@sfpl.org
URL: http://sfpl.org/locations/main-library/art-music
Scope: Visual arts; performing arts; music; sports and recreation. **Services:** Center open to the public. **Holdings:** Books; serials; scores; CD-ROMs; DVDs.

11304 ■ University of Nevada, Las Vegas Music Library (UNLV)
4505 S Maryland Pky.
  Las Vegas, NV 89154-7002
Ph: (702)895-2541
Co. E-mail: music.library@unlv.edu
URL: http://www.library.unlv.edu/music
Contact: Deanna Stefanelli, Contact
Facebook: www.facebook.com/unlvlib
X (Twitter): x.com/unlvlibraries
Instagram: www.instagram.com/unlvlibraries
YouTube: www.youtube.com/user/unlvlibraries
Description: To inspire discovery, appreciation, and respect for animals and nature. **Scope:** Music. **Services:** Interlibrary loan (limited); open to faculty, students, and the las vegas music community. **Founded:** 2001. **Holdings:** 35,000 scores; 15,500 recordings; 3,000 DVDs; audiovisual materials; manuscripts.

11305 ■ University of North Carolina School of the Arts - Semans Library
1533 S Main St.
  Winston Salem, NC 27127-2738
Ph: (336)770-3399
URL: http://www.uncsa.edu/faculty-staff-hub/aroun
  d-campus/facilities-maintenance/design-and-cons
  truction-projects/semans-renovation.aspx
Description: Library collects, organizes, describes and preserves access to records of permanent administrative, legal, fiscal and historical value. **Scope:** Art and design. **Services:** Interlibrary loan; library open to the public; copying; printing; scanning. **Founded:** 1965. **Holdings:** Books; periodicals; music and media.

11306 ■ Weill-Lenya Research Center (WLRC) - Library
7 E 20th St.
  New York, NY 10003
Ph: (212)505-5240
Fax: (212)353-9663
Co. E-mail: wlrc@kwf.org
URL: http://www.kwf.org/research-center
Description: Research unit of the Kurt Weill Foundation for Music, Inc., a private, non-profit foundation. Offers information referral. **Scope:** Life and works of Kurt Julian Weill (1900-1950), German-born American composer, and Lotte Lenya (1898-1981), Austrian actress-singer and Weill's widow. Also studies music in the Weimar Republic and the American musical theater. **Services:** Copying at staff discretion; lending photos for reprinting; library open to the public by appointment. **Founded:** 1983. **Holdings:** Books; printed music; music manuscripts; scripts; correspondence; audio and video recordings; films; programs; photographs; posters; press clippings; business records; personal papers. **Publications:** *Guide to the Weill-Lenya Research Center*; *Kurt Weill Newsletter* (Semiannual). **Awards:** Kurt Weill Foundation Grant Program- Professional Performance (Annual).

ASSOCIATIONS AND OTHER ORGANIZATIONS

11307 ■ American Institute of Organbuilders (AIO)
PO Box 1695
Grass Valley, CA 95945
Ph: (415)806-9011
Co. E-mail: execsec@pipeorgan.org
URL: http://www.pipeorgan.org
Contact: Jeffrey Dexter, President
E-mail: jdexter@schantzorgan.com
Facebook: www.facebook.com/American-Institute-of
-Organbuilders-127681787268798
Description: Professional builders and service technicians of pipe organs. Advances the art of pipe organ building by encouraging discussion, inquiry, and research; furthers knowledge regarding pipe organ building through lectures and the exchange of information. Conducts examinations and small-group training seminars. **Founded:** 1974. **Publications:** *Journal of American Organbuilding* (Quarterly); *AIO Service Manual; Apprenticeship and Training Policy Manual; Member Directory.* **Educational Activities:** American Institute of Organbuilders Convention (Annual). **Geographic Preference:** National.

11308 ■ American Musical Instrument Society (AMIS)
c/o Jitasa
1750 W Front St.
Boise, ID 83702
URL: http://www.amis.org
Contact: Janet K. Page, President
Facebook: www.facebook.com/OfficialAMIS
Description: Promotes understanding of many aspects of musical instruments of all types, from all cultures and time periods. Publishes and disseminates information on all types of instruments through journals and newsletters. Hosts demonstrations and meetings. **Founded:** 1971. **Publications:** *Journal of the American Music Instrument Society* (Annual); *American Musical Instrument Society--Membership Directory and Handbook* (Annual). **Educational Activities:** AMIS Annual Meeting (Annual). **Awards:** Curt Sachs (Annual); Nicolas Bessaraboff Prize (Annual); Frances Densmore Prize (Annual); Curt Sachs Award (Annual); Nicholas Bessaraboff Prize (Annual); The William E. Gribbon Memorial Award for Student Travel (Annual). **Geographic Preference:** National.

11309 ■ Associated Pipe Organ Builders of America (APOBA)
11804 Martin Rd.
Waterford, PA 16441
Free: 800-473-5270
URL: http://www.apoba.com
Contact: Jonathan Ross, President
E-mail: jross@andoverorgan.com
Description: Manufacturers of pipe organs and pipe organ parts. Aims to expand and perfect the art of pipe organ building in the U.S. Sponsors educational programs and speakers' bureau. Compiles marketing statistics. **Founded:** 1941. **Publications:** *Success Stories: Five Pipe Organ Projects Summarized.* **Geographic Preference:** National.

11310 ■ International Association of Piano Builders and Technicians (IAPBT)
c/o Piano Technicians Guild
4444 Forest Ave.
Kansas City, KS 66106
Ph: (913)432-9975
Fax: (913)432-9986
Co. E-mail: exec@ptg.org
URL: http://my.ptg.org/iapbtw/home
Contact: Barbara Cassaday, Executive Director
E-mail: exec@ptg.org
Description: Trade organization for piano technicians and rebuilders around the world. Seeks to encourage and provide a forum for the exchange of technical information and related subjects and for cooperation in scientific research to improve the quality of pianos. **Founded:** 1979. **Geographic Preference:** Multinational.

11311 ■ National Association of Professional Band Instrument Repair Technicians Inc. (NAPBIRT)
2026 Eagle Rd.
Normal, IL 61761
Ph: (309)452-4257
Fax: (309)452-4825
Co. E-mail: napbirt@napbirt.org
URL: http://napbirt.org
Contact: William Mathews, Contact
E-mail: napbirt@napbirt.org
Instagram: www.instagram.com/napbirtofficial
Description: Aims to offer continuing education in the field of band instrument repair. Promotes technical integrity in the craft. Conducts self-evaluation programs, local parts and services exchange programs, and problem solution services. Surveys tools and procedures to improve work quality. Serves as liaison between manufacturers/suppliers and technicians by providing a technical audience for the introduction and evaluation of new products and policies. Has established a code of ethics. Provides placement service. Holds hands-on training sessions per year. **Founded:** 1976. **Geographic Preference:** National.

11312 ■ National Piano Foundation (NPF) [Piano Manufacturers Association International]
14070 Proton Rd., Ste. 100
Dallas, TX 75244
Ph: (972)233-9107
Fax: (972)490-4219
URL: http://pianonet.com
Contact: Richard Rejino, Executive Director
Description: Manufacturers of pianos and parts suppliers. Compiles monthly unit shipment and dollar volume reports. **Founded:** 1962. **Geographic Preference:** Multinational; National.

11313 ■ Piano Technicians Guild (PTG)
4444 Forest Ave.
Kansas City, KS 66106
Ph: (913)432-9975
Fax: (913)432-9986
Co. E-mail: ptg@ptg.org
URL: http://www.ptg.org/home
Contact: Paul Adams, President
E-mail: pres@ptg.org
Facebook: www.facebook.com/pianotechniciansguild
X (Twitter): x.com/pianotechguild
YouTube: www.youtube.com/user/PTGHomeOffice
Description: Piano tuners and technicians. Conducts technical institutes at conventions, seminars and local chapter meetings. Promotes public education in piano care; maintains liaison with piano manufacturers and teachers. Maintains hall of fame. **Founded:** 1958. **Publications:** *Piano Technicians Journal--Piano Technicians Guild Directory Issue; Piano Technicians Journal* (Annual). **Educational Activities:** PTG Annual Convention (Annual); MTNA National Conference (Annual). **Awards:** The Golden Hammer Award (Annual); The Hall of Fame (Annual); The Crowl-Travis Member of Note Award (Annual). **Geographic Preference:** Multinational.

REFERENCE WORKS

11314 ■ "The Faces Behind the Nation's Largest Instrument Repair Shop" in The Frederick News-Post (July 6, 2016)
URL(s): www.fredericknewspost.com/news/arts_an
.d_entertainment/the-faces-behind-the-nation-s
-largest-instrument-repair-shop/article_e475ec5e
-3319-5039-830f-da097ddbe77d.html
Ed: Jennifer Skinner. **Released:** July 06, 2016.
Description: The biggest instrument repair shop in the nation is is Frederick, Maryland. Music & Arts Repair Shop takes in musical instruments from schools where students rent or buy, and repairs them. Handling nearly 200,000 shipments a year, The Repair Shop is busiest in the summer months after school lets out. **Availability:** Online.

TRADE PERIODICALS

11315 ■ Acoustic Guitar Magazine
Pub: Acoustic Guitar
URL(s): store.acousticguitar.com/collections/back
-issues
Facebook: www.facebook.com/AcousticGui
tarMagazine
Released: Monthly **Price:** $35.99, for online one year; $90.99, for online 3 year; $66.99, for 2 year; $35.99, for print and online 1 year; $66.99, for print and online 2 year; $90.99, for print and online 3 year. **Description:** Magazine for professional and amateur acoustic guitar enthusiasts offering advice on choosing, maintaining, and playing acoustic guitar. **Availability:** Print; Download; Online.

11316 ■ *Premiere Guitar*
Pub: Gearhead Communications L.L.C.
Contact: Amy D. Plummer, Contact
URL(s): www.premierguitar.com
Facebook: www.facebook.com/premierguitar
X (Twitter): x.com/premierguitar
Instagram: www.instagram.com/premierguitar
YouTube: www.youtube.com/premierguitar

Released: Monthly **Price:** $12.99, for 1 year; $39.95, Two years for US print; $115, for print one year international; $119.90, Two years for Canada print; $230, Two years for international print; $55.95, Canada for print one year; $24.95, U.S. for print one year; $0.99, Single issue for digital; $12.95, Canada for 5 months; $4.95, U.S. for 5 months; $2.50, for back issues. **Description:** Consumer magazine covering equipment, services, and supplies for professional, performing musicians. **Availability:** Print; Download; Online.

RESEARCH CENTERS

11317 ■ University of Hartford College of Engineering, Technology and Architecture - Engineering Applications Center - Acoustics Laboratory
200 Bloomfield Ave.
  West Hartford, CT 06117

URL: http://www.hartford.edu/academics/schools-colleges/ceta/academics/department-of-mechanical-aerospace-and-acoustical-engineering/acoustical-engineering-programs.aspx

Description: Integral unit of Engineering Applications Center, College of Engineering, Technology and Architecture at University of Hartford. **Scope:** Noise and vibration control, machine diagnostics, musical instrument analysis, psychoacoustics, architectural acoustics, sound system design, optimization and materials testing, hearing loss, as well as sound quality design and optimization.

ASSOCIATIONS AND OTHER ORGANIZATIONS

11318 ■ **Professional Beauty Association (PBA)**

7755 E Gray Rd.
  Scottsdale, AZ 85260-3459
Ph: (480)281-0424
Free: 800-468-2274
Co. E-mail: info@probeauty.org
URL: http://www.probeauty.org
Contact: Nina Daily, Executive Director
Facebook: www.facebook.com/professionalbeau
  tyassociation
Linkedin: www.linkedin.com/company/professional
  -beauty-association
X (Twitter): x.com/probeautyassoc
Instagram: www.instagram.com/probeautyassoc
YouTube: www.youtube.com/user/professionalbeauty

Description: Manufacturer of beauty and barber products, cosmetics, equipment, and supplies used in or resold by beauty salons or barbershops. **Founded:** 1985. **Publications:** *American Salon Magazine* (Quarterly); *PBA Progress.* **Educational Activities:** Professional Beauty Africa (Annual); National Beauty Show - HAIRWORLD (Annual); Cosmoprof North America (CPNA) (Annual); International Salon & Spa Expo ('Annual). **Awards:** Sally Beauty Scholarships for High School Graduates (Annual). **Geographic Preference:** National.

REFERENCE WORKS

11319 ■ *"How Vietnamese Americans Took Over the Nails Business: A Documentary" in NPR (May 19, 2019)*
URL(s): www.npr.org/2019/05/19/724452398/how-vie
  tnamese-americans-took-over-the-nails-business-a
  -documentary
Ed: Lulu Garcia-Navarro. **Released:** May 19, 2019. **Description:** Discusses the new documentary, Nailed It, about the Vietnamese heritage in US nail salons and how these entrepreneurs launched this multi-billion dollar industry. **Availability:** Online.

11320 ■ *Marilyn Monroe-Themed Spas to Open in Orlando This Fall: Former Disney Exec Al Weiss Co-Heading Up Venture*
Pub: Baltimore Business Journal
Contact: Rhonda Pringle, President
E-mail: rpringle@bizjournals.com
Description: Former Walt Disney World executive Al Weiss and Niki Bryan Spa Management Company founder Niki Bryan are planning to create a chain of spas, salons, nail boutiques and other concepts with the Marily Monroe brand called Marilyn Monroe Spas LLC. The concept intends to bring a standard of service, feeling and identity in the spa industry in Orlando, Florida. **Availability:** Print; Online.

11321 ■ *"Nice Toes, Bro. Young Men Invade Nail Salons" in The Wall Street Journal (July 28, 2019)*
URL(s): www.wsj.com/articles/nice-toes-bro-young
  -men-invade-nail-salons-11564338047
Ed: Ray A. Smith. **Released:** July 28, 2019. **Description:** Young men are stepping up their grooming game and heading to the local nail salon for pedicures. Luxury fashion brands have popularized sandals, making nice toes a necessity, but it's causing some tension with their regular female customers who are finding themselves waiting in line. **Availability:** Online.

STATISTICAL SOURCES

11322 ■ *Hair & Nail Salons Industry in the US - Market Research Report*
URL(s): www.ibisworld.com/united-states/market-re
  search-reports/hair-nail-salons-industry/
Price: $925. **Description:** Downloadable report analyzing current and future trends in the hair and nail salon industries. **Availability:** Download.

CONSULTANTS

11323 ■ **Contempo Nails**
333 S Robertson Blvd.
  Beverly Hills, CA 90211
Contact: Hang Nguyen, Chief Executive Officer
Description: Provider of consulting services in sculptured acrylic nail application and care, and catering for special event such as birthdays, baby showers, and much more. **Scope:** Provider of consulting services in sculptured acrylic nail application and care, and catering for special event such as birthdays, baby showers, and much more.

ASSOCIATIONS AND OTHER ORGANIZATIONS

11324 ■ Au Pair in America (APIA)
1 High Ridge Pk.
  Stamford, CT 06905
Ph: (203)399-5419
Free: 800-928-7247
Fax: (203)399-5592
Co. E-mail: aupair.info@aifs.com
URL: http://www.aupairinamerica.com
Contact: Jean Quinn, Director
Facebook: www.facebook.com/AuPairInAmerica
X (Twitter): x.com/aupairinamerica
Instagram: www.instagram.com/theaupairinamerica
YouTube: www.youtube.com/user/aupairinamerica

Description: A program of the American Institute for Foreign Study, Inc. International youth exchange program to promote cross-cultural understanding between American families and Western European young adults. Provides the opportunity for young people overseas to learn about American culture and family life while living in the U.S. Arranges for foreigners between 18 and 26 to reside in the U.S. for a year while caring for the children of a host family; participants serve as an "au pair," or equal person, in the host family's household. Has developed a reciprocal program which allows young Americans to travel to Europe. **Founded:** 1986. **Geographic Preference:** National.

11325 ■ International Nanny Association (INA)
PO Box 70496
  Milwaukee, WI 53207
Free: 888-878-1477
Co. E-mail: info@nanny.org
URL: http://www.nanny.org
Contact: Marcia Hall, Executive Director
X (Twitter): x.com/IntlNannyAssoc
Instagram: www.instagram.com/intlnannyassoc
YouTube: www.youtube.com/user/INANanny

Description: An educational association for nannies and those who educate, place, employ, and support professional in-home child care. **Founded:** 1985. **Publications:** *A Nanny for Your Family; Directory of Nanny Training Programs, Placement Agencies and Special Services* (Annual); *INAVision; Recommended Practices for Nannies; So You Want to Be a Nanny; Annual Directory of Nanny Training Programs, Nanny Placement Agencies and Special Services.* **Educational Activities:** International Nanny Association Conference (Annual). **Awards:** INA Nanny of the Year (Annual). **Geographic Preference:** National.

REFERENCE WORKS

11326 ■ "Nanny Shortage Could Create a Crisis as Families Return to Work" in Crains New York (July 22, 2021)
Ed: Cara Eisenpress. **Released:** July 22, 2021. **Description:** Due to the disruption in work from Covid-19, many nannies in New York found work elsewhere. By the time industries opened back up, many parents have been scrambling to find someone to watch their children. **Availability:** Online.

11327 ■ "Vaccine 'Battle' Halts Child Care Business Operations" in Nashville Business Journal (July 29, 2021)
Ed: Emma Dooling. **Released:** July 29, 2021. **Description:** Now that Covid-19 vaccines are available, many families are requesting their nannies receive the vaccination in order to continue working within their homes. Some nannies are hesitant, and it's causing a disruption within the nanny industry. **Availability:** Online.

11328 ■ "What It Takes To Be a $200,000-a-Year Nanny" in CNN (June 13, 2019)
URL(s): www.cnn.com/2019/06/13/success/nanny -high-paying-job/index.html
Ed: Anna Bahney. **Released:** June 13, 2019. **Description:** Top-tier nannies are in demand, especially if they have specializations, certifications, and a lot of experience. Those seeking the top paying positions often have to work long hours and overnight, plus some traveling with the family. **Availability:** Online.

11329 ■ "When the Nanny Leaves" in The New York Times (August 21, 2017)
URL(s): www.nytimes.com/2017/08/21/well/family/ when-the-nanny-leaves.html
Ed: Alexandra Sacks, M.D. **Released:** August 21, 2017. **Description:** Discusses the impact a nanny leaving a household has on the children they once cared for. **Availability:** Online.

STATISTICAL SOURCES

11330 ■ Maids, Nannies & Gardeners Industry in the US - Market Research Report
URL(s): www.ibisworld.com/united-states/market-re- search-reports/maids-nannies-gardeners-industry/
Price: $925. **Description:** Downloadable report analyzing current and future trends in the domestic help industries. **Availability:** Download.

FRANCHISES AND BUSINESS OPPORTUNITIES

11331 ■ Absolute Best Care Nanny Agency
110 Wall St., Office 2-041
  New York, NY 10005
Ph: (212)481-5705
Co. E-mail: info@absolutebestcare.com
URL: http://www.absolutebestcare.com
Facebook: www.facebook.com/absolutebes tcarenannies
X (Twitter): x.com/absolutenanny

Description: Firm provides placing nannies, baby nurses, housekeepers and babysitters. **Founded:** 2002. **Financial Assistance:** No **Managerial Assistance:** Firm provides placing nannies, baby nurses, housekeepers and babysitters.

11332 ■ Nanny Poppinz Corporate, Inc.
340 9th St.
  Naples, FL 34102
Ph: (239)690-6495
Free: 877-262-6694
URL: http://www.nannypoppinz.com
Contact: Susan McCloskey, President

Description: Nanny agency franchise. **No. of Franchise Units:** 3. **No. of Company-Owned Units:** 2. **Founded:** 1999. **Franchised:** 2004. **Equity Capital Needed:** $65,000-$107,000. **Franchise Fee:** $35,000. **Training:** Yes.

START-UP INFORMATION

11333 ■ *"Best In Show" in Pet Product News (Vol. 64, November 2010, No. 11, pp. 20)*
Ed: Lizett Bond. **Description:** Cherrybrook Premium Pet Supplies offers an expanded array of quality holistic products and is staffed by people who possess wide knowledge of these products. Aside from receiving the Outstanding Holistic Approach award, Cherrybrook has opened three stores in New Jersey. How a holistic approach to service kept customers coming back is discussed. **Availability:** Print; Online.

ASSOCIATIONS AND OTHER ORGANIZATIONS

11334 ■ **Acupuncture Canada**
Toronto, ON, Canada M3C 1W3
Ph: (416)752-3988
Fax: (416)752-4398
Co. E-mail: info@acupuncturecanada.org
URL: http://www.acupuncturecanada.org
Contact: Catharine Maxwell-Palmer, President
Facebook: www.facebook.com/AcupunctureCan
Linkedin: www.linkedin.com/company/acupuncture
-canada
X (Twitter): x.com/acupuncture_can
Instagram: www.instagram.com/acupuncture_can
Description: Promotes acupuncture's legitimate place in health care by initiating and supporting research in acupuncture. **Founded:** 1974. **Educational Activities:** Acupuncture Canada Board meeting. **Geographic Preference:** National.

11335 ■ **Alexander Technique International (ATI)**
6510 Telecom Dr. Ste. 370
Indianapolis, IN 46278
Ph: (317)932-3570
Co. E-mail: office@alexandertechniqueinternational
.org
URL: http://www.alexandertechniqueinternational.org
Facebook: www.facebook.com/Alexander-Technique
-International-168509932777
X (Twitter): x.com/ATInternational
Description: Worldwide organization of Alexander technique teachers, students and supporters of the technique, created to promote and advance the work discovered by F.M. Alexander. Alexander Technique can improve health by overcoming harmful habits that cause stress and pain which often restrict physical and mental capabilities. **Founded:** 1992. **Publications:** *Communique*; *ExChange* (Semiannual). **Geographic Preference:** Multinational.

11336 ■ **American Holistic Health Association (AHHA)**
PO Box 17400
Anaheim, CA 92817-7400
Ph: (714)779-6152
Co. E-mail: mail@ahha.org
URL: http://ahha.org
Contact: Suzan V. Walter, President

Facebook: www.facebook.com/AMHolistic
Linkedin: www.linkedin.com/company/american-holis
tic-health-association
X (Twitter): x.com/AmHolistic
Description: Promotes holistic health care, a concept that stresses the integration of physical, mental, emotional, and spiritual concerns with environmental harmony. **Founded:** 1989. **Geographic Preference:** Multinational.

11337 ■ **American Reflexology Certification Board (ARCB)**
4707 Schley Ave., Ste. A
Braddock Heights, MD 21714
Ph: (303)933-6921
Co. E-mail: info@arcb.net
URL: http://arcb.net
Contact: Lara Westdorp, President
E-mail: arcbpresident@gmail.com
Facebook: www.facebook.com/ARCB.net
Description: Works to protect the public; promotes advancement of field through recognition of competent reflexologists meeting national standards; provides National Board Certified Reflexologist certification. **Founded:** 1991. **Publications:** *Reflexology Today Newsletter*; *Reflexology Today*. **Geographic Preference:** National.

11338 ■ **American Tarot Association (ATA)**
1020 Liberty Rd.
Lexington, KY 40505-4035
Free: 888-211-1572
Fax: (859)514-9799
Co. E-mail: ata@ata-tarot.com
URL: http://www.ata-tarot.com
Contact: Tracy Hite, Treasurer
E-mail: treasurer@ata-tarot.com
Description: Works to bring together qualified students, teachers and masters of the Tarot, who are willing to subscribe to a high ethical standard, and use the Tarot for the benefit of those for whom they read. Recognizes Tarot as a useful tool for personal growth and spiritual development. **Publications:** *ATA Quarterly* (Quarterly); *Tarot Reflections* (Monthly). **Geographic Preference:** Multinational.

11339 ■ **Healing Touch Professional Association (HTPA)**
15610 Henderson Pass No. 700070
San Antonio, TX 78232
Ph: (210)497-5529
Co. E-mail: info@healingtouchprogram.com
URL: http://www.htprofessionalassociation.com
Contact: Christine Salas, Director
Facebook: www.facebook.com/
HealingTouchProfessionalAssociation
Description: Offers education and resources to practice the Healing Touch holistic method of healing along with providing accredited credentials. Networking is available throughout the community.

11340 ■ **The International Society for the Study of Ghosts and Apparitions (ISSGA) [Headquarters for Ghost Investigations]**
29 Washington Sq. W
Penthouse N
New York, NY 10011-9180
Co. E-mail: theghostpost@yahoo.com
URL: http://phantasm.mynetcologne.de/issga.html
Contact: Dr. Jeanne Keyes Youngson, President
E-mail: jeannekey@aol.com
Description: Professional ghost hunters; individuals interested in ghosts and apparitions. Provides information on ghosts, apparitions, and other phenomena. Sponsors private tours in Greenwich Village, NY, led by the president of the society. Compiles statistics; conducts research. **Founded:** 1986. **Geographic Preference:** National.

11341 ■ **Reflexology Association of America (RAA)**
1809 Rutledge
Madison, WI 53704
Ph: (608)571-5053
Co. E-mail: inforaa@reflexology-usa.org
URL: http://reflexology-usa.org
Contact: Debbie Hitt, President
E-mail: raapres@reflexology-usa.org
Description: Promotes and supports reflexology ("the systematic, manual stimulation of the reflex maps located on the feet, hands and outer ears that resemble the shape of the human body"). **Founded:** 1995. **Publications:** *Reflexology Across America Newsletter* (Quarterly); *Guidelines to Setting up a Reflexology Association*; *How do Reflexologists Earn a Living*; *Reflexology Across America* (Quarterly); *State Leadership Training Manual*; *State Organizational Development Guidelines*. **Geographic Preference:** Multinational.

REFERENCE WORKS

11342 ■ *"Ahead of the Trend: What Will the World Map Look Like in Five Years?" in Pet Product News (Vol. 66, September 2012, No. 9, pp. S1)*
Description: How Whiskers Holistic Pet Care has transformed itself into the go-to place for naturally inclined pet owners in New York City's East Village is discussed. Since 1988, Whiskers Holistic Pet Care has emphasized careful product selection and customer education to serve a wide array of customers. **Availability:** Print; Online.

11343 ■ *"Remember Those Great Volkswagen Ads?"*
Pub: Merrell Publishers
Contact: Hugh Merrell, Publisher
E-mail: hugh.merrell@merrellpublishers.com
Price: $65; C$72. **Description:** The Volkswagen advertising campaign of the 1960s and 1970s is rated the best and most influential of the century. Also included is a section on billboards signs used to advertise. **Availability:** Print.

STATISTICAL SOURCES

11344 ■ *Essential Oil Manufacturing Industry in the US - Market Research Report*
URL(s): www.ibisworld.com/united-states/market-research-reports/essential-oil-manufacturing-industry/
Price: $925. **Description:** Downloadable report analyzing current and future trends in the essential oil manufacturing industry. **Availability:** Online.

TRADE PERIODICALS

11345 ■ *Geocosmic Journal*
Pub: National Council for GeoCosmic Research
Contact: Pam Wenzel, Treasurer
E-mail: treasurer@geocosmic.org
URL(s): geocosmic.org/publications
Ed: Leigh Westin. **Released:** Annual **Price:** $15, Single issue for pdf format. **Description:** Trade magazine on astrology and cosmology. **Availability:** Print; PDF; Download.

11346 ■ *Light Lines*
Pub: L/L Research
Contact: Austin Bridges, Director
URL(s): www.llresearch.org/newsletters/light-lines/3
Released: Quarterly; Spring, Summer, Winter and Fall. **Description:** Provides news of interest regarding metaphysical evolution. **Availability:** Print; PDF.

11347 ■ *Revelations of Awareness*
Pub: Cosmic Awareness Communications
Contact: T. Vikki, Manager
E-mail: vikkit@cosmicawareness.org
URL(s): cosmicawareness.org/subscription
Released: Monthly **Price:** $77, for print + online; $52, for annual print subscription; $44, for annual online subscription; $3, for back issues 1-4; $2.50, for 5-7 back issues; $2.30, for back issues 8-9; $2.10, for 10 issues; $1.80, for 11 or more back issues. **Description:** Consists of a series of questions submitted by readers which are answered through channelings from a force describing itself as Cosmic Awareness or 'Universal Mind'. Offers deeply spiritual, yet practical and current information that can be applied to the daily life of the reader on such topics as holistic health, philosophy, and unsolved mysteries. Recurring features include letters to the editor, news of research, book reviews, notices of publications available, reports of meetings, and a calendar of events. Exposes UFO and New World Order conspiracies. **Availability:** Print; Download; Online.

11348 ■ *SCP Journal*
Pub: Spiritual Counterfeits Project
Contact: Tal Brooke, President
URL(s): scp-inc.org/product-category/journal/?orderby=date
Ed: George A. Koch, Tal Brooke. **Released:** Latest Issue Spring 2024. **Price:** $35, U.S. for annual; $7, Single issue. **Description:** Magazine covering spiritual phenomena and cultural trends such as near-death experiences, deep ecology, Gaia, witchcraft, and UFOs. Analyzes spiritual trends from a Christian perspective. **Availability:** Print.

11349 ■ *Triangles Bulletin*
Pub: Lucis Trust
Contact: Christine Morgan, President
URL(s): www.lucistrust.org/triangles/triangles_bulletin
Released: Quarterly; March, June, September, December. **Description:** Contains articles regarding the Triangles Network of Light, a service activity for men and women of goodwill who believe in the power of thought. Concerned with the principles of brotherhood, the one humanity, and with the global community preparing for the New Age and the Reappearance of the Christ. Reports on organizations and movements of interest to Network members. Recurring features include editorials and news from Network units. **Availability:** PDF; Download; Online.

LIBRARIES

11350 ■ Bastyr University Library
14500 Juanita Dr., NE
Kenmore, WA 98028
Ph: (425)602-3020
Co. E-mail: library@bastyr.edu
URL: http://bastyr.libguides.com/home
Contact: Ekaterini Papadopoulou, Director
E-mail: epapadopoulou@bastyr.edu
URL(s): www.bastyr.edu/student-life/library
Facebook: www.facebook.com/BastyrUniversity
X (Twitter): x.com/bastyr
Scope: Education; natural health arts; science. **Services:** Interlibrary loan; copying; library open to the public for reference use only. **Founded:** 1980. **Holdings:** DVDs; eBooks; journals.

11351 ■ Geisinger Medical Center (GMC) - Health Sciences Library
100 N Academy Ave.
Danville, PA 17822
Ph: (570)271-6211
URL: http://www.geisinger.org/patient-care/find-a-location/geisinger-medical-center
Description: Community radio station currently operating out of the French Quarter in New Orleans. **Scope:** Medical. **Services:** Library not open to public. **Founded:** 1996. **Holdings:** Figures not available.

START-UP INFORMATION

11352 ■ *"David Maus Debuting New Dealership" in Orlando Business Journal (Vol. 26, February 5, 2010, No. 36, pp. 1)*
Pub: Orlando Business Journal
Contact: Julie Swyers, Director
E-mail: jswyers@bizjournals.com

Ed: Anjali Fluker. **Description:** Automotive dealers David Maus Automotive Group and Van Tuyl Automotive Investment Group will launch David Maus Chevrolet in Sanford, Florida in fall 2010. The 12-acre site of the Chevy dealership will be located adjacent to the David Maus Toyota dealership. The new store is expected to generate nearly 125 new jobs. **Availability:** Print; Online.

11353 ■ *"Ex-NFL Players' Game Plan: 2 New Nissan Dealerships" in Crain's Detroit Business (Vol. 30, July 28, 2014, No. 30, pp. 1)*
Pub: Crain Communications Inc.
Contact: Barry Asin, President

Description: All Pro Motors LLC, a New Jersey automobile dealership management company, is bringing National Football League star power to both Dearborn and Clinton Township, Michigan opening new Nissan dealerships. Detail of the new retail stores is revealed. **Availability:** Print; Online.

11354 ■ *"Wheel Genius" in Entrepreneur (June 2014)*
Pub: Entrepreneur Media Inc.
Contact: Dan Bova, Director
E-mail: dbova@entrepreneur.com

Description: Electric car startup, Kenguru, has developed a hatchback that aims to improve mobility for wheelchair users, who enter the vehicle using a rear-opening tailgate and automatic ramp. The Kenguru, which is Hungarian for kangaroo, uses motorcycle-style handlebars instead of steering wheels. The 1,000-pound car has an estimated range of 60 miles and can travel up to 35 miles per hour. The Kenguru could sell for about $25,000. Founder Stacy Zoern partnered with Budapest, Hungary-based Istvan Kissaroslaki in developing the new car. **Availability:** Print; Online.

ASSOCIATIONS AND OTHER ORGANIZATIONS

11355 ■ **1953-54 Buick Skylark Club**
c/o Gary Di Lillo, Newsletter Editor
27315 Hemlock Dr.
Westlake, OH 44145
Fax: (440)871-5484
Co. E-mail: gary@avptc.com
URL: http://www.skylarkclub.org
Contact: Marvin Pickens, Treasurer
E-mail: marvinpickens@bellsouth.net

Description: Owners and admirers of Buick Skylark automobiles built in 1953 and 1954. Promotes preservation and maintenance of classic Buicks. Serves as a clearinghouse on 1953 and 1954 Buick Skylarks; facilitates communication and good fellowship among members. **Founded:** 1978. **Geographic Preference:** National.

11356 ■ **American Automotive Leasing Association (AALA)**
600 Pennsylvania Ave.SE
Washington, DC 20003
Ph: (202)531-1398
URL: http://www.aalafleet.com
Contact: Mike Joyce, Executive Director
E-mail: joyce@aalafleet.com

Description: Represents the commercial automotive fleet leasing and management industry. **Founded:** 1955. **Geographic Preference:** National.

11357 ■ **American International Automobile Dealers Association (AIADA)**
500 Montgomery St., Ste. 800
Alexandria, VA 22314
Ph: (703)519-7810
Free: 800-462-4232
Co. E-mail: goaiada@aiada.org
URL: http://www.aiada.org
Contact: Cody Lusk, President
Facebook: www.facebook.com/AIADA.News
Linkedin: www.linkedin.com/company/aiada
X (Twitter): x.com/AIADA_News
YouTube: www.youtube.com/user/aiadaorg2011

Description: Works to preserve a free market for international automobiles in the U.S. and is dedicated to increasing public awareness of the benefits derived from the auto industry. **Founded:** 1970. **Publications:** *Auto Dealer* (Quarterly); *AIADA's Showroom* (9/year). **Awards:** David F. Mungenast Sr. Lifetime Achievement Award (Annual). **Geographic Preference:** National.

11358 ■ *CADA Newsline*
123 Commerce Valley Dr. E Ste., 303
Thornhill, ON, Canada L3T 7W8
Ph: (905)940-4959
Free: 800-463-5289
Co. E-mail: privacy@cada.ca
URL: http://www.cada.ca
Contact: Tim Reuss, President
E-mail: treuss@cada.ca
URL(s): www.cada.ca/CADA/CADA/News1/Newsline -Echo-CADA.aspx
Released: Monthly; current update June 2024. **Availability:** Print.

11359 ■ **Corporation des Associations de Detaillants d'Automobiles (CADA)**
123 Commerce Valley Dr. E Ste., 303
Thornhill, ON, Canada L3T 7W8
Ph: (905)940-4959
Free: 800-463-5289
Co. E-mail: privacy@cada.ca
URL: http://www.cada.ca
Contact: Tim Reuss, President

E-mail: treuss@cada.ca
Facebook: www.facebook.com/Canadian-Automobile -Dealers-Association-CADA-764363147039168
X (Twitter): x.com/cdnautocada

Description: An automobile dealer member association principally engaged in representation and advocacy services for new car and truck dealership franchisees, including policy legislation, legal assistance, industry communication facilitation and public relations services as well as education and insurance programs. **Founded:** 1941. **Publications:** *CADA Newsline* (Monthly). **Educational Activities:** Canadian International AutoShow (Annual). **Awards:** Richard C. Gauthier CADA Scholarship (Annual). **Geographic Preference:** National.

11360 ■ **Ford Minority Dealers Association (FMDA)**
PO Box 760386
Southfield, MI 48075
Ph: (248)557-2500
Free: 866-559-1732
URL: http://fordmda.com
Contact: Dr. A. V. Fleming, Executive Director
E-mail: deedee0914@aol.com

Description: Minority-owned car dealerships. Promotes professional standards of minority dealerships. Strives to increase the number of minority dealerships. **Founded:** 1980. **Geographic Preference:** National.

11361 ■ **National Association of Minority Automobile Dealers (NAMAD)**
9475 Lottsford Rd., Ste. 150
Largo, MD 20774
Ph: (301)306-1614
Fax: (301)306-1493
URL: http://namad.org
Contact: Fernando Varela, Chairman
Facebook: www.facebook.com/namadusa
YouTube: www.youtube.com/user/NAMADVIDEOS

Description: To better the business conditions of its members on an ongoing basis. Serves as a confidential spokesperson for dealers. Offers business analysis, financial counseling, and short- and long-term management planning. Conducts research programs; compiles statistics. **Founded:** 1980. **Publications:** *NAMAD Newsletter*. **Geographic Preference:** National.

11362 ■ **National Auto Auction Association (NAAA)**
5320 Spectrum Dr., Ste. D
Frederick, MD 21703
Ph: (301)696-0400
Fax: (301)631-1359
Co. E-mail: naaa@naaa.com
URL: http://www.naaa.com
Contact: Tricia Heon, Chief Executive Officer
E-mail: theon@naaa.com
Facebook: www.facebook.com/National-Auto-Auction -Association-35704747404
X (Twitter): x.com/NAutoAuctionAsn

Description: Owners/operators of wholesale automobile and truck auctions; associate members are car and truck manufacturers, insurers of checks and titles, car and truck rental companies, publishers of auto price guide books, and others connected with the industry. Maintains hall of fame. **Founded:** 1948. **Publications:** *National Auto Auction Association--Membership Directory* (Annual); *On the Block* (6/year). **Educational Activities:** NAAA Annual Convention (Annual); NAAA Annual Convention (Annual). **Awards:** NAAA Hall of Fame (Annual). **Geographic Preference:** National.

11363 ■ National Automobile Dealers Association (NADA)
8484 Westpark Dr., Ste. 500
Tysons, VA 22102
Free: 800-557-6232
Co. E-mail: customerservice@nada.org
URL: http://www.nada.org
Contact: Mike Stanton, President
Facebook: www.facebook.com/NADAUpdate
YouTube: www.youtube.com/user/NADAUpdate
Description: Franchised new car and truck dealers. Provides representation for franchised new car and truck dealers in the areas of government, industry, and public affairs. Offers management services and retirement and insurance programs to member dealers. Maintains National Automobile Dealers Charitable Foundation. **Founded:** 1917. **Publications:** *NADA Appraisal Guides*; *NADA's AutoExec Magazine: Official Publication of the National Automobile Dealers Association* (Monthly); *Automotive Executive--Dealer Business Guide Issue*; *AutoExec* (Monthly); *DEAC Report* (Quarterly); *NADA Headlines* (Weekly). **Educational Activities:** ATD Convention & Expo (Annual); NADA Show (Annual). **Geographic Preference:** National.

11364 ■ National Independent Automobile Dealers Association (NIADA)
4621 S Cooper St., Ste. 131-524
Arlington, TX 76017
Ph: (817)640-3838
Co. E-mail: cpo@niada.com
URL: http://niada.com
Contact: Scott Allen, President
Facebook: www.facebook.com/NationalIndependentAutomobileDealersAssociation
Linkedin: www.linkedin.com/company/national-independent-automobile-dealers-association
X (Twitter): x.com/_niada
Instagram: www.instagram.com/_niada
YouTube: www.youtube.com/channel/UCwhk-6tS5PDMOpGDkxGMd_g
Description: Maintains speakers' bureau, services for children, and charitable programs. Sponsors competitions; compiles statistics. **Founded:** 1946. **Publications:** *Used Car Dealer* (Monthly); *Dealer Connection* (Quarterly); *Used Car Industry Report* (Annual). **Educational Activities:** NIADA Convention & Expo (Annual). **Awards:** NIADA National Quality Dealer of the Year Award (Annual); NIADA Ring of Honor (Annual); NIADA Eagle Award (Annual); NIADA Crystal Eagle Award (Biennial); NIADA Foundation Scholarships (Annual); NIADA State Association Executive of the Year (Annual). **Geographic Preference:** National.

11365 ■ Used Truck Association (UTA)
1502 W Broadway, Ste. 102
Madison, WI 53713
Free: 877-438-7882
Co. E-mail: contact@uta.org
URL: http://www.uta.org
Contact: Rick Clark, President
E-mail: rick@uta.org
Facebook: www.facebook.com/usedtruckassociation
Linkedin: www.linkedin.com/company/used-truck-association
X (Twitter): x.com/usedtruckassoc
Instagram: www.instagram.com/usedtruckassociation
Description: Truck dealerships with substantial used truck sales; truck manufacturers. Promotes professionalism among members; works to elevate the image of the used truck sales business. Monitors

federal regulatory developments affecting used truck sales; conducts lobbying activities. **Founded:** 1998. **Awards:** Marvin F. Gordon Lifetime Achievement Award (Annual). **Geographic Preference:** National.

REFERENCE WORKS

11366 ■ "$3 Million in Repairs Prep Cobo for Auto Show" in Crain's Detroit Business (Vol. 26, January 4, 2010, No. 1, pp. 1)
Pub: Crain Communications Inc.
Contact: Barry Asin, President

Ed: Nancy Kaffer. **Description:** Overview of the six projects priced roughly at $3 million which were needed in order to host the North American International Auto Show; show organizers stated that the work was absolutely necessary to keep the show in the city of Detroit. **Availability:** Print; Online.

11367 ■ "The 490 Made Chevy a Bargain Player" in Automotive News (Vol. 86, October 31, 2011, No. 6488, pp. S22)
Pub: Crain Communications Inc.
Contact: Barry Asin, President

Ed: David Phillips. **Description:** The first Chevrolet with the 490 engine was sold in 1913, but it was too expensive for masses. In 1914 the carmaker launched a lower-priced H-series of cars competitively priced. Nameplates such as Corvette, Bel Air, Camaro and Silverado have defined Chevrolet through the years. **Availability:** Online.

11368 ■ "1914 Proved to Be Key Year for Chevy" in Automotive News (Vol. 86, October 31, 2011, No. 6488, pp. S18)
Pub: Crain Communications Inc.
Contact: Barry Asin, President

Ed: Jamie LaReau. **Description:** Chevy Bow Tie emblem was born in 1914, creating the brand's image that has carried through to current days. **Availability:** Print; Online.

11369 ■ "2011 FinOvation Awards" in Farm Industry News (January 19, 2011)
Pub: Informa Business Media, Inc.
Contact: Charlie McCurdy, President

Ed: Karen McMahon, Jodie Wehrspann. **Description:** The 2011 FinOvation Award winners are announced, covering new products that growers need for corn and soybean crops. Winners range from small turbines and a fuel-efficient pickup to a Class 10 combine and drought-tolerant hybrids. **Availability:** Online.

11370 ■ "Advice at Entrepreneurs Event: Make Fast Decisions, See Trends" in Crain's Detroit Business (Vol. 30, July 28, 2014, No. 30, pp. 4)
Pub: Crain Communications Inc.
Contact: Barry Asin, President

Description: Crain's entrepreneurial event was held a The Henry Ford in Dearborn, Michigan. Panelists at the event advised entrepreneurs to make fast decisions and to be aware of small business trends in order to be successful. George Matick Chevrolet was honored. Details of the event are covered. **Availability:** PDF; Online.

11371 ■ "Alcoa's Quebec Deal Keeps Smelters Running" in Pittsburgh Business Times (Vol. 33, February 28, 2014, No. 33, pp. 3)
Pub: American City Business Journals, Inc.
Contact: Mike Olivieri, Executive Vice President

Released: Weekly. **Price:** $4, Introductory 4-week offer(Digital & Print). **Description:** Alcoa Inc. has renewed its power supply contract with the Quebec provincial government for three of its smelters in 2014. The aluminum company is investing $250 million in the smelters over the next five years to support growth in the automotive manufacturing industry. **Availability:** Print; Online.

11372 ■ "Alternative Fuels Take Center Stage at Houston Auto Show" in Houston Business Journal (Vol. 44, January 31, 2014, No. 39, pp. 8)
Pub: American City Business Journals, Inc.
Contact: Mike Olivieri, Executive Vice President

Released: January 31, 2014. **Price:** $4, Introductory 4-Week Offer(Digital & Print). **Description:** An energy summit was held at the Houston Auto Show in Texas on January 22, 2014, where energy executives discussed new technology and initiatives. They considered the market for electric and natural gas-fueled vehicles as well as other options including hydrogen, fuel cells, and biofuels. **Availability:** Print; Online.

11373 ■ The Art and Science of Running a Car Dealership
Ed: Max Zanan. **Released:** October 09, 2019. **Description:** An experienced general manager of a dealership explains the things he wishes he knew before taking the job. Key topics about today's car purchasing and how dealers operate are given. **Availability:** Print.

11374 ■ "Auction Company Grows with Much Smaller Sites" in Automotive News (Vol. 86, October 31, 2011, No. 6488, pp. 23)
Pub: Crain Communications Inc.
Contact: Barry Asin, President

Ed: Arlena Sawyers. **Description:** Auction Broadcasting Company has launched auction sites and is expanding into new areas. The family-owned business will provide auctions half the size traditionally used. The firm reports that 40 percent of the General Motors factory-owned vehicles sold on consignment were purchased by online buyers, up 30 percent over 2010. **Availability:** Online.

11375 ■ "Auto Asphyxiation" in Canadian Business (Vol. 85, August 13, 2012, No. 13, pp. 38)
Ed: Michael McCullough. **Description:** The declining car ownership and utlization has profound business implications for oil companies and automakers and may bring substantial benefit to other sectors and the economy as a whole. The transition to the post-automotive age may happen in places where there is the will to change transportation practices but not in others. **Availability:** Print; Online.

11376 ■ "Auto Bankruptcies Could Weaken Defense" in Crain's Detroit Business (Vol. 25, June 8, 2009, No. 23, pp. 1)
Pub: Crain Communications Inc.
Contact: Barry Asin, President

Ed: Chad Halcom. **Description:** Bankruptcy and supplier consolidation of General Motors Corporation and Chrysler LLC could interfere with the supply chains of some defense contractors, particularly makers of trucks and smaller vehicles. **Availability:** Print; Online.

11377 ■ "Auto Loan Demand On the Upswing" in Memphis Business Journal (Vol. 34, May 25, 2012, No. 6, pp. 1)
Pub: Baltimore Business Journal
Contact: Rhonda Pringle, President
E-mail: rpringle@bizjournals.com

Ed: Cole Epley. **Description:** Demand for auto loans in the US has increased in April 2012. Auto loans have surpassed consumerm loans during the first quarter of the year. **Availability:** Print; Online.

11378 ■ "Auto Show Aims to Electrify" in Crain's Detroit Business (Vol. 26, January 11, 2010, No. 2, pp. 1)
Pub: Crain Communications Inc.
Contact: Barry Asin, President

Ed: Ryan Beene. **Description:** Overview of the North American International Auto show include sixteen production and concept vehicles including eight from the Detroit 3. High-tech battery suppliers as well as hybrid and electric vehicles will highlight the show. **Availability:** Print; Online.

11379 ■ *"Baltimore Dealers Fear Shortages in Car Supply"* in *Boston Business Journal (Vol. 29, May 13, 2011, No. 1, pp. 1)*
Pub: Boston Business Journal
Contact: Carolyn M. Jones, President
E-mail: cmjones@bizjournals.com
Ed: Scott Dance. **Price:** $4, Introductory 4-Week Offer(Digital Only). **Description:** The earthquake and tsunami in Japan are seen to impact the automobile dealers in Baltimore, Maryland. Automobile supply in the area is seen to decrease dramatically during the summer sales season. Shortage of transmission parts and paint colors is also forecasted. **Availability:** Print; Online.

11380 ■ *"Bankruptcies"* in *Crain's Detroit Business (Vol. 24, March 24, 2008, No. 12, pp. 6)*
Pub: Crain Communications Inc.
Contact: Barry Asin, President
Description: Current list of business that filed for Chapter 7 or 11 protection in U.S. Bankruptcy Court in Detroit include a construction company, a medical care company, a physical therapy firm and a communications firm. **Availability:** Online.

11381 ■ *"Battered U.S. Auto Makers in Grip of Deeper Sales Slump"* in *Globe & Mail (April 4, 2007, pp. B1)*
Ed: Greg Keenan. **Description:** The fall in Canadian sales and market share of Ford Motor Co., General Motors Corp. and Chrysler Group is discussed. **Availability:** Print; Online.

11382 ■ *"BMW Revs Up for a Rebound"* in *Barron's (Vol. 89, July 13, 2009, No. 28, pp. M7)*
Pub: Dow Jones & Company Inc.
Contact: Almar Latour, Chief Executive Officer
Ed: Jonathan Buck. **Description:** Investors may like BMW's stocks because the company has maintained its balance sheet strength and has an impressive production line of new models that should boost sales in the next few years. The company's sales are also gaining traction, although their vehicle delivery was down 1.7 percent year on year on June 2009, this was still the best monthly sales figure for 2009. **Availability:** Online.

11383 ■ *"Brand Police Keep the Lines Distinct at GM"* in *Automotive News (Vol. 86, October 31, 2011, No. 6488, pp. 3)*
Pub: Crain Communications Inc.
Contact: Barry Asin, President
Ed: Mike Colias. **Description:** Joel Ewanick, marketing chief at General Motors, is working to keep General Motor's four brands distinct within their brands. **Availability:** Online.

11384 ■ *"Buick Prices Verano Below Rival Luxury Compacts"* in *Automotive News (Vol. 86, October 31, 2011, No. 6488, pp. 10)*
Pub: Crain Communications Inc.
Contact: Barry Asin, President
Ed: Mike Colias. **Description:** General Motors's Verano will compete with other luxury compacts such as the Lexus IS 250 and the Acura TSX, but will be prices significantly lower coming in with a starting price of $23,470, about $6,000 to $10,000 less than those competitors. **Availability:** Online.

11385 ■ *Buyology: Truth and Lies About Why We Buy*
Pub: Doubleday
Ed: Martin Lindstrom. **Released:** February 02, 2010. **Price:** $15, paperback. **Description:** Marketers study brain scans to determine how consumers rate Nokia, Coke, and Ford products. **Availability:** Print.

11386 ■ *"C-Class Could Boost Auto Suppliers"* in *Birmingham Business Journal (Vol. 31, June 27, 2014, No. 26, pp. 10)*
Pub: American City Business Journals, Inc.
Contact: Mike Olivieri, Executive Vice President
Released: June 27, 2014. **Description:** The 2014 model of the Mercedes-Benz C-Class will be the first to be built at the Vance, Alabama manufacturing

plant, increasing business opportunities for auto suppliers in the region. Jason Hoff, president and CEO of Mercedes-Benz US International Inc. notes that the move will impact the local economy as several companies in the area expand their operations to meet the growing demand from Mercedes.

11387 ■ *"Car Dealer Closings: Immoral, Slow-Death"* in *Crain's Detroit Business (Vol. 25, June 8, 2009, No. 23)*
Pub: Crain Communications Inc.
Contact: Barry Asin, President
Ed: Daniel Duggan. **Description:** Colleen McDonald discusses the closing of her two Chrysler dealerships located in Taylor and Livonia, Michigan, along with her Farmington Hills store, Holiday Chevrolet. **Availability:** Print; Online.

11388 ■ *"CarBiz Inc. Speaking At NABD"* in *Marketwired (May 14, 2007)*
Pub: Comtex News Network Inc.
Contact: Kan Devnani, President
Description: CarBiz Inc., a leading provider of software, consulting, and training solutions to the United States' automotive industry, had two of its executive officers speak at the National Alliance of Buy Here - Pay Here Dealers (NABD), a conference that draws over 2,000 dealers, service providers, and experts from across the United States. **Availability:** Print; Online.

11389 ■ *"CAW Hopes to Beat Xstrata Deadline"* in *Globe & Mail (January 30, 2007, pp. B3)*
Description: The decision of Canadian Auto Workers to strike work at Xstrata PLC over wage increase is discussed. **Availability:** Online.

11390 ■ *"Charged Up for Sales"* in *Charlotte Business Journal (Vol. 25, October 15, 2010, No. 30, pp. 1)*
Description: Li-Ion Motors Corporation is set to expand its production lines of electric cars in Sacramento, California. The plan is seen to create up to 600 jobs. The company's total investment is seen to reach $500 million. **Availability:** Print; Online.

11391 ■ *"Consumers Like Green, But Not Mandates"* in *Business Journal-Milwaukee (Vol. 28, December 10, 2010, No. 10, pp. A1)*
Pub: The Business Journal
Contact: Heather Ladage, President
E-mail: hladage@bizjournals.com
Ed: Sean Ryan. **Description:** Milwaukee, Wisconsin consumers are willing to spend more on green energy, a survey has revealed. Respondents also said they will pay more for efficient cars and appliances. Support for public incentives for homeowners and businesses that reduce energy use has also increased. **Availability:** Print; Online.

11392 ■ *"Dealer Gets a Lift with Acquisitions at Year's End"* in *Crain's Detroit Business (Vol. 26, January 11, 2010, No. 2, pp. 3)*
Pub: Crain Communications Inc.
Contact: Barry Asin, President
Ed: Ryan Beene. **Description:** Alta Equipment Co., a forklift dealer, closed 2009 with a string of acquisitions expecting to double the firm's employee headcount and triple its annual revenue. Alta Lift Truck Services, Inc., as the company was known before the acquisitions, was founded in 1984 as Michigan's dealer for forklift manufacturer Yale Materials Handling Corp. **Availability:** Print; Online.

11393 ■ *"Delphi Latest In Fight Over Offshore Tax Shelters"* in *Crain's Detroit Business (Vol. 30, July 7, 2014, No. 27, pp. 1)*
Pub: Crain Communications Inc.
Contact: Barry Asin, President
Description: Internal Revenue Service is investigating Delphi Automotive and other American companies over the use of offshore tax shelters. The latest in Delphi's dispute with the federal government over tax practices is expected to cost the supplier millions. Delphi manufactures electronics and technologies for vehicles. Apple Inc. and Google Inc. have also been

targeted by the IRS for incorporating portions of the businesses offshore allowing them to avoid U.S. taxes as well as other foreign taxes. **Availability:** Online.

11394 ■ *"The Doomsday Scenario"* in *Conde Nast Portfolio (Vol. 2, June 2008, No. 6, pp. 91)*
Ed: Jeffrey Rothfeder. **Description:** Detroit and the U.S. auto industry are discussed as well as the ramifications of the demise of this manufacturing base. Similarities and differences between the downfall of the U.S. steel business and the impact it had on Pittsburg, Pennsylvania is also discussed.

11395 ■ *"Everyone Has a Story Inspired by Chevrolet"* in *Automotive News (Vol. 86, October 31, 2011, No. 6488, pp. S003)*
Pub: Crain Communications Inc.
Contact: Barry Asin, President
Description: Besides being a great ad slogan, 'Baseball, Hot Dogs, Apple Pie and Chevrolet', the brand conjures up memories for most everyone in our society. Louis Chevrolet had a reputation as a race car driver and lent his name to the car that has endured for 100 years. **Availability:** Online.

11396 ■ *"Ex-Medical Student Stages Career In Event Planning: Barcelona Owner Makes Inroads with Luxury Car Dealerships"* in *Los Angeles Business Journal (Vol. 34, June 18, 2012, No. 25, pp. 10)*
Pub: CBJ L.P.
Contact: Terri Cunningham, Contact
Description: Barcelona Enterprises started as a company designing menus for restaurants, organizing food shows, to planning receptions for luxury car dealers. The fim will be launching the first Las Vegas Chocolate Festival & Pastry Show in July 2012. Presently, the company runs 24 wine and food festivals, organizes events for an upscale dog shampoo maker, and sports car dealerships. **Availability:** Print; Online.

11397 ■ *"Extra Rehab Time Boosts M-B's Off-Lease Profits"* in *Automotive News (Vol. 86, October 31, 2011, No. 6488, pp. 22)*
Pub: Crain Communications Inc.
Contact: Barry Asin, President
Ed: Arlena Sawyers. **Description:** Mercedes-Benz Financial Services USA is holding on to off-lease vehicles in order to recondition them and the move is boosting profits for the company. **Availability:** Print; Online.

11398 ■ *"Ford: Down, Not Out, and Still a Buy"* in *Barron's (Vol. 92, July 23, 2012, No. 30, pp. 14)*
Pub: Dow Jones & Company Inc.
Contact: Almar Latour, Chief Executive Officer
Ed: Vito J. Racanelli. **Description:** Stocks of Ford Motor Company could gain value as the company continues to improve its finances despite fears of slower global economic growth. The company's stock prices could double from $9.35 per share within three years. **Availability:** Online.

11399 ■ *"Former Schaefer & Strohminger Dealerships to Hit Auction Block"* in *Baltimore Business Journal (Vol. 28, September 10, 2010)*
Pub: Baltimore Business Journal
Contact: Rhonda Pringle, President
E-mail: rpringle@bizjournals.com
Ed: Gary Haber. **Description:** Maryland's real estate developers have a chance to vie for almost 11 acres of prime Baltimore County real estate that are on the auction block. The five properties were once home to Schaefer and Strohminger car dealerships and were located in the county's busiest areas. Other potential uses for the properties are also discussed.

11400 ■ *"From American Icon to Global Juggernaut"* in *Automotive News (Vol. 86, October 31, 2011, No. 6488, pp. S003)*
Pub: Crain Communications Inc.
Contact: Barry Asin, President

Ed: Peter Brown. **Description:** Chevrolet celebrates its 100th Anniversary. The brand revolutionized its market with affordable cars that bring technology to the masses. Chevys have been sold in 140 countries and the company is responding to a broader market. **Availability:** Print; Online.

11401 ■ *"From the Moon to Malibu" in Canadian Business (Vol. 87, July 2014, No. 7, pp. 106)*
Description: The new BMW i8 plug-in hybrid sports car accelerates from zero to 100 kilometers per hour in 4.4 seconds but consumes fuel at an average of just 4.8 liters per 100 kilometers. The drivetrain features a 131-horsepower electric motor and a 231-horsepower internal combustion engine. **Availability:** Print; Online.

11402 ■ *"Full Speed Ahead: How to Get the Most Out of Your Company Vehicles" in Entrepreneur (Vol. 37, October 2009, No. 10, pp. 78)*
Pub: Entrepreneur Media Inc.
Contact: Dan Bova, Director
E-mail: dbova@entrepreneur.com
Ed: Jill Amadio. **Description:** Methods of saving costs on purchasing and maintaining vehicles are described. Tips include shopping online, choosing hybrid vehicles, and choosing cars with incentives and lower insurance costs.

11403 ■ *"Future Autoworkers will Need Broader Skills" in Crain's Detroit Business (Vol. 25, June 8, 2009, No. 23, pp. 13)*
Pub: Crain Communications Inc.
Contact: Barry Asin, President
Ed: Ryan Beene. **Description:** Auto industry observers report that new workers in the industry will need advanced skills and educational backgrounds in engineering and technical fields because jobs in the factories will become more technology-based and multidisciplinary. **Availability:** Online.

11404 ■ *"General Electric Touts Going Green for Business Fleet Services" in America's Intelligence Wire (June 1, 2012)*
Description: General Capital Fleet Services if featuring alternative-fuel vehicles in Eden Prairie for its corporate customers. GE Capital is the world's largest fleet management service and is offering its customers the first of its kind service that allows corporate lease customers to test drive alternative fuel cars from 20 different manufacturers. **Availability:** Print; Online.

11405 ■ *"GM Scores High Marks For Its Use of Solar Power" in Blade (September 13, 2012)*
Pub: McClatchy Tribune Information Services
Contact: Patrick J. Talamantes, President
Ed: Tyrel Linkhorn. **Description:** General Motors scores high among top corporate generators of solar power in the United States. The Solar Energy Industries Assocation ranked GM's on-site solar power generation capacity at number 13, making GM the first in the automotive sector. Details of GM's solar projects are outlined. **Availability:** Online.

11406 ■ *"GM's Decision to Boot Dealer Prompts Sale" in Baltimore Business Journal (Vol. 27, November 6, 2009, No. 26, pp. 1)*
Pub: Baltimore Business Journal
Contact: Rhonda Pringle, President
E-mail: rpringle@bizjournals.com
Ed: Daniel J. Sernovitz. **Description:** General Motors Corporation's (GM) decision to strip Baltimore's Anderson Automotive Group Inc. of its GM franchise has prompted the owner, Bruce Mortimer, to close the automotive dealership and sell the land to a developer. The new project could make way for new homes, a shopping center and supermarket. **Availability:** Print; Online.

11407 ■ *"GM's Volt Woes Cast Shadow on E-Cars" in Wall Street Journal Eastern Edition (November 28, 2011, pp. B1)*
Pub: Dow Jones & Company Inc.
Contact: Almar Latour, Chief Executive Officer

Ed: Sharon Terlep. **Description:** The future of electric cars is darkened with the government investigation by the National Highway Traffic Safety Administration into General Motor Company's Chevy Volt after two instances of the car's battery packs catching fire during crash tests conducted by the Agency. **Availability:** Online.

11408 ■ *"Here's Why I Went Broke as a Used Car Dealer" in AutoTrader (February, 2017)*
URL(s): www.autotrader.com/car-video/heres-why-i-went-broke-used-car-dealer-261353
Ed: Tyler Hoover. **Released:** February 2017. **Description:** A former used car dealer talks about his time working on the lot and how his passion for cars almost financially ruined him. **Availability:** Online.

11409 ■ *"High-Yield Turns Into Road Kill" in Barron's (Vol. 88, July 7, 2008, No. 27, pp. M7)*
Pub: Dow Jones & Company Inc.
Contact: Almar Latour, Chief Executive Officer
Ed: Emily Barrett. **Description:** High-yield bonds have returned to the brink of collapse after profits have recovered from the shock brought about by the collapse of Bear Stearns. The high-yield bond market could decline again due to weakness in the automotive sector, particularly in Ford and General Motors. **Availability:** Online.

11410 ■ *"How Detroit Built Its Marquee Auto Show" in Crain's Detroit Business (Vol. 30, January 6, 2014, No. 1, pp. 17)*
Pub: Crain Communications Inc.
Contact: Barry Asin, President
Description: Detroit-area automobile dealers and business leaders, along with staff from the Detroit Auto Dealers Association, promoted Detroit as the premier North American International Auto Show event, upstaging New York. Few would have considered cold and snowy Detroit as a January destination, but they succeeded in their marketing campaign and the show has continued to grow since. **Availability:** Online.

11411 ■ *"How Much Profit is Enough?" in Automotive News (Vol. 86, October 31, 2011, No. 6488, pp. 12)*
Pub: Crain Communications Inc.
Contact: Barry Asin, President
Description: Workers at the big three automobile companies are unhappy about the issues of class wealth, like the high compensations offered to CEOs. **Availability:** Print; Online.

11412 ■ *"How to Start a Car Dealership Business in 9 Simple Steps" in Starting Business (September 4, 2020)*
URL(s): www.startingbusiness.com/blog/start-business-car-dealership
Ed: Andrew Moran. **Released:** September 4, 2020. **Availability:** Online.

11413 ■ *"Hyannis Mercedes Franchise Sold" in Cape Cod Times (December 2, 2010)*
Pub: Cape Cod Times
Contact: Anne Brennan, Executive Editor
E-mail: abrennan@capecodonline.com
Ed: Sarah Shemkus. **Description:** Trans-Atlantic Motors franchise has been sold to Mercedes-Benz of Westwood. **Availability:** Print; Online.

11414 ■ *"Hyundai Enters Minivan Market" in Globe & Mail (February 15, 2006, pp. B7)*
Ed: Greg Keenan. **Description:** The reasons behind the launch of minivan by Hyundai Auto Canada Inc. are presented. **Availability:** Online.

11415 ■ *"Japan-Brand Shortages Will Linger Into '12" in Automotive News (Vol. 86, October 31, 2011, No. 6488, pp. 1)*
Pub: Crain Communications Inc.
Contact: Barry Asin, President

Ed: Amy Wilson, Mark Rechtin. **Description:** Floods in Thailand and the tsunami in Japan have caused shortages of Japanese-brand vehicle parts. These shortages are expected to linger into 2012. **Availability:** Online.

11416 ■ *"Keeping the Vehicle On the Road--A Survey On On-Road Lane Detection Systems" in ACM Computing Surveys (Vol. 46, Spring 2014, No. 1, pp. 2)*
Pub: Association for Computing Machinery - University of Wyoming
Contact: Ed Seidel, President
E-mail: uwpres@uwyo.edu
Description: The development of wireless sensor networks, such as researchers Advanced Driver Assistance Systems (ADAS) requires the ability to analyze the road scene in the same as a human. Road scene analysis is an essential, complex, and challenging task and it consists of: road detection and obstacle detection. The detection of the road borders, the estimation of the road geometry, and the localization of the vehicle are essential tasks in this context since they are required for the lateral and longitudinal control of the vehicle. A comprehensive review of vision-based road detection systems vision in automobiles and trucks is examined. **Availability:** Online.

11417 ■ *"Kroger Launches Car-Buying Program" in Supermarket News (November 7, 2019)*
URL(s): www.supermarketnews.com/retail-financial/kroger-launches-car-buying-program
Ed: Russell Redman. **Released:** November 07, 2019. **Description:** Kroger is entering the car buying industry by partnering with TrueCar Inc. to form Kroger Auto, Powered by TrueCar. Kroger customers can now access vehicle pricing information to compare savings plus receive discounts on new and used vehicles. Consumers who participate will also receive a free Fuel VIP membership. **Availability:** Online.

11418 ■ *"LatinWorks Cozies Up to Chevy in Detroit" in Austin Business Journal (Vol. 31, August 12, 2011, No. 23, pp. A1)*
Pub: Austin Business Journal
Contact: Rachel McGrath, Director
E-mail: rmcgrath@bizjournals.com
Ed: Sandra Zaragoza. **Description:** Hispanic marketing agency LatinWorks opened an office in Detroit to better serve its client Chevrolet and to potentially secure more contracts from its parent company General Motors, whose offices are located nearby. **Availability:** Print; Online.

11419 ■ *"Mercury (1939-2010)" in Canadian Business (Vol. 83, June 15, 2010, No. 10, pp. 27)*
Ed: Steve Maich. **Released:** 2018. **Description:** Ford's Mercury brand of cars began in 1939 and it was designed by Ford to attract a wealthier clientele. Mercury was mentioned in a 1949 song by K.C. Douglas and was driven in the movie, "Rebel Without a Cause". However, the brand was too expensive for the mass market and not exclusive enough through the years, so Ford Motor Company decided to discontinue the brand in 2010. **Availability:** Print; Online.

11420 ■ *"Mobis to Set Up Lancaster Distribution Center" in Dallas Business Journal (Vol. 35, April 6, 2012, No. 30, pp. 1)*
Pub: Baltimore Business Journal
Contact: Rhonda Pringle, President
E-mail: rpringle@bizjournals.com
Description: Irvine, California-based Mobis Parts America bought a 442,000-square-foot Saint Pointe Building in Lancaster, Texas from KTR Capital Partners for an undisclosed price. Mobisplans to make the building a distribution center for regional Hyundai and Kia dealerships, creating more than 30 jobs to start. **Availability:** Print; Online.

11421 ■ *"The New Frontier" in Crain's Detroit Business (Vol. 26, January 18, 2010, No. 3, pp. S025)*

Description: Due to the changing consumer preference resulting from new fuel-efficiency standards, concern about climate change and higher gasoline prices, Detroit car designers are beginning to shift focus onto smaller vehicles. **Availability:** Print; Online.

11422 ■ *"New Life for Porsche's VW Dreams" in Barron's (Vol. 89, July 6, 2009, No. 27, pp. 9)*

Pub: Dow Jones & Company Inc.

Contact: Almar Latour, Chief Executive Officer

Ed: Vito J. Racanelli. **Description:** Porsche and Volkswagen moved closer to a merger after the Qatar Investment Authority offered to take a stake in Porsche. The QIA could take up to a 30 percent stake in Porsche and purchase all Volkswagen calls for up to $6 billion. **Availability:** Online.

11423 ■ *"No Frills - And No Dodge" in Crain's Detroit Business (Vol. 24, September 22, 2008, No. 38, pp. 3)*

Pub: Crain Communications Inc.

Contact: Barry Asin, President

Ed: Bradford Wernle. **Description:** Chrysler LLC is in the middle of a business plan known as Project Genesis, a five-year strategy in which the company will reduce the dealer count by combining its Jeep, Chrysler and Dodge brands under one rooftop wherever possible. Not every dealer will be able to arrange this deal because of the investment required to expand stores in which have low-overhead; many of these stores feel that low-overhead structures are more likely to survive difficult times than the larger stores in which the Genesis consolidation plan intends to implement. **Availability:** Online.

11424 ■ *"No End to the Nightmare; America's Car Industry" in The Economist (Vol. 390, January 3, 2009, No. 8612, pp. 46)*

Description: Detroit's struggling auto industry and the government loan package is discussed as well as the United Auto Worker union, which is loathed by Senate Republicans. **Availability:** Print; Online.

11425 ■ *"Older, But Not Wiser" in Canadian Business (Vol. 85, July 16, 2012, No. 11-12, pp. 54)*

Ed: Matthew McClearn, Michael McCullough. **Description:** Data from Statistics Canada revealed that two-thirds of workers aged 55 and above have some form of debt from mortgage to credit card balance while its one-third among the retired. Some factors contributing to the trend are the decline in borrowing costs, real estate, and older Canadians' car purchasing behavior. **Availability:** Print; Online.

11426 ■ *"Pennsylvania DEP To Conduct Natural Gas Vehicle Seminar" in Travel & Leisure Close-Up (October 8, 2012)*

Description: Pennsylvania Department of Environmental Protection is holding a Natural Gas Vehicle seminar at the Bayfront Convention Center in Erie, PA, as well as other locations throughout the state. The seminars will help municipal and commercial fleet owners make better informed decisions when converting fleets from compressed natural gas and liquefied natural gas. **Availability:** Print; Online.

11427 ■ *"Penske Opens Its First Smart Car Dealership In Bloomfield Hills" in Crain's Detroit Business (Vol. 24, January 21, 2008, No. 3)*

Pub: Crain Communications Inc.

Contact: Barry Asin, President

Ed: Sheena Harrison. **Description:** Information about Penske Automotive Group's Smart Car addition to its dealership lineup. Smart Car pricing starts at $11,590, with more than 30,000 individuals reserving vehicles. **Availability:** Print; Online.

11428 ■ *"Quonset Steering To Import Records" in Providence Business News (Vol. 29, May 19, 2014, No. 7, pp. 1)*

Pub: American City Business Journals, Inc.

Contact: Mike Olivieri, Executive Vice President

Released: May 17, 2014. **Description:** The growing automobile import business at Port of Davisville in North Kingstown, Rhode Island is marked by four consecutive record-breaking years of imports, with 250,000 vehicles expected to arrive by the end of 2014. Quonset Development Corporation managing director, Steven J. King, attributes the success of the auto import business to North Atlantic Distribution Inc. **Availability:** Print; Online.

11429 ■ *"The Road Warrior: Pamela Rodgers Kept Rodgers Chevrolet On Course Despite Numerous Obstacles" in Black Enterprise (Vol. 44, June 2014, No. 10, pp. 76)*

Pub: Earl G. Graves Ltd.

Contact: Earl Graves, Jr., President

Description: Profile of Pamela Rodgers, who built her company into one of General Motor's flagship franchises and ranked among the largest black-owned dealerships. Rodgers addresses the importance of customer service in order to grow her business. She is a 30-year veteran with her Chevrolet dealership located in the Detroit area.

11430 ■ *"The Role of Leadership In Successful International Mergers and Acquisitions: Why Renault-Nissan Succeeded and DaimlerChrysler-Mitsubishi Failed" in Human Resource Management (Vol. 51, May-June 2012, No. 3, pp. 433-456)*

Pub: John Wiley & Sons, Inc.

Contact: Christina Van Tassell, Executive Vice President Chief Financial Officer

Ed: Carol Gill. **Released:** May 25, 2012. **Description:** The effects of national and organizational culture on the performance of Nissan and Mitsubishi after their mergers with Renault and DaimlerChrysler respectively are examined. Japanese national culture was found to influence organizational culture and human resource management practices, while leadership affected the success of their turnaround efforts.

11431 ■ *"Ross: There's Still Money In the Auto Industry" in Crain's Detroit Business (Vol. 24, January 28, 2008, No. 4, pp. 12)*

Pub: Crain Communications Inc.

Contact: Barry Asin, President

Ed: Brent Snavely. **Description:** Wilbur Ross, chairman and CEO of WL Ross and Company LLC, a private equity firm, predicts U.S. vehicle sales will fall by about 750,000 in 2008, but continues to look for supplier bargains. **Availability:** Online.

11432 ■ *"Russia: Uncle Volodya's Flagging Christmas Spirit" in The Economist (Vol. 390, January 3, 2009, No. 8612, pp. 22)*

Description: Overview of Russia's struggling economy as well as unpopular government decisions such as raising import duties on used foreign vehicles so as to protect Russian carmakers. **Availability:** Print; Online.

11433 ■ *"Selling Michigan; R&D Pushed as Reason For Chinese To Locate In State" in Crain's Detroit Business (Vol. 24, January 14, 2008)*

Pub: Crain Communications Inc.

Contact: Barry Asin, President

Ed: Marti Benedetti. **Description:** Southeast Michigan Economic Development organizations are working to develop relationships with Chinese manufacturers so they will locate their automotive research and development operations in the state.

11434 ■ *"Sizing Up Bentley" in Barron's (Vol. 92, September 17, 2012, No. 38, pp. 16)*

Description: The energy efficiencies of cars produced by Bentley Motors have shown little improvement over time. The company needs to invest in improving the fuel efficiencies of its vehicles to attract new customers and remain competitive. **Availability:** Online.

11435 ■ *"Slimmer Interiors Make Small Cars Seem Big" in Automotive News (Vol. 86, October 31, 2011, No. 6488, pp. 16)*

Pub: Crain Communications Inc.

Contact: Barry Asin, President

Ed: David Sedgwick. **Description:** Cost-conscious buyers want luxury car amenities in their smaller vehicles, so automakers are rethinking interiors. Style, efficiency and value could be the next trend in vehicles. **Availability:** Print; Online.

11436 ■ *"Small is the New Big in Autos" in Globe & Mail (February 16, 2006, pp. B3)*

Ed: Greg Keenan. **Description:** The reasons behind the introduction of subcompact cars by companies such as Ford Motor Co. are presented. The automobiles were unveiled at Canadian International Auto Show in Toronto.

11437 ■ *"Steering Toward Profitability" in Black Enterprise (Vol. 41, December 2010, No. 5, pp. 72)*

Pub: Earl G. Graves Ltd.

Contact: Earl Graves, Jr., President

Ed: Alan Hughes. **Description:** Systems Electro Coating LLC had to make quick adjustments when auto manufacturers were in a slump. The minority father-daughter team discuss their strategies during the auto industry collapse.

11438 ■ *"Stock Car Racing" in Canadian Business (Vol. 81, September 15, 2008, No. 14-15, pp. 29)*

Description: Some analysts predict a Chapter 11-style tune-up making GM and Ford a speculative turnaround stock. However, the price of oil could make or break the shares of the Big Three U.S. automobile manufacturers and if oil goes up too high then a speculative stock to watch is an electric car company called Zenn Motor Co. **Availability:** Online.

11439 ■ *"Subaru of America Releases September Sales Figures" in Travel & Leisure Close-Up (October 8, 2012)*

Description: Subaru of America Inc. reports a 32 percent increase in sales in September 2012 compared to September 2011. Sales were shown at 27,683 vehicles for the month. Statistical data included. **Availability:** Print; Online.

11440 ■ *"Suppliers May Follow Fiat: Local Group Says Italian Firms are Inquiring" in Crain's Detroit Business (Vol. 25, June 15, 2009, No. 24, pp. 1)*

Pub: Crain Communications Inc.

Contact: Barry Asin, President

Ed: Ryan Beene. **Description:** Italian suppliers to Fiat SpA are looking toward Detroit after the formation of Chrysler Group LLC, the Chrysler-Fiat partnership created from Chrysler's bankruptcy. The Italian American Alliance for Business and Technology is aware of two Italy-based powertrain component suppliers that are considering a move to Detroit. **Availability:** Online.

11441 ■ *"Supply-Chain Collaboration, Image of Industry are OESA Chief's Top Tasks; Q&A Julie Fream, Original Equipment Suppliers Association" in Crain's Detroit Business (Vol. 30, January 6, 2014, No. 1, pp. 4)*

Pub: Crain Communications Inc.

Contact: Barry Asin, President

Description: Julie Fream is the new CEO of the Original Equipment Suppliers Assocation. Fream is a former Visteon Corporation executive and has held numerous positions in automotive manufacturing, sales and marketing. She is committed to holding transparency and collaboration within the industry. **Availability:** Online.

11442 ■ *"The 'Supply Side' of the Auto Industry" in Montly Labor Review (Vol. 133, September 2010, No. 9, pp. 72)*

Pub: U.S. Department of Labor Bureau of Labor Statistics

Contact: Amrit Kohli, Director

E-mail: kohli.amrit@bls.gov

Description: Restructuring and geographic change in the automobile industry is discussed. **Availability:** PDF; Online.

11443 ■ *"Survey: Confident Parts Makers Plan to Expand, Hire" in Crain's Detroit Business (Vol. 30, August 18, 2014, No. 33, pp. 5)*
Pub: Crain Communications Inc.
Contact: Barry Asin, President

Description: North American automotive suppliers are increasing capital expenditure, hiring new workers, and raising funds for possible mergers and acquisitions. Automotive manufacturing suppliers are forecasting a rebound in new vehicle sales. Statistical data included. **Availability:** Online.

11444 ■ *"Sustainable Advantage" in Inc. (Vol. 36, September 2014, No. 7, pp. 86)*
Pub: Mansueto Ventures L.L.C.
Contact: Stephanie Mehta, Chief Executive Officer

Price: $8.95, hardcopy black and white. **Description:** Four startup companies committed to providing sustainable, eco-friendly products and services while protecting the environment and bettering human health are profiled. Holganix(TM) offers organic lawn care products; Motiv Power Systems electrifies large vehicles; Clean Energy Collective Solar Power builds lareg community solar panel arrays; and Protein Bar offers healthy alternatives to fast food in its chain of restaurants. The company also works with nonprofits focused on wellness and education and has created 167 Learning Gardens nationwide. **Availability:** Print; PDF; Online.

11445 ■ *"Tesla Eyes Two Sites for New Battery-Pack Plant" in San Antonio Business Journal (Vol. 28, May 16, 2014, No. 14, pp. 8)*
Pub: American City Business Journals, Inc.
Contact: Mike Olivieri, Executive Vice President

Released: Weekly. **Price:** $4, introductory 4-week offer(Digital only). **Description:** The City of San Antonio, Texas is competing with other cities in five states to land the contract for the $5 million battery-pack plant of Texla Motors. Bill Avila of Bracewell & Giuliani LLPO law firm believes that San Antonio has an edge over some of the cities competing for the Tesla manufacturing plant because of its successful recruitment of Toyota in 2003. **Availability:** Print; Online.

11446 ■ *"This Just In: TechTown, Partners Get $1M to Start Tech Exchange" in Crain's Detroit Business (Vol. 25, June 1, 2009, No. 22, pp. 1)*
Pub: Crain Communications Inc.
Contact: Barry Asin, President

Ed: Daniel Duggan. **Description:** Three veterans of the auto industry have partnered to create, Revitalizing Michigan, a nonprofit dedicated to help manufacturers improve their processes. The firm is seeking federal, state and private grants to fund the mission. **Availability:** Print; Online.

11447 ■ *"Toyota Marks Record Profit Sales" in Globe & Mail (February 7, 2007, pp. B10)*

Description: The record quarterly sales and earnings reported by Japanese automaker Toyota Motor Corp. are discussed. The company sold 2.16 million vehicles during the quarter while registering 426.8 billion yen in profits. **Availability:** Print; Online.

11448 ■ *"Turning Drivers Into Geeks; Auto Dealers Debate Need for Technology Specialists to Bring Buyers Up to Speed" in Crain's Detroit Business (Vol. 30, January 6, 2014, No. 1, pp. 3)*
Pub: Crain Communications Inc.
Contact: Barry Asin, President

Description: Dealers at the 2014 North American International Auto Show discuss the need for technology specialists to educate sales staff as well as customers on the new high-tech items manufactured on today's automobiles and trucks. **Availability:** Print; Online.

11449 ■ *"Volvo: Logistics Agreement to Reduce Environmental Impact" in Ecology, Environment & Conservation Business (July 19, 2014, pp. 28)*
Pub: NewsRX LLC.
Contact: Kalani Rosell, Contact

Description: Scandinavian Logistics Partners AB (Scanlog) will sell surplus capacity in rail transport from Belgium to Sweden to the Volvo Group. The partnership benefits both costs and environmental impact. The Volvo group is committed to optimizing transport of their manufactured cars and trucks. **Availability:** Online.

11450 ■ *"'We're Full," Car Dealers Say as Auto Sales Slow after a Long Boom" in The New York Times (July 23, 2019)*
URL(s): www.nytimes.com/2019/07/23/business/were-full-car-dealers-say-as-auto-sales-slow-after-a-long-boom.html
Ed: Neal E. Boudette. **Released:** July 23, 2019. **Description:** Car sales to individual buyers are slowing down, even with discounts and other incentives. The past decade saw a big boom in car and truck sales, but now these vehicles aren't moving off the lots fast enough and dealers are ordering less from manufacturers. **Availability:** Online.

11451 ■ *Why GM Matters: Inside the Race to Transform an American Icon*
Ed: William Holstein. **Price:** $26, Hardback. **Description:** A timely examination of General Motors Corporation and the problems it is facing. **Availability:** Audio.

11452 ■ *"With Traffic Jam in Super Bowl, Can Any Auto Brand Really Win?" in Advertising Age (Vol. 81, December 6, 2010, No. 43, pp. 1)*
Pub: Crain Communications, Inc.
Contact: Jessica Botos, Manager, Marketing
E-mail: jessica.botos@crainsnewyork.com

Ed: Rupal Parekh. **Description:** Car marketers are doubling down for Super Bowl XLV in Arlington, Texas and asking their ad agencies to craft commercials unique enough to break through the clutter and to capture viewers' attention. **Availability:** Online.

11453 ■ *"Worry No. 1 at Auto Show: Recession" in Crain's Detroit Business (Vol. 24, January 21, 2008, No. 3, pp. 1)*
Pub: Crain Communications Inc.
Contact: Barry Asin, President

Ed: Brent Snavely. **Description:** Recession fears clouded activity at the 2008 Annual North American International Auto Show. Automakers are expecting to see a drop in sales due to slow holiday retail spending as well as fallout from the subprime lending crisis. **Availability:** Online.

11454 ■ *"Xstrata and CAW Get Tentative Deal" in Globe & Mail (February 2, 2007, pp. B3)*

Description: The agreement between Xstrata PLC and Canadian Auto Workers union over wage hike is discussed. **Availability:** Print; Online.

STATISTICAL SOURCES

11455 ■ *RMA Annual Statement Studies*
Pub: Risk Management Association
Contact: Nancy Foster, President

Released: Annual. **Description:** Contains composite balance sheets and income statements for more than 360 industries, including the accounting, auditing, and bookkeeping industries. Also contains five years of comparative historical data for discerning trends. Includes 16 commonly used ratios, computed for most of the size groupings for nearly every industry.

11456 ■ *Standard & Poor's Industry Surveys*
Pub: Standard And Poor's Financial Services LLC.
Contact: Douglas L. Peterson, President

Description: Two-volume book that examines the prospects for specific industries, including trucking. Also provides analyses of trends and problems, statistical tables and charts, and comparative company analyses.

TRADE PERIODICALS

11457 ■ *Auto Dealer*
Pub: American International Automobile Dealers Association
Contact: Cody Lusk, President
URL(s): www.aiada.org/news/magazine
Released: Quarterly; Spring, Winter, Fall, Summer. **Description:** Offers international auto dealers current news on the issues impacting the business. **Availability:** Print; Online.

11458 ■ *AutoWeek*
Pub: Crain Communications Inc.
Contact: Barry Asin, President
URL(s): www.autoweek.com
Facebook: www.facebook.com/AutoWeekUSA
X (Twitter): x.com/autoweekusa
Instagram: www.instagram.com/AutoweekUSA
YouTube: www.youtube.com/user/AutoweekUSA
Description: Magazine for car enthusiasts, includes news coverage and features on vehicles, personalities, and events. Provides coverage of Formula One, CART, NASCAR, and IMSA races. **Availability:** Print; Online. **Type:** Full-text.

11459 ■ *Car and Driver*
Pub: Hearst Magazines Inc.
Contact: Jonathan Wright, President
URL(s): www.caranddriver.com
Facebook: www.facebook.com/caranddriver
X (Twitter): x.com/caranddriver
YouTube: www.youtube.com/user/caranddriver
Released: 6/year **Price:** $40, for Car and Driver + Popular Mechanics 1 year; $15, for print 1 year. **Availability:** Print; Online.

11460 ■ *FDA Newsletter*
Released: Bimonthly **Price:** Included in membership. **Description:** Covers factory-dealer relations focusing on factory encroachment on dealer equity in their own franchise. Discusses fleet subsidies, sales agreements, terminations, add points, warranty administration, and product distribution. Examines individual dealer problems. Recurring features include letters to the editor, news of research, book reviews, reports of meetings, and interviews.

11461 ■ *Road & Track*
Pub: Hearst Magazines Inc.
Contact: Jonathan Wright, President
URL(s): www.roadandtrack.com
X (Twitter): x.com/RoadandTrack
Instagram: www.instagram.com/RoadandTrack
YouTube: www.youtube.com/user/roadandtrack
Pinterest: www.pinterest.com/roadandtrack
Released: 6/year; Feb/Mar, Apr/May, Jun/Jul, Aug/Sept, Oct/Nov, Dec/Jan. **Price:** $13.99, Single issue; $30, for 1 year print subscription; $50, for print + online. **Description:** Automotive magazine. **Availability:** Print; Online.

11462 ■ *Used Car Dealer*
Pub: National Independent Automobile Dealers Association
Contact: Scott Allen, President
URL(s): niada.com/used-car-dealer-magazine
Ed: Steve Hamilton. **Released:** Monthly **Price:** $100, Members; $8, Members for per year; $80, Nonmembers for per year. **Description:** Trade magazine for the used car market. **Availability:** Print; Online.

TRADE SHOWS AND CONVENTIONS

11463 ■ *North American International Auto Show (NAIAS)*
Adient Plymouth CTU
49200 Halyard Dr.
Plymouth, MI 48170

Ph: (734)254-5000
Fax: (734)254-5843
Contact: Doug del Grosso, President
URL(s): detroitautoshow.com
Facebook:
Price: $7, seniors; $13. **Frequency:** Annual. **Description:** New automobile and trucks introductions, concept cars, and manufacturer-related displays. **Audience:** Industry Professionals. **Principal Exhibits:** New automobile and trucks introductions, concept cars, and manufacturer-related displays. **Telecommunication Services:** hgeorge@loviogeorge.com.

11464 ■ SSA Convention
Service Specialists Association (SSA)
  1531 Springside Pl.
  Downers Grove, IL 60516
Ph: (224)990-1005
Co. E-mail: servicespecialists@outlook.com
URL: http://www.servicespecialistsassociation.com
Contact: Adm. (Ret.) Warren Wild, President
URL(s): www.servicespecialistsassociation.com/
  ssaconvention2024
Frequency: Annual. **Description:** Exhibits related to truck repair operations, equipment, supplies, and services. **Audience:** Members and industry professionals. **Principal Exhibits:** Exhibits related to truck repair operations, equipment, supplies, and services.

11465 ■ VAIS Annual Professional Conference
Packaging Machinery Manufacturers Institute (PMMI)
  12930 Worldgate Dr., Ste. 200
  Herndon, VA 20170-6037
Ph: (571)612-3200
Free: 888-ASK-PMMI
Co. E-mail: info@pmmi.org
URL: http://www.pmmi.org
Contact: James E. Pittas, President
URL(s): https://westvirginiaautoshow.com/show-info
Frequency: Annual. **Description:** Exhibits related to new cars, trucks and SUVs. **Audience:** Car enthusiasts and industry professionals. **Principal Exhibits:** Exhibits related to new cars, trucks and SUVs.

FRANCHISES AND BUSINESS OPPORTUNITIES

11466 ■ J.D. Byrider
Byrider Franchising L.L.C.
  12802 Hamilton Crossing Blvd.
  Carmel, IN 46032
Free: 888-663-5739
URL: http://www.byriderfranchise.com
Contact: Craig Peters, Chief Executive Officer
Facebook: www.facebook.com/byridercorporate
X (Twitter): x.com/byridercorp
YouTube: www.youtube.com/channel/UCcw9pV
  tSaG731WN918t7cWA
Description: Retailer of cars. **Founded:** 1989. **Franchise Fee:** $35,000-$50,000. **Royalty Fee:** 0.025. **Financial Assistance:** Yes **Training:** Yes.

11467 ■ Thrifty Car Sales, Inc.
The Hertz Corporation
  5310 E 31st St.
  Tulsa, OK 74135
Ph: (239)390-8380
Free: 800-654-4173
Co. E-mail: hertzracap@hertz.com
URL: http://www.hertz.com/rentacar/reservation
Description: Retailer of automobiles. **Founded:** 1998. **Franchised:** 1998. **Training:** Available at headquarters, with ongoing support.

COMPUTERIZED DATABASES

11468 ■ *Tire Business*
Crain Communications Inc.
  1155 Gratiot Ave.
  Detroit, MI 48207-2732
Ph: (313)446-6000
Co. E-mail: info@crain.com
URL: http://www.crain.com
Contact: Barry Asin, President

URL(s): www.tirebusiness.com
Facebook: www.facebook.com/TireBusinessCrain
Linkedin: www.linkedin.com/company/tire-business
X (Twitter): x.com/tirebusiness
Instagram: www.instagram.com/tirebusinesscrain
Released: Latest issue July 15, 2024. **Price:** $99, for digital only annual; $225, Other countries for Print + Digital; $119, for print+ digital. **Description:** Edited for independent tire retailers and wholesalers. **Availability:** Print; PDF; Download; Online. **Type:** Full-text; Numeric.

LIBRARIES

11469 ■ American Automobile Association, Inc. (AAA) - Research Library
American Automobile Association, Inc. (AAA)
  1000 AAA Dr.
  Heathrow, FL 32746
Ph: (407)444-4240
Fax: (407)444-4247
URL: http://www.aaa.com/International
URL(s): www.aaasouth.com
Facebook: www.facebook.com/AAAFlorida
Description: Provides emergency roadside service, discounts and travel bookings. **Scope:** Travel guide books; market studies; highway and traffic safety; driver education; automobiles - history, statistics, insurance. **Services:** Interlibrary loan; library open to researchers with permission. **Founded:** 1902. **Holdings:** 10,000 books; 20 VF drawers of pamphlets; reports. **Publications:** *Southern California/Las Vegas TourBook*; *Arkansas/Kansas/Missouri/Oklahoma TourBook* (Annual); *New York TourBook* (Annual); *Alabama/Louisiana/Mississippi TourBook* (Annual); *Oregon/Washington TourBook* (Annual); *New Jersey/Pennsylvania TourBook* (Annual); *Arizona/New Mexico TourBook* (Annual); *Atlantic Provinces/Quebec TourBook* (Annual); *Texas TourBook*; *Western Canada/Alaska TourBook* (Annual); *AAA Bridge and Ferry Directory* (Annual); *Great Lakes CampBook* (Annual); *Japan Travel Book* (Annual); *Kenya Travel Book* (Annual); *Malta and Gozo Travel Book* (Annual); *Mexico Travel Book* (Annual); *Morocco Travel Book* (Annual); *New Zealand Travel Book* (Annual); *Portugal Travel Book* (Annual); *Scotland Travel Book* (Annual); *South Africa Travel Book* (Annual); *Switzerland Travel Book* (Annual); *Thailand Travel Book* (Annual); *Tunisia Travel Book* (Annual); *Turkey South Coast Travel Book* (Annual); *Turkey West Coast Travel Book* (Annual); *Europe Travel Book* (Annual).

11470 ■ Crain Communications Inc.
1155 Gratiot Ave.
  Detroit, MI 48207-2732
Ph: (313)446-6000
Co. E-mail: info@crain.com
URL: http://www.crain.com
Contact: Barry Asin, President
Facebook: www.facebook.com/CrainCommunica
  tionsInc
Linkedin: www.linkedin.com/company/crain
  -communications
X (Twitter): x.com/craincomm
Instagram: www.instagram.com/craincommunications
Description: Publisher of newspaper covering news, sports, business information, and much more. **Founded:** 1922. **Publications:** *Plastics News* (Weekly); *Automotive News Europe* (Monthly); *Automotive News Canada* (Monthly); *Plastics News* (Weekly); *Crain's Phoenix*; *Crain's Philadelphia*; *Crain's Toronto*; *Crain's Utah*; *Crain's Indianapolis*; *Directory of Dental Plan Providers*; *Directory of Consumer-Driven Health Care Plan*; *Directory of Insurance Wholesalers*; *Directory of Prescription Benefit Managers* (Annual); *RCR's Cellular Database* (Annual); *Automotive News* (Weekly); *AutoWeek*; *Crain's Detroit Business* (Weekly); *Detroit Monthly* (Monthly); *Automotive News Market Data Book* (Semiannual); *Crain's List--Chicago's Largest Banks*; *Banking and Finance--Chicago's Largest Thrifts*; *Banking and Finance--Chicago's Money Managers*; *Banking and Finance--Chicago's SBA Lenders*; *Banking and Finance--Chicago's Venture-Capital and*

Private-Equity Firms; *Crain's List--Best Places to Work*; *Crain's List--Largest Commercial Real Estate Brokers: Leasing*; *Crain's List--Largest Commercial Real Estate Brokers: Sales*; *Crain's List--Commercial Real Estate: Chicago's Largest Property Management Firms*; *Crain's List--Chicago's Commercial Real Estate: Contractors*; *Crain's List--Chicago's Commercial Real Estate Dealmakers Directory*; *Crain's List--Largest Industrial Leases*; *Crain's List--Leases in the Suburban Market*; *Crain's List--Leases in the Chicago Office Market*; *Crain's List--Corporate Giving Programs*; *Crain's 500*; *Crain's List--Chicago-area Web Developers*; *Crain's List--Chicago's Largest Festivals*; *Crain's List--Chicago's Largest Integrated Marketing Agencies*; *Crain's List--Chicago's Largest Law Firms*; *Crain's List--Chicago's Largest Tourist Attractions*; *Crain's List--MBA Program Directory*; *Crain's List--Mergers and Acquisitions*; *Crain's List--Minority Owned*; *Crain's List--Non-Profit Directory*; *Crain's List--Non-Profits' Highest Earners: Other Employees*; *Crain's List--Non-profits' Highest Earners: Top Executives*; *Crain's List--Chicago's Largest Physician Groups*; *Crain's List--Chicago's Largest Public Relations Firms*; *Crain's List--Sports Franchises*; *Crain's Top Performing Arts Venues*; *Crain's List--Who's Who in Chicago Real Estate*; *Crain's List--Chicago's Largest Employers*; *Crain's List--Chicago's Largest Executive Recruiters*; *Crain's List--Fast 50*; *Crain's List--Chicago-area Foundations*; *Crain's List--Chicago's Largest Health Insurers* (Annual); *Crain's List--The Highest Paid Non-CEOs*; *Crain's List--Chicago's Largest Homebuilders*; *Crain's List--Chicago's Largest Hospitals*; *Crain's List--Chicago's Largest Hotels*; *Crain's List--Chicago's Largest Insurance Brokers*; *Crain's List--Chicago's Largest Privately Held Companies*; *Crain's List--Publicly-Traded Companies*; *Who's Who in Chicago Business*; *Business Insurance--Agent/Broker Profiles* (Annual); *Business Insurance--Captive Managers Issue* (Annual); *Business Insurance--Risk Management Consultants Issue* (Annual); *Oakland Life* (Monthly); *Modern Healthcare: The Weekly Healthcare Business News Magazine* (Weekly); *Directory of Safety Consultants and Rehabilitation Management Providers* (Annual); *Crain's Sacramento*; *Crain's Tampa Bay*; *Euromarketing* (Annual); *Pensions & Investments--1,000 Largest Retirement Funds* (Annual); *Pensions & Investments--Money Managers Directory Investment Adviser Profiles* (Annual); *Business Insurance--Directory of HMOs, POSs and PPOs Issue* (Annual); *Business Marketing--Directory of Marketing Software*; *Crain's Chicago Business--Book of Top Business Lists* (Annual); *Crain's Detroit Business--Metrofacts* (Annual); *Advertising Age--Leading National Advertisers Issue* (Annual); *Crain's Nonprofit News* (Weekly); *American Clean Car* (Bimonthly); *American Coin-Op: The Magazine for Coin-Operated Laundry and Drycleaning Businessmen* (Monthly); *American Drycleaner* (Monthly); *RCR and Global Wireless' International Database* (Annual); *RCR's PCS Database* (Annual); *Automotive News* (Daily); *Modern Healthcare*; *Workforce Management: HR Trends and Tools for Business Results* (Monthly); *Business Insurance* (Biweekly); *City & State* (Biweekly); *Creativity* (Monthly); *Modern Physician* (Monthly); *Rubber News* (Biweekly); *RCR's SPEC Guide*; *Business Insurance--Employee Benefit Information Systems Issue* (Annual); *Business Insurance--Risk Management Information Systems Issue* (Annual); *Business Insurance--Environmental Risk Management Consultants Issue* (Annual); *Business Insurance--International Insurers & Benefits Networks Issue* (Annual); *Automotive News--Market Data Book*; *Workforce*; *Advertising Age--Agencies Ranked by Gross Income Issue* (Annual); *Crain's List--Chicago's Largest Accounting Firms*; *Crain's List--Chicago's Largest Advertising Agencies*; *Crain's List--Banking and Finance: Chicago-Area Bank Performance Rankings*; *Crain's List--Banking and Finance: Investment Bankers*; *Pensions & Investments--Annual Equity/Fixed Income Investment Performance Report Issue* (Quarterly); *Business Insurance--Third-Party Claims Administrators Issue* (Annual); *Franchise Buyer*; *BtoB*; *InvestmentNews* (Semimonthly); *Modern Physician*; *Tire Business*; *BtoB Magazine: The Magazine for Marketing Strategists* (Monthly); *Modern Healthcare: The Newsmagazine for Administrators* and Managers in Hospitals and Other Healthcare Institutions (Weekly); Modern Physician: Essential Business News for the Executive Physician; Directory of Rehabilitation Management Service Providers; Business Insurance--Directory of Employee Assistance Program Providers and Dependent Care Resource and Referral Services (Annual); Waste & Recycling News (Biweekly); Plastics & Rubber Weekly (Weekly); City & State's Government Manager Resource Guide (Annual); Business Insurance--Directory of Property Loss Control Consultants (Annual); Crain's Pittsburgh; Crain's Las Vegas (Daily); Crain's Houston (Weekly); Crain's Connecticut; Crain's Raleigh-Durham; Business Insurance--Employee Benefit Consultants Issue (Annual); Pensions & Investments--Directory of Investment Management Consultants Issue (Annual); Pensions & Investments--Master Trust/Custody and Global Custody Banks (Annual); Pension & Investment Age--Directory of Cash Management Services Issue (Annual); Pensions & Investments--Investment Managers (Annual); Pensions & Investment Age--Directory: Disks and Data Issue; Business Insurance--Directory of Excess/Surplus Lines Insurers Issue (Annual);

Business Insurance Directory of 401(K) Plan Administrators (Monthly); Investment News (Weekly); Guide to Business/Industrial Advertising Agencies (Annual); Crain's Small Business (Monthly); Crain's Chicago Business (Weekly); TelevisionWeek (Daily). **Educational Activities:** Plastics Encounter Midwest; Plastics Encounter Southeast.

11471 ■ NAFA Fleet Management Association - Library
180 Talmadge R.d, IGO Bldg., Ste. 558
Edison, NJ 08817
Ph: (609)720-0882
Fax: (609)452-8004
Co. E-mail: info@nafa.org
URL: http://www.nafa.org
Contact: Ray Brisby, President
Facebook: www.facebook.com/nafafleet
Linkedin: www.linkedin.com/company/nafa-fleet-management-association
X (Twitter): x.com/nafafleet
YouTube: www.youtube.com/user/nafafleetmanagement

Description: Persons responsible for the administration of a motor vehicle fleet of 25 or more units for a firm not commercially engaged in the sale, rental, or lease of motor vehicles. Compiles statistics. Maintains placement service and speaker's bureau; conducts research programs. Operates Fleet Information Resource Center. Sponsors professional Certified Automotive Fleet Manager certification. **Scope:** Motor vehicle fleets. **Founded:** 1957. **Holdings:** Figures not available. **Publications:** FleetSolutions (Bimonthly); NAFA Annual Reference Book; National Association of Fleet Administrators--Annual Reference Book (Annual); NAFA Fleet Executive: The Magazine for Vehicle Management (Monthly); FleetFocus (Biweekly); NAFA Roster. **Educational Activities:** NAFA Institute and Expo (NAFA I&E) (Annual). **Awards:** NAFA Distinguished Service Award (Annual); NAFA Excellence in Education Award (Irregular); Larry Goill Memorial Quality Fleet Management Idea Award (Annual); NAFA Outstanding Chapter Service Award (Annual). **Geographic Preference:** National.

ASSOCIATIONS AND OTHER ORGANIZATIONS

11472 ■ Local Media Association (SNA)
116 W Rhoby Rd.
 Lake City, MI 49651-0450
Ph: (410)838-3018
Fax: (888)317-0856
Co. E-mail: info@localmedia.org
URL: http://localmedia.org
Contact: Nancy Lane, Chief Executive Officer
Facebook: www.facebook.com/localmediaassociation
Linkedin: www.linkedin.com/in/local-media-associa
 tion-23a04032
X (Twitter): x.com/LocalMediaAssoc
Instagram: www.instagram.com/localmediaassoc
Description: Represents publishing firms or individual community-oriented newspapers in suburban or urban areas (regular members) and companies in related professions and industries (associate and professional members). Services the trade, research, and marketing needs of its members. Holds annual advertising, circulation, editorial, and management seminars. Sponsors advertising and editorial contests. **Founded:** 1971. **Publications:** *Local Media Today* (Weekly); *Local Media Association--Membership Directory* (Annual). **Educational Activities:** Circulation Managers and Classified Managers; Classified Advertising Conference; Publishers and Advertising Directors. **Awards:** LMA Editorial Contest Awards (Annual); LMA Advertising and Promotions Contest Awards (Annual); LMA Advertising Director of the Year (Annual); LMA Journalist of the Year (Annual); Dean S. Lesher Award (Annual); LMA General Excellence/Newspaper of the Year (Annual). **Geographic Preference:** National.

EDUCATIONAL PROGRAMS

11473 ■ EEI Communications Creating Successful Newsletters
URL(s): www.eeicom.com
Description: Covers development of audience profile, understanding publishing goals, writing and editing skills, and publication design. **Audience:** Writers and editors . **Principal Exhibits:** Covers development of audience profile, understanding publishing goals, writing and editing skills, and publication design. **Telecommunication Services:** train@eeicom.com.

11474 ■ EEI Communications Writing News (Onsite)
URL(s): www.eeicom.com
Description: Covers current techniques for newsletter and news periodical writing, including using more compelling reporting techniques; avoiding common grammar and punctuation errors in condensed writing; formulating dynamic leads and conclusions;

understanding and using tone to convey news appropriately; using spoken and printed quotations correctly; checking statistics and logical generalizations; and finding resources for research and story ideas. **Audience:** Writers and editors. **Principal Exhibits:** Covers current techniques for newsletter and news periodical writing, including using more compelling reporting techniques; avoiding common grammar and punctuation errors in condensed writing; formulating dynamic leads and conclusions; understanding and using tone to convey news appropriately; using spoken and printed quotations correctly; checking statistics and logical generalizations; and finding resources for research and story ideas. **Telecommunication Services:** train@eeicom.com.

REFERENCE WORKS

11475 ■ "How Newsletter Innovations Are Driving Publisher Revenue" in What's New in Publishing (June 6, 2019)
URL(s): whatsnewinpublishing.com/how-newsletter
 -innovations-are-driving-publisher-revenue
Ed: Simon Owens. **Released:** June 06, 2019. **Description:** Email newsletter distribution is still an active way to engage with consumers to get them to subscribe to a publication. However, just sending out emails isn't what's driving sales, algorithms and applied machine learning are helping companies target consumers based on their interests. **Availability:** Online.

11476 ■ "Why You Don't Get Published: An Editor's View" in Accounting and Finance (Vol. 52, June 2012, No. 2, pp. 343)
Ed: Michael E. Bradbury. **Released:** March 12, 2012. **Description:** This paper uses content analysis to examine 66 reviews on 33 manuscripts submitted to 'Accounting and Finance'. Selected extracts from reviews are provided to illustrate the issues considered important to reviewers. The main message is that papers need to be work-shopped and more care taken over editorial matters. A checklist for prospective authors is provided. **Availability:** Print; Online.

TRADE PERIODICALS

11477 ■ Oregon Publisher
Pub: Oregon Newspaper Publishers Association
Contact: Laurie Hieb, Executive Director
E-mail: laurie@orenews.com
URL(s): www.orenews.com/onpa-publications
Released: Quarterly **Description:** Covers journalism and publishing topics. **Availability:** PDF; Online.

CONSULTANTS

11478 ■ Editorial Code and Data Inc. (ECDI)
814 Wolverine Dr., Ste. 2
 Wolverine Lake, MI 48390

Ph: (248)245-4500
Co. E-mail: monique.magee@gmail.com
URL: http://www.marketsize.com
Contact: Arsen J. Darnay, Editor
Facebook: www.facebook.com/EditorialCodeAn
 dData
Description: Developer of statistical publishing and software development services. **Scope:** Developer of statistical publishing and software development services. **Founded:** 1990. **Holdings:** ECDI has wide holdings of U.S. government data in print and electronic format. **Publications:** "Market Share Reporter"; "Encyclopedia of Products & Industries"; "Economic Indicators Handbook"; "American Salaries and Wages Survey"; "Dun and Bradstreet & Gale: Industrial Handbook"; "Reference American Cost of Living Survey".

11479 ■ Heidelberg Graphics (HG)
2 Stansbury Ct.
 Chico, CA 95928
Ph: (530)342-6582
Fax: (530)342-6582
Co. E-mail: service@heidelberggraphics.com
URL: http://www.heidelberggraphics.com
Contact: Larry S. Jackson, Owner
Description: Publisher of books and also provides publishing, layout, printing and e-Book solutions. **Founded:** 1972. **Publications:** "Chronicles of the Clandestine Knights: Hyacinth Blue," 2003; "A Book of Thoughts II," 2001; "Historic Shot Glasses: The pre-Prohibition," 1992; "After the War," 1981; "Phantasm," 1980.

FRANCHISES AND BUSINESS OPPORTUNITIES

11480 ■ Coffee News
PO Box 503
 Hampden, ME 04444
Ph: (207)217-3293
Co. E-mail: hello@mhcoffeenews.com
URL: http://www.coffeenewsbangor.com
Description: Weekly publication for distribution in coffee shops and restaurants. **Founded:** 1988. **Training:** Quarterly training sessions, open to all franchisees and personal mentor program.

COMPUTERIZED DATABASES

11481 ■ Daily Brief
Oxford Analytica
 5 Alfred St.
 Oxford OX1 4EH, United Kingdom
Ph: 44 1865 261-600
URL: http://www.oxan.com
Contact: Nick Redman, Director
URL(s): www.oxan.com/services/daily-brief
Released: Daily **Availability:** Online. **Type:** Full-text.

ASSOCIATIONS AND OTHER ORGANIZATIONS

11482 ■ The Toy Association Inc.
1375 Broadway 10th Fl.
New York, NY 10018
Ph: (212)675-1141
Co. E-mail: info@toyassociation.org
URL: http://www.toyassociation.org
Contact: Steve Pasierb, President
Facebook: www.facebook.com/TheToyAssociation
Linkedin: www.linkedin.com/company/thetoyassociation
X (Twitter): x.com/TheToyAssoc
YouTube: www.youtube.com/TheToyAssociation
Description: Provides business services to US. manufacturers and importers of toys. Manages American International Toy Fair; represents the industry before Federal, State and Local government on issues of importance; provides legal and legislative counsel; conducts educational programs; compiles industry statistics. **Founded:** 1916. **Publications:** *American International Toy Fair Official Directory* (Annual); *Toy Challenges and Opportunities* (Annual); *The Official American International Toy Fair Directory* (Annual). **Educational Activities:** Toy Fair (Annual). **Awards:** TIA Toy of the Year Award (Annual). **Geographic Preference:** National.

SOURCES OF SUPPLY

11483 ■ *Souvenirs, Gifts & Novelties Magazine--Buyer's Guide Issue*
Kane Communications Inc.
Contact: Scott Borowsky, President
URL(s): sgnmag.com
Facebook: www.facebook.com/SouvenirGiftsAndNovelties
Linkedin: www.linkedin.com/company/souvenirs-gifts-novelties
X (Twitter): x.com/sgnmagazine
Instagram: www.instagram.com/souvenirsgiftsandnovelties
Pinterest: www.pinterest.com/SGNMag
Released: 6/year **Description:** Publication includes list of 1,000 manufacturers, wholesalers, and importers of souvenirs, gifts, apparel, toys, jewelry novelty, and candle items. **Entries include:** Company name, address, phone, products, whether firm is manufacturer, wholesaler, or importer. **Arrangement:** Classified by product. **Indexes:** Alphabetical. **Availability:** Print; Online.

TRADE PERIODICALS

11484 ■ *The Toy Book*
Pub: Adventure Publishing Group Inc.
Contact: Laurie Schacht, President
E-mail: laurieschacht@aol.com
URL(s): toybook.comwww.adventurepublishinggroup.com/ap-toy-book.html
Facebook: www.facebook.com/TheToyBook
X (Twitter): x.com/toybook
Instagram: www.instagram.com/thetoybook
Released: Annual **Price:** $200, for 1 year foreign; $48, for print 6 issue; $56, Canada for per year. **Description:** Tabloid for buyers in the toy and hobby industries. **Availability:** Print; PDF; Download; Online.

TRADE SHOWS AND CONVENTIONS

11485 ■ IAFE Trade Show
International Association of Fairs and Expositions (IAFE)
3043 E Cairo St.
Springfield, MO 65802
Ph: (417)862-5771
Free: 800-516-0313
Co. E-mail: iafe@fairsandexpos.com
URL: http://www.fairsandexpos.com
Contact: Marla Calico, President
URL(s): www.iafeconvention.com
Frequency: Annual. **Description:** Talent agencies, concessionaires, novelties, amusement devices, insurance, ribbons, plaques, attractions, and equipment. Products and services for the fair industry. **Audience:** IAFE members, special event producers, entertainment buyers, carnival executives, concessionaires, facility managers, Fair industry professionals. **Principal Exhibits:** Talent agencies, concessionaires, novelties, amusement devices, insurance, ribbons, plaques, attractions, and equipment. Products and services for the fair industry. **Telecommunication Services:** registration@fairsandexpos.com.

FRANCHISES AND BUSINESS OPPORTUNITIES

11486 ■ Watch It! Inc.
100 City Ctr. Dr., Ste. 1-151
Missisauga, ON, Canada L5B 2C9
Ph: (905)276-5147
Co. E-mail: squareone@watchit.ca
URL: http://www.watchit.ca
Description: Retailer of watches, sunglasses and accessories for men and women. **Founded:** 1999. **Training:** Yes.

LIBRARIES

11487 ■ Haystack Mountain School of Crafts Library
PO Box 518
Deer Isle, ME 04627
Ph: (207)348-2306
Co. E-mail: haystack@haystack-mtn.org
URL: http://www.haystack-mtn.org
Contact: Ayumi Horie, President
Facebook: www.facebook.com/Haystack-Mountain-School-of-Crafts-90810472119
Instagram: www.instagram.com/haystack_school
YouTube: www.youtube.com/channel/UC25-NaGw3xPfkcTejEYqzzg
Scope: Fine arts; weaving; design and architecture. **Founded:** 1950. **Holdings:** 1,000 Books; Craft; Art; Design and Architecture.

11488 ■ Museum of Contemporary Craft Library
724 NW Davis St.
Portland, OR 97209
Ph: (503)223-2654
Fax: (503)223-0190
Co. E-mail: info@museumofcontemporarycraft.org
URL: http://www.museumofcontemporarycraft.org
Contact: Kathy Abraham, President
Scope: Modern and contemporary craft heritage. **Services:** Library open during Museum hours. **Founded:** 1937. **Holdings:** 1,300 objects of modern and contemporary craft ; photographs; slides; ephemera.

START-UP INFORMATION

11489 ■ *"Bond Hill Cinema Site To See New Life" in Business Courier (Vol. 27, October 29, 2010, No. 26, pp. 1)*
Pub: Business Courier

Ed: Dan Monk. **Description:** Avondale, Ohio's Corinthian Baptist Church will redevelop the 30-acre former Showcase Cinema property to a mixed-use site that could feature a college, senior home, and retail. Corinthian Baptist, which is one of the largest African-American churches in the region, is also planning to relocate the church. **Availability:** Print; Online.

11490 ■ *How to Start a Home-Based Senior Care Business: Develop a Winning Business Plan*

Ed: James L. Ferry. **Released:** Second edition. **Price:** paperback; softback; Electronic Book. **Description:** Everything needed to know in order to start and run a profitable, ethical, and satisfying senior care business from your home. Information covers writing a good business plan, marketing services to families, creating a fee structure, and developing a network of trusted caregivers and service providers. **Availability:** E-book; Print.

ASSOCIATIONS AND OTHER ORGANIZATIONS

11491 ■ **Aging Life Care Association (ALCA)**
3275 W Ina Rd., Ste. 130
Tucson, AZ 85741-2198
Ph: (520)881-8008
Fax: (520)325-7925
Co. E-mail: marketing@aginglifecare.org
URL: http://www.aginglifecare.org
Contact: Julie Wagner, Chief Executive Officer
E-mail: jwagner@aginglifecare.org
Facebook: www.facebook.com/AgingLifeCareAssociation
Linkedin: www.linkedin.com/company/national-association-of-professional-geriatric-care-managers
X (Twitter): x.com/AgingLifeCare
YouTube: www.youtube.com/channel/UCclUMV4s_TYh2rRmPk45y8A
Description: Promotes quality services and care for elderly citizens. Provides referral service and distributes information to individuals interested in geriatric care management. Maintains referral network. **Founded:** 1985. **Publications:** *Journal of Aging Life Care* (Semiannual); *Inside ALCA* (3/year). **Geographic Preference:** National.

11492 ■ **AMDA - The Society for Post-Acute and Long-Term Care Medicine (AMDA)**
10500 Little Patuxent Pky., Ste. 210
Columbia, MD 21044
Ph: (410)740-9743
Free: 800-876-2632
Fax: (410)740-4572
Co. E-mail: info@paltc.org
URL: http://paltc.org
Contact: David A. Nace, President
Facebook: www.facebook.com/AMDAtheSocietyforPALTCMed
Linkedin: www.linkedin.com/company/american-medical-directors-association-amda-
X (Twitter): x.com/AMDApaltc
Description: Physicians providing care in long-term facilities including nursing homes. Sponsors continuing medical education in geriatrics and medical administration. Promotes improved long-term care. **Founded:** 1978. **Publications:** *Caring for the Ages* (8/year); *JAMDA* (Monthly); *State Network News (SNN)* (Quarterly). **Educational Activities:** AMDA Long Term Care Medicine Annual Conference (Annual). **Geographic Preference:** National.

11493 ■ **American College of Health Care Administrators (ACHCA)**
1101 Connecticut Ave. NW, Ste. 450
Washington, DC 20036
Free: 800-561-3148
Co. E-mail: info@achca.org
URL: http://www.achca.org
Contact: Amanda Charles, Business Manager
E-mail: acharles@achca.org
Facebook: www.facebook.com/pages/The-American-College-of-Health-Care-Administrators/326597784597
X (Twitter): x.com/ACHCA
Description: Persons actively engaged in the administration of long-term care facilities, such as nursing homes, retirement communities, assisted living facilities, and sub-acute care programs. Administers professional certification programs for assisted living, sub-acute and nursing home administrators. Works to elevate the standards in the field and to develop and promote a code of ethics and standards of education and training. Seeks to inform allied professions and the public that good administration of long-term care facilities calls for special formal academic training and experience. Encourages research in all aspects of geriatrics, the chronically ill, and administration. Maintains placement service. Holds special education programs; facilitates networking among administrators. **Founded:** 1962. **Publications:** *Continuum* (Quarterly); *Balance: The Source for Administrators in Long-Term Health Care* (8/year); *ACHCA E-News* (Bimonthly). **Educational Activities:** ACHCA Annual Winter Marketplace (Annual). **Awards:** New Administrator Award (Annual); ACHCA Education Award (Annual); ACHCA Journalism Award (Annual); W.Phillip McConnell Student Scholarship Fund (Irregular); Richard L. Thorpe Fellowship (Annual); ACHCA Distinguished Assisted Living Administrator Award (Annual); ACHCA Distinguished Nursing Home Administrator Award (Annual); ACHCA New Nursing Home Administrator Award (Annual). **Geographic Preference:** National.

11494 ■ **American Health Care Association (AHCA)**
1201 L St. NW
Washington, DC 20005
Ph: (202)842-4444
Fax: (202)842-3860
Co. E-mail: help@ltctrendtracker.com
URL: http://www.ahcancal.org/Pages/default.aspx
Contact: Mark Parkinson, President
Facebook: www.facebook.com/ahcancal
X (Twitter): x.com/ahcancal
YouTube: www.youtube.com/user/ahcancalstream
Description: Federation of state associations of long-term health care facilities. Promotes standards for professionals in long-term health care delivery and quality care for patients and residents in a safe environment. Focuses on issues of availability, quality, affordability, and fair payment. Operates as liaison with governmental agencies, Congress, and professional associations. Compiles statistics. American Health Care Association is an association of long term and post-acute care providers and advocates for quality care and services for frail, elderly and disabled Americans. **Founded:** 1949. **Publications:** *Focus* (Weekly); *Provider--LTC Buyers' Guide Issue* (Annual); *American Health Care Association: Provider* (Monthly); *Choosing a Nursing Home Pamphlet*; *Choosing An Assisted Living Residence: A Consumer's Guide*; *Having Your Say: Advance Directives Fact Sheet*; *Understanding Long Term Care Insurance Fact Sheet*; *Assisted Living State Regulatory Review* (Annual); *NCAL Connections* (Weekly); *Resident Assistant Newsletter*; *Assessing Your Needs: Consumer Guides to Nursing and Assisted Living Facilities*; *Caring for Someone with Alzheimer's Fact Sheet*; *Living in a Nursing Home: Myths and Realities Fact Sheet*; *Tips on Visiting Friends and Relatives Fact Sheet*; *Family Questions: The First Thirty Days Fact Sheet*; *Moving Into an Assisted Living Residence: Making a Successful Transition Fact Sheet*; *Making the Transition to Nursing Facility Life Fact Sheet*; *Paying for Long Term Care Pamphlet*; *Glossary of Terms Pamphlet*; *Advice for Families Pamphlet*; *Advance Preparation: Having the Conversation About Long Term Care Pamphlet*; *Coping with the Transition Pamphlet*; *Talking To Your Loved Ones About Their Care Pamphlet*; *Capitol Connection Newsletter* (Biweekly); *NCAL Focus Newsletter* (Monthly); *AHCA Notes* (Monthly); *Provider: For Long Term Care Professionals* (Monthly). **Educational Activities:** American Health Care Association Annual Convention and Exposition (Annual). **Awards:** AHCA/NCAL National Quality Award - Bronze Level (Annual); AHCA/NCAL Adult Volunteer of the Year (Annual); AHCA Group Volunteer of the Year (Annual); AHCA/NCAL Young Adult Volunteer of the Year Award (Annual); AHCA/NCAL National Quality Award - Silver Level (Annual); AHCA/NCAL National Quality Award - Gold Level (Annual). **Geographic Preference:** National.

11495 ■ **American Hospital Association (AHA) - Resource Center**
155 N Wacker Dr.
Chicago, IL 60606
Ph: (312)422-3000
Free: 800-424-4301
Co. E-mail: ahahelp@aha.org

URL: http://www.aha.org
Contact: Richard J. Pollack, President
E-mail: rick@aha.org
Description: Represents hospitals and health care provider organizations. Seeks to advance the health of individuals and communities. Leads, represents, and serves health care provider organizations that are accountable to the community and committed to health improvement. **Scope:** Health services information. **Services:** Interlibrary loan; copying. **Founded:** 1898. **Holdings:** Periodicals; books; reference materials; electronic information sources. **Publications:** *Hospital Statistics* (Annual); *Hospital Database* (Annual); *AHA Healthcare IT Database*; *AHA Guide®* (Annual); *AHA Hospital Statistics*; *AHA Annual Survey Database*; *Health Services Research* (Bimonthly); *Directory of Health Care Coalitions in the United States* (Annual); *Healthcare QuickDisc*; *Guide to the Health Care Field* (Annual); *Hospitals & Health Networks (H&HN)*; *American Hospital Association--Ambulatory Outreach*; *AHA Directory of Health Care Professionals*; *Directory of Planning and Design Professionals for Health Facilities* (Annual); *American Hospital Association--Guide to the Health Care Field* (Annual); *AHA News Now* (Daily); *AHA Guide to the Health Care Field* (Annual); *Coding Clinic for ICD-10-CM Newsletter* (Quarterly); *AHA Integrated Delivery Network Directory: U.S. Health Care Systems, Networks, and Alliances*. **Awards:** Hospital Awards for Volunteer Excellence (HAVE) (Annual); AHA Honorary Life Membership (Annual); AHA Board of Trustees Award (Annual); NHPCO Circle of Life Awards (Annual); AHA Federal Health Care Executive Special Achievement Award (Annual); AHA Award of Honor (Annual); AHA Distinguished Service Award (Annual); Justin Ford Kimball Innovators Award (Irregular). **Geographic Preference:** National.

11496 ■ American Seniors Housing Association (ASHA)
5225 Wisconsin Ave. NW, Ste. 500
Washington, DC 20015
Ph: (202)237-0900
URL: http://www.ashaliving.org
Contact: David S. Schless, President
E-mail: david@ashaliving.org
Description: Represents the interests of firms participating in seniors housing and has played an integral role in seniors housing advocacy. **Founded:** 1991. **Publications:** *Seniors Housing Construction Trends Report*; *Seniors Housing Legal Notes*; *Seniors Housing Research Notes*; *Seniors Housing Statistical Handbook*; *Seniors Housing Update*. **Educational Activities:** Executive Board Meeting (Annual); Rising Leaders Meeting (Annual). **Geographic Preference:** National.

11497 ■ Argentum
1650 King St.
Alexandria, VA 22314
Ph: (703)894-1805
Co. E-mail: info@argentum.org
URL: http://www.argentum.org
Contact: James Balda, President
E-mail: jbalda@argentum.org
Facebook: www.facebook.com/ArgentumSeniorLiving
Linkedin: www.linkedin.com/company/argentum1
X (Twitter): x.com/argentum
Instagram: www.instagram.com/argentumadvocates
YouTube: www.youtube.com/user/assistedlivingfed
Description: Promotes the interests of the assisted living industry and works to enhance the quality of life for the population it serves. **Founded:** 1990. **Publications:** *ALFA Alert* (Periodic); *Senior Housing Directory*; *Guide to Choosing an Assisted Living Residence*; *Senior Living Executive* (Bimonthly); *ALFA Public Policy Bulletins* (Monthly). **Awards:** Argentum Hero Awards (Annual). **Geographic Preference:** National.

11498 ■ Association of Jewish Aging Services (AJAS)
6101 Montrose Rd., Ste. 207
Rockville, MD 20852
Ph: (202)543-7500
Co. E-mail: info@ajas.org

URL: http://www.ajas.org
Contact: Ruth Katz, President
Facebook: www.facebook.com/AJASdc
Linkedin: www.linkedin.com/company/association-of
-jewish-aging-services-ajas-
YouTube: www.youtube.com/channel/UCeSps7tU
-YQLU0Xs5bqdwgQ
Description: Represents charitable Jewish homes and nursing homes; retirement and housing units; independent and assisted living, geriatric hospitals, and special facilities for Jewish aged and chronically ill. Conducts institutes and conferences; undertakes legislative activities; compiles statistics. Conducts studies and maintains demographic and other information on Jewish aging. Publishes journals and periodicals on aging. **Founded:** 1960. **Publications:** *Journal on Jewish Aging* (Semiannual); *Directory of Jewish Homes and Housing for the Aged in the United States and Canada* (Biennial). **Awards:** AJAS Humanitarian Award (Annual); AJAS Mentor of the Year (Annual); AJAS Young Executive Award (Annual); AJAS Jewish Programming Award (Annual); Trustee of the Year Award (Annual); Dr. Herbert Shore Award of Honor (Annual); Professional of the Year Award (Annual). **Geographic Preference:** Multinational.

11499 ■ Foundation Aiding the Elderly (FATE)
3430 American River Dr., Ste. 105
Sacramento, CA 95864
Ph: (916)481-8558
Free: 877-481-8558
Fax: (916)481-2239
Co. E-mail: caroleh@4fate.org
URL: http://www.4fate.org
Contact: Carole Herman, President
E-mail: caroleh@4fate.org
Facebook: www.facebook.com/4fate.org
Description: Assists the public with relatives and friends in long-term care nursing homes. Provides awareness of the existence of, and potential for, abuse, neglect, and lack of dignity of the elderly in nursing homes. Initiates action to make improvements. Raises funds to bring about nursing home reform. Offers referrals for senior issues and advocates for legislation. **Founded:** 1982. **Geographic Preference:** National.

11500 ■ Health Industry Distributors Association (HIDA)
310 Montgomery St.
Alexandria, VA 22314
Ph: (703)549-4432
Co. E-mail: hida@hida.org
URL: http://www.hida.org
Contact: Doug Bryant, President
Facebook: www.facebook.com/hida.org
Linkedin: www.linkedin.com/company/hidaorg
X (Twitter): x.com/HIDAorg
Description: Represents distributors of medical, laboratory, surgical, and other health care equipment and supplies to hospitals, physicians, nursing homes, and industrial medical departments. Conducts sales training, management seminars, and research through the HIDA Educational Foundation. **Founded:** 1902. **Publications:** *HIDA--Membership Directory and Buyer's Guide*. **Educational Activities:** HIDA Executive Conference (Annual); HIDA Streamlining Healthcare Expo and Business Exchange (Annual). **Awards:** John F. Sasen Leadership Award (Annual). **Geographic Preference:** National.

11501 ■ LeadingAge
2519 Connecticut Ave. NW
Washington, DC 20008
Ph: (202)783-2242
Co. E-mail: info@leadingage.org
URL: http://www.leadingage.org
Contact: Amma Addo, Director
E-mail: aaddo@leadingage.org
Facebook: www.facebook.com/LeadingAge
Linkedin: www.linkedin.com/company/leadingage
X (Twitter): twitter.com/LeadingAge
Instagram: www.instagram.com/leadingage

Description: Works to advance the vision of healthy, affordable and ethical aging services for America. **Founded:** 1961. **Publications:** *LeadingAge* (Bimonthly); *HCBS Report* (Monthly); *American Association of Homes for the Aging--Directory of Consulting Firms*; *American Association of Homes and Services for the Aging--Directory of Members* (Biennial); *Aging Services: The Not-for-Profit Difference*; *Savings and Solutions*; *The Consumer's Directory of Continuing Care Retirement Communities*. **Educational Activities:** Future of Aging Services; LeadingAge Annual Meeting and Expo (Annual). **Awards:** LeadingAge Award of Honor (Annual); LeadingAge Meritorious Service Award; Hobart Jackson Diversity and Inclusion Award (Annual); Dr. Herbert Shore Outstanding Mentor Award (Annual); LeadingAge Excellence in Not-for-Profit Leadership Award (Annual). **Geographic Preference:** Multinational.

11502 ■ National Association of Directors of Nursing Administration in Long Term Care (NADONA/LTC)
1329 E Kemper Rd., Ste. 4100A
Springdale, OH 45246
Ph: (513)791-3628
Free: 800-222-0539
Co. E-mail: info@nadona.org
URL: http://www.nadona.org
Contact: Robin Arnicar, President
Facebook: www.facebook.com/nadona
Linkedin: www.linkedin.com/company/nadona-ltc
X (Twitter): x.com/NAD0NA
Instagram: www.instagram.com/nadonaofficial
YouTube: www.youtube.com/channel/UCwhsUCK
55-E9h48XKMCLPGQ
Description: Aims are: to establish an acceptable ethical standard for practices in long term care nursing administration; promote research in the profession; to develop a consistent program of education and certification for the positions of director, associate director, and assistant director. **Founded:** 1986. **Awards:** NADONA Nurse Administrator of the Year (Annual). **Geographic Preference:** National.

11503 ■ National Association of Long Term Care Administrator Boards (NAB)
1120 20th St. NW, Ste. 750
Washington, DC 20036
Ph: (202)712-9040
Co. E-mail: nab@nabweb.org
URL: http://www.nabweb.org
Contact: Randy Lindne, President
Facebook: www.facebook.com/NABengaged
Linkedin: www.linkedin.com/company/nabweb
X (Twitter): x.com/NABengaged
Description: State boards responsible for licensing nursing homes administrators. Produces exam to test the competence of nursing home administrators; operates continuing education review service; disseminates information and educational materials on nursing home administration. **Founded:** 1972. **Publications:** *State Licensure Requirements and College Directory* (Biennial). **Educational Activities:** NAB Mid-Year Meeting (Annual). **Geographic Preference:** National.

11504 ■ National Association of States United for Aging and Disabilities (NASUAD)
241 18th St. S, Ste. 403
Arlington, VA 22202
URL: http://www.advancingstates.org
Contact: Martha Roherty, Executive Director
Description: Provides information, technical assistance, and professional development support to State Units on Aging. (A state unit is an agency of state government designated by the governor and state legislature to administer the Older Americans Act and to serve as a focal point for all matters relating to older people.) Serves as a channel for officially designated state leadership in aging to exchange information and to join together for appropriate action on behalf of the elderly. Services include: information on federal policy and program developments in aging; training and technical assistance on a wide range of

program and management issues; liaison with organizations representing the public and private sectors. **Founded:** 1964. **Geographic Preference:** National.

11505 ■ **National Consumer Voice for Quality Long-Term Care**
1025 Connecticut Ave. NW, Ste. 1000
  Washington, DC 20036
Ph: (202)332-2275
Fax: (866)230-9789
Co. E-mail: info@theconsumervoice.org
URL: http://theconsumervoice.org
Contact: Jonathan Evans, President
Facebook: www.facebook.com/theconsumervoice
X (Twitter): x.com/ConsumerVoices

Description: National, state and local consumer/citizen groups and individuals seeking nursing home and board and care reform. Seeks to provide a consumer voice at the national, state, and local levels in the development and implementation of the long-term care system. Provides a platform through which groups can keep informed of current movements for change and can make their views known. Conducts seminars and training programs and utilizes a speakers' bureau consisting of advocates from around the country. Serves as a clearinghouse for information on nursing home and board care issues, and publishes consumer books and pamphlets. **Founded:** 1975. **Publications:** *Avoiding Physical Restraint Use: New Standards in Care*; *Nursing Home Staffing: A Guide for Residents, Families, Friends, and Caregivers*; *Piecing Together Quality Long-Term Care: A Consumer's Guide to Choices and Advocacy*; *Quality Care Advocate* (Quarterly); *Where Do I Go From Here A Guide for Nursing Home Residents, Families, and Friends a Consulting on Attorney.* **Geographic Preference:** National.

REFERENCE WORKS

11506 ■ *"Advancing the Ball" in Inside Healthcare (Vol. 6, December 2010, No. 7, pp. 31)*
Description: Profile of Medicalodges an elder-care specialty company that provides both patient care and technology development. President and CEO of the firm believes that hiring good employees is key to growth for any small business. **Availability:** Online.

11507 ■ *"Con Roundup: Novi Eyed for $11 Million, 100-Bed Medilodge" in Crain's Detroit Business (Vol. 25, June 1, 2009, No. 22, pp. M032)*
Pub: Crain Communications Inc.
Contact: Barry Asin, President
Description: Novi, Michigan is one of the cities being considered for construction of a new 110-bed skilled nursing facility. Details of the project are included. **Availability:** Online.

11508 ■ *"Elder Care Costs Surge" in National Underwriter Life & Health (Vol. 114, November 8, 2020, No. 21, pp. 25)*
Ed: Trevor Thomas. **Description:** Nursing home and assisted living rates rose from 2009 to 2010, according to MetLife Mature Market Institute. Statistical data included. **Availability:** Online.

11509 ■ *"Elder Care, Rx Drug Reforms Top Zoeller's Agenda" in Times (December 21, 2010)*
Pub: The Times
Ed: Sarah Tompkins. **Description:** Indiana Attorney General Greg Zoeller is hoping to develop a program in the state that will help regulate care for the elderly; freeze medical licenses for doctors involved in criminal investigations; address illegal drug use; and to establish a program to help individuals dispose of old prescription medications easily at pharmacies. **Availability:** Online.

11510 ■ *"Elder-Care Seminar to Teach Ways to Avoid Falls" in Virginian-Pilot (November 25, 2010)*
Pub: The Virginian-Pilot
Contact: Kevin Goyette, Director

E-mail: kgoyette@dailypress.com
Ed: Amy Jeter. **Description:** ResCare HomeCare, a home health services firm, offers free seminars on helping to make residences safer for seniors prone to falling. **Availability:** Print; Online.

11511 ■ *"EVMS Gets Grant to Train Providers for Elder Care" in Virginian-Pilot (October 29, 2010)*
Pub: The Virginian-Pilot
Contact: Kevin Goyette, Director
E-mail: kgoyette@dailypress.com
Ed: Elizabeth Simpson. **Description:** Eastern Virginia Medical School received a federal grant to train health providers in elder care. Details of the program are provided. **Availability:** Online.

11512 ■ *"Ground Readied for Construction of $4.5 Million Senior Care Center in Crown Point" in Times (August 9, 2012)*
Description: Bickford Senior Living will begin construction on a $4.5 million senior care center in Munster, Indiana. The facility will include assisted living apartments for seniors with various needs. Sixteen of the units will care for individuals with memory loss. Nurses and caregivers will be on staff 24 hours a day. **Availability:** Print; Online.

11513 ■ *"Los Angeles Jewish Home to Expand to Westside With New Senior Care Community and In-Home Services" in PR Newswire (September 12, 2012)*
Pub: PR Newswire Association LLC.
Description: Los Angeles Jewish Home plans to develop a senior care community at The Village at Playa Vista on the west side of Los Angeles, California. They will serve residential, healthcare and in-home care for seniors living on the west side of LA. Gonda Healthy Aging Westside Campus, donated by Leslie and Susan Gonda (Goldschmied) Foundation, will be part of the Jewish Home's mission to serve seniors in the area. Statistical data included.

11514 ■ *"MMRGlobal Home Health and Senior Care Programs to Be Showcased at Visiting Nurse Associations of America's Annual Meeting" in Marketwired (April 12, 2012)*
Pub: Comtex News Network Inc.
Contact: Kan Devnani, President
Description: MMR Global Inc. will highlight its storage and solutions and electronic document management and imaging systems for healthcare professionals at the Visiting Nurse Associations of America (VNAA) 30th Annual Meeting in Phoenix, Arizona. Personal Health Records (PHRs), MyEsafeDepositBox and other programs are profiled. **Availability:** Print; Online.

11515 ■ *"New Government Tool Opens Window into Nursing-Home Abuse" in The Wall Street Journal (November 19, 2019)*
URL(s): www.wsj.com/articles/new-government-tool
  -opens-window-into-nursing-home-abuse-1157
  4159400
Ed: Yuka Hayashi. **Released:** November 19, 2019. **Description:** The government database, Nursing Home Compare, has a new feature that marks facilities cited for abuse or neglect with a small red icon. So far, 760 facilities have been indicated, and the symbols are updated monthly. **Availability:** Online.

11516 ■ *"New York Identifies Hospitals and Nursing Homes with Deadly Fungus" in The New York Times (November 13, 2019)*
URL(s): www.nytimes.com/2019/11/13/health/candida
  -auris-resistant-hospitals.html
Ed: Matt Richtel, Andrew Jacobs. **Released:** November 13, 2019. **Description:** New York became the first state to release the names of the medical facilities that treated patients with Candida auris, a fungus that has been spreading globally and is very hard to treat. Hospitals and nursing homes have been susceptible to the fungus, and the state wants to remain transparent to consumers and to encourage facilities to help stop its spread. **Availability:** Online.

11517 ■ *"A Nursing Home Chain Grows Too Fast and Collapses, and Elderly and Disabled Residents Pay the Price" in NBCnews (July 19, 2019)*
URL(s): www.nbcnews.com/health/aging/nursing
  -home-chain-grows-too-fast-collapses-elderly
  -disabled-residents-n1025381
Ed: Laura Strickler, Stephanie Gosk, Shelby Hanssen. **Released:** July 19, 2019. **Description:** Profile of Skyline Healthcare, a nursing home chain that ran out of money or had facilities shut down due to documented neglect. Owned and operated by Joseph Schwartz, who quickly bought numerous nursing homes but mismanaged many aspects of the business. Residents and employees were not prepared for this news and found themselves in vulnerable situations. **Availability:** Online.

11518 ■ *"Nursing Home Group Put on the Block" in Globe & Mail (February 23, 2006, pp. B1)*
Ed: Elizabeth Church. **Description:** The reasons behind the decision of Exetendicare Inc. to go for sale are presented. **Availability:** Online.

11519 ■ *"Physicians Development Groupn Kicks Off $13M Skilled Nursing Facility in NE Wichita" in Wichita Business Journal (Vol. 27, January 20, 2012, No. 3, pp. 1)*
Pub: Baltimore Business Journal
Contact: Rhonda Pringle, President
E-mail: rpringle@bizjournals.com
Description: Physicians Development Group has started construction of a skilled nursing facility in Wichita, Kansas. The 80-bed nursing facility is estimated to cost around $13 million. **Availability:** Print; Online.

11520 ■ *"Silver Dollars" in Small Business Opportunities (September 2008)*
Description: Profile of Always Best Care Senior Services, a franchise created by Michael Newman, which offers non-medical In-Home Care, Personal Emergency Response Systems, and Assisted Living Placement Services to seniors; the company offers franchisees the opportunity to fill what is oftentimes a void for the seniors and their families in the community. **Availability:** Online.

11521 ■ *"Stay In Your Home" in Consumer Reports Money (Vol. 9, May 20, 2012, No. 5, pp. 1)*
Pub: Consumer Reports Books
Contact: Marta L. Tellado, President
Description: Renovations to help the elderly remain in their homes are covered. **Availability:** Online.

11522 ■ *"SunLink Health Systems Subsidiaries Open Senior Behavioral Care Units in Dahlonega, GA and Fulton, MO" in Mental Health Weekly Digest (July 16, 2012, pp. 326)*
Pub: NewsRX LLC.
Contact: Kalani Rosell, Contact
Description: SunLink Health Systems Inc. opened Changing Seasons, a 10-bed geriatric psychiatric unit in Dahlonega, Georgia and Kingdom Senior Solutions opened a 19-bed geriatric psychiatric unit in Fulton, Georgia. Details of the new facilities are defined.

11523 ■ *"They've Fallen, But Can Senior-Housing Stocks Get Up" in Barron's (Vol. 88, March 10, 2008, No. 10, pp. 43)*
Pub: Dow Jones & Company Inc.
Contact: Almar Latour, Chief Executive Officer
Ed: Kopin Tan. **Description:** Shares of senior housing companies present buying opportunities to investors because of their low prices. Companies such as Brookdale Senior Living are not as dependent on housing prices but have suffered declines in share prices. **Availability:** Online.

11524 ■ *"VA Seeking Bidders for Fort Howard" in Baltimore Business Journal (Vol. 28, June 25, 2010, No. 7, pp. 1)*
Pub: Baltimore Business Journal
Contact: Rhonda Pringle, President
E-mail: rpringle@bizjournals.com

Ed: Daniel J. Servnoitz. **Description:** The Veterans Affairs Maryland Health Care Systems has requested proposals from developers to build a retirement community at Fort Howard in Baltimore County. The historic site, which has about 36 mostly vacant buildings, could become the home to hundreds of war veterans. Details of the proposed development are discussed. **Availability:** Print; Online.

STATISTICAL SOURCES

11525 ■ *RMA Annual Statement Studies*
Pub: Risk Management Association
Contact: Nancy Foster, President

Released: Annual. **Description:** Contains composite balance sheets and income statements for more than 360 industries, including the accounting, auditing, and bookkeeping industries. Also contains five years of comparative historical data for discerning trends. Includes 16 commonly used ratios, computed for most of the size groupings for nearly every industry.

11526 ■ *Standard & Poor's Industry Surveys*
Pub: Standard And Poor's Financial Services LLC.
Contact: Douglas L. Peterson, President

Description: Two-volume book that examines the prospects for specific industries, including trucking. Also provides analyses of trends and problems, statistical tables and charts, and comparative company analyses.

TRADE PERIODICALS

11527 ■ *Abbeyfield Houses Society of Canada Newsletter*
Pub: Abbeyfield Houses Society of Canada
Contact: Denis Laframboise, President
URL(s): abbeyfield.ca/start-a-house

Description: Reports on news of Abbeyfield Houses Society of Canada, a provider of care and companionship for the elderly. Also features articles related to aging, housing, and lifestyle in Canada and internationally. Recurring features include letters to the editor, and columns titled News of Local Societies and Bits 'n Bites. **Availability:** PDF; Download.

11528 ■ *Clinical Gerontologist: The Journal of Aging and Mental Health*
Pub: Taylor And Francis Group
Contact: Annie Callanan, Chief Executive Officer
URL(s): www.tandfonline.com/journals/wcli20
X (Twitter): x.com/clinical_gero

Ed: Dolores Gallagher-Thompson, PhD. **Released:** 5/year **Price:** $2,284, Institutions for online only; $340, Individuals for online only. **Description:** Contains practical information and research on assessment and intervention of mental health needs of aged patients. **Availability:** Print; Download; PDF; Online.

11529 ■ *Physical Medicine and Rehabilitation Clinics of North America*
Pub: Elsevier Inc.
URL(s): www.pmr.theclinics.com

Ed: Santos F. Martinez. **Price:** $491, Individuals for International online + print. **Description:** Journal focused on physical medicine and rehabilitation, including trends in patient management and newest advances in the field. **Availability:** Print; Download; PDF; Online.

11530 ■ *Topics in Geriatric Rehabilitation (TGR)*
Pub: Lippincott Williams & Wilkins
URL(s): journals.lww.com/topicsingeriatricrehabilita tion/pages/default.aspx
Facebook: www.facebook.com/people/Topics-in -Geriatric-Rehabilitation/100069909094080
X (Twitter): x.com/TGROnline

Ed: Carole B. Lewis, PhD. **Released:** Quarterly **Price:** $94, for in training print online 1 year USA, Canada/Mexico; $142, Individuals for online 1 year US, international; $284, Individuals for online 2 year US, international; $426, Individuals for online 3 year US, international; $188, for in training print online 2 year USA, Canada/Mexico; $282, for in training print online 3 year USA, Canada/Mexico; $282, Individuals for print and online international /UK / Australia 1 year; $268, Individuals for print and online Canada / Mexico 1 year; $1,481, Institutions for print International and Uk/Australia; $147, Individuals for online 1 year US, international; $196, Individuals for print and online USA 1 year; $1,467, Institutions for print Canada /Mexico; $1,148, Institutions for print US. **Description:** Journal presenting clinical, basic, and applied research, as well as theoretical information, for the health care professional practicing in the area of geriatric rehabilitation. **Availability:** Print; PDF; Online.

TRADE SHOWS AND CONVENTIONS

11531 ■ **American Health Care Association Annual Convention and Exposition**
American Health Care Association (AHCA)
1201 L St. NW
Washington, DC 20005
Ph: (202)842-4444
Fax: (202)842-3860
Co. E-mail: help@ltctrendtracker.com
URL: http://www.ahcancal.org/Pages/default.aspx
Contact: Mark Parkinson, President
URL(s): deliveringsolutionsorg.eventscribe.net

Frequency: Annual. **Description:** Supplies for the long-term healthcare industry. **Audience:** Health care professionals. **Principal Exhibits:** Supplies for the long-term healthcare industry. **Telecommunication Services:** meetings@ahca.org.

11532 ■ **LeadingAge Annual Meeting and Expo**
LeadingAge
2519 Connecticut Ave. NW
Washington, DC 20008
Ph: (202)783-2242
Co. E-mail: info@leadingage.org
URL: http://www.leadingage.org
Contact: Amma Addo, Director
E-mail: aaddo@leadingage.org
URL(s): leadingage.org/annualmeeting/home

Frequency: Annual. **Description:** Equipment, supplies, and services for housing and long-term care facilities for the aged. **Audience:** Health care professionals, members, and industry professionals. **Principal Exhibits:** Equipment, supplies, and services for housing and long-term care facilities for the aged. Dates and Locations: 2025 Nov 02-05 Boston Convention & Exhibition Center, Boston, MA; 2026 Oct 25-28 Pennsylvania Convention Center, Philadelphia, PA; 2027 Nov 07-10 Minneapolis Convention Center, Minneapolis, MN; 2028 Oct 22-22 Ernest N. Morial Convention Center, New Orleans, LA; 2029 Oct 28-31 San Diego Convention Center, San Diego, CA; 2030 Nov 03-06 Henry B. Gonzalez Convention Center, San Antonio, TX. **Telecommunication Services:** meetings@leadingage.org.

CONSULTANTS

11533 ■ **Diversified Health Resources Inc.**
1209 N Astor St., No. 2N
Chicago, IL 60610-2655
Contact: Andrea Rice Rozran, President

Description: Offers health care consulting for hospitals, nursing homes including homes for the aged and other health related facilities and companies. Specializes in planning and marketing. Also conducts executive searches for top level health care administrative positions. Serves private industries as well as government agencies. **Scope:** Offers health care consulting for hospitals, nursing homes including homes for the aged and other health related facilities and companies. Specializes in planning and

marketing. Also conducts executive searches for top level health care administrative positions. Serves private industries as well as government agencies. **Publications:** "City Finance".

FRANCHISES AND BUSINESS OPPORTUNITIES

11534 ■ **Age Advantage Home Care Franchising Inc.**
2910 Jefferson St., Ste. 206
Carlsbad, CA 92008
Ph: (760)720-7272
Co. E-mail: susanna.kinnefors@ageadvantage.com
URL: http://ageadvantage.com/location-CA.html
Contact: Susanna Kinnefors, Owner
E-mail: susanna.kinnefors@ageadvantage.com

Description: Firm provides home and senior care services. **Founded:** 1998. **Financial Assistance:** Yes

11535 ■ **Home Instead Inc.**
13323 California St.
Omaha, NE 68154
Ph: (402)205-8392
Free: 888-331-3242
URL: http://www.homeinstead.com
Contact: Lori Hogan, Co-Founder
Facebook: www.facebook.com/homeinsteadinc
Linkedin: www.linkedin.com/company/homeinstea dinc
X (Twitter): x.com/homeinstead
Instagram: www.instagram.com/homeinstea dseniorcare
YouTube: www.youtube.com/user/HomeInsteadInc

Description: Non-medical companionship and home-care services for elderly people. **Founded:** 1994. **Franchise Fee:** $55,000. **Royalty Fee:** 5%. **Financial Assistance:** No **Training:** Yes.

COMPUTERIZED DATABASES

11536 ■ *Consumer InSite*
Type: Full-text.

11537 ■ *Health & Wellness InSite*
Type: Full-text.

LIBRARIES

11538 ■ **American College of Health Care Administrators (ACHCA)**
1101 Connecticut Ave. NW, Ste. 450
Washington, DC 20036
Free: 800-561-3148
Co. E-mail: info@achca.org
URL: http://www.achca.org
Contact: Amanda Charles, Business Manager
E-mail: acharles@achca.org
Facebook: www.facebook.com/pages/The-American -College-of-Health-Care-Administrators/32659778 4597
X (Twitter): x.com/ACHCA

Description: Persons actively engaged in the administration of long-term care facilities, such as nursing homes, retirement communities, assisted living facilities, and sub-acute care programs. Administers professional certification programs for assisted living, sub-acute and nursing home administrators. Works to elevate the standards in the field and to develop and promote a code of ethics and standards of education and training. Seeks to inform allied professions and the public that good administration of long-term care facilities calls for special formal academic training and experience. Encourages research in all aspects of geriatrics, the chronically ill, and administration. Maintains placement service. Holds special education programs; facilitates networking among administrators. **Founded:** 1962. **Publications:** *Continuum* (Quarterly); *Balance: The Source for Administrators in Long-Term Health Care* (8/year); *ACHCA E-News* (Bimonthly). **Educational Activities:** ACHCA Annual Winter Marketplace (Annual). **Awards:** New Administrator Award (Annual); ACHCA

Education Award (Annual); ACHCA Journalism Award (Annual); W.Phillip McConnell Student Scholarship Fund (Irregular); Richard L. Thorpe Fellowship (Annual); ACHCA Distinguished Assisted Living Administrator Award (Annual); ACHCA Distinguished Nursing Home Administrator Award (Annual); ACHCA New Nursing Home Administrator Award (Annual). **Geographic Preference:** National.

11539 ■ AnMed Health Medical Center - Cancer Learning Center
800 N Fant St. 1st fl.
  Anderson, SC 29621
Ph: (864)512-3477
Co. E-mail: foundation@anmedhealth.org
URL: http://anmedhealth.org/give-back/our-foundation
Description: Provides healthcare and medical services. **Scope:** Cancer, oncology, therapy. **Founded:** 1985. **Subscriptions:** journals Booklets; brochures; pamphlets; handbooks; textbooks; cookbooks; treatment guides; survivor stories; video cassette tapes; DVDs.

11540 ■ Clemson University-College of Health, Education & Human Development-Learning Resource Center
209 Gantt Cir., Clemson University
  Clemson, SC 29634
Ph: (864)656-7645
URL: http://www.clemson.edu/centers-institutes/clrc/index.html
Contact: Debi Switzer, Department Chairman
E-mail: debi@clemson.edu
Scope: Health; education. **Holdings:** Figures not available.

11541 ■ Evangelical Lutheran Good Samaritan Society (ELGSS) [Good Samaritan Society]
4800 W 57th St.
  Sioux Falls, SD 57108
Ph: (605)362-3100
Free: 866-928-1635
Co. E-mail: moreinfo@good-sam.com
URL: http://www.good-sam.com
Contact: Nate Schema, President
Facebook: www.facebook.com/goodsamaritansociety
Linkedin: www.linkedin.com/company/the-good-samaritan-society
YouTube: www.youtube.com/user/goodsamaritansociety
Description: Owns, operates, and manages 240 Christian institutions in 25 states, including nursing homes with levels of care ranging from senior living to skilled nursing. Provides each center with computerized accounting, comparative data, administrator and staff training programs, a regional director, special purchasing agreements, life enrichment programming, emergency financial backing, and specialists in other fields. Conducts meetings to provide administrators with credits for continuing education. **Founded:** 1922. **Publications:** *Donor eNewsletter* (Weekly); *The Evangelical Lutheran Good Samaritan Society--Directory* (Annual). **Geographic Preference:** National; Local.

11542 ■ Genesis Medical Center - Illini Campus - Perlmutter Library of the Health Sciences
801 Illini Dr.
  Silvis, IL 61282-2904
URL: http://www.genesishealth.com
Description: Healthcare center. **Scope:** Clinical medicine; healthcare management; nursing; consumer health; emergency medical services; geriatrics; quality improvement. **Services:** Interlibrary loan; literature searches; PUBMED training; open to the public. **Founded:** 1980. **Holdings:** Figures not available. **Preferred Investment Size:** Genesis Medical Center, Illini Hospital and Dewitt Hospital.

11543 ■ Lexington Medical Center - LMC Health Library
2720 Sunset Blvd.
  West Columbia, SC 29169
Ph: (803)791-2000

URL: http://www.lexmed.com/?aspxerrorpath=/about/community-involvement/health-library
Scope: Medical science; psychology; nutrition; childcare; sports medicine; health care law; general health. **Holdings:** 1,000 books; 500 audiovisual titles.

11544 ■ Millcreek Community Hospital/ LECOM Medical Library
5515 Peach St.
  Erie, PA 16509
Ph: (814)868-8217
Co. E-mail: admissions@lecom.edu
URL: http://lecomhealth.com/sports-medicine-fellowship
Facebook: www.facebook.com/1LECOM
Linkedin: www.linkedin.com/school/lake-erie-college-of-osteopathic-medicine
X (Twitter): twitter.com/1LECOM
Description: An osteopathic acute care hospital offering comprehensive inpatient and outpatient services and 24-hour emergency care in Erie, Pennsylvania. **Scope:** Medicine. **Services:** Interlibrary loan; copying; library open to the public. **Holdings:** Figures not available.

11545 ■ Princeton Community Hospital Library
122 12th St.
  Princeton, WV 24740
URL: http://wvumedicine.org/princeton
Contact: James Sarver, III, President
Scope: Information on cancer. **Founded:** 1970. **Holdings:** Figures not available.

11546 ■ Southwest Health Center - Medical Library
1400 E Side Rd.
  Platteville, WI 53818
Ph: (608)348-2331
Co. E-mail: worekj@southwesthealth.org
URL: http://www.southwesthealth.org
Contact: Doug Rogers, Chairman
Facebook: www.facebook.com/southwesthealth
X (Twitter): x.com/SouthwestHealth
YouTube: www.youtube.com/user/SouthwestHealth
Description: Medical library. **Scope:** Health; medicine; nursing. **Founded:** 1975. **Holdings:** Figures not available.

11547 ■ Toronto Rehabilitation Institute - Library
550 University Ave.
  Toronto, ON, Canada M5G 2A2
Ph: (416)597-3422
URL: http://www.uhn.ca/TorontoRehab
Facebook: www.facebook.com/torontorehabinstitute
Linkedin: www.linkedin.com/company/toronto-rehabilitation-institute
X (Twitter): x.com/TRI_UHN
YouTube: www.youtube.com/user/UHNToronto
Scope: Rehabilitation. **Founded:** 1978. **Holdings:** Figures not available. **Awards:** Annie Kirshenblatt Memorial Scholarship (Annual); Shoshana Philipp (Kirshenblatt) R.N. Memorial Scholarships (Annual); Toronto Rehab Scholarships in Rehabilitation-Related Research (Annual); Toronto Rehabilitation Institute Graduate Student Scholarships - Ontario Student Opportunities Trust Fund (OSOTF). **Geographic Preference:** Multinational.

11548 ■ United Way of Dane County - Imagination Library
2059 Atwood Ave.
  Madison, WI 53704
Ph: (608)246-4350
Fax: (608)246-4349
Co. E-mail: writeus@uwdc.org
URL: http://www.unitedwaydanecounty.org
Contact: Renee Moe, President
E-mail: renee.moe@uwdc.org
Facebook: www.facebook.com/unitedwaydaneco
X (Twitter): x.com/unitedwaydaneco
Instagram: www.instagram.com/unitedwaydaneco
YouTube: www.youtube.com/channel/UCmBN7K8KWKsci6yaVqU-wmg

Description: Unite the community to achieve measurable results and change lives. **Scope:** School. **Founded:** 1971. **Holdings:** Books. **Geographic Preference:** Local.

11549 ■ University of South Florida College of Medicine - Suncoast Gerontology Center - The Eastern Star Library on Alzheimer's Disease
4001 E Fletcher Ave.
  Tampa, FL 33613
URL: http://health.usf.edu/medicine/byrd
Scope: Alzheimer's disease; aging; caregiving; long-term care; dementia. **Services:** Interlibrary loan; copying; SDI; library open to the public for reference use only. **Founded:** 1985. **Holdings:** 800 books; 450 reports; 50 archival materials; 25 videocassettes.

11550 ■ Virginia Commonwealth University School of Allied Health Professions - Virginia Center on Aging - Information Resources Center
900 E Leigh St., Ste. 7020
  Richmond, VA 23219
Ph: (804)828-1525
Co. E-mail: vcoa@vcu.edu
URL: http://www.sahp.vcu.edu/vcoa/video-library/index.html
Contact: Dr. Edward F. Ansello, Director
E-mail: eansello@vcu.edu
Facebook: www.facebook.com/vcuvcoa
YouTube: www.youtube.com/user/alliedhelp/videos
Scope: Gerontology; mental health; sociology and the politics of aging; geriatrics; family relationships; long-term care; lifelong learning. **Services:** Library open to the public with restrictions (audio/visual materials available to Virginia residents only). **Founded:** 1978. **Holdings:** 1,500 books; 4 archives; 150 videos and DVDs.

11551 ■ Western Illinois Area Agency on Aging (WIAAA) - Greta J. Brook Elderly Living and Learning Facility [Elderly Living and Learning Facility (ELLF)]
729 34th Ave.
  Rock Island, IL 61201
Ph: (309)793-6800
Free: 800-322-1051
Co. E-mail: information@wiaaa.org
URL: http://www.wiaaa.org
Contact: Barbara Eskildsen, Executive Director
E-mail: beskildsen@wiaaa.org
Facebook: www.facebook.com/Western-Illinois-Area-Agency-on-Aging-502130799853006
Scope: Gerontology; senior housing; family caregiving; Medicare; Medicaid; social security; retirement planning; intergenerational programs; program development. **Services:** Interlibrary loan; senior computer center open to those fifty years of age or older; facility open to the public. **Founded:** 1973. **Holdings:** 1,108 books; 260 videotapes; 130 audio/visual materials; 35 DVDs and CDs. **Subscriptions:** 2 journals and other serials; 12 periodicals (includes journals).

RESEARCH CENTERS

11552 ■ Center for Health Care Strategies Inc. (CHCS)
200 American Metro Blvd., Ste. 119
  Hamilton, NJ 08619
Ph: (609)528-8400
Fax: (609)586-3679
Co. E-mail: hr@chcs.org
URL: http://www.chcs.org
Contact: Stephen A. Somers, Consultant
Facebook: www.facebook.com/CenterForHealthCareStrategies
Linkedin: www.linkedin.com/company/chcshealth
X (Twitter): x.com/CHCShealth
Description: Independent, nonprofit health care policy resource center. **Scope:** Development and implementation of effective health and social policy for all Americans. **Founded:** 1995. **Publications:**

Case studies; *CHCS Fact sheets*; *Policy and issue briefs* (Monthly); *CHCS Reports*; *Resource papers*; *Technical assistance tools* (Annual).

11553 ■ Sherbrooke University - Centre de Recherche sur le Vieillissement (CDRV) [Sherbrooke University - Research Centre on Aging]
Sherbrooke, QC, Canada
URL: http://www.cdrv.ca/en/home
Contact: Isabelle Dionne, Director
E-mail: isabelle.dionne@usherbrooke.ca
URL(s): www.usherbrooke.ca/recherche/en/udes/clusters/institutes/cdrv

Description: Integral unit of Sherbrooke University. **Scope:** Biology of aging, oxidative stress, biosignalisation, rehabilitation, validation of measurement tools and methods, psychological distress, cognitive decline, family caregivers, quality of care, integrated services, Alzheimer's disease, diabetes, nutrition, epidemiology and prevention of functional decline, physical activity, gait and balance, psycho-sociology of aging, sleep disorders, medicine. consumption, actualization of potential, psychological well-being, abuse and crime issues, road safety, consent, ethics, tissue regeneration, energy and lipid metabolism, telerehabilitation, emotion recognition, continuity of care, hobbies, social participation, memory, long-term consequences of cerebrovascular accident, professional practice in gerontology, etc.

11554 ■ University of Arizona - Arizona Center on Aging (ACOA)
1501 N Campbell, Ste. 7401
 Tucson, AZ 85724-5027
URL: http://aging.medicine.arizona.edu
Contact: Dr. Mindy J. Fain, Officer
Description: Integral unit of College of Medicine at University of Arizona. **Scope:** Long-term care, retirement communities, minority elderly, health and long-term care policy, and aging. Conducts applied research in service delivery system development and provides technical assistance and research dissemination. **Founded:** 1980. **Publications:** *ACOA Papers*.

11555 ■ University of Massachusetts Boston - Gerontology Institute
100 Morrissey Blvd.
 Boston, MA 02125
Ph: (617)287-7300
Fax: (617)287-7080
Co. E-mail: gerontologyinstitute@umb.edu
URL: http://www.umb.edu/gerontologyinstitute
Contact: Len Fishman, Professor
E-mail: len.fishman@umb.edu
Facebook: www.facebook.com/umassgerontology

Description: Integral unit of University of Massachusetts, Boston. **Scope:** Gerontology Institute deals with aging social policy, including health care, economics, security, long-term care, productive aging, systems delivery, older women's issues, pension assistance, retirement, older drivers, demographics and minority issues. **Founded:** 1984. **Publications:** *Journal of Aging & Social Policy* (Quarterly). **Educational Activities:** Gerontology Institute Seminars, Offers exemplary teaching and training programs.

START-UP INFORMATION

11556 ■ *"Do Cool Sh*t: Quit Your Day Job, Start Your Own Business, and Live Happily Ever After"*
Pub: Harper Business
Contact: Hollis Heimbouch, Senior Vice President Publisher
Released: January 20, 2015. **Price:** $16.61, hardcover; $11.97, paperback; $11.49, e-book; $3.13, kindle; $0.05, hardcover(99 used from $0.05); $8, hardcover(44 new from $8.00); $2, paperback(76 used from $2.00); $5.47, paperback(64 new from $5.47). **Description:** Serial social entrepreneur, angel investor, and woman business leader, Miki Agrawal, teaches how to start and run a successful new business. She covers all issues from brainstorming, to raising money to getting press without any connections, and still have time to enjoy life. She created WILD, a farm-to-table pizzeria in New York City and Las Vegas. She also partnered in a children's multimedia company called Super Sprowtz--a story-driven nutrition program for children, and she launched a patented high-tech underware business called THINX. Agrawal also discusses the growth in her businesses. **Availability:** E-book; Print.

ASSOCIATIONS AND OTHER ORGANIZATIONS

11557 ■ **Academy of Nutrition and Dietetics (AND) - Library**
120 S Riverside Plz., Ste. 2190
Chicago, IL 60606-6995
Ph: (312)899-0040
Free: 800-877-1600
URL: http://www.eatright.org
Contact: Kevin L. Sauer, President
X (Twitter): x.com/eatright
YouTube: www.youtube.com/user/EatRightTV
Pinterest: www.pinterest.com/kidseatright

Description: Represents food and nutrition professionals. Promotes nutrition, health and well-being. **Scope:** Food and nutrition. **Services:** Library not open to the public. **Founded:** 1917. **Holdings:** Figures not available. **Publications:** *Weight Loss Matters: Your Weight and Your Health Pamphlet*; *Find a Nutrition Professional Consumer Search*; *Directory of Columbus Registered Dietitians*; *Directory of Registered Dietitians*; *Directory of Dietetics Programs* (Annual); *Directory of Consulting Dietitians in Private Practice*; *Journal of the Academy of Nutrition and Dietetics* (Monthly). **Educational Activities:** Food Nutrition Conference Expo (FNCE) (Annual).

11558 ■ **American Association of Nutritional Consultants (AANC)**
220 Parker St.
Warsaw, IN 46580
Ph: (574)269-6165
Free: 888-828-2262
Fax: (574)268-2120

Co. E-mail: registrar@aanc.net
URL: http://www.aanc.net
Facebook: www.facebook.com/AmericanAccocia tionofNutritionalConsultants

Description: Seeks to create a forum for exchange of nutritional information. Offers benefits such as car rental and laboratory discounts. **Founded:** 1985. **Publications:** *American Association of Nutritional Consultants Brochure*. **Geographic Preference:** National.

11559 ■ **American Nutrition Association (ANA)**
211 W Chicago Ave., Ste. 217
Hinsdale, IL 60521
URL: http://www.theana.org
Contact: Jeffrey Blumberg, Board Member
Facebook: www.facebook.com/AmericanNutri tionAssociation
Linkedin: www.linkedin.com/company/american-nutri tion-association
X (Twitter): x.com/AmNuAssn
Instagram: www.instagram.com/americannutri tionassociation
YouTube: www.youtube.com/channel/UC5MfCwoHAs 2iaBMfwhRLslw

Description: Aims to promote optimal health through nutrition and wellness education. Performs at the cutting edge of science-based nutrition, educating both laypeople and professionals about the health benefits of nutrition and wellness. **Founded:** 1959. **Publications:** *Nutrition Digest*. **Geographic Preference:** National.

11560 ■ **Association of Nutrition and Foodservice Professionals (ANFP)**
406 Surrey Woods Dr.
Saint Charles, IL 60174
Ph: (630)587-6336
Free: 800-323-1908
Fax: (630)587-6308
Co. E-mail: info@anfponline.org
URL: http://www.anfponline.org
Contact: Joyce Gilbert, President
Facebook: www.facebook.com/ANFPonline
Linkedin: www.linkedin.com/company/association-of -nutrition-&-foodservice-professionals
X (Twitter): x.com/_ANFP
Instagram: www.instagram.com/anfponline
Pinterest: www.pinterest.com/anfp3581

Description: Dietary managers united to maintain a high level of competency and quality in dietary departments through continuing education. Provides educational programs and placement service. **Founded:** 1960. **Publications:** *Nutrition & Foodservice Edge Magazine* (6/year); *ANFP Publications Catalog*; *Nutrition & Foodservice Edge* (6/year); *DMA Master Track Human Resources Series*; *DMA Master Track Management Series*. **Educational Activities:** ANFP Annual Conference & Expo (ANFPACE) (Annual). **Awards:** ANFP State Achievement Award (Semiannual). **Geographic Preference:** National; State.

11561 ■ **Canadian Health Food Association (CHFA) [Association Canadienne des Aliements de Sante]**
235 Yorkland Blvd., Ste. 201
Toronto, ON, Canada M2J 4Y8
Free: 800-661-4510
Co. E-mail: info@chfa.ca
URL: http://chfa.ca/en
Contact: Aaron Skelton, President
Facebook: www.facebook.com/CAhealthfood
X (Twitter): x.com/cdnhealthfood
Instagram: www.instagram.com/cahealthfood
YouTube: www.youtube.com/user/cdnhealthfood

Description: Seeks to advance the health food industries. Facilitates communication and cooperation among members; represents the commercial and regulatory interests of the health food industries; sponsors educational and promotional programs. **Publications:** *The Natural Voice* (5/year). **Educational Activities:** CHFA West (Annual); CHFA East Tradeshow (Annual). **Geographic Preference:** National.

11562 ■ *Canadian Journal of Dietetic Practice and Research*
99 Yorkville Ave., 2nd Fl.
Toronto, ON, Canada M5R 1C1
Ph: (416)596-0857
Fax: (416)596-0603
Co. E-mail: contactus@dietitians.ca
URL: http://www.dietitians.ca
Contact: Alexis Williams, Chief Executive Officer
URL(s): dcjournal.ca/journal/cjdpr

Ed: Dawna Royall. **Released:** Quarterly **Price:** $62, Individuals for one year online only; $340, Institutions for one year online only. **Description:** Peer-reviewed professional journal for dietitians and nutritionists in Canada (English and French). **Availability:** Print; PDF; Online.

11563 ■ **Canadian Nutrition Society (CNS) [Société Canadienne de Nutrition (SCN)]**
Toronto, ON, Canada
Free: 888-414-7188
Co. E-mail: info@cns-scn.ca
URL: http://cns-scn.ca
Contact: Sukhinder Cheema, President
Facebook: www.facebook.com/canadiannutri tionsociety
Linkedin: www.linkedin.com/company/canadian-nutri tion-society
X (Twitter): x.com/CNS_SCN
Instagram: www.instagram.com/canadiannutri tionsociety

Description: Dietitians and other scientists and health care professionals with an interest in nutrition. Seeks to advance the study and practice of the nutritional sciences. Serves as a forum for the exchange of information among members; sponsors research and educational programs. **Founded:** 2010. **Awards:** CNS Young Investigator Award for Outstanding Research (Annual). **Geographic Preference:** National.

11564 ■ Dietetics in Health Care Communities (DHCC)

PO Box 4489
 Carol Stream, IL 60197-4489
Free: 800-877-1600
Co. E-mail: dhcc@quidnunc.net
URL: http://www.dhccdpg.org
Contact: Marcus Sam, Contact
Facebook: www.facebook.com/dieteticsinheal
thcarecommunities15
Linkedin: www.linkedin.com/groups

Description: A special interest group of the American Dietetic Association. Dietitians employed in extended care facilities, nursing homes, homecare, and a variety of food service operations. Disseminates information; assists in solving their problems in the field. Conducts workshops; offers networking opportunities for professionals. **Founded:** 1975. **Publications:** *Reasons to Believe* (Bimonthly); *Inservice Manual.* **Awards:** Gaynold Jensen Education Stipends (Annual); DHCC Best Practice Award (Annual); DHCC Circle Award (Annual); DHCC Distinguished Member Award (Annual); DHCC Up and Coming Member of the Year Award (Annual); DHCC Scholarship (Annual). **Geographic Preference:** National.

11565 ■ Dietitians of Canada

99 Yorkville Ave., 2nd Fl.
 Toronto, ON, Canada M5R 1C1
Ph: (416)596-0857
Fax: (416)596-0603
Co. E-mail: contactus@dietitians.ca
URL: http://www.dietitians.ca
Contact: Alexis Williams, Chief Executive Officer
Facebook: www.facebook.com/DietitiansCAN
X (Twitter): twitter.com/dietitianscan
YouTube: www.youtube.com/user/DietitiansCAN

Description: Leads and supports members to promote health and well being through expertise in food and nutrition. **Founded:** 1935. **Publications:** *Canadian Journal of Dietetic Practice and Research* (Quarterly). **Geographic Preference:** National.

11566 ■ Fondation Canadienne de la Recherche en Diététique (CFDR) [Canadian Foundation for Dietetic Research (CFDR)]

99 Yorkville Ave. Second Fl.
 Toronto, ON, Canada M5R 1C1
Ph: (416)642-9309
Co. E-mail: info@cfdr.ca
URL: http://cfdr.ca
Contact: Carol Clarke, Chairman
Facebook: www.facebook.com/CFDRcan
Linkedin: www.linkedin.com/company/cfdrcan
X (Twitter): x.com/cfdrcan
Instagram: www.instagram.com/cfdrcan

Description: Dietitians and other individuals with an interest in nutrition. Seeks to advance dietetic research. Provides support and assistance to nutrition research projects. Conducts educational programs. **Founded:** 1991. **Publications:** *Keeping in Touch* (3/year). **Awards:** CFDR Regular Research Grant Competition (Annual). **Geographic Preference:** National.

11567 ■ International Union of Nutritional Sciences (IUNS)

c/o Prof. J. Alfredo Martinez, Pres.
 Dept. de Fisiologia y Nutricion
 Universidad de Navarra, Edificio de Investigacion
 C/Irunlarrea, 1
 31008 Pamplona, Spain
Co. E-mail: office@iuns.org
URL: http://iuns.org
Contact: Dr. Lynnette M. Neufeld, President

Description: Promotes advancement in nutrition science, research and development through international cooperation at the global level. Encourages communication and collaboration among nutrition scientists as well as to disseminate information in nutritional sciences through modern communication technology. **Founded:** 1946. **Publications:** *International Union of Nutritional Sciences--Annual Report* (Quadrennial). **Educational Activities:** International Congress of Nutrition (Quadrennial). **Geographic Preference:** Multinational.

11568 ■ *Keeping in Touch*

99 Yorkville Ave. Second Fl.
 Toronto, ON, Canada M5R 1C1
Ph: (416)642-9309
Co. E-mail: info@cfdr.ca
URL: http://cfdr.ca
Contact: Carol Clarke, Chairman
URL(s): uat.cfdr.ca/Publications/Newsletters-Archive
.aspx

Released: 3/year **Description:** Contains the latest foundation activities. **Availability:** PDF; Online.

11569 ■ National Eating Disorder Information Centre (NEDIC) - Library

200 Elizabeth St., ES 7-421
 Toronto, ON, Canada M5G 2C4
Ph: (416)340-4156
Free: 866-633-4220
Co. E-mail: nedic@uhn.ca
URL: http://nedic.ca
Contact: Suzanne Phillips, Program Manager
E-mail: suzanne.phillips@uhn.ca
Facebook: www.facebook.com/thenedic
X (Twitter): x.com/theNEDIC
Instagram: www.instagram.com/the_nedic
YouTube: www.youtube.com/user/nedic85

Description: Provides information and resources on causes, symptoms of, and therapeutic and health care treatments for eating disorders and the preoccupation with food and weight. Aims to raise awareness on eating disorders through conducting lectures and workshops. **Scope:** Eating disorders. **Holdings:** Figures not available. **Educational Activities:** Eating Disorder Awareness Week (EDAW) (Annual). **Geographic Preference:** National.

11570 ■ Organic & Natural Health Association

PO Box 42385
 Washington, DC 20015
Co. E-mail: info@organicandnatural.org
URL: http://organicandnatural.org
Contact: Karen Howard, Chief Executive Officer
Facebook: www.facebook.com/organicandna
turalhealthassociation
Linkedin: www.linkedin.com/company/organic-and-na
tural-health-association
X (Twitter): x.com/orgnathealth
YouTube: www.youtube.com/user/OrgNatHealth

Description: Dedicated to creating and promoting transparent business practices that safeguard access to organic and natural food, products and services. **Founded:** 2014.

11571 ■ University of Mississippi School of Applied Sciences - Institute of Child Nutrition (ICN)

97 Jeanette Phillips Dr.
 University, MS 38677
Ph: (662)915-7658
Free: 800-321-3054
Fax: (800)321-3061
Co. E-mail: helpdesk@theicn.org
URL: http://theicn.org
Contact: Aleshia Hall-Campbell, PhD, MPH, Executive Director
Facebook: www.facebook.com/ichildnutrition
Linkedin: www.linkedin.com/company/theicn
X (Twitter): x.com/ichildnutrition
Instagram: www.instagram.com/theicn
YouTube: www.youtube.com/channel/UC4tz7o6PmB
4-1fJTXN9K1Uw

Description: Seeks to be the leader in providing education, research, and resources to promote excellence in child nutrition programs. Provides information, conducts applied research, and offers training and education opportunities using appropriate technology. **Scope:** Improvement of child nutrition programs. **Founded:** 1989. **Publications:** *Insight* (Quarterly); *Mealtime Memo for Child Care* (Bimonthly); *Resource Guide*; *Update* (Semiannual); *NFSMI Newsletters*; *Resource guide.* **Educational Activities:** National Food Service Management Institute Convention; NFSMI Workshops. **Geographic Preference:** National.

REFERENCE WORKS

11572 ■ *"Communicating Nutrition Research" in Today's Dietitian (Vol. 20, May 2018, No. 5, p. 38)*

URL(s): www.todaysdietitian.com/newarchives/0518p
38.shtml

Ed: Emily A. Callahan, MPH, RDN, Karen Collins, MS, RDN, CDN, FAND. **Released:** May 2018. **Description:** A guide to helping dietitians understand the latest research in nutrition and how to translate studies and pass that knowledge along to their clients. **Availability:** Print; Online.

11573 ■ *"Dietetic Technicians Bring Nutrition To the Table" in Occupational Outlook Quarterly (Vol. 58, Summer 2014, No. 2, pp. 26)*

Pub: Government Publishing Office
Contact: Hugh Nathanial Halpern, Director

Description: Employment growth for dietetic technicians is projected to grow at a faster pace than average employment sectors over the 2012-22 decade. Working as a dietetic technician combines an individual's love for food and a desire to work with others to help with their nutritional health. **Availability:** Print; Online.

11574 ■ *Everything is Possible: Life and Business Lessons from a Self-Made Billionaire and the Founder of Slim-Fast*

Released: First edition. **Description:** A profile of the founder of Slim-Fast nutritional diet drink used to help people lose weight. **Availability:** E-book.

11575 ■ *"Experts Strive to Educate on Proper Pet Diets" in Pet Product News (Vol. 64, November 2010, No. 11, pp. 40)*

Ed: Joan Hustace Walker. **Description:** Pet supply manufacturers have been bundling small mammal food and treats with educational sources to help retailers avoid customer misinformation. This action has been motivated by the customer's quest to seek proper nutritional advice for their small mammal pets. **Availability:** Online.

11576 ■ *"Food as Nature Intended" in Pet Product News (Vol. 64, November 2010, No. 11, pp. 30)*

Ed: Nikki Moustaki. **Description:** Dog owners have been extending their health-consciousness to their pets by seeking natural products that will address their pets' raw food diet. Retailers response to this trend are outlined. **Availability:** Online.

11577 ■ *"GNC Reaches 'A Pivotal Moment" in Pittsburgh Business Times (Vol. 34, August 15, 2014, No. 4, pp. 4)*

Pub: American City Business Journals, Inc.
Contact: Mike Olivieri, Executive Vice President

Released: Weekly. **Price:** $4, introductory 4-week offer(Digital & Print). **Description:** Goldman analyst, Stephen Tanal, states Michael Archbold is taking over as CEO of GNC Holdings Inc. at a pivotal moment as the company shifts from heavy dependence on promotions to sustaining sales growth beyond 2015. Analysts discuss the recent problems faced by the vitamin, health and fitness retailer and the implications of a possible merger between GNC and Archbolds' former company, the Vitamin Shoppe Inc. **Availability:** Print; Online.

11578 ■ *"In the Raw: Karyn Calabrese Brings Healthy Dining to a New Sophisticated Level" in Black Enterprise (Vol. 41, September 2010)*

Pub: Earl G. Graves Ltd.
Contact: Earl Graves, Jr., President

Ed: Sonia Alleyne. **Description:** Profile of Karyn Calabrese whose businesses are based in Chicago, Illinois. Calabrese has launched a complete line of products (vitamins and beauty items), services (spa, chiropractic, and acupuncture treatments), and restaurants to bring health dining and lifestyles to a better level. **Availability:** Online.

11579 ■ "Making It Work" in Pet Product News (Vol. 64, December 2010, No. 12, pp. S8)

Ed: Kerri Chladnicek. **Description:** How focusing on service and flexibility allowed New Jersey-based pet supply store B.C. Woof to achieve success is discussed. B.C. Woof began as a pet-sitting business which eventually concentrated on natural foods. Aside from conducting a do-it-yourself approach in food formulation for customers, B.C. Woof has also been guiding customers on nutrients they need for their pets. **Availability:** Print; Online.

11580 ■ "Supplements Mix Nutrition With Convenience" in Pet Product News (Vol. 64, November 2010, No. 11, pp. 44)

Ed: Karen Shugart. **Description:** Pet supply manufacturers have been making supplements and enhanced foods that improve mineral consumption, boost bone density, and sharpen appetite in herps. Customers seem to enjoy the convenience as particular herps demands are being addressed by these offerings. Features of other supplements and enhanced foods for herps are described. **Availability:** Print; Online.

TRADE PERIODICALS

11581 ■ American Journal of Clinical Nutrition (AJCN)
Pub: American Society for Nutrition
Contact: Paul M. Coates, President
URL(s): ajcn.nutrition.orgnutrition.org/publications
X (Twitter): x.com/AJCNutrition

Released: Monthly **Description:** Peer-reviewed journal publishing basic and clinical studies relevant to human nutrition. **Availability:** Print; PDF; Download; Online.

11582 ■ EatingWell
Pub: Dotdash Meredith
Contact: Neil Vogel, Chief Executive Officer
URL(s): www.eatingwell.com
Facebook: www.facebook.com/EatingWell
X (Twitter): x.com/EatingWell
Instagram: www.instagram.com/eatingwell
YouTube: www.youtube.com/@eatingwell
Pinterest: www.pinterest.com/eatingwell
Ed: Lisa Valente, Jim Romanoff, Victoria Seaver. **Released:** Quarterly **Price:** $25, for 4 issue; $14.99, for cover price. **Description:** Food magazine with emphasis on delicious low-fat cooking and sensible nutrition. **Availability:** Print; Online.

11583 ■ Journal of Culinary Science & Technology
Pub: Taylor & Francis Group (Journals)
Contact: Annie Callanan, Chief Executive Officer
URL(s): www.tandfonline.com/journals/wcsc20
Released: 6/year **Price:** $275, Individuals for print and online; $745, Institutions for print and online; $234, Individuals for online only; $745, Institutions for online only. **Description:** The Journal of Culinary Science & Technology covers current developments in fine and applied culinary science research. **Availability:** Print; Download; PDF; Online.

11584 ■ Journal of Nutrition (JN)
Pub: American Society for Nutrition
Contact: Paul M. Coates, President
URL(s): nutrition.org/publicationswww.elsmediakits.com/The%20Journal-of-Nutrition/TJNUT/2024
Released: Monthly **Description:** Peer-reviewed journal covering on all aspects of experimental nutrition. **Availability:** Print; PDF; Online.

11585 ■ Nutrition Today
Pub: Lippincott Williams & Wilkins
URL(s): journals.lww.com/nutritiontodayonline/pages/default.aspx
Facebook: www.facebook.com/100033470302155
X (Twitter): x.com/Ntjournalonline
Ed: Johanna Dwyer. **Released:** 6/year; volume 59 - issue 3. **Price:** $82, for print online training one year USA & Canada/Mexico; $98, for print online international & UK/Australia one year in training; $72, for

online intraning international & USA one year; $1,028, Institutions for print international & UK /Australia one year; $122, Individuals for online USA & international one year; $166, Individuals for print online Canada/Mexico one year; $300, Individuals for international print online one year; $257, Individuals for print online UK/Australia one year; $757, for print one year Canada/Mexico; $144, Individuals for print+ online USA one year; $1,012, Institutions for print USA one year. **Description:** Health science journal. **Availability:** Print; PDF; Online.

11586 ■ Topics in Clinical Nutrition (TICN)
Pub: Lippincott Williams & Wilkins
URL(s): journals.lww.com/topicsinclinicalnutrition/pages/default.aspx
Facebook: www.facebook.com/100028714222254/wall#!/pages/Topics-in-Clinical-Nutrition/124938497585061
X (Twitter): x.com/TCN_online
Released: Quarterly **Price:** $1,258, Institutions for print international, up//Australia 1 year; $144, Individuals for online 1 year US International; $288, Individuals for online 2 year US International; $432, Individuals for online 3 year US International; $142, for online 2 year In Training US; $213, for online 3 year In Training US; $71, for online 1 year In Training US; $1,231, Institutions for print 1 year Canada/Mexico; $1,357, Institutions for print 1 year International; $2,462, Institutions for print 2 year Canada/Mexico; $2,714, Institutions for print 2 year International; $3,693, Institutions for print 3 year Canada/Mexico; $4,071, Institutions for print 3 year International; $1,357, Institutions for print 1 year UK/Australia; $2,714, Institutions for print 2 year UK/Australia; $4,071, Institutions for print 3 year UK/Australia; $1,097, Institutions for print 1 year US; $2,194, Institutions for print 2 year US; $3,291, Institutions for print 3 year US. **Description:** Peer-reviewed journal addressing the challenges and problems of dietitians and others involved in dietary care in a health care setting. **Availability:** Print; PDF; Online.

TRADE SHOWS AND CONVENTIONS

11587 ■ ASPEN Nutrition Science & Practice Conference
American Society for Parenteral and Enteral Nutrition (ASPEN)
 8401 Colesville Rd., Ste. 510
 Silver Spring, MD 20910
Ph: (301)587-6315
Fax: (301)587-2365
Co. E-mail: aspen@nutritioncare.org
URL: http://www.nutritioncare.org
Contact: Gail A. Cresci, President
URL(s): www.nutritioncare.org/conference
Frequency: Annual. **Description:** Physicians, dietitians, nurses, pharmacists, and members of the industry. **Audience:** Industry professionals. **Principal Exhibits:** Physicians, dietitians, nurses, pharmacists, and members of the industry. Dates and Locations: 2025 Mar 22-25 Greater Columbus Convention Center, Columbus, OH. **Telecommunication Services:** aspen@nutritioncare.org.

11588 ■ Food Nutrition Conference Expo (FNCE)
Academy of Nutrition and Dietetics (AND)
 120 S Riverside Plz., Ste. 2190
 Chicago, IL 60606-6995
Ph: (312)899-0040
Free: 800-877-1600
URL: http://www.eatright.org
Contact: Kevin L. Sauer, President
URL(s): www.eatrightpro.org/events/fnce
X (Twitter): twitter.com/eatrightFNCE
Frequency: Annual; usually held in October. **Description:** Food products, food service equipment, nutrition supplements, health care books, resource materials, and computers. **Audience:** Dietitians, nutrition science researchers, policymakers, health-care providers and industry leaders. **Principal Exhibits:** Food products, food service equipment, nutrition

supplements, health care books, resource materials, and computers. Dates and Locations: 2025 Oct 11-14 Nashville, TN; 2026 Oct 24-27 San Antonio, TX; 2027 Oct 23-26 Washington, DC; 2028 Oct 07-10 Salt Lake City, UT; 2029 Oct 27-30 New Orleans, LA; 2030 Oct 12-15 Indianapolis, IN; 2031 Oct 25-28 Boston, MA. **Telecommunication Services:** fnce@corcexpo.com.

11589 ■ IFT Food Expo
Almond Board of California (ABC)
 1150 9th St., Ste. 1500
 Modesto, CA 95354
Ph: (209)549-8262
Fax: (209)549-8267
Co. E-mail: careers@almondboard.com
URL: http://www.almonds.com
Contact: Richard Waycott, President
URL(s): www.iftevent.org/attend/about
Price: $380, Pre-registered, members; $620, Pre-registered, non-members. **Frequency:** Annual; held between Monday through Wednesday. **Description:** Includes food exposition. **Audience:** Industry professionals. **Principal Exhibits:** Includes food exposition. Dates and Locations: 2025 Jul 13-16; 2026 Jul 12-15; 2027 Jul 11-14; 2028 Jul 09-12; 2029 Jul 15-18; 2030 Jul 14-17. McCormick Place, Chicago, IL. **Telecommunication Services:** info@ift.org.

11590 ■ School Nutrition Industry Conference (SNIC)
School Nutrition Association (SNA)
 2900 S Quincy St., Ste. 700
 Arlington, VA 22206
Ph: (703)824-3000
Fax: (703)824-3015
Co. E-mail: servicecenter@schoolnutrition.org
URL: http://schoolnutrition.org
Contact: Beth Wallace, President
URL(s): https://schoolnutrition.org/conferences-events/school-nutrition-industry-conference
Frequency: Annual. **Description:** With networking opportunity and educational programs. **Audience:** Industry professionals. **Principal Exhibits:** With networking opportunity and educational programs. Dates and Locations: 2025 Jan 19-21 Phoenix, AZ; 2026 Jan 11-13 Austin, TX; 2027 Jan 10-12 Tampa, FL; 2028 Jan 23-25 San Diego, CA.

11591 ■ Society for Nutrition Education and Behavior Annual Conference
Society for Nutrition Education and Behavior (SNEB)
 3502 Woodview Trace, Ste. 300
 Indianapolis, IN 46268
Ph: (317)328-4627
Free: 800-235-6690
Fax: (317)280-8527
Co. E-mail: info@sneb.org
URL: http://www.sneb.org
Contact: Nicole Brandt, Executive Director
E-mail: nbrandt@sneb.org
URL(s): www.sneb.org/sneb-2024
Price: $405, SNEB Member; $505, Professional Member; $540, Non-members; $225, SNEB Student Member; $265, Student Member; $300, Non-Member Student; $250, One Day for SNEB Member; $305, One Day for Non-Member; $120, Student Day One Day. **Frequency:** Annual. **Description:** Nutrition-related, for educating the public and educators. **Audience:** Nutrition educators, dietitians, public health professionals, home economists, food service personnel, university and high school faculty. **Principal Exhibits:** Nutrition-related, for educating the public and educators. **Telecommunication Services:** info@sneb.org.

11592 ■ Soho Expo
Southeast National Products Association (SENPA)
 5946 Main St.
 New Port Richey, FL 34652
Ph: (727)846-0320
Fax: (800)545-1374
URL: http://www.southeastnpa.org
Contact: Michelle Dufresne, President
URL(s): www.senpa.org/soho-expo.html
Frequency: Annual; held on first weekend in December. **Description:** Nutritional foods and related equipment, supplies, and services. **Audience:** Buyers,

retailers and business professionals. **Principal Exhibits:** Nutritional foods and related equipment, supplies, and services. **Telecommunication Services:** soho@southeastnpa.org.

11593 ■ SupplySide East
URL(s): east.supplysideshow.com/en/home.html
Frequency: Annual. **Description:** Features ingredients, solutions, and information for nutrition-based beverages and meals prominent in the health and nutrition industry. **Principal Exhibits:** Features ingredients, solutions, and information for nutrition-based beverages and meals prominent in the health and nutrition industry.

CONSULTANTS

11594 ■ Center for Lifestyle Enhancement-Columbia Medical Center of Plano
3901 West 15th St
 Plano, TX 75075
Ph: (972)596-6800
Fax: (972)519-1299
URL: http://medicalcityplano.com
Contact: Erol R. Akdamar, President
Facebook: www.facebook.com/medicalcityplano
X (Twitter): twitter.com/MedCityPlano
Description: Firm provides professional health counseling in the areas of general nutrition for weight management, eating disorders, diabetic education, cholesterol reduction and adolescent weight management. Offers work site health promotion and preventive services. Also coordinates speaker's bureau, cooking classes and physician referrals. **Scope:** Firm provides professional health counseling in the areas of general nutrition for weight management, eating disorders, diabetic education, cholesterol reduction and adolescent weight management. Offers work site health promotion and preventive services. Also coordinates speaker's bureau, cooking classes and physician referrals. **Founded:** 1975. **Training:** Rx Diet and Exercise; Smoking Cessation; Stress Management; Health Fairs; Fitness Screenings; Body Composition; Nutrition Analysis; Exercise Classes; Prenatal Nutrition; SHAPEDOWN; Successfully Managing Diabetes; Gourmet Foods for Your Heart; The Aging Heart; Heart Smart Saturday featuring Day of Dance; Weight-Loss Management Seminars; The Right Stroke for Men; Peripheral Artery Disease Screening; Menstruation: The Cycle Begins; Boot Camp for New Dads; Grand parenting 101: Caring for Kids Today; Teddy Bear C New Baby Day C Safe Sitter Babysitting Class.

11595 ■ Debra F. Latimer Nutrition and Diabetes Associates L.L.C.
6300 W Loop., S Ste. 333
 Bellaire, TX 77401
Contact: Debra F. Latimer, President
Description: Provider of nutritional consultancy services like fitness, diet, diabetes control. **Scope:** Provider of nutritional consultancy services like fitness, diet, diabetes control. **Training:** Diabetes-Self Management and Training Program, Houston, Jul, 2007; Preventive and Treatment Plans for Cardiac Care; Pre and Post-natal Nutrition; Pre-menstrual Syndrome; Eating for the Health of It; Weight Management and Wellness Program; Supermarket Nutrition Tours; Diabetes education and training. The Diabetes-Self Management and Education Program.

11596 ■ Krumkill Stables
c/o Jean Bigaouette, 460 Krumkill Rd.
 Albany, NY 12203
Ph: (518)482-8704
URL: http://www.krumkillstables.com/home
Contact: Jean Bigaouette, Contact
Description: Firm provides training, trail ride, and camping services. **Scope:** Firm provides training, trail ride, and camping services.

11597 ■ Marisa Moore Nutrition, LLC
2625 Piedmont Rd., Ste. 56-160
 Atlanta, GA 30324
Co. E-mail: questions@marisamoore.com

URL: http://marisamoore.com
Contact: Marisa Moore, Contact
E-mail: marisa@marisamoore.com
Facebook: www.facebook.com/MarisaMooreNutrition
X (Twitter): x.com/marisamoore
Instagram: www.instagram.com/MarisaMoore
Pinterest: www.pinterest.com/marisamoore
Description: Food and nutrition expert working on the business side of health and wellness. Works with startups, chefs, food vendors, marketers, food scientists, brand managers, nutritionists, and researchers.

FRANCHISES AND BUSINESS OPPORTUNITIES

11598 ■ The Dentist's Choice, Inc. (TDC)
246 W Shaw Ave.
 Fresno, CA 93704
Contact: Steven Paganetti, Contact
Description: Provider of dental hand piece rebuild, repair and maintenance services and also retailer of dental hand piece models. **Founded:** 1994. **Financial Assistance:** Yes **Training:** Provides 1 week at headquarters and ongoing support.

11599 ■ Discount Sport Nutrition (DSN)
7324 Gaston Ave., Ste. No. 124-422
 Dallas, TX 75214
Ph: (972)489-7925
Free: 833-GET-SWOLE
Fax: (214)292-8619
Co. E-mail: sales@sportsupplements.com
URL: http://www.sportsupplements.com
Contact: Charles Moser, President
Facebook: www.facebook.com/DiscountSportsNutrition
X (Twitter): x.com/DSNutrition
Instagram: www.instagram.com/DSNTULSA
YouTube: www.youtube.com/user/dsnspor
tsupplements
Description: Nutritional sport supplements retail store. **No. of Franchise Units:** 6. **Founded:** 1998. **Franchised:** 2000. **Equity Capital Needed:** $92,774-$185,344. **Franchise Fee:** $25,000. **Financial Assistance:** Yes **Training:** 3 phase initial hands on training program located at current stores, as well as your location. Provides assistance with site location, leases, layout design, suppliers, advertising, marketing, and ongoing assistance.

11600 ■ GNC Holdings, Inc.
Harbin Pharmaceutical Group Co. Ltd. (HPGC)
 300 Sixth Ave.
 Pittsburgh, PA 15222
Ph: 86 451 51870077
Free: 400-900-1111
Fax: 86 451 51870277
URL: http://www.hayao.com
Contact: Rachel Jones, Vice President
Facebook: www.facebook.com/GNCLiveWell
X (Twitter): x.com/GNCLiveWell
Instagram: www.instagram.com/gnclivewell
YouTube: www.youtube.com/user/GNCvids
Pinterest: www.pinterest.com/gnclivewell
Description: Operates as a retailer of health and wellness products including vitamins, minerals, and herbal supplement, sports nutrition and diet products. **Founded:** 1935. **Training:** Training and support provided.

11601 ■ The Hungry Heart
28202 Cabot Rd., Ste. 300
 Laguna Niguel, CA 92677
Ph: (949)887-2600
Free: 877-486-4797
Co. E-mail: questions@thehungryheart.org
URL: http://thehungryheart.org
Contact: Lauren Grant, President
Facebook: www.facebook.com/TheHungryHeart
Description: A caring approach to out of control eating. **Founded:** 1996. **Franchised:** 2006. **Training:** Yes.

COMPUTERIZED DATABASES

11602 ■ Health & Wellness InSite
Type: Full-text.

LIBRARIES

11603 ■ Abbott Nutrition Manufacturing Inc. - Library
Abbott Laboratories
 100 Abbott Pk. Rd.
 Abbott Park, IL 60064
Ph: (224)667-6100
Co. E-mail: reach@abbott.com
URL: http://www.abbott.com
Contact: Robert B. Ford, Chief Executive Officer
Facebook: www.facebook.com/Abbott
Linkedin: www.linkedin.com/company/abbott-
X (Twitter): x.com/AbbottNews
YouTube: www.youtube.com/c/abbott
Description: Manufacturer of nutritional and healthcare products for adults, infant and new mothers, therapeutic, and much more. **Scope:** Nutrition. **Founded:** 1903. **Holdings:** Figures not available.

11604 ■ Academy of Nutrition and Dietetics (AND) - Library
120 S Riverside Plz., Ste. 2190
 Chicago, IL 60606-6995
Ph: (312)899-0040
Free: 800-877-1600
URL: http://www.eatright.org
Contact: Kevin L. Sauer, President
X (Twitter): x.com/eatright
YouTube: www.youtube.com/user/EatRightTV
Pinterest: www.pinterest.com/kidseatright
Description: Represents food and nutrition professionals. Promotes nutrition, health and well-being. **Scope:** Food and nutrition. **Services:** Library not open to the public. **Founded:** 1917. **Holdings:** Figures not available. **Publications:** *Weight Loss Matters: Your Weight and Your Health Pamphlet*; *Find a Nutrition Professional Consumer Search*; *Directory of Columbus Registered Dietitians*; *Directory of Registered Dietitians*; *Directory of Dietetics Programs* (Annual); *Directory of Consulting Dietitians in Private Practice*; *Journal of the Academy of Nutrition and Dietetics* (Monthly). **Educational Activities:** Food Nutrition Conference Expo (FNCE) (Annual).

11605 ■ American Institute for Biosocial and Medical Research (AIBMR) - Library [AIBMR Life Sciences, Inc.]
Seattle, WA
Co. E-mail: info@aibmr.com
URL: http://aibmr.com
Contact: Dr. Alexander Schauss, Senior Director Founder
Description: Offers natural products and nutraceutical consulting specializing in the areas of scientific research coordination, regulatory compliance, research consulting and product development. Offers the service of technical writing for product dossiers, evaluation of scientific literature, research reports and manuscript preparation. Industries served: insurance companies, hospitals, federal, state and local government agencies, colleges and universities, food processors, food distributors, food manufacturers, and informational database developers. **Scope:** Offers natural products and nutraceutical consulting specializing in the areas of scientific research coordination, regulatory compliance, research consulting and product development. Offers the service of technical writing for product dossiers, evaluation of scientific literature, research reports and manuscript preparation. Industries served: insurance companies, hospitals, federal, state and local government agencies, colleges and universities, food processors, food distributors, food manufacturers, and informational database developers. **Services:** Library not open to the public. **Founded:** 1978. **Subscriptions:** 500 journals and other serials. **Publications:** "Probiotic metabolites from Bacillus coagulans GanedenBC30 support maturation of antigen-presenting cells in vitro," Apr, 2012; "Mitigation of Inflammation with

Foods," Apr, 2012; "Effect of the novel low molecular weight hydrolyzed chicken sternal cartilage extract, BioCell Collagen, on improving osteoarthritis-related symptoms: a randomized, double-blind, placebo-controlled trial," Apr, 2012; "SupplySide Insights - R and D," Apr, 2012; "Efficacy and tolerability assessment of a topical formulation containing copper sulfate and hypericum perforatum on patients with herpes skin lesions: a comparative, randomized controlled trial," Feb, 2012; "Safety evaluation of a proprietary food-grade, dried fermentate preparation of Saccharomyces cerevisiae," Jan, 2012; "The effect of ergothioneine on clastogenic potential and mutagenic activity: genotoxicity evaluation," Aug, 2011; "One-year chronic oral toxicity with combined reproduction toxicSafety aspects and cholesterol-lowering efficacy of chitosan tablets.Safety aspects and cholesterol-lowering efficacy of chitosan tablets. study of a novel probiotic, Bacillus coagulans, as a food ingredient," May, 2011; "Evaluation of the safety of the dietary antioxidant ergothioneine using the bacterial reverse mutation assay," Jan, 2010; "Single- and repeated-dose oral toxicity studies of citicoline freebase (choline cytidine 5'-pyrophosphate) in Sprague-Dawley rats," Nov, 2009 Safety assessment of a proprietary preparation of a novel Probiotic, Bacillus coagulans, as a food ingredient," Jun, 2009; "Absorption, uptake and tissue affinity of high-molecular-weight hyaluronan after oral administration in rats and dogs," Nov, 2008; "In vitro and in vivo antioxidant and anti-inflammatory capacities of an antioxidant-rich fruit and berry juice blend. Results of a pilot and randomized, double-blinded, placebo-controlled, crossover study," Sep, 2008; Safety aspects and cholesterol-lowering efficacy of chitosan tablets," Feb, 2008; "Acai (Euterpe oleracea): An Extraordinary Antioxidant-Rich Palm Fruit from the Amazon," Alexander G. Schauss, Aug, 2008; "Feed My Brain," Alexander Schauss, Dec, 2004.

11606 ■ Bastyr University Library
14500 Juanita Dr., NE
  Kenmore, WA 98028
Ph: (425)602-3020
Co. E-mail: library@bastyr.edu
URL: http://bastyr.libguides.com/home
Contact: Ekaterini Papadopoulou, Director
E-mail: epapadopoulou@bastyr.edu
URL(s): www.bastyr.edu/student-life/library
Facebook: www.facebook.com/BastyrUniversity
X (Twitter): x.com/bastyr
Scope: Education; natural health arts; science. **Services:** Interlibrary loan; copying; library open to the public for reference use only. **Founded:** 1980. **Holdings:** DVDs; eBooks; journals.

11607 ■ Beech-Nut Nutrition Corp. - Library
Hero Gruppe
  1 Nutritious Pl.
  Amsterdam, NY 12010
Ph: 41 62 885-5111
Co. E-mail: info@hero.ch
URL: http://www.hero-group.ch
Contact: Ashley LeBlanc, Manager
Facebook: www.facebook.com/beechnutfoods
X (Twitter): x.com/beechnutfoods
Instagram: www.instagram.com/beechnutfoods
YouTube: www.youtube.com/user/beechnutfoods
Pinterest: www.pinterest.com/beechnutfoods
Description: Manufacturing: Infant and toddler food, including cereals, beverages and canned fruits, vegetables and meals. **Scope:** Food; babies. **Founded:** 1891. **Holdings:** Figures not available.

11608 ■ Campbell Soup Company Research Information Center
1 Campbell Pl.
  Camden, NJ 08103-1701
Ph: (856)342-4800
Free: 800-257-8443
URL: http://www.campbellsoupcompany.com
Contact: Mark A. Clouse, President
Facebook: www.facebook.com/campbells
Linkedin: www.linkedin.com/company/campbell-soup
  -company/about
X (Twitter): x.com/CampbellSoupCo
Instagram: www.instagram.com/campbellsoupco

YouTube: www.youtube.com/campbellsoup
Scope: Food technology, biochemistry, microbiology, nutrition. **Services:** Interlibrary loan; library not open to the public. **Founded:** 1869. **Holdings:** 5000 books; 2200 bound periodical volumes; 3500 patents.

11609 ■ Case Western Reserve University (CMLA) - Cleveland Health Sciences Library
11000 Euclid Ave.
  Cleveland, OH 44106
Ph: (216)368-3643
Co. E-mail: chslreference@case.edu
URL: http://case.edu/chslibrary
Contact: Jessica DeCaro, Director
E-mail: jessica.decaro@case.edu
Scope: Health science. **Services:** Interlibrary loan; copying; SDI; scanning and digitization; library open to the public for reference use only. **Founded:** 1965. **Holdings:** 4,30,000 books and journal volumes.

11610 ■ Geisinger Medical Center (GMC) - Health Sciences Library
100 N Academy Ave.
  Danville, PA 17822
Ph: (570)271-6211
URL: http://www.geisinger.org/patient-care/find-a-loca
  tion/geisinger-medical-center
Description: Community radio station currently operating out of the French Quarter in New Orleans. **Scope:** Medical. **Services:** Library not open to public. **Founded:** 1996. **Holdings:** Figures not available.

11611 ■ General Mills, Inc.
General Mills, Inc.
  1 General Mills Blvd.
  Minneapolis, MN 55426
Ph: (763)764-7600
Free: 800-248-7310
Fax: (763)764-2268
Co. E-mail: corporate.response@generalmills.com
URL: http://www.generalmills.com
Contact: Jeffrey L. Harmening, Chief Executive Officer
Facebook: www.facebook.com/GeneralMills
Linkedin: www.linkedin.com/company/general-mills
X (Twitter): twitter.com/generalmills
Instagram: www.instagram.com/generalmills/
YouTube: www.youtube.com/user/generalmills
Description: Producer and distributor of branded consumer foods sold through retail stores. **Founded:** 1866. **Educational Activities:** GSF West; Natural Products Expo East (Annual); Natural Products Expo West (Annual). **Awards:** Pillsbury Bake-Off® Contest (Annual).

11612 ■ The Gottesman Libraries at Teachers College
Columbia University, Russell Hall
  525 W 120th St.
  New York, NY 10027
Ph: (212)755-3144
Co. E-mail: library@tc.columbia.edu
URL: http://library.tc.columbia.edu
Facebook: www.facebook.com/
  teacherscollegecolumbia
X (Twitter): x.com/teacherscollege
Instagram: www.instagram.com/teacherscollege
YouTube: www.youtube.com/teacherscollege
Description: Resources which are primarily electronic and accessible on and off campus, have been selected as ones relevant to the focus of the practicum. **Scope:** Educational material. **Services:** Interlibrary loan; consultations; copying. **Founded:** 1887. **Holdings:** 500,000 monograph and serial volumes; 224,227 microforms; 6,679 nonprint materials; 3,694 cubic feet of manuscript material; 93,639 photographs; 8,361 titles in microform; 5,251 computer files; sound recordings; 65 cartographic; 2,345 graphic; 1,488 audio; 2,781 film and video. **Subscriptions:** journals.

11613 ■ Kellanova - Information Center
Kellanova
  One Kellogg Square, PO Box 3599
  Battle Creek, MI 49016-3599
Ph: (269)961-2000
Free: 800-962-1413

Co. E-mail: investor.relations@kellogg.com
URL: http://www.kelloggcompany.com
Contact: Steven Cahillane, Chief Executive Officer
URL(s): www.kelloggs.com
Facebook: www.facebook.com/KelloggsCareers
Linkedin: www.linkedin.com/company/kellogg-com
  pany/
X (Twitter): twitter.com/KelloggCompany
YouTube: https://www.youtube.com/user/KelloggsUS
Pinterest: https://in.pinterest.com/kelloggs/
Description: Producer and wholesaler of ready-to-eat cereal, snack, and convenience foods. **Scope:** Food science and nutrition. **Services:** Document delivery (for Kellogg employees); center not open to the public. **Founded:** 1906. **Holdings:** 3000 books. **Subscriptions:** 115 journals and other serials.

11614 ■ Le Cordon Bleu College of Culinary Arts Library
350 Rhode Island St.
  San Francisco, CA 94103
URL: http://www.careered.com/closedschool/loca
  tions
Scope: Culinary arts; nutrition; restaurant and hospitality industry. **Services:** Library open to the public by special appointment only. **Founded:** 1989. **Holdings:** 3,500 books.

11615 ■ Lemmen-Holton Cancer Pavilion Library
145 Michigan St. NE
  Grand Rapids, MI 49503
Ph: (616)486-5700
URL: http://findadoctor.spectrumhealth.org/location/
  profile/7989
Description: Provide a full range of cancer services including, prevention, screening and diagnosis, personalized cancer treatment, integrative therapies, supportive care services, access to clinical trials and leading edge technology. **Scope:** Medicine; literature. **Holdings:** Books.

11616 ■ National Eating Disorder Information Centre (NEDIC) - Library
200 Elizabeth St., ES 7-421
  Toronto, ON, Canada M5G 2C4
Ph: (416)340-4156
Free: 866-633-4220
Co. E-mail: nedic@uhn.ca
URL: http://nedic.ca
Contact: Suzanne Phillips, Program Manager
E-mail: suzanne.phillips@uhn.ca
Facebook: www.facebook.com/thenedic
X (Twitter): x.com/theNEDIC
Instagram: www.instagram.com/the_nedic
YouTube: www.youtube.com/user/nedic85
Description: Provides information and resources on causes, symptoms of, and therapeutic and health care treatments for eating disorders and the preoccupation with food and weight. Aims to raise awareness on eating disorders through conducting lectures and workshops. **Scope:** Eating disorders. **Holdings:** Figures not available. **Educational Activities:** Eating Disorder Awareness Week (EDAW) (Annual). **Geographic Preference:** National.

11617 ■ Price-Pottenger Nutrition Foundation (PPNF) - Library [Health and Healing Wisdom; PPNF]
7890 Broadway
  Lemon Grove, CA 91945
Ph: (619)462-7600
Free: 800-366-3748
Co. E-mail: info@price-pottenger.org
URL: http://price-pottenger.org
Contact: Mark Bielsky, President
Facebook: www.facebook.com/pricepottenger
Linkedin: www.linkedin.com/company/price-pottenger
  -nutrition-foundation
Instagram: www.instagram.com/pricepottenger
YouTube: www.youtube.com/user/PricePottengerNF
Description: Seeks to increase awareness of natural health, organic gardening, nutrition and ecology. Disseminates information to the medical and dental professions, as well as to the public, through publications, seminars, classes, study groups, and scientific

exhibits. Stresses the benefits of chemically-untreated "whole" foods. Named in honor of Weston A. Price, DDS and Francis M. Pottenger, Jr., MD, known for their work in nutrition research. Publishes nutritional books. Reaches market through direct mail and wholesalers. **Scope:** Health, organic gardening, nutrition, and the environment. **Founded:** 1952. **Holdings:** 5,000 health books. **Publications:** *Price-Pottenger Journal of Health and Healing* (Quarterly). **Geographic Preference:** Multinational.

11618 ■ Tufts University - Hirsh Health Sciences Library (HHSL)
145 Harrison Ave.
  Boston, MA 02111
Ph: (617)636-6705
Fax: (617)636-3805
Co. E-mail: hhsl@tufts.edu
URL: http://hirshlibrary.tufts.edu
Contact: Eric Albright, Director
E-mail: eric.albright@tufts.edu
Facebook: www.facebook.com/hirshlibrary
X (Twitter): x.com/tuftshhsl
Scope: Health resources. **Services:** Interlibrary loan; copying; library open to the public. **Founded:** 1973. **Holdings:** books; articles; Volumes; print.

11619 ■ U.S.D.A. Agricultural Research Service (USDA ARS) - Western Regional Research Center (WRRC) - Library
800 Buchanan St.
  Albany, CA 94710
URL: http://www.ars.usda.gov/pacific-west-area/albany-ca/wrrc
Contact: William Orts, Director (Acting)
E-mail: bill.orts@ars.usda.gov
Description: It consists of books, magazines, journals, and newsletters on agriculture. **Scope:** Cereals; fruits and vegetables; field and industrial crops; food technology; chemistry; nutrition. **Founded:** 1940. **Holdings:** Figures not available.

11620 ■ U.S.D.A. National Agricultural Library (NAL) - Food and Nutrition Information Center (FNIC)
10301 Baltimore Ave.
  Beltsville, MD 20705
Ph: (301)504-5414
URL: http://www.nal.usda.gov/programs/fnic
Contact: James Cain, Contact
E-mail: james.cain@usda.gov
Scope: Food; human nutrition education. **Services:** library not open to the public. **Founded:** 1977. **Holdings:** Figures not available.

11621 ■ U.S. Food & Drug Administration Biosciences Library (FDA) - Center for Food Safety and Applied Nutrition Branch Library (CFSAN) [FDA]
5001 Campus Dr., HFS-009
  College Park, MD 20740-3835
Free: 888-723-3366
URL: http://www.fda.gov/about-fda/fda-organization/center-food-safety-and-applied-nutrition-cfsan
Contact: Dr. Susan T. Mayne, Director
Scope: Food technology; nutrition; cosmetics. **Services:** Interlibrary loan; Library open to the public. **Founded:** 1961. **Holdings:** Printed material; Videos. **Subscriptions:** 100 journals and other serials.

11622 ■ University of California, Berkeley - Marian Koshland Bioscience, Natural Resources & Public Health Library
2101 Valley Life Sciences Bldg.
  Berkeley, CA 94720-6500
Ph: (510)642-2531
Fax: (510)642-8217
Co. E-mail: bios@library.berkeley.edu

URL: http://www.lib.berkeley.edu/visit/bioscience
Contact: Brian Quigley, Head
E-mail: bquigley@berkeley.edu
Facebook: www.facebook.com/ucberkeleylibrary
X (Twitter): x.com/ucberkeleylib
Instagram: www.instagram.com/ucberkeleylibrary
YouTube: www.youtube.com/channel/UCrwP3Cw1FHwqslSAG5JkLTQ
Scope: Agriculture; anatomy; botany; cell biology; environmental sciences; molecular biology; biology; nutrition; pest management; physiology; forestry; entomology; paleontology. **Services:** Interlibrary loan (through General Library); copying; library open to the public for reference use with restricted circulation; printing; scanning. **Founded:** 1930. **Holdings:** 542,000 volumes; 50,633 pamphlets and reprints; 1,543 reels of microfilm; 24,005 microfiche.

11623 ■ University of Hawaii - John A. Burns School of Medicine Health Sciences Library
651 Ilalo St., MEB 101
  Honolulu, HI 96813
Ph: (808)692-0810
Fax: (808)692-1244
Co. E-mail: hslinfo@hawaii.edu
URL: http://hslib.jabsom.hawaii.edu
Contact: Kristen Anderson, Director
E-mail: krisa@hawaii.edu
Facebook: www.facebook.com/hslibjabsom
Instagram: www.instagram.com/jabsom.library
YouTube: www.youtube.com/channel/UCakn9yk5kzGeEwgrfXec7tQ/playlists
Description: Serves as an information resource not only for the John A. Burns School of Medicine, but also for the University of Hawai'i at Mānoa campus, the UH system, and the State. **Scope:** Clinical science. **Services:** Interlibrary loan; printing; library open to the public. **Founded:** 1968. **Holdings:** E-books; e-journal.

11624 ■ University of Nebraska-Lincoln - Dinsdale Family Learning Commons - Library
1625 N 38th St., E Campus
  University of Nebraska-Lincoln
  Lincoln, NE 68583-0717
Ph: (402)472-4401
URL: http://libraries.unl.edu/dinsdale-family-learning-commons
Contact: Gayleen Hill, Contact
E-mail: ghill1@unl.edu
Scope: Agriculture. **Services:** Copying; library open to the public; Wi-Fi; printing; copying; scanning. **Founded:** 1964. **Holdings:** Figures not available.

RESEARCH CENTERS

11625 ■ Columbia University College of Physicians and Surgeons - Institute of Human Nutrition (IHN)
630 W 168 St. PH15E-1512
  New York, NY 10032
Ph: (212)305-4808
Co. E-mail: nutrition@cumc.columbia.edu
URL: http://www.ihn.cuimc.columbia.edu
Contact: Dr. Sabrina Diano, Director
E-mail: sd3449@cumc.columbia.edu
Facebook: www.facebook.com/InstituteHumanNutrition
Linkedin: www.linkedin.com/in/institute-of-human-nutrition-2a6360173
X (Twitter): twitter.com/ColumbiaIhn
Instagram: www.instagram.com/columbia.ihn/
YouTube: www.youtube.com/channel/UCCfMkv0yUN-dye_Jk49fT-w

Description: Integral unit of College of Physicians and Surgeons at Columbia University, jointly operated by its Post-Graduate Education Division and Division of Basic Sciences, located at Columbia-Presbyterian Medical Center. **Scope:** Atherosclerosis, lipoprotein-receptor-cell interaction; lipid emulsion metabolism; free fatty acids and cell lipid metabolism; basic retinoid and vitamin A physiology, biochemistry, and molecular biology; food and nutrition policy and law; intestinal ion transport mechanisms; enteric nervous system; human lipoprotein metabolism; lipolytic enzymes and endothelial cell biology; atherosclerosis; mineral metabolism and toxicology; carbohydrate and lipid metabolism, obesity, diabetes mellitus, food intake regulation; calcium metabolism; vascular cell biology; pathogenesis of thrombosis; regulation of intracellular cholesterol metabolism; endocytic pathways in macrophages; Cholesteryl ester transfer; protein structure/function and mutagenesis; regulation of gene expression; molecular nutrition; molecular mechanisms of carcinogenesis. **Founded:** 1957.

11626 ■ Ohio State University - Wilbur A. Gould Food Industries Center
2015 Fyffe Rd.
  Columbus, OH 43210
Ph: (614)292-7004
Free: 800-752-2751
Fax: (614)688-5459
Co. E-mail: osufic@osu.edu
URL: http://foodindustries.osu.edu
Contact: Dr. Valente Alvarez, Director
Description: Integral unit of Ohio State University, but with its own advisory board. **Scope:** Food industries (plant and animal products), including technology, processing, engineering, marketing, food service, and food science and nutrition. Serves as the focal point of food activities on campus, including University-food industry cooperation, research coordination, and service programs. Maintains the Endowed Chair in Food Industries. **Founded:** 1982. **Publications:** *FIC Annual Reports*; *FIC Bulletins*; *Newsletter Quarterly* (Quarterly). **Educational Activities:** Better Process Control School, Hands-on basic training in laboratory techniques and skills.; FIC Seminars, Offer exemplary teaching programs.

11627 ■ University of Florida - Institute of Food and Agricultural Sciences - Center for Nutritional Sciences
PO Box 11018
  Gainesville, FL 32611-0180
Ph: (352)392-1971
URL: http://fshn.ifas.ufl.edu/center-for-nutritional-sciences
Contact: Dr. Robert J. Cousins, Director
E-mail: cousins@ufl.edu
Description: Integral unit of University of Florida but operating under its own board of control. **Scope:** Nutritional science research center. **Founded:** 1985. **Educational Activities:** Center for Nutritional Sciences Graduate Research Assistantships, To support a campus-wide initiative to bring together scientists and faculty from multiple disciplines whose research and academic interests include nutrition.; Center for Nutritional Sciences Seminars (Irregular), For nutritional sciences research and studies.

11628 ■ University of Texas Southwestern Medical Center at Dallas - Center for Human Nutrition
5323 Harry Hines Blvd.
  Dallas, TX 75390
URL: http://www.utsouthwestern.edu/education/medical-school/departments/center-human-nutrition
Contact: Dr. Jay Horton, Director
Description: Integral unit of University of Texas Southwestern Medical Center at Dallas. **Scope:** Human nutrition. Investigates the preventive effects of vitamins C and E on atherosclerosis. **Founded:** 1943.

ASSOCIATIONS AND OTHER ORGANIZATIONS

11629 ■ Business and Institutional Furniture Manufacturer's Association (BIFMA)
678 Front Ave. NW, Ste. 150
Grand Rapids, MI 49504-5368
Ph: (616)285-3963
Co. E-mail: email@bifma.org
URL: http://www.bifma.org
Contact: Deirdre Jimenez, President
E-mail: djimenez@bifma.org
Facebook: www.facebook.com/bifmaHQ
X (Twitter): x.com/BIFMA
Instagram: www.instagram.com/bifma_hq
Description: Organized group of furniture manufacturers and suppliers addressing issues of common concern to the contract furnishings industry. Works to develop, expand, and promote work environments that enhance the productivity and comfort of customers. **Founded:** 1973. **Publications:** *The Download, BIFMA International* (Quarterly). **Educational Activities:** BIFMA Leadership Conference (Annual). **Geographic Preference:** National.

11630 ■ International Interior Design Association (IIDA)
111 E Wacker Dr., Ste. 222
Chicago, IL 60601
Ph: (312)467-1950
Free: 888-799-4432
Co. E-mail: iidahq@iida.org
URL: http://iida.org
Contact: Cheryl S. Durst, Chief Executive Officer
Facebook: www.facebook.com/IIDAHQ
Linkedin: www.linkedin.com/company/iida
X (Twitter): x.com/IIDA_HQ
Instagram: www.instagram.com/iida_hq
Description: Represents professional interior designers, including designers of commercial, healthcare, hospitality, government, retail, residential facilities; educators; researchers; representatives of allied manufacturing sources. Conducts research, student programs and continuing education programs for members. Has developed a code of ethics for the professional design membership. **Founded:** 1994. **Publications:** *GRAction.* **Geographic Preference:** Multinational.

11631 ■ MTM Association for Standards and Research [Methods Time Measurements Association for Standards and Research]
Elbchaussee 352
22609 Hamburg, Germany
URL: http://mtm.org/en/mtm-standard/mtm-standard
Contact: Dr. Peter Kuhlang, Managing Director
E-mail: peter.kuhlang@mtm.org
Description: Provides information on fatigue, optimum methods of performance, the effect of practice on motion performance, and the use of motion information for determining allowances and predicting total performance time. **Scope:** Work measurement techniques and productivity improvement. Activities focus on human motion, including internal studies concerned with velocity, acceleration, tension, and control characteristics of a given motion under several conditions. **Founded:** 1951. **Publications:** *Research Reports Monograph Series.* **Educational Activities:** MTM-CNM Family Conference (Biennial), To equip families with the conections and resources. **Geographic Preference:** National.

REFERENCE WORKS

11632 ■ "100 Brilliant Companies" in Entrepreneur (May 2014)
Pub: Entrepreneur Media Inc.
Contact: Dan Bova, Director
E-mail: dbova@entrepreneur.com
Description: Entrepreneur magazine annually selects 100 companies, ideas, innovations and applications which the editors feel offer unique, simple and high-tech solutions to various everyday problems. These may include design developments, innovations in wearable gadgets, travel applications and other new ideas which represent 21st Century breakthroughs and thinking outside the box. The list is divided into ten categories, including Fashion, The Human Factor, and Travel and Transportation. **Availability:** Online.

11633 ■ "Co-Working a Hit in Seattle Market" in Puget Sound Business Journal (Vol. 34, March 14, 2014, No. 48, pp. 8)
Pub: American City Business Journals, Inc.
Contact: Mike Olivieri, Executive Vice President
Released: Weekly. **Price:** $4, introductory 4-week offer(Digital & Print). **Description:** Companies in Seattle, Washington are learning about the new trend in co-working. The city's co-working industry continues to grow, which is why competitors have established a trade group. Co-working is the process of sharing office space within business centers. Regus, which manages 21 business centers in the city, plans to introduce private booths called WorkBoxes. **Availability:** Print; Online.

11634 ■ "Declutter Your Office by Updating Your Personal Tech" in Entrepreneur (May 2014)
Pub: Entrepreneur Media Inc.
Contact: Dan Bova, Director
E-mail: dbova@entrepreneur.com
Description: Office designers provide tips for organizing the shared office space model. Jessica Mowery of MOW Design Studio emphasizes the importance of employee productivity while making changes that result in more efficient and motivated people. Sonya Dufner of Gensler says they design with flexibility while making sure that the office space will work for clients in the long term. Some suggested solutions for decluttering the office are the HP Officejet Pro 8600 e-All-In-One Printer, David Hsu's Desk 117 and Herman Miller's SAYL Work Chair with Suspension Back. **Availability:** Print; Online.

11635 ■ "Designing an Office Around Your Company's Goals How Eventbrite Learned That a Workspace Becomes Much More Than an Office Once Your Team Weighs In" in Inc. (Vol. 36, September 2014, No. 7, pp. 122)
Pub: Mansueto Ventures L.L.C.
Contact: Stephanie Mehta, Chief Executive Officer
Released: September 2014. **Description:** Julia Hartz, co-founder and president of an online ticketing and event planning service, Eventbrite, shares insight into designing her firm's new office space. She opened suggestions from all employees to come up with the right environment to suit her workers. **Availability:** Print; Online.

11636 ■ "Evolutionary Psychology in the Business Sciences"
Pub: Springer Publishing Co.
Contact: Bernhard Springer, Founder
Released: First edition. **Description:** All individuals operating in the business sphere share a common biological heritage, including consumers, employers, employees, entrepreneurs, or financial traders, to name a few. The evolutionary behavioral sciences and specific business contexts including marketing, consumer behavior, advertising, innovation and creativity and invention, intertemporal choice, negotiations, competition and cooperation in organizational settings, sex differences in workplace patterns, executive leadership, business ethics, store and office design, behavioral decision making, and electronic communications and commerce are all addressed. **Availability:** E-book; Print.

11637 ■ "Glenmede at Liberty To Show Off Space" in Philadelphia Business Journal (Vol. 32, January 24, 2014, No. 50, pp. 8)
Pub: American City Business Journals, Inc.
Contact: Mike Olivieri, Executive Vice President
Released: Weekly. **Price:** $4, introductory 4-week offer(Digital & Print). **Description:** Glenmede Trust Company decided to undertake a full office renovation after renewing its lease at One Liberty Place. The investment company decided to replace drywall with glass and more informal meeting places were constructed. The firm, which focuses on employee engagement, aims to improve the work environment. **Availability:** Print; Online.

11638 ■ "Healthcare Facilities Increasingly Embracing Dynamic Glass to Benefit Patients" in Ecology, Environment & Conservation Business (May 24, 2014)
Pub: NewsRX LLC.
Contact: Kalani Rosell, Contact
Description: According to research, optimizing natural daylight and outdoor views in healthcare facilities helps to improve outcomes and shorter recovery times for patients. Therefore, a growing number of healthcare facilities are incorporating SageGlass(R) dynamic glass, a product of Saint-Gobain, into their new construction and remodeling/renovation designs. **Availability:** Online.

11639 ■ *"Intel Joins Movement to Turn Cube Farms Into Wide-Open Spaces"* in *Sacramento Business Journal (Vol. 28, May 27, 2011, No. 13, pp. 1)*
Pub: Sacramento Business Journal
Contact: Stephanie Fretwell, Director
E-mail: sfretwell@bizjournals.com
Ed: Melanie Turner. **Description:** Intel Corporation has remodeled its facility in Folsom, California. The renovation has required some workers to give up their cubicles. Comments from executives are included.

11640 ■ *"Millennials Driving New Types of Space"* in *Philadelphia Business Journal (Vol. 33, April 25, 2014, No. 11, pp. 8)*
Pub: American City Business Journals, Inc.
Contact: Mike Olivieri, Executive Vice President
Description: The trends in the layout of office spaces catering to millennial workers are discussed by a panel of experts at a meeting of the Central Philadelphia Development Corporation and Center City District in Pennsylvania. These tenants like older buildings with wide open spaces, urban areas and the ability to work by bike or foot and co-working spaces. **Availability:** Online.

11641 ■ *"Office Design: The Latest Trends in Workspace Architecture"* in *Wallpaper.com (October 25, 2019)*
URL(s): www.wallpaper.com/gallery/architecture/office-design-latest-trends-workspace-architecture
Released: October 25, 2019. **Description:** Innovative office designs from around the world are shown and discussed. **Availability:** Online.

11642 ■ *"Office Space"* in *Business Strategy Review (Vol. 25, Summer 2014, No. 2, pp. 18)*
Description: Author talks about his working environment at Wild Wadi Waterpark where screams from excited customers are all part of the daily backdrop. **Availability:** Print; Online.

11643 ■ *"Open For Business"* in *Baltimore Business Journal (Vol. 30, June 22, 2012, No. 7, pp. 1)*
Ed: James Briggs. **Description:** The demand for offices with open floor plans has risen as companies look to improve collaboration while cutting costs. Incorporating glass walls and low desks to open office design allow the flow of natural light, which in turn, reduces energy bills. How companies are addressing the challenge of maintaining privacy in an open office design are also discussed. **Availability:** Print; Online.

11644 ■ *"Open Office Design of Today Focuses on Choice and Collaboration"* in *Buildings (September 24, 2019)*
URL(s): www.buildings.com/news/industry-news/articleid/22110/title/open-office-design-collaboration
Ed: Valerie Dennis Craven. **Released:** September 24, 2019. **Description:** The history of the open office plan is discussed and how this concept has shifted over the years. A one-size-fits-all approach to office design is not working well, and office designers are encouraging managers to communicate what types of work needs to be done during the day so a variety of spaces can be created and implemented. **Availability:** Online.

11645 ■ *"Real Estate Firm Joins Trend Toward Functional Offices"* in *Pacific Business News (Vol. 52, April 25, 2014, No. 9, pp. 3)*
Pub: American City Business Journals, Inc.
Contact: Mike Olivieri, Executive Vice President
Released: April 25, 2014. **Price:** $4, Introductory 4-Week Offer(Digital & Print). **Description:** CBRE Inc. Hawaii has adopted the Workplace 360 model at its headquarters in downtown Honolulu as part of a companywide effort to support the way its employees work. Employees can choose nine different ways of working including height-adjustable workstations, standard wraparound desk workstations, huddle rooms and conference rooms. **Availability:** Print; Online.

TRADE PERIODICALS

11646 ■ *Facility Executive*
Pub: Group C Media Inc.
Contact: Bill Corsini, Director
E-mail: bcorsini@groupc.com
URL(s): facilityexecutive.comgroupcmedia.com/print-publications
Facebook: www.facebook.com/FacilityExecutive
Linkedin: www.linkedin.com/company/facility-executive-magazine
X (Twitter): x.com/facilityexec
Instagram: www.instagram.com/FacilityExecutive
YouTube: www.youtube.com/user/tfmmagazine
Pinterest: www.pinterest.com/commercial_industry_news/facility-executive-magazine-news
Ed: Heidi Schwartz. **Released:** 6/year **Description:** Tabloid for facility design and management. **Availability:** Print; PDF; Download; Online.

11647 ■ *Human Factors and Ergonomics Society Bulletin*
Pub: Human Factors and Ergonomics Society
Contact: Carolyn Sommerich, President
E-mail: president@hfes.org
URL(s): www.hfes.org/About-HFES/HFES-History
Released: Monthly **Description:** Recurring features include letters to the editor, news of research, a calendar of events, reports of meetings, news of educational opportunities, job listings, and notices of publications available. **Availability:** Online.

11648 ■ *Interior Design*
Pub: Sandow
Contact: Peter Fain, Chief Operating Officer
URL(s): interiordesign.net
Facebook: www.facebook.com/InteriorDesignMagazine
Linkedin: www.linkedin.com/company/interior-design-magazine
X (Twitter): x.com/InteriorDesign
Instagram: www.instagram.com/interiordesignmag
Pinterest: www.pinterest.com/intdesmag
Released: Last edition 2024. **Price:** $12.95, Single issue for print. **Description:** Interior designing and furnishings magazine. **Availability:** Print; Online.

CONSULTANTS

11649 ■ **Alfred Swenson Pao-Chi Chang Architects**
Chicago, IL
URL: http://www.swensonchangcasina.com
Contact: Pao-Chi Chang, Contact
Description: Firm provides architectural and conceptual design for small, mid-rise, high-rise and ultra-tall buildings. **Scope:** Firm provides architectural and conceptual design for small, mid-rise, high-rise and ultra-tall buildings. **Founded:** 1973.

11650 ■ **Cassway/Albert Ltd.**
1528 Walnut St., Ste. 1100
Philadelphia, PA 19102
Contact: Robert L. Cassway, President
Description: Consultants in architecture, landscape architecture, urban planning, interior design and space planning. **Scope:** Consultants in architecture, landscape architecture, urban planning, interior design and space planning.

11651 ■ **Hewitt Architects**
101 Stewart St., Ste. 200
Seattle, WA 98101
Ph: (206)624-8154
Co. E-mail: info@hewittseattle.com
URL: http://hewittseattle.com
Contact: Paul Shema, President
E-mail: pshema@hewittseattle.com
Facebook: www.facebook.com/HewittSeattle
Linkedin: www.linkedin.com/company/hewitt
Instagram: www.instagram.com/hewittseattle
Description: Provider of architecture, urban design and landscape architecture services. **Founded:** 1975.

11652 ■ **The Hezner Corp.**
678 Broadway St., Ste. 100
Libertyville, IL 60048-2325
Ph: (847)918-3800
Fax: (847)549-7633
Co. E-mail: hezner@hezner.biz
URL: http://www.hezner.com
Contact: Kurt Hezner, President
Facebook: www.facebook.com/theheznercorporation
Linkedin: www.linkedin.com/company/the-hezner-corporation
Description: Firm offers architectural and construction services. **Founded:** 1932.

11653 ■ **HLW International L.L.P.**
5 Penn Plz.
New York, NY 10001
Ph: (212)353-4600
Fax: (212)353-4666
Co. E-mail: info@hlw.com
URL: http://www.hlw.design
Contact: Andrew Mangan, Director
E-mail: amangan@hlw.com
Facebook: www.facebook.com/HLWIntl
Linkedin: www.linkedin.com/company/hlw
X (Twitter): x.com/hlwintl
Instagram: www.instagram.com/hlwinternational
Description: Firm provides engineering and architectural services and also interior designing, strategic planning, landscape architecture and design consulting services. **Scope:** Provider of comprehensive services for many diverse projects located throughout the United States and the world. **Founded:** 1885. **Publications:** Offers design, architecture and planning services. **Training:** Rehabilitation of Office Facilities; R & D Facilities Costs and Cost Analysis; Renovation of R & D Buildings and Labs; Trends and New Developments for Medical Research Facilities; New Technologies for R & D Building Systems; New Labs for Pharmaceutical, Biotechnology, Medical Device and Personal Care Products. **Special Services:** Design, architecture and planning firm.

11654 ■ **Site Design Group Ltd.**
888 S Michigan Ave., Ste. 1000
Chicago, IL 60605
Ph: (312)427-7240
Fax: (312)427-7241
Co. E-mail: hello@site-design.com
URL: http://www.site-design.com
Contact: Ernest C. Wong, President
E-mail: ecwong@site-design.com
Linkedin: www.linkedin.com/company/sitedesigngroupltd
X (Twitter): x.com/sitedesigngroup
Pinterest: www.pinterest.com/sitedesigngroup
Description: Architectural and engineering consulting firm engages in food facilities design, interior design, landscape planning, plant, office layout and design. **Scope:** Architectural and engineering consulting firm engages in food facilities design, interior design, landscape planning, plant, office layout and design. **Founded:** 1986. **Publications:** "Wilderness Experiences inspire Urban design," Apr, 2004; "A Cultural Revolution: In Chicago's Chinatown, carving a public space out of an urban wasteland," Landscape Architecture, Jul, 2002.

FRANCHISES AND BUSINESS OPPORTUNITIES

11655 ■ **California Closet Company Inc. (CC)**
FirstService Brands
1414 Harbour Way S, Ste. 1750
Richmond, CA 94804
Free: 866-366-0420
Fax: (601)549-7973
URL: http://www.fsvbrands.com
Contact: Carolyn Musher, Vice President, Sales
URL(s): www.fsvbrands.com/our_companies/california_closets.html
Facebook: www.facebook.com/CaliforniaClosets
X (Twitter): x.com/caclosets
Instagram: www.instagram.com/caclosets
Pinterest: www.pinterest.com/caclosets

Description: Custom closet design, manufacture, and installation. **Founded:** 1978. **Financial Assistance:** Yes **Training:** Includes training at headquarters, franchisee's location and ongoing support.

COMPUTERIZED DATABASES

11656 ■ Art Index™
EBSCO Information Services
  10 Estes St.
  Ipswich, MA 01938
Ph: (978)356-6500
Free: 800-653-2726
Co. E-mail: information@ebsco.com
URL: http://www.ebsco.com

Contact: Tim Collins, Chief Executive Officer
URL(s): www.ebsco.com/products/research-da
  tabases/art-index
Description: Indexing for over 680 periodicals and 14,000 art dissertations. **Availability:** Online. **Type:** Bibliographic.

RESEARCH CENTERS

11657 ■ Western Michigan University - College of Engineering and Applied Sciences - Department of Industrial and Manufacturing Engineering - Human Performance Institute (HPI)
1903 W Michigan Ave.
  Kalamazoo, MI 49008-5336

URL: http://wmich.edu/ieeem/humanperformance
Contact: Dr. Tycho K. Fredericks, Contact
Description: Integral unit of Department of Industrial and Manufacturing Engineering, College of Engineering and Applied Sciences at Western Michigan University. Offers in-house presentations and ergonomic audits. **Scope:** Ergonomics, work analysis and design, human capabilities in the workplace, job safety, and product design. Research focuses on analysis of job requirements such as strength, coordination, reaction time flexibility and dexterity, heart rate variations, oxygen use, and environmental factors. **Founded:** 1903.

ASSOCIATIONS AND OTHER ORGANIZATIONS

11658 ■ Business Technology Association (BTA)
12411 Wornall Rd., Ste. 200
Kansas City, MO 64145
Ph: (816)941-3100
Free: 800-505-2821
Co. E-mail: info@bta.org
URL: http://www.bta.org
Contact: David Polimeni, President
Facebook: www.facebook.com/BTAORG
Linkedin: www.linkedin.com/company/business
-technology-association
X (Twitter): x.com/BTA_ORG
YouTube: www.youtube.com/channel/
UCBSsarYTnpYafmHxiMDGQWw

Description: Dealers and resellers of office equipment and networking products and services. Offers 60 seminars on management, service, technology, and business systems. Conducts research, provides business-supporting services and benefits, including insurance, and legal counsel. **Founded:** 1926. **Publications:** *Business Owner* (Bimonthly); *BTA Membership Directory.* **Awards:** Channel's Choice Award (Annual); Channel's Choice Award (Annual). **Geographic Preference:** National.

11659 ■ Envelope Manufacturers Association (EMA)
700 S Washington St., Ste. 260
Alexandria, VA 22314
Ph: (703)739-2200
Co. E-mail: tbrooks@envelope.org
URL: http://www.envelope.org
Contact: Maynard H. Benjamin, President
E-mail: mhbenjamin@envelope.org
Facebook: www.facebook.com/1Envelope

Description: Represents envelope manufacturers and their suppliers. **Founded:** 1933. **Publications:** *Family Album* (Annual). **Geographic Preference:** National.

11660 ■ Information Technology Industry Council (ITI)
700 K St. NW, Ste. 600
Washington, DC 20001
Ph: (202)737-8888
Fax: (202)638-4922
Co. E-mail: info@itic.org
URL: http://www.itic.org
Contact: Jason Oxman, President
Facebook: www.facebook.com/ITI.dc
Linkedin: www.linkedin.com/company/information
-technology-industry-council
X (Twitter): x.com/iti_techtweets
YouTube: www.youtube.com/channel/UCo4j-sW0
ti0RiiXupgo2L_A

Description: Represents manufacturers of information technology products. Serves as secretariat and technology for ANSI-accredited standards committee X3 information technology group. Conducts public

policy programs; compiles industry statistics. **Founded:** 1916. **Publications:** *Washington Letter* (Biweekly). **Geographic Preference:** National.

11661 ■ Print Services and Distribution Association (PSDA)
330 N Wabash Ave., Ste. 2000
Chicago, IL 60611
Free: 800-230-0175
Fax: (312)673-6880
Co. E-mail: psda@psda.org
URL: http://brandchaincommunity.org
Contact: Eric Granata, Vice President
Facebook: www.facebook.com/PrintAssociation
X (Twitter): x.com/psda
Instagram: www.instagram.com/printassociation
YouTube: www.youtube.com/channel/
UC8OxverBGzSUMVNAFWZy8nQ

Description: Independent distributors, manufacturers and suppliers to the forms, business printing and document management industries. Sponsors educational and channel marketing programs. Compiles statistics. **Founded:** 1947. **Publications:** *Who's Who Among Business Printing Independents* (Annual); *Print Solutions: Award-Winning Coverage of the Printing Industry* (Monthly); *PERF Print Report* (Quarterly); *Print Solutions Weekly* (Weekly); *Who's Who in the Business Printing and Document Management Industry* (Annual); *Brand Chain Supplier Directory*; *Print Solutions--Buyers' Guide Issue* (Annual). **Awards:** Print Excellence and Knowledge Awards (Annual); PSDA Member of the Year (Annual); PSDA President's Award (Annual). **Geographic Preference:** Multinational.

REFERENCE WORKS

11662 ■ *"Bringing Charities More Bang for Their Buck"* in Crain's Chicago Business (Vol. 34, May 23, 2011, No. 21, pp. 31)
Pub: Crain Communications Inc.
Contact: Barry Asin, President

Ed: Lisa Bertagnoli. **Description:** Marcy-Newberry Association connects charities with manufacturers in order to use excess items such as clothing, janitorial and office supplies. **Availability:** Online.

11663 ■ *"The Definitive Office Supplies Checklist for Small Businesses"* in Small Business Trends(January 27, 2023)
URL(s): smallbiztrends.com/2018/12/office-supplies
-checklist-small-business.html

Ed: Annie Pilon. **Released:** January 27, 2023. **Description:** Small businesses need supplies and equipment just as much as larger offices. Included here is a list of basic supplies plus lists of needed technology, furniture, and other items to help your business thrive. **Availability:** Online.

11664 ■ *"Does Staples Rebranding Foretell the Fall of Another Retailer to Private Equity?"* in Forbes (April 10, 2019)
URL(s): www.forbes.com/sites/sanfordstein/2019/04/
10/does-staples-rebranding-foretell-the-fall-of-ano
ther-retailer-to-private-equity/#7e9d73a659b3

Ed: Sanford Stein. **Released:** April 10, 2019. **Description:** With the launch of the new Staples logo and rebranding efforts, there is a lot of speculation on what the future holds for this chain. It's possible they could offer an IPO if Sycamore Partners, their owners, cash out. Staples also seems to be transitioning to a B2B model instead of the old B2C model that worked for so many years. **Availability:** Online.

11665 ■ *"Macroeconomic Policy and U.S. Competitiveness: A Reformed Fiscal Policy Is Vital To Renewing America's Productivity"* in Harvard Business Review (Vol. 90, March 2012, No. 3, pp. 112)
Pub: Harvard Business Review Press
Contact: Moderna V. Pfizer, Contact

Ed: Matthew Weinzierl, Richard H.K. Vietor. **Description:** Improving productivity requires increasing physical capital (such as equipment or technology), raising human capital, or using both of these types of capital more efficiently. The authors promote a plan that blends cuts in defense and health care spending, adjustments to Social Security, and carbon and gas taxes.

11666 ■ *"Office Depot Closing 400 Stores"* in San Antonio Business Journal (Vol. 28, May 9, 2014, No. 13, pp. 3)
Pub: American City Business Journals, Inc.
Contact: Mike Olivieri, Executive Vice President

Released: Weekly. **Description:** Boca Raton, Florida-based Office Depot announced a plan to close at least 400 stores in the U.S. by the end of 2016. Office Depot joins a growing list of national retailers decreasing store locations in order to increase their bottom line. The problems facing the big players in the office supplies/equipment industry are presented. **Availability:** Print; Online.

11667 ■ *"Office Depot Enhances Customer Experience with New Business Services"* in Stores.org (June 25, 2018)
URL(s): stores.org/2018/06/25/one-stop-small-busi
ness-shop/

Released: June 25, 2018. **Description:** Office Depot is selling more than just office supplies — they are offering IT support services to small and medium-sized businesses. **Availability:** Online.

11668 ■ *"Sharp Restarts Toner Manufacturing: Production Moved from Japan to Serve China Market"* in Memphis Business Journal (Vol. 34, May 11, 2012, No. 4, pp. 1)
Pub: Baltimore Business Journal
Contact: Rhonda Pringle, President
E-mail: rpringle@bizjournals.com

Ed: Michael Sheffield. **Description:** Sharp Manufacturing Company of America has decided to reopen its ink toner production plant in Memphis, Tennessee because of cheaper material, labor and freight costs. The company's move was also attributed to local economic growth and the government support they received after a 2008 tornado hit the area surrounding the area. **Availability:** Print; Online.

11669 ■ *"A Stylish New Labelmaker" in Inc. (Vol. 33, October 2011, No. 8, pp. 48)*
Pub: Inc. Magazine
Ed: John Brandon. **Description:** Epson's first label-maker, the LabelWorks LW-400 offers many design options and has a full QWERTY keyboard that allows users to create and print labels in various sizes. **Availability:** Online.

11670 ■ *"Time For a Change at Canon?' in Barron's (Vol. 92, July 23, 2012, No. 30, pp. 17)*
Pub: Dow Jones & Company Inc.
Contact: Almar Latour, Chief Executive Officer
Ed: Neil A. Martin. **Description:** Stocks of Japanese imaging equipment maker Canon could lose value unless the company undergoes changes in operations and governance. Prices of the company's American Depositary Receipts could fall 20 percent from $37.22 per share within 12 months. **Availability:** Online.

11671 ■ *"U.S. Office Supply Revenue to Rise 8% in 2021" in Progressive Grocer (August 30, 2021)*
Released: August 30, 2021. **Description:** With students going back to school after missing a year due to COVID-19, office supply stores are primed to see an increase in sales for the first time in a few years. **Availability:** Online.

STATISTICAL SOURCES

11672 ■ *The American Demand for Office Furniture and Anticipated Trends*
Released: Fifth edition.

11673 ■ *Office Supply Stores Industry in the US - Market Research Report*
URL(s): www.ibisworld.com/united-states/market-research-reports/office-supply-stores-industry/

Price: $925. **Description:** Downloadable report analyzing the current and future trends in the office supply stores industry. **Availability:** Download.

11674 ■ *RMA Annual Statement Studies*
Pub: Risk Management Association
Contact: Nancy Foster, President
Released: Annual. **Description:** Contains composite balance sheets and income statements for more than 360 industries, including the accounting, auditing, and bookkeeping industries. Also contains five years of comparative historical data for discerning trends. Includes 16 commonly used ratios, computed for most of the size groupings for nearly every industry.

FRANCHISES AND BUSINESS OPPORTUNITIES

11675 ■ California Closet Company Inc. (CC)
FirstService Brands
1414 Harbour Way S, Ste. 1750
Richmond, CA 94804
Free: 866-366-0420
Fax: (601)549-7973
URL: http://www.fsvbrands.com
Contact: Carolyn Musher, Vice President, Sales
URL(s): www.fsvbrands.com/our_companies/california_closets.html
Facebook: www.facebook.com/CaliforniaClosets
X (Twitter): x.com/caclosets
Instagram: www.instagram.com/caclosets
Pinterest: www.pinterest.com/caclosets
Description: Custom closet design, manufacture, and installation. **Founded:** 1978. **Financial Assistance:** Yes **Training:** Includes training at headquarters, franchisee's location and ongoing support.

11676 ■ Island Ink-Jet Systems Inc.
200 Edgeley Blvd., Unit 17, 2nd Fl.
Vaughan, ON, Canada L4K 3Y8
Ph: (647)966-0029
Free: 877-446-5538
Co. E-mail: vaughan@islandinkjet.com

URL: http://www.islandinkjet.com
Description: Retailer of laser toners, ink toners, laser printer drum, wireless air print and much more. **Training:** Yes.

11677 ■ PostNet
1312 17th St.
Denver, CO 80202
Ph: (303)595-0500
Co. E-mail: co149@postnet.com
URL: http://locations.postnet.com/co/denver/1312-17th-street
Facebook: www.facebook.com/PostNetCO149
X (Twitter): x.com/PostNetDenCO149
Description: Offers an array of high demand services and products, tailored to meet the needs of small business owners and today's busy consumer. We like to think of our company as an entrepreneur's store, helping the small office, home office and small business owners get what they need, when they need it. At the same time, Firm caters to the general consumer, offering a host of products and services to help them complete their personal business needs quickly and efficiently. **Founded:** 1993. **Franchised:** 2004. **Training:** Provides 7 days training full-time.

11678 ■ Proforma Inc.
8800 E Pleasant Valley Rd.
Cleveland, OH 44131
Free: 800-825-1525
Co. E-mail: comments@proforma.com
URL: http://www.proforma.com
Contact: Doug Kordel, President
Linkedin: www.linkedin.com/company/proforma
X (Twitter): x.com/proforma
Description: Firm provides promotional products, commercial printing services, advertising specialties and much more. **Founded:** 1978. **Training:** 1 week franchise training at headquarters, local development agent support, ongoing classroom and regional training. Local and national campaigns. Regional meetings and annual national conventions.

START-UP INFORMATION

11679 ■ *"Amazon Selling Secrets: How to Make an Extra $1K - $10K a Month Selling Your Own Products on Amazon"*

Released: July 06, 2014. **Price:** $8.99. **Description:** Secrets for finding and selling popular items on Amazon.com are shared. The tools, resources and system for earning extra money each month selling on Amazon are presented.

11680 ■ *The Complete Idiot's Guide to Starting an eBay® Business*

Pub: Penguin Publishing Group

Released: April 03, 2012. **Price:** $19.95, paperback; $12.99, e-book. **Description:** Guide for starting an eBay business includes information on products to sell, how to price merchandise, and details for working with services like PayPal, and how to organize fulfillment services. **Availability:** E-book; Print.

11681 ■ *"E-Commerce Jewelry Startup Gemvara Won't Pursue Retail Store in Boston"* in *Boston Business Journal (Vol. 34, March 14, 2014, No. 6)*

Pub: American City Business Journals, Inc.

Contact: Mike Olivieri, Executive Vice President

Released: Weekly. **Description:** Janet Holian is CEO of Gemvara, a Boston, Massachusetts-based online jewelry retailer. She ran a pop-up store from November through February and considered opening a traditional brick and mortar store. In the end, Holian decided to focus on the online store. Customers can still make private appointments to Gemvara's One Financial Center location. The company specializes in customizable fine jewelry. **Availability:** Print; Online.

11682 ■ *eBay Business the Smart Way*

Released: 3rd edition. **Description:** eBay commands ninety percent of all online auction business. Computer and software expert and online entrepreneur shares information to help online sellers get started and move merchandise on eBay. Tips include the best ways to build credibility, find products to sell, manage inventory, create a storefront Website, and more. **Availability:** Print; PDF.

11683 ■ *The eBay Business Start-Up Kit: With 100s of Live Links to All the Information & Tools You Need*

Pub: Nolo

Contact: Chris Braun, President

Ed: Richard Stim. **Description:** Interactive kit that provides in-depth information and practical advice in launching an eBay business. **Availability:** Print.

11684 ■ *EBay Income: How ANYONE of Any Age, Location, and/or Background Can Build a Highly Profitable Online Business with eBay*

Pub: Atlantic Publishing Co.

Contact: Dr. Heather L. Johnson, Contact

Description: A complete overview of eBay is given and guides any small company through the entire process of creating the auction and auction strategies, photography, writing copy, text and formatting, multiple sales, programming tricks, PayPal, accounting, creating marketing, merchandising, managing email lists, advertising, plans, taxes and sales tax, best time to list items and for how long, sniping programs, international customers, opening a storefront, electronic commerce, buy-it now pricing, keywords, Google marketing and eBay secrets.

11685 ■ *"Etsy: Etsy Business for Beginners! Master Etsy and Build a Profitable Business In No Time"*

Released: December 23, 2014. **Price:** $6.99, regular price is $13.99. **Description:** Craft artisans take note: information is offered to start an online business through Etsy. Whether handmade home accessories, clothing, or knick-knacks, Etsy is the perfect option for artists and crafters to start a home-based, online retail operation. **Availability:** Print; Download.

11686 ■ *How to Open and Operate a Financially Successful Bookstore on Amazon and Other Web Sites: With Companion CD-ROM*

Pub: Atlantic Publishing Co.

Contact: Dr. Heather L. Johnson, Contact

Description: This book was written for every used book aficionado and bookstore owner who currently wants to take advantage of the massive collection of online resources available to start and run your own online bookstore business.

11687 ■ *"How to Open and Operate a Financially Successful Florist and Floral Business Online and Off"*

Pub: Atlantic Publishing Co.

Contact: Dr. Heather L. Johnson, Contact

Released: Revised second edition. **Description:** A concise and easy to follow guide for opening a retail florist or floral business online or a traditional brick and mortar store. Knowledge shared includes: cost control systems, retail math and competitive pricing, legal concerns, tax reporting requirements and reporting, profit and loss statements, management skills, sales advertising, and marketing techniques, customer service, direct sales, internal marketing ideas, and more. **Availability:** CD-ROM; Print; Online.

11688 ■ *How to Use the Internet to Advertise, Promote, and Market Your Business or Web Site: With Little or No Money*

Pub: Atlantic Publishing Co.

Contact: Dr. Heather L. Johnson, Contact

Ed: Bruce C. Brown. **Released:** Revised third edition. **Description:** Information is given to help build, promote, and make money from your Website or brick and mortar store using the Internet, with minimal costs.

11689 ■ *"No. 381: Metallica and Other Forms of Hardware"* in *Inc. (Vol. 36, September 2014, No. 7, pp. 107)*

Pub: Mansueto Ventures L.L.C.

Contact: Stephanie Mehta, Chief Executive Officer

Released: August 20, 2014. **Description:** Profile of Mikhail Orlov, who stayed in American instead of fighting a war he did not believe in while living in Chechnya, Russia. Orlov discovered his entrepreneurial spirit when he began importing Russian army surplus gear. He operates his startup online store selling guns, ammo, and hunting accessories. **Availability:** Print; Online.

11690 ■ *Selling Online: Canada's Bestselling Guide to Becoming a Successful E-Commerce Merchant*

Description: Helps individuals build online retail enterprises; this updated version includes current tools, information and success strategies, how to launch an online storefront, security, marketing strategies, and mistakes to avoid. **Availability:** Online.

ASSOCIATIONS AND OTHER ORGANIZATIONS

11691 ■ Internet Society
11710 Plz. America Dr., Ste. 400
Reston, VA 20190
Ph: (703)439-2120
Fax: (703)326-9881
Co. E-mail: isoc@isoc.org
URL: http://www.internetsociety.org
Contact: Dan York, Director
Facebook: www.facebook.com/InternetSociety
Linkedin: www.linkedin.com/company/internet-society
X (Twitter): x.com/internetsociety
Instagram: www.instagram.com/internetsociety
YouTube: www.youtube.com/user/InternetSocie
tyVideo

Description: Seeks to ensure global cooperation and coordination for the Internet and related internetworking technologies and applications. **Founded:** 1992. **Publications:** *IETF Journal*; *Internet Society Newsletter* (Monthly). **Educational Activities:** Internet Society Conference (Annual); Network and Distributed System Security Symposium (NDSS) (Annual). **Awards:** Internet Society Fellowships to the IETF; Jonathan B. Postel Service Award (Annual). **Geographic Preference:** National.

REFERENCE WORKS

11692 ■ *"1 in 4 Food Delivery Drivers Admit to Eating Your Food"* in *NPR (July 30, 2019)*

URL(s): www.npr.org/2019/07/30/746600105/1-in-4-food-delivery-drivers-admit-to-eating-your-food

Released: June 30, 2019. **Description:** Results from a recent US Foods survey found that 54% of respondents, who are drivers for food delivery apps such as DoorDash, admit to being tempted by the smell of customers' food and half actually took a bite. To help solve this problem customers want tamper-evident stickers on their food containers. Other delivery services are stepping up and creating strategies to prevent this in the first place. **Availability:** Online.

11693 ■ *"5 E-Commerce Landmines You Need to Avoid"* in Legal Zoom (February 15, 2023)

URL(s): www.legalzoom.com/articles/5-e-commerce -landmines-you-need-to-avoid

Ed: Gwen Moran. **Released:** February 15, 2023. **Description:** Keep your online business running smoothly and provide great customer service with the tips given in this article. **Availability:** Online.

11694 ■ *"5 E-Commerce Must-Haves That Will Save You Time and Money"* in Legal Zoom (March 15, 2023)

URL(s): www.legalzoom.com/articles/5-e-commerce -must-haves-that-will-save-you-time-and-money

Ed: Jane Haskins, Esq. **Released:** March 15, 2023. **Description:** Delivers the pros and cons of using third-party software to help you track orders, inventory, etc. **Availability:** Online.

11695 ■ *"5 Tips to Attract New Online Customers"* in Legal Zoom (March 9, 2023)

URL(s): www.legalzoom.com/articles/5-tips-to-attrac t-new-online-customers

Ed: Sandra Beckwith. **Released:** March 09, 2023. **Availability:** Online.

11696 ■ *"6 Top Online Consignment Shops for Selling Your Clothes"* in U.S. News & World Report (February 21, 2019)

URL(s): money.usnews.com/money/personal-finance/ saving-and-budgeting/articles/6-top-online -consignment-shops-for-selling-your-clothes

Ed: Maryalene LaPonsie. **Released:** February 21, 2019. **Description:** Online consignment shops and apps are trending upwards, making it easier for consumers to upload photos of their items and reaching more potential buyers. Some online shops focus solely on high-end brands, while some will take everyday clothes. A discussion of six popular online consignment shops with pros and cons listed, along with their fees is given. **Availability:** Online.

11697 ■ *"18 Online Cooking Classes for the Busy Budding Chef"* in SheKnows (March 27, 2019)

URL(s): www.sheknows.com/food-and-recipes/ar ticles/1079046/best-online-cooking-classes/

Ed: Heather Barnett. **Released:** March 27, 2019. **Description:** Cooking classes don't have to taken at a traditional school. Instead, if you are short on time there are online courses you can enroll in. Included is a list of 18 options so you can find the best fit for you and your wallet. **Availability:** Online.

11698 ■ *"25 Best Genealogy Websites for Beginners"* in Family Tree

URL(s): www.familytreemagazine.com/premium/ 25-best-genealogy-websites-for-beginners/

Ed: Sunny Jane Morton. **Description:** A list of the best internet resources available for those interested in conducting genealogy research. Gives the price and a description of the service, which services are free, and which are membership only. **Availability:** Online.

11699 ■ *"All Hail: How Taxi Companies Stay Competitive in an Evolving Marketplace"* in SmartcitiesDive (March 28, 2019)

URL(s): www.smartcitiesdive.com/news/taxi-compa nies-ride-hailing-competitition/551449/

Ed: Katie Pyzyk. **Released:** March 28, 2019. **Description:** It's no surprise that Uber an Lyft have taken a good deal of market share from the traditional taxi business, so how do taxis still make a living? By adapting the same business model as Uber and Lyft, several taxi cab companies are still profitable and gaining back that market share. **Availability:** Online.

11700 ■ *"Amazon Beats Best Buy As Top Electronics Retailer"* in RetailDive (April 17, 2018)

URL(s): www.retaildive.com/news/amazon-beats-bes t-buy-as-top-electronics-retailer/521505/

Ed: Daphne Howland. **Released:** April 17, 2018. **Description:** Dealerscope released it's Top 101 Consumer Electronics Retailers list, and Amazon has taken over the lead from Best Buy. Amazon grew its electronics sales by more than 18.5%. **Availability:** Online.

11701 ■ *"Amazon to End Its Restaurant Delivery Service"* in The New York Times (June 11, 2019)

URL(s): www.nytimes.com/2019/06/11/business/ama zon-restaurant-delivery-service-ending.html

Ed: David Yaffe-Bellany. **Released:** June 11, 2019. **Description:** Amazon Restaurants will officially close on June 24 and according to Amazon the move will let them focus more on grocery delivery, since they now own Whole Foods. Amazon Restaurants never really took off in popularity as compared to the other food delivery apps and they can no longer keep up with the competition. **Availability:** Online.

11702 ■ *"Amazon Hits Back at Bloomberg Report About Small Suppliers Purge"* in Fast Company (May 28, 2019)

URL(s): www.fastcompany.com/90355900/amazon-is -about-to-halt-orders-from-small-suppliers-report# :~:targetText=A%20purge%20is%20on%20 the,selling%20platform%2C%20according%20to% 20Bloomberg.

Ed: Cale Guthrie Weissman. **Released:** May 28, 2019. **Description:** Bloomberg reported that Amazon would be purging small wholesalers in favor of large suppliers in order to maintain a competitive edge. However, Amazon is claiming that report is false and there will be no large-scale purge, even if they do review their vendors and make periodic changes as needed. **Availability:** Online.

11703 ■ *"Amazon Is Poised to Unleash a Long-Feared Purge of Small Suppliers"* in Bloomberg (May 28, 2019)

URL(s): www.bloomberg.com/news/articles/2019-0 5-28/amazon-is-poised-to-unleash-long-feare d-purge-of-small-suppliers

Ed: Spencer Soper. **Released:** May 28, 2019. **Description:** Online giant Amazon is planning a permanent purge of thousands of small wholesale vendors in favor of larger suppliers. **Availability:** Online.

11704 ■ *"Amazon Launches Free Creator University with Guides for Affiliates and Influencers"* in Small Business Trends (February 9, 2023)

URL(s): smallbiztrends.com/2023/02/amazon -launches-free-creator-university.html

Ed: Gabrielle Pickard-Whitehead. **Released:** February 09, 2023. **Description:** Amazon Creator University has launched, which can be a useful tool for managing an Amazon store. Details how online store owners and influencers can benefit. **Availability:** Online.

11705 ■ *"Amazon Launches a Personal Shopper Service That Sends Monthly Curated Clothing Boxes"* in The Verge (July 31, 2019)

URL(s): www.theverge.com/2019/7/31/20748632/ amazon-personal-shopper-prime-wardrobe-service -style-subscription-box

Ed: Ashley Carman. **Released:** July 31, 2019. **Description:** Amazon launched a new fashion service called Personal Shopper by Prime Wardrobe. Prime members who sign up will need to answer a survey about their fit and trend preferences and will then receive a curated box of clothing. Up to eight pieces will be included and the member can preview it before it ships and they will only pay for what they keep. Services costs $4.99 a month. **Availability:** Online.

11706 ■ *"Amazon Makes Inroads Selling Medical Supplies to the Sick"* in The Wall Street Journal (November 29, 2018)

URL(s): www.wsj.com/articles/amazon-makes-inroa ds-selling-medical-supplies-to-the-sick-1543487401

Ed: Melanie Evans. **Released:** November 29, 2018. **Description:** A new app is allowing doctors to direct patients towards medical supplies that can be purchased on Amazon.com, raising some privacy concerns. However, doctors are saying its the same as handing over a handwritten note which are often lost or sparing patients from having to spend time trying to track down the needed supplies. **Availability:** Online.

11707 ■ *"Amazon Targets Denton-Based Sally Beauty's Professional Salon Customers"* in The Dallas Morning News (June 24, 2019)

URL(s): www.dallasnews.com/business/retail/2019/0 6/24/amazon-targets-denton-based-sally-beauty-s -professional-salon-customers/

Ed: Maria Halkias. **Released:** June 24, 2019. **Description:** Amazon launched a beauty store for salon professionals, which is in direct competition with Denton-based Sally Beauty Supply, which has been a staple in the industry for decades. Amazon is now selling online, what Sally's carries inside their stores, which is going to make Sally's add new products and improve their own technology in order to remain competitive. **Availability:** Print; Online.

11708 ■ *"Amazon Will Regret Building Private Label Brands"* in Marketplace Pulse (September 25, 2019)

URL(s): www.marketplacepulse.com/articles/amazon -will-regret-building-private-label-brands

Ed: Jouzas Kaziukenas. **Released:** September 25, 2019. **Description:** Amazon is receiving backlash from launching its own private label items and pushing those items on its site before other brands. Often copying other brands for its products, there are antitrust concerns as well since they gather data about various products being sold on its platform. **Availability:** Online.

11709 ■ *"Amazon's Booze Business in Jeopardy with Investigation into Fake LA Liquor Store"* in Vinepair (August 20, 2019)

URL(s): vinepair.com/booze-news/amazons-fake-la -liquor-store/

Ed: Tim McKirdy. **Released:** August 20, 2019. **Description:** The California Department of Alcoholic Beverage Control has opened an investigation into Amazon for not maintaining a physical liquor store in the state, thus violating its liquor license requirements. **Availability:** Online.

11710 ■ *"Americans Spend Billions on Takeout. But Food Delivery Apps Are Still a Terrible Business"* in Barron's (November 15, 2019)

URL(s): www.barrons.com/articles/food-delivery -grubhub-doordash-and-uber-eats-51573859107

Ed: Eric J. Savitz. **Released:** November 15, 2019. **Description:** Discusses the negative issues with food-delivery apps. **Availability:** Online.

11711 ■ *"Baltimore Entrepreneur Develops an Event-Themed Wish List App"* in Baltimore Business Journal (Vol. 32, July 25, 2014, No. 12, pp. 7)

Pub: American City Business Journals, Inc.
Contact: Mike Olivieri, Executive Vice President

Released: Weekly. **Price:** $4, introductory 4-week offer(Digital only). **Description:** Baltimore-based entrepreneur Patrick Nagle has developed an online event-themed gift registry named Glist, a mobile application (app) and Website that assists in gift buying. Glist allows users to photograph items they want, put them on the online birthday wish list, or 'glist', and share the registries via social media. **Availability:** Print; Online.

11712 ■ *"Best Baby Clothing Stores of 2019"* in Babylist (January 1, 2019)

URL(s): www.babylist.com/hello-baby/best-baby-clo thing-stores

Released: January 01, 2019. **Description:** Top online places to shop for baby clothes. Some offer either instore or online deals, so it may be best to check both if you are looking for a steal. **Availability:** Online.

11713 ■ *"Best Days and Weekends to Shop for Clothing" in U.S. News and World Report (April 23, 2018)*

Ed: Kristin McGrath. **Released:** April 23, 2018. **Description:** General tips for clothes shopping throughout the year and when to hit the stores and online for the best deals to stretch your budget. **Availability:** Online.

11714 ■ *"Best Online Stores for Personal Electronics" in Money Crashers*

URL(s): www.moneycrashers.com/best-online-stores -consumer-electronics/

Ed: Chris Bibey. **Description:** If you are looking for a deal and larger selection on electronics, check out the online stores that specialize in these gadgets. Six of the best online sites are listed with a description of their merchandise and deals. **Availability:** Online.

11715 ■ *"Boom and Bust in the Book Biz" in Canadian Business (Vol. 83, August 17, 2010, No. 13-14, pp. 16)*

Pub: Rogers Media Inc.

Contact: Neil Spivak, Chief Executive Officer

Ed: Jordan Timm. **Description:** Electronic book marketplace is booming with Amazon.com's e-book sales for the Kindle e-reader exceeding the hardcover sales. Kobo Inc. has registered early success with its Kobo e-reader and has partnered with Hong Kong telecom giant on an e-book store. **Availability:** Print; Online.

11716 ■ *"Borrow Baby Couture Launch Rocks Fasion World - Provides Couture Fashion for Girls" in Benzinga.com (June 18, 2012)*

Description: Borrow Baby Couture allows parents, family and friends to rent couture clothing by top fashion designers for girls ages 9 months to 4 years. The retailer has launched an online site. Purchases are wrapped in tissue arriving ready to wear and includes return shipping costs. **Availability:** Online.

11717 ■ *"Brite-Strike Tactical Launches New Internet Marketing Initiatives" in Marketwired (September 15, 2009)*

Pub: Comtex News Network Inc.

Contact: Kan Devnani, President

Description: Brite-Strike Tactical Illumination Products, Inc. has enlisted the expertise of Internet marketing guru Thomas J. McCarthy to help revamp the company's Internet campaign. An outline of the Internet marketing strategy is provided. **Availability:** Print; Online.

11718 ■ *"Can You Really Manage Engagement Without Managers? Zappos May Soon Find Out, as the Online Retailer is Eliminating the Traditional Manager Role" in Gallup Business Journal (April 24, 2014)*

Pub: Gallup, Inc.

Contact: Jon Clifton, Chief Executive Officer

Description: Online retailer, Zappos, will do away with the traditional manager role to lessen the chain of control within the organization. The concept of self-managed teams is explored. **Availability:** Online.

11719 ■ *"CBS Radio Group Seeks New Space for Growing Event, Online Business" in Dallas Business Journal (Vol. 35, June 15, 2012, No. 40, pp. 1)*

Pub: Baltimore Business Journal

Contact: Rhonda Pringle, President

E-mail: rpringle@bizjournals.com

Ed: Candace Carlisle. **Description:** CBS Radio Dallas/Fortworth is planningto move to a larger facility to accommodate new business segments. The company has begun developing content for online and events.

11720 ■ *"Check It Out! The Professional Beauty Association Launches New Website" in Modern Salong (November 11, 2019)*

URL(s): www.modernsalon.com/618285/check-it-ou t-the-professional-beauty-association-launches-new -website

Released: November 11, 2019. **Description:** The Professional Beauty Association launched a new website. The newly enhanced site includes sections on member resources, events and programming, advocacy, and also has expanded resources for inspiration. **Availability:** Online.

11721 ■ *"Check Out How a Nurse Made Millions with Her Etsy Business" in Small Business Trends(February 22, 2023)*

URL(s): smallbiztrends.com/2023/02/nurse-makes -millions-etsy-side-business.html

Ed: Gabrielle Pickard-Whitehead. **Released:** February 22, 2023. **Description:** Profile of Stephanee Beggs, a nurse who made millions from her side-hustle Etsy store. **Availability:** Online.

11722 ■ *"Chipotle Mexican Grill Adds Alexa for Reorders of Favorite Meals" in Nation's Restaurant News (November 21, 2019)*

URL(s): www.nrn.com/fast-casual/chipotle-mexican -grill-adds-alexa-reorders-favorite-meals

Ed: Nancy Luna. **Released:** November 21, 2019. **Description:** Chipotle has added Amazon's voice ordering assistant, Alexa, to its list of ways consumers can order. However, there are limitations since it's only set up to reorder meals for delivery once a Chipotle loyalty member links their profile to the Alexa app. **Availability:** Online.

11723 ■ *"Citadel EFT (CDFT) Contracts With New Search Engine Optimization (SEO) and Banner Ad Web Marketing Companies" in Internet Wire (August 8, 2012)*

Pub: Comtex News Network Inc.

Contact: Kan Devnani, President

Description: Citafel EFT Inc. provides credit card terminals, online, mail order and retail credit card processing services. The firm has contracted with two Web marketing companies to increase its awareness on the Internet. **Availability:** Print; Online.

11724 ■ *"Clicks Vs. Bricks" in Birmingham Business Journal (Vol. 31, April 25, 2014, No. 17, pp. 4)*

Pub: American City Business Journals, Inc.

Contact: Mike Olivieri, Executive Vice President

Released: May 22, 2018. **Description:** Birmingham, Alabama's retail industry has been evolving as investment to brick-and-mortar stores by mall and shopping center owners double. The hope is that the social shopping experience, economic recovery, and Fair Marketplace legislation for an online sales tax will make co-existence with Internet stores more viable. The survival and expansion of retail are discussed. **Availability:** Print; Online.

11725 ■ *The Complete Guide to Google Adwords: Secrets, Techniques, and Strategies You Can Learn to Make Millions*

Pub: Atlantic Publishing Co.

Contact: Dr. Heather L. Johnson, Contact

Released: 2012. **Description:** Google AdWords, when it launched in 2002 signaled a fundamental shift in what the Internet was for so many individuals and companies. Learning and understanding how Google AdWords operates and how it can be optimized for maximum exposure, boosting click through rates, conversions, placement, and selection of the right keywords, can be the key to a successful online business. **Availability:** Print; Online.

11726 ■ *The Complete Guide to Selling on Amazon: Tips and Tricks for Profitable Sales*

URL(s): www.barnesandnoble.com/w/the-complete -guide-to-selling-on-amazon-james-dickson/ 1143168570?ean=2940185599174

Released: March 05, 2023. **Price:** $4.99, e-book. **Description:** A resource guide for starting your own online shop on the Amazon platform. Goes into detail about products, marketing, customer service, and sourcing products to sell. **Availability:** E-book.

11727 ■ *"Consumers Love Food Delivery. Restaurants and Grocers Hate It." in The Wall Street Journal (March 9. 2019)*

URL(s): www.wsj.com/articles/consumers-love-foo d-delivery-restaurants-and-grocers-hate-i t-11552107610

Ed: Heather Haddon, Julie Jargon. **Released:** March 09, 2019. **Description:** Food delivery services are tricky for restaurants, with most being unprofitable due to the cost of delivery. Consumers have very high expectations because they are used to instant gratification with online services, but grocers and restaurants are struggling to keep up with the demand. **Availability:** Online.

11728 ■ *"Custom Picture Framing Is Too Expensive — and Framebridge Has a Fix for That" in Forbes (January 4, 2019)*

URL(s): www.forbes.com/sites/pamdanziger/2019/01/ 04/custom-picture-framing-is-too-expensive -framebridge-has-a-fix-for-that/#7c5100ff2489

Ed: Pamela N. Danziger. **Released:** January 04, 2019. **Description:** After Susan Tynan tried to get several posters custom framed and found out how expensive that was, she founded an online frame shop called Framebridge, which will frame pictures for a fraction of the price. The demand in cheaper framing options has caused smaller shops to close, while online stores and bigger chains are taking up more of the market. **Availability:** Online.

11729 ■ *"The Cutest Houston-Made Kids' Clothes Will Soon Come in Mom Versions" in Houstonia (August 7, 2019)*

URL(s): www.houstoniamag.com/articles/2019/8/7/ bee-and-birdie-kids-clothes-etsy-shop

Ed: Abby Ledoux. **Released:** August 07, 2019. **Description:** The small online shop, Bee + Birdie has made a name for itself selling affordable toddler clothing that has a more subdued aesthetic instead of the in-your-face fashion that most stores carry. With its current success, the brand is now launching "mom" versions of their fashions. **Availability:** Online.

11730 ■ *"Cyber Thanksgiving Online Shopping a Growing Tradition" in Marketing Weekly News (December 12, 2009, pp. 137)*

Pub: Investment Weekly News

Description: According to e-commerce analysts, Thanksgiving Day is becoming increasingly important to retailers in terms of online sales. Internet marketers are realizing that consumers are already searching for Black Friday sales and if they find deals on the products they are looking for, they are highly likely to make their purchase on Thanksgiving Day instead of waiting. **Availability:** Online.

11731 ■ *"The Death of the Local Bike Shop" in Outside (November 2, 2016)*

URL(s): www.outsideonline.com/2126741/death-local -bike-shop

Ed: Robbie Carver. **Released:** November 02, 2016. **Description:** With the advent of popular bike brands Trek and Giant moving to an online sales model, the decline of the local bike shop is explored. **Availability:** Online.

11732 ■ *"Designing an Office Around Your Company's Goals How Eventbrite Learned That a Workspace Becomes Much More Than an Office Once Your Team Weighs In" in Inc. (Vol. 36, September 2014, No. 7, pp. 122)*

Pub: Mansueto Ventures L.L.C.

Contact: Stephanie Mehta, Chief Executive Officer

Released: September 2014. **Description:** Julia Hartz, co-founder and president of an online ticketing and event planning service, Eventbrite, shares insight into designing her firm's new office space. She opened suggestions from all employees to come up with the right environment to suit her workers. **Availability:** Print; Online.

11733 ■ *"Does the Gig Economy Have a Future in Grocery Stores?" in Grocery Dive (November 7, 2019)*

URL(s): www.grocerydive.com/news/does-the-gig -economy-have-a-future-in-grocery-stores/566797/

Ed: Jeff Wells. **Released:** November 07, 2019. **Description:** The gig economy has entered the grocery business by filling jobs for workers who shop for customers and deliver the goods. This type of work is expanding in the market as e-commerce demand accelerates, and traditional grocers have taken notice and started to provide their own on-demand labor. **Availability:** Online.

11734 ■ *"The Downfall of Trustify" in PInow.com (November 11, 2019)*
URL(s): www.pinow.com/articles/2779/the-downfall-of
-trustify
Ed: Stephanie Irvine. **Released:** November 11, 2019. **Description:** Profile of Trustify, Inc., a start-up company founded in 2015 that helped people hire private investigators online. It's popularity was fueled by its forward-thinking business model, but quickly died out within a few years due to financial troubles, hiring unlicensed investigators, and taking on cases that normally shouldn't be investigated. **Availability:** Online.

11735 ■ *"The Downfall of the Virtual Assistant (So Far)" in ComputerWorld (June 20, 2019)*
URL(s): www.computerworld.com/article/3403332/
downfall-virtual-assistant.html
Ed: JR Raphael. **Released:** June 20, 2019. **Description:** Virtual assistants such as Alexa, Siri, and Google Assistant are all features that people are starting to rely on more and more. However, the success rate isn't as high as expected when it comes to completing tasks. More simple tasks, such as pulling up the weather, are easily accomplished by these virtual assistants, but consumers are becoming frustrated when complex tasks can't be completed by the AI. **Availability:** Online.

11736 ■ *"E-Cards Are Back, Thanks to the Pandemic" in The New York Times (June 22, 2021)*
Ed: Anna Schaverien. **Released:** June 22, 2021. **Description:** Due to the COVID-19 pandemic causing stores to close and reducing social gatherings, many people resurrected the old e-card to send along over the internet in order to stay connected. **Availability:** Online.

11737 ■ *"Easier Options Orders" in Barron's (Vol. 92, August 25, 2012, No. 35, pp. 28)*
Pub: Dow Jones & Company Inc.
Contact: Almar Latour, Chief Executive Officer
Ed: Theresa W. Carey. **Description:** Online brokerage optionsXpress introduced the Walk Limit, a service that allows traders to improve pricing for options and save money. Online brokerage TradeMonster introduced portfolio margining to qualified customers. **Availability:** Online.

11738 ■ *"Etsy Alternatives for Crafty Entrepreneurs" in Business News Daily (February 21, 2023)*
URL(s): www.businessnewsdaily.com/5287-etsy-al
ternatives-handmade-sites.html
Ed: Max Freedman. **Released:** February 21, 2023. **Description:** Sometimes the craft website Etsy is not the best option to sell your handmade crafts. Listed are various other sites to help you launch or expand your online business. **Availability:** Online.

11739 ■ *"Etsy Sellers Experience Payment Delays after Silicon Valley Bank Collapse" in Small Business Trends (March 11, 2023)*
URL(s): smallbiztrends.com/2023/03/etsy-sellers-ex
perience-payment-delays-after-silicon-valley-bank
-collapse.html
Ed: Joshua Sophy. **Released:** March 11, 2023. **Description:** With the fail of Silicon Valley Bank came bad news for Etsy shop owners. They received word that since Etsy uses Silicon Valley Bank, their payments would have a delay in processing. This could have severe consequences for these small online shop owners. **Availability:** Online.

11740 ■ *The Everything Store: Jeff Bezos and the Age of Amazon*
Pub: Little, Brown and Company
Contact: Judy Clain, Editor-in-Chief
Released: October 15, 2013. **Price:** $28, hardcover; $30, audiobook CD; $24.98, audiobook downloadable; $12.99, e-book; $18, paperback; $30, hardcov-

er(large print); $28. **Description:** Amazon.com started as a bookseller, a company delivering books through the mail. Today, the online store, offers a limitless selection of goods at competitively low prices. Profile of entrepreneur Jeff Bezos that outlines his endless pursuit of new markets and risky new ventures to transform retail. **Availability:** audiobook; CD-ROM; E-book; Print.

11741 ■ *"Expedia Tells Hotels Adding Resort Fees Will Lower Your Listings on Its Pages" in Skift (November 14, 2019)*
URL(s): skift.com/2019/11/14/expedia-tells-hotels-a
dding-resort-fees-will-lower-your-listings-on-its
-pages/
Ed: Dennis Schaal. **Released:** November 14, 2019. **Description:** Expedia acted upon it's earlier stance that it will send hotel listings lower in its sort order if they add resort fees to the base room rates. This is part of Expedia's effort to be more transparent in their pricing because often, consumers do not understand the resort fee and forget it's there until checkout. **Availability:** Online.

11742 ■ *"Extreme Temperatures May Pose Risks to Some Mail-Order Meds" in NPR (January 7, 2019)*
URL(s): www.npr.org/sections/health-shots/2019/01/
07/673806506/extreme-temperatures-may-pose
-risks-to-some-mail-order-meds
Ed: Alex Smith. **Released:** January 07, 2019. **Description:** With most medications instructing to store at room temperature, what happens when a mail delivery service leaves your meds in extreme weather conditions? Many prescriptions are filled online and home delivered, with packages being left in either extreme cold or heat, depending on the season and the location. A push is being made to go back to retail pharmacy services unless the mail-order services can prove that the drugs are being delivered at the right temperatures. **Availability:** Online.

11743 ■ *"Facebook Launches Online Dating Service in US" in Financial Times (September 5, 2019)*
URL(s): www.ft.com/content/fd63af00-cb38-11e9-a1f
4-3669401ba76f
Ed: Camilla Hodgson. **Released:** September 05, 2019. **Description:** Facebook Dating is launching in order to help users have meaningful relationships. However, concerns about how this social media platform is going to use personal data are being raised. **Availability:** Online.

11744 ■ *"Facebook Marketplace vs. the Competition for E-Commerce Businesses" in Business News Daily (March 20, 2023)*
URL(s): www.businessnewsdaily.com/9481-p2p
-marketplace-apps.html
Ed: Leslie Pankowski. **Released:** March 20, 2023. **Description:** Many small businesses engage in e-commerce marketplaces and choosing a platform that will be capable of successfully selling your product may be hit or miss. This article discusses selling on Facebook Marketplace. **Availability:** Online.

11745 ■ *"Fishbrain Launches in-App Fishing Tackle Shop" in Fishing Tackle Retailer (October 10, 2019)*
URL(s): fishingtackleretailer.com/fishbrain-launches
-in-app-fishing-tackle-shop/
Released: October 10, 2019. **Description:** The popular social networking site for anglers, Fishbrain, launched it's own in-app marketplace after partnering with Marketplacer. Various categories of merchandise is available for so that users can easily locate what they need to purchase. **Availability:** Print; Online.

11746 ■ *"FTC Sues Owner of Online Dating Service Match.com For Using Fake Love Interest Ads to Trick Consumers into Paying for a Match.com Subscription" in Federal Trade Commission (September 25, 2019)*
URL(s): www.ftc.gov/news-events/press-releases/20
19/09/ftc-sues-owner-online-dating-service-ma
tchcom-using-fake-love

Released: September 25, 2019. **Description:** The FTC has sued Match.com over unfair business practices, resulting in consumers being tricked into buying paid subscriptions to Match.com. Users need a paid subscription to Match.com in order to respond to messages they may receive from potential suitors, and those with free accounts were sent ads by the company in an effort to get them to sign up and pay for a paid account. **Availability:** Online.

11747 ■ *"Full Speed Ahead: How to Get the Most Out of Your Company Vehicles" in Entrepreneur (Vol. 37, October 2009, No. 10, pp. 78)*
Pub: Entrepreneur Media Inc.
Contact: Dan Bova, Director
E-mail: dbova@entrepreneur.com
Ed: Jill Amadio. **Description:** Methods of saving costs on purchasing and maintaining vehicles are described. Tips include shopping online, choosing hybrid vehicles, and choosing cars with incentives and lower insurance costs.

11748 ■ *"Goodwill, the Original Thrift Store, Goes Digital" in The Business of Fashion (June 11, 2019)*
URL(s): www.businessoffashion.com/articles/news-bi
tes/goodwill-the-original-thrift-store-goes-digital
Released: June 11, 2019. **Description:** Goodwill, America's staple thrift store chain, has teamed up with OfferUp to sell it's goods online. **Availability:** Online.

11749 ■ *"The Great Concierge Debate: Digital or Personal?" in The New York Times (October 20, 2017)*
URL(s): www.nytimes.com/2017/10/20/travel/digital
-vs-personal-concierges.html
Ed: Mike Seely. **Released:** October 20, 2017. **Description:** When in Roam, a new concierge app, was launched by Krista Krauss Miller and is competing with other well-known concierge apps. Miller's app is able to reach people staying in an Airbnb or a hotel without a concierge service. **Availability:** Online.

11750 ■ *"Great News for the Dead: The Funeral Industry Is Being Disrupted" in The Economist (April 14, 2018)*
URL(s): www.economist.com/leaders/2018/04/14/
great-news-for-the-dead-the-funeral-industry-is-
being-disrupted
Released: April 14, 2018. **Description:** Old-fashioned funeral services typically cost around $9,000 with very few options for those left behind to deal with. However, with the advancement of online tools, those left grieving can search for options and compare competitors in the privacy of their own homes. **Availability:** Online.

11751 ■ *"Here's How You Boycott Amazon" in Puget Sound Business Journal (Vol. 35, June 13, 2014, No. 8, pp. 12)*
Pub: American City Business Journals, Inc.
Contact: Mike Olivieri, Executive Vice President
Description: Critic, Kimberly Mills, says she boycotted Amazon.com because of its lack of corporate philanthropy and poor working conditions. She also boycotted the firm by purchasing directly from the listed company Websites when purchasing retail products, instead of buying directly from Amazon's site. Other online retailers are increasing customer services corporate social responsibility. **Availability:** Online.

11752 ■ *"Here's One Market Amazon Can't Easily Crack: Car Parts" in CNN (November 29, 2018)*
URL(s): www.cnn.com/2018/11/29/business/advance
-auto-parts-oreilly-autozone/index.html
Ed: Nathaniel Meyersohn. **Released:** November 29, 2018. **Description:** Amazon is trying to move into the car parts industry, but is hitting a snag due to smaller brick-and-mortar stores being able to provide customer service and helping to guide consumers

through their purchases. Amazon is looking into partnering with other retail outlets, which may help their bottom line in this industry. **Availability:** Online.

11753 ■ *"Home Security Systems That Are Fast, Easy and Totally Not Creepy" in The Wall Street Journal (August 26, 2018)*
URL(s): www.wsj.com/articles/home-security-systems -that-are-fast-easy-and-totally-not-creepy -1535288400
Ed: David Pierce. **Released:** August 26, 2018. **Description:** Reviews for four different home security kits that are easy to install and pair with an app on the phone. Each one is slightly different from the other and descriptions of what comes in the kit and how invasive they to your privacy are given. **Availability:** Online.

11754 ■ *"Hoop Culture Opens Showroom, Expands Reach Globally" in Orlando Business Journal (Vol. 30, February 28, 2014, No. 36, pp. 3)*
Pub: American City Business Journals, Inc.
Contact: Mike Olivieri, Executive Vice President
Released: Weekly. **Description:** Hoop Culture Inc. president, Mike Brown, shares how the online basketball apparel retailer/wholesaler online store has expanded globally. He mentions that Orlando, Florida is one of their biggest markets. **Availability:** Print; Online.

11755 ■ *"How Are Digital Marketplaces Affecting the Wholesale Model?" in Business of Home (November 5, 2019)*
URL(s): businessofhome.com/articles/how-are-digital -marketplaces-affecting-the-wholesale-model
Ed: Warren Shoulberg. **Released:** November 05, 2019. **Description:** Discusses the B2B wholesale initiative in the gift and home markets industry. Typically, wholesalers sold directly to shops via trade shows, seasonal markets, and buying days, but two digital platforms, Faire and ModMart, are now offering an online alternative. **Availability:** Online.

11756 ■ *"How Concierge Roles Are Changing in an Internet Age" in Hotel News Now (July 9, 2018)*
URL(s): www.hotelnewsnow.com/Articles/287216/ How-concierge-roles-are-changing-in-an-interne t-age
Ed: Laura Koss-Feder. **Released:** July 09, 2018. **Description:** With so many people plugged into their phones, they have everything they need to enjoy a trip. Online reviews of restaurants, shows, and attractions are at their fingertips. How do traditional concierges compete? . **Availability:** Online.

11757 ■ *"How COVID-19 Has Changed Customer Behavior, and How Businesses Can Respond" in Legal Zoom (February 22, 2023)*
URL(s): www.legalzoom.com/articles/how-covid-19 -has-changed-customer-behavior-and-how-busi nesses-can-respond
Ed: Kylie Ora Lobell. **Released:** February 22, 2023. **Description:** The worldwide pandemic altered a lot of human behaviors as we adjusted to a new normal, and that is especially true when it comes to behaviors about shopping. Find out what changed, what's new, and how businesses can adapt. **Availability:** Online.

11758 ■ *"How I Did It: Best Buy's CEO On Learning to Love Social Media" in Harvard Business Review (Vol. 88, December 2010, No. 12, pp. 43)*
Pub: Harvard Business Publishing
Contact: Diane Belcher, Managing Director
Ed: Brian J. Dunn. **Price:** $8.95, PDF. **Description:** Effective utilization of online social networks to enhance brand identity, connect with consumers, and address bad publicity scenarios is examined. **Availability:** Online; PDF.

11759 ■ *"How Plumbing Facebook Groups Have Changed the Industry" in Plumber (November 20, 2019)*
URL(s): www.plumbermag.com/how-to-articles/ communication-networking-industry-social/how -plumbing-facebook-groups-have-changed-the-in dustry

Ed: Anthony Pacilla. **Released:** November 20, 2019. **Description:** Online Facebook books are providing a powerful tool for today's plumbers, which is easy-access online content about the industry. Once available only through national associations, the library, or on the job, answers to questions plumbers may come across can be easily solved within groups populated by industry experts. **Availability:** Online.

11760 ■ *"How to (Realistically) Start an Online Ecommerce Busines That Actually Grows in 2019" in Big Commerce*
URL(s): www.bigcommerce.com/blog/how-to-create -online-store/#learn-how-to-create-your-own-online -store
Ed: Tracey Wallace. **Description:** A 9-chapter guide on everything you need to know to start an online business. Topics include how to find niche products to sell; how to evaluate the market; online market research; conducting a competitive analysis; business laws; how to analyze your target market; how to source and manufacture products; and how to create, setup, and launch an online store. **Availability:** PDF; Online.

11761 ■ *"How Small, Independent Hotels Are Using Tech to Be More Competitive" in Skift (November 11, 2019)*
URL(s): skift.com/2019/11/11/how-small-independen t-hotels-are-using-tech-to-be-more-competitive/
Released: November 11, 2019. **Description:** Consumers are used to using online methods to search for the best deals on hotel prices, which often leaves smaller hotels out of the equation due to them just not having the high-tech systems that big chains can afford. However, online travel agencies like Expedia are trying to bridge the technology gap by offering easy to use solutions for these smaller hotels. **Availability:** Online.

11762 ■ *"How to Transition Your Brick and Mortar Business to an Online Entity" in Legal Zoom (February 22, 2023)*
URL(s): www.legalzoom.com/articles/how-to-transi tion-your-brick-and-mortar-business-to-an-online-en tity
Ed: Sandra Beckwith. **Released:** February 22, 2023. **Description:** Read about the advantages of transforming your brick and mortar business into an online presence. **Availability:** Online.

11763 ■ *"Iconic Boise Skateboard Shop to Close" in Idaho Business Review (August 19, 2014)*
Pub: BridgeTower Media
Contact: Adam Reinebach, President
Description: Lori Wright and Lori Ambur have owned Newt & Harold's for over 30 years. The partners are closing the firm that sold skateboards and snowboards. Wright focused on the marketing and inventory aspects of the retail shop, while Ambur ran the organizational and financial end. Wright and Ambur say they are leaving retail because the industry has faced so many changes since they first opened, particularly competing with online stores.

11764 ■ *"In the 2019 Dating World, Nobody Meets in Person Anymore" in The Philadelphia Inquirer (February 13, 2019)*
URL(s): www.inquirer.com/news/online-dating-tinder -bumble-okcupid-match-meet-cute-20190213.html
Ed: Anna Orso. **Released:** February 13, 2019. **Description:** Technology has changed how people date, where users can look up profiles on their phones and try to find their ideal match. Old-fashioned face-to-face meetings are becoming rare as people prefer the ease of using apps where most of the guesswork is eliminated, which eases fears and decreases anxiety of having to walk up and introduce oneself. **Availability:** Online.

11765 ■ *"Internet Sales of Pet Products Increasingly 'Big Box'" in Pet Product News (Vol. 66, September 2012, No. 9, pp. 4)*
Description: Internet sales account for nearly 4 percent of the $30 billion U.S. market for pet products in 2011, or about $1.2 billion retail. Meanwhile, overall

pet product retail sales growth and overall Internet retail sales growth of 10 percent can be outpaced as Internet sales of pet products is seen to grow at a 12 percent compound annual rate through 2015. **Availability:** Online.

11766 ■ *"Jab, Jab, Jab, Right Hook: How to Tell Your Story in a Noisy Social World"*
Pub: Harper Business
Contact: Hollis Heimbouch, Senior Vice President Publisher
Released: November 26, 2013. **Price:** $23.99, hardcover. **Description:** Author and social media expert shares advice on ways to connect with customers and beat the competition. Social media strategies for marketers and managers need to convert Internet traffic to sales. Communication is the key to online sales that are adapted to high quality social media platforms and mobile devices. **Availability:** E-book; Print.

11767 ■ *"Jo-Ann Fabric and Craft Stores Joins ArtFire.com to Offer Free Online Craft Marketplace" in Marketwired (January 26, 2010)*
Pub: Comtex News Network Inc.
Contact: Kan Devnani, President
Description: Jo-Ann Fabric and Craft Stores has entered into a partnership with ArtFire.com which will provide sewers and crafters all the tools they need in order to make and sell their products from an online venue. **Availability:** Print; Online.

11768 ■ *"Kinek Offers Secure Prescription Drop-Off For Online Shoppers" in Pittsburgh Post-Gazette (June 14, 2012)*
Description: Canadian firm, Kinek, founded in 2009 in New Brunswick, provides drop-off point locations for online shoppers. Med-Fast Pharmacy in Western Pennsylvania joined the Kinek network to provide prescription pickup. The service can be used for most online purchases, including those made on Amazon or eBay. Some drop off sites charge a fee, others are free. **Availability:** Print; Online.

11769 ■ *"LivingSocial's New 'Glue'" in Washington Business Journal (Vol. 33, May 2, 2014, No. 2, pp. 10)*
Pub: American City Business Journals, Inc.
Contact: Mike Olivieri, Executive Vice President
Description: LivingSocial Inc. CFO, John Bax, shares his views on the confluence of forces that shaped the company's first quarter results. Bax reports the company is pouring resources into the creation of a new retail merchant solution platform to help market products and services. Bax named the project Glue because it is geared to encouraging customer loyalty to merchants along with repeat business. **Availability:** Print; Online.

11770 ■ *"Major Publishers Are Selling a Ton of Ebooks in 2021" in Good E-Reader (May 7, 2021)*
URL(s): goodereader.com/blog/e-book-news/major -publishers-are-selling-a-ton-of-ebooks-in-2021
Ed: Michael Kozlowski. **Released:** May 07, 2021. **Description:** Ebook and audiobooks sales are doing quite well in 2021, which is due mainly to people staying home and not shopping at bookstores. Harpercollins, S&S, and Hachette had increased sales. **Availability:** Download.

11771 ■ *"Modern Meal Offers Recipe Inspiration, Curation and Home Delivery" in Orlando Business Journal (Vol. 30, April 4, 2014, No. 41, pp. 3)*
Pub: American City Business Journals, Inc.
Contact: Mike Olivieri, Executive Vice President
Released: Weekly. **Price:** $8, introductory 4-week offer(Digital & Print). **Description:** Modern Meal LLC's CEO, Mark Hudgins, works to get people to the dinner table for a good meal. The social network with a Pinterest look is in early-beta-launch and users are trying out the features by curating recipes from

popular cooking Websites and looking at recipes of other users. Modern' Meal's plan to tap into the e-grocery market is also discussed. **Availability:** Print; Online.

11772 ■ *"MyReviewsNow.net Announces New Affiliate Partner Gift Baskets Overseas" in M2 EquityBites (EQB) (June 22, 2012)*
Description: MyReviewsNow.net has partnered with Gift Baskets Overseas in order to offer gift baskets to be shipped overseas. Gift Baskets Oversease works with local florists and shippers worldwide. No financial details were disclosed. **Availability:** Online.

11773 ■ *"A Neat SocialTrade" in Barron's (Vol. 92, July 23, 2012, No. 30, pp. 23)*
Pub: Dow Jones & Company Inc.
Contact: Almar Latour, Chief Executive Officer
Ed: Theresa W. Carey. **Description:** SocialTrade is a Website that allows users to exchange ideas and data with each other through video. Online broker DittoTrade launched a mobile applications that allows investors to connect to other traders and follow their trades. **Availability:** Online.

11774 ■ *"The New and Improved Ski Shop" in Powder (January 11, 2017)*
URL(s): www.powder.net/stories/news/the-new-an d-improved-ski-shop/
Ed: Devon O'Neil. **Released:** January 11, 2017. **Description:** Traditional ski shop have found they must compete with online sales, especially since consumers bought about $1 billion worth of snow sports equipment from the internet. Big chains have closed but some smaller shops are actually thriving due to innovations and an eye for great customer service. **Availability:** Online.

11775 ■ *"The One Thing You Must Get Right When Building a Brand" in Harvard Business Review (Vol. 88, December 2010, No. 12, pp. 80)*
Pub: Harvard Business Publishing
Contact: Diane Belcher, Managing Director
Ed: Patrick Barwise, Sean Meehan. **Price:** $8.95, PDF. **Description:** Four uses for new media include: communicating a clearly defined customer promise, creating trust via delivering on the promise, regularly improving on the promise, and innovating past what is familiar. **Availability:** Online; PDF.

11776 ■ *"Online Alcohol Purchasing Comes of Age" in Supermarket News (September 16, 2021)*
Ed: Amber Roberts. **Released:** September 16, 2021. **Description:** The demand for online alcohol sales increases during the COVID-19 pandemic, so more traditional brick-and-mortar stores are beginning to add online sales. However, regulations are often strict, which has led to online delivery platform companies dominating the industry.

11777 ■ *"Online Consignment Is Big Business and a Bargain Hunter's Heaven" in CBS News (April 13, 2017)*
URL(s): www.cbsnews.com/news/clothing -consignment-fashion-bargain-online/
Released: April 03, 2017. **Description:** There is a big boom in online consignment shops, with it now being an $18 billion industry. ThredUp is one of the main online sites dealing with used clothing, while The RealReal is another site dealing with mostly high-end designer items. Both sites cash in because so many people out there are looking for good bargains on quality clothing. **Availability:** Online.

11778 ■ *"Online Security Crackdown" in Chain Store Age (Vol. 84, July 2008, No. 7, pp. 46)*
Ed: Samantha Murphy. **Description:** Online retailers are beefing up security on their Websites. Cyber thieves use retail systems in order to gain entry to consumer data. David's Bridal operates over 275 bridal showrooms in the U.S. and has a one-stop wedding resource for new brides planning weddings. **Availability:** Online.

11779 ■ *"Online Shopping Overtakes a Major Part of Retail for the First Time Ever" in CNBC.com (April 2. 2019)*
URL(s): www.cnbc.com/2019/04/02/online-shopping -officially-overtakes-brick-and-mortar-retail-for-the -first-time-ever.html
Released: April 02, 2019. **Description:** The total market share of "non-store," or online U.S. retail sales was higher than general merchandise sales for the first time in history. Online stores, led by Amazon, are seeing sales increase over the decades with no sign of slowing down. **Availability:** Online.

11780 ■ *"Open Source Intelligence for Private Investigators" in PInow.com (October 14, 2019)*
URL(s): www.pinow.com/articles/2646/open-source-in telligence-for-private-investigators
Released: October 14, 2019. **Description:** Examines the role of Open Source Intelligence (OSINT) that private investigators use. Even though it is accessible to everyone it can still be a great tool to use since data it provides could be useful. Several open source tools are described with their benefits along with links. **Availability:** Online.

11781 ■ *"Over-50 Singles Might Have the Best Luck Online" in USA Today (August 31, 2019)*
URL(s): www.usatoday.com/story/life/2019/08/31/ online-dating-over-50/2129198001/
Ed: Valerie Finholm. **Released:** August 31, 2019. **Description:** Dating past 50 can be nerve-wracking, but online dating seems to be helping to ease those jitters. There are sites such as OurTime.com and Stitch that are designed specifically for people in their 50s, and even eHarmony.com and Match.com are being used by people in this demographic. **Availability:** Online.

11782 ■ *"Pa. Pushes for Collection of Online Sales Tax" in Philadelphia Business Journal (Vol. 31, March 2, 2012, No. 3, pp. 1)*
Pub: Baltimore Business Journal
Contact: Rhonda Pringle, President
E-mail: rpringle@bizjournals.com
Description: The government of Pennsylvania is seeking to increase taxes from e-sales. The government estimates that it could lose $380 million in uncollected online sales and use tax to the e-commerce retail sector in 2012. It has also introduced tax forms that instruct taxpayers to report and remit use tax. **Availability:** Print; Online.

11783 ■ *"The Power of Online" in Advertising Age (Vol. 85, October 13, 2014, No. 21, pp. 4)*
Pub: Crain Communications Inc.
Contact: Barry Asin, President
Description: According to Shop.org, online sales could increase by as much as 11 percent this holiday season. Retailers are not only focusing on when customers will start holiday shopping, but whether they will use online stores or shop at brick-and-mortar stores. Many retailers are expanding their online services using digital showrooms on their Websites. **Availability:** Online.

11784 ■ *"Powering Intelligent Commerce: eCommera Rebrands as OrderDynamics, Helping Retailers Activate Commerce from First Interaction to Fulfillment" in Computer Business Week (August 28, 2014, pp. 20)*
Pub: NewsRX LLC.
Contact: Kalani Rosell, Contact
Description: OrderDynamics, a new global brand created by eCommera, is profiled. The firm will continue to provide an integrated suite of software-as-a-service (SaaS) big data products and service that power intelligent commerce for retailers and brands around the world. Details of the integration of the new brand are included. **Availability:** Online.

11785 ■ *"ReachLocal Plans to Double DFW Space, is Hunting for 150K Square Feet" in Dallas Business Journal (Vol. 35, March 23, 2012, No. 28, pp. 1)*
Pub: Baltimore Business Journal
Contact: Rhonda Pringle, President

E-mail: rpringle@bizjournals.com
Description: Online marketing firm ReachLocal Inc. is planning to double its presence in North Texas. The company is considering building up to 150,000-square-feet of space in the area. Construction plans are included. **Availability:** Print; Online.

11786 ■ *"Recycling Old Cellphones" in San Jose Mercury News (September 26, 2012)*
Description: Gazelle.com buys old gadgets, including mobile phones, on its Website. The firm either resells the gadgets through retail channels such as eBy or turns them over to wholesalers. Recycling electronic waste information is provided. **Availability:** Online.

11787 ■ *"Report Challenges Internet Providers' Advertised Speeds" in U.S. News & World Report (August 31, 2019)*
URL(s): www.usnews.com/news/best-states/pennsyl-vania/articles/2019-08-31/report-challenges-interne t-providers-advertised-speeds
Ed: Jon O'Connell, Bill Wellock. **Released:** August 31, 2019. **Description:** New research has uncovered that internet service providers aren't being truthful when it comes to disclosing their internet speeds. While boasting about high speeds, the reality is that consumers aren't receiving these high speeds. This has been having detrimental effects on people, especially in rural communities, because it causes a lack of availability to access educational, health care, and commerce tools. **Availability:** Online.

11788 ■ *"The Rise of Digital Currencies and Atlanta's Key Role" in Atlanta Business Chronicle (July 4, 2014, pp. 25A)*
Pub: American City Business Journals, Inc.
Contact: Mike Olivieri, Executive Vice President
Released: Weekly. **Price:** $4, introductory 4-week offer(Digital only). **Description:** Virtual currency bit-coin, which is an Internet protocol that defines a decentralized online payment system is discussed. A description of how bitcoin and other virtual currencies are used and concerns over its future use are examined. A short profile of Atlanta-based startup BitPay, which provides software solutions to help businesses accept bitcoin payments without risking operating cash flow is included. BitPay also enables rapid currency conversion through bitcoin ATMs or kiosks. **Availability:** Print; Online.

11789 ■ *"Same-Day Delivery's Second Act" in Inc. (Vol. 36, March 2014, No. 2, pp. 87)*
Pub: Mansueto Ventures L.L.C.
Contact: Stephanie Mehta, Chief Executive Officer
Description: New technology is helping electronic commerce to be reliable and profitable while offering same day delivery. Profiles of delivery services competing for retail contracts include Instacart, Zoo-kal, Postmates, to name a few. Statistical data included. **Availability:** Online.

11790 ■ *"Save-A-Lot Adds Amazon PayCode and Hub Locker to St. Louis Stores" in Grocery Dive (November 5, 2019)*
URL(s): www.grocerydive.com/news/save-a-lot-adds -amazon-paycode-and-hub-locker-to-st-louis-stores/ 566608/
Ed: Lauren Stine. **Released:** November 05, 2019. **Description:** Save-A-Lot is adding Amazon PayCode to several stores in St. Louis, which allows for picking up and paying for Amazon packages with cash. Amazon Hub Locker will also be available. **Availability:** Online.

11791 ■ *"Say Yes to the New Wedding Collection from Pinhole Press" in Benzinga.com (May 1, 2012)*
Pub: Benzinga.com
Contact: Jason Raznick, Founder
Ed: Aaron Wise. **Description:** Online retailer, Pinhole Press, providing personalized photo gifts has introduced a new Edding Collection that includes wedding invitations, save the dates, bridal shower sets, wedding gifts and more. Further details of the new wedding collection are included. **Availability:** Online.

11792 ■ *"Search and Discover New Opportunities" in DM News (Vol. 31, December 14, 2009, No. 29, pp. 13)*
Pub: Haymarket Media Inc.
Contact: Kevin Costello, Chief Executive Officer
Ed: Chantal Tode. **Description:** Although other digital strategies are gaining traction in Internet marketing, search marketing continues to dominate this advertising forum. Companies like American Greetings, which markets e-card brands online, are utilizing social networking sites and affiliates to generate a higher demand for their products. **Availability:** Print; Online.

11793 ■ *Selling Online for Dummies*
Pub: John Wiley & Sons, Inc.
Contact: Christina Van Tassell, Executive Vice President Chief Financial Officer
Ed: Paul Waddy. **Released:** September 2023. **Price:** $26.99, paperback. **Description:** Guide instructs readers on how to set up an online shopping site and how to manage the business aspects such as taxes and duties. **Availability:** Print.

11794 ■ *"Shop Happy: Harvesting Happiness Announces Grassroots Crowdfunding Site for HH4Heroes" in Marketwired (July 2, 2012)*
Pub: Comtex News Network Inc.
Contact: Kan Devnani, President
Description: Shop Happy online store has created a fundraising aspect to their customers' shopping experience. Shoppers can assist in helping to heal post combat veterans suffering from PTSD, TBI, MST, andMSA who have served as combat warriors in Operations Iraqi and Enduring Freedom. Lisa Cypers Kamen, founder of Harvesting Happiness believes this program will help both veterans and customers to empower themselves and our veterans in a positive way (HH4Heroes.org).

11795 ■ *Shopify for Dummies*
Pub: John Wiley & Sons, Inc.
Contact: Christina Van Tassell, Executive Vice President Chief Financial Officer
URL(s): www.wiley.com/en-us/Shopify+For+Dummies -p-9780730394457
Ed: Paul Waddy. **Released:** August 2022. **Price:** $16, e-book; $26.99, paperback. **Description:** A guide on how to set up and run your own online Shopify store. **Availability:** E-book; Print.

11796 ■ *"Soda Says, a Curated Consumer Electronics Retail Platform, Launches in the US" in TechCrunch (May 29, 2019)*
URL(s): techcrunch.com/2019/05/29/soda-says-a -curated-consumer-electronics-retail-platform -launches-in-the-u-s/
Ed: Jordan Crook. **Released:** May 29, 2019. **Description:** Soda Says, a new e-commerce marketplace launched in the US. This platform focuses on lifestyle gadgets that are useful and pleasing to the eye. They are also offering pop-up stores within traditional department stores. **Availability:** Online.

11797 ■ *"The Soon To Be $200B Online Food Delivery Is Rapidly Changing the Global Food Industry" in Forbes September 9, 2019)*
URL(s): www.forbes.com/sites/sarwantsingh/2019/ 09/09/the-soon-to-be-200b-online-food-delivery-is -rapidly-changing-the-global-food-industry/#738 268e0b1bc
Ed: Sarwant Singh. **Released:** September 09, 2019. **Description:** Discusses the growing demand for online food delivery services in the United States and worldwide. There are currently ten major players in this game just in the United States, and each is trying to take bigger and bigger pieces of the industry. **Availability:** Online.

11798 ■ *Starting an Etsy Business for Dummies*
Pub: John Wiley & Sons, Inc.
Contact: Christina Van Tassell, Executive Vice President Chief Financial Officer
URL(s): www.wiley.com/en-us/Starting+an+Etsy +Business+For+Dummies%2C+4th+Edition-p-978 1394168705

Ed: Kate Shoup, Kate Gatski. **Released:** 4th edition. **Price:** $24.99, paperback. **Description:** A guide on how to start selling products on Etsy and setting up a shop on their website. New updates about the current changes to Etsy are included, how to market your products, how to generate better search results, plus more guidance is included. **Availability:** Print.

11799 ■ *"StubHub Launches in the UK" in Entertainment Close-Up (March 25, 2012)*
Description: StubHub, an eBay company, is expanding to the United Kingdom. The firm sells tickets, third party, to music, sport, and entertainment events by connecting buyers and sellers. Details of the service and expansion are explored. **Availability:** Online.

11800 ■ *"Survey: People Willing to Pay More for Food Delivery" in U.S. News & World Report (July 30, 2019)*
URL(s): www.usnews.com/news/national-news/ar ticles/2019-07-30/survey-people-willing-to-pay-more -for-food-delivery
Ed: Alexa Lardieri. **Released:** July 30, 2019. **Description:** With consumers using food delivery apps more and more, a new survey from U.S. Foods concluded that Uber Eats is the most popular app followed by GrubHug, DoorDash, and Postmates. People are also unwilling to wait for more than 40 minutes for their delivery and there are caps on the amount of money they will spend on fees and tips. **Availability:** Online.

11801 ■ *"Target to Power New Toys 'R' Us Online Business" in Reuters (October 8, 2019)*
URL(s): www.reuters.com/article/us-target-toys-r-us/ target-to-power-new-toys-r-us-online-business-i dUSKBN1WN1GG
Released: October 08, 2019. **Description:** Target announced a partnership with Tru Kids, which is the parent of the Toys 'R' Us brand, in order to run their toy website, ToysRUs.com. Consumers have the option to complete their purchase at Target.com. **Availability:** Online.

11802 ■ *"Therealreal's Online Luxury Consignment Shop" in The New Yorker (October 14, 2019)*
URL(s): www.newyorker.com/magazine/2019/10/21/ therealreals-online-luxury-consignment-shop
Ed: Susan Orlean. **Released:** October 14, 2019. **Description:** TheRealReal's online consignment site specializes in high-end designer clothes, jewelry, and handbags. With the online presence to go along with their brick-and-mortar store, items can be seen by more people around the world, especially since the used-clothes market is trending upward. **Availability:** Online.

11803 ■ *"ThredUp Is Helping Big Stores Sell Recyled Clothes" in Quartzy (August 21, 2019)*
URL(s): qz.com/quartzy/1692050/thredup-is-giving-re tailers-a-plug-and-play-platform-to-sell-used-clo thes/
Ed: Marc Bain. **Released:** August 21, 2019. **Description:** ThredUp has announced its new program, Resale-As-A-Servie (RAAS), which will allow big box clothes retailers to sell directly from its used clothing inventory. **Availability:** Online.

11804 ■ *"ThredUP Launches Online Concierge Service to Compete With Children's Consignment" in Benzinga.com (January 25, 2012)*
Description: Concierge is a new service offered by thredUP, the top online site for used children's clothing. Concierge simplifies the process of recycling children's clothing. Users sign up at the Website and request a prepaid, ready to ship recycling bag. After filling the bag, it is placed on the doorstep, and thredUp takes it from there. After consignors inspect the items, senders are given rewards up to $5 per piece, based on quality and quantity of items shipped. The received items are then sold on thredUP's online shop.

11805 ■ *"The Top 4 Tips for Virtual Startups" in Legal Zoom (February 24, 2023)*
URL(s): www.legalzoom.com/articles/the-top-tips-for -virtual-startups
Ed: Brette Sember, J.D. **Released:** February 24, 2023. **Description:** A virtual startup has a rather unique setting since it's all online, so how does one manage employees when everyone is remote? Follow these guidelines to keep your business running smoothly. **Availability:** Online.

11806 ■ *"Top 10 Most Popular Online Makeup Stores in the U.S." in US Unlocked*
URL(s): www.usunlocked.com/top-10-us-makeup-s tores/
Ed: Linda Hemerik. **Description:** Online beauty stores are more popular than ever thanks to beauty vloggers and influencers. Included are some of the best places to buy cosmetics online. **Availability:** Online.

11807 ■ *Trade Show Calendar*
URL(s): www.expomarketing.com/trade-show-calen dar/
Released: 2019. **Description:** Hundreds of trade shows are presented in an online website, complete with links directly to the events' webpages. **Availability:** Online.

11808 ■ *"Trader Joe's Secret Sauce? An Army of Influencers" in Grocery Dive (November 8, 2019)*
URL(s): www.grocerydive.com/news/trader-joes -secret-sauce-an-army-of-influencers/566912/
Ed: Jennifer Sweeney. **Released:** November 08, 2019. **Description:** Influencer marketing is giving Trader Joe's a boost on Instagram thanks to several social media accounts from fans of the company. Featuring products and recipes, these digital influencers have inadvertently created a whole marketing campaign for the grocer. **Availability:** Online.

11809 ■ *"The Truth about Ecommerce You Might Not Realize" in Small Business Trends(February 1, 2023)*
URL(s): smallbiztrends.com/2023/01/truth-abou t-ecommerce.html
Ed: Holly Chavez. **Released:** February 01, 2023. **Description:** Steve Chou, founder of MyWifeQuitHerJob.com, is interviewed about ecommerce and small businesses. **Availability:** Online.

11810 ■ *"Uptick in Clicks: Nordstrom's Online Sales Surging" in Puget Sound Business Journal (Vol. 29, August 22, 2008, No. 18, pp. 1)*
Description: Nordstrom Inc.'s online division grew its sales by 15 percent in the second quarter of 2008, compared to 2007's 4.3 percent in overall decline. The company expects their online net sales to reach $700 million in 2008 capturing eight percent of overall sales. **Availability:** Print; Online.

11811 ■ *"Wakefern's ShopRite Tests Online Meal Planning Service" in Supermarket News (November 4, 2019)*
URL(s): www.supermarketnews.com/online-retail/ wakefern-s-shoprite-tests-online-meal-planning -service
Ed: Russell Redman. **Released:** November 04, 2019. **Description:** Wakefern Food Corp. is partnering with Locai Solutions and piloting an online meal planning and recipe experience called CookIt. The technology uses artificial intelligence which recommends recipes based off of customers' online shopping baskets. **Availability:** Online.

11812 ■ *"Want to Work for Amazon? You May Get the Chance Soon" in Pharmacy Times (May 17, 2017)*
URL(s): www.pharmacytimes.com/contributor/timothy -aungst-pharmd/2017/05/want-to-work-for-amazon -you-may-get-the-chance-soon
Ed: Timothy Aungst. **Released:** May 17, 2017. **Description:** Online retail giant, Amazon, is making a play to break into the pharmacy industry. More staff

is being hired for Amazon's health care division, which could lead to quick home deliveries for prescriptions. **Availability:** Online.

11813 ■ *"Watch Out, Uber Eaters: Online Food Delivery Can Lead to Overspending and Isolation" in Tennessean (June 25, 2019)*
URL(s): www.tennessean.com/story/money/2019/06/25/online-food-delivery-can-lead-addiction-overspending/1490064001/
Ed: Sandy Mazza, Brad Schmitt. **Released:** June 25, 2019. **Description:** Food delivery services and apps are quickly growing and people love the convenience they provide. However, it's often hard to stop ordering food online because it's so accessible and easy, which if not checked will lead to overspending. **Availability:** Online.

11814 ■ *"Wayfair Unveils New Mobile App Features" in Home Accents Today (November 13, 2019)*
URL(s): www.homeaccentstoday.com/e-commerce/wayfair-unveils-new-mobile-app-features/
Released: November 13, 2019. **Description:** Wanting to make it easier for their customers to discover products and have the ability to design rooms on the go, Wayfair added some new features to its mobile shopping app. Now consumers have access to an augmented reality (AR) tool and a Room Planner 3-D. **Availability:** Online.

11815 ■ *"Web Move Puts Rack Ahead of Pack" in Puget Sound Business Journal (Vol. 35, May 16, 2014, No. 4, pp. 8)*
Pub: American City Business Journals, Inc.
Contact: Mike Olivieri, Executive Vice President
Description: Upscale retailer, Norstrom Inc., launched a Website for Nordstrom Rack in the hopes of boosting sales for its discount arm by 10 to 20 percent. Terry Boyle, present of Nordstrom Rack's online store, is not concerned that the site might steal traffic from their retail establishments. **Availability:** Online.

11816 ■ *"Web Tax Holiday About to End" in Silicon Valley/San Jose Business Journal (Vol. 30, September 7, 2012, No. 24, pp. 1)*
Pub: Baltimore Business Journal
Contact: Rhonda Pringle, President
E-mail: rpringle@bizjournals.com
Description: Retailers outside California will be required to charge sales tax to customers in the state making online purchases. It is believed that the sales tax will provide an additional boost for independent booksellers. These sellers claim that they have been at a disadvantage becazuse they were required to automatically charge customers with an 8.375 percent tax. **Availability:** Print; Mailing list; Online.

11817 ■ *"What's Amazon Doing in the Pet Consumables Market?" in veterinarynews.dvm360.com (October 2, 2018)*
URL(s): veterinarynews.dvm360.com/whats-amazon-doing-pet-consumables-market
Ed: Katie James. **Released:** October 02, 2018. **Description:** Amazon provides insight into its pet business model, which has local veterinarians worried about the competition. In the meantime, Amazon is growing its share of pet consumables, which include food, healthcare products, and litter by applying it's successful business strategy that works with other consumers. **Availability:** Online.

11818 ■ *"Why Messaging Is the Future of Market Research" in Entrepreneur (July 2, 2019)*
URL(s): www.entrepreneur.com/article/332354
Ed: Andrew Reid. **Released:** July 02, 2019. **Availability:** Online.

11819 ■ *"With Funeral Home Rules Due for an Update, There's a Push for Online Prices" in The New York Times (March 29, 2019)*
URL(s): www.nytimes.com/2019/03/29/your-money/funeral-homes-pricing.html

Ed: Ann Carrns. **Released:** March 29, 2019. **Description:** Consumer advocates are pushing for change when it comes to funeral services by advocating for online pricing. Federal regulators are taking a look at an old rule that governs how funeral homes share information, and advocates want these prices online so that consumers can be better informed ahead of time. **Availability:** Online.

11820 ■ *"Wolferman's Bakery Introduces New Brand Positioning" in Snack Food & Wholesale Bakery Magazine (October 3, 2019)*
URL(s): www.snackandbakery.com/articles/93542-wolfermans-bakery-introduces-new-brand-positioning
Released: October 03, 2019. **Description:** Wolferman's is introducing a new brand positioning to help consumers be aware they sell more than just English Muffins. They have a full online bakery, which complements it's partnership with Harry & David and 1-800-FLOWERS.COM Inc. **Availability:** Print; Online.

11821 ■ *"Women Clicking to Earn Virtual Dollars" in Sales and Marketing Management (November 11, 2009)*
Ed: Stacy Straczynski. **Description:** According to a new report from Internet marketing firm Q Interactive, women are increasingly playing social media games where they are able to click on an ad or sign up for a promotion to earn virtual currency. Research is showing that this kind of marketing may be a potent tool, especially for e-commerce and online stores. **Availability:** Print; Online.

11822 ■ *"WordPress May NOT Be Right for This Type of Business" in Small Business Trends(January 10, 2023)*
URL(s): smallbiztrends.com/2023/01/why-use-wordpress.html
Ed: Holly Chavez. **Released:** January 10, 2023. **Description:** While WordPress is a great option for many small businesses to present an online presence, it is not a good option for those that rely on e-commerce. **Availability:** Online.

11823 ■ *"You Call It Craft, I Call It Art" in The New York Times (August 23, 2019)*
URL(s): www.nytimes.com/2019/08/23/arts/design/folk-art-market-santa-fe.html
Ed: Guy Trebay. **Released:** August 23, 2019. **Description:** Explores the creative process of craftspeople and discusses the shifting perceptions of art, folk art, and crafting within the context of social media. With the rise of social media, more people are exposed to new ideas and various artistic work. **Availability:** Online.

11824 ■ *"Young Entrepreneur Gets Some Recognition and Some Help for College" in Philadelphia Inquirer (August 30, 2010)*
Pub: The Philadelphia Inquirer
Contact: Elizabeth H. Hughes, Chief Executive Officer
Ed: Susan Snyder. **Description:** Profile of Zachary Gosling, age 18, who launched an online auction Website from his bedroom, using advertising and sponsorship funds rather than charging fees to users.

11825 ■ *Zotero for Genealogy: Harnessing the Power of Your Research*
Ed: Donna Cox Baker. **Price:** $21.99, Paperback; $9.99, E-book. **Description:** A guide on how to use the Zotero download for genealogy research. The product eliminates bulky files, binders, papers and allows the user to keep all notes and citations on any computing device. **Availability:** E-book; Print.

11826 ■ *"Zuckerberg Says Ecommerce Trends After Pandemic Led to Mass Layoffs" in Small Business Trends(November 17, 2022)*
URL(s): smallbiztrends.com/2022/11/meta-ceo-says-ecommerce-trends-after-pandemic-led-to-mass-layoffs.html

Ed: Gabrielle Pickard-Whitehead. **Released:** November 17, 2022. **Description:** After miscalculating ecommerce trends during the pandemic, Meta CEO Mark Zuckerberg laid off 11,000 employees. **Availability:** Online.

STATISTICAL SOURCES

11827 ■ *Black Consumers: Digital Trends & Impact of COVID-19 One Year Later - US - April 2021*
URL(s): store.mintel.com/report/black-consumers-digital-trends-impact-of-covid-19-one-year-later-us-april-2021
Price: $4,366.35. **Description:** Downloadable report detailing the purchase power of the Black consumer and the relationship to digital products and services. Report includes an executive summary, interactive databook, PowerPoint presentation, infographic overview, report PDF, and previous years data. **Availability:** PDF.

11828 ■ *Digital Printing Industry in the US - Market Research Report*
URL(s): www.ibisworld.com/united-states/market-research/digital-printing-industry/
Price: $925. **Description:** Downloadable report analyzing the current and future trends in the digital printing industry. **Availability:** Online.

11829 ■ *E-Book Publishing Industry in the US - Market Research Report*
URL(s): www.ibisworld.com/united-states/market-research/e-book-publishing-industry/
Price: $925. **Description:** Downloadable report analyzing the current and future trends of e-book publishing. **Availability:** Download.

11830 ■ *eCommerce Behaviors: Gen Z vs. Millennials: Incl Impact of Covid-19 - US - June 2020*
Price: $4,366.35. **Description:** Downloadable report discussing the analysis done on Gen Z and Millennials and their consumer habits. Report includes an executive summary, interactive databook, PowerPoint presentation, infographic overview, report PDF, and previous years data. **Availability:** PDF.

11831 ■ *Evolving eCommerce: Vitamins, Minerals & Supplements: Incl Impact of COVID-19 - US - December 2020*
URL(s): store.mintel.com/report/evolving-ecommerce-vitamins-minerals-supplements-incl-impact-of-covid-19-us-december-2020
Price: $4,366.35. **Description:** Downloadable report discussing data analysis about the vitamin, mineral, and supplement market and it's growth in online shopping. **Availability:** PDF.

11832 ■ *Hispanics: Digital Trends & Impact of COVID-19 One Year Later - US - April 2021*
URL(s): store.mintel.com/report/hispanics-digital-trends-impact-of-covid-19-one-year-later-us-april-2021
Price: $4,366.35. **Description:** Downloadable report discussing the impact the COVID-19 pandemic has had on the Hispanic community and their shopping habits. Provides data on Hispanics' approach to technology and attitudes about digital products. Report includes an executive summary, interactive databook, PowerPoint presentation, infographic overview, report PDF, and previous years data. **Availability:** PDF.

11833 ■ *Online Beauty Retailing - US - 2021*
URL(s): store.mintel.com/report/online-beauty-retailing-us-2021
Price: $4,366.35. **Description:** A downloadable report with insights on how the Covid-19 pandemic affected consumers and the way they shop. However, people still bought beauty products and this report gives the reasons, methods, considerations, and attitudes towards these purchases. The full report includes an executive summary, interactive databook, PowerPoint presentation, infographic overview, report PDF, and previous years data. **Availability:** PDF.

11834 ■ *Online Beer, Wine & Liquor Sales Industry in the US - Market Research Report*
URL(s): www.ibisworld.com/united-states/market-re-search-reports/online-beer-wine-liquor-sales-indus
try/

Price: $925. **Description:** Downloadable report analyzing the online beer, wine, and liquor retail industry. **Availability:** Online.

11835 ■ *Online Greeting Card Sales Industry in the US - Market Research Report*
URL(s): www.ibisworld.com/united-states/market-re-search-reports/online-greeting-card-sales-industry/

Price: $925. **Description:** Downloadable report analyzing the online greeting card industry. **Availability:** Online.

11836 ■ *Online Insurance Brokers Industry in the US - Market Research Report*
URL(s): www.ibisworld.com/united-states/market-re-search-reports/online-insurance-brokers-industry/

Price: $925. **Description:** Downloadable report analyzing the current and future trends in the online insurance broker industry. **Availability:** Download.

11837 ■ *U.S. Key Elements of Ecommerce Market Report 2021*
URL(s): store.mintel.com/report/us-key-elements-of
-ecommerce

Price: $4,366.35. **Description:** Downloadable report providing data on the online shopping habits of US consumers. Report includes an executive summary, interactive databook, PowerPoint presentation, infographic overview, report PDF, and previous years data. **Availability:** PDF.

11838 ■ *US Alcoholic Beverages Online Market Report 2021*
URL(s): store.mintel.com/report/us-alcoholic-bever-ages-online-market-report

Price: $4,366.35. **Description:** When the Covid-19 pandemic hit, online alcoholic beverage sales went up, due to people not wanting to shop instore. This downloadable report covers the reasons online sources are used to purchase alcohol, barriers to doing so, and consumer behavior trends. Included are an executive summary, interactive databook, PowerPoint presentation, infographic overview, report PDF, and previous years data. **Availability:** PDF.

11839 ■ *US Digital Advertising Market Report 2021*
URL(s): store.mintel.com/report/us-digital-advertising
-market-report

Price: $4,366.35. **Description:** Downloadable report examining recent trends in digital advertising, especially with the impact the Covid-19 pandemic has had on the way people consume advertising. Includes an executive summary, interactive databook, PowerPoint Presentation, Infographic Overview, report PDF, and previous years data. **Availability:** PDF.

11840 ■ *US Footwear Online Retailing Market Report 2021*
URL(s): store.mintel.com/report/us-footwear-online-re-tailing-market-report

Price: $4,366.35. **Description:** Downloadable report providing data on the online footwear retailing market. Report includes an executive summary, interactive databook, PowerPoint presentation, infographic overview, report PDF, and previous years data. **Availability:** PDF.

11841 ■ *US Online Apparel Retailing (Men's and Women's) Market Report 2021*
URL(s): store.mintel.com/report/us-online-apparel-re-tailing-mens-womens-market-report

Price: $4,366.35. **Description:** Downloadable report examining the shopping habits, both online and in-store, for clothing. Details how the Covid-19 pandemic affected shoppers. Report includes and executive summary, interactive databook, PowerPoint presentation, infographic overview, report pdf, and previous years data. **Availability:** PDF.

TRADE PERIODICALS

11842 ■ *Online Searcher*
Pub: Information Today Inc.
Contact: Thomas H. Hogan, President
URL(s): www.infotoday.com/OnlineSearcher

Released: Bimonthly; January/February, March/April, May/June, July/August, September/October, and November/December. **Description:** Edited for librarians, Webmasters, site designers, content managers, and others concerned with knowledge/information management. Includes critical reviews of Web sites, software, search engines, and information services. (Formerly published by Online, Inc.). **Availability:** Print; Online.

VIDEO/AUDIO MEDIA

11843 ■ *How I Built This: Paperless Post: James and Alexa Hirschfeld*
URL(s): wondery.com/shows/how-i-built-this/episode/10386-paperless-post-james-and-alexa-hirschfeld

Ed: Guy Raz. **Released:** October 07, 2024. **Description:** Founders discuss the challenges of starting an online invitation company, including convincing investors that it would work and settling on the right business model.

11844 ■ *Profit First Nation: Mastering Inventory for E-Commerce Success*
URL(s): www.profitfirstnation.com/episodes/ep-133-mastering-inventory-for-e-commerce-success-expert-tips-from-certified-profit-first-professional-cyndi-thomason

Ed: Danielle Mulvey. **Released:** August 22, 2023. **Description:** Podcast offers tips on managing inventory and explains why you need an inventory account.

11845 ■ *Recurring, Repeatable, Reliable Online Income with Dan R. Morris*
URL(s): www.eofire.com/podcast/danrmorris3

Ed: Jon Lee Dumas. **Released:** October 02, 2024. **Description:** Podcast explains what's needed to succeed as an online solopreneur: focus, tenacity, a homebase or website, a product or content, and a way to take the money.

11846 ■ *The Solopreneur Hour: 3 Steps to a Great Online Business with Chris Farrell*
URL(s): solopreneurhour.com/podcast/864-3-steps-to-a-great-online-business-w-chris-farrell-best-of

Ed: Michael O'Neal. **Released:** July 25, 2022. **Description:** Podcast discusses online marketing.

11847 ■ *The Solopreneur Hour: A Massive Passive Income Opportunity in Payment Processing*
URL(s): solopreneurhour.com/podcast/841-a-massive-passive-income-opportunity-in-payment-processing

Ed: Michael O'Neal. **Released:** July 25, 2022. **Description:** Podcast discusses payment processing.

11848 ■ *Uncovered: The Business of True Crime*
URL(s): www.thepitch.show/118-uncovered-the-business-of-true-criime

Released: September 13, 2023. **Description:** Podcast asks if a media company can scale returns by solving murders on a website.

PUBLICATIONS

11849 ■ *Plunkett's E-Commerce & Internet Business Almanac: Your Reference Source to All Facets of the Internet Business*
PO Box 541737
Houston, TX 77254-1737
Ph: (713)932-0000
Fax: (713)932-7080
Co. E-mail: customersupport@plunkettresearch.com
URL: http://www.plunkettresearch.com
Contact: Jack W. Plunkett, Chief Executive Officer
URL(s): www.plunkettresearch.com/7-keys-for-job
-seekers

Released: Latest issue 2023. **Price:** $399.99, Single issue. **Description:** Covers 400 of the largest companies working in all facets of e-commerce and Internet business, including Internet service providers, Web site operators, equipment and others. Includes financial details, growth and hiring plans, research, marketing, acquisitions, and technology. **Entries include:** Company name, address, phone, fax, Internet address, names and titles of key personnel, type of business. **Indexes:** Industry, location, sales rank, profit rank. **Availability:** E-book; Print.

LIBRARIES

11850 ■ *Alabama A & M University - J.F. Drake Memorial Learning Resources Center*
4900 Meridian St. N
Normal, AL 35762
Ph: (256)372-4725
URL: http://alabamam.ent.sirsi.net/client/en_US/default
Contact: Linda McClellan, Coordinator
Scope: Arts; sciences; business; engineering; education; agriculture and technology. **Services:** Interlibrary loan; copying; media services; Center open to the public (courtesy card must be purchased for check out of materials by persons not enrolled at the university or at one of the cooperating institutions). **Founded:** 1875. **Holdings:** 236,147 books; 25,517 bound periodical volumes; 5,044 AV programs; 20,869 periodicals on microfilm; 1,053 college catalogs; various telephone directories; 16,166 ERIC microfiche; 141,376 government documents; Wall Street Journal on microfiche (11,643); 359 microfilm subscriptions. **Subscriptions:** 1,657 journals and other serials; 93 newspapers.

START-UP INFORMATION

11851 ■ *"Franchises with an Eye on Chicago"* in Crain's Chicago Business (Vol. 34, March 14, 2011, No. 11, pp. 20)
Pub: Crain Communications Inc.
Contact: Barry Asin, President

Ed: Kevin McKeough. **Description:** Profiles of franchise companies seeking franchisees for the Chicago area include: Extreme Pita, a sandwich shop; Hand and Stone, offering massage, facial and waxing services; Molly Maid, home-cleaning service; Primrose Schools, private accredited schools for children 6 months to 6 hears and after-school programs; Protect Painters, residential and light-commercial painting contractor; and Wingstop, a restaurant offering chicken wings in nine flavors, fries and side dishes. **Availability:** Online.

11852 ■ *"Green Business Plan Competition"* in Chemical & Engineering News (Vol. 90, July 9, 2012, No. 28, pp. 34)
Pub: American Chemical Society Philadelphia Section
Contact: Dr. David Cichowicz, Director

Ed: Stephen K. Ritter. **Description:** Startup anticorrosion coatings firm AnCatt Inc. won the inaugural chemistry business plan competition at the Green Chemistry & Engineering Conference held in July 2012 in Washington, DC. AnCatt was honored for its conducting-polymer-based anticorrosion paint system aimed at replacing chromate, lead, and cadmium paint pigments. **Availability:** Online.

11853 ■ *How to Start a Faux Painting or Mural Business*
Pub: Allworth Press
Contact: Tad Crawford, Founder

Ed: Rebecca Pittman. **Released:** Second edition. **Price:** $24.95, paperback. **Description:** Updated and expanded to cover better ways to advertise, innovative supplies (such as Venetian plasters and stained cements), unique bidding and studio setups required for new plasters and varnishes. **Availability:** E-book; Print.

ASSOCIATIONS AND OTHER ORGANIZATIONS

11854 ■ **American Coatings Association (ACA)**
901 New York Ave. NW, Ste. 300 W
Washington, DC 20001
Ph: (202)462-6272
Fax: (202)462-8549
URL: http://www.paint.org
Facebook: www.facebook.com/AmericanCoatingsAssociation
Linkedin: www.linkedin.com/company/american-coatings-association
YouTube: www.youtube.com/user/acapaint

Description: Manufacturers of paints and chemical coatings; suppliers of raw materials and equipment. Conducts statistical surveys and research, government, and public relations programs. Provides management information programs and management and technician development programs. Compiles statistics. **Founded:** 1933. **Publications:** *Paint & Coatings Buyers Guide*; *Journal of Coatings Technology and Research* (6/year); *Insider News*; *Member Services Directory*; *Technical Bulletin*; *Trademark Directory* (Irregular; Periodic); *Guide to Coatings Courses, Symposia, and Seminars*; *American Coatings Association--Yearbook and Membership Directory* (Annual); *JCT: Journal of Coatings Technology* (6/year). **Educational Activities:** American Coatings Show (ACS) (Biennial); International Coatings Expo (Annual). **Awards:** George Baugh Heckel Award (Irregular). **Geographic Preference:** National.

11855 ■ **Wallcoverings Association (WA)**
35 E Wacker Dr., Ste. 850
Chicago, IL 60601
Ph: (312)224-2574
Co. E-mail: info@wallcoverings.org
URL: http://www.wallcoverings.org
Contact: Sarah Tiwana, Executive Director
E-mail: stiwana@wallcoverings.org
Facebook: www.facebook.com/WallcoveringsAssociation
X (Twitter): x.com/TheWA_Tweets
Instagram: www.instagram.com/wallcoveringsassociation
Pinterest: www.pinterest.ca/thewallcoveringsassociation

Description: Association for manufacturers, converters, distributors and suppliers in the wall coverings industry. **Founded:** 1920. **Publications:** *Wallcoverings Association--Directory of Members* (Annual). **Awards:** WA Allman Award (Annual). **Geographic Preference:** National.

REFERENCE WORKS

11856 ■ *"Baltimore Dealers Fear Shortages in Car Supply"* in Boston Business Journal (Vol. 29, May 13, 2011, No. 1, pp. 1)
Pub: Boston Business Journal
Contact: Carolyn M. Jones, President
E-mail: cmjones@bizjournals.com

Ed: Scott Dance. **Price:** $4, Introductory 4-Week Offer(Digital Only). **Description:** The earthquake and tsunami in Japan are seen to impact the automobile dealers in Baltimore, Maryland. Automobile supply in the area is seen to decrease dramatically during the summer sales season. Shortage of transmission parts and paint colors is also forecasted. **Availability:** Print; Online.

11857 ■ *"The Case for Thousand Dollar Wallpaper"* in Architectural Digest (February 22, 2017)
URL(s): www.architecturaldigest.com/story/hand-painted-chinoiserie-wallpaper-de-gournay-gracie-voutsa

Ed: Hadley Keller. **Released:** February 22, 2017. **Description:** The history of hand-painted chinoiserie wallpaper and wallpanels is given with commentary from the New York-based studio, Gracie. **Availability:** Online.

11858 ■ *"Contractors Must be Lead Certified"* in Contractor (Vol. 57, February 2010, No. 2, pp. 3)

Description: Contractors should be trained and certified to comply with the U.S. Environmental Protection Agency's Lead Renovation, Repair, and Painting regulation if they work on housing built before 1978 by April 2010. Contractors with previous lead abatement training must be trained and certified under this new program. **Availability:** Print; Online.

11859 ■ *"Hotels Make Wallcoverings a Sticking Trend"* in Hotel News Now (April 17, 2019)
URL(s): www.hotelnewsnow.com/Articles/294815/Hotels-make-wallcoverings-a-sticking-trend

Ed: Dana Miller. **Released:** April 17, 2019. **Description:** Wallcoverings, the term used to describe the more durable wallpaper used in hotels, are being used in innovative colors and patterns in hotel settings. Often cheaper than repainting, wallcoverings are a good way to switch up the look of a hotel when it's time to renovate or add a personal touch that is unique to the area the hotel is located. **Availability:** Online.

11860 ■ *"Paint Price Hikes Continue"* in American Painting Contractor (October 11, 2021)

Released: October 11, 2021. **Description:** As raw material pricing continues to rise, due to such events as Hurricane Ida that hit the Gulf Coast, those price hikes are being passed down to paint companies and eventually to the painter contractor. **Availability:** Online.

11861 ■ *PDRA Decorating Registry*
Pub: Paint and Decorating Retailers Association
Contact: Craig Bond, Chairman of the Board
E-mail: craig@pdra.org
URL(s): pdrmag.com/registry

Description: Publication includes list of about 1,500 manufacturers, manufacturers' representatives, distributors, and suppliers of decorating merchandise; a comprehensive trademark and brand name directory; associations, societies, and trade shows related to the home decorating industry. **Entries include:** For companies and manufacturer representatives-- Firm name, address, phone, fax, name and title of contact, trademark, brand names. For associations-- Name, address, phone, statement of purpose or description of service, key personnel, trade shows sponsored with dates and locations. Principal content of publication is decorative products (coatings, wallcoverings, window treatments, flooring, sundries). **Arrangement:** Alphabetical. **Indexes:** Brand and trade name. **Availability:** Print.

11862 ■ *"Pittsburgh Paint Maker Aims to Shake the Sales Blues" in The Wall Street Journal (July 2, 2019)*

URL(s): www.wsj.com/articles/ppg-battles-to-brighten -lackluster-paint-business-11562072413

Ed: Austen Hufford. **Released:** July 02, 2019. **Description:** Pittsburgh-based paint company, PPG, will not be breaking its paint and industrial-coatings units to two separate companies, but investors are concerned and the company will need to prove that it can boost it's domestic paint sales to homeowners and builders. **Availability:** Online.

11863 ■ *"Synthetic Drywall Rots Mechanical Product" in Contractor (Vol. 56, December 2009, No. 12, pp. 50)*

Ed: Robert P. Mader. **Description:** Chinese-made synthetic drywalls have been found to corrode mechanical and electrical products in homes. Drywalls always contain a certain amount of sulfur. The hydrogen sulfide gas component of synthetic drywalls causes copper and silver sulfide corrosion. **Availability:** Print; Online.

11864 ■ *"This Home Necessity Is Disappearing From Store Shelves" in Best Life (May 20, 2021)*

URL(s): bestlifeonline.com/paint-shortage-news/

Ed: Kali Coleman. **Released:** May 20, 2021. **Description:** The supply chain issues due to COVID-19 are also hitting paint supply stores. Expect shortages in the near future and plan to put aside painting your home until the colors you want are in stock. Also adding to the issue is the winter storm that hit Texas and the petrochemical companies. **Availability:** Online.

STATISTICAL SOURCES

11865 ■ *Paint Stores Industry in the US - Market Research Report*

URL(s): www.ibisworld.com/united-states/market-research-reports/paint-stores-industry/

Price: $925. **Description:** Downloadable report analyzing the current and future trends in the paint store industry. **Availability:** Online.

11866 ■ *RMA Annual Statement Studies*

Pub: Risk Management Association

Contact: Nancy Foster, President

Released: Annual. **Description:** Contains composite balance sheets and income statements for more than 360 industries, including the accounting, auditing, and bookkeeping industries. Also contains five years of comparative historical data for discerning trends. Includes 16 commonly used ratios, computed for most of the size groupings for nearly every industry.

TRADE PERIODICALS

11867 ■ *Paint & Decorating Retailer*

Pub: Paint and Decorating Retailers Association

Contact: Craig Bond, Chairman of the Board

E-mail: craig@pdra.org

URL(s): pdrmag.com/pdr-magazine-overview

Facebook: www.facebook.com/PaintandDecora tingRetailer

X (Twitter): x.com/PDRMagazine

Released: Monthly **Description:** Includes information on legislation and regulation affecting the industry. For paint and wallpaper, window and floor covering and paint retailers. **Availability:** Print; Online.

START-UP INFORMATION

**11868 ■ "Franchises with an Eye on Chicago"
in Crain's Chicago Business (Vol. 34, March
14, 2011, No. 11, pp. 20)**
Pub: Crain Communications Inc.
Contact: Barry Asin, President

Ed: Kevin McKeough. **Description:** Profiles of
franchise companies seeking franchisees for the
Chicago area include: Extreme Pita, a sandwich
shop; Hand and Stone, offering massage, facial and
waxing services; Molly Maid, home-cleaning service;
Primrose Schools, private accredited schools for
children 6 months to 6 hears and after-school
programs; Protect Painters, residential and light-
commercial painting contractor; and Wingstop, a
restaurant offering chicken wings in nine flavors, fries
and side dishes. **Availability:** Online.

**11869 ■ "Green Business Plan Competition"
in Chemical & Engineering News (Vol. 90,
July 9, 2012, No. 28, pp. 34)**
Pub: American Chemical Society Philadelphia
Section
Contact: Dr. David Cichowicz, Director

Ed: Stephen K. Ritter. **Description:** Startup anticorrosion coatings firm AnCatt Inc. won the inaugural
chemistry business plan competition at the Green
Chemistry & Engineering Conference held in July
2012 in Washington, DC. AnCatt was honored for its
conducting-polymer-based anticorrosion paint system
aimed at replacing chromate, lead, and cadmium
paint pigments. **Availability:** Online.

**11870 ■ How to Start a Faux Painting or
Mural Business**
Pub: Allworth Press
Contact: Tad Crawford, Founder

Ed: Rebecca Pittman. **Released:** Second edition.
Price: $24.95, paperback. **Description:** Updated and
expanded to cover better ways to advertise, innovative supplies (such as Venetian plasters and stained
cements), unique bidding and studio setups required
for new plasters and varnishes. **Availability:** E-book;
Print.

ASSOCIATIONS AND OTHER ORGANIZATIONS

**11871 ■ American Coatings Association
(ACA)**
901 New York Ave. NW, Ste. 300 W
Washington, DC 20001
Ph: (202)462-6272
Fax: (202)462-8549
URL: http://www.paint.org
Facebook: www.facebook.com/AmericanCoa
tingsAssociation

Linkedin: www.linkedin.com/company/american-coa
tings-association
YouTube: www.youtube.com/user/acapaint

Description: Manufacturers of paints and chemical
coatings; suppliers of raw materials and equipment.
Conducts statistical surveys and research, government, and public relations programs. Provides
management information programs and management
and technician development programs. Compiles
statistics. **Founded:** 1933. **Publications:** Paint &
Coatings Buyers Guide; Journal of Coatings Technology and Research (6/year); Insider News; Member
Services Directory; Technical Bulletin; Trademark
Directory (Irregular; Periodic); Guide to Coatings
Courses, Symposia, and Seminars; American Coatings Association--Yearbook and Membership Directory (Annual); JCT: Journal of Coatings Technology
(6/year). **Educational Activities:** American Coatings
Show (ACS) (Biennial); International Coatings Expo
(Annual). **Awards:** George Baugh Heckel Award (Irregular). **Geographic Preference:** National.

**11872 ■ American Subcontractors
Association (ASA)**
1004 Duke St.
Alexandria, VA 22314
Ph: (703)684-3450
Co. E-mail: asaoffice@asa-hq.com
URL: http://www.asaonline.com
Contact: Richard Bright, Chief Operating Officer
E-mail: rbright@asa-hq.com
Facebook: www.facebook.com/subcontractors
X (Twitter): x.com/ASAupdate

Description: Construction subcontractors of trades
and specialties such as foundations, concrete,
masonry, steel, mechanical, drywall, electrical, painting, plastering, roofing and acoustical. Formed to deal
with issues common to subcontractors. Works with
other segments of the construction industry in
promoting ethical practices, beneficial legislation and
education of construction subcontractors and suppliers. Manages the Foundation of the American
Subcontractors Association (FASA). **Founded:** 1966.
Publications: ASAtoday (Weekly); The Subcontractor (Monthly); Action ASA; The Contractor's Compass
(Monthly). **Geographic Preference:** National.

**11873 ■ Paint and Decorating Retailers
Association (PDRA)**
1401 Triad Ctr. Dr.
Saint Peters, MO 63376
Free: 800-737-0107
Co. E-mail: info@pdra.org
URL: http://www.pdra.org
Contact: Craig Bond, Chairman of the Board
E-mail: craig@pdra.org
X (Twitter): x.com/PaintDecoRetail
Pinterest: www.pinterest.com/pdra0036

Description: Serves as a trade association of locally-
owned paint and decorating stores in the U.S.,
Canada and around the world. Offers professional
advice, personal service and quality products for
every paint, wall covering, window treatment and floor
covering project. **Founded:** 1947. **Publications:**
PDRA Gold Book (Annual); Paint & Decorating
Retailer (Monthly); Gold Book (Annual); Decorating
Retailer--Directory of the Wallcoverings Industry Issue (Annual); Gold Book: Directory of the Wallcovering Industry (Annual); PDRA Decorating Registry.
Educational Activities: PDRA Show. **Geographic
Preference:** Multinational.

**11874 ■ Painting Contractors Association
(PCA)**
2316 Millpark Dr.
Maryland Heights, MO 63043
Free: 800-332-7322
Co. E-mail: support@pcapainted.org
URL: http://www.pcapainted.org
Contact: Nigel Costolloe, Executive Director
E-mail: ncostolloe@pcapainted.org
Facebook: www.facebook.com/PCAsocial
Linkedin: www.linkedin.com/company/pcasocial
X (Twitter): x.com/PCAsocial
Instagram: www.instagram.com/pcasocial
YouTube: www.youtube.com/channel/
UCBTMBYTowqtaZJvPCRL4TtA

Description: Painting and wall covering contractors.
Operates educational and charitable programs.
Compiles statistics. **Founded:** 1884. **Publications:**
Hazardous Waste Handbook; Painting and Wallcovering Contractor; PCA Membership Directory; Painting and Wallcovering Contractor--PDCA Roster (Annual). **Awards:** PCA A.E. Robert Friedman Scholarship (Annual); PDCA Picture It Painted Professionally
Awards; PDCA Humanitarian Award; Al Quilici Outstanding Member Award; L.E. Travis, Jr. PDCA
Craftsman of the Year Award (Annual); PDCA Safety
Achievement Awards (Annual). **Geographic Preference:** National.

**11875 ■ Wallcovering Installers Association
(WIA)**
PO Box 1166
Lebanon, OH 45036
Free: 800-254-6477
Fax: (888)505-1929
Co. E-mail: info@wallcoveringinstallers.org
URL: http://www.wallcoveringinstallers.org
Contact: Mike Digilio, President
E-mail: michaeldigilio@mac.com
Linkedin: www.linkedin.com/company/wallcovering
-installers-association
X (Twitter): x.com/wecoverwalls
YouTube: www.youtube.com/c/Wallcoveringins
tallersOrg1
Pinterest: www.pinterest.com/wecoverwalls

Description: Paperhangers united to promote use of wall coverings; upgrade the skills of paperhangers and the quality of materials; foster unity among members; encourage good business practices and ethics in the industry. Conducts charitable programs. Sponsors educational programs. **Founded:** 1974. **Publications:** *American Painting Contractor (APC)*; *Jobsite*; *Paint Pro*. **Educational Activities:** WIA Convention and Vendor Showcase (Annual); National Paperhangers Forum. **Awards:** Sam Kovnat Award (Annual); Skip Lowe Award (Annual); Bob Isenberger Paperhanger Member of the Year (Annual); WIA Golden Shears Award (Annual); Guy Cooper Golden Plumbline Award (Annual). **Geographic Preference:** National.

11876 ■ Wallcoverings Association (WA)

35 E Wacker Dr., Ste. 850
  Chicago, IL 60601
Ph: (312)224-2574
Co. E-mail: info@wallcoverings.org
URL: http://www.wallcoverings.org
Contact: Sarah Tiwana, Executive Director
E-mail: stiwana@wallcoverings.org
Facebook: www.facebook.com/WallcoveringsAssociation
X (Twitter): x.com/TheWA_Tweets
Instagram: www.instagram.com/wallcoveringsassociation
Pinterest: www.pinterest.ca/thewallcoveringsassociation

Description: Association for manufacturers, converters, distributors and suppliers in the wall coverings industry. **Founded:** 1920. **Publications:** *Wallcoverings Association--Directory of Members* (Annual). **Awards:** WA Allman Award (Annual). **Geographic Preference:** National.

REFERENCE WORKS

11877 ■ *American Painting Contractor--Buyers' Guide*

Pub: Communication Publications & Resources
URL(s): www.paintmag.comwww.ppgpaints.com/store-locator
X (Twitter): twitter.com/PaintMag/status/1301958370266697730?ref_src=twsrc%5Etfw%7Ctwcamp%5Eembeddedtimeline%7Ctwterm%5Eprofile%3APaintMag%7Ctwcon%5Etimelinechrome&ref_url=http%3A%2F%2Fwww.paintmag.com%2F

Released: Annual **Description:** Publication includes list of more than 600 manufacturers of products, tools, and equipment for the paint and wallcoverings application industry. **Entries include:** Name, address, phone, fax, e-mail, URL, and contact name; some listings include logo and products. **Arrangement:** Alphabetical by product. **Indexes:** Product. **Availability:** Diskette; CD-ROM; Print; Online; Magnetic tape.

11878 ■ *"Baltimore Dealers Fear Shortages in Car Supply"* in Boston Business Journal (Vol. 29, May 13, 2011, No. 1, pp. 1)

Pub: Boston Business Journal
Contact: Carolyn M. Jones, President
E-mail: cmjones@bizjournals.com

Ed: Scott Dance. **Price:** $4, Introductory 4-Week Offer(Digital Only). **Description:** The earthquake and tsunami in Japan are seen to impact the automobile dealers in Baltimore, Maryland. Automobile supply in the area is seen to decrease dramatically during the summer sales season. Shortage of transmission parts and paint colors is also forecasted. **Availability:** Print; Online.

11879 ■ *"Contractors Must be Lead Certified"* in Contractor (Vol. 57, February 2010, No. 2, pp. 3)

Description: Contractors should be trained and certified to comply with the U.S. Environmental Protection Agency's Lead Renovation, Repair, and Painting

regulation if they work on housing built before 1978 by April 2010. Contractors with previous lead abatement training must be trained and certified under this new program. **Availability:** Print; Online.

11880 ■ *"Paint Price Hikes Continue"* in American Painting Contractor (October 11, 2021)

Released: October 11, 2021. **Description:** As raw material pricing continues to rise, due to such events as Hurricane Ida that hit the Gulf Coast, those price hikes are being passed down to paint companies and eventually to the painter contractor. **Availability:** Online.

11881 ■ *"Synthetic Drywall Rots Mechanical Product"* in Contractor (Vol. 56, December 2009, No. 12, pp. 50)

Ed: Robert P. Mader. **Description:** Chinese-made synthetic drywalls have been found to corrode mechanical and electrical products in homes. Drywalls always contain a certain amount of sulfur. The hydrogen sulfide gas component of synthetic drywalls causes copper and silver sulfide corrosion. **Availability:** Print; Online.

11882 ■ *"Three Productivity Solutions"* in Contractor (Vol. 57, February 2010, No. 2, pp. 26)

Ed: William Feldman, Patti Feldman. **Description:** Singletouch is a real-time data capture solution for mechanical and other contractors that work in jobs that require materials and workload tracking. Contractors get information on extreme weather and sudden changes in the cost of materials. The OptimumHVAC optimization software by Optimum Energy is designed to optimize energy savings in commercial buildings. **Availability:** Print; Online.

SOURCES OF SUPPLY

11883 ■ PDRA Decorating Registry

Paint and Decorating Retailers Association
Contact: Craig Bond, Chairman of the Board
E-mail: craig@pdra.org
URL(s): pdrmag.com/registry

Description: Publication includes list of about 1,500 manufacturers, manufacturers' representatives, distributors, and suppliers of decorating merchandise; a comprehensive trademark and brand name directory; associations, societies, and trade shows related to the home decorating industry. **Entries include:** For companies and manufacturer representatives-- Firm name, address, phone, fax, name and title of contact, trademark, brand names. For associations-- Name, address, phone, statement of purpose or description of service, key personnel, trade shows sponsored with dates and locations. Principal content of publication is decorative products (coatings, wallcoverings, window treatments, flooring, sundries). **Arrangement:** Alphabetical. **Indexes:** Brand and trade name. **Availability:** Print.

STATISTICAL SOURCES

11884 ■ *Painters Industry in the US - Market Research Report*

URL(s): www.ibisworld.com/united-states/market-research-reports/painters-industry/

Price: $925. **Description:** Downloadable report analyzing current and future trends in the painters industry. **Availability:** Download.

11885 ■ *RMA Annual Statement Studies*

Pub: Risk Management Association
Contact: Nancy Foster, President

Released: Annual. **Description:** Contains composite balance sheets and income statements for more than 360 industries, including the accounting, auditing, and bookkeeping industries. Also contains five years

of comparative historical data for discerning trends. Includes 16 commonly used ratios, computed for most of the size groupings for nearly every industry.

CONSULTANTS

11886 ■ Historic Exterior Paint Colors Consulting

3661 Waldenwood Dr.
  Ann Arbor, MI 48105
Ph: (734)668-0298
Co. E-mail: robs@umich.edu
URL: http://historichousecolors.com
Contact: Robert Schweitzer, Contact

Description: Provider of exterior paint color consulting services for historic, contemporary, and much more. **Scope:** Provider of exterior paint color consulting services for historic, contemporary, and much more. **Publications:** "Proof that Paint Color Lends Detail," Arts and Crafts Homes, 2006; "Bungalow Colors- Exteriors," Gibbs-Smith Publishers, 2002; "Color Scheming," Design NJ, 2002; "Colonial Revival Homes," Victorian Homes, Feb, 2003; "America's Favorite Homes"; "Color a New World," 60s Ranch Color Makeover, Romantic Homes, Aug, 2001; "How Shall I Paint my House," American Bungalow, 1999; "Color Concepts and Bungalow Basics," Cottages & Bungalows.

FRANCHISES AND BUSINESS OPPORTUNITIES

11887 ■ CertaPro Painters Ltd.

FirstService Brands
  2621 Van Buren Ave., Ste. 550A
  Audubon, PA 19403
Free: 866-366-0420
Fax: (601)549-7973
URL: http://www.fsvbrands.com
Contact: Michael Stone, President
URL(s): www.fsvbrands.com/our_companies/certa_pro_painters.html
Facebook: www.facebook.com/certapropainters
Linkedin: www.linkedin.com/company/certapro-painters
X (Twitter): x.com/CertaPro
Instagram: www.instagram.com/certapro
YouTube: www.youtube.com/user/certaproyt
Pinterest: www.pinterest.com/certapro

Description: Provider of residential and commercial building painting services. **Founded:** 1992.

11888 ■ Color World Housepainting Inc.

94 Village Pointe Dr.
  Powell, OH 43065
Ph: (614)739-9240
Free: 888-324-0313
Co. E-mail: info@colorworldhousepainting.com
URL: http://www.colorworldpainting.com
Contact: Tom Hodgson, President
E-mail: tomh@colorworldhousepainting.com
Facebook: www.facebook.com/ColorWorldColumbus
X (Twitter): x.com/cwhousepainting
Instagram: www.instagram.com/colorworldhousepainting
YouTube: www.youtube.com/channel/UC1eX2s7g3oiaxG9NQ2IWdWg
Pinterest: www.pinterest.com/colorworldhousepaintingcorp

Description: Provider of house painting services such as commercial painting, power washing, gutter installation, holiday lighting, minor drywall, carpentry work and much more. **Founded:** 1997. **Franchise Fee:** $25,000. **Training:** Includes 2 weeks training.

11889 ■ Hester Painting & Decorating

7340 N Monticello Ave.
  Skokie, IL 60076
Ph: (847)677-5130
Co. E-mail: info@hesterdecorating.com

URL: http://hesterdecorating.com
Contact: Stephen Hester, President
Facebook: www.facebook.com/hesterpainting
Linkedin: www.linkedin.com/company/hester-painting
 -&-decorating
Instagram: www.instagram.com/hesterpaintingdecora
 ting
YouTube: www.youtube.com/channel/UCYZVwV3H
 _Hx5JOfjDidz6vg
Pinterest: www.pinterest.com/hesterpainting
Description: Firm provides painting and decorating services for walls, ceilings, doors, cabinets and

furniture. **Founded:** 1968. **Franchised:** 2007. **Franchise Fee:** $50,000. **Training:** Provides 9 days management training at headquarters covering award winning business systems along with over 3 weeks of hands on training for your staff at training facility and at your new showroom. You will learn approximately 30 faux and decorative finishing techniques.

11890 ■ Protect Painters
Neighborly
 Ann Arbor, MI 48103

Free: 800-490-7501
Fax: (877)496-2356
URL: http://www.neighborlybrands.com

Description: Firm provides painting services for interior and exterior residential buildings and much more. **Founded:** 1995. **Training:** 8-10 days hands-on training courses. Ongoing support includes marketing, sales, weekly analysis of marketing and production, weekly teleconferences, workshops, personal visits and regional meetings.

START-UP INFORMATION

11891 ■ *"Military Vet Uses SBA Program to Help Fund His Business"* in *Philadelphia Business Journal (Vol. 33, May 9, 2014, No. 13, pp. 6)*
Pub: American City Business Journals, Inc.
Contact: Mike Olivieri, Executive Vice President

Released: Weekly. **Description:** Colonel Richard Elam and his wife Kimberly, both with the Florida Army National Guard, secured funding through the Small Business Administration's (SBA's) Veterans Advantage program to launch iPlay, which rents mobile entertainment equipment such as rock walls and laser-tag setups for group events. The capital access initiative, launched in January 2014, waives the origination fee for SBA Express loans to qualified veteran entrepreneurs. **Availability:** Print; Online.

ASSOCIATIONS AND OTHER ORGANIZATIONS

11892 ■ **Clowns of America International (COAI)**
PO Box 122
Eustis, FL 32727-0122
Ph: (352)357-1676
Free: 877-816-6941
Co. E-mail: coaioffice@aol.com
URL: http://mycoai.com
Contact: Adam Schill, President
Facebook: www.facebook.com/coaiofficialpage
YouTube: www.youtube.com/channel/UCDg 65FJ9RjO63UtoXiC00jA

Description: Professional and amateur clowns, magicians, puppeteers, jugglers, and others who present a humorous program for the circus, radio, television, stage, and screen; friends of clowns and persons interested in clowning as a profession or hobby. Includes activities such as: training sessions, and entertaining in parades and shows. Provides entertainment for charitable organizations and events. Promotes first week of August as National Clown Week. **Publications:** *The New Calliope* (6/year). **Awards:** COAI Best of Press Award (Irregular); COAI Charlie Award (Annual); COAI Clown of the Year (Irregular); COAI Lifetime Achievement Award (Annual). **Geographic Preference:** National.

REFERENCE WORKS

11893 ■ *"Green It Like You Mean It"* in *Special Events Magazine (Vol. 28, February 1, 2009, No. 2)*
Description: Eco-friendly party planners offer advice for planning and hosting green parties or events. Tips include information for using recycled paper products, organic food and drinks. The Eco Nouveau Fashion Show held by Serene Star Productions reused old garments to create new fashions as well as art pieces from discarded doors and window frames for the show; eco-friendly treats and gift bags were highlighted at the event.

11894 ■ *"NACE Becomes the National Association for Catering and Events"* in *Entertainment Close-Up (July 29, 2012)*
Pub: Close-Up Media Inc.
Contact: Caroline S. Moore, President
E-mail: cms@closeupmedia.com
Description: National Association for Catering and Events (NACE) is committed to event and catering professionals seeking the highest training in all aspects of event planning, design and execution. In a recent survey, NACE reports that 44 percent of its members chose catering and event planning as a second career. **Availability:** Online.

STATISTICAL SOURCES

11895 ■ *U.S. The Future of Live Events Market Report 2021*
URL(s): store.mintel.com/report/us-the-future-of-live-events-market-report
Price: $4,366.35. **Description:** Downloadable report containing data on the live events market in the US and the impact COVID-19 has had on it. Report includes an executive summary, interactive databook, PowerPoint presentation, infographic overview, report PDF, and previous years data. **Availability:** PDF.

FRANCHISES AND BUSINESS OPPORTUNITIES

11896 ■ **Complete Weddings + Events**
110 N 9th St.
Omaha, NE 68102
Ph: (402)339-3535
Co. E-mail: events@completewedo.com
URL: http://completewedo.com/omaha/?utm_source =NationalWebsite&utm_medium=internal
Contact: Christian Maas, Manager
E-mail: christian.maas@completewedo.com
Facebook: www.facebook.com/completeweddings
Linkedin: www.linkedin.com/company/completewedo
X (Twitter): x.com/completewedo
Instagram: www.instagram.com/completeomaha
Pinterest: www.pinterest.com/completemvp
Description: Mobile entertainment service. Entertainment for special events. Franchise owners hire and train a staff of DJs to perform at these events. **Founded:** 1974. **Training:** 10 days at corporate office, covering day-to-day operations, including marketing, training of staff, hiring procedures, etc. Additional 4 day onsite provided.

11897 ■ **Cool Daddy's**
Atlanta, GA
Ph: (678)394-8009
Co. E-mail: info@cooldaddys.com
URL: http://www.cooldaddys.com
Description: Producer and retailer of frozen drinks for private parties, festivals and events. **Training:** Provides 2 weeks at headquarters. 1 week at franchisee's location, with ongoing support.

11898 ■ **Party Land**
113A W Ridge Pke.
Plymouth Meeting, PA 19462
Description: Retailer of party products such as plates, cups, napkins, accessories, table covers, balloons. **Founded:** 1986. **Franchised:** 1988. **Training:** 1 week training.

RESEARCH CENTERS

11899 ■ **International Clown Hall of Fame and Research Center (ICHOF)**
102 4th Ave.
Baraboo, WI 53913
Ph: (608)852-6767
URL: http://www.theclownmuseum.com
Contact: Greg Desanto, Executive Director
Facebook: www.facebook.com/International-Clown-Hall-of-Fame-and-Research-Center-3403129 40051
Description: Independent, nonprofit research and educational organization. **Scope:** Clowns and clowning. **Founded:** 1986. **Publications:** *ICHOF Newsletter* (Quarterly).

START-UP INFORMATION

11900 ■ *"Event-Planning Startup Extends Its Reach" in Indianapolis Business Journal (Vol. 33, June 18, 2012, No. 16, pp. 2A)*
Description: Snappening.com offers a searchable database of central Indiana event venues ad professional planners and is expanding its service to four new markets. **Availability:** Print; Online.

ASSOCIATIONS AND OTHER ORGANIZATIONS

11901 ■ **National Association of Casino Party Operators (NACPO)**
712 H St. NE, Ste. 1079
Washington, DC 20002
Ph: (202)838-6843
Co. E-mail: admin@nacpo.org
URL: http://nacpo.org
Contact: Elaine Davidson, President
E-mail: info@elitecasinoevent.com
URL(s): nacpo.wildapricot.org
Facebook: www.facebook.com/nacpo
Linkedin: www.linkedin.com/company/national
-association-of-casino-party-operators
YouTube: www.youtube.com/channel/
UCWXsJx0GBzvLS-ZR-uxCdAA
Description: Casino party operators, party planners, party rental shop owners, theme party and special events operators, and others involved in casino party rental business. Strives to strengthen the casino and theme party industry and advance the industry into more geographical markets. Promotes members' interests. **Founded:** 1992. **Geographic Preference:** National.

REFERENCE WORKS

11902 ■ *"2012 Outlook: ROI Still Piles on the Pressure" in Conference & Incentive Travel (March 1, 2012, pp. 14)*
Description: According to a recnt poll, more than one-third of 500 event planners preict lower budgets for 2012 than last year. Event planners for EDF Energy, Deloitte, Allianz Insurance, Sanofi Pasteur MSD, and Fico discuss their predictions for the industry for 2012. **Availability:** Online.

11903 ■ *"Best Places to Work; No. 2 Tasty Catering Inc." in Crain's Chicago Business (Vole 35, April 2, 2012, No. 14, pp. 18)*
Pub: Crain Communications Inc.
Contact: Barry Asin, President

Ed: Sachiko Yoshitsugu. **Description:** Tasty Catering Inc., located in Elk Grove Village, Illinois was rated Number 2 in Crain's Best Places to Work category. The event planning and catering firm offers a family style lunch to employees weekly. CEO Tom Walters enjoys this meal with his workers. The company offers an educational program called Tasty Catering University that provides up to 30 hours of paid class time in courses ranging from English to business. **Availability:** Online.

11904 ■ *"Businesses Encouraged to Imagine the Possibilities With Meeting Planner Package" in Internet Wire (May 23, 2012)*
Pub: Comtex News Network Inc.
Contact: Kan Devnani, President
Description: Courtyard Orlando Lake Buena Vista, Florida is featuring an inclusive room rate and Double Event Planning Rewards Points for business planners using the hotel's professional event managers for their future meetings and events. Details of the program are included. **Availability:** Print; Online.

11905 ■ *The Complete Guide to Successful Event Planning*
Ed: Shannon C. Kilkenny. **Released:** July 30, 2016. **Price:** $31.22, Paperback; $23.99, E-book. **Description:** The newly-revised 3rd edition now includes sections on social media, social networking, cultural sensitivity, ethics, and diversity to help you plan special events. **Availability:** E-book; Print.

11906 ■ *"Green It Like You Mean It' in Special Events Magazine (Vol. 28, February 1, 2009, No. 2)*
Description: Eco-friendly party planners offer advice for planning and hosting green parties or events. Tips include information for using recycled paper products, organic food and drinks. The Eco Nouveau Fashion Show held by Serene Star Productions reused old garments to create new fashions as well as art pieces from discarded doors and window frames for the show; eco-friendly treats and gift bags were highlighted at the event.

11907 ■ *"Holiday Bloom: Event Designer Collin Abraham Heightens Glamour With Florals" in Black Enterprise (Vol. 41, November 2010, No. 4)*
Description: Profile of Collin Abraham, who works out of his Harlem boutique to arrange unique floral pieces to complement the social gatherings and main events he plans for his clients. **Availability:** Print; Online.

11908 ■ *"NACE Becomes the National Association for Catering and Events" in Entertainment Close-Up (July 29, 2012)*
Pub: Close-Up Media Inc.
Contact: Caroline S. Moore, President

E-mail: cms@closeupmedia.com
Description: National Association for Catering and Events (NACE) is committed to event and catering professionals seeking the highest training in all aspects of event planning, design and execution. In a recent survey, NACE reports that 44 percent of its members chose catering and event planning as a second career. **Availability:** Online.

11909 ■ *"On Your Marks, American Airlines, Now Vote! Contest Creating Possibilities and Opportunities for Delray Beach Wedding Planner" in Benzinga.com (2011)*
Pub: Benzinga.com
Contact: Jason Raznick, Founder
Description: Wedding planner, Aviva Samuels, owner of Kiss the Planner boutique wedding and event planning agency in Florida, says that winning this contest would help her increase her knowledge base and provide in-depth, personal experience offering more destination wedding destinations.

11910 ■ *"Person To Watch: Wedding Planner Brings Energy to Her Job" in Chattanooga Times/Free Press (April 24, 2012)*
Ed: Karen Nazor Hill. **Description:** Profile of Morgan Holland, 28-year-old founder of Soirees of Chattanooga. Weddings are a large part of Holland's event planning business, with parties for nonprofits, birthday parties, and private parties making up the other 15 percent. **Availability:** Print; Online.

11911 ■ *"Plan Your Wedding with Cleveland Airport Marriott's Certified Event Planners" in Benzinga.com (February 2, 2011)*
Description: Cleveland's Airport Marriott makes wedding planning easy with its venue spaces and a full team of wedding planners. **Availability:** Print; Online.

11912 ■ *"Prepare for Your Fourth of July Party With a Maid Service" in Internet Wire (July 3, 2012)*
Pub: Comtex News Network Inc.
Contact: Kan Devnani, President
Description: Merry Maids will assist in preparing a house for special occasions and holiday parties. The firm still specializes in house cleaning, but has expanded its services. Details of services offered are included. **Availability:** Print; Online.

TRADE PERIODICALS

11913 ■ *The Polar Bear ROARS*
Pub: Polar Bear Alumni Association
Contact: Dick Wilson, President
URL(s): www.northhighpolarbears.org/roars.html
Released: Quarterly **Description:** Provides news of current events regarding reunion information, memories of alumni, history of school and articles about alumni and faculty. Recurring features include reports of reunions. **Availability:** Print.

ASSOCIATIONS AND OTHER ORGANIZATIONS

11914 ■ **National Pawnbrokers Association (NPA)**
2920 W Southlake Blvd., Ste. 120
Southlake, TX 76092-6781
Ph: (817)337-8830
Co. E-mail: info@nationalpawnbrokers.org
URL: http://www.nationalpawnbrokers.org
Contact: Johnny Whiteside, President
Facebook: www.facebook.com/na
tionalpawnbrokersassociation
Linkedin: www.linkedin.com/company/national
-pawnbrokers-association-us
X (Twitter): x.com/pawntweet
Instagram: www.instagram.com/national_pawnbro-
kers
YouTube: www.youtube.com/natlpawnbrokersassoc
Description: Pawnbrokers and interested others. Seeks to educate and inform the public on the pawn-broking industry. Provides continuing education on technological changes. **Founded:** 1989. **Publications:** *National Pawnbroker* (Quarterly); *Pawnbroker News* (Periodic). **Educational Activities:** NPA Legislative Conference (Annual); National Pawnbrokers Association Annual Convention and Tradeshow (Annual); National Pawnbrokers Association PAWN EXPO (Annual). **Geographic Preference:** National.

REFERENCE WORKS

11915 ■ *"B-N Pawn Shop Auctions Off Jimmy Hoffa's Rifle" in Pantagraph (September 14, 2010)*
Pub: The Pantagraph
Ed: Ryan Denham. **Description:** Midwest Exchange pawn shop located in IAA Drive in Bloomington, Illinois auctioned a rifle once belonging to Jimmy Hoffa. **Availability:** Print; Online.

11916 ■ *"BRIEF: Montana Street Pawn Shop Closing Doors" in Montana Standard (November 6, 2010)*
Pub: Montana Standard
Ed: John Grant Emeigh. **Description:** First National Pawn located in Butte, Montana will close its doors after losing its lease. Co-owner Pat Evenson reported the lease situation coupled with the economy prompted the decision to close. **Availability:** Online.

11917 ■ *"Detroit Pawn Shop to be Reality TV Venue" in UPI NewsTrack (July 10, 2010)*
Pub: United Press International Inc.
Contact: Nicholas Chiaia, President
Description: TruTV will present a new series called 'Hardcore Pawn' to compete with the History Channel's successful show 'Pawn Stars'. The show will feature American Jewelry and Loan in Detroit, Michigan and its owner Les Gold, who runs the store with his wife and children. **Availability:** Online.

11918 ■ *"Family Feud: Pawn Shop Empire Stalls with Transition to Second Generation" in Billings Gazette (December 19, 2010)*
Pub: The Billings Gazette
Ed: Jan Falstad. **Description:** Profile of Ben L. Brown Sr. and his pawn shop located in Billings, Montana is presented. Brown discusses his plan to transition his business to his children. **Availability:** Print; Online.

11919 ■ *"Federal Employees Turn to Pawnshops Amid Shutdown's Financial Pinch" in The New York Times (January 19, 2019)*
URL(s): www.nytimes.com/2019/01/19/us/politics/fe
deral-workers-pawnshops-government-shutdown
.html
Ed: Mihir Zaveri. **Released:** January 19, 2019. **Description:** During the longest government shutdown in American history, federal workers who haven't seen a paycheck turned to pawnbrokers for short-term loans. Many of these employees are hoping that they can get a paycheck soon and reclaim their items before the pawnshop gets to sell them. Some pawnshops are offering to waive interest payments for four months for furloughed federal workers. **Availability:** Online.

11920 ■ *"Pawn Shop Plan Snubbed by Citizen Group" in North County Times (October 14, 2010)*
Ed: Ray Huard. **Description:** A citizens advisory group is against the opening of an upscale pawn shop in downtown Oceanside, California. The group contends that a pawn shop does not fit the plans for revitalizing the area. **Availability:** Online.

11921 ■ *"Waco Pawn Shop Owners Say Reality Isn't Much Like 'Pawn Stars' TV Show" in Waco Tribune-Herald (August 15, 2010)*
Pub: Waco Tribune-Herald
Contact: Ken Sury, Editor
E-mail: ken.sury@wacotrib.com
Ed: Mike Copeland. **Description:** Area pawn shop owners report that the television show on cable TV does not represent the true life operations of a pawn shop. The Las Vegas shop represented on TV boasts 30 employees and 21 on-call experts, which is not the case in reality. **Availability:** Print; Online.

STATISTICAL SOURCES

11922 ■ *Pawn Shops Industry in the US - Market Research Report*
URL(s): www.ibisworld.com/united-states/market-re-
search-reports/pawn-shops-industry/
Price: $925. **Description:** Downloadable report analyzing the current and future trends in the pawn shop industry. **Availability:** Download.

ASSOCIATIONS AND OTHER ORGANIZATIONS

11923 ■ American Payroll Association (APA)
660 N Main Ave., Ste. 100
San Antonio, TX 78205
Ph: (210)224-6406
Fax: (210)224-6038
URL: http://www.americanpayroll.org
Contact: Dan Maddux, Executive Director
Facebook: www.facebook.com/
AmericanPayrollAssociation
X (Twitter): x.com/PayNews
Instagram: www.instagram.com/americanpayroll
YouTube: www.youtube.com/user/PayNewsNetwork
Description: Works to increase member's skills and professionalism through education and mutual support. Represents the interest of members before legislative bodies. Conducts training courses. Administers the certified payroll professional program of recognition. **Founded:** 1982. **Publications:** Creates opportunities and forge a community by providing the education, skills, and resources necessary for payroll professionals to become successful. **Training:** Standard Foundation of Payroll Administration; Implementing Payroll Best Practices; Payroll System Selection and Implementation; Accounts Payable or Disbursements Preparing for Year-End and 2009; Canadian Payrolls Preparing for Year-End and 2009; Government/Public Sector Preparing for Year-End and 2009; Payroll Issues For Multi-State Employers. **Educational Activities:** Educational Institutions Payroll Conference (EIPC) (Annual). **Awards:** Payroll Education Grants (Annual). **Geographic Preference:** State.

11924 ■ Dialogue Magazine
250 Bloor St. E, Ste. 1600
Toronto, ON, Canada M4W 1E6
Ph: (416)487-3380
Free: 800-387-4693
Fax: (416)487-3384
Co. E-mail: infoline@payroll.ca
URL: http://payroll.ca
Contact: Peter Tzanetakis, President
URL(s): payroll.ca/dialogue-magazine
Released: Quarterly **Availability:** Print; PDF; Download; Online.

11925 ■ National Payroll Institute
[Association canadienne de la paie (ACP)]
250 Bloor St. E, Ste. 1600
Toronto, ON, Canada M4W 1E6
Ph: (416)487-3380
Free: 800-387-4693
Fax: (416)487-3384
Co. E-mail: infoline@payroll.ca
URL: http://payroll.ca
Contact: Peter Tzanetakis, President
Facebook: www.facebook.com/nationalpayrollinsti
tute
Linkedin: www.linkedin.com/company/national-payroll
-institute

X (Twitter): x.com/NatPayrollInst
YouTube: www.youtube.com/c/nationalpayrollinstitute
Description: Represents the payroll community in Canada; offers education programs, advocacy efforts, products and services to help members enhance and adapt payroll operations. **Founded:** 1978. **Publications:** Dialogue Magazine (Quarterly); CPA E-Source (Bimonthly). **Awards:** Diana Ferguson Award (Annual); The CPA Partner Award (Annual); CPA Board of Directors Award (Annual). **Geographic Preference:** National.

REFERENCE WORKS

11926 ■ "6 Lessons from Audit Experts Who Adopted AI Early" in Journal of Accountancy (November 23, 2021)
Ed: Andrew Kenney. **Released:** November 23, 2021. **Description:** With the advance of AI, the best thing those in the accountancy industries can do is learn about various AI platforms and how to incorporate them into their businesses. The technology is still evolving, but tips are given on how to use AI to benefit customers. **Availability:** Online.

11927 ■ "APA Creates 2020 Form W-4 Webpage. Sample Letter to Explain Changes" in American Payroll Association (November 14, 2019)
URL(s): www.americanpayroll.org/news-resources/
apa-news/2019/11/14/apa-creates-2020-form-w
-4-webpage-sample-letter-to-explain-changes

Ed: Jyme Mariani, Esq. **Released:** November 14, 2019. **Description:** In order to keep members informed, the American Payroll Association has added a new Compliance Hot Topic on its website to provide information on the new 2020 From W-4. APA resources, IRS resources, and education links will also be provided. **Availability:** Online.

11928 ■ "Best Payroll Services for 2023" in Business News Daily (March 6, 2023)
URL(s): www.businessnewsdaily.com/7509-best-pay-
roll-services.html
Ed: Jamie Johnson. **Released:** March 06, 2023. **Description:** Contains reviews of the best payroll software available for small businesses to use. **Availability:** Online.

11929 ■ "Best Payroll Software for Small Businesses" in NerdWallet (April 9, 2018)
Ed: Steve Nicastro. **Released:** April 09, 2018. **Description:** Offers comparisons of five different payroll software options for small businesses. **Availability:** Online.

11930 ■ "Choosing the Right Small Business Software for Collecting Payments" in Business 2 Community (October 4, 2021)
URL(s): www.business2community.com/small-busi-
ness/choosing-the-right-small-business-software-for
-collecting-payments-02434457

Ed: Haiden Hibbert. **Released:** October 04, 2021. **Description:** Reviews the reasons a small business needs to choose payment processing software. **Availability:** Online.

11931 ■ Employer Legal Forms Simplified
Released: First edition. **Description:** Business reference containing the following forms needed to handle employees in any small business environment: application, notice, confidentiality, absence, federal employer forms and notices, and many payroll forms. All forms are included on a CD that comes in both PDF and text formats. Adobe Acrobat Reader software is also included on the CD. The forms are valid in all fifty states and Washington, DC. **Availability:** Print.

11932 ■ "Etsy Says Payment Delays from SVB Collapse are Resolved" in Small Business Trends (March 17, 2023)
URL(s): smallbiztrends.com/2023/03/etsy-says
-payment-delays-from-svb-collapse-have-been-re-
solved.html

Ed: Gabrielle Pickard-Whitehead. **Released:** March 17, 2023. **Description:** There were payment delays to Etsy vendors due to the collapse of the Silicon Valley Bank (SVB). However, those issues have been resolved. Details about the collapse and the affects on Etsy are discussed. **Availability:** Online.

11933 ■ "Feds Finalize I-9 Form Rules Allowing Electronic Storage" in HR Specialist (Vol. 8, September 2010, No. 9, pp. 5)
Pub: Capitol Information Group Inc.
Contact: Allie Ash, Chief Executive Officer

Description: U.S. Department of Homeland Security issued regulations that give employers more flexibility to electronically sing and store I-9 employee verification forms. **Availability:** Print; PDF; Online.

11934 ■ I Just Started My Small Business—Do I Need Payroll Software?
URL(s): articles.bplans.com/i-just-started-my-small
-business-do-i-need-payroll-software/

Ed: Jenna Lee. **Description:** Discusses the advantages of utilizing payroll software for your small business and what to look for in a good payroll service. **Availability:** Online.

11935 ■ The Payroll Book: A Guide for Small Businesses and Startups
Pub: John Wiley & Sons, Inc.
Contact: Christina Van Tassell, Executive Vice President Chief Financial Officer
URL(s): www.wiley.com/en-us/The+Payroll+Book%
3A+A+Guide+for+Small+Businesses+and+Startups
-p-9781119704430

Ed: Charles Read. **Released:** July 2020. **Price:** $18, e-book; $29.95, paperback. **Description:** Dealing with payroll for employees can often be confusing because it's not straightforward — there are taxes, withholding, and other requirements on top of calculating base pay. This guide discusses what you need to know to run a successful payroll department. **Availability:** E-book; Print.

11936 ■ *"Privacy Concern: Are 'Group' Time Sheets Legal?" in HR Specialist (Vol. 8, September 2010, No. 9, pp. 4)*
Pub: Capitol Information Group Inc.
Contact: Allie Ash, Chief Executive Officer
Description: Under the Fair Labor Standards Act (FLSA) employers are required to maintain and preserve payroll or other records, including the number of hours worked, but it does not prescribe a particular order or form in which these records must be kept. **Availability:** PDF; Online.

11937 ■ *"Reconsidering Pay Dispersion's Effect On the Performance of Interdependent Work: Reconciling Sorting and Pay Inequality" in Academy of Management Journal (Vol. 55, June 1, 2012, No. 3, pp. 585)*
Pub: Academy of Management
Contact: Sharon Alvarez, President
Ed: Charlie O. Trevor, Greg Reilly, Barry Gerhart. **Description:** The use of pay dispersion in interdependent work settings to secure valued employee inputs is investigated. Results show that the strategy positively affects interdependent team performance. Potential constraints on the sorting perspective on pay dispersion are also studied. **Availability:** Electronic publishing; Download; PDF; Online.

11938 ■ *"Visa Wants Creators to Get Paid Faster" in Small Business Trends (November 8, 2022)*
URL(s): smallbiztrends.com/2022/11/visa-ready-creator-commerce-program.html
Ed: Gabrielle Pickard-Whitehead. **Released:** November 08, 2022. **Description:** Visa launched a new program, Visa Ready Creator Commerce, which will help online content creators have a reliable and fast avenue for payment from viewers and subscribers. **Availability:** Online.

STATISTICAL SOURCES

11939 ■ *Payroll & Bookkeeping Services Industry in the US - Market Research Report*
URL(s): www.ibisworld.com/united-states/market-research-reports/payroll-bookkeeping-services-industry/
Price: $925. **Description:** Downloadable report analyzing the current and future trends in the payroll and bookkeeping industries. **Availability:** Download.

TRADE PERIODICALS

11940 ■ *Keep Up to Date on Payroll*
Pub: American Future Systems Inc.
Contact: Edward G. Rendell, Governor
URL(s): www.pbp.com/divisions/publishing/newsletters/financial-management/keep-up-to-date-on-payroll
Released: Semimonthly **Description:** Presents the latest on federal and state tax laws and unemployment insurance. Recurring features include interviews, a calendar of events, news of educational opportunities, and columns titled Law and Reg Update, Real Problems/Real Solutions, and Sharpen Your Judgment. **Availability:** Online.

TRADE SHOWS AND CONVENTIONS

11941 ■ **American Payroll Association Annual Congress**
URL(s): www.americanpayroll.org/congress

Price: $1,660, Members; $1,710, for colleague; $1,860, Non-members. **Frequency:** Annual. **Audience:** Payroll professionals. **Telecommunication Services:** APA_Events@americanpayroll.org.

CONSULTANTS

11942 ■ **Tax Preparations Etc. Inc.**
77 Remsen Rd.
Yonkers, NY 10710
Contact: Anna Faustini, Chief Executive Officer
Description: Provider of payroll, tax preparation, and bookkeeping services. **Scope:** Provider of payroll, tax preparation, and bookkeeping services.

FRANCHISES AND BUSINESS OPPORTUNITIES

11943 ■ **Universal Payroll Company**
290 Main St., Ste. 300
Alpharetta, GA 30009
URL(s): http://www.unipayroll.com
Description: Full service payroll company.

COMPUTER SYSTEMS/ SOFTWARE

11944 ■ *Aatrix Top Pay™*
Aatrix Software Inc.
2617 S Columbia Rd.
Grand Forks, ND 58201
Ph: (701)746-6017
Free: 800-426-0854
Co. E-mail: sales@aatrix.com
URL: http://www.aatrix.com
URL(s): www.aatrix.com/solutions/mac/top-pay
Price: $259.95, for annual. **Description:** Handles payroll calculations and tax deductions for both salaried and hourly employees. **Availability:** Download; Online.

11945 ■ *Aatrix Ultimate Payroll™*
Aatrix Software Inc.
2617 S Columbia Rd.
Grand Forks, ND 58201
Ph: (701)746-6017
Free: 800-426-0854
Co. E-mail: sales@aatrix.com
URL: http://www.aatrix.com
URL(s): www.aatrix.com/solutions/mac/ultimate-payroll
Price: $259.95, for 12 month subscription. **Description:** Available for Apple Macintosh computers. Features payroll functions as well as restaurant tips reporting, unlimited pay rates, piecework, and deductions. Also prints information on federal forms, and tracks check amounts, sick, vacation, and holiday pay. **Availability:** Online.

11946 ■ *Comprehensive Integrated Payroll System*
FREY Municipal Software
40 N Grand Ave., Ste. 303
Fort Thomas, KY 41075
Ph: (859)441-6566
Free: 800-659-3739
Co. E-mail: sales@freymunicipalsoftware.com
URL: http://www.freymunicipalsoftware.com
URL(s): www.freymunicipalsoftware.com/chips
Description: CHIPS (CompreHensive Integrated Payroll System) is designed to provide the special functional and reporting capabilities required for fund based accounting operations. **Availability:** Online.

11947 ■ *Custom Payroll*
LPI Datasmith Inc.
10020 Fontana
Overland Park, KS 66207

Ph: (913)381-9118
Free: 888-729-2020
Fax: (913)381-9118
URL: http://datasmithpayroll.com
URL(s): www.datasmithpayroll.com/forms/catalog/pg1.htm
Price: Contact vendor for pricing. **Description:** Contact Datasmith product cost. **Availability:** Print; Online.

LIBRARIES

11948 ■ **Ernst & Young Library**
833 E Michigan St.
Milwaukee, WI 53202
Ph: (414)273-5900
Fax: (414)223-7200
URL: http://www.ey.com
Contact: Carmine di Sibio, Chief Executive Officer
Facebook: www.facebook.com/EY
Linkedin: www.linkedin.com/company/ernstandyoung
X (Twitter): x.com/EYnews
YouTube: www.youtube.com/ernstandyoungglobal
Scope: Taxation; tax law; accounting; auditing. **Services:** Performs searches on fee basis for clients only. **Holdings:** 1,200 books.

11949 ■ **International Public Management Association for Human Resources (IPMA-HR) - Library**
1617 Duke St.
Alexandria, VA 22314
Ph: (703)549-7100
URL: http://www.ipma-hr.org
Contact: Jennifer Fairweather, President
Facebook: www.facebook.com/International-Public-Management-Association-for-Human-Resources-IPMA-HR-38098732966
Linkedin: www.linkedin.com/company/ipma-hr
X (Twitter): x.com/ipmahr
Instagram: www.instagram.com/ipmahr
Description: Seeks to improve human resource practices in government through provision of testing services, advisory service, conferences, professional development programs, research, and publications. Sponsors seminars, conferences, and workshops on various phases of public personnel administration. Compiles statistics. **Scope:** Human resources. **Founded:** 1906. **Holdings:** Figures not available. **Publications:** *PSHRA's --Membership Directory*; *Public Personnel Management (PPM)* (Quarterly); *HR Bulletin* (Weekly); *Public Eye* (Monthly); *International News* (Bimonthly). **Educational Activities:** International Training (Annual); PSHRA Annual Conference (Annual). **Awards:** Graduate Study Fellowship (Annual); Agency Award for Excellence (Annual); Honorary Life Membership (Annual); Warner W. Stockberger Achievement Award (Annual). **Geographic Preference:** Multinational; State.

RESEARCH CENTERS

11950 ■ **University of Waterloo School of Accounting and Finance - Centre for Accounting Research and Education (CARE)**
School of Accounting & Finance
200 University Ave. W
Waterloo, ON, Canada N2L 3G1
Ph: (519)888-4567
Fax: (519)888-7562
URL: http://uwaterloo.ca/school-of-accounting-and-finance/care
Contact: Steve Fortin, Director
E-mail: steve.fortin@uwaterloo.ca
Description: Integral unit of University of Waterloo, but operated under its own board of control. **Scope:** Assurance services, financial accounting, finance, management accounting and information systems, and taxation. Encourages interdisciplinary research at the University, including research in ethics. **Founded:** 1981. **Publications:** *CARE Working Papers.*

ASSOCIATIONS AND OTHER ORGANIZATIONS

11951 ■ Alliance of Area Business Publishers (AABP)
287 Richards Ave.
 Norwalk, CT 06850
Ph: (203)515-9294
Co. E-mail: sandersonmgt@gmail.com
URL: http://www.bizpubs.org
Contact: Cate Sanderson, Executive Director
E-mail: cate@sandersonmgt.com
Description: Local area business publications. Encourages high journalistic standards among area business publications. Acts as a forum for the exchange of ideas and information, especially on common issues such as editorial excellence, postal regulations, government regulations, and advertising. Compiles statistics of business patterns in markets of members and engages in cooperative member market research. **Founded:** 1979. **Publications:** *Association of Area Business Publications--Directory* (Annual); *Alliance of Area Business Publications--Membership Directory.* **Awards:** AABP Editorial Excellence Awards (Annual). **Geographic Preference:** National.

11952 ■ Alliance for Audited Media (AAM)
4513 Lincoln Ave., Ste. 105B
 Lisle, IL 60532
Ph: (224)366-6939
Free: 800-285-2220
Co. E-mail: service@auditedmedia.com
URL: http://auditedmedia.com
Contact: Tom Drouillard, President
Facebook: www.facebook.com/auditedmedia
Linkedin: www.linkedin.com/company/alliance-for-au
 dited-media
X (Twitter): x.com/auditedmedia
Instagram: www.instagram.com/auditedmedia
YouTube: www.youtube.com/user/auditedmedia
Description: Represents advertisers, advertising agencies, and publishers of daily and weekly newspapers, farm publications, consumer magazines, and business publications in the United States and Canada. Issues standardized statements on the circulation of publisher members; verifies the figures shown in these statements by auditors' examination of publishers' records; disseminates circulation data. Provides academic associate support; conducts forums and seminars. **Founded:** 1914. **Publications:** *ABC Audit Report and Publisher's Statements* (Annual); *Canadian Circulation of U.S. Magazines* (Annual); *Snapshot* (Semiannual); *Periodical Statement Library* (Semiannual); *Snapshot* (Periodic); *Magazine Market Coverage; Periodical Analyzer; Newspaper Analyzer; Magazine Trends; Newspaper County Penetration Reports* (Semiannual). **Geographic Preference:** National.

11953 ■ American Court and Commercial Newspapers, Inc. (ACCN)
PO Box 5337
 Arlington, VA 22205-5337
Ph: (703)237-9806
Fax: (703)237-9808
URL: http://accnnotices.wordpress.com
Contact: Eric Barnes, President
Description: Newspapers of general circulation devoted to lawyers and courts, financial and real estate professionals, contractors, and business interests. Functions as an advertising medium for business and legal vendors, marketers, advertising agencies, and related businesses. Operates speakers' bureau; conducts research reports. Compiles statistics. **Founded:** 1930. **Geographic Preference:** National.

11954 ■ American Society of Magazine Editors (ASME)
2807 Jackson Ave.
 Long Island City, NY 11101
Ph: (212)872-3737
Co. E-mail: asme@asme.media
URL: http://www.asme.media
Contact: Amanda Kludt, President
Facebook: www.facebook.com/ASME1963
Linkedin: www.linkedin.com/company/asme1963
X (Twitter): x.com/asme1963
Instagram: www.instagram.com/asme1963
Description: Represents magazine editors. Sponsors annual editorial internship program for college juniors and the National Magazine Awards. **Founded:** 1963. **Awards:** ASME Magazine Editor's Hall of Fame (Periodic); National Magazine Awards (Annual). **Geographic Preference:** National.

11955 ■ American Society of Media Photographers (ASMP)
Four Embarcadero Ctr., Ste. 1400
 San Francisco, CA 94111
Free: 844-762-3386
Co. E-mail: info@asmp.org
URL: http://www.asmp.org
Contact: Michael Shay, Chairman of the Board
E-mail: chair@asmp-board.org
Facebook: www.facebook.com/asmpnational
Linkedin: www.linkedin.com/company/asmp-the
 -american-society-of-media-photographers
X (Twitter): x.com/asmp
Instagram: www.instagram.com/asmpnational
Description: Professional society of freelance photographers. Works to evolve trade practices for photographers in communications fields. Provides business information to photographers and their potential clients; promotes ethics and rights of members. Holds educational programs and seminars. Compiles statistics. **Founded:** 1944. **Publications:** *American Society of Media Photographers--Membership Directory; ASMP Bulletin* (Quarterly). **Geographic Preference:** National.

11956 ■ Association of Alternative Newsmedia (AAN)
4780 I-55N., Ste. 100-225
 Jackson, MS 39211
Co. E-mail: accounting@aan.org
URL: http://aan.org
Contact: Todd Stauffer, Executive Director
E-mail: todd@aan.org
Facebook: www.facebook.com/Altweeklies
X (Twitter): x.com/AltWeeklies
Description: Members include Village Voice, L. A. Weekly, Chicago Reader and Washington City Paper. Provides members with information and communication relevant to the business of publishing an alternative newspaper. Holds annual convention. Compiles financial standards report, publishes monthly newsletter and administers annual editorial awards contest. **Founded:** 1978. **Publications:** *Association of Alternative Newsmedia Newsweekly Directory.* **Educational Activities:** AAN Leadership Conference (Annual). **Awards:** AAN Awards (Annual). **Geographic Preference:** National.

11957 ■ Baker's Journal
111 Gordon Baker Rd., Ste. 400
 Toronto, ON, Canada M2H 3R1
Ph: (416)442-5600
Free: 800-268-7742
Fax: (416)510-5134
Co. E-mail: apotal@annexbusinessmedia.com
URL: http://www.mromagazine.com
Contact: Beata Olechnowicz, Manager
E-mail: bolechnowicz@annexbusinessmedia.com
URL(s): www.bakersjournal.com
Facebook: www.facebook.com/BakersJournal
YouTube: www.youtube.com/user/bakersjournal
Released: 9/year; Jan/Feb, Mar, Apr, May/Jun, Jul, Aug/Sept, Oct, Nov, Dec. **Description:** Provides new marketing trends, product information, industry events, and new ideas. **Availability:** Print; Download; Online.

11958 ■ Book and Periodical Council (BPC)
192 Spadina Ave., Ste. 107
 Toronto, ON, Canada M5T 2C2
Ph: (416)975-9366
Co. E-mail: info@thebpc.ca
URL: http://www.thebpc.ca
Contact: Anne McClelland, Executive Director
Facebook: www.facebook.com/BookandPerio
 dicalCouncil
X (Twitter): x.com/intent/follow
Description: Associations representing writers, editors, and publishers of books and periodicals and manufacturers, distributors, and sellers and lenders of printed materials. **Geographic Preference:** National.

11959 ■ Canadian Association of Journalists (CAJ) [L'Association Canadienne des Journalistes]
PO Box 117, Station F
 Toronto, ON, Canada M4Y 2L4
URL: http://caj.ca
Contact: Brent Jolly, President
E-mail: brent@caj.ca
Facebook: www.facebook.com/CdnAssocJournalists
Linkedin: www.linkedin.com/company/canadian
 -association-of-journalists
X (Twitter): x.com/caj

Description: Professional organization representing the interests of journalists in Canada. Promotes high professional standards. Disseminates information. **Founded:** 1978. **Publications:** *CAJ Media* (3/year); *Directory of Canadian Journalists* (Annual). **Awards:** CAJ Code of Silence Award (Annual); Awards for Investigative Journalism (Annual); Investigative Journalist Award (Annual). **Geographic Preference:** National.

11960 ■ *Canadian Contractor*

111 Gordon Baker Rd., Ste. 400
Toronto, ON, Canada M2H 3R1
Ph: (416)442-5600
Free: 800-268-7742
Fax: (416)510-5134
Co. E-mail: apotal@annexbusinessmedia.com
URL: http://www.mromagazine.com
Contact: Beata Olechnowicz, Manager
E-mail: bolechnowicz@annexbusinessmedia.com
URL(s): www.canadiancontractor.ca
Facebook: www.facebook.com/CanadianContractor
Instagram: www.instagram.com/canadiancontractor

Ed: Stephen Payne. **Released:** Irregular **Description:** Canadian magazine for contractors and builders in the residential and light commercial building industry. **Availability:** Print; Online.

11961 ■ Canadian Copyright Institute (CCI)

192 Spadina Ave., Ste. 107
Toronto, ON, Canada M5T 2C2
Ph: (416)975-9366
Co. E-mail: info@thecci.ca
URL: http://thecci.ca/default.html
Contact: Anne McClelland, Administrator

Description: Creators, producers, and distributors of copyrighted works. Encourages a more complete understanding of copyright laws among members and the public. Consults with government and judicial bodies regarding reform of copyright laws. Conducts and sponsors research on copyright laws worldwide. Works with organizations pursuing similar goals to improve copyright legislation and enforcement. **Founded:** 1965. **Publications:** *Copyright Reform Legislation Reporting Service* (Periodic). **Geographic Preference:** National.

11962 ■ Canadian University Press (CUP)

Canada
URL: http://cup.ca
Contact: Andrew Mrozowski, President
E-mail: president@cup.ca

Description: Student newspapers. Serves as a communication and support network for members; promotes exchange of news and features among members; seeks to develop journalistic skills among Canadian students; provides mechanism for sharing of national advertising by members. Encourages cultural diversity in Canadian student media. Conducts political action caucuses. **Founded:** 1938. **Publications:** *House Organ* (Monthly); *This Week and More* (Weekly). **Geographic Preference:** National.

11963 ■ City and Regional Magazine Association (CRMA)

287 Richards Ave.
Norwalk, CT 06850
Ph: (203)515-9294
Co. E-mail: admin@citymag.org
URL: http://citymag.org
Contact: Ray Paprocki, President

Description: City and regional consumer-oriented magazines; related businesses involved in printing, advertising, and circulation. Strives to gain presence in the marketplace and command an increased following among national advertisers. Serves as a channel of communication between city and regional consumer magazines and coordinates research projects. Distributes information; creates press materials. Compiles statistics. **Founded:** 1978. **Awards:** National City and Regional Magazine Award for Writer of the Year (Annual). **Geographic Preference:** National; Local.

11964 ■ *Computing Canada*

55 Town Ctr. Ct., Ste. 302
Scarborough, ON, Canada M1P 4X4
Ph: (416)290-0240
Free: 800-565-4007
Co. E-mail: info@itbusiness.ca
URL: http://www.itbusiness.ca
Contact: Fawn Annan, President
E-mail: fannan@itworldcanada.com
URL(s): www.itworldcanada.com/computing-canada
Ed: Dave Webb. **Availability:** Print; Online.

11965 ■ International News Media Association (INMA) [The International Newspaper Marketing Association; National Newspaper Promotion Association]

PO Box 740186
Dallas, TX 75374
Ph: (214)373-9111
Fax: (214)373-9112
URL: http://www.inma.org
Contact: Maribel Perez Wadsworth, President
Facebook: www.facebook.com/inma.newsmedia
X (Twitter): x.com/inmaorg
Instagram: www.instagram.com/inmaorg

Description: Identifies the best ideas to grow audience, revenue, and brand of news media companies through sharing of global best practices. **Founded:** 1930. **Educational Activities:** Annual INMA World Congress (Annual); INMA World Congress (Annual). **Awards:** Silver Shovel Award; INMA Awards; Silver Shovel Award (Annual). **Geographic Preference:** Multinational.

11966 ■ Magazines Canada

RPO 14th
Markham, ON, Canada L3S 4T1
Ph: (416)994-6471
Free: 877-238-8354
Fax: (416)504-0437
Co. E-mail: info@magazinescanada.ca
URL: http://magazinescanada.ca
Contact: Chris Radley, Executive Director
E-mail: chrisradley@magazinescanada.ca
Linkedin: www.linkedin.com/company/magazines -canada
Instagram: www.instagram.com/magscanada
YouTube: www.youtube.com/user/magazinescanada

Description: Represents members' interests before government agencies and provides support and assistance to magazine publishers. **Scope:** A professional magazine industry association, representing more than 300 consumer titles of all scope and size. **Founded:** 1973. **Publications:** "Kenya: Healing the Nation," Apr, 2008; "Finding a good fit with a new recruit". **Training:** You built it but do they come?; The Naked Truth About Magazines; Powerhouse Websites: On a Budget. **Awards:** Outstanding Volunteer (Annual); Magazines Canada - Volunteer of the Year (Annual).

11967 ■ MPA - The Association of Magazine Media (MPA)

4401 N Fairfax Dr., Ste. 300
Arlington, VA 22203
Ph: (571)366-1000
Co. E-mail: info@newsmediaalliance.org
URL: http://www.newsmediaalliance.org
Contact: Mark Adams, President
Facebook: www.facebook.com/NewsMediaAlliance
Linkedin: www.linkedin.com/company/news-media -alliance
X (Twitter): x.com/newsalliance
YouTube: www.youtube.com/c/NewsMediaAlliance

Description: Publishers of more than 1000 consumer and other magazines issued not less than four times a year. Activities include: Advertising Marketing Department to promote magazines as an advertising medium; Washington office to report on federal legislation and postal rates and regulations; Consumer Marketing Department to provide information services and assistance to members in all areas of circulation marketing. **Founded:** 1919. **Holdings:** Books; magazine publishers research reports; circulation reports; magazine advertising expenditures statistics; 400 vertical files of information on markets

and media. **Publications:** *Newsletter of International Publishing*; *MPA Washington Newsletter*. **Educational Activities:** American Magazine Media Conference (Annual). **Awards:** MPA Lifetime Achievement Awards (Annual); Kelly Awards (Annual). **Geographic Preference:** National.

11968 ■ *NASJA Directory*

22 Cavalier Way Latham
Latham, NY 12110
URL: http://www.nasja.org
Contact: Jeff Blumenfeld, President
E-mail: jeff@blumenfeldpr.com
URL(s): www.nasja.org/explore-nasja/member-benefi ts
Availability: Print.

11969 ■ National Association of Hispanic Publications, Inc. (NAHP)

National Press Bldg.
529 14th St. NW, Ste. 923
Washington, DC 20045
URL: http://nahp.org
Contact: Álvaro Gurdián, President
Facebook: www.facebook.com/NAHPofficial

Description: Promotes adherence to high standards of ethical and professional standards by members; advocates continuing professional development of Hispanic journalists and publishers. Provides technical assistance to members in areas including writing and editing skills, circulation and distribution methods, attracting advertisers, obtaining financing, design and layout, and graphic arts. Conducts public service programs including voter registration drives. **Founded:** 1982. **Publications:** *The Hispanic Press* (Quarterly). **Educational Activities:** NAHP Annual Convention (Annual). **Geographic Preference:** National.

11970 ■ News Media Canada

37 Front St. E, Ste. 200
Toronto, ON, Canada M5E 1B3
Ph: (416)923-3567
Free: 877-305-2262
Fax: (416)923-7206
Co. E-mail: info@newsmediacanada.ca
URL: http://nmc-mic.ca
Contact: Paul Deegan, President
E-mail: pdeegan@newsmediacanada.ca
Facebook: www.facebook.com/newsmediacanada
Linkedin: www.linkedin.com/groups/3349657
X (Twitter): x.com/NewsMediaCanada
Instagram: www.instagram.com/newsmediacanada
YouTube: www.youtube.com/channel/UCtaZw _hUrzWo617mOTLhegw

Description: Represents more than 800 print and digital media outlets in Canada. Represents the interests of media members before labor and industrial organizations, government agencies, and the public. Conducts educational and promotional activities. Conducts industry research. **Founded:** 2016. **Publications:** *Community Markets Canada Membership Directory* (Annual). **Awards:** Canadian Community Newspaper Awards (Annual). **Geographic Preference:** National.

11971 ■ North American Snowsports Journalists Association (NASJA)

22 Cavalier Way Latham
Latham, NY 12110
URL: http://www.nasja.org
Contact: Jeff Blumenfeld, President
E-mail: jeff@blumenfeldpr.com
Facebook: www.facebook.com/Nasjasnowmedia
X (Twitter): x.com/NASJAsnowscoops

Description: Newspaper, magazine, book, television, radio writers and broadcasters, and photographers who report on skiing and other snow sports. Covers skiing and other snow sports. **Founded:** 1963. **Publications:** *North American Snowsports Journalists Association--Membership Directory* (Annual); *The Inside Edge* (Quinquennial); *NASJA Directory*. **Educational Activities:** North American Snowsports Journalists Association Meeting (Annual). **Awards:** Harold S. Hirsch Award for Excellence in Snowsports Journalism - Blogs (Annual); Harold S. Hirsch Award for Excellence in Snowsports Journalism - Books (Triennial); Harold S. Hirsch Award for Excellence in Snowsports Journalism - Feature Writing (Annual); Carson White Snowsports Achievement Award (Annual); Harold S. Hirsch Award for Excellence in Snowsports Journalism - Columns (Annual); Harold S. Hirsch Award for Excellence in Snowsports Journalism - Video (Annual); Harold S. Hirsch Award for Excellence Image (Annual); Paul Robbins Outstanding Competitor Award (Annual); NASJA Lifetime Achievement Award (Annual). **Geographic Preference:** Multinational.

11972 ■ Printing United Alliance Center for Technology and Research - Library [Printing Industries of America's Center for Technology and Research]

2000 Corporate Dr., Ste. 205
 Wexford, PA 15090
Ph: (412)259-1710
Co. E-mail: info@printing.org
URL: http://www.printing.org/programs/technology
 -research
Facebook: www.facebook.com/printingunited
Linkedin: www.linkedin.com/company/printingunited
Instagram: www.instagram.com/printingind

Description: Serves the international graphic communications industries. Conducts research in graphic processes and their commercial applications, along with seminars and forums on graphic arts and environmental subjects. Conducts educational programs, including the publishing of graphic arts textbooks and learning modules, in addition to training and certification program in sheet-fed offset press operating, Web offset press operating, image assembly, and desktop publishing. Produces test images and quality control devices for the industry. Performs technical services for the graphic arts industry, including problem-solving, material evaluation, and plant audits. **Scope:** Human resources; economics; technologies; business growth. **Founded:** 1924. **Holdings:** Figures not available. **Publications:** "Re-Energize Your Printing Business," Partnership Publishing L.L.C.; "Handbook for Digital Printing and Variable-Data Printing"; "Flexography Primer"; "Process Controls Primer"; "The PDF Print Production Guide". **Training:** Creating Print Ready Files that Work Every Time; What Designers Need to Know about Sustainability; What Every Designer Must Know About Color and Press Oks; New Frontiers for the 21st Century Graphic Designer; Color Management for Printing and Packaging; Web to Print Primer; Designing for Prepress Success; Profit Opportunity Expanding into New Markets with Ancillary Services; Winning Ways to Market Web to Print Work flow to Customers; PDF Preflight and Repair for Newbies; Cross Media Methods n Magic URLS, Microsites and More; Good Jobs Gone Bad 2009 Edition; Fine Tune Your Color Management; Automating for Survival; Best Practice Primer Winning Digital Printing Workflows; Maximize Press time with Pit Stop Maintenance; A How to Tactical Plan for Sustainability Success; Optimizing Your Digital Press Where it Works and Where its Broken; Offset Press Optimization How to Troubleshoot, Control and Accelerate; Performance Dashboard Stalking Waste in the Printers Processes; Technology Forecast What's Hot and What's Not; Lean n Green Tactics and Techniques for Removing Waste; Controlling the Print Process How to Avoid Customer Rejects; Process Control for Color Management Prepress through Press. **Educational Activities:** President's Conference (Annual). **Awards:** Naomi Berber Memorial Award (Annual); Printing Industries of America Education Award of Excellence (Annual); InterTech Technology Awards (Annual); Robert F. Reed Technology Medal (Annual); William D. Schaeffer Environmental Award (Annual); Frederick D. Kagy Education Award of Excellence (Annual). **Geographic Preference:** National.

11973 ■ Society of Publication Designers (SPD)

1120 Ave. of the Americas, 4th Flr.
 New York, NY 10036
Ph: (212)223-3332
Co. E-mail: mail@spd.org
URL: http://www.spd.org

Contact: Agnethe Glatved, President
Facebook: www.facebook.com/SPD.org
Linkedin: www.linkedin.com/company/the-society-of
 -publication-designers
X (Twitter): x.com/SPDtweets
Instagram: www.instagram.com/spdesigners
Description: Represents art directors, designers, editors, photographers and illustrators with the responsibility of layout and design of consumer, business and professional publications and newspapers. Holds speakers' luncheons and auctions. **Founded:** 1965. **Publications:** GRIDS; Solid Gold. **Educational Activities:** Annual SPD Awards Gala (Annual). **Awards:** SPD Magazine of the Year Award (Annual). **Geographic Preference:** National.

REFERENCE WORKS

11974 ■ "Calista Sells Rural Newspapers" in Alaska Business Monthly (Vol. 27, October 2011, No. 10, pp. 8)

Pub: Alaska Business Publishing Company Inc.
Contact: Charles Bell, Vice President, Sales and Marketing
E-mail: cbell@akbizmag.com
Ed: Nancy Pounds. **Description:** Calista sold its six newspapers, a magazine, shoppers and its printing house. Details of the sales are given.

11975 ■ "Copyright Clearance Center (CCC) Partnered with cSubs" in Information Today (Vol. 28, November 2011, No. 10, pp. 14)

Description: Copyright Clearance Center (CCC) partnered with cSubs to integrate CCC's point-of-content licensing solution RightsLink Basic directly into cSubs workflow. The partnership will allow cSubs' customers a user-friendly process for obtaining permissions. Csubs is a corporate subscription management service for books, newspapers, and econtent. **Availability:** Online.

11976 ■ "Crain's Makes Ad Sales, Custom Marketing Appointments" in Crain's Chicago Business (Vol. 34, October 24, 2011, No. 42, pp. 13)

Pub: Crain Communications Inc.
Contact: Barry Asin, President
Description: Crain's Chicago Business announced key appointments in its sales department: David Denor has been named first director of custom marketing services and Kate Van Etten will succeed Denor as advertising director. **Availability:** Online.

11977 ■ Directory of Small Press/Magazine Editors & Publishers

Pub: Dustbooks
URL(s): www.dustbooks.com/de.htm
Ed: Len Fulton. **Released:** Annual; latest edition 2017-2018. **Description:** Covers about 7,500 publishers and editors. **Entries include:** Individual name, title of press or magazine, address and phone number. **Arrangement:** Alphabetical. **Availability:** Print.

11978 ■ The Facebook Effect: The Inside Story of the Company That Is Connecting the World

Ed: David Kirkpatrick. **Released:** 2011. **Price:** $18, paperback; $13.99, e-book. **Description:** There's never been a Website like Facebook: more than 350 million people have accounts, and if the growth rate continues, by 2013 every Internet user worldwide will have his or her own page. No one's had more access to the inner workings of the phenomenon than Kirkpatrick, a senior tech writer at Fortune magazine. Written with the full cooperation of founder Mark Zuckerberg, the book follows the company from its genesis in a Harvard dorm room through its successes over Friendster and MySpace, the expansion of the user base, and Zuckerberg's refusal to sell. **Availability:** E-book; Print.

11979 ■ "FCC Adopts New Media Ownership Rules" in Black Enterprise (Vol. 38, March 1, 2008, No. 8, pp. 26)

Pub: Earl G. Graves Ltd.
Contact: Earl Graves, Jr., President

Ed: Joyce Jones. **Description:** Federal Communications Commission approved a ruling that lifts a ban on newspaper and/or broadcast cross ownership. Because of declining sales in newspaper advertising and readership the ban will allow companies to share local news gathering costs across multiple media platforms. **Availability:** Online.

11980 ■ "Gannett Looks to Spare Journalists' Jobs after Big Newspaper Merger" in The Wall Street Journal (November 19, 2019)

URL(s): www.wsj.com/articles/gannett-looks-to-spare
 -journalists-jobs-after-big-newspaper-merger-1157
 4197800
Ed: Lukas I. Alpert. **Released:** November 19, 2019. **Description:** CEO Paul Bascobert of Gannett Media Corp., vowed to avoid big layoffs of journalists when Gannett Co. and GateHouse Media merge. However, there will be cuts to eliminate duplicate jobs and functions from regional printing, distribution, and copy-editing. **Availability:** Online.

11981 ■ "Growth of Free Dailies Dropping" in Globe & Mail (March 24, 2007, pp. B7)

Ed: Grant Robertson. **Description:** The decrease in the readership of free newspapers in Canada, in view of growing preference for online news, is discussed. **Availability:** Online.

11982 ■ How to Get Rich

Ed: Felix Dennis. **Released:** 2013. **Price:** $8.16, paperback. **Description:** The author, publisher of Maxim, The Week, and Stuff magazines, discusses the mistakes he made running his companies. He didn't understand that people who buy computer gaming magazines wanted a free game with each copy, as one of his rivals was offering. And he laments not diversifying into television and exploiting the Internet. **Availability:** E-book; Print.

11983 ■ The International Directory of Little Magazines & Small Presses

Pub: Dustbooks
URL(s): www.dustbooks.com/d.htm
Ed: Len Fulton. **Released:** Annual **Description:** Covers over 4,000 small, independent magazines, presses, and papers. **Entries include:** Name, address, size, circulation, frequency, price, type of material used, number of issues or books published annually, and other pertinent data. **Arrangement:** Alphabetical. **Indexes:** Subject, regional.

11984 ■ "Joanna Crangle Named MBJ Publisher" in Sacramento Business Journal (Vol. 31, March 28, 2014, No. 5)

Pub: American City Business Journals, Inc.
Contact: Mike Olivieri, Executive Vice President
Released: Weekly. **Description:** Joanna Crangle has been appointed the new publisher of the 'Memphis Business Journal'. She will succeed Stuart Chamblin, who is retiring as of March 31, 2014. Crangle has previously served as the newspaper's circulation director and advertising director. **Availability:** Print; Online.

11985 ■ "Joe Wikert, General Manager, O'Reilly Technology Exchange" in Information Today (Vol. 26, February 2009, No. 2, pp. 21)

Description: Joe Wikert, general manager of O'Reilly Technology Exchange discusses his plans to develop a free content model that will evolve with future needs. O'Reilly's major competitor is Google. Wikert plans to expand the firm's publishing program to include print, online, and in-person products and services. **Availability:** Online.

11986 ■ "Lessons From My Father" in Crain's Chicago Business (Vol. 31, November 10, 2008, No. 45, pp. 28)

Pub: Crain Communications Inc.
Contact: Barry Asin, President
Ed: Rance Crain. **Description:** Rance Crain discusses his father, G.D. Crain Jr., who founded Crain Communications Inc. during the Great Depression. Advice is given for sustaining a business, even one that seems to be failing, during tough economic times. **Availability:** Online.

11987 ■ *The Library and Book Trade Almanac*

Pub: Information Today Inc.

Contact: Thomas H. Hogan, President

URL(s): store.infotoday.com/product/the-library-and-book-trade-almanac

Released: Annual; latest edition 68th; 2023. **Price:** $339.50, U.S.; $371.50, for outside north America; $361.50, for Canada or Mexico; $339.50, for annual. **Description:** Publication includes lists of accredited library schools; scholarships for education in library science; library organizations; library statistics; publishing and bookselling organizations. Includes lists of notable books, best-sellers, literary prize winners; library and trade statistics; calendar of events. **Entries include:** Directory listings give name of institution, address, phone, fax, name of officer or contact, publications; scholarship listings include requirements, value of grant, contact name. Principal content is articles and special reports on topics of interest to those in library/information science and publishers; international reports; annual reports from federal agencies and libraries and from national associations; information on legislation, funding, etc. **Arrangement:** Topical. **Indexes:** Organization; subject. **Availability:** Print; Online.

11988 ■ *"Life's Work: Ben Bradlee"* in *Harvard Business Review* (Vol. 88, September 2010, No. 9, pp. 128)

Pub: Harvard Business Publishing

Contact: Diane Belcher, Managing Director

Ed: Alison Beard. **Price:** $8.95, PDF. **Description:** Newspaper publisher Ben Bradlee discusses factors that lead to success, including visible supervisors, enthusiasm, appropriate expansion, and the importance in truth in reporting. **Availability:** Online; PDF.

11989 ■ *Media, Organizations and Identity*

Pub: Palgrave Macmillan

Released: First edition. **Description:** The mass media, press, and television are essential in the formation of corporate identity and the promotion of business image and reputation. This book offers a new perspective into the interrelationships between media and organizations over three dimensions: media as business, media in business and business in the media.

11990 ■ *"A New Globe - In Print and Online"* in *Marketing to Women* (Vol. 22, August 2009, No. 8, pp. 3)

Description: Seventeen magazine is unifying its print and Online editions with complementary content, a strategy that seems to be working as every aspect of Seventeen drives the reader to another component. **Availability:** Online.

11991 ■ *"New Sony HD Ads Tout Digital"* in *Brandweek* (Vol. 49, April 21, 2008, No. 16, pp. 5)

Description: Looking to promote Sony Electronics' digital imaging products, the company has launched another campaign effort known as HDNA, a play on the words high-definition and DNA; originally Sony focused the HDNA campaign on their televisions, the new ads will include still and video cameras as well and marketing efforts will consist of advertising in print, Online, television spots and publicity at various venues across the country. **Availability:** Online.

11992 ■ *"Paper Tigers"* in *Conde Nast Portfolio* (Vol. 2, June 2008, No. 6, pp. 84)

Ed: Roger Lowenstein. **Description:** Newspapers are losing their advertisers and readers and circulation today is equal to that of 1950, a time when the U.S. population was half its present size. **Availability:** Print; Online.

11993 ■ *"People; E-Commerce, Online Games, Mobile Apps"* in *Advertising Age* (Vol. 80, October 19, 2009, No. 35, pp. 14)

Pub: Crain Communications, Inc.

Contact: Jessica Botos, Manager, Marketing

E-mail: jessica.botos@crainsnewyork.com

Ed: Nat Ives. **Description:** Profile of People Magazine and the ways in which the publisher is moving its magazine forward by exploring new concepts in a time of declining newsstand sales and advertising pages; among the strategies are e-commerce such as the brand People Style Watch in which consumers are able highlight clothing and jewelry and then connect to retailers' sites and a channel on Taxi TV, the network of video-touch screens in New Your City taxis. **Availability:** Online.

11994 ■ *"Printing Company Edwards Brothers Grapples With a Shrinking Market"* in *Crain's Detroit Business* (Vol. 26, Jan. 4, 2010)

Pub: Crain Communications Inc.

Contact: Barry Asin, President

Ed: Bill Shea. **Description:** Overview of the publishing industry, which has seen a huge decline in revenue; Edwards Brothers, Inc., a family printing business that was founded 117 years ago is struggling due to a variety of factors, many of which are explored. **Availability:** Print; Online.

11995 ■ *"Reducing the Book's Carbon Footprint"* in *American Printer* (Vol. 128, July 1, 2011, No. 7)

Description: Green Press Initiative's Book Industry Environmental Council is working to achieve a 20 percent reduction in the book industry's carbon footprint by 2020. The Council is made up of publishers, printers, paper suppliers, and non-governmental organizations. **Availability:** Online.

11996 ■ *"Renren Partners With Recruit to Launch Social Wedding Services"* in *Benzinga.com* (June 7, 2011)

Pub: PR Newswire Association LLC.

Description: Renren Inc., the leading real name social networking Internet platform in China has partnered with Recruit Company Limited, Japan's largest human resource and classified media group to form a joint venture to build a wedding social media catering to the needs of engaged couples and newlyweds in China.

11997 ■ *"Scaife's Legacy to Live On in Black and White"* in *Pittsburgh Business Times* (Vol. 33, July 11, 2014, No. 52, pp. 3)

Pub: American City Business Journals, Inc.

Contact: Mike Olivieri, Executive Vice President

Released: Weekly. **Price:** $4, introductory 4-week offer(Digital only). **Description:** Pittsburgh Tribune Review owner, Richard Mellon Scaife, before his death on July 4, 2014, took the necessary steps to ensure that his media empire would continue after his demise. Scaife's most cherished legacy has grown over four decades into Trib Total Media and the Pittsburgh Tribune Review, a conservative newspaper alternative to Pittsburgh Post-Gazette. **Availability:** Print; Online.

11998 ■ *"Study: New Moms Build A Lot of Brand Buzz"* in *Brandweek* (Vol. 49, April 21, 2008, No. 16, pp. 7)

Description: According to a new survey which sampled 1,721 pregnant women and new moms, this demographic is having 109 word-of-mouth conversations per week concerning products, services and brands. Two-thirds of these conversations directly involve brand recommendations. The Internet is driving these word-of-mouth, or W-O-M, conversations among this segment, beating out magazines, television and other forms of media. **Availability:** Online.

11999 ■ *"The Sunday Newspaper (est. 1891): the Death of Three Postmedia Sunday Papers Leaves Few Remaining"* in *Canadian Business* (Vol. 85, July 16, 2012, No. 11-12, pp. 14)

Ed: Conan Tobias. **Description:** Postmedia Network Canada Corporation announced the cancellation of the Sunday editions of three of its newspapers, namely 'Calgary Herald', Edmonton Journal', and 'Ottawa Citizen', in order to focus on digital distribution.

The first newspaper in Canada to publish a Sunday edition was 'The World' on May 24, 1891 but law required it to be delivered on Saturday. **Availability:** Print; Online.

12000 ■ *"A Turn in the South"* in *The Economist* (Vol. 390, January 3, 2009, No. 8612, pp. 34)

Description: Overview of Charleston, South Carolina, a region that lost its navy base in 1996, which had provided work for more than 22,000 people; the city developed a plan called Noisette in order to redevelop the area and today the economy is healthier and more diversified than it was a decade ago. Charleston was described as among the best cities for doing business by Inc. Magazine and seems to be handling the downturn of the economy fairly well. Statistical data regarding growth, business and population is included. **Availability:** Print; Online.

STATISTICAL SOURCES

12001 ■ *RMA Annual Statement Studies*

Pub: Risk Management Association

Contact: Nancy Foster, President

Released: Annual. **Description:** Contains composite balance sheets and income statements for more than 360 industries, including the accounting, auditing, and bookkeeping industries. Also contains five years of comparative historical data for discerning trends. Includes 16 commonly used ratios, computed for most of the size groupings for nearly every industry.

TRADE PERIODICALS

12002 ■ *Canastota Bee-Journal*

Contact: Richard K. Keene, President

E-mail: rkeene@cnylink.com

Released: Weekly (Wed.) **Price:** $28, Individuals in-state (NY); $45, Two years in-state (NY); $60, Individuals 3 years; in-state (NY); $33, Out of state out-of-state; $60, Out of state 2 years; out-of-state; $79, Out of state 3 years; out-of-state; $28, Out of country; $46, Out of country 2 years; $63, Out of country; $23, Individuals senior rate in-county. **Description:** Community newspaper serving the Syracuse suburban towns of Lenox, Lincoln, and Canastota. **Availability:** Print.

12003 ■ *Hamilton/Morrisville Tribune*

Contact: Richard K. Keene, President

URL(s): cnylink.com/aboutcny

Released: Weekly (Wed.) **Price:** $25, Individuals in-state, one year; $30, Individuals out-of-state, one year; $28, Individuals in-state outside Ononandoga and Madison Counties; $23, Individuals senior in-county, one year; $19, Individuals college, one year; $99, Individuals outside the U.S., one year; $15, Individuals Syracuse parent, one year; $10, Individuals prime for senior citizens, one year. **Description:** Community newspaper serving the Syracuse suburban communities of Hamilton, Madison, Eaton, Lebanon, and Morrisville. **Availability:** Print.

12004 ■ *La Jolla Village News*

Pub: San Diego Community Newspaper Group

Contact: Heather Long, Manager

E-mail: heather@sdnews.com

URL(s): sdnews.com/la-jolla-village-news

Facebook: www.facebook.com/LJVillageNews

X (Twitter): x.com/ljvillagenews

Ed: Blake Bunch. **Released:** Biweekly; published every other week. **Price:** $24, for 12 issues print; $52, for 26 issues print. **Description:** Community newspaper. **Availability:** Print; PDF; Download; Online.

12005 ■ *Redlands Daily Facts*

Pub: Southern California News Group

URL(s): www.redlandsdailyfacts.com

Facebook: www.facebook.com/RedlandsDailyFacts

X (Twitter): x.com/RedlandsNews

Instagram: www.instagram.com/inlandempirereport

Released: Daily **Price:** $3.50, for digital per week; $4.50, for premium digital per week; $1, for 6 month; $14, for print and online; $1, for standard 1 year. **Description:** General interest newspaper. **Availability:** Print; Online.

VIDEO/AUDIO MEDIA

12006 ■ *How I Built This: Politico & Axios: Jim VandeHei*
URL(s): wondery.com/shows/how-i-built-this/episode/ 10386-politico-amp-axios-jim-vandehei
Ed: Guy Raz. **Released:** February 27, 2023. **Description:** Podcast discusses how a political reporter co-founded a media company when the only thing he'd ever managed was a night shift at Little Caesar's.

CONSULTANTS

12007 ■ Heidelberg Graphics (HG)
2 Stansbury Ct.
  Chico, CA 95928
Ph: (530)342-6582
Fax: (530)342-6582
Co. E-mail: service@heidelberggraphics.com
URL: http://www.heidelberggraphics.com
Contact: Larry S. Jackson, Owner
Description: Publisher of books and also provides publishing, layout, printing and e-Book solutions. **Founded:** 1972. **Publications:** "Chronicles of the Clandestine Knights: Hyacinth Blue," 2003; "A Book of Thoughts II," 2001; "Historic Shot Glasses: The pre-Prohibition," 1992; "After the War," 1981; "Phantasm," 1980.

12008 ■ J. S. Eliezer Associates Inc. (JSEA)
300 Atlantic St.
  Stamford, CT 06902
Contact: Peter M. Harding, Chief Executive Officer
Description: Management and market research consultants offering design and implementation of manufacturing strategy, feasibility analysis, and systems analysis, as well as management information systems and prepress systems, manufacturing proposals analysis, negotiations and contracts, paper purchasing strategy and contract negotiations, and catalog distribution effectiveness analysis and serves the publishing and catalog industries. **Scope:** Management and market research consultants offering design and implementation of manufacturing strategy, feasibility analysis, and systems analysis, as well as management information systems and prepress systems, manufacturing proposals analysis, negotiations and contracts, paper purchasing strategy and contract negotiations, and catalog distribution effectiveness analysis and serves the publishing and catalog industries.

FRANCHISES AND BUSINESS OPPORTUNITIES

12009 ■ EasyChair Media
800 3rd St.
  Windsor, CO 80550
Ph: (970)686-5805
Co. E-mail: office@easychairmedia.com
URL: http://www.easychairmedia.com
Facebook: www.facebook.com/EasyChairMedia
Description: Firm is a provider of marketing services. **Founded:** 2000. **Franchised:** 2002. **Publications:** *EasyChair* (Quarterly). **Training:** Create captivating design that evokes emotion and ensures reaction.

12010 ■ Frontier Publications Inc.
24425 Wax Orchard Rd. SW
  Vashon, WA 98070-7514
Contact: Tara Snowden, Governor
Description: Sell franchises for the Bingo Bugle Newspaper nationally. The Bingo Bugle is a monthly publication for bingo players. desktop publishing, typesetting and paste-up, bookkeeping and billing, distribution and multiple-edition advertising. **Founded:** 1979. **Financial Assistance:** No **Training:** Available 2 days at franchisee's location, headquarters or regional location and ongoing support.

PUBLICATIONS

12011 ■ Cincinnati Business Courier
120 E 4th St., Ste. 230
  Cincinnati, OH 45202
Ph: (513)621-6665
Fax: (513)621-2462
Co. E-mail: cincinnati@bizjournals.com
URL: http://www.bizjournals.com/cincinnati
Contact: Kelly Snyder, Director
E-mail: ktassos@bizjournals.com
Facebook: www.facebook.com/BusinessCourier
Linkedin: www.linkedin.com/company/business -courier
X (Twitter): x.com/BusinessCourier
Instagram: www.instagram.com/cincinna tibusinesscourier
Description: Publisher of business journals. **Founded:** 1984. **Publications:** *Business Courier* (Weekly).

12012 ■ Houston Business Journal (HBJ)
5444 Westheimer, Ste. 1560
  Houston, TX 77056
Ph: (713)688-8811
Fax: (713)963-0482
Co. E-mail: houston@bizjournals.com
URL: http://www.bizjournals.com/houston
Contact: Bob Charlet, President
E-mail: bcharlet@bizjournals.com
Facebook: www.facebook.com/hous tonbusinessjournals
Linkedin: www.linkedin.com/company/houston -business-journal
X (Twitter): x.com/HOUBizjournal
Instagram: www.instagram.com/houbizjournal
Description: Publisher: Newspaper. **Founded:** 1987.

12013 ■ Philadelphia Business Journal
400 Market St., Ste. 1200
  Philadelphia, PA 19106
Ph: (215)238-1450
Fax: (215)238-9489
Co. E-mail: philadelphia@bizjournals.com
URL: http://www.bizjournals.com/philadelphia
Contact: Sierra Quinn, Director
E-mail: squinn@bizjournals.com
Facebook: www.facebook.com/PhilaBusinessJournal
Linkedin: www.linkedin.com/company/philadelphia -business-journal
X (Twitter): x.com/PHLBizJournal
Description: Publishes business directories. **Publications:** *Philadelphia Business Journal* (Weekly); *Philadelphia Business Journal--Book of Business Lists Issue* (Annual).

COMPUTERIZED DATABASES

12014 ■ *Daily Brief*
Oxford Analytica
  5 Alfred St.
  Oxford OX1 4EH, United Kingdom
Ph: 44 1865 261-600
URL: http://www.oxan.com
Contact: Nick Redman, Director
URL(s): www.oxan.com/services/daily-brief
Released: Daily **Availability:** Online. **Type:** Full-text.

12015 ■ *Ethnic NewsWatch: A History™*
URL(s): proquest.libguides.com/enew
Type: Full-text; Directory.

LIBRARIES

12016 ■ MPA - The Association of Magazine Media (MPA)
4401 N Fairfax Dr., Ste. 300
  Arlington, VA 22203
Ph: (571)366-1000
Co. E-mail: info@newsmediaalliance.org
URL: http://www.newsmediaalliance.org
Contact: Mark Adams, President
Facebook: www.facebook.com/NewsMediaAlliance
Linkedin: www.linkedin.com/company/news-media -alliance
X (Twitter): x.com/newsalliance
YouTube: www.youtube.com/c/NewsMediaAlliance
Description: Publishers of more than 1000 consumer and other magazines issued not less than four times a year. Activities include: Advertising Marketing Department to promote magazines as an advertising medium; Washington office to report on federal legislation and postal rates and regulations; Consumer Marketing Department to provide information services and assistance to members in all areas of circulation marketing. **Founded:** 1919. **Holdings:** Books; magazine publishers research reports; circulation reports; magazine advertising expenditures statistics; 400 vertical files of information on markets and media. **Publications:** *Newsletter of International Publishing*; *MPA Washington Newsletter*. **Educational Activities:** American Magazine Media Conference (Annual). **Awards:** MPA Lifetime Achievement Awards (Annual); Kelly Awards (Annual). **Geographic Preference:** National.

12017 ■ Trusted Media Brands Inc. (TMB)
485 Lexington Ave.
  New York, NY 10017
Free: 877-732-4438
URL: http://www.trustedmediabrands.com
Contact: Marty Moe, President
Linkedin: www.linkedin.com/company/trusted-media -brands-inc
X (Twitter): x.com/trustedmediainc
Description: A global multi-brand media and marketing company that educates, entertains and connects audiences around the world and the company markets and publishes books, magazines, educational products, recorded music collections and home video products worldwide. **Founded:** 1922. **Publications:** *Birds & Blooms* (Bimonthly); *Reader's Digest* (9/year); *Country: The Land and Life We Love* (Bimonthly); *Reminisce* (6/year); *Country EXTRA: The Land and Life We Love*; *New Choices: The Magazine for Your Health, Money & Travel* (Monthly); *Walking* (Bimonthly).

REFERENCE WORKS

12018 ■ *"11 Secrets of Personal Shoppers" in Mental Floss (September 15, 2017)*

Ed: Suzanne Raga. **Released:** September 15, 2017. **Description:** Personal shoppers aren't just for big spenders—they can help regular folks find clothing and accessories that are flattering, stylish, and budget-friendly, too. This article describes what personal shoppers do in addition to shopping, their fee structure, their varying clientele, and their personal attention. **Availability:** Online.

12019 ■ *"Amazon Launches a Personal Shopper Service That Sends Monthly Curated Clothing Boxes" in The Verge (July 31, 2019)*

URL(s): www.theverge.com/2019/7/31/20748632/ amazon-personal-shopper-prime-wardrobe-service -style-subscription-box

Ed: Ashley Carman. **Released:** July 31, 2019. **Description:** Amazon launched a new fashion service called Personal Shopper by Prime Wardrobe. Prime members who sign up will need to answer a survey about their fit and trend preferences and will then receive a curated box of clothing. Up to eight pieces will be included and the member can preview it before it ships and they will only pay for what they keep. Services costs $4.99 a month. **Availability:** Online.

12020 ■ *Become a Personal Shopper for Seniors*

Ed: Craig Wallin. **Description:** This article discusses what is entailed in becoming a personal shopper for senior citizens. **Availability:** Online.

12021 ■ *"Become a Personal Shopper: Step-by-Step Career Guide" in Study.com (March 4, 2020)*

Released: March 04, 2020. **Description:** A personal shopper helps clients who don't have the time, interest or ability to shop for themselves by doing it for them. This article provides information on career requirements, licensing, as well as 5 steps to take to start your personal shopper business. **Availability:** Online.

12022 ■ *How to Start a Home-Based Senior Care Business*

Ed: James L. Ferry. **Released:** 2nd edition. **Price:** Paperback,softback; Electronic Book. **Description:** Information is provided to start a home-based senior care business. **Availability:** E-book; Print.

12023 ■ *"How to Start a Personal Grocery Shopping Business" in ToughNickel (May 28, 2020)*

Ed: Shawna Wilson. **Released:** May 28, 2020. **Description:** If you are looking for a way to earn some extra money, personal grocery shopping might be a great option for you. Unlike other small business ventures, the start-up costs for this endeavor are

minimal. This article discusses things to think about before getting started, fees to charge, and how to keep customers coming. **Availability:** Online.

12024 ■ *"How to Start a Personal Shopper Business" in The Balance Small Business (November 17, 2019)*

Ed: Ron Dicker. **Released:** November 17, 2019. **Description:** Personal shoppers get paid to shop and run errands, serving clients who are too busy or simply unable to shop for themselves. This article describes the skills, education and experience needed, potential earnings, what personal shoppers need to get their business off the ground, and marketing strategies. **Availability:** Online.

12025 ■ *"Professional Help: Cross That Off Your To-Do List" in Inc. (November 2007, pp. 89-90, 92)*

Ed: Alison Stein Wellner. **Description:** Small business owners are finding that it pays to hire someone to takeover the personal tasks of daily living, including hiring a personal assistant, chauffeur, chef, stylist, pet caregiver, or concierge service. **Availability:** Online.

12026 ■ *"Q&A With Devin Ringling: Franchise's Services Go Beyond Elder Care" in Gazette (October 2, 2010)*

Pub: The Gazette

Contact: Vicki Cederholm, Director, Operations

E-mail: vicki.cederholm@gazette.com

Ed: Bill Radford. **Description:** Profile of franchise, Interim HealthCare, in Colorado Springs, Colorado; the company offers home care services that include wound care and specialized feedings to shopping and light housekeeping. It also runs a medical staffing company that provides nurses, therapists and other health care workers to hospitals, prisons, schools and other facilities. **Availability:** Online.

12027 ■ *Shop 'til You Drop: Starting a Personal Shopping Business*

Description: If you love shopping and possess a knack for paying attention to details, you may want to consider starting a part-time business as a personal shopper. This article provides details on skills required to do the job, startup expenses, monthly expenses, and possible bumps in the road to be aware of. **Availability:** Online.

12028 ■ *"Starting a Grocery Shopping Business in 6 Easy Steps" in Grocery Shopping Business website (April 19, 2019)*

Ed: Maggie Thurston. **Released:** April 19, 2019. **Description:** The business of hiring a personal grocery shopper is booming. This article provides details on how to start your own business including information on legal structure, insurance, supplies, services, and prices. **Availability:** Online.

12029 ■ *Starting a Personal Shopper Business*

Description: A complete guide to starting a personal shopper business. Includes information on market research, legal matters, certification, manpower, and marketing plan. **Availability:** Online.

12030 ■ *"Trying Out a Forgotten (and Free) Service: Personal Shoppers" in The New York Times (November 11, 2016)*

URL(s): www.nytimes.com/2016/11/11/style/trying-ou t-a-forgotten-and-free-service-personal-shoppers .html

Ed: Susan Lehman. **Released:** November 11, 2016. **Description:** Review of personal shoppers at Bergdorf Goodman, Macy's, and Saks Fifth Avenue stores in NYC. **Availability:** Online.

12031 ■ *"Twelve Things I Never Knew About Clothes Until I Became a Personal Shopping for Barneys" in Bloomberg (November 14, 2018)*

Ed: Brandon Presser. **Released:** November 14, 2018. **Description:** This article details hands-on experience from a Barneys personal shopper. **Availability:** Online.

FRANCHISES AND BUSINESS OPPORTUNITIES

12032 ■ Decorating Den Interiors (DDI)
8659 Commerce Dr.
Easton, MD 21601
Ph: (410)648-4793
Free: 800-DEC-DENS
Co. E-mail: info@decoratingden.com
URL: http://decoratingden.com
Contact: Jim Bugg, Sr., President
Facebook: www.facebook.com/DecoratingDen
X (Twitter): x.com/decoratingden
Instagram: www.instagram.com/decoratingden
YouTube: www.youtube.com/user/DecoratingDen
Pinterest: www.pinterest.com/decorating
dencorporate

Description: Interiors by Decorating is one of the oldest, international, shop-at-home interior decorating franchises in the world. **Founded:** 1969. **Training:** Training combines classroom work, home study, meetings, seminars and on-the-job experience including working with an experienced interior decorator. Secondary, advanced and graduate certification training continue throughout the franchise owner's career with Interiors by Decorating Den.

12033 ■ Foot Solutions, Inc.
3000 Old Alabama Rd., Ste. 121
Alpharetta, GA 30022
Ph: (678)587-5329
URL: http://footsolutions.com
Contact: John Prothro, Chief Executive Officer
Facebook: www.facebook.com/FootSolutions
Linkedin: www.linkedin.com/company/foot-solutions
Instagram: www.instagram.com/footsolutionsofficial_

Description: Personalized and custom designed products. **Founded:** 2000. **Financial Assistance:** No **Training:** Yes.

12034 ■ Instant Imprints
6615 Flanders Dr., Ste. B
San Diego, CA 92121

Ph: (858)642-4848
Free: 800-542-3437
Fax: (858)453-6513
Co. E-mail: info@instantimprints.com
URL: http://instantimprints.com
Contact: Ralph Askar, President

Facebook: www.facebook.com/instantimprints
Linkedin: www.linkedin.com/company/instant-imprints
X (Twitter): x.com/instantimprints
Description: Firm provides embroidery, promotional products, print services. **Founded:** 2002. **Franchised:** 2002. **Equity Capital Needed:** Net Worth of

$350,000; Liquid Assets of $100,000. **Franchise Fee:** 39950. **Royalty Fee:** 0.06. **Training:** Yes.

START-UP INFORMATION

12035 ■ *"Monsanto Acquires Targeted-Pest Control Technology Start-Up; Terms Not Disclosed"* in Benzinga.com (September 2011)
Pub: Benzinga.com
Contact: Jason Raznick, Founder
Ed: Eddie Staley. **Description:** Monsanto Company acquired Beelogics, a firm that researches and develops biological tools that control pests and diseases. Research includes a product that will help protect bee health. **Availability:** Online.

12036 ■ *"Termite Trouble"* in Arkansas Business (Vol. 28, March 28, 2011, No. 13, pp. 5)
Description: Thomas Pest Control of Little Rock, Arkansas has had liens placed against it by the Internal Revenue Service. The owner's daughter took over the business after her father passed away and is trying to rectify the situation. **Availability:** Online.

ASSOCIATIONS AND OTHER ORGANIZATIONS

12037 ■ **Association of Applied IPM Ecologists (AAIE)**
PO Box 27317
Fresno, CA 93729
URL: http://www.aaie.net
Contact: Celeste Gilbert, President
Description: Professional agricultural pest management consultants, entomologists, and field personnel. Promotes the implementation of integrated pest management in agricultural and urban environments. Provides a forum for the exchange of technical information on pest control. Offers placement service. **Founded:** 1967. **Educational Activities:** Association of Applied IPM Ecologists Annual Conference (Annual). **Awards:** AAIE Outstanding Member of the Year (Annual); AAIE Outstanding Lifetime Achievement (Annual). **Geographic Preference:** National.

12038 ■ **National Pest Management Association (NPMA) - Library**
10460 N St.
Fairfax, VA 22030
Ph: (703)352-6762
Free: 800-678-6722
Fax: (703)352-3031
Co. E-mail: npma@pestworld.org
URL: http://www.npmapestworld.org
Contact: Dominique Stumpf, CMP, CAE, Chief Executive Officer
E-mail: dstumpf@pestworld.org
URL(s): my.npmapestworld.org
Facebook: www.facebook.com/NationalPestManagementAssn
Linkedin: www.linkedin.com/company/nationalpestmgmt
X (Twitter): x.com/nationalpestmgt
Instagram: www.instagram.com/nationalpestmgt

Description: Represents firms engaged in control of insects, rodents, birds, and other pests, in or around structures, through use of insecticides, rodenticides, miticides, fumigants, and non-chemical methods. Provides advisory services on control procedures, new products, and safety and business administration practices. Promotes June as National Pest Control Month. Sponsors research, periodic technical and management seminars. **Scope:** Pest control. **Founded:** 1933. **Holdings:** Figures not available. **Publications:** *National Pest Control Association--Technical Release* (Monthly); *National Pest Management Association--Series of Management Reports* (Periodic); *Pest Gazette.* **Educational Activities:** PestWorld (Annual). **Awards:** PWIPM Professional Empowerment Grant (Annual); NPMA Committee of the Year Award (Annual). **Geographic Preference:** Multinational.

12039 ■ **Responsible Industry for a Sound Environment (RISE)**
4201 Wilson Bld., Ste. 700
Arlington, VA 22203
Ph: (202)872-3860
Co. E-mail: rise@pestfacts.org
URL: http://www.pestfacts.org
Contact: Megan J. Provost, President
Linkedin: www.linkedin.com/company/risepestfacts
X (Twitter): x.com/pestfacts
Description: Manufacturers, formulators, distributors, and representatives of the specialty pesticides industry. Promotes the environmental, health, and safety benefits of the proper use of specialty pesticides. **Founded:** 1991. **Geographic Preference:** National.

REFERENCE WORKS

12040 ■ *"Autumn Rat Control Essential for Poultry Units"* in Poultry World (Vol. 165, September 2011, No. 9, pp. 32)
Description: Dr. Alan Buckle discusses the use of rodenticides control, focusing on poultry units. **Availability:** Online.

12041 ■ *"Bedbugs Are Here, But Help Is At Hand"* in Register-Guard (June 26, 2011)
Description: A survey conducted by the National Pest Control Association found that 95 percent of its 7,000 members have treated buildings for bed bugs. That number is up 25 percent from 2000. **Availability:** Print; Online.

12042 ■ *"Don't Let the Bed Bugs Bite"* in Yuma Sun (April 22, 2011)
Ed: Mara Knaub. **Description:** Bug specialists note that bed bugs are returning. Exterminators say that eliminating these pests can be costly. Most bed bugs are picked up while traveling. **Availability:** Download; PDF; Online.

12043 ■ *"Faulkner Pest Service Has Been Providing Quality Pest Control Solutions for 23 Years"* in OfficialSpin (September 30, 2011)
Description: Profile of Faulkner Pest Service, which has been providing pest control services in Amarillo for twenty-three years. **Availability:** Online.

12044 ■ *"Hearing Damage Leads to Settlement"* in Register-Guard (August 13, 2011)
Description: Cynergy Pest Control lost a court battle when a rural Cottage Grove man was granted a $37,000 settlement after his hearing was damaged by the pest control companies method to eradicate gophers, using blasts in his neighbor's yard. **Availability:** Print; Online.

12045 ■ *"The Pre-Tail Revolution"* in Canadian Business (Vol. 87, October 2014, No. 10, pp. 10)
Description: A number of products that succeeded in security support from crowdfunding platforms, Kickstarter and Indiegogo, and those that failed are presented. Included are the do-it-yourself computer kit Kano, Bluetooth speakers Edge.sound, three-dimensional printer The Micro, Coolest Cooler the insect control device BugASalt, hexacopter Hexo+, and the Ubuntu Edge. **Availability:** Print; Online.

12046 ■ *"Rose Pest Solutions Acquires Indiana Pest Control"* in PCTonline (November 18, 2019)
URL(s): www.pctonline.com/article/rose-acquires-in diana-pest-control/
Ed: Brad Harbison. **Released:** November 18, 2019. **Description:** Troy, Michigan-based Rose Pest Solutions announced it acquired Indiana Pest Control. Both companies offer similar services in residential and commercial pest management along with wildlife control, but clients in Indiana will now benefit from Rose's canine bed bug inspections and professional fumigation. **Availability:** Online.

12047 ■ *"US Hygiene Adds Bed Bug Fix to Its Line of Highly Effective Cleaning and Pest Control Products"* in Benzinga.com (October 29, 2011)
Pub: Benzinga.com
Contact: Jason Raznick, Founder
Description: US Hygiene LLC introduced its newest product called Bed Bug Fix, which is a naturally-derived, nontoxic insecticide that kills a multitude of bugs including bed bugs and dust mites. The product is safe to use around children, plants and pets. **Availability:** Print; Online.

STATISTICAL SOURCES

12048 ■ **Pest Control Industry in the US - Market Research Report**
URL(s): www.ibisworld.com/united-states/market-research-reports/pest-control-industry/
Price: $925. **Description:** Downloadable report analyzing the current and future trends in the pest control industry. **Availability:** Download.

12049 ■ **RMA Annual Statement Studies**
Pub: Risk Management Association
Contact: Nancy Foster, President

Released: Annual. **Description:** Contains composite balance sheets and income statements for more than 360 industries, including the accounting, auditing, and bookkeeping industries. Also contains five years of comparative historical data for discerning trends. Includes 16 commonly used ratios, computed for most of the size groupings for nearly every industry.

TRADE PERIODICALS

12050 ■ *Biological Control*
Pub: Elsevier Inc.
Contact: Jan Herzhoff, President
URL(s): www.sciencedirect.com/journal/biological -control
Ed: E.E. Lewis, J. Liu, M.D. Eubanks, J.H. Hoffmann. **Released:** Monthly; latest edition: volume 196. **Description:** Journal containing information on the means of reducing or mitigating pets and pest effects through the use of natural enemies. **Availability:** Print; PDF; Download; Online.

12051 ■ *Common Sense Pest Control Quarterly*
Pub: Bio-Integral Resource Center
Contact: Andrew Pollack, Chief Executive Officer
URL(s): www.birc.org/descjrnls.htm#Common% 20Sense%20Pest%20Control%20Quarterly
Released: Quarterly **Description:** Presents information regarding least-toxic pest management in layperson's terms. Evaluates alternative strategies for many pest problems still being treated exclusively with pesticides. Discusses such concerns as least-toxic management of pests on indoor plants, pests that damage paper, controlling fleas and ticks on pets, and garden pants, pests that damage paper, controlling fleas and ticks on pets, and garden pests. Recurring features include letters to the editor, interviews, news of research, book reviews, and notices of. **Availability:** Print; Online.

12052 ■ *The IPM Practitioner*
Pub: Bio-Integral Resource Center
Contact: Andrew Pollack, Chief Executive Officer
URL(s): www.birc.org/descjrnls.htm#The%20IPM% 20Practitioner
Description: Supports the Center in its efforts to publish information on all aspects of environmentally-sound pest control. Investigates the least-toxic methods of controlling pests in agriculture, urban landscapes and structures, greenhouse and general horticulture, forestry, medical/veterinary, range, and other settings. Recurring features include letters to the editor, interviews, news of research, reports of meetings, news of educational opportunities and job listings, notices and reviews of publications available, and a calendar of events. Contains yearly listings of products. **Availability:** Print; Online.

12053 ■ *Pest Control Technology (PCT)*
Pub: GIE Media Inc.
Contact: Chris Foster, President
URL(s): www.pctonline.com
Facebook: www.facebook.com/PCTMagazine
Linkedin: www.linkedin.com/company/pctmagazine
X (Twitter): twitter.com/pctmagazine
Ed: Jodi Dorsch. **Released:** Monthly **Description:** Provides technical and business management information for personnel in the pest control industry. **Availability:** Print; PDF; Download; Online.

12054 ■ *Pesticide Biochemistry and Physiology (PBP)*
Pub: Elsevier Inc.
URL(s): www.sciencedirect.com/journal/pesticide -biochemistry-and-physiology
Ed: J.M. Clark. **Released:** 9/year **Price:** $524, Individuals for print us, Canada and India; $3,375, Institutions for print us, Canada and India. **Description:** Journal covering research related to to the mode of action of plant protection agents such as insecticides, fungicides, herbicides, and similar compounds, including nonlethal pest control agents, biosynthesis of pheromones, hormones, and plant resistance agents. **Availability:** Print; PDF; Download; Online.

12055 ■ *Tri-Ology*
Pub: Florida Department of Agriculture and Consumer Services Division of Plant Industry
Contact: Dr. Trevor Smith, Director
E-mail: plantindustry@fdacs.gov
URL(s): www.fdacs.gov/About-Us/Publications/Plan t-Industry-Publications/TRI-OLOGY
Ed: P. J. Anderson, G. S. Hodges. **Released:** Quarterly **Description:** Government scientific publication covering plant pests and disease. **Availability:** Online; Download; PDF.

TRADE SHOWS AND CONVENTIONS

12056 ■ Florida Pest Management Association Convention and Exposition
Description: Equipment, services, and supplies for the chemical industry. **Audience:** Pest control operators and professionals. **Principal Exhibits:** Equipment, services, and supplies for the chemical industry.

12057 ■ Pest Control Operators of California Convention
Pest Control Operators of California (PCOC)
3031 Beacon Blvd.
West Sacramento, CA 95691
Ph: (916)372-4363
Fax: (916)372-5437
URL: http://www.pcoc.org
Contact: Dean Wiley, President
URL(s): web.pcoc.org/events/Best-Pest-2024-PMPs -5/details
Frequency: Annual. **Description:** Equipment, supplies, and services for owners and operators of structural pest control companies in California. **Audience:** Pest control operators and professionals. **Principal Exhibits:** Equipment, supplies, and services for owners and operators of structural pest control companies in California.

FRANCHISES AND BUSINESS OPPORTUNITIES

12058 ■ Critter Control, Inc.
Rollins, Inc.
9435 E Cherry Bend Rd.
Traverse City, MI 49684
Ph: (404)888-2000
URL: http://www.rollins.com
Description: Animal & wildlife control services. **No. of Franchise Units:** 109. **No. of Company-Owned Units:** 1. **Founded:** 1983. **Franchised:** 1987. **Equity Capital Needed:** $12,750-$80,500 total investment. **Franchise Fee:** $5,000-$47,000. **Royalty Fee:** 7%. **Financial Assistance:** Yes **Training:** Available 1 week at headquarters, franchisees' locations and annual conferences with ongoing support.

12059 ■ Mosquito Squad
Authority Brands
3101 Northside Ave.
Richmond, VA 23228
Free: 800-496-9019
URL: http://www.authoritybrands.com
Facebook: www.facebook.com/MosquitoSquadCorp
X (Twitter): x.com/mosquitosquadco
Instagram: www.instagram.com/mosquitosquadco
YouTube: www.youtube.com/c/MosquitoSquadCo
Description: Provider of mosquito control services for residential and commercial sectors. **Founded:** 2005. **Training:** Yes.

12060 ■ MosquitoNix
2145 Chenault Dr., Ste. 100
Carrollton, TX 75006
Free: 866-934-2002
Co. E-mail: info@mosquitonix.com
URL: http://mosquitonix.com
Contact: Mike O'Neal, President
Description: Firm offers mosquito control and pest control services. **Founded:** 2003. **Franchised:** 2003. **Franchise Fee:** $12,500. **Training:** Offers 5 days at headquarters and ongoing support.

12061 ■ Terminix Termite & Pest Control
Terminix Global Holdings, Inc.
4114 Willow Lake Blvd.
Memphis, TN 38118
Free: 877-837-6464
Co. E-mail: jesse.jenkins@terminix.com
URL: http://www.terminix.com
Facebook: www.facebook.com/terminix
Linkedin: www.linkedin.com/company/terminix
X (Twitter): x.com/Terminix
Instagram: www.instagram.com/terminix
YouTube: www.youtube.com/terminix
Description: Commercial, industrial and residential pest control and termite protection. **Founded:** 1927. **Training:** 1 week at headquarters, in-field training and ongoing self-tutorial.

12062 ■ Truly Nolen
3636 E Speedway Blvd.
Tucson, AZ 85716
Free: 800-468-7859
Co. E-mail: info@trulymail.net
URL: http://www.trulynolen.com
Facebook: www.facebook.com/TrulyNolen
X (Twitter): x.com/TrulyNolen
Instagram: www.instagram.com/trulynolen
Pinterest: www.pinterest.com/TrulyNolenPest
Description: Firm provides pest, termite and rodent control services. **Founded:** 1938. **Financial Assistance:** Yes **Training:** Yes.

COMPUTERIZED DATABASES

12063 ■ *National Pesticide Information Retrieval System (NPIRS)*
Purdue University Entomology Department Center for Environmental and Regulatory Information Systems
1435 Win Hentschel Blvd., Ste. 215
West Lafayette, IN 47906
Ph: (765)494-6616
URL: http://ceris.purdue.edu/ceris
Contact: Michael Hill, Director
E-mail: mikehill@purdue.edu
URL(s): www.npirs.org
Price: $500, for tier 1; $2,500, for tier 2; $5,000, for tier 3; $7,500, for tier 4; $10,000, for tier 5. **Availability:** Online. **Type:** Full-text; Numeric.

LIBRARIES

12064 ■ California Department of Pesticide Regulation Library (DPR)
1001 I St.
Sacramento, CA 95814
Co. E-mail: publicrecords@cdpr.ca.gov
URL: http://apps.cdpr.ca.gov/ereglib
Contact: Julie Henderson, Director
Scope: Pesticides. **Services:** Library not open to the public. **Founded:** 1981. **Holdings:** 81,900 volumes. **Subscriptions:** 150 journals and other serials.

12065 ■ National Pest Management Association (NPMA) - Library
10460 N St.
Fairfax, VA 22030
Ph: (703)352-6762
Free: 800-678-6722
Fax: (703)352-3031
Co. E-mail: npma@pestworld.org
URL: http://www.npmapestworld.org
Contact: Dominique Stumpf, CMP, CAE, Chief Executive Officer
E-mail: dstumpf@pestworld.org
URL(s): my.npmapestworld.org
Facebook: www.facebook.com/NationalPes tManagementAssn
Linkedin: www.linkedin.com/company/nationalpes tmgt
X (Twitter): x.com/nationalpestmgt
Instagram: www.instagram.com/nationalpestmgt
Description: Represents firms engaged in control of insects, rodents, birds, and other pests, in or around structures, through use of insecticides, rodenticides, miticides, fumigants, and non-chemical methods.

Provides advisory services on control procedures, new products, and safety and business administration practices. Promotes June as National Pest Control Month. Sponsors research, periodic technical and management seminars. **Scope:** Pest control. **Founded:** 1933. **Holdings:** Figures not available. **Publications:** *National Pest Control Association-- Technical Release* (Monthly); *National Pest Management Association--Series of Management Reports* (Periodic); *Pest Gazette*. **Educational Activities:** PestWorld (Annual). **Awards:** PWIPM Professional Empowerment Grant (Annual); NPMA Committee of the Year Award (Annual). **Geographic Preference:** Multinational.

12066 ■ Rachel Carson Council (RCC)
8600 Irvington Ave.
  Bethesda, MD 20817
Ph: (301)214-2400
Co. E-mail: office@rachelcarsoncouncil.org
URL: http://rachelcarsoncouncil.org
Contact: Dr. Robert K. Musil, President
Facebook: www.facebook.com/RachelCarsonCouncil
Linkedin: www.linkedin.com/company/rachel-carson
  -council-inc-
X (Twitter): x.com/RachelCarsonDC
Instagram: www.instagram.com/rachelcarsondc

Description: Seeks to advise about the effects of pesticides that threaten the health, welfare, and survival of living organisms and biological systems. Promotes alternative, environmentally benign pest management strategies to encourage healthier life styles. Fosters a sense of wonder and respect towards nature. **Founded:** 1965. **Geographic Preference:** National.

12067 ■ U.S. Environmental Protection Agency (AWBERC Library) - Andrew W. Breidenbach Environmental Research Center Library
26 W Martin Luther King Dr., Rm. 406
  Cincinnati, OH 45268
Ph: (513)569-7703
Fax: (513)569-7709
Co. E-mail: ci_awberc_library@epa.gov
URL: http://www.epa.gov/epalibraries/andrew-w-brei
  denbach-environmental-research-center-library
  -services

Scope: Bacteriology; biotechnology; hazardous waste; risk assessment; toxicology; wastewater treatment; water pollution and water quality. **Services:** Interlibrary loan; copying. **Founded:** 1971. **Holdings:** 19,000 books, 2,00,000 technical reports, and 1,000 journal titles.

12068 ■ U.S. Environmental Protection Agency (EPA) - National Enforcement Investigations Center Environmental Forensics Library
1595 Wynkoop St.
  Denver, CO 80202-1129
URL: http://www.epa.gov/enforcement/national
  -enforcement-investigations-center-neic

Scope: Environmental law; water quality; industrial and agricultural pollution abatement practices; air and water pollution; hazardous waste. **Services:** Interlibrary loan (OCLC=EOB); copying; library open to the public by appointment. **Holdings:** EPA technical reports.

RESEARCH CENTERS

12069 ■ Bio-Integral Resource Center (BIRC)
PO Box 7414
  Berkeley, CA 94707
Ph: (510)524-2567
Fax: (510)524-1758
Co. E-mail: birc@igc.org
URL: http://www.birc.org
Contact: Andrew Pollack, Chief Executive Officer
Facebook: www.facebook.com/Bio-Integral-Resource
  -Center-434226623308463
X (Twitter): x.com/BIRChelp

Description: Provides consultations for pest management professionals, farmers, foresters, park service resource managers. **Scope:** Provides information on managing pests and land resource problems. **Founded:** 1979. **Publications:** *IPM Practitioner* (10/year); *The IPM Practitioner*; *Common Sense Pest Control Quarterly* (Quarterly); *Common Sense Pest Control Quarterly* (Quarterly). **Geographic Preference:** National.

12070 ■ Cornell University - Cornell Cooperative Extension - New York State Integrated Pest Management Program
607 W North St.
  Geneva, NY 14456
Ph: (315)787-2360
Fax: (315)787-2360
Co. E-mail: nysipm@cornell.edu
URL: http://nysipm.cornell.edu
Contact: Alejandro Calixto, Director
E-mail: aac273@cornell.edu
Facebook: www.facebook.com/NYSIPM
X (Twitter): twitter.com/NYSIPM
YouTube: www.youtube.com/user/NYSIPM

Description: Integral unit of Cornell Cooperative Extension at Cornell University and the New York State Department of Agriculture and Markets. **Scope:** Management alternatives for farmers; maintaining productivity and decreasing risks to the environment; computers and electronic weather equipment to assist with pest management decisions on potatoes, sweet corn, onions, tomatoes, apples, and grapes; pesticide reduction; and biological controls to combat pests; and management alternatives for schools, homes, parks and golf courses. **Publications:** *New York State Integrated Pest Management Program Annual Report* (Annual); *New York State Integrated Pest Management Program Articles*; *New York State Integrated Pest Management Program Brochures*; *Cornell Urban IPM News* (Quarterly); *IPM Today* (Monthly); *New York State Integrated Pest Management Program Manuals*.

12071 ■ Kerr Center for Sustainable Agriculture (KCSA)
24456 Kerr Rd.
  Poteau, OK 74953-5215
Ph: (918)647-9123
Co. E-mail: mailbox@kerrcenter.com
URL: http://kerrcenter.com
Contact: David Redhage, President
Facebook: www.facebook.com/kerrcenter
X (Twitter): x.com/KerrCenter

Description: Center provides training in sustainable agriculture to extension and agriculture professionals. Offers field days, ranch tours, and speaking engagements. **Scope:** Fertility management and soil health; water management; stream and pond conservation; nutrient cycling and waste management; insect, disease, and predator management; weed management; biological diversity; plant and animal adaptation; energy use and conservation; effects of farm decisions on people; and economic and biological accounting. **Founded:** 1965. **Publications:** *Kerr Center's newsletter* (Monthly). **Educational Activities:** KCSA Conferences; KCSA Workshops. **Awards:** Kerr Center Oklahoma Producer Grant Program (Annual).

12072 ■ Purdue University Department of Entomology - Center for Urban and Industrial Pest Management
615 Mitch Daniels Blvd.
  West Lafayette, IN 47907-2053
URL: http://extension.entm.purdue.edu/urban
Contact: John M. Medendorp, Associate Director
E-mail: jmedendo@purdue.edu

Description: Integral unit of Purdue University. Offers undergraduate and graduate degree programs in urban and industrial pest management in conjunction with the School of Agriculture at the University; conferences, workshops, seminars, and correspondence courses. **Scope:** Pest management, especially cockroach and termite control. **Founded:** 1989.

12073 ■ University of Florida - Institute of Food and Agricultural Sciences - Entomology and Nematology Department - Florida Medical Entomology Laboratory (FMEL) - Reference Collection
200 9th St SE
  Vero Beach, FL 32962
Ph: (772)778-7200
URL: http://fmel.ifas.ufl.edu
Contact: Jorge Rey, Director
E-mail: jrey@ufl.edu
Facebook: www.facebook.com/FMELUF
X (Twitter): twitter.com/UFEntomology

Description: Integral unit of Institute of Food and Agricultural Sciences, Entomology and Nematology Department at University of Florida. Offers state organizations and districts assistance. **Scope:** Biology and control of biting insects and other arthropods with emphasis on transmitters of disease and pest annoyances. Studies the entomological aspects of public health, veterinary science, sanitation, mosquito control, drainage and irrigation design, and wetlands management. **Founded:** 1956. **Holdings:** 5,500 volumes. **Subscriptions:** 10000 volumes; 131 journals and other serials. **Educational Activities:** FMEL Training, Focusing on medical entomology.

START-UP INFORMATION

12074 ■ *"Groomers Eye Profit Growth Through Services" in Pet Product News (Vol. 64, December 2010, No. 12, pp. 26)*
Ed: Kathleen M. Mangan. **Description:** Pet groomers can successfully offer add-on services by taking into account insider customer knowledge, store image, and financial analysis in the decision-making process. Many pet groomers have decided to add services such as spa treatments and training due to a slump in the bathing and grooming business. How some pet groomers gained profitability through add-on services is explored. **Availability:** Online.

12075 ■ *"Keep The (Cage) Customer Satisfied" in Pet Product News (Vol. 64, December 2010, No. 12, pp. 10)*
Ed: Devon McPhee. **Description:** Windsor, California-based Debbie's Pet Boutique, recipient of Pet Product News International's Outstanding Customer Service Award, has been dedicated to combining topnotch grooming services with a robust retail selection. These features might gain return customers for Debbie's Pet Boutique. **Availability:** Online.

12076 ■ *"Succeed With the Right Equipment" in Pet Product News (Vol. 64, November 2010, No. 11, pp. 42)*
Ed: Sandi Cain. **Description:** Grooming shop owners have been focusing on obtaining ergonomic, durable, and efficient products such as restraints, tables, and tubs. These products enhance the way grooming tasks are conducted. Ways pet supply manufacturers have responded to this trend are examined. **Availability:** Online.

ASSOCIATIONS AND OTHER ORGANIZATIONS

12077 ■ **Canine Journal**
2622 Bartram Pl.
Winston Salem, NC 27106
URL: http://www.caninejournal.com
Contact: Alex Schenker, Chief Executive Officer
Facebook: www.facebook.com/CanineJournal
Instagram: www.instagram.com/caninejournal
YouTube: www.youtube.com/c/Caninejournal
Pinterest: www.pinterest.com/caninejournal

Description: An online resource for all things dog-related, from health concerns and food to pet insurance and dog resorts. **Founded:** 2007.

12078 ■ **National Association of Professional Pet Sitters (NAPPS)**
1120 Rte. 73, Ste. 200
Mount Laurel, NJ 08054
Ph: (856)439-0324
Co. E-mail: napps@petsitters.org
URL: http://petsitters.org
Contact: Amy Sparrow, President
Facebook: www.facebook.com/TheNAPPS
X (Twitter): x.com/TheNAPPS

Instagram: www.instagram.com/the_napps
YouTube: www.youtube.com/channel/UCNeb5zv
dxvqDCJY-WmuJQ-g
Description: Owners or employees of pet-sitting services. Promotes professional and ethical standards in pet sitting and fosters cooperation among members of the pet-care industry. Serves as a network for the exchange of ideas and information on pet sitting and current industry practices. Disseminates information educating the pet-owning public on the advantages of leaving pets in a home environment and how to choose a reliable sitter. **Founded:** 1989. **Educational Activities:** NAPPS Annual Conference Virtually (Annual). **Geographic Preference:** National.

12079 ■ **National Dog Groomers Association of America, Inc. (NDGAA)**
PO Box 101
Clark, PA 16113
Ph: (724)962-2711
Co. E-mail: info@ndgaa.com
URL: http://nationaldoggroomers.com
Contact: Jeff Reynolds, Executive Director
Facebook: www.facebook.com/National-Dog-Groomers-Assoc-of-America-Inc-154513854614846

Description: Dog groomers and supply distributors organized to upgrade the profession. Conducts state and local workshops; sponsors competitions and certification testing. Makes groomer referrals. **Founded:** 1969. **Geographic Preference:** National.

12080 ■ **The Pet Advocacy Network (PIJAC)**
1615 Duke St., Ste. 100
Alexandria, VA 22314
Ph: (202)452-1525
Fax: (703)997-4270
Co. E-mail: info@petadvocacy.org
URL: http://petadvocacy.org
Contact: Mike Bober, President
E-mail: mbober@petadvocacy.org
Facebook: www.facebook.com/PetAdvocacyNetwork
Linkedin: www.linkedin.com/company/pet-advocacy
-network
X (Twitter): x.com/PetAdvocacy

Description: Pet retailers, manufacturers and distributors; companion animal suppliers; pet industry trade associations. Works to monitor federal and state regulations and legislation affecting the industry. Sponsors research projects and industry-related educational programs. **Founded:** 1971. **Publications:** *Our Pets, Our Health*; *PetLetter* (Periodic); *Tips on Travel With Your Pets*. **Geographic Preference:** National.

REFERENCE WORKS

12081 ■ *7 Tips for Great Pet Boarding Business Management*
Ed: Chad Halvorson. **Description:** Pet boarding is a great business opportunity for animal lovers. This article details 7 tips to help you start the pet boarding business of your dreams. **Availability:** Online.

12082 ■ *Are You Cut Out to Run a Kennel or Pet Boarding Business?*
Ed: Bruce Hakutizwi. **Description:** Discusses things to consider for pet lovers who are thinking of starting their own kennel or pet boarding business, including potential costs and challenges. Includes details on business planning, market research, pricing, job skills, advertising, and startup costs. **Availability:** Online.

12083 ■ *"Bark Up The Right Tree" in Small Business Opportunities (Winter 2009)*
Released: February 09, 2016. **Description:** Profile of Central Bark, a daycare company catering to pets that offers franchise opportunities and is expanding rapidly despite the economic downturn; the company's growth strategy is also discussed.

12084 ■ *"The Best (and Worst) Parts of Starting a Pet Grooming Business" in The Balance Small Business (July 28, 2019)*
Ed: Alyssa Gregory. **Released:** July 28, 2019. **Description:** Provides pros and cons to consider when operating a pet grooming business. This article also provides salary information. **Availability:** Online.

12085 ■ *"Facials for Fido? Retail: Kriser's Pet Store Grows With High-End Pet Products Market" in San Fernando Valley Business Journal (Vol. 17, February 20, 2012, No. 4, pp. 1)*
Description: Sherman Oaks all-natural pet food and supply retailer, Kriser's, is expanding with seven new stores. The company is known for its health options in pet food, tasty treats, and fancy toys by catering to a high-end clientele. They also offer upscale pet grooming services, including blueberry facials and de-shedding treatments. **Availability:** Online.

12086 ■ *"How to Get an Animal Boarding License" in DailyPuppy (March 8, 2018)*
Ed: Elle Smith. **Released:** March 08, 2018. **Description:** To operate your boarding business, regardless of the need in your jurisdiction for a specific animal boarding license, you will at least need to be licensed at the state, county or municipal level to run a business. Where you obtain your business license depends on the jurisdiction where you operate. Failure to obtain a business license is a misdemeanor in many areas. This article provides resources to help ensure you are properly licensed. **Availability:** Online.

12087 ■ *"How to Start a Dog Boarding Business" in The Balance Careers (August 9, 2019)*
Ed: Mary Hope Kramer. **Released:** August 09, 2019. **Description:** Pet services is one of the fastest growing segments of the pet industry and boarding services represent a key component of this growth. This article offers things to consider and steps to follow to start your own dog boarding business. **Availability:** Online.

12088 ■ *"How to Start a Dog Boarding Business" in Entrepreneur (February 18, 2020)*

Ed: Shipra Singh. **Released:** February 18, 2020. **Description:** Dog boarding, also known as Dog daycare, is a service which allows owners to drop their dogs off for a certain period of time by paying a fee. This article details things to consider and how to get started with your dog boarding business. **Availability:** Online.

12089 ■ *"How to Start a Dog Grooming Business" in 123 Pet Software Blog (October 2, 2020)*

Ed: Jennifer Phillips April. **Released:** October 02, 2020. **Description:** Pet grooming is a fast-growing segment of the pet industry. This article provides information on how to start a dog grooming business, from having a physical storefront or mobile grooming service to developing your business concept, training and certification, business software, advertising, pricing, equipment, and customer retention. **Availability:** Online.

12090 ■ *"How to Start a Pet Grooming Business" in Starting Your Business website (November 15, 2020)*

Released: November 15, 2020. **Description:** This article discusses the fast-growing field of pet grooming and what you need to know to start your own pet grooming business including industry trends, experience and skills, startup costs, and earning potential. **Availability:** Online.

12091 ■ *How to Start Your Dog Boarding Business: What to Know about Dogs, Kennels, and the Business*

Ed: Sarah Clark. **Released:** September 19, 2021. **Description:** A successful dog boarding business owner gives her take on how to set up and run this type of business. **Availability:** E-book.

12092 ■ *"Jersey Pet Store Regs Poised for Change" in Pet Product News (Vol. 66, March 2012, No. 3, pp. 18)*

Description: Bills at the New Jersey Assembly could mandate the state's Department of Health and Senior Services to review and update requirements for establishments that sell live animals. Assembly Bill 147 would direct the department to prohibit overcrowdng animals in pet stores, kennels, and similar establishments. The bill would also revise the state's cruelty laws. **Availability:** Online.

12093 ■ *"Mobile Pet Grooming Business" in The Balance Careers (January 26, 2019)*

Ed: Alissa Wolf. **Released:** January 26, 2019. **Description:** Mobile pet grooming is a companion animal service sector that is rapidly growing. This article discusses the advantages of owning a mobile pet grooming business, how to get started, what tools and equipment you'll need, important business requirements, how to create a business plan, and tips on advertising. **Availability:** Online.

12094 ■ *"Paid Petsitting in Homes Is Illegal in New York. That's News to Some Sitters" in The New York Times (July 21, 2017)*

URL(s): www.nytimes.com/2017/07/21/nyregion/dogsitting-new-york-illegal.html **Ed:** Sarah Maslin Nir. **Released:** July 21, 2017. **Description:** People running petsitting services in NYC where shocked to discover that their businesses were not legal, since they must be licensed to board animals and in a permitted kennel, which is not allowed in the city. However, the rules for this are rarely enforced, unless a complaint is filed. This is starting to change with the advent of large, app-based petcare businesses and law makers are cracking down on these services. The app owners are not backing down. **Availability:** Online.

12095 ■ *Pet Business 101: From Puppy School to Running With the Big Dogs*

Ed: Brooke Faulkner. **Released:** September 10, 2018. **Description:** Provides business tips for entrepreneurs looking to break into the pet industry to open a business such as behavior training, grooming, or pet sitting. **Availability:** Online.

12096 ■ *"Pet Care Services in Rhode Island to be Taxed' in Pet Product News (Vol. 66, September 2012, No. 9, pp. 1)*

Description: Pet care services will be subject to a 7 percent sales tax in Rhode Island starting October 1, 2012, potentially resulting in more expensive pet boardng, grooming, sitting, and training. The tax is part of the state's efforts to close a $120 million budget deficit. How pet supplies retailers have reacted to the new tax is presented. **Availability:** Online.

12097 ■ *Pet Groomers Business Insurance*

Description: Working with animals at your pet grooming business can expose your business to significant risks. This article discusses pet grooming insurances coverages available to your business. **Availability:** Online.

12098 ■ *"Professional Grooming Marketplace: Cash In On Green Products and Services" in Pet Product News (Vol. 66, September 2012, No. 9, pp. 84)*

Ed: Lizett Bond. **Description:** Pet grooming salons can build customer reputation by providing sustainable and environment-friendly products and services. Energy efficiency and electricity conservation can also be focused upon as pet grooming salons aspire for green marketing goals. **Availability:** Online.

12099 ■ *"Woof Gang Bakery & Grooming Claws Through Recession" in Orlando Business Journal (Vol. 29, July 6, 2012, No. 3, pp. 1)*

Pub: Baltimore Business Journal **Contact:** Rhonda Pringle, President **E-mail:** rpringle@bizjournals.com **Ed:** Anjali Fluker. **Description:** Woof Gang Bakery and Grooming has reported increased sales des;pite the economic crisis. The company is set to open its 30th store by the end of 2012. **Availability:** Print; Online.

STATISTICAL SOURCES

12100 ■ *Pet Grooming & Boarding Industry in the US - Market Research Report*

URL(s): www.ibisworld.com/united-states/market-research-reports/pet-grooming-boarding-industry/ **Price:** $925. **Description:** Downloadable report analyzing current and future trends in the pet grooming and boarding industries. **Availability:** Download.

VIDEO/AUDIO MEDIA

12101 ■ *How To!: How to Follow Your Small Business Dream*

URL(s): slate.com/podcasts/how-to/2023/09/how-to-start-small-business-entrepreneur-startup **Ed:** Carvell Wallace. **Released:** December 19, 2023. **Description:** Podcast brings in a business coach to advise a part-time pet groomer on starting her own business.

TRADE SHOWS AND CONVENTIONS

12102 ■ **All American Grooming Show**

URL(s): www.aagroom.com **Frequency:** Annual. **Description:** Provides education for pet groomers. Also hosts a show featuring the newest products and services. **Audience:** Pet groomers, boarders, day care operators, veterinarians, and pet store retailers. **Principal Exhibits:** Provides education for pet groomers. Also hosts a show featuring the newest products and services.

12103 ■ **Super Zoo**

World Pet Association (WPA) 11801 Pierce St., Ste. 200 Riverside, CA 92505 **Ph:** (626)447-2222 **Co. E-mail:** info@wpamail.org **URL:** http://www.worldpetassociation.org

Contact: Victor Mason, President **E-mail:** vic.mason@wpamail.org **URL(s):** ww.superzoo.org/about/ **Frequency:** Annual. **Description:** Includes demonstrations, speakers, product exhibits, hobbyist shows and rides for children and contests. **Audience:** Industry professionals. **Principal Exhibits:** Includes demonstrations, speakers, product exhibits, hobbyist shows and rides for children and contests. **Telecommunication Services:** info@SuperZoo.org.

CONSULTANTS

12104 ■ **Best in Show Consulting L.L.C.**

2643 Snowmass Cir. Minnetonka, MN 55305 **Co. E-mail:** bestinshowconsulting@gmail.com **URL:** http://www.bestinshowconsulting.com **Contact:** Renee Shanesy, Owner **Facebook:** www.facebook.com/PetResortstartup **Description:** Helps entrepreneurs with startup and operation of dog daycare and boarding facilities. **Founded:** 2003.

FRANCHISES AND BUSINESS OPPORTUNITIES

12105 ■ **Adventure Pet**

8885 Terabyte Ct. Reno, NV 89521 **Ph:** (775)742-9378 **Co. E-mail:** info@adventurepet.com **URL:** http://adventurepet.com **Contact:** Troy Herrera, Owner **Facebook:** www.facebook.com/adventurepetdogs **Description:** Pet care franchise offering boarding, day camp, and grooming services for dogs.

12106 ■ **All American Pet Resorts**

41850 W 11 Mile Rd., Ste. 202 Novi, MI 48375 **Ph:** (248)513-3006 **Co. E-mail:** info@allamericanpetresorts.com **URL:** http://www.allamericanpetresorts.com **Facebook:** www.facebook.com/allamericanpetresorts **Description:** An all-inclusive, upscale dog boarding and daycare resort providing dog boarding, dog daycare, and dog grooming.

12107 ■ **Aussie Pet Mobile Inc. (APM)**

95 Argonaut, Ste. 890 Aliso Viejo, CA 92656 **Contact:** Paul Ebert, Chief Executive Officer **Description:** Mobile pet grooming service. **Founded:** 1999. **Franchised:** 2007. **Equity Capital Needed:** $73,000. **Franchise Fee:** $29,000. **Training:** Yes.

12108 ■ **Barkefellers**

9400 Corporation Dr. Indianapolis, IN 46256 **Ph:** (317)913-9400 **URL:** http://barkefellers.com **Contact:** Rick Coffey, Co-Founder **Facebook:** www.facebook.com/Bark.IndyNortheast **X (Twitter):** x.com/barkefellers **Description:** A family-owned and operated luxurious pet resort providing lavish overnight accommodations, a salon spa, spacious doggie daycare, and obedience training.

12109 ■ **Camp Bow Wow Franchising, Inc. (CBW)**

7577 W 103rd Ave., Ste. 209 Westminster, CO 80021 **Free:** 877-700-2275 **Co. E-mail:** info@campbowwowusa.com **URL:** http://www.campbowwow.com **Contact:** Julie Turner, President **Facebook:** www.facebook.com/CampBowWow **Linkedin:** www.linkedin.com/company/62821 **X (Twitter):** x.com/campbowwow **Instagram:** www.instagram.com/campbowwow **YouTube:** www.youtube.com/user/CampBowWow

Description: We provide doggy day camp, as well as overnight boarding for travelers. We utilize consistent start-up and operations systems that keep the franchise locations similar in look and customer experience. We oversee the growth of the company in a thoughtful, strategic manner that allows franchises to be successful in each location. **No. of Franchise Units:** 200. **No. of Company-Owned Units:** 1. **Founded:** 2000. **Franchised:** 2002. **Equity Capital Needed:** Cash investment $80,000 liquid; $300,000-$600,000 total investment; minimum net worth $100,000. **Franchise Fee:** $50,000. **Training:** Yes.

12110 ■ Camp Run-A-Mutt (CRAM)
2900 Fourth Ave., Ste. 206
 San Diego, CA 92103
URL: http://www.camprunamutt.com
Contact: Dennis Quaglia, President
Facebook: www.facebook.com/camprunamutt
Instagram: www.instagram.com/camprunamutt

Description: A cage-free dog daycare and boarding franchise featuring indoor and outdoor fun for your furry companion in a fully supervised, clean and safe environment. **Founded:** 2007.

12111 ■ Canine Campus
3116 Karen Pl.
 Colorado Springs, CO 80907
Ph: (719)448-9600
Fax: (719)448-0496
Co. E-mail: fido@caninecampus.us
URL: http://www.caninecampus.us
Contact: Joelle Audette, Founder
Facebook: www.facebook.com/CanineCampusCO
X (Twitter): x.com/CanineCampusCO
Instagram: www.instagram.com/caninecampusdog
 daycareboarding
YouTube: www.youtube.com/user/TheCanineCampus
Pinterest: www.pinterest.com/caninecampus

Description: Provider of day care, boarding, grooming and training services for dogs. **Founded:** 1999. **Training:** Offers 7 days training at headquarters, 7 days at franchisee's location and ongoing support.

12112 ■ D Pet Hotels
15060 N Northsight Blvd.
 Scottsdale, AZ 85260
Ph: (480)781-4151
URL: http://dpethotels.com
Facebook: www.facebook.com/DPetHotelsScottsdale
X (Twitter): x.com/dph_scottsdale

Description: Franchise offering luxury dog care and amenities, including grooming, boarding, and daycare.

12113 ■ Dog Miami Beach LLC
920 Alton Rd.
 Miami Beach, FL 33139
Ph: (305)397-8549
Co. E-mail: miamibeach@doghotels.com
URL: http://doghotels.com

Description: Franchise of retail stores specializing in top-of-the-line dog services, including dog boarding, dog daycare, and dog grooming.

12114 ■ The Dog Stop
Pittsburgh, PA
Free: 855-635-3935
Co. E-mail: thedogstop@thedogstop.com
URL: http://thedogstop.com

Description: All-inclusive indoor/outdoor dog care facility offering dog grooming, dog daycare, dog boarding, dog obedience training, in-home services, and a pet retail store. **Founded:** 2009.

12115 ■ Doggies Gone Wild
1675 NW 97th Ave.
 Miami, FL 33172
Ph: (305)740-6456
URL: http://doggies-gonewild.com
X (Twitter): x.com/DoggiesGoneWild

YouTube: www.youtube.com/channel/UCR9V
 5rSKZCS154rv8Uu2VkQ

Description: Provides a deluxe home-away-from-home for dogs. Services include dog boarding, dog daycare, and dog grooming. **Founded:** 2008.

12116 ■ Dogs Rule Resort
2501 Pecan St.
 Carrollton, TX 75010
Ph: (972)306-3647
Co. E-mail: info@dogsruleresort.com
URL: http://www.dogsruleresort.com
X (Twitter): x.com/DogsRule_Resort

Description: Provider of all-inclusive doggie daycare, boarding, and grooming services with a mission to give dogs happy experiences in safe, clean environments.

12117 ■ Dogtopia
4920 Wyaconda Rd.
 North Bethesda, MD 20852
Ph: (240)389-5124
URL: http://www.dogtopia.com
Contact: Chris Kempner, Chairman
Facebook: www.facebook.com/dogtopia
X (Twitter): x.com/dogtopia
Instagram: www.instagram.com/dogsofdogtopia
YouTube: www.youtube.com/channel/
 UCpWpoOofGfyQgYuJIYH1_jw

Description: A dog daycare, boarding and spa facility center. **Founded:** 2000. **Financial Assistance:** Yes **Training:** Available 2-4 weeks at headquarters, 5 days at franchisee's location, and onging support.

12118 ■ Happy Tails Dog Spa
3574 Redondo Beach Blvd.
 Torrance, CA 90504
Ph: (310)415-3355
URL: http://www.happytailsdogspa.net
Contact: Jonathan Sperling, Owner
Facebook: www.facebook.com/happytailsdogspa
Instagram: www.instagram.com/happytailsdogspa
 _grooming

Description: Provider of dog grooming and spa services. **Training:** Yes.

12119 ■ Hounds Town USA
12 Garrity Ave.
 Ronkonkoma, NY 11779
Ph: (631)467-1643
Co. E-mail: info@houndstownusa.com
URL: http://houndstownusa.com
Contact: Michael Gould, Founder
URL(s): www.houndstownfranchise.com
Facebook: www.facebook.com/hounds.town
Instagram: www.instagram.com/houndstownusa
YouTube: www.youtube.com/channel/UCi6laqS
 3-ES0cmmqfvt6qFw

Description: A fully interactive dog daycare, boarding, and pet spa facility. **Founded:** 2000.

12120 ■ K9 Resorts
43 S Ave.
 Fanwood, NJ 07023
Ph: (908)889-7387
Co. E-mail: info@k9resorts.com
URL: http://www.k9franchise.com
Facebook: www.facebook.com/k9resorts

Description: Luxury pet hotel franchise that provides unmatched services and facilities for pet owners who care about how their dogs are boarded and cared for when they are away. Offers a premium product & pricing strategy that allows our franchisees to provide a differentiated offering in the marketplace while driving top line revenue and profitability in the business. **Founded:** 2005.

12121 ■ Kennelwood Village Inc.
2008 Kratky Rd.
 Saint Louis, MO 63114
Ph: (314)429-2100
Fax: (314)429-6647

URL: http://www.kennelwood.com
Contact: Brooke Lorenz, Manager
E-mail: pagegrooming@kennelwood.com
Facebook: www.facebook.com/kennelwoodpetresorts
X (Twitter): x.com/Kennelwood
Instagram: www.instagram.com/kennelwoodpe
 tresorts
YouTube: www.youtube.com/user/KennelwoodPe
 tResort
Pinterest: www.pinterest.com/kennelwood

Description: Firm offers dog boarding and grooming services for pets. **Founded:** 1974.

12122 ■ Preppy Pet
57 W Michigan St.
 Orlando, FL 32806
Ph: (407)420-1060
Fax: (407)420-1068
URL: http://preppypet.com
Facebook: www.facebook.com/preppypet

Description: Operator of dog care center. **Founded:** 2003. **Franchised:** 2006. **Equity Capital Needed:** $75,000 - $150,000. **Franchise Fee:** $19,900 - $34,500. **Royalty Fee:** 6.5% Monthly. **Financial Assistance:** No **Training:** Yes.

12123 ■ PSP Group, LLC
Franchise Group, Inc. (FRG)
 29493 7 Mile Rd.
 Livonia, MI 48152-1909
Ph: (740)363-2222
Free: 800-790-3863
Fax: (800)880-6432
URL: http://www.franchisegrp.com
Facebook: www.facebook.com/petsuppliesplus
X (Twitter): x.com/petsuppliesplus
Instagram: www.instagram.com/petsuppliesplus

Description: Distributor of pet supplies and provider of grooming services. **No. of Operating Units:** 315. **Founded:** 1988. **Franchised:** 2002. **Equity Capital Needed:** $549,400-$1,097,400. **Franchise Fee:** $49,900. **Royalty Fee:** 2-3%. **Financial Assistance:** Yes **Training:** Provides 4 weeks training at headquarters.

12124 ■ Ryan's Pet Food Inc.
70 Don Caster Ave.
 Thornhill, ON, Canada L3T 1L3
Ph: (905)771-9227
Co. E-mail: gpf78@globalpetfoods.com
URL: http://globalpetfoods.com
Contact: Dino Fragaglia, President
X (Twitter): x.com/GlobalPetFoods

Description: Chain of pet food stores. **Founded:** 1979. **Financial Assistance:** No **Training:** Yes.

12125 ■ Scenthound
1070 E Indiantown Rd., Ste. 300
 Jupiter, FL 33477
Contact: Jessica D. Vogel, Manager

Description: Membership-based dog grooming franchise with a focus on pet wellness.

12126 ■ TailWaggers Doggy Daycare
4528 Summerside Rd.
 Cincinnati, OH 45245
Ph: (920)882-8000
URL: http://www.tailwaggersdoggydaycare.com
Facebook: www.facebook.com/tailwaggersdoggy
 daycarecincinnati

Description: Offers dog daycare, boarding, grooming, and retail services. Franchises available.

12127 ■ U-Wash Doggie
Description: Self and full service pet grooming. **No. of Franchise Units:** 1. **No. of Company-Owned Units:** 5. **Founded:** 1992. **Franchised:** 1997. **Equity Capital Needed:** $98,000. **Franchise Fee:** $15,000. **Training:** Yes.

12128 ■ Woofie's
44200 Waxpool Rd.
  Ashburn, VA 20147
Ph: (571)426-6503
URL: http://ownawoofies.com
Contact: Amy Reed, Co-Founder
Description: Provides customized, professional care and services to pets and their owners in your com-munity. Services include daily dog walks, pet sitting visits, loyalty member program, and ongoing groom-ing appointments. **Founded:** 2004.

12129 ■ Zoomin Groomin
780 Lynnhaven Pky., Ste. 240
  Virginia Beach, VA 23452
Free: 855-825-7387
URL: http://www.zoomingroomin.com
Contact: Katie Stow, Contact
URL(s): discoverzoomingroomin.com
Facebook: www.facebook.com/zoomingroomin
Linkedin: www.linkedin.com/company/zoomin
  -groomin-mobile-pet-grooming-franchises
Description: A full-service mobile pet spa designed to bring comfort and convenience to pets and pet parents.

START-UP INFORMATION

12130 ■ *"Biz Pays Tribute: Franchise Helps Owners Grieve and Honor Their Beloved Pets" in Small Business Opportunities (November 2007)*

Description: Paws and Remember is a franchise company that provides pet cremation and memorial products while assisting veterinary clinics and other pet specialists to help clients when they lose a pet.

ASSOCIATIONS AND OTHER ORGANIZATIONS

12131 ■ **International Association of Pet Cemeteries and Crematories (IAOPCC)**
4103 Winder Hwy., Ste. 7604
  Chestnut Mountain, GA 30502
Free: 800-952-5541
Fax: (404)800-6331
Co. E-mail: info@iaopc.com
URL: http://www.iaopc.com/default.aspx
Contact: Martin Hopp, President
Description: Educates the public on pet burials and the disposal of sick and diseased animals to eliminate contamination and pollution of the ground and water. Facilitates exchange of information among members. Revitalizes inactive and unkept cemeteries. **Founded:** 1971. **Publications:** *News & Views* (Semiannual). **Educational Activities:** International Association of Pet Cemeteries Annual Convention (Annual); Prospective Pet Cemeterian Seminars. **Geographic Preference:** National.

REFERENCE WORKS

12132 ■ *Minding Your Dog Business: A Practical Guide to Business Success for Dog Professionals*
Pub: Dogwise Publishing
Ed: Veronica Boutelle. **Released:** 2010. **Price:** $11. 95, Shopworn,plus S&H. **Description:** Setting up and running a successful dog-related business is an achievement in itself, but the real test is to build success and growth for the long haul. **Availability:** E-book; Print.

TRADE SHOWS AND CONVENTIONS

12133 ■ **International Association of Pet Cemeteries Annual Convention**
International Association of Pet Cemeteries and
  Crematories (IAOPCC)
  4103 Winder Hwy., Ste. 7604
  Chestnut Mountain, GA 30502
Free: 800-952-5541
Fax: (404)800-6331
Co. E-mail: info@iaopc.com
URL: http://www.iaopc.com/default.aspx
Contact: Martin Hopp, President
URL(s): www.iaopc.com

Frequency: Annual. **Audience:** Industry professionals.

ASSOCIATIONS AND OTHER ORGANIZATIONS

12134 ■ National Association of Dog Obedience Instructors (NADOI)
1430 Gadsden Hwy., Ste. 116-613
Birmingham, AL 35235
Ph: (205)202-1323
Co. E-mail: info@nadoi.org
URL: http://nadoi.org
Contact: Clare Reece-Glore, Officer
E-mail: president@nadoi.org
Facebook: www.facebook.com/NADOI
X (Twitter): x.com/NADOIORG
YouTube: www.youtube.com/channel/UC2lme4Hzjx
2ff_RZtIC1mNQ
Pinterest: www.pinterest.com/dogobedience

Description: Dog obedience instructors who have met certain standards as established by the association. Promotes improved dog obedience instruction. Endorses instructors; serves as a network for communication among members. Maintains speakers' bureau. **Founded:** 1965. **Publications:** NADOI News (Bimonthly). **Geographic Preference:** National.

REFERENCE WORKS

12135 ■ 5 Marketing Tips for Dog Trainers
Released: November 08, 2019. **Description:** Marketing a dog training business doesn't have to be a difficult task because there are so many different options out there. This article provides a variety of marketing tips and strategies to implement in your dog training business. **Availability:** Online.

12136 ■ "The 8 Best Online Dog Training Certification Programs of 2020" in The Spruce Pets (September 19, 2020)
Ed: Ashley Knierim. **Released:** September 19, 2020. **Description:** Provides detailed information on eight online dog training certification programs to help you get started on your dog training business. **Availability:** Online.

12137 ■ "9 Low-Cost Business Ideas for Animal Lovers" in Entrepreneur (February 21, 2019)
Ed: Grace Reader. **Released:** February 21, 2019. **Description:** Provides 9 low-cost business ideas that animal lovers can explore as business startup ideas. **Availability:** Online.

12138 ■ "50 Unusual Pet Businesses to Start" in Small Business Trends (January 16, 2016)
Ed: Annie Pilon. **Released:** January 16, 2016. **Description:** For those who love animals and have an entrepreneurial spirit, there are a wide variety of businesses you can start that allow you to work around dogs, cats, and other pets. This article provides a list of 50 unique pet-related businesses you could consider starting. **Availability:** Online.

12139 ■ "Does Your Dog Need Obedience School?" in WebMD
URL(s): pets.webmd.com/dogs/features/dog-obe
dience-school#1
Ed: Jennifer Dixon. **Description:** Advice on when to send your dog to obedience school for training. Includes signs to look for, typical ages of when dogs are ready, and suggestions for keeping the training going at home. **Availability:** Online.

12140 ■ Dog Obedience School Business Plan
Description: Walks the reader through the process of creating a business plan for a pet obedience school. **Availability:** Online.

12141 ■ "How to Become a Dog Trainer" in American Kennel Club website (March 12, 2020)
Ed: Stephanie Gibeault. **Released:** March 12, 2020. **Description:** Being a dog trainer can be an incredibly rewarding job. This article details information about how to become an experienced training and how to become certified. **Availability:** Online.

12142 ■ "How to Start a Dog Training Business" in The Balance Careers (October 31, 2019)
Ed: Mary Hope Kramer. **Released:** October 31, 2019. **Description:** Dog training services are in high demand as pet owners continue to demonstrate a willingness to invest in the well-being of their animals. A dog training business can be a profitable option for entrepreneurs. This article details the necessary experience desired, how to launch your business, how to market and network, pricing models, and a general business outlook. **Availability:** Online.

12143 ■ "How to Start a Dog Training Business: A Complete Guide" in K9 of Mine website (September 19, 2019)
Ed: Kayla Fratt. **Released:** September 19, 2019. **Description:** This article provides information to entrepreneurs who are considering starting their own dog training business. Includes information on choosing an area of expertise, becoming a pro through training or mentorship, certification, deciding what services you will offer, marketing, business plans, and insurance. **Availability:** Online.

12144 ■ "How to Start and Grow a Successful Dog Training Business" in Dog Matters (April 12, 2018)
Ed: Tenille Williams. **Released:** April 12, 2018. **Description:** A guide to starting and growing a successful dog training business. Includes information about training and certification, insurance, and marketing. **Availability:** Online.

12145 ■ "Is It Cruel to Use a Choke Collar on Your Dog?" in Dog Training Central
URL(s): www.dog-obedience-training-review.com/i
t-cruel-use-choke-collar-your-dog

Description: Discusses the pros and cons of using a choke collar while training your dog, and gives safety tips to make sure the collar is being used correctly. **Availability:** Online.

12146 ■ Minding Your Dog Business: A Practical Guide to Business Success for Dog Professionals
Pub: Dogwise Publishing
Ed: Veronica Boutelle. **Released:** 2010. **Price:** $11. 95, Shopworn,plus S&H. **Description:** Setting up and running a successful dog-related business is an achievement in itself, but the real test is to build success and growth for the long haul. **Availability:** E-book; Print.

12147 ■ "Navigating Dog Trainer Partnerships" in Pet Product News (Vol. 66, September 2012, No. 9, pp. 47)
Ed: Steven Appelbaum. **Description:** Benefits and disadvantages of partnerships between pet supplies retailers and dog trainers are discussed. With the proper approach to partnering with dog trainers who are duly specialized in dog behavior modification, pet supplies retailers can realize improved business and stronger customer loyalty. Tips on cross-promoting pet-related services are also provided. **Availability:** Online.

12148 ■ Pet Business 101: From Puppy School to Running With the Big Dogs
Ed: Brooke Faulkner. **Released:** September 10, 2018. **Description:** Provides business tips for entrepreneurs looking to break into the pet industry to open a business such as behavior training, grooming, or pet sitting. **Availability:** Online.

12149 ■ "Pet Care Services in Rhode Island to be Taxed" in Pet Product News (Vol. 66, September 2012, No. 9, pp. 1)
Description: Pet care services will be subject to a 7 percent sales tax in Rhode Island starting October 1, 2012, potentially resulting in more expensive pet boardng, grooming, sitting, and training. The tax is part of the state's efforts to close a $120 million budget deficit. How pet supplies retailers have reacted to the new tax is presented. **Availability:** Online.

12150 ■ "Planet Dog Foundation Awards $25,000 In Grants" in Pet Product News (Vol. 66, September 2012, No. 9, pp. 13)
Description: Portland, Maine-based Planet Dog Foundation has selected eight dog servic organizations to share $25,000 in grants. Aside from financing assitance dog, therapy dogs, and canine search and rescue programs across the U.S., the foundation supports programs that help children and adults. **Availability:** Online.

12151 ■ Puppy Training: A Step-by-Step Guide to Crate Training, Potty Training, and Obedience Training
Ed: Alexa Parsons. **Released:** November 09, 2017. **Price:** $8.95, Paperback; $2.99, E-book. **Descrip-**

tion: A guide for people new to having a puppy and who need suggestions and help with training their new pet. **Availability:** E-book; Print.

FRANCHISES AND BUSINESS OPPORTUNITIES

12152 ■ Bark Busters
PO Box 2558
  Garibaldi Highlands, BC, Canada V0N 1T0
Free: 866-418-4584
Co. E-mail: inquiries@barkbusters.ca
URL: http://www.barkbusters.ca
Facebook: www.facebook.com/barkbusterscanada
Linkedin: www.linkedin.com/company/bark-busters
  -canada
X (Twitter): x.com/barkbusters
YouTube: www.youtube.com/channel/UCq1ga9Trn
  tyellIuYKMt9rQ
Description: Dog training company. **No. of Franchise Units:** 30. **Founded:** 1989. **Franchised:** 1994. **Equity Capital Needed:** $55,000-$65,000. **Franchise Fee:** $33,000. **Training:** Provides 23 days training.

12153 ■ Bark Busters Home Dog Training
250 W Lehow Ave.
  Englewood, CO 80110
Free: 877-500-2275
URL: http://www.barkbusters.com
Contact: Adrienne Greene, Contact
X (Twitter): twitter.com/BarkBustersUSA
YouTube: www.youtube.com/barkbustershomedog
  training
Description: Firm that trains dogs on its behavior. **Founded:** 2000. **Financial Assistance:** Yes **Training:** Offers a minimum 120 hours at headquarters with ongoing support.

12154 ■ Canine Dimensions
Phoenix, AZ
URL: http://caninedimensions.com
Contact: Phil Guida, Chief Executive Officer
Facebook: www.facebook.com/pg/caninedimensions
X (Twitter): twitter.com/K9Dimensions
YouTube: www.youtube.com/user/caninedimensions
Description: Dog training center. **No. of Franchise Units:** 1. **No. of Company-Owned Units:** 1. **Founded:** 1997. **Franchised:** 2007. **Equity Capital Needed:** $44,050-$50,050. **Franchise Fee:** $22,500. **Training:** Yes.

12155 ■ The Dog Stop
Pittsburgh, PA
Free: 855-635-3935
Co. E-mail: thedogstop@thedogstop.com
URL: http://thedogstop.com
Description: All-inclusive indoor/outdoor dog care facility offering dog grooming, dog daycare, dog boarding, dog obedience training, in-home services, and a pet retail store. **Founded:** 2009.

12156 ■ The Dog Wizard
216 Foster Ave.
  Charlotte, NC 28203
Free: 866-867-0381
URL: http://thedogwizard.com/franchise
Contact: Gretchen Hollifield, Chief Executive Officer
YouTube: www.youtube.com/TheDogWizard
Description: A mobile dog training and facility-based franchise designed to give dog owners a better choice in dog training.

12157 ■ Hot Dog on a Leash
1308 Oak Ave.
  Carlsbad, CA 92008
Free: 866-546-8364

Co. E-mail: info@hotdogonaleash.com
URL: http://hotdogonaleash.com
Contact: Heather Oakes, Owner
Description: Dog training and behavior specialists utilizing lure and focus training. Franchise offers a proven system combining high values and standards for pets.

12158 ■ Ryan's Pet Food Inc.
70 Don Caster Ave.
  Thornhill, ON, Canada L3T 1L3
Ph: (905)771-9227
Co. E-mail: gpf78@globalpetfoods.com
URL: http://globalpetfoods.com
Contact: Dino Fragaglia, President
X (Twitter): x.com/GlobalPetFoods
Description: Chain of pet food stores. **Founded:** 1979. **Financial Assistance:** No **Training:** Yes.

LIBRARIES

12159 ■ American Kennel Club Library (AKC Library)
101 Pk. Ave.
  New York, NY 10178
Ph: (919)233-9767
Co. E-mail: info@akc.org
URL: http://www.akc.org/about/archive
Instagram: www.instagram.com/akclibrary
Description: Contains a repository of unique data devoted to dogs that consists of approximately 15,000 volumes on purebred dog. **Scope:** Dogs - breeds, training, health, literature, art. **Services:** Copying; library open to the public by appointment. **Founded:** 1934. **Holdings:** 18,000 volumes; VF drawers of clippings, videocassettes, fine art collection; 5 dissertations. **Subscriptions:** 300 journals and other serials.

START-UP INFORMATION

12160 ■ *"Birdcage Optimization"* in *Pet Product News (Vol. 64, November 2010, No. 11, pp. 54)*

Ed: Cheryl Reeves. **Description:** Manufacturers have been emphasizing size, security, quality construction, stylish design, and quick cleaning when guiding consumers on making birdcage options. Selecting a birdcage is gaining importance considering that cage purchases have become the highest expense associated with owning a bird. Other avian habitat trends are also examined. **Availability:** Online.

12161 ■ *"Business Builders: Tradeshow Attendance Incentives Add Up"* in *Pet Product News (Vol. 64, December 2010, No. 12, pp. 14)*

Ed: Mark E. Battersby. **Description:** Pointers on how pet specialty retailers can claim business travel tax and income tax deductions for expenses paid or incurred in participation at tradeshows, conventions, and meetings are presented. Incentives in form of these deductions could allow pet specialty retailers to gain business benefits, aside from the education and enjoyment involved with the travel. **Availability:** Online.

12162 ■ *"Come Together: A Thematic Collection of Times Articles, Essays, Maps and More About Creating Community"* in *Pet Product News (Vol. 64, December 2010, No. 12, pp. 28)*

Ed: Lizett Bond. **Description:** Pet supply retailers have posted improved sales and improved customer service by bundling their offerings. Bundling pertains to grouping related items such as collars and leashes into a single unit for marketing purposes. Aside from providing convenience and enhanced product information to customers, bundling has facilitated more efficient purchases. **Availability:** Online.

12163 ■ *"Experts Strive to Educate on Proper Pet Diets"* in *Pet Product News (Vol. 64, November 2010, No. 11, pp. 40)*

Ed: Joan Hustace Walker. **Description:** Pet supply manufacturers have been bundling small mammal food and treats with educational sources to help retailers avoid customer misinformation. This action has been motivated by the customer's quest to seek proper nutritional advice for their small mammal pets. **Availability:** Online.

12164 ■ *"Food as Nature Intended"* in *Pet Product News (Vol. 64, November 2010, No. 11, pp. 30)*

Ed: Nikki Moustaki. **Description:** Dog owners have been extending their health-consciousness to their pets by seeking natural products that will address their pets' raw food diet. Retailers response to this trend are outlined. **Availability:** Online.

12165 ■ *"Helping Customers Fight Pet Waste"* in *Pet Product News (Vol. 64, November 2010, No. 11, pp. 52)*

Ed: Sandy Robins. **Description:** Pet cleaning products manufacturers have been enjoying high sales figures by paying attention to changing pet ownership trends and environmental awareness. Meanwhile, the inclusion of user-friendly features in these products has also been boosted by the social role of pets and the media attention to pet waste. How manufacturers have been responding to this demand is explored. **Availability:** Print; Online.

12166 ■ *"Making It Work"* in *Pet Product News (Vol. 64, December 2010, No. 12, pp. S8)*

Ed: Kerri Chladnicek. **Description:** How focusing on service and flexibility allowed New Jersey-based pet supply store B.C. Woof to achieve success is discussed. B.C. Woof began as a pet-sitting business which eventually concentrated on natural foods. Aside from conducting a do-it-yourself approach in food formulation for customers, B.C. Woof has also been guiding customers on nutrients they need for their pets. **Availability:** Print; Online.

12167 ■ *"Natural Pet Product Merchandiser Roundtable: Functional Foods and Treats"* in *Pet Product News (Vol. 64, December 2010, No. 12, pp. S1)*

Released: January 18, 2013. **Description:** Executives and business owners from the pet supplies industries deliberate on the role of functional foods in the retail sector. Functional foods pertain to foods with specified health benefits. Insight into marketing functional foods and convincing pet owners to make the transition to these products is examined. **Availability:** Online.

12168 ■ *"Nestle Acquires Waggin' Train Dog Treat Company"* in *Pet Product News (Vol. 64, November 2010, No. 11, pp. 7)*

Description: Vevey, Switzerland-based Nestle has acquired South Carolina-based dog treat firm Waggin' Train LLC from private equity firm VMG Partners in September 2010. Waggin' Train LLC, which will be operated as a wholly owned subsidiary, is expected to fill a gap in Nestle's dog treat product portfolio. **Availability:** Online.

12169 ■ *"North American Pet Health Insurance Market Poised for Growth"* in *Pet Product News (Vol. 64, December 2010, No. 12, pp. 4)*

Ed: David Lummis. **Description:** The pet health insurance market is expected to further grow after posting about $350 million in sales in 2009, a gain of more than $40 million. Pet insurance firms have offered strategies such as product humanization in response to this growth forecast. Meanwhile, pet insurance shoppers have been provided more by insurance firms with wider choices. **Availability:** Online.

12170 ■ *"Perfecting Customer Services"* in *Pet Product News (Vol. 64, November 2010, No. 11, pp. 18)*

Ed: Alison Bour. **Description:** Pet supply retailers are encouraged to emphasize customer experience and sales representatives' knowledge of the store's product offerings to foster repeat business. Employee protocols could be implemented to improve customer interaction. Other guidelines on developing a pet supply retail environment that advances repeat business are presented. **Availability:** Online.

12171 ■ *"Pet Food Bank 'Shares the Love"* in *Pet Product News (Vol. 64, December 2010, No. 12, pp. 6)*

Description: Winston-Salem, North Carolina-based nonprofit Share the Love Pet Food Bank has donated 60,000 pounds of pet food since its establishment in 2009. It has been linking pet food manufacturers and rescue groups to supply unsold pet food to needy animals. The nonprofit intends to reach out to more animal welfare groups by building more warehouses. **Availability:** Online.

12172 ■ *"Promotions Create a Path to Better Profit"* in *Pet Product News (Vol. 64, December 2010, No. 12, pp. 1)*

Ed: Joan Hustace Walker. **Description:** Pet store retailers can boost small mammal sales by launching creative marketing and promotions such as social networking and adoption days.

12173 ■ *"Smarts Drive Sales"* in *Pet Product News (Vol. 64, December 2010, No. 12, pp. 1)*

Ed: Karen Shugart. **Description:** Retailers could make smart decisions by deciding how to best attract customers into their stores or resolving whether to nurture in-store or buy herps (reptiles) from suppliers. Paying attention to these smart decisions could help boost customer interest in herps and address customer demands. **Availability:** Online.

12174 ■ *"Solutions for the Frustrating Feline"* in *Pet Product News (Vol. 64, November 2010, No. 11, pp. 46)*

Ed: Lori Luechtefeld. **Description:** Products that can help customers deal with problematic cat behaviors, such as out-of-the-box urination and scratching are described. Information on such products including litter box deodorants and disposable scratchers is provided. Feline territorial behaviors can also be addressed by pheromone products that can calm hyperactive cats. **Availability:** Online.

12175 ■ *"Supplements Mix Nutrition With Convenience"* in *Pet Product News (Vol. 64, November 2010, No. 11, pp. 44)*

Ed: Karen Shugart. **Description:** Pet supply manufacturers have been making supplements and enhanced foods that improve mineral consumption, boost bone density, and sharpen appetite in herps. Customers seem to enjoy the convenience as particular herps demands are being addressed by these offerings. Features of other supplements and enhanced foods for herps are described. **Availability:** Print; Online.

12176 ■ *"Tapping the 'Well' in Wellness"* in *Pet Product News (Vol. 64, November 2010, No. 11, pp. 1)*
Ed: Wendy Bedwell-Wilson. **Description:** Healthy food and treats are among the leading wellness products being sought by customers from specialty retailers to keep their pets healthy. With this demand for pet wellness products, retailers suggest making sure that staff know key ingredients to emphasize to customers. Other insights into this trend and ways to engage customers are discussed. **Availability:** Online.

12177 ■ *"Teachable Moments: Worth Every Penny"* in *Pet Product News (Vol. 64, December 2010, No. 12, pp. 34)*
Ed: Cheryl Reeves. **Description:** Pet bird retailers can attain both outreach to customers and enhanced profitability by staging educational events such as the annual Parrot Palooza event of Burlington, New Jersey-based Bird Paradise. Aside from attracting a global audience, Parrot Palooza features seminars, workshops, classes, and bird-related contests. **Availability:** Print; Online.

12178 ■ *"Young Adults, Childless May Help Fuel Post-Recession Rebound"* in *Pet Product News (Vol. 64, November 2010, No. 11, pp. 4)*
Ed: David Lummis. **Description:** Pet industry retailers and marketers are encouraged to tap into the young adult and childless couple sectors to boost consumer traffic and sales to pre-recession levels. Among young adult owners, pet ownership increased from 40 percent in 2003 to 49 percent in 2009. Meanwhile, the childless couple sector represented 63 percent of all dog/cat owners in 2009. **Availability:** Online.

ASSOCIATIONS AND OTHER ORGANIZATIONS

12179 ■ American Pet Products Association (APPA)
225 High Ridge Rd., Ste. W200
Stamford, CT 06905
Ph: (203)532-0000
Free: 800-452-1225
Fax: (203)532-0551
Co. E-mail: info@americanpetproducts.org
URL: http://www.americanpetproducts.org
Contact: Steve King, President
E-mail: sking@americanpetproducts.org
Facebook: www.facebook.com/AmericanPetProducts
Linkedin: www.linkedin.com/company/american-pet-products-association-appa
X (Twitter): x.com/APPAtweets
Instagram: www.instagram.com/americanpetproducts
YouTube: www.youtube.com/user/AmericanPetProducts
Description: U.S. Manufacturers and importers of pet products. Provides public relations program to promote pet ownership and pet care. Sponsors the association's annual National Pet Products Trade Show; publishes the National Pet Owner's Survey, the association's research study in the pet industry. **Founded:** 1958. **Publications:** *APPMA Advisor* (Quarterly). **Educational Activities:** Global Pet Expo (Annual). **Awards:** APPA New Product Showcase Awards (Annual). **Geographic Preference:** Multinational.

12180 ■ The Pet Advocacy Network (PIJAC)
1615 Duke St., Ste. 100
Alexandria, VA 22314
Ph: (202)452-1525
Fax: (703)997-4270
Co. E-mail: info@petadvocacy.org
URL: http://petadvocacy.org
Contact: Mike Bober, President
E-mail: mbober@petadvocacy.org
Facebook: www.facebook.com/PetAdvocacyNetwork
Linkedin: www.linkedin.com/company/pet-advocacy-network
X (Twitter): x.com/PetAdvocacy
Description: Pet retailers, manufacturers and distributors; companion animal suppliers; pet industry trade associations. Works to monitor federal and state regulations and legislation affecting the industry. Sponsors research projects and industry-related educational programs. **Founded:** 1971. **Publications:** *Our Pets, Our Health*; *PetLetter* (Periodic); *Tips on Travel With Your Pets.* **Geographic Preference:** National.

12181 ■ Pet Food Institute (PFI)
1020 19th St. NW, Ste. 225
Washington, DC 20036
Ph: (202)791-9440
Co. E-mail: info@petfoodinstitute.org
URL: http://www.petfoodinstitute.org
Contact: Dana Brooks, President
Facebook: www.facebook.com/PetFoodInstitute
Linkedin: www.linkedin.com/company/69679972
X (Twitter): x.com/uspetfood
YouTube: www.youtube.com/channel/UCC tKmC7Wiwoe0nZXmutQtPg
Description: Represents the manufacturers of 97% of the commercial pet food produced in the United States. Serves as the voice of the industry before legislative and regulatory bodies at both the federal and state levels. **Founded:** 1958. **Educational Activities:** Suppliers Mart (Annual). **Geographic Preference:** National.

12182 ■ Pet Industry Distributors Association (PIDA)
1000 W Valley Rd.
Southeastern, PA 19399
Ph: (610)257-7893
Co. E-mail: pida@kingmgmt.org
URL: http://www.pida.org
Contact: Celeste Powers, President
E-mail: cpowers@msp-amc.com
Linkedin: www.linkedin.com/company/petindustrydistributorsassociation
Description: Strives to enhance the well-being of the pet product wholesaler-distributor. Promotes partnerships between suppliers and customers. Fosters the human-companion animal bond. **Founded:** 1968. **Publications:** *Pet Industry Distributors Association-Membership Directory*; *PIDA Bulletin* (Bimonthly). **Educational Activities:** University of Innovative Distribution (Annual); Annual Pet Industry Leadership Conference (Annual); Global Pet Expo (Annual). **Awards:** PIDA Lifetime Achievement Award (Occasionally); PIDA Performance Benchmarking Awards Program (Annual). **Geographic Preference:** National.

12183 ■ World Pet Association (WPA) [American Pet Society (APS)]
11801 Pierce St., Ste. 200
Riverside, CA 92505
Ph: (626)447-2222
Co. E-mail: info@wpamail.org
URL: http://www.worldpetassociation.org
Contact: Victor Mason, President
E-mail: vic.mason@wpamail.org
Linkedin: www.linkedin.com/in/world-pet-association-12700323
Description: Manufacturers, retailers and distributors of pet food and services and of avian, aquarium and companion animal care products, equipment and services. Seeks to advance the economic interests of members; promotes responsible pet ownership. Conducts trade shows, certificate training courses and seminars for pet shop retailers, grooming establishments, veterinary clinics. **Founded:** 1951. **Educational Activities:** Super Zoo (Annual); America's Family Pet Expo (Annual); WWPSA Annual Pet Industry Trade Show (Annual). **Geographic Preference:** National; Multinational.

REFERENCE WORKS

12184 ■ *"Add Aquatics to Boost Business"* in *Pet Product News (Vol. 64, December 2010, No. 12, pp. 20)*
Ed: David Lass. **Description:** Pet stores are encouraged to add aquatics departments to increase profitability through repeat sales. This goal can be realized by sourcing, displaying, and maintaining high quality live fish. Other tips regarding the challenges associated with setting up an aquatics department are presented. **Availability:** Online.

12185 ■ *"Ahead of the Trend: What Will the World Map Look Like in Five Years?"* in *Pet Product News (Vol. 66, September 2012, No. 9, pp. S1)*
Description: How Whiskers Holistic Pet Care has transformed itself into the go-to place for naturally inclined pet owners in New York City's East Village is discussed. Since 1988, Whiskers Holistic Pet Care has emphasized careful product selection and customer education to serve a wide array of customers. **Availability:** Print; Online.

12186 ■ *"Almost Like Home"* in *Pet Product News (Vol. 66, September 2012, No. 9, pp. S18)*
Description: Treats Unleashed, a natural and functional pet foods and supplies store chain in Medwestern U.S., has been known for creating an aura that kept customers returning to each of its seven stores. It has also been reputed for a laidback atmosphere that prioritizes customer education over sales. The chain's promotional and growth-related plans are also discussed. **Availability:** Online.

12187 ■ *"Aquatic Medications Engender Good Health"* in *Pet Product News (Vol. 64, November 2010, No. 11, pp. 47)*
Ed: Madelaine Heleine. **Description:** Pet supply manufacturers and retailers have been exerting consumer education and preparedness efforts to help aquarium hobbyists in tackling ornamental fish disease problems. Aquarium hobbyists have been also assisted in choosing products that facilitate aquarium maintenance before disease attacks their pet fish. **Availability:** Online.

12188 ■ *"Backer Christmas Trade Show Preview"* in *Pet Product News (Vol. 66, September 2012, No. 9, pp. 12)*
Description: The 46th Annual H.H. Backer Pet Industry Christmas Trade Showand Educational Conference will beheld at the Donald E. Stephens Convention Center in Rosemont, Illinois from October 12-14, 2012. More than 600 pet supply manufacturers and about 9,000 industry professionals will attend. **Availability:** Print; Online.

12189 ■ *"Best In Show"* in *Pet Product News (Vol. 64, November 2010, No. 11, pp. 20)*
Ed: Lizett Bond. **Description:** Cherrybrook Premium Pet Supplies offers an expanded array of quality holistic products and is staffed by people who possess wide knowledge of these products. Aside from receiving the Outstanding Holistic Approach award, Cherrybrook has opened three stores in New Jersey. How a holistic approach to service kept customers coming back is discussed. **Availability:** Print; Online.

12190 ■ *"Branding Spree"* in *Pet Product News (Vol. 66, September 2012, No. 9, pp. 40)*
Ed: Michael Ventre. **Description:** The extent to which pet security firm PetSafe has continued to diversify into new product categories to realize growth opportunities is explored. An arm of Radio Systems Corporation, PetSafe has been known for manufacturing products such as wireless fences and electronic pet collars. **Availability:** Print; Online.

12191 ■ *"California Forces Pet Stores to Sell Only Dogs and Cats from Shelters"* in *The New York Times (January 2, 2019)*
URL(s): www.nytimes.com/2019/01/02/us/california-pet-store-rescue-law.html

Ed: Christine Hauser. **Released:** January 02, 2019. **Description:** A new law in California has required all pet stores to sell only dogs, cats, and rabbits from animal shelters instead of obtaining animals from breeding mills, which have a history of very poor conditions. Stores who do not comply will be subjected to a $500 per animal fine. **Availability:** Online.

12192 ■ *"Canadian Pet Charities Won't Go Hungry"* in Pet Product News (Vol. 66, September 2012, No. 9, pp. 15)

Description: Premium dog and cat food manufacturer Petcurean will donate more than 42,000 pounds of Go! and Now Fresh dry foods to 25 animal rescue organizations across Canada. The donation is deemed invaluable to Petcurean's network of dog and cat foster activities. **Availability:** Online.

12193 ■ *"Canine Cuisine: AKC Tips for a Healthful Diet"* in Seattle Times (September 13, 2008, pp. D9)

Pub: Associated Press

Contact: Ken Dale, Chief Financial Officer Senior Vice President

Description: The American Kennel Club recommends feeding dogs food with balanced essential nutrients, including proteins, carbohydrates, fats, vitamins, minerals, and water; types of food, feeding practices and what not to feed a dog is discussed. **Availability:** Online.

12194 ■ *"Celebrate Holiday Spirit With Sparkling Sales"* in Pet Product News (Vol. 66, September 2012, No. 9, pp. 48)

Ed: Cheryl Reeves. **Description:** Pet supplies retailers can increase frequency of holiday sales, from Halloween through New Year's, by integrating creative marketing strategies into merchandise and incentives that elicit customer attention. The impression of fun should also be emphasized on customers. Guidelines for presenting displays and organizing special store-related events are also provided. **Availability:** Print; Online.

12195 ■ *"Dog Marketplace: Pet Waste Products Pick Up Sales"* in Pet Product News (Vol. 66, September 2012, No. 9, pp. 58)

Ed: Sandi Cain. **Description:** Pet supplies manufacturers are developing dog waste pickup bags and other convenient cleanup tools characterized by environment-friendliness and fashion. The demand for these cleanup tools has been motivated by dog owners' desire to minimize their and their dogs' environmental footprints. **Availability:** Online.

12196 ■ *"Elanco Challenges Bayer's Advantage, K9 Advantix Ad Claims"* in Pet Product News (Vol. 64, November 2010, No. 11, pp. 11)

Description: Elanco Animal Health has disputed Bayer Animal Health's print and Web advertising claims involving its flea, tick, and mosquito control products Advantage and K9 Advantix. The National Advertising Division of the Council of Better Business Bureaus recommended the discontinuation of ads, while Bayer Animal Health reiterated its commitment to self-regulation. **Availability:** Online.

12197 ■ *"Ex-Medical Student Stages Career In Event Planning: Barcelona Owner Makes Inroads with Luxury Car Dealerships"* in Los Angeles Business Journal (Vol. 34, June 18, 2012, No. 25, pp. 10)

Pub: CBJ L.P.

Contact: Terri Cunningham, Contact

Description: Barcelona Enterprises started as a company designing menus for restaurants, organizing food shows, to planning receptions for luxury car dealers. The fim will be launching the first Las Vegas Chocolate Festival & Pastry Show in July 2012. Presently, the company runs 24 wine and food festivals, organizes events for an upscale dog shampoo maker, and sports car dealerships. **Availability:** Print; Online.

12198 ■ *"Facials for Fido? Retail: Kriser's Pet Store Grows With High-End Pet Products Market"* in San Fernando Valley Business Journal (Vol. 17, February 20, 2012, No. 4, pp. 1)

Description: Sherman Oaks all-natural pet food and supply retailer, Kriser's, is expanding with seven new stores. The company is known for its health options in pet food, tasty treats, and fancy toys by catering to a high-end clientele. They also offer upscale pet grooming services, including blueberry facials and de-shedding treatments. **Availability:** Online.

12199 ■ *"Foods for Thought"* in Pet Product News (Vol. 64, December 2010, No. 12, pp. 16)

Ed: Maddy Heleine. **Description:** Manufacturers have been focused at developing species-specific fish foods due to consumer tendency to assess the benefits of the food they feed their fish. As retailers stock species-specific fish foods, manufacturers have provided in-store items and strategies to assist in efficiently selling these food products. Trends in fish food packaging and ingredients are also discussed. **Availability:** Online.

12200 ■ *"Help Wanted: Only the Best Need Apply"* in Pet Product News (Vol. 66, April 2012, No. 4, pp. 24)

Description: Simi Valley, California-based pet supplies store, Theresa's Country Feed and Pet is said to have achieved success by hiring quality customer-oriented employees. In view of its receipt of the Pet Product News International's 2011-2012 Retailer of the Year Award for Outstanding General Pet Store, Theresa's approach to recruitment and customer relations are discussed. **Availability:** Print; Online.

12201 ■ *"Howl-o-ween"* in Decatur Daily (October 25, 2011)

Description: Animal Friends Humane Society provides free pet food and cat litter to Meals on Wheels clients. **Availability:** Online.

12202 ■ *"In the Wake of Pet-Food Crisis, Iams Sales Plummet Nearly 17 Percent"* in Advertising Age (Vol. 78, May 14, 2007, No. 18, pp. 3)

Pub: Crain Communications, Inc.

Contact: Jessica Botos, Manager, Marketing

E-mail: jessica.botos@crainsnewyork.com

Ed: Jack Neff. **Description:** Although the massive U.S. pet-food recall impacted more than 100 brands, Procter & Gamble Co.'s Iams lost more sales and market share than any other industry player. According to Information Resources Inc. data, the brand's sales dropped 16.5 percent in the eight-week period ended April 22. Many analysts feel that the company could have handled the crisis in a better manner. **Availability:** Online.

12203 ■ *"International Waters: Hawaii Aquarium Legislation Dead...Or Is It?"* in Pet Product News (Vol. 66, September 2012, No. 9, pp. 76)

Ed: John Dawes. **Description:** SB 580 is deemed as one of the Hawaiin Senate bills that would lead to prohibition of, or heavy restrictions to, the collection of marine reef fish for home aquaria. Implications of these Senate bill on marine life conservation and stakeholder submissions are discussed. **Availability:** Online.

12204 ■ *"Internet Sales of Pet Products Increasingly 'Big Box"* in Pet Product News (Vol. 66, September 2012, No. 9, pp. 4)

Description: Internet sales account for nearly 4 percent of the $30 billion U.S. market for pet products in 2011, or about $1.2 billion retail. Meanwhile, overall pet product retail sales growth and overall Internet retail sales growth of 10 percent can be outpaced as Internet sales of pet products is seen to grow at a 12 percent compound annual rate through 2015. **Availability:** Online.

12205 ■ *"Invest in Energy-Efficient Equipment for Your Pet Store"* in Pet Product News (Vol. 66, September 2012, No. 9, pp. 72)

Ed: Leila Meyer. **Description:** Aquatic retailers can achieve business growth by offering lighting products, pumps, heaters, filters, and other aquarium supplies that would help customers realize energy efficiency. Aside from offering an education in energy efficiency as a customer service opportunity, retailers are encouraged to determine what supplies are crucial in helping customers achieve energy usage goals. **Availability:** Online.

12206 ■ *"Jersey Pet Store Regs Poised for Change"* in Pet Product News (Vol. 66, March 2012, No. 3, pp. 18)

Description: Bills at the New Jersey Assembly could mandate the state's Department of Health and Senior Services to review and update requirements for establishments that sell live animals. Assembly Bill 147 would direct the department to prohibit over-crowdng animals in pet stores, kennels, and similar establishments. The bill would also revise the state's cruelty laws. **Availability:** Online.

12207 ■ *"Keep The (Cage) Customer Satisfied"* in Pet Product News (Vol. 64, December 2010, No. 12, pp. 10)

Ed: Devon McPhee. **Description:** Windsor, California-based Debbie's Pet Boutique, recipient of Pet Product News International's Outstanding Customer Service Award, has been dedicated to combining topnotch grooming services with a robust retail selection. These features might gain return customers for Debbie's Pet Boutique. **Availability:** Online.

12208 ■ *"Marketer Bets Big on U.S.'s Growing Canine Obsession"* in Advertising Age (Vol. 79, April 14, 2008, No. 15, pp. 14)

Pub: Crain Communications, Inc.

Contact: Jessica Botos, Manager, Marketing

E-mail: jessica.botos@crainsnewyork.com

Ed: Emily Bryson York. **Description:** Overview of FreshPet, a New Jersey company that began marketing two brands of refrigerated dog food-Deli Fresh and FreshPet Select-which are made from fresh ingredients such as beef, rice and carrots. The company projects continued success due to the amount of money consumers spend on their pets as well as fears derived from the 2007 recalls that inspired consumers to look for smaller, independent manufacturers that are less likely to source ingredients from China. **Availability:** Online.

12209 ■ *"Melamine Analytical Methods Released"* in Feedstuffs (Vol. 80, October 6, 2008, No. 41, pp. 2)

Pub: Miller Publishing Company

Description: Romer Labs has released new validations for its AgraQuant Melamine enzyme-linked immunosorbent assay. The test kit screens for melamine in feed and diary products, including pet foods, milk and milk powder. Melamine by itself is nontoxic in low doses, but when combined with cyanuric acid it can cause fatal kidney stones. The Chinese dairy industry is in the midst of a huge melamine crisis; melamine-contaminated dairy and food products from China have been found in more than 20 countries. **Availability:** Print; Online.

12210 ■ *Minding Your Dog Business: A Practical Guide to Business Success for Dog Professionals*

Pub: Dogwise Publishing

Ed: Veronica Boutelle. **Released:** 2010. **Price:** $11. 95, Shopworn,plus S&H. **Description:** Setting up and running a successful dog-related business is an achievement in itself, but the real test is to build success and growth for the long haul. **Availability:** E-book; Print.

12211 ■ *"Navigating Dog Trainer Partnerships"* in Pet Product News (Vol. 66, September 2012, No. 9, pp. 47)

Ed: Steven Appelbaum. **Description:** Benefits and disadvantages of partnerships between pet supplies retailers and dog trainers are discussed. With the proper approach to partnering with dog trainers who are duly specialized in dog behavior modification, pet supplies retailers can realize improved business and stronger customer loyalty. Tips on cross-promoting pet-related services are also provided. **Availability:** Online.

12212 ■ *"New Developments in Cat's Play" in Pet Product News (Vol. 66, September 2012, No. 9, pp. 1)*
Description: Developments in toys for cats have been characterized by items that bring out a cat's natural instincts, toxin-free composition, and durability, among other trends. Meanwhile, consumers are encouraged to try these toys so follow-up purchases can be made. Ways in which manufacturers have addressed the demand for these toys is also discussed. **Availability:** Online.

12213 ■ *"New Pet Product Launches IndieGoGo Crowdfunding to Remain American Made" in Benzinga.com (June 11, 2012)*
Pub: Benzinga.com
Contact: Jason Raznick, Founder
Ed: Aaron Wise. **Description:** The Supercollar (r) is a new dog collar and leash combination launched on an Indiegogo crowdfunding campaign in order to raise fund to help the firm keep their business in America. The firm is striving to design and manufacture the Supercollar here in the US in order to create and save American jobs. The Supercollar's technology is also discussed. **Availability:** Print; Online.

12214 ■ *"New Recipes Added to IAMS Naturals Pet Food Line" in MMR (Vol. 28, August 1, 2011, No. 11, pp. 17)*
Description: Procter & Gamble Company's IAMS brand has created a new pet food line called IAMS Naturals for pet owners wishing to feed their pets natural, wholesome food. IAMS Sensitive Naturals has ocean fish and its first ingredient for dogs with sensitivities. IAMS Simple & Natural features chicken with no fillers. **Availability:** Print; Online.

12215 ■ *"Optimum Nutrition, Maximum Profit" in Pet Product News (Vol. 66, September 2012, No. 9, pp. S1)*
Description: How pet food manufacturers have expanded brand lines to address pet owners' demand for fresh, balanced superfood diets that provide optimum pet nutrtion and foster rapid digestion among pets is explored. Retailers have been maximizing profits by guiding pet owners in selecting he appropriate superfood brands for their pets. **Availability:** Online.

12216 ■ *"Options Abound in Winter Wares" in Pet Product News (Vol. 64, November 2010, No. 11, pp. 1)*
Ed: Maggie M. Shein. **Description:** Pet supply manufacturers emphasize creating top-notch construction and functional design in creating winter clothing for pets. Meanwhile, retailers and pet owners seek human-inspired style, quality, and versatility for pets' winter clothing. How retailers generate successful sales of pets' winter clothing outside of traditional brand marketing is also examined. **Availability:** Online.

12217 ■ *"Organic Dog Food Options" in Pet Product News (Vol. 66, September 2012, No. 9, pp. 54)*
Ed: Keith Loria. **Description:** How pet supplies manufacturers have responded to dog owners' demand for natural and organic dog food is discussed. This demand has been generated by increasing health-consciousness, leading to greater tendency to look more closely at food ingredients. Reasons why the switch to organic dog food should be done are presented, along with marketing tips for organic dog food products. **Availability:** Print; Online.

12218 ■ *"Organic Dog Treats" in Veterinary Economics (Vol. 49, November 2008, No. 11, pp. 52)*
Description: Wet Noses all-natural dog treats come in six flavors: dogranola, pumpkin, sweet potato curry, apples and carrots, cheddar, and peanut butter and

molasses. The treats are made without animal by-products, added chemicals, preservatives, corn, soy or wheat. **Availability:** Online.

12219 ■ *"Pet Care Services in Rhode Island to be Taxed" in Pet Product News (Vol. 66, September 2012, No. 9, pp. 1)*
Description: Pet care services will be subject to a 7 percent sales tax in Rhode Island starting October 1, 2012, potentially resulting in more expensive pet boardng, grooming, sitting, and training. The tax is part of the state's efforts to close a $120 million budget deficit. How pet supplies retailers have reacted to the new tax is presented. **Availability:** Online.

12220 ■ *"Pet Store Pro Adds New Curriculum" in Pet Product News (Vol. 66, February 2012, No. 2, pp. 2012)*
Description: Pet Store Pro, the Pet Industry Distributors Association's free online training program, is going to launch chapters of a curriculum intended to assist pet store managers learn effective approaches to motivate employees and boost profitability. Other management-level chapters to be added by Pet Store Pro throughout 2012 are listed. **Availability:** Print; Online.

12221 ■ *"PetSmart: A Barking Buy" in Barron's (Vol. 89, July 6, 2009, No. 27, pp. 15)*
Pub: Dow Jones & Company Inc.
Contact: Almar Latour, Chief Executive Officer
Ed: Jay Palmer. **Description:** Shares of PetSmart could climb from $21.70 to about $28 due to the company's improving profits, cash flow, and product portfolio. The company's shares are trading at 14 times projected 2010 earnings of $1.64 a share. **Availability:** Online.

12222 ■ *"Portability and Durability Are Key When It Comes to Pet Containment" in Pet Product News (Vol. 66, September 2012, No. 9, pp. 64)*
Ed: Wendy Bedwell-Wilson. **Description:** Containment products that have been offered by pet supply manufacturers are marked by features such as portability and durability. Some of these products include crates, partitions, and adjustable pens to cordon off dog and ensure their safety within the household premises. **Availability:** Online.

12223 ■ *"Progress Means Business" in Pet Product News (Vol. 66, September 2012, No. 9, pp. 88)*
Description: Pet supplies retailers are encouraged to promote devices featuring technologies that will assist herp hobbyists to properly monitor temperature, humidity and UVB in tanks with improved control and precision. Customer connction should also be taken into consideration by retailers to generate more sales. Other marketing tips for promoting sophisticated monitoring devices for herp tanks are given. **Availability:** Online.

12224 ■ *"Sales of What's Under Feet Add Up Fast" in Pet Product News (Vol. 66, September 2012, No. 9, pp. S8)*
Description: Pet supplies retailers and manufacturers have been emphasizing the type of substances in creating new approaches to developing environment-friendly natural litters and beddings for small mammals and cats. Some of these approaches are highlighted, along with marketing strategies retailers have implemented. **Availability:** Print; Online.

12225 ■ *"Secaucus-Based Freshpet is Barking Up the Right Tree" in Record (September 8, 2011)*
Pub: North Jersey Media Group
Contact: Scott Muller, Director
E-mail: muller@northjersey.com
Ed: Rebecca Ollales. **Description:** Freshpet produces a variety of nutritious, refrigerated pet foods and treats for cats and dogs. The firm introduced five new recipes and treats to its grain-free line called Vital line. The Vital line mimics the ancestral diets of dogs and cats. **Availability:** Online.

12226 ■ *"Specialize in Cat Nutrition" in Pet Product News (Vol. 66, September 2012, No. 9, pp. 80)*
Ed: Karen Shugart. **Description:** Cat food manufacturers have been developing a widely expanding variety of specialty diets that target numerous feline needs as cat owners' interest in their pets' nutrition becomes more intense. In view of this trend, insights into the growth of specialty diets in the cat food category are presented, along with descriptions of some of these diets. **Availability:** Online.

12227 ■ *"Staying Social Complements Retail Goals" in Pet Product News (Vol. 66, September 2012, No. 9, pp. 34)*
Description: Pet supplies retailers can take advantage of social media to brand the store and its products and facilitate dialogue with consumers. As these retail goals are realized, profits can be attained. Strategies that can enable pet supplies retailers to create business networks through social media marketing are also presented. **Availability:** Online.

12228 ■ *"Store Front: Invest in Energy-Efficient Equipment for Your Pet Store" in Pet Product News (Vol. 66, September 2012, No. 9, pp. 43)*
Ed: Leila Meyer. **Description:** Developments in energy-efficient lighting, heating, and air conditioning have allowed pet supplies stores to conduct upgrades that result in savings. Pet supplies stores have also been impressing customers by obtaining Energy Start or LEED certification. **Availability:** Print; Online.

12229 ■ *"Tax Tip: Streamlining Sales Tax Collections" in Pet Product News (Vol. 66, September 2012, No. 9, pp. 38)*
Ed: Mark E. Battersby. **Description:** Pointers on how pet supplies retailers and managers can streamline sales taxes are presented. Businesses are being challenge by the pressure to collect taxes on goods sold to local customers and competititon from Internet merchants that are not required to collect sales taxes. **Availability:** Online.

12230 ■ *"To Catch Up, Colgate May Ratchet Up Its Ad Spending" in Advertising Age (Vol. 81, December 6, 2010, No. 43, pp. 1)*
Pub: Crain Communications, Inc.
Contact: Jessica Botos, Manager, Marketing
E-mail: jessica.botos@crainsnewyork.com
Ed: Jack Neff. **Description:** Colgate-Palmolive Company has been losing market share in the categories of toothpaste, deodorant, body wash, dish soap and pet food. **Availability:** Online.

12231 ■ *"Wegmans Uses Database for Recall" in Supermarket News (Vol. 56, September 22, 2008, No. 38)*
Pub: Informa USA, Inc.
Contact: Stephen A. Carter, Chief Executive Officer
Ed: Carol Angrisani. **Description:** Wegmans used data obtained through its loyalty card that, in turn, sent automated telephone calls to every customer who had purchased tainted pet food when Mars Petcare recalled dog food products.

12232 ■ *"What's Amazon Doing in the Pet Consumables Market?" in veterinarynews.dvm360.com (October 2, 2018)*
URL(s): veterinarynews.dvm360.com/whats-amazon-doing-pet-consumables-market
Ed: Katie James. **Released:** October 02, 2018. **Description:** Amazon provides insight into its pet business model, which has local veterinarians worried about the competition. In the meantime, Amazon is growing its share of pet consumables, which include food, healthcare products, and litter by applying it's successful business strategy that works with other consumers. **Availability:** Online.

12233 ■ *"Where Pet Nutrition Meets Love" in Pet Product News (Vol. 66, September 2012, No. 9, pp. S14)*
Description: Michael Landa, coowner of Nulo Pet Products, discusses the role of his company in reducing pet obesity through the manufacture of high-

protein foods. Aside from explaining his interest in pet obesity, Landa also describes how the company differentiates itself from competitors. **Availability:** Online.

TRADE PERIODICALS

12234 ■ *Dog World: Active Dogs, Active People*
Contact: Damian Durio, Editor
E-mail: editor@dogworld.co.uk

Ed: Damian Durio, Chrissy Smith. **Description:** Magazine serving breeders, exhibitors, hobbyists and professionals in kennel operations, groomers, veterinarians, animal hospitals/clinics and pet suppliers. **Availability:** Print; Online.

VIDEO/AUDIO MEDIA

12235 ■ *How I Built This: Freshpet: Scott Morris*
URL(s): wondery.com/shows/how-i-built-this/episode/10386-freshpet-scott-morris

Ed: Guy Raz. **Released:** October 09, 2023. **Description:** Podcast explains how Freshpet transformed pet food by making slice-and-serve meals.

TRADE SHOWS AND CONVENTIONS

12236 ■ Super Zoo
World Pet Association (WPA)
11801 Pierce St., Ste. 200
Riverside, CA 92505
Ph: (626)447-2222
Co. E-mail: info@wpamail.org
URL: http://www.worldpetassociation.org
Contact: Victor Mason, President
E-mail: vic.mason@wpamail.org
URL(s): ww.superzoo.org/about/

Frequency: Annual. **Description:** Includes demonstrations, speakers, product exhibits, hobbyist shows and rides for children and contests. **Audience:** Industry professionals. **Principal Exhibits:** Includes demonstrations, speakers, product exhibits, hobbyist shows and rides for children and contests. **Telecommunication Services:** info@SuperZoo.org.

CONSULTANTS

12237 ■ Turnkey Inc.
58 Parker Rd.
Houston, TX 77076
Ph: (713)695-6846
URL: http://turn-keyinc.com
Contact: Al Locker, Jr., President
E-mail: al@turn-keyinc.com

Description: Provides pet care facility design and build services including project consulting, business plans, site selection, construction, remodeling, and custom design. **Founded:** 1960.

FRANCHISES AND BUSINESS OPPORTUNITIES

12238 ■ Multi-Menu
2852 boul Le Corbusier
Laval, QC, Canada H7L 3S1
Ph: (450)682-5056
Free: 877-462-0056
Fax: (450)682-5054
Co. E-mail: multimenu@multimenu.ca
URL: http://www.multimenu.ca
Contact: Gerald Tremblay, Contact
X (Twitter): x.com/MultiMenuen

Description: Retailer of pet food and accessories for dogs, cats and birds. **No. of Franchise Units:** 160. **Founded:** 1996. **Equity Capital Needed:** $5,000-$15,000. **Training:** Ongoing support and training.

12239 ■ Petland Inc.
250 Riverside St.
Chillicothe, OH 45601
Ph: (740)775-2464
Free: 800-221-5935
Co. E-mail: customerservice@petlandinc.com
URL: http://petland.com
Contact: Cynthia G. Schumaker, Contact
Facebook: www.facebook.com/PetlandUSA
X (Twitter): x.com/petland
Instagram: www.instagram.com/petlandusa
YouTube: www.youtube.com/channel/UChOvesecYqmTGHnes1irMCA

Description: Retailer of pets, pet supplies, and pet-related services. **Founded:** 1967. **Financial Assistance:** Yes **Managerial Assistance:** Field representative visits to retail store.

12240 ■ Pets Are Inn Inc.
7625 Metro Blvd., Ste. 120
Minneapolis, MN 55439
Ph: (952)944-8298
Co. E-mail: mpls_office@petsareinn.com
URL: http://www.petsareinn.com
Contact: Ann Platt, Owner

Description: Chain of pet franchise. **Founded:** 1982. **Franchised:** 1982. **Equity Capital Needed:** $23,400-$56,650. **Franchise Fee:** $10,000- $35,000. **Royalty Fee:** 10% of the first $5,000 of gross sales revenue ; 7.5% of the next $5,000 of gross sales revenue ; 5% of all gross sales revenue in excess of $10,000. **Financial Assistance:** Yes

12241 ■ PSP Group, LLC
Franchise Group, Inc. (FRG)
29493 7 Mile Rd.
Livonia, MI 48152-1909
Ph: (740)363-2222

Free: 800-790-3863
Fax: (800)880-6432
URL: http://www.franchisegrp.com
Facebook: www.facebook.com/petsuppliesplus
X (Twitter): x.com/petsuppliesplus
Instagram: www.instagram.com/petsuppliesplus

Description: Distributor of pet supplies and provider of grooming services. **No. of Operating Units:** 315. **Founded:** 1988. **Franchised:** 2002. **Equity Capital Needed:** $549,400-$1,097,400. **Franchise Fee:** $49,900. **Royalty Fee:** 2-3%. **Financial Assistance:** Yes **Training:** Provides 4 weeks training at headquarters.

12242 ■ Ruffin's Pet Centres
209 Queen St.
Campbelltown, NSW 2560, Australia
Ph: 61 905 774-6373
URL: http://www.ruffinspet.com
Facebook: www.facebook.com/RuffinsPetCentre
YouTube: www.youtube.com/channel/UCUnSelHRnIz0oYsqlk7BKTA/videos
Pinterest: www.pinterest.com/ruffinspet

Description: Operator of pet center and also retailer of pet foods and accessories. **Founded:** 1981. **Training:** As required.

12243 ■ Ryan's Pet Food Inc.
70 Don Caster Ave.
Thornhill, ON, Canada L3T 1L3
Ph: (905)771-9227
Co. E-mail: gpf78@globalpetfoods.com
URL: http://globalpetfoods.com
Contact: Dino Fragaglia, President
X (Twitter): x.com/GlobalPetFoods

Description: Chain of pet food stores. **Founded:** 1979. **Financial Assistance:** No **Training:** Yes.

12244 ■ Wild Bird Centers of America Inc.
4611 C Sangamore Rd.
Bethesda, MD 20816

Description: Franchises "one-stop" bird seed and supply stores. **Founded:** 1985. **Franchised:** 1990. **Financial Assistance:** No **Training:** Yes.

12245 ■ Wild Birds Unlimited Inc. (WBU)
11711 N College Ave., Ste. 146
Carmel, IN 46032
Ph: (317)571-7100
Free: 888-730-7108
Co. E-mail: wbu@a11y.com
URL: http://www.wbu.com
Contact: Jim Carpenter, President
Facebook: www.facebook.com/wildbirdsunlimited
Linkedin: www.linkedin.com/company/wild-birds-unlimited-inc.
X (Twitter): x.com/wbu_inc
Instagram: www.instagram.com/wildbirdsunlimited
YouTube: www.youtube.com/user/WildBirdsUnlimited

Description: Retail outlets for birdseed, bird feeders and gift items. **Founded:** 1981. **Franchise Fee:** $25,000. **Training:** Training available 6 days at headquarters, 2 days at franchisee's location, 5 days at annual meeting and ongoing support.

START-UP INFORMATION

12246 ■ *"Pet Project Pays Off' in Small Business Opportunities (March 2011)*
Description: Pet sitting goes big time, reporting $40 million annually for Camp Bow Wow. Pet-oriented businesses are recession-proof because of Americans love for pampering their canines. **Availability:** Online.

ASSOCIATIONS AND OTHER ORGANIZATIONS

12247 ■ Care.com, Inc.
IAC Inc.
  201 Jones Rd.
  Waltham, MA 02451
Ph: (212)314-7300
Co. E-mail: info@iac.com
URL: http://www.iac.com
Contact: Tim Allen, President
Facebook: www.facebook.com/caredotcom
X (Twitter): x.com/caredotcom
Instagram: www.instagram.com/caredotcom
YouTube: www.youtube.com/user/caredotcom
Pinterest: www.pinterest.com/caredotcom
Description: Provider of an online search platform for caregiving, housekeeping services, and pet sitting services.

12248 ■ National Association of Professional Pet Sitters (NAPPS)
1120 Rte. 73, Ste. 200
  Mount Laurel, NJ 08054
Ph: (856)439-0324
Co. E-mail: napps@petsitters.org
URL: http://petsitters.org
Contact: Amy Sparrow, President
Facebook: www.facebook.com/TheNAPPS
X (Twitter): x.com/TheNAPPS
Instagram: www.instagram.com/the_napps
YouTube: www.youtube.com/channel/UCNeb5zv
  dxvqDCJY-WmuJQ-g
Description: Owners or employees of pet-sitting services. Promotes professional and ethical standards in pet sitting and fosters cooperation among members of the pet-care industry. Serves as a network for the exchange of ideas and information on pet sitting and current industry practices. Disseminates information educating the pet-owning public on the advantages of leaving pets in a home environment and how to choose a reliable sitter. **Founded:** 1989. **Educational Activities:** NAPPS Annual Conference Virtually (Annual). **Geographic Preference:** National.

12249 ■ Pet Care Trust (PCT)
3465 Box Hill Corporate Ctr Dr., Ste. H
  Abingdon, MD 21009
Ph: (443)921-2825
Co. E-mail: csmall@msp-amc.com
URL: http://www.petsintheclassroom.org
Contact: Chris Clevers, President
Facebook: www.facebook.com/PetsintheClassroom
Instagram: www.instagram.com/petsintheclassroom
YouTube: www.youtube.com/user/petcaretrust
Pinterest: www.pinterest.com/classroompets
Description: Promotes public understanding regarding the value of and the right to enjoy companion animals; enhances society's knowledge about companion animals through research and education; promotes professionalism among members of the companion animal community. Compiles statistics. Provides animals in the classroom teacher education workshops. **Founded:** 1990. **Geographic Preference:** National.

12250 ■ Pet Sitters Associates LLC
2924 Northwinds Dr.
  Eau Claire, WI 54701
Free: 855-737-1598
Co. E-mail: info@petsitllc.com
URL: http://www.petsitllc.com
Description: Member organization providing pet business insurance coverage, listings in their nationwide pet director, and access to a library of resources to help grow your business. **Founded:** 1998.

12251 ■ Pet Sitters International (PSI)
213 E Dalton Rd.
  King, NC 27021
Ph: (336)983-9222
Co. E-mail: info@petsit.com
URL: http://www.petsit.com
Contact: Michelle Boles, Manager
X (Twitter): x.com/petsittersintl
Instagram: www.instagram.com/petsittersinternational
YouTube: www.youtube.com/user/PetSittersIntl
Pinterest: www.pinterest.com/petsittersintl
Description: Represents professional pet sitters. Serves as an educational organization for professional pet sitters and advocates of at-home pet care. Promotes, recognizes and supports excellence in pet sitting. Provides a forum of communication for members who share a common vision of excellence in at-home pet care. **Founded:** 1994. **Publications:** *Pet Owner's World* (Semiannual); *The World of Professional Pet Sitting* (Bimonthly). **Educational Activities:** Quest for Excellence (Annual). **Awards:** PSI Pet Sitter of the Year (Annual). **Geographic Preference:** Multinational.

12252 ■ Professional United Pet Sitters (PUPS)
Kingsland, GA 31548
Ph: (267)225-3799
Co. E-mail: mail@petsits.com
URL: http://petsits.com
Description: Promotes the pet sitting industry by fostering an online environment of collaboration, professionalism, and support for experienced pet sitters as well as individuals looking to launch a pet sitting business. Offers information on a variety of pet sitting topics, as well as a library of pet sitting and dog walking resources that include business start-up guides, pet sitting contracts and forms, analysis tools, guides, and more. **Founded:** 2005.

12253 ■ Rover.com [A Place for Rover]
711 Capitol Way S, Ste. 204
  Olympia, WA 98501
Free: 888-453-7889
URL: http://www.rover.com
Contact: Brent Turner, President
Facebook: www.facebook.com/RoverDotCom
X (Twitter): x.com/roverdotcom
Instagram: www.instagram.com/roverdotcom
Pinterest: www.pinterest.com/roverdotcom
Description: A network of pet sitters and dog walkers. The company offers a platform in which consumers can connect pet parents with service providers for their pets, including in-home dog boarding, pet sitting, dog walking, or day care. **Founded:** 2011.

12254 ■ Wag Labs Inc. [Wag!]
55 Francisco St., Ste. 360
  San Francisco, CA 94133
Ph: (707)324-4219
URL: http://wagwalking.com
Contact: Adam Storm, President
Facebook: www.facebook.com/WagWalking/
X (Twitter): twitter.com/wagwalking
Instagram: www.instagram.com/wag/
Description: Developer of a mobile app that allows pet caregivers to connect with pet parents. The platform allows pet parents to book specific pet care services including dog walking, pet sitting and boarding, advice from licensed pet experts, home visits, training, and access to other services.

REFERENCE WORKS

12255 ■ *"Bark Up The Right Tree" in Small Business Opportunities (Winter 2009)*
Released: February 09, 2016. **Description:** Profile of Central Bark, a daycare company catering to pets that offers franchise opportunities and is expanding rapidly despite the economic downturn; the company's growth strategy is also discussed.

12256 ■ *"Making It Work" in Pet Product News (Vol. 64, December 2010, No. 12, pp. S8)*
Ed: Kerri Chladnicek. **Description:** How focusing on service and flexibility allowed New Jersey-based pet supply store B.C. Woof to achieve success is discussed. B.C. Woof began as a pet-sitting business which eventually concentrated on natural foods. Aside from conducting a do-it-yourself approach in food formulation for customers, B.C. Woof has also been guiding customers on nutrients they need for their pets. **Availability:** Print; Online.

12257 ■ *Minding Your Dog Business: A Practical Guide to Business Success for Dog Professionals*
Pub: Dogwise Publishing
Ed: Veronica Boutelle. **Released:** 2010. **Price:** $11.95, Shopworn, plus S&H. **Description:** Setting up and running a successful dog-related business is an

achievement in itself, but the real test is to build success and growth for the long haul. **Availability:** E-book; Print.

12258 ■ *"Paid Petsitting in Homes Is Illegal in New York. That's News to Some Sitters"* in *The New York Times (July 21, 2017)*

URL(s): www.nytimes.com/2017/07/21/nyregion/dogsitting-new-york-illegal.html

Ed: Sarah Maslin Nir. **Released:** July 21, 2017. **Description:** People running petsitting services in NYC where shocked to discover that their businesses were not legal, since they must be licensed to board animals and in a permitted kennel, which is not allowed in the city. However, the rules for this are rarely enforced, unless a complaint is filed. This is starting to change with the advent of large, app-based pet-care businesses and law makers are cracking down on these services. The app owners are not backing down. **Availability:** Online.

12259 ■ *Pet Business 101: From Puppy School to Running With the Big Dogs*

Ed: Brooke Faulkner. **Released:** September 10, 2018. **Description:** Provides business tips for entrepreneurs looking to break into the pet industry to open a business such as behavior training, grooming, or pet sitting. **Availability:** Online.

12260 ■ *"Pet Care Services in Rhode Island to be Taxed' in Pet Product News (Vol. 66, September 2012, No. 9, pp. 1)*

Description: Pet care services will be subject to a 7 percent sales tax in Rhode Island starting October 1, 2012, potentially resulting in more expensive pet boardng, grooming, sitting, and training. The tax is part of the state's efforts to close a $120 million budget deficit. How pet supplies retailers have reacted to the new tax is presented. **Availability:** Online.

12261 ■ *"Professional Help: Cross That Off Your To-Do List' in Inc. (November 2007, pp. 89-90, 92)*

Ed: Alison Stein Wellner. **Description:** Small business owners are finding that it pays to hire someone to takeover the personal tasks of daily living, including hiring a personal assistant, chauffeur, chef, stylist, pet caregiver, or concierge service. **Availability:** Online.

12262 ■ *"Understanding Pet Sitting Certifications" in TimeToPet Blog (Feb. 25, 2022)*

URL(s): www.timetopet.com/blog/understanding-pet-sitting-certifications

Ed: Michael Grenier. **Released:** February 25, 2022. **Description:** Provides information on pet sitting and dog walking certifications and licenses. Discusses the differences and whether you need either for your business. **Availability:** Online.

STATISTICAL SOURCES

12263 ■ *2022 Pet Sitting and Dog Walking Services Global Market Size & Growth Report with Updated Forecasts*

URL(s): www.marketresearch.com/Kentley-Insights-v4035/Pet-Sitting-Dog-Walking-Services-32298745/

Price: $295. **Description:** Report that utilizes in-depth survey results from companies that offer pet sitting and dog walking services. Provides a complete worldwide view of market size, revenue, growth, and forecasts across 216 countries. **Availability:** Download.

12264 ■ *Dog Walking Services in the US - Industry Market Research Report*

URL(s): www.marketresearch.com/IBISWorld-v2487/Dog-Walking-Services-Research-30066349/

Price: $1,020. **Description:** Report covering the scope, size, disposition and growth of the dog walking industry including the key sensitivities and success factors. Also included are five-year industry forecasts, growth rates and an analysis of the industry key players and their market shares. **Availability:** Download.

12265 ■ *Pet Sitting Market Research Report by Pet Type, Application, Region - Global Forecast to 2027 - Cumulative Impact of COVID-19*

URL(s): www.marketresearch.com/360iResearch-v4164/Pet-Sitting-Research-Type-Application-32399462/

Price: $4,949. **Description:** Research report that categorizes the pet sitting industry to forecast the revenues and analyze trends based on pet type. **Availability:** PDF.

CONSULTANTS

12266 ■ **The Dog Gurus**
1312 Harvard St.
Houston, TX 77008-4245
Ph: (732)997-6537
Co. E-mail: info@thedoggurus.com
URL: http://thedoggurus.com

Description: Pet care business consulting and staff training company. Offers programs, resources, and training to help you start your own pet-sitting business. **Founded:** 2013.

12267 ■ **Jump Consulting**
2550 E Rose Garden Ln., No. 73225
Phoenix, AZ 85050
URL: http://jumpconsulting.net
Contact: Bella Vasta, Owner Founder
E-mail: bella@jumpconsulting.net
Facebook: www.facebook.com/jumpconsulting
Instagram: www.instagram.com/bellavasta
YouTube: www.youtube.com/channel/UCpQaXkTp44_9A2CZxHCWrjQ

Description: Helps pet-sitting business owners start or expand their businesses. **Founded:** 2007.

FRANCHISES AND BUSINESS OPPORTUNITIES

12268 ■ **Central Bark Doggy Day Care**
PO Box 14217
West Allis, WI 53214
Free: 866-799-2275
Fax: (866)398-1349
Co. E-mail: info@centralbarkusa.com
URL: http://www.centralbarkusa.com/doggy-day-care
Contact: Jackie Jordan, Co-Founder
Facebook: www.facebook.com/CentralBarkUSA
YouTube: www.youtube.com/channel/UC4zP6mOXoxlC0rRy-4_JAOA

Description: Provider of personalized pet care in an environment that is clean, safe and fun as an alternative to kennel boarding and lonely days at home. **Founded:** 1997. **Equity Capital Needed:** $255,118-$389,046. **Franchise Fee:** $40,000. **Royalty Fee:** 0.05. **Training:** Yes.

12269 ■ **Dogs Love Running! Inc.**
7 Miami Ct.
Naperville, IL 60563
Free: 877-738-7786
URL: http://www.dogsloverunning.com
Contact: John Reh, President

Description: Provider of pet care services including pet exercise, pet sitting, pet boarding, and pet day care. Specializes in helping your pets live longer and behave better through exercise. **Founded:** 2007.

12270 ■ **Fetch! Pet Care**
Livonia, MI
Free: 866-338-2463
Co. E-mail: hello@fetchpetcare.com
URL: http://www.fetchpetcare.com
Facebook: www.facebook.com/FetchHomeOffice
Linkedin: www.linkedin.com/company/fetchhomeoffice
X (Twitter): x.com/fetchpetcare
Instagram: www.instagram.com/fetchpetcare

Description: Home pet care service provider. Services include puppy sitting, dog walking, pet sitting, overnight pet care, pet taxi, and pet medical administration. **Founded:** 2002.

12271 ■ **In Home Pet Services Inc. (IHPS)**
88-25 247th St.
Bellerose, NY 11426
Ph: (718)347-7387
Co. E-mail: info@inhomepetservices.com
URL: http://www.inhomepetservices.com
Contact: Robyn Elman, President
Facebook: www.facebook.com/InHomePetServices

Description: Firm provides pet sitting and dog walking services. **Founded:** 2001. **Training:** Includes 1 week training at headquarters.

12272 ■ **Kitten Sittin'**
116 W Wildwood St.
Tampa, FL 33613
Ph: (813)846-6717
Co. E-mail: info@kittensittin.biz
URL: http://www.kittensittin.biz

Description: Professional cat sitting service providing in-home cat care, including consultation, standard care visits, and medication administration.

12273 ■ **Out-U-Go! Pet Care Services Inc.**
7020 W N Ave.
Chicago, IL 60707
Free: 877-268-8846
URL: http://outugo.com
X (Twitter): x.com/outugo

Description: Provider of custom dog walking and pet sitting services. Additional services include cat sitting, house sitting, puppy care, and critter care. **Founded:** 1996.

12274 ■ **Pawsitively Spoiled**
2601 Sherman Dr.
Kokomo, IN 46902
Ph: (765)860-5983
Co. E-mail: pawsitivelyspoiledrjtc@gmail.com
URL: http://pawsitivelyspoiled.net
Contact: Nicole Peel, Member
Facebook: www.facebook.com/PawsitivelySpoiled
Instagram: www.instagram.com/pawsitivelyspoiledkokomo

Description: Pet franchise offering pet sitting and dog walking services.

12275 ■ **Pet Assist**
15 Moose Hill Pky.
Sharon, MA 02067
Ph: (781)806-5722
Co. E-mail: service@petassist.com
URL: http://petassist.com

Description: Pet care franchise offering pet sitting, dog walking, cat sitting, and pet waste cleanup services.

12276 ■ **Pet Sit Pros Inc. (PSP)**
1951 S Magnolia Ave.
Long Beach, CA 90806
Free: 855-856-7387
URL: http://www.petsitpros.com
Contact: Jay Goldfisher, Chief Executive Officer
E-mail: jay@petsitpros.com
Facebook: www.facebook.com/PetSitPros

Description: A full-service professional pet sitting and dog walking business that treats the health, safety, and well-being of your pet as its top priority. Offers a variety of in-home pet care services.

12277 ■ **Pet-Tenders**
PO Box 23622
San Diego, CA 92193
Ph: (619)298-3033
Co. E-mail: info@pet-tenders.com
URL: http://pet-tenders.com
Contact: Lou Gurnick, President

Description: In-home and house sitting service. **No. of Franchise Units: 4. No. of Company-Owned Units: 1. Founded:** 1983. **Franchised:** 1990. **Equity Capital Needed:** $2,000-$5,400. **Franchise Fee:** $8,500. **Financial Assistance:** Yes **Training:** Yes.

12278 ■ Preppy Pet
57 W Michigan St.
  Orlando, FL 32806
Ph: (407)420-1060
Fax: (407)420-1068
URL: http://preppypet.com
Facebook: www.facebook.com/preppypet
Description: Operator of dog care center. **Founded:**
2003. **Franchised:** 2006. **Equity Capital Needed:**
$75,000 - $150,000. **Franchise Fee:** $19,900 -
$34,500. **Royalty Fee:** 6.5% Monthly. **Financial Assistance:** No **Training:** Yes.

12279 ■ Sitter4Paws
436 Coronado Ter., Ste. 2
  Los Angeles, CA 90026
Ph: (323)316-0673

Co. E-mail: info@sitter4paws.com
URL: http://www.sitter4paws.com
Contact: Alexandra Alvarez, Founder
Facebook: www.facebook.com/Sitter
  4PawsLosAngeles
X (Twitter): x.com/sitter4paws
Description: A professional pet sitting and dog walking service. **Founded:** 2009.

12280 ■ Snaggle Foot LLC
CO
Free: 877-609-7387
Co. E-mail: info@snagglefoot.com
URL: http://www.snagglefoot.com
Facebook: www.facebook.com/SnaggleFootCorp
X (Twitter): twitter.com/SnaggleFootCorp
Pinterest: www.pinterest.com/SnaggleFootPetCare

Description: Provider of professional pet care and
pet sitting services. Each independently owned and
operated franchise sets their own prices and range of
services. **Founded:** 2008.

PUBLICATIONS

**12281 ■ *The Balanced Pet Sitter: What You
Wish You Knew Before Starting Your Pet
Care Business***
Ed: Renee Stilson. **Released:** November 13, 2019.
Price: $9.99, Kindle; $18.99, Paperback. **Description:** Comprehensive handbook providing a complete
set of practical tools that take the reader from startup
to success as they begin their pet care business.
Availability: E-book; Print.

REFERENCE WORKS

12282 ■ *"Interactive Stores a Big Part of Borders' Turnaround Plan" in Crain's Detroit Business (Vol. 24, February 18, 2008, No. 7, pp. 4)*
Pub: Crain Communications Inc.
Contact: Barry Asin, President
Ed: Nathan Skid. **Description:** Borders Group Inc. is using digital technology and interactive media as a part of the firm's turnaround plan. The digital store will allow shoppers to create CDs, download audio books, publish their own works, print photos and search family genealogy. **Availability:** Online.

STATISTICAL SOURCES

12283 ■ *Photofinishing Industry in the US - Market Research Report*
URL(s): www.ibisworld.com/united-states/market-research-reports/photofinishing-industry/

Price: $925. **Description:** Downloadable report analyzing current and future trends in the photofinishing industry. **Availability:** Download.

12284 ■ *RMA Annual Statement Studies*
Pub: Risk Management Association
Contact: Nancy Foster, President
Released: Annual. **Description:** Contains composite balance sheets and income statements for more than 360 industries, including the accounting, auditing, and bookkeeping industries. Also contains five years of comparative historical data for discerning trends. Includes 16 commonly used ratios, computed for most of the size groupings for nearly every industry.

LIBRARIES

12285 ■ **International Center of Photography (ICP) - Library**
79 Essex St.
New York, NY 10002

Ph: (212)857-0000
Co. E-mail: info@icp.org
URL: http://www.icp.org
Contact: Jeffrey A. Rosen, President
Facebook: www.facebook.com/internationalcenterofphotography
X (Twitter): x.com/icphotog
Instagram: www.instagram.com/icp
YouTube: www.youtube.com/user/icplive

Description: Presents exhibitions of the finest works of some of the most talented photographers in the world; features an extensive array of historical and contemporary photographs, revealing the power and diversity of the medium from documentary photography to digital imaging. **Scope:** Visual culture. **Services:** Open to staff, faculty, students, members, researchers by appointment. **Founded:** 1974. **Holdings:** 20,000 volumes; 50 periodical; photography; photobooks; bibliography. **Awards:** ICP Infinity Awards for Special Presentation (Annual). **Geographic Preference:** Multinational.

START-UP INFORMATION

12286 ■ *Setting Up a Successful Photography Business*
Released: August 12, 2020. **Description:** A guide on how to set up a professional photographer business. Contains checklists, charts, and business templates. **Availability:** E-book.

ASSOCIATIONS AND OTHER ORGANIZATIONS

12287 ■ American Photographic Artists (APA)
9190 W Olympic Blvd. No.212
Beverly Hills, CA 90212-3540
Ph: (323)933-1631
Co. E-mail: membershiprep@apanational.org
URL: http://la.apanational.org
Contact: Patti Silverstein, Director
E-mail: director@apa-la.com
Facebook: www.facebook.com/APALosAngeles
X (Twitter): x.com/apanational
Instagram: www.instagram.com/apa_la
Description: Enhances dialogue among professional photographers and their clients. Suggests standards and business practices to improve the quality of professional photography; and acts as a forum for discussion of problems and solutions. Conducts discussion groups. **Founded:** 1981. **Publications:** *1999 APA National Photographer's Survey Report.* **Geographic Preference:** National.

12288 ■ American Society of Media Photographers (ASMP)
Four Embarcadero Ctr., Ste. 1400
San Francisco, CA 94111
Free: 844-762-3386
Co. E-mail: info@asmp.org
URL: http://www.asmp.org
Contact: Michael Shay, Chairman of the Board
E-mail: chair@asmp-board.org
Facebook: www.facebook.com/asmpnational
Linkedin: www.linkedin.com/company/asmp-the
 -american-society-of-media-photographers
X (Twitter): x.com/asmp
Instagram: www.instagram.com/asmpnational
Description: Professional society of freelance photographers. Works to evolve trade practices for photographers in communications fields. Provides business information to photographers and their potential clients; promotes ethics and rights of members. Holds educational programs and seminars. Compiles statistics. **Founded:** 1944. **Publications:** *American Society of Media Photographers-- Membership Directory; ASMP Bulletin* (Quarterly). **Geographic Preference:** National.

12289 ■ American Society of Photographers (ASP)
Greenville, SC
URL: http://asofp.com
Contact: Ella Carlson, President

Facebook: www.facebook.com/aspexcellence
X (Twitter): x.com/aspexcellence
Instagram: www.instagram.com/aspexcellence
Description: Photographers who have earned the degrees of Master of Photography, Photographic Craftsman, and Photographic Specialist through the Professional Photographers of America. Sponsors annual traveling exhibit of Masters' photographs and annual National Student Competition and Exhibit. **Founded:** 1937. **Awards:** ASP Service Award (Annual). **Geographic Preference:** National.

12290 ■ Canadian Association of Professional Image Creators (CAPIC) [L'Association Canadienne des Createurs Professionnels de L'Image]
RPO Galleria
 Toronto, ON, Canada M6H 4H7
Ph: (416)462-3677
Free: 888-252-2742
Co. E-mail: info@capic.org
URL: http://www.capic.org
Contact: Hai Au Bui, President
E-mail: natlpresident@capic.org
Facebook: www.facebook.com/CAPICnational
X (Twitter): x.com/CapicNational
Instagram: www.instagram.com/capicnational
Description: Photographers and illustrators employed in communications. Promotes professional and artistic advancement of members. Represents members' interests before industrial organizations; formulates standards of ethics and practice for members. **Founded:** 1978. **Geographic Preference:** National.

12291 ■ Photographic Society of America (PSA)
8241 S Walker Ave., Ste. 104
 Oklahoma City, OK 73139
Ph: (405)843-1437
Free: 855-772-4636
URL: http://psa-photo.org
Contact: J. R. Schnelzer, President
E-mail: prespsa@psa-photo.org
X (Twitter): x.com/PSA_Photo
Instagram: www.instagram.com/photographicsocie
 tyofamerica
Description: Camera clubs; amateur, advanced amateur photographers. Sponsors competitions. Conducts slide and print contests, provides instruction slide sets, slide analysis, print portfolios, and other technical services. **Founded:** 1919. **Publications:** *PSA Journal* (Monthly). **Geographic Preference:** National.

12292 ■ Pictorial Photographers of America (PPA)
147-10 41st Ave.
 Flushing, NY 11355
Ph: (917)403-5023
URL: http://www.ppa-photoclub.org
Contact: Kathryn Buck, President
E-mail: kathryn@ppa-photoclub.org

Facebook: www.facebook.com/PictorialPho
 tographersOfAmerica
X (Twitter): x.com/PPAPhotoclub
Instagram: www.instagram.com/ppaphotoclub
Description: Amateur and professional photographers. Aids members in perfecting their photographic techniques. Sponsors individual print and slide analysis, exhibitions, and field trips. **Founded:** 1916. **Publications:** *Light and Shade* (Monthly). **Educational Activities:** Pictorial Photographers of America Dinner. **Geographic Preference:** National.

12293 ■ Professional Photographers of America (PPA)
229 Peachtree St. NE, Ste. 2300
 Atlanta, GA 30303
Free: 800-786-6277
Co. E-mail: csc@ppa.com
URL: http://www.ppa.com
Contact: Jeffrey Dachowski, President
E-mail: jdachowskippa@mail.com
Facebook: www.facebook.com/OurPPA
Linkedin: www.linkedin.com/company/ourppa
X (Twitter): x.com/ourppa
Instagram: www.instagram.com/ourPPA
YouTube: www.youtube.com/c/ourppa
Description: Trade association for professional photographers. Offers education, resources, and industry standards. **Founded:** 1880. **Publications:** *Who's Who in Professional Imaging* (Annual); *PP of A Today* (Monthly).

12294 ■ Professional Women Photographers (PWP)
119 W 72nd St., No. 223
 New York, NY 10023
Co. E-mail: pwp@pwponline.org
URL: http://www.pwponline.org
Contact: Megan Green, President
Facebook: www.facebook.com/
 ProfessionalWomenPhotographers
X (Twitter): x.com/PWPonlineorg
Description: Women professional photographers; other interested individuals. Supports and promotes the work of women photographers through the sharing of ideas, resources, and experience. **Founded:** 1975. **Publications:** *PWP Newsletter* (10/year). **Awards:** PWP Student Awards (Annual). **Geographic Preference:** National.

12295 ■ San Francisco Camerawork (SFC) - SF Camerawork Video Archive
Fort Mason Ctr., 2 Marina Blvd., Bldg. A
 San Francisco, CA 94123
Ph: (415)487-1011
Co. E-mail: info@sfcamerawork.org
URL: http://sfcamerawork.org
Contact: Michelle Branch, President
Facebook: www.facebook.com/sfcamerawork
Linkedin: www.linkedin.com/company/sf-camerawork
X (Twitter): x.com/sfcamerawork
Instagram: www.instagram.com/sfcamerawork
YouTube: www.youtube.com/channel/UC
 _YWTsT8NGq9eygrcHjH__Q

Description: Represents nationally recognized artists' organization whose purpose is to stimulate dialogue, encourage inquiry, and communicate ideas about contemporary photography and related media through a variety of artistic and professional programs. **Scope:** Photography; art theory. **Founded:** 1974. **Holdings:** Audio and video recordings. **Publications:** *Camerawork: A Journal of Photographic Arts* (Semiannual). **Geographic Preference:** National.

REFERENCE WORKS

12296 ■ *4 Things Commercial Photographers Need to Discuss with Their Small Business Clients*
Ed: Natalia Robert. **Description:** Provides key factors for commercial photographers to discuss with your small business client during an initial consultation so that conflicts can be avoided. **Availability:** Online.

12297 ■ *"9 Photographers Share What They Love (and Hate) about Their Jobs" in Business News Daily (October 5, 2018)*
URL(s): www.businessnewsdaily.com/8295-pho tography-pros-cons.html
Ed: Saige Driver. **Released:** October 05, 2018. **Description:** Nine different interviews of professional photographers asking what they love and hate about their jobs. **Availability:** Online.

12298 ■ *"10 Dirty Little Secrets of the Commerical Photography Industry" in PetaPixel (July 24, 2019)*
Ed: Jamie Piper. **Released:** July 24, 2019. **Description:** An honest discussion of the 10 downfalls of commercial photography which will help anyone going into this field to be prepared for what goes on behind the scenes.

12299 ■ *A Complete Guide to Commercial Photography*
Ed: Amrish Mudgal. **Released:** November 05, 2019. **Description:** Discusses what commercial photography is and what it isn't as well as the types of commercial photography, equipment needed, and tips to get started. **Availability:** Online.

12300 ■ *"CPI Corp. Acquires Assets of Bella Pictures" in Benzinga.com (January 28, 2011)*
Pub: PR Newswire Association LLC.
Description: CPI Corporation acquired assets of Bella Pictures Inc., a leading provider of branded wedding photography services. Details of the acquisition are explained. **Availability:** Online.

12301 ■ *"Education Required to Be a Photographer" in Chron (July 24, 2018)*
Ed: Elvis Michael. **Released:** July 24, 2018. **Description:** Although there are no standard education requirements for many photography careers, formal training or education can increase job opportunities and salaries. This article details how to gain experience in the photography field and what type of salary you can expect. **Availability:** Online.

12302 ■ *How to Break Into the Commercial Photography Business*
Ed: Tracy Stefan. **Description:** Discusses the types of assignments commercial photographers work on and provides six steps to follow to start your business. **Availability:** Online.

12303 ■ *"How to Get Professional Product Photography on a Small Business Budget" in 99 Designs*
Description: Small businesses can get professional-looking product shots without blowing the budget. This article details how to photograph products on a small business budget. **Availability:** Online.

12304 ■ *"How to Get Started in Commercial Photography" in Photography Spark (April 27, 2019)*
Ed: Jamie Piper. **Released:** April 27, 2019. **Description:** Offers steps to get you started offering commercial photography to clients on a scale that is unintimidating, manageable, and scalable. **Availability:** Online.

12305 ■ *How to Price Commercial Photography*
Description: A guide to commercial photography pricing including information on pricing your time, pricing number of photographs, and pricing different types of photography. **Availability:** Online.

12306 ■ *How to Set Up a Commercial Photography Business*
Description: Commercial photography is a broad category with a huge playing field. This article discusses different types of photography, such as headshots, product, event, stock, fine art, and how to decide what to specialize in. **Availability:** Online.

12307 ■ *"How Technology Has Changed News Photography over 40 Years" in The New York Times (September 27, 2017)*
URL(s): www.nytimes.com/2017/09/27/technology/ personaltech/how-technology-has-changed-news -photography-over-40-years.html
Ed: Jim Wilson. **Released:** September 27, 2017. **Description:** New York Times photographer, Jim Wilson, discusses the technology he uses to shoot photos. **Availability:** Online.

12308 ■ *Marketing 101 for Commercial Photographers*
Description: One of the more challenging aspects of being a commercial photographer is the marketing, which is ironic because these photographers work in a commercial marketing environment, yet reaching prospective clients can seem difficult. This article discusses marketing options to consider for your business. **Availability:** Online.

12309 ■ *The New Lighting for Product Photography: The Digital Photographer's Step-by-Step Guide to Sculpting with Light*
Ed: Allison Earnest. **Released:** August 15, 2019. **Price:** $32.49, Paperback. **Description:** A guide for commercial photographers on how to successfully set up and design images for publications, websites, and advertising campaigns. **Availability:** Print.

12310 ■ *"What Is Commercial Photography? Great Tips to Get Started" in Expert Photography*
Description: Discusses what commercial photography is and how to get started in this business. Includes information on common types of photography shoots, what gear to use, trends, marketing, and working with clients. **Availability:** Online.

TRADE PERIODICALS

12311 ■ *Applied Arts Magazine*
Pub: Applied Arts Inc.
Facebook: www.facebook.com/AppliedArtsMag
Linkedin: www.linkedin.com/company/applied-arts -magazine
X (Twitter): x.com/appliedarts
Instagram: www.instagram.com/appliedartsmag
Pinterest: www.pinterest.ca/Appliedartsawards
Ed: Will Novosedlik. **Released:** Semiannual; Summer and Winter. **Price:** $60, for 1 year print & digital US; $75, for 1 year print & digital international; C$40, for print & digital only Canada 1 years; C$19.99, for 1 year digital only USA & international; $19.99, for 1 year digital only Canada; $30, for cover price per annual; C$9.99, for single issue online. **Description:** Visual communication arts magazine for designers, art directors, photographers, illustrators and other professionals in related fields. **Availability:** Print; Online.

12312 ■ *ICG Magazine*
Pub: International Cinematographers Guild
Contact: John Lindley, President
URL(s): www.icgmagazine.com/web
Facebook: www.facebook.com/theicgmag
X (Twitter): x.com/theicgmag
Instagram: www.instagram.com/theicgmag

Ed: David Geffner. **Released:** Monthly **Price:** $24, for 1 year online 10 digital issues; $88, Single issue. **Description:** Trade magazine covering cinematography lighting techniques in film and video. **Availability:** Print; PDF; Download; Online.

12313 ■ *The Photo Review*
Pub: The Photo Review
URL(s): photoreview.org/publications/journal
Facebook: www.facebook.com/thephotoreview
Instagram: www.instagram.com/thephotoreview
Released: Quarterly **Price:** $90, U.S. for two years; $65, Canada and Mexico for one year; $120, Canada and Mexico for two years; $50, U.S. for one year; $75, for outside north America on year; $140, Two years for outside north America; $45, for per year in the US; $130, for two years Mexico; $70, for one year Mexico; $7, Single issue. **Description:** Photography journal. **Availability:** Print; PDF. **Telecommunication Services:** Email: info@thephotoreview. org .

12314 ■ *PSA Journal*
Pub: Photographic Society of America
Contact: J. R. Schnelzer, President
E-mail: prespsa@psa-photo.org
URL(s): psa-photo.org/page/journal
Released: Monthly **Price:** $10, for back Issues. **Description:** Photographic journal. **Availability:** Print; Download; PDF; Online.

12315 ■ *Shutterbug*
Pub: Shutterbug Productions
URL(s): www.shutterbug.com
Facebook: www.facebook.com/shutterbug
X (Twitter): x.com/shutterbug
Instagram: www.instagram.com/shutterbugpix
YouTube: www.youtube.com/shutterbug
Description: Photography magazine. **Availability:** Print; Online.

VIDEO/AUDIO MEDIA

12316 ■ *Professional on the Go: How Are Professional Photographers Getting in on the Real Estate Game?*
URL(s): www.spreaker.com/user/11226745/profes- sional-real-estate-photography
Ed: Chinwe Onyeagoro. **Released:** August 26, 2019. **Description:** Podcast discusses the growing niche of real estate photography.

12317 ■ *Turning Artistic Passion into Profit with Jonah Allen*
URL(s): www.eofire.com/podcast/jonahallen
Ed: Jon Lee Dumas. **Released:** June 18, 2024. **Description:** Podcast discusses entrepreneurship with an underwater photographer.

CONSULTANTS

12318 ■ *Carlson Communications Corp. (CC)*
276 W Main St.
Northborough, MA 01532
Ph: (508)217-9031
Co. E-mail: info@carlcomm.com
URL: http://www.carlcomm.com
Contact: Rich Carlson, President
Facebook: www.facebook.com/Carlson-Communica tions-82528201445
Linkedin: www.linkedin.com/company/carlson -communications
Description: Marketing firm provides web developments, graphic design, video, online advertising and more. **Founded:** 1989.

FRANCHISES AND BUSINESS OPPORTUNITIES

12319 ■ *A Day to Cherish Wedding Videos*
10174 S Memorial Dr.
South Jordan, UT 84095
Contact: Murry L. Dalton, Contact

Description: Wedding and special occasion videos. **Founded:** 2004. **Training:** Provides 6 days at headquarters and 2 days at franchisee's location with ongoing support.

12320 ■ EagleShotz
6621 Westerly Ln.
  Gainesville, GA 30506
Description: Event photography specializing in corporate, charity and celebrity golf events. **Founded:** 2007. **Training:** Offered at franchisee's location 24 hours with ongoing support.

12321 ■ Kids At Heart Photography
NJ
Ph: (609)587-0547
Co. E-mail: service.schoolphotos@gmail.com
URL: http://kidsatheartphotos.com
Description: School & sports photography. **Franchised:** 2006. **Training:** Yes.

12322 ■ Print Three Franchising Corp. (PTFC)
20 Great Gulf Dr., Unit 14
  Concord, ON, Canada L4K 0k7
Ph: (905)669-8895
Free: 800-335-5918
Fax: (905)669-0712
Co. E-mail: support@printthree.com
URL: http://www.printthree.com
Facebook: www.facebook.com/PrintThree
Linkedin: www.linkedin.com/company/print-three
  -franchising
X (Twitter): x.com/PrintThreeHQ
Instagram: www.instagram.com/printthreehq
YouTube: www.youtube.com/user/PrintThreeCorp
Description: Provider of commercial and digital printing services including web-to-print solutions, web services and professional marketing. **Founded:** 1970. **Training:** Yes.

12323 ■ TSS Photography
Candid Color Systems Inc. (CCS)
  1300 Metropolitan Ave.
  Oklahoma City, OK 73108
Ph: (405)947-8747
Fax: (405)951-7343
Co. E-mail: ccssupport@candid.com
URL: http://www.candid.com
Facebook: www.facebook.com/TSSPhotographyHQ
X (Twitter): x.com/tssphotos
Instagram: www.instagram.com/_tssphotography_
YouTube: www.youtube.com/channel/UC8J5iH4H
  1Rxs2fSMOf_UaCA
Pinterest: www.pinterest.com/tssphotography
Description: Firm provides photography services such as school, sports and event photography. **No. of Franchise Units:** 220. **Founded:** 1983. **Franchised:** 1984. **Equity Capital Needed:** $40,000-$60,000. **Financial Assistance:** Yes **Training:** Available 3 days at headquarters, 5 days at franchisee's location with ongoing support.

COMPUTERIZED DATABASES

12324 ■ Earthshots™
Digital Wisdom Inc.
  300 Jeanette Dr.
  Tappahannock, VA 22560-0011

Ph: (804)443-9000
Free: 800-800-8560
Co. E-mail: info@digitalwisdom.net
URL: http://digiwis.com
URL(s): www.digiwis.com/dwi_maps.htm
Price: $19, Single issue. **Availability:** Online. **Type:** Image.

12325 ■ Photography Collections Online
George Eastman House International Museum of
  Photography and Film
  900 E Ave.
  Rochester, NY 14607
Ph: (585)327-4800
Co. E-mail: info@eastman.org
URL: http://www.eastman.org
URL(s): www.eastman.org/photography
Availability: Online. **Type:** Directory; Bibliographic.

LIBRARIES

12326 ■ Ringling College of Art and Design - Kimbrough Memorial Library
2700 N Tamiami Trl.
  Sarasota, FL 34234
Ph: (941)351-5100
Co. E-mail: admissions@ringling.edu
URL: http://www.ringling.edu/news/dr-thompson-in
  -srq-daily
Contact: Dr. Larry Thompson, President
Description: Contains reference materials, journals, books, online materials, and video and audio materials on arts. **Scope:** Art history; interior design; graphic design; computer animation; photography; architecture; fine arts; decorative arts; illustration. **Services:** Interlibrary loan; copying; library open to artists and researchers. **Founded:** 1932. **Holdings:** 49,000 books; 110,000 art slides; 34 16mm films; 3,000 videocassettes and DVDs. **Subscriptions:** 320 journals and other serials.

12327 ■ San Francisco Public Library - Bernard Osher Foundation Art, Music & Recreation Center
100 Larkin St.
  San Francisco, CA 94102
Ph: (415)557-4525
Co. E-mail: artmusicrec@sfpl.org
URL: http://sfpl.org/locations/main-library/art-music
Scope: Visual arts; performing arts; music; sports and recreation. **Services:** Center open to the public. **Holdings:** Books; serials; scores; CD-ROMs; DVDs.

12328 ■ School of Visual Arts Library (SVA)
380 2nd Ave., 2nd Fl.
  New York, NY 10010
Ph: (212)592-2660
Co. E-mail: admissions@sva.edu
URL: http://sva.edu/life-at-sva/academic-life/library
Contact: Caitlin Kilgallen, Director
E-mail: ckilgallen@sva.edu
Facebook: www.facebook.com/SVALibrary
Instagram: www.instagram.com/svalibrary
Scope: Art and design study. **Services:** Copying; library open to students, faculty, staff, and alumni (METRO passes honored). **Founded:** 1978. **Holdings:** Figures not available.

12329 ■ SF Camerawork Reference Library
1150 25th St.
  San Francisco, CA 94107
Ph: (415)487-1011
Co. E-mail: info@sfcamerawork.org
URL: http://www.sfcamerawork.org
Contact: Michelle Branch, President
Facebook: www.facebook.com/sfcamerawork
X (Twitter): x.com/sfcamerawork
Instagram: www.instagram.com/sfcamerawork
Scope: Photography; contemporary art; art theory and criticism. **Services:** Library open for the reference use of students, educators, scholars, and visitors. **Founded:** 1974. **Holdings:** 3,500 volumes; 700 bound periodical volumes.

12330 ■ Smithsonian Institution - Smithsonian American Art Museum - National Portrait Gallery Library
Victor Bldg., Ste. 2100, 750 9th St. NW
  Washington, DC 20001
Ph: (202)633-8230
Fax: (202)633-8232
Co. E-mail: aapglibrary@si.edu
URL: http://library.si.edu/libraries/american-art-an
  d-portrait-gallery
Contact: Anne Evenhaugen, Librarian Head
Description: Supports the research of the Smithsonian American Art Museum, the National Portrait Gallery and the Archives of American Art, the AA/PG Library collection of 180,000 volumes, exhibition catalogs, catalogues raisonnes, serials and dissertations is concentrated in the area of American art, history, and biography with supportive materials on European art. **Scope:** American art, history; European art. **Founded:** 1937. **Holdings:** 23,000 works.

12331 ■ Springfield Art Museum Library (SAM)
1111 E Brookside Dr.
  Springfield, MO 65807
Ph: (417)837-5700
Co. E-mail: artmuseum@springfieldmo.gov
URL: http://www.sgfmuseum.org
Contact: Nick Nelson, Director
E-mail: nnelson@springfieldmo.gov
Facebook: www.facebook.com/sgfmuseum
X (Twitter): x.com/sgfmuseum
Instagram: www.instagram.com/sgfmuseum
Scope: Cultural; art. **Services:** Library open to the research by appointment only. **Founded:** 1926. **Holdings:** 10,000 art; 6,000 volumes. **Awards:** Springfield Art Museum Watercolor U.S.A. (Annual). **Geographic Preference:** National.

12332 ■ Walker Art Center - Library & Archives
725 Vineland Pl.
  Minneapolis, MN 55403
Ph: (612)375-7680
Co. E-mail: library.archives@walkerart.org
URL: http://walkerart.org/library-research
Contact: Jill Vuchetich, Archivist Head
Description: Library consists of Walker's artist's book collections. **Scope:** Art; history. **Services:** Copying; reference services; open to the public by appointment. **Founded:** 1950. **Subscriptions:** 150 journals 35,000 books; 1,800 art books; 5,200 artist files; 4,000 linear feet records; 6,000 audio, video, and film titles; 640,000 still images.

START-UP INFORMATION

12333 ■ *Setting Up a Successful Photography Business*
Released: August 12, 2020. **Description:** A guide on how to set up a professional photographer business. Contains checklists, charts, and business templates. **Availability:** E-book.

ASSOCIATIONS AND OTHER ORGANIZATIONS

12334 ■ **Photographic Society of America (PSA)**
8241 S Walker Ave., Ste. 104
Oklahoma City, OK 73139
Ph: (405)843-1437
Free: 855-772-4636
URL: http://psa-photo.org
Contact: J. R. Schnelzer, President
E-mail: prespsa@psa-photo.org
X (Twitter): x.com/PSA_Photo
Instagram: www.instagram.com/photographicsocie
  tyofamerica
Description: Camera clubs; amateur, advanced amateur photographers. Sponsors competitions. Conducts slide and print contests, provides instruction slide sets, slide analysis, print portfolios, and other technical services. **Founded:** 1919. **Publications:** *PSA Journal* (Monthly). **Geographic Preference:** National.

12335 ■ **Professional Photographers of America (PPA)**
229 Peachtree St. NE, Ste. 2300
Atlanta, GA 30303
Free: 800-786-6277
Co. E-mail: csc@ppa.com
URL: http://www.ppa.com
Contact: Jeffrey Dachowski, President
E-mail: jdachowskippa@mail.com
Facebook: www.facebook.com/OurPPA
Linkedin: www.linkedin.com/company/ourppa
X (Twitter): x.com/ourppa
Instagram: www.instagram.com/ourPPA
YouTube: www.youtube.com/c/ourppa
Description: Trade association for professional photographers. Offers education, resources, and industry standards. **Founded:** 1880. **Publications:** *Who's Who in Professional Imaging* (Annual); *PP of A Today* (Monthly).

12336 ■ **San Francisco Camerawork (SFC) - SF Camerawork Video Archive**
Fort Mason Ctr., 2 Marina Blvd., Bldg. A
San Francisco, CA 94123
Ph: (415)487-1011
Co. E-mail: info@sfcamerawork.org
URL: http://sfcamerawork.org
Contact: Michelle Branch, President
Facebook: www.facebook.com/sfcamerawork
Linkedin: www.linkedin.com/company/sf-camerawork
X (Twitter): x.com/sfcamerawork

Instagram: www.instagram.com/sfcamerawork
YouTube: www.youtube.com/channel/UC
  _YWTsT8NGq9eygrcHjH__Q

Description: Represents nationally recognized artists' organization whose purpose is to stimulate dialogue, encourage inquiry, and communicate ideas about contemporary photography and related media through a variety of artistic and professional programs. **Scope:** Photography; art theory. **Founded:** 1974. **Holdings:** Audio and video recordings. **Publications:** *Camerawork: A Journal of Photographic Arts* (Semiannual). **Geographic Preference:** National.

12337 ■ **Wedding and Portrait Photographers International (WPPI)**
Las Vegas, NV
Co. E-mail: info@wppievents.com
URL: http://wppiexpo.com
Facebook: www.facebook.com/wppievents
X (Twitter): x.com/RfWPPI
Instagram: www.instagram.com/wppievents
YouTube: www.youtube.com/user/rfwppi

Description: Represents wedding portrait and digital photographers and photographers employed at general photography studios. Promotes high artistic and technical standards in wedding photography. **Publications:** *Wedding Photography Monthly* (Monthly); *Marketing and Technical Manual* (Quarterly); *Rangefinder* (Monthly); *Wedding Photographer* (Monthly); *WPPI Photography Monthly* (Monthly). **Educational Activities:** Wedding and Portrait Photographers International Competition (Semiannual). **Awards:** Honors of excellence Award (Annual). **Geographic Preference:** Multinational.

REFERENCE WORKS

12338 ■ *5 Must Ask Questions Before You Open a Photography Studio*
Ed: Sarah Petty. **Description:** Based on real-life experience, this article discusses five important questions to ask yourself before you open a photography studio. **Availability:** Online.

12339 ■ *6 Tips That Will Increase Your Photo Studio Production*
Description: Discusses six specific tips to help you increase your photo studio production including maximizing your workspace, hiring and training helpful staff, developing efficient workflows, using workflow software, using effective lighting techniques, and minimizing the time between photography and image QA. **Availability:** Online.

12340 ■ *26 Things I Wish I'd Known Before Starting My Photography Business*
Ed: Lauren Lim. **Released:** March 18, 2020. **Description:** Mistakes are learning opportunities in disguise. The author shares 26 things learned from running her own photography business that you can hopefully avoid. **Availability:** Online.

12341 ■ *The Complete Guide to Building a Photography Studio*
Ed: Anand Paul. **Released:** January 09, 2020. **Description:** Setting up your own photography studio is a significant investment. This article explains how to set up your own photography studio, which provides for complete autonomy for your photography work process. **Availability:** Online.

12342 ■ *"A Complete Marketing Plan for the Photography Studio I Just Got Beautiful Portraits From" in The Better Marketing Brief (April 7, 2020)*
Ed: Paul Myers. **Released:** April 07, 2020. **Description:** Provides detailed information to help you formulate a complete marketing plan for you photography business studio including information on business philosophy, consumer feedback, segmentation and marketing, and branding. **Availability:** Online.

12343 ■ *"CPI Corp. Acquires Assets of Bella Pictures" in Benzinga.com (January 28, 2011)*
Pub: PR Newswire Association LLC.
Description: CPI Corporation acquired assets of Bella Pictures Inc., a leading provider of branded wedding photography services. Details of the acquisition are explained. **Availability:** Online.

12344 ■ *How to Build Your First Photography Studio*
Ed: Scott Choucino. **Released:** April 02, 2018. **Description:** Discusses factors to consider when looking for your first photography studio space including location, space, access, facilities, equipment, and cost. **Availability:** Online.

12345 ■ *"How Mini Sessions Can Make a Big Impact for Your Photography Studio" in H+H Color Lab Blog (December 15, 2016)*
Released: December 15, 2016. **Description:** Discusses how marketing mini sessions for your photography business can boost your overall client base and how to go about doing mini sessions. **Availability:** Online.

12346 ■ *How to Start My Own Picture Studio Store*
Description: The picture studio store business has multiple niche or specialty opportunities, such as pets, high school senior, graduation, children, babies, family, weddings, boudoir and business photography. This article discusses steps to take to start your own picture studio business. **Availability:** Online.

12347 ■ *"How to Start a Photography Business" in Photography Spark (July 3, 2020)*
Ed: Zach Prez. **Released:** July 03, 2020. **Description:** Discusses steps to take to start your own photography business including setting business goals, choosing the types of clients you'd like to work with, setting a budget for startup costs, setting revenue and schedule expectations, salary informa-

tion, creating a business plan, marketing, branding, business licensing and finances, and insurance. **Availability:** Online.

12348 ■ *"Small Business Loans for Photography Business"* in *SmartBiz (April 17, 2020)*

Released: April 17, 2020. **Description:** Provides information on how to obtain small business loans with low-cost financing so that you can obtain equipment for you business and can market your business to meet your goals. **Availability:** Online.

STATISTICAL SOURCES

12349 ■ *RMA Annual Statement Studies*
Pub: Risk Management Association
Contact: Nancy Foster, President

Released: Annual. **Description:** Contains composite balance sheets and income statements for more than 360 industries, including the accounting, auditing, and bookkeeping industries. Also contains five years of comparative historical data for discerning trends. Includes 16 commonly used ratios, computed for most of the size groupings for nearly every industry.

TRADE PERIODICALS

12350 ■ *The Polar Bear ROARS*
Pub: Polar Bear Alumni Association
Contact: Dick Wilson, President
URL(s): www.northhighpolarbears.org/roars.html
Released: Quarterly **Description:** Provides news of current events regarding reunion information, memories of alumni, history of school and articles about alumni and faculty. Recurring features include reports of reunions. **Availability:** Print.

12351 ■ *Popular Photography*
Pub: Bonnier LLC
Contact: David Ritchie, Co-Chief Executive Officer
URL(s): www.popphoto.com
Facebook: www.facebook.com/popularphotography
X (Twitter): x.com/popphoto
Instagram: www.instagram.com/popphotomag
Released: Monthly **Description:** Photography magazine. **Availability:** Print; Online.

12352 ■ *PSA Journal*
Pub: Photographic Society of America
Contact: J. R. Schnelzer, President
E-mail: prespsa@psa-photo.org
URL(s): psa-photo.org/page/journal
Released: Monthly **Price:** $10, for back Issues. **Description:** Photographic journal. **Availability:** Print; Download; PDF; Online.

12353 ■ *Shutterbug*
Pub: Shutterbug Productions
URL(s): www.shutterbug.com
Facebook: www.facebook.com/shutterbug
X (Twitter): x.com/shutterbug
Instagram: www.instagram.com/shutterbugpix
YouTube: www.youtube.com/shutterbug
Description: Photography magazine. **Availability:** Print; Online.

TRADE SHOWS AND CONVENTIONS

12354 ■ Wedding and Portrait Photographers International Competition
Wedding and Portrait Photographers International (WPPI)
Las Vegas, NV
Co. E-mail: info@wppievents.com
URL: http://wppiexpo.com
URL(s): www.wppionline.com/competitions.shtml

Frequency: Semiannual. **Audience:** Wedding and portrait photographers.

FRANCHISES AND BUSINESS OPPORTUNITIES

12355 ■ Glamour Shots Licensing Inc. (GS)
1300 Metropolitan Ave.
 Oklahoma City, OK 73108
Free: 800-750-0494
Co. E-mail: gsservice@glamourshots.com
URL: http://glamourshots.com
Contact: Jack E. Counts, Jr., Contact
Facebook: www.facebook.com/glamourshots
X (Twitter): x.com/GlamourShots
Instagram: www.instagram.com/glamourshots
YouTube: www.youtube.com/channel/
 UC8bwQvEWZeqUKsM-Y9vRXAA
Pinterest: www.pinterest.com/glamourshots
Description: High fashion photography studio. **No. of Franchise Units:** 40.0. **Franchised:** 1992. **Equity Capital Needed:** $218,420 - $264,950. **Royalty Fee:** 0.03. **Financial Assistance:** Yes **Training:** Yes.

12356 ■ Lil' Angels Photography
PO Box 2426
 Cleveland, TN 37320-2426
Ph: (404)567-1704
URL: http://lilangelsphoto.com
Contact: Paul Kimball, Manager
E-mail: pkimball@cpq.com
Facebook: www.facebook.com/lilangelspho
 tofranchise
Description: Manufacturer of studio equipment. **Founded:** 1996. **Franchised:** 1998. **Training:** 6 days provided at corporate headquarters, 2 days of onsite, and regional and annual convention included.

12357 ■ Lil'Pals Pet Photography
1007 Savoy Pl.
 Fredericksburg, VA 22401
Ph: (540)903-3895
URL: http://www.bestshotgroup.com/lil-pals-prices
Contact: Teri Beardsley, Owner
E-mail: teri@bestshotgroup.com
Description: Firm provides photographic services. **Training:** Yes.

12358 ■ PoGoPix Studios
4916 139th Ave. SE, Unit 218
 Calgary, AB, Canada T2Z 0G4
Ph: (403)269-6790
URL: http://www.pogopix.ca
Facebook: www.facebook.com/pages/category/Local
 -Business
Description: Operator of professional portrait photography studio. **Founded:** 2000.

12359 ■ TSS Photography
Candid Color Systems Inc. (CCS)
 1300 Metropolitan Ave.
 Oklahoma City, OK 73108
Ph: (405)947-8747
Fax: (405)951-7343
Co. E-mail: ccssupport@candid.com
URL: http://www.candid.com
Facebook: www.facebook.com/TSSPhotographyHQ
X (Twitter): x.com/tssphotos
Instagram: www.instagram.com/_tssphotography_
YouTube: www.youtube.com/channel/UC8J5iH4H
 1Rxs2fSMOf_UaCA
Pinterest: www.pinterest.com/tssphotography
Description: Firm provides photography services such as school, sports and event photography. **No. of Franchise Units:** 220. **Founded:** 1983. **Franchised:** 1984. **Equity Capital Needed:** $40,000-$60,000. **Financial Assistance:** Yes **Training:** Available 3 days at headquarters, 5 days at franchisee's location with ongoing support.

COMPUTERIZED DATABASES

12360 ■ *Earthshots™*
Digital Wisdom Inc.
 300 Jeanette Dr.
 Tappahannock, VA 22560-0011
Ph: (804)443-9000
Free: 800-800-8560
Co. E-mail: info@digitalwisdom.net
URL: http://digiwis.com
URL(s): www.digiwis.com/dwi_maps.htm
Price: $19, Single issue. **Availability:** Online. **Type:** Image.

LIBRARIES

12361 ■ George Eastman Museum - Richard And Ronay Menschel Library
900 E Ave.
 Rochester, NY 14607
Ph: (585)327-4800
Co. E-mail: info@eastman.org
URL: http://www.eastman.org
Contact: Bruce Barnes, Director
Facebook: www.facebook.com/georgeeas
 tmanmuseum
X (Twitter): x.com/EastmanMuseum
Instagram: www.instagram.com/eastmanmuseum
YouTube: www.youtube.com/c/GeorgeEas
 tmanMuseum
Description: Museum collects and interprets images, films and equipment in the disciplines of photography and motion picture. **Scope:** Local History. **Services:** Copying; Open to the public by an appointment. **Founded:** 1947. **Holdings:** Books; Periodicals; photography; Moving images; Manuscripts; Papers; Monographs; Ephemera. **Publications:** *George Eastman House Interactive Catalog.*

12362 ■ International Center of Photography (ICP) - Library
79 Essex St.
 New York, NY 10002
Ph: (212)857-0000
Co. E-mail: info@icp.org
URL: http://www.icp.org
Contact: Jeffrey A. Rosen, President
Facebook: www.facebook.com/internationalcen
 terofphotography
X (Twitter): x.com/icphotog
Instagram: www.instagram.com/icp
YouTube: www.youtube.com/user/icplive
Description: Presents exhibitions of the finest works of some of the most talented photographers in the world; features an extensive array of historical and contemporary photographs, revealing the power and diversity of the medium from documentary photography to digital imaging. **Scope:** Visual culture. **Services:** Open to staff, faculty, students, members, researchers by appointment. **Founded:** 1974. **Holdings:** 20,000 volumes; 50 periodical; photography; photobooks; bibliography. **Awards:** ICP Infinity Awards for Special Presentation (Annual). **Geographic Preference:** Multinational.

12363 ■ University of Arizona - Center for Creative Photography Archives
1030 N Olive Rd.
 Tucson, AZ 85721
URL: http://ccp.arizona.edu/collections/archives
 -manuscripts
Description: Publishes archive, bibliography and guides. Also publishes books about or by photographers as well as exhibition catalogs and announcements. Offers posters, T-shirts, books and cards. Reaches market through direct mail and wholesalers. Does not accept unsolicited manuscripts. **Scope:** Educational material. **Services:** Interlibrary loan; copying; archives open to the public. **Founded:** 1975. **Holdings:** Photographs; archival material; manuscript; rare books.

START-UP INFORMATION

12364 ■ *"Former Boxer Lou Savarese Fits Into New Business Role" in Houston Business Journal (Vol. 40, January 8, 2010, No. 35, pp. 1)*
Pub: Houston Business Journal
Contact: Bob Charlet, President
E-mail: bcharlet@bizjournals.com

Ed: Greg Barr. **Description:** Lou Savarese explains how the lessons he learned as a professional boxer help him to manage his new business venture, a gym called Savarese Fight Gym. Customers who desire to learn boxing and to stay fit like a boxer comprise the fitness center's target market. **Availability:** Print; Online.

12365 ■ *"Land Swap Key to Ending Royal Oak Project Impasse" in Crain's Detroit Business (Vol. 25, June 8, 2009, No. 23, pp. 20)*
Pub: Crain Communications Inc.
Contact: Barry Asin, President

Ed: Chad Halcom. **Description:** Details of the new construction of the LA Fitness health club near Woodward and Washington Avenues in Royal Oak, Michigan are discussed. **Availability:** Online.

12366 ■ *"Pump Up the Profits" in Small Business Opportunities (Summer 2010)*
Pub: Harris Publishing, Inc.
Contact: Janet Chase, Contact

Description: New fitness franchise offers customized personal training at bargain rates. Profile of Alan Katz, president of EduFit, a concept that allows small groups of people to workout with customized training is provided.

12367 ■ *"Riches In Recreation" in Small Business Opportunities (March 2011)*
Pub: Harris Publishing, Inc.
Contact: Janet Chase, Contact

Description: Making money is child's play thanks to new gym concept that makes parents and franchisors happy. Profile of Great Play, the franchised children's gym is provided. **Availability:** Download; PDF; Online.

ASSOCIATIONS AND OTHER ORGANIZATIONS

12368 ■ **Aerobics and Fitness Association of America (AFAA)**
355 E Germann Rd., Bldg. 6
Gilbert, AZ 85297
Free: 800-446-2322
Co. E-mail: customerservice@afaa.com
URL: http://www.afaa.com
Facebook: www.facebook.com/afaa.fit
Linkedin: www.linkedin.com/company/2224802
X (Twitter): x.com/afaa_fit
Instagram: www.instagram.com/afaa_certified
YouTube: www.youtube.com/user/AFAAfitness

Pinterest: www.pinterest.com/afaa
Description: Promotes safety and excellence in exercise instruction. Offers certifications in Primary Group Exercise, Personal Trainer, Advanced Personal Trainer, Yoga, Step, KickBoxing, Emergency Response, Fitness Practitioner, and the New Wave Workout. **Founded:** 1983. **Geographic Preference:** Multinational.

12369 ■ **American Council on Exercise (ACE)**
4933 Paramount Dr.
San Diego, CA 92123
Ph: (858)576-6500
Free: 888-825-3636
Fax: (858)576-6564
Co. E-mail: support@acefitness.org
URL: http://www.acefitness.org
Contact: Scott Goudeseune, Chief Executive Officer
Facebook: www.facebook.com/ACEfitness
Linkedin: www.linkedin.com/company/american-council-on-exercise
X (Twitter): x.com/acefitness
Instagram: www.instagram.com/acefitness
Pinterest: www.pinterest.com/acefitness
Description: Promotes the benefits of physical activity and protects consumers against unsafe and ineffective fitness products and instruction. Sponsors university-based exercise science research and testing that targets fitness products and trends. Sets standards for fitness professionals. **Founded:** 1985. **Publications:** *ACE FitnessMatters* (Bimonthly); *ACE ProSource* (Monthly). **Educational Activities:** Annual NIRSA Conference and Campus Rec & Wellness Expo (Annual). **Geographic Preference:** National.

12370 ■ **American Sports Builders Association (ASBA)**
2331 Rock Spring Rd.
Forest Hill, MD 21050
Ph: (443)640-1042
Free: 866-501-2722
Co. E-mail: info@sportsbuilders.org
URL: http://sportsbuilders.org
Contact: Fred Stringfellow, Executive Director
Facebook: www.facebook.com/sportsbuilders
Linkedin: www.linkedin.com/company/sportsbuilders
X (Twitter): x.com/sportsbuilders

Description: Contractors who install running tracks, synthetic turf fields, tennis courts and indoor sports surfaces; manufacturers who supply basic materials for construction; accessory suppliers, designers, architects, and consultants of facilities. Provides guidelines for tennis court construction, running track construction, fencing, synthetic turf field construction and lighting. Offers certification and awards programs. **Founded:** 1965. **Publications:** *American Sports Builders Association--Membership Directory* (Annual); *Buyers Guide for Tennis Court Construction; Running Tracks: A Construction & Maintenance Manual; Tennis and Track Construction Guidelines* (Periodic); *U.S. Tennis Court and Track Builders Association Membership Directory* (Annual). **Educational Activities:** ASBA Technical Meeting (Annual); ASBA Winter Meeting (Annual). **Geographic Preference:** National.

12371 ■ **Aquatic Exercise Association (AEA) [World Aquatic Coalition, Inc.]**
1618 Ellis St.
Brunswick, GA 31520
Ph: (912)289-3559
Free: 888-232-9283
Co. E-mail: info@aeawave.org
URL: http://aeawave.org
Contact: Angie Proctor, Executive Director
E-mail: angie@aeawave.org
Facebook: www.facebook.com/aeawave
Description: Aquatic fitness instructors and therapists, pool and club owners, recreation departments, and manufacturers of pool products and services. Fosters members' professional development; serves as a resource center for services and products related to the aquatic fitness and therapy industries. Compiles and disseminates information through educational events and networking opportunities; offers certification to aquatic exercise instructors. Conducts educational programs. **Founded:** 1984. **Publications:** *AKWA Magazine* (Bimonthly); *Aquatic Therapy and Fitness Research Journal* (Semiannual). **Educational Activities:** International Aquatic Fitness Conference (IAFC) (Annual). **Awards:** AEA Global Award for Aquatic Fitness Professional (Annual). **Geographic Preference:** Multinational.

12372 ■ **Exercise Safety Association (ESA)**
PO Box 554
Dana Point, CA 92629
Ph: (407)951-6222
Co. E-mail: askesaoffice@gmail.com
URL: http://www.exercisesafety.com
Description: Fitness instructors, personal trainers, health spas, YMCAs, community recreation departments, and hospital wellness programs. Purposes are: to improve the qualifications of exercise instructors; to train instructors to develop safe exercise programs that will help people avoid injury while exercising; to prepare instructors for national certification. Offers training in aerobics and exercise and on the physiological aspects of exercise. Conducts exercise safety and research programs. Sponsors charitable program; maintains speakers' bureau. Offers instructor placement services. **Founded:** 1978. **Publications:** *ESA Member Directory* (Annual); *Exercise Safety Association Newsletter* (Bimonthly). **Awards:** ESA STAR Certification. **Geographic Preference:** National.

12373 ■ **The Fitness Business Association (AFS)**
121 Washington Ave., N 4th Fl.
Minneapolis, MN 55401
Ph: (612)213-2375
Fax: (612)217-8659
Co. E-mail: info@fbafitness.com
URL: http://www.fbafitness.com
Contact: Josh Leve, Chief Executive Officer

Description: Strives to provide an array of business-specific products, services, and benefits to fitness studio owners in order to help them more effectively manage and grow their businesses. **Founded:** 2019.

12374 ■ IDEA Health and Fitness Association
10190 Telesis Ct.
 San Diego, CA 92121
Ph: (858)535-8979
Free: 800-999-4332
Co. E-mail: contact@ideafit.com
URL: http://www.ideafit.com
Contact: Kathie Davis, Co-Founder
Facebook: www.facebook.com/ideafit
Linkedin: www.linkedin.com/company/idea-health-&-fi
 tness
X (Twitter): x.com/ideafit
Instagram: www.instagram.com/ideafit
YouTube: www.youtube.com/ideafitness
Pinterest: www.pinterest.com/ideafit

Description: Provides continuing education for fitness professionals including; fitness instructors, personal trainers, program directors, and club/studio owners. Offers workshops for continuing education credits. **Founded:** 1982. **Publications:** *IDEA Fitness Journal* (Quarterly); *IDEA Health & Fitness Source* (10/year); *IDEA Personal Trainer* (10/year); *Trainer Success* (5/year). **Educational Activities:** IDEA World Fitness and Personal Trainer Convention (Annual). **Awards:** IDEA Fitness Instructor of the Year (Annual); IDEA Personal Trainer of the Year Award (Annual); IDEA Fitness Leader of the Year (Annual); Fitness Instructor of the Year (Annual); Personal Trainer of the Year (Annual); Program Director of the Year (Annual). **Geographic Preference:** National.

12375 ■ Institut Canadien de la Recherche sur la Condition Physique et le Mode de Vie (ICRCP) [Canadian Fitness and Lifestyle Research Institute (CFLRI)]
230 - 2733 Lancaster Rd.
 Ottawa, ON, Canada K1B 0A9
Ph: (613)233-5528
Fax: (613)233-5536
Co. E-mail: contact.us.cflri@cflri.ca
URL: http://cflri.ca
Contact: Dr. Christine Cameron, President
Facebook: www.facebook.com/cflri
X (Twitter): x.com/cflri_icrcp
Instagram: www.instagram.com/cflri_icrcp

Description: Conducts research on physical activities in Canada and distributes information about physical activity. **Scope:** A national research organization concerned with monitoring the physically activity levels of Canadians and sharing knowledge about the importance of leading healthy, active lifestyles. **Founded:** 1980. **Publications:** *Physical Activity Monitor* (Annual); *The Research File* (Monthly). **Geographic Preference:** National.

12376 ■ International Federation of Bodybuilding and Fitness (IFBB)
C/ Dublin, no 39 I 28232 Europolis, Las Rozas
 28232 Madrid, Spain
Ph: 34 91 5352819
Co. E-mail: contact@ifbb.com
URL: http://www.ifbb.com
Contact: Dr. Rafael Santonja, President
Facebook: www.facebook.com/International.Federa
 tion.Body.Building.Fitness
X (Twitter): x.com/IFBB_OFFICIAL
Instagram: www.instagram.com/ifbb_official
YouTube: www.youtube.com/channel/
 UCohZwr7VQLSkXBjAD83T-og

Description: National federations of bodybuilding enthusiasts united to promote better health and fitness through bodybuilding, physical culture, proper nutrition, and weight training. Conducts research dealing with physical culture, bodybuilding, weight training, nutrition, sports injuries, and sports medicine. Compiles statistics on the results of competitions and evaluates judges' accuracy. Sanctions amateur, professional, and open world and continental bodybuilding competitions for men and women. Sponsors the Mr./Ms. Olympia contests and the World Amateur Men's and Women's Championships. Establishes rules and appoints qualified judges. **Founded:** 1948. **Publications:** *Congress Report* (Annual); *Flex* (Monthly); *Scientific Athletic Reports* (Periodic). **Geographic Preference:** Multinational.

12377 ■ International Fitness Professionals Association (IFPA)
PO Box 46248
 Tampa, FL 33646
Ph: (813)979-1925
Free: 800-785-1924
Fax: (813)979-1978
Co. E-mail: info@ifpa-fitness.com
URL: http://www.ifpa-fitness.com
Contact: Dr. James Bell, Chief Executive Officer
Facebook: www.facebook.com/ifpa.fitness
X (Twitter): x.com/ifpa_inc

Description: Promotes the interests of fitness professionals. Fosters the learning experience and professional recognition of fitness instructors. Provides practical and scientifically based health and fitness information to members. **Founded:** 1994. **Geographic Preference:** Multinational.

12378 ■ International Health, Racquet and Sportsclub Association (IHRSA) - Library
70 Fargo St.
 Boston, MA 02210
Ph: (617)951-0055
Free: 800-228-4772
Co. E-mail: info@ihrsa.org
URL: http://www.IHRSA.org
Contact: Chris Craytor, Chairman of the Board
Facebook: www.facebook.com/IHRSA
Linkedin: www.linkedin.com/company/ihrsa
X (Twitter): x.com/IHRSA
Instagram: www.instagram.com/ihrsa
YouTube: www.youtube.com/user/IHRSALive

Description: Promotes the continued growth of the health, racket, and sports club industry in 70 countries. Aids member clubs in making educated business decisions. Sets standards for club management; offers group purchasing program. **Scope:** Fitness industry. **Founded:** 1980. **Holdings:** Figures not available. **Publications:** *Club Business International (CBI)* (Monthly); *Profiles of Success* (Annual). **Educational Activities:** IHRSA International Convention & Trade Show (Annual).

12379 ■ International Physical Fitness Association, Inc. (IPFA)
MI
URL: http://www.ipfaus.com

Description: Physical fitness centers. Facilitates the transfer of individual memberships from one member club to another. **Founded:** 1960. **Publications:** *IPFA Roster* (Annual). **Geographic Preference:** National.

12380 ■ Medical Fitness Association (MFA)
PO Box 3602
 Pinehurst, NC 28374
Ph: (910)420-8610
Free: 844-312-3541
Fax: (910)420-8733
URL: http://www.medicalfitness.org
Contact: David Flench, President
Facebook: www.facebook.com/medicalfitness
Linkedin: www.linkedin.com/company/medical-fitness
 -association
X (Twitter): x.com/MFAGlobal

Description: Promotes strengthened operations and standards in fitness centers maintained by hospitals and organizations; works to improve the financial viability of fitness facilities. **Founded:** 1991. **Publications:** *Medical Fitness Centers, 5th Edition* (Biennial); *Medical Fitness Centers, 4th Edition* (Biennial); *Re: Source, Journal of the Medical Fitness Association* (Quarterly). **Educational Activities:** Strategies for Today's Healthcare Leaders (Annual); Strategies for Today's Healthcare Leaders (Annual). **Awards:** Facility Awards (Annual); MFA Distinguished Service Award (Annual); Medical Fitness Association Regional Rising Star Award (Annual); Hank Boerner Pioneer Award (Annual). **Geographic Preference:** National.

12381 ■ National Association for Health and Fitness (NAHF)
Albany, NY
Ph: (518)456-1058
Co. E-mail: aerobic2@aol.com
URL: http://www.physicalfitness.org

Facebook: www.facebook.com/people/National
 -Association-for-Health-and-Fitness-NAHF/1000
 64548706188
X (Twitter): x.com/nahfofficial

Description: State governor's fitness councils, corporations/nonprofit and public sector organizations, and individuals. Works with states to establish and maintain governor's councils and or state coalitions on physical fitness and health. Seeks to promote the quality of life for individuals in the U.S. through physical fitness, sports, and healthy lifestyles. Conducts Annual National conference; regional meetings; trainings/technical assistance, networking, national newsletters, resources and members benefits program, and Annual Gold Star Awards program. **Founded:** 1979. **Educational Activities:** Global Employee Health & Fitness Month (GEHFM). **Geographic Preference:** National.

12382 ■ National Federation of Professional Trainers (NFPT)
PO Box 4579
 Lafayette, IN 47901
Free: 800-729-6378
Co. E-mail: info@nfpt.com
URL: http://www.nfpt.com
Contact: April Pattee, Director, Human Resources
 Director, Customer Service
Facebook: www.facebook.com/TheNFPT
X (Twitter): x.com/TheNFPT
YouTube: www.youtube.com/channel/
 UCsFBSznPQPvivGSYKDK2NVg

Description: Offers organizational certification credentials for consumer recognition of competence; provides certified affiliates with ongoing education; establishes a network of support, and provides professional products and services to trainers and consumers. **Founded:** 1978. **Geographic Preference:** National.

12383 ■ Physical and Health Education Canada (PHE Canada)
2451 Riverside Dr.
 Ottawa, ON, Canada K1H 7X7
Ph: (613)523-1348
Free: 888-837-7678
Fax: (613)523-1206
Co. E-mail: info@phecanada.ca
URL: http://www.phecanada.ca
Contact: Dr. Jo Sheppard, President
Facebook: www.facebook.com/PHECanada
X (Twitter): x.com/PHECanada
Instagram: www.instagram.com/phecanada
YouTube: www.youtube.com/user/phecanada

Description: Promotes the long-term health benefits of health and active lifestyles. Seeks to facilitate the professional development of members and teachers, teacher education in the education field. **Founded:** 1933. **Publications:** *Avante* (Triennial; 3/year); *Physical & Health Education Journal* (Quarterly); *In Touch* (Monthly). **Awards:** R. Tait Mckenzie Award (Annual); Dr. Andy Anderson Young Professional Awards (Annual); PHE Canada Student Award (Annual); North American Society Award (Annual); Dr. Andy Anderson Young Professional Award (Annual); North American Society Award (NAS) (Annual); PHE Canada National Award for Teaching Excellence in Physical Education (Annual); R. Tait McKenzie Honour Award; Quality Daily Physical Education Award Program (Annual). **Geographic Preference:** National.

12384 ■ Physical & Health Education Journal
2451 Riverside Dr.
 Ottawa, ON, Canada K1H 7X7
Ph: (613)523-1348
Free: 888-837-7678
Fax: (613)523-1206
Co. E-mail: info@phecanada.ca
URL: http://www.phecanada.ca
Contact: Dr. Jo Sheppard, President
URL(s): journal.phecanada.ca

Released: Quarterly **Price:** C$65, Individuals; C$175, Institutions. **Description:** Peer-reviewed journal covering physical and health education. **Availability:** Print; Online.

12385 ■ Society of Health and Physical Educators (SHAPE)

PO Box 225
 Annapolis Junction, MD 20701
Ph: (703)476-3400
Free: 800-213-7193
Fax: (703)476-9527
Co. E-mail: education@shapeamerica.org
URL: http://www.shapeamerica.org
Contact: Terri Drain, President
Facebook: www.facebook.com/SHAPEAmericaFB
X (Twitter): x.com/SHAPE_America
Instagram: www.instagram.com/shapeamerica
YouTube: www.youtube.com/SHAPEAmericaYT
Description: Students and educators in physical education, dance, health, athletics, safety education, recreation, and outdoor education. Works to improve its fields of education at all levels through such services as consultation, periodicals and special publications, leadership development, determination of standards, and research. Sponsors placement service. **Founded:** 1885. **Publications:** *AAHE Directory of Institutions Offering Undergraduate and Graduate Degree Programs in Health Education* (Biennial); *Dance Directory--Programs of Professional Preparation in American Colleges and Universities* (Biennial); *Journal of Physical Education, Recreation & Dance (JOPERD)* (9/year); *Directory of Institutions Offering Undergraduate and Graduate Degree Programs in Health Education* (Biennial); *American Journal of Health Education (AJHE)* (Bi-monthly); *Health Education Teaching Techniques Journal*; *The International Electronic Journal of Health Education* (Annual); *Directory of Professional Preparation Programs in Recreation, Parks, and Related Areas*; *AAHPERD Update* (Bimonthly); *Dance Film and Video Guide*; *AALReporter* (Quarterly); *UpdatePLUS* (Bimonthly); *Health Education*; *Strategies: A Journal for Physical and Sport Educators* (6/year); *Research Quarterly for Exercise and Sport (RQES)* (Quarterly). **Educational Activities:** The SHAPE America National Convention & Expo (Annual); SHAPE America National Convention & Expo (Annual); SHAPE America National Convention and Expo (Annual); National Association for Sport and Physical Education Convention (Annual). **Awards:** Ruth Abernathy Presidential Scholarship (Annual); Joy of Effort Award (Annual); Barbara A. Cooley Master's Scholarship (Annual); Bill Kane Undergraduate Scholarship (Annual); SHAPE America Graduate Student Research Award (Annual); SHAPE America Research Council Distinguished Service Award (Annual); Margie R. Hanson Elementary Physical Education Distinguished Service Award (Annual); Joy of Effort (Annual); SHAPE America Scholar Award (Annual); SHAPE America Teacher of the Year Award (Annual); Luther Halsey Gulick Award (Annual); SHAPE America Honor Award (Irregular); Mabel Lee Award (Annual); R. Tait McKenzie Award (Annual); William G. Anderson Award (Annual); SHAPE America Research Writing Award (Annual); SHAPE America College/University Physical Health Education Professional of the Year Awards (Annual); SHAPE America Major of the Year (Annual); Charles D. Henry Award (Annual); Ruth Abernathy Presidential Undergraduate Scholarship (Annual); SHAPE Hall of Fame Award (Annual); SHAPE America Guiding Woman in Sport (Annual); Rachel Bryant Award (Annual); SHAPE America Honor Awards (Annual). **Geographic Preference:** National.

12386 ■ United States Association of Independent Gymnastic Clubs (USAIGC)

PO Box 20937
 Floral Park, NY 11001
Ph: (212)227-9792
Co. E-mail: paul.spadaro@usaigc.com
URL: http://usaigc.com
Facebook: www.facebook.com/IGCUSA
X (Twitter): x.com/usaigc
Description: Gymnastic clubs and independent gymnastic club businesses offering professional class instruction and coaching; manufacturers of gymnastic equipment, apparel, and supplies. Aims to provide services, programs, and business advice to help gymnastic businesses to grow and prosper; locate organizations and individuals that will provide needed services for member's clientèle; further coaching knowledge; advance the U.S. in gymnastic competitions throughout the world. Offers certification for coaches and developmental-training programs for gymnasts to prepare for international competitions. **Founded:** 1973. **Publications:** *ClubNews* (Quarterly). **Educational Activities:** National Club Owners Meeting. **Geographic Preference:** National.

12387 ■ United States Competitive Aerobics Federation (USCAF)

8033 Sunset Blvd., No. 920
 Los Angeles, CA 90046
URL: http://www.sportaerobics-nac.com
Contact: Bri Zamorano, Contact
Description: Governs and organizes sports fitness and aerobic competitions for youth and adults. Seeks to maintain high standards and consistency in the sport. Conducts educational programs. **Founded:** 1989. **Geographic Preference:** National.

12388 ■ United States Water Fitness Association (USWFA) - Library

6415 N Ocean Blvd.
 Boynton Beach, FL 33435
Ph: (561)742-6000
Co. E-mail: info@uswfa.org
URL: http://www.uswfa.org
Contact: John R. Spannuth, Contact
Description: Promotes aquatics, including water fitness, through activities such as water aerobics, water walking, water running, and deep water exercise. Awards certification for water fitness instructors, program coordinators, and aquatic directors. **Scope:** Water fitness. **Founded:** 1989. **Holdings:** Figures not available. **Publications:** *National Aquatics Newsletter* (Quarterly). **Geographic Preference:** National.

12389 ■ USA Racquetball (USAR)

1661 Mesa Ave.
 Colorado Springs, CO 80906-2917
Ph: (719)635-5396
Fax: (719)635-0685
Co. E-mail: communications@usaracquetball.com
URL: http://www.usaracquetball.com
Contact: Mike Grisz, Executive Director
E-mail: ed@usaracquetball.com
Facebook: www.facebook.com/USARacquetball
X (Twitter): x.com/usaracquetball
Instagram: www.instagram.com/usaracquetball
YouTube: www.youtube.com/user/usaracquetball
Description: Represents racquetball players and enthusiasts. Promotes racquetball as a sport; organizes racquetball to be a self-governing sport of, by, and for the players; encourages building of facilities for the sport; conducts racquetball events including annual national and international tournaments. Maintains hall of fame, junior player programs, and charitable programs. **Founded:** 1969. **Publications:** *Racquetball Magazine* (Quarterly). **Educational Activities:** United States Racquetball Association Competition; High Performance Camp. **Awards:** Hall of Fame (Annual); Racquetball Hall of Fame (Irregular); Joe Sobek Outstanding Contribution Award (Annual); John Halverson Fair Play Award (Annual). **Geographic Preference:** National.

REFERENCE WORKS

12390 ■ "4 Tasty Ways to Work Nutrition into Your Fitness Business" in Glofox blog (February 14, 2019)

Ed: Eamonn Curley. **Released:** February 14, 2019. **Description:** For your gym members, nutrition can be one of the trickiest parts of hitting their fitness goals. Investing in the nutrition side of your fitness business can be extremely beneficial as it can work as a great retention tool and it can function as an additional revenue stream for your business. This article provides 4 ways you can begin implementing nutrition into your fitness business. **Availability:** Online.

12391 ■ "4 Types of Gym Employees Who Will Power Your Hybrid Success" in Glofox blog (October 26, 2020)

Ed: Eamonn Curley. **Released:** October 26, 2020. **Description:** As the fitness industry changes, so will the types of roles and skills needed to make a fitness business successful. Digital technology is here to stay and is only going to be more critical in the day-to-day running of a business, so you will need the right people on your team to take on this challenge. This article details the four types of employees you need to be successful. **Availability:** Online.

12392 ■ "5 Best Fitness Apps for Kids" in MentalUP (June 24, 2022)

URL(s): www.mentalup.co/blog/fitness-apps-for-kids
Released: June 24, 2022. **Description:** Discusses the benefits of five difference fitness apps that are aimed at children and their physical fitness. **Availability:** Online.

12393 ■ The 5 Best Personal Trainer Certifications

Description: Discusses five programs offering personal trainer certification. These programs are all lead by venerable fitness institutions, combining cutting-edge fitness science and methodologies with the convenience of distance learning. **Availability:** Online.

12394 ■ "5 Great Corporate Wellness Program Ideas for Your Fitness Business" in Glofox blog (August 14, 2019)

Ed: Eamonn Curley. **Released:** August 14, 2019. **Description:** With an emphasis on corporate workplace fitness programs, many companies now offer employees gym memberships or discounts. This article details steps a small fitness business can take to get involved in corporate wellness to add an additional revenue stream. **Availability:** Online.

12395 ■ "5 Things Every Fitness Founder Needs to Know About Gym Membership Sales" in Glofox blog (February 12, 2019)

Ed: Eamonn Curley. **Released:** February 12, 2019. **Description:** In fitness, you will not increase membership sales by being a pushy salesperson trying to close a deal. Instead, you need to approach sales with the potential member and their needs totally in mind. This article presents five key things to know to help increase gym membership sales for you fitness business. **Availability:** Online.

12396 ■ "6 Effective Yoga Marketing Tips to Take Your Studio to the Next Level" in Glofox blog (April 2, 2019)

Ed: Eamonn Curley. **Released:** April 02, 2019. **Description:** Whether you're a yoga teacher, opening a yoga studio or own an existing business, your marketing plan is crucial to growing your business. This article will go through 6 effective tips to help you grow your studio today. **Availability:** Online.

12397 ■ "6 Steps to Creating an Effective Gym Lead Management Process" in Glofox blog (July 23, 2019)

Ed: Eamonn Curley. **Released:** July 23, 2019. **Description:** Lead management is a process that bridges the gap between sales and marketing. This article details the importance, for fitness businesses, of taking leads and turning them into full paying members and provides six steps to an effective lead management process. **Availability:** Online.

12398 ■ "7 Fool-Proof Tactics to Boost Class Attendance in 2019" in Glofox blog (July 17, 2019)

Ed: Eamonn Curley. **Released:** July 17, 2019. **Description:** Fitness entrepreneurs rely on class attendance for business success. This article offers a variety of tactics that can boost class attendance. **Availability:** Online.

12399 ■ "7 Lead Generation Strategies for Gyms in Year One of Business" in Glofox blog (June 16, 2019)

Ed: Eamonn Curley. **Released:** June 16, 2019. **Description:** Discusses the basics of lead generation for gyms, the typical lead generation channels for a gym, and the best lead generation strategies for gyms in their first year of business. **Availability:** Online.

12400 ■ *"8 Practical Product and Service Ideas to Boost Gym Revenue" in Glofox blog (August 19, 2019)*
Ed: Lucy Connor. **Released:** August 22, 2019. **Description:** Discusses the importance of memberships to the fitness business, while pointing out that fitness businesses can't survive on revenue from memberships alone. This article discusses how to diversify into other revenue streams. **Availability:** Online.

12401 ■ *"9 Skills Your Trainers Need to Deliver an Incredible Online Experience" in Glofox blog (October 30, 2020)*
Ed: Jenny Weller. **Released:** October 30, 2020. **Description:** With a rise in on-demand and streaming fitness platforms, many studios and gyms are now running a hybrid fitness business, providing both onsite and online services. There are some essential skills that your team will need to deliver an incredible online experience for members. This article looks at the difference between running a class online vs. in person and how you can support your coaches with the transition. **Availability:** Online.

12402 ■ *"14 First Class Gym Event Ideas to Boost Your Acquisition and Retention" in Glofox blog (February 8, 2019)*
Ed: Eamonn Curley. **Released:** February 08, 2019. **Description:** Discusses the fact that offering a range of marketing strategies will boost your businesses. This article focuses on how you can use events to meet potential customers face to face. The author divides a list of gym event ideas into challenges, community, expertise, and brand awareness and goes through the steps you need to ensure you successfully implement your own gym event ideas. **Availability:** Online.

12403 ■ *"24 Fitness Marketing Strategies to Grow Your Gym or Training Business" in Maniac Marketing Blog (August 3, 2020)*
Ed: Joy Gendusa. **Released:** August 03, 2020. **Description:** Offers a variety of marketing strategies for gym and personal training businesses to utilize to help generate more new clients. **Availability:** Online.

12404 ■ *"Are You Using Fitness Content Marketing to Grow Your Business?" in Glofox blog (May 19, 2019)*
Ed: Eamonn Curley. **Released:** May 24, 2019. **Description:** Content marketing is one of the best ways to grow your fitness business organically. This article discusses reasons to invest in content marketing, fitness content marketing trends, the best content marketing platforms, and how to approach fitness content marketing. **Availability:** Online.

12405 ■ *Athletic Business--Buyers Guide Issue*
Pub: Athletic Business Publications Inc.
Contact: Jason Scott, Managing Editor
E-mail: jason@athleticbusiness.com
URL(s): www.athleticbusiness.com/directory
Description: Publication includes listings of about 2,000 manufacturers and suppliers of athletic equipment, trainers' supplies, conditioning and testing equipment, building and facility equipment, sports surfaces, aquatic components, and outdoor recreation equipment; related trade associations and consultants and other professionals in the field. **Entries include:** Name, address, phone, fax, e-mail address. **Arrangement:** Separate alphabetical sections for manufacturers and suppliers, associations, and professionals. **Indexes:** Product, advertiser name. **Availability:** Print; Online.

12406 ■ *"Because 10 Million Zumba Lovers Can't Be Wrong" in Inc. (Volume 32, December 2010, No. 10, pp. 106)*
Pub: Mansueto Ventures L.L.C.
Contact: Stephanie Mehta, Chief Executive Officer

Ed: Christine Lagorio. **Released:** December 01, 2010. **Description:** Profile of partners, Alberto Perez, Alberto Perlman, and Alberto Aghion, founders of Zumba, a form of dance used for fitness. **Availability:** Online.

12407 ■ *"'Biggest Loser' Adds Bit of Muscle to Local Economy" in Crain's Detroit Business (Vol. 26, January 4, 2010, No. 1, pp. 1)*
Pub: Crain Communications Inc.
Contact: Barry Asin, President
Ed: Chad Halcom. **Description:** NBC's weight-loss reality show, "The Biggest Loser" has helped the local economy and generated a new crop of local startup businesses due to past contestants that were from the Detroit area. **Availability:** Print; Online.

12408 ■ *"Cancer Survivor Becomes Marathoner, Author" in Business Journal-Serving Phoenix & the Valley of the Sun (Vol. 30, August 20, 2010, No. 50, pp. 1)*
Pub: Phoenix Business Journal
Contact: Alex McAlister, Director
E-mail: amcalister@bizjournals.com
Ed: Angela Gonzales. **Description:** Cancer survivor Helene Neville has finished a record-breaking 2,520-mile run in 93 days and then celebrated her 50th birthday despite being diagnosed with Hodgkins' lymphoma in 1991. Neveille, who is also a Phoenix area registered nurse, made stops along the way to promote her book, 'Nurses in Shape'. Neville also discusses how she fought her cancer through running. **Availability:** Print; Online.

12409 ■ *"Celebrate Innovation, No Matter Where It Occurs" in Harvard Business Review (Vol. 90, April 2012, No. 4, pp. 36)*
Pub: Harvard Business Review Press
Contact: Moderna V. Pfizer, Contact
Ed: Nitin Nohria. **Price:** $6, hardcover. **Description:** Yoga is used to illustrate the global success of a given concept not originally construed as a product or service. Although yoga emerged in ancient India, it is now practiced worldwide and is at the center of many businesses and disciplines, from the health care industry to clothing and accessories. **Availability:** PDF; Online.

12410 ■ *"Corrales Site of New Senior Living/ Care Complex" in America's Intelligence Wire (August 13, 2012)*
Description: David Dronet, developer of Corrales Senior Living LLC, has chosen Corrales, New Mexico as its newest site to construct a continuum of care for senior citizens. The project entails a $60 million complex of private homes and health care units with amenities like a restaurant, fitness areas, and gardens. **Availability:** Print; Online.

12411 ■ *"Digital Marketing Trends for Gyms in 2019" in Glofox blog (July 26, 2019)*
Ed: Jenny Weller. **Released:** July 26, 2019. **Description:** As digital trends evolve, marketers and small business owners should be aware so they can quickly adapt to emerging technologies to grow their business. This article discusses twelve digital marketing trends for gym and fitness business owners. **Availability:** Online.

12412 ■ *"First Look at Downtown's JW Marriott" in Houston Business Journal (Vol. 45, June 27, 2014, No. 7, pp. 10A)*
Pub: American City Business Journals, Inc.
Contact: Mike Olivieri, Executive Vice President
Released: Weekly. **Price:** $4, Introductory 4-week offer(Digital & Print). **Description:** The JW Marriott is one of several new hotels being developed for downtown Houston and construction scheduled to be completed in time for the 2017 Super Bowl to be held in the city. The hotel includes two ballrooms, the Picasso and the Monet, a spa with eight treatment rooms, a yoga studio, and an executive lounge for platinum and gold members. **Availability:** Print; Online.

12413 ■ *"The Fitness Marketing Guide for the Modern Fitness Founder" in Glofox blog (March 20, 2019)*
Ed: Eamonn Curley. **Released:** March 20, 2019. **Description:** Acquiring customers is the most important part of running a fitness business. To grow you need to make sure your message is getting out to potential clients. This article shares a range of strategies you can use to acquire new clients and grow your fitness business. **Availability:** Online.

12414 ■ *"From Fat to Fit" in Canadian Business (Vol. 79, September 22, 2006, No. 19, pp. 100)*
Ed: Graham Scott. **Description:** The increase in physical fitness clubs across Canada is discussed. **Availability:** Online.

12415 ■ *"GNC Reaches 'A Pivotal Moment" in Pittsburgh Business Times (Vol. 34, August 15, 2014, No. 4, pp. 4)*
Pub: American City Business Journals, Inc.
Contact: Mike Olivieri, Executive Vice President
Released: Weekly. **Price:** $4, introductory 4-week offer(Digital & Print). **Description:** Goldman analyst, Stephen Tanal, states Michael Archbold is taking over as CEO of GNC Holdings Inc. at a pivotal moment as the company shifts from heavy dependence on promotions to sustaining sales growth beyond 2015. Analysts discuss the recent problems faced by the vitamin, health and fitness retailer and the implications of a possible merger between GNC and Archbolds' former company, the Vitamin Shoppe Inc. **Availability:** Print; Online.

12416 ■ *"Gym Insurance: Cost, Coverage & Providers" in Fit Small Business (September 15, 2020)*
Ed: Virginia Hamill. **Released:** September 15, 2020. **Description:** Gym owners have more risk than many other business owners because your operations include engaging people in strenuous exercise. Gym insurance covers the costs associated with injuries and lawsuits. This article discusses what gym insurance is, who needs it, how much it costs, the different types of policies, and top insurance providers. **Availability:** Online.

12417 ■ *"Hot to Use Instagram Stories for Your Fitness Business" in Glofox blog (July 13, 2019)*
Ed: Jenny Weller. **Released:** July 13, 2019. **Description:** Instagram Stories give businesses the opportunity to increase their visibility. This article details why you should include Instagram stories in your social media and marketing strategy and ways you can use it to grow your business. **Availability:** Online.

12418 ■ *"How I Did It: Mel Zuckerman, Chairman, Canyon Ranch" in Inc. (December 2007, pp. 140-142)*
Ed: Daniel McGinn. **Description:** Profile of Mel Zuckerman, who tells how transformed his life as a middle-aged, overweight homebuilder to a healthy addition to the fitness and spa industry with his posh Canyon Ranch retreats. **Availability:** Online.

12419 ■ *"How to Put on a Successful Gym Grand Opening" in Glofox blog (June 10, 2019)*
Ed: Eamonn Curley. **Released:** June 10, 2019. **Description:** Discusses why your gym should have a grand opening day, what you need to do for it, and offers ideas to help make it a success. **Availability:** Online.

12420 ■ *"How to Start an Insanely Successful Personal Training Business" in Small Business Trends (January 11, 2017)*
Ed: Jeff Charles. **Released:** January 11, 2017. **Description:** Provides helpful tips to help you get your personal training business started the right way. Includes information on certification, understanding your clients, specialization, insurance, and marketing. **Availability:** Online.

12421 ■ *"How to Start a Personal Training Business From Home"* in The Balance Small Business (December 8, 2019)
Ed: Leslie Truex. **Released:** December 08, 2019. **Description:** Provides a list of pros and cons of a personal training home business, what you need to get started, and how to start. **Availability:** Online.

12422 ■ *"How to Start a Small Gym Business"* in Chron (March 8, 2019)
Ed: Andra Picincu. **Released:** March 08, 2019. **Description:** Discusses different types of small gym businesses, business plans, business model, licensing, and advertising. **Availability:** Online.

12423 ■ *"IMPACT Fitness Boot Camp Training Now Approved for NESTA Credits for Personal Trainer Certification"* in Marketing Weekly News (January 28, 2012)
Description: Intense Mixed Performance Accelerated Cross Training (IMPACT) helps personal trainers impact their clients' lives as well as their own income. However, the IMPACT fitness certification program now qualifies trainers for continuing education credits through the National Exercise & Sports Trainers Assocation's (NESTA) Personal Fitness Trainer program. The online IMPACT fitness training and business systems helps personal trainers create a successful fitness business in any 30x30 foot space. **Availability:** Online.

12424 ■ *"Little Gyms Are Getting Bigger"* in Sacramento Business Journal (Vol. 31, April 25, 2014, No. 9)
Pub: American City Business Journals, Inc.
Contact: Mike Olivieri, Executive Vice President
Released: Weekly. **Price:** $4, Introductory 4-week offer(Digital & Print). **Description:** The boutique gym is a growing segment of the consumer fitness market. One such smaller boutique gym is Orangetheory Fitness in Roseville, California. It focuses on small groups and commaraderie along with a promise of more personal attention for the fitness center members. The company is part of a national chain with plans to expand to 12 more locations in the Sacramento area in the next five years. **Availability:** Print; Online.

12425 ■ *"One Personal Trainer's Fitness Goal: Help Cancer Patients Feel Better During and After Treatment"* in America's Intelligence Wire (February 1, 2012)
Description: Laura Rosencrantz quit her job as a fitness instructor to develop a specialized training program to help cancer patients remain stronger while in treatment, stronger in recovery, or to help them feel better in their final months. She watched her grandfather grow weak during his cancer treatment and she knew she could help others during this time. **Availability:** Print; Online.

12426 ■ *"Personal Trainer to Attempt to Break World Record"* in Pantagraph (August 23, 2012)
Description: Dan Seaway, personal trainer, will attempt to break the Guinness record for the most miles run on a treadmill at Gold's Gym in Bloomington, Illinois. Details are included. **Availability:** Online.

12427 ■ *"The Picture Perfect Guide on How to Make a Fitness Video Strategy"* in Glofox blog (April 17, 2019)
Ed: Eamonn Curley. **Released:** April 17, 2019. **Description:** Discusses the effective combination of fitness and video, tips on creating great video, and how you can distribute your video content effectively on organic and paid platforms. **Availability:** Online.

12428 ■ *"A Quick Guide to Creating an Effective Gym Referral Program"* in Glofox blog (April 30, 2019)
Ed: Eamonn Curley. **Released:** April 30, 2019. **Description:** Discusses how to create an effective referral strategy for your fitness business including the basics of a referral program, how to start a referral program, and the key to its success. **Availability:** Online.

12429 ■ *"Relief for Gyms on Track, Congress Passes Infrastructure Bill"* in IHRSA (November 15, 2021)
Ed: Helen Durkin. **Released:** November 15, 2021. **Description:** During the COVID-19 pandemic, many gyms and athletic centers suffered business-wise due to shutdowns and members being weary of spreading the disease. With the passage of a new bill, these businesses will be able to collect federal relief money. **Availability:** Online.

12430 ■ *"Ritz Kapalua Sells 93 Suites for $176M to Fund Renovation"* in Commercial Property News (March 17, 2008)
Description: Ritz-Carlton, Kapalua in Lahaina, Hawaii sold ninety-three of its units in order to fund renovations of 463 rooms and suites along with construction of a new spa and fitness center, new and expanded restaurants and pools and an environmental education center for children. **Availability:** Online.

12431 ■ *"Sell a Movement Within a Smoothie"* in Canadian Business (Vol. 87, July 2014, No. 7, pp. 58)
Description: Vega is a nutritional and fitness supplement maker based in Vancouver, British Columbia that has increased its sales sevenfold from 2008 to 2013, earning the 9th spot in the 2014 Profit 500 ranking of fastest growing companies in Canada. The firm's strategy is to promote its flagship product Vega One using an in-store bicycle-powered blender. **Availability:** Online.

12432 ■ *"The Six Reasons the Fitness Industry is Booming"* in Forbes (September 26, 2018)
URL(s): www.forbes.com/sites/benmidgley/2018/09/26/the-six-reasons-the-fitness-industry-is-booming/#597f0a4e506d
Ed: Ben Midgley. **Released:** September 26, 2018. **Description:** The International Health, Racquet & Sportsclub Association has released statistics showing that the US health and fitness industry has been growing by at least 3 - 4% annually for the last ten years. Consumer habits and lifestyles are changing, with many Americans taking their health seriously. Many fitness centers are popping up and people are buying memberships and working on getting healthy. **Availability:** Online.

12433 ■ *"Step-by-Step Guide to Starting a Personal Training Business"* in NASM (March 24, 2020)
Released: March 24, 2020. **Description:** Provides nine tips for starting an independent personal training business for those who are considering becoming an independent personal trainer, working in clients' homes, or offering online coaching programs. **Availability:** Online.

12434 ■ *"Targeted Personal Trainer Business Strategies Build Clients, Income, Business and Success"* in Marketing Weekly News (August 4, 2012)
Description: Various business strategies can help personal trainers build their business include getting certified, creating postcards or flyers, and partnering with other fitness professionals. **Availability:** Print; PDF; Online.

12435 ■ *"Top Tips for a Killer Facebook Ad Campaign, for Your Gym or Studio'* in Glofox blog (April 18, 2017)
Ed: Eamonn Curley. **Released:** April 18, 2017. **Description:** This article describes everything you need to know to create a Facebook Ad Campaign that generates high quality leads for your fitness business. **Availability:** Online.

12436 ■ *"The Ultimate 5 Step Fitness Studio Branding Framework"* in Glofox blog (February 6, 2019)
Ed: Eamonn Curley. **Released:** February 06, 2019. **Description:** A brand is not just the logo or a tagline or some marketing materials. It is the essence of what your fitness business means inside and outside

of the studio. This article discusses steps to help you build your own brand and shows fitness studios who have succeeded with their branding. **Availability:** Online.

12437 ■ *"The Ultimate Guide to Push Notifications for Fitness Businesses"* in Glofox blog (July 29, 2019)
Ed: Eamonn Curley. **Released:** July 29, 2019. **Description:** Push notifications, brief messages or alerts sent through a mobile app, can enhance your fitness business. This article details how push notifications can be used to take your fitness business to the next level. **Availability:** Online.

12438 ■ *"Weightplan.com Launches 'Gymcodes' the Virtual Personal Trainer - Scan QR Codes on Gym Equipment for on the Spot Exercise Tuition"* in America's Intelligence Wire (June 11, 2012)
Description: The Weightplan.com iPhone app provides instant gym tuition simply by scanning QR codes on pieces of gym equipment. Details of the 'Gymcode' program are provided. **Availability:** Print; Online.

12439 ■ *"Wenmat Sells Last Fitness Clubs"* in Sacramento Business Journal (Vol. 31, June 6, 2014, No. 15, pp. 6)
Pub: American City Business Journals, Inc.
Contact: Mike Olivieri, Executive Vice President
Released: Weekly. **Price:** $4, Introductory 4-week offer(Digital & Print). **Description:** Wenmat Fitness sold all of its health clubs while expanding its presence in Sacramento, California. Fitness Evolution purchased Wenmat's Signature Athletic Club as well as its Incentive Fitness. Meanwhile, California Family Fitness bought two Wenmat locations. **Availability:** Print; Online.

12440 ■ *"What I Learned Starting a Small Fitness Business"* in Salon business strategy (September 18, 2019)
Ed: Rosa Anderson-Jones. **Released:** September 18, 2019. **Description:** A discussion with a small business owner who details what she learned when she started her small fitness business. Includes learning curve, things she got right, and tips. **Availability:** Online.

12441 ■ *"What It Takes to Run a Personal Training Business"* in Entrepreneur (November 1, 2016)
Released: November 01, 2016. **Description:** Describes the variety of things a personal trainer has to offer and discusses things to think about to determine whether this business is right for you. **Availability:** Online.

12442 ■ *"Why the Gap is Stalking Lululemon"* in Canadian Business (Vol. 85, August 22, 2012, No. 14, pp. 7)
Ed: Jim Sutherland. **Description:** Lululemon Athletica is facing competition against Gap Inc.'s Athleta as the retail giant plans to have about 50 new shops across Canada by the end of 2012. Athleta is also carrying lines of yoga- and activewear similar to that of Lululemon's and are even located near their stores. **Availability:** Online.

STATISTICAL SOURCES

12443 ■ *Boxing Gyms & Clubs Industry in the US - Market Research Report*
URL(s): www.ibisworld.com/united-states/market-research-reports/boxing-gyms-clubs-industry/
Price: $925. **Description:** Downloadable report analyzing the current and future trends in the boxing gyms and clubs industry. **Availability:** Download.

12444 ■ *RMA Annual Statement Studies*
Pub: Risk Management Association
Contact: Nancy Foster, President
Released: Annual. **Description:** Contains composite balance sheets and income statements for more than 360 industries, including the accounting, auditing,

and bookkeeping industries. Also contains five years of comparative historical data for discerning trends. Includes 16 commonly used ratios, computed for most of the size groupings for nearly every industry.

TRADE PERIODICALS

12445 ■ *Muscular Development*
Pub: Advanced Research Media, Inc.
Contact: Steve Blechman, Chief Executive Officer
URL(s): www.musculardevelopment.com/contact-us
.html
Facebook: www.facebook.com/MuscularDevelopmen
tMagazine
X (Twitter): x.com/MuscularDevelop
Instagram: www.instagram.com/muscular
development
YouTube: www.youtube.com/channel/UC9xC
5ClCMLOShjp1Ms0dbRw
Released: Monthly **Price:** $6.99, for cover price; $34.
95, U.S. for annual. **Description:** Bodybuilding and physical fitness magazine. **Availability:** Print; Online.

12446 ■ *Shape*
Pub: Dotdash Meredith
Contact: Neil Vogel, Chief Executive Officer
URL(s): www.shape.com
Facebook: www.facebook.com/SHAPEmagazine
X (Twitter): x.com/Shape_Magazine
Instagram: www.instagram.com/shape
YouTube: www.youtube.com/c/SHAPEMagazine
Pinterest: www.pinterest.com/shapemagazine
Released: Semiannual **Description:** Magazine for women covering nutrition, weight control, physical fitness, psychology, fashion, beauty and travel. **Availability:** Print; Online.

TRADE SHOWS AND CONVENTIONS

12447 ■ California Association for Health, Physical Education, Recreation, and Dance State Conference
California Association for Health, Physical Education, Recreation, and Dance (CAHPERD)
1501 El Camino Ave., Ste. 3
Sacramento, CA 95815
Ph: (916)922-3596
Co. E-mail: reception@cahperd.org
URL: http://www.cahperd.org
Contact: Joanie Verderber, Treasurer
URL(s): www.cahperd.org/Public/Public/Conferences
.aspx
Frequency: Annual. **Description:** Event includes reception and awards. **Audience:** Member and nonmember professionals, presenters, guests, and vendors. **Principal Exhibits:** Event includes reception and awards. Dates and Locations: 2025 Jan 22-25 Pasadena Convention Center, Pasadena, CA. **Telecommunication Services:** reception@cahperd.
org.

12448 ■ NATA Clinical Symposia & AT Expo
National Athletic Trainers' Association (NATA)
1620 Valwood Pky., Ste. 115
Carrollton, TX 75006
Ph: (214)637-6282
Fax: (214)637-2206
Co. E-mail: membership@nata.org
URL: http://www.nata.org
Contact: Tory Lindley, President
URL(s): convention.nata.org
Frequency: Annual. **Description:** Sports medicine products and services. **Audience:** Athletic Trainers. **Principal Exhibits:** Sports medicine products and services. Dates and Locations: 2025 Jun 24-27 Orlando, FL. **Telecommunication Services:** membership@nata.org.

12449 ■ The Yoga Expo
URL(s): theyogaexpo.org
Facebook: www.facebook.com/theyogaexpo?fref=ts
Linkedin: www.linkedin.com/company/the-yoga-expo
Instagram: www.instagram.com/yogaexpoworld

Price: $35. **Frequency:** Annual. **Description:** Provides classes in yoga plus product booths. **Audience:** Anyone interested in yoga, meditation, and wellness. **Principal Exhibits:** Provides classes in yoga plus product booths.

FRANCHISES AND BUSINESS OPPORTUNITIES

12450 ■ American Ramp Systems
45 School St., Ste. 202
Boston, MA 02108
Contact: Nathan Bemo, President
Description: Sales and rentals of accessibility ramps. **Founded:** 1970. **Financial Assistance:** Yes **Training:** Provides 1 week at headquarters with ongoing support.

12451 ■ Anytime Fitness LLC
Almuftah Group
1355 S Frontage Rd., Ste. 340
Hastings, MN 55033
Ph: 974 44 446-868
Co. E-mail: almuftah@almuftah.com
URL: http://www.almuftah.com
Facebook: www.facebook.com/anytimefitness
Instagram: www.instagram.com/anytimefitness
Pinterest: www.pinterest.com/anytimefitness
Description: Operator of fitness centers with branches worldwide. **Founded:** 2002. **Financial Assistance:** Yes **Training:** Provides 3 days minimum at headquarters and 3 days minimum onsite with ongoing support. **Educational Activities:** IFA Annual Convention (Annual).

12452 ■ CKO Kickboxing
900 Madison St., Ste. 2
Hoboken, NJ 07030
Ph: (201)963-7774
Co. E-mail: info@ckouppereastside.com
URL: http://www.ckokickboxing.com
Contact: Charles Osinowo, Owner
Facebook: www.facebook.com/CKOKickboxingGyms
X (Twitter): x.com/ckokickboxing
Instagram: www.instagram.com/ckokickboxing
Description: Firm provides health fitness and kickboxing gym franchise. **Founded:** 1997. **Training:** Consists of intensive training in the following areas: class structure and size, pre-opening and set-up, marketing, operations and customer service with ongoing mentoring and support.

12453 ■ CoachMeFit
2300 E Stadium Blvd.
Ann Arbor, MI 48104
Ph: (734)477-9430
Co. E-mail: info@coachmefit.com
URL: http://coachmefit.com
Contact: Lindsay Bogdasarian, Founder
Facebook: www.facebook.com/coachmefitAnnarbor
Linkedin: www.linkedin.com/company/coachmefit
Instagram: www.instagram.com/coachmefit
Description: Provider of personal training services for health, wellness and fitness. **Founded:** 2001. **Royalty Fee:** 5%. **Financial Assistance:** Yes **Training:** 3-5 days at headquarters.

12454 ■ Fit Zone for Women
2455 E Sunrise Blvd., Ste. 1204
Fort Lauderdale, FL 33304
Free: 800-988-4712
URL: http://www.fitzoneforwomen.com
Facebook: www.facebook.com/fitzone.sturgis
Description: Provider of women fitness services. **Founded:** 2004. **Training:** Provides 7 days at headquarters and 3 days onsite and ongoing support.

12455 ■ Gold's Gym International Inc.
RSG Group GmbH
5420 Lyndon B. Johnson Fwy., Ste. 610
Dallas, TX 75240
URL: http://rsggroup.com
Contact: Brandon Bean, Chief Executive Officer
Facebook: www.facebook.com/goldsgym
Linkedin: www.linkedin.com/company/gold%27s-gym
X (Twitter): x.com/GoldsGym

Instagram: www.instagram.com/goldsgym
YouTube: www.youtube.com/channel/
UCxAJiokP8vMPu4RGeeRJfdg
Description: The operator of health and fitness clubs around the world. **Founded:** 1965. **Royalty Fee:** $43. **Financial Assistance:** Yes **Training:** Yes.

12456 ■ IM=X Pilates Studio
265 Madison Ave., 2nd Fl.
New York, NY 10016
Ph: (212)997-1167
Free: 800-469-1336
Co. E-mail: info@imxpilates.com
URL: http://www.imxpilates.com
Contact: Lauren Fakete, President
Facebook: www.facebook.com/imxpilatesnyc
X (Twitter): x.com/imxpilatesnyc
Instagram: www.instagram.com/imxpilatesnyc
Description: Develops patented equipment and helping customers grow pilates programs. Studio offers pilates, barre, yoga, cycling, personal training and back wellness programs. **Founded:** 2003. **Training:** Operations Manual and Training course prepare you to grow and operate your own studio or studio chain. Every year we will train and certify up to 12 of your staff in the Basic And Advanced IM=X Pilates program.

12457 ■ Lucille Roberts Fitness Express (LR)
1387 St. Nicholas Ave.
New York, NY 10033
Co. E-mail: heretohelp@tsiclubs.com
URL: http://www.lucilleroberts.com
Facebook: www.facebook.com/lucilleroberts
X (Twitter): x.com/lucilleroberts
Instagram: www.instagram.com/lucilleroberts
Description: Women fitness and weight-loss center. **No. of Operating Units:** 50. **Founded:** 1973. **Financial Assistance:** Yes **Training:** Offers 1 week at headquarters with ongoing support.

12458 ■ My Gym Enterprises
15300 Ventura Blvd., Ste. 414
Sherman Oaks, CA 91403
Ph: (818)907-6966
Co. E-mail: info@mygym.com
URL: http://www.mygym.com
Facebook: www.facebook.com/mygymfun
X (Twitter): x.com/mygymfun
Instagram: www.instagram.com/mygymfun
YouTube: www.youtube.com/mygymfun
Pinterest: www.pinterest.com/mygymfun
Description: Firm provides children learn and growth through unique and exciting activities. **No. of Operating Units:** 170.0. **Founded:** 1983. **Equity Capital Needed:** $36,000-$55,000. **Franchise Fee:** 25000. **Royalty Fee:** $150 - $250 a month. **Training:** 21 day training course-Ref. Manuals and videos-Complete bus. operating systems-Detailed class curricula-Full hand holding process through Grand Opening and 1st session-Exceptional ongoing support w/ onsite visits, written materials, phone calls program innovations, promotions, My Gym National and Regional Seminars.

12459 ■ One 2 One Bodyscapes
1197 Walnut St.
Newton, MA 02461
Ph: (617)796-8808
Co. E-mail: info@bodyscapesfitness.com
URL: http://www.one2onebodyscapes.com
Contact: Brent Pendleton, Contact
Facebook: www.facebook.com/BodyScapesFitness
X (Twitter): x.com/BodyScapesFit
Description: Provider of an unsurpassed personal training. **Founded:** 1997. **Training:** Yes.

12460 ■ Oogles N Googles
10051 Cedar Point Dr.
Carmel, IN 46032
Description: Birthday parties and preschool enrichment. **No. of Franchise Units:** 10. **Founded:** 2001. **Franchised:** 2003. **Equity Capital Needed:** $33,400-$40,700. **Franchise Fee:** $19,900. **Royalty Fee:** 7%. **Training:** Available at headquarters for 10 days.

12461 ■ Platoon Fitness
899 Penn St.
 Bryn Mawr, PA 19010
Ph: (215)752-8666
Co. E-mail: info@platoonfitness.com
URL: http://platoonfitness.com
Contact: Todd Scott, Owner
E-mail: todd@platoonfitness.com
Facebook: www.facebook.com/platoonfitness
Linkedin: www.linkedin.com/company/platoon-fitness
Instagram: www.instagram.com/platoonfitness
Description: Fitness center provides of personal training, outdoor boot camp, nutrition, massage, corporate wellness, sport specific training and more. **Founded:** 1996. **Training:** Offers 2 weeks training at headquarters, 2 months onsite, additional training 5 times a year at franchise's location, and ongoing support.

12462 ■ Retro Fitness L.L.C.
1601 Belvedere Rd., Ste. E-500
 West Palm Beach, FL 33406
Ph: (732)431-0062
Co. E-mail: corporate@retrofitness.com
URL: http://retrofitness.com
Contact: Andrew Alfano, Chief Executive Officer
Facebook: www.facebook.com/RetroFitness
Linkedin: www.linkedin.com/company/retrofitness-llc
X (Twitter): x.com/retrofitness
YouTube: www.youtube.com/channel/UCn4hR1Gq
 6mAumL4P0-IVqSQ
Description: A franchiser of 1980s-themed fitness centers. **Founded:** 2004. **Training:** Provides 8 days training at headquarters, 8 days at franchiser's location and ongoing support.

12463 ■ Snap Fitness
2411 Galpin Ct., Ste. 110
 Chanhassen, MN 55317
Ph: (952)567-5800
Co. E-mail: chanhassen@snapfitness.com
URL: http://www.snapfitness.com/us
Facebook: www.facebook.com/snapfi
 tnesschanhassen
Instagram: www.instagram.com/snapfi
 tnesschanhassen
YouTube: www.youtube.com/user/snapfitness247
Description: Operator of fitness centers. **No. of Franchise Units:** 1500. **Founded:** 2003. **Franchised:** 2005. **Franchise Fee:** $25,000. **Financial Assistance:** Yes **Training:** Provides 2 days at headquarters with ongoing support.

12464 ■ Sportball Systems Inc.
39 Glen Cameron Rd., Unit 8
 Thornhill, ON, Canada L3T 1P1
Ph: (905)882-4473
Free: 877-678-5437
Fax: (905)882-8453
Co. E-mail: registration@sportball.ca
URL: http://www.sportball.ca
Contact: Sharon Balasbas, Manager
Facebook: www.facebook.com/SportballGTA
X (Twitter): x.com/sportball
Instagram: www.instagram.com/sportballgta
Description: Provider of kids sports programs including children soccer, T-ball and ball hockey for toddlers, preschoolers and school-aged kids. **Founded:** 1995. **Training:** Yes.

12465 ■ Survivor Bootcamp
Queen Victoria School, 1850 E 3rd at Victoria
 Vancouver, BC, Canada V5N 4K2
Ph: (604)349-4199
Co. E-mail: eastvan@survivorfitness.com
URL: http://www.survivorfitness.com
Contact: Daniela Duva, Contact
X (Twitter): x.com/wekickyourbutt
Pinterest: www.pinterest.ca/wekickbutt
Description: Chain of fitness centers. **Founded:** 2004. **Training:** Provides 1 week training in Vancouver.

12466 ■ Tumbles
1221 Encinitas Blvd.
 Encinitas, CA 92024
Ph: (760)942-7411

Co. E-mail: encinitas@tumbles.net
URL: http://encinitas.tumbles.net
Facebook: www.facebook.com/TEncinitas
Instagram: www.instagram.com/tumblesgym
Description: Provider of physical activities and growth development classes to motor skills, spatial awareness, coordination, balance, agility, flexibility and sports preparation for children. **Founded:** 1985. **Training:** Yes.

12467 ■ Twist Sport Conditioning Centers
Unit 3, 3rd Fl., 68 E 2nd St.
 Vancouver, BC, Canada V5T 1B1
Ph: (604)904-6556
URL: http://www.twistperformance.com
Description: Sport conditioning center provides athletic training, fitness training, hockey conditioning and other sports training services. **Founded:** 1999.

12468 ■ UG Franchise Operations L.L.C.
1501 Quail St., Ste. 100
 Newport Beach, CA 92660
Contact: Becky DeGeorge, Contact
Description: The business you will conduct as an LA Boxing Franchise is a membership physical fitness system consisting of unique boxing and kickboxing training regiment, utilizing a system and products that are proprietary to the company. **Founded:** 1992. **Training:** 5 days of initial training at corporate training facilities, and 1 day onsite. Initial training includes instruction in owner/operator responsibilities, instructor training, equipment, membership sales, administration, operations, product and services sales and marketing.

COMPUTERIZED DATABASES

12469 ■ *Smoking and Tobacco Use Data and Statistics*
U.S. Centers for Disease Control and Prevention
 1600 Clifton Rd.
 Atlanta, GA 30329
Free: 800-232-4636
Co. E-mail: hrcs@cdc.gov
URL: http://www.cdc.gov
Contact: Dr. Mandy K. Cohen, Director
URL(s): www.cdc.gov/ophdst/data-research/index
 .html
Availability: Online. **Type:** Bibliographic.

12470 ■ *SPORTDiscus*
EBSCO Information Services
 10 Estes St.
 Ipswich, MA 01938
Ph: (978)356-6500
Free: 800-653-2726
Co. E-mail: information@ebsco.com
URL: http://www.ebsco.com
Contact: Tim Collins, Chief Executive Officer
URL(s): www.ebsco.com/products/research-da
 tabases/sportdiscus
Availability: Online. **Type:** Bibliographic.

LIBRARIES

12471 ■ Lemmen-Holton Cancer Pavilion Library
145 Michigan St. NE
 Grand Rapids, MI 49503
Ph: (616)486-5700
URL: http://findadoctor.spectrumhealth.org/location/
 profile/7989
Description: Provide a full range of cancer services including, prevention, screening and diagnosis, personalized cancer treatment, integrative therapies, supportive care services, access to clinical trials and leading edge technology. **Scope:** Medicine; literature. **Holdings:** Books.

12472 ■ Springfield College - Babson Library
263 Alden St.
 Springfield, MA 01109-3739
URL: http://springfield.edu/node/36
Contact: Andrea Taupier, Contact
E-mail: ataupier@springfield.edu

Description: Library serves students and faculties of Springfiled College. **Scope:** Sport; physical education; recreation; ymca. **Services:** Interlibrary loan; Accessible for the students, faculty and staffs. **Founded:** 1885. **Holdings:** Figures not available.

12473 ■ State University of New York at Cortland Memorial Library
PO Box 2000
 Cortland, NY 13045
Ph: (607)753-2011
URL: http://www2.cortland.edu/library
Contact: Jennifer L. Kronenbitter, Director
Scope: Technology; research. **Services:** Interlibrary loan; copying; library open to the public. **Founded:** 1868. **Holdings:** Books; newspapers; journals.

12474 ■ Tuality Healthcare Health Sciences Library
Tuality Health Education Ctr.
 335 SE 8th Ave.
 Hillsboro, OR 97123
Ph: (503)681-1702
Co. E-mail: community.relations@tuality.org
URL: http://www.tuality.org
Contact: Lori James-Nielsen, President
Facebook: www.facebook.com/HillsboroMedCtr
Linkedin: www.linkedin.com/company/ohsu-health
 -hillsboro-medical-center
X (Twitter): x.com/HillsboroMedCtr
Instagram: www.instagram.com/hillsboromedctr
YouTube: www.youtube.com/user/TualityHealthcare
Scope: Clinical medicine; pharmacology; nursing; therapeutics; cardiovascular medicine. **Services:** Interlibrary loan; copying; library open to the public by appointment. **Founded:** 1980. **Holdings:** Books; pamphlets; videos.

12475 ■ Université de Montréal - Bibliothèque de Kinésiologie
2100, boul. Edouard-Montpetit, Rm. 8259
 Montreal, QC, Canada H3C 3J7
Ph: (514)343-7643
Co. E-mail: unequestion@bib.umontreal.ca
URL: http://bib.umontreal.ca/sciences-sante
Contact: Alain Borsi, Director
E-mail: alain.borsi@umontreal.ca
Facebook: www.facebook.com/bibUdeM
X (Twitter): x.com/bibUdeM
YouTube: www.youtube.com/user/Biblio
 thequesUdeM
Scope: Physical and health education; kinesiology. **Founded:** 1966. **Holdings:** Figures not available.

12476 ■ University of North Carolina at Greensboro - Martha Blakeney Hodges Special Collections & University Archives - History of Physical Education and Dance Collection
320 College Ave.
 Greensboro, NC 27412-0001
URL: http://library.uncg.edu/info/depts/scua/collec
 tions/rare_books/items.aspx#authors
Description: Central library provides access to millions of digital items. **Scope:** Physical education; sports; gymnastics; dance; general recreation. **Services:** Wi-Fi access; collection open to the public for research. **Founded:** 1891. **Holdings:** 230 pamphlets; books; articles; photographs; manuscript.

RESEARCH CENTERS

12477 ■ Cooper Institute (CI)
12330 Preston Rd.
 Dallas, TX 75230
Ph: (972)341-3200
Free: 800-635-7050
Fax: (972)341-3227
Co. E-mail: news@cooperinst.org
URL: http://www.cooperinstitute.org
Contact: Dr. Laura DeFina, President
Facebook: www.facebook.com/TheCooperInstitute
Linkedin: www.linkedin.com/company/the-cooper-insti
 tute
YouTube: www.youtube.com/user/TheCooperInstitute

Description: Promotes understanding of the relationship between living habits and health. Provides leadership in enhancing the physical and emotional well-being of individuals. **Scope:** Aims to evaluate the benefits of regular exercise, healthy lifestyle, and preventive healthcare; effectively proving again and again that exercise truly is medicine. **Founded:** 1970. **Publications:** *Aerobics Center Longitudinal Study; Providing Dietary Guidance Course; Steps to Better Health; The Walking Handbook.* **Educational Activities:** SHAPE America National Convention and Expo (Annual). **Geographic Preference:** Multinational.

12478 ■ Institut Canadien de la Recherche sur la Condition Physique et le Mode de Vie (ICRCP) [Canadian Fitness and Lifestyle Research Institute (CFLRI)]
230 - 2733 Lancaster Rd.
  Ottawa, ON, Canada K1B 0A9
Ph: (613)233-5528
Fax: (613)233-5536
Co. E-mail: contact.us.cflri@cflri.ca
URL: http://cflri.ca
Contact: Dr. Christine Cameron, President
Facebook: www.facebook.com/cflri

X (Twitter): x.com/cflri_icrcp
Instagram: www.instagram.com/cflri_icrcp

Description: Conducts research on physical activities in Canada and distributes information about physical activity. **Scope:** A national research organization concerned with monitoring the physically activity levels of Canadians and sharing knowledge about the importance of leading healthy, active lifestyles. **Founded:** 1980. **Publications:** *Physical Activity Monitor* (Annual); *The Research File* (Monthly). **Geographic Preference:** National.

ASSOCIATIONS AND OTHER ORGANIZATIONS

12479 ■ Academie Canadienne de Medecine du Sport et de l'Exercice (ACMSE) [Canadian Academy of Sport and Exercise Medicine]
House of Sport RA Ctr., 2451 Riverside Dr.
Ottawa, ON, Canada K1H 7X7
Ph: (613)748-5851
Co. E-mail: admin@casem-acmse.org
URL: http://casem-acmse.org
Contact: Dr. Erika Persson, President
Facebook: www.facebook.com/CanadianAca
demyofSportandExerciseMedicine
X (Twitter): twitter.com/CASEMACMSE
Instagram: www.instagram.com/cansportmed

Description: Physicians committed to excellence in the practice of medicine as it applies to all aspects of physical activity. Seeks to be a leader in advancing the art and science of sport medicine, including health promotion and disease prevention, for the benefit of all Canadians through programs of education, research, and service. **Founded:** 1970. **Publications:** *Clinical Journal of Sport Medicine* (6/year). **Geographic Preference:** National.

12480 ■ Acupuncture Canada
Toronto, ON, Canada M3C 1W3
Ph: (416)752-3988
Fax: (416)752-4398
Co. E-mail: info@acupuncturecanada.org
URL: http://www.acupuncturecanada.org
Contact: Catharine Maxwell-Palmer, President
Facebook: www.facebook.com/AcupunctureCan
Linkedin: www.linkedin.com/company/acupuncture
-canada
X (Twitter): x.com/acupuncture_can
Instagram: www.instagram.com/acupuncture_can

Description: Promotes acupuncture's legitimate place in health care by initiating and supporting research in acupuncture. **Founded:** 1974. **Educational Activities:** Acupuncture Canada Board meeting. **Geographic Preference:** National.

12481 ■ American Alternative Medical Association (AAMA)
2200 Market St., Ste. 803
Galveston, TX 77550-1530
Ph: (409)621-2600
Free: 888-764-2237
Fax: (775)703-5334
Co. E-mail: office@joinaama.com
URL: http://www.joinaama.com
Contact: Donald A. Rosenthal, MD, Director

Description: Fosters unity among "grassroots practitioners" and those with advanced academic credentials. Educates the public that good health can be obtained without the use of drugs. Encourages improved public awareness of the benefits of alternative health care. **Founded:** 1990. **Geographic Preference:** National.

12482 ■ American Physical Therapy Association (APTA)
3030 Potomac Ave., Ste. 100
Alexandria, VA 22305-3085
Ph: (703)684-2782
Free: 800-999-2782
Fax: (703)684-7343
Co. E-mail: memberservices@apta.org
URL: http://www.apta.org
Contact: Roger Herr, President
Facebook: www.facebook.com/
AmericanPhysicalTherapyAssociation
Linkedin: www.linkedin.com/company/american
-physical-therapy-association
X (Twitter): x.com/aptatweets
Instagram: www.instagram.com/aptapics
YouTube: www.youtube.com/user/APTAvideo

Description: Publishes reference guides, monographs, brochures and periodicals for physical therapy professionals on education, practice, research and administration. **Founded:** 1921. **Holdings:** 3,000 books; photographs; reports; dissertations; oral histories; conference proceedings; annual reports; board of directors meeting minutes; House of Delegates minutes. **Subscriptions:** 200 journals and other serials. **Publications:** *APTA Magazine* (11/year); *Physical Therapy & Rehabilitation Journal (PTJ)* (Monthly); *Clinical Management: The Magazine of the American Physical Therapy Association* (Bimonthly); *Physical Therapy Reimbursement News.* **Awards:** Dorothy E. Baethke - Eleanor J. Carlin Award for Excellence in Academic Teaching (Annual); Lucy Blair Service Award (Periodic); Dorothy Briggs Memorial Scientific Inquiry Award (Irregular); Signe Brunnstrom Award for Excellence in Clinical Teaching (Annual); Chattanooga Research Award (Annual); Jules M. Rothstein Golden Pen Award for Scientific Writing (Annual); APTA Honorary Membership (Periodic); Henry O. and Florence P. Kendall Practice Award (Irregular); Mary McMillan Lecture Award (Irregular); Eugene Michels New Investigator Award (Annual); APTA Minority Initiatives Award (Periodic); Margaret L. Moore Award for Outstanding New Academic Faculty Member (Annual); Jack Walker Award (Periodic); Marian Williams Award for Research in Physical Therapy (Annual); Catherine Worthingham Fellows Award (Annual); Helen J. Hislop Award for Outstanding Contributions to Professional Literature (Annual); APTA Minority Scholarships - Faculty Development Scholarship Award (Annual); APTA Minority Scholarships - Scholarship Awards for Student Physical Therapy Assistants (Annual); APTA Minority Scholarships - Scholarship Award for Student Physical Therapists (Annual). **Geographic Preference:** National.

12483 ■ American Physical Therapy Association - Academy of Orthopaedic Physical Therapy (APTA AOPT)
2920 E Ave. S, Ste. 200
La Crosse, WI 54601
Free: 800-444-3982
Fax: (608)788-3965
URL: http://www.orthopt.org

Contact: Dr. Bob Rowe, President
E-mail: browe@orthopt.org
Facebook: www.facebook.com/OrthopaedicAPTA
Linkedin: www.linkedin.com/company/aopt
X (Twitter): x.com/OrthopaedicAPTA
Instagram: www.instagram.com/apta_orthopaedic

Description: Orthopaedic physical therapists and physical therapist assistants who belong to the American Physical Therapy Association; physical therapy educators and students. Supports the continued growth of the physical therapy profession through education and research; promotes development of a standard certification procedure for the field. Seeks to assure the quality of physical therapy curricula at both the undergraduate and postgraduate levels. Facilitates communication among orthopedic physical therapists and other health care professionals. Gathers and disseminates information on the care of musculoskeletal disorders. Provides access to a network of orthopaedic study groups. **Founded:** 1974. **Publications:** *The Journal of Orthopaedic and Sports Physical Therapy (JOSPT)* (Monthly); *Orthopaedic Physical Therapy Practice* (Quarterly). **Awards:** James A. Gould Excellence in Teaching Orthopaedic Physical Therapy Award (Annual); APTA Outstanding PT & PTA Student Award (Annual); Paris Distinguished Service Award (Annual). **Geographic Preference:** National.

12484 ■ Association Canadienne des Thérapeutes du Sport (CATA)
Ste 300, 400 5th Ave SW
Calgary, AB, Canada T2P 0L6
Ph: (403)509-2282
Free: 888-509-2282
Co. E-mail: internationalcandidateliaison@athletic
therapy.org
URL: http://athletictherapy.org
Facebook: www.facebook.com/cata.acts
Linkedin: www.linkedin.com/company/cata-acts
Instagram: www.instagram.com/cata_canada

Description: Promotes advancement of the study and practice of sports medicine and athletic therapy. **Founded:** 1965. **Awards:** CATA Writing Award (Annual); Larry Ashley Award (Annual); CATA Human Kinetics Writing Awards; CATA Distinguished Athletic Therapy Educator Award (Annual); Larry Ashley Memorial Scholarship Award (Annual); CATA Special Recognition Award (Annual); CATA Merit Award (Annual). **Geographic Preference:** National.

12485 ■ Canadian Association of Physical Medicine & Rehabilitation (CAPMR) [Association canadienne de médecine physique et de réaptation]
4 Cataraqui St., Ste. 310
Kingston, ON, Canada K7K 1Z7
Ph: (613)507-0480
Fax: (866)303-0626
Co. E-mail: info@capmr.ca
URL: http://capmr.ca
Contact: Dr. Larry Robinson, President
Facebook: www.facebook.com/capmr.ca
X (Twitter): x.com/capm_r

Description: Aims to provide and maintain a national professional forum and network for the exchange of information and opinion. **Founded:** 1952. **Publications:** *CAPM&R Newsletter* (3/year); *Canadian Association of Physical Medicine and Rehabilitation News.* **Educational Activities:** CAPM&R Annual Scientific Meeting (Annual). **Awards:** Medical Student Essay Contest (Annual); CAPM&R Resident Essay Contest (Annual); CAPM&R Resident Research Contest (Annual); CAPM&R Visiting Professorship program (Annual); Canadian Medical Student Essay Award (Annual). **Geographic Preference:** National.

12486 ■ Foundation for Physical Therapy (FPT)

3030 Potomac Ave., Ste. 110
Alexandria, VA 22305-3085
Free: 800-875-1378
Co. E-mail: info@foundation4pt.org
URL: http://foundation4pt.org
Contact: Paul A. Rockar, President
Facebook: www.facebook.com/foundation4pt
Linkedin: www.linkedin.com/company/foundation-for
-physical-therapy-research
X (Twitter): x.com/foundation4pt
YouTube: www.youtube.com/user/Foundation4PT1
Description: Supports the physical therapy profession's research needs by funding scientific and clinically-relevant physical therapy research. **Founded:** 1979. **Awards:** Charles M. Magistro Distinguished Service Award (Annual); Innovation in Fundraising Award (Periodic); FPT Spirit of Philantrophy Award (Annual). **Geographic Preference:** National.

12487 ■ Institute for Traditional Medicine and Preventive Health Care (ITM)

2017 SE Hawthorne Blvd.
Portland, OR 97214
Ph: (503)233-4907
Fax: (503)233-1017
Co. E-mail: itm@itmonline.org
URL: http://www.itmonline.org
Contact: Subhuti Dharmananda, PhD, Director
E-mail: subhuti@itmonline.org

Description: Helps people seeking traditional medicine knowledge and services by clarifying the nature of traditional medicine and demonstrating how it can be utilized in the modern setting. Provides educational materials and articles on traditional medicine and related topics. Conducts background research in traditional medicine including journal searches in China and computer searches in the U.S. **Founded:** 1979. **Publications:** *A Bag of Pearls; Internet Journal of the Institute for Traditional Medicine.* **Geographic Preference:** Multinational.

12488 ■ International Journal of Disability, Community & Rehabilitation

URL(s): www.ijdcr.ca
Released: Annual **Price:** $20, Individuals For one year. **Description:** Journal consisting of two international and two Canadian publication per year. **Availability:** Print; Online.

12489 ■ National Ayurvedic Medical Association (NAMA)

2455 E Sunrise Blvd., Ste. 816
Fort Lauderdale, FL 33304
Ph: (213)628-6291
Co. E-mail: nama@ayurvedanama.org
URL: http://www.ayurvedanama.org
Contact: Jayarajan Kodikannath, President
Facebook: www.facebook.com/Ayurvedanama
Linkedin: www.linkedin.com/company/national-ayurve
dic-medical-association
Instagram: www.instagram.com/ayurveda_nama
YouTube: www.youtube.com/channel/UCOv
2WJRz9mODO3nDVX1aw8g

Description: Aims to preserve, improve, and promote the philosophy, science and practice of Ayurveda. Maintains the professional competency and licensing of Ayurveda through enhancement of knowledge, practice and application of Ayurvedic profession. Encourages the public to appreciate and accept Ayurveda. **Founded:** 2000. **Educational Activities:**

Annual AHG Symposium (Annual); Ayurveda: Healing People, Healing Communities. **Geographic Preference:** National.

12490 ■ Private Practice Section of the American Physical Therapy Association (PPS)

1421 Prince St., Ste. 300
Alexandria, VA 22314
Free: 800-517-1167
Co. E-mail: info@ppsapta.org
URL: http://ppsapta.org
Contact: Mike Horsfield, President
E-mail: mike.horsfield@rockvalleypt.com
Facebook: www.facebook.com/PrivatePracticeSec
tion
Linkedin: www.linkedin.com/company/private-practice
-section-apta
X (Twitter): x.com/PPS_APTA
Instagram: www.instagram.com/pps_apta

Description: To provide physical therapists with information on establishing and managing a private practice; to promote high standards of private practice physical therapy. **Founded:** 1956. **Publications:** *Private Practice Section of the American Physical Therapy Association--Membership Directory* (Biennial); *Hire for Fit; IMPACT* (11/year); *Private Practice Section Membership Directory; Safeguarding Your Practice: The Corporate Compliance Manual* (Annual); *Twenty Questions About Private Practice.* **Awards:** Robert G. Dicus Award (Annual). **Geographic Preference:** National.

12491 ■ Sound Healers Association (SHA)

PO Box 2240
Boulder, CO 80306
Ph: (303)443-8181
Co. E-mail: info@soundhealersassociation.org
URL: http://www.soundhealersassociation.org
Contact: Andi Goldman, Director

Description: Promotes research and awareness for the use of sound and music as therapeutic and transformational modalities for healing. Phonograph Records Tapes & Disks. **Founded:** 1982. **Educational Activities:** Concerts; Healing Sounds Seminars. **Geographic Preference:** National.

12492 ■ Vocational Rehabilitation Association of Canada (VRA)

2-555 Hall Ave. E
Renfrew, ON, Canada K7V 4M7
Co. E-mail: info@vracanada.com
URL: http://www.vracanada.com
Contact: Tracey Kibble, President
X (Twitter): x.com/VRACanada

Description: Promotes excellence in rehabilitation education, training, and practice. Formulates and enforces code of ethics. Facilitates communication to its members and stakeholders. **Founded:** 1970. **Publications:** *Rehab Review* (Quarterly). **Geographic Preference:** National.

REFERENCE WORKS

12493 ■ "Celebrate Innovation, No Matter Where It Occurs" in Harvard Business Review (Vol. 90, April 2012, No. 4, pp. 36)

Pub: Harvard Business Review Press
Contact: Moderna V. Pfizer, Contact

Ed: Nitin Nohria. **Price:** $6, hardcover. **Description:** Yoga is used to illustrate the global success of a given concept not originally construed as a product or service. Although yoga emerged in ancient India, it is now practiced worldwide and is at the center of many businesses and disciplines, from the health care industry to clothing and accessories. **Availability:** PDF; Online.

12494 ■ "Q&A With Devin Ringling: Franchise's Services Go Beyond Elder Care" in Gazette (October 2, 2010)

Pub: The Gazette
Contact: Vicki Cederholm, Director, Operations
E-mail: vicki.cederholm@gazette.com

Ed: Bill Radford. **Description:** Profile of franchise, Interim HealthCare, in Colorado Springs, Colorado; the company offers home care services that include wound care and specialized feedings to shopping and light housekeeping. It also runs a medical staffing company that provides nurses, therapists and other health care workers to hospitals, prisons, schools and other facilities. **Availability:** Online.

12495 ■ "Victory Healthcare Moves Into Dallas-Fort Worth Market" in Dallas Business Journal (Vol. 35, May 18, 2012, No. 36, pp. 1)

Pub: Baltimore Business Journal
Contact: Rhonda Pringle, President
E-mail: rpringle@bizjournals.com

Ed: Bill Hethcock. **Description:** Victory Healthcare Holdings is to open Victory Medical Center in Plano, Texas. The company is also planning two more health facilities in the Dallas-Fort Worth area. Victory Medical will provide rehabilitative care as well as spinal and orthopedic surgery, which both have high demands. **Availability:** Print; Online.

TRADE PERIODICALS

12496 ■ APTA Magazine

Pub: American Physical Therapy Association
Contact: Roger Herr, President
URL(s): www.apta.org/apta-magazine
Released: 11/year **Description:** Magazine for physical therapy professionals. **Availability:** Online.

12497 ■ Pediatric Physical Therapy

Pub: Wolters Kluwer Health Inc.
Contact: Greg Samios, President
URL(s): www.wolterskluwer.com/en/solutions/ovid/pe
diatric-physical-therapy--apta-academy-of-pediatric
-physical-therapy-1120journals.lww.com/pedpt/
pages/default.aspx
Facebook: www.facebook.com/PEDPT
X (Twitter): x.com/PedPTJournal
Instagram: www.instagram.com/pedptjournal
YouTube: www.youtube.com/c/Pedia
tricPhysicalTherapy
Released: Quarterly **Description:** Peer-reviewed journal reporting on new clinical care for pediatric patients. **Availability:** Print; PDF; Online.

12498 ■ Physical Medicine and Rehabilitation Clinics of North America

Pub: Elsevier Inc.
URL(s): www.pmr.theclinics.com
Ed: Santos F. Martinez. **Price:** $491, Individuals for International online + print. **Description:** Journal focused on physical medicine and rehabilitation, including trends in patient management and newest advances in the field. **Availability:** Print; Download; PDF; Online.

12499 ■ Physical & Occupational Therapy In Pediatrics: A Quarterly Journal of Developmental Therapy (POTP)

Pub: Taylor & Francis Group (Journals)
Contact: Annie Callanan, Chief Executive Officer
URL(s): www.tandfonline.com/journals/ipop20
Ed: Robert J. Palisano, Annette Majnemer. **Released:** 6/year; volume 44, issue 4 2024. **Price:** $3,222, Institutions for print and online.; $2,642, Institutions for online only. **Description:** Journal for therapists involved in developmental and physical rehabilitation of infants and children. **Availability:** Print; Download; PDF; Online.

12500 ■ Physical Therapy & Rehabilitation Journal (PTJ)

Pub: Oxford University Press Oxford Journals
URL(s): academic.oup.com/ptj
Facebook: www.facebook.com/
PhysicalTherapyJournal
X (Twitter): x.com/PTJournal
Released: Monthly **Price:** $285, Institutions for online only. **Description:** Features peer-reviewed scientific and professional articles, continuing education course listings, abstracts of current literature, and book reviews. **Availability:** Print; Online; PDF.

TRADE SHOWS AND CONVENTIONS

12501 ■ American Academy of Physical Medicine and Rehabilitation Annual Assembly
American Academy of Physical Medicine and
  Rehabilitation (AAPM&R)
9700 W Bryn Mawr Ave., Ste. 200
Rosemont, IL 60018-5701
Ph: (847)737-6000
Fax: (847)754-4368
Co. E-mail: memberservices@aapmr.org
URL: http://www.aapmr.org
Contact: Adm. Stuart M. M. Weinstein, President
URL(s): www.aapmr.org/education/annual-assembly
Frequency: Annual. **Description:** Innovative learning opportunities, non-stop networking, and a variety of educational sessions and hands-on workshops. **Audience:** Physicians specializing in physical medicine and rehabilitation. **Principal Exhibits:** Innovative learning opportunities, non-stop networking, and a variety of educational sessions and hands-on workshops. Dates and Locations: 2025 Oct 22-25 Hyatt Regency/Salt Palace Convention Center, Salt Lake City, UT; 2026 Nov 11-14 Hyatt Regency Orlando/Orange County Convention Center, Orlando, FL; 2027 Nov 10-13 Phoenix Convention Center, Phoenix, AZ; 2028 Oct 11-14 Colorado Convention Center, Denver, CO. **Telecommunication Services:** registration@aapmr.org.

12502 ■ NEXT
URL(s): www.apta.org/NEXT/FutureDates
Frequency: Annual. **Description:** With networking opportunity and educational programs. **Audience:** Physical therapists, physical therapists assistants, and allied health professionals. **Principal Exhibits:** With networking opportunity and educational programs. **Telecommunication Services:** conferences@apta.org.

12503 ■ Texas Physical Therapy Association Annual Conference
Texas Physical Therapy Association (TPTA)
166 Hargraves Dr., Ste. C-400-148
Austin, TX 78701
Ph: (512)477-1818
Fax: (512)477-1434
Co. E-mail: info@ptot.texas.gov
URL: http://www.tpta.org
Contact: Michael Geelhoed, President
URL(s): tpta.memberclicks.net/annual-conference-24
Frequency: Annual. **Description:** Physical therapy recruiters, equipment, supplies, books, and services. **Audience:** Physical therapists, physical therapists assistants, and physical therapy students. **Principal Exhibits:** Physical therapy recruiters, equipment, supplies, books, and services. **Telecommunication Services:** lmaxwell@tpta.org.

LIBRARIES

12504 ■ American Physical Therapy Association (APTA)
3030 Potomac Ave., Ste. 100
Alexandria, VA 22305-3085
Ph: (703)684-2782
Free: 800-999-2782
Fax: (703)684-7343
Co. E-mail: memberservices@apta.org
URL: http://www.apta.org
Contact: Roger Herr, President
Facebook: www.facebook.com/
  AmericanPhysicalTherapyAssociation
Linkedin: www.linkedin.com/company/american
  -physical-therapy-association
X (Twitter): x.com/aptatweets
Instagram: www.instagram.com/aptapics
YouTube: www.youtube.com/user/APTAvideo

Description: Publishes reference guides, monographs, brochures and periodicals for physical therapy professionals on education, practice, research and administration. **Founded:** 1921. **Holdings:** 3,000 books; photographs; reports; dissertations; oral histories; conference proceedings; annual

reports; board of directors meeting minutes; House of Delegates minutes. **Subscriptions:** 200 journals and other serials. **Publications:** *APTA Magazine* (11/year); *Physical Therapy & Rehabilitation Journal (PTJ)* (Monthly); *Clinical Management: The Magazine of the American Physical Therapy Association* (Bimonthly); *Physical Therapy Reimbursement News.* **Awards:** Dorothy E. Baethke - Eleanor J. Carlin Award for Excellence in Academic Teaching (Annual); Lucy Blair Service Award (Periodic); Dorothy Briggs Memorial Scientific Inquiry Award (Irregular); Signe Brunnstrom Award for Excellence in Clinical Teaching (Annual); Chattanooga Research Award (Annual); Jules M. Rothstein Golden Pen Award for Scientific Writing (Annual); APTA Honorary Membership (Periodic); Henry O. and Florence P. Kendall Practice Award (Irregular); Mary McMillan Lecture Award (Irregular); Eugene Michels New Investigator Award (Annual); APTA Minority Initiatives Award (Periodic); Margaret L. Moore Award for Outstanding New Academic Faculty Member (Annual); Jack Walker Award (Periodic); Marian Williams Award for Research in Physical Therapy (Annual); Catherine Worthingham Fellows Award (Annual); Helen J. Hislop Award for Outstanding Contributions to Professional Literature (Annual); APTA Minority Scholarships - Faculty Development Scholarship Award (Annual); APTA Minority Scholarships - Scholarship Awards for Student Physical Therapy Assistants (Annual); APTA Minority Scholarships - Scholarship Award for Student Physical Therapists (Annual). **Geographic Preference:** National.

12505 ■ Community Therapy Services Inc. (CTS)
101-1555 St. James St.
  Winnipeg, MB, Canada R3H 1B5
Ph: (204)949-0533
Fax: (204)942-1428
Co. E-mail: cts@ctsinc.mb.ca
URL: http://www.ctsinc.mb.ca
Contact: Janis Lumsden, Executive Director
Founded: 1980.

12506 ■ Florida A&M University (FAMU) - Frederick S. Humphries Science Research Center Library
309 W Pershing St., Ste. 401
  Tallahassee, FL 32301
Ph: (850)599-3393
URL: http://library.famu.edu/index/src
Description: Coleman Library was built in 1948, renovated in 1972, expanded in 1990 and again in 2004. The 88,964 square foot facility includes group study rooms, a student study lounge and cafe, graduate/faculty study carrels, teleconference rooms, and a state of the art information literacy classroom. **Scope:** Pharmacy and pharmaceutical sciences; nursing and allied health science; environmental science; physics; computer science and other related disciplines. **Services:** Library open to the public. **Founded:** 1957. **Holdings:** Monographs; periodicals; print and online journals; indexes; books.

12507 ■ Texas Woman's University - Dallas Center Library
5500 SW Medical Ave.
  Dallas, TX 75235
Ph: (214)689-6580
Co. E-mail: dallaslibrary@twu.edu
URL: http://libguides.twu.edu/dallascenterlibrary
Scope: Nursing; healthcare administration; occupational therapy. **Services:** Interlibrary loan.

12508 ■ University of South Dakota - Christian P. Lommen Health Sciences Library
414 E Clark St.
  Vermillion, SD 57069
Ph: (605)357-1400
Co. E-mail: wegner@usd.edu
URL: http://www.usd.edu/library
Facebook: www.facebook.com/wegnerlibrary
X (Twitter): x.com/WegnerLibrary
Instagram: www.instagram.com/wegnerlibrary
Scope: Anatomy, physiology, pharmacology, microbiology, pathology, biochemistry, nursing, dental hygiene, medical technology, physical therapy, oc-

cupational therapy, physician assistant, clinical medicine, social work. **Services:** Interlibrary loan; copying; SDI; consultation services for hospitals; library open to the public. **Founded:** 1907. **Holdings:** 35,000 books; 60,000 bound periodical volumes; 300 AV programs.

RESEARCH CENTERS

12509 ■ Ball State University - Human Performance Laboratory (HPL)
Ball State University
1340 N McKinley
  Muncie, IN 47306
Ph: (765)285-1158
Co. E-mail: hbl@bsu.edu
URL: http://www.bsu.edu/academics/centersandinsti
  tutes/hpl
Contact: Scott Trappe, PhD, Director
E-mail: strappe@bsu.edu

Description: Integral unit of Ball State University. **Scope:** Human performance, including studies on effects of physical training on skeletal muscular metabolism, strength development, aging, research, biomechanics, youth fitness and health, nutritional studies, endocrine mechanisms (e.g. GH), fluid replacement during and following acute dehydration, muscle glycogen utilization during prolonged exertion, and swimming research. **Founded:** 1965.

12510 ■ Brigham Young University - Human Performance Research Center (HPRC)
PO Box 26800
  Provo, UT 84602-6800
Ph: (801)422-2927
URL: http://byuorg.lib.byu.edu/index.php/Brigham
  _Young_University._Human_Performance_Re-
  search_Center
Contact: Dr. Garth Fisher, Director

Description: Integral unit of College of Health and Human Performance at Brigham Young University. **Scope:** Exercise physiology, including studies of cardiovascular changes due to exercise, muscle changes with exercise, energy cost of various types of exercise, and body composition changes due to exercise; athletic injury rehabilitation, including therapeutic exercise, therapeutic modality, neural control. Biomechanics, including EMG, motion analysis, and muscle force generation. **Founded:** 1972.

12511 ■ Case Western Reserve University Department of Biology - Skeletal Research Center (SRC)
10900 Euclid Ave.
  Cleveland, OH 44106-7080
URL: http://artsci.case.edu/skeletal
Contact: Dr. Arnold I. Caplan, Director
E-mail: aic@cwru.edu

Description: Integral unit of Department of Biology at Case Western Reserve University. Offers medical services through the Musculoskeletal Institute. **Scope:** Tissue engineered regeneration and clinical aspects of skeletal tissue, including cartilage, bones, tendons, and ligaments; bone development and repair; cancer bone metastasis. **Founded:** 1986.

12512 ■ Cleveland FES Center
10701 East Blvd.
  Cleveland, OH 44106
Ph: (216)231-3257
Co. E-mail: info@fescenter.org
URL: http://fescenter.org
Contact: Robert Kirsch, Executive Director
E-mail: rfk3@case.edu
Facebook: www.facebook.com/ClevelandFEScenter
Linkedin: www.linkedin.com/company/cleveland-func
  tional-electrical-stimulation-fes-center
X (Twitter): twitter.com/ClevelandFES
Instagram: www.instagram.com/Cleveland_FES
  _Center
YouTube: www.youtube.com/channel/
  UCSPDNnTSbIX8ieevZb9GUmw
Pinterest: www.pinterest.com/fescenter

Description: Research consortium of Case Western University, Cleveland VA Medical Center and Metro Health Medical Center. Offers consulting services. **Scope:** Functional electrical stimulation (FES) in the restoration of muscle control or sensory function, particularly in the areas of lower and upper extremity deficits, scoliosis, spasticity, respiratory insufficiency, and bladder function. Studies focus on computer-controlled and implanted FES systems for paraplegic and quadriplegic users, persons with hemiplegia due to cerebral trauma or stroke, and persons with spinal cord injuries. **Founded:** 1991. **Educational Activities:** Neural Prothesis Seminar Series (Monthly), Held at 8:30 am in CWRU Biomedical Research Building Room 105.; FESC Seminars (Irregular), Held at 8:30 am in CWRU Biomedical Research Building Room 105.; FESC Workshops, Offer exemplary teaching and training programs.; Neural Prosthesis Seminar Series (Monthly), Presentations focusing on all aspects of FES research from leading researchers throughout the world. Open to all students, researchers, and professionals.

12513 ■ Colorado State University Department of Health and Exercise Science - Human Performance Clinical Research Laboratory (HPCRL)
910 Moby Dr., 1582 Campus Delivery
Fort Collins, CO 80523-1582
Ph: (970)491-6120
Co. E-mail: hpcrl_research_operations@colostate
.edu
URL: http://www.chhs.colostate.edu/hes-hpcrl
Contact: Tiffany Lipsey, Director
E-mail: tiffany.lipsey@colostate.edu

Description: Integral unit of Department of Health and Exercise Science, Colorado State University. Offers stress testing to the community. **Scope:** Human performance, body composition, metabolism, nutrition and sports performance, and exercise physiology. **Founded:** 2000.

12514 ■ Georgia Institute of Technology College of Architecture - Center for Assistive Technology and Environmental Access (CATEA)
512 Means St. NW Ste. 250
Atlanta, GA 30318
Co. E-mail: cidi-support@design.gatech.edu
URL: http://cidi.gatech.edu/about
Facebook: www.facebook.com/CIDIaccess
Linkedin: www.linkedin.com/company/cidiaccess
X (Twitter): twitter.com/cidiaccess
Instagram: www.instagram.com/cidiaccess
YouTube: www.youtube.com/user/AccessibleMe
diaTube/featured

Description: Integral unit of College of Architecture, Georgia Institute of Technology. **Scope:** Universal design and assistive technology in accessible education and online information, workplace accommodations, wheeled mobility and seating, and environmental accessibility. **Founded:** 1980. **Publications:** CATEA Newsletter (Quarterly); CATEA Access Newsletter (Quarterly).

12515 ■ National Institute for Fitness and Sport (NIFS)
250 University Blvd.
Indianapolis, IN 46202
Ph: (317)274-3432
Co. E-mail: membership@nifs.org
URL: http://www.nifs.org
Contact: Jerry Taylor, Chief Executive Officer
E-mail: jtaylor@nifs.org
X (Twitter): x.com/NIFSIndy
Instagram: www.instagram.com/nifsindy
YouTube: www.youtube.com/user/nifsindy

Description: National institute for fitness and sport. **Scope:** Exercise physiology, sports medicine, and health and fitness education. **Founded:** 1985. **Publications:** NIF Source (Bimonthly). **Awards:** NIFS Corporate Fitness Management Internship.

12516 ■ Rehabilitation Institute of Michigan (RIM)
261 Mack Blvd.
Detroit, MI 48201
Ph: (313)745-1203
Co. E-mail: adarim@dmc.org
URL: http://www.rimrehab.org
Contact: Patty Jobbitt, Chief Executive Officer
Facebook: www.facebook.com/RehabInstitute
X (Twitter): x.com/dmc_rehab
Instagram: www.instagram.com/rehabinstitu
temichigan

Description: Incorporated nonprofit 93-bed specialized, physical rehabilitation hospital and research organization within the Detroit Medical Center and School of Medicine, Wayne State University. **Scope:** Physical medicine and rehabilitation medicine, including electromyography, neuropsychology, measures of rehabilitation outcome, and methods of evaluation and treatment of patients with closed head injuries, spinal cord injuries, cerebrovascular accidents, and other diagnoses. Offers inpatient and outpatient medical and rehabilitation services in rheumatology, internal medicine, cardiology, orthopedic surgery, urology, psychiatry, neuropsychology, rehabilitation psychology, rehabilitation nursing, and occupational, speech, and physical therapy. **Founded:** 1951. **Publications:** RIM Research report (Annual); Thinking Cap. **Educational Activities:** RIM Meetings, Focus on rehabilitation clinical interventions and research.

12517 ■ Shirley Ryan AbilityLab - Sensory Motor Performance Program (SMPP)
355 East Erie
Chicago, IL 60611
Co. E-mail: cstarinfo@sralab.org
URL: http://sralab.org/research/labs/single-motor/
people
Contact: Dr. William Zev Rymer, Director
E-mail: zrymer@ric.org

Description: Separately incorporated organization affiliated with Northwestern University Medical School. **Scope:** Rehabilitation medicine, brain trauma, stroke, atherosclerosis, neuromuscular diseases, applied neurophysiology, deep venous thrombosis, spinal cord injury, arthritis, prosthetics/orthotics, rehabilitation nursing, allied health, and communicative disorders. **Founded:** 1954.

12518 ■ University of Calgary Faculty of Kinesiology - Human Performance Laboratory (HPL)
2500 University Dr. NW
Calgary, AB, Canada T2N 1N4
URL: http://kinesiology.ucalgary.ca/research/labs-an
d-centres/human-performance-lab
Contact: Dr. Benno M. Nigg, Founder

Description: Integral unit of University of Calgary. Offers high performance team testing and sport surface/shoe testing. **Scope:** Researches on mobility and longevity; biomechanics, including load on the musculoskeletal system, basic muscle mechanics, joint mechanics, lower back biomechanics, orthoses, sport shoes, and sports equipment. **Founded:** 1981. **Publications:** HPL Annual report (Annual). **Educational Activities:** HPL Congress.

12519 ■ University of Delaware - College of Health Sciences - Department of Kinesiology and Applied Physiology - Human Performance Laboratory
540 S College Ave.
Newark, DE 19713
URL: http://sites.udel.edu/chs-atep/iac

Description: Integral unit of Department of Kinesiology and Applied Physiology, College of Health Sciences, University of Delaware. **Scope:** Sports science, biomechanics, exercise physiology, bone density, and elite skaters. **Founded:** 1933.

12520 ■ University of Florida - College of Health and Human Performance - Department of Applied Physiology and Kinesiology - Center for Exercise Science (CES)
c/o David Vaillancourt
Director

PO Box 118205
FLG 100
Gainesville, FL 32611-8205
Ph: (352)294-1770
Co. E-mail: vcourt@hhp.ufl.edu
URL: http://hhp.ufl.edu/faculty-research/centers-insti
tutes/ces
Contact: Dr. David Vaillancourt, Director
E-mail: vcourt@ufl.edu

Description: Integral unit of Colleges of Medicine and Health and Human Performance at University of Florida. **Scope:** Fitness as it relates to athletic performance, as well as the general population, including research on biomechanics and skill acquisition; health risk factors; exercise and the lumbar and cervical spine, sports, aging, menopause, diabetes, and athletic performance.

12521 ■ University of Texas at Arlington College of Engineering - Human Performance Institute (HPI)
701 S Nedderman Dr.
Arlington, TX 76019
URL: http://www.uta.edu/academics/faculty/profile
?username=kondrask
Contact: George Vincent Kondraske, Director
E-mail: george.kondraske@uta.edu

Description: Integral unit of College of Engineering, University of Texas at Arlington. Offers assistive device services to rehabilitation providers; cooperative research program with outside organizations enabling them to obtain a replica of the instrumented measurement system. **Scope:** Research center carries out research in the following areas; Methods of measurement of human performance, including performance theory, human performance conceptual framework, and specialized instrumentation; studies have broad applications in the fields of space, rehabilitation, the military, and industry. **Founded:** 1986. **Publications:** HPI Newsletter (Semiannual); Progress Report (Annual). **Educational Activities:** Workshops focusing on human performance measurement and rehabilitation technology.

12522 ■ University of Utah - College of Health - Department of Exercise and Sport Science - Human Performance Research Laboratory
383 Colorow Dr., No.4
Salt Lake City, UT 84108
Co. E-mail: julie.wambaugh@health.utah.edu
URL: http://health.utah.edu/health-kinesiology-recrea
tion/kinesiology/research/u-sprt

Description: Integral unit of Department of Exercise and Sport Science, College of Health, University of Utah. Offers Peak Academy, an applied sport science service for the University and surrounding community. **Scope:** Effects of exercise and environment on muscular, cardiovascular, respiratory, nervous, and thermoregulatory systems of the human body. Programs are conducted on exercise and multiple sclerosis patients, women at risk for osteoporosis, exercise and functional abilities and health benefits. **Founded:** 1972.

12523 ■ University of Vermont - College of Medicine - Department of Orthopaedics and Rehabilitation (MMRC) - McClure Musculoskeletal Research Center
4th Fl. 95 Carrigan Dr.
Burlington, VT 05405-0084
URL: http://med.uvm.edu/orthopaedics/MMRC
Contact: Omar Khan, President

Description: Integral unit of Department of Orthopaedics and Rehabilitation, College of Medicine at University of Vermont. Research and development consultation to industry, business, government, and public agencies. **Scope:** Occupational and sports injuries and nontraumatic and congenital disorders, including how musculoskeletal structures are injured and how they heal. Research focuses on lower back pain, including studies of vehicle vibration, exercise, and different low back pain treatments; sports medicine, including knee, shoulder, and ankle injuries; scoliosis, including the etiology of idiopathic scoliosis and growth asymmetry research; osteoarthritis; and joint replacement studies.

START-UP INFORMATION

12524 ■ *"Blaze Pizza Adds Nine Franchise Groups" in FastCasual.com (September 2, 2014)*
Pub: Networld Media Group
Contact: Kathy Doyle, President
E-mail: publisher@networldmediagroup.com
Description: Blaze Fast Fire'd Pizza has signed nine new San Diego area development agreements that will add 67 franchise restaurants to its firm. The company will also open 315 company-owned and franchised pizza restaurants in 33 states by the end of 2015. **Availability:** Online.

12525 ■ *"Do Cool Sh*t: Quit Your Day Job, Start Your Own Business, and Live Happily Ever After"*
Pub: Harper Business
Contact: Hollis Heimbouch, Senior Vice President Publisher
Released: January 20, 2015. **Price:** $16.61, hardcover; $11.97, paperback; $11.49, e-book; $3.13, kindle; $0.05, hardcover(99 used from $0.05); $8, hardcover(44 new from $8.00); $2, paperback(76 used from $2.00); $5.47, paperback(64 new from $5.47). **Description:** Serial social entrepreneur, angel investor, and woman business leader, Miki Agrawal, teaches how to start and run a successful new business. She covers all issues from brainstorming, to raising money to getting press without any connections, and still have time to enjoy life. She created WILD, a farm-to-table pizzeria in New York City and Las Vegas. She also partnered in a children's multimedia company called Super Sprowtz--a story-driven nutrition program for children, and she launched a patented high-tech underware business called THINX. Agrawal also discusses the growth in her businesses. **Availability:** E-book; Print.

12526 ■ *"In a Twist, Pretzel Vendors Will Be Selling Pizza: Wetzels to Launch Blaze Fast-Fire'd Concept with Two SoCal Locations" in Los Angeles Business Journal (Vol. 34, June 4, 2012, No. 23, pp. 12)*
Pub: CBJ L.P.
Contact: Terri Cunningham, Contact
Ed: Bethany Firnhaber. **Description:** Rick and Elise Wetzel, cofounders of Wetzel's Pretzels is launching its new restaurants featuring fast-casual pizza. The concept is of an assembly line process where customers can make 11-inch personalized pizzas with toppings like artichokes, gorgonzola cheese, roasted red peppers and arugula. The pizzas bake in two minutes. **Availability:** Online.

REFERENCE WORKS

12527 ■ *"All Fired Up!" in Small Business Opportunities (November 2008)*
Description: Profile of Brixx Wood Fired Pizza, which has launched a franchising program due to the amount of interest the company's founders received

over the years; franchisees do not need experience in the food industry or pizza restaurant service business in order to open a franchise of their own because all franchisees receive comprehensive training in which they are educated on all of the necessary tools to effectively run the business. **Availability:** Print; Online.

12528 ■ *"Chuck E. Cheese's CEO to Retire" in Dallas Business Journal (Vol. 37, March 28, 2014, No. 29, pp. 6)*
Pub: American City Business Journals, Inc.
Contact: Mike Olivieri, Executive Vice President
Released: Weekly. **Price:** $4, introductory 4-week offer(Digital only). **Description:** CEC Entertainment Inc. president and CEO, Michael Magusiak, is retiring after spending almost 27 years with the parent company Chuck E. Cheese. Magusiak is confident that the future of Chuck E. Cheese's brand will continue to grow in the U.S. and globally. **Availability:** Print; Online.

12529 ■ *"Doyle: Domino's New Pizza Seasoned with Straight Talk" in Crain's Detroit Business (Vol. 26, January 11, 2010, No. 2, pp. 8)*
Pub: Crain Communications Inc.
Contact: Barry Asin, President
Ed: Nathan Skid. **Description:** Interview with J. Patrick Doyle, the CEO of Domino's Pizza, Inc.; the company has launched a new marketing campaign that focuses on its bold new vision. **Availability:** Online.

12530 ■ *"Local Firm Snaps up 91 Area Pizza Huts" in Orlando Business Journal (Vol. 26, January 8, 2010, No. 32, pp. 1)*
Pub: Orlando Business Journal
Contact: Julie Swyers, Director
E-mail: jswyers@bizjournals.com
Ed: Alexis Muellner, Anjali Fluker. **Description:** Orlando, Florida-based CFL Pizza LLC bought the 91 Orlando-area Pizza Hut restaurants for $35 million from parent company Yum! Brands Inc. CFL Pizza plans to distribute parts of the business to Central Florida vendors and the first business up for grabs is the advertising budget. **Availability:** Print; Online.

12531 ■ *"Meet the Maker: Sean Dempsey, Dempsey's Brewery Restaurant & Pub, SD" in Pizza Today (October 24, 2019)*
URL(s): www.pizzatoday.com/news/pizza-headlines/meet-the-maker-sean-dempsey-dempseys-brewery-restaurant-pub-sd/
Ed: Denise Greer. **Released:** October 24, 2019. **Description:** An interview of Sean Dempsey, the owner of Dempsey's Brewery Restaurant & Pub in Watertown, South Dakota about his pizzeria. **Availability:** Online.

12532 ■ *"Ohio Franchisee Buys 21 Jacksonville-Area Papa John's" in Florida Times-Union (December 20, 2010)*
Pub: Florida Times-Union

Ed: Mark Basch. **Description:** Ohio-based Papa John's pizza franchise acquired 21 of the restaurants in Duval, Clay and St. Johns counties in Jacksonville, Florida. **Availability:** Online.

12533 ■ *"Pizza or Beer? Why Kalil Made Right Call" in Business Journal (Vol. 31, January 31, 2014, No. 36, pp. 6)*
Pub: American City Business Journals, Inc.
Contact: Mike Olivieri, Executive Vice President
Released: January 31, 2014. **Price:** $4, Introductory 4-week offer(Digital & Print). **Description:** Businessman, Matt Kalil, purchased the Pieology franchise rights for Minnesota. Kalil will open his first locations in Maple Grove and Saint Paul's Highland Park. The restaurant franchise is expected to have six locations by the end of 2014. **Availability:** Print; Online.

12534 ■ *"Pizza Chain Enters Boston" in Boston Business Journal (Vol. 34, April 25, 2014, No. 12, pp. 3)*
Pub: American City Business Journals, Inc.
Contact: Mike Olivieri, Executive Vice President
Released: April 25, 2014. **Description:** Mitch Roberts and David Peterman have decided to sign a franchise agreement with Blaze Pizza. The two restaurateurs will bring the California-based restaurant chain to Boston, Massachusetts.

12535 ■ *"Study: Restaurants Should Use Compostable Dinnerware to Reduce Food Waste" in PMQ Pizza Magazine (November 2019)*
URL(s): www.pmq.com/reducing-food-waste/
Ed: Brett Jordan. **Released:** November 2019. **Description:** A new study conducted by Eco-Cycle says that restaurants can reduce food waste in landfills by offering compostable plates, cups, and utensils. The study also found that to succeed in composting, restaurants should use either all compostable serviceware or all durable serviceware, in order to cut down on confusion of how to sort the materials after use. **Availability:** Online.

12536 ■ *"Such Crust: Domino's Disses Pizza Hut Dough in Latest Spots" in Advertising Age (Vol. 83, October 1, 2012, No. 35, pp. 3)*
Pub: Crain Communications Inc.
Contact: Barry Asin, President
Ed: Maureen Morrison. **Description:** Domino's Pizza reports Pizza Hut using frozen crusts in its latest advertising campaign, whereas Domino's always uses fresh dough for all of its pizzas. **Availability:** Print; Online.

VIDEO/AUDIO MEDIA

12537 ■ *Main Street Business Insights: Jennifer Jones, Owner of Good Times Coal Fired Pizza & Pub*
URL(s): mainstreet.org/resources/knowledge-hub/podcast/jennifer-jones-owner-of-good-times-coal-fired-pizza-pub-2

Ed: Matt Wagner. **Released:** February 22, 2024. **Description:** Podcast discusses buying a business in a new community.

CONSULTANTS

12538 ■ Riedel Marketing Group (RMG)
5327 E Pinchot Ave.
  Phoenix, AZ 85018
Contact: Ann Riedel, Member
E-mail: ajr@4rmg.com

Description: The house wares and food service industry strategic marketing planning experts. Help manufacturers of house wares and food products solve marketing problems and identify and exploit marketing opportunities. Provides a full-range of strategic marketing planning services including development of marketing strategy, development of fact-based sales presentations, category management, definition of market opportunities and new product development exclusively to the house wares and food service industries. **Scope:** The house wares and food service industry strategic marketing planning experts. Help manufacturers of house wares and food products solve marketing problems and identify and exploit marketing opportunities. Provides a full-range of strategic marketing planning services including development of marketing strategy, development of fact-based sales presentations, category management, definition of market opportunities and new product development exclusively to the house wares and food service industries. **Founded:** 1991. **Publications:** "Your Key Consumer: Her Take on the International Home & Housewares Show," Mar, 2008; "What's Hot, What's Not: The Consumer Speaks," Mar, 2006; "HIPsters SPEAK: What We Love to Buy and Why," Apr, 2005; "Influentials: Who They Are and Why You Should Care," Jun, 2004; "The Seven Secrets to Selling More Housewares," Jan, 2003. **Training:** Consumers Speak: What We Love to Buy and Why, What Do Those Consumers Think; The Seven Secrets to Selling More House wares. **Special Services:** Home Trend Influentials Panel.

FRANCHISES AND BUSINESS OPPORTUNITIES

12539 ■ Bellacino's Pizza and Grinders Inc.
1891 Holton Rd., Ste. B
  Muskegon, MI 49445
Ph: (231)744-3111
URL: http://bellacinos.com
Facebook: www.facebook.com/BellacinosPizzaan
  dGrinders

Description: Firm engages in the production of fast-food products. **Franchised:** 1995. **Training:** Provides 14 days at headquarters, 10 days onsite with ongoing support.

12540 ■ Blaze Pizza, LLC
35 N Lake Ave., Ste. 810
  Pasadena, CA 91101
Ph: (626)585-5880
Fax: (844)270-1480
URL: http://www.blazepizza.com
Contact: Beto Guajardo, Chief Executive Officer

Description: Operates the Blaze Pizza chain of more than 150 mostly franchised fast-casual pizza restaurants. **Founded:** 2011.

12541 ■ Boston's The Gourmet Pizza
14850 Quorum Dr., Ste. 201
  Dallas, TX 75254
Ph: (972)484-9022
Free: 866-277-8721
Fax: (972)484-7630
Co. E-mail: contact@bostons.com
URL: http://www.bostons.com
Facebook: www.facebook.com/BostonsPizzaUSA
Linkedin: www.linkedin.com/company/boston's-res
  taurant-&-sports-bar
X (Twitter): x.com/bostonspizzausa
Instagram: www.instagram.com/bostonspizzausa
YouTube: www.youtube.com/c/BostonsPizzaUSA

Description: Operator of casual restaurant specializes in pizza. **No. of Operating Units:** 400. **Franchised:** 1968. **Equity Capital Needed:** $1,500,000 net worth, $500,000 liquid assets. **Franchise Fee:** $50,000. **Royalty Fee:** 5% of gross sales. **Training:** Yes.

12542 ■ Breadeaux Pizza
825 17th Ave. SW
  Altoona, IA 50009
Ph: (515)967-3708
Co. E-mail: marketing@askarbrands.com
URL: http://breadeauxpizza.com
Facebook: www.facebook.com/PizzaBreadeaux
X (Twitter): x.com/BreadeauxPizza1

Description: Fast pizza operation. **No. of Franchise Units:** 95. **No. of Company-Owned Units:** 3. **Founded:** 1985. **Franchised:** 1985. **Equity Capital Needed:** $69,500-$310,000. **Franchise Fee:** $15,000/15 years. **Training:** Yes.

12543 ■ Buck's Pizza Franchising Corporation, Inc.
PO Box 405
  Dubois, PA 15801
Free: 800-310-8848
Co. E-mail: info@buckspizza.com
URL: http://buckspizza.com
Contact: Lance Benton, Founder

Description: Chain of pizza restaurants. **Founded:** 1994. **Equity Capital Needed:** $163,450–$341,400. **Training:** Provides onsite training at opening.

12544 ■ Chicken Delight
395 Berry St.
  Winnipeg, MB, Canada R3J 1N6
Ph: (204)885-7570
Fax: (204)831-6176
URL: http://www.chickendelight.com
Facebook: www.facebook.com/ChickenDelightInterna
  tional
YouTube: www.youtube.com/user/ChickenDelightDo
  tCom

Description: Chain of restaurant. **Founded:** 1952. **Franchised:** 1952. **Equity Capital Needed:** $273,000-$306,000. **Franchise Fee:** $20,000. **Royalty Fee:** 5%. **Training:** Offers an intensive 4 week, in-field training program at our corporate stores.

12545 ■ CiCi Enterprises, LP
SSCP Management
  120 S Denton Tap Rd.
  Coppell, TX 75019
URL: http://sscpmanagement.com
Facebook: www.facebook.com/Cicis
X (Twitter): x.com/MyCiCis
Instagram: www.instagram.com/officialcicis
YouTube: www.youtube.com/user/cicispizza1985

Description: Operates a chain of pizza restaurants. **Founded:** 1985.

12546 ■ Domino's Pizza of Canada Ltace.
Domino's Pizza, Inc.
  301 Tecumseh Rd., E
  Windsor, ON, Canada N8X 2R5
Ph: (734)930-3030
Fax: (800)253-8182
Co. E-mail: communitygiving@dominos.com
URL: http://biz.dominos.com
X (Twitter): x.com/DominosCanada

Description: Chain of fast food restaurant. It offers menu pizza and sandwiches. **Training:** Required to successfully complete an initial 6 week training program in a designated training center with ongoing support.

12547 ■ Domino's Pizza, Inc.
Domino's Pizza, Inc.
  30 Frank Lloyd Wright Dr.
  Ann Arbor, MI 48105
Ph: (734)930-3030
Fax: (800)253-8182
Co. E-mail: communitygiving@dominos.com
URL: http://biz.dominos.com
Contact: Joseph H. Jordan, President
URL(s): www.dominos.com
Facebook: www.facebook.com/Dominos

Linkedin: www.linkedin.com/company/domino's-pizza
X (Twitter): twiter.com/dominos
Instagram: www.instagram.com/dominos

Description: Pizza restaurant chain engaged in the retail sale of food and related delivery and carryout services through its network of franchise owners and company-owned stores. **Founded:** 1960. **Training:** Yes.

12548 ■ East of Chicago Pizza Co.
121 W High St.
  Lima, OH 45801
Ph: (419)225-7116
Co. E-mail: info@eastofchicago.com
URL: http://www.eastofchicago.com
Contact: Robert J. Honigford, Contact
Facebook: www.facebook.com/EOCPizza
X (Twitter): x.com/eocpizza
Instagram: www.instagram.com/eas
  tofchicagocorporate

Description: Chain of pizza restaurants. **No. of Franchise Units:** 105. **No. of Company-Owned Units:** 5. **Founded:** 1990. **Franchised:** 1991. **Equity Capital Needed:** $130,000-$250,000, store type. **Franchise Fee:** $20,000. **Training:** Yes.

12549 ■ Famous Famiglia
DeBartolo Holdings L.L.C.
  245 Main St., Ste. 410
  White Plains, NY 10601
Ph: (813)908-8400
Fax: (813)908-2206
URL: http://debartoloholdings.com
Contact: Paul Kolaj, President
Facebook: www.facebook.com/FamousFamiglia1
X (Twitter): twitter.com/FamousFamiglia
Instagram: www.instagram.com/famousfamiglia

Description: Chain of pizza restaurants. **Founded:** 1986. **Financial Assistance:** No

12550 ■ Figaro's Pizza
1500 Liberty St. SE, Ste. 160
  Salem, OR 97302
Co. E-mail: contact@figaros.com
URL: http://figaros.com
Facebook: www.facebook.com/figarospizza
X (Twitter): x.com/FigarosPizza
YouTube: www.youtube.com/channel/UCUI9sRseo2B
  1DkX2X82K2bA

Description: Firm is an operator of Pizza restaurant. **Founded:** 1981. **Training:** 18 days in-store and classroom training.

12551 ■ Flying Wedge Pizza Co.
333 Brooksbank Ave., Unit 140
  Vancouver, BC, Canada V7J 3S8
Ph: (604)929-3343
Co. E-mail: flyingwedgeparkandtilford@gmail.com
URL: http://flyingwedgepizza.square.site
Facebook: www.facebook.com/people/Flying-Wedge
  -Park-and-Tilford/100070704920446

Description: Chain of fast food restaurants that serves menu pizza and sandwiches. **No. of Operating Units:** 20. **Founded:** 1989. **Equity Capital Needed:** 359000; Minimum of $139,000 in unencumbered cash. **Franchise Fee:** $35,000. **Training:** Provides 6 weeks training.

12552 ■ Fox's Pizza Den, Inc.
4810 Old William Penn Hwy.
  Murrysville, PA 15632
Ph: (724)519-9686
URL: http://www.foxspizza.com
Contact: Jim Fox, Founder
Facebook: www.facebook.com/foxspizzaden
X (Twitter): x.com/FoxsPizzaDen
Instagram: www.instagram.com/foxspizzaden

Description: Provider of pizza and sandwich restaurants. **No. of Franchise Units:** 275. **Founded:** 1971. **Franchise Fee:** $10,000. **Royalty Fee:** $300. **Financial Assistance:** No **Managerial Assistance:** Complete assistance with business plan, site location, assistance with lease, financing, equipment set-up, supervise renovation and onsite training of franchisee and employees. Assistance with bookkeeping and inventory control.

12553 ■ Garlic Jim's Famous Gourmet Pizza

9796 Edmonds Way
 Edmonds, WA 98020
Ph: (425)771-5467
URL: http://garlicjims.com
Facebook: www.facebook.com/garlicjims
X (Twitter): x.com/garlicjim
Instagram: www.instagram.com/garlicjims
YouTube: www.youtube.com/garlicjim
Description: Chain of pizza restaurants. **Founded:** 2004. **Franchised:** 2003. **Financial Assistance:** Yes **Training:** Initial and ongoing training.

12554 ■ Godfather's Pizza Inc.

2808 N 108th St.
 Omaha, NE 68164
Ph: (402)391-1452
Free: 800-456-8347
Co. E-mail: cservice@godfathers.com
URL: http://www.godfathers.com/home
Contact: Ronald B. Gartlan, President
Facebook: www.facebook.com/godfatherspizza
X (Twitter): x.com/godfatherspizza
Instagram: www.instagram.com/godfatherspizza
YouTube: www.youtube.com/user/GodfathersPizza
Pinterest: www.pinterest.com/godfatherspizza
Description: Pizza restaurant serving 2 types of pizza crust, salads, beverages and sandwiches. **No. of Operating Units:** 640. **Founded:** 1973. **Franchised:** 1974. **Franchise Fee:** $25,000. **Royalty Fee:** 6% . **Training:** Operator of pizza restaurants.

12555 ■ Greco Pizza Donair

165 Rosebury Str.
 Campbellton, NB, Canada E3N 2H2
Ph: (506)759-8822
Co. E-mail: customerservice@greco.ca
URL: http://greco.ca
X (Twitter): x.com/Greco_Pizza
Instagram: www.instagram.com/grecopizza
YouTube: www.youtube.com/channel/UCw9jX4SZr
 59lJTm2BiFnJNw
Description: Home-delivery chain of pizza, donair and oven-sub sandwiches in Atlantic Canada. Specializes in fast, free delivery. **No. of Franchise Units:** 101. **No. of Company-Owned Units:** 2. **Founded:** 1977. **Franchised:** 1977. **Equity Capital Needed:** $40,000 total investment; $140,000-$180,000 Canadian. **Franchise Fee:** $15,000 Canadian. **Training:** Yes.

12556 ■ Happy Joe's Pizza and Ice Cream

5239 Grand Ave.
 Davenport, IA 52807
Ph: (563)332-8811
Co. E-mail: contact@happyjoes.com
URL: http://happyjoes.com
Contact: Thomas Sacco, Chief Executive Officer
Facebook: www.facebook.com/HappyJoes
Linkedin: www.linkedin.com/company/happy-joes
 -pizza
X (Twitter): x.com/HappyJoesPizza
Instagram: www.instagram.com/happyjoespizza
Description: Operator of pizza restaurant. **Founded:** 1972. **Equity Capital Needed:** Full Size?/?PIZZA-GRILLE ($310,250 - $1,045,625); Delivery?/?Carry-out Only ($189,00 - $358,000). **Franchise Fee:** $25,000-$30,000. **Royalty Fee:** 4.5%-5% of Sales. **Training:** Yes.

12557 ■ Hungry Howie's Pizza Inc.

30300 Stephenson Hwy.
 Madison Heights, MI 48071
Ph: (248)414-3300
Fax: (248)414-3301
Co. E-mail: marketing@hungryhowies.com
URL: http://www.hungryhowies.com
Facebook: www.facebook.com/hungryhowies
X (Twitter): x.com/hungryhowies
Instagram: www.instagram.com/hungryhowies
Description: Firm produces pizzas, bread, fresh salads and operates restaurant. **No. of Operating Units:** 600. **Founded:** 1973. **Franchised:** 1982. **Equity Capital Needed:** $300,000 net worth; $100,000 liquid asest. **Franchise Fee:** $25,000. **Royalty Fee:** 0.05. **Training:** Comprehensive class-

room and in-store training program. Field supervision provided for site selection, construction, lease negotiations, store layout, and store opening.

12558 ■ Italo's Pizza Shop Inc.

3560 Middlebranch Rd., NE
 Canton, OH 44705
Ph: (330)455-7443
URL: http://italospizza.com
Contact: Italo Ventura, Owner
Facebook: www.facebook.com/ItalosPizzaMi
 ddlebranch
Description: Operator of pizza restaurant. **No. of Franchise Units:** 11. **No. of Company-Owned Units:** 2. **Founded:** 1966. **Equity Capital Needed:** $15,000. **Franchise Fee:** $20,000. **Royalty Fee:** 5%. **Training:** An intensive 3 weeks of training at corporate headquarters is provided, with additional assistance, if necessary, at the franchisee's location.

12559 ■ Jerry's Subs and Pizza

Jerry's Systems, Inc.
 16260 S Frederick Rd.
 Gaithersburg, MD 20877
Free: 800-990-9176
Fax: (301)948-3508
X (Twitter): x.com/jerrysusa
Description: Fresh-dough pizza and stuffed submarine sandwiches, served in upscale retail outlets, featuring take-out service and self-service dining. **No. of Franchise Units:** 135. **No. of Company-Owned Units:** 3. **Founded:** 1954. **Franchised:** 1981. **Equity Capital Needed:** $250,000-$350,000. **Franchise Fee:** $25,000. **Royalty Fee:** 6%. **Financial Assistance:** Yes **Training:** Available 5 weeks at headquarters.

12560 ■ Jet City Pizza Co.

2323 E Section
 Mount Vernon, WA 98274
Ph: (360)424-2000
URL: http://www.jetcitypizza.com
Facebook: www.facebook.com/jetcitypizza
X (Twitter): x.com/jetcitypizza
Instagram: www.instagram.com/explore/tags/jetci
 typizza
Description: Chain of pizza restaurants. **Founded:** 1994. **Franchised:** 1996. **Training:** Offers 5 week training program that consists of in-store operations at one of our corporate locations and classroom business seminars at headquarters.

12561 ■ Jet's America Inc.

37501 Mound Rd.
 Sterling Heights, MI 48310
Ph: (586)268-5870
Fax: (586)268-6762
URL: http://www.jetspizza.com
Contact: Eugene Jetts, Founder
Facebook: www.facebook.com/JetsPizza
Linkedin: www.linkedin.com/company/jets-pizza
X (Twitter): x.com/JetsPizza
Instagram: www.instagram.com/jetspizza
YouTube: www.youtube.com/user/jetspizza
Description: Manufacturer and distributor of pizza, sidekicks, salads, jetzee, boats, drinks. **Founded:** 1978.

12562 ■ Ledo Pizza Systems Inc.

41 Old Solomons Island Rd., Ste. 201
 Annapolis, MD 21401
Ph: (410)721-6887
URL: http://ledopizza.com
Contact: James Beall, Chief Executive Officer
Facebook: www.facebook.com/ledopizza
X (Twitter): x.com/ledopizza
Instagram: www.instagram.com/ledopizza
Description: Operator of pizza restaurant. **Founded:** 1955. **Franchise Fee:** $30,000. **Training:** Yes.

12563 ■ Little Caesars Pizza

Ilitch Holdings Inc.
 2211 Woodward Ave.
 Detroit, MI 48201
URL: http://www.ilitchholdings.com
Contact: Christopher Ilitch, President
Facebook: www.facebook.com/LittleCaesars

Linkedin: www.linkedin.com/company/little-caesars
X (Twitter): x.com/littlecaesars
Instagram: www.instagram.com/LittleCaesars
Description: Operator of a chain of pizza restaurants. **Founded:** 1959. **Franchised:** 1962. **Equity Capital Needed:** $100,000-net worth of $250,000. **Training:** Training school is 6 weeks in duration and covers every aspect of the business. Provides continuing ongoing classes.

12564 ■ Marco's Inc.

5248 Monroe St.
 Toledo, OH 43623
Ph: (419)882-3300
Co. E-mail: datainquiry@marcos.com
URL: http://www.marcos.com
Contact: Tony Libardi, President
Facebook: www.facebook.com/MarcosPizza
X (Twitter): x.com/marcospizza
Instagram: www.instagram.com/marcospizza
Description: Pizza restaurant chain. **No. of Company-Owned Units:** 25. **Founded:** 1978. **Franchised:** 1979. **Equity Capital Needed:** $224,092 to $549,092. **Franchise Fee:** $25,000. **Financial Assistance:** Yes **Training:** Trained in each and every aspect of the system, including marketing, advertising and administration. Approximately 6 weeks in duration, 2 of which are held at the corporate training center. Prior food service or related experience is required.

12565 ■ Mazzio's Italian Eatery

4441 S 72nd E Ave.
 Tulsa, OK 74145
Ph: (918)663-8880
Fax: (918)641-1236
Co. E-mail: wecare@mazzios.com
URL: http://www.mazzios.com
Facebook: www.facebook.com/Mazzios
X (Twitter): x.com/mazzios
YouTube: www.youtube.com/user/MazziosItalian
Description: Operator of the fast-food restaurant. **No. of Operating Units:** 140. **Founded:** 1961. **Financial Assistance:** No **Training:** Yes.

12566 ■ Me-n-Ed's Pizzerias

5776 N 1st St.
 Fresno, CA 93710
Ph: (559)431-4810
URL: http://www.meneds.com
Contact: John A. Ferdinandi, Contact
Facebook: www.facebook.com/menedspizzeria
X (Twitter): x.com/menedspizzeria
Instagram: www.instagram.com/menedspizzeria
Description: Pizza restaurant chain. **Founded:** 1958. **Training:** Training provided at headquarters, franchisee's location and ongoing support.

12567 ■ MOD Super Fast Pizza Holdings L.L.C. [MOD Pizza]

2035 158th Ct. NE, Ste. 200
 Bellevue, WA 98008
Free: 877-212-0465
Co. E-mail: feedback@modpizza.com
URL: http://www.modpizza.com
Contact: Scott Svenson, Chief Executive Officer
Facebook: www.facebook.com/MODPizza
X (Twitter): x.com/modpizza
Instagram: www.instagram.com/modpizza
Description: Chain of fast casual pizza restaurants. **Founded:** 2008.

12568 ■ New Orleans Pizza (NOP)

50 Main St. E
 Beeton, ON, Canada L0G 1A0
Ph: (905)729-0101
URL: http://neworleanspizza.com
X (Twitter): x.com/neworleanscan
Description: Operator of fast food restaurant. It offers menu pizzas, wings, submarines and much more. **Founded:** 1978. **Training:** Yes.

12569 ■ NYPD Pizza

2589 S Hiawassee Rd.
 Orlando, FL 32835
Ph: (407)293-8880
URL: http://www.nypdpizzeria.com

Contact: Paul Russo, Founder
Facebook: www.facebook.com/OfficialNYPDpizza
X (Twitter): x.com/nypdpizzeria
Instagram: www.instagram.com/nypdpizza
Description: Chain of pizza restaurants. **Founded:** 1996. **Franchised:** 2004. **Royalty Fee:** 6%. **Training:** Training program is mandatory for franchise owner, management team and the pie cooks. First hand experience where the franchisee learns what it takes to operate a franchise. The training and support includes opening to closing, advertising and marketing.

12570 ■ Old Chicago Pizza & Taproom
SPB Hospitality
3550 S Wadsworth Blvd.
Lakewood, CO 80235
URL: http://www.spbhospitality.com
Facebook: www.facebook.com/OCLakewood
Instagram: www.instagram.com/oldchicago
Description: Restaurant offering craft beer, pizza. **Founded:** 1976. **Training:** Yes.

12571 ■ OOC Inc.
3550 San Pablo Dam Rd.
El Sobrante, CA 94820
Contact: James Todd Parent, Chief Executive Officer
Description: Chain of pizza restaurants. **Founded:** 1994. **Financial Assistance:** Yes **Training:** Provides 4 weeks at headquarters, 2 weeks at franchisee's location and ongoing support.

12572 ■ Panago Pizza Inc.
109 Atlantic Ave., Unit 302A
Toronto, ON, Canada M6K 1X4
URL: http://www.panagofranchise.com
Description: Operator of pizza restaurant. It offers menu salads, wings, breadsticks, dips, shakers and sauces. **Founded:** 1986. **Equity Capital Needed:** $160,000-$ 478,000. **Franchise Fee:** $25,000. **Royalty Fee:** 0.05. **Training:** 6 week intensive training program complemented with ongoing operational support.

12573 ■ Papa Gino's, Inc.
600 Providence Hwy.
Dedham, MA 02026
Ph: (781)329-1946
Free: 800-727-2446
Co. E-mail: hallard@thecastlegrp.com
URL: http://www.papaginos.com
Facebook: www.facebook.com/papa.ginos
Linkedin: www.linkedin.com/company/papa-gino's
X (Twitter): x.com/papaginos
Instagram: www.instagram.com/papaginos
Description: Operator of pizza restaurants. **Founded:** 1961. **Financial Assistance:** No **Training:** Yes.

12574 ■ Papa John's International, Inc.
Papa John's International, Inc.
2002 Papa John's Blvd.
Louisville, KY 40299-2367
Ph: (502)261-7272
Free: 888-777-7272
Co. E-mail: online@papajohns.com
URL: http://www.papajohns.com
Contact: Elias Reyna, Chief People Officer Chief Diversity Officer
Facebook: www.facebook.com/papajohnsus
X (Twitter): twitter.com/papajohns
Instagram: www.instagram.com/papajohns
YouTube: www.youtube.com/user/papajohns
Description: Operates and franchises pizza delivery and carryout restaurants and in certain international markets, dine-in and delivery restaurants. **Founded:** 1984. **Training:** Provides initial management training program and offers ongoing assistance regarding operations, marketing, real estate and development, food and equipment supply.

12575 ■ Papa Murphy's Holdings, Inc.
Papa Murphy's Holdings, Inc.
8000 NE Pk. Dr., Ste. 350
Vancouver, WA 98662
Ph: (360)260-7272
Free: 844-620-2501

Co. E-mail: guestservices@papamurphys.com
URL: http://www.papamurphys.com
Contact: Victoria Tullett, General Counsel
Facebook: www.facebook.com/papamurphyspizza
X (Twitter): x.com/papamurphys
Instagram: www.instagram.com/papamurphys
Pinterest: www.pinterest.com/papamurphys
Description: Operator of pizza restaurants offering made-to-order pizza, salads, and desserts. **Founded:** 1981. **Training:** Offers extensive training for new franchise owners, including in-store skill training and structured classroom training at our headquarters.

12576 ■ Papa's Pizza To-Go Inc.
94 Town Sq.
Blairsville, GA 30512
Ph: (706)745-1999
URL: http://papaspizzatogo.com
Facebook: www.facebook.com/PapasPizzaToGo
Instagram: www.instagram.com/papaspizzatogo_
Description: Pizzeria. **Founded:** 1986. **Training:** Operator of pizza restaurants.

12577 ■ Paul Revere's Pizza
1935 51st St. NE
Cedar Rapids, IA 52402
Ph: (319)399-1500
URL: http://paulreverespizza.com
Contact: Jeffrey A. Schuster, Contact
Facebook: www.facebook.com/PRPCR
Description: Distributor of pizza, pasta, sandwiches, ribs, salads and much more. **Equity Capital Needed:** $100,700 to $213,000. **Franchise Fee:** $15,000. **Royalty Fee:** 4% of the gross sales. **Financial Assistance:** No **Training:** Yes.

12578 ■ Pizza Depot
2 Automatic Rd., Unit 122
Brampton, ON, Canada L6S 6K8
Ph: (416)289-9711
Free: 866-597-9711
Fax: (905)458-8644
Co. E-mail: info@pizzadepot.ca
URL: http://www.pizzadepot.ca
Facebook: www.facebook.com/PizzaDepot
X (Twitter): x.com/CdnPizzaDepot
Instagram: www.instagram.com/pizzadepotca
Description: Operator of pizza restaurant. It offers menu pizza, sandwiches, salads, wings, sides and much more. **Founded:** 2000. **Training:** Yes.

12579 ■ Pizza Factory Inc.
40120 Hwy. 41
Oakhurst, CA 93644
Ph: (559)683-2700
Free: 800-654-4840
Co. E-mail: info@pizzafactoryinc.com
URL: http://www.pizzafactory.com
Contact: Mary Jane Riva, Chief Executive Officer
Facebook: www.facebook.com/pizzafactoryinc
X (Twitter): x.com/PizzaFactoryInc
Instagram: www.instagram.com/pizzafactoryinc
Description: Family-oriented pizza restaurant, serving pizza, pasta, sandwiches and salad bar. Specializing in communities of 15,000 or less. **No. of Franchise Units:** 100. **Founded:** 1979. **Franchised:** 1985. **Financial Assistance:** No **Training:** Offers 325 hours training.

12580 ■ Pizza Nova Take Out Ltd.
1260 Lawrence Ave., E
Toronto, ON, Canada M3A 1C4
Ph: (416)439-0000
Co. E-mail: call.center@pizzanova.com
URL: http://www.pizzanova.com
Contact: Domenic Primucci, President
Facebook: www.facebook.com/PizzaNova
X (Twitter): x.com/PizzaNova
Description: Chain of pizza restaurants. Strives to meet the demands of the consumers, planning and opening many more restaurants across Ontario and beyond. **Founded:** 1963. **Franchised:** 1963. **Equity Capital Needed:** $80,000-$100,000. **Franchise Fee:** $20,000. **Royalty Fee:** 0.06. **Training:** Yes.

12581 ■ Pizza Patron Inc.
510 Portland Rd.
San Antonio, TX 78216
Ph: (210)614-7888
Fax: (210)614-8876
URL: http://www.pizzapatron.com
Contact: Charles M. Loflin, President
Facebook: www.facebook.com/PizzaPatron
X (Twitter): x.com/pizzapatron
Instagram: www.instagram.com/pizzapatron
Description: Operator of pizza restaurant. **No. of Operating Units:** 97.0. **Founded:** 1986. **Equity Capital Needed:** $241,550-$515,490. **Franchise Fee:** $20,000. **Royalty Fee:** 5% of sales. **Training:** A comprehensive hands-on training program, onsite, at our company store and concludes with a 4 day owner simulation where you run our company store as if it were your own and ongoing support.

12582 ■ The Pizza Pipeline
3633 E Sanson
Spokane, WA 99217
Ph: (509)326-1977
URL: http://www.pizzapipeline.com
Facebook: www.facebook.com/pizzapipeline
Description: Pizza delivery. **Founded:** 1988. **Financial Assistance:** No **Training:** Includes 4-6 weeks training at corporate headquarters, 2 weeks at franchisee's location and ongoing support.

12583 ■ Pizza Pit
6306 Monona Dr.
Monona, WI 53716
Ph: (608)221-6777
Fax: (608)819-6625
URL: http://pizzapit.biz
X (Twitter): x.com/pizzapit
Instagram: www.instagram.com/realpizzapit
YouTube: www.youtube.com/channel/
UCgYICB8NoAJ7gozfaF94IUQ
Description: Operator of a chain of pizza restaurants. **Founded:** 1969. **Equity Capital Needed:** $80,000-$300,000. **Franchise Fee:** $25,000. **Royalty Fee:** 0.0325. **Training:** Yes.

12584 ■ Pizza Pizza
500 Kipling Ave.
Toronto, ON, Canada M8Z 5E5
Ph: (416)967-1111
Co. E-mail: feedback@pizzapizza.ca
URL: http://www.pizzapizza.ca/store/1/delivery
Facebook: www.facebook.com/PizzaPizzaCanada
X (Twitter): x.com/pizzapizzaltd
Instagram: www.instagram.com/pizzapizzaltd
Description: Operator of pizza restaurant. Franchised Canadian pizza quick-service restaurant. **Founded:** 1967. **Training:** Offers 8 weeks training and ongoing support. **Educational Activities:** Toronto International Boat Show (Annual).

12585 ■ Pizza Schimizza
Schmizza International, Inc.
1500 Liberty St. SE
Salem, OR 97302
Ph: (503)371-9318
Fax: (503)363-5364
Description: Gourmet New York style pizza. **No. of Franchise Units:** 24. **Founded:** 1993. **Franchised:** 2001. **Equity Capital Needed:** $150,000 liquid. **Franchise Fee:** $35,000 1st; $10,000 2nd; $5,000 additional. **Training:** Yes.

12586 ■ Pizzaville Inc.
741 Rowntree Dairy Rd.
Woodbridge, ON, Canada L4L 5T9
Ph: (416)736-3636
Fax: (905)850-0339
Co. E-mail: info@pizzaville.ca
URL: http://www.pizzaville.ca
Contact: Angelo Contardi, President
Facebook: www.facebook.com/pizzavilleinc
X (Twitter): x.com/pizzaville
Description: Operator of pizza restaurant offers menu salads, wings, breadsticks, organic juices, dips, shakers and sauces. **Founded:** 1963. **Equity Capital Needed:** $275,000-$300,000. **Royalty Fee:** $300/

week for all new stores, and progressively increases annually at a rate of$50/week for the first term of the Franchise Agreement (new stores only). **Training:** Yes.

12587 ■ Pizzeria Valdiano (PV)
Ligman Franchise group
 1610 Town Ctr. Dr.
 Lakeland, FL 33803
Ph: (813)935-5087
Fax: (813)425-5799
Contact: Joe Liguori, Contact
E-mail: joe@pizzeriavaldiano.com
X (Twitter): x.com/ValdianoPizza

Description: Pizzeria in Orlando. **No. of Franchise Units:** 1. **No. of Company-Owned Units:** 1. **Founded:** 2006. **Franchised:** 2007. **Equity Capital Needed:** $276,000-$394,000. **Franchise Fee:** $27,500. **Training:** Yes.

12588 ■ Pizzicato Gourmet Pizza
2420 5th Ave.
 San Diego, CA 92101
URL: http://www.pizzicatopizza.com
Facebook: www.facebook.com/PizzicatoPDX
Instagram: www.instagram.com/pizzicatopdx

Description: Upscale gourmet pizza & salads. **Franchised:** 2004. **Training:** Yes.

12589 ■ RAVE Restaurant Group, Inc.
RAVE Restaurant Group, Inc.
 3551 Plano Pky.
 The Colony, TX 75056-5245
Ph: (469)384-5000
Free: 877-574-9924
Co. E-mail: media@raverg.com
URL: http://www.raverg.com
Contact: Brandon Solano, Chief Executive Officer

Description: Owner, franchisor, and supplier of pizza restaurants. **Founded:** 2011.

12590 ■ Rocky Rococo Pizza and Pasta
105 E Wisconsin Ave., Ste. 101
 Oconomowoc, WI 53066
Free: 800-888-7625
Co. E-mail: rockycares@rockyrococo.com
URL: http://rockyrococo.com
Facebook: www.facebook.com/rockyrococo
Linkedin: www.linkedin.com/company/rockyrococo
X (Twitter): x.com/rockyrococo

Description: Operator of pizza restaurant. **Founded:** 1974. **Franchised:** 1995. **Franchise Fee:** $25,000. **Training:** Yes.

12591 ■ Rotelli Pizza & Pasta
501 E Atlantic Ave.
 Delray Beach, FL 33483
Ph: (561)272-7270
Co. E-mail: info@rotellipp.com
URL: http://rotellipizzapasta.com
Contact: Joseph Bilotti, Contact

Description: Operator of pizza and pasta restaurant. **Founded:** 1999. **Training:** Provides a total of 6 weeks training between headquarters and franchisee's location and ongoing support.

12592 ■ San Francisco Oven
1736 E Sunshine, Ste. 1011
 Springfield, MO 65804

Description: Producer and distributor of pizza, sandwiches, and soups. **Founded:** 2001. **Franchised:** 2002. **Training:** Yes.

12593 ■ Snappy Tomato Pizza Co.
6111 A Burgundy Hill Dr., Ste. C
 Burlington, KY 41005
Ph: (859)525-4680
Free: 888-463-7627
Fax: (859)525-4686
Co. E-mail: snappyfeedback@snappytomato.com
URL: http://www.snappytomato.com
Contact: Tim Gayhart, President
Facebook: www.facebook.com/SnappyTomatoPizza
X (Twitter): x.com/Snappy_Tomato
Instagram: www.instagram.com/snappytomato

Description: A delivery, dine-in and carry-out pizzeria that makes the highest-quality pizza available. Menu features hoagies, salads and award-winning "Ranch Pizza.". **No. of Franchise Units:** 59. **Equity Capital Needed:** $99,000-$241,000. **Franchise Fee:** $14,000. **Royalty Fee:** 5% of weekly gross sales. **Training:** Training program covers every aspect of the business, including actual time in stores getting hands-on experience.

12594 ■ Straw Hat Pizza
901 Marina Village Pkwy
 Alameda, CA 94501
Ph: (510)864-8600
URL: http://www.strawhatpizzaalameda.com

Description: Operator of pizza restaurants. **No. of Operating Units:** 50.0. **Founded:** 1959. **Financial Assistance:** Yes **Training:** Yes.

12595 ■ Stuft Pizza, Stuft Pizza Bar & Grill, Stuft Pizza Pronto
78015 Main St., Ste. 100
 La Quinta, CA 92253

Ph: (760)777-9989
URL: http://www.stuftpizzabarandgrill.com
Facebook: www.facebook.com/StuftPizzaBarAndGrill
Instagram: www.instagram.com/stuftpizzabarandgrill

Description: Chain of restaurants. **Founded:** 1976. **Training:** Yes.

12596 ■ Villa Restaurant Group Inc. (VRG)
25 Washington St.
 Morristown, NJ 07960
Ph: (973)285-4800
Co. E-mail: customerservice@villarestaurantgroup .com
URL: http://www.villarestaurantgroup.com
Contact: Biagio Scotto, President
Linkedin: www.linkedin.com/company/villa-restaurant-group

Description: Quick service pizza and Italian restaurant. **Founded:** 1964. **Training:** Yes.

12597 ■ Vocelli Pizza
4740 Baum Blvd.
 Pittsburgh, PA 15213
Ph: (412)246-4444
URL: http://www.vocellipizza.com
Contact: Varol Ablak, Contact
Facebook: www.facebook.com/vocellipizza
X (Twitter): x.com/vocellipizza

Description: Pizza, subs, wings; delivery or carryout. **Founded:** 1988. **Franchised:** 1988. **Financial Assistance:** Yes **Training:** Yes.

12598 ■ Whata Lotta Pizza
7011 Warner Ave.
 Huntington Beach, CA 92647
Ph: (714)848-6148
URL: http://www.whatalottapizza.com
Contact: Wayne Lavigne, Founder

Description: Chain of restaurants. **Founded:** 1992. **Training:** Yes.

12599 ■ Z Pizza
30822 S Coast Hwy.
 Laguna Beach, CA 92651
Ph: (949)499-4949
URL: http://www.zpizza.com
Facebook: www.facebook.com/zpizza
X (Twitter): x.com/zpizza
Instagram: www.instagram.com/zpizza
Pinterest: www.pinterest.com/zpizza

Description: They serve delicious gourmet style pizza, pasta and sandwiches. **Founded:** 1986. **Franchised:** 1999. **Training:** 4 weeks at headquarters, 2 weeks at franchisee's location, and ongoing support.

REFERENCE WORKS

12600 ■ *"How Does Plant Leasing Work?" in Natura (July, 2013)*
URL(s): naturahq.com/2013/07/how-does-plant-leasing-work/
Released: July 2013. **Description:** An introduction to plant leasing and its benefits. Most businesses do not have time to take care of plants, so hiring someone to lease and care for plants in your building is a solid solution. It also allows an opportunity to change things around each season, add more plants, or thin them out if they are too much. **Availability:** Online.

TRADE SHOWS AND CONVENTIONS

12601 ■ Nursery/Landscape Expo
Texas Nursery & Landscape Association (TNLA)
7730 S IH-35
Austin, TX 78745-6698
Ph: (512)280-5182
Co. E-mail: info@tnlaonline.org
URL: http://www.tnlaonline.org
Contact: Amy Graham, President
E-mail: agraham@tnlaonline.org
URL(s): www.nurserylandscapeexpo.org
Frequency: Annual. **Description:** Plant materials including foliage, bedding plants, trees, and palms, allied products including machinery, equipment, and supplies for horticulture and landscape industry. **Audience:** Industry professionals. **Principal Exhibits:** Plant materials including foliage, bedding plants, trees, and palms, allied products including machinery, equipment, and supplies for horticulture and landscape industry. **Telecommunication Services:** expo@nurserylandsca.wpengine.com.

CONSULTANTS

12602 ■ Foliage Service by Concepts
PO Box 30387
Portland, OR 97294
Ph: (503)234-3459
Co. E-mail: info@foliage-services.com

URL: http://www.foliage-services.com
Contact: Carl D. Mark, Contact
Description: Firm provides designs, placements, cares, and retails interior plants for various office and building environments. **Scope:** Firm provides designs, placements, cares, and retails interior plants for various office and building environments. **Founded:** 1968.

FRANCHISES AND BUSINESS OPPORTUNITIES

12603 ■ Foliage Design Systems (FDS)
7048 Narcoossee Rd.
Orlando, FL 32822
Ph: (407)245-7776
Free: 800-933-7351
Co. E-mail: info@foliagedesign.com
URL: http://www.foliagedesign.com
Contact: David Liu, President
Facebook: www.facebook.com/FoliageDesignOrlando
Linkedin: www.linkedin.com/company/foliage-design-systems-of-orlando
X (Twitter): x.com/interiorscape
Description: Provides the sale, lease and short-term rental of live, artificial and preserved interior foliage and decorative containers. Related products include seasonal decorative items. Designs, installs and maintains interior foliage in office buildings, hotels, residences, and restaurants. **No. of Franchise Units:** 37. **No. of Company-Owned Units:** 3. **Founded:** 1971. **Franchised:** 1980. **Equity Capital Needed:** $49,400-$144,000, includes initial franchise fee. **Franchise Fee:** $25,000-$100,000. **Training:** followed by onsite training covering all facets of business from plant care and plant identification to sales and marketing to office procedures. Complete operations manuals provided.

RESEARCH CENTERS

12604 ■ Ohio State University College of Food, Agricultural, and Environmental Sciences - C. Wayne Ellett Plant and Pest Diagnostic Clinic (PPDC)
1680 Madison Ave.
Wooster, OH 44691

Ph: (614)292-5006
Fax: (614)466-9754
Co. E-mail: ppdc@osu.edu
URL: http://ppdc.osu.edu
Description: Multidisciplinary testing laboratory at Ohio State University. Offers diagnosis of plant problems, plant diseases, insects, weeds. **Scope:** Plant disease diagnosis, including insect and mite identification, plant and weed identification, and nematode extractions. **Founded:** 1985.

12605 ■ University of British Columbia - Botanical Garden - Library & Archives
6804 SW Marine Dr.
Vancouver, BC, Canada V6T 1Z4
Ph: (604)822-4208
Fax: (604)822-2016
Co. E-mail: garden.info@ubc.ca
URL: http://botanicalgarden.ubc.ca
Contact: Daniel Mosquin, Manager
E-mail: daniel.mosquin@ubc.ca
Facebook: www.facebook.com/UBCgarden
X (Twitter): twitter.com/ubcgarden
Instagram: www.instagram.com/ubcgarden
Pinterest: www.pinterest.com/ubcgarden
Description: Integral unit of University of British Columbia. Develops professional training programs for the British Columbia nursery industry. Offers plant information and identification services. **Scope:** Plant genomics; evolution of plant development and plant molecular systematics; biosystematics of flora of British Columbia and development of horticultural material from existing ornamentals and indigenous plants, including cytological, morphological, biochemical, and phytogeographical evaluation and specific breeding and selection programs of ornamentals. The Plant Introduction Scheme of the Botanical Garden is a cooperative research program with nursery trades and landscape architects established to facilitate research, introduction, and production of new plant cultivars to the public. Collects and evaluates superior forms of native British Columbia plants for commercial introduction. **Founded:** 1916. **Holdings:** 3,000 books; 2,500 slides; 150 magazine; negatives; journal; monographs; periodicals; manuals; ephemera; documents; records; audio and video recordings. **Publications:** *Davidsonia*; *UBC Botanical Garden Newsletter* (Monthly). **Educational Activities:** UCB Botanical Garden Workshops.

ASSOCIATIONS AND OTHER ORGANIZATIONS

12606 ■ American Society of Plumbing Engineers (ASPE)
6400 Shafer Ct., Ste. 350
Rosemont, IL 60018-4914
Ph: (847)296-0002
Co. E-mail: info@aspe.org
URL: http://www.aspe.org
Contact: Jim Zebrowski, President
Facebook: www.facebook.com/AmericanSocie
tyofPlumbingEngineers
Linkedin: www.linkedin.com/company/american-socie
ty-of-plumbing-engineers
X (Twitter): x.com/ASPEorg
Instagram: www.instagram.com/aspe_org
YouTube: www.youtube.com/channel/UCJFy5ih
4JvM9KDBE3EOglRw

Description: Engineers and designers involved in the design and specification of plumbing systems; manufacturers, governmental officials, and contractors related to the industry may become members on a limited basis. Resolves professional problems in plumbing engineering; advocates greater cooperation among members and plumbing officials, contractors, laborers, and the public. Code committees examine regulatory codes pertaining to the industry and submit proposed revisions to code writing authorities to simplify, standardize, and modernize all codes. Sponsors American Society of Plumbing Engineers Research Foundation. **Founded:** 1964. **Educational Activities:** ASPE Convention & Expo (Biennial); ASPE Technical Symposium (Biennial); American Society of Plumbing Engineers Convention & Expo (Biennial). **Awards:** Alfred Steele Engineering Scholarship (Annual); ASPE'S Honor Roll of Employers (Periodic); ASPE Industry Award (Biennial); George W. Runkle Award of Merit (Biennial). **Geographic Preference:** National.

12607 ■ American Society of Sanitary Engineering (ASSE)
18927 Hickory Creek Dr., Ste. 220
Mokena, IL 60448
Ph: (708)995-3019
Co. E-mail: general.info@asse-plumbing.org
URL: http://www.asse-plumbing.org
Contact: Scott Hamilton, Senior Director
E-mail: scott.hamilton@asse-plumbing.org
Facebook: www.facebook.com/ASSE1906
X (Twitter): x.com/ASSE_Intl

Description: Plumbing officials, sanitary engineers, plumbers, plumbing contractors, building officials, architects, engineers, designing engineers, physicians, and others interested in health. Conducts research on plumbing and sanitation, and develops performance standards for components of the plumbing system. Sponsors disease research program and other studies of water-borne epidemics. **Founded:** 1906. **Awards:** Henry B. Davis Award (Annual); Dewey R. Dedrick, Jr. Award (Periodic); ASSE Fellowship Award (Annual). **Geographic Preference:** National.

12608 ■ American Supply Association (ASA)
1200 N Arlington Heights Rd., Ste. 150
Itasca, IL 60143
Ph: (630)467-0000
Fax: (630)467-0001
Co. E-mail: info@asa.net
URL: http://www.asa.net
Contact: Bill Condron, President
Facebook: www.facebook.com/
americansupplyassociation
Linkedin: www.linkedin.com/company/american
-supply-association-asa
X (Twitter): x.com/ASA_HQ

Description: Represents wholesale, distributors, and manufacturers of plumbing and heating, cooling, pipes, valves, and fittings. Compiles statistics on operating costs and makes occasional studies of compensation, fringe benefits, wages, and salaries. Conducts research studies and forecasting surveys. Maintains management institutes, home study courses under the ASA Education Foundation and Endowment program, provides technology and produces a CD-ROM and internet catalogue of manufacturers. **Founded:** 1969. **Publications:** *American Supply Association--Membership Directory*; *ASA News*; *Operating Performance Report* (Annual); *Operating Performance Report (OPR)* (Annual); *American Supply Association--Member Directory* (Annual). **Educational Activities:** University of Innovative Distribution (Annual). **Geographic Preference:** National.

12609 ■ Association of Independent Manufacturers'/Representatives, Inc. (AIM/R)
800 Roosevelt Rd., Ste. C-312
Glen Ellyn, IL 60137
Ph: (630)942-6581
Co. E-mail: info@aimr.net
URL: http://www.aimr.net
Contact: Mike Powers, President
E-mail: mpowers@keylinesales.com
Facebook: www.facebook.com/AIMR.Rep
Linkedin: www.linkedin.com/company/aim-r
X (Twitter): x.com/aimr_r
Instagram: www.instagram.com/aimr.rep

Description: Manufacturers' representative companies in the plumbing-heating-cooling-piping industry promoting the use of independent sales representatives. Conducts educational programs and establishes a code of ethics between members and customers. **Founded:** 1972. **Publications:** *AIM/R News and Views* (Quarterly). **Geographic Preference:** National.

12610 ■ Plumbing & Drainage Institute (PDI)
800 Tpke., St., Ste. 300
North Andover, MA 01845
Ph: (978)557-0720
Free: 800-589-8956
Co. E-mail: pdi@pdionline.org
URL: http://www.pdionline.org

Description: Represents manufacturers of engineered plumbing and drainage products. Promotes the advancement of engineered plumbing products through publicity, public relations, research and standardization of plumbing requirements. Works on codes and standards for plumbing drainage products. **Founded:** 1928. **Geographic Preference:** National.

12611 ■ Plumbing Manufacturers International (PMI)
1750 Tysons Blvd., Ste. 1500
McLean, VA 22102
Ph: (847)481-5500
Co. E-mail: pmiadmin@safeplumbing.org
URL: http://www.safeplumbing.org
Contact: Martin Knieps, President
Facebook: www.facebook.com/pmihome
X (Twitter): x.com/safeplumbing
YouTube: www.youtube.com/user/SafePlumbing

Description: Manufacturers of plumbing products. **Founded:** 1974. **Geographic Preference:** Multinational.

REFERENCE WORKS

12612 ■ *"3 Hard Parts of Starting a Plumbing Business"* in Home Business (December 12, 2019)
Released: December 12, 2019. **Description:** Discusses three areas of a plumbing business that can create challenges: licensing/insurance, choosing the right location, and advertising. **Availability:** Online.

12613 ■ *"7 Plumbing Business Management Tips to Streamline and Grow"* in Service Titan Blog (November 5, 2020)
Released: November 05, 2020. **Description:** Managing a plumbing business in today's digital world requires a few more skills than simply knowing how to tweak a water pressure regulator or install a sump pump. For best plumbing business management, plumbing contractors must also know how to price their services correctly, create effective marketing campaigns to gain new customers, and recruit new hires to fill the technician gap in a highly competitive field. This article discusses how to position your plumbing business for growth by taking your management approach to the next level. **Availability:** Online.

12614 ■ *9 Plumbing Digital Marketing Ideas for Small Business Owners*
Description: Lack of a strong online presence will affect how well you compete in the market as a business owner. This article details the importance of internet marketing to reach wider audiences for your plumbing business. **Availability:** Online.

12615 ■ *"11 Tips for Starting a Successful Plumbing Business"* in Design Hill Blog (July 11, 2018)
Ed: Charles Darwin. **Released:** July 11, 2018. **Description:** Discusses the varying specialties

involved in owning a plumbing business as well as tips on business planning as you start your plumbing business. **Availability:** Online.

12616 ■ *"Be Safe: CSE Requires a Series of Steps" in Contractor (Vol. 56, October 2009, No. 10, pp. 40)*

Ed: Dave Yates. **Description:** Confined Space Entry claims 91 lives each year and plumbers can prevent this by following several steps starting with the use of a four-gas analyzer which costs $1,262. It measures oxygen levels, as well as combustible gases, carbon monoxide, and hydrogen sulfide. **Availability:** Print; Online.

12617 ■ *"BIM and You: Know Its Benefits and Risks" in Contractor (Vol. 57, January 2010, No. 1, pp. 46)*

Ed: Susan Linden McGreevy. **Description:** Building Information Modeling is intended to be "collaborative" and this could raise legal issues if a contractor sends an electronic bid and it is filtered out. Other legal issues that mechanical contractors need to consider before using this technology are discussed. **Availability:** Print; Online.

12618 ■ *"A Burning Issue: Lives Are at Stake Every Day" in Contractor (Vol. 56, October 2009, No. 10, pp. 29)*

Description: American Society of Plumbing Engineers has been accused of being biased for supporting rules that require residential fire sprinklers although the society's members will not receive any benefit from their installation. The organization trains and certifies plumbing engineers who design life-saving fire protection systems. **Availability:** Online.

12619 ■ *"The Business End of Staying in Business" in Contractor (Vol. 56, September 2009, No. 9, pp. 51)*

Ed: Al Schwartz. **Description:** Advice on how to manage a new plumbing business in the United States is offered. The transition from being a workman to an employer is seen as one that accompanies a steep learning curve. The importance of managing cash flow is also highlighted. **Availability:** Print; Online.

12620 ■ *"Charlotte Pipe Launches Satirical Campaign" in Contractor (Vol. 57, January 2010, No. 1, pp. 6)*

Description: Charlotte Pipe and Foundry Co. launched an advertising campaign that uses social media and humor to make a point about how it can be nearly impossible to determine if imported cast iron pipes and fittings meet the same quality standards as what is made in the U.S. The campaign features 'pipe whisperers' and also spoofs pipe sniffing dogs. **Availability:** Print; Online.

12621 ■ *"Commercial Water Efficiency Initiatives Announced" in Contractor (Vol. 56, November 2009, No. 11, pp. 5)*

Ed: Robert P. Mader. **Description:** Plumbing engineers John Koeller and Bill Gauley are developing a testing protocol for commercial toilets. The team said commercial toilets should have a higher level of flush performance than residential toilets for certification. The Environmental Protection Agency's WaterSense program wants to expand the program into the commercial/institutional sector. **Availability:** Print; Online.

12622 ■ *"Contractors Can't Do It Alone, PHCC's Pfeffer Says" in Contractor (Vol. 56, October 2009, No. 10, pp. 3)*

Ed: Robert P. Mader. **Description:** President Herbert "Skip" Pfeffer of the Plumbing-Heating-Cooling Contractors National Association says lobbying and education are the services that the association offers that a contractor cannot do individually. Pfeffer says the dues for the association are set up in a manner that allows members to pay monthly. **Availability:** Print; Online.

12623 ■ *"Corporate Park Retrofits for Water Savings" in Contractor (Vol. 56, October 2009, No. 10, pp. 5)*

Description: Merrit Corporate Park in Norwalk, Connecticut has been interested in improving building efficiency and one of their buildings has been retrofit-

ted with water-efficient plumbing systems which will allow them to save as much as two million gallons of water. ADP Service Corp. helped the park upgrade their plumbing system. **Availability:** Online.

12624 ■ *"CSE: Contractors Are Always Responsible" in Contractor (Vol. 56, November 2009, No. 11, pp. 34)*

Ed: Dave Yates. **Description:** Plumbing contractors should purchase a long snorkel hose, a tripod with manual-crank hoist, and a sump pump in order to prevent accidents associated with Confined Space Entry. Liability issues surrounding confined space entry prevention and accidents are discussed. **Availability:** Print; Online.

12625 ■ *"The Customer Is Always Right Even When He's Wrong" in Contractor (Vol. 57, February 2010, No. 2, pp. 12)*

Ed: Al Schwartz. **Description:** Mechanical contractors should note that customers will make a judgment based upon the impression that they form on their first meeting. Contractors can maintain a professional image by washing their trucks and having the personnel dress uniformly. Contractors have every right to demand that employees clean up and make a better impression on customers. **Availability:** Print; Online.

12626 ■ *Directory of Listed Plumbing Products*

Pub: International Association of Plumbing and Mechanical Officials

Contact: D. J. Nunez, President

URL(s): pld.iapmo.org

Description: Covers about 1,500 manufacturers of approximately 10,000 plumbing products and appliances. **Entries include:** Manufacturer name, address, product name, model number, product description. **Arrangement:** Alphabetical. **Indexes:** Manufacturer, product. **Availability:** Print.

12627 ■ *"Do the Right Thing" in Contractor (Vol. 56, December 2009, No. 12, pp. 16)*

Ed: Robert P. Mader. **Description:** Applewood Plumbing, Heating and Electric has won Contractor magazine's 2009 Contractor of the Year Award. The company has ranked eighth among more than 300 service companies in the United States. A brief history of the company is also provided. **Availability:** Print; Online.

12628 ■ *"EPA Finalizes WaterSense for Homes" in Contractor (Vol. 57, January 2010, No. 1, pp. 70)*

Ed: Robert P. Mader. **Description:** U.S. Environmental Protection Agency released its "final" version of the WaterSense for Homes standard. The standard's provisions that affect plumbing contractors include the specification that everything has to be leak tested and final service pressure cannot exceed 60 psi. **Availability:** Print; Online.

12629 ■ *"Expect Action on Health Care and the Economy" in Contractor (Vol. 57, January 2010, No. 1, pp. 30)*

Ed: Kevin Schwalb. **Description:** The Plumbing-Heating-Cooling Contractors National Association is working to solidify its standing in the public policy arena as the legislative agenda will focus on health care reform, estate tax and immigration reform, all of which will impact the industries. **Availability:** Print; Online.

12630 ■ *"Federal Buildings to Achieve Zero-Net Energy by 2030" in Contractor (Vol. 56, December 2009, No. 12, pp. 5)*

Ed: Candace Roulo. **Description:** United States president Barack Obama has issued sustainable goals for federal buildings. Federal agencies are also required to increase energy efficiency, conserve water and support sustainable communities. Obama has also announced a $3.4 billion investment in a smart energy creed. **Availability:** Print; Online.

12631 ■ *"Ga. PMA Launches Online Education Program" in Contractor (Vol. 56, October 2009, No. 10, pp. 8)*

Description: Plumbing & Mechanical Association of Georgia launched an online program that covers technical and business management that will help

contractors run their businesses. Future courses will include math for plumbers, graywater systems, and recession-proofing your business. **Availability:** Print; Online.

12632 ■ *"Get Online Quick in the Office Or in the Field" in Contractor (Vol. 56, October 2009, No. 10, pp. 47)*

Ed: William Feldman, Patti Feldman. **Description:** Contractors can set up a web site in minutes using the www.1and1.com website. Verizon's Novatel MIFI 2372 HSPA personal hotspot device lets contractors go online in the field. The StarTech scalable business management system helps contractors manage daily operations. **Availability:** Print; Online.

12633 ■ *"Got to be Smarter than the Average Bear" in Contractor (Vol. 56, September 2009, No. 9, pp. 82)*

Ed: Robert P. Mader. **Description:** International Association of Plumbing and Mechanical Officials Green Technical Committee has debated the need for contractors to have certifications in installing green plumbing. Some have argued that qualifications would discourage homeowners from improving their properties. Comments from executives are also included. **Availability:** Print; Online.

12634 ■ *Guide to Marketing Your Plumbing Business*

Description: A step-by-step guide to creating an effective marketing strategy for your plumbing business. **Availability:** Online.

12635 ■ *"How to Improve Your Mobile Marketing" in Contractor (Vol. 56, October 2009, No. 10, pp. 54)*

Ed: Matt Michel. **Description:** Plumbers can improve their mobile advertising by making their logos as large as possible and positioning their logo on top of the truck so people can see it over traffic. They should also make the phone numbers small because people only take note of these when the truck is parked. **Availability:** Online.

12636 ■ *How to Open a Plumbing Business*

Ed: Morgan Rush. **Description:** Provides information on how to open a plumbing business including licensing, insurance, plumbing equipment, vehicles, office equipment, and marketing. **Availability:** Online.

12637 ■ *"How Plumbing Facebook Groups Have Changed the Industry" in Plumber (November 20, 2019)*

URL(s): www.plumbermag.com/how-to-articles/ communication-networking-industry-social/how -plumbing-facebook-groups-have-changed-the-in dustry

Ed: Anthony Pacilla. **Released:** November 20, 2019. **Description:** Online Facebook books are providing a powerful tool for today's plumbers, which is easy-access online content about the industry. Once available only through national associations, the library, or on the job, answers to questions plumbers may come across can be easily solved within groups populated by industry experts. **Availability:** Online.

12638 ■ *How to Start a Plumbing Business: A Step-by-Step Guide to Set You Up for Success*

Description: A guide to starting a plumbing business, including extensive research and interviews with established plumbers. **Availability:** Online.

12639 ■ *"IAPMO GTC Debates Supplement" in Contractor (Vol. 56, September 2009, No. 9, pp. 3)*

Ed: Robert P. Mader. **Description:** Green Technical Committee of the International Association of Plumbing and Mechanical Officials is developing a Green Plumbing and Mechanical Supplement. The supplement provides for installation of systems by licensed contractors and installers. Comments from officials are also presented. **Availability:** Print; Online.

12640 ■ *"IAPMO GTC Votes to Limit Showers to 2.0-GPM"* in *Contractor (Vol. 56, September 2009, No. 9, pp. 1)*
Description: Green Technical Committee of the International Association of Plumbing and Mechanical Officials has voted to limit showers to 2.0 GPM. It is also developing a Green Plumbing and Mechanical Supplement. Comments from executives are also supplied. **Availability:** Print; Online.

12641 ■ *"It's New or Improved, But Does It Work?"* in *Contractor (Vol. 57, January 2010, No. 1, pp. 22)*
Ed: Al Schwartz. **Description:** There is a place for skepticism in the HVAC and plumbing industry as not all new products that are specified may not always perform. The tradesman has the responsibility of integrating new technology into the field. **Availability:** Print; Online.

12642 ■ *"Kohler Building Earns LEED Silver Certification"* in *Contractor (Vol. 56, September 2009, No. 9, pp. 12)*
Description: United States Green Building Council has awarded Kohler Co. with the Silver Leadership in Energy and Environmental Design Status. The award has highlighted the company's work to transform its building into a more environmentally efficient structure. A description of the facility is also provided. **Availability:** Print; Online.

12643 ■ *"LA Passes HET Ordinance, California Greens Code"* in *Contractor (Vol. 56, September 2009, No. 9, pp. 1)*
Ed: Candace Roulo. **Description:** Los Angeles City Council has passed a Water Efficiency Requirements ordinance. The law mandates lower low-flow plumbing requirements for plumbing fixtures installed in new buildings and retrofits. Under the ordinance, a toilet's maximum flush volume may not exceed 1.28-gpf. **Availability:** Print; Online.

12644 ■ *"Lead-Free Products must Meet Requirements"* in *Contractor (Vol. 56, September 2009, No. 9, pp. 30)*
Ed: Robert Gottermeier. **Description:** United States Environmental Protection Agency's adoption of the Safe Drinking Water Act is aimed at lowering lead extraction levels from plumbing products. Manufacturers have since deleaded brass and bronze potable water products. Meanwhile, California and Vermont have passed a law limiting lead content for potable water conveying plumbing products. **Availability:** Print; Online.

12645 ■ *"Major Advances in Heat Pump Technology"* in *Contractor (Vol. 57, January 2010, No. 1, pp. 42)*
Ed: Mark Eatherton. **Description:** Tax credits make ground-source heat pump technology more economically feasible. Suggestions on how to choose the right ground-source heat pump technology to install in a house are discussed. **Availability:** Print; Online.

12646 ■ *"Major Advances in Heat Pump Technology - Part Two"* in *Contractor (Vol. 57, February 2010, No. 2, pp. 22)*
Ed: Mark Eatherton. **Description:** Chinese and Japanese companies have come up with refrigerant based heat pump products that are air based which will significantly lower the installed cost of heat pump based systems. Some of these newer models have variable speed, soft start compressors and have the ability to perform high-efficiency heat pump operation on a modulating basis. **Availability:** Print; Online.

12647 ■ *"A Necessary Balancing Act: Bookkeeping"* in *Contractor (Vol. 56, November 2009, No. 11, pp. 22)*
Ed: Al Schwartz. **Description:** Pros and cons of getting a bookkeeper or a certified public accountant for the subcontractor are discussed. A bookkeeper can help a subcontractor get new accounting software up and running while an accountant will more than likely keep after the books at regular intervals throughout the year. **Availability:** Print; Online.

12648 ■ *"Online Training Requires Tools, Accessories"* in *Contractor (Vol. 56, September 2009, No. 9, pp. 67)*
Ed: Larry Drake. **Description:** Importance of the right equipment and tools to members of the United States plumbing industry undergoing online training is discussed. Portable devices such as BlackBerrys and I-phones could be used for online training. The use of headphones makes listening easier for the trainee. **Availability:** Print; Online.

12649 ■ *"PHCC Convention, Show Get High Marks"* in *Contractor (Vol. 56, December 2009, No. 12, pp. 1)*
Ed: Robert P. Mader. **Description:** Plumbing-Heating-Cooling Contractors National Association has held its first convention and trade show in New Orleans, Louisiana. Attendees were treated to a variety of seminars and exhibitors during the event. Comments from event organizers are also given. **Availability:** Print; Online.

12650 ■ *"Plumbing, Heating Products Shine at Greenbuild Expo"* in *Contractor (Vol. 56, December 2009, No. 12, pp. 1)*
Ed: Robert P. Mader. **Description:** Greenbuild Show held in Phoenix, Arizona has showcased the latest in plumbing and heating products. Zurn displayed its EcoVantage line of fixtures and valves during the event. Meanwhile, Sloan Valve offered its washdown 1-pint/flush Alphine urinal. **Availability:** Online.

12651 ■ *"Portland Home Is First in U.S. to Use Variable Speed Inverter Technology"* in *Contractor (Vol. 56, December 2009, No. 12, pp. 5)*
Description: Daikin Altherma heat pump with inverter drive has been installed in a Portland, Oregon home. The heat pump provides a high coefficient of performance while delivering hydronic and domestic hot water functionality. Other product features and dimensions are also supplied. **Availability:** Print; Online.

12652 ■ *"Pre-Certified LEED Hotel Prototype Reduces Energy Use, Conserves Water"* in *Contractor (Vol. 57, January 2010, No. 1, pp. 3)*
Pub: Informa USA, Inc.
Contact: Stephen A. Carter, Chief Executive Officer
Ed: Candace Roulo. **Released:** January 01, 2010. **Description:** Marriott International Inc.'s LEED pre-certified prototype hotel will reduce a hotel's energy and water consumption by 25 percent and save owners approximately $100,000. Their Courtyard Settler's Ridge in Pittsburgh will be the first hotel built based on the prototype.

12653 ■ *"Public Bathroom Pressure Woes Resolved"* in *Contractor (Vol. 56, September 2009, No. 9, pp. 44)*
Ed: Dave Yates. **Description:** Design and construction of a public bathroom's plumbing system in the United States are discussed. Installed plumbing fixtures with flush valves would not function properly. The installation of Grundfos SQE variable-speed pumps has resolved problems with the bathroom's water pressure. **Availability:** Print; Online.

12654 ■ *"Put Power in Your Direct Mail Campaigns"* in *Contractor (Vol. 56, September 2009, No. 9, pp. 64)*
Ed: Matt Michel. **Description:** Advice on how members of the United States plumbing industry should manage direct mail marketing campaigns is offered. Determining the purpose of a campaign is recommended. Focusing on a single message, product or service is also encouraged. **Availability:** Print; Online.

12655 ■ *"Rehab Center Slashes Energy Bills By Going Tankless"* in *Contractor (Vol. 56, December 2009, No. 12, pp. 3)*
Description: Melburne Health and Rehabilitation Center in Florida has reduced its energy bills by installing a tankless hot water system. Sun Plumbing

was selected to install the system. The system was installed on a mechanical room that housed the old tank-type heaters. **Availability:** Print; Online.

12656 ■ *"Route Optimization Impacts the Bottom Line"* in *Contractor (Vol. 56, November 2009, No. 11, pp. 48)*
Ed: Dave Beaudry. **Description:** Plumbing and HVAC businesses can save a significant amount of money from route optimization. The process begins with gathering information on a fleet and a routing software tool can determine the effectiveness of current route configurations and identify preferable route plans. **Availability:** Print; Online.

12657 ■ *"Selling a Job When There's Buyer's Remorse"* in *Contractor (Vol. 56, December 2009, No. 12, pp. 37)*
Ed: H. Kent Craig. **Description:** Advice on how contractors should manage low-profit jobs in the United States is presented. Efforts should be made to try and find at least one quality field foreman or superintendent. Contractors should also try to respectfully renegotiate the terms of the job. **Availability:** Online.

12658 ■ *"Small Business, Big Mentality"* in *Plumber Magazine (October 2017)*
Ed: Cory Dellenbach. **Released:** October 2017. **Description:** An interview with Dave Banghart, owner of Banghart Plumbing in Everett, Washington, talks about how his small operation finds big ways to draw in customers. **Availability:** Online.

12659 ■ *"Solar Choices"* in *Contractor (Vol. 56, October 2009, No. 10, pp. 32)*
Ed: Tom Scheel. **Description:** Price, performance, and ease of installation of a flat plate versus an evacuated tube collector for a plumbing and heating job are compared. The better choice with regards to weight, aesthetics, efficiency in warm or cool climates, year round load, and space heating is discussed. **Availability:** Print; Online.

12660 ■ *"Solar Hot Water Sales Are Hot, Hot, Hot"* in *Contractor (Vol. 56, December 2009, No. 12, pp. 22)*
Ed: Dave Yates. **Description:** Plumbing contractors in the United States can benefit from the increased sales of solar thermal water systems. Licensed plumbers have the base knowledge on the risks associated from heating and storing water. Safety issues associated with solar water heaters are also included. **Availability:** Online.

12661 ■ *"Sprinkler Advocates Beat Builders Again"* in *Contractor (Vol. 56, November 2009, No. 11, pp. 58)*
Ed: Robert P. Mader. **Description:** Proponents of residential fire sprinklers were able to fend off the attempt by the National Association of Home Builders to do away with mandated fire sprinklers on the International Residential Code by the International Code Council (ICC). The ICC's vote on the issue is good news for fire sprinkler contractors and plumbing contractors. **Availability:** Print; Online.

12662 ■ *"Three Productivity Solutions"* in *Contractor (Vol. 57, February 2010, No. 2, pp. 26)*
Ed: William Feldman, Patti Feldman. **Description:** Singletouch is a real-time data capture solution for mechanical and other contractors that work in jobs that require materials and workload tracking. Contractors get information on extreme weather and sudden changes in the cost of materials. The OptimumHVAC optimization software by Optimum Energy is designed to optimize energy savings in commercial buildings. **Availability:** Print; Online.

12663 ■ *"Three Steps to Follow when Job Hunting"* in *Contractor (Vol. 56, September 2009, No. 9, pp. 62)*
Ed: H. Kent Craig. **Description:** Advice on how project managers in the United States plumbing industry should look for jobs in view of the economic crisis. Job seekers should consider relocating to

places where there are an abundance of project management jobs. Resumes should also be revised to make an applicant stand out. **Availability:** Print; Online.

12664 ■ *"Tips to Improve Your Direct Mail Results" in Contractor (Vol. 57, January 2010, No. 1, pp. 55)*
Ed: Matt Michel. **Description:** Plumbers can improve their direct mail efforts by buying quality lists and writing good headlines. The mail should also tell a story and urge its readers to action. **Availability:** Print; Online.

12665 ■ *"Tracking Your Fleet Can Increase Bottom Line" in Contractor (Vol. 56, November 2009, No. 11, pp. 26)*
Ed: Candace Roulo. **Description:** GPS fleet management system can help boost a contractor's profits, employee productivity, and efficiency. These are available as a handheld device or a cell phone that employees carry around or as a piece of hardware installed in a vehicle. These lets managers track assets and communicate with employees about jobs. **Availability:** Online.

12666 ■ *"Trade Craft: Take Pride in Your Trade, Demand Excellence" in Contractor (Vol. 56, October 2009, No. 10, pp. 24)*
Ed: Al Schwartz. **Description:** There is a need for teaching, developing, and encouraging trade craft. An apprentice plumber is not only versed in the mechanical aspects of the trade but he also has a working knowledge of algebra, trigonometry, chemistry, and thermal dynamics. Contractors should be demanding on their personnel regarding their trade craft and should only keep and train the very best people they can hire. **Availability:** Print; Online.

12667 ■ *"The Ultimate Guide to Growing Your Plumbing Business" in Blue Corona Blog (October 17, 2018)*
Ed: Jenny Mott. **Released:** October 17, 2018. **Description:** A detailed guide to marketing your plumbing business based on years of study and meticulous tracking. **Availability:** Online.

12668 ■ *Ultimate Guide: Plumbing*
Released: January 03, 2017. **Price:** $13.57, Paperback. **Description:** A complete guide on plumbing for homeowners. Includes 800 photos along with numerous diagrams to show the user how complete simple to complex plumbing tasks. **Availability:** Print.

12669 ■ *Unclog the Workflow: The Perks of Answering Services for Plumbing Businesses*
Ed: Markie Johansen. **Description:** Describes how an answering service for your plumbing business allows you to work smarter, not harder. **Availability:** Online.

12670 ■ *"Use Social Media to Enhance Brand, Business" in Contractor (Vol. 56, December 2009, No. 12, pp. 14)*
Ed: Elton Rivas. **Description:** Advice on how plumbing contractors should use online social networks to increase sales is presented including such issues as clearly defining goals and target audience. An additional advantage to this medium is that advertisements can easily be shared with other users.

12671 ■ *"Water Conservation Helps GC's Building Attain LEED Gold Status" in Contractor (Vol. 56, September 2009, No. 9, pp. 5)*
Description: Green contractor Marshall Erdman has built a new office building using green design. The facility is seen to become a prime Leadership in Energy and Environmental Design (LEED) building model. Details of the building's design and features are also provided. **Availability:** Print; Online.

12672 ■ *"Water Efficiency Bills Move Through Congress" in Contractor (Vol. 56, July 2009, No. 7, pp. 20)*
Ed: Kevin Schwalb. **Description:** National Association, a plumbing-heating-cooling contractor, was instrumental in drafting the Water Advanced Technolo-

gies for Efficient Resource Use Act of 2009 and they are also backing the Water Accountability Tax Efficiency Reinvestment Act. The first bill promotes WaterSense-labeled products while the other promotes water conservation through tax credits. **Availability:** Print; Online.

12673 ■ *"Web-Based Solutions Streamline Operations" in Contractor (Vol. 56, December 2009, No. 12, pp. 28)*
Ed: William Feldman, Patti Feldman. **Description:** Sage Project Lifecycle Management is a Web-based service platform for plumbing and HVAC contractors. It enables effective workflow and document management. Projectmates, on the other hand, is a Web-based enterprise-wide solution for managing both commercial plumbing and HVAC projects. **Availability:** Print; Online.

12674 ■ *"WQA Develops Certification Program" in Contractor (Vol. 57, January 2010, No. 1, pp. 56)*
Ed: Dennis Sowards. **Description:** Water Quality Association is now offering a new certification program for companies that may be affected by California's law that prohibits any products intended to convey or dispense water for human consumption that is not lead-free. All pipe or plumbing fixtures must be certified by a third party certification body. **Availability:** Print; Online.

SOURCES OF SUPPLY

12675 ■ *American Supply Association--Member Directory*
American Supply Association
Contact: Bill Condron, President
URL(s): www.asa.net/Join-ASA/Member-Directory-PUBLIC
Released: Annual **Description:** Covers 4,000 member wholesalers handling plumbing, heating, and cooling materials and supplies. **Entries include:** Company name, address, phone, names of executives, list of products or services, fax numbers, email and website. **Arrangement:** Geographical and alphabetical. **Indexes:** Special interest divisions. **Availability:** Print.

STATISTICAL SOURCES

12676 ■ *RMA Annual Statement Studies*
Pub: Risk Management Association
Contact: Nancy Foster, President
Released: Annual. **Description:** Contains composite balance sheets and income statements for more than 360 industries, including the accounting, auditing, and bookkeeping industries. Also contains five years of comparative historical data for discerning trends. Includes 16 commonly used ratios, computed for most of the size groupings for nearly every industry.

TRADE PERIODICALS

12677 ■ *Contractor Connection*
Pub: Indiana Association of Plumbing Heating Cooling Contractors
Contact: Tyler Frame, President
URL(s): www.iaphcc.com/contractor-connection
Released: Quarterly; Jan/Feb/Mar; Apr/May/June; July/Aug/Sept; and Oct/Nov/Dec. **Description:** Official publication of the Indiana Association of Plumbing, Heating, Cooling Contractors, Inc. **Availability:** Print; PDF.

12678 ■ *Plumbing Engineer*
Pub: PHCPPros
Contact: Nicole Meyer, Manager
E-mail: nicole@phcppros.com
URL(s): www.phcppros.com/publications/1-plumbing-engineer
Released: Monthly **Description:** Trade journal for consulting engineering, mechanical engineering, architecture, and contracting professionals. **Availability:** Print; Online.

TRADE SHOWS AND CONVENTIONS

12679 ■ *CMPX: Canadian Mechanical & Plumbing Exposition (CMPX)*
Shield Associates Ltd.
 25 Bradgate Rd.
 Toronto, ON, Canada M3B 1J6
URL(s): www.cmpxshow.com
X (Twitter): twitter.com/CMPXShow
Frequency: Biennial. **Description:** Heating, air conditioning, refrigeration, ventilation, energy-saving products and technologies, indoor air quality products, building automation, renewable energy equipment, emerging technologies, and mechanical plumbing equipment. **Audience:** Plumbing, HVACR & mechanical contractors, installers, technicians, wholesalers, engineers, architects, building managers, renovators, specifiers, government personnel, manufacturers reps, retailers, journalists, teachers & students. **Principal Exhibits:** Heating, air conditioning, refrigeration, ventilation, energy-saving products and technologies, indoor air quality products, building automation, renewable energy equipment, emerging technologies, and mechanical plumbing equipment. Dates and Locations: 2026 Mar 25-27 Metro Toronto Convention Centre, South Building, ON. **Telecommunication Services:** cmpxshow@newcom.ca.

12680 ■ *MCEE: Mecanex/Climatex/ Expolectriq/Eclairage (MECANEX)*
Corporation of Master Pipe Mechanics of Quebec (CMMTQ)
 8175, Blvd., Saint-Laurent
 Montreal, QC, Canada QC H2P 2M1
Ph: (514)382-2668
Free: 800-465-2668
Fax: (514)382-1566
URL: http://www.cmmtq.org
Contact: Mylène Sagala, Director, Legal Services
E-mail: msagala@cmmtq.org
URL(s): www.mcee.ca/a-propos
Frequency: Biennial. **Description:** New products, services and technologies in plumbing, heating, air-conditioning, fire-protection, ventilation, and refrigeration. Also features tools, equipment, and services for contractors. **Audience:** Contractors, wholesalers, builders, engineers, architects, designers, renovators, and maintenance personnel. **Principal Exhibits:** New products, services and technologies in plumbing, heating, air-conditioning, fire-protection, ventilation, and refrigeration. Also features tools, equipment, and services for contractors. Dates and Locations: 2025 Apr 24-25 Palais des congres de Montreal, Montreal, QC. **Telecommunication Services:** mcee@mcee.ca.

CONSULTANTS

12681 ■ *GHT Ltd.*
1110 N Glebe Rd., Ste. 300
 Arlington, VA 22201
Ph: (703)243-1200
Fax: (703)276-1376
Co. E-mail: info@ghtltd.com
URL: http://www.ghtltd.com
Contact: Patrick Kunze, President
Facebook: www.facebook.com/GHTLimited
Linkedin: www.linkedin.com/company/ght-limited
Description: Firm provides consulting on engineering design services such as telecommunications and security engineering service, life safety engineering service, utilities planning service and much more. **Scope:** Firm provides consulting on engineering design services such as telecommunications and security engineering service, life safety engineering service, utilities planning service and much more. **Founded:** 1965. **Publications:** "Critical spaces keep the pace of business humming," May, 2004; "To avoid staticlater, hire right telecom consultant," Oct, 2007. **Special Services:** LEED®.

FRANCHISES AND BUSINESS OPPORTUNITIES

12682 ■ **Ace DuraFlo Systems L.L.C.**
2926 W Pendleton Ave.
Santa Ana, CA 92704
Free: 888-775-0220
Co. E-mail: info@aceduraflo.com
URL: http://aceduraflo.com
Contact: Larry Gillanders, Chief Executive Officer
X (Twitter): x.com/ace_duraflo
YouTube: www.youtube.com/user/aceduraflo
Description: Provider of pipe restoration, leak repair and corroded pipe repair services. **Founded:** 1990. **Training:** Provider of 1 week at headquarters, 2 weeks at franchisee's location with ongoing support.

12683 ■ **American Leak Detection Inc. (ALD)**
888 Research Dr., Ste. 105
Palm Springs, CA 92262
Ph: (760)465-1368
Free: 866-701-5306
URL: http://www.americanleakdetection.com
Contact: Dr. Patrick J. DeSouza, President
Facebook: www.facebook.com/AmericanLeakDetection
X (Twitter): x.com/leakdetection
YouTube: www.youtube.com/user/ALDJosh

Description: Detection of water or sewer leaks under concrete slabs of homes, pools, spas, fountains, commercial buildings, etc., with electronic equipment manufactured by the company. **Founded:** 1974. **Training:** Provides 6-12 weeks at headquarters, 1 week at franchisee's location with ongoing support.

12684 ■ **Canadian Poolplayers Association (CPA) [American Poolplayers Association (APA)]**
1000 Lake St. Louis Blvd., Ste. 325
Lake Saint Louis, MO 63367
Ph: (636)625-8611
Free: 888-327-8752
Fax: (636)265-6556
URL: http://poolplayers.com/canada
Contact: Larry Hubbart, Founder
Facebook: www.facebook.com/poolplayers
Linkedin: www.linkedin.com/company/236406
X (Twitter): x.com/poolplayers
Instagram: www.instagram.com/poolplayers
YouTube: www.youtube.com/apaleagues

Description: Oversees and provides ongoing support to recreational pool league operators. **No. of Franchise Units:** 17. **No. of Company-Owned Units:** 5. **Founded:** 1979. **Franchised:** 1989. **Equity Capital Needed:** $17,080-$24,150. **Franchise Fee:** $5,000. **Royalty Fee:** $2.50 plus/team/wk. **Geographic Preference:** National.

12685 ■ **Handyman Connection**
Mamar Inc.
11115 Kenwood Rd.
Blue Ash, OH 45242
Facebook: www.facebook.com/HandymanConnectionCorporate
Linkedin: www.linkedin.com/company/handyman-connection
X (Twitter): x.com/handymancorp
Instagram: www.instagram.com/handymanconnection_homeoffice

YouTube: www.youtube.com/user/handymancorporate
Description: Small to medium home repairs and remodeling. **No. of Franchise Units:** 160. **No. of Company-Owned Units:** 1. **Founded:** 1990. **Franchised:** 1993. **Equity Capital Needed:** $90,000-$125,000. **Franchise Fee:** $25,000-$40,000. **Training:** 2 weeks at corporate training center and 1 week grand opening onsite.

12686 ■ **Mr. Rooter Plumbing**
1020 N University Parks Dr.
Waco, TX 76707
Ph: (231)903-6029
Free: 833-647-7779
URL: http://www.mrrooter.com
Facebook: www.facebook.com/MrRooterLLC
Linkedin: www.linkedin.com/company/mr-rooter-llc
Instagram: www.instagram.com/mrrooterllc
YouTube: www.youtube.com/c/mrrooter
Pinterest: www.pinterest.com/mrrooterplumbing

Description: Firm provides plumbing and drain cleaning services for commercial, residential and emergency sectors. **Founded:** 1970. **Training:** Initial, on-site, intranet and ongoing support.

12687 ■ **Potty Doctor Plumbing Service**
424 N Dixie Hwy.
Lake Worth, FL 33460
Ph: (561)582-0334
Free: 888-377-6889
Co. E-mail: sales@pottydoctor.com
URL: http://www.pottydoctor.com
Facebook: www.facebook.com/PottyDoctor
Description: Firm provides plumbing services. **Founded:** 1948. **Training:** Yes.

ASSOCIATIONS AND OTHER ORGANIZATIONS

12688 ■ Porcelain Enamel Institute (PEI)
PO Box 920220
Norcross, GA 30010
Ph: (770)676-9366
Fax: (770)409-7280
Co. E-mail: info@porcelainenamel.com
URL: http://www.porcelainenamel.com
Contact: Michael Cukier, President
Linkedin: www.linkedin.com/company/porcelain
-enamel-institute-inc
X (Twitter): x.com/penamel
Description: Trade association of the porcelain enamel industry. Manufacturers of major appliances, sanitary ware, architectural porcelain enamel, signs, and other porcelain enamel products; suppliers to the industry such as producers of steel, aluminum, and porcelain enamel frit; chemical companies. Conducts market development and promotion programs, develops test methods for evaluation of porcelain enamel properties, and maintains weather resistance testing sites jointly with the National Bureau of Standards. Serves as information clearinghouse. **Founded:** 1930. **Publications:** *Technical Forum; First Firing* (Bimonthly). **Educational Activities:** Porcelain Enamel Institute Meeting; PEI Technical Forum (Annual). **Geographic Preference:** National.

REFERENCE WORKS

12689 ■ *"Reglazing Tile Is the Most Transformative Fix for a Dated Bathroom" in Architectural Digest (August 31, 2017)*
URL(s): www.architecturaldigest.com/story/reglazing
-tile-transformative-fix-for-a-dated-bathroom
Ed: Amanda Sims. **Released:** August 31, 2017. **Description:** Not everyone has the time or resources to renovate an old bathroom when the tiles, tub, and sink are outdated and in need of a new color. Reglazing, or refinishing, is an option and is offered by professionals who can transform the look of a whole bathroom in a few hours. The time and cost are also a lot lower than a whole bathroom renovation. **Availability:** Online.

FRANCHISES AND BUSINESS OPPORTUNITIES

12690 ■ BMR Bathmaster Reglazing Ltd.
No. 5 651 Wilton Grove Rd
London, ON, Canada N6N 1N7
Ph: (519)653-8823
Free: 877-767-2336
Fax: (888)789-0947
Co. E-mail: info@bathmaster.com
URL: http://www.bathmaster.com
Facebook: www.facebook.com/people/BathMaster/
100063765061246
Linkedin: www.linkedin.com/in/bmr-bathmaster-10b
28987
Instagram: www.instagram.com/bmrbathmaster
Description: Provider of remodeling services for bathroom. **Founded:** 1989. **Training:** 10 day training and full support.

12691 ■ Kott Koatings Inc.
27161 Burbank St.
Foothill Ranch, CA 92610
Ph: (949)770-5055
Co. E-mail: thebathtubpeople@yahoo.com
URL: http://www.thebathtubpeople.com
Contact: John M. Kott, Chief Executive Officer
Description: A porcelain, fiberglass, and bathtub reglazing business. **Founded:** 1950. **Financial Assistance:** Yes **Training:** Yes.

12692 ■ Perma-Glaze Inc., Multi-Surface Restoration
150 S Camino Seco, Ste. 108
Tucson, AZ 85710
Free: 800-332-7397
Co. E-mail: acepermaglaze@permaglaze.com
URL: http://permaglaze.com
Description: Restoration and refinishing of bathroom and kitchen fixtures, such as bathtubs, sinks and ceramic tiles. **Founded:** 1978. **Financial Assistance:** Yes **Training:** Training includes 5-10 day technical, hands-on training and all tools and equipment.

12693 ■ PremierGarage Serving Scottsdale
Scottsdale, AZ 85258
URL: http://www.premiergarage.com/near-me/scotts
dale-az
Contact: Kevin Kinney, Owner
E-mail: kkinney@premiergarage.com
Description: Offers premium quality Garage Floor Coatings, Cabinetry and Organizers for residential applications. **No. of Franchise Units:** 74. **No. of Company-Owned Units:** 1. **Founded:** 1999. **Franchised:** 2002. **Equity Capital Needed:** $76,200-$429,500. **Franchise Fee:** $7,500-150,000. **Training:** Yes.

12694 ■ Surface Specialists Systems Inc.
621-B Stallings Rd.
Matthews, NC 28104
Free: 866-239-8707
Co. E-mail: info@surfacespecialists.com
URL: http://surfacespecialists.com
Contact: Dan Kaplan, President
Facebook: www.facebook.com/Surface-Specialists
-Systems-Inc-117560751628241
Linkedin: www.linkedin.com/company/surface
-specialists-systems-inc-
X (Twitter): x.com/thetubexperts
YouTube: www.youtube.com/user/tubmanone/fea
tured
Description: Provides bathroom, kitchen refinishing and repair services for tubs, sinks and counter tops including acrylic tub-liner and wall installation, converting tubs to whirlpools, glass scratch removal and turning existing bathtubs. **Founded:** 1981. **Franchised:** 1981. **Equity Capital Needed:** $43,200-56,000. **Franchise Fee:** $36,000. **Financial Assistance:** Yes **Training:** Provides 15 days hands-on training, annual convention, and 24/7 direct access to company president.

REFERENCE WORKS

12695 ■ "Butane Heated Pressure Washer Offers Diverse Cleaning Options" in Product News Network (March 8, 2011)
Description: Profile of the Super Max (TM) 6000B power sprayer the can clean with cold or heated water and wet steam. Daimer Industries, provider of janitorial supplies, announced the availability of the machine that offers a variety of cleaning options for a range of applications. **Availability:** Online.

12696 ■ The Costs, Benefits and Dangers of Pressure Washing
URL(s): www.mercurynews.com/2018/10/26/the-costs-benefits-and-dangers-of-pressure-washing/
Ed: AP McClatchy. **Released:** October 26, 2018.
Description: Reviews the benefits of pressure washing along with several warnings and considerations homeowners should be be aware of when tackling a project. **Availability:** Online.

FRANCHISES AND BUSINESS OPPORTUNITIES

12697 ■ Sparkle Wash International
Sparkle International, Inc.
7599 First Pl.
Oakwood Village, OH 44146
Ph: (800)321-0770
Fax: (216)464-8869
Contact: Pat Baker, President
E-mail: pbaker@sparklewash.com
Description: Offers mobile pressure cleaning and restoration service. **No. of Franchise Units:** 172. **No. of Company-Owned Units:** 1. **Founded:** 1965. **Franchised:** 1967. **Equity Capital Needed:** Approximately $50,000. **Franchise Fee:** Minimum $25,000. **Training:** 5 day initial program at headquarters, includes classroom, shop, and in-field training on the franchisees own equipment. An optional 6th day of in-field experience is available at no added charge. Sparkle Wash sends a qualified trainer to work with the franchisee for 3 Days at his location.

12698 ■ Window Gang Inc.
Morehead City, NC 28557
Free: 877-946-4264
Co. E-mail: info@windowgang.com
URL: http://www.windowgang.com
Contact: Tim McCullen, Founder
Facebook: www.facebook.com/WindowGangCorp
X (Twitter): x.com/windowgang
YouTube: www.youtube.com/user/WindowGang101
Description: Firm provides residential window washing, gutter cleaning and house washing. **Founded:** 1986. **Managerial Assistance:** Marketing materials and regional meetings. **Training:** Up to 14 days of training in both the corporate location and in your territory that includes successful technical, sales, marketing, and business procedures. Provides non-stop customer leads.

12699 ■ Window Genie (WG)
Neighborly
40 W Crescentville Rd.
Cincinnati, OH 45246
Free: 800-490-7501
Fax: (877)496-2356
URL: http://www.neighborlybrands.com
Contact: John Marshall, Contact
Facebook: www.facebook.com/windowgenie
Linkedin: www.linkedin.com/company/window-genie
X (Twitter): twitter.com/thewindowgenie
Instagram: www.instagram.com/windowgenie
YouTube: www.youtube.com/channel/UC8CEiBA9H-Dj6B1BQOZlpYQ
Pinterest: www.pinterest.com/windowgenie
Description: Provider of window cleaning, window tinting, pressure washing, gutter cleaning services. **Founded:** 1994. **Franchised:** 1998. **Equity Capital Needed:** $80,000 - $150,000. **Franchise Fee:** $32,000-$57,000,. **Financial Assistance:** Yes **Training:** Offers 5 days at headquarters, 5 days at franchisees location with ongoing support.

REFERENCE WORKS

12700 ■ *"The Key to Cheap Internet Service: A Local SIM Card" in The New York Times (April 9, 2019)*
Ed: Geoffrey Morrison. **Released:** April 09, 2019. **Description:** Tips on using a SIM card and pay-as-you-go service to obtain cheaper rates on your cell phone while traveling, instead of letting the SIM card installed by your service provider tell the provider you are roaming. **Availability:** Online.

TRADE SHOWS AND CONVENTIONS

12701 ■ **NTCA Rural Telecom Industry Meeting & EXPO (RTIME)**
NTCA - The Rural Broadband Association
4121 Wilson Blvd.
Arlington, VA 22203
Ph: (703)351-2000
Fax: (703)351-2001
Co. E-mail: benefitsresource@ntca.org
URL: http://www.ntca.org
Contact: Shirley Bloomfield, Chief Executive Officer
E-mail: sbloomfield@ntca.org
URL(s): www.ntca.org/events-education/events/save-date-rtime
Frequency: Annual. **Description:** Equipment, supplies, and services for the telecommunications industry. Event will be live streamed and available in person. **Audience:** Telco owners, executives and key employees. **Principal Exhibits:** Equipment, supplies, and services for the telecommunications industry. Event will be live streamed and available in person. Dates and Locations: 2025 Feb 23-26 Grand Hyatt San Antonio, Marriott Riverwalk and Marriott Rivercenter, San Antonio, TX; 2026 Feb 22-25 Walt Disney World Swan/Dolphin, Orlando, FL; 2027 Feb 14-17 Manchester Grand Hyatt, San Diego, CA; 2028 Feb 20-23 Sheraton Dallas, Dallas, TX. **Telecommunication Services:** meetings@ntca.org.

RESEARCH CENTERS

12702 ■ **University of Nebraska-Omaha College of Information Science & Technology - Center for Management of Information Technology (CMIT)**
6001 Dodge St.
Omaha, NE 68182
URL: http://www.unomaha.edu/college-of-information-science-and-technology/engagement/centers/center-for-management-information-technology/index.php
Contact: Dr. Deepak Khazanchi, Professor
E-mail: khazanchi@unomaha.edu

Description: Integral unit of College of Information Science and Technology at the University of Nebraska at Omaha. **Scope:** Management of information technology.

ASSOCIATIONS AND OTHER ORGANIZATIONS

12703 ■ Print Council of America (PCA)
Portland Art Museum
219 SW Pk. Ave.
Portland, OR 97205
URL: http://printcouncil.org
Contact: Mary Weaver Chapin, President
E-mail: mary.chapin@pam.org

Description: Museum professionals. Fosters the study and appreciation of new and old prints, drawings, and photographs; stimulates discussion. Sponsors educational programs and research publications; offers placement services. **Founded:** 1956. **Geographic Preference:** National.

12704 ■ Professional Picture Framers Association (PPFA)
330 Mounts Corner Dr. 313
Freehold, NJ 07728
Ph: (848)444-5138
Co. E-mail: info@ppfadirectory.com
URL: http://ppfadirectory.com
Contact: Tim O'Neill, President
Facebook: www.facebook.com/ProfessionalPic
tureFramersfacebook.com/ProfessionalPic
tureFramers
X (Twitter): x.com/pfmmag

Description: Individuals, firms, or corporations engaged in the picture framing and fine art businesses (art dealers, manufacturers, wholesalers, importers, and publishers). Provides guidance and service in developing quality craftsmanship in the art of picture framing. Sponsors certification program and national consumer marketing program. Provides education and trade show programming. **Founded:** 1971. **Publications:** *Who's Who in Picture Framing & Fine Art* (Annual). **Awards:** PPFA Paul Frederick Distinction for Leadership Award (Annual); PPFA Service Award (Annual); PPFA International Print Framing Competition (Annual). **Geographic Preference:** Multinational.

REFERENCE WORKS

12705 ■ "Custom Picture Framing Is Too Expensive — and Framebridge Has a Fix for That" in Forbes (January 4, 2019)
URL(s): www.forbes.com/sites/pamdanziger/2019/01/
04/custom-picture-framing-is-too-expensive
-framebridge-has-a-fix-for-that/#7c5100ff2489

Ed: Pamela N. Danziger. **Released:** January 04, 2019. **Description:** After Susan Tynan tried to get several posters custom framed and found out how expensive that was, she founded an online frame shop called Framebridge, which will frame pictures for a fraction of the price. The demand in cheaper framing options has caused smaller shops to close, while online stores and bigger chains are taking up more of the market. **Availability:** Online.

12706 ■ "Innovation Incubators Attract Printers, Designers" in PrintingImpressions October 16, 2019)
URL(s): www.piworld.com/article/innovation-incuba
tors-attract-printers-designers/

Ed: Vince Cahill. **Released:** October 16, 2019. **Description:** Five innovation centers in Brooklyn are examined as they focus on design and print. These centers are part of a bigger plan to mix a variety of industries to drive growth in their respective sectors. Printing studios for a variety of needs such as wallpaper, fabrics, retail, promotion, and others work with graphic designers and other professionals to increase manufacturing growth. **Availability:** Online.

12707 ■ Printworld Directory of Contemporary Prints and Prices
Pub: Printworld International Inc.
URL(s): www.printworlddirectory.com

Released: Irregular; latest edition 16th; February 15, 2017. **Price:** $50, for Canada and Mexico airmail; $80, for Europe, Asia & Africa; $359, for print; $99, U.S.; $149, Canada and Mexico; $179, Other countries for Europe, Asia & Africa. **Description:** Publication includes biographical data on 5,000 international artists in contemporary printmaking; thousands of galleries who handle prints and hundreds of print publishers, and 600,000 print/price listings. Includes documentation on approximately 600,000 prints which have appeared in limited editions of no more than 500 and have a retail value of $100-1,000,000, and approximately 500 photos of recent & vintage prints. **Entries include:** For artists--Name, address, personal and educational data, major exhibits, collections, publishers, printers, galleries, awards, teaching positions and documentation of prints. For galleries and publishers--Name, address. **Arrangement:** Alphabetical. **Indexes:** Artist name, printer/print workshop, publisher, gallery, art appraiser. **Availability:** Print.

TRADE PERIODICALS

12708 ■ Picture Framing Magazine: Online
Contact: Bruce Gherman, Publisher
URL(s): www.pictureframingmagazine.com

Released: Monthly **Price:** $20, U.S. for print and digital,1 year; $20, U.S. for print,1 year; $40, Canada for print and digital,1 year; $40, Canada for print,1 year; $60, Other countries for print and digital,1 year; $60, Other countries for print,1 year; $30, U.S. for print and digital,2 year; $30, U.S. for print,2 year; $70, Canada for print and digital,2 year; $70, Canada for print,2 year; $110, Other countries for print and digital,2 year; $110, Other countries for print,2 year; $8.95, for digital,1 year; $11.95, for digital,2 year. **Description:** Trade magazine for the picture framing industry. **Availability:** Print; Online.

FRANCHISES AND BUSINESS OPPORTUNITIES

12709 ■ Big Picture Framing
60 Needham St.
Newton, MA 02461
Ph: (617)527-0144
Free: 800-315-0024
Co. E-mail: info@bigpictureframing.com
URL: http://www.bigpictureframing.com
Contact: Barry Stahl, Chief Executive Officer
E-mail: barry@bigpictureframing.com
Facebook: www.facebook.com/bigpictureframing
X (Twitter): x.com/bigpictureframe
Instagram: www.instagram.com/big.picture.framing
Pinterest: www.pinterest.com/big_picture

Description: Provider of framing services for craft, picture and more. **Founded:** 2000. **Training:** Offers a comprehensive 2 1/2 week training program that provides you with everything you need to know to operate a store, including store operations, framing, sales and design, marketing and advertising, purchasing, hiring and business management.

12710 ■ Deck the Walls
5700 Mexico Rd., Ste.6
Saint Peters, MO 63376
Free: 866-719-8200
Co. E-mail: dtwcontact@fcibiz.com
URL: http://deckthewalls.com
Facebook: www.facebook.com/
DeckTheWallsCorporate
X (Twitter): x.com/Deck_The_Walls
Instagram: www.instagram.com/deckthewalls
Pinterest: www.pinterest.com/deckthewalls

Description: Firm engages in both custom framing and specialty prints in retail outlets and online. **Founded:** 1979. **Training:** Classroom and in-store training prepare franchisees for all aspects of business, including custom framing.

12711 ■ Fastframe USA Inc.
3739 Thousand Oaks Bd
Thousand Oaks, CA 91362
Ph: (805)497-3173
Co. E-mail: info@fastframe.com
URL: http://fastframe.com
Facebook: www.facebook.com/FastframeUSA
X (Twitter): x.com/FastframeUSA
Instagram: www.instagram.com/fastframe_usa
Pinterest: www.pinterest.co.uk/ffusa

Description: Custom picture framing franchise. Provide high-quality custom framing and art sales in both the retail and commercial markets. Offers a turn-key package from site selection to final store build-out. **No. of Franchise Units:** 300. **Founded:** 1986. **Franchised:** 1986. **Equity Capital Needed:** $115,800- $159,300. **Financial Assistance:** Yes **Training:** Provides 2 weeks of training at the corporate training center. Topics include in-store operations, marketing, and advertising, framing, business management, and the FAST system. Ongoing field support and 1-week on-site training.

12712 ■ Framing and Art Centre
2000 Appleby Line
Unit G4 Millcroft Shopping Centre
Burlington, ON, Canada L7L 6M6
Ph: (905)315-9183
Co. E-mail: facburlington@cogeco.net

URL: http://burlington.framingartcentre.ca
Facebook: www.facebook.com/FramingArtCen
  treBurlington
X (Twitter): x.com/FramingArtCtr
Instagram: www.instagram.com/framingartcentre
Pinterest: www.pinterest.com/framingartctr
Description: Provider of framing, wall décor, testimo-
nials and art services for business and shops.
Founded: 1974. **Franchised:** 1974. **Financial As-
sistance:** Yes **Training:** Yes.

12713 ■ The Great Frame Up Inc. (TFGU)
5700 Mexico Rd., Ste. 6
  Saint Peters, MO 63376
Free: 866-719-8200
Co. E-mail: tgfucontact@fcibiz.com
URL: http://thegreatframeup.com
Facebook: www.facebook.com/tgfucustomframing
X (Twitter): x.com/tgfuframing
Instagram: www.instagram.com/thegreatframeup

Pinterest: www.pinterest.com/thegreatframeup
Description: Firm provides custom framing services.
Founded: 1971. **Financial Assistance:** Yes **Training:** 2 weeks classroom and instore training including
custom framing, covering all aspects of framing, as
well as hands-on training in an actual store situation.
Workshops and a toll-free number to the training
center are provided for ongoing education.

ASSOCIATIONS AND OTHER ORGANIZATIONS

12714 ■ Amalgamated Printers' Association (APA)
c/o Lisa & TH Groves
160 S Dewey Rd.
Dewey, AZ 86327-7099
Ph: (928)642-6590
Co. E-mail: apamailer2021@gmail.com
URL: http://apa-letterpress.com
Contact: Mark Barbour, President
Facebook: www.facebook.com/AmalgamatedPrintersAssociation

Description: Active printers interested in furthering of the art and craft of printing. Encourages excellence of printing content, design and techniques among members. Sponsors competitions. **Founded:** 1958. **Educational Activities:** APA Wayzgoose. **Geographic Preference:** Multinational.

12715 ■ American Institute of Graphic Arts (AIGA)
228 Pk. Ave. S, Ste. 58603
New York, NY 10003
Ph: (212)807-1990
Co. E-mail: general@aiga.org
URL: http://www.aiga.org
Contact: Ashleigh Axios, President
Facebook: www.facebook.com/AIGAdesign
Linkedin: www.linkedin.com/company/aiga
X (Twitter): x.com/AIGAdesign
Instagram: www.instagram.com/AIGAdesign
YouTube: www.youtube.com/user/AIGAdesign
Pinterest: www.pinterest.com/aigadesign

Description: Publishes books. A national nonprofit membership organization with chapters in forty-two cities. It conducts an interrelated program of competitions, exhibitions, publications and educational activities to promote excellence in graphic design. Reaches market through direct mail. Does not accept unsolicited manuscripts. **Scope:** History of American communication design. **Services:** Library not open to the public. **Founded:** 1914. **Holdings:** Rare book; manuscript. **Publications:** *Trace: AIGA Journal of Design* (Triennial); *Gain: AIGA Journal of Business and Design* (Semiannual); *Voice: Journal of Design* (Quarterly); *365: AIGA Year in Design* (Annual). **Educational Activities:** AIGA Design Conference (Annual). **Awards:** AIGA Corporate Leadership Award (Periodic); AIGA Medal (Annual); AIGA 50 Books/50 Covers Competition (Annual). **Geographic Preference:** National.

12716 ■ Association for PRINT Technologies
450 10th Cir. N
Nashville, TN 37203
Ph: (703)264-7200
Co. E-mail: aptech@aptech.org
URL: http://printtechnologies.org
Contact: Thayer Long, President
E-mail: tlong@aptech.org

Description: Companies engaged in the manufacture and distribution of equipment, systems, software and/or supplies used in the printing, publishing and converting industries. Represents members before federal agencies and allied trade groups. Funds programs at educational institutions to train graphic arts personnel. Organizes a monthly industry statistical program that compiles and distributes data on orders and shipments. **Founded:** 1993. **Publications:** *Directory of International Suppliers of Printing, Publishing, and Converting Technologies* (Annual); *Vanguard* (Semiannual); *Guide to Audio Visual Materials and Public Speakers in the Printing and Publishing Technologies Industry* (Annual). **Educational Activities:** GRAPH EXPO (Annual). **Awards:** Harold W. Gegenheimer Awards for Industry Service (Annual). **Geographic Preference:** National.

12717 ■ Flexographic Technical Association (FTA)
3920 Veterans Memorial Hwy., Ste. 9
Bohemia, NY 11716-1074
Ph: (631)737-6020
Co. E-mail: memberinfo@flexography.org
URL: http://www.flexography.org
Contact: Mark Cisternino, President
Facebook: www.facebook.com/flextechassn
Linkedin: www.linkedin.com/company/flextechassn
X (Twitter): x.com/flextechassn
Instagram: www.instagram.com/flextechassn

Description: Firms engaged in printing by flexographic process suppliers to the industry; end users. Seeks to advance the science of flexographic printing, assist and recommend developments in flexography. Conducts educational activities for production, supervisory, and management personnel, and annual technical forum. Sponsors the Foundation of Flexographic Technical Association. **Founded:** 1958. **Publications:** *SourceBook* (Annual); *FLEXO: Converting Technology.* **Educational Activities:** Flexographic Technical Association Forum (Annual). **Awards:** FTA Hall of Fame (Annual); FTA Presidents' Award (Annual); FTA Technical Innovation Award (Annual); Excellence in Flexography Awards (Annual); FIRST Operator Certification Awards (Annual). **Geographic Preference:** Multinational.

12718 ■ Idealliance - Library [International Digital Enterprise Alliance]
1800 Diagonal Rd., Ste. 320
Alexandria, VA 22314-2862
Ph: (703)837-1070
Fax: (703)837-1072
Co. E-mail: membership@idealliance.org
URL: http://idealliance.org
Contact: Jordan Gorski, Executive Director
E-mail: jgorski@idealliance.org
Facebook: www.facebook.com/idealliance
Linkedin: www.linkedin.com/company/idealliance
X (Twitter): x.com/Idealliance
Instagram: www.instagram.com/idealliance
YouTube: www.youtube.com/c/idealliance

Description: Works to advance user-driven, cross-industry solutions for all publishing and content-related processes by developing standards fostering business alliances and identifying best practices. **Scope:** Training; graphics; designers. **Founded:** 1966. **Holdings:** Figures not available. **Publications:** *EDIrectory*; *Prepress Bulletin*; *Graphic Communications Association--Membership Directory* (Semiannual); *GCA Audio-Visual Listing.* **Geographic Preference:** Multinational.

12719 ■ In-Plant Printing and Mailing Association (IPMA) - Library
103 N Jefferson St.
Kearney, MO 64060
Ph: (816)919-1691
Co. E-mail: ipmainfo@ipma.org
URL: http://ipma.org
Contact: Kelly Hogg, President
E-mail: kah5z@virginia.edu
Facebook: www.facebook.com/ipma.headquarters
X (Twitter): x.com/ipmahq
Instagram: www.instagram.com/ipmahq
YouTube: www.youtube.com/channel/UCtVGu4PAx6hYmWebcf3la0w

Description: Managers of in-house corporate publishing or distribution activities. Offers continuing education courses and certification programs. Conducts research, surveys, and studies on industrial and technological trends. **Scope:** Mailing; printing. **Founded:** 1964. **Holdings:** Figures not available. **Publications:** *In-House Salary and Compensation Survey* (Biennial); *Inside Edge* (Monthly); *IPMA Bookstore*; *IPMA International Directory* (Annual). **Awards:** IPMA Mail Center Award (Annual); James M. Brahney Scholarship (Annual); In-House Promotional Excellence Award (Annual); IPMA Print Center Award (Annual); IPMA In-Print Award (Annual). **Geographic Preference:** National.

12720 ■ National Association of Printing Ink Manufacturers (NAPIM)
180 Admiral Cochrane Dr., Ste. 370
Annapolis, MD 21401
Ph: (410)940-6589
URL: http://www.napim.org
Contact: Molly Alton Mullins, Executive Director
E-mail: mmullins@napim.org

Description: Represents printing ink manufacturers and suppliers. Sponsors National Printing Ink Research Institute. **Founded:** 1916. **Awards:** NAPIM Ault Award (Annual); NAPIM Printing Ink Pioneer Award (Annual). **Geographic Preference:** National.

12721 ■ Printing Brokerage/Buyers Association International (PB/BA) - Library
1530 Locust St., Mezzanine 124
Philadelphia, PA 19102
Ph: (215)821-6581
URL: http://pbba.org

Description: Promotes understanding, cooperation, and interaction among members while obtaining the highest standard of professionalism in the graphic arts industry. **Scope:** Printing and publishing marketing and corporate development specialists, whose services include start ups, joint ventures, acquisitions, mergers, contract negotiation, international trade, seminars, workshops, facilities planning, and cost reduction programs. Serves private industries as well as government agencies. **Founded:** 1985. **Holdings:** Figures not available. **Publications:** "Hot Markets for 2007-2008," Jan, 2005. **Training:** How to Sell Printing Effectively; Sales Compensation and Management; How to Buy Printing Effectively; Hot Markets; International Priority Commerce. **Awards:** PBBA Printing Broker Reseller of the Year (Annual). **Geographic Preference:** Multinational. **Special Services:** Findprint®; Salesort®.

12722 ■ Printing United Alliance Center for Technology and Research - Library [Printing Industries of America's Center for Technology and Research]
2000 Corporate Dr., Ste. 205
　Wexford, PA 15090
Ph: (412)259-1710
Co. E-mail: info@printing.org
URL: http://www.printing.org/programs/technology
　-research
Facebook: www.facebook.com/printingunited
Linkedin: www.linkedin.com/company/printingunited
Instagram: www.instagram.com/printingind
Description: Serves the international graphic communications industries. Conducts research in graphic processes and their commercial applications, along with seminars and forums on graphic arts and environmental subjects. Conducts educational programs, including the publishing of graphic arts textbooks and learning modules, in addition to training and certification program in sheet-fed offset press operating, Web offset press operating, image assembly, and desktop publishing. Produces test images and quality control devices for the industry. Performs technical services for the graphic arts industry, including problem-solving, material evaluation, and plant audits. **Scope:** Human resources; economics; technologies; business growth. **Founded:** 1924. **Holdings:** Figures not available. **Publications:** "Re-Energize Your Printing Business," Partnership Publishing L.L.C.; "Handbook for Digital Printing and Variable-Data Printing"; "Flexography Primer"; "Process Controls Primer"; "The PDF Print Production Guide". **Training:** Creating Print Ready Files that Work Every Time; What Designers Need to Know about Sustainability; What Every Designer Must Know About Color and Press Oks; New Frontiers for the 21st Century Graphic Designer; Color Management for Printing and Packaging; Web to Print Primer; Designing for Prepress Success; Profit Opportunity Expanding into New Markets with Ancillary Services; Winning Ways to Market Web to Print Work flow to Customers; PDF Preflight and Repair for Newbies; Cross Media Methods n Magic URLS, Microsites and More; Good Jobs Gone Bad 2009 Edition; Fine Tune Your Color Management; Automating for Survival; Best Practice Primer Winning Digital Printing Workflows; Maximize Press time with Pit Stop Maintenance; A How to Tactical Plan for Sustainability Success; Optimizing Your Digital Press Where it Works and Where its Broken; Offset Press Optimization How to Troubleshoot, Control and Accelerate; Performance Dashboard Stalking Waste in the Printers Processes; Technology Forecast What's Hot and What's Not; Lean n Green Tactics and Techniques for Removing Waste; Controlling the Print Process How to Avoid Customer Rejects; Process Control for Color Management Prepress through Press. **Educational Activities:** President's Conference (Annual). **Awards:** Naomi Berber Memorial Award (Annual); Printing Industries of America Education Award of Excellence (Annual); InterTech Technology Awards (Annual); Robert F. Reed Technology Medal (Annual); William D. Schaeffer Environmental Award (Annual); Frederick D. Kagy Education Award of Excellence (Annual). **Geographic Preference:** National.

REFERENCE WORKS

12723 ■ "Agfa To Debut New: M-Press Leopard" in American Printer (Vol. 128, June 1, 2011, No. 6)
Description: M-Press Leopard is a new version of the machine that offers advanced ink jet technology

at a lower price point. Agfa Graphics introduced the new version that allows for new applications that require more manual handling. **Availability:** Print; Online.

12724 ■ "Avanti Hosts 19th Annual User's Conference in Washington, DC" in American Printer (Vol. 128, July 1, 2011, No. 7)
Description: Avanti Computer Systems Ltd. hosted its 19th annual users conference in Washington DC. In-plant and commercial printers were in attendance. **Availability:** Online.

12725 ■ "Avoid a Tablet Generation Gap" in American Printer (Vol. 128, July 1, 2011, No. 7)
Description: Individuals between the ages of 18-34 are the only generation that is more likely to own a laptop computer or netbook insead of a desktop computer. Statistical data included. **Availability:** Online.

12726 ■ "Bankruptcies" in Crain's Detroit Business (Vol. 24, March 24, 2008, No. 12, pp. 6)
Pub: Crain Communications Inc.
Contact: Barry Asin, President
Description: Current list of business that filed for Chapter 7 or 11 protection in U.S. Bankruptcy Court in Detroit include a construction company, a medical care company, a physical therapy firm and a communications firm. **Availability:** Online.

12727 ■ "Calista Sells Rural Newspapers" in Alaska Business Monthly (Vol. 27, October 2011, No. 10, pp. 8)
Pub: Alaska Business Publishing Company Inc.
Contact: Charles Bell, Vice President, Sales and
　Marketing
E-mail: cbell@akbizmag.com
Ed: Nancy Pounds. **Description:** Calista sold its six newspapers, a magazine, shoppers and its printing house. Details of the sales are given.

12728 ■ "Challenges Await Quad in Going Public" in Milwaukee Business Journal (Vol. 27, January 29, 2010, No. 18, pp. A1)
Pub: The Business Journal
Contact: Heather Ladage, President
E-mail: hladage@bizjournals.com
Ed: Rich Rovito. **Description:** Sussex, Wisconsin-based Quad/Graphics Inc.'s impending acquisition of rival Canadian World Color Press Inc. will transform it into a publicly held entity for the first time. Quad has operated as a private company for nearly 40 years and will need to adjust to changes, such as the way management shares information with Quad/Graphics' employees. Details of the merger are included. **Availability:** Print; Online.

12729 ■ "ContiTech Celebrates 100 Years" in American Printer (Vol. 128, July 1, 2011, No. 7)
Description: ContiTech celebrated 100 years in business. The firm started in 1911 after developing the first elastic printing blanket. Other milestones for the firm include its manufacturing process for compressible printing blankets, the Conti-Air brand and climate-neutral printing blankets. **Availability:** Print; Online.

12730 ■ "Crouser Releases Offline UV Coating Price Report" in American Printer (Vol. 128, June 1, 2011, No. 6)
Description: Crouser and Associates will offer the 'Pricing Off-Line UV Coating' report that provides background information on all three types of protective printing coatings and price guidance. The report will also offer comparisons of four popular types of offline equipment.

12731 ■ "Design Center Shows Quality of Digital Paper" in American Printer (Vol. 128, June 1, 2011, No. 6)
Description: Digital Design Centers allows printers to customize marketing tools in order to promote their own digital printing capabilities. **Availability:** Online.

12732 ■ "Digital Printing Walks the Plank" in American Printer (Vol. 128, August 1, 2011, No. 8)
Description: Digital print manufacturing is discussed. **Availability:** Online.

12733 ■ "Feeding the Elephants While Searching for Greener Pastures" in American Printer (Vol. 128, July 1, 2011, No. 7)
Ed: Bob Rosen. **Description:** Three steps to help printers to build a new business while facing the challenges to the existing business are outlined. **Availability:** Print.

12734 ■ "Flint Group Raises Prices of Offset Inks in EMEA" in American Printer (Vol. 128, August 1, 2011, No. 8)
Description: Due to the rising cost for raw materials, Flint Group is raising their prices for inks and coatings in North American. **Availability:** Online.

12735 ■ "Four Exhibition Considerations" in American Printer (Vol. 128, August 1, 2011, No. 8)
Description: Four questions to ask at the Graph Expo will help printers improve their own business. **Availability:** Print; Download; PDF.

12736 ■ "France Telecom Takes Minitel Offline" in Canadian Business (Vol. 85, August 13, 2012, No. 13, pp. 12)
Ed: Matthew McClearn. **Description:** The Minitel online service was developed to reduce the costs of printing phone directories in the French postal and telecommunications ministry in 1978 and became popular in Paris in 1982. With its user-based halved annually and services declining in its waning years, France Telecom opted to terminate the service on June 30, 2012. **Availability:** Print; Online.

12737 ■ "Fujifilm Invites Printers to Take the 'Onset Challenge" in American Printer (Vol. 128, August 1, 2011, No. 8)
Description: Fujifilm North American Corporation's Graphic Systems Division offers a new five-step product selection and return-on-investment calculator for the Onset family of wide-format printers. **Availability:** Online.

12738 ■ "Graphic Tech Acquires First U.S. :M-Press Tiger with Inline Screen Printing" in American Printer (Vol. 128, June 1, 2011, No. 6)
Description: Graphic Tech located in California bought M-Press Tiger, the first in North America with an inline screen printing unit. **Availability:** Online.

12739 ■ "Hard-To-Read Fonts Promote Better Recall" in Harvard Business Review (Vol. 90, April 2012, No. 4, pp. 32)
Pub: Harvard Business Review Press
Contact: Moderna V. Pfizer, Contact
Ed: Daniel Oppenheimer. **Price:** $6, hardcover. **Description:** Elaborate fonts have been found to boost reading comprehension because they make text harder to skim. However, because elaborate fonts are more difficult to read, it raises the likelihood that individuals might simply stop reading. **Availability:** PDF; Online.

12740 ■ "Having a Head for Security Means Being In the Know: Security Print Explored" in Print Week (July 4, 2012)
Ed: Jon Severs. **Description:** The security market is expanding and presenting opportunities for printers, a fundamental part of security procedures. Print is an environment where digital media is not used. Details for printers wishing to enter the print security market are presented. **Availability:** Print; Online.

12741 ■ "Interchangeable or Irreplaceable?" in American Printer (Vol. 128, August 1, 2011, No. 8)
Description: Creating and maintaining customers is important for all graphic design and printing companies. Tips are shared to help maintain good customer satisfaction and repeat business. **Availability:** Online.

12742 ■ *"KBA, Graphic Art System Partner on Cold Foil" in American Printer (Vol. 128, June 1, 2011, No. 6)*

Description: KBA North America has partnered with Graphic Art System to retrofit and equip presses with cold foil machines. **Availability:** Online.

12743 ■ *"Kodak Offers Cloud-Based Operating Option" in American Printer (Vol. 128, June 1, 2011, No. 6)*

Description: Kodak partnered with VMware to offer its first Virtual Operating Environment option for Kodak Unified Workflow Solutions. The new feature enables cost savings, increased efficiency and failover protection. **Availability:** Online.

12744 ■ *"New Approach to Mechanical Binding" in American Printer (Vol. 128, July 1, 2011, No. 7)*

Description: EcoBinder coil binding system from Kugler-Womako eliminates traditional plastic combs or wire spiral with the use of 22-mm wide printable paper rings. **Availability:** Online.

12745 ■ *"One World" in American Printer (Vol. 128, August 1, 2011, No. 8)*

Description: Graph Expo will highlight entrepreneurs focused on the connection between content, technology and business models. **Availability:** Print; Online.

12746 ■ *"Paper Replaces PVC for Gift Cards" in American Printer (Vol. 128, June 1, 2011, No. 6)*

Description: Monadnock Envi Card Stock replaces paper for gift cards, loyalty cards, membership cards, hotel keys and durable signage. This renewable wood fiber alternative to PVC card materials comes from Monadock Paper Mills. **Availability:** Online.

12747 ■ *"Please Pass the Mayo" in Crain's Chicago Business (Vol. 31, April 28, 2008, No. 17, pp. 32)*

Pub: Crain Communications Inc.

Contact: Barry Asin, President

Ed: Samantha Stainburn. **Description:** Fort Dearborn Co. has come a long way since it started as on one-press print shop; the family-owned company was struggling to keep up with the technology of making consumer product labels for curvy bottles of products like V8 V-Fusion juice and in 2006 sold off to Genstar Capital LLC which has pushed for acquisitions; last year, Fort Derborn bought its biggest competitor, Renaissance Mark Inc., doubling its size and adding spirit and wine makers to its client roster. **Availability:** Online.

12748 ■ *"PrintCity Shares Guide for Carbon Footprinting" in American Printer (Vol. 128, June 1, 2011, No. 6)*

Description: PrintCity Alliance published its new report, 'Carbon Footprint & Energy Reduction for Graphic Industry Value Chain.' The report aims to help improve the environmental performance of printers, converters, publishers, brand owners and their suppliers. **Availability:** Online.

12749 ■ *"Printers to the Trade" in American Printer (Vol. 128, July 1, 2011, No. 7)*

Description: Wholesale printing is discussed. Two wholesale printers share insight into their success, from business philosophies in general to practices that build strong relationships. **Availability:** Online.

12750 ■ *Printing Impressions--400 List*

Pub: NAPCO Media

Contact: Mark J. Subers, President

E-mail: msubers@napco.com

URL(s): www.piworld.com

Ed: Erik Cagle, Julie Greenbaum. **Released:** Daily **Description:** Publication includes list of the leading 500 commercial, financial, directory, publication, check, book, business form, packaging, and specialty printers. **Entries include:** Company name, city and state, sales, name of president or chief executive officer, number of press units, number of employees, coded list of printing specialties (periodicals, commercial, specialty, etc.), whether publicly or privately owned. **Arrangement:** Ranked by annual sales. **Availability:** Print; Online.

12751 ■ *"Reducing the Book's Carbon Footprint" in American Printer (Vol. 128, July 1, 2011, No. 7)*

Description: Green Press Initiative's Book Industry Environmental Council is working to achieve a 20 percent reduction in the book industry's carbon footprint by 2020. The Council is made up of publishers, printers, paper suppliers, and non-governmental organizations. **Availability:** Online.

12752 ■ *"Sappi Announces North American 'Printers of the Year' Gold Winners" in American Printer (Vol. 128, July 1, 2011, No. 7)*

Description: Sappi Fine Paper North America honored ten gold winners of its 14th North American Printers of the Year awards. Each gold winning printer will receive $20,000 to support marketing and brand initiatives. **Availability:** Print; Online.

12753 ■ *"Say Yes to the New Wedding Collection from Pinhole Press" in Benzinga.com (May 1, 2012)*

Pub: Benzinga.com

Contact: Jason Raznick, Founder

Ed: Aaron Wise. **Description:** Online retailer, Pinhole Press, providing personalized photo gifts has introduced a new Edding Collection that includes wedding invitations, save the dates, bridal shower sets, wedding gifts and more. Further details of the new wedding collection are included. **Availability:** Online.

12754 ■ *"Seeing the Light" in American Printer (Vol. 128, July 1, 2011, No. 7)*

Description: Four printing demos on sheetfed, digital, label and pad printing equipment were highlighted at the Fifth UV Days held in Stuttgart, Germany in May 2011. **Availability:** Online.

12755 ■ *"Seven Tips for Continuous Improvement" in American Printer (Vol. 128, July 1, 2011, No. 7)*

Description: Seven tips are given to help any graphic arts or printing company improve by integrating lean manufacturing into operations. **Availability:** Online.

12756 ■ *"Successful First Year for Twin Rivers" in American Printer (Vol. 128, June 1, 2011, No. 6)*

Description: Profile of Twin Rivers located in Maine. The firm manufactured 380,000 tons of free sheet and hybrid-groundwood papers in its first year. **Availability:** Online.

12757 ■ *"Sudden Shift Leaves Wells Fargo Vendor Scrambling" in Charlotte Business Journal (Vol. 25, July 9, 2010, No. 16, pp. 1)*

Pub: Charlotte Business Journal

Contact: Robert Morris, Editor

E-mail: rmorris@bizjournals.com

Ed: Adam O'Daniel. **Description:** Rubber stamps vendor Carolina Marking Devices is facing a 30 percent drop in business after banking firm Wells Fargo & Company decided to buy its rubber stamps from another vendor. Carolina Marking Devices had provided rubber to First Union Corporation and its successor Wachovia Corporation, which was eventually acquired by Wells Fargo. Other reactions from Carolina Marking Device owners are given. **Availability:** Print; Online.

12758 ■ *"Tic-Tac-Show: Line Up the Opportunities at Graph Expo" in American Printer (Vol. 128, August 1, 2011, No. 8)*

Description: Graph Expo has become the US print industry's main event. There will be as many as 500 exhibitors at this year's event and the Graphic Arts Show Company lists over 30 co-located events as well as 53 new sessions in the seminar program's 28 education categories. **Availability:** PDF; Online.

12759 ■ *"Transcontinental to Exchange Assets with Quad/Graphics" in American Printer (Vol. 128, August 1, 2011, No. 8)*

Description: Transcontinental Inc. and Quad/Graphics Inc. entered into an agreement where Transcontinental will indirectly acquire all shares of Quad Graphics Canada Inc. **Availability:** Print; Online.

12760 ■ *"Try a Little Social Media" in American Printer (Vol. 128, June 1, 2011, No. 6)*

Description: Social media helps keep Ussery Printing on customers radar. Jim David, VP of marketing for the firm, states that 350 people following them on Facebook are from the local area. **Availability:** Print; Mailing list; Online.

12761 ■ *"Web to Print" in American Printer (Vol. 128, August 1, 2011, No. 8)*

Description: Jerry Kennelly, CEO and founder of Tweak.com believes that Web-to-Design is middleware with no content. His firm offers an easy to use interface that flows right into the printer's workflow with no additional costs. **Availability:** Online.

12762 ■ *Women in 3D Printing: From Bones to Bridges and Everything in Between*

Ed: Stacey M. DelVecchio. **Released:** 2021. **Description:** Discusses the contribution women engineers have made to the 3D printing industry. **Availability:** Print.

STATISTICAL SOURCES

12763 ■ *Digital Printing Industry in the US - Market Research Report*

URL(s): www.ibisworld.com/united-states/market-research-reports/digital-printing-industry/

Price: $925. **Description:** Downloadable report analyzing the current and future trends in the digital printing industry. **Availability:** Online.

12764 ■ *RMA Annual Statement Studies*

Pub: Risk Management Association

Contact: Nancy Foster, President

Released: Annual. **Description:** Contains composite balance sheets and income statements for more than 360 industries, including the accounting, auditing, and bookkeeping industries. Also contains five years of comparative historical data for discerning trends. Includes 16 commonly used ratios, computed for most of the size groupings for nearly every industry.

TRADE PERIODICALS

12765 ■ *American Printer: The Graphic Arts Managers Magazine*

URL(s): www.americanprinter.com/about/american-printer

Facebook: Facebook.com/American-Printer-Magazine-48526382394/

X (Twitter): Twitter.com/AMPRINTMAG

Description: Magazine covering the printing and publishing market. **Availability:** Print.

12766 ■ *FLEXO: Converting Technology*

Pub: Foundation of the Flexographic Technical Association

Contact: Laura Wright, Chairman of the Board

URL(s): www.flexography.org/flexo-magazine

Ed: Brad Pareso. **Description:** Magazine covering the flexographic printing method. **Availability:** Print.

12767 ■ *Guild of Book Workers Newsletter*

Pub: Guild of Book Workers

Contact: Bexx Caswell, President

E-mail: president@guildofbookworkers.org

URL(s): guildofbookworkers.org/newsletter

Released: 6/year **Description:** Covers issues in book arts, binding, book conservation, calligraphy, and printing. Recurring features include letters to the editor, interviews, news of research, a calendar of events, reports of meetings, news of educational opportunities, job listings, book reviews, and notices of publications available. **Availability:** PDF; Online.

12768 ■ *Printing Impressions: America's Most Influential and Widely Read Publication for Commercial Printers*
Pub: NAPCO Media
Contact: Mark J. Subers, President
E-mail: msubers@napco.com
URL(s): www.piworld.com
Facebook: www.facebook.com/PIconnects
Linkedin: www.linkedin.com/company/printing -impressions
X (Twitter): x.com/PIconnects
Ed: Mark T. Michelson. **Released:** Monthly **Description:** Trade magazine. **Availability:** Print; Download; PDF; Online.

12769 ■ *Quick Printing: The Information Source for Commercial Copyshops & Printshops*
Contact: Kelly Holmes, Publisher
E-mail: kelly@quickprinting.com
Ed: Karen Lowery Hall. **Released:** Monthly **Price:** Free. **Description:** For Quick and Small Commercial Printers. **Availability:** Print; Online.

VIDEO/AUDIO MEDIA

12770 ■ *The Print-on-Demand Revolution*
URL(s): www.startuphustlepodcast.com/the-print-on -demand-revolution
Ed: Matt Watson. **Released:** February 14, 2024. **Description:** Podcast discusses the logistics of custom printing, the challenges of managing a remote team, policing copyright infringement, and ensuring quality control. .

TRADE SHOWS AND CONVENTIONS

12771 ■ **Graphics of the Americas**
Florida Graphics Alliance (FGA)
    10524 Moss Pk. Rd., Ste. 204
    Orlando, FL 32822
Ph: (407)240-8009
Co. E-mail: gabe@floridagraphics.org
URL: http://www.floridagraphics.org
Contact: Art Abbott, Contact
E-mail: art@abbottcg.com
URL(s): www.floridagraphics.org/member-news
X (Twitter): twitter.com/goaexpo
Description: Graphic arts and specialty printing equipment, supplies, and services. **Audience:** Commercial printers, digital printers, label printers, wide format printers, graphic designers, screen printers, packaging printers, specialty printers, sign printers, book printers, publishers, binders, converting professionals, print and media buyers. **Principal Exhibits:** Graphic arts and specialty printing equipment, supplies, and services.

CONSULTANTS

12772 ■ **J. S. Eliezer Associates Inc. (JSEA)**
300 Atlantic St.
    Stamford, CT 06902
Contact: Peter M. Harding, Chief Executive Officer
Description: Management and market research consultants offering design and implementation of manufacturing strategy, feasibility analysis, and systems analysis, as well as management information systems and prepress systems, manufacturing proposals analysis, negotiations and contracts, paper purchasing strategy and contract negotiations, and catalog distribution effectiveness analysis and serves the publishing and catalog industries. **Scope:** Management and market research consultants offering design and implementation of manufacturing strategy, feasibility analysis, and systems analysis, as well as management information systems and prepress systems, manufacturing proposals analysis, negotiations and contracts, paper purchasing strategy and contract negotiations, and catalog distribution effectiveness analysis and serves the publishing and catalog industries.

FRANCHISES AND BUSINESS OPPORTUNITIES

12773 ■ **AlphaGraphics Inc. (AG)**
143 Union Blvd., Ste. 650
    Lakewood, CO 80228
Ph: (720)603-1389
Free: 800-955-6246
Co. E-mail: opportunity@alphagraphics.com
URL: http://www.alphagraphicsfranchise.com
Contact: Randy Anderson, Director
URL(s): www.alphagraphics.com
Facebook: www.facebook.com/agidahofalls
X (Twitter): x.com/agidahofalls
Pinterest: www.pinterest.com/alphagraphicsid
Description: Provides mobile marketing, brand development, digital copying and email marketing. **No. of Franchise Units:** 300. **Founded:** 1970. **Training:** 4 weeks new franchisee training, 1 week in-store training and advanced franchisee training.

12774 ■ **Babies 'N' Bells Inc.**
4489 Mira Vista Dr.
    Frisco, TX 75034
URL: http://thefranchisemall.com/franchises/details/ 10282-0-babies_n_bells.htm
Contact: Dara Craft, Contact
Description: Chain of franchising store. **Founded:** 1997. **Franchised:** 1997. **Financial Assistance:** Yes **Training:** Offers 1 week at headquarters with ongoing support.

12775 ■ **Cartridge Express**
Canada
Ph: (780)960-9413
URL: http://www.cartridgeexpress.io
Facebook: www.facebook.com/CartridgeExpressCA
Description: Manufacturer of ink toner printer cartridges. **Training:** Yes.

12776 ■ **Cartridge World**
3917 Mercy Dr.
    McHenry, IL 60050
Ph: (815)321-4400
Fax: (815)271-5896
Co. E-mail: info@cartridgeworldglobal.com
URL: http://www.cartridgeworldusa.com
Contact: Mark Pinner, Co-Chief Executive Officer
E-mail: mpinner@cartridgeworld.com
Facebook: www.facebook.com/CartridgeWorldNA
X (Twitter): twitter.com/cartridgeworld
YouTube: www.youtube.com/user/cartridgeworldusa1
Description: Provider of cartridge refilling services. **Founded:** 1997. **Training:** An intensive 2 week training course.

12777 ■ **Kwik Kopy Business Centers, Inc.**
12715 Telge Rd.
    Cypress, TX 77429
Contact: Jay Groot, President
Description: Provider of printing and copying services. **Founded:** 2001. **Financial Assistance:** Yes **Managerial Assistance:** Provide business support, advertising, and marketing materials. **Training:** Owners attend classroom and field training, as well as ongoing training through workshops and conferences.

12778 ■ **Minuteman Press International Inc.**
61 Executive Blvd.
    Farmingdale, NY 11735
Ph: (631)249-1370
Co. E-mail: info@mpihq.com
URL: http://www.minutemanpress.com
Contact: Nick Titus, President
Facebook: www.facebook.com/Minu temanPressFranchise
Linkedin: www.linkedin.com/company/minuteman -press
X (Twitter): x.com/minutemanintl
YouTube: www.youtube.com/c/minutemanpress
Description: Offers commercial offset printing, computer typesetting, saddle stitch and sewn binding services. **Founded:** 1974. **Financial Assistance:** Yes **Training:** Provides 2 weeks plus additional onon-site training.

12779 ■ **PIP, Inc.**
26722 Plz.
    Mission Viejo, CA 92691
Co. E-mail: marketing@pip.com
URL: http://www.pip.com
Contact: Richard Lowe, President
Facebook: www.facebook.com/PIPCorporate
Linkedin: www.linkedin.com/company/pip-inc
X (Twitter): x.com/pipcorp
YouTube: www.youtube.com/user/pipcorp
Description: Firm provides printing, marketing and signage services. **Founded:** 1963. **Financial Assistance:** Yes **Training:** 2 1/2 weeks of training at PIP University and field visit within the first six months of operation.

12780 ■ **Postal Connections of America (PCA)**
6136 Frisco Sq., Blvd., Ste. 400
    Frisco, TX 75034
Free: 800-767-8257
Co. E-mail: info@postalconnections.com
URL: http://www.postalconnections.com
Contact: Fred Morache, Managing Director Owner
Facebook: www.facebook.com/PostalConnectionsInc
Linkedin: www.linkedin.com/company/postal-connec tions
X (Twitter): x.com/PCA_CORP
YouTube: www.youtube.com/channel/UCPO 3Pi7Wgc9BZwbZ2zO1Ftw
Description: Firm provides packaging supplies, notary services, mail box rentals, printing, copying, fax services, shipping, office and shipping supplies and computer services. **Founded:** 1985. **Financial Assistance:** Yes **Training:** Extensive training prior to & after opening. Franchisee's receive 5 days live action training in a regional training store, Unique Act video training program & 4 days onsite.

12781 ■ **Print Three Franchising Corp. (PTFC)**
20 Great Gulf Dr., Unit 14
    Concord, ON, Canada L4K 0k7
Ph: (905)669-8895
Free: 800-335-5918
Fax: (905)669-0712
Co. E-mail: support@printthree.com
URL: http://www.printthree.com
Facebook: www.facebook.com/PrintThree
Linkedin: www.linkedin.com/company/print-three -franchising
X (Twitter): x.com/PrintThreeHQ
Instagram: www.instagram.com/printthreehq
YouTube: www.youtube.com/user/PrintThreeCorp
Description: Provider of commercial and digital printing services including web-to-print solutions, web services and professional marketing. **Founded:** 1970. **Training:** Yes.

12782 ■ **Sir Speedy Inc. [Sir Speedy Print Signs Marketing]**
26722 Plz.
    Mission Viejo, CA 92691
Free: 800-854-3321
Co. E-mail: marketing@sirspeedy.com
URL: http://www.sirspeedy.com
Contact: Richard Lowe, President
Facebook: www.facebook.com/SirSpeedyCorporate
Linkedin: www.linkedin.com/company/sir-speedy
X (Twitter): x.com/sirspeedycorp
YouTube: www.youtube.com/user/sirspeedycorp
Description: Provider of printing, signage and marketing services. **Founded:** 1968. **Training:** Available at headquarters 2 weeks, 2 weeks at franchisee's location, at regional meeings 1-3 days, and ongoing support.

12783 ■ **The UPS Store Canada**
1115 N Service Rd. W, Unit 1
    Oakville, ON, Canada L6M 2V9
Free: 800-661-6232
Co. E-mail: custsvccaen@ups.com
URL: http://www.theupsstore.ca
Contact: David Druker, President
Facebook: www.facebook.com/TheUPSStoreCA
Linkedin: www.linkedin.com/company/the-ups-store -canada

X (Twitter): x.com/theupsstore_can
Instagram: www.instagram.com/theupsstoreca
YouTube: www.youtube.com/user/TheUPSS toreCanada
Description: Provider of small business solutions, digital printing, mailbox services, packaging and shipping and postal services. **No. of Franchise Units:** 360. **Founded:** 1988. **Equity Capital Needed:** $80,000-$100,000. **Educational Activities:** ACUHO-I Conference & Expo (Annual).

LIBRARIES

12784 ■ Carnegie Mellon University-Special Collections
5000 Forbes Ave.
 Pittsburgh, PA 15213-3890
Ph: (412)268-2444
URL: http://www.library.cmu.edu/distinctive-collec tions/special-collections
Contact: Samuel Lemley, Curator

Description: Contains many `of Carnegie Mellon University's rare and unique materials and the rare book collection. **Scope:** History of science; cryptology; computing; early Shakespeare editions; graphic arts. **Services:** Library open to the public. **Founded:** 1964. **Holdings:** Books.

RESEARCH CENTERS

12785 ■ Gravure Association of the Americas, Inc. (GAA) - Library
150 Executive Ctr., Dr., Ste. 201
 Greenville, SC 29615
Ph: (803)948-9470
Fax: (803)948-9471
URL: http://gaa.org
Contact: Tony Donato, Director, Operations
E-mail: tdonato@gaa.org

Description: Promotes the use of the gravure printing process for publication printing, package printing and specialty product printing. Collects, analyzes and disseminates current and historical information pertaining to gravure technology, marketing, environmental issues, government regulations, education and training. Exchanges information with the European Rotogravure Association. Compiles statistics. **Scope:** Gravure printing, electronic imaging, laser applications, environmental control, and computer process control. Research focuses on press, paper, ink, color reproduction, cylinder preparation, system, and the environment. **Services:** Library open to members. **Founded:** 1987. **Subscriptions:** magazines Articles; PDF manuals; textbook. **Publications:** *Gravure* (Quarterly); *Gravure Association of America-- Membership Roster* (Annual); *INTERFACE* (Monthly). **Educational Activities:** GAA Conferences and seminars; GAA Annual Convention, Promotes the use of the gravure printing process for publication printing, package printing and specialty product printing. **Awards:** Gravure Cylinder Society Award (Annual); Gravure Person of the Year (Annual); Gravure Golden Cylinder Awards (Annual). **Geographic Preference:** National.

ASSOCIATIONS AND OTHER ORGANIZATIONS

12786 ■ Council of International Investigators (CII)
PO Box 267
Elmhurst, IL 60126
Ph: (630)333-5729
Co. E-mail: office@cii2.org
URL: http://www.cii2.org
Contact: Toine Goorts, President
E-mail: tgoorts@goorts-international.com

Description: Provide an enhanced quality of service for all clients by offering continuing education. **Founded:** 1955. **Publications:** *International Councilor* (Quarterly). **Awards:** CII International Investigator of the Year (Annual); Malcolm W. Thomson, C.I.I. Memorial Award (Annual); CII Meritorious Service Award (MSA) (Annual). **Geographic Preference:** Multinational.

12787 ■ International Foundation for Protection Officers (IFPO)
1076 6th Ave. N
Naples, FL 34102
Ph: (239)430-0534
Co. E-mail: adminifpo@ifpo.org
URL: http://www.ifpo.org
Contact: Sandi J. Davies, Chief Executive Officer
E-mail: sandi@ifpo.com
Facebook: www.facebook.com/ifpo.org
X (Twitter): x.com/ifponews

Description: Seeks to provide for the education, training, and certification of protection officers worldwide. **Publications:** *Business Crime Prevention*; *Careers in Security and Investigation*; *Protection Officer News* (Quarterly); *Protection Officer Survival*. **Geographic Preference:** National.

12788 ■ JS Consulting Inc.
1701 E Edgewood Ave., No. 47802
Indianapolis, IN 46227
URL: http://www.jsconsulting.com

Description: Offers private investigation and digital forensics services. **Scope:** Offers private investigation and digital forensics services. **Holdings:** The computer-readable database containing information on more than 36,000 agencies in all 50 states and 152 countries; updated daily. **Publications:** "Email Dangers And Pitfalls To Be Aware Of"; "Will Private Investigation Survive?"; "Amazing Feats and Gadgets"; "A License to Learn"; "Being A Professional PI"; "Brain Surgery by Appointment"; "Clients: Who and What are they?"; "Investigators Investigating Investigators"; "Stan Comstock's Million Dollar Investigative Service"; "Celebrating Investigation"; "Bizarre Job Description for a Private Investigator"; "Sales and the Art of Private Investigation"; "Telephone Technique"; "The K.I.S.S. Online Glossary"; "The Truth About Your Sleuth"; "The Real HP Culprits"; "Private Investigation and the Good Life". **Educational Activities:** ION Conference. **Geographic Preference:** Multinational.

12789 ■ National Association of Investigative Specialists (NAIS)
9513 Burnet Rd.
Austin, TX 78758
Ph: (512)719-3595
Fax: (512)719-3594
URL: http://www.pimall.com/nais
Contact: Ralph D. Thomas, Contact

Description: Promotes professionalism and provides for information exchange among private investigators. Lobbies for investigative regulations. **Founded:** 1984. **Publications:** *How to Find Anyone Anywhere: Secret Sources and Techniques for Locating Missing Persons* (Annual); *Physical Surveillance Training Manual* (Annual); *PI Bites*; *PI Daily* (Daily); *PI CATALOG*; *Private Investigator's Connection* (Bi-monthly); *Investigator's International All-in-One Directory* (Annual); *Investigator's Information Access Directory* (Annual). **Educational Activities:** Super Conference. **Geographic Preference:** National.

12790 ■ National Association of Legal Investigators (NALI)
PO Box 278
Bath, MI 48808
Ph: (517)702-9835
Fax: (517)372-1501
Co. E-mail: info@nalionline.org
URL: http://www.nalionline.org
Contact: Ken Shelton, Chairman
E-mail: ken@sheltoninvestigations.com

Description: Legal investigators, both independent and law firm staff, who specialize in investigation of personal injury matters for the plaintiff and criminal defense. Promotes professionalization of the legal investigator, accomplished by seminars and a professional certification program. Provides nationwide network of contact among members. Compiles statistics. **Founded:** 1967. **Publications:** *Legal Investigator*. **Awards:** NALI Editor-Publisher Award (Annual). **Geographic Preference:** National.

12791 ■ National Association of Professional Background Screeners (NAPBS)
110 Horizon Dr., Ste. 210
Raleigh, NC 27615
Ph: (919)459-2082
Fax: (919)459-2075
Co. E-mail: info@thepbsa.org
URL: http://thepbsa.org
Contact: Melissa Sorenson, Executive Director
E-mail: melissa.sorenson@napbs.com
Facebook: www.facebook.com/National-Association-of-Professional-Background-Screeners-159461350758108
Linkedin: www.linkedin.com/company/1317358
X (Twitter): x.com/NAPBS

Description: Represents the interests of companies offering employment and background screening. Promotes ethical business practices. Fosters awareness of issues related to consumer protection and privacy rights. Maintains the standard of the background screening industry. **Founded:** 2003. **Educa-**tional Activities:** National Association of Professional Background Screeners Meeting. **Geographic Preference:** National.

12792 ■ National Council of Investigation and Security Services Inc. (NCISS)
PO Box 200615
Evans, CO 80620
Free: 800-445-8408
Fax: (970)480-7794
URL: http://www.nciss.org
Contact: Tina Thomas, President
E-mail: tthomas@subrosapi.com

Description: Monitors national and state legislative and regulatory activities. Encourages the practice of high standards of personal and professional conduct. Acquires and disseminates information. Provides information about state legislation and regulatory activities that could have an impact on a particular firm or on the industry in general; acts as spokesman for the industry before legislative and regulatory bodies at both federal and state levels. **Founded:** 1975. **Publications:** *NCISS Report* (Semiannual). **Awards:** John J. Duffy Memorial Achievement Award (Annual); Wayne J. Wunder Memorial Award (Annual). **Geographic Preference:** National.

12793 ■ Nine Lives Associates (NLA)
c/o Executive Protection Institute
16 Penn Pl., Ste. 1130
New York, NY 10001
URL: http://www.personalprotection.com/Home/NLA

Description: Provides professional recognition for qualified individuals engaged in executive protection assignments. **Founded:** 1978. **Educational Activities:** Nine Lives Associates Conference (Annual). **Geographic Preference:** Multinational.

12794 ■ Society of Professional Investigators (SPI)
Church St. Station, Ste. 2032
New York, NY 10008
Ph: (212)840-0349
URL: http://spinyc.org
Contact: Paul G. Babakitis, President
E-mail: president@spinyc.org
Linkedin: www.linkedin.com/company/society-of-professional-investigators
X (Twitter): x.com/SPINYC_org
YouTube: www.youtube.com/channel/UCrinAS0J06uU62dlypjiGpw

Description: Seeks to advance knowledge of the science and technology of professional investigation, law enforcement, and police science; maintains high standards and ethics; promotes efficiency of investigators in the services they perform. **Founded:** 1956. **Publications:** *SPI Newsletter*. **Geographic Preference:** National.

REFERENCE WORKS

12795 ■ *American Polygraph Association--Member Directory* (Internet only)
Pub: American Polygraph Association
Contact: Roy Ortiz, President

E-mail: president@polygraph.org

URL(s): members.polygraph.org/members/directory/ search_bootstrap.php?twocol&org_id=APAS

Ed: Stuart Senter, PhD. **Description:** Covers approximately 2,500 member individuals and companies involved the polygraph field. **Arrangement:** Geographical. **Availability:** Print.

12796 ■ *"The Downfall of Trustify" in PInow.com (November 11, 2019)*

URL(s): www.pinow.com/articles/2779/the-downfall-of -trustify

Ed: Stephanie Irvine. **Released:** November 11, 2019. **Description:** Profile of Trustify, Inc., a start-up company founded in 2015 that helped people hire private investigators online. It's popularity was fueled by its forward-thinking business model, but quickly died out within a few years due to financial troubles, hiring unlicensed investigators, and taking on cases that normally shouldn't be investigated. **Availability:** Online.

12797 ■ *"Open Source Intelligence for Private Investigators" in PInow.com (October 14, 2019)*

URL(s): www.pinow.com/articles/2646/open-source-in telligence-for-private-investigators

Released: October 14, 2019. **Description:** Examines the role of Open Source Intelligence (OSINT) that private investigators use. Even though it is accessible to everyone it can still be a great tool to use since data it provides could be useful. Several open source tools are described with their benefits along with links. **Availability:** Online.

12798 ■ *"Private Investigators and Cold Cases" in PInow.com (September 16, 2019)*

URL(s): www.pinow.com/articles/2662/private-inves tigators-and-cold-cases

Ed: Carie McMichael. **Released:** September 16, 2019. **Description:** Examines the role private investigators play in helping solve cold cases when law enforcement agencies do not have the time or resources to dedicate to the process. Private investigators can also work on their own without a chain of command to disrupt the work, unlike police detectives who must also follow certain procedures. **Availability:** Online.

STATISTICAL SOURCES

12799 ■ *RMA Annual Statement Studies*

Pub: Risk Management Association

Contact: Nancy Foster, President

Released: Annual. **Description:** Contains composite balance sheets and income statements for more than 360 industries, including the accounting, auditing, and bookkeeping industries. Also contains five years of comparative historical data for discerning trends. Includes 16 commonly used ratios, computed for most of the size groupings for nearly every industry.

TRADE PERIODICALS

12800 ■ *Criminal Justice*

Pub: American Bar Association

Contact: Mary L. Smith, President

URL(s): www.americanbar.org/groups/criminal_jus tice/publications/criminal-justice-magazine

Released: Quarterly **Price:** $100, Nonmembers for annual subscription, US. **Description:** Magazine covering criminal law designed for members of the ABA's Section of Criminal Justice and legal professionals. **Availability:** Print; Online.

FRANCHISES AND BUSINESS OPPORTUNITIES

12801 ■ **Case In Point, Inc. (CIP)**

PO Box 1286

Londonderry, NH 03053

Free: 800-370-2116

Fax: (800)397-2963

Co. E-mail: info@cipnow.com

URL: http://cipnow.com

Contact: Peter Carl, President

E-mail: pcarl@cipnow.com

Description: Firm engages in providing investigation services such as surveillance, criminal, civil investigation and investigative research. **Founded:** 1992. **Franchised:** 2002. **Training:** Offers 2 weeks at headquarters, 1 week at franchisees location and ongoing support.

ASSOCIATIONS AND OTHER ORGANIZATIONS

12802 ■ Private Label Manufacturers Association (PLMA)
630 3rd Ave.
New York, NY 10017
Ph: (212)972-3131
Co. E-mail: info@plma.com
URL: http://plma.com
Contact: Peggy Davies, President
Linkedin: www.linkedin.com/company/private-label
-manufacturers-association
X (Twitter): x.com/PLMA_USA
Description: Membership consists of manufacturers, brokers, suppliers, and consultants. Educates consumers on the quality and value of private label or store brand products; promotes private label industry. Compiles statistics; conducts research programs for members. **Founded:** 1979. **Publications:** *PLMA E-Scanner* (Monthly). **Educational Activities:** Private Label Trade Show (Annual); Domestic Trade Show; International Trade Show (Annual). **Awards:** PLMA Salute to Excellence (Annual). **Geographic Preference:** Multinational.

REFERENCE WORKS

12803 ■ "Amazon Will Regret Building Private Label Brands" in Marketplace Pulse (September 25, 2019)
URL(s): www.marketplacepulse.com/articles/amazon
-will-regret-building-private-label-brands
Ed: Jouzas Kaziukenas. **Released:** September 25, 2019. **Description:** Amazon is receiving backlash from launching its own private label items and pushing those items on its site before other brands. Often copying other brands for its products, there are antitrust concerns as well since they gather data about various products being sold on its platform. **Availability:** Online.

12804 ■ "The Rise and Premiumization of Private Label: Sales Surpass $143bn, Notes Nielsen" in Food Navigator-USA (August 30, 2019)
URL(s): www.foodnavigator-usa.com/Article/2019/08/
30/The-rise-and-premiumization-of-private-label
-Sales-surpass-143bn-notes-Nielsen
Ed: Mary Ellen Shoup. **Released:** August 30, 2019. **Description:** Consumers are buying private label products at a much higher rate than in the past, with many of them declaring that the quality is just as good or better than the name brand. Stores are also launched more higher-end store brand products, which consumers are also buying. **Availability:** Online.

TRADE SHOWS AND CONVENTIONS

12805 ■ PLMA's Annual Private Label Trade Show
URL(s): plma.com/events/plmas-annual-private-label
-trade-show
Frequency: Annual. **Description:** Private label product show. Buyers include: supermarkets, drug chains, mass merchandisers, supercenters, specialty retailers, dollar stores, club stores, and military exchanges. **Principal Exhibits:** Private label product show. Buyers include: supermarkets, drug chains, mass merchandisers, supercenters, specialty retailers, dollar stores, club stores, and military exchanges. **Telecommunication Services:** exhibit@plma.com.

FRANCHISES AND BUSINESS OPPORTUNITIES

12806 ■ Cap-It International Inc.
4954 275th St.
Langley, BC, Canada V4W 0A3
Free: 855-857-1211
Co. E-mail: info@capitfranchise.com
URL: http://cap-it.com
Contact: Andrew Funk, President
Facebook: www.facebook.com/CapItIntl
Description: Retailer of truck caps, wheels, tires, hitches, racking and lights. **Founded:** 1977. **Equity Capital Needed:** $350,000-$750,000. **Franchise Fee:** $49,000. **Royalty Fee:** 0.05. **Training:** Provides 6 weeks of training.

START-UP INFORMATION

12807 ■ *"5 Things to Know Before Becoming a Professional Organizer" in Pro Organizer Studio Blog*

URL(s): proorganizerstudio.com/blog/professional
-organizer-career/

Ed: Jen Obermeier. **Description:** Provides information for those interested in becoming professional organizers and outlines five tips to consider when getting started. **Availability:** Online.

12808 ■ *How to Start a Home-Based Professional Organizing Business*

Ed: Dawn Noble. **Released:** April 01, 2011. **Price:** paperback, softback. **Description:** Tips for starting a home-based professional organizing business are presented. **Availability:** E-book; Print.

12809 ■ *"How to Start a Professional Organizer Business" in MyCorporation blog*

URL(s): blog.mycorporation.com/2021/07/profes-sional-organizer-business/

Ed: Deborah Sweeney. **Released:** 2021. **Description:** Describes what a professional organizer does as well as steps involved in starting your own business as a professional organizer. **Availability:** Online.

12810 ■ *"How to Start a Professional Organizing Business" in LiveAbout website (Nov. 16, 2019)*

URL(s): www.liveabout.com/how-to-start-a-profes-sional-organizer-business-from-home-3952102

Ed: Leslie Truex. **Released:** November 16, 2019. **Description:** Presents information on how to start a professional organizer business including a list of pros and cons, association information, and what you need to get started. **Availability:** Online.

12811 ■ *How to Start a Professional Organizing Business*

URL(s): howtostartanllc.com/business-ideas/
professional-organizing

Released: October 08, 2022. **Description:** A professional organizing business helps clients develop critical organizing skills through training and can jumpstart the process by providing a full range of organizing services. This article provides a 10-step guide to starting your own professional organizing business. **Availability:** Online.

12812 ■ *How to Start a Professional Organizing Business in 30 Days*

URL(s): www.udemy.com/course/proorganizerboo
tcamp/

Price: $99.99. **Description:** A course on how to start a professional home organization business in one month. This course covers the business structure side of things and includes 3.5 hours of video, 5 articles + resources, and a certificate of completion. **Availability:** Video; Print.

12813 ■ *"Planning Your (Successful!) Professional Organizing Business" in A Personal Organizer blog*

URL(s): apersonalorganizer.com/starting-professional
-organizing-business/

Ed: Helena Alkhas. **Description:** Describes steps to consider when planning to turn your passion for organizing into a professional organizer business. **Availability:** Online.

12814 ■ *"Professional Organizer" in Entrepreneur*

URL(s): www.entrepreneur.com/businessideas/
personal-organizer

Description: Provides information on how to start a professional organization business. **Availability:** Online.

12815 ■ *"Starting an Organizing Business for Little or No Money" in ZenBusiness blog (Dec. 13, 2021)*

URL(s): www.zenbusiness.com/blog/starting-an-orga-nizing-business-for-little-or-no-money/

Released: December 13, 2021. **Description:** Being a successful organizer often boils down to asking the right questions, sizing up your client's personality, and developing a system that is clear, intuitive, and simple to implement. This article provides information for organizing entrepreneurs to think about when starting a business as a professional organizer. **Availability:** Online.

ASSOCIATIONS AND OTHER ORGANIZATIONS

12816 ■ **American Society of Professional Organizers (ASPO)**
1657 The Fairway 1090
  Jenkintown, PA 19046
Ph: (267)223-5044
Co. E-mail: membership@amspo.org
URL: http://www.amspo.org
Contact: Thalia Poulos, President
Facebook: www.facebook.com/amsocietypo
Instagram: www.instagram.com/amsocietypo

Description: Works to educate and certify members to ensure their goal to become Professional Organizers is attainable. **Founded:** 2018. **Publications:** *Simple Systems: Professional Organizing*; *Simple Systems: The Business of Organizing*.

12817 ■ **National Association of Black Professional Organizers (NABPO)**
PO Box 723021
  Atlanta, GA 31139
Co. E-mail: nabporganizers@gmail.com
URL: http://nabpo.org
Contact: Takilla Combs, President
E-mail: president@nabpo.org
Facebook: www.facebook.com/nabpo
Linkedin: www.linkedin.com/company/nabpo
Instagram: www.instagram.com/nabpo_inc

Description: Works to provide education and support to professional organizers of all ethnic backgrounds. **Founded:** 2017.

12818 ■ **National Association of Professional Organizers (NAPO)**
1120 Rte. 73, Ste. 200
  Mount Laurel, NJ 08054
Ph: (856)380-6828
Fax: (856)439-0525
Co. E-mail: napo@napo.net
URL: http://www.napo.net
Contact: Mindy Godding, President
E-mail: mindy@abundanceorganizing.com
Facebook: www.facebook.com/NAPONatl
Linkedin: www.linkedin.com/company/naponational
X (Twitter): x.com/NAPOnatl
Instagram: www.instagram.com/napo_natl
YouTube: www.youtube.com/user/NAPOHQ
Pinterest: www.pinterest.com/NapoNatl

Description: Professional organizers providing organization, time management, or productivity improvement services; persons in related fields such as organizational product sales and organizational development. Works to promote and educate the public about the profession and to offer support, education, and networking opportunities to members. **Founded:** 1983. **Publications:** *NAPO Directory*; *NAPO Newsletter* (Bimonthly); *National Association of Professional Organizers--Directory* (Annual). **Educational Activities:** National Association of Professional Organizers Conference (Annual). **Awards:** Founders (Annual); Organizing Excellence Award (Annual); Founders' Award (Annual); NAPO Organizer's Choice (Annual); Organizing Excellence (Annual); NAPO President's Award (Irregular); Corporate Associate Member of the Year Award (Annual). **Geographic Preference:** National.

EDUCATIONAL PROGRAMS

12819 ■ *Simple Systems: Professional Organizing*
1657 The Fairway 1090
  Jenkintown, PA 19046
Ph: (267)223-5044
Co. E-mail: membership@amspo.org
URL: http://www.amspo.org
Contact: Thalia Poulos, President
URL(s): www.amspo.org/certification

Price: $175, Single issue. **Description:** Self-paced certification course that provides the knowledge, confidence and credentials to stand out as a leader in the field of professional organizers. Includes 12 modules. **Availability:** Print.

12820 ■ *Simple Systems: The Business of Organizing*
1657 The Fairway 1090
  Jenkintown, PA 19046
Ph: (267)223-5044
Co. E-mail: membership@amspo.org
URL: http://www.amspo.org
Contact: Thalia Poulos, President

URL(s): www.amspo.org/certification

Price: $175, Individuals. **Description:** Self-paced certification course that provides the knowledge, confidence and credentials to stand out as a leader in the field of professional organizers. Includes 11 modules. **Availability:** Print.

REFERENCE WORKS

12821 ■ "6 Steps for Starting a Professional Organizing Business" in Metropolitan Organizing Blog (November 12, 2018)
Ed: Geralin Thomas. **Released:** November 12, 2018. **Description:** A comprehensive list for new professional organizers starting a productivity consulting or professional organizing business. **Availability:** Online.

12822 ■ "6 Worth-the-Price Fix-Ups" in Realtor Magazine (Vol. 44, April-May 2011, No. 44, pp. 23)
Pub: Realtor Magazine
Contact: Sara Geimer, Manager
E-mail: sgeimer@nar.realtor

Description: Advice on how realtors could increase a home's resale value through do-it-yourself projects is given. Removal of personal items and clutter is recommended, along with rearrangement of furniture. A clutter consultant could also be used. **Availability:** Online.

12823 ■ 7 Ways to Find Clients for Your Professional Organizing Business
URL(s): myspacematters.com/7-ways-to-get-clients -for-your-professional-organizing-business/
Ed: Katherine Lawrence. **Description:** Clients are the bread and butter of maintaining a successful organizing business. This article presents seven different ways to find clients so that you can establish credibility and start making money. **Availability:** Online.

12824 ■ 7 Ways to Get Clients for Your Professional Organizing Business
Ed: Katherine Lawrence. **Description:** A list of several ways to get clients for your professional organizing business from a certified professional organizer. **Availability:** Online.

12825 ■ "25 Tasks to Do When You're a Professional Organizer With No Clients" in Organizers Connect website (Sept. 15, 2021)
URL(s): www.organizersconnect.com/professional -organizer-with-no-clients/
Released: September 15, 2021. **Description:** This article explains that there are slow times and busy times for professional organizers and provides a list of tasks to do when you are a professional organizer with no clients. **Availability:** Online.

12826 ■ "Android Users Can Now Manage Life On-the-Go With New AboutOne Family Organizer Companion Application" in PR Newswire (August 1, 2012)
Pub: PR Newswire Association LLC.

Description: AboutOne Family Organizer allows customers to handle family memories and paperwork using android and iPhone mobile phones. The Family Organizer app allows users to organize all household information and is password protected. Details of the app are included. **Availability:** Online.

12827 ■ "Are You Interested in Becoming a Professional Organizer?" in Peace of Mind Blog (January 26, 2020)
Released: January 26, 2020. **Description:** Provides information and tips from a professional organizer on how to start your own professional organizer business. **Availability:** Online.

12828 ■ Born to Organize: Everything You Need to Know About a Career As a Professional Organizer
URL(s): www.timetoorganize.com/coaching-products/ book/

Ed: Sara Pedersen. **Released:** January 01, 2008. **Price:** $18.95. **Description:** Designed to give prospective and new professional organizers the inside scoop on today's organizing industry and answers questions about careers in professional organizing. **Availability:** Print; PDF.

12829 ■ Do Professional Organizers Need Insurance?
URL(s): www.amspo.org/latest-news/do-professional -organizers-need-insurance

Description: As a home service provider, you want to make sure you are offering quality, professional services to your clients. But what if you break something or damage property? This article provides information on the importance of obtaining insurance for your professional organizer business. **Availability:** Online.

12830 ■ Ethical Pitfalls for Professional Organizers
Ed: Debbie Stanley. **Released:** January 01, 2020. **Price:** $19.95. **Description:** Presents a strategic and organized approach for professional organizers to understanding ethics, mitigating risk, avoiding harm, and encouraging honor. **Availability:** E-book; Print.

12831 ■ "HatchedIt.com Social Organizer for Families Launches New Phone App at BlogHer '12" in PR Newswire (August 3, 2012)
Pub: PR Newswire Association LLC.

Description: HatchedIt.com is a free social organizer for families. The new phone app includes two new updates: shareable to do lists and an inbox for members to accept or decline invitations for events or to connect with members.

12832 ■ How to Become a Professional Organizer
Ed: Lauren Williams. **Released:** July 22, 2019. **Description:** Contains tips from eight different professional organizers on how to succeed as a professional organizer. **Availability:** Online.

12833 ■ How Much Money Do Professional Organizers Make Annually?
Ed: Rick Suttle. **Description:** Discusses the average income a professional organizer may make by state as well as qualifications, contributing factors to salary, and job outlook. **Availability:** Online.

12834 ■ "Inesoft Cash Organizer Desktop: A New Approach to Personal Accounts Bookkeeping" in America's Intelligence Wire (August 7, 2012)
Description: Inesoft Cash Organizer Desktop application is offering a new product for financial management on a home PC and mobile devices. The program supports the classification of money transactions by category, sub-category, project, sub-project, budget planning, and world currencies (including current exchange rates), credit calculators, special reports, and more. Multiple users in the family can use the appllication. Details of the program are outlined. **Availability:** Online.

12835 ■ Learn to Organize: A Professional Organizer's Tell-All Guide to Home Organizing
URL(s): www.timetoorganize.com/coaching-products/ learn-to-organize-book/
Ed: Sara Pedersen. **Released:** January 16, 2013. **Price:** $18.95, paperback; $15, pdf. **Description:** A book for professional organizers who are looking to steamline their skills. Provides a six-step process for streamlining. **Availability:** Print; PDF.

12836 ■ "Make It Easier On Yourself" in Women In Business (Vol. 63, Fall 2011, No. 3, pp. 28)
Pub: American Business Women's Association
Contact: Rene Street, Executive Director
Released: September 22, 2011. **Description:** Getting and staying organized helps avoid wasting time on deciding which priorities to address first. Taking

help and avoiding hoarding are examples of how to become organized. The use of technology for organizing priorities is also explained. **Availability:** Online.

12837 ■ Managing Client Expectations: A Guide for Organizing Professionals
Ed: Standolyn Robertson. **Released:** July 01, 2020. **Price:** $9.95. **Description:** A step-by-step guide for professional organizers to help you manage your clients' expectations. Presents information on the three critical stages of a client relationship. **Availability:** E-book; Print.

12838 ■ Mastering the Business of Organizing: A Guide to Plan, Launch, Manage, Grow, and Leverage a Profitable, Professional Organizing Business
Released: February 11, 2019. **Price:** $20.99, Paperback; $8.69, E-book. **Description:** A guide for people interested in starting their own professional organizing business. From start-up to growing your company, the author compiles all of the necessary tools needed to make your business a success. **Availability:** E-book; Print.

12839 ■ "Monday Organizer: Clean and De-Clutter in 15 Minutes" in Tulsa World (June 13, 2011)
Pub: The McClatchy Company
Contact: Tony W. Hunter, Chief Executive Officer
Ed: Kim Brown. **Description:** New weekly series highlights practical tips and helpful ideas to simply life by taking 15 minutes to de-clutter your home or office. Paper clutter can be eliminated in 15 minutes by gathering up newspapers and magazines to recycle; sort mail as soon as you receive it and throw away any junk mail at that time. If watching TV, use commercial time to accomplish small tasks. **Availability:** Print; Online.

12840 ■ The No-Nonsense Home Organization Plan: 7 Weeks to Declutter in Any Space
Ed: Kim Davidson Jones. **Released:** October 15, 2019. **Price:** $10.99, Paperback; $7.99, E-book. **Description:** A guide for the person who wants to organize their own home or personal space. The 7-week plan makes use of what you already have so there is no need to purchase any supplies while the emphasis is on learning how to break down large tasks into smaller ones and to maximize the space that needs help. **Availability:** E-book; Print.

12841 ■ Professional Organizer: How to Organize a Business
URL(s): www.universalclass.com/articles/self-help/ business/professional-organizer-how-to-organize-a -business.htm
Description: Describes the six main areas to focus on when organizing your own small business or when looking to hire someone to organize it for you. **Availability:** Online.

12842 ■ Professional Organizers Specializing In Small Businesses
URL(s): mchorganizing.com/?p=156
Ed: Mark Higgins. **Released:** August 29, 2021. **Description:** Details the value that a professional organizer can bring to your small business. **Availability:** Online.

12843 ■ "The Pros and Cons of Starting a Professional Organizer Business" in The Balance Small Business (January 14, 2020)
Ed: Alyssa Gregory. **Released:** January 14, 2020. **Description:** Professional organizers can work with many types of people and businesses to help them clean out their accumulated clutter, get organized, and create a system for managing documents or possessions going forward. This article discusses the benefits and challenges of starting your own professional organizing business. **Availability:** Online.

12844 ■ "Reclaim Your Office" in Greater Baton Rouge Business Report (Vol. 30, June 12, 2012, No. 22, pp. 12)
Ed: Regina Leeds. **Description:** The 8-Minute Organizer provides easy solutions to simplify life. **Availability:** Online.

12845 ■ *"Resolve to Make the Most of Your Space With Professional Organizer Julie Morgenstern and Lowe's" in Marketwired (January 24, 2012)*
Pub: Comtex News Network Inc.
Contact: Kan Devnani, President
Description: Five tips for organizing a home are provided by Julie Morgenstern, a professional organizer for Lowe's. Placing user manuals for the home in one central place makes for an easier life. It is best to work in one room at a time when starting the task of organizing a household.

12846 ■ *Six Ways a Professional Organizer Can Help Your Small Business*
URL(s): sabrinasadminservices.com/ways-a-professional-organizer-can-help-your-small-business/
Ed: Sabrina Quairoli. **Released:** October 29, 2021. **Description:** Provides a specific list of tasks that may inspire you to get an organizer for your small business with the ultimate goal of achieving increased productivity. **Availability:** Online.

12847 ■ *Small Business Organizing*
Ed: Karen York. **Description:** Discusses the value of getting your small business organized with a goal of increased productivity and better workflow. **Availability:** Online.

12848 ■ *"StorageByMail Lets Customers Ship Away Their Clutter" in Inc. (Vol. 33, April 2011, No. 3, pp. 92)*
Pub: Inc. Magazine
Ed: Issie Lapowsky. **Description:** StorageByMail allows people to put items into storage by mailing them to the company. The firm charges a monthly fee, customers describe contents of each box, and ship to the Jersey City facility using a preprinted label. StorageByMail pays the $25 shipment charge. **Availability:** Online.

12849 ■ *Top 11 Local SEO Strategies for Professional Organizers*
Ed: Edward Winslow. **Description:** To successfully build your brand and dominate your market, you need a local SEO strategy for your website. This refers to your plan for content marketing on search engines and social media as success on these platforms is sure to bring many new clients. This article provides eleven strategies for professional organizers to follow to ensure good SEO results. **Availability:** Online.

12850 ■ *The Ultimate Social Media Marketing Guide for Pro Organizers*
Description: Discusses how powerful social media marketing is for professional organizers. Provides specific guidelines detailing the types of content you should post on each social media platform, along with some ideas you may not have considered about why you should be on each network. **Availability:** Online.

12851 ■ *"Uncontained Enthusiasm: Container Store Readies for post IPO Growth" in Dallas Business Journal (Vol. 37, January 10, 2014, No. 18, pp. 4)*
Pub: American City Business Journals, Inc.
Contact: Mike Olivieri, Executive Vice President
Released: January 10, 2014. **Price:** $4, introductory 4-week offer(Digital only). **Description:** The Container Store CEO, Kip Tindell, and his team have been balancing the organization and storage retailer's culture of conscious capitalism with executing an aggressive growth plan and returning shareholder value. Tindell could set the stage for large-scale expansion after a successful initial public offering (IPO). Details of Tindells' growth plan are also discussed. **Availability:** Print; Online.

12852 ■ *"What No One Told Me about Running an Organizing Business" in A Personal Organizer blog*
URL(s): apersonalorganizer.com/what-no-one-told-me-about-running-an-organizing-business/

Ed: Helena Alkhas. **Description:** A guide from an experienced professional organizer that details lessons learned in the first ten years of a career. Provides information on entrepreneurship, career longevity, utilizing your assets, and creating multiple revenue streams. **Availability:** Online.

12853 ■ *"What Professional Organizers Really Do, and How They Can Help You" in The New York Times (January 16, 2019)*
URL(s): www.nytimes.com/2019/01/16/smarter-living/professional-organizers-productivity-clutter.html
Ed: Jolie Kerr. **Released:** January 16, 2019. **Description:** Professional organizers are here to help everyday people organize any of the physical or digital spaces in their lives. They will handle just about any tasks that will help their clients have a cleaner, de-cluttered space, especially when they are too overwhelming to handle alone or if there just isn't enough time. One thing potential clients need to consider is that they will need to be there for the process, since the primary function of a professional organizer is not housekeeping, but changing the system of the space. **Availability:** Online.

FRANCHISES AND BUSINESS OPPORTUNITIES

12854 ■ **California Closet Company Inc. (CC)**
FirstService Brands
1414 Harbour Way S, Ste. 1750
Richmond, CA 94804
Free: 866-366-0420
Fax: (601)549-7973
URL: http://www.fsvbrands.com
Contact: Carolyn Musher, Vice President, Sales
URL(s): www.fsvbrands.com/our_companies/california_closets.html
Facebook: www.facebook.com/CaliforniaClosets
X (Twitter): x.com/caclosets
Instagram: www.instagram.com/caclosets
Pinterest: www.pinterest.com/caclosets
Description: Custom closet design, manufacture, and installation. **Founded:** 1978. **Financial Assistance:** Yes **Training:** Includes training at headquarters, franchisee's location and ongoing support.

12855 ■ **Closet Factory**
12800 S Broadway
Los Angeles, CA 90061
Free: 800-838-7995
Co. E-mail: info@closetfactory.com
URL: http://www.closetfactory.com
Contact: Stephen Newman, Chief Executive Officer
Facebook: www.facebook.com/closetfactory
X (Twitter): x.com/ClosetFactory
Instagram: www.instagram.com/closet_factory
Description: Firm engages in the design, distribution, manufacturing and installation of custom closets. **Founded:** 1983. **Financial Assistance:** Yes **Training:** Yes.

12856 ■ **Closets by Design Franchising**
3850 Capitol Ave.
Whittier, CA 90601
Free: 800-500-9210
Co. E-mail: cbdclientissues@closetsbydesign.com
URL: http://www.closetsbydesign.com
Facebook: www.facebook.com/closetsbydesign
X (Twitter): x.com/ClosetsByDesign
Instagram: www.instagram.com/closetsbydesign
YouTube: www.youtube.com/channel/UCCdjd9ErW3iz2qUAfRjfHKA
Description: Firm engages in design, build and install custom closets, garage cabinets, home offices, laundries, pantries, wardrobe mirror doors and much more. **Founded:** 1982. **Franchised:** 1998. **Equity Capital Needed:** $126,000 to $296,500. **Franchise Fee:** $20,000. **Financial Assistance:** Yes **Training:** Provides 3 weeks at headquarters, and additional 3 weeks at franchisee's location.

12857 ■ **Closets and Storage Concepts**
436 Commerce Ln., Ste. D
West Berlin, NJ 08091

Ph: (856)627-5700
Free: 888-843-2567
URL: http://www.closetandstorageconcepts.com
Facebook: www.facebook.com/ClosetandStorageConceptsofNorthAmerica
X (Twitter): x.com/ClosetSystem
Instagram: www.instagram.com/csc_nj
Pinterest: www.pinterest.com/ClosetStorage
Description: Manufacturer and retailer of closet, wall beds, office products and other accessories. **Founded:** 1987. **Financial Assistance:** Yes **Training:** Creates custom closet designs, manufacturing, and installing custom closet solutions for closet storage, mudroom, pantry, laundry room, garage, home office and more.

12858 ■ **Floorguard Inc.**
340 Marshall Ave., Unit 101
Aurora, IL 60506
Free: 800-694-2724
Co. E-mail: office@floorguard.com
URL: http://www.floorguard.com
Description: Garage flooring and storage systems. **Founded:** 1988. **Training:** Yes.

12859 ■ **Garagetek**
206 Bethpage-Sweet Hollow Rd.
Old Bethpage, NY 11804
Free: 866-664-2724
Co. E-mail: hq@garagetek.com
URL: http://www.garagetek.com
Contact: Marc Shuman, President
Facebook: www.facebook.com/GarageTek
Instagram: www.instagram.com/garagetek
Pinterest: www.pinterest.com/garagetek
Description: Firm provides garage storage solutions. **Founded:** 2000. **Training:** Provides 2 weeks at corporate and ongoing field support.

12860 ■ **Granite Transformations**
1565 NW 36th St.
Miami, FL 33142
Ph: (954)435-5538
Co. E-mail: rsgmarketing@trend-group.com
URL: http://www.granitetransformations.com
X (Twitter): x.com/granite_trans
Instagram: www.instagram.com/granitetrendtransformations
YouTube: www.youtube.com/user/GraniteTrans
Pinterest: www.pinterest.com/granitetrans
Description: Provider of Construction, remodeling and bath and closets services. **Founded:** 1996. **Training:** Training program consists of operations, installations, and sales training. Each training module is supported with training material. Training facility is an actual working location allowing trainees to evaluate, test, and see results. Grand opening supported by sales manager onsite and ongoing support.

12861 ■ **HouseWall Garage System**
4530 N Hiatus Rd., Ste. 115
Sunrise, FL 33351
Ph: (954)533-8351
Free: 855-854-9255
Co. E-mail: info@housewall.com
URL: http://www.housewall.com
Facebook: www.facebook.com/housewall
X (Twitter): x.com/housewallGO
Instagram: www.instagram.com/housewallgarageorganizer
Description: Retailer of garage system such as paneling, cabinets, flooring and accessories. **Royalty Fee:** 6-5.5%. **Training:** Offers 1 week at headquarters and ongoing support.

12862 ■ **Parties By Terrye**
12115 Long Lake Dr.
Owings Mills, MD 21117
Ph: (410)581-1080
URL: http://partiesbyterrye.com
Description: Provider of party and event planning services for residents and businesses. **Founded:** 1983. **Training:** Yes.

Property Management

ASSOCIATIONS AND OTHER ORGANIZATIONS

12863 ■ Institute of Real Estate Management (IREM)
430 N Michigan Ave., Ste. 500
 Chicago, IL 60611
Ph: (312)329-6000
Free: 800-837-0706
Fax: (800)338-4736
Co. E-mail: getinfo@irem.org
URL: http://www.irem.org
Contact: Libby Ekre, President
Facebook: www.facebook.com/InstituteofRealEstateManagement
Linkedin: www.linkedin.com/company/institute-of-real-estate-management
X (Twitter): x.com/IREM_info
YouTube: www.youtube.com/user/IREMinfo
Description: Professional organization of real property and asset managers. Awards professional designation Certified Property Manager (CPM) to qualifying individuals, Accredited Management Organization (AMO) to qualifying management firms and also awards Accredited Residential Manager (ARM) accreditation to qualifying individuals who are primarily residential site managers. Monitors legislation affecting real estate management. Offers management courses and seminars; conducts research and educational programs, publishes books and reports; maintains formal code of ethics; compiles statistics; maintains employment Website for real estate management industry. **Founded:** 1933. **Publications:** *Journal of Property Management* (Bimonthly); *Real Estate Income/Expense Analysis National Summary.* **Awards:** IREM Academy of Authors (Annual); Lloyd D. Hanford Sr. Distinguished Instructor Award (Annual); IREM Foundation Diversity Outreach Scholarship (Annual); Paul H. Rittle, Sr. Scholarship; Donald M. Furbush Scholarship (Annual); J. Wallace Paletou Award (Annual); Paul H. Rittle Sr. Memorial Scholarship Award (Quarterly); George M. Brooker, CPM Diversity Collegiate Scholarship (Semiannual); Donald M. Furbush Professional Development Grants; Paul H. Rittle Sr. Professional Development Grants. **Geographic Preference:** National.

12864 ■ Intellectual Property Owners Association (IPO)
1501 M St. NW, Ste. 1150
 Washington, DC 20005
Ph: (202)507-4500
Fax: (202)507-4501
Co. E-mail: info@ipo.org
URL: http://ipo.org
Contact: Karen Cochran, President
Facebook: www.facebook.com/IPOAssociation
Linkedin: www.linkedin.com/company/ipoassociation
X (Twitter): x.com/ipo
Description: Corporations, lawyers, and individuals interested in intellectual property (patents, trademarks, copyrights, and trade secrets). Seeks to support and strengthen the patent, trademark, copyright, and trade secret laws. Monitors related legislative activities. **Founded:** 1972. **Publications:** *IPO Daily News* (Daily). **Educational Activities:** Intellectual Property Owners Association Education Foundation & EPO Conference (Annual). **Awards:** IPO National Inventor of the Year (Annual). **Geographic Preference:** National.

12865 ■ International Facility Management Association (IFMA) - Library
800 Gessner Rd., Ste. 900
 Houston, TX 77024
Ph: (713)623-4362
Fax: (713)623-6124
Co. E-mail: ifma@ifma.org
URL: http://www.ifma.org
Contact: Don Gilpin, President
X (Twitter): x.com/IFMA
YouTube: www.youtube.com/ifmaglobal
Description: International association for facility management professionals. Provides educational opportunities, produces conferences and expositions, and conducts research on and for the facility management industry. **Scope:** Facility management. **Founded:** 1980. **Holdings:** Figures not available. **Publications:** *Operations and Maintenance Benchmarks Survey; FMJ magazine* (6/year). **Educational Activities:** World Workplace Europe (Annual); World Workplace (Annual). **Awards:** IFMA Associate Member Award (Annual); IFMA Fellows (Annual); IFMA Chapter Award for Excellence in Membership Marketing (Annual); IFMA Chapter Award for Excellence in Newsletter Publishing (Annual); IFMA Large Chapter of the Year Award (Annual); IFMA Student Chapter of the Year Award (Annual); IFMA Council of the Year Award (Annual). **Geographic Preference:** Multinational.

12866 ■ National Association of Residential Property Managers (NARPM)
1403 Greenbrier Pky., Ste. 150
 Chesapeake, VA 23320
Free: 800-782-3452
Fax: (866)466-2776
Co. E-mail: info@narpm.org
URL: http://www.narpm.org
Contact: Gail S. Phillips, Chief Executive Officer
E-mail: ceo@narpm.org
Facebook: www.facebook.com/narpmnational
X (Twitter): x.com/NARPM
Instagram: www.instagram.com/narpmnational
YouTube: www.youtube.com/channel/UC8Yi_NazIBrQlmOHRg_KMOA
Description: Sponsors educational programs. Supports the professional and ethical practices of rental home management through networking, education and certification. **Founded:** 1988. **Publications:** *Property Manager Directory.* **Geographic Preference:** National.

12867 ■ National Property Management Association (NPMA)
One Glenlake Pky., NE, Ste. 1200
 Atlanta, GA 30328
Ph: (404)477-5811
Fax: (404)240-0998
Co. E-mail: membership@npma.org
URL: http://www.npma.org
Contact: Bill Franklin, President
Description: Aims to build leadership by educating, training and promoting standards of competency and ethical behavior in the asset management of personal property. Serves property professionals throughout the U.S.; companies and organizations the public and private sectors, including scientific laboratories, universities, hospitals, public school systems, and local, state and federal government agencies. **Founded:** 1970. **Publications:** *NPMA Survey; Property Manual.* **Awards:** NPMA Chapter of the Year (Annual); NPMA Federal Property Manager of the Year (Annual). **Geographic Preference:** National.

12868 ■ Property Management Association (PMA)
7508 Wisconsin Ave., 4th Fl.
 Bethesda, MD 20814
Ph: (301)657-9200
Fax: (301)907-9326
Co. E-mail: info@pma-dc.org
URL: http://www.pma-dc.org
Contact: Elaine de Lude, President
Facebook: www.facebook.com/PropertyManagementAssociation
Linkedin: www.linkedin.com/company/property-management-association-inc
X (Twitter): x.com/PMAAssociation
Instagram: www.instagram.com/propertymanagementassociation
Description: Represents property management professionals who own and operate multifamily residential, commercial, retail, industrial and other income-producing properties and firms that provide goods and services used in real property management. **Founded:** 1952. **Publications:** *Property Management Association--Membership Directory; Property Management Association--Directory; Property Management Association--Bulletin* (Monthly). **Geographic Preference:** National.

12869 ■ Vacation Rental Management Association (VRMA)
2001 K St. NW, 3rd Fl., N
 Washington, DC 20006
Ph: (202)367-1179
Fax: (202)367-2179
Co. E-mail: vrma@vrma.org
URL: http://www.vrma.org
Contact: Miller Hawkins, President
Facebook: www.facebook.com/TheVRMA
X (Twitter): x.com/VRMA
Instagram: www.instagram.com/thevrma
YouTube: www.youtube.com/channel/UC-a4QnB0B8bHczSLFCe3w2w
Description: Companies that rent and manage vacation properties, resorts, townhomes and condominiums on a short-term basis. Promotes the interests of the vacation rental industry to the public. **Founded:** 1985. **Geographic Preference:** National.

REFERENCE WORKS

12870 ■ *"1Q Office Vacancies Mainly Up; Class A Space Bucks Trend, Falls"* in Crain's Detroit Business (Vol. 24, April 14, 2008, No. 15)
Pub: Crain Communications Inc.
Contact: Barry Asin, President

Ed: Daniel Duggan. **Description:** Although more office space became vacant in the first quarter, Class A space went in the opposite direction with several local businesses are moving from less-desirable to more desirable areas. **Availability:** Online.

12871 ■ *"5 Tips for a Top-Notch Residential Lease"* in Legal Zoom (March 27, 2023)
URL(s): www.legalzoom.com/articles/5-tips-for-a-top -notch-residential-lease
Ed: Michelle Kaminsky, Esq. **Released:** March 27, 2023. **Description:** Gives advice on how to structure a rental agreement for your property in order to maintain legal integrity. **Availability:** Online.

12872 ■ *"2015 Marketing Calendar for Real Estate Pros: Own It"*
Pub: CreateSpace

Released: October 14, 2014. **Price:** $9.56, paperback. **Description:** Real estate agents, mortgage loan agents, and new home builders and site and listing agents are shown how to use low-cost, high yield, proven marketing techniques to create digital real estate listings, find more customers, and sell more homes. Advice for building a brand and public relations; attracting renters and buyers; developing a good Website; and a digital marketing plan are explained. **Availability:** Print.

12873 ■ *Airbnb for Dummies*
Pub: John Wiley & Sons, Inc.
Contact: Christina Van Tassell, Executive Vice President Chief Financial Officer
URL(s): www.wiley.com/en-us/Airbnb+For+Dummies%2C+2nd+Edition-p-9781394154630
Ed: Symon He, James Svetec. **Released:** 2nd edition. **Description:** This guide explains how to turn your rentable property into an Airbnb in order to earn an income. Tips on using the Airbnb website, navigating their policies, and even setting up your property to rent out are all included. **Availability:** paperback; Print.

12874 ■ *"Apartment Action: A Renewal in Rentals"* in Barron's (Vol. 88, March 17, 2008, No. 11, pp. 17)
Pub: Dow Jones & Company Inc.
Contact: Almar Latour, Chief Executive Officer

Ed: Robin Goldwyn Blumenthal. **Description:** Discusses the projected entry of the estimated 82 million echo-boomers into the rentals market and the influx of immigrants and displaced homeowners which could turn apartments into lucrative investments again. While apartment-building completions rose slowly since 2003, demand is expected to increase steeply until 2015. **Availability:** Online.

12875 ■ *"Bangles, BMWs Elbow Out Delis and Discount Shops"* in Crain's New York Business (Vol. 24, January 13, 2008, No. 2, pp. 35)
Pub: Crain Communications, Inc.
Contact: Jessica Botos, Manager, Marketing
E-mail: jessica.botos@crainsnewyork.com
Ed: Wendy Davis. **Description:** Lured by a growing number of affluent residents and high-earning professionals, a number of upscale retailers have opened locations downtown which is driving up rents and forcing out longtime independent merchants.

12876 ■ *"Battelle Given Keys to CompeteColumbus"* in Business First-Columbus (October 15, 2007, pp. 1)
Pub: Business First
Contact: Nick Fortine, President
E-mail: nfortine@bizjournals.com

Ed: Kevin Kemper. **Description:** Battelle Memorial Institute has been contracted by Compete Columbus to manage the organization's daily operations. Compete Columbus was formerly managed by a single executive, David Powell, who resigned in September 2006. Profile of Compete Columbus is included. **Availability:** Print; Online.

12877 ■ *"Bellevue Collection Collects 4 New Towers"* in Puget Sound Business Journal (Vol. 35, May 16, 2014, No. 4, pp. 4)
Pub: American City Business Journals, Inc.
Contact: Mike Olivieri, Executive Vice President
Description: A number of real estate development projects planned by Kemper Development Company, as part of the massive expansion of its Bellevue Collection in Washington are presented. Kemper is the builder, owner and operator of the properties that include office space on Lincoln Square, the New Lincoln Square Hotel/Apartments, Bellevue Square Hotel/Apartment Tower and Bellevue Square Apartment Tower. **Availability:** Online.

12878 ■ *"Briarcliff Office Building Fills Up Fast"* in The Business Journal-Serving Metropolitan Kansas City (Vol. 26, Sept. 5, 2008, pp. 1)
Pub: American City Business Journals, Inc.
Contact: Mike Olivieri, Executive Vice President
Ed: Rob Roberts. **Description:** Prior to its opening the Hilltop Office Building in Kansas City Missouri has attained 80 percent occupancy. FCStone Group Inc.'s plan to move to the building has boosted the facility's occupancy. Description and dimensions of the office building are also provided. **Availability:** Online.

12879 ■ *Commercial Real Estate Investing for Dummies*
Pub: John Wiley & Sons, Inc.
Contact: Christina Van Tassell, Executive Vice President Chief Financial Officer
URL(s): www.wiley.com/en-us/Commercial+Real+Estate+Investing+For+Dummies%2C+2nd+Edition-p-9781119858515
Ed: Peter Conti, Peter Harris. **Released:** 2nd edition. **Price:** $15, e-book; $24.99, paperback. **Description:** Learn about making the most of commercial real estate strategies along with getting started techniques and the latest tax laws. **Availability:** E-book; Print.

12880 ■ *"A Conversation With: Ron Gantner, Jones Lang LaSalle"* in Crain's Detroit Business (Vol. 24, October 6, 2008, No. 40, pp. 9)
Pub: Crain Communications Inc.
Contact: Barry Asin, President
Description: Interview with Ron Gantner who is a corporate real estate adviser with the real estate company Jones Lang LaSalle as well as the company's executive vice president and part of the tenant advisory team; Gantner speaks about the impact that the Wall Street crisis is having on the commercial real estate market in Detroit. **Availability:** Print; Online.

12881 ■ *"Cool on Chicago Office Properties"* in Crain's Chicago Business (Vol. 31, March 31, 2008, No. 13, pp. 16)
Pub: Crain Communications Inc.
Contact: Barry Asin, President
Ed: Eddie Baeb. **Description:** Investors predict values on Chicago office buildings to drop 1.3 percent over the next year. **Availability:** Online.

12882 ■ *"Crescent to Add Two Restaurants"* in Memphis Business Journal (Vol. 33, April 6, 2012, No. 52, pp. 1)
Pub: Baltimore Business Journal
Contact: Rhonda Pringle, President
E-mail: rpringle@bizjournals.com
Description: Highwoods Properties Inc. is planning to open two restaurants at its Crescent Center in Memphis, Tennessee. The new establishment are both upscale concepts from Darden Restaurants Inc. **Availability:** Print; Online.

12883 ■ *"Detroit Residential Market Slows; Bright Spots Emerge"* in Crain's Detroit Business (Vol. 24, October 6, 2008, No. 40, pp. 11)
Pub: Crain Communications Inc.
Contact: Barry Asin, President
Ed: Daniel Duggan. **Description:** Discusses the state of the residential real estate market in Detroit; although condominium projects receive the most attention, deals for single-family homes are taking place in greater numbers due to financing issues. Buyers can purchase a single family home with a 3.5 percent down payment compared to 20 percent for some condo deals because of the number of first-time homebuyer programs under the Federal Housing Administration.

12884 ■ *"East-Side Real Estate Forum Detours To Grand Rapids"* in Crain's Detroit Business (Vol. 24, October 6, 2008, No. 40, pp. 17)
Pub: Crain Communications Inc.
Contact: Barry Asin, President
Ed: Daniel Duggan. **Description:** Tom Wackerman was elected chairman of the University of Michigan-Urban Land Institute Real Estate Forum and proposed that the annual conference be held in Grand Rapids due to the brisk economic activity he was finding there; although the idea was initially met with resistance, the plan to introduce East-siders to the West side began receiving more enthusiasm due to the revitalization of the area, which was once considered to have a bleak outlook. Many are hoping to learn the lessons of those who were able to change a negative economic climate into a positive one in which the cooperation of private business and government can work together to accomplish goals. **Availability:** Print; Online.

12885 ■ *"Firms Start Increasing their Space"* in Philadelphia Business Journal (Vol. 31, March 23, 2012, No. 6, pp. 1)
Pub: Baltimore Business Journal
Contact: Rhonda Pringle, President
E-mail: rpringle@bizjournals.com
Description: Office occupancies in Philadelphia, Pennsylvania have grown in 2012. The economic recovery is seen to drive this trend. Comments from office/property management brokers are also included. **Availability:** Print; Online.

12886 ■ *"Golf Club Plan Raises Hackles"* in Philadelphia Business Journal (Vol. 31, April 6, 2012, No. 8, pp. 1)
Pub: Baltimore Business Journal
Contact: Rhonda Pringle, President
E-mail: rpringle@bizjournals.com
Description: VRJ Associates' proposal to redevelop its Westover Country Club golf course into an athletic and recreational facility has been opposed by neighboring residents. The proposed facility would include 12 tennis courts softball and baseball fields, among other things. **Availability:** Print; Online.

12887 ■ *"Hot Real Estate Market Means Hard Work for Investors"* in Business Journal (Vol. 31, March 21, 2014, No. 3, pp. 14)
Pub: American City Business Journals, Inc.
Contact: Mike Olivieri, Executive Vice President
Description: Real estate investors are finding it difficult to improve the residential real estate market due to higher prices. Investors who purchase properties to use as rentals are struggling with the high home values in Portland, Oregon. **Availability:** Print; Online.

12888 ■ *"ICC Works on Prescriptive Green Construction Code"* in Contractor (Vol. 56, October 2009, No. 10, pp. 1)
Ed: Robert P. Mader. **Description:** International Code Council launched an initiative to create a green construction code that focuses on existing commercial buildings. The initiative's timeline will include public meetings leading up to a final draft that will be available in 2010. **Availability:** Print; Online.

12889 ■ "Industrial Vacancies Hit High" in Crain's Chicago Business (Apr. 21, 2008)
Pub: Crain Communications Inc.
Contact: Barry Asin, President
Ed: Alby Gallun. **Description:** Hitting its highest level in four years in the first quarter is the Chicago-area industrial vacancy rate, a sign that the slumping economy is depressing demand for warehouse and manufacturing space. **Availability:** Online.

12890 ■ "James Donnelly on Keeping His Company's Edge: 'We Have Documented Best Practice for Everything'" in South Florida Business Journal (Vol. 34, May 23, 2014, No. 44, pp. 15)
Pub: American City Business Journals, Inc.
Contact: Mike Olivieri, Executive Vice President
Description: James Donnelly, CEO of Castle Group, a community management firm specializing in home-owners and condominium associations, believes that organizational culture is an important driver of business success. He reveals that the company keeps its edge by maintaining the best office technology and the best employees. His views about the importance of customer satisfaction are stressed. **Availability:** Print; Online.

12891 ■ Landlord's Legal Kit for Dummies
Pub: John Wiley & Sons, Inc.
Contact: Christina Van Tassell, Executive Vice President Chief Financial Officer
URL(s): www.wiley.com/en-us/Landlord%27s+Legal +Kit+For+Dummies%2C+2nd+Edition-p-978111989 6357
Ed: Robert S. Griswold, Laurence C. Harmon. **Released:** 2nd edition. **Price:** $21, e-book; $34.99, paperback. **Description:** This kit will help landlords with all aspects of renting their properties. Templates and worksheets are provided. **Availability:** E-book; Print.

12892 ■ "Local Industrial Vacancies Climb" in Crain's Chicago Business (Vol. 31, November 17, 2008, No. 46, pp. 18)
Pub: Crain Communications Inc.
Contact: Barry Asin, President
Ed: Eddie Baeb. **Description:** Demand for local industrial real estate has declined dramatically as companies that use warehouse and factory space struggle to survive in an ailing economy. According to a report by Colliers Bennett & Kahnweiler Inc., a commercial real estate brokerage, the regional vacancy rate has risen to 9.86 percent in the third quarter, the fourth straight increase and the highest in the past 14 years. **Availability:** Online.

12893 ■ "Look Before You Lease" in Women Entrepreneur (February 3, 2009)
Description: Top issues to consider before leasing an office space are discussed including: additional charges that may be expected on top of the basic rental price; determining both short- and long-term goals; the cost of improvements to the space; the cost of upkeep; and the conditions of the lease. **Availability:** Online.

12894 ■ "Magellan Companies Establishes Century 21 Beachhead in Boise" in Idaho Business Review (September 15, 2014)
Pub: BridgeTower Media
Contact: Adam Reinebach, President
Description: New Jersey-based Century 21, the largest real estate franchise worldwide, has entered the Idaho market under the name Century 21 Magellan Realty with five agents. Wesley Flacker, builder, home renovator, broker, and property manager purchased the franchise and expects to have 60 agents by 2015.

12895 ■ "Mall On a Mission: KOP to Get $150 Million Makeover" in Philadelphia Business Journal (Vol. 33, March 14, 2014, No. 5, pp. 6)
Pub: American City Business Journals, Inc.
Contact: Mike Olivieri, Executive Vice President
Released: Weekly. **Price:** $4, introductory 4-week offer(Digital & Print). **Description:** Philadelphia, Pennsylvania-based King of Prussia Mall is set to

undergo a $150 million renovation. The plan involves construction of about 250,000 square feet of space for retailers. Mall owner, Simon Property Group, has contracted IMC Construction to handle the project. **Availability:** Print; Online.

12896 ■ "A New Mix of Tenants Settles In Downtown" in Crain's New York Business (Vol. 24, January 13, 2008, No. 2, pp. 26)
Pub: Crain Communications, Inc.
Contact: Jessica Botos, Manager, Marketing
E-mail: jessica.botos@crainsnewyork.com
Ed: Andrew Marks. **Description:** More and more nonfinancial firms are relocating downtown due to the new retailers and restaurants that are reshaping the look and feel of lower Manhattan.

12897 ■ "Owners Consider Remodeling Westlake Center" in Puget Sound Business Journal (Vol. 33, September 28, 2012, No. 23, pp. 1)
Pub: Baltimore Business Journal
Contact: Rhonda Pringle, President
E-mail: rpringle@bizjournals.com
Ed: Jeanne Lang Jones. **Description:** General Growth Properties Inc. is considering a major remodel of the Westlake Center shopping mall in Seattle, Washington and international fashion chain Zara is negotiating for space at Westlake. Such activities benefit the city's retailers and landlords along with providing a broader civic benefit to the town square. **Availability:** Print; Online.

12898 ■ "Peabody Launching 464-Room Renovation" in Memphis Business Journal (Vol. 34, July 13, 2012, No. 13, pp. 1)
Pub: Baltimore Business Journal
Contact: Rhonda Pringle, President
E-mail: rpringle@bizjournals.com
Ed: Michael Sheffield. **Description:** The Peabody Memphis has announced preparations for a massive renovation that will affect all 464 rooms of the hotel starting in November. Peabody Hotel Group, which manages the hotel fo rBelz Enterprises, has estimated the renovations to cost between $10 million and $20 million. **Availability:** Print; Online.

12899 ■ Property Management Association--Directory (Washington DC)
Pub: Property Management Association
Contact: Elaine de Lude, President
URL(s): www.pma-dc.org/product-service-directory ?CategoryView=true
Description: Covers over 539 property managers and 336 related supplier firms. **Entries include:** For property managers--Name, firm name, address, phone, fax, specialty. For supplier firms--Company name, name of contact, address, phone, fax. **Arrangement:** Each list is alphabetical. **Indexes:** Supplier product/service. **Availability:** Print.

12900 ■ "Rent Laws' Impact: Tenant Paradise or Return of the 'Bronx is Burning'?" in The New York Times (June 17, 2019)
URL(s): www.nytimes.com/2019/06/17/nyregion/ren t-regulation-nyc.html
Released: June 17, 2019. **Description:** New York's new rent laws are having an impact in the New York City real estate market by establishing new rules from rent increases to security deposits to evictions. The Bronx is being affected the most since they have the highest number of rent-regulated apartments, which residents are cheering on, but the real estate industry is having doubts about the changes. **Availability:** Online.

12901 ■ "Rubicon Is the Latest Small Real Estate Firm to Break Out" in Dallas Business Journal (Vol. 35, June 29, 2012, No. 42, pp. 1)
Pub: Baltimore Business Journal
Contact: Rhonda Pringle, President
E-mail: rpringle@bizjournals.com
Ed: Candace Carlisle. **Description:** Stream Realty Partners LP partnered with Chad Hennings, Kyle Jacobs and John Pope to form the real estate firm

Rubicon Representation. The new company will provide tenant representation (property management) services. **Availability:** Print; Online.

12902 ■ "Suburban Retailers Go Urban" in Philadelphia Business Journal (Vol. 28, August 17, 2012, No. 27, pp. 1)
Pub: Baltimore Business Journal
Contact: Rhonda Pringle, President
E-mail: rpringle@bizjournals.com
Description: Traditional suburban retailers in the retail corridor of Philadelphia, Pennsylvania such as cosmetics retailer Ulta Beauty have been seeking population density and are relocating to urban settings, which represent untapped markets. How Vesper Property Group signed with Ulta Beauty a long-term lease on three levels totaling 13,600 square feet is also discussed. **Availability:** Print; Online.

12903 ■ "Troy Complex has New Brand, New Leases" in Crain's Detroit Business (Vol. 24, April 14, 2008, No. 15, pp. 32)
Pub: Crain Communications Inc.
Contact: Barry Asin, President
Ed: Daniel Duggan. **Description:** Discusses the re-branding of the 1.2 million-square-foot collection of office buildings in Troy purchased by New York-based Emmes Co. The firm has also pledged more than $6 million in upgrades, hired a new leasing company and completed 67,000 square feet of leasing with another 100,000 in negotiations. **Availability:** Print; Online.

12904 ■ "Walnut Hill Sheds Its Past, Name" in Philadelphia Business Journal (Vol. 33, April 4, 2014, No. 8, pp. 8)
Pub: American City Business Journals, Inc.
Contact: Mike Olivieri, Executive Vice President
Released: Weekly. **Price:** $4, introductory 4-week offer(Digital & Print). **Description:** Walnut Hill Plaza was bought by a fund comprised of Miller Investment Management and Hayden Real Estate at an auction in 2012 for $11 million and they spent $2 million in construction renovations. The property was also re-branded as 150 Walnut Warner and the once forlorn building is up to 100% leased space. The tenants renting space in the building are also highlighted. **Availability:** Print; Online.

TRADE PERIODICALS

12905 ■ Journal of Property Management
Pub: Institute of Real Estate Management
Contact: Libby Ekre, President
URL(s): jpmonline.org
Released: Bimonthly **Description:** Magazine serving real estate managers. **Availability:** Print; PDF; Online; Download.

TRADE SHOWS AND CONVENTIONS

12906 ■ Apartment Association of Greater Dallas Annual Trade Show
Apartment Association of Greater Dallas (AAGD)
5728 LBJ Fwy., Ste. 100
Dallas, TX 75240
Ph: (972)385-9091
Co. E-mail: membership@aagdallas.com
URL: http://www.aagdallas.com
Contact: Ian Mattingly, President
URL(s): www.aagdallas.com/2024-trade-show
Frequency: Annual. **Description:** Industry-related equipment, supplies, and services, research and development. **Audience:** Owners, and management company personnel. **Principal Exhibits:** Industry-related equipment, supplies, and services, research and development. **Telecommunication Services:** pkelley@aagdallas.com.

12907 ■ Apartment Association of Greater Orlando Tradeshow
Apartment Association of Greater Orlando (AAGO)
340 N Maitland Ave.
Maitland, FL 32751

Ph: (407)644-0539
URL: http://www.aago.org
Contact: Debbie Gentry, Director
URL(s): www.aago.org/events/2025tradeshow
Frequency: Annual. **Description:** suppliers to the apartment industry. **Audience:** Contractors, marketing professionals, paint manufacturers, furniture suppliers, landscaping professionals, and refinishers. **Principal Exhibits:** suppliers to the apartment industry. Dates and Locations: 2025 Apr 22-22 Event Place at Dezerland Park Orlando, Orlando, FL. **Telecommunication Services:** carina@aago.org.

12908 ■ Apartment Association of Metro Denver Seminar and Trade Show
URL(s): www.aamdhq.org
Description: Apartment management equipment, supplies, and services. **Audience:** Trade professionals. **Principal Exhibits:** Apartment management equipment, supplies, and services.

12909 ■ Building Owners and Managers Association International Annual Convention
URL(s): www.boma.org/events/Pages/default.aspx
Frequency: Annual. **Description:** Products, supplies and equipment for the office building industry, including architectural and building hardware, asbestos abatement, building automation, carpeting, control systems, doors, elevators and elevator maintenance, electrical and lighting, environmental services, financial services, fire protection, flooring and floor machines, hazardous waste removal, interior design, landscaping, locks, paper products, parking, pest control, plumbing and fixtures, recycling, renovation and restoration, roofing, security, signage, water treatment, windows. **Audience:** Owners and managers of office buildings, developers, brokers, and real estate professionals. **Principal Exhibits:** Products, supplies and equipment for the office building industry, including architectural and building hardware, asbestos abatement, building automation, carpeting, control systems, doors, elevators and elevator maintenance, electrical and lighting, environmental services, financial services, fire protection, flooring and floor machines, hazardous waste removal, interior design, landscaping, locks, paper products, parking, pest control, plumbing and fixtures, recycling, renovation and restoration, roofing, security, signage, water treatment, windows. **Telecommunication Services:** info@boma.org.

12910 ■ The Cooperator Expo
URL(s): coopexpofall.com
Frequency: Annual. **Description:** One day show for property managers, apartment owners, board members, shareholders, and real estate professionals in the co-op, condo, and apartment building industries. **Principal Exhibits:** One day show for property managers, apartment owners, board members, shareholders, and real estate professionals in the co-op, condo, and apartment building industries.

12911 ■ Florida Buildings & Facilities Maintenance Show
URL(s): www.maintenanceshows.info/attend-florida.html
Frequency: Annual. **Description:** Products and service booths promoting the latest in the property facilities management industry. **Principal Exhibits:** Products and service booths promoting the latest in the property facilities management industry.

12912 ■ International Facilities Management Association's Facility Fusion Conference and Expo
URL(s): facilityfusion.ifma.org

Frequency: Annual. **Description:** Provides opportunities for leadership and career development in the facilities management industry. **Principal Exhibits:** Provides opportunities for leadership and career development in the facilities management industry.

12913 ■ PM Springfest
URL(s): informaconnect.com/pm-springfest
Frequency: Annual. **Description:** Provides education, talks, and support for property managers. **Principal Exhibits:** Provides education, talks, and support for property managers.

CONSULTANTS

12914 ■ Beer-Wells Real Estate Services Inc.
430 N Center St.
Longview, TX 75601
Ph: (903)753-2191
URL: http://beerwellseasttexas.com
Facebook: www.facebook.com/Beer-Wells-Real-Estate-Services-East-Texas-105027860967639
Description: Real estate firm is engaged in the management, leasing, and marketing of retail, office and industrial properties and they represent buyers, sellers, and tenants. **Founded:** 1994.

12915 ■ Gates, Hudson & Associates Inc.
3020 Hamaker Ct., Ste. 300
Fairfax, VA 22031
Ph: (703)876-9590
Contact: Patricia Blackburn, President
Facebook: www.facebook.com/GatesHudson
Linkedin: www.linkedin.com/company/gates-hudson
Description: Firm specializes in condominium, cooperative and homeowner associations. **Founded:** 1980. **Publications:** "A British Invasion," Jul, 2009.

12916 ■ Hanford-Freund & Co.
47 Kearny St.
San Francisco, CA 94108
Ph: (415)981-5780
Co. E-mail: info@hanfordfreund.com
URL: http://www.hanfordfreund.com
Contact: J. Timothy Falvey, Senior Vice President
Facebook: www.facebook.com/hanfordfreund
Description: Full-service real estate firm specializes in residential and commercial property management and homeowner association management services such as commercial and residential real estate sales and leasing, as well as apartment leasing and rental services and provides non-emergency, repair, and maintenance online request services. **Founded:** 1930.

12917 ■ Investors' Property Services
26020 Acero, Ste. 200
Mission Viejo, CA 92691
Ph: (949)900-6160
Co. E-mail: info@investorshq.com
URL: http://www.investorshq.com
Contact: Robert C. Warren, III, President
X (Twitter): x.com/InvestorsHQ
Description: Firm provides property management consulting services such as core and association management, and much more services. **Scope:** Firm provides property management consulting services such as core and association management, and much more services. **Founded:** 1980.

FRANCHISES AND BUSINESS OPPORTUNITIES

12918 ■ Parker Finch & Associates, LLC
209 E Baseline Rd., Ste. E-208
Tempe, AZ 85283
Contact: James R. Small, Contact

Description: Property management services for condos & home owners associations. **Training:** 2 weeks training provided at headquarters and ongoing support.

COMPUTERIZED DATABASES

12919 ■ ABI/INFORM
ProQuest LLC
789 E Eisenhower Pky.
Ann Arbor, MI 48108
Ph: (734)761-4700
Free: 800-521-0600
URL: http://www.proquest.com
Contact: Matti Shem Tov, Chief Executive Officer
URL(s): about.proquest.com/en/products-services/abi_inform_complete
Availability: Online. **Type:** Full-text; Bibliographic; Image.

LIBRARIES

12920 ■ California Department of Housing and Community Development Housing Resource Center
2020 W El Camino Ave.
Sacramento, CA 95833
Ph: (916)263-7400
Co. E-mail: communications@hcd.ca.gov
URL: http://www.hcd.ca.gov
Contact: Gustavo Velasquez, Director
Facebook: www.facebook.com/CaliforniaHCD
Linkedin: www.linkedin.com/company/californiahcd
X (Twitter): x.com/California_HCD
YouTube: www.youtube.com/channel/UC7ciVAlNzF0vHlJ9kkMm1HA
Scope: Housing; planning; community development; redevelopment; land use. **Services:** Center open to the public with restrictions. **Founded:** 1987. **Holdings:** 4,000 reports. **Subscriptions:** 175 journals.

12921 ■ Steven Winter Associates Inc. (SWA) - Library
61 Washington St., Fl. 2
Norwalk, CT 06854
Ph: (203)857-0200
Co. E-mail: clients@swinter.com
URL: http://www.swinter.com
Contact: Marc Zuluaga, Chief Executive Officer
Facebook: www.facebook.com/StevenWinterAssociates
X (Twitter): x.com/_SWinter
Description: Provides research, consulting and advisory services such as green building certification, energy efficiency, energy optimization, and accessibility consulting. **Scope:** Housing technology; energy conservation; engineering; construction technology; LEED consulting. **Services:** Library not open to the public. **Founded:** 1972. **Holdings:** 2,008 books; 1,200 bound periodical volumes; 700 microfiche. **Publications:** "Getting to Energy Star or Equivalent Ratings in Affordable Housing"; "Green Building Guidelines"; "Energy-Efficient Design and Construction for Commercial Buildings"; "Home Rehab Handbook"; "A Basic Guide to Fair Housing Accessibility"; "The Passive Solar Design and Construction Handbook"; "High Performance School Buildings Resource and Strategy Guide"; "The Whole Building Design Guide"; "Taking the LEED," Mar, 2007. **Training:** Green Building, Energy Efficiency and Historic Preservation, Dec, 2009; Managing Lean and Green; Multifamily Housing Building Operator Training; Energy Efficiency Multifamily Building Training; Taking the Mystery Out of Green Building; Basic Water and Hot Water Efficiency.

Public Relations Consultant

ASSOCIATIONS AND OTHER ORGANIZATIONS

12922 ■ Agricultural Relations Council (ARC)
c/o Kristy Mach, Executive Director
126 W Main St.
New Prague, MN 56071
Ph: (952)758-5811
Fax: (952)758-5813
Co. E-mail: arc@gandgcomm.com
URL: http://www.agrelationscouncil.org
Contact: John Blue, President
E-mail: jlblue@trufflemedia.com

Description: Professional society of agricultural public relations executives employed by private business firms, associations, publications, and government agencies. Operates placement service. **Publications:** *ARClight; Agricultural Relations Council--Members Directory.* **Educational Activities:** Agricultural Relations Council Conference (Annual). **Awards:** Golden ARC Award for Agricultural Image PR Campaigns (Annual). **Geographic Preference:** National.

12923 ■ Canadian Public Relations Society (CPRS)
1 Yonge St.
Toronto, ON, Canada M5A 3S5
Ph: (416)360-1988
Co. E-mail: executivedirector@cprs.ca
URL: http://www.cprs.ca
Contact: Claire Ryan, President
Facebook: www.facebook.com/CPRSToronto
X (Twitter): x.com/cprstoronto
Instagram: www.instagram.com/cprstoronto

Description: Seeks to advance the practice of public relations; promotes ongoing professional development of members. **Founded:** 1953. **Educational Activities:** CPRS National Conference (Annual). **Awards:** CPRS Major Awards (Annual); Torchia Scholarship in Public Relations (Annual); CPRS Awards of Excellence (Annual); Philip A. Novikoff Memorial Award (Annual); Don Rennie Memorial Award (Annual); CPRS Award of Attainment (Annual); CPRS Shield of Service (Annual); CPRS Outstanding Achievement Award (Annual); CPRS Lamp of Service (Annual); Norman A. Dann Lectern Award (Annual); CN-Emery Leblanc Award (Annual); CPRS/CNW Student Award of Excellence (Annual). **Geographic Preference:** National.

12924 ■ Public Relations Society of America (PRSA) - Resource Library
120 Wall St., 21st Fl.
New York, NY 10005-4024
Ph: (212)460-1400
Co. E-mail: memberservices@prsa.org
URL: http://www.prsa.org
Contact: Linda Thomas Brooks, Chief Executive Officer
Facebook: www.facebook.com/PRSANational
Linkedin: www.linkedin.com/company/prsa
X (Twitter): x.com/PRSA

Instagram: www.instagram.com/prsanational
Description: Professional society of public relations practitioners in business and industry, government, associations, hospitals, schools, and nonprofit organizations. Advocates for best practices in the field, as well as greater understanding and adoption of public relations services. Offers job board and networking opportunities. **Scope:** Public relations firm specializes in counseling firms and training programs. **Founded:** 1947. **Holdings:** Articles. **Publications:** "Tactics"; "Professional Development"; "Best Practices"; "How and Why High Technology Companies Use Corporate Identity Principles in Image Building"; "How Much Does My Baby Cost An Analysis of Gender Differences in Income, Career Interruption and Child Bearing"; "Public Relations Practitioners Relationships with Media and Each Other as Moderators of Excellent Health Information and the Local Public Health Agenda". **Training:** PR Boot Camp: Key Concepts and Techniques of Effective Public Relations, New York, Dec, 2009; Not a Bond Cocktail Shaking and Stirring the Right Ingredients for Effective Online Membership Engagement; Jun, 2011; Social Media Its a Jungle Out There, Mar, 2010; Show Me the Members Money The Power of Association and Nonprofit Marketing & Public Relations, July, 2009. **Educational Activities:** PRSA Conferences. **Awards:** Public Relations Professional of the Year Award (Annual); Gold Anvil Award (Annual); Paul M. Lund Public Service Award (Annual); PRSA Outstanding Educator Award (Annual); Bronze Anvil Awards (Annual); Silver Anvil Awards (Annual); MacEachern Chief Executive Officer Award (Annual); Chester Burger Scholarship for Excellence in Public Relations (Annual). **Geographic Preference:** National.

12925 ■ Public Relations Student Society of America (PRSSA)
120 Wall St., 21st Fl.
New York, NY 10005-4024
Ph: (212)460-1474
Free: 800-452-8266
Fax: (212)995-0757
Co. E-mail: prssa@prsa.org
URL: http://www.prsa.org/prssa
Contact: Milagros Orcoyen, President
E-mail: nationalpresident@prsa.org
Facebook: www.facebook.com/prssanational
Linkedin: www.linkedin.com/company/prssanational
X (Twitter): x.com/PRSSANational
Instagram: www.instagram.com/prssanational

Description: Professionally oriented student association organized to cultivate a favorable and mutually advantageous relationship between students and professional public relations practitioners. Fosters understanding of public relations theories and procedures; encourages students to adhere to high ideals and principles of public relations. **Founded:** 1967. **Awards:** Axia Public Relations Scholarship (Annual); Robin M. Urbanski Memorial Scholarship (Annual); Ofield Dukes Multicultural Student Award (Annual); Neumeier Family Leadership Award (Annual); Ron Culp Scholarship for Mentorship (Annual); John D. Graham Scholarship (Annual); Betsy Plank/

PRSSA Scholarships (Annual); PRSA Diversity Multicultural Scholarships (Annual); Gary Yoshimura Scholarship (Annual); PRSSA National Gold Key Awards (Annual); Stephen D. Pisinski Memorial Scholarship (Annual); Lawrence G. Foster Award for Excellence in Public Relations (Annual). **Geographic Preference:** National.

REFERENCE WORKS

12926 ■ "1914 Proved to Be Key Year for Chevy" in Automotive News (Vol. 86, October 31, 2011, No. 6488, pp. S18)
Pub: Crain Communications Inc.
Contact: Barry Asin, President

Ed: Jamie LaReau. **Description:** Chevy Bow Tie emblem was born in 1914, creating the brand's image that has carried through to current days. **Availability:** Print; Online.

12927 ■ "Another California Firm Moving to Austin" in Austin Business Journal (Vol. 31, May 6, 2011, No. 9, pp. 1)
Pub: Austin Business Journal
Contact: Rachel McGrath, Director
E-mail: rmcgrath@bizjournals.com

Ed: Christopher Calnan. **Description:** Main Street Hub Inc. is planning to build a facility in Austin, Texas. The company helps businesses manage their online reputations. Main Street has selected Aquila Commercial LLC as its real estate broker. **Availability:** Print; Online.

12928 ■ "The Buck Stops Here" in Canadian Business (Vol. 81, November 10, 2008, No. 19, pp. 25)
Ed: Sarka Halas. **Description:** Reputation strategist Leslie Gaines-Ross says that minimizing the damage followed by the identification of what went wrong are the first steps that companies need to take when trying to salvage their reputation. Gaines-Ross states that it is up to the CEO to ensure the company's speedy recovery and they need to be at the forefront of the process. **Availability:** Online.

12929 ■ "Column: It's Time to Take Full Responsibility" in Harvard Business Review (Vol. 88, October 2010, No. 10, pp. 42)
Pub: Harvard Business Publishing
Contact: Diane Belcher, Managing Director

Ed: Rosabeth Moss Kanter. **Price:** $6, PDF. **Description:** A case for corporate responsibility is cited, focusing on long-term impact and the effects of public accountability. **Availability:** Online; PDF.

12930 ■ "Deskside Story: As the Latest Buzzword Suggests, PR Firms Are Happy To Drop By" in Inc. (December 2007, pp. 70, 73)
Ed: Nitasha Tiku. **Description:** Setting up a meeting between a company's CEO and a journalist is known as deskside and is becoming popular again whereby a publicist offers clients deskside visits, briefings and alerts to help promote public relations for a company. **Availability:** Print; Online.

12931 ■ *"Empowered" in Harvard Business Review (Vol. 88, July-August 2010, No. 7-8, pp. 94)*
Pub: Harvard Business Publishing
Contact: Diane Belcher, Managing Director
Ed: Josh Bernoff, Ted Schadler. **Price:** $8.95, PDF. **Description:** HERO concept (highly empowered and resourceful operative) which builds a connection between employees, managers, and IT is outlined. The resultant additional experience and knowledge gained by employees improves customer relationship management. **Availability:** Online; PDF.

12932 ■ *"The HBR Interview:"We Had to Own the Mistakes"" in Harvard Business Review (Vol. 88, July-August 2010, No. 7-8, pp. 108)*
Pub: Harvard Business Publishing
Contact: Diane Belcher, Managing Director
Ed: Adi Ignatius. **Description:** Interview with Howard Schultz, CEO of Starbucks, covers topics that include investment in retraining, the impact of competition, premium quality, authenticity, customer services, strategy development, work-and-life issues, and international presence. **Availability:** Online.

12933 ■ *"Hennelly Aims to Increase Building Work in Great Lakes Region for Ryan Cos." in Crain's Chicago Business (Vol. 34, May 23, 2011, No. 21, pp. 6)*
Pub: Crain Communications Inc.
Contact: Barry Asin, President
Ed: Eddie Baeb. **Description:** Profile of Tim Hennelly, who is working to make Ryan Company known as a pure builder rather than a developer-builder. **Availability:** Print; Online.

12934 ■ *"Hopkins' Security, Reputation Face Challenges in Wake of Slaying" in Baltimore Business Journal (Vol. 28, August 6, 2010, No. 13)*
Pub: Baltimore Business Journal
Contact: Rhonda Pringle, President
E-mail: rpringle@bizjournals.com
Ed: Gary Haber. **Description:** The slaying of Johns Hopkins University researcher Stephen Pitcairn has not tarnished the reputation of the elite school in Baltimore, Maryland among students. Maintaining Hopkins' reputation is important since it is Baltimore's largest employer with nearly 32,000 workers. Insights on the impact of the slaying among the Hopkins' community are also given.

12935 ■ *"How Do You Measure Your PR's Return On Investment?" in Puget Sound Business Journal (Vol. 34, March 21, 2014, No. 49, pp. 9)*
Pub: American City Business Journals, Inc.
Contact: Mike Olivieri, Executive Vice President
Description: The process of measuring public relations and its return on investment (ROI) is difficult because not all expenditures are directed towards media relations and public image. Public relations covers leadership programs, speaking engagements, and word of mouth campaigns. The possibility of linking PR efforts towards bottom line marketing as a goal is discussed. **Availability:** Online.

12936 ■ *"How I Did It: Timberland's CEO On Standing Up to 65,000 Angry Activists" in Harvard Business Review (Vol. 88, September 2010, No. 9, pp. 39)*
Pub: Harvard Business Publishing
Contact: Diane Belcher, Managing Director
Ed: Jeff Swartz. **Price:** $8.95, PDF. **Description:** Timberland Company avoided a potential boycott by taking a two-way approach. It addressed a supplier issue that posed a threat to the environment, and launched an email campaign to keep Greenpeace activists informed of the development of a new supplier agreement. **Availability:** Online; PDF.

12937 ■ *"How One Company Joins Corporate Public Relations and Community Engagement" in Denver Business Journal (Vol. 65, January 17, 2014, No. 36, pp. A6)*
Pub: American City Business Journals, Inc.
Contact: Mike Olivieri, Executive Vice President

Description: Denver, Colorado-based Barefoot PR was formed by Cori Streetman and Sarah Hogan in 2010 to change corporate views on philanthropy. The partners made a commitment to make community investment the driving force of business. Insights on the next-generation of community relations consultants are also given. **Availability:** Online.

12938 ■ *"How To Be a Twitter Ninja" in Canadian Business (Vol. 87, October 2014, No. 10, pp. 51)*
Description: Robert Palmer, public relations manager at WestJet, shares some rules when it comes to customer engagement on Twitter. He emphasizes the importance of communication when dealing with customer complaints as quickly as possible. **Availability:** Print; Online.

12939 ■ *If You Have to Cry, Go Outside: And Other Things Your Mother Never Told You*
Pub: HarperCollins Publishers L.L.C.
Contact: Brian Murray, President
Ed: Kelly Cutrone, Meredith Bryan. **Released:** February 02, 2010. **Price:** $10.99, e-book; $7.24, e-book. **Description:** Women's mentor advices on how to make it in one of the most competitive industries in the world, fashion. She has kicked people out of fashion shows, forced some of reality television's shiny start to fire their friends, and built her own company which is one of the most powerful public relations firms in the fashion business. **Availability:** E-book; Print.

12940 ■ *"Lessons from SeaWorld's 'Blackfish' Nightmare" in Orlando Business Journal (Vol. 30, January 3, 2014, No. 28, pp. 7)*
Pub: American City Business Journals, Inc.
Contact: Mike Olivieri, Executive Vice President
Released: January 03, 2014. **Price:** $8, introductory 4-week offer(Digital only). **Description:** University of Florida's crisis communications specialist and public relations (PR) professor, W. Timothy Coombs, shares his views about the PR backlash from SeaWorld's refusal to participate in the filming of the documentary 'Blackfish'. Coombs believes SeaWorld must create a public statement that defends its character and actions. **Availability:** Print; Online.

12941 ■ *"The List: Public Relations Agencies" in South Florida Business Journal (Vol. 35, August 8, 2014, No. 2, pp. 12)*
Pub: American City Business Journals, Inc.
Contact: Mike Olivieri, Executive Vice President
Description: Rankings of public relations agencies in the South Florida region are presented. Rankings were based on the 2013 public relations net fee income in the region. **Availability:** Print; Online.

12942 ■ *Media, Organizations and Identity*
Pub: Palgrave Macmillan
Released: First edition. **Description:** The mass media, press, and television are essential in the formation of corporate identity and the promotion of business image and reputation. This book offers a new perspective into the interrelationships between media and organizations over three dimensions: media as business, media in business and business in the media.

12943 ■ *O'Dwyer's Directory of Public Relations Firms*
Pub: J.R. O'Dwyer Company Inc.
Contact: Christine O'Dwyer, Director, Marketing
URL(s): www.odwyerpr.com/pr_firms_database/index_form.php
Ed: Kevin McCauley, Melissa Werbell. **Released:** Annual **Price:** $250, for featured database listing. **Description:** Covers over 1,600 public relations firms; international coverage. Includes list of top 50 public relations firms. **Entries include:** Firm name, address, phone, principal executives, branch and overseas offices, billings, date founded, and 7,750 clients are cross-indexed. **Arrangement:** Geographical by country. **Indexes:** Specialty (beauty and fashions, finance/investor, etc.), geographical, client. **Availability:** Print; Download; Online; PDF.

12944 ■ *"Offer Your Own Authentic Truth" in South Florida Business Journal (Vol. 34, July 25, 2014, No. 53, pp. 13)*
Pub: American City Business Journals, Inc.
Contact: Mike Olivieri, Executive Vice President
Released: Weekly. **Price:** $8, introductory 4-week offer(Digital only). **Description:** Turkel Brands CEO, Bruce Turkel, was born in Miami Beach, Florida and has a bachelor's degree in design at the University of Florida. Turkel was a respected advertising agency owner and executive creative director before he began blogging on marketing and branding. He shares three tips for building a brand and creating a positive public image. **Availability:** Print; Online.

12945 ■ *"Optima Public Relations Gains Partners" in Alaska Business Monthly (Vol. 27, October 2011, No. 10, pp. 10)*
Pub: Alaska Business Publishing Company Inc.
Contact: Charles Bell, Vice President, Sales and Marketing
E-mail: cbell@akbizmag.com
Ed: Nancy Pounds. **Description:** Optima Public Relations has partnered with Gogerty Marriott of Seattle and Seattle Design Group. **Availability:** Print; Online.

12946 ■ *Public Relations Campaigns: An Integrated Approach*
Ed: Regina M. Luttrell, Luke W. Capizzo. **Released:** March 08, 2018. **Price:** $80.02, Paperback; $68.39, E-book. **Description:** While using case studies and real-life examples, the authors guide the reader into the process of creating a public relations campaign. **Availability:** E-book; Print.

12947 ■ *"Reputation Warfare" in Harvard Business Review (Vol. 88, December 2010, No. 12, pp. 70)*
Pub: Harvard Business Publishing
Contact: Diane Belcher, Managing Director
Ed: Leslie Gaines-Ross. **Price:** $8.95, PDF. **Description:** Steps are presented for addressing attacks on corporate public image. These include responding promptly, avoiding disproportionate displays of force, empowering employees to present the firm's position, and stockpiling credentials to bolster credence. **Availability:** Online; PDF.

12948 ■ *"Voice: Rebuilding Trust" in Business Strategy Review (Vol. 21, Summer 2010, No. 2, pp. 79-80)*
Ed: David De Cremer. **Released:** June 24, 2010. **Description:** The financial world's attempts to rebuild trust are charted. Three steps to jump-start that process are outlined. **Availability:** Print; PDF; Online.

12949 ■ *When the Headline Is You: An Insider's Guide to Handling the Media*
Pub: Jossey-Bass
Ed: Jeff Ansell, Jeff Lesson. **Released:** August 01, 2010. **Price:** $29.95, hardcover; $29.95, hardcover. **Description:** How-to guide for executives and other professionals whose high-visibility requires frequent interviews with the media. Tested techniques, tools, and insights for how to respond to all types of media in tough situation are provided. The book also reveals the lessons learned and the pitfalls to avoid by referencing actual news stores from around the world and provides exercises for readers who wish to sharpen their media-handling skills. **Availability:** E-book; Print.

12950 ■ *"Why Marketing Slogans Matter" in Canadian Business (Vol. 85, June 11, 2012, No. 10, pp. 18)*
Ed: Bruce Philp. **Description:** Slogans earn their meaning in popular culture through dramatic beginnings and repetition over the years so marketers should consider whether the brand can earn it before replacing the tag lines. People in the branding business should not use the tag line exercise as a substitute for creating a strategy. **Availability:** Online.

TRADE PERIODICALS

12951 ■ *Public Relations Review: A Global Journal of Research and Comment*
Pub: Elsevier Inc.
Contact: Jan Herzhoff, President
URL(s): www.sciencedirect.com/journal/public-rela
tions-review
Released: 5/year; volume 1. **Price:** $242, Individuals for print us Canada India; $1,984, Institutions for print us Canada India. **Description:** Communications journal covering public relations education, government, survey research, public policy, history, and bibliographies. **Availability:** Print; Download; PDF; Online.

CONSULTANTS

12952 ■ Ashland Group L.P.
1560 W Bby Area Blvd. No. 350
Friendswood, TX 77546
Ph: (281)484-1700
Co. E-mail: info@ashlandgroup.com
URL: http://ashlandgroup.com
Contact: Dwayne Humphrey, Vice President, Business Development

Description: Government and political affairs agency that specializes in government relations, advocacy communications, media relations, campaign management and government contract lobbying. Offers creative and innovative tax issues. **Scope:** Government and political affairs agency that specializes in government relations, advocacy communications, media relations, campaign management and government contract lobbying. Offers creative and innovative tax issues. **Publications:** "State Tax Guide," Jan, 2009; "State Tax Guide," Jan, 2007.

12953 ■ Campaign Solutions
117 N Saint Asaph St.
Alexandria, VA 22314
Ph: (202)664-7711
Co. E-mail: info@campaignsolutions.com
URL: http://www.campaignsolutions.com
Contact: Becki Donatelli, President
Facebook: www.facebook.com/pages/campaign-solu
tions/50710138582
Linkedin: www.linkedin.com/company/campaign-solu
tions
X (Twitter): x.com/campsol
Instagram: www.instagram.com/campaignsolutions
Description: Republican campaign consultants. Brings a breadth and depth of knowledge and experience not found in any other republican voter contact and communications firm. **Scope:** Republican campaign consultants. Brings a breadth and depth of knowledge and experience not found in any other republican voter contact and communications firm. **Founded:** 1998. **Training:** Absolutely Interactive e-marketing Solution.

12954 ■ The Da Vinci Group Inc.
18609 Foundry Rd.
Purcellville, VA 20132
Contact: Mark Smith, President
Description: Provider of consulting and management services for government and public relations, public affairs, and corporate development. **Scope:** Provider of consulting and management services for government and public relations, public affairs, and corporate development.

12955 ■ The Harwood Institute for Public Innovation
4915 St. Elmo Ave., Ste. 402
Bethesda, MD 20814
Ph: (301)656-3669
Co. E-mail: info@theharwoodinstitute.org
URL: http://www.theharwoodinstitute.org
Contact: Rich Harwood, President
Facebook: www.facebook.com/HarwoodInstitute
Linkedin: www.linkedin.com/company/the-harwoo
d-institute
X (Twitter): x.com/HarwoodInst
Instagram: www.instagram.com/harwoodinst
YouTube: www.youtube.com/user/HarwoodInstitute

Description: Works to understand the essence of society's complex challenges and understands how to create effective action. **Scope:** Works to understand the essence of society's complex challenges and understands how to create effective action. **Founded:** 1988. **Publications:** "Hope Unraveled: The People's Retreat and Our Way Back," Kettering Foundation Press; "Public Engagement and School Facilities Conversation Workbook," 2004; "Telling Stories of Self-Trust and Hope: A Tool for Engaging Youth in Community Change," 2003; "Making it Real: How to Make Civic Engagement a Public Sensibility," 2003; "New Political Covenant: America's Aspirations for Political Conduct," 2002; "Public Engagement and Small Schools Conversation Guide," 2002; "Creating A New Story: Flint's Struggle to Move Forward," 2001. **Training:** Devotion: Declaring Our Intentions in Public Life; Creating A New Public Story; Originating Civic Faith and Self-Trust in America; Moving From a Flat World to a Round World in Public Life; The Public Realm: Where America Must Address Its Concerns.

12956 ■ The Media Guys Inc.
718 W Monte Cir.
Mesa, AZ 85210
Contact: Robert Grossfeld, President
Description: A strategic communications firm specializing in public affairs and issues management. Expertise in social marketing, strategic communications and political campaigns. **Scope:** A strategic communications firm specializing in public affairs and issues management. Expertise in social marketing, strategic communications and political campaigns. **Founded:** 1992.

12957 ■ Midwest Computer Group L.L.C. (MCG)
6060 Franks Rd.
House Springs, MO 63051
Contact: Leon Sanford, Jr., Contact
Description: Specializes in helping businesses create accounting, marketing and business information systems, software development and database design and management. **Scope:** Specializes in helping businesses create accounting, marketing and business information systems, software development and database design and management.

12958 ■ ReCourses Inc.
4851 Vincion Rd.
Murfreesboro, TN 37130-7909
Ph: (615)831-2277
Fax: (615)831-2277
URL: http://www.davidcbaker.com
Contact: Bob Lalasz, Chief Executive Officer
X (Twitter): x.com/ReCourses
Description: A privately held advisory firm providing business management advice to entrepreneurial experts worldwide. It is committed to a research-based, educational contribution to principals of expert firms through free position papers, webinars, a podcast, books (print, ebook, audible), and speaking engagements, as well as affordable seminars and advisory services. **Scope:** A privately held advisory firm providing business management advice to entrepreneurial experts worldwide. It is committed to a research-based, educational contribution to principals of expert firms through free position papers, webinars, a podcast, books (print, ebook, audible), and speaking engagements, as well as affordable seminars and advisory services. **Founded:** 1996. **Publications:** -"Managing (Right) for the First Time"; "Financial Management of a Marketing Firm". - "Financial Management of a Marketing Firm"; "Guidebook used worldwide for independent agencies". - "The Business of Expertise"; "How Entrepreneurial Experts Convert Insight to Impact and Wealth". **Training:** 10th Annual New Business Summit, Jan, 2013; Event - TEDx Nashville: Success from the Inside Out-Alignment & Engagement, Apr, 20163; Event - AIGA Brand Academy (Emory Executive Education @ Goizueta Business School), Apr, 2013; Measuring Economic Performance: Measuring and Enhancing Performance in a Marketing Firm, Dec, 2012; Managing Client Relationships: Being Indispensable, Growing the Account, Making Money, Nov, 2012; The Busi-

ness of Design Oct, 2012; Getting a Good Start in Your Creative Career, Nov, 2011; Research and Insights, Nov, 2011; Managing Client Relationships; Research and Strategy; Financial Management: Measuring and Enhancing Performance in a Marketing Firm, Sep, 2009; Building and Leading a Staff: The When, How, and What of Growth and Culture, Sep, 2009; Doing Effective Work: Adding Significance to the Strategic Portion of Your Work for Clients, Sep, 2009; Resourcing the Creative Process: Managing Pricing, Deadlines, Budgets, Quality, and Capacity, Apr, 2009.

12959 ■ The Rothschild Image
13900 Tahiti Way, Ste. 308
Marina del Rey, CA 90292
Ph: (310)574-6018
Co. E-mail: info@rothschildimage.com
URL: http://www.rothschildimage.com
Contact: Ashley Rothschild, Founder
Description: Provider of VIP consulting, corporate seminars, and training services. **Scope:** Provider of VIP consulting, corporate seminars, and training services. **Publications:** "Is There an O'Neal Family Curse? - ABC News," Feb, 2007; "Can an Image Consultant Help You Dress for Success? - Wall Street Journal," Feb, 2006; "Reality Check - Paris Hilton and Amber Moore," Jan, 2004; "Britney's Mystery Man - Britney Spears," Dec, 2003; "People who need to redo their image," Jun, 2003; "Reshaping an Image," Jun, 2003; "Dress to Impress the World International Business Fashion," Apr, 2003. **Training:** S.T.A.R.POWER: A Professional Image Consultant Training Program; Learn How to Have More Success, Power and Romance in Your Life.

12960 ■ Smith, Dawson & Andrews (SDA)
1150 Connecticut Ave. NW, Ste. 1025
Washington, DC 20036
Ph: (202)835-0740
Co. E-mail: info@sda-inc.com
URL: http://www.sda-inc.com
Contact: James P. Smith, President
E-mail: jims@sda-inc.com
Linkedin: www.linkedin.com/company/smith-dawson
-&-andrews
Description: A government relations/public affairs firm specializing in public policy, communications, legislative strategy and business development. **Scope:** A government relations/public affairs firm specializing in public policy, communications, legislative strategy and business development. **Founded:** 1981.

12961 ■ Stevens, Reed, Curcio and Potholm Media
201 N Union St., Ste. 200
Alexandria, VA 22314
Ph: (703)683-8326
Co. E-mail: srcpmedia@srcpmedia.com
URL: http://srcpmedia.com
Contact: Ben Burger, Managing Partner
X (Twitter): x.com/srcpmedia
Description: Republican media consulting firm that specializes in media production, public opinion research, direct mail design, opposition research and political strategy. **Scope:** Republican media consulting firm that specializes in media production, public opinion research, direct mail design, opposition research and political strategy. **Founded:** 1993.

12962 ■ The Tarrance Group
201 N Union St., Ste. 410
Alexandria, VA 22314
Ph: (703)684-6688
Co. E-mail: tarrance@tarrance.com
URL: http://www.tarrance.com
Contact: Ed Goeas, President
Facebook: www.facebook.com/thetarrancegroup
Description: Specializes in research and international polling. Services include: political polling/political campaign consulting, corporate affairs, reputation management, issue advocacy, national political and environment research. **Scope:** Specializes in research and international polling. Services include: political polling/political campaign consulting, corpo-

rate affairs, reputation management, issue advocacy, national political and environment research. **Founded:** 1977.

12963 ■ Triad Strategies L.L.C.
300 N 2nd St., Ste. 1200
 Harrisburg, PA 17101
Ph: (717)238-2970
Co. E-mail: advocacy@triadstrategies.com
URL: http://www.triadstrategies.com
Contact: Roy Wells, President
E-mail: rwells@triadstrategies.com
Facebook: www.facebook.com/triadstrategies
Linkedin: www.linkedin.com/company/triad-strategies
X (Twitter): x.com/triadstrategies
Instagram: www.instagram.com/triadstrategies
YouTube: www.youtube.com/channel/UC_y9-DXXzey
 -oZPrH9K3fRA
Description: Government relations firm. Services include legislative and regulatory monitoring, legislative and executive branch lobbying, independent and quasi-public agency lobbying, issue research, issue management, grassroots organizing, public relations,

strategic planning and network marketing. **Scope:** Government relations firm. Services include legislative and regulatory monitoring, legislative and executive branch lobbying, independent and quasi-public agency lobbying, issue research, issue management, grassroots organizing, public relations, strategic planning and network marketing. **Founded:** 2002.

LIBRARIES

12964 ■ University of Illinois at Urbana-Champaign - Communications Library
122 Gregory Hall
 810 S Wright St.
 Urbana, IL 61801
Ph: (217)333-2216
Co. E-mail: comlibrarian@illinois.edu
URL: http://www.library.illinois.edu/commedia
Contact: Lisa Romero, Librarian Associate Professor
E-mail: l-romero@illinois.edu
X (Twitter): x.com/CommLibraryUIUC

Scope: Telecommunications; popular culture; public relations; communication theory and radio and television broadcasting. **Services:** Interlibrary loan; Library open to the public with permit from Main Library. **Founded:** 1933. **Holdings:** 16,000 volumes of books, journals, newspapers; e-journals.

12965 ■ University of Missouri - Columbia - Frank Lee Martin Memorial Journalism Library
120 Neff Hall
 Columbia, MO 65211
Ph: (573)882-7502
URL: http://journalism.missouri.edu/real-worl
 d-experiences/centers-and-institutes/frank-lee-mar
 tin-journalism-library
Contact: Vera Elwood, Contact
E-mail: velwood@missouri.edu

Description: Journalism Library founded in 1908. **Scope:** Journalism. **Services:** Interlibrary loan; copying. **Founded:** 1908. **Holdings:** Books; videos; DVDs; CDs.

ASSOCIATIONS AND OTHER ORGANIZATIONS

12966 ■ Affiliated Warehouse Companies (AWC)
PO Box 295
Hazlet, NJ 07730-0295
Ph: (732)739-2323
Co. E-mail: sales@awco.com
URL: http://www.awco.com
Facebook: www.facebook.com/AffiliatedWarehouse
Linkedin: www.linkedin.com/company/affiliate
d-warehouse-companies
X (Twitter): x.com/AffiliatedWCO

Description: Represents franchised public merchandise warehouse companies united for national sales work, advertising, and public relations. Assists in gathering rates and data pertaining to warehousing and distribution. Offers free consultation services to industry. Maintains placement service; compiles statistics. **Founded:** 1953. **Publications:** *Affiliated Warehouse Companies--Directory* (Biennial). **Geographic Preference:** National.

12967 ■ American Chain of Warehouses (ACWI)
c/o Partners Warehouse L. L. C., 26634 S Walton Dr.
Elwood, IL 60421
Ph: (708)946-9792
Co. E-mail: info@acwi.org
URL: http://acwi.org
Contact: Bob Shaunnessey, Vice President
E-mail: bob.shaunnessey@partnerswarehouse.com

Description: Represents commercial warehouses. Provides national sales representation. Disseminates information. **Founded:** 1911. **Publications:** *American Chain of Warehouses--Membership Directory* (Annual). **Geographic Preference:** National.

12968 ■ Global Cold Chain Alliance (GCCA) - Library
241 18th St. South Ste. 620
Arlington, VA 22202
Ph: (703)373-4300
Fax: (703)373-4301
Co. E-mail: email@gcca.org
URL: http://www.gcca.org
Contact: Matthew Ott, President
Facebook: www.facebook.com/globalcol
dchainalliance
Linkedin: www.linkedin.com/groups
X (Twitter): x.com/gccaorg
YouTube: www.youtube.com/channel/UCpC7fCh
-trouA14JTilKHFQ

Description: Aims to improve business operations. Works to carry out insurance survey work. Acts as a clearinghouse for technical information. Compiles industry statistics. **Scope:** A free, convenient way to find third-party logistics providers, contractors and suppliers. **Holdings:** Figures not available. **Publications:** *Global Cold Chain Directory*; *Cold Facts* (Bimonthly); *Crisis Management Manual*; *Directory of*

Public Refrigerated Warehouses (Annual); *Guide to Effective Warehouse Design, Maintenance, and Modernization*; *Commodity Storage Manual*; *International Directory of Refrigerated Warehouses and Distribution Centers* (Continuous); *International Association of Cold Storage Contractors--Membership Directory* (Annual). **Educational Activities:** IARW-WFLO Annual Convention (Annual). **Geographic Preference:** National.

12969 ■ International Warehouse Logistics Association (IWLA)
2800 S River Rd., Ste. 260
Des Plaines, IL 60018
Ph: (847)813-4699
Fax: (847)813-0115
Co. E-mail: mail@iwla.com
URL: http://www.iwla.com
Contact: Steve W. DeHaan, President
E-mail: sdehaan@iwla.com
Facebook: www.facebook.com/IWLA1891/timeline
Linkedin: www.linkedin.com/company/international
-warehouse-logistics-association
X (Twitter): x.com/IWLA_US
Instagram: www.instagram.com/iwla1891
YouTube: www.youtube.com/user/IWLA1891

Description: Promotes the growth and success of public and contract warehousing and related logistics services. Serves as the voice of the global outsourced warehouse logistics industry, representing 3PLs (third party logistics providers), 4PLs (fourth party logistics providers), public and contract warehouse logistics companies and their suppliers, setting standards, legal frameworks and best practices for the warehousing logistics industry for 110 years. Members of the Association receive services including legal assistance, marketing assistance and group buying programs. **Founded:** 1891. **Publications:** *International Warehouse Logistics Association--Membership Directory & Resource Guide* (Annual); *This Week at IWLA* (Weekly); *International Warehouse Logistics Association--Roster of Members* (Annual). **Educational Activities:** IWLA Convention & Expo (Annual). **Geographic Preference:** National.

12970 ■ Material Handling Industry of America - Order Fulfillment Solutions (MHI)
8720 Red Oak Blvd., Ste. 201
Charlotte, NC 28217
URL: http://www.mhi.org/OFC
Contact: Anupam Berry Bose, Executive
E-mail: abose@mhi.org

Description: Trade associations comprising storage industries. Compiles statistics; sponsors research and educational programs. **Founded:** 1986. **Awards:** MHEFI scholarship (Annual). **Geographic Preference:** National.

12971 ■ Recreational Vehicle Aftermarket Association (RVAA)
One ParkView Plaza
Oakbrook Terrace, IL 60181
Ph: (630)596-9004
Co. E-mail: info@rvaahq.org

URL: http://www.rvaahq.org
Contact: Susan Carpenter, President
E-mail: scarpenter@robacompany.com
Facebook: www.facebook.com/RVAAHQ
X (Twitter): twitter.com/rvaahq

Description: Distributors, suppliers, and manufacturer's agents in the RV aftermarket industry. **Founded:** 1969. **Educational Activities:** Aftermarket Executive Conference (Annual). **Geographic Preference:** National.

12972 ■ Self Storage Association (SSA) - Library
1001 N Fairfax St., Ste. 505
Alexandria, VA 22314
Ph: (703)575-8000
Free: 888-735-3784
Fax: (703)575-8901
Co. E-mail: info@selfstorage.org
URL: http://www.selfstorage.org
Contact: Timothy J. Dietz, President
E-mail: tdietz@selfstorage.org
Linkedin: www.linkedin.com/company/self-storage
-association-ssa---usa
X (Twitter): x.com/selfstorageassn
YouTube: www.youtube.com/channel/
UCSkTZUCyawpnIVlQSagjYTQ

Description: Represents owners and operators of self-storage facilities. Improves the quality of management, customer service, facilities; promotes public management, marketing, security and related topics. Lobbies for state legislation protecting and recognizing self-storage owners and operators. **Scope:** Self-storage operation and management. **Founded:** 1975. **Holdings:** Figures not available. **Publications:** *SSA Globe Magazine* (Monthly). **Educational Activities:** Self Storage Association Spring Conference and Tradeshow (Annual). **Geographic Preference:** National.

12973 ■ SOLE - The International Society of Logistics
14625 Baltimore Ave., Ste. 303
Laurel, MD 20707-4902
Ph: (301)459-8446
Fax: (301)459-1522
Co. E-mail: solehq@erols.com
URL: http://www.sole.org
Contact: Timothy H. Overstreet, President

Description: Represents corporate and individual management and technical practitioners in the field of logistics, including scientists, engineers, educators, managers, and other specialists in commerce, aerospace, and other industries, government, and the military. (Logistics is the art and science of management engineering and technical activities concerned with requirements, and designing, supplying, and maintaining resources to support objectives, plans, and operations.) Covers every logistics specialty, including reliability, maintainability, systems and equipment maintenance, maintenance support equipment, human factors, training and training equipment, spare parts, overhaul and repair, handbooks, field site activation and operation, field engineering, facilities, packaging, supply chain management, materials handling, and transportation. Sponsors on-line job referral service; conducts specialized education programs. **Founded:** 1966. **Publications:** *Annual International Conference and Exposition Proceedings* (Annual); *Logistics Spectrum* (Quarterly); *SOLE-The International Society of Logistics--Membership Directory* (Annual). **Educational Activities:** SOLE Annual International Logistics Conference and Exhibition (Annual); District 02 Professional Development Forum. **Awards:** SOLE Doctoral Dissertation Award/Scholarships (Annual). **Geographic Preference:** Multinational.

12974 ■ Warehousing Education and Research Council (WERC)
8720 Red Oak Blvd., Ste. 201
  Charlotte, NC 28217
Ph: (630)990-0001
Co. E-mail: wercoffice@werc.org
URL: http://www.werc.org
Contact: Krys Slovacek, Director
E-mail: kslovacek@werc.org
Facebook: www.facebook.com/WERChq
Linkedin: www.linkedin.com/company/werc
X (Twitter): x.com/werc
Instagram: www.instagram.com/werc_hq

Description: Represents distribution and warehousing professionals who lead, direct, and manage the efficient flow of information, materials, and finished goods throughout the supply chain. Provides practical ways that can be apply to improve service and reduce costs. **Scope:** Warehousing industry and executive professionalism, including improving service within the industry. **Founded:** 1977. **Educational Activities:** WERC DX Annual Conference (Annual). **Geographic Preference:** Multinational.

REFERENCE WORKS

12975 ■ "$560 Million Acquisition in Storage for CubeSmart" in Orlando Business Journal (Vol. 28, September 7, 2012, No. 30, pp. 1)
Pub: Baltimore Business Journal
Contact: Rhonda Pringle, President
E-mail: rpringle@bizjournals.com

Description: CubeSmart has completed its $560 million acquisition of 22 storage facilities in late August 2012, making it one of the leading self-storage companies in the US. In light of this growth, an overview of CubeSmart is explored. **Availability:** Print; Online.

12976 ■ "Company Hopes To Pack Profits With Self-Storage" in Crain's Detroit Business (Vol. 24, February 18, 2008, No. 7, pp. 15)
Pub: Crain Communications Inc.
Contact: Barry Asin, President

Ed: Daniel Duggan. **Description:** Storage Opportunity Partners has purchased a vacant building to convert into a self-storage facility. **Availability:** Online.

12977 ■ "How to Invest in Self-Storage Real Estate" in U.S. News & World Report (August 12, 2019)
URL(s): money.usnews.com/investing/real-estate -investments/articles/how-to-invest-in-self-storage -real-estate

Ed: Kayleigh Kulp. **Released:** August 12, 2019. **Description:** Investors looking for real-estate to buy into may want to consider self-storage facilities since they are a relatively stable and long-term investment. Even when the economy isn't doing well, self-storage lots are often still being used by people who need to store household items and business that need a space for warehouse products overflow. **Availability:** Online.

12978 ■ Leonard's Guide Freight Transportation & Warehouse Directory (FTWD)
Pub: G.R. Leonard and Co.
URL(s): www.leonardsguide.com/ftwd.asp

Released: Continuous **Price:** $495, Single issue. **Description:** Covers approximately 4,000 warehouses in the U.S. and Canada. **Entries include:** Name, address, phone, storage areas, facilities, truck dock capacity, rail siding, geographical area served, products handled, services offered, year established, number of employees, distribution service, insurance and general information. **Arrangement:** Geographical by state. **Indexes:** Geographical by ZIP code, alphabetical, categorical. **Availability:** Download; Online.

12979 ■ "Manufacturing Boom Leads to Local Warehouse Leasing Fury" in Houston Business Journal (Vol. 44, April 11, 2014, No. 49, pp. 10A)
Pub: American City Business Journals, Inc.
Contact: Mike Olivieri, Executive Vice President

Released: Weekly. **Price:** $4, introductory 4-week offer(Digital only). **Description:** The growth of Houston, Texas manufacturing sector has resulted in companies' investment in local warehouse space. Siemens AG and Emerson Electric Company have leased new warehouse space in the area. Meanwhile, other energy companies have also contributed to the decline of industrial vacancy rates. **Availability:** Print; Online.

12980 ■ "Marine-Services Firm Eyes Expansion" in Providence Business News (Vol. 29, August 25, 2014, No. 21, pp. 8)
Pub: American City Business Journals, Inc.
Contact: Mike Olivieri, Executive Vice President

Released: August 23, 2014. **Description:** Jamestown, Rhode Island-based Conanicut Marine Services Inc. is looking to expand the business with a bigger marina, the addition of a third boat to his ferry fleet, and a climate-controlled storage shed. Owner, Bill Munger, discusses his efforts to overcome the challenges of sustaining the business during the economic recession. **Availability:** Print; Online.

12981 ■ "Safety Products Firm Expanding" in Memphis Business Journal (Vol. 33, March 16, 2012, No. 49, pp. 1)
Pub: Baltimore Business Journal
Contact: Rhonda Pringle, President
E-mail: rpringle@bizjournals.com

Description: Safety products importer and supplier International Sourcing Company Inc., the parent firm of Cordova Safety Products and Cordova Consumer Products, has purchased the 1 million-square-foot Cleo property in southeast Memphis, Tennessee. Aside from relocating its warehouse and office operations to the facility, the firm will add 20 new jobs as part of its growth initiative. **Availability:** Print; Online.

12982 ■ "Substantial Deal Expected to Create Jobs, Help Industrial Market" in Tampa Bay Business Journal (Vol. 30, January 8, 2010, No. 3)
Pub: Tampa Bay Business Journal
Contact: Ian Anderson, President
E-mail: ianderson@bizjournals.com

Ed: Janet Leiser. **Description:** Food distribution firm Gordon Food Service (GFS) is on the brink of purchasing Albertson's million-square-foot warehouse along with 158 acres of space. The deal between GFS and Albertson's could expand GFS' presence in west Central Florida. A history of GFS' growth is included. **Availability:** Print; Online.

12983 ■ "Supermercado El Rancho Chain Grows Along with Hispanic Population" in Dallas Business Journal (Vol. 35, July 13, 2012, No. 44, pp. 1)
Pub: Baltimore Business Journal
Contact: Rhonda Pringle, President
E-mail: rpringle@bizjournals.com

Ed: Matt Joyce. **Description:** Garland, Texas-based Supermercado El Rancho has grown rapidly wit its take on the Hispanic grocery market and is planning to open 12 stores in six years. La Bodega Meat Inc.,

the chain's affiliate distribution company, is planning a $13.1 million renovation and double the size of its warehouse to accommodate the plans for more stores.

12984 ■ "Trammell Crow Facility in Houston is a Late Bloomer" in Houston Business Journal (Vol. 40, August 28, 2009, No. 16, pp. 1A)
Pub: Houston Business Journal
Contact: Bob Charlet, President
E-mail: bcharlet@bizjournals.com

Ed: Jennifer Dawson. **Released:** Weekly. **Description:** Trammell Crow Company leased half of the 61,000 square foot IAH International Air Cargo Centre II to Tradewinds Cargo Handling. The facility, located at George Bush Intercontinental Airport, is intended to be a destination of fresh flowers and food from Latin America. **Availability:** Print; Online.

12985 ■ Where Does the Tidiness Craze Leave Self-Storage Stocks?
URL(s): www.bloomberg.com/opinion/articles/2019-0 3-04/where-does-the-tidiness-craze-leave-self-s torage-stocks

Released: March 04, 2019. **Description:** The tidiness and organization craze has done a lot for people looking to declutter their spaces, but not everyone is happy. Self-storage lots bank on renters who will store their items on their property and part of the new trend in cleaning up is also letting go of items that are no longer needed. Cleaning out these self-storage units and closing out on leases has caused demand to fall. **Availability:** Online.

STATISTICAL SOURCES

12986 ■ RMA Annual Statement Studies
Pub: Risk Management Association
Contact: Nancy Foster, President

Released: Annual. **Description:** Contains composite balance sheets and income statements for more than 360 industries, including the accounting, auditing, and bookkeeping industries. Also contains five years of comparative historical data for discerning trends. Includes 16 commonly used ratios, computed for most of the size groupings for nearly every industry.

12987 ■ Storage & Warehousing Leasing Industry in the US - Market Research Report
URL(s): www.ibisworld.com/united-states/market-re search-reports/storage-warehouse-leasing-industry/

Price: $925. **Description:** Downloadable report analyzing the current and future trends in the storage and warehouse leasing industries. **Availability:** Download.

12988 ■ Transportation and Warehousing Industry in the US - Market Research Report
URL(s): www.ibisworld.com/united-states/market-re search-reports/transportation-warehousing-industry/

Price: $925. **Description:** Downloadable report analyzing current and future trends in the transportation and warehousing industries. **Availability:** Download.

TRADE PERIODICALS

12989 ■ Self-Storage Now!
Pub: Mini-Storage Messenger
Contact: Travis M. Morrow, Chief Executive Officer
E-mail: travis.morrow@storelocal.com
URL(s): www.modernstoragemedia.com/selfs toragenow

Released: Quarterly **Description:** Written to help mini-storage management personnel increase profits through marketing tips, business advice, new products, space rental sales techniques, and the sale of products and services to tenants. **Availability:** Online.

TRADE SHOWS AND CONVENTIONS

12990 ■ Self Storage Association Executive Ski Workshop
URL(s): www.selfstorage.org/Events-Education/Even ts/Executive-Ski-Workshop

Description: Networking conference and ski trip for members of the Self Storage Association. **Audience:** SSA members only. **Principal Exhibits:** Networking conference and ski trip for members of the Self Storage Association.

12991 ■ Self Storage Association Spring Conference and Tradeshow

Self Storage Association (SSA)
  1001 N Fairfax St., Ste. 505
  Alexandria, VA 22314
Ph: (703)575-8000
Free: 888-735-3784
Fax: (703)575-8901
Co. E-mail: info@selfstorage.org
URL: http://www.selfstorage.org
Contact: Timothy J. Dietz, President
E-mail: tdietz@selfstorage.org
URL(s): www.selfstorage.org/Events-Education/Even ts/National-Spring-Conference/Conference-Procee dings

Frequency: Annual; held spring. **Description:** Equipment, supplies, and services designed for and pertinent to construction, maintenance, and operation of self storage facilities. Meal functions held in exhibit hall. **Audience:** Self storage professionals. **Principal Exhibits:** Equipment, supplies, and services designed for and pertinent to construction, maintenance, and operation of self storage facilities. Meal functions held in exhibit hall. Dates and Locations: 2025 Mar 12-14 Rosen Shingle Creek, Orlando, FL. **Telecommunication Services:** membership@selfstorage.org.

12992 ■ WERC DX Annual Conference

Dematic Corp.
  507 Plymouth Ave. NE
  Grand Rapids, MI 49505
Free: 877-725-7500
URL: http://www.dematic.com/en-us
Contact: Hasan Dandashly, President
URL(s): na.eventscloud.com/website/63567

Frequency: Annual. **Description:** Provides educational programs that cater to the needs of warehouse and distribution management professionals. Provides networking opportunities. **Audience:** Warehousing and Logistics Professionals. **Principal Exhibits:** Provides educational programs that cater to the needs of warehouse and distribution management professionals. Provides networking opportunities. **Telecommunication Services:** conference@werc.org.

CONSULTANTS

12993 ■ K.B. Ackerman Co. (KBA)

PO Box 163395
  Columbus, OH 43216
Ph: (614)946-9436
Fax: (614)488-9243
Co. E-mail: ken@warehousingforum.com
URL: http://www.warehousingforum.com
Contact: Kenneth B. Ackerman, President
E-mail: ken@warehousingforum.com

Description: Firm provides warehousing and logistics management services such as auditing warehouse performance, merger and acquisition, warehouse real estate, site selection and construction consulting, layout and space planning, and much more. **Scope:** Firm provides warehousing and logistics management services such as auditing warehouse performance, merger and acquisition, warehouse real estate, site selection and construction consulting, layout and space planning, and much more. **Founded:** 1981. **Publications:** "Warehousing Tips"; "Lean Warehousing"; "Fundamentals of Supply Chain Management"; "Auditing Warehouse Performance"; "Warehousing Tips"; "Warehousing Fundamentals"; "Words of Warehousing 2". **Training:** Family Business-Perpetuating Success; Best Practices In Warehouse Management; Quality and Leadership in the Warehouse; Improving Warehouse Performance; Warehousing as a Competitive Weapon; Lean Warehousing.

12994 ■ KEOGH Consulting Inc.

10217 Brecksville Rd.
  Brecksville, OH 44141
Ph: (440)526-2002
Fax: (440)526-9466
Co. E-mail: information@keogh1.com
URL: http://www.keogh1.com
Contact: Ravi Madala, President

Description: Provider of consulting services material handling and logistics operations such as supply chain strategy, operation planning, software solutions, and opportunity assessment. **Scope:** Provider of consulting services material handling and logistics operations such as supply chain strategy, operation planning, software solutions, and opportunity assessment. **Founded:** 1983. **Operations & Fulfillment - Work WITH me"; "Supply Chain Optimization101"; "Don't Waste Your Space!"; "Finding Hidden Productivity"; "Product Slotting The Secret to Increased Productivity"; "New Equipment Digest". **Training:** Keys to DC Automation Excellence, Oct, 2008; Keys to Operations and Integration Success, Sep, 2008.

12995 ■ Wesley-Kind Associates Inc.

6 E 43 St.
  New York, NY 10017
Contact: Daniel A. Kind, Officer

Description: Material handling and distribution consultants offering advice on plant and warehouse layouts and operating systems for the movement, storage and control of materials and products. **Scope:** Material handling and distribution consultants offering advice on plant and warehouse layouts and operating systems for the movement, storage and control of materials and products. **Publications:** "How to Reengineer the Storage Function," Penton Publishing, 1995.

RESEARCH CENTERS

12996 ■ Warehousing Education and Research Council (WERC)

8720 Red Oak Blvd., Ste. 201
  Charlotte, NC 28217
Ph: (630)990-0001
Co. E-mail: wercoffice@werc.org
URL: http://www.werc.org
Contact: Krys Slovacek, Director
E-mail: kslovacek@werc.org
Facebook: www.facebook.com/WERChq
Linkedin: www.linkedin.com/company/werc
X (Twitter): x.com/werc
Instagram: www.instagram.com/werc_hq

Description: Represents distribution and warehousing professionals who lead, direct, and manage the efficient flow of information, materials, and finished goods throughout the supply chain. Provides practical ways that can be apply to improve service and reduce costs. **Scope:** Warehousing industry and executive professionalism, including improving service within the industry. **Founded:** 1977. **Educational Activities:** WERC DX Annual Conference (Annual). **Geographic Preference:** Multinational.

ASSOCIATIONS AND OTHER ORGANIZATIONS

12997 ■ Automotive Oil Change Association (AOCA)
2443 Fair Oaks Blvd., Ste. 1177
Sacramento, CA 95825
Ph: (916)329-1888
Free: 800-230-0702
Co. E-mail: info@aoca.org
URL: http://www.aoca.org
Contact: Christina Bauders, Executive Director
Facebook: www.facebook.com/aocasocial

Description: Owners and operators of oil change shops. Works to solve problems and advance interests of members. Offers group insurance and credit card program. Compiles statistics; disseminates information, employee training programs. **Founded:** 1987. **Publications:** *Oil Changing Times*. **Educational Activities:** Fast Lube Expo (Annual). **Geographic Preference:** National.

REFERENCE WORKS

12998 ■ "Competing in the Growing Quick Lube Market" in Ratchet + Wrench (July 5, 2018)
URL(s): www.ratchetandwrench.com/articles/6568 -competing-in-the-growing-quick-lube-market
Ed: Alex Van Abbema. **Released:** July 05, 2018. **Description:** The quick lube industry is steadily growing with sales increasing from in 2017 from $5.8 billion to $6 billion. With quick lube shops doing well and expanding their operations, other types of car shops are taking note and offering oil change services in order to take back some of the market share. **Availability:** Online.

STATISTICAL SOURCES

12999 ■ Oil Change Services Industry in the US - Market Research Report
URL(s): www.ibisworld.com/united-states/market-research-reports/oil-change-services-industry/
Price: $925. **Description:** Downloadable report analyzing current and future trends in the oil change services industry. **Availability:** Download.

TRADE PERIODICALS

13000 ■ Oil and Automotive Service Marketing News
Pub: KAL Publications Inc.
Contact: Kathy Laderman, Editor
URL(s): www.kalpub.com/OANews/oa.html
Ed: Kathy Laderman. **Released:** 7/year **Price:** $25, for 1 year 7 issue; $40, for 2 year 14 issue. **Description:** News magazine (tabloid) targeting people engaged in the marketing, distribution, merchandising, installation, and servicing of gasoline, fuels, oil, tires, batteries, accessories, and automotive aftermar-

ket products for service stations, convenience stores and carwashes in the thirteen Pacific Western states. **Availability:** Print; PDF; Online.

FRANCHISES AND BUSINESS OPPORTUNITIES

13001 ■ All Tune and Lube (ATL)
8334 Veterans Hwy.
Millersville, MD 21108
Free: 800-935-8863
URL: http://www.alltuneandlube.com
Facebook: www.facebook.com/ATL-Total-Car-Care -Corporate-Office-239957309236
X (Twitter): x.com/alltuneandlube

Description: Provider of automotive maintenance and repair services. **Founded:** 1985. **Financial Assistance:** Yes **Training:** All Tune and Lube provides extensive training at headquarters and in the individual center locations. Provides 1 week of center management training and operational support.

13002 ■ Econo Lube N' Tune Inc.
440 S Church St., Ste. 700
Charlotte, NC 28202
Free: 855-325-5444
URL: http://www.econolube.com

Description: Provider of automotive repair and maintenance services. **Founded:** 1973. **Franchise Fee:** $39,500. **Financial Assistance:** Yes **Training:** Yes.

13003 ■ Express Oil Change & Tire Engineers (ETE)
3635 Lorna Rd.
Birmingham, AL 35216
Ph: (205)985-0770
URL: http://www.expressoil.com
Facebook: www.facebook.com/expressoil
X (Twitter): x.com/expressoil
Instagram: www.instagram.com/expressoil
YouTube: www.youtube.com/expressoilchange tireengineers

Description: Provider of automotive repairing services. **No. of Franchise Units:** 12. **No. of Company-Owned Units:** 2. **Founded:** 1979. **Franchised:** 1985. **Equity Capital Needed:** $1.4 million-$1.8 million. **Franchise Fee:** $35,000. **Royalty Fee:** 5%. **Training:** Provides 8 to 10 weeks of training for franchisee and/or key operator and 2 weeks training for franchisee's store crew.

13004 ■ Fresh Coat
4755 Lake Forest Dr.
Cincinnati, OH 45242
Ph: (859)208-1223
Free: 855-912-6928
URL: http://freshcoatpainters.com
Facebook: www.facebook.com/FreshCoatPainters
Instagram: www.instagram.com/freshcoatpainters
Pinterest: www.pinterest.com/freshcoat

Description: Homeowners spend millions of dollars everyday on painting kitchens, family rooms, every room in the house. Fresh coat has captured a niche in the multi-billion dollar industry. As a franchisee, you build your business through proven marketing, expertise and a system exclusive to Fresh Coat. This business is about building an organization and managing people; not doing the work yourself. **Founded:** 2004. **Franchised:** 2005. **Financial Assistance:** Yes **Training:** A complete turnkey operation. Training program provides tools needed to operate a successful and profitable business, including getting the business, payroll, computer training, market knowledge, recruitment, operations, scheduling and bidding.

13005 ■ Grease Monkey International Inc.
5575 DTC Pkwy., Ste. 100
Greenwood Village, CO 80111
Free: 800-822-7706
URL: http://www.greasemonkeyauto.com
Facebook: www.facebook.com/greasemonkeyintl
Linkedin: www.linkedin.com/company/grease-monkey -international-inc-
Instagram: www.instagram.com/greasemonkeyintl
YouTube: www.youtube.com/channel/ UCoAGqYWO0cyzJ9EfWcMFKqA

Description: Provides quick, convenient vehicle maintenance services. Offers quick oil change and lubrication services. **Founded:** 1978. **Training:** Training is provided at corporate headquarters and onsite. Franchisor also assists with site selection and construction.

13006 ■ Jiffy Lube Canada
1227 Appleby Line
Burlington, ON, Canada L7L 5H9
URL: http://www.jiffylube.ca

Description: Fast oil change and preventative maintenance services. **Founded:** 1979. **Training:** Initial and ongoing training provided.

13007 ■ Jiffy Lube International Inc.
PO Box 4427
Houston, TX 77210-4458
Free: 800-344-6933
URL: http://www.jiffylube.com
Contact: Edward Hymes, President
Facebook: www.facebook.com/jiffylube
X (Twitter): x.com/jiffylube
YouTube: www.youtube.com/user/JiffyLubeIntl

Description: Quick oil change and preventative maintenance. **Founded:** 1979. **Educational Activities:** NAFA Institute and Expo (NAFA I&E) (Annual).

13008 ■ Oil Butler International Corp.
1599 Rte. 22 W
Union, NJ 07083

Description: Provides oil change service. **Founded:** 1987. **Training:** Yes.

13009 ■ Precision Tune Auto Care Inc.
Icahn Enterprises L.P.
748 Miller Dr. SE
Leesburg, VA 20175

Ph: (305)422-4100
Free: 800-255-2737
URL: http://www.ielp.com

Description: Firm provides automotive repairs and maintenance services. **Founded:** 1975. **Training:** Yes.

13010 ■ Valvoline Instant Oil Change (VIOC)

Valvoline Inc.
100 Valvoline Way
Lexington, KY 40509

Ph: (859)357-7777
Free: 800-832-6825
Co. E-mail: feedback@valvoline.com
URL: http://www.valvoline.com
Contact: David Fint, Contact
Facebook: www.facebook.com/viocofficial

Description: Provider of oil changes and maintenance services. **Founded:** 1986. **Training:** Yes.

13011 ■ Victory Lane Quick Oil Change

45550 Helm St.
Plymouth, MI 48170

Ph: (734)667-4304
Fax: (734)667-4401
Co. E-mail: customerservice@victorylane.net
URL: http://www.victorylane.net
Contact: Justin Cialella, President
Facebook: www.facebook.com/victorylaneqoc

Description: Quick oil and lube service. **Founded:** 1980. **Financial Assistance:** Yes **Training:** Yes.

START-UP INFORMATION

13012 ■ *"Radio Producer Launches Food Truck, New Show"* in Dickinson Press (April 18, 2012)
Description: Jason Spiess left his radio job to open The Rolling Stove mobile food truck in Dickinson, North Dakota. He will broadcast a new radio show from the food truck called, 'Talkin' Bakken' while serving breakfast and barbecue. He's using a 1973 Indian Winnebago that he bought from Craigslist.com and converted it into a barbecue smoker. **Availability:** Online.

ASSOCIATIONS AND OTHER ORGANIZATIONS

13013 ■ Alliance of Canadian Cinema Television and Radio Artists (ACTRA)
625 Church St., Ste. 300
  Toronto, ON, Canada M4Y 2G1
Ph: (416)489-1311
Free: 800-387-3516
Co. E-mail: actraonline@actra.ca
URL: http://www.actra.ca
Contact: Eleanor Noble, President
Facebook: www.facebook.com/ACTRANational
X (Twitter): twitter.com/ACTRAnational
Instagram: www.instagram.com/actranational
YouTube: www.youtube.com/ACTRANational

Description: Seeks to obtain equitable compensation and safe working conditions for members. **Founded:** 1943. **Publications:** *InterACTRA News* (Quarterly); *ACTRASCOPE* (Quarterly). **Geographic Preference:** National.

13014 ■ Associated Press Broadcast Services (AP)
200 Liberty St.
  New York, NY 10281
Ph: (212)621-1500
Co. E-mail: info@ap.org
URL: http://www.ap.org/en
Contact: Daisy Veerasingham, President
Facebook: www.facebook.com/APNews
Linkedin: www.linkedin.com/company/associate
  d-press
X (Twitter): x.com/AP
YouTube: www.youtube.com/ap

Description: Broadcast stations in the United States that are members of the Associated Press. Advances journalism through radio and television. Cooperates with the AP in order to make available accurate and impartial news. Serves as a liaison between radio and television stations that are members of the AP and representatives of those stations. **Founded:** 1946. **Geographic Preference:** National; Middle Atlantic States.

13015 ■ Association Canadienne des Radiodiffuseurs (ACR) [Canadian Association of Broadcasters (CAB)]
770-45 O' Connor St.
  Ottawa, ON, Canada K1P 1A4

Ph: (613)233-4035
URL: http://cab-acr.ca
Contact: Kevin Desjardins, President
Linkedin: www.linkedin.com/company/canadian
  -association-of-broadcasters
X (Twitter): x.com/CAB_ACR

Description: Collective voice of the majority of Canada's private radio and television stations, networks, and specialty services. Develops industry-wide strategic plans, works to improve the financial health of the industry, and promotes private broadcasting's role as Canada's leading programmer and local service provider. **Founded:** 1926. **Geographic Preference:** National.

13016 ■ Broadcast Cable Credit Association (BCCA)
550 W Frontage Rd. Ste. 3600
  Northfield, IL 60093
Ph: (847)881-8757
Fax: (847)784-8059
Co. E-mail: info@bccacredit.com
URL: http://www.bccacredit.com/webroot/index.asp
Contact: Mary Collins, President
E-mail: mary.collins@mediafinance.org

Description: Enables members to efficiently manage credit risk and increase profitability. Provides industry specific credit reports on individual agencies, advertisers, or buying services (local or national). **Founded:** 1972. **Publications:** *BCCA Credit Handbook* (Annual); *Credit and Collection Survey*; *The Financial Manager* (Bimonthly); *Update* (Monthly). **Educational Activities:** Broadcast Cable Credit Association Annual Conference (Annual). **Geographic Preference:** National.

13017 ■ Canadian Disc Jockey Association (CDJA)
Abbey Market
  Oakville, ON, Canada L6M 3H5
Free: 844-235-2357
Co. E-mail: info@cdja.ca
URL: http://cdja.ca
Contact: Luka Miller, President
E-mail: president@cdja.ca
Facebook: www.facebook.com/cdja.ca
Instagram: www.instagram.com/canadian
  discjockeyassociation
YouTube: www.youtube.com/channel/UCCh
  -ZlzkvlEnvESz79x5_dg

Description: Represents the Canadian disc jockey industry. Promotes excellence in service through education, information, networking, and support. **Founded:** 1976. **Publications:** *CUED-UP Street*; *DJ Pulse* (Quarterly). **Awards:** CDJA National President's Award (Annual). **Geographic Preference:** National.

13018 ■ Country Radio Broadcasters Inc. (CRB)
1009 16th Ave. S
  Nashville, TN 37212
Ph: (615)327-4487
Co. E-mail: info@crb.org

URL: http://www.countryradioseminar.com
Contact: Kurt Johnson, President
Facebook: www.facebook.com/CountryRadioSeminar
X (Twitter): x.com/CRSOfficial
Instagram: www.instagram.com/crsofficial
YouTube: www.youtube.com/channel/UCgOrqcvFRg
  6gn-2x9k3tXBg

Description: Seeks to advance and promote the study of the science of broadcasting through the mutual exchange of ideas by conducting seminars and workshops, as well as providing scholarships to broadcasting students. **Founded:** 1969. **Publications:** *Country Radio Broadcasters--Program Book and Directory* (Annual). **Educational Activities:** Country Radio Seminar (CRS); Country Radio Broadcasters Seminar (CRS) (Annual). **Awards:** Country Radio Broadcasters Inc. Artist Humanitarian Award (Annual); Artist Career Achievement Award (Annual); Country Radio Hall of Fame (Annual); Country Radio Hall of Fame (Annual); Country Radio Broadcasters Inc. President's Award (Annual); Country Radio Broadcasters Inc. Radio Humanitarian Award (Annual); Tom Rivers Humanitarian Award (Occasionally). **Geographic Preference:** National.

13019 ■ International Radio and Television Society Foundation (IRTS)
1697 Broadway, Ste. 404
  New York, NY 10019
Ph: (212)867-6650
Co. E-mail: info@irts.org
URL: http://irtsfoundation.org
Contact: Joyce Tudryn, President
Facebook: www.facebook.com/TheIRTS
Linkedin: www.linkedin.com/company/the-irts-founda
  tion
Instagram: www.instagram.com/irts.foundation

Description: Individuals interested in management, sales, or executive production in the radio, television, and cable industries and their allied fields. Seeks to educate members through seminars. Conducts summer internships for college students majoring in communications. **Founded:** 1939. **Publications:** *International Radio and Television Society Foundation--Roster Yearbook* (Annual); *International Radio* (Annual). **Educational Activities:** International Radio and Television Society Foundation Luncheon. **Awards:** IRTS Gold Medal Award (Annual); International Radio and Television Society Foundation Summer Fellowships Program (Annual). **Geographic Preference:** National.

13020 ■ National Association of Black Owned Broadcasters (NABOB) [National Black Owned Broadcasters Association]
1001 Conn. Ave., NW, Ste. 504
  Washington, DC 20036
Ph: (202)463-8970
Co. E-mail: info@usbcnetwork.com
URL: http://nabob.org
Contact: Jim Winston, President
E-mail: jwinston@nabob.org

Description: Black broadcast station owners; black formatted stations not owned or controlled by blacks; organizations having an interest in the black consumer market or black broadcast industry; individuals interested in becoming owners; and communications schools, departments and professional groups and associations. Works with the Office of Federal Procurement Policy to determine which government contracting major advertisers and advertising agencies are complying with government initiatives to increase the amount of advertising dollars received by minority-owned firms. Conducts lobbying activities; provides legal representation for the protection of minority ownership policies. Sponsors annual Communications Awards Dinner each March. Publishes to improve and increase the opportunities for success for black and minority owners in the broadcast industry. **Founded:** 1976. **Publications:** *Black Owned Station Directory* (Quarterly); *NABOB News.* **Geographic Preference:** National.

13021 ■ National Association of Broadcasters (NAB)
1 M St. SE
  Washington, DC 20003
Ph: (202)429-5300
Co. E-mail: nab@nab.org
URL: http://www.nab.org
Contact: Gordon H. Smith, President
Facebook: www.facebook.com/Broadcasters
Linkedin: www.linkedin.com/company/national-association-of-broadcasters
X (Twitter): x.com/nabtweets
Instagram: www.instagram.com/wearebroadcasters
YouTube: www.youtube.com/user/nabroadcasters

Description: Serves as the voice for the nation's radio and television broadcasters. Advances the interests of members in federal government, industry and public affairs; improves the quality and profitability of broadcasting; encourages content and technology innovation; and spotlights the important and unique ways stations serve their communities. Delivers value to its members through advocacy, education and innovation. Relies on the grassroots strength of its television and radio members and state broadcast associations. Helps broadcasters seize opportunities in the digital age. Offers broadcasters a variety of programs to help them grow in their careers, promote diversity in the workplace and strengthen their businesses. **Founded:** 1922. **Educational Activities:** NAB Show. **Awards:** NAB Crystal Radio Awards (Annual); NAB Distinguished Service Award (Annual); NAB Engineering Achievement in Radio Award (Annual); NAB Engineering Achievement in Television Award (Annual); NAB National Radio Award (Annual); NAB Celebration of Service to America Awards (Annual); Marconi Radio Awards (Annual); NAB Spirit of Broadcasting Award (Periodic); NAB International Broadcasting Excellence Award (Annual); Wally Jorgenson Award. **Geographic Preference:** National.

13022 ■ National Federation of Community Broadcasters (NFCB)
PO Box 806
  Paonia, CO 81428
Ph: (970)279-3411
URL: http://nfcb.org
Contact: Nathan Moore, President
Facebook: www.facebook.com/CommunityRadio
Linkedin: www.linkedin.com/company/nfcb
X (Twitter): x.com/NFCB
Instagram: www.instagram.com/nfcborg

Description: Independent, community-licensed radio and radio production organizations. Fosters the development of public policy at the legislative, regulatory and administrative levels. **Founded:** 1975. **Publications:** *Community Radio News* (Monthly); *The NFCB Public Radio Legal Handbook: A Guide to FCC Rules and Regulations*; *NFCB's Guide to Underwriting for Public Radio.* **Educational Activities:** Community Radio Conference (Annual). **Awards:** NFCB Bader Award (Annual); NFCB Volunteer of the Year (Annual). **Geographic Preference:** National.

13023 ■ North American Broadcasters Association (NABA)
NABA c/o Canadian Broadcasting Centre (CBC)
  205 Wellington St. W, Ste. 9C200
  Toronto, ON, Canada M5V 3G7
Ph: (416)205-3363
Fax: (416)205-2901
Co. E-mail: contact@nabanet.com
URL: http://nabanet.com
Contact: Richard Friedel, President
Facebook: www.facebook.com/North-American-Broadcasters-Association-NABA-2705058279524102
Linkedin: www.linkedin.com/company/north-american-broadcasters-association
X (Twitter): x.com/NABA_ORG

Description: Network broadcasters in North America concerned with international matters that affect broadcasting. Seeks to identify, study and provide solutions to international questions concerning broadcasting. Creates opportunities for North American broadcasters to share information, identify common interests and reach on issues of an international nature. Works with other international broadcasters' associations and unions toward gaining an effective voice in international circles on matters that affect broadcasting. Organizes international conferences in conjunction with other broadcasting associations. **Founded:** 1972. **Educational Activities:** North American Broadcasters Association Meeting (Annual). **Awards:** NABA International Achievement Award (Annual). **Geographic Preference:** Multinational.

13024 ■ Radio Advertising Bureau (RAB) - Reference Collection
400 E Las Colinas Blvd., Ste. 350
  Irving, TX 75039
Free: 800-232-3131
Co. E-mail: memberresponse@rab.com
URL: http://www.rab.com
Contact: Erica Farber, President
E-mail: efarber@rab.com
Facebook: www.facebook.com/RadioAdvBureau
Linkedin: www.linkedin.com/company/radio-advertising-bureau
X (Twitter): twitter.com/RadioAdvBureau
Instagram: www.instagram.com/radioadvertisingbureau

Description: Includes radio stations, radio networks, station sales representatives, and allied industry services, such as producers, research firms, schools, and consultants. Calls on advertisers and agencies to promote the sale of radio time as an advertising medium. Sponsors program to increase professionalism of radio salespeople, awarding Certified Radio Marketing Consultant designation to those who pass examination. **Scope:** Radio broadcasting. **Founded:** 1951. **Holdings:** Figures not available. **Publications:** *RAB.com*; *RAB Co-op Directory* (Weekly). **Educational Activities:** Managing Sales Conference. **Awards:** Best of Show (Annual); Radio Marketer of the Year (Annual). **Geographic Preference:** National.

13025 ■ Radio Television Digital News Association - Canada (RTDNA)
Toronto, ON, Canada V6E 2V2
Co. E-mail: admin@rtdnacanada.com
URL: http://rtdnacanada.com
Contact: Lis Travers, President
Linkedin: www.linkedin.com/company/rtdna-canada
YouTube: www.youtube.com/channel/UCjfaGm3YaUnOlsnKHFFXxZw

Description: Radio and television news executives and personnel. Promotes the professional development of broadcast journalists in Canada. Sponsors national scholarship program. **Founded:** 1962. **Awards:** RTDNA National Awards (Annual); RTDNA Lifetime Achievement Award (Annual); RTDNA President's Award (Annual). **Geographic Preference:** National.

REFERENCE WORKS

13026 ■ *"Abacast, Citadel Strike Radio Ad Deal" in Business Journal Portland (Vol. 27, December 31, 2010, No. 44, pp. 3)*
Pub: Portland Business Journal
Contact: Andy Giegerich, Managing Editor

E-mail: agiegerich@bizjournals.com

Ed: Erik Siemers. **Description:** Software firm Abacast Inc. has partnered with Citadel Media to aid the latter's advertising sales. Citadel provides radio networks and syndicated programs to 4,200 affiliate stations. **Availability:** Print; Online.

13027 ■ *"America's Rural Radio Stations Are Vanishing - and Taking the Country's Soul with Them" in The Guardian (June 6, 2019)*
URL(s): www.theguardian.com/tv-and-radio/2019/jun/06/radio-silence-how-the-disappearance-of-rural-stations-takes-americas-soul-with-them

Ed: Debbie Weingarten. **Released:** June 06, 2019. **Description:** As radio stations across the country are struggling to gain advertisers, they are being sold to media conglomerates who are relocating them to urban areas leaving rural areas without their local stations. The 1996 Telecommunications Act was the beginning of the end when it allowed deregulation which led to larger stations buying smaller ones and creating ten parent companies who controlled all of the revenue. **Availability:** Online.

13028 ■ *"Branded Entertainment: Dealmaking Strategies & Techniques for Industry Professionals"*
Pub: J. Ross Publishing Inc.
Contact: Stephen Buda, President

Released: October 01, 2014. **Price:** $39.95, hardcover, plus shipping charge extra. FL sale tax $3.36. **Description:** Branded entertainment, also known as branded content or advertainment, is an entertainment-based method that is funded by and complementary to a brand's marketing strategy. These projects are usually a partnership between brands, television or radio producers, and broadcasters. **Availability:** E-book; Print; Download.

13029 ■ *"CBS Radio Group Seeks New Space for Growing Event, Online Business" in Dallas Business Journal (Vol. 35, June 15, 2012, No. 40, pp. 1)*
Pub: Baltimore Business Journal
Contact: Rhonda Pringle, President
E-mail: rpringle@bizjournals.com

Ed: Candace Carlisle. **Description:** CBS Radio Dallas/Fortworth is planningto move to a larger facility to accommodate new business segments. The company has begun developing content for online and events.

13030 ■ *"Cincinnati Reds Hit Ratings Homer" in Business Courier (Vol. 27, July 30, 2010, No. 13, pp. 1)*
Pub: Business Courier

Ed: Steve Watkins, John Ourand. **Description:** Cincinnati Reds fans have tuned in to their TVs and radios as their team made a hottest start to a season. The Reds TV ratings have increased 49 percent during the first six months of 2010 and continued to rise while the Reds' games broadcast on WLW-AM reported the highest average audience share per game of any Major League Baseball team. **Availability:** Print; Online.

13031 ■ *"Executive Decision: XM Mulls Betting the Bank in Competitive Game of Subscriber Growth" in Globe & Mail (March 18, 2006, pp. B3)*
Ed: Grant Robertson. **Description:** Canadian Satellite Radio Inc., XM Canada, president and Chief Operating Officer Stephen Tapp feel that establishing a profile in satellite radio to attract subscribers is a very big challenge. His views on the Canadian radio market are detailed. **Availability:** Print; Online.

13032 ■ *"A Family's Fortune" in Canadian Business (Vol. 80, Winter 2007, No. 24, pp. 103)*
Price: $23. **Description:** James Richardson started as a tailor before moving into the grain business because his clients paid him in sacks of wheat and barley. The James Richardson and Sons Ltd. entered the radio business in 1927 but later sold it off in 1951. **Availability:** Print; Online.

13033 ▪ *"Far Out: Satellite Radio Finds New Way to Tally Listeners"* in *Globe & Mail* (March 14, 2007, pp. B14)

Description: The marketing strategy adopted by satellite radio broadcasting firm XM Satellite Radio Inc. in Canada for increasing its subscriber based is discussed. **Availability:** Online.

13034 ▪ *Investing in Radio Market Report*

Pub: BIA/Kelsey

Contact: Tom Buono, Chief Executive Officer

URL(s): www.bia.com/publications

Released: Quarterly; April, June, August and December. **Price:** $2,130, Individuals for pdf. **Description:** Covers U.S. Radio industry markets and inclusive stations. Includes market data, including revenues, demographics, and economic indicators. **Entries include:** For stations--Call letters, technical attributes, format, estimated revenues, owner, last acquisition date and price, ratings for eight books. **Arrangement:** Numerical by market rank size. **Indexes:** Market name, station call letters, city of license. **Availability:** PDF; Online.

13035 ▪ *"It Could Be Worse"* in *Barron's* (Vol. 89, July 27, 2009, No. 30, pp. 5)

Pub: Dow Jones & Company Inc.

Contact: Almar Latour, Chief Executive Officer

Ed: Alan Abelson. **Description:** Media sources are being fooled by corporate America who is peddling an economic recovery rather than reality as shown by the report of a rise in existing home sales which boosted the stock market even if it was a seasonal phenomenon. The phrase "things could be worse" sums up the reigning investment philosophy in the U.S. and this has been stirring up the market. **Availability:** Online.

13036 ▪ *"Liberty Media Pushes to Close on Sirius XM While Cable Deals Wait"* in *Denver Business Journal* (Vol. 65, February 28, 2014, No. 42)

Pub: American City Business Journals, Inc.

Contact: Mike Olivieri, Executive Vice President

Released: Weekly. **Description:** Liberty Media Corporation CEO, Greg Maffei, notes that various cable TV mergers are on hold while everyone awaits the decision if Comcast and Time Warner will be allowed to go through with their $45.2 billion merger. Liberty Media had supported Charter Communications plans to buy Time Warner for cash and stock. That deal was pushed aside when Comcast came along with a larger, all-stock offer. **Availability:** Print; Online.

13037 ▪ *"Marketing: You Are On the Air: Radio and TV Producers Are Looking For Shows Starring Smart CEOs"* in *Inc.* (December 2007, pp. 67-69)

Ed: Sarah Goldstein. **Description:** Many successful entrepreneurs are being hired to host television and radio shows in order to share business expertise. **Availability:** Print; Online.

13038 ▪ *Media, Organizations and Identity*

Pub: Palgrave Macmillan

Released: First edition. **Description:** The mass media, press, and television are essential in the formation of corporate identity and the promotion of business image and reputation. This book offers a new perspective into the interrelationships between media and organizations over three dimensions: media as business, media in business and business in the media.

13039 ▪ *"Out of This World"* in *Black Enterprise* (November 2007)

Pub: Earl G. Graves Ltd.

Contact: Earl Graves, Jr., President

Ed: Anthony Calypso. **Description:** Profile of Noah Samara, CEO of WorldSpace Inc. who raised $1 billion to help create the technological architecture for satellite radio. **Availability:** Online.

13040 ▪ *"Radio"* in *MarketingMagazine* (Vol. 115, September 27, 2010, No. 13, pp. 24)

Pub: Rogers Media Inc.

Contact: Neil Spivak, Chief Executive Officer

Description: Market data in the radio broadcasting industry in Canada is outlined. **Availability:** Print; Online.

13041 ▪ *"Radio Feels Heat from iPod Generation"* in *Globe & Mail* (March 16, 2006, pp. B1)

Ed: Simon Tuck, Grant Robertson. **Description:** Conventional radio stations are losing the younger generation listeners to new technology such as MP3 players, satellite radio and music-playing cell phones. The report of Canadian Association of Broadcasters (CAB) is detailed. **Availability:** Online.

13042 ▪ *"Regent's Signal, Once Powerful, Fading From Local Scene"* in *Business Courier* (Vol. 27, June 4, 2010, No. 5, pp. 1)

Pub: Business Courier

Ed: Dan Monk. **Description:** Los Angeles, California-based Oaktree Capital Management bought former Regent Communications Inc. from Chapter 11 bankruptcy and transformed it into Townsquare Media Inc., a privately held firm. Regent's corporate presence has faded fast in Cincinnati, Ohio as its operations wind down. Insights on Regent's failed business model are also given. **Availability:** PDF; Online.

13043 ▪ *"Research Reports"* in *Barron's* (Vol. 90, August 23, 2010, No. 34, pp. M13)

Pub: Barron's Editorial & Corporate Headquarters

Description: Shares of Sirius XM Radio, Target and Deere and Company received an eBuyE rating, while shares of Research in Motion got an eNeutralE rating. **Availability:** Online.

13044 ▪ *"Steering a Steady Course Through Turbulent Waters"* in *Providence Business News* (Vol. 29, June 2, 2014, No. 9, pp. 22)

Pub: American City Business Journals, Inc.

Contact: Mike Olivieri, Executive Vice President

URL(s): pbn.com/steering-a-steady-course-through -turbulent-waters97424

Description: Barbara Haynes, Cumulus Broadcasting Market Manager, continues to remain clear sighted amid changing ownership, competition and technology propelling radio through dramatic transformation. Some of the elements that have driven her to success include resilience and dedication to community service.

STATISTICAL SOURCES

13045 ▪ *Radio Broadcasting Industry in the US - Market Research Report*

URL(s): www.ibisworld.com/united-states/market-re search-reports/radio-broadcasting-industry

Price: $925. **Description:** Downloadable report analyzing the current and future trends in the radio broadcasting industry. **Availability:** Download.

TRADE PERIODICALS

13046 ▪ *Community Radio News*

Pub: National Federation of Community Broadcasters

Contact: Nathan Moore, President

URL(s): nfcb.org/newsletter

Released: Monthly **Description:** Serves as a medium of communication for independent, community-licensed radio stations. Contains brief articles and news items on such topics as public broadcasting and programming, legislative developments, activities of the Federal Communications Commission, and local stations. Recurring features include notices of grants and awards, job openings, and a calendar of events/conferences for noncommercial broadcasters. **Availability:** Print.

13047 ▪ *Radio World*

Pub: Future P.L.C.

Contact: Zilah Byng-Thorne, Chief Executive Officer

URL(s): www.radioworld.com

Facebook: www.facebook.com/RadioWorldMagazine

X (Twitter): x.com/Radioworld_News

Released: Biweekly **Description:** Technical newspaper (tabloid) covering radio broadcast industry. **Availability:** Print; Online.

13048 ▪ *TelevisionWeek*

Pub: Crain Communications Inc.

Contact: Barry Asin, President

URL(s): www.tvweek.com

Released: Daily **Description:** Newspaper covering management, programming, cable and trends in the television and the media industry. **Availability:** Print.

TRADE SHOWS AND CONVENTIONS

13049 ▪ **Country Radio Seminar (CRS)**

Alan Jackson

  Nashville, TN

URL: http://www.alanjackson.com/last-call-tour

URL(s): countryradioseminar.com

Description: Country radio broadcasting exhibition. **Audience:** Radio broadcasters. **Principal Exhibits:** Country radio broadcasting exhibition.

13050 ▪ **RTNDA International Conference & Exhibition/Radio-Television News Directors Association**

Radio Television Digital News Association (RTDNA)

  The National Press Bldg., 529 14th St. NW, Ste. 1240

  Washington, DC 20045

Ph: (202)221-4282

Co. E-mail: membership@rtdna.org

URL: http://www.rtdna.org

Contact: Dan Shelley, Executive Director

E-mail: dans@rtdna.org

URL(s): www.rtdna.org/events/rtdna25-new-orleans

Frequency: Annual. **Description:** Offer exemplary teaching programs. **Audience:** Actors, directors, producers, reporters, correspondents, and radio and television announcers and newscasters. **Principal Exhibits:** Offer exemplary teaching programs. Dates and Locations: 2025 Jun 11-13 Hotel Monteleone, New Orleans, LA. **Telecommunication Services:** events@rtdna.org.

CONSULTANTS

13051 ▪ **Baker Scott & Co.**

34 North Lenhome Dr., Ste. 107

  Cranford, NJ 07016

Ph: (973)263-3355

Co. E-mail: exec.search@bakerscott.com

URL: http://www.bakerscott.com

Description: Firm provides consulting services for executive search process such as telecommunications industry, residential and commercial, assisting executives, and much more. **Scope:** Firm provides consulting services for executive search process such as telecommunications industry, residential and commercial, assisting executives, and much more. **Founded:** 1979. **Training:** Offers seminar programs on interview techniques, management skills, and customer service.

13052 ▪ **The Benchmark Co.**

200-C Parker Dr., Ste. 100

  Austin, TX 78728

Ph: (512)310-4000

Free: 833-246-2400

URL: http://www.bench.com

Contact: Mark Ogburn, General Manager

Description: Firm provides advertising, health care, financial, e-commerce, broadcasting and other related services. **Scope:** Firm provides advertising, health care, financial, e-commerce, broadcasting and other related services. **Publications:** "Radio in the 90S; Audience, Promotion and Marketing Strategies". **Training:** The Rules of the Ratings Game Seminar.

13053 ▪ **D.E.M. Allen & Associates Ltd. (DEMA)**

Winnipeg, MB, Canada

Ph: (204)889-9202
Co. E-mail: info@dema.ca
URL: http://www.dema.ca
Description: Firm provides planning, design, supervision and adjustment of broadcast transmitting facilities. **Scope:** Telecommunications consultants, experienced in AM, FM and television broadcasting, CATV systems, LF/HF, VHF/UHF and microwave systems and satellite earth stations, RF measurements and evaluations related to SCADA, LMCS in the millimeters portion of the spectrum as well as the 2.5Ghz MDS/MMDS field, electromagnetic compatibility and electromagnetic immunity including non-ionizing radiation evaluation and measurement. Services include planning, design, supervision and adjustment of broadcast transmitting facilities, including specifications, tender evaluation, preparation of reports, technical briefs for Federal Regulatory bodies, evaluation and measurements associated with RF propagation and electromagnetic energy throughout the radio frequency spectrum. **Founded:** 1965.

13054 ■ DeMers Programming Media Consultants
617 Newcomen Rd.
Exton, PA 19341
Ph: (610)363-2626
URL: http://www.demersprogramming.com
Contact: Peter Smith, Consultant
E-mail: peter@demersprogramming.com
Description: Firm is engaged in advisory services to radio broadcasters and provides market visits, competitive analysis, product maintenance, informatics, stationality, creative benchmarks, promotional tactics, marketing strategies, personality management, managerial development, research strategies and much more. **Founded:** 1986. **Publications:** "12 Steps To A One Share - Uncovering The Clutter," Feb, 2005; "Get Your Mind Out Of The Clutter - DeMers Dispatch Winter '05"; "See Spot Run...Over The Golden Goose"; "Radio's Attention Deficit Disorder"; "Program The Seller"; "At Issue: Staying Creative"; "Take A Hard Look At Your Special Programming"; "A Fresh Coat Of Paint"; "Guerrilla Radio". **Training:** Diary Keepers Plus Research; Marketing, Merchandising and Money.

13055 ■ Engineering Harmonics Inc.
326 Carlaw Ave. Unit 105
Toronto, ON, Canada M4M 3N8
Ph: (416)465-3378
Fax: (416)465-9037
Co. E-mail: info@engineeringharmonics.com
URL: http://engineeringharmonics.com
Contact: Gary Tibshirani, Director
Linkedin: www.linkedin.com/company/engineering-harmonics-inc.
Description: Consulting firm engages in the conception and design of audiovisual, performance sound and digital signage solutions. **Scope:** Consulting firm engages in the conception and design of audiovisual, performance sound and digital signage solutions. **Founded:** 1988. **Publications:** "Designing Sound for Frank Gehry's Vision"; "Precis of WDCH PSVC System"; "PSVC Design Challenges at WDCH"; "Power and Ground Update"; "Noise Reduction Systems"; "Mandating the House Audio System," Overture Hall; "Betting on Legends," Nov, 2008; "Examining our Roots, Defining our Future," Dec, 2008; "Walking The Hall: A Guide to Tuning a Loudspeaker System," Nov, 2007; "National Ballet School," Nov, 2007; "The Puzzle of PA for a Hall-in-the-Round," Aug, 2007; "A House for All Seasons," Aug, 2006; "Hooray for LA," Jan, 2004; "A Kodak Moment," Apr, 2002.

13056 ■ Financial Solutions Inc.
309 W Jefferson St.
La Grange, KY 40031
Ph: (502)225-9900
URL: http://www.oldhamfinancial.com
Contact: Robin Lawson, President
E-mail: robin@oldhamfinancialsolutions.com
Facebook: www.facebook.com/financial.solutions.inc
Linkedin: www.linkedin.com/company/oldhamfinancialsolutions

Description: Firm is engaged in developing, implementing, and monitoring financial strategy and provides services such as financial and insurance planning, and investment management. **Scope:** Firm is engaged in developing, implementing, and monitoring financial strategy and provides services such as financial and insurance planning, and investment management. **Publications:** "Eighty percent of Americans agree they would benefit from having basic financial education and information," 2009; "Finra Investor Education Survey, 2007"; "How Are Mutual Funds Taxed". **Training:** Long Term Care, Estate Planning, Retirement, Financial Management.

13057 ■ Radiotechniques Engineering, LLC
402 10th Ave.
Haddon Heights, NJ 08035-0367
Ph: (856)546-8008
Fax: (856)546-1841
Co. E-mail: sales@radiotechniques.com
URL: http://www.radiotechniques.com
Contact: Barbara Albano, Officer
Description: Firm offers variety of radio broadcasting related services such as station design, field engineering and construction supervision. **Founded:** 1979. **Special Services:** Point Manager™; Palm Pilot™; Treo™.

13058 ■ Sellmeyer Engineering
Two Pecan Grove Cir.
Lucas, TX 75002
Ph: (972)542-2056
Fax: (972)636-5940
URL: http://www.sellmeyereng.com
Contact: J. S. Sellmeyer, Contact
Description: Firm provides consulting services such as FCC applications, transmitter plant designs, construction supervision, broadcast studio facilities planning and construction, AM directional antenna design, adjustment and measurements. **Founded:** 1980.

13059 ■ Strategic Computer Solutions Inc.
2625 Shefman Ter., No. 200
Ann Arbor, MI 48105-3441
Ph: (248)888-0666
Fax: (248)888-0665
Co. E-mail: info@stratcom.com
URL: http://www.stratcom.com
Description: Firm offers business consulting, system analysis, web development and consulting. **Scope:** Firm offers business consulting, system analysis, web development and consulting. **Founded:** 1987. **Special Services:** gloEMR™.

LIBRARIES

13060 ■ Canadian Broadcasting Corporation - Reference Library/Image Research Library
PO Box 500, Sta. A
Toronto, ON, Canada M5W 1E6
URL: http://www.cbc.ca/mediacentre/program/the-heart
Description: The Library has thousands of subject and biography files and books selected for their visual content. It also features an historic serials collection, including the Eaton's catalogue back to 1910. **Scope:** Radio and television broadcasting. **Services:** Interlibrary loan; copying; library open to the public for research on CBC or broadcasting in Canada. **Founded:** 1946. **Holdings:** Books; documentaries; digital archives.

13061 ■ CBS News Reference Library
51 W 52nd St.
New York, NY 10019
URL: http://www.cbsnews.com
Facebook: www.facebook.com/CBSNews
X (Twitter): x.com/cbsnews
Instagram: www.instagram.com/cbsnews
YouTube: www.youtube.com/user/CBSNewsOnline
Scope: Reference material. **Founded:** 1940. **Holdings:** 38,000 books; 2,500 bound periodical volumes; 15,000 clippings files; 7,700 reels of microfilm; 50,000 microfiche. **Subscriptions:** 270 journals and other serials; 10 newspapers.

13062 ■ Library of Congress - Moving Image Resource Center
James Madison Memorial Bldg., LM 336
101 Independence Ave. SE
Washington, DC 20540-4810
Ph: (202)707-8572
Co. E-mail: mpref@loc.gov
URL: http://www.loc.gov/research-centers/moving-image/about-this-research-center
Contact: Carla Hayden, Librarian
Scope: Animated films related. **Services:** Collections open to the public with restrictions. **Holdings:** 3,000 books, bound volumes of early periodicals, and vertical files; 300,000 film items; 350,000 television items; 3 million sound recordings preserved on cylinders, discs, tapes, wires, Dictaphone belts, music box discs, and piano rolls.

13063 ■ National Association of Broadcasters (NAB)
1 M St. SE
Washington, DC 20003
Ph: (202)429-5300
Co. E-mail: nab@nab.org
URL: http://www.nab.org
Contact: Gordon H. Smith, President
Facebook: www.facebook.com/Broadcasters
Linkedin: www.linkedin.com/company/national-association-of-broadcasters
X (Twitter): x.com/nabtweets
Instagram: www.instagram.com/wearebroadcasters
YouTube: www.youtube.com/user/nabroadcasters
Description: Serves as the voice for the nation's radio and television broadcasters. Advances the interests of members in federal government, industry and public affairs; improves the quality and profitability of broadcasting; encourages content and technology innovation; and spotlights the important and unique ways stations serve their communities. Delivers value to its members through advocacy, education and innovation. Relies on the grassroots strength of its television and radio members and state broadcast associations. Helps broadcasters seize opportunities in the digital age. Offers broadcasters a variety of programs to help them grow in their careers, promote diversity in the workplace and strengthen their businesses. **Founded:** 1922. **Educational Activities:** NAB Show. **Awards:** NAB Crystal Radio Awards (Annual); NAB Distinguished Service Award (Annual); NAB Engineering Achievement in Radio Award (Annual); NAB Engineering Achievement in Television Award (Annual); NAB National Radio Award (Annual); NAB Celebration of Service to America Awards (Annual); Marconi Radio Awards (Annual); NAB Spirit of Broadcasting Award (Periodic); NAB International Broadcasting Excellence Award (Annual); Wally Jorgenson Award. **Geographic Preference:** National.

13064 ■ The Paley Center for Media - Research Services
25 W 52 St.
New York, NY 10019
URL: http://www.paleycenter.org/about/about-faq
Description: Assists individuals doing extensive media research and offers facilities and staff to help researchers utilize the microfiched clippings file and extensive collections of television and radio programs to the fullest potential. **Scope:** Television and radio history. **Founded:** 1975. **Holdings:** Figures not available.

13065 ■ Radio Advertising Bureau (RAB) - Reference Collection
400 E Las Colinas Blvd., Ste. 350
Irving, TX 75039
Free: 800-232-3131
Co. E-mail: memberresponse@rab.com
URL: http://www.rab.com
Contact: Erica Farber, President
E-mail: efarber@rab.com
Facebook: www.facebook.com/RadioAdvBureau
Linkedin: www.linkedin.com/company/radio-advertising-bureau
X (Twitter): twitter.com/RadioAdvBureau

Instagram: www.instagram.com/radioadver
tisingbureau

Description: Includes radio stations, radio networks, station sales representatives, and allied industry services, such as producers, research firms, schools, and consultants. Calls on advertisers and agencies to promote the sale of radio time as an advertising medium. Sponsors program to increase professionalism of radio salespeople, awarding Certified Radio Marketing Consultant designation to those who pass examination. **Scope:** Radio broadcasting. **Founded:** 1951. **Holdings:** Figures not available. **Publications:** *RAB.com*; *RAB Co-op Directory* (Weekly). **Educational Activities:** Managing Sales Conference. **Awards:** Best of Show (Annual); Radio Marketer of the Year (Annual). **Geographic Preference:** National.

**13066 ■ Temple University Libraries -
Blitman Resource Center**
1301 W Norris St.
  Philadelphia, PA 19122
URL: http://tfma.temple.edu/facilities-technology

Scope: Communications. **Services:** Center open to the public. **Founded:** 1884. **Holdings:** Figures not available.

**13067 ■ University of Maryland Libraries -
Hornbake Library**
4130 Campus Dr.
  College Park, MD 20740
Ph: (301)405-9212
Co. E-mail: askhornbake@umd.edu
URL: http://www.lib.umd.edu/visit/libraries/hornbake

URL(s): www.lib.umd.edu/special/collections/marylan
  d/home; www.lib.umd.edu/prange; www
  .prangecollection.wordpress.com; www.lib.guides
  .umd.edu/DjunaBarnes
Facebook: www.facebook.com/HornbakeLibrary
X (Twitter): x.com/hornbakelibrary

Scope: History. **Services:** Collection open to the public by appointment. **Founded:** 2007. **Holdings:** 35,000 lin.ft.; manuscripts; microfilm; archives.; 1.5 million photographs; 60,000 books; 2,500 maps.; 8700 books; 250 periodical titles; 320 VF drawers and boxes of archives, clippings, research studies, scripts, scrapbooks, documents, and correspondence; 1000 oral histories, including interviews with prominent broadcasters; 5445 audiotapes; 25,000 photographs; 1500 subject files; 6000 pamphlets. **Subscriptions:** ; 300 journals and other serials.

ASSOCIATIONS AND OTHER ORGANIZATIONS

13068 ■ American Association of Radon Scientists and Technologists (AARST)
527 N Justice St.
Hendersonville, NC 28739
Ph: (828)348-0185
Co. E-mail: info@aarst.org
URL: http://aarst.org
Contact: Kyle Hoylman, President
E-mail: kyle@protectenv.com
Facebook: www.facebook.com/Ra
donProfessionalsSavingLives
X (Twitter): x.com/StopRadon
YouTube: www.youtube.com/channel/UC4zz1o8Lvb
6zUixZdZJR7mg
Description: Scientists and tradespeople engaged in radon gas testing and remediation and advocacy on behalf of radon lung cancer victims. **Founded:** 1986. **Publications:** *Annual Proceedings International Radon Symposium* (Annual); *Radon Reporter* (3/year). **Educational Activities:** International Radon Symposium (Annual). **Geographic Preference:** National.

REFERENCE WORKS

13069 ■ *"Does Your Home or Building Need Radon Testing?" in U.S. News & World Report (February 24, 2016)*
URL(s): health.usnews.com/health-news/patient-a
dvice/articles/2016-02-24/does-your-home-or-buil
ding-need-radon-testing
Ed: Lisa Esposito. **Released:** February 24, 2016.
Description: Details the dangers of radon in our homes and who is susceptible to falling sick from exposure. Short-term testing is available, but long-term testing is recommended because radon levels can fluctuate which will give a better sample. DIY testing kits are also available for a low price. **Availability:** Online.

13070 ■ *"New Push for Mainers to Test for Radon in Homes" in News Center Maine (January 28, 2019)*
URL(s): www.newscentermaine.com/article/news/
new-push-for-mainers-to-test-for-radon-in-homes/
97-d24c0b79-a28f-4ed8-8dc7-42fed9462654
Ed: Lindsey Mills. **Released:** January 28, 2019.
Description: Maine CDC director Dr. Bruce Bates is urging everyone in Maine to have their homes tested for radon after 12 of their 16 counties were found to have have high radon amounts. If radon is detected, there are various measures residents can take, with the simplest being opening the windows to ventilate the house. **Availability:** Online.

FRANCHISES AND BUSINESS OPPORTUNITIES

13071 ■ Professional House Doctors Inc.
3020 48th St.
Des Moines, IA 50310
Ph: (515)278-1884
Co. E-mail: radoninfo@aol.com
URL: http://www.prohousedr.com
Contact: Charles J. Stephenson, Contact
Facebook: www.facebook.com/ProHouseDr
Description: Provider of environmental and building science services to residential and commercial clients. Services include radon testing and mitigation, building inspections, indoor air quality analysis, asbestos and lead analysis and much more. **Founded:** 1982. **Franchised:** 1991. **Training:** Offers 2 weeks at headquarters and ongoing support.

LIBRARIES

13072 ■ Institut de Radioprotection du Canada (RSI) - Library [Radiation Safety Institute of Canada]
100 Sheppard Ave. E Ste. 760
Toronto, ON, Canada M2N 6N5
Ph: (416)650-9090
Free: 800-263-5803
Fax: (416)650-9920
Co. E-mail: info@radiationsafety.ca
URL: http://radiationsafety.ca
Contact: Natalia Mozayani, President
E-mail: nmozayani@radiationsafety.ca
Facebook: www.facebook.com/RadiationSafetyInsti
tute
Linkedin: www.linkedin.com/company/radiation-safety
-institute-of-canada
X (Twitter): x.com/rsicanada
YouTube: www.youtube.com/channel/uc5v13of
dn0sscqfv5iwo-wa
Description: Promotes radiation safety in homes, schools and the environment. Conducts radiation research and studies and serves as a clearinghouse on radiation and radiation safety. Makes available radiation monitoring services and personal alpha dosimeter services for miners. Sponsors public educational and training programs and maintains mediation and consulting services. **Scope:** Radiation, radiation safety, radon, radiation and health, radioactive waste, nuclear power, training, and mediation. **Services:** Copying; library open to the public. **Founded:** 1980. **Holdings:** Figures not available. **Geographic Preference:** National.

START-UP INFORMATION

13073 ■ *"First-Time Landlord: Your Guide to Renting Out a Single-Family Home"*
Pub: Nolo
Contact: Chris Braun, President
Released: 6th Edition. **Price:** $17.49, e-book (downloadable); $19.99, book and e-book. **Description:** The basics for becoming an landlord for anyone wishing to start an entrepreneurial pursuit in home rentals are outlined. Concise information for renting out a single-family home includes, how to determine whether the property will turn a profit, landlord business basics, finding the right tenants, preparing and signing a lead, handling repairs, complying with state rental laws, dealing with problem tenants, and preparing for the sale of the property. **Availability:** E-book.

13074 ■ *"'Passion Is the Key to Accomplishment" in South Florida Business Journal (Vol. 35, August 15, 2014, No. 3, pp. 11)*
Pub: American City Business Journals, Inc.
Contact: Mike Olivieri, Executive Vice President
Released: Weekly. **Price:** $8, introductory 4-week offer(Digital only). **Description:** Metro 1 president and CEO, Tony Cho, made his name by shaping neighborho9ods and large-scale urban projects in Miami, Florida. Cho says he got his first job when he was 11 years old working with a maintenance crew. Cho started his real estate firm during the economic downturn and believes surviving during the recession is his greatest entrepreneurial accomplishment to date. **Availability:** Print; Online.

13075 ■ *"Younger, Permenter Build New Real Estate Firm in Dallas" in Dallas Business Journal (Vol. 35, May 18, 2012, No. 36, pp. 1)*
Pub: Baltimore Business Journal
Contact: Rhonda Pringle, President
E-mail: rpringle@bizjournals.com
Ed: Candace Carlisle. **Description:** Former Grubb and Ellis brokers Moody Younger and Kathy Permenter have started Younger Partners Commercial LLC, a new commercial real estate firm based in Dallas. The idea for Younger Partners came about after Grubb and Ellis was acquired by BGC Partners Inc. The firm plans to concentrate on office leasing and corporate service. **Availability:** Print; Online.

ASSOCIATIONS AND OTHER ORGANIZATIONS

13076 ■ **Alabama Association of REALTORS (AAR)**
522 Washington Ave.
  Montgomery, AL 36104
Ph: (334)262-3808
Co. E-mail: mailbox@alabamarealtors.com
URL: http://www.alabamarealtors.com
Contact: Jeremy S. Walker, Chief Executive Officer
Facebook: www.facebook.com/AlabamaREALTORS

Linkedin: www.linkedin.com/company/alabamareal tors
X (Twitter): x.com/alrealtors
Instagram: www.instagram.com/alabamarealtors
YouTube: www.youtube.com/user/
  AlabamaREALTORtv
Description: Promotes professionalism among Realtors in Alabama. **Founded:** 1922. **Educational Activities:** Alabama Association of Realtors Annual Convention (Annual). **Geographic Preference:** State.

13077 ■ **American Land Title Association (ALTA)**
1800 M St. NW, Ste. 300S
  Washington, DC 20036-5828
Ph: (202)296-3671
Free: 800-787-2582
Fax: (202)223-5843
Co. E-mail: service@alta.org
URL: http://www.alta.org
Contact: Lauren Dollerschell, Director, Meetings
E-mail: ldollerschell@alta.org
Facebook: www.facebook.com/altaonline
Linkedin: www.linkedin.com/groups
X (Twitter): x.com/altaonline
YouTube: www.youtube.com/altavideos
Description: Represents the abstracters, title insurance companies, and attorneys specializing in real property law. **Founded:** 1907. **Publications:** *American Land Title Association--Directory* (Annual); *Title News* (Monthly). **Educational Activities:** ALTA Advocacy Summit (Annual). **Geographic Preference:** National.

13078 ■ **American Real Estate Society (ARES)**
PO Box 500
  Athens, OH 45701
Ph: (740)239-2737
Fax: (740)593-6758
Co. E-mail: membership@aresnet.org
URL: http://www.aresnet.org
Contact: Dr. Spenser J. Robinson, President
E-mail: s.robinson@cmich.edu
Facebook: www.facebook.com/americanrealesta tesociety
X (Twitter): x.com/ARESconference
Description: College and university professors; high-level practicing professionals involved in real estate finance, investment, development, valuation, marketing, consulting, management, education, and law; and institutions. Acts as a forum for the exchange of information and research on applied business and individual decision-making within real estate finance, real estate market analysis, investment, valuation, development, and other areas related to real estate in the private sector. Operates ARES Case Clearinghouse, which makes available copies of instructional cases pertinent to real estate practice. **Founded:** 1985. **Publications:** *Journal of Real Estate Practice and Education (JREPE)* (Continuous); *Journal of Real Estate Portfolio Management (JREPM)* (Semiannual); *ARES Newsletter* (Semiannual); *Journal of Housing*

Research (JHR) (Semiannual); *Journal of Real Estate Literature (JREL)* (Semiannual); *Journal of Real Estate Research (JRER)* (Quarterly). **Educational Activities:** American Real Estate Society Annual Meeting (Annual). **Awards:** The Graaskamp Award (Annual). **Geographic Preference:** National.

13079 ■ **American Real Estate and Urban Economics Association (AREUEA)**
c/o Travelink
  404 BNA Dr., No. 650
  Nashville, TN 37217
Free: 800-242-0528
Fax: (615)367-0012
Co. E-mail: areuea@travelink.com
URL: http://www.areuea.org
Contact: Ingrid Gould Ellen, President
Description: University faculty, individuals in real estate and related areas, and firms and organizations active in real estate and research. Promotes education and encourages research in real estate, urban land economics, and allied fields; improves communication in real estate and allied matters among college and university faculty who are teaching or conducting research in fields of interest to the association; facilitates the mutual association of academic and research persons in real estate, urban land economics, and allied fields. **Founded:** 1964. **Publications:** *Real Estate Economics* (6/year). **Awards:** Homer Hoyt Doctoral Dissertation Award (Annual); George Bloom Service Award (Annual). **Geographic Preference:** National.

13080 ■ **Arizona Association of Realtors (AAR)**
255 E Osborn Rd., Ste. 200
  Phoenix, AZ 85012
Ph: (602)248-7787
Fax: (602)351-2474
Co. E-mail: afterhours@aaronline.com
URL: http://www.aaronline.com
Contact: K. Michelle Lind, Co-Chief Executive Officer
E-mail: michellelind@aaronline.com
Facebook: www.facebook.com/azrealtors
X (Twitter): x.com/AARSuccess
YouTube: www.youtube.com/AZREALTORS
Description: Represents and advocates for licensed realtors in Arizona. Provides education and advocacy for legislative and political affairs, risk management, professional and business development, and professional standards. Also offers business tools and networking. **Founded:** 1945. **Geographic Preference:** State.

13081 ■ **Association of Commercial Real Estate Professionals (ACRP)**
1233 W Loop S, Ste. 900
  Houston, TX 77027
Ph: (713)830-2184
Fax: (713)986-4996
Co. E-mail: info@acrp.org
URL: http://acrp.org
Contact: Chris Heath, President
Facebook: www.facebook.com/acrphouston

Linkedin: www.linkedin.com/groups/142636
X (Twitter): x.com/ACRPHouston
Instagram: www.instagram.com/arcphouston
Description: Supports commercial real estate professionals through educational and networking opportunities. **Founded:** 1987.

13082 ■ California Association of Realtors (CAR)
525 S Virgil Ave.
  Los Angeles, CA 90020
Ph: (213)739-8200
Fax: (213)480-7724
Co. E-mail: cs@car.org
URL: http://www.car.org
Contact: Otto Catrina, President
E-mail: ottoc@car.org
Facebook: www.facebook.com/CAREALTORS
X (Twitter): x.com/carealtors
Instagram: www.instagram.com/carealtors
YouTube: www.youtube.com/user/CAREALTORS
Pinterest: www.pinterest.com/carealtors

Publications: *California Real Estate Magazine* (Quarterly). **Educational Activities:** California Realtor Expo (Annual). **Geographic Preference:** State.

13083 ■ The Canadian Real Estate Association (CREA) [L'Association Canadienne de L'immeuble]
200 Catherine St., 6th Fl.
  Ottawa, ON, Canada K2P 2K9
Ph: (613)237-7111
Free: 800-842-2732
Fax: (613)234-2567
Co. E-mail: info@crea.ca
URL: http://www.crea.ca
Contact: Michael Bourque, Chief Executive Officer
Facebook: www.facebook.com/CREA.ACI
Linkedin: www.linkedin.com/company/1400987
X (Twitter): x.com/CREA_ACI
Instagram: www.instagram.com/crea_aci
YouTube: www.youtube.com/user/CREACHANNEL

Description: Represents real estate professionals. Seeks the professional advancement of members and to increase the profitability of the real estate industry. **Founded:** 1943. **Geographic Preference:** National.

13084 ■ Chicago Association of Realtors (CAR)
430 N Michigan Ave., Ste. 800
  Chicago, IL 60611
Ph: (312)803-4900
Fax: (312)803-4905
Co. E-mail: membership@chicagorealtor.com
URL: http://chicagorealtor.com
Contact: Antje Gehrken, President
Facebook: www.facebook.com/
  CHICAGOASSOCIATIONOFREALTORS
Linkedin: www.linkedin.com/company/chicago
  -association-of-realtors
X (Twitter): x.com/ChicagoREALTORS
Instagram: www.instagram.com/chicagorealtors

Description: Strives to develop real estate business practices. Advocates the right to own, use and transfer real property. Provides a facility for professional development, research and exchange of information among members. **Founded:** 1883. **Geographic Preference:** Local.

13085 ■ Colorado Association of REALTORS (CAR)
309 Inverness Way S
  Englewood, CO 80112
Ph: (303)790-7099
Free: 800-944-6550
Co. E-mail: communications@coloradorealtors.com
URL: http://www.coloradorealtors.com
Contact: Tyrone Adams, Chief Executive Officer
E-mail: tadams@coloradorealtors.com
Facebook: www.facebook.com/ColoradoREALTORS
Linkedin: www.linkedin.com/company/coloradoreal
  tors
X (Twitter): x.com/corealtors
YouTube: www.youtube.com/user/ColoradoRealtors

Description: Trade association representing REALTORs across Colorado. **Geographic Preference:** State.

13086 ■ Counselors of Real Estate (CRE)
140 S Dearborn St., Ste. 1500A
  Chicago, IL 60603
Ph: (312)329-8427
Fax: (312)329-8881
Co. E-mail: info@cre.org
URL: http://cre.org
Contact: Mary Walker Fleischmann, President
E-mail: mfleischmann@cre.org
Facebook: www.facebook.com/counselorsofreales
  tate
X (Twitter): x.com/CounselorsofRE

Description: Professional society of individuals with extensive experience in all phases of real estate who provide a counseling service. **Founded:** 1953. **Publications:** *CRE Member Directory* (Annual); *Counselors Real Estate--Membership Directory* (Semiannual); *Real Estate Issues* (Biweekly). **Awards:** James D. Landauer/John R. White Award (Annual); James Felt Creative Counseling Award (Annual); William S. Ballard Award (Annual). **Geographic Preference:** Multinational.

13087 ■ Delaware Association of Realtors (DAR)
134 E Water St.
  Dover, DE 19901
Ph: (302)734-4444
Fax: (302)734-1341
Co. E-mail: info@delawarerealtor.com
URL: http://www.delawarerealtor.com
Contact: Dr. Susan N. Giove, President
Facebook: www.facebook.com/DEREALTORS
Linkedin: www.linkedin.com/company/delaware-real
  tors
X (Twitter): x.com/DEREALTORS
YouTube: www.youtube.com/channel/UCi5kXVkYro
  3hrhVRn80ub3w

Description: Develops and provides programs that support Realtors across Delaware. Promotes to the public the value of working with Realtors. Advocates at the local, state, and federal levels to ensure individuals' rights to own, use, and transfer property, and to eliminate unfair and counter-productive government regulations on real estate professionals. **Geographic Preference:** State.

13088 ■ Detroit Association of Realtors
18701 Grand River Ave., Ste. 126
  Detroit, MI 48223
Ph: (313)962-1313
Co. E-mail: detroitassociation@gmail.com
URL: http://detroitassociationofrealtors.com
Contact: Michael Poole, Treasurer
E-mail: mmpoole@ameritech.net
Facebook: www.facebook.com/detroitrealtors

Description: Strives to develop real estate business practices. Advocates the right to own, use and transfer real property. Provides a facility for professional development, research and exchange of information among members. **Founded:** 1890. **Geographic Preference:** Local.

13089 ■ FIABCI-USA [International Real Estate, U.S. Chapter]
347 Fifth Ave., Ste. 1402-147
  New York, NY 10016
Ph: (646)979-9769
Co. E-mail: info@fiabci-usa.com
URL: http://www.fiabciusamember.com
Contact: Evan G. Bennett, President
Facebook: www.facebook.com/FIABCIUSANEWS

Description: Brings together nearly 1,000,000 members in 57 countries; members represent all specializations in real estate, including brokerage, development, counseling, management, appraisal and financing. Conducts discussion among members in global real estate trends, emerging markets, case studies of international real estate transactions and refer business to each other. **Founded:** 1954. **Publications:** *World Directory* (Annual); *FIABCI Press* (5/year). **Educational Activities:** FIABCI-U.S.A. Congress (Annual). **Geographic Preference:** National; Local.

13090 ■ Florida Realtors
7025 Augusta National Dr.
  Orlando, FL 32822
Ph: (407)438-1400
Fax: (407)438-1411
Co. E-mail: support@floridarealtors.org
URL: http://www.floridarealtors.org
Contact: Christina Pappas, President
E-mail: christinap@floridarealtors.org
Facebook: www.facebook.com/therealfloridarealtors
Linkedin: www.linkedin.com/company/florida-realtors
X (Twitter): x.com/floridarealtors
Instagram: www.instagram.com/therealfloridarealtors
YouTube: www.youtube.com/user/FloridaReal
  torsTube

Description: Provides services and information to more than 170,000 individuals who are professional real estate agents in Florida. Services include free legal hotline and technology helpline, free websites, online electronic business information, real estate business news, license renewal courses, and political/legislative/governmental affairs advocacy. **Founded:** 1916. **Publications:** *Florida Realtor* (Monthly). **Educational Activities:** Florida Association of Realtors Convention & Trade Show (Annual). **Awards:** Florida Realtors Associate Realtor of the Year (Annual); Commercial Realtor Achievement Awards (Annual); Florida Realtors Education Award (Annual); Environmental Award for Residential Developments (Annual); Environmental Award for Commercial Developments (Annual); Florida Realtors Newcomer Award (Annual); Realtor Achievement Award (Annual); Florida Realtors - Realtor of the Year (Annual); Florida Realtors Humanitarian of the Year (Annual). **Geographic Preference:** State.

13091 ■ Georgia Association of Realtors (GAR)
6065 Barfield Rd. NE
  Atlanta, GA 30328-4402
Ph: (770)451-1831
Free: 866-280-0576
Co. E-mail: info@garealtor.com
URL: http://www.garealtor.com
Contact: Joey B. Tucker, President
Facebook: www.facebook.com/garealtor
Linkedin: www.linkedin.com/company/georgia-real
  tors
X (Twitter): x.com/garealtors
YouTube: www.youtube.com/user/
  GeorgiaREALTORS

Description: Trade association representing and supporting Realtors across Georgia. **Founded:** 1920. **Geographic Preference:** State.

13092 ■ Greater Regional Alliance of REALTORS (GRAR)
660 Kenmoor Ave., SE
  Grand Rapids, MI 49546
Ph: (616)940-8200
Free: 888-940-GRAR
Fax: (616)940-8216
URL: http://www.grar.com
Contact: Julie Rietberg, Chief Executive Officer

Description: Strives to develop real estate business practices. Advocates the right to own, use and transfer real property. Provides a facility for professional development, research and exchange of information among members. **Geographic Preference:** Local.

13093 ■ Indiana Association of Realtors (IAR)
143 W Market St., Ste. 100
  Indianapolis, IN 46204
Free: 800-284-0084
Co. E-mail: news@indianarealtors.com
URL: http://indianarealtors.com
Contact: Karl Berron, Chief Executive Officer
E-mail: kberron@indianarealtors.com
Facebook: www.facebook.com/indianarealtors
X (Twitter): x.com/indianarealtors

Description: Represents real estate professionals dedicated to the protection and preservation of the free enterprise system and the right of the individual to own real property. Seeks to sustain a healthy real estate market in Indiana. **Founded:** 1913. **Publications:** *Indiana Realtor* (Monthly). **Awards:** IAR REALTOR of the Year (Annual). **Geographic Preference:** State.

13094 ■ Institute of Real Estate Management (IREM)
430 N Michigan Ave., Ste. 500
  Chicago, IL 60611
Ph: (312)329-6000
Free: 800-837-0706
Fax: (800)338-4736
Co. E-mail: getinfo@irem.org
URL: http://www.irem.org
Contact: Libby Ekre, President
Facebook: www.facebook.com/InstituteofRealEstateManagement
Linkedin: www.linkedin.com/company/institute-of-real-estate-management
X (Twitter): x.com/IREM_info
YouTube: www.youtube.com/user/IREMinfo
Description: Professional organization of real property and asset managers. Awards professional designation Certified Property Manager (CPM) to qualifying individuals, Accredited Management Organization (AMO) to qualifying management firms and also awards Accredited Residential Manager (ARM) accreditation to qualifying individuals who are primarily residential site managers. Monitors legislation affecting real estate management. Offers management courses and seminars; conducts research and educational programs, publishes books and reports; maintains formal code of ethics; compiles statistics; maintains employment Website for real estate management industry. **Founded:** 1933. **Publications:** *Journal of Property Management* (Bimonthly); *Real Estate Income/Expense Analysis National Summary.* **Awards:** IREM Academy of Authors (Annual); Lloyd D. Hanford Sr. Distinguished Instructor Award (Annual); IREM Foundation Diversity Outreach Scholarship (Annual); Paul H. Rittle, Sr. Scholarship; Donald M. Furbush Scholarship (Annual); J. Wallace Paletou Award (Annual); Paul H. Rittle Sr. Memorial Scholarship Award (Quarterly); George M. Brooker, CPM Diversity Collegiate Scholarship (Semiannual); Donald M. Furbush Professional Development Grants; Paul H. Rittle Sr. Professional Development Grants. **Geographic Preference:** National.

13095 ■ Maine Association of Realtors (MAR)
19 Community Dr.
  Augusta, ME 04330
Ph: (207)622-7501
Fax: (207)623-3590
Co. E-mail: info@mainerealtors.com
URL: http://www.mainerealtors.com
Contact: Sherri Dunbar, Treasurer
E-mail: sherri@dunhamrealty.com
Facebook: www.facebook.com/mainerealtors
Instagram: www.instagram.com/mainerealtors
Founded: 1936. **Geographic Preference:** State.

13096 ■ Michigan Realtors (MR)
720 N Washington Ave.
  Lansing, MI 48906
Free: 800-454-7842
Fax: (517)334-5568
URL: http://www.mirealtors.com
Contact: James Iodice, President
Facebook: www.facebook.com/mirealtors
X (Twitter): x.com/MichREALTORS
YouTube: www.youtube.com/user/MICHREALTORS
Description: Real estate professionals united to provide members with programs, products, and services to enhance their businesses. Advocates and promotes the preservation and advancement of property rights. **Founded:** 1915. **Publications:** *Michigan Realtor* (Quarterly). **Awards:** Michigan Realtors Scholarship Trust (Annual); Realtor of the Year (Annual); Michigan Realtors Scholarship (An-

nual); Michigan Realtors' Realtor of the Year (Annual); Realtor Active in Politics Award (RAP) (Annual). **Geographic Preference:** State.

13097 ■ Minnesota Association of Realtors (MNAR)
11100 Bren Rd. W
  Minnetonka, MN 55343
Ph: (952)935-8313
Free: 800-862-6097
Co. E-mail: info@mnrealtor.com
URL: http://www.mnrealtor.com/home
Contact: Jason Miller, President
Facebook: www.facebook.com/MinnRealtor
Linkedin: www.linkedin.com/company/mnrealtors
X (Twitter): x.com/Minn_Realtors
Instagram: www.instagram.com/Minnesota_realtors
YouTube: www.youtube.com/user/mnarealtor
Description: Provides business support to real estate professionals throughout Minnesota. Advocates for laws in support of the real estate industry. Offers members legal support, and facilitates ethics hearings and arbitrations. Provides opportunities for continuing education and networking. **Founded:** 1919. **Geographic Preference:** State.

13098 ■ Mississippi Association of Realtors (MAR)
4274 Lakeland Dr.
  Jackson, MS 39232-1000
Ph: (601)932-5241
Free: 800-747-1103
Fax: (601)932-0382
Co. E-mail: mar@msrealtors.org
URL: http://msrealtors.org
Contact: Beth Hansen, Chief Executive Officer
Facebook: www.facebook.com/msrealtors
Linkedin: www.linkedin.com/company/mississippi-association-of-realtors/about
X (Twitter): x.com/msrealtors
YouTube: www.youtube.com/user/MSAssocofREALTORS
Description: Strives to develop real estate business practices. Advocates the right to own, use and transfer real property. Provides a facility for professional development, research and exchange of information among members. **Geographic Preference:** State.

13099 ■ Mortgage Bankers Association (MBA)
1919 M St. NW, 5th Fl.
  Washington, DC 20036
Ph: (202)557-2700
Free: 800-793-6222
Co. E-mail: education@mba.org
URL: http://www.mba.org
Contact: Susan Stewart, Chairman
Facebook: www.facebook.com/mbamortgage
Linkedin: www.linkedin.com/company/mortgage-bankers-association
X (Twitter): x.com/mbamortgage
Instagram: www.instagram.com/mortgage_bankers_association
Description: Principal lending and investor interests in the mortgage finance field, including mortgage banking firms, commercial banks, life insurance companies, title companies, and savings and loan associations. **Founded:** 1913. **Holdings:** Figures not available. **Publications:** *MBA Directory of Members*; *Mortgage Banking Magazine: The Magazine of Real Estate Finance* (Monthly); *State and Local MBA Directory* (Semiannual); *Mortgage Banking Sourcebook*; *Real Estate Finance Today* (Weekly); *Mortgage Banking: The Magazine of Real Estate Finance Managers and Employees*; *Mortgage Bankers Performance Study* (Quarterly); *Mortgage Banking: The Magazine of Real Estate Finance* (Monthly); *National Delinquency Survey (NDS)* (Quarterly). **Educational Activities:** MBA's Commercial Real Estate Finance/Multi-Family Housing Convention Expo (Annual). **Geographic Preference:** National.

13100 ■ National Association of Real Estate Brokers (NAREB) - Willis E. Carson Library
9831 Greenbelt Rd.
  Lanham, MD 20706

Ph: (301)552-9340
Fax: (301)552-9216
Co. E-mail: nareb@nareb.com
URL: http://www.nareb.com
Contact: Lawrence Bastiste, Chairman
Facebook: www.facebook.com/realtistnareb
X (Twitter): x.com/realtist_nareb
YouTube: www.youtube.com/user/RealtistUSA/videos
Description: Research, educational and certification programs include: Real Estate Management Brokers Institute; National Society of Real Estate Appraisers; Real Estate Brokerage Institute; United Developers Council. Encourages unity among those who are engaged in real estate. Promotes and maintains high standards of conduct. Protects the public against unethical, improper, or fraudulent practices connected with the real estate business. Conducts research; compiles statistics on productivity, marketing and development. **Scope:** Real estate. **Founded:** 1947. **Holdings:** Figures not available. **Publications:** *Realtist Membership Directory* (Annual). **Geographic Preference:** National.

13101 ■ National Association of Realtors (NAR) - Library & Archives
430 N Michigan Ave.
  Chicago, IL 60611-4087
Free: 800-874-6500
Co. E-mail: infocentral@realtors.org
URL: http://www.nar.realtor
Contact: Bob Goldberg, Chief Executive Officer
Facebook: www.facebook.com/NARdotRealtor
Linkedin: www.linkedin.com/company/national-association-of-realtors
X (Twitter): x.com/nardotrealtor
Instagram: www.instagram.com/NARdotRealtor
YouTube: www.youtube.com/user/NAREALTORS
Description: Promotes education, high professional standards and modern techniques in specialized real estate work such as brokerage, appraisal, property management, land development, industrial real estate, farm brokerage and counseling. Conducts research programs. **Scope:** Real estate topics. **Services:** Interlibrary loan. **Founded:** 1908. **Holdings:** 500,000 documents and images; 7,500 e-books; audiobooks and videos; 6,000 e-journal; 12,000 books; reports; and guides; 150 journals; newsletters; periodicals; magazines. **Publications:** *Realtor Magazine* (Quarterly); *Realtor Magazine: The Business tool for Real Estate Professionals* (Quarterly); *NAR Commercial Real Estate Outlook* (Quarterly); *Real Estate Today: Official Publication of the National Association of Realtors* (10/year); *REALTORS Land Institute* (6/year); *Existing-Home Sales* (Monthly). **Awards:** National Association of Realtors Distinguished Service Award (Annual). **Geographic Preference:** National.

13102 ■ National Association of Review Appraisers and Mortgage Underwriters (NARA/MU)
PO Box 879
  Palm Springs, CA 92263
Free: 877-743-6805
Fax: (760)327-5631
Co. E-mail: info@naramu.org
URL: http://www.naramu.org
Contact: Brent Felstead, Associate Manager

Description: Real estate professionals and mortgage underwriters who aid in determining value of property. Acts as umbrella group for real estate appraisers. Conducts educational seminars; maintains speakers' bureau; operates placement service. **Founded:** 1975. **Educational Activities:** National Association of Review Appraisers and Mortgage Underwriters Convention - National Conference & Expo. **Geographic Preference:** National.

13103 ■ National Council of Exchangors (NCE)
11 W Main St., Ste. 223
  Belgrade, MT 59714
Ph: (858)222-1608
Co. E-mail: admin@ncexchangors.com
URL: http://www.ncexchangors.com
Contact: Tom DeSollar, President

Description: Real estate professionals who possess specialized training in the fields of real estate exchanging, real estate tax law, investment analysis, client counseling, and equity marketing. **Founded:** 1977. **Publications:** *NCE News* (Periodic). **Educational Activities:** NCE Marketing Conference (Quarterly). **Geographic Preference:** National.

13104 ■ Nevada Realtors (NVAR)
760 Margrave Dr., No. 200
  Reno, NV 89502
Ph: (775)829-5911
Free: 800-748-5526
Co. E-mail: info@nvrealtors.org
URL: http://nevadarealtors.org
Contact: Doug McIntyre, President
Facebook: www.facebook.com/NevadaRealtors
X (Twitter): x.com/NVARnevada
YouTube: www.youtube.com/user/NVARvideo
Description: Advocates for private property rights.
Geographic Preference: State.

13105 ■ New Hampshire Association of Realtors (NHAR)
11 S Main St., Ste. 301
  Concord, NH 03301
Ph: (603)225-5549
Co. E-mail: info@nhar.org
URL: http://www.nhar.org
Contact: Adam Gaudet, President
Facebook: www.facebook.com/newhampshire.realtors
X (Twitter): x.com/nhrealtors
YouTube: www.youtube.com/channel/UCGQJbhOKBM7KM2lGuPac_Xw
Description: Realtors. Provides services in governmental affairs, education, professional standards, and media relations. **Founded:** 1933. **Publications:** *New Hampshire Realtor eNews*; *NHAReport* (Monthly); *Realtor Referral Network* (Annual). **Educational Activities:** NHAR Fall Business and Education Conference. **Awards:** NHAR Distinguished Service Award (Annual); NHAR Honor Society (Annual); NHAR Realtor of the Year (Annual). **Geographic Preference:** State.

13106 ■ New Jersey Realtors (NJR)
10 Hamilton Ave.
  Trenton, NJ 08611
Ph: (609)341-7100
Co. E-mail: info@njrealtor.com
URL: http://www.njrealtor.com
Contact: Robert White, President
E-mail: robert@msn.com
Facebook: www.facebook.com/NJREALTORS
X (Twitter): x.com/NJ_REALTORS
Instagram: www.instagram.com/njrealtors
YouTube: www.youtube.com/user/RealStoryNJ
Description: Supports all segments of its membership by developing and delivering programs, services and related products that enhance the ability to conduct business successfully and ethically. Promotes the extension and preservation of the right to own, transfer and use real property. **Founded:** 1917. **Publications:** *New Jersey Realtors* (Bimonthly); *New Jersey Realtor Magazine* (Bimonthly). **Educational Activities:** Triple Play Realtors Convention and Trade Expo (Annual). **Geographic Preference:** State.

13107 ■ North Carolina Association of Realtors (NCAR)
4511 Weybridge Ln.
  Greensboro, NC 27407
Ph: (336)294-1415
Fax: (336)299-7872
Co. E-mail: hello@ncrealtors.org
URL: http://www.ncrealtors.org
Contact: Andrea Bushnell, Chief Executive Officer
E-mail: abushnell@ncrealtors.org
Facebook: www.facebook.com/ncrealtors
X (Twitter): x.com/ncrealtors
Instagram: www.instagram.com/ncrealtors
YouTube: www.youtube.com/user/ncrealtors

Description: Realtors organized to protect and advance industry and member interests. Lobbies and conducts workshops and seminars. **Founded:** 1921. **Publications:** *Tar Heel Realtor* (Monthly). **Geographic Preference:** State.

13108 ■ Ohio Association of Realtors (OAR)
200 E Town St.
  Columbus, OH 43215
Ph: (614)228-6675
Co. E-mail: oar@ohiorealtors.org
URL: http://ohiorealtors.org
Contact: Shauna Brown, Vice President
E-mail: brown@ohiorealtors.org
Facebook: www.facebook.com/OhioRealtors
Linkedin: www.linkedin.com/company/ohio-realtors
X (Twitter): x.com/OhioRealtors
Instagram: www.instagram.com/ohiorealtors
YouTube: www.youtube.com/user/OhioRealtorsAssn
Geographic Preference: State.

13109 ■ Oklahoma Association of Realtors (OAR)
9807 Broadway Ext.
  Oklahoma City, OK 73114-6312
Ph: (405)848-9944
Free: 800-375-9944
Fax: (405)848-9947
Co. E-mail: support@okrealtors.com
URL: http://okrealtors.com
Contact: Susanna Lorg, President
E-mail: slorg@oklahomahometeam.com
Facebook: www.facebook.com/OKRealtors
Linkedin: www.linkedin.com/company/okrealtors
X (Twitter): x.com/OKRealtors
YouTube: www.youtube.com/channel/UClOfyyN1yu2-lesfkowRYow
Founded: 1921. **Publications:** *Opening Doors* (Bimonthly). **Geographic Preference:** State.

13110 ■ Oregon REALTORS
2110 Mission St. SE, No. 230
  Salem, OR 97302
Ph: (503)362-3645
Free: 800-252-9115
Fax: (503)362-9615
Co. E-mail: info@oregonrealtors.org
URL: http://oregonrealtors.org
Contact: Jenny Pakula, Chief Executive Officer
Facebook: www.facebook.com/OregonREALTORS
Linkedin: www.linkedin.com/company/oregonrealtors
X (Twitter): x.com/ORREALTORS
Instagram: www.instagram.com/oregonrealtors
YouTube: www.youtube.com/oregonrealtors
Description: Supports Realtors in Oregon through business, educational, and legislative advocacy. **Founded:** 1932. **Geographic Preference:** State.

13111 ■ Pennsylvania Association of Realtors (PAR)
500 N 12th St.
  Lemoyne, PA 17043-1213
Free: 800-555-3390
URL: http://www.parealtors.org
Contact: Christopher S. Beadling, President
Facebook: www.facebook.com/PARealtors
Linkedin: www.linkedin.com/company/parealtors
X (Twitter): x.com/PARealtors
Instagram: www.instagram.com/parealtors
Description: Promotes education, high professional standards, and modern techniques in specialized real estate work. Operates bookstore and real estate school. Conducts lobbying. Provides group insurance program. Makes available grants and scholarships. **Founded:** 1920. **Publications:** *The Pennsylvania Realtor* (Monthly). **Awards:** PAR Lifetime Achievement Award (Annual); PAR Realtor Active in Politics of the Year Award (RAP) (Annual); PAR Realtor of the Year (Annual). **Geographic Preference:** State.

13112 ■ Real Property Association of Canada (REALPAC) [Association des biens Immobiliers du Canada]
77 King St. W, TD North Twr., Ste. 4030
  Toronto, ON, Canada M5K 1H1
Ph: (416)642-2700
Free: 855-732-5722

Fax: (416)642-2727
Co. E-mail: info@realpac.ca
URL: http://realpac.ca
Contact: Dr. Michael Brooks, Chief Executive Officer
E-mail: mbrooks@realpac.ca
Linkedin: www.linkedin.com/company/realpac
X (Twitter): x.com/realpac_news
YouTube: www.youtube.com/channel/UCgyTGYy289DxHoBGPeY5Qzg
Description: Real estate and development companies and related businesses. Promotes growth in the real estate development and related industries. Serves as a forum for discussion of issues facing the industry; represents members' interests before the public. **Founded:** 1970. **Geographic Preference:** National.

13113 ■ Realtors Land Institute (RLI)
430 N Michigan Ave., Ste. 600
  Chicago, IL 60611
Free: 800-441-5263
Fax: (312)329-8633
Co. E-mail: rli@realtors.org
URL: http://www.rliland.com
Contact: Dean Saunders, President
Facebook: www.facebook.com/RLILand
X (Twitter): x.com/rliland
Instagram: www.instagram.com/realtors_land_institute
Description: Maintains educational programs for real estate brokers; promotes competence and accredits members. Sponsors courses for realtors and others seeking professional excellence on Land Brokerage, Agricultural Land Brokerage, Exchanging Properties, Estate Planning, Subdivision Development and Financial Analysis of Land Investment. **Publications:** *Terra Firma* (Semiannual). **Geographic Preference:** National.

13114 ■ Rhode Island Association of Realtors (RIAR)
100 Bignall St.
  Warwick, RI 02888
Ph: (401)785-9898
Co. E-mail: info@rirealtors.org
URL: http://www.rirealtors.org
Contact: Agueda Del Borgo, President
E-mail: agueda@placesandspacesrealtyri.com
Facebook: www.facebook.com/RIRealtors
Linkedin: www.linkedin.com/company/rirealtors
X (Twitter): x.com/RI_REALTORS
Instagram: www.instagram.com/rirealtors
YouTube: www.youtube.com/channel/UCsSbc4_NXIYReNfNS00bpxw
Description: To support its members in conducting their real estate businesses ethically and competently. **Founded:** 1948. **Geographic Preference:** State.

13115 ■ South Carolina Association of Realtors (SCR)
3780 Fernandina Rd.
  Columbia, SC 29210
Ph: (803)772-5206
Fax: (803)620-4730
Co. E-mail: info@screaltors.org
URL: http://www.screaltors.org
Contact: Nick Kremydas, Chief Executive Officer
E-mail: nick@screaltors.org
Facebook: www.facebook.com/SCREALTORS
Linkedin: www.linkedin.com/company/screaltors
X (Twitter): x.com/screaltors
Description: Real estate agents, brokers, and affiliates organized to raise standards of professionalism in the industry. Provides member services. Conducts educational seminars and public service programs. Extensive lobbying on real estate issues and the protection of property rights. **Founded:** 1944. **Publications:** *Legislative/Legal Outlook*; *Realtor Magazine South Carolina Edition* (Bimonthly). **Geographic Preference:** State.

13116 ■ Tennessee Association of Realtors (TAR)
901 19th Ave., S
  Nashville, TN 37212
Free: 877-321-1477
URL: http://tnrealtors.com

Contact: Travis Close, President
Facebook: www.facebook.com/Tennessee-REAL-
TORS-15041383689
Linkedin: www.linkedin.com/company/tennessee-real
tors
X (Twitter): x.com/TNAOR
Instagram: www.instagram.com/tnrealtors
YouTube: www.youtube.com/channel/
UCMoDHWJzCVneHr9eYFgOkkA
Description: Engaged in real-estate business in Ten-
nessee. **Publications:** *TAR Digest* (Weekly). **Geo-
graphic Preference:** State.

13117 ■ Texas Association of Realtors (TAR)
1115 San Jacinto Blvd., Ste. 200
  Austin, TX 78701
Ph: (512)480-8200
Free: 800-873-9155
Co. E-mail: info@texasrealtors.com
URL: http://www.texasrealtors.com
Contact: Travis Kessler, President
URL(s): www.texasrealestate.com
Facebook: www.facebook.com/texasrealtors
X (Twitter): x.com/TXRealtors
Instagram: www.instagram.com/txrealtors
YouTube: www.youtube.com/user/TexasRealtors
Description: Advocates for realtors and private
property rights in Texas. **Founded:** 1920. **Publica-
tions:** *Texas Realtor* (10/year); *Texas Association of
Realtors Referral Directory.* **Geographic Preference:**
State; Local.

13118 ■ Utah Association of Realtors (UAR)
230 W Towne Ridge Pky., Ste. 500
  Sandy, UT 84070
Ph: (801)676-5200
Co. E-mail: info@utahrealtors.com
URL: http://utahrealtors.com
Contact: Randy Day, President
Facebook: www.facebook.com/utahassociationofreal
tors
X (Twitter): x.com/UtRealtors
YouTube: www.youtube.com/user/uarnews
Description: Advocates for realtors and their clients
by promoting the preservation and extension of the
right to own, transfer and use real property. Provides
professional development services to help its mem-
bers prosper, including risk reduction training,
educational opportunities, and business tools.
Founded: 1998. **Geographic Preference:** State.

**13119 ■ Vermont Association of Realtors
(VAR)**
148 State St.
  Montpelier, VT 05602
Ph: (802)229-0513
Fax: (802)229-0995
Co. E-mail: info@vermontrealtors.com
URL: http://www.vermontrealtors.com
Contact: Vince Malta, President
Facebook: www.facebook.com/vermontrealtors
X (Twitter): x.com/vtrealtors
Instagram: www.instagram.com/vermontrealtors
Description: Realtors organized to advance the
interests of the industry. **Publications:** *R-GRAM*
(Monthly); *Vermont Association of Realtors--
Membership Directory and Referral Guide* (Annual).
Geographic Preference: State.

**13120 ■ Virginia Association of Realtors
(VAR)**
10231 Telegraph Rd.
  Glen Allen, VA 23059
Ph: (804)264-5033
Co. E-mail: members@virginiarealtors.org
URL: http://virginiarealtors.com
Contact: Denise Ramey, President
Facebook: www.facebook.com/VirginiaREALTORS
Linkedin: www.linkedin.com/company/virginiarealtors
X (Twitter): x.com/REALTORS_VA
Description: Represents the interests of professional
realtors. **Founded:** 1920. **Publications:** *The Virginia
REALTOR.* **Educational Activities:** Var Annual
Convention (Annual). **Awards:** Virginia's Realtor of
the Year (Annual). **Geographic Preference:** State.

13121 ■ Women's Council of Realtors (WCR)
430 N Michigan Ave.
  Chicago, IL 60611
Free: 800-285-2955
Co. E-mail: wcr@wcr.org
URL: http://www.wcr.org
Contact: Jeff Hornberger, Executive Vice President
E-mail: jhornberger@wcr.org
X (Twitter): x.com/womenscouncil
Instagram: www.instagram.com/womenscouncil
YouTube: www.youtube.com/channel/UCRQTF5B
1MFKtpyvjcFzR8yw
Pinterest: www.pinterest.com/womenscouncil
Description: Women and men real estate brokers
and salespeople. Provides opportunity for real estate
professionals to participate at local, state, and
national levels. Makes programs available for per-
sonal and career growth. Offers courses in leadership training, referral and relocation business.
Members may earn the Leadership Training Graduate (LTG) designation. **Founded:** 1938. **Publications:** *Women's Council of Realtors--Referral Roster*
(Annual); *eConnect.* **Geographic Preference:** National.

REFERENCE WORKS

**13122 ■ "1Q Office Vacancies Mainly Up;
Class A Space Bucks Trend, Falls" in Crain's
Detroit Business (Vol. 24, April 14, 2008, No.
15)**
Pub: Crain Communications Inc.
Contact: Barry Asin, President
Ed: Daniel Duggan. **Description:** Although more office space became vacant in the first quarter, Class A
space went in the opposite direction with several local
businesses are moving from less-desirable to more
desirable areas. **Availability:** Online.

**13123 ■ "5 Tips for a Top-Notch Residential
Lease" in Legal Zoom (March 27, 2023)**
URL(s): www.legalzoom.com/articles/5-tips-for-a-top
-notch-residential-lease
Ed: Michelle Kaminsky, Esq. **Released:** March 27,
2023. **Description:** Gives advice on how to structure
a rental agreement for your property in order to
maintain legal integrity. **Availability:** Online.

**13124 ■ "6 Worth-the-Price Fix-Ups" in
Realtor Magazine (Vol. 44, April-May 2011, No.
44, pp. 23)**
Pub: Realtor Magazine
Contact: Sara Geimer, Manager
E-mail: sgeimer@nar.realtor
Description: Advice on how realtors could increase
a home's resale value through do-it-yourself projects
is given. Removal of personal items and clutter is
recommended, along with rearrangement of furniture.
A clutter consultant could also be used. **Availability:**
Online.

**13125 ■ "A 16-Year Housing Slump? It Could
Happen" in Barron's (Vol. 88, March 17, 2008,
No. 11, pp. 27)**
Pub: Dow Jones & Company Inc.
Contact: Almar Latour, Chief Executive Officer
Ed: Gene Epstein. **Description:** Housing remains a
good protection against inflation but over very long
periods. Inflation-adjusted stock prices did even better but have greater volatility. Commodities, on the
other hand, underperformed both housing and stocks
as inflation hedges. House prices tend to rise faster
than the consumer price index is because land is
inherently limited. **Availability:** Online.

**13126 ■ "2009 Real Estate in Review: Median
Prices Drop, Sales Up" in Bellingham
Business Journal (Vol. February 2010, pp. 15)**
Description: Bellingham and Whatcom County,
Washington saw a rise in home sales in 2008. Single
family home sales were up 3.3 percent in Bellingham
and 0.5 percent for the entire county. Statistical data
included. **Availability:** Print; Online.

**13127 ■ "2010 Book of Lists" in Business
Courier (Vol. 26, December 26, 2009, No. 36,
pp. 1)**
Price: $49.95. **Description:** Rankings of companies
and organizations within the business services,
education, finance, health care, hospitality and tourism, real estate, and technology industries in the
Cincinnati, Ohio-Northern Kentucky area are presented. Rankings are based on sales, business size,
or other statistics. **Availability:** PDF; Online.

**13128 ■ "2015 Marketing Calendar for Real
Estate Pros: Own It"**
Pub: CreateSpace
Released: October 14, 2014. **Price:** $9.56, paper-
back. **Description:** Real estate agents, mortgage
loan agents, and new home builders and site and
listing agents are shown how to use low-cost, high
yield, proven marketing techniques to create digital
real estate listings, find more customers, and sell
more homes. Advice for building a brand and public
relations; attracting renters and buyers; developing a
good Website; and a digital marketing plan are
explained. **Availability:** Print.

**13129 ■ "After Recession, Texas Cities Lead
National Recovery" in Dallas Business
Journal (Vol. 37, June 27, 2014, No. 42, pp.
28)**
Pub: American City Business Journals, Inc.
Contact: Mike Olivieri, Executive Vice President
Released: Weekly. **Price:** $4, introductory 4-week
offer(Digital only). **Description:** A study of 510 U.S.
cities by NeredWallet finds that 11 Texas cities are
among those showing the fastest recovery since the
recession began. NerdWallet analyst Sreekar Jasthi
attributes this to growing business investment, rising
employment, and an increase in median home values
in cities such as Richardson and Gran Prairie. **Availability:** Print; Online.

**13130 ■ "Agricultural Community Implements
Green Technologies, Building Team" in
Contractor (Vol. 56, September 2009, No. 9,
pp. 5)**
Ed: Candace Roulo. **Description:** John DeWald and
Associates has initiated a residential development
project which uses green technologies in Illinois. The
community features a community center, organic farm
and recreational trails. Comments from executives
are also provided. **Availability:** Print; Online.

13131 ■ Airbnb for Dummies
Pub: John Wiley & Sons, Inc.
Contact: Christina Van Tassell, Executive Vice
  President Chief Financial Officer
URL(s): www.wiley.com/en-us/Airbnb+For+Dum-
mies%2C+2nd+Edition-p-9781394154630
Ed: Symon He, James Svetec. **Released:** 2nd edition. **Description:** This guide explains how to turn
your rentable property into an Airbnb in order to earn
an income. Tips on using the Airbnb website, navigating their policies, and even setting up your property
to rent out are all included. **Availability:** paperback;
Print.

**13132 ■ "All-Star Advice 2010" in Black
Enterprise (Vol. 41, October 2010, No. 3, pp.
97)**
Pub: Earl G. Graves Ltd.
Contact: Earl Graves, Jr., President
Ed: Renita Burns, Sheiresa Ngo, Marcia Wade Talbert. **Description:** Financial experts share tips on
real estate, investing, taxes, insurance and debt
management. **Availability:** Online.

**13133 ■ "Anderson Pitches Liberty Towne
Place" in Business Courier (Vol. 27, June 18,
2010, No. 7, pp. 1)**
Pub: Business Courier
Ed: Dan Monk. **Description:** Jeffrey R. Anderson
Real Estate Inc.'s plan for a retail center in Butler
County, Ohio could have three department stores in
the 1.1 million-square-foot property. An outdoor sports
retailer is also part of the plans. **Availability:** Print;
Online.

13134 ■ *"Another California Firm Moving to Austin"* in *Austin Business Journal (Vol. 31, May 6, 2011, No. 9, pp. 1)*
Pub: Austin Business Journal
Contact: Rachel McGrath, Director
E-mail: rmcgrath@bizjournals.com
Ed: Christopher Calnan. **Description:** Main Street Hub Inc. is planning to build a facility in Austin, Texas. The company helps businesses manage their online reputations. Main Street has selected Aquila Commercial LLC as its real estate broker. **Availability:** Print; Online.

13135 ■ *"Apartment Action: A Renewal in Rentals"* in *Barron's (Vol. 88, March 17, 2008, No. 11, pp. 17)*
Pub: Dow Jones & Company Inc.
Contact: Almar Latour, Chief Executive Officer
Ed: Robin Goldwyn Blumenthal. **Description:** Discusses the projected entry of the estimated 82 million echo-boomers into the rentals market and the influx of immigrants and displaced homeowners which could turn apartments into lucrative investments again. While apartment-building completions rose slowly since 2003, demand is expected to increase steeply until 2015. **Availability:** Online.

13136 ■ *"Apartment Tower in River North Fetches More Than $90 Million"* in *Crain's Chicago Business (Vol. 34, October 24, 2011, No. 42, pp. 17)*
Pub: Crain Communications Inc.
Contact: Barry Asin, President
Ed: Alby Gallun. **Description:** Apartment tower in River North was sold for over $90 million to a Texas pension fund adviser. Details are included. **Availability:** Online.

13137 ■ *"Ask Inc.: Managing and Real Estate to Build Value"* in *Inc. (December 2007, pp. 83-84)*
Ed: Ari Weinzweig. **Price:** $8.95. **Description:** Questions regarding knowledge management in the case of a retiring CFO, issues involved in opening a satellite office for a New York realtor, and information for hiring a multicultural workforce are all discussed. **Availability:** PDF; Online.

13138 ■ *"Athletes Face Wins and Losses After Pro Sports"* in *The Business Journal - Serving Phoenix and the Valley of the Sun (Vol. 29, September 21, 2008, No. 3, pp. 1)*
Pub: American City Business Journals, Inc.
Contact: Mike Olivieri, Executive Vice President
Ed: Chris Casacchia. **Description:** Professional athletes like hockey star Jeremy Roenick start businesses, while others like Joel Adamson work to boost local communities. Former athletes were found to be particularly interested with real estate businesses. Other views and information on former athletes and their life after sports are presented. **Availability:** Online.

13139 ■ *"Au Revoir Or Goodbye?"* in *Barron's (Vol. 88, July 14, 2008, No. 28, pp. 5)*
Pub: Dow Jones & Company Inc.
Contact: Almar Latour, Chief Executive Officer
Ed: Alan Abelson. **Description:** Former Senator Phil Gramm's opinion that the U.S. is a "nation of whiners" as they moan about recession is another example of the disconnection between Washington and Wall Street on one hand and the real world on the other. It would be a catastrophe for most of the world if Fannie Mae and Freddie Mac were to go under and take their trillions of mortgage debt with them. **Availability:** Online.

13140 ■ *"Austin Realtors Cozy Up To Trulia"* in *Austin Business Journal (Vol. 34, May 9, 2014, No. 12, pp. 6)*
Pub: American City Business Journals, Inc.
Contact: Mike Olivieri, Executive Vice President
Released: Weekly. **Price:** $4, Introductory 4-week offer(Digital & Print). **Description:** Austin Board of Realtors (ABOR) MLS Advisory Committee chairman Lisa Messana explains the organization's decision to share data exclusively with Trulia.com. She describes member response to the announcement to end ABOR's data license agreement with ListHub. **Availability:** Print; Online.

13141 ■ *"Baltimore Commercial Real Estate Foreclosures Continue to Rise"* in *Baltimore Business Journal (Vol. 28, October 1, 2010, No. 21, pp. 1)*
Pub: Baltimore Business Journal
Contact: Rhonda Pringle, President
E-mail: rpringle@bizjournals.com
Ed: Daniel J. Sernovitz. **Description:** Foreclosures of commercial real estate across the Greater Baltimore area have continued to rise. The region is now host to about $2 billion worth of commercial properties that carry a maturing debt or have been foreclosed. Commercial real estate owners are unable to finance their debts because banks have become stricter in passing out loans. **Availability:** Print; Online.

13142 ■ *"Bangles, BMWs Elbow Out Delis and Discount Shops"* in *Crain's New York Business (Vol. 24, January 13, 2008, No. 2, pp. 35)*
Pub: Crain Communications, Inc.
Contact: Jessica Botos, Manager, Marketing
E-mail: jessica.botos@crainsnewyork.com
Ed: Wendy Davis. **Description:** Lured by a growing number of affluent residents and high-earning professionals, a number of upscale retailers have opened locations downtown which is driving up rents and forcing out longtime independent merchants.

13143 ■ *"Banks Continue March Out of Bad-Loan Numbers: Total Loans Up, Non-Performing Loans Decline"* in *Memphis Business Journal (Vol. 34, August 24, 2012, No. 19, pp. 1)*
Pub: Baltimore Business Journal
Contact: Rhonda Pringle, President
E-mail: rpringle@bizjournals.com
Description: Banks in Memphis, Tennessee continue to improve their capital status throughout the second quarter of 2012. The twenty-five banks observed showed improvements in total loan volume, as well as in non-performing loans and real estate. Total loans grew $723.26 million, while non-performing loans and real-estate-owned assets fell $322.4 million. **Availability:** Print; Online.

13144 ■ *"Baupost Group Pours Money into Charlotte Real Estate Projects"* in *Charlotte Business Journal (Vol. 25, December 3, 2010, No. 37, pp. 1)*
Pub: Charlotte Business Journal
Contact: Robert Morris, Editor
E-mail: rmorris@bizjournals.com
Ed: Will Boye. **Description:** Boston-based hedge fund Baupost Group has been financing real estate project in Charlotte, North Carolina including more than 80 acres just north of uptown. Aside from purchasing the $23.8 million note for the Rosewood Condominiums from Regions Financial Corporation, the Baupost Group is also negotiating with Regions to buy the $93.9 million debt of the EipCentre real estate project. **Availability:** Print; Online.

13145 ■ *"'Better Together:' OCO LPA Executives Discuss Recent Merger"* in *San Antonio Business Journal (Vol. 28, July 4, 2014, No. 21, pp. 8)*
Pub: American City Business Journals, Inc.
Contact: Mike Olivieri, Executive Vice President
Released: Weekly. **Price:** $4, introductory 4-week offer(Digital & Print). **Description:** Texas-based OCO Architects agreed to merge with LPA Inc. of Irvine, California effective July 1, 2014 and the local firm will initially operate as OCO LPA before it officially becomes LPA in January 2015. The merger is expected to keep OCO LPA relevant in the residential and commercial real estate sectors. **Availability:** Print; Online.

13146 ■ *"Betting On Spec"* in *San Antonio Business Journal (Vol. 28, April 25, 2014, No. 11, pp. 4)*
Pub: American City Business Journals, Inc.
Contact: Mike Olivieri, Executive Vice President
Released: Weekly. **Price:** $4, Introductory 4-week offer(Digital only). **Description:** Real estate broker, Ty Bragg, believes that San Antonio, Texas is lacking space for the industrial-facilities market and that will limit opportunities within the real estate sector. However, Steve Raub of Investment Realty Company, thinks that more companies are noticing the city's industrial market as a site to consider. **Availability:** Print; Online.

13147 ■ *"Bills Would Regulate Mortgage Loan Officers"* in *Crain's Detroit Business (Vol. 24, February 25, 2008, No. 8, pp. 9)*
Pub: Crain Communications Inc.
Contact: Barry Asin, President
Ed: Amy Lane. **Description:** New legislation in Michigan, if passed, would create a registration process for mortgage loan officers in the state in order to address the mortgage loan crisis. **Availability:** Print; Online.

13148 ■ *"Bose Seeking Expansion Options in Framingham"* in *Boston Business Journal (Vol. 34, June 13, 2014, No. 19, pp. 15)*
Pub: American City Business Journals, Inc.
Contact: Mike Olivieri, Executive Vice President
Released: Weekly. **Description:** Bose Corporation, the Framingham-based high-end audio products manufacturer, is in talks to buy a 10-acre property near its headquarters. Bose is negotiating with the owner of three buildings on Pennsylvania Avenue near the Bose headquarters. Bose already owns five buildings in Framingham, but is looking at real estate for growth and expansion. **Availability:** Print; Online.

13149 ■ *"Bottom's Up: This Real-Estate Rout May Be Short-Lived"* in *Barron's (Vol. 88, July 14, 2008, No. 28, pp. 25)*
Pub: Dow Jones & Company Inc.
Contact: Almar Latour, Chief Executive Officer
Ed: Jonathan R. Laing. **Description:** Economist Chip Case believes that home prices are nearing a bottom based on his analysis of the history of the housing market; surprisingly, in the past the housing market has rebounded after a quarter from a massive housing start drop. The drop in early stage delinquencies is another sign of the housing market's recovery. **Availability:** Online.

13150 ■ *"A Bright Spot: Industrial Space in Demand Again"* in *Sacramento Business Journal (Vol. 28, October 21, 2011, No. 34, pp. 1)*
Description: Sacramento, California's industrial sites have been eyed by potential tenants who are actively seeking space larger than 50,000 square feet. **Availability:** Print; Online.

13151 ■ *"Brisk Activity in North Fulton Office Market"* in *Atlanta Business Chronicle (July 11, 2014, pp. 2B)*
Description: Activity appears to have pickup up briskly in the North Fulton office market during the first six months of 2014, mainly due to the high profile deals involving major players in the technology and health care sectors. **Availability:** Print; Online.

13152 ■ *"Brokerages Seek a Foothold in Charlotte Real Estate Market"* in *Charlotte Business Journal (Vol. 25, October 15, 2010, No. 30, pp. 1)*
Pub: Charlotte Business Journal
Contact: Robert Morris, Editor
E-mail: rmorris@bizjournals.com
Ed: Will Boye. **Description:** Charlotte, North Carolina has become an attractive destination for out-of-town brokerage firms. Colliers International has signed an affiliate deal with Anthony and Company to set up shop in Charlotte. Grubb and Ellis Company, on the other hand, is planning to open an office in the city. **Availability:** Print; Online.

13153 ■ *"Brookfield Asset Management: A Perfect Predator"* in *Canadian Business (Vol. 83, July 20, 2010, No. 11-12, pp. 50)*
Pub: Rogers Media Inc.
Contact: Neil Spivak, Chief Executive Officer
Ed: Joanna Pachner. **Description:** Brookfield Asset Management CEO Bruce Flatt manages $108 billion worth of real estate and the company has become one of the world's biggest prime real estate owners since he became leader. Flatt says their goal is to earn a 12-15 percent compound annual return per share and that they would shrink in size if it meant reaching that goal. **Availability:** Online.

13154 ■ *"Brown's Goal: 1,300 New Apartments and Condos"* in *Business First of Buffalo (Vol. 30, February 28, 2014, No. 24, pp. 6)*
Pub: American City Business Journals, Inc.
Contact: Mike Olivieri, Executive Vice President
Released: February 28, 2014. **Price:** $140, Digital & Print; $115, Digital only. **Description:** Buffalo, New York Mayor Bryan Brown is planning for at least 1,300 new, market-rate residential units in the city's central business district over the next four years. The additional residential units are incorporated in Brown's larger strategy for creating a 24/7 downtown Buffalo. The impact of the residential development plan on the area's periphery is examined. **Availability:** Print; Online.

13155 ■ *"Bubble Trouble? Many Experts Say Seattle Housing Market Is Headed for a Fall"* in *Puget Sound Business Journal (Vol. 34, April 18, 2014, No. 53, pp. 4)*
Pub: American City Business Journals, Inc.
Contact: Mike Olivieri, Executive Vice President
Description: Redfin disclosed that nearly one third of homes listed in the real estate market in King County, Washington were sold above the listing price in February 2014 and it is forecast that the housing market is headed into a new bubble. Statistics indicate that the trend in rising prices is slowing even in the face of a declining supply of available homes. The impact of international buyers is also discussed.

13156 ■ *"Builder's Bankruptcy Fans Fears"* in *Crain's Cleveland Business (Vol. 28, October 22, 2007, No. 42, pp. 1)*
Pub: Crain Communications Inc.
Contact: K. C. Crain, President
Ed: Stan Bullard. **Description:** Whitlatch & Co., Northeast Ohio's largest builder by unit volume in the early 1990s, has filed for Chapter 11 bankruptcy. This is causing builders and others in the real estate industry to wonder how long and severe the housing slump will be and which companies will survive. **Availability:** Online.

13157 ■ *"Builder's Comeback Highlights Uptick in Demand for New Homes"* in *Boston Business Journal (Vol. 29, June 3, 2011, No. 4, pp. 1)*
Pub: Boston Business Journal
Contact: Carolyn M. Jones, President
E-mail: cmjones@bizjournals.com
Ed: Gary Haber. **Description:** The return of builder Michael Canock after a series of credit crisis and the funding for his new projects are discussed in light of the recent upsurge in the home-building industry in the Baltimore area. New single-family homes numbered 318 in first quarter 2011 which is a 20 percent increase from first quarter 2010.

13158 ■ *"Builders: Land Prices Up, Bank Lending Down"* in *Orlando Business Journal (Vol. 30, January 31, 2014, No. 32, pp. 5)*
Pub: American City Business Journals, Inc.
Contact: Mike Olivieri, Executive Vice President
Released: Weekly. **Price:** $8, introductory 4-week offer(Digital & Print). **Description:** A look at the views of residential real estate executives on the rising land prices and financing of construction is presented. The limited supply of lots in great locations has resulted in landowners raising asking prices. The real

estate downturn has also resulted in the reluctance of many banks to lend money to home builders to finance construction in Central Florida. **Availability:** Print; Online.

13159 ■ *"Buying a Short Sale Property: A Guide to Understanding the Short Sale Process and How to Profit From Short Sale"*
Released: September 26, 2014. **Price:** $6.09, Paperback. **Description:** A short sale is the process where a house is sold for less than the amount of money actually owed on it in order to avoid foreclosure. This trend is becoming more prevalent so it is important to understand the requirements and processes involved in purchasing a foreclosed home or property. **Availability:** Print.

13160 ■ *"C. Fla. Notches $5B in Real Estate Property Sales in Last 12 Months"* in *Orlando Business Journal (Vol. 31, July 4, 2014, No. 1, pp. 4)*
Pub: American City Business Journals, Inc.
Contact: Mike Olivieri, Executive Vice President
Released: Weekly. **Price:** $8, Introductory 4-week offer(Digital & Print). **Description:** Real estate company Real Capital Analytics reports sales volumes totaling $5 billion in Central Florida's commercial real estate market between June 2013 and May 2014. Real estate deals in the region reflect investor interest in the Orlando market, as private equity and development firms renovate existing properties or build new construction projects, thus increasing property values, creating jobs and boosting the local economy. **Availability:** Print; Online.

13161 ■ *"Cash Deals Are King, But Don't Reign Supreme In Birmingham"* in *Birmingham Business Journal (Vol. 31, May 16, 2014, No. 20, pp. 6)*
Pub: American City Business Journals, Inc.
Contact: Mike Olivieri, Executive Vice President
Released: Weekly; 16 May 14. **Price:** $4, introductory 4-week offer(Digital & Print). **Description:** Data from market research firm, RealtyTrac found that all-cash transactions in Birmingham, Alabama accounted for less than 31 percent of home sales in the first quarter of 2014, compared with a stronger all-cash transactions recorded by Southern metropolitan areas like Atlanta, Memphis and Charlotte. Ben Chenault of MortgageBanc sees a trend among average homebuyers who prefer cash over finance. **Availability:** Print; Online.

13162 ■ *"Cedar Fair to Solicit Bids for Geauga Lake"* in *Crain's Cleveland Business (Vol. 28, October 8, 2007, No. 40, pp. 1)*
Pub: Crain Communications Inc.
Contact: K. C. Crain, President
Ed: Stan Bullard. **Description:** Cedar Fair Entertainment Co. plans to seek sealed bids for the redevelopment of nearly 540 acres of their amusement park site in southwest Geauga County and northwest Portage County. **Availability:** Online.

13163 ■ *"Central Florida Real Estate Values to Level Out this Year"* in *Orlando Business Journal (Vol. 29, June 15, 2012, No. 54, pp. 1)*
Pub: Baltimore Business Journal
Contact: Rhonda Pringle, President
E-mail: rpringle@bizjournals.com
Ed: Anjali Fluker. **Description:** Property values in Central Florida are stabilizing with only a 1.2 percent decline in combined 2012 taxable values projected in Orange, Seminole, Osceola and Lake Counties, compared with 2011. A stable real estate market is said to be critical for the region, as it makes up 25 percent of the gross metropolitan product. **Availability:** Print; Online.

13164 ■ *"CNL's James Seneff Jr. Reveals 7 Ways to Grow Your Firm, Even in Down Times"* in *Orlando Business Journal (Vol. 30, May 16, 2014, No. 47, pp. 3)*
Pub: American City Business Journals, Inc.
Contact: Mike Olivieri, Executive Vice President

Released: Weekly. **Price:** $8, introductory 4-week offer(Digital & Print). **Description:** CNL Financial Group Inc. founder and executive chairman, James Seneff, Jr., offers tips on ways to succeed during down times in his keynote address at a University of Central Florida Real Estate Conference in Orlando. He advises entrepreneurs to be a contrarian and avoid following the pack. **Availability:** Print; Online.

13165 ■ *"Colliers Shifts Its Brokerage Home"* in *Charlotte Business Journal (Vol. 25, November 5, 2010, No. 33, pp. 1)*
Pub: Charlotte Business Journal
Contact: Robert Morris, Editor
E-mail: rmorris@bizjournals.com
Ed: Will Boye. **Description:** Colliers International signed a long-term affiliate agreement with commercial real estate firm Clarus Properties, in a move that would allow Colliers to resume business in Charlotte, North Carolina. Colliers also hired well known brokers Brad Grow and Brent Royall. **Availability:** Print; Online.

13166 ■ *"Columbia's JPB Raising $175M to Acquire Companies, Real Estate"* in *Boston Business Journal (Vol. 29, May 27, 2011, No. 3, pp. 1)*
Pub: Boston Business Journal
Contact: Carolyn M. Jones, President
E-mail: cmjones@bizjournals.com
Ed: Gary Haber. **Description:** JPB Enterprises is preparing to raise $175 million in its goal of acquiring companies and real estate that are major names in America. The $75 million will be raised for a buyout fund that will target wide range of industries while the $100 million will be used for land investment projects in the Florida Panhandle. Baltimore firms are expected to benefit from this deal. **Availability:** Print; Online.

13167 ■ *"Coming Soon: Bailouts of Fannie and Freddie"* in *Barron's (Vol. 88, July 14, 2008, No. 28, pp. 14)*
Pub: Dow Jones & Company Inc.
Contact: Almar Latour, Chief Executive Officer
Ed: Jonathan R. Laing. **Description:** Assurances from the government that Fannie Mae and Freddie Mac are adequately capitalized and able to carry on their duties as guarantors or owners of over $5 trillion of U.S. home mortgages are designed to keep both entities afloat until they attempt to raise $10 billion in new equity. The government would assume any losses in a bailout and owners of the banks' papers would profit as yields drop. **Availability:** Online.

13168 ■ *"Commercial Real Estate Brokers See Steady Growth In 2014"* in *Sacramento Business Journal (Vol. 30, January 10, 2014, No. 46, pp. 3)*
Pub: American City Business Journals, Inc.
Contact: Mike Olivieri, Executive Vice President
Released: Weekly. **Price:** $4, introductory 4-week offer(Digital & Print). **Description:** Analysts believe that the outlook for commercial real estate in Sacramento, California is positive. However, Elliot Williams of Jones Lang LaSalle thinks that the office market's recovery will depend on leases by smaller companies. Sacramento reported 10,000-square-feet of positive absorption in the fourth quarter of 2013. **Availability:** Print; Online.

13169 ■ *"Commercial Real Estate May Be Cooling, While Residential Clamors to Meet Demand"* in *Houston Business Journal (Vol. 44, January 3, 2014, No. 35, pp. 6)*
Pub: American City Business Journals, Inc.
Contact: Mike Olivieri, Executive Vice President
Released: January 03, 2014. **Description:** Greater Houston Partnership has predicted that the real estate industry will remain active for the years ahead in Houston, Texas. However, commercial real estate might cool down while residential sales are expected to remain hot with demand outpacing supply. Houston's construction boom in each sector is also discussed. **Availability:** Print; Online.

13170 ■ *"Con-Way Development Back in High Gear" in Business Journal Portland (Vol. 27, November 5, 2010, No. 36, pp. 1)*
Pub: Portland Business Journal
Contact: Andy Giegerich, Managing Editor
E-mail: agiegerich@bizjournals.com

Ed: Wendy Culverwell. **Description:** Trucking firm Con-Way Inc. intends to sell parcels of land from a property comprising 16 blocks and 20 prime acres west of the Pearl District in Portland, Oregon. In 2009, Con-Way abandoned plans to sell the property. As Con-Way reclaims control over design and usage of the property, it also expressed willingness to cooperate with a master developer on a related real estate project. **Availability:** Print; Online.

13171 ■ *"Contingent Offers: Weighing the Risk" in Crain's Chicago Business (Vol. 31, April 21, 2008, No. 16, pp. 48)*
Pub: Crain Communications Inc.
Contact: Barry Asin, President

Ed: Darci Smith. **Description:** Interview with Greer Haseman, the broker-owner of Town Square Associates, who discusses contingent offers in a challenging housing market. **Availability:** Online.

13172 ■ *"A Conversation with: Renea Butler" in Crain's Detroit Business (Vol. 25, June 8, 2009, No. 23, pp. 12)*
Pub: Crain Communications Inc.
Contact: Barry Asin, President

Ed: Ryan Beene. **Description:** Renea Butler, vice president of administration and human resources for Real Estate One Inc. in Southfield as well as vice president for public relations for the Human Resource Association of Greater Detroit, talks about how the economy has affected human resource services. **Availability:** Print; Online.

13173 ■ *"A Conversation With: Ron Gantner, Jones Lang LaSalle" in Crain's Detroit Business (Vol. 24, October 6, 2008, No. 40, pp. 9)*
Pub: Crain Communications Inc.
Contact: Barry Asin, President

Description: Interview with Ron Gantner who is a corporate real estate adviser with the real estate company Jones Lang LaSalle as well as the company's executive vice president and part of the tenant advisory team; Gantner speaks about the impact that the Wall Street crisis is having on the commercial real estate market in Detroit. **Availability:** Print; Online.

13174 ■ *"Cool on Chicago Office Properties" in Crain's Chicago Business (Vol. 31, March 31, 2008, No. 13, pp. 16)*
Pub: Crain Communications Inc.
Contact: Barry Asin, President

Ed: Eddie Baeb. **Description:** Investors predict values on Chicago office buildings to drop 1.3 percent over the next year. **Availability:** Online.

13175 ■ *"Could Bond OK Bring Back the Charlotte Housing Battle?" in Charlotte Business Journal (Vol. 25, November 5, 2010, No. 33, pp. 1)*
Pub: Charlotte Business Journal
Contact: Robert Morris, Editor
E-mail: rmorris@bizjournals.com

Ed: Susan Stabley. **Description:** The approval of the $15 million housing bond in Charlotte, North Carolina could bring back the debates on housing in the region. Protesters have opposed affordable housing developments that were proposed in the area since 2008. Other information on the recently approved housing bond and on other real estate issues in North Carolina is presented. **Availability:** Print; Online.

13176 ■ *Crittenden Directory of Real Estate Financing*
Pub: Crittenden Research Inc.
Contact: Linda Frabl, Editor
URL(s): crittendenreport.com/directory

Released: Bimonthly **Description:** Covers over 300 major lenders, investors, and joint ventures engaged in commercial and residential real estate financing and investing. **Entries include:** Company name, nickname, total assets, typical rate, real estate investment portfolio value, production totals (broken down by type of investment), maximum and minimum loan/investment amounts; preferred types of loans, interest rates, fees, and related data; names, addresses, phone numbers of contacts, pension fund name. **Arrangement:** Geographical (by principal area of lending activity). **Indexes:** Type of real estate, company name, project type. **Availability:** Print.

13177 ■ *"Design '07 (Housing): Prince of the City" in Canadian Business (Vol. 80, November 19, 2007, No. 23, pp. 62)*
Pub: Rogers Media Inc.
Contact: Neil Spivak, Chief Executive Officer

Ed: Rachel Pulfer. **Description:** Robert Fung and the Salilent Group aim to revive the poverty-stricken communities in Vancouver by transforming the city's old buildings into designer condominiums using city incentives. Fung and his partners have increased property values in the most unlikely neighborhoods by creating luxury real estate. Fung's recommendations on Vancouver's real estate development are given. **Availability:** Online.

13178 ■ *"Detroit Residential Market Slows; Bright Spots Emerge" in Crain's Detroit Business (Vol. 24, October 6, 2008, No. 40, pp. 11)*
Pub: Crain Communications Inc.
Contact: Barry Asin, President

Ed: Daniel Duggan. **Description:** Discusses the state of the residential real estate market in Detroit; although condominium projects receive the most attention, deals for single-family homes are taking place in greater numbers due to financing issues. Buyers can purchase a single family home with a 3.5 percent down payment compared to 20 percent for some condo deals because of the number of first-time homebuyer programs under the Federal Housing Administration.

13179 ■ *"Developer Backs Out of Major Bastrop Project" in Austin Business JournalInc. (Vol. 28, December 19, 2008, No. 40, pp. 1)*

Description: Weingarten Realty Investors, a Houston, Texas-based real estate company, has backed out of its contract on more than 1 million square feet of retail space at the County Road 304 and State Highway 71 corner in Bastrop, Texas, according to landowner Tom Brundage. Analysts say that the Bastrop area is not ready for big retail projects. **Availability:** Print; Online.

13180 ■ *"Developer Tries to Bring Homes to Buda" in Austin Business JournalInc. (Vol. 28, December 26, 2008, No. 41, pp. 1)*

Description: Real estate developer Jeremiah Venture LP is planning a residential, single-family development on about 600 acres near Buda, Texas. The company also plans to construct a membrane waste treatment plant, and has applied to do land application. However, several groups have come forward to ask for more information on the application due to concerns about soil density. **Availability:** Print; Online.

13181 ■ *"Developers Give Big to Stephanie Rawlings-Blake Bid for Mayor" in Baltimore Business Journal (Vol. 29, August 26, 2011, No. 16, pp. 1)*
Pub: Boston Business Journal
Contact: Carolyn M. Jones, President
E-mail: cmjones@bizjournals.com

Ed: Scott Dance. **Description:** Mayor Stephanie Rawlings-Blake received thousands of dollars in her political campaign from companies of real estate developers who are vying to build key development projects in Baltimore, Maryland. Rawlings-Blake cre-

ated a major fundraising advantage over other mayoral candidates with the help of those contributions. **Availability:** Online.

13182 ■ *"Developers Give City Dwellings a Modern Spin" in Crain's Cleveland Business (Vol. 28, November 5, 2007, No. 44, pp. 18)*
Pub: Crain Communications Inc.
Contact: K. C. Crain, President

Ed: Stan Bullard. **Description:** Cleveland is increasingly becoming a canvas for fresh, cutting-edge design due to several recent projects, some at prominent sites. **Availability:** Online.

13183 ■ *"Developers Move Forward Along Seattle's Waterfront" in Puget Sound Business Journal (Vol. 35, July 25, 2014, No. 14, pp. 4)*
Pub: American City Business Journals, Inc.
Contact: Mike Olivieri, Executive Vice President

Released: Weekly. **Description:** Seattle, Washington's waterfront development continues to flourish with plans for two more projects on the horizon. Brick Road Holdings is planning construction of a seven-story Natasha market-rate project with 160 apartments. Six other new projects by the following companies are profiled: Schuster Group, Gerding Edlen, Mack Urban, Daniels Real Estate, Goodman Real Estate, and Martin Selig Real Estate. **Availability:** Print; Online.

13184 ■ *"Developers Poised to Pull Trigers" in Boston Business Journal (Vol. 30, November 12, 2010, No. 42, pp. 1)*

Description: Large residential projects are expected to break ground in Boston, Massachusetts in 2011, as real estate developers expect growth for the industry. Real estate experts expect more than 2,000 rental units to be available by 2011. Information on key real estate projects in Boston is presented. **Availability:** Print; Online.

13185 ■ *Dictionary of Real Estate Terms*
Pub: Barron's Educational Series Inc.
Contact: Manuel H. Barron, Contact

Ed: Jack P. Friedman, Jack C. Harris, J. Bruce Lindeman. **Released:** 9th edition. **Price:** $16.99, paperback, plus shipping charges $5.99. **Description:** More than 2,500 real estate terms relating to mortgages and financing, brokerage law, architecture, rentals and leases, property insurance, and more. **Availability:** E-book; Print.

13186 ■ *"Digital Realty Routes $50 Million for Data Center Improvements" in St.Louis Business Journal (Vol. 33, September 14, 2012, No. 3, pp. 1)*
Pub: Baltimore Business Journal
Contact: Rhonda Pringle, President
E-mail: rpringle@bizjournals.com

Description: Digital Realty Trust is planning to invest up to $50 millionto renovate its data center in Saint Louis, Missouri. The facility is expected to become one of the largest data centers in the region. **Availability:** Print; Online.

13187 ■ *"Docs Might Hold Cure for Baltimore-Area Real Estate, Banks" in Baltimore Business Journal (Vol. 28, November 5, 2010, No. 26, pp. 1)*
Pub: Baltimore Business Journal
Contact: Rhonda Pringle, President
E-mail: rpringle@bizjournals.com

Ed: Gary Haber. **Description:** Health care providers, including physicians are purchasing their office space instead of renting it as banks lower interest rates to 6 percent on mortgages for medical offices. The rise in demand offers relief to the commercial real estate market. It has also resulted in a boom in building new medical offices. **Availability:** Print; Online.

13188 ■ *"East-Side Real Estate Forum Detours To Grand Rapids" in Crain's Detroit Business (Vol. 24, October 6, 2008, No. 40, pp. 17)*
Pub: Crain Communications Inc.
Contact: Barry Asin, President

Ed: Daniel Duggan. **Description:** Tom Wackerman was elected chairman of the University of Michigan-Urban Land Institute Real Estate Forum and proposed that the annual conference be held in Grand Rapids due to the brisk economic activity he was finding there; although the idea was initially met with resistance, the plan to introduce East-siders to the West side began receiving more enthusiasm due to the revitalization of the area, which was once considered to have a bleak outlook. Many are hoping to learn the lessons of those who were able to change a negative economic climate into a positive one in which the cooperation of private business and government can work together to accomplish goals. **Availability:** Print; Online.

13189 ▪ "Eleni Reed: C&W Gets Green Star" in Crain's New York Business (Vol. 24, January 6, 2008, No. 1, pp. 25)
Pub: Crain Communications, Inc.
Contact: Jessica Botos, Manager, Marketing
E-mail: jessica.botos@crainsnewyork.com
Ed: Theresa Agovino. **Description:** Cushman & Wakefield Inc. has hired Eleni Reed as director of sustainability strategies; the real estate firm wants to ensure that the 500 million square feet of office space it manages around the globe meets environmental standards.

13190 ▪ "Empty Lots Could Be Full of Promise" in San Francisco Business Times (Vol. 28, March 14, 2014, No. 34, pp. 4)
Pub: American City Business Journals, Inc.
Contact: Mike Olivieri, Executive Vice President
Price: $4, Introductory 4-Week Offer(Digital Only).
Description: San Francisco, California officials are looking at the city's own landholdings in order to start constructing new homes. However, the use of city-owned land does not ensure that the home permit process will be trouble-free. **Availability:** Print; Online.

13191 ▪ "Energy Efficiency Ordinance Softened" in Austin Business JournalInc. (Vol. 28, October 3, 2008, No. 29)
Pub: Austin Business Journal
Contact: Rachel McGrath, Director
E-mail: rmcgrath@bizjournals.com
Ed: Jean Kwon. **Description:** City of Austin has eliminated mandatory energy efficiency upgrades to single-family housing as a condition for selling or renting homes or buildings. The new law proposes that an energy performance audit be conducted on single-family homes before being sold and the results of the audit disclosed to perspectives buyers. **Availability:** Print; Online.

13192 ▪ "Everyone Out of the Pool" in Barron's (Vol. 89, July 20, 2009, No. 29, pp. 18)
Pub: Dow Jones & Company Inc.
Contact: Almar Latour, Chief Executive Officer
Ed: Sandra Ward. **Description:** Shares of Pool Corp. could drop as continued weakness in the housing market weakens the market for swimming pool equipment. The company's shares are trading at $18.29, about 20 times projected 2009 earnings of $0.91 a share. **Availability:** Online.

13193 ▪ "Eyes to the Sky" in Canadian Business (Vol. 80, March 26, 2007, No. 7, pp. 33)
Description: The growth and prices of condominium market in the Canada are analyzed. **Availability:** Online.

13194 ▪ "Fifth Third Spinoff Eyes More Space" in Business Courier (Vol. 27, July 16, 2010, No. 11, pp. 1)
Pub: Business Courier
Ed: Dan Monk, Steve Watkins. **Description:** Electronic-funds transfer company Fifth Third Solutions (FTPS), a spinoff of Fifth Third Bancorp, is seeking as much as 200,000 square feet of new office space in Ohio. The bank's sale of 51 percent ownership stake to Boston-based Advent International Corporation has paved the way for the growth of

FTPS. How real estate brokers' plans have responded to FTPS' growth mode is discussed. **Availability:** Print; Online.

13195 ▪ "Florida Fast 100: D&D Construction Services" in South Florida Business Journal (Vol. 35, September 19, 2014, No. 8, pp. 16)
Pub: American City Business Journals, Inc.
Contact: Mike Olivieri, Executive Vice President
Description: Profile of D and D Construction, who reports increased earnings in 2013 totaling $26.5 million. The increase has been attributed to the commercial real estate market's recovery from the economic recession. The company is focusing on offering hospitality (restaurant, hotel) projects. **Availability:** Online.

13196 ▪ The Foreclosure of America: Life Inside Countrywide Home Loans and the Selling of the American Dream
Pub: Berkley Trade/Penguin Group USA Inc.
Ed: Adam Michaelson. **Released:** January 06, 2009.
Price: $6.99, E-book; Paperback. **Description:** An inside look at Countrywide Home Loans and the mortgage crisis. **Availability:** E-book; Print.

13197 ▪ "Former Schaefer & Strohminger Dealerships to Hit Auction Block" in Baltimore Business Journal (Vol. 28, September 10, 2010)
Pub: Baltimore Business Journal
Contact: Rhonda Pringle, President
E-mail: rpringle@bizjournals.com
Ed: Gary Haber. **Description:** Maryland's real estate developers have a chance to vie for almost 11 acres of prime Baltimore County real estate that are on the auction block. The five properties were once home to Schaefer and Strohminger car dealerships and were located in the county's busiest areas. Other potential uses for the properties are also discussed.

13198 ▪ "Gen Z May Value Ownership More than Millennials Do" inRealtor Magazine (November 22, 2019)
URL(s): magazine.realtor/daily-news/2019/11/22/gen-z-may-value-ownership-more-than-millennials-do
Released: November 22, 2019. **Description:** Freddie Mac researchers conducted a survey on people aged 14 to 23, Generation Z, and found that they are more likely to want to own a home and to purchase it by the time they turn 30. Millennials, on the other hand, did not have these same thoughts at the same age. **Availability:** Online.

13199 ▪ "Generation Y Driving Portland Multifamily" in Daily Journal of Commerce, Portland (October 29, 2010)
Ed: Nick Bjork. **Description:** Generation Y, young adults between the ages of 18-30, are interested in multifamily residents in the Portland, Oregon area. Developers in the area, particularly North Portland, have recognized this trend and are looking into multifamily investments.

13200 ▪ "GMREB/Analysis of the Resale Market-First Quarter 2007: Year Off to a Great Start" in Marketwired (May 14, 2007)
Pub: Comtex News Network Inc.
Contact: Kan Devnani, President
Description: According to statistics gathered by the Greater Montreal Real Estate Board (GMREB), the Montreal census metropolitan area (CMA) resale market was vigorous in the first quarter of 2007 yielding 10 percent more existing homes being than the first quarter of 2006. **Availability:** Print; Online.

13201 ▪ "GM's Mortgage Unit Deal Brings in $9 Billion" in Globe & Mail (March 24, 2006, pp. B3)
Ed: Shawn McCarthy. **Description:** General Motors Corp. sells General Motors Acceptance Corp.'s commercial real estate division to Kohlberg Kravis Roberts & Co. Five Mile Capital Partners LLC and Goldman Sachs Capital Partners. The reasons behind the deal are presented. **Availability:** Print; Online.

13202 ▪ "Goldbelt Inc.: Targeting Shareholder Development" in Alaska Business Monthly (Vol. 27, October 2011, No. 10, pp. 108)
Pub: Alaska Business Publishing Company Inc.
Contact: Charles Bell, Vice President, Sales and Marketing
E-mail: cbell@akbizmag.com
Ed: Tracy Kalytiak. **Description:** Profile of Goldbelt Inc., the company that has changed its original focus of timber to real estate to tourism and then to government contracting opportunities. **Availability:** Print; Online.

13203 ▪ "A Good Sign for Commercial Real Estate?" in Austin Business JournalInc. (Vol. 29, December 18, 2009, No. 41, pp. 1)
Pub: Austin Business Journal
Contact: Rachel McGrath, Director
E-mail: rmcgrath@bizjournals.com
Ed: Kate Harrington. **Description:** Factors that could contribute to the reemergence of the commercial mortgage-backed securities market in Texas are discussed. These securities can potentially boost the commercial real estate market statewide as well as nationwide. Commercial mortgage-backed securities origination in 2009 is worth less that $1 billion, compared with $238 billion in 2008. **Availability:** Online.

13204 ▪ "Gray Matters: An Aging Workforce Has Mass. Companies Scrambling to Deal with 'Silver Tsunami'" in Austin Business Journal (Vol. 34, May 30, 2014, No. 15, pp. 8)
Pub: American City Business Journals, Inc.
Contact: Mike Olivieri, Executive Vice President
Description: Profiles of Seniors Real Estate Inc. Institute founders Nikki and Bruce Buckelew are presented. Nikki has focused on providing real estate agents with training and Webinars. Their career achievements are also included. **Availability:** Print; Online.

13205 ▪ "The Great Fall of China" in Canadian Business (Vol. 85, June 11, 2012, No. 10, pp. 26)
Ed: Michael McCullough. **Description:** China has a growing influence over the future of Canada's economy as emerging economies and commodity prices recover from the recession. Among the problems unique to China which could impact the Canadian economy are the housing market, its demographic risk and the lack of transparency in the corporate and financial sector. **Availability:** Online.

13206 ▪ "Green Housing for the Rest of Us" in Inc. (November 2007, pp. 128-129)
Ed: Nitasha Tiku. **Description:** Profile of Full Spectrum NY, real estate developer firm, offering residences at the Kalahari, a green high-rise with state-of-the-art features at a reasonable price. **Availability:** Online.

13207 ▪ "Growth in Fits and Starts" in Canadian Business (Vol. 83, July 20, 2010, No. 11-12, pp. 18)
Description: US home sales and manufacturing indicators have dropped and fears of a double-dip recession are widespread. However, a chief economist says that this is endemic to what can be seen after a recession caused by a financial crisis. In Canada, consumer optimism is rising and anxiety over losing one's job is waning. **Availability:** Print; Online.

13208 ▪ "Hawaii Rides Retail Strength Into New Year" in Pacific Business News (Vol. 51, January 17, 2014, No. 48, pp. 3)
Pub: American City Business Journals, Inc.
Contact: Mike Olivieri, Executive Vice President
Released: Weekly. **Price:** $4, introductory 4-week offer(Digital only). **Description:** CBRE Hawaii's Fourth Quarter 2013 Hawaii Retail MarketView shows positive absorption, lower vacancy rates and stable lease rents with large transaction that will accelerate

major retail development and redevelopment. Hawaii's real estate market remained strong in 2013. **Availability:** Print; Online.

13209 ■ *"High-End Blunders" in Crain's Chicago Business (Vol. 31, April 21, 2008, No. 16, pp. 54)*
Pub: Crain Communications Inc.
Contact: Barry Asin, President
Ed: Laura Bianchi. **Description:** Discusses some of the biggest errors sellers make that keep their homes from selling including: pricing too high; expecting to recoup the cost of very high-end amenities and decor; avant-garde decorating; owners that hover when the house is being shown; stripping the home of top-quality light fixtures and hardware and replacing them with inferior versions with the assumption that the new buyer will come in with their own decorator and redo it; and poorly maintained properties. **Availability:** Online.

13210 ■ *"Home Developers Buy 9 Acres in Lakewood" in Dallas Business Journal (Vol. 35, August 10, 2012, No. 48, pp. 1)*
Pub: Baltimore Business Journal
Contact: Rhonda Pringle, President
E-mail: rpringle@bizjournals.com
Ed: Candace Carlisle. **Description:** Megatel Homes, together with Centurion American Development Group, has purchased a 9.4 acre land in Lakewood, Dallas for $35 million. Centurion plans to begin real estate development of 59 single-family home lots in the next three months, while Megatel plans construction to build Tudor style homes. The infill land is considered a prime investment for its desireable location.

13211 ■ *"Home Prices Sag" in Crain's Chicago Business (Vol. 31, April 28, 2008, No. 17, pp. 3)*
Pub: Crain Communications Inc.
Contact: Barry Asin, President
Ed: Alby Gallun. **Description:** Since the slump in the housing market is continuing with no sign of recovery, Chicago-area home prices are poised for an even steeper drop this year. In 2007, the region's home prices fell nearly 5 percent and according to a forecast by Fiserv Inc., they will decline 8.1 percent this year and another 2.2 percent in 2009. Statistical data included. **Availability:** Online.

13212 ■ *"Home Sweet (Second) Home" in Baltimore Business Journal (Vol. 30, May 25, 2012, No. 3, pp. 1)*
Ed: Leigh Somerville. **Description:** Home prices in Maryland have declined in 2012. A number of affluent homebuyers have been purchasing vacation homes in the state. **Availability:** Print; Online.

13213 ■ *"Homebuilder Confidence Buried Under Snow" in Birmingham Business Journal (Vol. 31, February 21, 2014, No. 8, pp. 7)*
Pub: American City Business Journals, Inc.
Contact: Mike Olivieri, Executive Vice President
Released: Weekly. **Description:** The National Association of Home Builders/Wells Fargo Housing Market Index has fallen by 10 points from the score of 56 in January to 46 in February as a result of 2014's harsh winter. The index is based on the survey of home builders' perceptions on the current and near-term housing market. **Availability:** Print; Online.

13214 ■ *"Homebuilding Thrives on Lot Prices" in Memphis Business Journal (Vol. 33, February 24, 2012, No. 46, pp. 1)*
Pub: Baltimore Business Journal
Contact: Rhonda Pringle, President
E-mail: rpringle@bizjournals.com
Ed: Christopher Sheffield. **Description:** Homebuilders in Memphis, Tennessee have survived the economic crises owing to the decrease in prices of lots. However, the increasein the purchase of lots is seen to adversely impact the sector in the long run. **Availability:** Print; Online.

13215 ■ *The Housing Boom and Bust*
Ed: Thomas Sowell. **Released:** Revised edition. **Price:** $10.99, e-book; $17.99; C$23.49. **Description:** An explanation of the economics and politics of the housing boom and its collapse. **Availability:** E-book; Print.

13216 ■ *"Housing Markets Still Struggling" in Montana Business Quarterly (Vol. 49, Spring 2011, No. 1, pp. 17)*
Pub: University of Montana Bureau of Business and Economic Research
Contact: Patrick Barkey, Director
E-mail: patrick.barkey@business.umt.edu
Ed: Scott Rickard. **Released:** Quarterly. **Description:** Montana's economic conditions are a bit better than national averages. Data ranked by state, year-over-year price change, and total price peak is presented, along with statistical data for the entire nation. **Availability:** Online.

13217 ■ *"Housing Slide Picks Up Speed" in Crain's Chicago Business (Vol. 31, April 19, 2008, No. 16, pp. 2)*
Pub: Crain Communications Inc.
Contact: Barry Asin, President
Ed: Eddie Baeb. **Description:** According to Tracy Cross & Associates Inc., a real estate consultancy, sales of new homes in the Chicago area dropped 61 percent from the year-earlier period which is more bad news for homebuilders, contractors and real estate agents who are eager for an indication that market conditions are improving. **Availability:** Online.

13218 ■ *"How To Make Finance Work: The U.S. Financial Sector Has Boomed, But That Hasn't Always Been Good News For the Rest of the Economy" in Harvard Business Review (Vol. 90, March 2012, No. 3, pp. 104)*
Pub: Harvard Business Review Press
Contact: Moderna V. Pfizer, Contact
Ed: David S. Scharfstein, Robin Greenwood. **Price:** $8.95, hardcover. **Description:** The growth of the financial sector has hindered overall US growth by shifting money from productive investments into residential real estate, and through high professional investment management costs. Private sector innovation and discipline will be needed to correct these flaws, as will regulatory changes. **Availability:** PDF; Online.

13219 ■ *"Identity Theft Can Have Long-Lasting Impact" in Providence Business News (Vol. 28, February 10, 2014, No. 45, pp. 7)*
Pub: American City Business Journals, Inc.
Contact: Mike Olivieri, Executive Vice President
URL(s): pbn.com/identity-theft-can-have-long-lasting -impact94959
Description: According to mortgage credit experts, recently reported massive data breaches at Nieman Marcus, Target, and other merchants could have negative impacts on several real estate deals scheduled for the upcoming months. Although victims are not liable for the unlawful debts, their credit reports and scores can be damaged for months, thus endangering loan applications for mortgages on home sale transactions. **Availability:** Online.

13220 ■ *"Illinois Farmland Tops $11,000 Per Acre" in Farm Industry News (June 27, 2011)*
Pub: Informa Business Media, Inc.
Contact: Charlie McCurdy, President
Ed: Karen McMahon. **Description:** Farmland property in Illinois continues to grow in value, selling for $11,000 per acre. Statistical data included. **Availability:** Online.

13221 ■ *"In Control: Tips For Navigating a Buyer's Market" in Black Enterprise (Vol. 38, December 2007, No. 5, pp. 64)*
Pub: Earl G. Graves Ltd.
Contact: Earl Graves, Jr., President
Ed: Erinn R. Johnson. **Description:** Tips are given to help would-be home buyers. The importance of finding a good real estate agent is stressed.

13222 ■ *"Industrial Vacancies Hit High" in Crain's Chicago Business (Apr. 21, 2008)*
Pub: Crain Communications Inc.
Contact: Barry Asin, President
Ed: Alby Gallun. **Description:** Hitting its highest level in four years in the first quarter is the Chicago-area industrial vacancy rate, a sign that the slumping economy is depressing demand for warehouse and manufacturing space. **Availability:** Online.

13223 ■ *Internet Resources and Services for International Real Estate Information*
Pub: Greenwood Electronic Media
URL(s): www.bloomsbury.com/us/internet-resources -and-services-for-international-real-estate-informa tion-9780313073779
Released: Latest edition: February 2001. **Price:** $56.88, for e-book; $86.39, for eBook (PDF) Australia; $83.16, for e-book (PDF) Canada; $103.95, for paperback Canada; $71.10, for paperback. **Description:** Covers internet sources related to international real estate, finance, and investment. **Availability:** E-book; Print.

13224 ■ *"Is Fannie Mae the Next Government Bailout?" in Barron's (Vol. 88, March 10, 2008, No. 10, pp. 21)*
Pub: Dow Jones & Company Inc.
Contact: Almar Latour, Chief Executive Officer
Ed: Jonathan R. Laing. **Description:** Fannie Mae may need a government bailout as it faces huge hits brought about by the effects of the housing crisis. The shares of the government-sponsored enterprise have dropped 65 percent since the housing crisis began. **Availability:** Online.

13225 ■ *"It Could Be Worse" in Barron's (Vol. 89, July 27, 2009, No. 30, pp. 5)*
Pub: Dow Jones & Company Inc.
Contact: Almar Latour, Chief Executive Officer
Ed: Alan Abelson. **Description:** Media sources are being fooled by corporate America who is peddling an economic recovery rather than reality as shown by the report of a rise in existing home sales which boosted the stock market even if it was a seasonal phenomenon. The phrase "things could be worse" sums up the reigning investment philosophy in the U.S. and this has been stirring up the market. **Availability:** Online.

13226 ■ *"KC Incentives Debate Rages on Unabated" in The Business Journal-Serving Metropolitan Kansas City (Vol. 26, September 5, 2008, No. 52)*
Pub: American City Business Journals, Inc.
Contact: Mike Olivieri, Executive Vice President
Ed: Rob Roberts. **Description:** Debate on the new economic development and incentives policy adopted by the Kansas City Council is still on. The city's Planned Industrial Expansion Authority has rejected a standard property tax abatement proposal. The real estate development community has opposed the rejection of proposed the tax incentives policy. **Availability:** Online.

13227 ■ *"Labor Shortage Creates Growing Pains" in Orlando Business Journal (Vol. 30, January 31, 2014, NO. 32, pp. 5)*
Pub: American City Business Journals, Inc.
Contact: Mike Olivieri, Executive Vice President
Released: January 31, 2014. **Description:** The reactions of residential real estate industry executives on the labor shortage created by the growing demand for new homes is presented. There were plenty of tradesmen and laborers on hand when the housing market recovery began, however, construction management faces labor competition from other builders and this trend slows the industry. **Availability:** Print; Online.

13228 ■ *"Land Squeeze Stalls Portland Homebuilders" in Business Journal Portland (Vol. 31, March 21, 2014, No. 3, pp. 4)*
Pub: American City Business Journals, Inc.
Contact: Mike Olivieri, Executive Vice President

Released: March 21, 2014. **Price:** $4, Introductory 4-Week Offer(Digital & Print). **Description:** Homebuilders in Portland, Oregon are building fewer homes that before the recession due to the impact of the 2008 economic collapse and the lack of available land on which to build. Prices in the residential real estate market are expected to increase as new single family home construction fails to keep pace with growing demand. **Availability:** Print; Online.

13229 ■ "Large Homes can be Energy Efficient Too" in Contractor (Vol. 56, October 2009, No. 10, pp. 5)

Ed: Candace Roulo. **Description:** Eco Estate at Briggs Chaney subdivision in Silver Spring, Maryland has model houses that use sustainable technologies and products and the homes that will be built on the subdivision will feature some of the technologies featured on the model home. The energy efficient HVAC system of the model homes are discussed. **Availability:** Print; Online.

13230 ■ "Largest Commercial Real Estate Brokerages" in Dallas Business Journal (Vol. 37, March 14, 2014, No. 27, pp. 8)

Pub: American City Business Journals, Inc.

Contact: Mike Olivieri, Executive Vice President

Description: The largest commercial real estate brokerages in Texas as of March 14, 2014, ranked by number of local licensed professionals, are listed. Jones Lang LaSalle got the top spot. Meanwhile, CBRE ranked second. **Availability:** Print; Online.

13231 ■ "Latino Real Estate Investments Are Increasing at High Rate" in Atlanta Agent Magazine (October 7, 2021)

Ed: Emily Mack. **Released:** October 07, 2021. **Description:** Discusses the trends released by the National Association of Hispanic Real Estate Professionals regarding homeownership and real estate holdings.

13232 ■ "Local Industrial Vacancies Climb" in Crain's Chicago Business (Vol. 31, November 17, 2008, No. 46, pp. 18)

Pub: Crain Communications Inc.

Contact: Barry Asin, President

Ed: Eddie Baeb. **Description:** Demand for local industrial real estate has declined dramatically as companies that use warehouse and factory space struggle to survive in an ailing economy. According to a report by Colliers Bennett & Kahnweiler Inc., a commercial real estate brokerage, the regional vacancy rate has risen to 9.86 percent in the third quarter, the fourth straight increase and the highest in the past 14 years. **Availability:** Online.

13233 ■ Loopholes of Real Estate: Secrets of Successful Real Estate Investing

Pub: Grand Central Publishing

Contact: Michael Pietsch, Chairman

Released: Second edition. **Description:** Knowledge, planning, and building a team of advisor and mentors is key to successful real estate investments. **Availability:** unabridged; Download; Audio.

13234 ■ "Magellan Companies Establishes Century 21 Beachhead in Boise" in Idaho Business Review (September 15, 2014)

Pub: BridgeTower Media

Contact: Adam Reinebach, President

Description: New Jersey-based Century 21, the largest real estate franchise worldwide, has entered the Idaho market under the name Century 21 Magellan Realty with five agents. Wesley Flacker, builder, home renovator, broker, and property manager purchased the franchise and expects to have 60 agents by 2015.

13235 ■ "A Matter of Perspective" in Business Journal-Portland (Vol. 24, November 2, 2007, No. 35, pp. 1)

Pub: Portland Business Journal

Contact: Andy Giegerich, Managing Editor

E-mail: agiegerich@bizjournals.com

Ed: Andy Giegerich. **Description:** Oregon Governor Ted Kulongoski assembled the Mortgage Lending Work Group, made up of members of the mortgage industry and consumer groups, to recommend possible bills for the Oregon Senate and House to consider. How its members try to balance philosophical differences in mortgage lending rules is discussed. **Availability:** Online.

13236 ■ "Md. Housing Leaders Race to Stem Rising Tide of Foreclosures: Neighborhood Watch" in Baltimore Business Journal (Vol. 28, July 23, 2010, No. 11, pp. 1)

Pub: Baltimore Business Journal

Contact: Rhonda Pringle, President

E-mail: rpringle@bizjournals.com

Ed: Daniel J. Sernovitz. **Description:** Maryland government and housing leaders are set to spend $100 million in federal funding to stem the increase in foreclosures in the area. The federal funding is seen as inadequate to resolve the problem of foreclosures. **Availability:** Print.

13237 ■ "Meet the Next Big Name in Residential Construction" in Houston Business Journal (Vol. 44, February 21, 2014, No. 42, pp. 8)

Pub: American City Business Journals, Inc.

Contact: Mike Olivieri, Executive Vice President

Released: Weekly. **Price:** $4, introductory 4-week offer(Digital only). **Description:** Hillwood Communities of Dallas, Texas will break ground on the Pomona master-planned community in Manvel, 20 miles south of downtown Houston. The development will include 2,100 single-family homes ranging from $250,000 to $400,000, a new elementary school and a new junior high school. **Availability:** Print; Online.

13238 ■ "A Model Development" in Crain's Cleveland Business (Vol. 28, October 1, 2007, No. 39, pp. 12)

Pub: Crain Communications Inc.

Contact: K. C. Crain, President

Ed: Scott Suttell. **Description:** Profile a Forest City Enterprises Inc., a firm that is developing a project in New Mexico called Mesa del Sol. The Albuquerque development is being seen as the vanguard of master-planned communities with its high-tech economic development center which is expected to become the site of 60,000 jobs, 38,000 homes and a town center. **Availability:** PDF.

13239 ■ "Myths of Deleveraging" in Barron's (Vol. 90, August 23, 2010, No. 34, pp. M14)

Pub: Barron's Editorial & Corporate Headquarters

Ed: Gene Epstein. **Description:** The opposite is true against reports about deleveraging or the decrease in credit since inflation-adjusted-investment factories and equipment rose 7.8 percent in the first quarter of 2010. On consumer deleveraging, sales of homes through credit is weak but there is a trend towards more realistic homeownership and consumer spending on durable goods rose 8.8 percent. **Availability:** Online.

13240 ■ "The Neighborhood Watch" in Hawaii Business (Vol. 53, March 2008, No. 9, pp. 36)

Pub: PacificBasin Communications

Contact: Chuck Tindle, Director

E-mail: chuckt@pacificbasin.net

Ed: David K. Choo. **Description:** OahuRe.com offers information on Hawaii real estate market, with spreadsheets and comparative market analysis page, which shows properties that are active, sold, or in escrow. Other details about OahuRe.com are discussed. A list of other top real estate websites in Hawaii and in the U.S. in general is provided.

13241 ■ "New Argentine Investment Taps Real Estate" in South Florida Business Journal (Vol. 32, June 22, 2012, No. 48, pp. 1)

Pub: Baltimore Business Journal

Contact: Rhonda Pringle, President

E-mail: rpringle@bizjournals.com

Description: Industry experts believe that Miami, Florida is becoming the go-to-investment destination of Argentines looking for real estate development

opportunities. For example, Consultatio paid $220 million for 5.5 acres in Bal Harbour where it plans to construct condominiums. It appears Argentines are selecting sites in Miami as investments. **Availability:** Print; Online.

13242 ■ "New Food Concepts Flood Market" in Business Journal (Vol. 30, June 8, 2012, No. 2, pp. 1)

Pub: American City Business Journals, Inc.

Contact: Mike Olivieri, Executive Vice President

Ed: John Vomhof, Jr. **Released:** Weekly. **Price:** $4, introductory 4-week offer(Digital only). **Description:** Twin Cities Metropolitan Area has seen the boom of the frozen yogurt segment over the past few years and the rise of fast casual sandwich shops, which are helping fuel activity in Minnesota's real estate market. However, there are skeptics who doubt whether all of the new concepts can survive. **Availability:** Print; Online.

13243 ■ "A New Mix of Tenants Settles In Downtown" in Crain's New York Business (Vol. 24, January 31, 2008, No. 2, pp. 26)

Pub: Crain Communications, Inc.

Contact: Jessica Botos, Manager, Marketing

E-mail: jessica.botos@crainsnewyork.com

Ed: Andrew Marks. **Description:** More and more nonfinancial firms are relocating downtown due to the new retailers and restaurants that are reshaping the look and feel of lower Manhattan.

13244 ■ "New York City-Based New Street Realty Advisors has Secured a New Flagship for David's Bridal" in Chain Store Age (August 2008)

Description: New York City-based New Street Realty Advisors secured a new flagship store for David's Bridal in the Chelsea district of Manhattan. David's Bridal will occupy 12,800 square feet on two floors in a retail condominium development. **Availability:** PDF; Online.

13245 ■ "The Next Real Estate Boom" in Canadian Business (Vol. 80, March 26, 2007, No. 7, pp. 25)

Description: The better places to invest in Canadian real estate market are presented. The future price performance of the industry is analyzed. **Availability:** Print; Online.

13246 ■ "Niche Areas Seeing the Bulk of Retail Activity" in San Antonio Business Journal (Vol. 28, August 29, 2014, No. 29, pp. 8)

Pub: American City Business Journals, Inc.

Contact: Mike Olivieri, Executive Vice President

Released: Weekly. **Price:** $4, introductory 4-week offer(Digital & Print). **Description:** Retail development projects in San Antonio, Texas have been focused on already established areas. Such projects have boosted the local real estate sector. Meanwhile, retail developers have been finding opportunities in redeveloping old retail centers. **Availability:** Print; Online.

13247 ■ "Nine Austin-Area Realtors on National Latino List" in Austin Business Journal (Vol. 34, July 11, 2014, No. 21, pp. 8)

Pub: American City Business Journals, Inc.

Contact: Mike Olivieri, Executive Vice President

Description: Nine Austin-based realtors have made it to the Top 250 Latino real estate agent list published by the National Association of Hispanic Real Estate Professionals. **Availability:** Print; Online.

13248 ■ "October 2009: Recovery Plods Along" in Hispanic Business (October 2009, pp. 10-11)

Description: Economist reports on a possible economic recovery which will not be allowed to rely on a strong domestic demand in order to sustain it. Consumers, looking to counterbalance years of leverage financing based on unrealistic, ever-increasing home and portfolio valuations, are saving rather than spending money.

13249 ■ *"OK, Bring in the Lawyers" in Crain's Chicago Business (Vol. 31, November 17, 2008, No. 46, pp. 26)*
Pub: Crain Communications Inc.
Contact: Barry Asin, President
Ed: Daniel Rome Levine. **Description:** Bankruptcy attorneys are finding the economic and credit crisis a benefit for their businesses due to the high number of business owners and mortgage holders that are need of their services. One Chicago firm is handling ten times the number of cases they did the previous year and of that about 80 percent of their new clients are related to the real estate sector. **Availability:** Online.

13250 ■ *"Old Ford Plant to Sign New Tenants" in Business Courier (Vol. 27, August 13, 2010, No. 15, pp. 1)*
Pub: Business Courier
Ed: Dan Monk. **Description:** Ohio Realty Advisors LLC, a company handling the marketing of the 1.9 million-square-foot former Ford Batavia plant is on the brink of landing one distribution and three manufacturing firms as tenants. These tenants are slated to occupy about 20 percent of the facility and generate as many as 250 jobs in Ohio. **Availability:** Print; Online.

13251 ■ *"Older, But Not Wiser" in Canadian Business (Vol. 85, July 16, 2012, No. 11-12, pp. 54)*
Ed: Matthew McClearn, Michael McCullough. **Description:** Data from Statistics Canada revealed that two-thirds of workers aged 55 and above have some form of debt from mortgage to credit card balance while its one-third among the retired. Some factors contributing to the trend are the decline in borrowing costs, real estate, and older Canadians' car purchasing behavior. **Availability:** Print; Online.

13252 ■ *"On the House: Housing Developers Try to Read Generation Y" in Philadelphia Inquirer (December 2, 2010)*
Pub: The Philadelphia Inquirer
Contact: Elizabeth H. Hughes, Chief Executive Officer
Ed: Al Heavens. **Description:** Results of a survey conducted with Generation Y individuals are examined, focusing on housing developments and whether this particular generation prefers suburban or rural lifestyles. Generation Y encompasses people ages 18 to 32 years old. Statistical data included. **Availability:** Online.

13253 ■ *"Outside Investors Hot On Detroit Commercial Real Estate" in Crain's Detroit Business (Vol. 24, January 28, 2008, No. 4, pp. 25)*
Pub: Crain Communications Inc.
Contact: Barry Asin, President
Ed: Daniel Duggan. **Description:** An overview of out-of-town investors seeking to purchase commercial real estate in Michigan is presented. Statistical data included. **Availability:** Print; Online.

13254 ■ *"Paying for the Recession: Rebalancing Economic Growth" in Montana Business Quarterly (Vol. 49, Spring 2011, No. 1, pp. 2)*
Pub: University of Montana Bureau of Business and Economic Research
Contact: Patrick Barkey, Director
E-mail: patrick.barkey@business.umt.edu
Ed: Patrick M. Barkey. **Released:** Quarterly. **Description:** Four key issues required to address in order to rebalance economic growth in America are examined. They include: savings rates, global trade imbalances, government budgets and most importantly, housing price correction. **Availability:** Online.

13255 ■ *Peggy's Corner: The Art of Staging*
Pub: Eaton-Moghannam Publishing
Ed: Peggy Selinger-Eaton, Gayla Moghannam. **Description:** Techniques to enhance the value of any home are given. Seven principles of staging a home for sale include making a great first impres-

sion, maximizing space and eliminating clutter, using lighting for open spacious feeling, de-emphasize flaws, make the home appealing to buyers with varied tastes, creating warmth, and modernizing the home.

13256 ■ *"Phila.-Area Foreclosures Rising" in Philadelphia Business Journal (Vol. 28, May 18, 2012, No. 14, pp. 1)*
Pub: Baltimore Business Journal
Contact: Rhonda Pringle, President
E-mail: rpringle@bizjournals.com
Description: California-based RealtyTrac has reported residential mortgage foreclosures increased in Pennsylvania's Philadelphia region by 36 percent in first quarter from 2011's fourth quarter. Experts believe the numbers will continue to rise up to the end of the year and will negatively affect home values and the broader regional economy. Insights on bank robo-signing practices are also explained. **Availability:** Print; Online.

13257 ■ *"Phillips Edison Launches $1.8B Retail REIT" in Business Courier (Vol. 27, October 15, 2010, No. 24, pp. 1)*
Pub: Business Courier
Ed: Dan Monk. **Description:** Retail center operator Phillips Edison & Company is organizing a real estate investment trust (REIT) to raise $1.8 billion to finance the planned purchase of 150 grocery-centered shopping centers around the U.S. The offering would be Phillips largest. Phillips Edison employs 174 workers and operates 250 shopping centers nationwide. **Availability:** Print; Online.

13258 ■ *"The Promise of the Promised Land" in San Francisco Business Times (Vol. 28, January 3, 2014, No. 24, pp. 4)*
Pub: American City Business Journals, Inc.
Contact: Mike Olivieri, Executive Vice President
Released: September 15, 2016. **Price:** $4, print. **Description:** San Francisco Bay Area in California has become the site selection for investment, technology and talent. The financing finding its way to the Bay Area has led to robust job creation, drawing people and increasing the population by 2.6 percent to 805,000. The impact of the Bay Area's technology boon in rents and home prices are also presented. **Availability:** Print; Online.

13259 ■ *"Proposed Accounting Changes Could Complicate Tenants' Leases" in Baltimore Business Journal (Vol. 28, July 2, 2010, No. 8, pp. 1)*
Pub: Baltimore Business Journal
Contact: Rhonda Pringle, President
E-mail: rpringle@bizjournals.com
Ed: Daniel J. Sernovitz. **Description:** The Financial Accounting Standards Board has proposed that companies must indicate the value of real estate leases as assets and liabilities on balance sheets instead of expenses. The proposals could cause some companies to document millions of dollars in charges on their books or find difficulty in getting loans. **Availability:** Print.

13260 ■ *"Proposed Triangle Redo in Motion" in Crain's Cleveland Business (Vol. 28, October 15, 2007, No. 41, pp. 1)*
Pub: Crain Communications Inc.
Contact: K. C. Crain, President
Ed: Stan Bullard. **Description:** Zaremba Homes and MRN Ltd. are partnering to redevelop the so-called Triangle section of University Circle. The proposed project will include a total of 434 new rental and for-sale residential suites and as much as 227,000 square feet of retail and restaurant space. **Availability:** Online.

13261 ■ *"Publix Could Be Downtown's Tipping Point" in Birmingham Business Journal (Vol. 31, May 23, 2014, No. 21, pp. 6)*
Pub: American City Business Journals, Inc.
Contact: Mike Olivieri, Executive Vice President
Released: Weekly. **Price:** $4, introductory 4-week offer(Digital & Print). **Description:** Publix Super Markets is planning to open a grocery store and pharmacy in downtown Birmingham, Alabama. Cus-

tomer demand is expected to increase due to the development of hundreds of apartments in the area. The project is also expected to boost the local real estate industry. **Availability:** Print; Online.

13262 ■ *"Real Estate Dealmakers of the Year: Where Are They Now?" in San Francisco Business Times (Vol. 28, March 28, 2014, No. 36)*
Pub: American City Business Journals, Inc.
Contact: Mike Olivieri, Executive Vice President
Released: Weekly. **Description:** Maria Ayerdi-Kaplan has been named the Business Times Dealmaker of the Year for 2013. Ayerdi-Kaplan is the Transbay Joint Powers Authority Executive Director and is in charge of oversight for the planned Transbay Transit Center. The center is part of a $4.5 billion construction project in San Francisco, California. **Availability:** Print; Online.

13263 ■ *"Real Estate Firm Joins Trend Toward Functional Offices" in Pacific Business News (Vol. 52, April 25, 2014, No. 9, pp. 3)*
Pub: American City Business Journals, Inc.
Contact: Mike Olivieri, Executive Vice President
Released: April 25, 2014. **Price:** $4, Introductory 4-Week Offer(Digital & Print). **Description:** CBRE Inc. Hawaii has adopted the Workplace 360 model at its headquarters in downtown Honolulu as part of a companywide effort to support the way its employees work. Employees can choose nine different ways of working including height-adjustable workstations, standard wraparound desk workstations, huddle rooms and conference rooms. **Availability:** Print; Online.

13264 ■ *"Real Estate Funds Raise More Than $350M" in Business Journal Portland (Vol. 27, December 31, 2010, No. 44, pp. 1)*
Pub: Portland Business Journal
Contact: Andy Giegerich, Managing Editor
E-mail: agiegerich@bizjournals.com
Ed: Wendy Culverwell. **Description:** Oregon-based real estate funds have raised around half of the $735 million that was raised by local companies. Investors have been purchasing distressed properties. Commercial real estate prices have declined since 2007. **Availability:** Print; Online.

13265 ■ *"Real Estate Market Still in a Slump" in Montana Business Quarterly (Vol. 49, Summer 2011, No. 2, pp. 15)*
Pub: University of Montana Bureau of Business and Economic Research
Contact: Patrick Barkey, Director
E-mail: patrick.barkey@business.umt.edu
Ed: Patrick M. Barkey. **Released:** Quarterly. **Description:** Montana's housing market is still in decline with no sign of improving in the near future. Statistical data included. **Availability:** Online.

13266 ■ *The Real Estate Recipe: Make Millions by Buying Small Apartment Properties in Your Spare Time*
Pub: DNA Press
Ed: Brian K. Friedman. **Released:** First edition. **Description:** Guide for anyone interested in property investments; the book provides information for choosing an apartment property and answers questions in a chronological workbook format. The author shares his own experiences in apartment investing and shares the entire process of analyzing and buying an apartment property using a hypothetical ten-unit complex. Sample worksheets, checklists, and tables are provided to help readers maintain their own records. **Availability:** Print.

13267 ■ *"The Real Estate Success Formula: 19 Proven Strategies to Making Money in Real Estate"*
Pub: CreateSpace
Released: September 28, 2014. **Price:** $19.99, paperback; $1.07, kindle; $99, paperback. **Description:** Nineteen proven strategies for selling real estate are provided by husband and wife real estate team. The book teaches how to buy, hold and sell

houses quickly without using your money or your credit. Tactics for marketing, systematizing and managing your real estate business are outlined. **Availability:** Print.

13268 ■ *"Real Estate's New Reality"* in *Entrepreneur (Vol. 37, July 2009, No. 7, pp. 32)*
Pub: Entrepreneur Media Inc.
Contact: Dan Bova, Director
E-mail: dbova@entrepreneur.com

Ed: Rosalind Resnick. **Description:** Investing in real estate is still an advisable move, as long as investors are prepared to hold on to the property and there is a rent roll to provide a decent return on investment. Among the key considerations when investing in real estate is the property's expenses and cash flow. Other suggestions for future real estate investors are given. **Availability:** Online.

13269 ■ *"Recovering Economy Puts Real Estate on Solid Ground"* in *San Antonio Business Journal (Vol. 28, February 7, 2014, No. 53, pp. 13)*
Pub: American City Business Journals, Inc.
Contact: Mike Olivieri, Executive Vice President

Released: Weekly. **Price:** $4, Introductory 4-week offer(Digital only). **Description:** With the economic recovery in San Antonio, the real estate market has shifted back to normal and a significant increase has been noted in new real estate deals and purchases. Pete Broderick, a shareholder at Cox Smith Mathews Inc. said that there have been more money-making deals of late, while another shareholder, Jimmy McDonough reports that banks are now willing to get into more long-term real estate deals. **Availability:** Print; Online.

13270 ■ *"Recovery on Tap for 2010?"* in *Orlando Business Journal (Vol. 26, January 1, 2010, No. 31, pp. 1)*
Pub: Orlando Business Journal
Contact: Julie Swyers, Director
E-mail: jswyers@bizjournals.com

Ed: Melanie Stawicki Azam, Richard Bilbao, Christopher Boyd, Anjali Fluker. **Description:** Economic forecasts for Central Florida's leading business sectors in 2010 are presented. These sectors include housing, film and TV, sports business, law, restaurants, aviation, tourism and hospitality, banking and finance, commercial real estate, retail, health care, insurance, higher education, and manufacturing. According to some local executives, Central Florida's economy will slowly recover in 2010. **Availability:** Online.

13271 ■ *"The REIT Stuff"* in *Canadian Business (Vol. 80, March 26, 2007, No. 7, pp. 72)*
Description: The stock performance of various real estate investment trusts in Canada is analyzed. **Availability:** Online.

13272 ■ *"REITs Decry Foreign Limits on Investment"* in *Globe & Mail (March 29, 2007, pp. B4)*
Ed: Elizabeth Church. **Description:** The planned legislation by Canadian government for regulation foreign investments by real estate investment trusts is discussed. **Availability:** Online.

13273 ■ *"The Residential Appraisal Process Needs a New Standard"* in *Forbes (June 20, 2018)*
URL(s): www.forbes.com/sites/forbesrealesta tecouncil/2018/06/20/the-residential-appraisal -process-needs-a-new-standard/#7e7b010f7742

Ed: Jason Mitchell. **Released:** June 20, 2018. **Description:** Discusses the value of having an algorithm to assess a property's value, instead of relying solely on an assessor. A larger lender has already adopted this method, which could lead to massive savings in the industry and for the buyer. **Availability:** Online.

13274 ■ *"Retail Remains Hot as More Stores Browse Around Houston"* in *Houston Business Journal (Vol. 44, January 17, 2014, No. 37, pp. 9A)*
Pub: American City Business Journals, Inc.
Contact: Mike Olivieri, Executive Vice President

Released: Weekly. **Price:** $4, Introductory 4-week offer(Digital & Print). **Description:** Houston, Texas-based Evergreen Commercial Realty president, Lilly Golden, has revealed that the city has 15 new retail projects under construction and about 30 other projects in the pipeline. Golden believes Houston's low vacancy rate and high rent growth in Class A assets cause high demand from investors nationally. The boom in the retail sector is also examined. **Availability:** Print; Online.

13275 ■ *"The Right Time for REITs"* in *Barron's (Vol. 88, July 14, 2008, No. 28, pp. 32)*
Pub: Dow Jones & Company Inc.
Contact: Almar Latour, Chief Executive Officer

Ed: Mike Hogan. **Description:** Discusses the downturn in U.S. real estate investment trusts so these are worth considering for investment. Several Websites that are useful for learning about real estate investment trusts for investment purposes are presented. **Availability:** Online.

13276 ■ *"A Rise in Rental Units"* in *Philadelphia Business Journal (Vol. 30, October 7, 2011, No. 34, pp. 1)*
Pub: Philadelphia Business Journal
Contact: Sierra Quinn, Director
E-mail: squinn@bizjournals.com

Ed: Natalie Kostelni. **Description:** Housing developers have been stepping up the construction of new apartment complexes throughout the suburbs of Pennsylvania in order to capture growing demand for rental properties. BPG Properties Ltd. has nearly 1,000 new apartments under construction. **Availability:** Online.

13277 ■ *"Rubicon Is the Latest Small Real Estate Firm to Break Out"* in *Dallas Business Journal (Vol. 35, June 29, 2012, No. 42, pp. 1)*
Pub: Baltimore Business Journal
Contact: Rhonda Pringle, President
E-mail: rpringle@bizjournals.com

Ed: Candace Carlisle. **Description:** Stream Realty Partners LP partnered with Chad Hennings, Kyle Jacobs and John Pope to form the real estate firm Rubicon Representation. The new company will provide tenant representation (property management) services. **Availability:** Print; Online.

13278 ■ *"Seen & Noted: A Home's Identity in Black and White"* in *Crain's Chicago Business (Vol. 31, April 21, 2008, No. 16, pp. 35)*
Pub: Crain Communications Inc.
Contact: Barry Asin, President

Ed: Lisa Bertagnoli. **Description:** Real estate agents are finding that showing customers a written floor plan is a trend that is growing since many buyers feel that Online virtual tours distort a room. Although floor plans cost up to $500 to have drawn up, they clearly show potential buyers the exact dimensions of rooms and how they connect. **Availability:** Online.

13279 ■ *"Sellers Face Excess Land Dilemma"* in *Crain's Cleveland Business (Vol. 28, November 12, 2007, No. 45, pp. 1)*
Pub: Crain Communications Inc.
Contact: K. C. Crain, President

Ed: Stan Bullard. **Description:** Overview on the way in which the housing slump is effecting builders, land developers and lot prices. Statistical data included. **Availability:** Online.

13280 ■ *"Signs Point To Improving CRE Market"* in *Birmingham Business Journal (Vol. 31, May 2, 2014, No. 18, pp. 7)*
Pub: American City Business Journals, Inc.
Contact: Mike Olivieri, Executive Vice President

Released: Weekly. **Price:** $4, introductory 4-week offer(Digital only). **Description:** Xceligent real estate research firm's data shows collective improvement in Birmingham, Alabama's retail, office and industrial markets over the first three months of 2014. The office market has a less than 10 percent vacancy rate for Class A office space. Vacancy rates for both retail and industrial markets are also provided. **Availability:** Print; Online.

13281 ■ *"Sitting, Sitting, Sitting-Snapshots of Homes that Just Won't Sell"* in *Crain's Chicago Business (Vol. 31, April 21, 2008, No. 16)*
Pub: Crain Communications Inc.
Contact: Barry Asin, President

Ed: Kevin Davis. **Description:** Listing of five Chicago-area homes that have been on the market for an extended length of time; also includes the original asking price, current asking price, special features and the biggest challenge of each home. **Availability:** Online.

13282 ■ *"Small Changes Can Mean Big Energy Savings"* in *Crain's Cleveland Business (Vol. 28, November 5, 2007, No. 44, pp. 21)*
Pub: Crain Communications Inc.
Contact: K. C. Crain, President

Ed: Harriet Tramer. **Description:** Many Northeast Ohio businesses are taking their cues from the residential real estate market to draw and capitalize on interest in energy efficiency and is regularly taken into account by local architects. **Availability:** Online.

13283 ■ *"South Loop Site Lands a Buyer"* in *Crain's Chicago Business (Vol. 31, March 24, 2008, No. 12, pp. 1)*
Pub: Crain Communications Inc.
Contact: Barry Asin, President

Ed: Alby Gallun. **Description:** Russland Capital Group, a little-known condominium developer from Skokie, recently purchased a 6.5-acre riverside property in the site known as Franklin Point for $40 million. **Availability:** Online.

13284 ■ *"Spec Homes are Back as Builders Gain Confidence"* in *Sacramento Business Journal (Vol. 29, August 31, 2012, No. 27, pp. 1)*
Pub: Baltimore Business Journal
Contact: Rhonda Pringle, President
E-mail: rpringle@bizjournals.com

Ed: Sanford Nax. **Description:** Home builders in California are looking to obtain more permits in anticipation of increased residential construction activity. Builders are also looking to rebuild housing supply and are more confident that these homes will sell quickly.

13285 ■ *"Staging a Martini-and-GQ Lifestyle"* in *Crain's Chicago Business (April 21, 2008)*
Pub: Crain Communications Inc.
Contact: Barry Asin, President

Ed: Kevin Davis. **Description:** Due to the competition of the slumping housing market, home stagers are becoming more prominent and are using creative ways to make an impression beyond de-cluttering, painting and cleaning by using accents such as casually placed magazines, candles and table settings. **Availability:** Online.

13286 ■ *"State Wants to Add Escape Clause to Leases"* in *Sacramento Business Journal (Vol. 28, October 14, 2011, No. 33, pp. 1)*
Pub: Sacramento Business Journal
Contact: Stephanie Fretwell, Director
E-mail: sfretwell@bizjournals.com

Ed: Michael Shaw. **Description:** California Governor Jerry Brown's administration has decided to add escape clauses to new lease agreements, which created new worry for building owners and brokers in Sacramento, California. Real estate brokers believe the appropriation of funds clauses have been making the lenders nervous and would result in less competition. **Availability:** Online.

13287 ■ *"Stuck With Two Mortgages" in Crain's Chicago Business (Vol. 31, April 21, 2008, No. 16)*

Pub: Crain Communications Inc.

Contact: Barry Asin, President

Ed: Darci Smith. **Description:** Discusses the problem a number of people are facing due to the slump in the housing market: being stuck with two mortgages when they move because their former homes have not sold. Many thought they could afford to move to a larger home, anticipating significant equity apprecia-tion that did not occur; now they are left with lowering their price and competing with the host of new developments. **Availability:** Online.

13288 ■ *"Survey Says Commercial Real Estate Headed for Turbulence" in Commercial Property News (March 17, 2008)*

Description: Commercial real estate sector is declin-ing due to the sluggish U.S. economy. According to a recent survey, national office, retail and hospitality markets are also on the decline. **Availability:** Online.

13289 ■ *"Tattooed Bellwethers of Economic Development" in Austin Business Journal (Vol. 34, May 2, 2014, No. 11, pp. A4)*

Pub: American City Business Journals, Inc.

Contact: Mike Olivieri, Executive Vice President

Released: Weekly. **Price:** $4, Introductory 4-week offer(Digital & Print). **Description:** The creative com-munity's art-centered business have helped Austin, Texas' growth by moving into transitional areas with low rents. Their kind of pioneering spirit primes the area for later commercial and residential develop-ment. The city's assistance programs for creative enterprises are also presented. **Availability:** Print; Online.

13290 ■ *"That Empty Feeling" in Crain's Cleveland Business (Vol. 28, October 15, 2007, No. 41, pp. 1)*

Pub: Crain Communications Inc.

Contact: K. C. Crain, President

Ed: Stan Bullard. **Description:** Townhouses, cluster homes and condominiums lured both buyers and builders for most of this decade but now that market is suffering to an even greater degree than the single-family home market. Statistical data included. **Avail-ability:** Online.

13291 ■ *"They've Fallen, But Can Senior-Housing Stocks Get Up" in Barron's (Vol. 88, March 10, 2008, No. 10, pp. 43)*

Pub: Dow Jones & Company Inc.

Contact: Almar Latour, Chief Executive Officer

Ed: Kopin Tan. **Description:** Shares of senior hous-ing companies present buying opportunities to inves-tors because of their low prices. Companies such as Brookdale Senior Living are not as dependent on housing prices but have suffered declines in share prices. **Availability:** Online.

13292 ■ *"Threat of New Office Space Records Rent Hikes" in Globe & Mail (March 21, 2007, pp. B4)*

Description: The increasing commercial rent prices in the Toronto region amid the high office building construction market are discussed. **Availability:** Online.

13293 ■ *"Toll Talker: CEO Takes Stock of His Company, the Housing Market" in Philadelphia Business Journal (Vol. 33, May 9, 2014, No. 13, pp. 4)*

Pub: American City Business Journals, Inc.

Contact: Mike Olivieri, Executive Vice President

Released: Weekly. **Price:** $4, introductory 4-week offer(Digital only). **Description:** Douglas C. Yearley, Jr., CEO of Toll Brothers Inc. discusses how his company capitalized on the economic recession in the housing market by acquiring large tracts of land between 2008 and 2010, including Shapell Homes in California for $1.2 billion. Yearley believes that while the housing downturn trend led to a rise in apartment

living, the concept of home ownership remains relatively strong in the U.S., thus spurring construc-tion. **Availability:** Print; Online.

13294 ■ *"Top 10 Retirement Mistakes and How to Avoid Them" in Canadian Business (Vol. 83, July 20, 2010, No. 11-12, pp. 39)*

Pub: Rogers Media Inc.

Contact: Neil Spivak, Chief Executive Officer

Ed: Jacqueline Nelson, Angelina Chapin. **Descrip-tion:** Some of the top retirement mistakes are relying on selling one's house to find a retirement. Other mistakes are paying too much for investments and planning to work in retirement since no one can be sure that they will be healthy enough to accomplish this. Suggestions to avoid these pitfalls are discussed. **Availability:** Print; Online.

13295 ■ *"Top Commercial Real Estate Developers" in South Florida Business Journal (Vol. 34, July 25, 2014, No. 53, pp. 14)*

Pub: American City Business Journals, Inc.

Contact: Mike Olivieri, Executive Vice President

Released: Weekly. **Description:** Rankings of the commercial real estate developers in South Florida are presented. Rankings are based on the total new rentable square feet developed and square feet sold in the region in 2013. **Availability:** Print; Online.

13296 ■ *"Top Statewide Commercial Real Estate Brokerages" in South Florida Business Journal (Vol. 34, April 4, 2014, No. 37, pp. 14)*

Pub: American City Business Journals, Inc.

Contact: Mike Olivieri, Executive Vice President

Description: Rankings of commercial real estate brokerages in South Florida area are presented. Rankings were based on total volume sales and leas-ing statewide in Florida. The top five real estate executives in the region are also listed. **Availability:** Print; Online.

13297 ■ *"Troy Complex has New Brand, New Leases" in Crain's Detroit Business (Vol. 24, April 14, 2008, No. 15, pp. 32)*

Pub: Crain Communications Inc.

Contact: Barry Asin, President

Ed: Daniel Duggan. **Description:** Discusses the re-branding of the 1.2 million-square-foot collection of office buildings in Troy purchased by New York-based Emmes Co. The firm has also pledged more than $6 million in upgrades, hired a new leasing company and completed 67,000 square feet of leasing with another 100,000 in negotiations. **Availability:** Print; Online.

13298 ■ *"University Place Building Gets an Anchor Tenant: Groundbreaking 2.0" in Philadelphia Business Journal (Vol. 30, September 23, 2011, No. 32, pp. 1)*

Pub: Philadelphia Business Journal

Contact: Sierra Quinn, Director

E-mail: squinn@bizjournals.com

Ed: Natalie Kostelni. **Description:** University Place Associates, the developer of 2.0 University Place in West Philadelphia, Pennsylvania, will break ground on a five-story, 97,000-square-foot office building in December 2011. The decision follows the Citizenship and Immigration Services signing of a 15-year lease as anchor tenant. **Availability:** Online.

13299 ■ *"Valenti: Roots of Financial Crisis Go Back to 1998" in Crain's Detroit Business (Vol. 24, October 6, 2008, No. 40, pp. 25)*

Pub: Crain Communications Inc.

Contact: Barry Asin, President

Ed: Tom Henderson, Nathan Skid. **Description:** Interview with Sam Valenti III who is the chairman and CEO of Valenti Capital L.L.C., a wealth-management firm; Valenti discusses in detail the his-tory that led up to the current economic crisis as well as his prediction for the future of the country. **Avail-ability:** Print; Online.

13300 ■ *"Vision for Camden in Better Focus" in Philadelphia Business Journal (Vol. 30, September 30, 2011, No. 33, pp. 1)*

Pub: Philadelphia Business Journal

Contact: Sierra Quinn, Director

E-mail: squinn@bizjournals.com

Ed: Natalie Kostelni. **Description:** More than $500 million worth of projects aimed at redeveloping the downtown and waterfront areas of Camden, New Jersey are being planned. These include the con-struction of residential, commercial, and education buildings. **Availability:** Online.

13301 ■ *"Walnut Hill Sheds Its Past, Name" in Philadelphia Business Journal (Vol. 33, April 4, 2014, No. 8, pp. 8)*

Pub: American City Business Journals, Inc.

Contact: Mike Olivieri, Executive Vice President

Released: Weekly. **Price:** $4, introductory 4-week offer(Digital & Print). **Description:** Walnut Hill Plaza was bought by a fund comprised of Miller Investment Management and Hayden Real Estate at an auction in 2012 for $11 million and they spent $2 million in construction renovations. The property was also re-branded as 150 Walnut Warner and the once forlorn building is up to 100% leased space. The tenants renting space in the building are also highlighted. **Availability:** Print; Online.

13302 ■ *"Wannabe Buyers Take Their Own Sweet Time" in Crain's Chicago Business (Vol. 31, April 21, 2008, No. 16, pp. 50)*

Pub: Crain Communications Inc.

Contact: Barry Asin, President

Ed: Lisa Bertagnoli. **Description:** Although all factors are in place for a robust real-estate market in the Chicago area: low interest rates, plenty of inventory and the region's relatively strong employment, buyers are taking their time and doing more research in order to see how bad the economy will get. **Availability:** Online.

13303 ■ *"What's Ahead for Fannie and Fred?" in Barron's (Vol. 90, August 30, 2010, No. 35, pp. 26)*

Pub: Barron's Editorial & Corporate Headquarters

Ed: Jonathan R. Laing. **Description:** A meeting presided by Treasury Secretary Timothy Geithner discussed the future of Fannie Mae and Freddie Mac. The two government sponsored enterprises were mismanaged and reforming these two agencies is critical. **Availability:** Online.

13304 ■ *"When Anything (And Everything) Goes" in Globe & Mail (January 20, 2007, pp. B4)*

Ed: Elizabeth Church. **Description:** The forecast on acquisition of different real estate firms is presented. **Availability:** Online.

13305 ■ *"Will Home Buyers Pay for Green Features?" in Contractor (Vol. 56, October 2009, No. 10, pp. 70)*

Ed: Robert P. Mader. **Description:** National Associa-tion of Home Builders commissioned a survey which shows that homeowners are interested in green as long as they do not have to pay much for it. The as-sociation did not allow a board member to read the survey which raises questions about how the ques-tions were phrased and how the sample was selected. **Availability:** Print; Online.

13306 ■ *"With Building Plans in Flux, County Could Sell Key Site" in Crain's Cleveland Business (Vol. 28, October 8, 2007, No. 40, pp. 1)*

Pub: Crain Communications Inc.

Contact: K. C. Crain, President

Ed: Jay Miller. **Description:** Due to such issues as financial and administrative problems, Cuyahoga County commissioners have pushed back the con-struction timeline for a planned county administration center and are saying that they are considering sell-ing the site in downtown Cleveland to developers who would erect a new office building that another large tenant could occupy. **Availability:** Online.

13307 ▪ *"You Better Shop Around: Four Steps to Getting the Best Deal on a Home Loan" in Black Enterprise (Vol. 40, July 2010, No. 12, pp. 78)*
Pub: Earl G. Graves Ltd.
Contact: Earl Graves, Jr., President

Ed: Tara-Nicholle Nelson. **Description:** Four steps to help anyone seeking a mortgage for a home purchase are listed. **Availability:** Online.

13308 ▪ *"You Won't Go Broke Filling Up On The Stock" in Barron's (Vol. 88, July 14, 2008, No. 28, pp. 38)*
Pub: Dow Jones & Company Inc.
Contact: Almar Latour, Chief Executive Officer

Ed: Assif Shameen. **Description:** Due to high economic growth, pro-business policies and a consumption boom, the Middle East is a good place to look for equities. The best ways in which to gain exposure to this market include investing in the real estate industry and telecommunications markets as well as large banks that serve corporations and consumers. **Availability:** Online.

13309 ▪ *"Your First Commercial Lease: How to Prepare and What to Expect" in Business News Daily (February 21, 2023)*
URL(s): www.businessnewsdaily.com/7619-negotiate-commercial-lease.html

Ed: Dock Treece. **Released:** February 21, 2023. **Description:** Many small businesses look for a commercial space to occupy. What do you need to know before signing that contract? This article takes a look at what should be included in the contract and what you need to understand in terms of finance and real estate. **Availability:** Online.

13310 ▪ *Your First Year in Real Estate: Making the Transition from Total Novice to Successful Professional*
Released: Second edition. **Price:** $22, paperback; $9.99, e-book. **Description:** Zeller helps new realtors to select the right company, develop mentor and client relationships, using the Internet and social networking to stay ahead of competition, to set and reach career goals, to stay current in the market, and more. **Availability:** E-book; Print.

STATISTICAL SOURCES

13311 ▪ *RMA Annual Statement Studies*
Pub: Risk Management Association
Contact: Nancy Foster, President

Released: Annual. **Description:** Contains composite balance sheets and income statements for more than 360 industries, including the accounting, auditing, and bookkeeping industries. Also contains five years of comparative historical data for discerning trends. Includes 16 commonly used ratios, computed for most of the size groupings for nearly every industry.

13312 ▪ *Standard & Poor's Industry Surveys*
Pub: Standard And Poor's Financial Services LLC.
Contact: Douglas L. Peterson, President

Description: Two-volume book that examines the prospects for specific industries, including trucking. Also provides analyses of trends and problems, statistical tables and charts, and comparative company analyses.

TRADE PERIODICALS

13313 ▪ *Commercial Investment Real Estate Magazine (CIRE)*
Pub: CCIM Institute
Contact: Timothy S. Blair, President
URL(s): www.ccim.com/cire-magazine/issues/fall-2022

Released: Quarterly; Fall, Summer, Spring, Winter. **Description:** Professional development magazine for commercial investment professionals and allied fields. **Availability:** Print; Online.

13314 ▪ *The duPont Registry: A Buyer's Gallery of Fine Boats*
Pub: duPont Publishing Inc.
Contact: William Chapman, Chief Executive Officer
URL(s): www.dupontregistry.com/about
Facebook: www.facebook.com/dupontregistry
X (Twitter): x.com/duPontREGISTRY
Instagram: www.instagram.com/dupontregistry
YouTube: www.youtube.com/channel/UCSWQ-ZuJ9lyHZFGfpoPz8wg
Pinterest: www.pinterest.com/dupontregistry

Released: Monthly **Price:** $89.95, for 12 issues; $149.95, for 24 issues; $189.95, for 36 issues. **Description:** Magazine featuring worldwide luxury homes for sale. **Availability:** Print; Online.

13315 ▪ *The Institutional Real Estate Letter*
Pub: Institutional Real Estate Inc.
Contact: Geoffrey Dohrmann, Chief Executive Officer
E-mail: g.dohrmann@irei.com
URL(s): tirel-na.irei.com/the-institutional-real-estate-letter-americas

Ed: Geoffrey Dohrmann. **Released:** 11/year **Price:** $2,695, for 1 year; $4,800, for 2 year; $6,050, for 3 year; $275, Single issue. **Description:** Monthly publication covering the pension, foundation, and endowment investment market. Provides information on investment patterns, trends, and strategies. **Availability:** Print; Online.

13316 ▪ *Journal of Property Management*
Pub: Institute of Real Estate Management
Contact: Libby Ekre, President
URL(s): jpmonline.org

Released: Bimonthly **Description:** Magazine serving real estate managers. **Availability:** Print; PDF; Online; Download.

13317 ▪ *National Delinquency Survey (NDS)*
Pub: Mortgage Bankers Association
Contact: Susan Stewart, Chairman
URL(s): www.mba.org/news-and-research/research-and-economics/single-family-research/national-delinquency-survey

Released: Quarterly **Price:** $600, Nonmembers for single copy; $300, Members for single copy; $275, Nonmembers; $150, Members. **Description:** Carries information on residential mortgage delinquency and foreclosure rates at national, regional, and state levels. Reports delinquency rates by length of time and type of loan. **Availability:** Download; Online; PDF. **Telecommunication Services:** Email: MBAResearch@mortgagebankers.org .

13318 ▪ *The Practical Real Estate Lawyer*
Pub: American Law Institute Continuing Legal Education
URL(s): www.ali-cle.org/legal-journals/PREL

Released: 6/year **Price:** $35, for digital issue; $119, for one year, print and online; $55, for one year, online. **Description:** Professional magazine offering advice on real estate for real estate practitioners. **Availability:** Print; Online.

13319 ▪ *Real Estate Forum: America's Premier Business Real Estate Magazine*
Pub: ALM Media Properties LLC.
Contact: Bill Carter, Chief Executive Officer
URL(s): www.globest.com/real-estate-forum/?slreturn=20210804023737

Released: 8/year; Jan/Feb, Mar/April, July/Aug and Nov/Dec. **Description:** Magazine providing national coverage of commercial, industrial, and corporate real estate. **Availability:** Print; Online.

13320 ▪ *Real Estate Weekly*
Contact: Linda O'Flanagan, Editor
E-mail: editor@rew-online.com
URL(s): rew-online.com
Facebook: www.facebook.com/RealEstateWeeklyNY
X (Twitter): twitter.com/RE_Weekly

Ed: Linda O'Flanagan. **Released:** Weekly **Price:** $49, for annual subscription; $72, for 2 year; $108, for 3 years. **Description:** Real estate newspaper. **Availability:** Print; Online.

13321 ▪ *Realtor Magazine: The Business tool for Real Estate Professionals*
Pub: National Association of Realtors
Contact: Bob Goldberg, Chief Executive Officer
URL(s): www.nar.realtor/magazine
Facebook: www.facebook.com/realtormag
X (Twitter): x.com/realtormag
Instagram: www.instagram.com/realtormag

Ed: Wendy Cole. **Released:** Quarterly **Price:** $56, Nonmembers for US. **Description:** Real estate magazine. **Availability:** Print; Online.

13322 ▪ *The Residential Specialist*
Pub: Residential Real Estate Council
Contact: Tricia Nekota, President
URL(s): trsmag.com/magazine

Ed: Kimberly Cure. **Released:** Bimonthly **Price:** $44.95, Canada for per year; $29.95, U.S. for per year; $89.95, for other international. **Description:** Trade magazine for residential real estate agents. **Availability:** Print; Online.

13323 ▪ *SIOR Report*
Pub: Society of Industrial and Office Realtors
Contact: Mark Duclos, President
E-mail: duclos@sentrycommercial.com
URL(s): www.sior.com/education-and-insights/insights/magazine/sior-report

Released: Quarterly **Description:** Dedicated to corporate real estate brokerage, development, and management. Recurring features include news of members and the Society, news of educational programs sponsored by the Society, book reviews, news of research, and statistics. **Availability:** Print; Online.

13324 ▪ *Terra Firma*
Pub: Realtors Land Institute
Contact: Dean Saunders, President
URL(s): www.rliland.com/Voices/Terra-Firma-magazine

Released: Semiannual; winter and summer. **Price:** $12.99, Single issue. **Description:** Contains articles of interest to realtors dealing with farm and land real estate. Recurring features include news of the Institute and tax information. **Availability:** Print; Online.

13325 ▪ *Wealth Management Real Estate*
Pub: Informa USA Inc.
Contact: Gareth Wright, Director
URL(s): www.wealthmanagement.com/real-estate

Ed: Elaine Misonzhnik. **Description:** Magazine on commercial real estate investment, development and management. **Availability:** Print; Online.

TRADE SHOWS AND CONVENTIONS

13326 ▪ *Chicago Build*
Frequency: Annual. **Description:** Provides networking, an exhibit hall, and key topic sessions about real estate, architecture, construction, and health and safety. **Audience:** Industry leaders in the building and construction trade. **Principal Exhibits:** Provides networking, an exhibit hall, and key topic sessions about real estate, architecture, construction, and health and safety.

13327 ▪ *The Cooperator Expo*
URL(s): coopexpofall.com
Frequency: Annual. **Description:** One day show for property managers, apartment owners, board members, shareholders, and real estate professionals in the co-op, condo, and apartment building industries. **Principal Exhibits:** One day show for property managers, apartment owners, board members, shareholders, and real estate professionals in the co-op, condo, and apartment building industries.

13328 ▪ *REALTORS Trade Expo*
URL(s): www.legislative.realtor
Frequency: Annual. **Description:** Provides talks, education, and vendor booths for realtors. **Audience:** Realtors. **Principal Exhibits:** Provides talks, education, and vendor booths for realtors.

CONSULTANTS

13329 ■ Lehrer Financial and Economic Advisory Services

5555 Del Monte Dr., Ste. 802
 Houston, TX 77056
Ph: (713)972-7912
Fax: (713)964-0444
URL: http://lehecoserv.com
Contact: Dr. Kenneth Eugene Lehrer, Contact
E-mail: drken@lehecoserv.com

Description: Firm provides economist and financial consulting and advisory services. **Scope:** Firm provides economist and financial consulting and advisory services. **Founded:** 1982. **Publications:** "The Petroleum Matter or Mess?"; An Easy Assist for an Overlooked but Tough Group"; "General Motors Joins Yogi Berra"; "The "Real" Real Estate Situation"; "Mortgage Securitization And Foreclosures"; "Creating World Certainty Via Petroleum Price Stability".

13330 ■ Real Resources (RR)

7520 Golden Valley Rd.
 Golden Valley, MN 55427
Ph: (612)729-5444
Co. E-mail: info@realresources.com
URL: http://realresources.com
Contact: Jim Olson, Chief Executive Officer
E-mail: jim.olson@realresources.com
Facebook: www.facebook.com/realresources
X (Twitter): x.com/realresources

Description: Provider of consulting services in areas of housing development, including site acquisition, market research, feasibility analysis, fiscal impact studies, zoning, mortgage underwriting, grant procurement, preparation, project and construction management, residential rent-up and marketing plans, retail and commercial leasing, small business plans and tax syndication analysis. **Scope:** Provider of consulting services in areas of housing development, including site acquisition, market research, feasibility analysis, fiscal impact studies, zoning, mortgage underwriting, grant procurement, preparation, project and construction management, residential rent-up and marketing plans, retail and commercial leasing, small business plans and tax syndication analysis. **Founded:** 1985.

13331 ■ White, Hutchinson, Leisure & Learning Group (WHLLG)

4036 Baltimore Ave.
 Kansas City, MO 64111
Ph: (816)931-1040
Fax: (816)756-5058
URL: http://www.whitehutchinson.com
Contact: Randy White, Chief Executive Officer
E-mail: randy@whitehutchinson.com
X (Twitter): x.com/whitehutchinson

Description: Provider of real estate development services for feasibility studies, concept development, design, production and project management, and financing solutions. **Scope:** Provider of real estate development services for feasibility studies, concept development, design, production and project management, and financing solutions. **Publications:** "Twenty Ways to Become More Family Friendly," Ialei Fun Extra, Feb, 2002; "The Importance of Food to Location-Based Leisure," Sep, 2001; "Guest Sacrifice: A Sure Trip to Prison Or a Path to Profitability," Entertainment Management, Aug, 2000; "Beyond Androcentrism: How to Design Lbls to Please Guests (Women & Children) Instead of Owners and Architects," Entertainment Management, Jun, 2000; "Child's Play: More Complicated Than it Looks," Entertainment Management, Feb, 2000; "How Can I Finance My Leisure Project?"; "The Feasibility Study: The Foundation for Success"; "New Luxury: Rich Design is No Longer Optional". **Training:** Renovation and Construction of Outdoor Play Environments Using Nature As The Play Element, Oct 2002; Designing and Renovating Outdoor Play Spaces Using Nature As Part Of The Play Element, Nov, 2002.

FRANCHISES AND BUSINESS OPPORTUNITIES

13332 ■ Advance Realty Inc.

8640 Ridgleys Choice Dr., Ste. 201
 Nottingham, MD 21236
Ph: (410)256-8700
Co. E-mail: noofficeemail@noofficeemail.com
URL: http://www.advancemls.com
Contact: Dawn Adamiak, Officer
Facebook: www.facebook.com/advancemls

Description: Real-estate developer of commercial and residential properties. **Financial Assistance:** No **Training:** Up to 5 days corporate based training and 2 days minimum onsite training and ongoing support.

13333 ■ Assist-2-Sell

6490 S McCarran Blvd., Ste. F 46
 Reno, NV 89509
Ph: (775)688-6060
Free: 800-528-7816
Co. E-mail: info@assist2sell.com
URL: http://assist2sell.com
Contact: Mary Lameres-Pomin, President
Facebook: www.facebook.com/assist2sell
X (Twitter): x.com/Assist2Sell
Pinterest: www.pinterest.com/assist2sellinc

Description: Discount real estate brokerage. **No. of Franchise Units:** 300. **Founded:** 1987. **Franchised:** 1993. **Equity Capital Needed:** $29,000-$34,000, including franchise fee. **Franchise Fee:** $9,995. **Training:** Yes.

13334 ■ Benham REO Group

8410 Pit Stop Ct., Ste. 140
 Concord, NC 28027
Ph: (704)270-2962
URL: http://www.redwoodrealtygroup.com

Description: Firm provides landscaping, information technology, communication and much more services. **Founded:** 2003. **Franchised:** 2007. **Financial Assistance:** Yes **Training:** 1 week training provided at headquarters and ongoing support.

13335 ■ The BrickKicker

849 N Ellsworth St.
 Naperville, IL 60563
Free: 800-821-1820
Fax: (630)420-2270
Co. E-mail: request@brickkicker.com
URL: http://www.brickkicker.com
Contact: Ron Ewald, Co-Founder
Facebook: www.facebook.com/The.BrickKicker
X (Twitter): x.com/BrickKickerHQ

Description: Building inspection service. **No. of Franchise Units:** 152. **Founded:** 1989. **Franchised:** 1995. **Equity Capital Needed:** $15,000-$40,000. **Franchise Fee:** $9,000-$40,000. **Financial Assistance:** Yes **Training:** Yes.

13336 ■ Century 21 Canada L.P. (C21)

700-1199 W Pender St.
 Vancouver, BC, Canada V6E 2R1
Ph: (604)606-2100
Fax: (604)606-2125
URL: http://www.c21.ca
Contact: Martin Charlwood, President
Facebook: www.facebook.com/CENTURY21Canada
X (Twitter): x.com/CENTURY21Canada
Instagram: www.instagram.com/century21canada
YouTube: www.youtube.com/channel/
 UCK9uFomKQuOUR8sSKHe7yWQ

Description: Real estate sales organization provides real estate careers, sales, training, technology, real estate marketing, real estate franchising, franchises, branding, networking, entrepreneurs. **Founded:** 1976. **Training:** Yes.

13337 ■ Flat Rate Realty (FR)

481 N Santa Cruz Ave., No. 104
 Los Gatos, CA 95030
Ph: (408)627-0030
URL: http://flatraterealty.com

Description: Firm engages in development of real-estate solutions and services. **Founded:** 1997. **Franchised:** 2006. **Financial Assistance:** Yes **Training:** Initial training, start up support, consultation and communication.

13338 ■ Help-U-Sell Real Estate

240 N Washington Blvd. No. 200
 Sarasota, FL 34236
Ph: (941)951-7707
Co. E-mail: info@helpusell.com
URL: http://www.helpusell.com
Contact: Robert Stevens, Chief Operating Officer
Facebook: www.facebook.com/helpusell
Linkedin: www.linkedin.com/company/help-u-sell-real
 -estate
X (Twitter): x.com/helpusell
YouTube: www.youtube.com/user/HelpUSellRealEs
 tate
Pinterest: www.pinterest.com/helpusellre

Description: Offers full-service real estate brokerage franchises. **Founded:** 1976. **Franchised:** 1976. **Equity Capital Needed:** $35,000 - $125,000. **Franchise Fee:** 17500. **Royalty Fee:** 6%. **Financial Assistance:** Yes **Training:** Offers 4 days at headquarters, at franchisee's location, 8 weeks by phone, retreats, regional meetings, convention, Help-U-Sell University and ongoing support.

13339 ■ Picket Fence Preview Inc.

Picket Fence Franchising Corp.
 1 Kennedy Dr., L-5
 South Burlington, VT 05403
Ph: (802)660-3167
Free: 800-201-0338
Contact: Toni Supple, Contact
E-mail: toni@picketfencepreview.com

Description: For sale by owner magazine. **No. of Franchise Units:** 5. **No. of Company-Owned Units:** 1. **Founded:** 1993. **Franchised:** 1994. **Equity Capital Needed:** $20,000-$35,000. **Franchise Fee:** $10,000. **Training:** Yes.

13340 ■ PropertyGuys.com Inc.

1133 St. George Blvd.
 Moncton, NB, Canada E1E 4E1
Free: 844-333-7017
URL: http://propertyguysfranchise.com
Contact: Ken LeBlanc, President
URL(s): propertyguys.com
X (Twitter): x.com/propertyguys
Pinterest: www.pinterest.ca/propertyguys

Description: Wholesaler and retailer of real estate properties. **Founded:** 1998. **Training:** Offers 5 days at PropertyGuys University.

13341 ■ RE/MAX, LLC [Re/Max International]

5075 S Syracuse St.
 Denver, CO 80237
Co. E-mail: customerservice@remax.com
URL: http://www.remax.com
Contact: Amy Lessinger, President
Facebook: www.facebook.com/remax
Linkedin: www.linkedin.com/company/remax
X (Twitter): twitter.com/remax
Instagram: www.instagram.com/remax
YouTube: www.youtube.com/remax
Pinterest: www.pinterest.com/remax

Description: International real estate franchise network. **No. of Franchise Units:** 3,207. **No. of Company-Owned Units:** 24. **Founded:** 1973. **Franchised:** 1973. **Equity Capital Needed:** $35,000-$194,000. **Franchise Fee:** $20,000-$35,000. **Royalty Fee:** 1%. **Financial Assistance:** Yes **Training:** Provides 5 days training at headquarters, annual conference, online training and ongoing support.

13342 ■ Realty Executives International Inc.

7600 N 16th St., Ste. 100
 Phoenix, AZ 85020
Ph: (480)239-2038
Free: 800-252-3366
Co. E-mail: customerservice@realtyexecutives.com
URL: http://www.realtyexecutives.com
Contact: David Boudreau, Contact
Facebook: www.facebook.com/realtyexecutivesintl

X (Twitter): x.com/realtyexec
YouTube: www.youtube.com/user/realtyexecutives
Pinterest: www.pinterest.com/realtyexecs
Description: Real estate franchise. **Founded:** 1965.
Financial Assistance: No **Training:** Yes.

13343 ■ Remerica Real Estate
41017 Ann Arbor Rd.
  Plymouth, MI 48170
Ph: (734)459-4500
Free: 844-736-3742
Co. E-mail: info@remerica.com
URL: http://www.remericarealestate.com
Contact: James Courtney, President
Facebook: www.facebook.com/RemericaofMichigan
Linkedin: www.linkedin.com/company/remerica-unite
  d-realty
Description: Real estate franchise. **Founded:** 1989.
Publications: *Remerica Real Estate.* **Training:**
Engaged in real estate business.

13344 ■ United Capital Mortgage Assistance, L.L.C. (UCMA)
402 Vine St.
  Woodstock, IL 60098
Free: 800-474-1407
URL: http://www.ucma.com
Description: Homeowner foreclosure service. **No. of
Company-Owned Units:** 1. **Founded:** 1997. **Fran-
chised:** 1998. **Equity Capital Needed:** $18,500-
$27,000, includes franchise fee. **Franchise Fee:**
$9,995, including training. **Training:** Yes.

13345 ■ Weichert Real Estate Affiliates Inc.
225 Littleton Rd.
  Morris Plains, NJ 07950
Free: 877-533-9007
Co. E-mail: franchising@weichertrealtors.net
URL: http://weichertfranchise.com
Facebook: www.facebook.com/weichertfranchising
Instagram: www.instagram.com/weichert_franchising
YouTube: www.youtube.com/channel/UCfa
  2oqhKPh0EUIrEjSLqlpw
Description: Provider of real-estate brokerage
services. **Founded:** 1969. **Training:** Offers 4 days at
corporate headquarters, on-site and annual confer-
ence, quarterly workshops and ongoing support.

PUBLICATIONS

13346 ■ Atlanta Agent Magazine
URL(s): atlantaagentmagazine.com
Facebook: www.facebook.com/AtlantaAgentMaga-
  zine
Linkedin: www.linkedin.com/company/agen
  t-publishing
X (Twitter): twitter.com/AtlantaAgentMag
Instagram: www.instagram.com/atlantaagentmaga-
  zine
YouTube: www.youtube.com/user/ChicagoAgen
  tMagazine
Description: An online magazine discussing the
Atlanta, GA real estate market. **Availability:** Online.

13347 ■ Heartland Real Estate Business
3535 Piedmont Rd. NE, Bldg. 14, Ste. 950
  Atlanta, GA 30305
Ph: (404)832-8262
Fax: (404)832-8260
URL: http://francemediainc.com
Contact: Scott France, Publisher
URL(s): rebusinessonline.com/commercial-real-esta
  te-magazines/heartland-real-estate
  -businessfrancemediainc.com/publications
Ed: Kristin Hiller, Matt Valley. **Released:** Monthly
Description: Magazine that covers the latest news,
developments and trends in commercial real estate
in the Midwest. **Availability:** Print; Online.

13348 ■ Real Estate Business Magazine (REB)
430 N Michigan Ave.
  Chicago, IL 60611
Ph: (312)321-4437
Free: 800-621-9738
Fax: (312)329-8882
Co. E-mail: info@rebinstitute.com
URL: http://www.rebinstitute.com
Contact: Sue Miller, President
URL(s): www.rebinstitute.com/REBInstitute/Maga-
  zine/REBMagazine.aspx?WebsiteKey=a696ee90
  -7e41-4183-888d-e06be2b76293
Released: Bimonthly **Description:** Magazine cover-
ing timely topics of concern to the real estate
industry's most dynamic brokers, owners, managers,
and sales associates. **Availability:** Print; PDF;
Download; Online.

13349 ■ Western Real Estate Business: Connecting Real Estate in the West
3535 Piedmont Rd. NE, Bldg. 14, Ste. 950
  Atlanta, GA 30305
Ph: (404)832-8262
Fax: (404)832-8260
URL: http://francemediainc.com
Contact: Scott France, Publisher
URL(s): rebusinessonline.com/commercial-real-esta
  te-magazines/western-real-estate-business
Ed: Amy Works, Nellie Day. **Released:** Monthly
Description: Magazine that covers the latest news,
developments and trends in commercial real estate
in the western states. **Availability:** Print; Online.

INTERNET DATABASES

13350 ■ Real Estate Industry: A Resource Guide
URL(s): guides.loc.gov/real-estate-industry-sources
Description: Provides links to research the residen-
tial and commercial real estate industries. Links to
print and online materials are given. **Availability:**
Online.

LIBRARIES

13351 ■ Baker Botts, L.L.P. Law Library
700 K St., NW
  Washington, DC 20001
Ph: (202)639-7700
Fax: (202)639-7890
URL: http://www.bakerbotts.com
Contact: Nancy Leap, Contact
E-mail: nancy.leap@bakerbotts.com
Scope: Law - banking, corporate, international, public
utilities, real estate, taxation, environmental, intel-
lectual property. **Services:** Interlibrary loan; copying;
library open to the public by appointment with restric-
tions. **Founded:** 1840. **Holdings:** 22,000 volumes;
microforms; videocassettes; audiocassettes; CD-
ROM.

13352 ■ Buset & Partners
1121 Barton St.
  Thunder Bay, ON, Canada P7B 5N3
Ph: (807)623-2500
Free: 866-532-8738
Fax: (807)622-7808
Co. E-mail: info@busetlaw.com
URL: http://busetlaw.com
Contact: Richard J. Buset, Partner Founder
E-mail: rbuset@busetlaw.com
Description: Full-service law firm located in the
central part of the City of Thunder Bay. **Founded:**
1980.

13353 ■ Landauer Realty Group Information Center
2 Science Rd.
  Glenwood, IL 60425-1586

Free: 800-323-8830
Fax: (708)755-7016
URL: http://www.landauer.com
Scope: Clinical optimization. **Services:** Center not
open to the public. **Holdings:** 375 books; 100 VF
drawers of reports; 16,000 clippings, offerings,
brochures, statistical data; 125 VF drawers of
research materials; U.S. maps; annual reports; 1960,
1970, 1980 census publications; government documents.

13354 ■ National Association of Realtors (NAR) - Library & Archives
430 N Michigan Ave.
  Chicago, IL 60611-4087
Free: 800-874-6500
Co. E-mail: infocentral@realtors.org
URL: http://www.nar.realtor
Contact: Bob Goldberg, Chief Executive Officer
Facebook: www.facebook.com/NARdotRealtor
Linkedin: www.linkedin.com/company/national
  -association-of-realtors
X (Twitter): x.com/nardotrealtor
Instagram: www.instagram.com/NARdotRealtor
YouTube: www.youtube.com/user/NAREALTORS
Description: Promotes education, high professional
standards and modern techniques in specialized real
estate work such as brokerage, appraisal, property
management, land development, industrial real
estate, farm brokerage and counseling. Conducts
research programs. **Scope:** Real estate topics.
Services: Interlibrary loan. **Founded:** 1908. **Holdings:** 500,000 documents and images; 7,500
e-books; audiobooks and videos; 6,000 e-journal;
12,000 books; reports; and guides; 150 journals;
newsletters; periodicals; magazines. **Publications:**
Realtor Magazine (Quarterly); *Realtor Magazine: The
Business tool for Real Estate Professionals* (Quarterly); *NAR Commercial Real Estate Outlook* (Quar-
terly); *Real Estate Today: Official Publication of the
National Association of Realtors* (10/year); *REAL-
TORS Land Institute* (6/year); *Existing-Home Sales*
(Monthly). **Awards:** National Association of Realtors
Distinguished Service Award (Annual). **Geographic
Preference:** National.

13355 ■ Polsinelli PC - Library
900 W 48th Pl., Ste. 900
  Kansas City, MO 64112
Ph: (816)753-1000
Fax: (816)753-1536
URL: http://www.polsinelli.com
Contact: Cara E. Stark, Director
E-mail: cstark@polsinelli.com
Linkedin: www.linkedin.com/company/polsinelli
Description: A full-service law firm serving clients in
health care, financial services, intellectual property,
middle-market corporate, labor and employment, real
estate, and business litigation. **Scope:** Law - tax,
bankruptcy, real estate; litigation; product liability.
Services: Interlibrary loan; copying; SDI; library open
to clients only. **Founded:** 1972. **Holdings:** 15,000
books. **Subscriptions:** 1,500 journals and other serials; 10 newspapers. **Educational Activities:** Winter
Leadership Conference (Annual); ABI Annual Spring
Meeting (Annual); International Car Rental Show (Annual).

13356 ■ University of New Orleans - Institute for Economic Development & Real Estate Research Library
2000 Lakeshore Dr.
  New Orleans, LA 70148
Ph: (504)280-6836
Fax: (504)280-3176
Co. E-mail: researchoffice@uno.edu
URL: http://www.uno.edu/research/collaborate/cen
  ters-and-institutes
Scope: Housing; retail; trade; real estate; economic
development; strategic planning for community
economic development. **Services:** Library open to

the public by appointment. **Holdings:** 900 volumes; reports; manuscripts; videotapes; microfiche; microfilms.

RESEARCH CENTERS

13357 ■ Ohio State University - Fisher College of Business - Ohio State Center for Real Estate
606 Fisher Hall
2100 Neil Ave.
Columbus, OH 43210-1144

Ph: (614)292-8916
Fax: (614)292-2418
Co. E-mail: realestate@osu.edu
URL: http://fisher.osu.edu/centers-partnerships/center-real-estate

Description: Research, education, and administrative unit in the College of Business, Ohio State University. **Scope:** Serves as a focal point for involvement of faculty from various disciplines in real estate research and education projects. **Founded:** 1976.

Educational Activities: Center for Real Estate Education and Research Assists in the development of educational programs in real estate offered by the University; Annual Real Estate Conference (Annual); Center for Real Estate Education and Research Seminars.

START-UP INFORMATION

13358 ■ *"First-Time Landlord: Your Guide to Renting Out a Single-Family Home"*
Pub: Nolo
Contact: Chris Braun, President
Released: 6th Edition. **Price:** $17.49, e-book (downloadable); $19.99, book and e-book. **Description:** The basics for becoming an landlord for anyone wishing to start an entrepreneurial pursuit in home rentals are outlined. Concise information for renting out a single-family home includes, how to determine whether the property will turn a profit, landlord business basics, finding the right tenants, preparing and signing a lead, handling repairs, complying with state rental laws, dealing with problem tenants, and preparing for the sale of the property. **Availability:** E-book.

ASSOCIATIONS AND OTHER ORGANIZATIONS

13359 ■ **International Real Estate Institute (IREI)**
PO Box 879
Palm Springs, CA 92263
Ph: (760)327-5284
Co. E-mail: info@irei-assoc.org
URL: http://irei-assoc.org

Description: Professionals in 120 countries specializing in the development, finance, investment and valuation of real estate. Conducts educational seminars and regional programs; operates speakers' bureau and placement service. Compiles statistics, consults United Nations on property issues. **Founded:** 1975. **Geographic Preference:** Multinational.

13360 ■ **Investments & Wealth Institute**
5619 DTC Pky., Ste. 500
Greenwood Village, CO 80111
Ph: (303)770-3377
Fax: (303)770-1812
URL: http://investmentsandwealth.org/home
Contact: Todd Wagenberg, Chairman of the Board
X (Twitter): x.com/iw_inst
YouTube: www.youtube.com/c/InvestmentsWealthInstitute

Description: Consultants, money managers, and others in the investment management consultant business. Seeks to increase public awareness of investment management consultants, provide educational programs to members, and encourage high business standards. Operates consulting industry certification program. Maintains a legislative network with state and federal legislative information affecting the industry. **Founded:** 1985. **Publications:** *Essentials of Investment Consulting*; *The Facts About Investing*; *The Journal of Investment Consulting* (Annual); *The Monitor* (Bimonthly); *Wealth Management Course*. **Educational Activities:** IMCA Annual Conference (Annual); Regional Consultants Conferences. **Awards:** Richard J. Davis Ethics, Legal,

Regulatory Insight Award (Annual); Stephen L. Kessler Writing Award (Annual). **Geographic Preference:** Multinational.

13361 ■ **NAIOP [National Association of Industrial and Office Properties (NAIOP); Commercial Real Estate Development Association]**
2355 Dulles Corner Blvd., Ste. 750
Herndon, VA 20171
Ph: (703)904-7100
Fax: (703)904-7942
Co. E-mail: info@naiop.org
URL: http://www.naiop.org
Contact: Molly Carson, Senior Vice President
Facebook: www.facebook.com/NAIOPCorporate
Linkedin: www.linkedin.com/company/naiop
X (Twitter): x.com/NAIOP
YouTube: www.youtube.com/NAIOPcorporate

Description: Organization for developers, owners and related professionals in office, industrial, retail and mixed-use real estate. Provides unparalleled industry networking and education, and advocates for effective legislation on behalf of members. **Founded:** 1967. **Publications:** *Development* (Quarterly); *Development Magazine* (Quarterly; Quarterly); *NAIOP News Online* (Biweekly); *Legislative News* (Weekly). **Educational Activities:** NAIOP Marketplace (Annual); National Association of Industrial and Office Properties Seminar. **Awards:** Developing Leaders Award (Annual); NAIOP Developer of the Year Award (Annual); NAIOP Developing Leaders Award (Annual); NAIOP Sustainable Development Award (Annual). **Geographic Preference:** Local; National.

13362 ■ **National Apartment Association (NAA)**
4300 Wilson Blvd., Ste. 800
Arlington, VA 22203
Ph: (703)518-6141
Fax: (703)248-9440
Co. E-mail: clientsolutions@naahq.org
URL: http://www.naahq.org
Contact: Robert Pinnegar, President
Facebook: www.facebook.com/NAAhq
Linkedin: www.linkedin.com/company/national-apartment-association
X (Twitter): x.com/naahq
YouTube: www.youtube.com/user/NAAhqVideos

Description: Provides education and certification for property management executives, on-site property managers, maintenance personnel, property supervisors, and leasing agents. Offers a nationwide legislative network concerned with governmental decisions at the federal, state, and local levels. **Founded:** 1939. **Publications:** *Units* (Monthly). **Educational Activities:** National Apartment Association Education Conference & Exposition (Annual). **Geographic Preference:** National.

13363 ■ **National Association of Real Estate Companies (NAREC)**
4908 Calhoun Canyon Loop
Austin, TX 78735

Ph: (773)283-6362
Co. E-mail: info@narec.org
URL: http://www.narec.org
Contact: Peter Ulstad, President
Linkedin: www.linkedin.com/groups/1859586/profile

Description: Individuals associated with companies involved in the financial management of real estate development companies. Purpose: Seeks to formulate positions and inform members on current accounting and financial reporting issues relating to real estate companies and to voice these positions to appropriate accounting rule-making bodies. Cooperates with such bodies in order to establish accounting and financial guidelines; provides a forum for members dealing with issues faced in managing the financial affairs of real estate companies such as financial reporting, financial management, tax planning, and information technology. **Founded:** 1978. **Publications:** *National Association of Real Estate Companies--Membership Directory*. **Educational Activities:** National Association of Real Estate Companies Conferences (Annual). **Geographic Preference:** National.

13364 ■ **National Association of Real Estate Investment Trusts (NAREIT)**
1875 I St. NW, Ste. 500
Washington, DC 20006
Ph: (202)739-9400
Free: 800-362-7348
Fax: (202)739-9401
URL: http://www.reit.com
Contact: Lisa Palmer, Chairman
Facebook: www.facebook.com/REITsNAREIT
Linkedin: www.linkedin.com/company/nareit
X (Twitter): x.com/REITs_NAREIT
YouTube: www.youtube.com/nareit1

Description: Real estate investment trusts; corporations, partnerships, or individuals (other than trusts) that manage multiple-owned real estate, or that have a business or professional interest in real estate trusts, associations, corporations and funds. Compiles statistics. **Founded:** 1960. **Publications:** *The REIT Directory*; *NAREIT Quick Member Guide* (Annual). **Educational Activities:** Institutional Investor Forum (Annual); Law, Accounting & Finance Conference (Annual). **Geographic Preference:** National.

13365 ■ **National Association of Realtors (NAR) - Library & Archives**
430 N Michigan Ave.
Chicago, IL 60611-4087
Free: 800-874-6500
Co. E-mail: infocentral@realtors.org
URL: http://www.nar.realtor
Contact: Bob Goldberg, Chief Executive Officer
Facebook: www.facebook.com/NARdotRealtor
Linkedin: www.linkedin.com/company/national-association-of-realtors
X (Twitter): x.com/nardotrealtor
Instagram: www.instagram.com/NARdotRealtor
YouTube: www.youtube.com/user/NAREALTORS

Description: Promotes education, high professional standards and modern techniques in specialized real estate work such as brokerage, appraisal, property management, land development, industrial real estate, farm brokerage and counseling. Conducts research programs. **Scope:** Real estate topics. **Services:** Interlibrary loan. **Founded:** 1908. **Holdings:** 500,000 documents and images; 7,500 e-books; audiobooks and videos; 6,000 e-journal; 12,000 books; reports; and guides; 150 journals; newsletters; periodicals; magazines. **Publications:** *Realtor Magazine* (Quarterly); *Realtor Magazine: The Business tool for Real Estate Professionals* (Quarterly); *NAR Commercial Real Estate Outlook* (Quarterly); *Real Estate Today: Official Publication of the National Association of Realtors* (10/year); *REALTORS Land Institute* (6/year); *Existing-Home Sales* (Monthly). **Awards:** National Association of Realtors Distinguished Service Award (Annual). **Geographic Preference:** National.

13366 ■ Real Property Association of Canada (REALPAC) [Association des biens Immobiliers du Canada]
77 King St. W, TD North Twr., Ste. 4030
  Toronto, ON, Canada M5K 1H1
Ph: (416)642-2700
Free: 855-732-5722
Fax: (416)642-2727
Co. E-mail: info@realpac.ca
URL: http://realpac.ca
Contact: Dr. Michael Brooks, Chief Executive Officer
E-mail: mbrooks@realpac.ca
Linkedin: www.linkedin.com/company/realpac
X (Twitter): x.com/realpac_news
YouTube: www.youtube.com/channel/UCgyTGYy
  289DxHoBGPeY5Qzg
Description: Real estate and development companies and related businesses. Promotes growth in the real estate development and related industries. Serves as a forum for discussion of issues facing the industry; represents members' interests before the public. **Founded:** 1970. **Geographic Preference:** National.

INCUBATORS/RESEARCH AND TECHNOLOGY PARKS

13367 ■ Plug and Play - Real Estate and Construction
440 N Wolfe Rd.
  Sunnyvale, CA 94085
URL: http://www.plugandplaytechcenter.com/real-es
tate-tech
Description: An accelerator for startups in the real estate and construction tech industry. Provides support with venture and angel partners, mentorship, a data center, office space, and networking opportunities. This program focuses on planning and design, project management, land use, construction, workforce optimization, safety and building analysis, asset and property management, financing and appraisal, smart cities, connected IoT and sensors, and energy and sustainability.

REFERENCE WORKS

13368 ■ "1Q Office Vacancies Mainly Up; Class A Space Bucks Trend, Falls" in Crain's Detroit Business (Vol. 24, April 14, 2008, No. 15)
Pub: Crain Communications Inc.
Contact: Barry Asin, President
Ed: Daniel Duggan. **Description:** Although more office space became vacant in the first quarter, Class A space went in the opposite direction with several local businesses are moving from less-desirable to more desirable areas. **Availability:** Online.

13369 ■ "9 Ways to Invest in Real Estate Without Buying Property in 2019" in Forbes (February 22, 2019)
URL(s): www.forbes.com/sites/jrose/2019/02/22/real
  -estate-investing-without-buying-property/#8cd19
  4071f54

Ed: Jeff Rose. **Released:** February 22, 2019. **Description:** If you're thinking about investing in real estate but are not quite ready to become a landlord, there are several other options to consider. Investing money through REITs and ETFs are popular and can give investors exposure to the industry. Also, investing in real estate companies and similar industries are another good way to invest money. **Availability:** Online.

13370 ■ "$1.2 Billion Master-Planned Community in Celina Back on Track" in Dallas Business Journal (Vol. 35, June 8, 2012, No. 39, pp. 1)
Pub: Baltimore Business Journal
Contact: Rhonda Pringle, President
E-mail: rpringle@bizjournals.com

Ed: Candace Carlisle. **Description:** Developer, Republic Property Group, has started at its $1.2 billion residential development project in Celina, Texas and aims to deliver 400 home lots in its initial phase to contruction home builders by April 2012. The Light Farms master-planned community will feature a $5 million amenity and welcome center as well as a $13 million greenbelt. **Availability:** Print; Online.

13371 ■ "113D Filings: Investors Report to the SEC" in Barron's (Vol. 88, March 24, 2008, No. 12, pp. M13)
Pub: Dow Jones & Company Inc.
Contact: Almar Latour, Chief Executive Officer

Released: April 02, 2016. **Description:** HealthCor Management called as problematic the plan of Magellan Health Services to use its high cash balances for acquisitions. Carlson Capital discussed with Energy Partners possible changes in the latter's board. Investor Carl Icahn suggested that Enzon Pharmaceuticals consider selling itself or divest some of its assets. **Availability:** Print; Online.

13372 ■ "A 16-Year Housing Slump? It Could Happen" in Barron's (Vol. 88, March 17, 2008, No. 11, pp. 27)
Pub: Dow Jones & Company Inc.
Contact: Almar Latour, Chief Executive Officer

Ed: Gene Epstein. **Description:** Housing remains a good protection against inflation but over very long periods. Inflation-adjusted stock prices did even better but have greater volatility. Commodities, on the other hand, underperformed both housing and stocks as inflation hedges. House prices tend to rise faster than the consumer price index is because land is inherently limited. **Availability:** Online.

13373 ■ "$100M Complex To Be Built on Purple People Bridge" in Business Courier (Vol. 27, November 12, 2010, No. 28, pp. 1)
Pub: Business Courier
Ed: Lucy May. **Description:** A development firm closed a deal with the Newport Southbank Bridge Company for a $100M entertainment complex that will be built on top of the Purple People Bridge. The proposed project will cover 150,000 square feet with attractions such as restaurants, a boutique hotel, and pubs. **Availability:** Print; Online.

13374 ■ "2009 Real Estate in Review: Median Prices Drop, Sales Up" in Bellingham Business Journal (Vol. February 2010, pp. 15)
Description: Bellingham and Whatcom County, Washington saw a rise in home sales in 2008. Single family home sales were up 3.3 percent in Bellingham and 0.5 percent for the entire county. Statistical data included. **Availability:** Print; Online.

13375 ■ "2010 Book of Lists" in Business Courier (Vol. 26, December 26, 2009, No. 36, pp. 1)
Price: $49.95. **Description:** Rankings of companies and organizations within the business services, education, finance, health care, hospitality and tourism, real estate, and technology industries in the Cincinnati, Ohio-Northern Kentucky area are presented. Rankings are based on sales, business size, or other statistics. **Availability:** PDF; Online.

13376 ■ "2015 Marketing Calendar for Real Estate Pros: Own It"
Pub: CreateSpace
Released: October 14, 2014. **Price:** $9.56, paperback. **Description:** Real estate agents, mortgage loan agents, and new home builders and site and listing agents are shown how to use low-cost, high yield, proven marketing techniques to create digital real estate listings, find more customers, and sell more homes. Advice for building a brand and public relations; attracting renters and buyers; developing a good Website; and a digital marketing plan are explained. **Availability:** Print.

13377 ■ "Actian, Data Transformed and Yellowfin BI Mashup Helps Kollaras Group Reap Big Data Rewards" in Computer Business Week (August 28, 2014, pp. 22)
Pub: NewsRX LLC.
Contact: Kalani Rosell, Contact
Description: Actian announced that Australian liquor, hospitality and property investment company, Kollaras Group can now access real-time analytics; fast, simple and accurate data warehousing; and Yellowfin's Business Intelligence (BI) platform is examined. The BI provides better insights and decision-making across diverse business units. **Availability:** Online.

13378 ■ "Agricultural Community Implements Green Technologies, Building Team" in Contractor (Vol. 56, September 2009, No. 9, pp. 5)
Ed: Candace Roulo. **Description:** John DeWald and Associates has initiated a residential development project which uses green technologies in Illinois. The community features a community center, organic farm and recreational trails. Comments from executives are also provided. **Availability:** Print; Online.

13379 ■ "All Aboard!" Austin Business Journal (Vol. 32, April 27, 2012, No. 8, pp. A1)
Ed: Sandra Zaragoza. **Description:** The MLK transit-oriented development in east Austin, Texas is attracting interest from real estate developers. About $22 million in real estate development projects are due to break ground in the vicinity of the station within 18 months. **Availability:** Online.

13380 ■ "All About The Benjamins" in Canadian Business (Vol. 81, September 29, 2008, No. 16, pp. 92)
Description: Discusses real estate developer Royal Indian Raj International Corp., a company that planned to build a $3 billion "smart city" near the Bangalore airport; to this day nothing has ever been built. The company was incorporated in 1999 by Manoj C. Benjamin one investor, Bill Zack, has been sued by the developer for libel due to his website that calls the company a scam. Benjamin has had a previous case of fraud issued against him as well as a string of liabilities and lawsuits. **Availability:** Online.

13381 ■ "All-Star Advice 2010" in Black Enterprise (Vol. 41, October 2010, No. 3, pp. 97)
Pub: Earl G. Graves Ltd.
Contact: Earl Graves, Jr., President
Ed: Renita Burns, Sheiresa Ngo, Marcia Wade Talbert. **Description:** Financial experts share tips on real estate, investing, taxes, insurance and debt management. **Availability:** Online.

13382 ■ "Anderson Pitches Liberty Towne Place" in Business Courier (Vol. 27, June 18, 2010, No. 7, pp. 1)
Pub: Business Courier
Ed: Dan Monk. **Description:** Jeffrey R. Anderson Real Estate Inc.'s plan for a retail center in Butler County, Ohio could have three department stores in the 1.1 million-square-foot property. An outdoor sports retailer is also part of the plans. **Availability:** Print; Online.

13383 ■ "Another California Firm Moving to Austin" in Austin Business Journal (Vol. 31, May 6, 2011, No. 9, pp. 1)
Pub: Austin Business Journal
Contact: Rachel McGrath, Director

E-mail: rmcgrath@bizjournals.com

Ed: Christopher Calnan. **Description:** Main Street Hub Inc. is planning to build a facility in Austin, Texas. The company helps businesses manage their online reputations. Main Street has selected Aquila Commercial LLC as its real estate broker. **Availability:** Print; Online.

13384 ▪ *"Apartment Action: A Renewal in Rentals"* in Barron's (Vol. 88, March 17, 2008, No. 11, pp. 17)
Pub: Dow Jones & Company Inc.
Contact: Almar Latour, Chief Executive Officer
Ed: Robin Goldwyn Blumenthal. **Description:** Discusses the projected entry of the estimated 82 million echo-boomers into the rentals market and the influx of immigrants and displaced homeowners which could turn apartments into lucrative investments again. While apartment-building completions rose slowly since 2003, demand is expected to increase steeply until 2015. **Availability:** Online.

13385 ▪ *"Apartment Tower in River North Fetches More Than $90 Million"* in Crain's Chicago Business (Vol. 34, October 24, 2011, No. 42, pp. 17)
Pub: Crain Communications Inc.
Contact: Barry Asin, President
Ed: Alby Gallun. **Description:** Apartment tower in River North was sold for over $90 million to a Texas pension fund adviser. Details are included. **Availability:** Online.

13386 ▪ *"Ask Inc.: Managing and Real Estate to Build Value"* in Inc. (December 2007, pp. 83-84)
Ed: Ari Weinzweig. **Price:** $8.95. **Description:** Questions regarding knowledge management in the case of a retiring CFO, issues involved in opening a satellite office for a New York realtor, and information for hiring a multicultural workforce are all discussed. **Availability:** PDF; Online.

13387 ▪ *"Assisted Living Facility Faces Bankruptcy and Care Issues"* in South Florida Business Journal (Vol. 33, August 17, 2012, No. 3, pp. 1)
Pub: Baltimore Business Journal
Contact: Rhonda Pringle, President
E-mail: rpringle@bizjournals.com
Description: FTMI Real Estate has filed for bankruptcy declaring a total debt of almost $29 million and assets of $19.6 million. The company owns The Lenox on the Lake, a 139-bed assisted living facility in Tamarac, which has at least one outstanding state complaint regarding patient care. **Availability:** Print; Online.

13388 ▪ *"Athletes Face Wins and Losses After Pro Sports"* in The Business Journal - Serving Phoenix and the Valley of the Sun (Vol. 29, September 21, 2008, No. 3, pp. 1)
Pub: American City Business Journals, Inc.
Contact: Mike Olivieri, Executive Vice President
Ed: Chris Casacchia. **Description:** Professional athletes like hockey star Jeremy Roenick start businesses, while others like Joel Adamson work to boost local communities. Former athletes were found to be particularly interested with real estate businesses. Other views and information on former athletes and their life after sports are presented. **Availability:** Online.

13389 ▪ *"Austin Realtors Cozy Up To Trulia"* in Austin Business Journal (Vol. 34, May 9, 2014, No. 12, pp. 6)
Pub: American City Business Journals, Inc.
Contact: Mike Olivieri, Executive Vice President
Released: Weekly. **Price:** $4, Introductory 4-week offer(Digital & Print). **Description:** Austin Board of Realtors (ABOR) MLS Advisory Committee chairman Lisa Messana explains the organization's decision to share data exclusively with Trulia.com. She describes member response to the announcement to end ABOR's data license agreement with ListHub. **Availability:** Print; Online.

13390 ▪ *Backstage Guide to Real Estate: Produce Passive Income, Write Your Own Story, and Direct Your Dollars Toward Positive Change*
Ed: Matt Picheny. **Released:** February 09, 2022. **Price:** $19.99, paperback; $9.99, e-book. **Description:** A guide on how to make real estate investments work for you. **Availability:** E-book; Print.

13391 ▪ *"Baltimore Commercial Real Estate Foreclosures Continue to Rise"* in Baltimore Business Journal (Vol. 28, October 1, 2010, No. 21, pp. 1)
Pub: Baltimore Business Journal
Contact: Rhonda Pringle, President
E-mail: rpringle@bizjournals.com
Ed: Daniel J. Sernovitz. **Description:** Foreclosures of commercial real estate across the Greater Baltimore area have continued to rise. The region is now host to about $2 billion worth of commercial properties that carry a maturing debt or have been foreclosed. Commercial real estate owners are unable to finance their debts because banks have become stricter in passing out loans. **Availability:** Print; Online.

13392 ▪ *"Baltimore Shopping Centers Go On the Block as Sellers See Demand"* in Baltimore Business Journal (Vol. 29, September 2, 2011, No. 17, pp. 1)
Pub: Boston Business Journal
Contact: Carolyn M. Jones, President
E-mail: cmjones@bizjournals.com
Ed: Daniel J. Sernovitz. **Description:** Maryland-based investors have been choosing to put their money in the supermarket business. Retail property sales have increased during the second quarter of 2011. **Availability:** Online.

13393 ▪ *"Bangles, BMWs Elbow Out Delis and Discount Shops"* in Crain's New York Business (Vol. 24, January 13, 2008, No. 2, pp. 35)
Pub: Crain Communications, Inc.
Contact: Jessica Botos, Manager, Marketing
E-mail: jessica.botos@crainsnewyork.com
Ed: Wendy Davis. **Description:** Lured by a growing number of affluent residents and high-earning professionals, a number of upscale retailers have opened locations downtown which is driving up rents and forcing out longtime independent merchants.

13394 ▪ *"Baupost Group Pours Money into Charlotte Real Estate Projects"* in Charlotte Business Journal (Vol. 25, December 3, 2010, No. 37, pp. 1)
Pub: Charlotte Business Journal
Contact: Robert Morris, Editor
E-mail: rmorris@bizjournals.com
Ed: Will Boye. **Description:** Boston-based hedge fund Baupost Group has been financing real estate project in Charlotte, North Carolina including more than 80 acres just north of uptown. Aside from purchasing the $23.8 million note for the Rosewood Condominiums from Regions Financial Corporation, the Baupost Group is also negotiating with Regions to buy the $93.9 million debt of the EipCentre real estate project. **Availability:** Print; Online.

13395 ▪ *"Bellevue Collection Collects 4 New Towers"* in Puget Sound Business Journal (Vol. 35, May 16, 2014, No. 4, pp. 4)
Pub: American City Business Journals, Inc.
Contact: Mike Olivieri, Executive Vice President
Description: A number of real estate development projects planned by Kemper Development Company, as part of the massive expansion of its Bellevue Collection in Washington are presented. Kemper is the builder, owner and operator of the properties that include office space on Lincoln Square, the New Lincoln Square Hotel/Apartments, Bellevue Square Hotel/Apartment Tower and Bellevue Square Apartment Tower. **Availability:** Online.

13396 ▪ *"'Better Together:' OCO LPA Executives Discuss Recent Merger"* in San Antonio Business Journal (Vol. 28, July 4, 2014, No. 21, pp. 8)
Pub: American City Business Journals, Inc.
Contact: Mike Olivieri, Executive Vice President
Released: Weekly. **Price:** $4, introductory 4-week offer(Digital & Print). **Description:** Texas-based OCO Architects agreed to merge with LPA Inc. of Irvine, California effective July 1, 2014 and the local firm will initially operate as OCO LPA before it officially becomes LPA in January 2015. The merger is expected to keep OCO LPA relevant in the residential and commercial real estate sectors. **Availability:** Print; Online.

13397 ▪ *"Betting On Spec"* in San Antonio Business Journal (Vol. 28, April 25, 2014, No. 11, pp. 4)
Pub: American City Business Journals, Inc.
Contact: Mike Olivieri, Executive Vice President
Released: Weekly. **Price:** $4, Introductory 4-week offer(Digital only). **Description:** Real estate broker, Ty Bragg, believes that San Antonio, Texas is lacking space for the industrial-facilities market and that will limit opportunities within the real estate sector. However, Steve Raub of Investment Realty Company, thinks that more companies are noticing the city's industrial market as a site to consider. **Availability:** Print; Online.

13398 ▪ *"Bills Would Regulate Mortgage Loan Officers"* in Crain's Detroit Business (Vol. 24, February 25, 2008, No. 8, pp. 9)
Pub: Crain Communications Inc.
Contact: Barry Asin, President
Ed: Amy Lane. **Description:** New legislation in Michigan, if passed, would create a registration process for mortgage loan officers in the state in order to address the mortgage loan crisis. **Availability:** Print; Online.

13399 ▪ *"Bose Seeking Expansion Options in Framingham"* in Boston Business Journal (Vol. 34, June 13, 2014, No. 19, pp. 15)
Pub: American City Business Journals, Inc.
Contact: Mike Olivieri, Executive Vice President
Released: Weekly. **Description:** Bose Corporation, the Framingham-based high-end audio products manufacturer, is in talks to buy a 10-acre property near its headquarters. Bose is negotiating with the owner of three buildings on Pennsylvania Avenue near the Bose headquarters. Bose already owns five buildings in Framingham, but is looking at real estate for growth and expansion. **Availability:** Print; Online.

13400 ▪ *"Bottom's Up: This Real-Estate Rout May Be Short-Lived"* in Barron's (Vol. 88, July 14, 2008, No. 28, pp. 25)
Pub: Dow Jones & Company Inc.
Contact: Almar Latour, Chief Executive Officer
Ed: Jonathan R. Laing. **Description:** Economist Chip Case believes that home prices are nearing a bottom based on his analysis of the history of the housing market; surprisingly, in the past the housing market has rebounded after a quarter from a massive housing start drop. The drop in early stage delinquencies is another sign of the housing market's recovery. **Availability:** Online.

13401 ▪ *"Briarcliff Office Building Fills Up Fast"* in The Business Journal-Serving Metropolitan Kansas City (Vol. 26, Sept. 5, 2008, pp. 1)
Pub: American City Business Journals, Inc.
Contact: Mike Olivieri, Executive Vice President
Ed: Rob Roberts. **Description:** Prior to its opening the Hilltop Office Building in Kansas City Missouri has attained 80 percent occupancy. FCStone Group Inc.'s plan to move to the building has boosted the facility's occupancy. Description and dimensions of the office building are also provided. **Availability:** Online.

13402 ■ "A Bright Spot: Industrial Space in Demand Again" in Sacramento Business Journal (Vol. 28, October 21, 2011, No. 34, pp. 1)

Description: Sacramento, California's industrial sites have been eyed by potential tenants who are actively seeking space larger than 50,000 square feet. **Availability:** Print; Online.

13403 ■ "Brisk Activity in North Fulton Office Market" in Atlanta Business Chronicle (July 11, 2014, pp. 2B)

Description: Activity appears to have pickup up briskly in the North Fulton office market during the first six months of 2014, mainly due to the high profile deals involving major players in the technology and health care sectors. **Availability:** Print; Online.

13404 ■ "Brokerages Seek a Foothold in Charlotte Real Estate Market" in Charlotte Business Journal (Vol. 25, October 15, 2010, No. 30, pp. 1)

Pub: Charlotte Business Journal
Contact: Robert Morris, Editor
E-mail: rmorris@bizjournals.com

Ed: Will Boye. **Description:** Charlotte, North Carolina has become an attractive destination for out-of-town brokerage firms. Colliers International has signed an affiliate deal with Anthony and Company to set up shop in Charlotte. Grubb and Ellis Company, on the other hand, is planning to open an office in the city. **Availability:** Print; Online.

13405 ■ "Brookfield Asset Management: A Perfect Predator" in Canadian Business (Vol. 83, July 20, 2010, No. 11-12, pp. 50)

Pub: Rogers Media Inc.
Contact: Neil Spivak, Chief Executive Officer

Ed: Joanna Pachner. **Description:** Brookfield Asset Management CEO Bruce Flatt manages $108 billion worth of real estate and the company has become one of the world's biggest prime real estate owners since he became leader. Flatt says their goal is to earn a 12-15 percent compound annual return per share and that they would shrink in size if it meant reaching that goal. **Availability:** Online.

13406 ■ "Brown's Goal: 1,300 New Apartments and Condos" in Business First of Buffalo (Vol. 30, February 28, 2014, No. 24, pp. 6)

Pub: American City Business Journals, Inc.
Contact: Mike Olivieri, Executive Vice President

Released: February 28, 2014. **Price:** $140, Digital & Print; $115, Digital only. **Description:** Buffalo, New York Mayor Bryan Brown is planning for at least 1,300 new, market-rate residential units in the city's central business district over the next four years. The additional residential units are incorporated in Brown's larger strategy for creating a 24/7 downtown Buffalo. The impact of the residential development plan on the area's periphery is examined. **Availability:** Print; Online.

13407 ■ "Bubble Trouble? Many Experts Say Seattle Housing Market Is Headed for a Fall" in Puget Sound Business Journal (Vol. 34, April 18, 2014, No. 53, pp. 4)

Pub: American City Business Journals, Inc.
Contact: Mike Olivieri, Executive Vice President

Description: Redfin disclosed that nearly one third of homes listed in the real estate market in King County, Washington were sold above the listing price in February 2014 and it is forecast that the housing market is headed into a new bubble. Statistics indicate that the trend in rising prices is slowing even in the face of a declining supply of available homes. The impact of international buyers is also discussed.

13408 ■ "Builder's Bankruptcy Fans Fears" in Crain's Cleveland Business (Vol. 28, October 22, 2007, No. 42, pp. 1)

Pub: Crain Communications Inc.
Contact: K. C. Crain, President

Ed: Stan Bullard. **Description:** Whitlatch & Co., Northeast Ohio's largest builder by unit volume in the early 1990s, has filed for Chapter 11 bankruptcy. This is causing builders and others in the real estate industry to wonder how long and severe the housing slump will be and which companies will survive. **Availability:** Online.

13409 ■ "Builders: Land Prices Up, Bank Lending Down" in Orlando Business Journal (Vol. 30, January 31, 2014, No. 32, pp. 5)

Pub: American City Business Journals, Inc.
Contact: Mike Olivieri, Executive Vice President

Released: Weekly. **Price:** $8, introductory 4-week offer(Digital & Print). **Description:** A look at the views of residential real estate executives on the rising land prices and financing of construction is presented. The limited supply of lots in great locations has resulted in landowners raising asking prices. The real estate downturn has also resulted in the reluctance of many banks to lend money to home builders to finance construction in Central Florida. **Availability:** Print; Online.

13410 ■ "C. Fla. Notches $5B in Real Estate Property Sales in Last 12 Months" in Orlando Business Journal (Vol. 31, July 4, 2014, No. 1, pp. 4)

Pub: American City Business Journals, Inc.
Contact: Mike Olivieri, Executive Vice President

Released: Weekly. **Price:** $8, Introductory 4-week offer(Digital & Print). **Description:** Real estate company Real Capital Analytics reports sales volumes totaling $5 billion in Central Florida's commercial real estate market between June 2013 and May 2014. Real estate deals in the region reflect investor interest in the Orlando market, as private equity and development firms renovate existing properties or build new construction projects, thus increasing property values, creating jobs and boosting the local economy. **Availability:** Print; Online.

13411 ■ "Cabi to Develop Major Retail Project" in South Florida Business Journal (Vol. 32, July 6, 2012, No. 50, pp. 1)

Pub: Baltimore Business Journal
Contact: Rhonda Pringle, President
E-mail: rpringle@bizjournals.com

Description: Aventura, Florida-based Cabi Developers has received a bankruptcy court approval to begin construction of a major retail project called Capital Brickell Place in the Brickell neighborhood. Mexican real estate developer GICSA will finance the project and Cabi has been talking with retailers like Costco, Targt and Trader Joe's as potential tenants. **Availability:** Print; Online.

13412 ■ "Cash Deals Are King, But Don't Reign Supreme In Birmingham" in Birmingham Business Journal (Vol. 31, May 16, 2014, No. 20, pp. 6)

Pub: American City Business Journals, Inc.
Contact: Mike Olivieri, Executive Vice President

Released: Weekly; 16 May 14. **Price:** $4, introductory 4-week offer(Digital & Print). **Description:** Data from market research firm, RealtyTrac found that all-cash transactions in Birmingham, Alabama accounted for less than 31 percent of home sales in the first quarter of 2014, compared with a stronger all-cash transactions recorded by Southern metropolitan areas like Atlanta, Memphis and Charlotte. Ben Chenault of MortgageBanc sees a trend among average homebuyers who prefer cash over finance. **Availability:** Print; Online.

13413 ■ "Cedar Fair to Solicit Bids for Geauga Lake" in Crain's Cleveland Business (Vol. 28, October 8, 2007, No. 40, pp. 1)

Pub: Crain Communications Inc.
Contact: K. C. Crain, President

Ed: Stan Bullard. **Description:** Cedar Fair Entertainment Co. plans to seek sealed bids for the redevelopment of nearly 540 acres of their amusement park site in southwest Geauga County and northwest Portage County. **Availability:** Online.

13414 ■ "Cincinnati Museum Center to Exhibit New Look" in Business Courier (Vol. 24, February 21, 2008, No. 46, pp. 1)

Pub: American City Business Journals, Inc.
Contact: Mike Olivieri, Executive Vice President

Ed: Dan Monk. **Description:** Discusses a $120 million renovation is being planned for the Cincinnati Museum Center complex at Union Terminal. The project aims to build a 14-acre park and office spaces in the area. Details of the Museum Center's renovation plans are given. **Availability:** Online.

13415 ■ "CNL's James Seneff Jr. Reveals 7 Ways to Grow Your Firm, Even in Down Times" in Orlando Business Journal (Vol. 30, May 16, 2014, No. 47, pp. 3)

Pub: American City Business Journals, Inc.
Contact: Mike Olivieri, Executive Vice President

Released: Weekly. **Price:** $8, introductory 4-week offer(Digital & Print). **Description:** CNL Financial Group Inc. founder and executive chairman, James Seneff, Jr., offers tips on ways to succeed during down times in his keynote address at a University of Central Florida Real Estate Conference in Orlando. He advises entrepreneurs to be a contrarian and avoid following the pack. **Availability:** Print; Online.

13416 ■ "Colliers Shifts Its Brokerage Home" in Charlotte Business Journal (Vol. 25, November 5, 2010, No. 33, pp. 1)

Pub: Charlotte Business Journal
Contact: Robert Morris, Editor
E-mail: rmorris@bizjournals.com

Ed: Will Boye. **Description:** Colliers International signed a long-term affiliate agreement with commercial real estate firm Clarus Properties, in a move that would allow Colliers to resume business in Charlotte, North Carolina. Colliers also hired well known brokers Brad Grow and Brent Royall. **Availability:** Print; Online.

13417 ■ "Columbia's JPB Raising $175M to Acquire Companies, Real Estate" in Boston Business Journal (Vol. 29, May 27, 2011, No. 3, pp. 1)

Pub: Boston Business Journal
Contact: Carolyn M. Jones, President
E-mail: cmjones@bizjournals.com

Ed: Gary Haber. **Description:** JPB Enterprises is preparing to raise $175 million in its goal of acquiring companies and real estate that are major names in America. The $75 million will be raised for a buyout fund that will target wide range of industries while the $100 million will be used for land investment projects in the Florida Panhandle. Baltimore firms are expected to benefit from this deal. **Availability:** Print; Online.

13418 ■ "Commercial Builders Take It on the Chin" in Crain's Chicago Business (Vol. 31, April 28, 2008, No. 17, pp. 16)

Pub: Crain Communications Inc.
Contact: Barry Asin, President

Ed: Alby Gallun. **Description:** Although the health care development sector has seen growth, the rest of Chicago's local commercial building industry has seen steep declines in the first quarter of this year. According to McGraw-Hill Construction, Chicago-area non-residential construction starts totaled $731 million in the quarter, a 60 percent drop from the year-earlier period. Volume in the retail, office and hotel markets fell by nearly 70 percent. **Availability:** Online.

13419 ■ "Commercial Real Estate Brokers See Steady Growth In 2014" in Sacramento Business Journal (Vol. 30, January 10, 2014, No. 46, pp. 3)

Pub: American City Business Journals, Inc.
Contact: Mike Olivieri, Executive Vice President

Released: Weekly. **Price:** $4, introductory 4-week offer(Digital & Print). **Description:** Analysts believe that the outlook for commercial real estate in Sacramento, California is positive. However, Elliot Williams of Jones Lang LaSalle thinks that the office market's recovery will depend on leases by smaller companies. Sacramento reported 10,000-square-feet of positive absorption in the fourth quarter of 2013. **Availability:** Print; Online.

13420 ■ *"Commercial Real Estate Developers"* **in Business Review Albany (Vol. 41, August 8, 2014, No. 20, pp. 8)**
Description: A listing of the top 22 commercial real estate developers in Albany, New York are ranked by square feet of property owned is presented. The Galesi Group is ranked number one, with Nigro Companies following in second place. **Availability:** Print; Online.

13421 ■ *"Commercial Real Estate May Be Cooling, While Residential Clamors to Meet Demand"* **in Houston Business Journal (Vol. 44, January 3, 2014, No. 35, pp. 6)**
Pub: American City Business Journals, Inc.
Contact: Mike Olivieri, Executive Vice President
Released: January 03, 2014. **Description:** Greater Houston Partnership has predicted that the real estate industry will remain active for the years ahead in Houston, Texas. However, commercial real estate might cool down while residential sales are expected to remain hot with demand outpacing supply. Houston's construction boom in each sector is also discussed. **Availability:** Print; Online.

13422 ■ *"Con-Way Development Back in High Gear"* **in Business Journal Portland (Vol. 27, November 5, 2010, No. 36, pp. 1)**
Pub: Portland Business Journal
Contact: Andy Giegerich, Managing Editor
E-mail: agiegerich@bizjournals.com
Ed: Wendy Culverwell. **Description:** Trucking firm Con-Way Inc. intends to sell parcels of land from a property comprising 16 blocks and 20 prime acres west of the Pearl District in Portland, Oregon. In 2009, Con-Way abandoned plans to sell the property. As Con-Way reclaims control over design and usage of the property, it also expressed willingness to cooperate with a master developer on a related real estate project. **Availability:** Print; Online.

13423 ■ *"Contingent Offers: Weighing the Risk"* **in Crain's Chicago Business (Vol. 31, April 21, 2008, No. 16, pp. 48)**
Pub: Crain Communications Inc.
Contact: Barry Asin, President
Ed: Darci Smith. **Description:** Interview with Greer Haseman, the broker-owner of Town Square Associates, who discusses contingent offers in a challenging housing market. **Availability:** Online.

13424 ■ *"A Conversation with: Renea Butler"* **in Crain's Detroit Business (Vol. 25, June 8, 2009, No. 23, pp. 12)**
Pub: Crain Communications Inc.
Contact: Barry Asin, President
Ed: Ryan Beene. **Description:** Renea Butler, vice president of administration and human resources for Real Estate One Inc. in Southfield as well as vice president for public relations for the Human Resource Association of Greater Detroit, talks about how the economy has affected human resource services. **Availability:** Print; Online.

13425 ■ *"A Conversation With: Ron Gantner, Jones Lang LaSalle"* **in Crain's Detroit Business (Vol. 24, October 6, 2008, No. 40, pp. 9)**
Pub: Crain Communications Inc.
Contact: Barry Asin, President
Description: Interview with Ron Gantner who is a corporate real estate adviser with the real estate company Jones Lang LaSalle as well as the company's executive vice president and part of the tenant advisory team; Gantner speaks about the impact that the Wall Street crisis is having on the commercial real estate market in Detroit. **Availability:** Print; Online.

13426 ■ *"Cool on Chicago Office Properties"* **in Crain's Chicago Business (Vol. 31, March 31, 2008, No. 13, pp. 16)**
Pub: Crain Communications Inc.
Contact: Barry Asin, President
Ed: Eddie Baeb. **Description:** Investors predict values on Chicago office buildings to drop 1.3 percent over the next year. **Availability:** Online.

13427 ■ *"Corus Eases Off Ailing Condo Market"* **in Crain's Chicago Business (April 28, 2008)**
Pub: Crain Communications Inc.
Contact: Barry Asin, President
Ed: H. Lee Murphy. **Description:** Corus Bankshares Inc., a specialist in lending for the condominium high-rise construction market, is diversifying its portfolio by making loans to office developers and expects to be investing in hotels through the rest of the year. Corus' $7.57 billion loan portfolio is also discussed in detail as well as the company's earnings and share price. Statistical data included. **Availability:** Online.

13428 ■ *"Could Bond OK Bring Back the Charlotte Housing Battle?"* **in Charlotte Business Journal (Vol. 25, November 5, 2010, No. 33, pp. 1)**
Pub: Charlotte Business Journal
Contact: Robert Morris, Editor
E-mail: rmorris@bizjournals.com
Ed: Susan Stabley. **Description:** The approval of the $15 million housing bond in Charlotte, North Carolina could bring back the debates on housing in the region. Protesters have opposed affordable housing developments that were proposed in the area since 2008. Other information on the recently approved housing bond and on other real estate issues in North Carolina is presented. **Availability:** Print; Online.

13429 ■ *"Council OKs Curtis Park Tax-Credit Plan"* **in Sacramento Business Journal (Vol. 31, June 13, 2014, No. 16, pp. 3)**
Pub: American City Business Journals, Inc.
Contact: Mike Olivieri, Executive Vice President
Released: June 13, 2014. **Description:** The Sacramento City Council of California approved an agreement intended to resolve the dispute over affordable housing tax credits between Bridge Housing and Curtis Park Village developers. Bridge Housing pulled out its application for nine percent tax credits for the rehabilitation of the Sutterview project to allow Curtis Park Court to get the tax credits in July 2014.

13430 ■ *"David Bugs Developer Goliaths"* **in Denver Business Journal (Vol. 64, August 17, 2012, No. 13, pp. 1)**
Pub: Baltimore Business Journal
Contact: Rhonda Pringle, President
E-mail: rpringle@bizjournals.com
Description: The ordinance allowing citizens to file petitions for the declaration of some Denver buildings as historic is affecting real estate developers. Experts are concerned that these efforts for the preservation of abandoned facilities may become a trend that would hinder new land development projects. Changes in the ordinance are being suggested to ease the impact on developers. **Availability:** Print; Online.

13431 ■ *"Design '07 (Housing): Prince of the City"* **in Canadian Business (Vol. 80, November 19, 2007, No. 23, pp. 62)**
Pub: Rogers Media Inc.
Contact: Neil Spivak, Chief Executive Officer
Ed: Rachel Pulfer. **Description:** Robert Fung and the Salient Group aim to revive the poverty-stricken communities in Vancouver by transforming the city's old buildings into designer condominiums using city incentives. Fung and his partners have increased property values in the most unlikely neighborhoods by creating luxury real estate. Fung's recommendations on Vancouver's real estate development are given. **Availability:** Online.

13432 ■ *"Detroit Residential Market Slows; Bright Spots Emerge"* **in Crain's Detroit Business (Vol. 24, October 6, 2008, No. 40, pp. 11)**
Pub: Crain Communications Inc.
Contact: Barry Asin, President
Ed: Daniel Duggan. **Description:** Discusses the state of the residential real estate market in Detroit; although condominium projects receive the most attention, deals for single-family homes are taking place in greater numbers due to financing issues. Buyers can purchase a single family home with a 3.5 percent down payment compared to 20 percent for some condo deals because of the number of first-time homebuyer programs under the Federal Housing Administration.

13433 ■ *"Developer Backs Out of Major Bastrop Project"* **in Austin Business JournalInc. (Vol. 28, December 19, 2008, No. 40, pp. 1)**
Description: Weingarten Realty Investors, a Houston, Texas-based real estate company, has backed out of its contract on more than 1 million square feet of retail space at the County Road 304 and State Highway 71 corner in Bastrop, Texas, according to landowner Tom Brundage. Analysts say that the Bastrop area is not ready for big retail projects. **Availability:** Print; Online.

13434 ■ *"Developer Tries to Bring Homes to Buda"* **in Austin Business JournalInc. (Vol. 28, December 26, 2008, No. 41, pp. 1)**
Description: Real estate developer Jeremiah Venture LP is planning a residential, single-family development on about 600 acres near Buda, Texas. The company also plans to construct a membrane waste treatment plant, and has applied to do land application. However, several groups have come forward to ask for more information on the application due to concerns about soil density. **Availability:** Print; Online.

13435 ■ *"Developers Give Big to Stephanie Rawlings-Blake Bid for Mayor"* **in Baltimore Business Journal (Vol. 29, August 26, 2011, No. 16, pp. 1)**
Pub: Boston Business Journal
Contact: Carolyn M. Jones, President
E-mail: cmjones@bizjournals.com
Ed: Scott Dance. **Description:** Mayor Stephanie Rawlings-Blake received thousands of dollars in her political campaign from companies of real estate developers who are vying to build key development projects in Baltimore, Maryland. Rawlings-Blake created a major fundraising advantage over other mayoral candidates with the help of those contributions. **Availability:** Online.

13436 ■ *"Developers Give City Dwellings a Modern Spin"* **in Crain's Cleveland Business (Vol. 28, November 5, 2007, No. 44, pp. 18)**
Pub: Crain Communications Inc.
Contact: K. C. Crain, President
Ed: Stan Bullard. **Description:** Cleveland is increasingly becoming a canvas for fresh, cutting-edge design due to several recent projects, some at prominent sites. **Availability:** Online.

13437 ■ *"Developers Move Forward Along Seattle's Waterfront"* **in Puget Sound Business Journal (Vol. 35, July 25, 2014, No. 14, pp. 4)**
Pub: American City Business Journals, Inc.
Contact: Mike Olivieri, Executive Vice President
Released: Weekly. **Description:** Seattle, Washington's waterfront development continues to flourish with plans for two more projects on the horizon. Brick Road Holdings is planning construction of a seven-story Natasha market-rate project with 160 apartments. Six other new projects by the following companies are profiled: Schuster Group, Gerding Edlen, Mack Urban, Daniels Real Estate, Goodman Real Estate, and Martin Selig Real Estate. **Availability:** Print; Online.

13438 ■ *"Developers Poised to Pull Trigers"* **in Boston Business Journal (Vol. 30, November 12, 2010, No. 42, pp. 1)**

Description: Large residential projects are expected to break ground in Boston, Massachusetts in 2011, as real estate developers expect growth for the industry. Real estate experts expect more than 2,000 rental units to be available by 2011. Information on key real estate projects in Boston is presented. **Availability:** Print; Online.

13439 ■ *"Developers Tout Benefits of Federal Tax Breaks"* **in Business First of Buffalo (Vol. 30, March 14, 2014, No. 26, pp. 4)**

Pub: American City Business Journals, Inc.
Contact: Mike Olivieri, Executive Vice President

Released: Weekly. **Price:** $140, Digital & Print; $115, Digital only. **Description:** President Obama has included a Federal tax credit program in the 2015 Federal budget that provides some relief to the local development community. Congressman Mark Higgins promised to support the program that offers tax breaks to urban developers who rehabilitate older buildings with new investments. The tax credit's economic benefits are also discussed. **Availability:** Print; Online.

13440 ■ *Dictionary of Real Estate Terms*

Pub: Barron's Educational Series Inc.
Contact: Manuel H. Barron, Contact

Ed: Jack P. Friedman, Jack C. Harris, J. Bruce Lindeman. **Released:** 9th edition. **Price:** $16.99, paperback, plus shipping charges $5.99. **Description:** More than 2,500 real estate terms relating to mortgages and financing, brokerage law, architecture, rentals and leases, property insurance, and more. **Availability:** E-book; Print.

13441 ■ *"Docs Might Hold Cure for Baltimore-Area Real Estate, Banks"* **in Baltimore Business Journal (Vol. 28, November 5, 2010, No. 26, pp. 1)**

Pub: Baltimore Business Journal
Contact: Rhonda Pringle, President
E-mail: rpringle@bizjournals.com

Ed: Gary Haber. **Description:** Health care providers, including physicians are purchasing their office space instead of renting it as banks lower interest rates to 6 percent on mortgages for medical offices. The rise in demand offers relief to the commercial real estate market. It has also resulted in a boom in building new medical offices. **Availability:** Print; Online.

13442 ■ *"East-Side Real Estate Forum Detours To Grand Rapids"* **in Crain's Detroit Business (Vol. 24, October 6, 2008, No. 40, pp. 17)**

Pub: Crain Communications Inc.
Contact: Barry Asin, President

Ed: Daniel Duggan. **Description:** Tom Wackerman was elected chairman of the University of Michigan-Urban Land Institute Real Estate Forum and proposed that the annual conference be held in Grand Rapids due to the brisk economic activity he was finding there; although the idea was initially met with resistance, the plan to introduce East-siders to the West side began receiving more enthusiasm due to the revitalization of the area, which was once considered to have a bleak outlook. Many are hoping to learn the lessons of those who were able to change a negative economic climate into a positive one in which the cooperation of private business and government can work together to accomplish goals. **Availability:** Print; Online.

13443 ■ *"Empty Lots Could Be Full of Promise"* **in San Francisco Business Times (Vol. 28, March 14, 2014, No. 34, pp. 4)**

Pub: American City Business Journals, Inc.
Contact: Mike Olivieri, Executive Vice President

Price: $4, Introductory 4-Week Offer(Digital Only). **Description:** San Francisco, California officials are looking at the city's own landholdings in order to start

constructing new homes. However, the use of city-owned land does not ensure that the home permit process will be trouble-free. **Availability:** Print; Online.

13444 ■ *"Empty Office Blues"* **in Business Journal Portland (Vol. 26, December 4, 2009, No. 39, pp. 1)**

Pub: Portland Business Journal
Contact: Andy Giegerich, Managing Editor
E-mail: agiegerich@bizjournals.com

Ed: Wendy Culverwell. **Description:** Portland's office vacancy rates could reach almost 15 percent by the end of 2010 due to job reductions and mergers. **Availability:** Print; Online.

13445 ■ *"Escape from Iron Mountain"* **in Barron's (Vol. 92, September 17, 2012, No. 38, pp. 23)**

Description: The stocks of Iron Mountain appear fully valued at their most recent price of $33/share. Activist investors Elliott Management and Davis Advisors pushed for the conversion into a real estate investment trust but have since sold their holdings in the company. **Availability:** Online.

13446 ■ *"Everyone Out of the Pool"* **in Barron's (Vol. 89, July 20, 2009, No. 29, pp. 18)**

Pub: Dow Jones & Company Inc.
Contact: Almar Latour, Chief Executive Officer

Ed: Sandra Ward. **Description:** Shares of Pool Corp. could drop as continued weakness in the housing market weakens the market for swimming pool equipment. The company's shares are trading at $18.29, about 20 times projected 2009 earnings of $0.91 a share. **Availability:** Online.

13447 ■ *"Exxon Mobil Campus 'Clearly Happening"* **in Houston Business Journal (Vol. 40, January 15, 2010, No. 36, pp. 1)**

Pub: Houston Business Journal
Contact: Bob Charlet, President
E-mail: bcharlet@bizjournals.com

Ed: Jennifer Dawson. **Description:** Oil and gas company Exxon Mobil intends to relocate its employees from Houston, Texas and Fairfax, Virginia into a 400-acre site near the town of Spring, Texas. Meanwhile, Exxon Mobil has refused to disclose further details of the relocation plan. Insights from real estate professionals on this relocation plan are examined. **Availability:** Print; Online.

13448 ■ *"Eyes to the Sky"* **in Canadian Business (Vol. 80, March 26, 2007, No. 7, pp. 33)**

Description: The growth and prices of condominium market in the Canada are analyzed. **Availability:** Online.

13449 ■ *"Fifth Third Spinoff Eyes More Space"* **in Business Courier (Vol. 27, July 16, 2010, No. 11, pp. 1)**

Pub: Business Courier

Ed: Dan Monk, Steve Watkins. **Description:** Electronic-funds transfer company Fifth Third Solutions (FTPS), a spinoff of Fifth Third Bancorp, is seeking as much as 200,000 square feet of new office space in Ohio. The bank's sale of 51 percent ownership stake to Boston-based Advent International Corporation has paved the way for the growth of FTPS. How real estate brokers' plans have responded to FTPS' growth mode is discussed. **Availability:** Print; Online.

13450 ■ *"A Fine Time for Timber"* **in Barron's (Vol. 92, August 25, 2012, No. 38, pp. 18)**

Pub: Dow Jones & Company Inc.
Contact: Almar Latour, Chief Executive Officer

Ed: Christopher C. Williams. **Description:** The stocks of timber firm and real estate investment trust Weyerhaeuser could have their dividend raised by as much as 50 percent. The company is poised to benefit from a housing sector recovery, which could raise the value of its real estate and timberland holdings. **Availability:** Online.

13451 ■ *"Florida Fast 100: D&D Construction Services"* **in South Florida Business Journal (Vol. 35, September 19, 2014, No. 8, pp. 16)**

Pub: American City Business Journals, Inc.
Contact: Mike Olivieri, Executive Vice President

Description: Profile of D and D Construction, who reports increased earnings in 2013 totaling $26.5 million. The increase has been attributed to the commercial real estate market's recovery from the economic recession. The company is focusing on offering hospitality (restaurant, hotel) projects. **Availability:** Online.

13452 ■ *"For One Homebuilder, It's Pretty Easy Being Green, Even in Houston"* **in Houston Business Journal (Vol. 44, April 11, 2014, No. 49, pp. 7)**

Pub: American City Business Journals, Inc.
Contact: Mike Olivieri, Executive Vice President

Released: Weekly. **Price:** $4, introductory 4-week offer(Digital only). **Description:** Frankel Building Group vice president, Scott Frankel, says new housing projects in Houston, Texas have been getting bigger. He also said that industry members are facing the problem of lack of residential lots in the region. Frankel added that the company builds its homes to LEED-certified standards. **Availability:** Print; Online.

13453 ■ *The Foreclosure of America: Life Inside Countrywide Home Loans and the Selling of the American Dream*

Pub: Berkley Trade/Penguin Group USA Inc.

Ed: Adam Michaelson. **Released:** January 06, 2009. **Price:** $6.99, E-book; Paperback. **Description:** An inside look at Countrywide Home Loans and the mortgage crisis. **Availability:** E-book; Print.

13454 ■ *"Former Schaefer & Strohminger Dealerships to Hit Auction Block"* **in Baltimore Business Journal (Vol. 28, September 10, 2010)**

Pub: Baltimore Business Journal
Contact: Rhonda Pringle, President
E-mail: rpringle@bizjournals.com

Ed: Gary Haber. **Description:** Maryland's real estate developers have a chance to vie for almost 11 acres of prime Baltimore County real estate that are on the auction block. The five properties were once home to Schaefer and Strohminger car dealerships and were located in the county's busiest areas. Other potential uses for the properties are also discussed.

13455 ■ *"Future Fuzzy at Former Pemco Plant"* **in Baltimore Business Journal (Vol. 32, July 25, 2014, No. 12, pp. 10)**

Pub: American City Business Journals, Inc.
Contact: Mike Olivieri, Executive Vice President

Released: Weekly. **Price:** $4, introductory 4-week offer(Digital only). **Description:** The abandoned Pemco Corporation site on Eastern Avenue in Southeast Baltimore faces an uncertain future as new owner, MCB Real Estate LLC, fails to specify its prospective development plans for the property. City Councilman, James B. Kraft, wants to restrict the amount of retail space to be built at the Pemco and might even delay filing legislation on the space until MCB provides more details for the 20-acre property. **Availability:** Print; Online.

13456 ■ *"Generation Y Driving Portland Multifamily"* **in Daily Journal of Commerce, Portland (October 29, 2010)**

Ed: Nick Bjork. **Description:** Generation Y, young adults between the ages of 18-30, are interested in multifamily residents in the Portland, Oregon area. Developers in the area, particularly North Portland, have recognized this trend and are looking into multifamily investments.

13457 ■ *"Glenmede at Liberty To Show Off Space"* **in Philadelphia Business Journal (Vol. 32, January 24, 2014, No. 50, pp. 8)**

Pub: American City Business Journals, Inc.
Contact: Mike Olivieri, Executive Vice President

Released: Weekly. **Price:** $4, introductory 4-week offer(Digital & Print). **Description:** Glenmede Trust Company decided to undertake a full office renovation after renewing its lease at One Liberty Place. The investment company decided to replace drywall with glass and more informal meeting places were constructed. The firm, which focuses on employee engagement, aims to improve the work environment. **Availability:** Print; Online.

13458 ■ *"GMREB/Analysis of the Resale Market-First Quarter 2007: Year Off to a Great Start"* in Marketwired (May 14, 2007)
Pub: Comtex News Network Inc.
Contact: Kan Devnani, President

Description: According to statistics gathered by the Greater Montreal Real Estate Board (GMREB), the Montreal census metropolitan area (CMA) resale market was vigorous in the first quarter of 2007 yielding 10 percent more existing homes being than the first quarter of 2006. **Availability:** Print; Online.

13459 ■ *"GM's Decision to Boot Dealer Prompts Sale"* in Baltimore Business Journal (Vol. 27, November 6, 2009, No. 26, pp. 1)
Pub: Baltimore Business Journal
Contact: Rhonda Pringle, President
E-mail: rpringle@bizjournals.com

Ed: Daniel J. Sernovitz. **Description:** General Motors Corporation's (GM) decision to strip Baltimore's Anderson Automotive Group Inc. of its GM franchise has prompted the owner, Bruce Mortimer, to close the automotive dealership and sell the land to a developer. The new project could make way for new homes, a shopping center and supermarket. **Availability:** Print; Online.

13460 ■ *"GM's Mortgage Unit Deal Brings in $9 Billion"* in Globe & Mail (March 24, 2006, pp. B3)
Ed: Shawn McCarthy. **Description:** General Motors Corp. sells General Motors Acceptance Corp.'s commercial real estate division to Kohlberg Kravis Roberts & Co. Five Mile Capital Partners LLC and Goldman Sachs Capital Partners. The reasons behind the deal are presented. **Availability:** Print; Online.

13461 ■ *"Goldbelt Inc.: Targeting Shareholder Development"* in Alaska Business Monthly (Vol. 27, October 2011, No. 10, pp. 108)
Pub: Alaska Business Publishing Company Inc.
Contact: Charles Bell, Vice President, Sales and Marketing
E-mail: cbell@akbizmag.com

Ed: Tracy Kalytiak. **Description:** Profile of Goldbelt Inc., the company that has changed its original focus of timber to real estate to tourism and then to government contracting opportunities. **Availability:** Print; Online.

13462 ■ *"A Good Sign for Commercial Real Estate?"* in Austin Business JournalInc. (Vol. 29, December 18, 2009, No. 41, pp. 1)
Pub: Austin Business Journal
Contact: Rachel McGrath, Director
E-mail: rmcgrath@bizjournals.com

Ed: Kate Harrington. **Description:** Factors that could contribute to the reemergence of the commercial mortgage-backed securities market in Texas are discussed. These securities can potentially boost the commercial real estate market statewide as well as nationwide. Commercial mortgage-backed securities origination in 2009 is worth less that $1 billion, compared with $238 billion in 2008. **Availability:** Online.

13463 ■ *"Green Housing for the Rest of Us"* in Inc. (November 2007, pp. 128-129)
Ed: Nitasha Tiku. **Description:** Profile of Full Spectrum NY, real estate developer firm, offering residences at the Kalahari, a green high-rise with state-of-the-art features at a reasonable price. **Availability:** Online.

13464 ■ *"Growth in Fits and Starts"* in Canadian Business (Vol. 83, July 20, 2010, No. 11-12, pp. 18)
Description: US home sales and manufacturing indicators have dropped and fears of a double-dip recession are widespread. However, a chief economist says that this is endemic to what can be seen after a recession caused by a financial crisis. In Canada, consumer optimism is rising and anxiety over losing one's job is waning. **Availability:** Print; Online.

13465 ■ *"Hawaii Rides Retail Strength Into New Year"* in Pacific Business News (Vol. 51, January 17, 2014, No. 48, pp. 3)
Pub: American City Business Journals, Inc.
Contact: Mike Olivieri, Executive Vice President
Released: Weekly. **Price:** $4, introductory 4-week offer(Digital only). **Description:** CBRE Hawaii's Fourth Quarter 2013 Hawaii Retail MarketView shows positive absorption, lower vacancy rates and stable lease rents with large transaction that will accelerate major retail development and redevelopment. Hawaii's real estate market remained strong in 2013. **Availability:** Print; Online.

13466 ■ *"High-End Blunders"* in Crain's Chicago Business (Vol. 31, April 21, 2008, No. 16, pp. 54)
Pub: Crain Communications Inc.
Contact: Barry Asin, President

Ed: Laura Bianchi. **Description:** Discusses some of the biggest errors sellers make that keep their homes from selling including: pricing too high; expecting to recoup the cost of very high-end amenities and decor; avant-garde decorating; owners that hover when the house is being shown; stripping the home of top-quality light fixtures and hardware and replacing them with inferior versions with the assumption that the new buyer will come in with their own decorator and redo it; and poorly maintained properties. **Availability:** Online.

13467 ■ *"Highland Row Joins Fray of Development Around U of M"* in Memphis Business Journal (No. 35, February 14, 2014, No. 45, pp. 7)
Released: February 14, 2014. **Description:** Real estate developer Milhaus is planning a 354-unit apartment complex and retail development project at the site of the Highland Church of Christ near the University of Memphis in Tennessee. other developers are also planning their own projects near the site including Shepherd Construction Company and Rael Development Corporation.

13468 ■ *"Hollander 95 Business Park Project Getting Bigger"* in Baltimore Business Journal (Vol. 29, September 23, 2011, No. 20, pp. 1)
Pub: Boston Business Journal
Contact: Carolyn M. Jones, President
E-mail: cmjones@bizjournals.com

Ed: Gary Haber. **Description:** Hollander 95 Business Park is in for a huge change as its new owners plan a $50 million expansion which calls for building as many as eight more buildings or a total of more than 500,000 square feed. FRP Development bought the site for $4.35 million at a foreclosure sale in July 2010 and is now seeking city approval for an Industrial Planned Unit Development designation. **Availability:** Online.

13469 ■ *"Home Prices Sag"* in Crain's Chicago Business (Vol. 31, April 28, 2008, No. 17, pp. 3)
Pub: Crain Communications Inc.
Contact: Barry Asin, President

Ed: Alby Gallun. **Description:** Since the slump in the housing market is continuing with no sign of recovery, Chicago-area home prices are poised for an even steeper drop this year. In 2007, the region's home prices fell nearly 5 percent and according to a forecast by Fiserv Inc., they will decline 8.1 percent this year and another 2.2 percent in 2009. Statistical data included. **Availability:** Online.

13470 ■ *"Homebuilder Confidence Buried Under Snow"* in Birmingham Business Journal (Vol. 31, February 21, 2014, No. 8, pp. 7)
Pub: American City Business Journals, Inc.
Contact: Mike Olivieri, Executive Vice President
Released: Weekly. **Description:** The National Association of Home Builders/Wells Fargo Housing Market Index has fallen by 10 points from the score of 56 in January to 46 in February as a result of 2014's harsh winter. The index is based on the survey of home builders' perceptions on the current and near-term housing market. **Availability:** Print; Online.

13471 ■ *"Hot Real Estate Market Means Hard Work for Investors"* in Business Journal Portland (Vol. 31, March 21, 2014, No. 3, pp. 14)
Pub: American City Business Journals, Inc.
Contact: Mike Olivieri, Executive Vice President
Description: Real estate investors are finding it difficult to improve the residential real estate market due to higher prices. Investors who purchase properties to use as rentals are struggling with the high home values in Portland, Oregon. **Availability:** Print; Online.

13472 ■ *"Hotel Could Move Into Former Movie Studio Site in Allen Park"* in Crain's Detroit Business (Vol. 35, September 1, 2014, No. 35, pp. 17)
Pub: Crain Communications Inc.
Contact: Barry Asin, President
Description: The former site of Unity Studios Inc. could become the site for a new hotel. The property was once owned by the former Visteon Corporation on Southfield Road in Allen Park, Michigan. Details of New York City-based Tim Equities Inc. plan for the hotel are included. **Availability:** Online.

13473 ■ *The Housing Boom and Bust*
Ed: Thomas Sowell. **Released:** Revised edition. **Price:** $10.99, e-book; $17.99; C$23.49. **Description:** An explanation of the economics and politics of the housing boom and its collapse. **Availability:** E-book; Print.

13474 ■ *"Housing Markets Still Struggling"* in Montana Business Quarterly (Vol. 49, Spring 2011, No. 1, pp. 17)
Pub: University of Montana Bureau of Business and Economic Research
Contact: Patrick Barkey, Director
E-mail: patrick.barkey@business.umt.edu

Ed: Scott Rickard. **Released:** Quarterly. **Description:** Montana's economic conditions are a bit better than national averages. Data ranked by state, year-over-year price change, and total price peak is presented, along with statistical data for the entire nation. **Availability:** Online.

13475 ■ *"Housing Slide Picks Up Speed"* in Crain's Chicago Business (Vol. 31, April 19, 2008, No. 16, pp. 2)
Pub: Crain Communications Inc.
Contact: Barry Asin, President

Ed: Eddie Baeb. **Description:** According to Tracy Cross & Associates Inc., a real estate consultancy, sales of new homes in the Chicago area dropped 61 percent from the year-earlier period which is more bad news for homebuilders, contractors and real estate agents who are eager for an indication that market conditions are improving. **Availability:** Online.

13476 ■ *"How To Make Finance Work: The U.S. Financial Sector Has Boomed, But That Hasn't Always Been Good News For the Rest of the Economy"* in Harvard Business Review (Vol. 90, March 2012, No. 3, pp. 104)
Pub: Harvard Business Review Press
Contact: Moderna V. Pfizer, Contact

Ed: David S. Scharfstein, Robin Greenwood. **Price:** $8.95, hardcover. **Description:** The growth of the financial sector has hindered overall US growth by shifting money from productive investments into residential real estate, and through high professional investment management costs. Private sector innovation and discipline will be needed to correct these flaws, as will regulatory changes. **Availability:** PDF; Online.

13477 ■ *"Hunt Valley Towne Center Gears Up for Growth; Ray Lewis Project Scrapped" in Baltimore Business Journal (Vol. 30, May 11, 2012, No. 1, pp. 1)*
Pub: American City Business Journals, Inc.
Contact: Mike Olivieri, Executive Vice President
Ed: James Briggs. **Description:** Greenberg Gibbons Commercial Corporation has plans for a 400-unit apartment complex and retail space at Hunt Valley Towne Centre in Baltimore, Maryland. The developer is also considering big-box stores to rent the vacant space that was supposed to be occuped by the failed bowling and entertainment venture MVP Lanes. **Availability:** Print; Online.

13478 ■ *"Hunter Capital's Malone Relishes Role of Renovator" in Puget Sound Business Journal (Vol. 35, June 13, 2014, No. 8, pp. 9)*
Pub: American City Business Journals, Inc.
Contact: Mike Olivieri, Executive Vice President
Description: Hunter Capital's founder, Michael Malone, says Seattle, Washington's real estate development needs to be balanced. He also stated that his company is set to renovate the old Dunn Automotive Building. He added that his firm will continue with its construction restoration projects. **Availability:** Online.

13479 ■ *"ICC Works on Prescriptive Green Construction Code" in Contractor (Vol. 56, October 2009, No. 10, pp. 1)*
Ed: Robert P. Mader. **Description:** International Code Council launched an initiative to create a green construction code that focuses on existing commercial buildings. The initiative's timeline will include public meetings leading up to a final draft that will be available in 2010. **Availability:** Print; Online.

13480 ■ *"IDI Plans Spec Industrial Space" in Memphis Business Journal (Vol. 33, February 10, 2012, No. 44, pp. 1)*
Pub: Baltimore Business Journal
Contact: Rhonda Pringle, President
E-mail: rpringle@bizjournals.com
Ed: Andy Ashby. **Description:** Industrial real estate company IDI is planning to start construction of two buildings in Memphis, Tennessee. The project is the company's first speculative new construction in four years. **Availability:** Print; Online.

13481 ■ *"If We Build Them, Will They Rent Them?" in Birmingham Business Journal (Vol. 31, August 1, 2014, No. 31, pp. 4)*
Pub: American City Business Journals, Inc.
Contact: Mike Olivieri, Executive Vice President
Released: August 1, 2014. **Description:** Developers and experts opine that the current demand for multifamily homes in Birmingham, Alabama will continue to grow, despite doubts by Housing and Urban Development over the city center's ability to sustain such growth. The key factors in the city's multi-family market as well as the risks and challenges facing developers are examined.

13482 ■ *"Illinois Farmland Tops $11,000 Per Acre" in Farm Industry News (June 27, 2011)*
Pub: Informa Business Media, Inc.
Contact: Charlie McCurdy, President
Ed: Karen McMahon. **Description:** Farmland property in Illinois continues to grow in value, selling for $11,000 per acre. Statistical data included. **Availability:** Online.

13483 ■ *"In Control: Tips For Navigating a Buyer's Market" in Black Enterprise (Vol. 38, December 2007, No. 5, pp. 64)*
Pub: Earl G. Graves Ltd.
Contact: Earl Graves, Jr., President
Ed: Erinn R. Johnson. **Description:** Tips are given to help would-be home buyers. The importance of finding a good real estate agent is stressed.

13484 ■ *"Incubator, Apartment Mix Eyed" in Providence Business News (Vol. 29, April 14, 2014, No. 2, pp. 1)*
Pub: American City Business Journals, Inc.
Contact: Mike Olivieri, Executive Vice President
URL(s): pbn.com/incubator-apartment-mix-eyed9 6427
Description: New York City-based developer, Frank Manaigo, has been working on plans to develop a culinary incubator in a vacant mill complex in the West End at the Armory District in Providence, Rhode Island. The "Rooms and Works" is a $6.5 million residential and commercial project that would feature the "Armory Kitchen". The apartment component of the project is also discussed. **Telecommunication Services:** Daddona@pbn.com.

13485 ■ *"Industrial Vacancies Hit High" in Crain's Chicago Business (Apr. 21, 2008)*
Pub: Crain Communications Inc.
Contact: Barry Asin, President
Ed: Alby Gallun. **Description:** Hitting its highest level in four years in the first quarter is the Chicago-area industrial vacancy rate, a sign that the slumping economy is depressing demand for warehouse and manufacturing space. **Availability:** Online.

13486 ■ *"Investment Market Heats Up on the Eastside" in Puget Sound Business Journal (Vol. 35, August 1, 2014, No. 15, pp. 4)*
Pub: American City Business Journals, Inc.
Contact: Mike Olivieri, Executive Vice President
Released: Weekly. **Price:** $4, Introductory 4-week offer(Digital & Print). **Description:** The real estate investment sales market in Puget Sound, Washington is experiencing growth along with construction activity. Office sales reached $787 million in the first half of the year, while the shortage of office space is driving up rents for office tenants and making the market attractive to investors. **Availability:** Print; Online.

13487 ■ *"Investors Eager to Buy Properties Regionwide" in Philadelphia Business Journal (Vol. 33, August 1, 2014, No. 25, pp. 10)*
Pub: American City Business Journals, Inc.
Contact: Mike Olivieri, Executive Vice President
Released: Weekly. **Price:** $4, introductory 4-week offer(Digital only). **Description:** Interest in multifamily homes in the Philadelphia region is growing in 2014, as buyers from across the country view Philadelphia as a key investment market. Investment brokers opine the present trend will continue as pricing remains strong and there are plenty of buyers with a limited number of properties. **Availability:** Print; Online.

13488 ■ *"Investors Eye Old Buildings" in Business Journal-Portland (Vol. 24, October 19, 2007, No. 34, pp. 1)*
Pub: Portland Business Journal
Contact: Andy Giegerich, Managing Editor
E-mail: agiegerich@bizjournals.com
Ed: Wendy Culverwell. **Description:** Office vacancy rates in downtown Portland has dipped to around five percent, causing brokers and investors to search for older buildings in the Class B and Class C categories where the rent is also cheaper. Some notable older and cheaper buildings will be renovated for use. **Availability:** Print; Online.

13489 ■ *"Is Fannie Mae the Next Government Bailout?" in Barron's (Vol. 88, March 10, 2008, No. 10, pp. 21)*
Pub: Dow Jones & Company Inc.
Contact: Almar Latour, Chief Executive Officer
Ed: Jonathan R. Laing. **Description:** Fannie Mae may need a government bailout as it faces huge hits brought about by the effects of the housing crisis. The shares of the government-sponsored enterprise have dropped 65 percent since the housing crisis began. **Availability:** Online.

13490 ■ *"KC Incentives Debate Rages on Unabated" in The Business Journal-Serving Metropolitan Kansas City (Vol. 26, September 5, 2008, No. 52)*
Pub: American City Business Journals, Inc.
Contact: Mike Olivieri, Executive Vice President
Ed: Rob Roberts. **Description:** Debate on the new economic development and incentives policy adopted by the Kansas City Council is still on. The city's Planned Industrial Expansion Authority has rejected a standard property tax abatement proposal. The real estate development community has opposed the rejection of proposed the tax incentives policy. **Availability:** Online.

13491 ■ *"KXAN Seeks Larger Studio, Office Space in Austin" in Austin Business Journal (Vol. 31, May 27, 2011, No. 12, pp. A1)*
Pub: Austin Business Journal
Contact: Rachel McGrath, Director
E-mail: rmcgrath@bizjournals.com
Ed: Cody Lyon. **Description:** Austin NBC affiliate KXAN Television is opting to sell its property north of downtown and relocate to another site. The station is now inspecting possible sites to house its broadcasting facility and employees totaling as many as 200 people. Estimated cost of the construction of the studios and offices is $13 million plus another million in moving the equipment. **Availability:** Print; Online.

13492 ■ *"Labor Shortage Creates Growing Pains" in Orlando Business Journal (Vol. 30, January 31, 2014, NO. 32, pp. 5)*
Pub: American City Business Journals, Inc.
Contact: Mike Olivieri, Executive Vice President
Released: January 31, 2014. **Description:** The reactions of residential real estate industry executives on the labor shortage created by the growing demand for new homes is presented. There were plenty of tradesmen and laborers on hand when the housing market recovery began, however, construction management faces labor competition from other builders and this trend slows the industry. **Availability:** Print; Online.

13493 ■ *"Land Squeeze Stalls Portland Homebuilders" in Business Journal Portland (Vol. 31, March 21, 2014, No. 3, pp. 4)*
Pub: American City Business Journals, Inc.
Contact: Mike Olivieri, Executive Vice President
Released: March 21, 2014. **Price:** $4, Introductory 4-Week Offer(Digital & Print). **Description:** Homebuilders in Portland, Oregon are building fewer homes that before the recession due to the impact of the 2008 economic collapse and the lack of available land on which to build. Prices in the residential real estate market are expected to increase as new single family home construction fails to keep pace with growing demand. **Availability:** Print; Online.

13494 ■ *"Largest Commercial Real Estate Brokerages" in Dallas Business Journal (Vol. 37, March 14, 2014, No. 27, pp. 8)*
Pub: American City Business Journals, Inc.
Contact: Mike Olivieri, Executive Vice President
Description: The largest commercial real estate brokerages in Texas as of March 14, 2014, ranked by number of local licensed professionals are listed. Jones Lang LaSalle got the top spot. Meanwhile, CBRE ranked second. **Availability:** Print; Online.

13495 ■ *"Largest North Texas Tenant Rep Firms" in Dallas Business Journal (Vol. 37, March 14, 2014, No. 27, pp. 6)*
Pub: American City Business Journals, Inc.
Contact: Mike Olivieri, Executive Vice President
Released: Weekly. **Price:** $22, all 22 records. **Description:** The largest tenant representative companies in North Texas as of March 14, 2014, ranked by number of tenant representative contracts are listed. CBRE got the top spot. Meanwhile, Jones Lang LaSalle ranked second. **Availability:** Print; Online.

13496 ■ *"Leaning Tower" in Business Courier (Vol. 27, June 4, 2010, No. 5, pp. 1)*
Pub: Business Courier

Ed: Jon Newberry. **Description:** New York-based developer Armand Lasky, owner of Tower Place Mall in downtown Cincinnati, Ohio has sued Birmingham, Alabama-based Regions Bank to prevent the bank's foreclosure on the property. Regions Bank claims Lasky was in default on an $18 million loan agreement. Details on the mall's leasing plan are also discussed. **Availability:** Online.

13497 ■ "Local Industrial Vacancies Climb" in Crain's Chicago Business (Vol. 31, November 17, 2008, No. 46, pp. 18)
Pub: Crain Communications Inc.
Contact: Barry Asin, President

Ed: Eddie Baeb. **Description:** Demand for local industrial real estate has declined dramatically as companies that use warehouse and factory space struggle to survive in an ailing economy. According to a report by Colliers Bennett & Kahnweiler Inc., a commercial real estate brokerage, the regional vacancy rate has risen to 9.86 percent in the third quarter, the fourth straight increase and the highest in the past 14 years. **Availability:** Online.

13498 ■ "Longtime Seattle Company Wards Cove Selling Last Seattle Properties" in Puget Sound Business Journal (Vol. 34, February 21, 2014, No. 45, pp. 4)
Pub: American City Business Journals, Inc.
Contact: Mike Olivieri, Executive Vice President

Description: Seattle, Washington-based Wards Cove Company is selling two renovated office buildings and a marina on Lake Union as the 86-year-old real estate investment firm winds down its operations. The company is also selling an industrial property on the lake's north side. Wards Cove history is profiled. **Availability:** Online.

13499 ■ Loopholes of Real Estate: Secrets of Successful Real Estate Investing
Pub: Grand Central Publishing
Contact: Michael Pietsch, Chairman

Released: Second edition. **Description:** Knowledge, planning, and building a team of advisor and mentors is key to successful real estate investments. **Availability:** unabridged; Download; Audio.

13500 ■ "Madison Partner Eyes Overton: French Quarter Suites May Become Luxury Hotel" in Memphis Business Journal (Vol. 34, April 27, 2012, No. 2, pp. 1)
Pub: Baltimore Business Journal
Contact: Rhonda Pringle, President
E-mail: rpringle@bizjournals.com

Description: Former hotel executive Mohammad Hakimian and a group of investors are planning to purchase and redevelop the French Quarter Suites into a hotel. Loeb Properties Inc. is planning to invest $19.2 million in the project. **Availability:** Print; Online.

13501 ■ "Magellan Companies Establishes Century 21 Beachhead in Boise" in Idaho Business Review (September 15, 2014)
Pub: BridgeTower Media
Contact: Adam Reinebach, President

Description: New Jersey-based Century 21, the largest real estate franchise worldwide, has entered the Idaho market under the name Century 21 Magellan Realty with five agents. Wesley Flacker, builder, home renovator, broker, and property manager purchased the franchise and expects to have 60 agents by 2015.

13502 ■ "Making Money on Foreclosures" in Memphis Business Journal (Vol. 33, March 9, 2012, No. 48, pp. 1)
Pub: Baltimore Business Journal
Contact: Rhonda Pringle, President
E-mail: rpringle@bizjournals.com

Ed: Cole Epley. **Description:** Investors and residential rental property buyers have benefited from home foreclosures in the US. Mortgage foreclosures have resulted in decreased home prices. **Availability:** Print; Online.

13503 ■ "Mall On a Mission: KOP to Get $150 Million Makeover" in Philadelphia Business Journal (Vol. 33, March 14, 2014, No. 5, pp. 6)
Pub: American City Business Journals, Inc.
Contact: Mike Olivieri, Executive Vice President

Released: Weekly. **Price:** $4, introductory 4-week offer(Digital & Print). **Description:** Philadelphia, Pennsylvania-based King of Prussia Mall is set to undergo a $150 million renovation. The plan involves construction of about 250,000 square feet of space for retailers. Mall owner, Simon Property Group, has contracted IMC Construction to handle the project. **Availability:** Print; Online.

13504 ■ "Managing the Federal HOME Program: Past and Future" in Real Estate Review (Vol. 41, Spring 2012, No. 1, pp. 29)
Released: Spring 2012. **Description:** The US Department of Housing and Urban Development's Home Investment Partnerships Program (HOME) is discussed. The program is allocated to eligible state and local governments, with the goal of increasing affordable housing. HOME has been criticized for idling home construction projects.

13505 ■ "Mapping the Gender Gap" in Business Journal Portland (Vol. 31, April 25, 2014, No. 8, pp. 4)
Pub: American City Business Journals, Inc.
Contact: Mike Olivieri, Executive Vice President

Released: April 25, 2014. **Price:** $4, introductory 4-week offer(Digital & Print). **Description:** The level of gender equality in the health care, banking, technology and commercial real estate industries of Oregon is examined. Gender bias in the workplace is one significant reason behind the wage gap and the lack of women in leadership positions. **Availability:** Print; Mailing list; Online.

13506 ■ "A Matter of Perspective" in Business Journal-Portland (Vol. 24, November 2, 2007, No. 35, pp. 1)
Pub: Portland Business Journal
Contact: Andy Giegerich, Managing Editor
E-mail: agiegerich@bizjournals.com

Ed: Andy Giegerich. **Description:** Oregon Governor Ted Kulongoski assembled the Mortgage Lending Work Group, made up of members of the mortgage industry and consumer groups, to recommend possible bills for the Oregon Senate and House to consider. How its members try to balance philosophical differences in mortgage lending rules is discussed. **Availability:** Online.

13507 ■ "Mayor Rawlings Pushes for South Dallas Development to Take Root" in Dallas Business Journal (Vol. 35, March 16, 2012, No. 27, pp. 1)
Pub: Baltimore Business Journal
Contact: Rhonda Pringle, President
E-mail: rpringle@bizjournals.com

Ed: Candace Carlisle. **Description:** Mayor Mike Rawlings has initiated efforts to create affordable housing options in southern Dallas, Texas. Rawlings has been exploring land opportunities and assessing how to leverage those land opportunities appropriately for home construction.

13508 ■ "Md. Housing Leaders Race to Stem Rising Tide of Foreclosures: Neighborhood Watch" in Baltimore Business Journal (Vol. 28, July 23, 2010, No. 11, pp. 1)
Pub: Baltimore Business Journal
Contact: Rhonda Pringle, President
E-mail: rpringle@bizjournals.com

Ed: Daniel J. Sernovitz. **Description:** Maryland government and housing leaders are set to spend $100 million in federal funding to stem the increase in foreclosures in the area. The federal funding is seen as inadequate to resolve the problem of foreclosures. **Availability:** Print.

13509 ■ "Meet the Next Big Name in Residential Construction" in Houston Business Journal (Vol. 44, February 21, 2014, No. 42, pp. 8)
Pub: American City Business Journals, Inc.
Contact: Mike Olivieri, Executive Vice President

Released: Weekly. **Price:** $4, introductory 4-week offer(Digital only). **Description:** Hillwood Communities of Dallas, Texas will break ground on the Pomona master-planned community in Manvel, 20 miles south of downtown Houston. The development will include 2,100 single-family homes ranging from $250,000 to $400,000, a new elementary school and a new junior high school. **Availability:** Print; Online.

13510 ■ "A Model Development" in Crain's Cleveland Business (Vol. 28, October 1, 2007, No. 39, pp. 12)
Pub: Crain Communications Inc.
Contact: K. C. Crain, President

Ed: Scott Suttell. **Description:** Profile a Forest City Enterprises Inc., a firm that is developing a project in New Mexico called Mesa del Sol. The Albuquerque development is being seen as the vanguard of master-planned communities with its high-tech economic development center which is expected to become the site of 60,000 jobs, 38,000 homes and a town center. **Availability:** PDF.

13511 ■ "Neighborhood Awaits Its 'Very Sexy Building" in Dallas Business Journal (Vol. 37, June 27, 2014, No. 42, pp. 12)
Pub: American City Business Journals, Inc.
Contact: Mike Olivieri, Executive Vice President

Released: Weekly. **Price:** $4, introductory 4-week offer(Digital only). **Description:** Crescent Real Estate Holdings LLC chairman and CEO, John Goff, described the upcoming 20-story, $225 million office and retail tower in Uptown Dallas as a 'sexy addition' to the neighborhood. Goff believes the location offers companies a unique marketing advantage. **Availability:** Print; Online.

13512 ■ "The Neighborhood Watch" in Hawaii Business (Vol. 53, March 2008, No. 9, pp. 36)
Pub: PacificBasin Communications
Contact: Chuck Tindle, Director
E-mail: chuckt@pacificbasin.net

Ed: David K. Choo. **Description:** OahuRe.com offers information on Hawaii real estate market, with spreadsheets and comparative market analysis page, which shows properties that are active, sold, or in escrow. Other details about OahuRe.com are discussed. A list of other top real estate websites in Hawaii and in the U.S. in general is provided.

13513 ■ "New Argentine Investment Taps Real Estate" in South Florida Business Journal (Vol. 32, June 22, 2012, No. 48, pp. 1)
Pub: Baltimore Business Journal
Contact: Rhonda Pringle, President
E-mail: rpringle@bizjournals.com

Description: Industry experts believe that Miami, Florida is becoming the go-to-investment destination of Argentines looking for real estate development opportunities. For example, Consultatio paid $220 million for 5.5 acres in Bal Harbour where it plans to construct condominiums. It appears Argentines are selecting sites in Miami as investments. **Availability:** Print; Online.

13514 ■ "New Food Concepts Flood Market" in Business Journal (Vol. 30, June 8, 2012, No. 2, pp. 1)
Pub: American City Business Journals, Inc.
Contact: Mike Olivieri, Executive Vice President

Ed: John Vomhof, Jr. **Released:** Weekly. **Price:** $4, introductory 4-week offer(Digital only). **Description:** Twin Cities Metropolitan Area has seen the boom of the frozen yogurt segment over the past few years and the rise of fast casual sandwich shops, which are helping fuel activity in Minnesota's real estate market. However, there are skeptics who doubt whether all of the new concepts can survive. **Availability:** Print; Online.

13515 ■ "New Ideas Urged for 'Superman' Reuse" in Providence Business News (Vol. 28, March 10, 2014, No. 49, pp. 1)
Pub: American City Business Journals, Inc.
Contact: Mike Olivieri, Executive Vice President

Released: March 08, 2014. **Description:** High Rock Development is requesting help from the public to architecturally renovate the 'Superman Building', the tallest building in Providence, Rhode Island. High Rock, the owner of the building, started a lobbying and marketing campaign in February 2014 to garner support. **Availability:** Print; Online.

13516 ■ "A New Mix of Tenants Settles In Downtown" in Crain's New York Business (Vol. 24, January 13, 2008, No. 2, pp. 26)
Pub: Crain Communications, Inc.
Contact: Jessica Botos, Manager, Marketing
E-mail: jessica.botos@crainsnewyork.com
Ed: Andrew Marks. **Description:** More and more nonfinancial firms are relocating downtown due to the new retailers and restaurants that are reshaping the look and feel of lower Manhattan.

13517 ■ "New York City-Based New Street Realty Advisors has Secured a New Flagship for David's Bridal" in Chain Store Age (August 2008)
Description: New York City-based New Street Realty Advisors secured a new flagship store for David's Bridal in the Chelsea district of Manhattan. David's Bridal will occupy 12,800 square feet on two floors in a retail condominium development. **Availability:** PDF; Online.

13518 ■ "New York Developer Revives Adams Morgan Hotel Project" in Washington Business Journal (Vol. 31, July 6, 2012, No. 11, pp. 1)
Pub: Baltimore Business Journal
Contact: Rhonda Pringle, President
E-mail: rpringle@bizjournals.com
Description: Real estate developer Brian Friedman brought on Andrew Zobler of Sydell Group LLC as a development partner for the Adams Morgan boutique hotel project. A previous plan for a $100 million property was shelved due to neighborhood opposition. **Availability:** Print; Online.

13519 ■ "The Next Real Estate Boom" in Canadian Business (Vol. 80, March 26, 2007, No. 7, pp. 25)
Description: The better places to invest in Canadian real estate market are presented. The future price performance of the industry is analyzed. **Availability:** Print; Online.

13520 ■ "Niche Areas Seeing the Bulk of Retail Activity" in San Antonio Business Journal (Vol. 28, August 29, 2014, No. 29, pp. 8)
Pub: American City Business Journals, Inc.
Contact: Mike Olivieri, Executive Vice President
Released: Weekly. **Price:** $4, introductory 4-week offer(Digital & Print). **Description:** Retail development projects in San Antonio, Texas have been focused on already established areas. Such projects have boosted the local real estate sector. Meanwhile, retail developers have been finding opportunities in redeveloping old retail centers. **Availability:** Print; Online.

13521 ■ "North Side Story: 1 Step Forward, 1 Step Back" in Puget Sound Business Journal (Vol. 35, June 6, 2014, No. 7, pp. 4)
Pub: American City Business Journals, Inc.
Contact: Mike Olivieri, Executive Vice President
Description: The City of Kenmore, Washington and private developers Benaroya Company and Real Property Investors agreed to discontinue the complementary commercial development project on the North Side because they failed to secure enough tenants for the planned Kenmore Village. The city is negotiating with another buyer and hopes to have a purchase-and-sale agreement in July 2014. **Availability:** Online.

13522 ■ "Observers See Different Messages if Voters Reject Ambassador Tax Rebate" in Wichita Business Journal (Vol. 27, February 17, 2012, No. 7, pp. 1)
Pub: Baltimore Business Journal
Contact: Rhonda Pringle, President

E-mail: rpringle@bizjournals.com
Description: Ambassador Hotel's room tax rebate has been put on a referendum in Wichita,Kansas and the rejection is expected to affect future downtown projects. However, the observers differ on the messages of a no vote would send to real estate investors. Insights on the ongoing debate on economic development policy are also given. **Availability:** Print; Online.

13523 ■ "October 2009: Recovery Plods Along" in Hispanic Business (October 2009, pp. 10-11)
Description: Economist reports on a possible economic recovery which will not be allowed to rely on a strong domestic demand in order to sustain it. Consumers, looking to counterbalance years of leverage financing based on unrealistic, ever-increasing home and portfolio valuations, are saving rather than spending money.

13524 ■ "Old Ford Plant to Sign New Tenants" in Business Courier (Vol. 27, August 13, 2010, No. 15, pp. 1)
Pub: Business Courier
Ed: Dan Monk. **Description:** Ohio Realty Advisors LLC, a company handling the marketing of the 1.9 million-square-foot former Ford Batavia plant is on the brink of landing one distribution and three manufacturing firms as tenants. These tenants are slated to occupy about 20 percent of the facility and generate as many as 250 jobs in Ohio. **Availability:** Print; Online.

13525 ■ "On the House: Housing Developers Try to Read Generation Y" in Philadelphia Inquirer (December 2, 2010)
Pub: The Philadelphia Inquirer
Contact: Elizabeth H. Hughes, Chief Executive Officer
Ed: Al Heavens. **Description:** Results of a survey conducted with Generation Y individuals are examined, focusing on housing developments and whether this particular generation prefers suburban or rural lifestyles. Generation Y encompasses people ages 18 to 32 years old. Statistical data included. **Availability:** Online.

13526 ■ "Outside Investors Help Fill Need for North Texas Businesses" in Dallas Business Journal (Vol. 35, March 16, 2012, No. 27, pp. 1)
Pub: Baltimore Business Journal
Contact: Rhonda Pringle, President
E-mail: rpringle@bizjournals.com
Description: Venture capitalists and private equity firms from outside North Texas have been filling the gap created by scarce capital for companies outside the enrgy and real estate industries. The increase in investments have been attributed to the entrepreneurial culture and gathering of big companies in the Dallas-Fort Worth area. **Availability:** Print; Online.

13527 ■ "Outside Investors Hot On Detroit Commercial Real Estate" in Crain's Detroit Business (Vol. 24, January 28, 2008, No. 4, pp. 25)
Pub: Crain Communications Inc.
Contact: Barry Asin, President
Ed: Daniel Duggan. **Description:** An overview of out-of-town investors seeking to purchase commercial real estate in Michigan is presented. Statistical data included. **Availability:** Print; Online.

13528 ■ "Paying for the Recession: Rebalancing Economic Growth" in Montana Business Quarterly (Vol. 49, Spring 2011, No. 1, pp. 2)
Pub: University of Montana Bureau of Business and Economic Research
Contact: Patrick Barkey, Director
E-mail: patrick.barkey@business.umt.edu
Ed: Patrick M. Barkey. **Released:** Quarterly. **Description:** Four key issues required to address in order to rebalance economic growth in America are examined.

They include: savings rates, global trade imbalances, government budgets and most importantly, housing price correction. **Availability:** Online.

13529 ■ Peggy's Corner: The Art of Staging
Pub: Eaton-Moghannam Publishing
Ed: Peggy Selinger-Eaton, Gayla Moghannam. **Description:** Techniques to enhance the value of any home are given. Seven principles of staging a home for sale include making a great first impression, maximizing space and eliminating clutter, using lighting for open spacious feeling, de-emphasize flaws, make the home appealing to buyers with varied tastes, creating warmth, and modernizing the home.

13530 ■ "Peter Bynoe Trades Up" in Black Enterprise (Vol. 38, July 2008, No. 12, pp. 30)
Pub: Earl G. Graves Ltd.
Contact: Earl Graves, Jr., President
Description: Chicago-based Loop Capital Markets L.L.C. has named Peter Bynoe managing director of corporate finance. Bynoe was previously a senior partner at the law firm DLA Piper U.S. L.L.P., where he worked on stadium deals.

13531 ■ "Phillips Edison Launches $1.8B Retail REIT" in Business Courier (Vol. 27, October 15, 2010, No. 24, pp. 1)
Pub: Business Courier
Ed: Dan Monk. **Description:** Retail center operator Phillips Edison & Company is organizing a real estate investment trust (REIT) to raise $1.8 billion to finance the planned purchase of 150 grocery-centered shopping centers around the U.S. The offering would be Phillips largest. Phillips Edison employs 174 workers and operates 250 shopping centers nationwide. **Availability:** Print; Online.

13532 ■ "Pop a Cork: Lofts' Sale Bodes Well for Urban Living" in Pittsburgh Business Times (Vol. 33, May 30, 2014, No. 46, pp. 3)
Pub: American City Business Journals, Inc.
Contact: Mike Olivieri, Executive Vice President
Released: May 30, 2014. **Price:** $4, introductory 4-week offer(Digital only). **Description:** Institutional apartment investor, GMH Capital Partners, has acquired the Cork Factory Lofts in the Strip District of Pittsburgh, Pennsylvania in an $8 billion deal with McCaffery Interests and local partners. The deal is anticipated to inspire more apartment rental development in the Pittsburg area. **Availability:** Print; Online.

13533 ■ "Portland's Hilton For Sale" in Business Journal Portland (Vol. 27, October 22, 2010, No. 34, pp. 1)
Pub: Portland Business Journal
Contact: Andy Giegerich, Managing Editor
E-mail: agiegerich@bizjournals.com
Ed: Wendy Culverwell. **Description:** Hilton Portland & Executive Tower, Portland's biggest hotel, is being sold by Cornerstone Real Estate Advisers LLC. Cornerstone hopes to close the deal for the 782-room complex by the end of 2010. Cornerstone contracted Jones Lang LaSalle to manage the sale, but terms to the deal are not available. **Availability:** Print; Online.

13534 ■ "Preleasing Drives Wedgewood Start" in Memphis Business Journal (Vol. 33, February 17, 2012, No. 45, pp. 1)
Pub: Baltimore Business Journal
Contact: Rhonda Pringle, President
E-mail: rpringle@bizjournals.com
Ed: Andy Ashby. **Description:** Austin-Texas-based StoneCrest Investments LLC has started construction on the second phase of its $32 million Wedgewood Commons Shopping Center in Olive Branch at Memphis, Tennessee. The commercial real estate development company has managed to complete enough preleasing to begin construction in the retail center. **Availability:** Print; Online.

13535 ■ "Private Equity Firms Focus on Failing Banks" in Baltimore Business Journal (Vol. 28, July 16, 2010, No. 10, pp. 1)
Pub: Baltimore Business Journal
Contact: Rhonda Pringle, President
E-mail: rpringle@bizjournals.com

Ed: Gary Haber. **Description:** Four deals in which assets of failed banks were acquired by private equity firms have been approved by the Federal Deposit Insurance Corporation in the past couple of years. Bay Bank FSK, for example, purchased Bay National Bank's assets in July 2010. Forecasts on more private equity acquisitions in the community banking industry are given. **Availability:** Print; Online.

13536 ■ *"Proposed Triangle Redo in Motion"* in Crain's Cleveland Business (Vol. 28, October 15, 2007, No. 41, pp. 1)
Pub: Crain Communications Inc.
Contact: K. C. Crain, President

Ed: Stan Bullard. **Description:** Zaremba Homes and MRN Ltd. are partnering to redevelop the so-called Triangle section of University Circle. The proposed project will include a total of 434 new rental and for-sale residential suites and as much as 227,000 square feet of retail and restaurant space. **Availability:** Online.

13537 ■ *"Publix Could Be Downtown's Tipping Point"* in Birmingham Business Journal (Vol. 31, May 23, 2014, No. 21, pp. 6)
Pub: American City Business Journals, Inc.
Contact: Mike Olivieri, Executive Vice President

Released: Weekly. **Price:** $4, introductory 4-week offer(Digital & Print). **Description:** Publix Super Markets is planning to open a grocery store and pharmacy in downtown Birmingham, Alabama. Customer demand is expected to increase due to the development of hundreds of apartments in the area. The project is also expected to boost the local real estate industry. **Availability:** Print; Online.

13538 ■ *"Real Estate Dealmakers of the Year: Where Are They Now?"* in San Francisco Business Times (Vol. 28, March 28, 2014, No. 36)
Pub: American City Business Journals, Inc.
Contact: Mike Olivieri, Executive Vice President

Released: Weekly. **Description:** Maria Ayerdi-Kaplan has been named the Business Times Deal-maker of the Year for 2013. Ayerdi-Kaplan is the Transbay Joint Powers Authority Executive Director and is in charge of oversight for the planned Trans-bay Transit Center. The center is part of a $4.5 billion construction project in San Francisco, California. **Availability:** Print; Online.

13539 ■ *"Real Estate Funds Raise More Than $350M"* in Business Journal Portland (Vol. 27, December 31, 2010, No. 44, pp. 1)
Pub: Portland Business Journal
Contact: Andy Giegerich, Managing Editor
E-mail: agiegerich@bizjournals.com

Ed: Wendy Culverwell. **Description:** Oregon-based real estate funds have raised around half of the $735 million that was raised by local companies. Investors have been purchasing distressed properties. Commercial real estate prices have declined since 2007. **Availability:** Print; Online.

13540 ■ *"Real Estate Market Still in a Slump"* in Montana Business Quarterly (Vol. 49, Summer 2011, No. 2, pp. 15)
Pub: University of Montana Bureau of Business and Economic Research
Contact: Patrick Barkey, Director
E-mail: patrick.barkey@business.umt.edu

Ed: Patrick M. Barkey. **Released:** Quarterly. **Description:** Montana's housing market is still in decline with no sign of improving in the near future. Statistical data included. **Availability:** Online.

13541 ■ *The Real Estate Recipe: Make Millions by Buying Small Apartment Properties in Your Spare Time*
Pub: DNA Press

Ed: Brian K. Friedman. **Released:** First edition. **Description:** Guide for anyone interested in property investments; the book provides information for choosing an apartment property and answers questions in a chronological workbook format. The author shares his own experiences in apartment investing and shares the entire process of analyzing and buying an apartment property using a hypothetical ten-unit complex. Sample worksheets, checklists, and tables are provided to help readers maintain their own records. **Availability:** Print.

13542 ■ *"The Real Estate Success Formula: 19 Proven Strategies to Making Money in Real Estate"*
Pub: CreateSpace

Released: September 28, 2014. **Price:** $19.99, paperback; $1.07, kindle; $99, paperback. **Description:** Nineteen proven strategies for selling real estate are provided by husband and wife real estate team. The book teaches how to buy, hold and sell houses quickly without using your money or your credit. Tactics for marketing, systematizing and managing your real estate business are outlined. **Availability:** Print.

13543 ■ *"Real Estate's New Reality"* in Entrepreneur (Vol. 37, July 2009, No. 7, pp. 32)
Pub: Entrepreneur Media Inc.
Contact: Dan Bova, Director
E-mail: dbova@entrepreneur.com

Ed: Rosalind Resnick. **Description:** Investing in real estate is still an advisable move, as long as investors are prepared to hold on to the property and there is a rent roll to provide a decent return on investment. Among the key considerations when investing in real estate is the property's expenses and cash flow. Other suggestions for future real estate investors are given. **Availability:** Online.

13544 ■ *"Receiver's Report Uncovers Trouble in Fashion Mall Redevelopment"* in South Florida Business Journal (Vol. 34, July 4, 2014, No. 50, pp. 4)
Pub: American City Business Journals, Inc.
Contact: Mike Olivieri, Executive Vice President

Released: Weekly. **Price:** $8, introductory 4-week offer(Digital only). **Description:** A report by receiver, Charles Lichtman, reveals possible fraud of fiduciary duty by Wei Chen, who manages the redevelopment of Fashion Mall in Plantation Florida. Chen used funds from the account of Tangshan Ganglu Iron and Steel Company to make a deposit on a purchase contract for the Sheraton Suites Plantation hotel and resort for a company he personally owned. **Availability:** Print; Online.

13545 ■ *"Recovering Economy Puts Real Estate on Solid Ground"* in San Antonio Business Journal (Vol. 28, February 7, 2014, No. 53, pp. 13)
Pub: American City Business Journals, Inc.
Contact: Mike Olivieri, Executive Vice President

Released: Weekly. **Price:** $4, Introductory 4-week offer(Digital only). **Description:** With the economic recovery in San Antonio, the real estate market has shifted back to normal and a significant increase has been noted in new real estate deals and purchases. Pete Broderick, a shareholder at Cox Smith Mathews Inc. said that there have been more money-making deals of late, while another shareholder, Jimmy Mc-Donough reports that banks are now willing to get into more long-term real estate deals. **Availability:** Print; Online.

13546 ■ *"Recovery on Tap for 2010?"* in Orlando Business Journal (Vol. 26, January 1, 2010, No. 31, pp. 1)
Pub: Orlando Business Journal
Contact: Julie Swyers, Director
E-mail: jswyers@bizjournals.com

Ed: Melanie Stawicki Azam, Richard Bilbao, Christopher Boyd, Anjali Fluker. **Description:** Economic forecasts for Central Florida's leading business sectors in 2010 are presented. These sectors include housing, film and TV, sports business, law, restaurants, aviation, tourism and hospitality, banking and finance, commercial real estate, retail, health care, insurance, higher education, and manufacturing. According to some local executives, Central Florida's economy will slowly recover in 2010. **Availability:** Online.

13547 ■ *"The REIT Stuff"* in Canadian Business (Vol. 80, March 26, 2007, No. 7, pp. 72)

Description: The stock performance of various real estate investment trusts in Canada is analyzed. **Availability:** Online.

13548 ■ *"REITs Decry Foreign Limits on Investment"* in Globe & Mail (March 29, 2007, pp. B4)

Ed: Elizabeth Church. **Description:** The planned legislation by Canadian government for regulation foreign investments by real estate investment trusts is discussed. **Availability:** Online.

13549 ■ *"Remington Developer Says Project May Not Include Second Big Box"* in Baltimore Business Journal (Vol. 30, June 8, 2012, No. 5, pp. 1)
Pub: American City Business Journals, Inc.
Contact: Mike Olivieri, Executive Vice President

Ed: James Briggs. **Price:** $4, introductory 4-week offer(Digital only). **Description:** WV Urban Developments will proceed with the 25th Street Station retail and housing project in Baltimore, Maryland with Wal-Mart Stores Inc. as the remaining retail anchor occupying 229,383 feet of space. Lowe's Cos. has backed out of the lease due to petitions filed by Wal-Mart components calling to overturn the plan. **Availability:** Print; Online.

13550 ■ *"Retail Remains Hot as More Stores Browse Around Houston"* in Houston Business Journal (Vol. 44, January 17, 2014, No. 37, pp. 9A)
Pub: American City Business Journals, Inc.
Contact: Mike Olivieri, Executive Vice President

Released: Weekly. **Price:** $4, Introductory 4-week offer(Digital & Print). **Description:** Houston, Texas-based Evergreen Commercial Realty president, Lilly Golden, has revealed that the city has 15 new retail projects under construction and about 30 other projects in the pipeline. Golden believes Houston's low vacancy rate and high rent growth in Class A assets cause high demand from investors nationally. The boom in the retail sector is also examined. **Availability:** Print; Online.

13551 ■ *"Retail Slump Deflates Greater Cincinnati Development"* in Business Courier (Vol. 24, February 28, 2008, No. 47, pp. 1)
Pub: American City Business Journals, Inc.
Contact: Mike Olivieri, Executive Vice President

Ed: Lisa Biank Fasig. **Description:** 2007 sales of the retail industry are the slowest since the year 2003, driving retail stores to reconsider their expansion plans for 2008. A number of retail projects have been delayed, cancelled or altered, including Newport Pavilion, Rivers Crossing, Wal-Mart Supercenters, Legacy Place and Millworks. The impacts of retail slowdown on development projects are analyzed further. **Availability:** Online.

13552 ■ *"A Rise in Rental Units"* in Philadelphia Business Journal (Vol. 30, October 7, 2011, No. 34, pp. 1)
Pub: Philadelphia Business Journal
Contact: Sierra Quinn, Director
E-mail: squinn@bizjournals.com

Ed: Natalie Kostelni. **Description:** Housing developers have been stepping up the construction of new apartment complexes throughout the suburbs of Pennsylvania in order to capture growing demand for rental properties. BPG Properties Ltd. has nearly 1,000 new apartments under construction. **Availability:** Online.

13553 ■ *"Roger Rechler Played Major Role in Long Island's Evolution"* in Commercial Property News (March 17, 2008)

Description: Profile of Roger Rechler, real estate developer on Long Island, New York, is presented. Rechler, who died in March 2008, was instrumental in the development, ownership and operations of the largest commercial real estate portfolio on Long Island. **Availability:** Online.

13554 ■ *"Roy MacDowell Jr. Version 2.0" in Boston Business Journal (Vol. 31, June 10, 2011, No. 20, pp. 1)*
Pub: Boston Business Journal
Contact: Carolyn M. Jones, President
E-mail: cmjones@bizjournals.com
Ed: Craig M. Douglas. **Description:** Real estate developer Roy MacDowell is selling his Boston, Massachusetts estate. The asking price for the property is $21.8 million. MacDowell recently suffered setbacks in his finances. **Availability:** Print; Online.

13555 ■ *"Sale of Owings Mills Solo Cup Plant Pending" in Boston Business Journal (Vol. 29, June 17, 2011, No. 6, pp. 1)*
Pub: Boston Business Journal
Contact: Carolyn M. Jones, President
E-mail: cmjones@bizjournals.com
Ed: Daniel J. Sernovitz. **Released:** Weekly; X. **Price:** $4, Print. **Description:** Baltimore developers Vanguard Equities Inc. and Greenberg Gibbons Commercial have contracted to buy the Solo Cup Company facility in Owing Mills and are now considering several plans for the property. Sale should be completed by September 2011 but no proposed sale terms are disclosed. **Availability:** Print; Online.

13556 ■ *"Salvation Army Prepares to Break Ground on South Mountain Community Center" in The Business Journal - Serving Phoenix and the Valley of the Sun (Vol. 28, September 12, 2008, No. 53, pp. 1)*
Pub: Phoenix Business Journal
Contact: Alex McAlister, Director
E-mail: amcalister@bizjournals.com
Ed: Jan Buchholz. **Description:** Construction will begin in early 2009 on an $80 million Ray and Joan Kroc Community Center in Phoenix, Arizona. It will be located adjacent to the Salvation Army, which received a $1.9 billion contribution from Joan Kroc after her death in 2003. This fund will be divided to construct 30 community centers across the country. **Availability:** Print; Online.

13557 ■ *"San Antonio Office Market: What a Difference a Year Makes" in San Antonio Business Journal (Vol. 28, August 8, 2014, No. 26, pp. 8)*
Pub: American City Business Journals, Inc.
Contact: Mike Olivieri, Executive Vice President
Released: August 08, 2014. **Price:** $4, Introductory 4-Week Offer(Digital & Print). **Description:** The San Antonio, Texas office market has grown in 2014. The market has absorbed over 610,000-square-feet of space during the first six months of the year. Meanwhile, a number of new office building construction projects are underway. **Availability:** Print; Online.

13558 ■ *"Sellers Face Excess Land Dilemma" in Crain's Cleveland Business (Vol. 28, November 12, 2007, No. 45, pp. 1)*
Pub: Crain Communications Inc.
Contact: K. C. Crain, President
Ed: Stan Bullard. **Description:** Overview on the way in which the housing slump is effecting builders, land developers and lot prices. Statistical data included. **Availability:** Online.

13559 ■ *"S.F. Leasing Off to Hottest Start Since 2000" in San Francisco Business Times (Vol. 28, January 17, No. 26, pp. 8)*
Pub: American City Business Journals, Inc.
Contact: Mike Olivieri, Executive Vice President
Description: Figures show that the demand for commercial space in San Francisco, California continues to increase. Companies such as LinkedIn, Trulia, DropBox, and Pinterest are expected to lease around 700,000 square feet of space. Colin Yasukochi, research director at CBRE Group, believes that commercial space is not being constructed fast enough to accommodate demand. **Availability:** Print; Online.

13560 ■ *"Signs Point To Improving CRE Market" in Birmingham Business Journal (Vol. 31, May 2, 2014, No. 18, pp. 7)*
Pub: American City Business Journals, Inc.
Contact: Mike Olivieri, Executive Vice President

Released: Weekly. **Price:** $4, introductory 4-week offer(Digital only). **Description:** Xceligent real estate research firm's data shows collective improvement in Birmingham, Alabama's retail, office and industrial markets over the first three months of 2014. The office market has a less than 10 percent vacancy rate for Class A office space. Vacancy rates for both retail and industrial markets are also provided. **Availability:** Print; Online.

13561 ■ *"Sitting, Sitting, Sitting-Snapshots of Homes that Just Won't Sell" in Crain's Chicago Business (Vol. 31, April 21, 2008, No. 16)*
Pub: Crain Communications Inc.
Contact: Barry Asin, President
Ed: Kevin Davis. **Description:** Listing of five Chicago-area homes that have been on the market for an extended length of time; also includes the original asking price, current asking price, special features and the biggest challenge of each home. **Availability:** Online.

13562 ■ *"Small Changes Can Mean Big Energy Savings" in Crain's Cleveland Business (Vol. 28, November 5, 2007, No. 44, pp. 21)*
Pub: Crain Communications Inc.
Contact: K. C. Crain, President
Ed: Harriet Tramer. **Description:** Many Northeast Ohio businesses are taking their cues from the residential real estate market to draw and capitalize on interest in energy efficiency and is regularly taken into account by local architects. **Availability:** Online.

13563 ■ *"Sneak Preview: Alamo Revamp" in Austin Business JournalInc. (Vol. 28, December 12, 2008, No. 39, pp. 1)*
Description: Austin, Texas-based Alamo Drafthouse Cinemas is planning to build a new Circle C Ranch. The new theater will showcase digital projectors and the latest sound systems to show 3-D movies. The company is in lease negotiations with developer Stratus Properties Inc. **Availability:** Print; Online.

13564 ■ *"South Loop Site Lands a Buyer" in Crain's Chicago Business (Vol. 31, March 24, 2008, No. 12, pp. 1)*
Pub: Crain Communications Inc.
Contact: Barry Asin, President
Ed: Alby Gallun. **Description:** Russland Capital Group, a little-known condominium developer from Skokie, recently purchased a 6.5-acre riverside property in the site known as Franklin Point for $40 million. **Availability:** Online.

13565 ■ *"Stadium Developers Seek a Win With the State" in The Business Journal-Serving Metropolitan Kansas City (Vol. 26, August 22, 2008)*
Description: Three Trails Redevelopment LLC is hoping to win $30 million in state tax credits from the Missouri Development Finance Board for the construction of an 18,500-seat Wizards stadium. The project is contingent on state tax incentives and the company remains optimistic about their goal.

13566 ■ *"Staging a Martini-and-GQ Lifestyle" in Crain's Chicago Business (April 21, 2008)*
Pub: Crain Communications Inc.
Contact: Barry Asin, President
Ed: Kevin Davis. **Description:** Due to the competition of the slumping housing market, home stagers are becoming more prominent and are using creative ways to make an impression beyond de-cluttering, painting and cleaning by using accents such as casually placed magazines, candles and table settings. **Availability:** Online.

13567 ■ *"State Center Lease Deal High for Md." in Baltimore Business Journal (Vol. 28, August 6, 2010, No. 13, pp. 1)*
Pub: Baltimore Business Journal
Contact: Rhonda Pringle, President
E-mail: rpringle@bizjournals.com

Ed: Daniel J. Sernovitz. **Description:** The proposed $1.5 billion State Center development project in Midtown Baltimore might cause the State of Maryland to pay the most expensive rental rates in the city. The state will have to pay an effective rental rate of $34 per square foot, including expenses, on the leasing. Other details of the redevelopment project are discussed. **Availability:** Print; Online.

13568 ■ *"State Wants to Add Escape Clause to Leases" in Sacramento Business Journal (Vol. 28, October 14, 2011, No. 33, pp. 1)*
Pub: Sacramento Business Journal
Contact: Stephanie Fretwell, Director
E-mail: sfretwell@bizjournals.com
Ed: Michael Shaw. **Description:** California Governor Jerry Brown's administration has decided to add escape clauses to new lease agreements, which created new worry for building owners and brokers in Sacramento, California. Real estate brokers believe the appropriation of funds clauses have been making the lenders nervous and would result in less competition. **Availability:** Online.

13569 ■ *"Stuck With Two Mortgages" in Crain's Chicago Business (Vol. 31, April 21, 2008, No. 16)*
Pub: Crain Communications Inc.
Contact: Barry Asin, President
Ed: Darci Smith. **Description:** Discusses the problem a number of people are facing due to the slump in the housing market: being stuck with two mortgages when they move because their former homes have not sold. Many thought they could afford to move to a larger home, anticipating significant equity appreciation that did not occur; now they are left with lowering their price and competing with the host of new developments. **Availability:** Online.

13570 ■ *"SunRail Route Apartments Coming in 2013" in Orlando Business Journal (Vol. 29, September 14, 2012, No. 13, pp. 1)*
Pub: Baltimore Business Journal
Contact: Rhonda Pringle, President
E-mail: rpringle@bizjournals.com
Ed: Anjali Fluker. **Description:** Real estate developers are planning to start construction of four apartment projects at SunRail stations in Florida. The projects are estimated to be worth $121 million. They are also seen to drive commercialization of the area. **Availability:** Print; Online.

13571 ■ *"Survey Says Commercial Real Estate Headed for Turbulence" in Commercial Property News (March 17, 2008)*
Description: Commercial real estate sector is declining due to the sluggish U.S. economy. According to a recent survey, national office, retail and hospitality markets are also on the decline. **Availability:** Online.

13572 ■ *"Swope: Breakup Won't Delay East Village" in The Business Journal-Serving Metropolitan Kansas City (Vol. 26, August 22, 2008, No. 50, pp. 1)*
Pub: American City Business Journals, Inc.
Contact: Mike Olivieri, Executive Vice President
Ed: Rob Roberts. **Description:** Swope Community Builders said that the Kansas City Redevelopment Project will not be delayed by the breakup of their partnership with Sherman Associates Inc. Swopes will be the sole master developer of the project. **Availability:** Online.

13573 ■ *"Tattooed Bellwethers of Economic Development" in Austin Business Journal (Vol. 34, May 2, 2014, No. 11, pp. A4)*
Pub: American City Business Journals, Inc.
Contact: Mike Olivieri, Executive Vice President
Released: Weekly. **Price:** $4, Introductory 4-week offer(Digital & Print). **Description:** The creative community's art-centered business have helped Austin, Texas' growth by moving into transitional areas with low rents. This kind of pioneering spirit primes the area for later commercial and residential development. The city's assistance programs for creative enterprises are also presented. **Availability:** Print; Online.

13574 ■ *"That Empty Feeling" in Crain's Cleveland Business (Vol. 28, October 15, 2007, No. 41, pp. 1)*
Pub: Crain Communications Inc.
Contact: K. C. Crain, President
Ed: Stan Bullard. **Description:** Townhouses, cluster homes and condominiums lured both buyers and builders for most of this decade but now that market is suffering to an even greater degree than the single-family home market. Statistical data included. **Availability:** Online.

13575 ■ *"This Is When You're Ready to Invest in Real Estate" in U.S. News & World Report (May 31, 2018)*
URL(s): money.usnews.com/investing/real-estate -investments/articles/2018-05-31/this-is-when-youre -ready-to-invest-in-real-estate
Ed: Debbie Carlson. **Released:** May 31, 2018. **Description:** Details the signs of when you are ready to start investing in real estate. Real estate is often touted as being a safe bet, but that's not necessarily true if your personal finances aren't in order, you have a low credit score, and you have no clue how to be a landlord. Taking steps to learn about the process will increase your chance at being successful in this type of investment. **Availability:** Online.

13576 ■ *"Threat of New Office Space Records Rent Hikes" in Globe & Mail (March 21, 2007, pp. B4)*
Description: The increasing commercial rent prices in the Toronto region amid the high office building construction market are discussed. **Availability:** Online.

13577 ■ *"Three Trails Blazes Tax Credit Deal" in The Business Journal-Serving Metropolitan Kansas City (Vol. 27, November 7, 2008, No. 9)*
Description: Three Trails Redevelopment LLC plans to redevelop the Bannister Mall area. The Missouri Development Finance Board is expected to approve $30 million in tax credits for the project. A verbal agreement on the terms and conditions has already been reached according to the agency's executive director.

13578 ■ *"Thriving Small Businesses Boost Real Estate Values" in Business News Daily (February 21, 2023)*
URL(s): www.businessnewsdaily.com/1583-small -business-real-estate.html
Ed: Alex Halperin. **Released:** February 21, 2023. **Description:** Small businesses add value to local communities by making them more viable and by hiring local people. This article explores the impact of small businesses on local real estate values. **Availability:** Online.

13579 ■ *"TMC Development Closes $1.1 Million Real Estate Purchase for Mansa, LLC Using SBA 504 Real Estate Financing" in Marketwired (September 17, 2009)*
Pub: Comtex News Network Inc.
Contact: Kan Devnani, President
Description: TMC Development announced the closing of a $1.1 million real estate purchase for Mansa, LLC dba Kwikee Mart, a Napa-based convenience store; TMC helped the company secure a Small Business Administration 504 loan in order to purchase the acquisition of a 3,464 square foot building. SBA created the 504 loan program to provide financing for growing small and medium-sized businesses. **Availability:** Online.

13580 ■ *"Toll Talker: CEO Takes Stock of His Company, the Housing Market" in Philadelphia Business Journal (Vol. 33, May 9, 2014, No. 13, pp. 4)*
Pub: American City Business Journals, Inc.
Contact: Mike Olivieri, Executive Vice President
Released: Weekly. **Price:** $4, introductory 4-week offer(Digital only). **Description:** Douglas C. Yearley, Jr., CEO of Toll Brothers Inc. discusses how his company capitalized on the economic recession in

the housing market by acquiring large tracts of land between 2008 and 2010, including Shapell Homes in California for $1.2 billion. Yearley believes that while the housing downturn trend led to a rise in apartment living, the concept of home ownership remains relatively strong in the U.S., thus spurring construction. **Availability:** Print; Online.

13581 ■ *"Top Commercial Real Estate Developers" in South Florida Business Journal (Vol. 34, July 25, 2014, No. 53, pp. 14)*
Pub: American City Business Journals, Inc.
Contact: Mike Olivieri, Executive Vice President
Released: Weekly. **Description:** Rankings of the commercial real estate developers in South Florida are presented. Rankings are based on the total new rentable square feet developed and square feet sold in the region in 2013. **Availability:** Print; Online.

13582 ■ *"Top Statewide Commercial Real Estate Brokerages" in South Florida Business Journal (Vol. 34, April 4, 2014, No. 37, pp. 14)*
Pub: American City Business Journals, Inc.
Contact: Mike Olivieri, Executive Vice President
Description: Rankings of commercial real estate brokerages in South Florida area are presented. Rankings were based on total volume sales and leasing statewide in Florida. The top five real estate executives in the region are also listed. **Availability:** Print; Online.

13583 ■ *"Troy Complex has New Brand, New Leases" in Crain's Detroit Business (Vol. 24, April 14, 2008, No. 15, pp. 32)*
Pub: Crain Communications Inc.
Contact: Barry Asin, President
Ed: Daniel Duggan. **Description:** Discusses the rebranding of the 1.2 million-square-foot collection of office buildings in Troy purchased by New York-based Emmes Co. The firm has also pledged more than $6 million in upgrades, hired a new leasing company and completed 67,000 square feet of leasing with another 100,000 in negotiations. **Availability:** Print; Online.

13584 ■ *"Two New Apartment Complexes on Tap for West Orange County" in Orlando Business Journal (Vol. 29, September 7, 2012, No. 12, pp. 1)*
Pub: Baltimore Business Journal
Contact: Rhonda Pringle, President
E-mail: rpringle@bizjournals.com
Ed: Anjali Fluker. **Description:** Unicorp National Development Inc. and Altamonte Springs, Florida-based LeCesse Development Inc. are seeking the City of Ocoee's approval for the construction of 458 apartment units on vacant land on Maguire Road. The two real estate developers are scheduled to meet with city planners to discuss the project and submit building plans.

13585 ■ *"University Place Building Gets an Anchor Tenant: Groundbreaking 2.0" in Philadelphia Business Journal (Vol. 30, September 23, 2011, No. 32, pp. 1)*
Pub: Philadelphia Business Journal
Contact: Sierra Quinn, Director
E-mail: squinn@bizjournals.com
Ed: Natalie Kostelni. **Description:** University Place Associates, the developer of 2.0 University Place in West Philadelphia, Pennsylvania, will break ground on a five-story, 97,000-square-foot office building in December 2011. The decision follows the Citizenship and Immigration Services signing of a 15-year lease as anchor tenant. **Availability:** Online.

13586 ■ *"Village at Waugh Chapel $275M Expansion Begins" in Baltimore Business Journal (Vol. 28, August 27, 2010, No. 16, pp. 1)*
Pub: Baltimore Business Journal
Contact: Rhonda Pringle, President
E-mail: rpringle@bizjournals.com
Ed: Daniel J. Sernovitz. **Description:** Developer Greenberg Gibbons Corporation has broken ground on a $275 million, 1.2 million-square-foot addition to its Village at the Waugh Chapel mixed-use complex.

Aside from creating 2,600 permanent jobs, the addition, named Village South, is expected to lure Target and Wegmans Food Markets to Crofton, Maryland. Funding for this project is discussed. **Availability:** Print.

13587 ■ *"Vision for Camden in Better Focus" in Philadelphia Business Journal (Vol. 30, September 30, 2011, No. 33, pp. 1)*
Pub: Philadelphia Business Journal
Contact: Sierra Quinn, Director
E-mail: squinn@bizjournals.com
Ed: Natalie Kostelni. **Description:** More than $500 million worth of projects aimed at redeveloping the downtown and waterfront areas of Camden, New Jersey are being planned. These include the construction of residential, commercial, and education buildings. **Availability:** Online.

13588 ■ *"Walnut Hill Sheds Its Past, Name" in Philadelphia Business Journal (Vol. 33, April 4, 2014, No. 8, pp. 8)*
Pub: American City Business Journals, Inc.
Contact: Mike Olivieri, Executive Vice President
Released: Weekly. **Price:** $4, introductory 4-week offer(Digital & Print). **Description:** Walnut Hill Plaza was bought by a fund comprised of Miller Investment Management and Hayden Real Estate at an auction in 2012 for $11 million and they spent $2 million in construction renovations. The property was also re-branded as 150 Walnut Warner and the once forlorn building is up to 100% leased space. The tenants renting space in the building are also highlighted. **Availability:** Print; Online.

13589 ■ *"Wannabe Buyers Take Their Own Sweet Time" in Crain's Chicago Business (Vol. 31, April 21, 2008, No. 16, pp. 50)*
Pub: Crain Communications Inc.
Contact: Barry Asin, President
Ed: Lisa Bertagnoli. **Description:** Although all factors are in place for a robust real-estate market in the Chicago area: low interest rates, plenty of inventory and the region's relatively strong employment, buyers are taking their time and doing more research in order to see how bad the economy will get. **Availability:** Online.

13590 ■ *"Weyerhaeuser's REIT Decision Shouldn't Scare Investors Away" in Barron's (Vol. 88, June 30, 2008, No. 26, pp. 18)*
Pub: Dow Jones & Company Inc.
Contact: Almar Latour, Chief Executive Officer
Ed: Christopher Williams. **Description:** Weyerhaeuser Co.'s management said that a conversion to a real estate investment trust was not likely in 2009 since the move is not tax-efficient as of the moment and would overload its non-timber assets with debt. The company's shares have fallen by 19.5 percent. However, the company remains an asset-rich outfit and its activist shareholder is pushing for change. **Availability:** Online.

13591 ■ *"What Do Developers Want?" in Real Estate Review (Vol. 41, Summer 2012, No. 2, pp. 77)*
Description: The results of a survey on real estate developers' decision-making process are presented. Most developers said they are not expecting much development in the next five years. They also said decision-making is based on minimizing risk and uncertainty. **Availability:** Print; Online; PDF.

13592 ■ *"What Happens in Vegas Could Happen in Baltimore, Too" in Boston Business Journal (Vol. 29, June 17, 2011, No. 6, pp. 1)*
Pub: Boston Business Journal
Contact: Carolyn M. Jones, President
E-mail: cmjones@bizjournals.com
Ed: Daniel J. Sernovitz. **Description:** At least 36 companies expressed their interest in developing a casino in South Baltimore following the state commission's announcement for bids. Developers have until July 28, 2011 to submit their proposals. Baltimore's

strong economy is the major factor for the interest, yet the fact that blackjack and poker are outlawed in Maryland could be a drawback. **Availability:** Print; Online.

13593 ■ *"What's Ahead for Fannie and Fred?"* **in Barron's (Vol. 90, August 30, 2010, No. 35, pp. 26)**
Pub: Barron's Editorial & Corporate Headquarters

Ed: Jonathan R. Laing. **Description:** A meeting presided by Treasury Secretary Timothy Geithner discussed the future of Fannie Mae and Freddie Mac. The two government sponsored enterprises were mismanaged and reforming these two agencies is critical. **Availability:** Online.

13594 ■ *"When Anything (And Everything) Goes"* **in Globe & Mail (January 20, 2007, pp. B4)**
Ed: Elizabeth Church. **Description:** The forecast on acquisition of different real estate firms is presented. **Availability:** Online.

13595 ■ *"The White Flint Plan: Planning a Transit Oriented District in Suburbia"* **in Real Estate Review (Vol. 41, Summer 2012, No. 2, pp. 53)**
Released: Summer 2012. **Description:** The planning and development of a real estate project around the Washington Metro mass transit station are discussed. The site was designated as a single family zone. A brief history of the project is also included.

13596 ■ *"With Building Plans in Flux, County Could Sell Key Site"* **in Crain's Cleveland Business (Vol. 28, October 8, 2007, No. 40, pp. 1)**
Pub: Crain Communications Inc.
Contact: K. C. Crain, President

Ed: Jay Miller. **Description:** Due to such issues as financial and administrative problems, Cuyahoga County commissioners have pushed back the construction timeline for a planned county administration center and are saying that they are considering selling the site in downtown Cleveland to developers who would erect a new office building that another large tenant could occupy. **Availability:** Online.

13597 ■ *"The Worst Lies Ahead for Wall Street: More Losses Certain; More Expensive Capital to Be Needed"* **in Crain's New York Business (Vol. 24, January 20, 2008, No. 3, pp. 1)**
Pub: Crain Communications, Inc.
Contact: Jessica Botos, Manager, Marketing
E-mail: jessica.botos@crainsnewyork.com

Ed: Aaron Elstein. **Description:** Due to the weakening economy, many financial institutions will face further massive losses forcing them to borrow more at higher interest rates and dragging down their earnings for years to come. The effects on commercial real estate and credit card loans are also discussed as well as the trend to investing in Asia and the Middle East. **Availability:** Online.

13598 ■ *"You Won't Go Broke Filling Up On The Stock"* **in Barron's (Vol. 88, July 14, 2008, No. 28, pp. 38)**
Pub: Dow Jones & Company Inc.
Contact: Almar Latour, Chief Executive Officer

Ed: Assif Shameen. **Description:** Due to high economic growth, pro-business policies and a consumption boom, the Middle East is a good place to look for equities. The best ways in which to gain exposure to this market include investing in the real estate industry and telecommunications markets as well as large banks that serve corporations and consumers. **Availability:** Online.

13599 ■ *Your First Year in Real Estate: Making the Transition from Total Novice to Successful Professional*
Released: Second edition. **Price:** $22, paperback; $9.99, e-book. **Description:** Zeller helps new realtors to select the right company, develop mentor and client relationships, using the Internet and social

networking to stay ahead of competition, to set and reach career goals, to stay current in the market, and more. **Availability:** E-book; Print.

TRADE PERIODICALS

13600 ■ *Commercial Investment Real Estate Magazine (CIRE)*
Pub: CCIM Institute
Contact: Timothy S. Blair, President
URL(s): www.ccim.com/cire-magazine/issues/fall -2022

Released: Quarterly; Fall, Summer, Spring, Winter. **Description:** Professional development magazine for commercial investment professionals and allied fields. **Availability:** Print; Online.

13601 ■ *Daily Record (Parsippany, New Jersey)*
Pub: USA Today Network
Contact: Mike Reed, Chairman
URL(s): www.dailyrecord.com
Facebook: www.facebook.com/DailyRecordNJ
X (Twitter): x.com/dailyrecord

Ed: Joe Ungaro. **Price:** $29.95, for archive 6 months; $7.95, for archive per month; $45, for 1 year digital. **Description:** Newspaper reporting legal and business news. **Availability:** Print; Online. **Type:** Full-text.

13602 ■ *The Institutional Real Estate Letter*
Pub: Institutional Real Estate Inc.
Contact: Geoffrey Dohrmann, Chief Executive Officer
E-mail: g.dohrmann@irei.com
URL(s): tirel-na.irei.com/the-institutional-real-estate-le tter-americas

Ed: Geoffrey Dohrmann. **Released:** 11/year **Price:** $2,695, for 1 year; $4,800, for 2 year; $6,050, for 3 year; $275, Single issue. **Description:** Monthly publication covering the pension, foundation, and endowment investment market. Provides information on investment patterns, trends, and strategies. **Availability:** Print; Online.

13603 ■ *New England Real Estate Journal*
Contact: Joanne Connolly, Publisher
URL(s): nerej.com
Facebook: www.facebook.com/nerejournal
X (Twitter): twitter.com/NEREJ

Released: Monthly **Price:** $69.50, for first time subscription. **Description:** Newspaper publishing commercial, industrial, and investment real estate news. **Availability:** Print; Online.

13604 ■ *Realtor Magazine: The Business tool for Real Estate Professionals*
Pub: National Association of Realtors
Contact: Bob Goldberg, Chief Executive Officer
URL(s): www.nar.realtor/magazine
Facebook: www.facebook.com/realtormag
X (Twitter): x.com/realtormag
Instagram: www.instagram.com/realtormag

Ed: Wendy Cole. **Released:** Quarterly **Price:** $56, Nonmembers for US. **Description:** Real estate magazine. **Availability:** Print; Online.

13605 ■ *The Residential Specialist*
Pub: Residential Real Estate Council
Contact: Tricia Nekota, President
URL(s): trsmag.com/magazine

Ed: Kimberly Cure. **Released:** Bimonthly **Price:** $44. 95, Canada for per year; $29.95, U.S. for per year; $89.95, for other international. **Description:** Trade magazine for residential real estate agents. **Availability:** Print; Online.

13606 ■ *SIOR Report*
Pub: Society of Industrial and Office Realtors
Contact: Mark Duclos, President
E-mail: duclos@sentrycommercial.com
URL(s): www.sior.com/education-and-insights/insigh ts/magazine/sior-report

Released: Quarterly **Description:** Dedicated to corporate real estate brokerage, development, and management. Recurring features include news of

members and the Society, news of educational programs sponsored by the Society, book reviews, news of research, and statistics. **Availability:** Print; Online.

13607 ■ *Wealth Management Real Estate*
Pub: Informa USA Inc.
Contact: Gareth Wright, Director
URL(s): www.wealthmanagement.com/real-estate

Ed: Elaine Misonzhnik. **Description:** Magazine on commercial real estate investment, development and management. **Availability:** Print; Online.

VIDEO/AUDIO MEDIA

13608 ■ *Strategies for Success: A Conversation with a Multi-Talented Real Estate Entrepreneur with Timothy Lyons*
URL(s): www.eofire.com/podcast/timothylyons
Ed: Jon Lee Dumas. **Released:** January 17, 2024. **Description:** Podcast discusses real estate investing as an entrepreneurial endeavor.

13609 ■ *Why Multifamily - All the Reasons to be All in Now with Arleen Garza*
URL(s): www.eofire.com/podcast/arleengarza
Ed: Jon Lee Dumas. **Released:** November 23, 2023. **Description:** Podcast explains how multifamily real estate works for generating steady cash flow.

CONSULTANTS

13610 ■ *Arnheim & Neely Inc.*
425 N Craig St., Ste. 100
Pittsburgh, PA 15213-1147
Contact: Robert J. Gillenberger, President
Description: Firm provides real estate management services.

13611 ■ *Boston Consulting Group, Inc. (BCG)*
Boston Consulting Group, Inc. (BCG)
200 Pier 4 Blvd.
Boston, MA 02210-2457
Ph: (617)973-1200
Fax: (617)973-1339
URL: http://www.bcg.com
Contact: Christoph Schweizer, Chief Executive Officer
Facebook: www.facebook.com/BostonConsul tingGroup
Linkedin: www.linkedin.com/company/boston-consul ting-group
X (Twitter): twitter.com/BCG
Instagram: www.instagram.com/bcg
YouTube: www.youtube.com/user/TheBCGVideo

Description: Global firm providing international strategy and general management consulting services. **Founded:** 1963. **Educational Activities:** EMBL International PhD Symposium.

13612 ■ *Cantey & Company Inc.*
3300 Harrison Rd.
Columbia, SC 29204
Fax: (803)256-4632
Co. E-mail: cantey@cantey.com
URL: http://www.cantey.com
Contact: Billy Cantey, President
E-mail: cantey@cantey.com
Facebook: www.facebook.com/canteyco
Linkedin: www.linkedin.com/company/cantey -&-company-inc

Description: Firm offers residential, commercial and investment real estate and as an independent counselor analyzes various real estate situations, either proposed or existing, for individuals and for institutions and clients include investors, home buyers and sellers, developers, syndicates, bank trust departments, attorneys and corporate realtors. **Scope:** Firm offers residential, commercial and investment real estate and as an independent counselor analyzes various real estate situations, either proposed or existing, for individuals and for institutions and clients include investors, home buyers and sellers, developers, syndicates, bank trust departments, attorneys and corporate realtors. **Founded:** 1977.

13613 ■ Coldwell Banker Commercial Reliant Realty
2181 Victory Pky., Ste. 102
Cincinnati, OH 45206
Ph: (513)241-8725
Co. E-mail: info@cbcreliantrealty.com
URL: http://reliantrealty-cincinnati-oh.cbcworldwide
.com
Contact: Jim Bastin, President
E-mail: bastin@cbcreliantrealty.com
Description: Firm provides real estate brokerage and property management for office, retail, industrial, multifamily, land, and much more. **Scope:** Firm provides real estate brokerage and property management for office, retail, industrial, multifamily, land, and much more. **Founded:** 1925.

13614 ■ Colliers International
601 Union St., Ste. 5300
Seattle, WA 98101
Ph: (202)223-0866
URL: http://www.colliers.com/en
Contact: Reid Erickson, Managing Director
E-mail: reid.erickson@colliers.com
Description: Advises clients regarding commercial and industrial development properties, suburban acreage, retail centers, office buildings, warehouses, manufacturing facilities, and deepwater-oriented industrial sites. Serves companies, government agencies, and individuals in Texas and the Gulf Coast area. **Founded:** 1978.

13615 ■ Continental Appraisal Co.
50 W Broad St.
Columbus, OH 43215
Contact: John R. Garvin, Contact
Description: Provider of counseling and appraisal services regarding real estate investment properties. Includes portfolio analysis, tax reviews, investment projects and market studies on commercial, multi family and industrial property. Specializes in private investors, trust advisors, financial institutions, corporate owners, pension funds and government agencies. **Scope:** Provider of counseling and appraisal services regarding real estate investment properties. Includes portfolio analysis, tax reviews, investment projects and market studies on commercial, multi family and industrial property. Specializes in private investors, trust advisors, financial institutions, corporate owners, pension funds and government agencies.

13616 ■ Fredericton Appraisal Associates Ltd.
500 Brookside Dr., Unit F
Fredericton, NB, Canada E3A 8V2
Ph: (506)458-9533
Fax: (506)458-1334
Co. E-mail: fappraisals@ara.ca
URL: http://www.frederictonappraisals.ca
Contact: Andrew L. Leech, President
E-mail: aleech@ara.ca
Description: Firm provides real estate advisory and valuation services. **Scope:** Firm provides real estate advisory and valuation services. **Founded:** 1973.

13617 ■ Goldman Associates, Inc. (GAI)
1014 Bridge Rd.
Charleston, WV 25314
Ph: (304)343-5695
Fax: (304)343-5694
URL: http://goldmanassociates.org
Contact: Jay Goldman, President
E-mail: jgoldman@goldmanassociates.org
Description: Provider of real-estate brokerage, appraising, consulting and asset management services. **Scope:** Provider of real-estate brokerage, appraising, consulting and asset management services. **Founded:** 1964.

13618 ■ M. C. O'Brien Inc.
4718 Ave., N
Brooklyn, NY 11234
Ph: (718)252-9191
Co. E-mail: info@mcobrien.com
URL: http://mcobrien.site
Contact: Jennifer Grosskopf, Executive Officer
Description: Firm provides consulting, real estate and management services. **Founded:** 1909. **Publications:** "M.C. O'Brien Brokers 27, 115 SF Lease in Marine Park," Mar, 2012; "O'Brien Brokers 40, 000 s/f Industrial Lease," Jun, 2011; "M.C. O'Brien Launches New Website," Mar, 2011; "O'Brien Brokers 23, 700 s/f Lease to Shindler Fish Co.," Feb, 2011.

13619 ■ Merritt & Harris Inc. (MH)
Jones Lang LaSalle Incorporated
330 Madison Ave., 3rd Fl.
New York, NY 10018
Ph: (312)782-5800
Fax: (312)782-4339
Co. E-mail: info@am.jll.com
URL: http://www.us.jll.com
Contact: Manny P. Kratsios, Managing Director
E-mail: manny.kratsios@am.jll.com
Description: Firm offers construction monitoring, property condition assessments, plan, cost review and various other real estate related consultation services. **Scope:** Firm offers construction monitoring, property condition assessments, plan, cost review and various other real estate related consultation services. **Founded:** 1937. **Publications:** "M and H Observations"; "Formula 1 Texas Style," 2011; "Spring Cost Corner," 2011; "The Construction Consultant's Role on the Workout Team," 2011; "What's New In Green for 2011?," 2011; "Taylor Made in New Jersey," 2010. **Training:** Preclosing Project Analysis for Construction Loans; Construction Monitoring for Lenders; Workout Seminar; Engineering Due Diligence; Basic Construction for Lenders and Investors; Analyzing the Development Team.

13620 ■ Paul Hornsby & Co.
7600 N Capital of Texas Hwy., Bldg. B, Ste. 210
Austin, TX 78731-1123
Contact: Edgar Paul Hornsby, Contact
Description: Firm engages in providing eminent domain, general commercial valuation and counselling services. **Publications:** "Real Estate Appraisal Issues and Ethics Eminent Domain for Attorneys Central Texas Commercial Property Exchange," 2007; "Contemporary Appraisal Issues," 2007; "Capitalization Theory & Techniques Chartered Financial Analysts," 2007; "Material and Substantial Impairment of Access CLE International," 2003; Fee Simple Versus Leased Fee Valuation: "A Study of Appraisal Models," 2001; "Regulatory Takings International Right of Way Association," 2000. **Training:** Fee Simple Estate - How Many Sticks in the Bundle- Ad Valorem Taxation, 2008.

13621 ■ Robert W. Neill Cos, Jr.
204 Washington St.
Carrollton, MS 38917
Contact: Robert W. Neill, Jr., Manager
X (Twitter): x.com/rwneilljr
Description: Provider of real estate brokerage services for residential, commercial, investment, agricultural, hunting and recreational properties. **Scope:** Provider of real estate brokerage services for residential, commercial, investment, agricultural, hunting and recreational properties.

13622 ■ Schostak Brothers and Company Inc.
17800 Laurel Pk. Dr. N, Ste. 200C
Livonia, MI 48152
Ph: (248)262-1000
Fax: (248)262-1814
Co. E-mail: schostakjj@schostak.com
URL: http://www.schostak.com
Contact: Steven Fisher, Chief Executive Officer
E-mail: fisher@schostak.com
Facebook: www.facebook.com/SchostakBrothers
Linkedin: www.linkedin.com/company/schostak-bro
thers-&-company-inc-
X (Twitter): x.com/schostakbroscre

Description: Real estate firm which performs feasibility and market studies, as well as valuations for industrial, commercial and investment property. **Founded:** 1920.

13623 ■ Stephen M. Segal Inc.
1545 Lamberton Rd.
Trenton, NJ 08611
URL: http://segal-labate.com/services
Description: Provider of counseling on all areas of real estate including marketing of industrial, commercial, office, and investment properties, land acquisition, financing, market and feasibility studies, site selection and analysis, and property management and also offers complete appraisal services for sale, lease, or acquisition, investment analyses, real estate tax assessments, and eminent domain matters and serves industry, financial institutions, individuals, attorneys, government agencies, and utilities. **Scope:** Provider of counseling on all areas of real estate including marketing of industrial, commercial, office, and investment properties, land acquisition, financing, market and feasibility studies, site selection and analysis, and property management and also offers complete appraisal services for sale, lease, or acquisition, investment analyses, real estate tax assessments, and eminent domain matters and serves industry, financial institutions, individuals, attorneys, government agencies, and utilities. **Founded:** 1968.

13624 ■ Stevenson Real Estate Group Ltd.
200 - 55 Donald St.
Winnipeg, MB, Canada R3C 1L8
Ph: (204)928-5000
URL: http://cwstevenson.ca
Contact: Martin McGarry, Chief Executive Officer
Description: Real estate consulting firm providing advice and appraisal services regarding investment, commercial and industrial properties for individuals, government and industry. Acts on behalf of clients in all areas of real estate investment. Industries served commercial real estate sales and leasing, commercial appraisals and property management. **Scope:** Real estate consulting firm providing advice and appraisal services regarding investment, commercial and industrial properties for individuals, government and industry. Acts on behalf of clients in all areas of real estate investment. Industries served commercial real estate sales and leasing, commercial appraisals and property management. **Founded:** 1901. **Publications:** "National survey finds Winnipeg office space in big demand"; "Destination Winnipeg-Economic Highlights".

13625 ■ West Virginia Commercial L.L.C.
803 Quarrier St., Ste. 220
Charleston, WV 25301
Contact: Brooks F. McCabe, Jr., Manager
E-mail: bmccabe@wv-commercial.com
Description: Comprehensive real estate service provider specializing in brokerage, development, and property management services including tenant-landlord relations, building and grounds maintenance, accounting, financial analysis, partnership arrangements, land assembly, design and construction services, the company serves national retailers, local entrepreneurs, public agencies, and other commercial office users. **Publications:** "Times West Virginian Published," Jun, 2007; "The Charleston Gazette," Dec, 2004; "Views and Visions," Nov, 2004; "WASHINGTON POST," Sep, 2004.

FRANCHISES AND BUSINESS OPPORTUNITIES

13626 ■ The Charlwood Pacific Group (CPG)
The Charlwood Pacific Group (CPG)
1285 W Pender St., Ste. 500
Vancouver, BC, Canada V6E 4B1
Ph: (604)718-2612
Fax: (604)718-2638
URL: http://www.charlwoodpacificgroup.com
Contact: Martin H. Charlwood, President
Description: Group company engages in travel, real estate, property management and mortgage brokerage businesses. **Founded:** 1975. **Training:** Yes.

13627 ■ HomeVestors of America, Inc.
Levine Leichtman Capital Partners (LLCP)
6500 Greenville Ave., No. 400
Dallas, TX 75206
Ph: (310)275-5335
Fax: (310)275-1441
Co. E-mail: main@llcp.com
URL: http://www.llcp.com
Contact: David Hicks, Co-President
Facebook: www.facebook.com/HomeVestors
Description: Real estate investors specializing in buying and selling undervalued houses. **Founded:** 1996. **Training:** 2 weeks initial training in Dallas, TX, annual convention, bi-annual advanced training; and year-round support.

13628 ■ Royal LePage Real Estate Services Ltd.
39 Wynford Dr.
Don Mills, ON, Canada M3C 3K5
Ph: (416)380-7500
Free: 877-RLP-4545
Co. E-mail: royallepage@cable-lynx.net
URL: http://www.royallepage.ca
Contact: Phil Soper, President
E-mail: president@royallepage.ca
Facebook: www.facebook.com/RoyalLePage
Linkedin: www.linkedin.com/company/royal-lepage
X (Twitter): twitter.com/Royal_LePage
YouTube: www.youtube.com/user/
   RoyalLePageCanada
Description: Retailer of homes and cottages. **Founded:** 1913. **Franchise Fee:** Varies. **Training:** Yes.

LIBRARIES

13629 ■ Building Owners and Managers Association International (BOMA) - Library [BOMA]
1101 15th St. NW, Ste. 800
Washington, DC 20005
Ph: (202)326-6300
Fax: (202)326-6377
Co. E-mail: info@boma.org
URL: http://www.boma.org
Contact: Henry Chamberlain, President
E-mail: hchamberlain@boma.org
X (Twitter): x.com/BOMAIntl
YouTube: www.youtube.com/user/BOMAInternational
Description: Building owners, managers, developers, leasing professionals, facility managers, asset managers and the providers of goods and services. Represents all facets of the commercial real estate industry. **Scope:** Real estate. **Founded:** 1907. **Holdings:** Figures not available. **Publications:** *Building Owners and Managers Association International-- Buyer's Guide to Products and Services* (Annual); *Boma Magazine; BOMA/Cushman and Wakefield Market Intelligence Report* (Quarterly); *Experience Exchange Report (EER); BOMA Global Office Tenant Survey; Who's Who in the Commercial Real Estate Industry* (Annual). **Educational Activities:** International Conference and Expo (Annual). **Awards:** Earth Awards; Office Building of the Year Earth Award (Annual); BOMA Government Affairs Award of Recognition - Outstanding Ongoing Advocacy Program; Earth Award; BOMA TOBY Award for Office Buildings Under 100,000 Square Feet (Annual); BOMA TOBY Award for Office Buildings Between 100,000 and 249,999 Square Feet (Annual); BOMA TOBY Award for Office Buildings Between 250,000 and 499,999 Square Feet (Annual); BOMA TOBY Award for Office Buildings Between 500,000 and One Million Square Feet (Annual); BOMA TOBY Award for Office Buildings Over One Million Square Feet (Annual); BOMA Government Affairs Award of Recognition - Single Government Affairs Issue. **Geographic Preference:** Multinational.

13630 ■ Buset & Partners
1121 Barton St.
Thunder Bay, ON, Canada P7B 5N3
Ph: (807)623-2500
Free: 866-532-8738
Fax: (807)622-7808

Co. E-mail: info@busetlaw.com
URL: http://busetlaw.com
Contact: Richard J. Buset, Partner Founder
E-mail: rbuset@busetlaw.com
Description: Full-service law firm located in the central part of the City of Thunder Bay. **Founded:** 1980.

13631 ■ Landauer Realty Group Information Center
2 Science Rd.
Glenwood, IL 60425-1586
Free: 800-323-8830
Fax: (708)755-7016
URL: http://www.landauer.com
Scope: Clinical optimization. **Services:** Center not open to the public. **Holdings:** 375 books; 100 VF drawers of reports; 16,000 clippings, offerings, brochures, statistical data; 125 VF drawers of research materials; U.S. maps; annual reports; 1960, 1970, 1980 census publications; government documents.

13632 ■ Polsinelli PC - Library
900 W 48th Pl., Ste. 900
Kansas City, MO 64112
Ph: (816)753-1000
Fax: (816)753-1536
URL: http://www.polsinelli.com
Contact: Cara E. Stark, Director
E-mail: cstark@polsinelli.com
Linkedin: www.linkedin.com/company/polsinelli
Description: A full-service law firm serving clients in health care, financial services, intellectual property, middle-market corporate, labor and employment, real estate, and business litigation. **Scope:** Law - tax, bankruptcy, real estate; litigation; product liability. **Services:** Interlibrary loan; copying; SDI; library open to clients only. **Founded:** 1972. **Holdings:** 15,000 books. **Subscriptions:** 1,500 journals and other serials; 10 newspapers. **Educational Activities:** Winter Leadership Conference (Annual); ABI Annual Spring Meeting (Annual); International Car Rental Show (Annual).

RESEARCH CENTERS

13633 ■ Indiana University Bloomington - Kelley School of Business - Benecki Center for Real Estate Studies (BCRES)
1309 E 10th St.
Bloomington, IN 47405-1701
Ph: (812)855-7794
URL: http://kelley.iu.edu/faculty-research/centers-insti
   tutes/real-estate/index.html
Contact: Dr. Jeffrey Fisher, Founder
Description: Integral unit of Kelley School of Business at Indiana University Bloomington. **Scope:** Housing affordability, income property, real estate valuation and the role of real estate in multi-asset portfolios. Special projects include development of homepage for several national organizations. **Founded:** 1985.

13634 ■ Massachusetts Institute of Technology - Center for Real Estate (CRE)
105 Massachusetts Ave.
Samuel Tak Lee Bldg. 9-343
Cambridge, MA 02139
Ph: (617)253-5000
Co. E-mail: cre-info@mit.edu
URL: http://cre.mit.edu
Contact: Kairos Shen, Executive Director
E-mail: kaiross@mit.edu
Facebook: www.facebook.com/MIT.CRE
Linkedin: www.linkedin.com/company/mit-center-for
   -real-estate
X (Twitter): x.com/MITCRE
Description: Integral unit of Massachusetts Institute of Technology, operating under an advisory committee composed of alumni, faculty, and business professionals. Offers seminars and professional development courses. **Scope:** Personal and work environment, focusing on real estate issues such as affordable housing, new investment and development strategies, returns to real estate across the business

cycle, public/private development strategies, international capital markets, impact of demographic trends, the markets for different products, and the design of future environments, including future U.S. office needs. **Founded:** 1983. **Publications:** *CRE Working Papers.* **Educational Activities:** CRE Executive education programs.

13635 ■ Northwestern University - Kellogg School of Management - Guthrie Center for Real Estate Research
2211 Campus Dr.
Evanston, IL 60208
URL: http://www.kellogg.northwestern.edu/departmen
   ts/real-estate/faculty-research/guthrie-center.aspx
Contact: Efraim Benmelech, Director
E-mail: e-benmelech@kellogg.northwestern.edu
Description: Integral unit of Northwestern University. **Scope:** Tax, real estate, and urban development and economics. **Founded:** 1987. **Publications:** *Guthrie Center for Real Estate Research Newsletter* (Annual). **Educational Activities:** Conferences, panel discussions and executive speakers luncheon series (Irregular), Offers exemplary teaching and training programs.

13636 ■ Real Estate Research Institute (RERI)
100 Pearl St., 13th Fl.
Hartford, CT 06103
Ph: (860)692-6341
Fax: (860)692-6351
Co. E-mail: reri@reri.org
URL: http://www.reri.org
Contact: Martha Peyton, President
Description: Independent, nonprofit organization, formerly affiliated with California State University, Fullerton. **Scope:** Real estate and urban land economics, including highest and best use studies, feasibility analyses, and real estate investment and valuation studies. **Founded:** 1987.

13637 ■ Southern Methodist University - Cox School of Business - Center for Research in Real Estate and Land Use Economics
PO Box 750100
Dallas, TX 75275-0100
URL: http://www.smu.edu/Academics/Centers-Insti
   tutes
Description: Integral unit of Edwin L. Cox School of Business, Southern Methodist University. **Scope:** Real estate and land use economics, including studies on the effect of high rise office buildings on residential property values, relocation opportunities and mortgage default, intermetropolitan variation in real housing price fluctuations, effect of municipal zoning ordinances on real property values, home ownership rates of married couples, and spatial variation in rates of economic depreciation for residential real estate. **Publications:** *Occasional Paper Series; Working Paper Series.* **Educational Activities:** Center for Research in Real Estate and Land Use Economics Semiannual Executive Seminars.

13638 ■ Texas A&M University - Real Estate Center (REC)
1700 Research Pky.
College Station, TX 77845
Ph: (979)845-2031
Co. E-mail: info@recenter.tamu.edu
URL: http://trerc.tamu.edu
Contact: Gary Maler, Executive Director
E-mail: gmaler@tamu.edu
Facebook: www.facebook.com/recentertx
Linkedin: www.linkedin.com/company/recentertx
X (Twitter): x.com/recentertx
Description: Research activity at Texas A&M University, operating under a nine-member advisory committee appointed by the governor of Texas. **Scope:** Real estate, including appraisal, brokerage, computer software, demography, development, economics education, financing, home buying and selling, investment, law, marketing, mineral leasing, mortgage instruments, multifamily housing, reference materials, rural properties, and tax. Assists real estate professionals, educators, and consumers by providing

information on the economy, taxation, law, finance, population, and households. **Founded:** 1971. **Publications:** *Tierra Grande: Journal of the Real Estate Center at Texas A&M University* (Quarterly); *Real Estate Applications Software Directory* (Annual); *English/Spanish Glossary of Real Estate Terms*; *Special Reports*; *Real Estate Center Technical Reports* (Monthly); *Tierra Grande* (Quarterly). **Educational Activities:** Annual Texas Land Market Outlook Conference (Annual); Conferences for real estate professionals, educators, and the general public, For research and development.

13639 ■ University of Florida - Warrington College of Business Administration - Bergstrom Center for Real Estate Studies
1384 Union Rd Bryan Hall 125
  Gainesville, FL 32611
Ph: (352)273-0311
Fax: (352)392-0301
URL: http://warrington.ufl.edu/real-estate-center
Contact: Wayne R. Archer, Executive Director
E-mail: wayne.archer@warrington.ufl.edu

Description: Integral unit of Warrington College of Business Administration at University of Florida. **Scope:** Real estate and urban analysis, including economic impact; market share study, including analysis of conceptual issues in appraisal, investment, and finance. **Publications:** *Survey of Emerging Market Conditions.* **Educational Activities:** Alfred Ring Distinguished Speaker Series (Annual), Offer exemplary teaching and training programs.; Appraisal seminars and professional education, Offer exemplary teaching and training programs.; Bergstrom Center for Real Estate Studies Conferences (Annual), Offer exemplary teaching and training programs.; Bergstrom Center for Real Estate Studies Lectures, Offer exemplary teaching and training programs.; Undergraduate and graduate instruction and research training on real estate problems and urban analyses, Offer exemplary teaching and training programs.

13640 ■ University of Illinois at Urbana, Champaign College of Business - Office of Real Estate Research
515 East Gregory Dr.
  Champaign, IL 61820
Co. E-mail: dejanir@illinois.edu
URL: http://giesbusiness.illinois.edu
Facebook: www.facebook.com/giesbusiness
Linkedin: www.linkedin.com/school/giesbusiness
X (Twitter): twitter.com/giesbusiness
Instagram: www.instagram.com/giesbusiness

YouTube: www.youtube.com/channel/UCvn1b9uPKrX
  dmzY_c5foz7Q
Description: Integral unit of College of Business at University of Illinois at Urbana-Champaign. **Scope:** Ongoing and contract studies on real estate issues, including appraisal and valuation, marketing and brokerage, environmental issues, land markets, municipal finance, property management, real estate investment, real estate financial markets, tenure choice, law, and public policy issues such as property rights, rent control, taxation, eminent domain, and impact fees. **Founded:** 1980. **Educational Activities:** Office of Real Estate Research Lecture Series, Offer exemplary teaching programs. **Awards:** CCIM Scholarship (Annual); Harold E. Eisenberg Foundation Scholarship (Annual); Morgan L. Fitch Scholarship (Annual); SIOR Scholarship (Annual).

13641 ■ University of Nevada, Las Vegas - Lied Institute for Real Estate Studies
4505 S Maryland Pkwy
  Las Vegas, NV 89154
Co. E-mail: shawn.mccoy@unlv.edu
URL: http://liedcenter.unlv.edu

Description: Integral unit of the University of Nevada, Las Vegas. **Scope:** Education institution that provides coaching on the below fields real estate, economic development, mortgage lending, common interest communities, investments, land use policy, taxation, development, and other related topics. **Founded:** 1989. **Publications:** *Annual Real Estate White Paper*; *Nevada Law and Reference Guide*; *Reserve Fund Guidelines for Common Interest Communities.* **Educational Activities:** Commercial Real Estate Certification; Lied Institute for Real Estate Studies Executive Education, Includes BOMA series, online mortgage lending training.; Lied Online Mortgage Training; Mentor Program, Providing professional development experiences for students.; Lied Institute for Real Estate Studies Roundtables; Real Estate and Business Society, Real estate, economic development, mortgage lending, common interest communities, investments, land use policy, taxation, development, and other related topics. **Awards:** Lieder Award (Annual); Lied Institute for Real Estate Studies Mentorship/Internship.

13642 ■ University of Pennsylvania - Samuel Zell and Robert Lurie Real Estate Center at Wharton
The Wharton School · University of Pennsylvania
  4th Fl., Vance Hall
  3733 Spruce St.
  Philadelphia, PA 19104-6302

Ph: (215)746-8098
Co. E-mail: wrec@wharton.upenn.edu
URL: http://realestate.wharton.upenn.edu
Contact: Joseph Gyourko, Director
E-mail: gyourko@wharton.upenn.edu
Facebook: www.facebook.com/pages/ZellLurie-Real
  -Estate-Center-at-Wharton/10150110573625277
Description: Integral unit of Wharton School, University of Pennsylvania. **Scope:** Deals with contemporary real estate issues and problems and the analysis of real estate markets, including real estate finance and macro environment, governmental regulation and constraints, energy costs and availability, demographic dynamics, and urban revitalization. **Founded:** 1983. **Publications:** *Wharton Real Estate Center Newsletter* (Semiannual); *Wharton Real Estate Review.* **Educational Activities:** Samuel Zell and Robert Lurie Real Estate Center at Wharton Public conferences; Samuel Zell and Robert Lurie Real Estate Center at Wharton Seminars, lectures; Samuel Zell and Robert Lurie Real Estate Center Fall Members' Meeting. **Awards:** Andrew Murphy Fellowship in Real Estate (Annual); Benjamin Franklin Kahn/WRIT Real Estate Scholarship (Annual); Jerome Freedman Memorial Award in Real Estate (Annual); Jimmy Goettee Award for Entrepreneurial Excellence (Annual); William Mack Award (Annual); William Zucker Award (Annual); Herbert K. Brown Scholastic Foundation Scholarship (Annual); Martin Bucksbaum Memorial Fellowship (Annual); Robert E. Linneman Memorial Fellowship (Annual).

13643 ■ University of South Carolina at Columbia - South Carolina Real Estate Center (SCCRE)
c/o Stephen Martin, Director, South Carolina Center
  for Real Estate
  Darla Moore School of Business, Rm. 451B
  Columbia, SC 29208
URL: http://sc.edu/study/colleges_schools/moore/
  research_and_centers/centers/real_estate_center/
  index.php

Description: Integral unit of Moore School of Business, University of South Carolina at Columbia. Offers media interviews. **Scope:** South Carolina real estate development, investment, marketing, finance, and appraising. Studies the economic impact of developments and evaluates labor market conditions in the state. **Founded:** 1973. **Publications:** *South Carolina Real Estate Center Newsletter* (Semiannual). **Educational Activities:** South Carolina Real Estate Center Conference, Offer exemplary teaching and training programs.; South Carolina Real Estate Center Seminars, Offer exemplary teaching programs.

ASSOCIATIONS AND OTHER ORGANIZATIONS

13644 ■ Audio Engineering Society, Inc. (AES)
697 3rd Ave., Ste. 405
New York, NY 10017
Ph: (212)661-8528
URL: http://aes2.org
Contact: Joshua Reiss, President
Linkedin: www.linkedin.com/company/audio-engineering-society
X (Twitter): x.com/AESorg
Instagram: www.instagram.com/aes_org
YouTube: www.youtube.com/user/AESorg
Description: Engineers, administrators, and technicians who design or operate recording and reproducing equipment for radio, television, motion picture, and recording studios, or who produce, install, and operate disc, magnetic tape, and sound amplifying equipment; educators who use recording in teaching, or who teach acoustics, electronics, and other sciences basic to the recording and reproducing of sound; administrators, sales engineers, and technicians in the sound industry and related fields. Operates educational and research foundation. **Founded:** 1948. **Publications:** *Journal of the Audio Engineering Society; Audio Engineering Society--Directory of Educational Programs; Journal of the Audio Engineering Society: Audio/Acoustics/Applications* (Monthly). **Educational Activities:** AES Convention (Annual). **Awards:** AES Publications Award (Annual); AES Bronze Medal Award (Annual); AES Board of Governors Award (Annual); AES Gold Medal Award (Annual); AES Gold Medal Award (Annual); AES Graduate Studies Grants (Annual). **Geographic Preference:** National.

13645 ■ Canadian Academy of Recording Arts and Sciences (CARAS)
219 Dufferin St., Ste. 211C
Toronto, ON, Canada M6K 3J1
Ph: (416)485-3135
Free: 888-501-3135
Fax: (416)485-4978
Co. E-mail: info@carasonline.ca
URL: http://carasonline.ca
Contact: Allan Reid, President
Facebook: www.facebook.com/theJunoAwards
X (Twitter): x.com/TheJUNOAwards
Instagram: www.instagram.com/TheJUNOAwards
YouTube: www.youtube.com/user/TheJUNOAwards
Description: Individuals actively working within the Canadian music industry. Promotes advancement in the field of recording and related disciplines. Conducts educational and charitable programs; maintains hall of fame. **Awards:** CARAS Juno Awards (Annual). **Geographic Preference:** National.

13646 ■ Canadian Independent Music Association (CIMA)
30 St. Patrick St., 2nd Fl.
Toronto, ON, Canada M5T 3A3
Ph: (416)485-3152
Co. E-mail: cima@cimamusic.ca
URL: http://cimamusic.ca
Contact: Andrew Cash, President
Facebook: www.facebook.com/CIMAmusic75
X (Twitter): x.com/cimamusic75
Instagram: www.instagram.com/cimamusic75
Description: Works to secure a strong and economically stable Canadian independent music and sound recording industry. **Founded:** 1975. **Geographic Preference:** National.

13647 ■ Content Delivery and Security Association (CDSA)
1775 W State St., No. 394
Boise, ID 83702
Ph: (208)629-1735
Co. E-mail: info@cdsaonline.org
URL: http://www.cdsaonline.org
Contact: Richard Atkinson, President
Facebook: www.facebook.com/CDSAonline
Linkedin: www.linkedin.com/company/cdsaonline
X (Twitter): x.com/CDSAonline
Description: Serves as the advocate for the growth and development of all recording media and as a forum for the exchange of information regarding global trends and innovations. Provides members an opportunity to join forces and be a strong industry voice allowing them to grow and expand their business. Encompasses all facets of the recording media. **Founded:** 1970. **Publications:** *Mediaware* (9/year); *IRMA International Source Directory* (Annual); *International Recording Media Associaton--Source Directory--the Buyer's Guide for the Recording Media Industry* (Annual). **Geographic Preference:** Multinational.

13648 ■ Music Business Association (MBA)
PO Box 746
Marlton, NJ 08053
Co. E-mail: info@musicbiz.org
URL: http://musicbiz.org
Contact: Portia Sabin, President
E-mail: portia@musicbiz.org
Facebook: www.facebook.com/MusicBizAssoc
X (Twitter): x.com/musicbizassoc
Instagram: www.instagram.com/musicbizassoc
Description: Serves the music and other prerecorded entertainment software industry as a forum for insight and dialogue; members include retailers, wholesalers, distributors, entertainment software suppliers, and suppliers of related products and services. **Founded:** 1958. **Publications:** *Music Biz Membership Directory; NARM Convention Official Guide* (Annual); *NARM News Bits* (Monthly); *NARM Research Briefs* (Monthly). **Educational Activities:** Insights and Sounds. **Awards:** Harry Chapin Memorial Humanitarian Award (Periodic); Music Business Association Presidential Award for Sustained Executive Achievement (Periodic). **Geographic Preference:** National.

13649 ■ Music Canada [Canadian Recording Industry Association (CRIA)]
85 Mowat Ave.
Toronto, ON, Canada M6K 3E3
Ph: (416)967-7272
Co. E-mail: info@musiccanada.com
URL: http://musiccanada.com
Contact: Patrick Rogers, Chief Executive Officer
E-mail: progers@musiccanada.com
Facebook: www.facebook.com/MusicCanada
X (Twitter): x.com/intent/user
Instagram: www.instagram.com/music_canada
Description: Record companies and manufacturers. Promotes high standards of ethics and practice in the recording industry. Represents members' interests. **Founded:** 1964. **Awards:** Music Canada Gold and Platinum (Annual). **Geographic Preference:** National.

13650 ■ National Academy of Recording Arts and Sciences (NARAS) [The Recording Academy]
3030 Olympic Blvd.
Santa Monica, CA 90404
URL: http://www.grammy.com
Contact: Tammy Hurt, Chairman
Facebook: www.facebook.com/RecordingAcademy
Description: Musicians, producers and other recording professionals. Dedicated to improving the cultural environment and quality of life for music and its makers. The Recording Academy is internationally known for the Grammy Awards and is responsible for numerous groundbreaking outreach, professional development, cultural enrichment, education and human service programs. **Founded:** 1957. **Publications:** *Grammy Magazine*. **Educational Activities:** The Grammy Awards (Annual). **Awards:** Latin GRAMMY (Annual); Grammy Hall of Fame Award (Annual); The Grammy Award (Annual). **Geographic Preference:** National.

13651 ■ Society of Professional Audio Recording Services (SPARS)
456 Commerce St.
Palacios, TX 77465-5444
Co. E-mail: info@spars.com
Contact: Paul Christensen, Contact
Facebook: www.facebook.com/spars.sessions
Description: Recording and video studio owners; manufacturers, producers, engineers, and recording service users involved with audio commercial facilities. Works to improve business operations and provide members with the opportunity to play an effective role in shaping the future of the industry. Maintains a high technical cultural standard. Analyzes, evaluates, and comments upon the use of professional audio equipment; fosters the dissemination of information concerning techniques of studio management and technical innovation; conducts educational activities. Assists in the development of projects, undertakings, and studies related to the industry; considers and deals with intratrade prob-

lems; attempts to reform abuses and inculcate principles of justice and equity in the audio recording industry. **Founded:** 1979. **Geographic Preference:** National.

REFERENCE WORKS

13652 ■ *"8 Things You Need to Set Up your Home Recording Studio" in Rolling Stone (February 6, 2019)*
URL(s): www.rollingstone.com/music/music-news/home-studio-setup-recording-how-to-790937/

Ed: Tim Chan. **Released:** February 06, 2019. **Description:** With technology and online access, many artists are able to release their own music in the comfort of their own homes. Booking time at a recording studio is not the only option anymore but before tackling that new album, there are several things needed to set up an ideal home recording studio. A list with links to products is included and discussed. **Availability:** Online.

13653 ■ *The Big Payback: The History of the Business of Hip-Hop*
Ed: Dan Charnas. **Released:** November 01, 2011. **Price:** $17, paperback; $13.99. **Description:** The complete history of hip-hop music is presented, by following the money and the relationship between artist and merchant. In its promise of economic security and creative control for black artist-entrepreneurs, it is the culmination of dreams of black nationalists and civil rights leaders. **Availability:** E-book; Print.

13654 ■ *"HBR Case Study: When the Longtime Star Fades" in Harvard Business Review (Vol. 88, September 2010, No. 9, pp. 117)*
Pub: Harvard Business Publishing
Contact: Diane Belcher, Managing Director

Ed: Jimmy Guterman. **Price:** $8.95, PDF. **Description:** A fictitious aging employee scenario is presented, with contributors offering advice. The scenario focuses on an older employee's match with a rapidly changing industry; suggestions include consolidating a niche business around the employee, and also engaging the older employee in solving the productivity issue. **Availability:** Online; PDF.

13655 ■ *The Rhythm of Success: How an Immigrant Produced His Own American Dream*
Pub: Penguin Publishing Group

Ed: Emilio Estefan. **Description:** Emilio Estefan, husband to singer Gloria Estefan and founder of the Latin pop legend Miami Sound Machine, is the classic example of the American dream. He shares his guiding principles that entrepreneurs need to start and grow a business. **Availability:** E-book; Print.

13656 ■ *"Welcome to Babesland" in Women In Business (Vol. 62, June 2010, No. 2, pp. 33)*
Description: Music group, Four Bitchin' Babes will be performing at the 2010 American Business Women's Association's National Women's Leadership Conference. The group has been in the industry for 20 years and has released nine albums. The Four Bitchin' Babes consist of Sally Fingerett, Nancy Moran, Deirdre Flint, and Debi Smith. **Availability:** Online.

TRADE PERIODICALS

13657 ■ *Journal of the Audio Engineering Society: Audio/Acoustics/Applications*
Pub: Audio Engineering Society UK
Contact: Dr. Neil Johnson, Chairman
URL(s): aes2.org/publications/journal

Released: Monthly **Price:** $350, for print per year; $595, for online. **Description:** Includes book reviews, calendar of events, information on new members, and reviews of acoustical patents. **Availability:** Print; Download; PDF; Online.

13658 ■ *Sound & Video Contractor*
Pub: Future P.L.C.
Contact: Zilah Byng-Thorne, Chief Executive Officer
URL(s): www.svconline.com
Facebook: www.facebook.com/svconline
X (Twitter): x.com/SVC_Online

Ed: Cynthia Wisehart. **Price:** $10, U.S. for back issues; $15, for outside the USA back issues. **Description:** Magazine covering management and technical topics for the systems contracting industry. **Availability:** Print; Online.

VIDEO/AUDIO MEDIA

13659 ■ *How I Built This: Merge Records: Laura Ballance and Mac McCaughan*
URL(s): www.npr.org/2021/12/03/1061221770/merge-records-laura-ballance-and-mac-mccaughan

Ed: Guy Raz. **Released:** December 06, 2021. **Description:** Podcast explains how a scrappy record label became one of the most influential in the industry.

TRADE SHOWS AND CONVENTIONS

13660 ■ **The NAMM Show**
National Association of Music Merchants (NAMM)
5790 Armada Dr.
Carlsbad, CA 92008
Ph: (760)438-8001
Free: 800-767-6266
Fax: (760)438-7327
Co. E-mail: info@namm.org
URL: http://www.namm.org
Contact: Joe Lamond, President
URL(s): registration.namm.org

Frequency: Annual. **Description:** Platform for the music, sound and event technology communities to promote music products. **Audience:** Music retailers, corporate buyers, manufacturer representatives, global distributors, artists, music educators, and sound contractors. **Principal Exhibits:** Platform for the music, sound and event technology communities to promote music products. Dates and Locations: 2025 Jan 21-25 Anaheim Convention Center, Anaheim, CA. **Telecommunication Services:** tradeshowsales@namm.org.

13661 ■ **Summer NAMM**
National Association of Music Merchants (NAMM)
5790 Armada Dr.
Carlsbad, CA 92008
Ph: (760)438-8001
Free: 800-767-6266
Fax: (760)438-7327
Co. E-mail: info@namm.org
URL: http://www.namm.org
Contact: Joe Lamond, President
URL(s): next.namm.org

Frequency: Annual. **Description:** Musical instruments and accessories, acoustical equipment, and sheet music publications. **Audience:** Pro audio professionals and buyers, manufacturer representatives, and music educators. **Principal Exhibits:** Musical instruments and accessories, acoustical equipment, and sheet music publications. **Telecommunication Services:** tradeshowsales@namm.org.

CONSULTANTS

13662 ■ **Engineering Harmonics Inc.**
326 Carlaw Ave. Unit 105
Toronto, ON, Canada M4M 3N8
Ph: (416)465-3378
Fax: (416)465-9037
Co. E-mail: info@engineeringharmonics.com
URL: http://engineeringharmonics.com
Contact: Gary Tibshirani, Director
Linkedin: www.linkedin.com/company/engineering-harmonics-inc.

Description: Consulting firm engages in the conception and design of audiovisual, performance sound and digital signage solutions. **Scope:** Consulting firm engages in the conception and design of audiovisual, performance sound and digital signage solutions. **Founded:** 1988. **Publications:** "Designing Sound for Frank Gehry's Vision"; "Precis of WDCH PSVC System"; "PSVC Design Challenges at WDCH"; "Power and Ground Update"; "Noise Reduction Systems"; "Mandating the House Audio System," Overture Hall; "Betting on Legends," Nov, 2008; "Examining our Roots, Defining our Future," Dec, 2008; "Walking The Hall: A Guide to Tuning a Loudspeaker System," Nov, 2007; "National Ballet School," Nov, 2007; "The Puzzle of PA for a Hall-in-the-Round," Aug, 2007; "A House for All Seasons," Aug, 2006; "Hooray for LA," Jan, 2004; "A Kodak Moment," Apr, 2002.

13663 ■ **Jess Barker, Document Research/Retrieval L.L.C.**
209 A S Macoupin St.
Gillespie, IL 62033
Contact: Barbara Barker, Manager

Description: Provides property title search for banks, lenders and real-estate investors.

13664 ■ **Lougheed Resource Group Inc. (LRG)**
17608 Deer Isle Cir.
Winter Garden, FL 34787
Ph: (407)654-1212
Co. E-mail: info@lrgconstruction.com
URL: http://lrgconstruction.com
Contact: Karen Lougheed, Owner
E-mail: karen@lrgconstruction.com

Description: Provider of building diagnostics, forensic and construction document analysis, litigation support, customized on-site risk reduction workshops, and much more for construction fields and trades related to commercial, residential, institutional, industrial, and recreational projects. **Scope:** Provider of building diagnostics, forensic and construction document analysis, litigation support, customized on-site risk reduction workshops, and much more for construction fields and trades related to commercial, residential, institutional, industrial, and recreational projects. **Founded:** 1987.

LIBRARIES

13665 ■ **Bowling Green State University (ML BSSA) - Music Library and Sound Recordings Archives**
William. T. Jerome Library, 3rd Fl.
Bowling Green, OH 43403
Ph: (419)372-2307
Co. E-mail: mlbssa@libanswers.bgsu.edu
URL: http://www.bgsu.edu/library/music.html
Contact: William L. Schurk, Archivist
E-mail: wschurk@bgsu.edu
X (Twitter): x.com/mlbssa
Instagram: www.instagram.com/mlbssa

Scope: Music. **Services:** Library open to the public with restrictions; researchers should contact Library prior to making extended visit. **Founded:** 1967. **Holdings:** 60,000 books and scores; 1,700 bound periodical volumes; 16,000 pieces of popular sheet music; 6 drawers of popular music posters.

13666 ■ **Delaware State Museums Division of Historical and Cultural Affairs - Johnson Victrola Museum Collection**
375 S New St.
Dover, DE 19904
Ph: (302)739-3262
Co. E-mail: jvmuseum@delaware.gov
URL: http://history.delaware.gov/johnson-victrola-museum
Contact: Reeves Johnson, Contact
Facebook: www.facebook.com/JohnsonVictrolaMuseum
Instagram: www.instagram.com/johnsonvictrolamuseum

Scope: History of the victor talking machine company; sound-recording industry. **Services:** Copying; library open to the public for reference and by appointment only. **Founded:** 1967. **Holdings:** Figures not available.

13667 ■ Recording Industry Association of America (RIAA)
1000 F St. NW, 2nd Fl.
  Washington, DC 20004

Ph: (202)775-0101
Fax: (202)775-7253
Co. E-mail: legal@riaa.com
URL: http://www.riaa.com
Contact: Mitch Glazier, Chief Executive Officer
Facebook: www.facebook.com/RIAA
X (Twitter): x.com/RIAA
Instagram: www.instagram.com/riaa_awards

Description: Promotes the mutual interests of recording companies, manufacturers and distributors, as well as the music industry through government relations, intellectual property protection, anti-piracy activities, research and public relations. **Founded:** 1952. **Publications:** *Fast Tracks* (Biweekly). **Geographic Preference:** National.

START-UP INFORMATION

13668 ■ *Recreational Vehicle Dealers Industry in the US - Market Research Report*
URL(s): ww.ibisworld.com/united-states/market-research-reports/recreational-vehicle-dealers-industry/
Price: $925. **Description:** Downloadable report analyzing the current and future trends in the recreational vehicle industry. **Availability:** Online.

ASSOCIATIONS AND OTHER ORGANIZATIONS

13669 ■ **BlueRibbon Coalition (BRC)**
PO Box 5449
 Pocatello, ID 83202
Ph: (208)237-1008
Co. E-mail: brc@sharetrails.org
URL: http://www.sharetrails.org
Contact: John Stewart, President
Facebook: www.facebook.com/BlueRibbonCoalition
X (Twitter): x.com/sharetrails

Description: Represents individuals, organizations and businesses involved in off highway recreation such as snowmobiling, motorcycle trail riding, mountain biking, ATVing, hiking, horseback riding, 4x4ing, rock hounding and boating. Seeks to preserve access for off highway recreation; promotes conservation of natural resources; encourages cooperation among members and government land managers. **Founded:** 1987. **Publications:** *BlueRibbon Magazine.* **Educational Activities:** BlueRibbon Coalition Spring Board meeting (Annual). **Geographic Preference:** National.

13670 ■ **Canadian Recreational Vehicle Association (CRVA) [Association Canadienne du Vehicule Recreatif]**
1100 Burloak Dr., Ste. 300
 Burlington, ON, Canada L7L 6B2
Ph: (905)315-3156
URL: http://crva.ca
Contact: Shane Devenish, President
E-mail: shane.devenish@crva.ca
Facebook: www.facebook.com/canadianrvassociation
Linkedin: www.linkedin.com/company/canadian
 -recreational-vehicle-association
X (Twitter): x.com/canadianrvassn
Instagram: www.instagram.com/canadianrvassociation
YouTube: www.youtube.com/channel/UCpQbywZfe
 _w1y82jjJanSEg/featured

Description: Suppliers (122) and manufacturers (49) of recreational vehicles. Represents the interests of the industry before consumers and government agencies; provides for information exchange. Collects statistics; sponsors educational programs; presents awards. Ensures a continuity of professional standards beneficial to the RV industry and ultimately to the interest of the consumer. **Founded:** 1975. **Geographic Preference:** National.

13671 ■ **Recreation Vehicle Industry Association (RVIA)**
1899 Preston White Dr.
 Reston, VA 20191
Ph: (703)620-6003
Fax: (703)620-5071
Co. E-mail: memberservices@rvia.org
URL: http://www.rvia.org
Contact: Craig Kirby, President
Facebook: www.facebook.com/RVIndustryAssoc
Linkedin: www.linkedin.com/company/rvia
X (Twitter): x.com/RV_Industry
Instagram: www.instagram.com/rvindustryassociation
YouTube: www.youtube.com/user/RVIACommunications

Description: Recreation vehicle manufacturers, manufacturers' representatives, and suppliers of accessories and equipment used by manufacturers. Provides a unified recreation vehicle organization for manufacturers and component parts suppliers of motorhomes, travel trailers, fifth wheel trailers, horse trailer conversions, sport-utility trailers, truck campers and folding camping trailers. Represents the growth and concerns of the industry to federal and state government departments, the media, and the public. Collects shipment statistics, technical data, and consumer and media information. Monitors industry compliance with safety standards and the activities of federal and state governments that affect the RV industry. **Founded:** 1910. **Publications:** *Recreation Vehicle Industry Association--Industry Profile Report* (Annual); *Recreation Vehicle Market Report* (Monthly); *Survey of RV Financing* (Annual); *RVIA Today* (Monthly); *Recreation Vehicle Industry Association--Membership Directory* (Annual). **Educational Activities:** The National RV Trade Show (Annual). **Awards:** Distinguished Achievement in RV Journalism Award (Annual); Distinguished Achievement in RV Standards Award (Annual); Distinguished Service to the RV Industry Award (Annual); RVIA National Legislative Award (Annual); RVIA National Service Award (Annual); RV Automotive Achievement Award (Annual); RVIA National Scholastic Award (Annual); RVIA Special Award (Annual); RVIA National Education Service Award (Annual); RVIA Spirit of America Award (Annual). **Geographic Preference:** National.

13672 ■ **Recreation Vehicle Rental Association (RVRA)**
3930 University Dr.
 Fairfax, VA 22030
Ph: (703)591-7130
Co. E-mail: info@rvda.org
URL: http://www.rvda.org/RVDA/Find_A_Dealer/About_RVRA.aspx
Contact: Phil Ingrassia, President
E-mail: pingrassia@rvda.org

Description: Represents dealers involved in the rental of recreation vehicles such as folding trailers, travel trailers, and motor homes. Works to improve the professionalism of the RV rental dealer through educational programs and promote the use of rentals by disseminating information. Compiles statistics; conducts seminars. **Founded:** 1982. **Geographic Preference:** National.

13673 ■ **RVDA, The National RV Dealers Association (RVDA)**
3930 University Dr.
 Fairfax, VA 22030
Ph: (703)591-7130
Co. E-mail: info@rvda.org
URL: http://www.rvda.org
Contact: Phil Ingrassia, CAE, President
E-mail: pingrassia@rvda.org
Facebook: www.facebook.com/rvlearningcenter
X (Twitter): x.com/rvlearningctr
YouTube: www.youtube.com/user/rvlearningcenter

Description: Firms that have as their principal business the retail sale of recreation vehicles (commonly known as travel trailers, camping trailers, truck campers, and motor homes) and who maintain a permanent business establishment open for business and service on what they sell year-round. Provides information and liaison on government regulation of safety, trade, warranty, and franchising; fosters improved dealer-manufacturer relations; encourages communications among dealers and state and local RV associations. Offers education programs and training, advertising, sales, and service information. Provides public relations and publicity among the RV dealers and the rest of the industry, the public, and the government; works to improve standards of service to the consumer; sponsors local retail RV shows and dealer seminars. Supports improved availability and quality of campgrounds. Maintains speakers' bureau; compiles statistics; sponsors educational programs. Maintains the Recreation Vehicle Rental Association and Recreation Vehicle Aftermarket Division to help improve the professional quality of rental and service businesses. **Founded:** 1970. **Publications:** *RV Executive Today* (Monthly); *RV Technician Magazine* (Bimonthly); *RVDA Online Membership Directory & Resource Guide* (Annual). **Educational Activities:** RV Dealers International Convention/Expo (Annual). **Geographic Preference:** National.

REFERENCE WORKS

13674 ■ *"An Economic Warning Sign: RV Shipments are Slipping" in The Wall Street Journal (August 19, 2019)*
URL(s): www.wsj.com/articles/one-countys-rv-industry-points-to-recession-around-the-bend-11566207001
Ed: Shayndi Raice. **Released:** August 19, 2019. **Description:** A strong indicator of the economy's health is whether or not consumers are purchasing luxury items such as RVs. When those sales start to wane, it's a good sign that the economy is in a recession or is headed for one. Elkhart, IN is the capital of the RV industry and so far, shipments to dealers have fallen 20% after a short drop last year. However, the slowdown could be due to manufacturing too many vehicles after a big demand for them in 2017 and dealers just have too many in stock. **Availability:** Online.

13675 ■ "RV Sales Have Slumped. Here's Why the Stocks Have Rallied" in Barron's (August 20, 2019)
URL(s): www.barrons.com/articles/rv-industry-slump
-inventory-elkhart-recession-economy-thor
-winnebago-51566240571
Ed: Nicholas Jasinski. **Released:** August 20, 2019.
Description: Even though sales of RVs have dropped 20% during the first half of the year, stocks at companies like Winnebago Industries have increased. A discussion of the RV industry and their sales cycle since the recession are given to explain how the stocks have increased. **Availability:** Online.

13676 ■ RVDA Online Membership Directory & Resource Guide (Recreation vehicles)
Pub: RVDA, The National RV Dealers Association
Contact: Phil Ingrassia, CAE, President
E-mail: pingrassia@rvda.org
URL(s): www.officialmediaguide.com/rvd/print2
Released: Annual **Description:** Covers over 900 retail sales firms handling travel trailers, camping trailers, truck campers, and motor homes in the United States and Canada that are open for business twelve months of the year. **Entries include:** Company name, address, phone, and owner's or manager's name. **Arrangement:** Alphabetical. **Indexes:** Geographical, membership status. **Availability:** Online.

13677 ■ "Sewage from RVs May Be Contaminating Waterways, Seattle Businesses Warn" in King5News (October 24, 2019)
URL(s): www.king5.com/article/news/sewage-from
-rvs-may-be-contaminating-waterways/281-717e50
5f-57e7-4de1-957d-349ee97946a4
Ed: Ted Land. **Released:** October 24, 2019. **Description:** Seattle Public Utilities ran tests in SODO and found elevated fecal coliform levels, which was due to incorrect private sewer connections. Locals fear that these elevated levels are due to people living in nearby RVs who have nowhere to dump their waste. **Availability:** Online.

13678 ■ "Survey Reveals RV Owners' Internet Needs" in RV News (November 24, 2021)
Released: November 24, 2021. **Description:** Even though many campers hit the road to leave behind their hectic lives for awhile, having a good Internet connection is become more and more vital for RV owners. Discusses the various needs for Internet and full results of the survey. **Availability:** Online.

13679 ■ "Your Cold Calling?" in Inc. (December 2007, pp. 34)
Ed: Elaine Appleton Grant. **Description:** Profile of a recreational outfitting company in northern New England with an asking price of $6.185 million, with gross revenue of $9.4 million in 2007. **Availability:** Online.

STATISTICAL SOURCES

13680 ■ RMA Annual Statement Studies
Pub: Risk Management Association
Contact: Nancy Foster, President
Released: Annual. **Description:** Contains composite balance sheets and income statements for more than 360 industries, including the accounting, auditing, and bookkeeping industries. Also contains five years of comparative historical data for discerning trends. Includes 16 commonly used ratios, computed for most of the size groupings for nearly every industry.

TRADE PERIODICALS

13681 ■ Escapees Magazine
Pub: Escapees, Inc.
Contact: Cathie Carr, President
URL(s): escapees.com/escapees-magazine
Released: Bimonthly **Description:** Provides members with the opportunity to exchange ideas and information on traveling in recreational vehicles. Carries hints for modifying vehicles for full-time living, saving and earning money, and keeping in touch with others. Recurring features include technical advice,

travel in Mexico and abroad, housekeeping hints, where to find free and inexpensive parking, book reviews, announcements of rallies and other events, and information about the Escapee support network and RV Park system. **Availability:** Print; Online; PDF.

TRADE SHOWS AND CONVENTIONS

13682 ■ Maryland RV Show
Maryland Recreational Vehicle Dealer's Association (MRVDA)
729 MD Rte. 3 N
Gambrills, MD 21054
Ph: (410)987-6300
Fax: (410)987-6300
Co. E-mail: info@mdrv.com
URL: http://www.mdrv.com/index.php
Contact: Greg Merkel, Treasurer
URL(s): www.mdrv.com/RV-show-RVs-dealer
-Maryland-MD-trailer-camper-motorhome.php
Frequency: Semiannual; first show at last two full weekends of February and second show on one weekend in September. **Audience:** RV dealers and professionals.

13683 ■ The National RV Trade Show
Recreation Vehicle Industry Association (RVIA)
1899 Preston White Dr.
Reston, VA 20191
Ph: (703)620-6003
Fax: (703)620-5071
Co. E-mail: memberservices@rvia.org
URL: http://www.rvia.org
Contact: Craig Kirby, President
URL(s): www.rvia.org/events/rvx-rv-experience#p-26
Frequency: Annual. **Description:** Recreational vehicles, component parts, services, and accessories. **Audience:** General public. **Principal Exhibits:** Recreational vehicles, component parts, services, and accessories. **Telecommunication Services:** hdang@rvia.org.

ASSOCIATIONS AND OTHER ORGANIZATIONS

13684 ■ **Association Canadienne des Industries du Recyclage (ACIR) [Canadian Association of Recycling Industries (CARI)]**
PO Box 67094 Westboro
  Ottawa, ON, Canada K2A 4E4
Ph: (613)728-6946
Co. E-mail: info@cari-acir.org
URL: http://cari-acir.org
Contact: Tracy Shaw, President
E-mail: tracy@cari-acir.org
Facebook: www.facebook.com/CARIACIRScrap
X (Twitter): x.com/CARI_Recycling

Description: Companies engaged in the recycling of used materials and products. Seeks to advance the recycling industries; promotes reuse of products containing nonrenewable resources. Represents members' interests; conducts promotional and advocacy activities. **Founded:** 1941. **Publications:** *The Pulse.* **Geographic Preference:** National.

13685 ■ **Canadian Environmental Network [Reseau canadien de l'environnement (RCEN)]**
136F Billings Ave.
  Ottawa, ON, Canada K1H 5K9
Co. E-mail: info@rcen.ca
URL: http://www.rcen.ca/en/home
Contact: Jade Scognamillo, Executive Director
Facebook: www.facebook.com/CanadianEnvironmentalNetwork
Linkedin: www.linkedin.com/company/canadian-environmental-network-rcen-
X (Twitter): x.com/rcen
Instagram: www.instagram.com/canadianenvironmentalnetwork

Description: Environmental organizations. Seeks to advance the projects and activities of members. Promotes ecologically sustainable development. Serves as a clearinghouse on environmental issues; provides support and assistance to members. **Founded:** 1977. **Publications:** *Canadian Environmental Network News.* **Geographic Preference:** Multinational.

13686 ■ **EarthSave Canada - Library**
422 Richards St., Ste. 170
  Vancouver, BC, Canada V6B 2Z4
Ph: (604)731-5885
Co. E-mail: office@earthsave.ca
URL: http://www.earthsave.ca
Contact: Dr. David Steele, President
Facebook: www.facebook.com/earthsavecanada
X (Twitter): x.com/earthsavecanada
Instagram: www.instagram.com/earthsavecanada
YouTube: www.youtube.com/user/earthsavecanada

Description: Seeks to increase the awareness of the health, ethical, and environmental impacts of food choices. Promotes transition to a plant-based diet for optimum health, environmental sustainability, and compassion. **Scope:** Charity. **Founded:** 1989. **Hold-**

ings: Figures not available. **Publications:** *Canada EarthSaver* (Quarterly); *Earthsave Canada--Veg Directory.* **Geographic Preference:** National.

13687 ■ *Enviro Business Guide*
PO Box 23
  Bluffton, AB, Canada T0C 0M0
Ph: (403)843-6563
Co. E-mail: info@recycle.ab.ca
URL: http://recycle.ab.ca
Contact: Don Hughes, President
E-mail: don.hughes@hughesenvironmentalservices.net
URL(s): recycle.ab.ca/enviro-businesses
Availability: Print.

13688 ■ **Institute of Scrap Recycling Industries (ISRI)**
1250 H St. NW, Ste. 400
  Washington, DC 20005
Ph: (202)662-8500
Fax: (202)624-9256
Co. E-mail: info@isri.org
URL: http://www.isri.org
Contact: Robin K. Wiener, President
Facebook: www.facebook.com/isri1987
X (Twitter): x.com/ISRI
Instagram: www.instagram.com/isrinews
YouTube: www.youtube.com/user/ISRI1987

Description: Represents processors, brokers, and consumers engaged in the recycling of ferrous, nonferrous, paper, plastics, glass, textiles, rubber and electronics scrap. Conducts specialized education and research programs. **Founded:** 1987. **Publications:** *Institute of Scrap Recycling Industries Directory of Members*; *ISRI Focus*; *Scrap Magazine*; *Institute of Scrap Recycling Industries--Membership Directory*; *IAER Electronics Recycling Newsletter* (Monthly). **Geographic Preference:** Multinational.

13689 ■ **Municipal Waste Association (MWA)**
10C Shared Space, 42 Carden St.
  Guelph, ON, Canada N1H 3A2
Ph: (519)837-6863
Co. E-mail: mwa@municipalwaste.ca
URL: http://municipalwaste.ca
Contact: David Douglas, Chairman

Description: Promotes more effective and environmentally sustainable removal of solid wastes. Facilitates sharing of municipal waste management, reduction, recycling, and reuse information and facilities. **Founded:** 1987. **Publications:** *For R Information* (Quarterly). **Awards:** MWA Promotion and Education Campaign Award (Annual). **Geographic Preference:** National.

13690 ■ *The Pulse*
PO Box 67094 Westboro
  Ottawa, ON, Canada K2A 4E4
Ph: (613)728-6946
Co. E-mail: info@cari-acir.org
URL: http://cari-acir.org
Contact: Tracy Shaw, President
E-mail: tracy@cari-acir.org
URL(s): cari-acir.org/blog

Availability: Print.

13691 ■ *RCA Connector*
PO Box 23
  Bluffton, AB, Canada T0C 0M0
Ph: (403)843-6563
Co. E-mail: info@recycle.ab.ca
URL: http://recycle.ab.ca
Contact: Don Hughes, President
E-mail: don.hughes@hughesenvironmentalservices.net
URL(s): recycle.ab.ca/newsyear/2024
Released: Monthly **Availability:** Print; Online.

13692 ■ **Recycling Council of Alberta (RCA)**
PO Box 23
  Bluffton, AB, Canada T0C 0M0
Ph: (403)843-6563
Co. E-mail: info@recycle.ab.ca
URL: http://recycle.ab.ca
Contact: Don Hughes, President
E-mail: don.hughes@hughesenvironmentalservices.net
Facebook: www.facebook.com/RecyclingCouncilOfAlberta
Linkedin: www.linkedin.com/company/recycling-council-of-alberta
X (Twitter): x.com/3RsAB
Instagram: www.instagram.com/recyclingcouncilab

Description: Promotes and facilitates waste reduction, recycling and resource conservation in the province of Alberta. **Founded:** 1987. **Publications:** *RCA Connector* (Monthly); *Enviro Business Guide.* **Awards:** R's of Excellence (Annual); Rs of Excellence Awards (Annual). **Geographic Preference:** State.

13693 ■ **Saskatchewan Environmental Society (SES)**
Offices No. 204 & No. 205a€"220 20th St. W
  Saskatoon, SK, Canada S7K 3N9
Ph: (306)665-1915
Co. E-mail: info@environmentalsociety.ca
URL: http://environmentalsociety.ca
Contact: Margret Asmuss, President
Facebook: www.facebook.com/environmentalsociety
Linkedin: www.linkedin.com/company/saskatchewan-environmental-society
X (Twitter): x.com/skenvsociety
Instagram: www.instagram.com/skenvsociety
YouTube: www.youtube.com/user/EnvironmentalSociety

Description: Seeks to support and encourage the creation of a global community in which all needs are met in sustainable ways. **Founded:** 1970. **Publications:** *SES Newsletter* (Quarterly). **Geographic Preference:** National.

13694 ■ **Secondary Materials and Recycled Textiles Association (SMART)**
1300 Piccard Dr., Ste. LL-14
  Rockville, MD 20850
Ph: (443)640-1050
Co. E-mail: smartinfo@msp-amc.com
URL: http://www.smartasn.org

Contact: Steve Rees, President
Facebook: www.facebook.com/smarttextiles
Linkedin: www.linkedin.com/company/secondary-ma
terials-and-recycled-textiles
X (Twitter): x.com/smarttextile
YouTube: www.youtube.com/channel/UCQ70gosA
dc9Zr3G6oaNmu9Q

Description: Manufacturers and distributors of
industrial wiping materials, recycled clothing, recycled
textile products, fibers and other cloth products. Monitors international trade activities, recycling and
environmental issues. **Founded:** 1932. **Geographic
Preference:** National.

**13695 ■ Society Promoting Environmental
Conservation (SPEC) - Library**
2305 W 7th Ave.
  Vancouver, BC, Canada V6K 1Y4
Ph: (604)736-7732
Co. E-mail: admin@spec.bc.ca
URL: http://www.spec.bc.ca
Contact: Jennifer Henry, Executive Director
Facebook: www.facebook.com/SPEC.bc.ca
X (Twitter): x.com/specbc
Instagram: www.instagram.com/specbc
YouTube: www.youtube.com/user/specbc

Description: Promotes environmental research,
advocacy, and education. **Scope:** Urban living.
Founded: 1969. **Holdings:** Figures not available.
Publications: *SPECTRUM* (Quarterly). **Geographic
Preference:** Multinational.

13696 ■ Steel Recycling Institute (SRI)
25 Massachusetts Ave. NW, Ste. 800
  Washington, DC 20001
URL: http://www.steel.org/sustainability

Description: Educates the solid waste management
industry, government, business and the consumer
about the economic and environmental benefits of
recycling steel. **Geographic Preference:** National.

13697 ■ U.S. Composting Council (USCC)
1053 E Whitaker Mill Rd., Ste. 115
  Raleigh, NC 27604
Ph: (301)897-2715
Co. E-mail: uscc@compostingcouncil.org
URL: http://www.compostingcouncil.org
Contact: Frank Franciosi, Executive Director
E-mail: ffranciosi@compostingcouncil.org
Facebook: www.facebook.com/USCompos
tingCouncil
Linkedin: www.linkedin.com/company/us-composting
-council
YouTube: www.youtube.com/USCompostingCouncil

Description: Supports the recycling of all organic
materials in the waste stream, including compostable
materials from solid waste, wastewater, and agricul-
ture that are not otherwise recycled. **Founded:** 1990.
Publications: *U.S. Composting Council--
Membership Directory*; Compost Facility Operating
Guide. **Awards:** Hi Kellogg Award (Annual); Rufus
Chaney Award (Annual); USCC Clean Water Award
(Annual); USCC Composter of the Year Award (An-
nual); H. Clark Gregory Award (Annual); Jerome
Goldstein Lifetime Achievement Award (Annual).
Geographic Preference: National.

**13698 ■ Yukon Conservation Society (YCS) -
Library**
302 Hawkins St.
  Whitehorse, YT, Canada Y1A 1X6
Ph: (867)668-5678
Co. E-mail: coservices@yukon.ca
URL: http://www.yukonconservation.org
Contact: Kim Melton, Director
Facebook: www.facebook.com/yukonconserva
tionsociety
X (Twitter): x.com/YukonConservati
Instagram: www.instagram.com/yukonconservation

Description: Seeks to protect Canada's natural
environment; particularly that of the Yukon region.
Encourages the conservation of Yukon wilderness,
wildlife and natural resources. **Scope:** Canada's
natural environment, particularly that of the Yukon

region. **Founded:** 1968. **Holdings:** Figures not avail-
able. **Publications:** *Walk Softly*. **Awards:** Ted Parnell
Scholarship (Annual). **Geographic Preference:**
National.

REFERENCE WORKS

**13699 ■ *"22 Top Recycling Tips for the
Workplace That You Can Implement Today"* in
*Recycle Coach (October 9, 2020)***
URL(s): recyclecoach.com/blog/22-top-recycling-tips
-for-the-workplace-that-you-can-implement-today
-rcaw/

Released: October 09, 2020. **Description:** As more
companies turn to green policies, more ways to
recycle are becoming available. Listed are 22 ways
to incorporate recycling and how to get employees
on board in participating.

**13700 ■ *"As Costs Skyrocket, More U.S.
Cities Stop Recycling"* in *The New York
Times (March 16, 2019)***
URL(s): www.nytimes.com/2019/03/16/business/local
-recycling-costs.html
Ed: Michael Corkery. **Description:** After China
stopped buying recyclable material from the US in
2018 due to it being mixed in with too much actual
trash, many communities across the nation are
canceling their recycling programs. With fewer buyers, recycling companies are charging cities more,
and these communities have to pass down the cost
somehow, either by raising taxes or cutting other
services. Many just close their recycling centers, and
it's having a detrimental impact the environment.
Availability: Online.

**13701 ■ *"California Water Treatment Facility
Turns to Solar Power"* in *Chemical Business
Newsbase (September 11, 2012)***
Description: Ramona, California municipal water
district providing water, sewer, recycled water, fire
protection, emergency medical services, and park
services to the community has commissioned a
530KWp solar energy installation. Enfinity America
Corporation developed and financed the solar panels
and EPC services were provided by manufacturer
Siliken. **Availability:** Print; Online.

**13702 ■ *"California's Largest Recycling
Business Closes, 750 Laid Off"* in *U.S. News
& World Report (August 5, 2019)***
URL(s): www.usnews.com/news/business/articles/20
19-08-05/californias-largest-recycling-business
-closes-750-laid-off
Released: August 05, 2019. **Description:** RePlant,
California's largest operator of recycling centers,
closed down all 284 of its centers and laid off 750
workers. The close comes after increased business
costs and falling prices for several recyclable materials. **Availability:** Online.

**13703 ■ *"Carrington Co. LLC Revolutionizes
the Hot Tea Market with First-Ever, Organic
Tea in Eco-Friendly Packaging"* in *Ecology,
Environment & Conservation Business (May
3, 2014, pp. 6)***
Pub: NewsRX LLC.
Contact: Kalani Rosell, Contact

Description: Carrington Company makes organic
non-genetically modified products including flax
seeds, hemp, chia, and organic coconut oil and teas.
The firm is launching its Carrington Organics Tea to
its lineup of healthy products, packed in a 100
percent eco-friendly packaging that will fully and
safely biodegrade when composted. It is the first tea
available packaged in fully recyclable packaging.
Availability: Online.

**13704 ■ *"Cascades Awarded 'Innovative
Product of the Year' and 'Environmental
Strategy of the Year' by Pulp & Paper
International PPI"* in *Ecology, Environment &
Conservation Business (January 4, 2014, pp.
4)***
Pub: NewsRX LLC.
Contact: Kalani Rosell, Contact

Description: Cascades Tissue Group was awarded
'Innovative Product of the Year' for its bathroom and
facial tissues made from unbleached recycled fiber,
the first of its kind in the U.S. Cascades also won the
'Environmental Strategy of the Year' based on its
commitment to reducing its ecological impact through
continuous improvement of processes, unique recycling infrastructure, and use of recycled fibers in
packaging and tissue products. Pulp and Paper
recognizes companies for these efforts annually.
Availability: Print; Online.

**13705 ■ *"Cash for Kiosks: EcoATM Pulls in
Series B Funding"* in *San Diego Business
Journal (Vol. 33, May 7, 2012, No. 19, pp. 10)***
Pub: CBJ L.P.
Contact: Terri Cunningham, Contact

Ed: Brad Graves. **Description:** EcoATM received
$17 million in Series B venture funds as well as a $1
million grant from the National Science Foundation.
The Series B funds will be used to install mall kiosks
that offer cash for used cellphones and other small
electronic devices. **Availability:** Online.

**13706 ■ *"Christmas Trees Keep Giving in St.
Louis Area"* in *St. Louis Post-Dispatch
(January 11, 2012)***
Pub: Tribune News Service
Contact: Jack Barry, Vice President, Operations
E-mail: jbarry@tribpub.com
Ed: Jonah Newman. **Description:** Missouri state law
prohibiting disposing of Christmas trees into area
lakes has forced citizens to find new ways to use
their old trees. Saint Louis and other municipalities
offers ways to recycle Christmas trees while creating
a good habitat for fish. Cities have sunk a portion of
the trees, then created mulch and is offered free to
residents. **Availability:** Online.

**13707 ■ *"Crucible: Battling Back from
Betrayal"* in *Harvard Business Review (Vol.
88, December 2010, No. 12, pp. 130)***
Pub: Harvard Business Publishing
Contact: Diane Belcher, Managing Director
Ed: Daniel McGinn. **Price:** $8.95, PDF. **Description:**
Stephen Greer's scrap metal firm, Hartwell Pacific,
lost several million dollars due to a lack of efficient
and appropriate inventory audits, accounting procedures, and new-hire reference checks for his foreign
operations. Greer believes that balancing growth with
control is a key component of success. **Availability:**
Print; PDF.

**13708 ■ *"Developer Tries to Bring Homes to
Buda"* in *Austin Business JournalInc. (Vol.
28, December 26, 2008, No. 41, pp. 1)***
Description: Real estate developer Jeremiah Venture LP is planning a residential, single-family
development on about 600 acres near Buda, Texas.
The company also plans to construct a membrane
waste treatment plant, and has applied to do land
application. However, several groups have come
forward to ask for more information on the application due to concerns about soil density. **Availability:**
Print; Online.

**13709 ■ *"DTE Energy Foundation Expands
'Greening' Programs at Michigan Festivals"* in
*Ecology, Environment & Conservation
Business (June 28, 2014, pp. 3)***
Pub: NewsRX LLC.
Contact: Kalani Rosell, Contact

Description: DTE Energy Foundation is expanding
its support for its 'Greening' or recycling programs to
the GrandJazz Fest in Grand Rapids and the Lakeshore Art Festival in Michigan. The Foundation
already supports recycling programs at the Detroit
Jazz Festival and the National Cherry Festival in
Traverse City. The foundation is committed to reduce
the carbon footprint at these events by recycling
plastic, aluminum cans, glass and other materials.
Availability: Online.

**13710 ■ *"Electronics Recyclers Poised to
Grow"* in *Austin Business Journal (Vol. 31,
July 22, 2011, No. 20, pp. A1)***
Pub: Austin Business Journal
Contact: Rachel McGrath, Director

E-mail: rmcgrath@bizjournals.com

Ed: Cody Lyon. **Description:** Electronic Recycling and Trading Inc. has leased 138,000 square feet of space in North Austin, Texas. The company requires more space for bigger equipment. **Availability:** Print; Online.

13711 ■ "Encore Container, Manufacturer of Plastic Drums and IBC Totes, Leads the Way in Environmental Sustainability" in Ecology, Environment & Conservation Business (January 25, 2014, pp. 33)
Pub: NewsRX LLC.
Contact: Kalani Rosell, Contact

Description: Encore Container, a leading reconditioner of IBC totes and manufacturer and reconditioner of plastic drums describes its efforts to promote environmental sustainability within the company: container reconditioning, plastic and steel recycling, water conservation and waste minimization. **Availability:** Online.

13712 ■ "From Scarcity to Plenty" in Inc. (Vol. 36, March 2014, No. 2, pp. 76)
Pub: Mansueto Ventures L.L.C.
Contact: Stephanie Mehta, Chief Executive Officer
Description: Profile of Mom's Organic Market which started in Scott Nash's mom's garage. Nash describes the healthy food choices offered at the store as well as its Environmental Restoration program which addressed issues including carbon offsets, recycling, and composting. **Availability:** Print; Online.

13713 ■ The Green Guide for Business: The Ultimate Environment for Businesses of All Sizes
Pub: Profile Books Limited
Contact: Stephen Brough, Co-Founder
Ed: Chris Goodball, Roger East, Hannah Bullock. **Released:** March 09, 2010. **Description:** Everyone wants to go green these days, but for small businesses that's easier said than done. How do you measure a company's carbon footprint? Are dryers or hand towels more eco-friendly? Recycled paper or FSC-certified? All these questions and more are explored. **Availability:** E-book.

13714 ■ Greening Your Small Business: How to Improve Your Bottom Line, Grow Your Brand, Satisfy Your Customers and Save the Planet
Price: $19.95. **Description:** A definitive resource for anyone who wants their small business to be cutting-edge, competitive, profitable, and eco-conscious. Stories from small business owners address every aspect of going green, from basics such as recycling waste, energy efficiency, and reducing information technology footprint, to more in-depth concerns such as green marketing and communications, green business travel, and green employee benefits.

13715 ■ "Groups Seek Donations to Recycle Christmas Trees" in The Register-Guard (January 7, 2012, pp. B11)
Description: Groups wishing to recycle used Christmas trees in the Eugene, Oregon area are listed. Some of the groups offer incentives as well as free pickup. Contact information for each group is provided. **Availability:** Print; Online.

13716 ■ "Health Care Briefs: Survey Says Most Approve of Donating Used Pacemakers to Medically Underserved" in Crain's Detroit Business (Vol. 25, June 1, 2009)
Pub: Crain Communications Inc.
Contact: Barry Asin, President
Description: According to a survey conducted by University of Michigan Cardiovascular Center, 87 percent of those with pacemakers and 71 percent of the general population would donate the device to patients in underserved nations.

13717 ■ "How to Reuse Or Recycle Your Old Tech: eWaste Is on the Rise but You Can Help Combat It By Using Old PCs and Electronics in Different Ways" in PC Magazine (Vol. 31, February 2012, No. 2, pp. 108)
Description: US recycling businesses employ 30,000 workers to recycle 3.5 million tons of electronic waste,

that does not include the number of devices that go to landfills. Simple and cheap ways to recycle or put old electronics to work are examined. **Availability:** Online.

13718 ■ "How to Sell, Donate, or Recycle Your Stuff" in The New York Times (January 11, 2019)
URL(s): www.nytimes.com/2019/01/11/realestate/how-to-sell-donate-or-recycle-your-stuff.html
Ed: Ronda Kaysen. **Released:** January 11, 2019. **Description:** If you are taking the time to clean out your home, resist the urge to throw away the old items and instead sell, donate, or recycle. You may be able to make some quick cash too. Various tips for getting rid of your unwanted items, including selling at consignment shops, are given. **Availability:** Online.

13719 ■ Institute of Scrap Recycling Industries--Membership Directory
Pub: Institute of Scrap Recycling Industries
Contact: Robin K. Wiener, President
URL(s): www.isri.org/membership/member-direc tories
Description: Covers member processors, brokers, and consumers of scrap ferrous and nonferrous metals, paper, glass, plastics, rubber, and textiles; suppliers to the industry. **Entries include:** Company name, address, phone, contact name, product or service provided. **Arrangement:** Information is arranged geographically, by firm name and by individual name in separate sections. **Availability:** Print.

13720 ■ "Kiosk Outfit ecoATM Now Recycling Video Games" in San Diego Union-Tribune (October 7, 2010)
Pub: The San Diego Union-Tribune
Contact: Phyllis Pfeiffer, President
E-mail: ppfeiffer@lajollalight.com
URL(s): www.sandiegouniontribune.com/sdut-kiosk-outfit-ecoatm-now-recycling-video-games-2010oct07-story.html
Ed: Mike Freeman. **Description:** ecoATM makes automated kiosks to buy back cell phones,it will now include video games as part of their recycling center for consumer electronics. **Availability:** Print; Online.

13721 ■ "Malarkey Using Upcycled Plastics in Shingles" in Roofing Contractor (December 28, 2018)
URL(s): www.roofingcontractor.com/articles/9 3334-malarkey-using-upcycled-plastics-in-shingles
Released: December 28, 2018. **Description:** Malarkey Roofing Products is going ot offer NEX polymer modified asphalt in all of its roofing shingles, keeping many materials out of the landfill. The company is focused on using upcycled materials to keep unnecessary waste from entering the environment. **Availability:** Online.

13722 ■ "New Earth Poised to Expand as Organic Recycling Grows" in San Antonio Business Journal (Vol. 28, May 23, 2014, No. 15, pp. 12)
Pub: American City Business Journals, Inc.
Contact: Mike Olivieri, Executive Vice President
Released: Weekly. **Price:** $4, introductory 4-week offer(Digital & Print). **Description:** New Earth Soils & Compost is expected to benefit from San Antonio, Texas' efforts to bring organic recycling to more homes. The company will invest $1 million into new facilities in order to facilitate growth. New Earth recycles manure, paper, food and wood in San Antonio and Conroe, Texas. **Availability:** Print; Online.

13723 ■ "Recession Creating Surge in Business for Auto Recyclers" in Business Journal-Serving Phoenix & the Valley of the Sun (Vol. 31, November 12, 2010, No. 10, pp. 1)
Pub: Phoenix Business Journal
Contact: Alex McAlister, Director
E-mail: amcalister@bizjournals.com

Ed: Patrick O'Grady. **Description:** Automotive parts recyclers in Arizona are benefiting from the challenging national economic conditions as well as from the green movement. Recyclers revealed that customers prefer recycled parts more because they are cheaper and are more environmentally friendly. Other information about the automotive parts recycling industry is presented. **Availability:** Print; Online.

13724 ■ "Recycling 202: How to Take Your Recycling Practices to the Next Level" in Black Enterprise (Vol. 41, September 2010, No. 2, pp. 38)
Pub: Earl G. Graves Ltd.
Contact: Earl Graves, Jr., President
Ed: Tamara E. Holmes. **Description:** Consumer Electronics Association and other organizations, manufacturers and retailers list ways to recycle all household items. **Availability:** Online.

13725 ■ "Recycling Old Cellphones" in San Jose Mercury News (September 26, 2012)
Description: Gazelle.com buys old gadgets, including mobile phones, on its Website. The firm either resells the gadgets through retail channels such as eBy or turns them over to wholesalers. Recycling electronic waste information is provided. **Availability:** Online.

13726 ■ "Reduce, Reuse, Recycle, Reupholster, Is Motto of Willmar, Minn., Upholstery Hobbyist Turned Pro" in West Central Tribune (August 14, 2012)
Ed: David Little. **Description:** American craftsmanship in furniture is foremost to Mr. Rousseau, owner of PrairieUpholstery of Willmar, Minnesota. He learned to reupholster furniture from an expert and opened his own shop in the historic downtown district. Rousseau will reupholster new and used furniture, car and truck seats, as well as boat seats and he can repair canvas. He also will rent upholstery cleaning and carpet shampoo machines, as well as refinishing wood furniture. **Availability:** Online.

13727 ■ "Repairing - Not Recycling - Is the First Step to Tackling E-Waste From Smartphones. Here's Why." in World Economic Forum (July 19, 2021)
Ed: Mo Chatterji. **Released:** July 19, 2021. **Description:** While smartphones have gained popularity throughout the years, so has the electronic waste from these devices. Recycling may not be the only answer unless the phone has truly reached the end of usefulness. Instead, repairing smartphones is making more sense because the process doesn't produce as much carbon emissions as recycling, and is therefore more environmentally friendly.

13728 ■ "Saving the Planet: A Tale of Two Strategies: Thomas Malthus Advised Restraint; Robert Solow Promotes Innovation. Let's Pursue Both To Solve the Environmental Crisis" in Harvard Business Review (Vol. 90, April 2012, No. 4, pp. 48)
Pub: Harvard Business Review Press
Contact: Moderna V. Pfizer, Contact
Ed: Roger Martin, Alison Kemper. **Price:** $8.95, hardcover. **Description:** Theories of economists Thomas Malthus and Robert Solow are merged to address specific environmental problems. Malthusian restraint includes fuel economy, refillable bottles, and recycling. Solovian innovation includes water supply chlorination, solar cooking, and geothermal energy. **Availability:** PDF; Online.

13729 ■ "Study: Restaurants Should Use Compostable Dinnerware to Reduce Food Waste" in PMQ Pizza Magazine (November 2019)
URL(s): www.pmq.com/reducing-food-waste/
Ed: Brett Jordan. **Released:** November 2019. **Description:** A new study conducted by Eco-Cycle says that restaurants can reduce food waste in landfills by offering compostable plates, cups, and utensils. The study also found that to succeed in composting, restaurants should use either all compostable ser-

viceware or all durable serviceware, in order to cut down on confusion of how to sort the materials after use. **Availability:** Online.

13730 ■ *"Unilever to Sustainably Source All Paper and Board Packaging" in Ice Cream Reporter (Vol. 23, July 20, 2010, No. 8, pp. 1)*
Description: Unilever, a leader in the frozen dessert market, has developed a new sustainable paper and board packaging sourcing policy that will reduce environmental impact by working with suppliers to source 75 percent of paper and board packaging from sustainably managed forests or from recycled material. Unilever is parent company to Breyers, Haagen-Dazs, Klondike, Popsicle and other ice cream brands.

13731 ■ *"Waste Management Exec First 'Undercover Boss' in Series Kicking Off on Super Bowl Sunday" in Houston Business Journal (Vol. 40, January 22, 2010, No. 37, pp. A1)*
Pub: Houston Business Journal
Contact: Bob Charlet, President
E-mail: bcharlet@bizjournals.com
Ed: Christine Hall. **Description:** Houston, Texas-based Waste Management Inc.'s president and chief operation officer, Larry O'Donnell shares some of his experience as CBS Television Network reality show 'Undercover Boss' participant. O'Donnell believes the show was a great way to show the customers how tough their jobs are and reveals that the most difficult job was being a sorter at the recycling center. **Availability:** Print; Online.

13732 ■ *"Wave of Resale, Consignment Shops Pop Up In Springs" in Gazette (March 19, 2012)*
Ed: Bill Radford. **Description:** The depressed economy has spurred the growth of consignment shops across the nation. Colorado Springs, Colorado area urges people to shop at these resale locations because they promote green initiatives by recycling goods. WeeCycle, Knit Wits, Once Upon a Child and Re-Generation, Moutain Equipment Recyclers, and Gearonimo, are among the established consignment stores in the area. **Availability:** Print.

13733 ■ *"Xerox Diverts Waste from Landfills" in Canadian Electronics (Vol. 23, February 2008, No. 1, pp. 1)*
Description: Xerox Corporation revealed that it was able to divert more than two billion pounds of electronic waste from landfills through waste-free initiatives. The company's program, which was launched in 1991, covers waste avoidance in imaging supplies and parts reuse. Environmental priorities are also integrated into manufacturing operations. **Availability:** Print; Online; PDF.

STATISTICAL SOURCES

13734 ■ *Cell Phone Recycling Industry in the US - Market Research Report*
URL(s): www.ibisworld.com/united-states/market-research-reports/cell-phone-recycling-industry/
Price: $925. **Description:** Downloadable report analyzing the current and future trends in the cell phone recycling industry. **Availability:** Download.

13735 ■ *Recycling Facilities Industry in the US - Market Research Report*
URL(s): www.ibisworld.com/united-states/market-research-reports/recycling-facilities-industry/
Price: $925. **Description:** Downloadable report analyzing data on current and future trends in the recycling industry. **Availability:** Download.

13736 ■ *Standard & Poor's Industry Surveys*
Pub: Standard And Poor's Financial Services LLC.
Contact: Douglas L. Peterson, President
Description: Two-volume book that examines the prospects for specific industries, including trucking. Also provides analyses of trends and problems, statistical tables and charts, and comparative company analyses.

TRADE PERIODICALS

13737 ■ *Composting News*
Pub: McEntee Media Corp.
URL(s): compostingnews.com
Facebook: www.facebook.com/CompostingNews
X (Twitter): x.com/CompostingNews
Released: Monthly **Price:** $83, Individuals for one year; $140, Individuals for two years. **Description:** Covers news and trends in the composting industry. Also reports on compost product prices. Recurring features include letters to the editor, interviews, news of research, a calendar of events, reports of meetings, and notices of publications available. **Availability:** Print; Download; Online.

13738 ■ *Environmental Quality Management*
Pub: Wiley Periodicals Inc.
Contact: Brian Napack, Chief Executive Officer
URL(s): onlinelibrary.wiley.com/journal/15206483
Released: Continuous **Price:** $1,933, Institutions for online US Canada India; $938, Individuals for online US Canada India. **Description:** Journal covering theories, applications, and social systems of resource recovery and concentrate management for a sustainable future. **Availability:** Print; Download; PDF; Online.

13739 ■ *Plastics Recycling Update*
Pub: Resource Recycling Inc.
Contact: Scott Beck, Manager
E-mail: scott@resource-recycling.com
URL(s): resource-recycling.com/plastics
Released: Quarterly **Description:** Markets newsletter that covers all aspects of plastic waste recovery. **Availability:** Print; Online.

13740 ■ *Recycling Today*
Pub: Recycling Today Media Group
Contact: James R. Keefe, Publisher
E-mail: jkeefe@gie.net
URL(s): www.recyclingtoday.com
Facebook: www.facebook.com/RecyclingTodaymag
Linkedin: www.linkedin.com/company/recycling-today-magazine
X (Twitter): x.com/recyclingtoday
Ed: Kristin Smith, Brian Taylor. **Released:** Monthly **Description:** Magazine covering recycling of secondary raw materials and solid-waste management. **Availability:** Print; PDF; Download; Online.

13741 ■ *Scrap Magazine*
Pub: Institute of Scrap Recycling Industries
Contact: Robin K. Wiener, President
URL(s): www.isri.org/about-rema/isri-connect
Ed: Cynthia Wagner. **Description:** Magazine providing articles and columns to member professionals that will help increase the profitability of their businesses for their process, broker, and consume scrap commodities. **Availability:** Online.

TRADE SHOWS AND CONVENTIONS

13742 ■ *Composting & Organics Recycling Conference*
URL(s): www.wasteexpo.com/en/conference-and-events/composting-and-organics-recycling.html
Frequency: Annual. **Description:** Educational and technical sessions for the recycling of organics industry. **Principal Exhibits:** Educational and technical sessions for the recycling of organics industry.

13743 ■ *GLOBE: Conference and Exhibition on Business and the Environment*
URL(s): 2016.globeseries.com
X (Twitter): twitter.com/GLOBE_Series
Frequency: Biennial. **Description:** Solutions for problems associated with climate change, energy security, and rising fuel prices. **Audience:** Business professionals. **Principal Exhibits:** Solutions for problems associated with climate change, energy security, and rising fuel prices.

13744 ■ *Plastics Recycling Conference*
URL(s): www.plasticsrecycling.com

Facebook: www.facebook.com/ResourceRecycling
X (Twitter): twitter.com/rrecycling
Description: Provides networking and seminars on the latest in plastics recycling. A tradeshow of innovative products is also held. **Principal Exhibits:** Provides networking and seminars on the latest in plastics recycling. A tradeshow of innovative products is also held. **Telecommunication Services:** nfo@plasticsrecycling.com.

13745 ■ *Re/focus Sustainability & Recycling Summit*
URL(s): events.plasticsindustry.org/2021Refocus
Frequency: Annual. **Description:** Recycling topic seminars for those in plastic manufacturing industry. **Principal Exhibits:** Recycling topic seminars for those in plastic manufacturing industry.

13746 ■ *Resource Recycling Conference*
URL(s): www.rrconference.com
Frequency: Annual. **Description:** Promotes the recycling industry through networking, a vendor show, and educational sessions. **Audience:** Policy leaders, CEO's, and government officials involved in the recycling industry. **Principal Exhibits:** Promotes the recycling industry through networking, a vendor show, and educational sessions.

13747 ■ *Waste360 Business Leadership Forum*
URL(s): www.wasteexpo.com/en/conference-and-events/Waste360BusinessLeadershipForum.html
Frequency: Annual. **Description:** Provides seminars and resources for small to midsized environmental services with the goal of growing their businesses. **Principal Exhibits:** Provides seminars and resources for small to midsized environmental services with the goal of growing their businesses.

LIBRARIES

13748 ■ *California Department of Conservation - Division of Recycling - Resource Center*
801 K St., MS 24-01
Sacramento, CA 95814
URL: http://www.conservation.ca.gov/dlrp/watershedportal/InformationResources/Pages/informationResources.aspx
Contact: David Shabazian, Director
Scope: Recycling; waste reduction; resource conservation. **Services:** Copying; library open to the public with restrictions. **Founded:** 1989. **Holdings:** 300 books; 400 reports; 277 videocassettes.

13749 ■ *California Department of Resources Recycling and Recovery Library*
1001 I St.
Sacramento, CA 95814
Ph: (916)341-6199
URL: http://www.calrecycle.ca.gov/LGCENTRAL/Library/CandDModel
Scope: Waste management; recycling. **Services:** Interlibrary loan; copying; library open to the public for reference use only. **Founded:** 1995. **Holdings:** Brochures; fact sheets; pamphlets; newsletters; reports.

13750 ■ *Institute for Local Self-Reliance (ILSR) - Agriculture Rules Library*
1200 18th St., NW Ste. 700
Washington, DC 20036
Ph: (202)898-1610
Co. E-mail: info@ilsr.org
URL: http://ilsr.org
Contact: Christopher Mitchell, Director
E-mail: christopher@ilsr.org
Linkedin: www.linkedin.com/company/institute-for-local-self-reliance
X (Twitter): x.com/ilsr
Instagram: www.instagram.com/ilsr_org
YouTube: www.youtube.com/user/ilsr08
Description: Provides the conceptual framework, strategies, and information to aid the creation of ecologically-sound and economically equitable communities. Works with citizens, activists, policymakers,

and entrepreneurs to design systems, policies and enterprises that meet local or regional needs; maximize local human, material, natural, and financial resources; and ensure that the benefits of these systems and resources accrue to all local citizens. **Scope:** Promotes the self-reliance of local, city, and state governments and citizen groups. Focuses on community organizations acquiring equity in environmentally sustainable economic development and on monitoring and establishing community control over material, natural, financial, and human resources. Provides policy analysis on materials policy, waste utilization, and energy use. **Founded:** 1974. **Holdings:** Figures not available. **Publications:** *The Carbohydrate Economy; New Rules* (Quarterly); *Recycling Economic Development Through Scrap-Based Manufacturing.* **Educational Activities:** Institute for Local Self-Reliance Workshops. **Geographic Preference:** National.

13751 ■ Long Island Lighting Company Resource Center
131 S Hoffman Ln.
  Islandia, NY 11749
Free: 800-490-0075
URL: http://www.psegliny.com

Scope: Energy, electricity, public utilities, business management. **Services:** Library not open to the public. **Founded:** 1986. **Holdings:** 1570 books; 100 periodical titles; videocassettes; audiocassettes.

13752 ■ Pennsylvania Environmental Council (PEC) - Library
1617 JFK Blvd., Ste. 543
  Philadelphia, PA 19103
Ph: (215)545-4570
Co. E-mail: paenvironmentalcouncil@gmail.com
URL: http://pecpa.org
Contact: Tom Gilbert, President
Facebook: www.facebook.com/
  PennsylvaniaEnvironmentalCouncil
X (Twitter): twitter.com/pecpa
YouTube: www.youtube.com/channel/UCfKnE9
  5ObJLP-A3zie0JtMw

Description: Independent, nonprofit advocacy organization. **Scope:** Growth management, land use, air quality and transportation; water resource allocation, groundwater, wetlands, open space preservation. **Services:** Copying; faxing; library open to the public by appointment. **Founded:** 1969. **Holdings:** 400 books; 100 reports; 40 videotapes; 10 slide shows. **Subscriptions:** 200 journals and other serials. **Publications:** *PEC Fact Sheets; Pennsylvania Environmentalist; Special Reports.* **Educational**

Activities: PEC Seminars; Speakers; PEC Deep Decarbonization Conferences; PEC Annual Members Meeting; Slide Shows and videos.

RESEARCH CENTERS

13753 ■ Brown University - Institute at Brown for Environment & Society (IBES)
85 Waterman St.
  Providence, RI 02912
Ph: (401)863-3449
Fax: (401)863-3839
Co. E-mail: environment@brown.edu
URL: http://ibes.brown.edu
Contact: Michael Burger, Executive Director
Facebook: www.facebook.com/brownenvsoc
X (Twitter): x.com/brownenvt
YouTube: www.youtube.com/channel/UCwi73X-v_0N
  1v2qdHMvy4Aw

Description: Integral unit of Brown University. Offers science and policy-related courses. **Scope:** Environmental studies with a focus on natural systems, food and water, human health and well-being, equity and governance, climate science, land change science, conservation science, environmental health, and institutions and human behavior. **Services:** Library open to the public for reference use only. **Holdings:** 500 books; 200 reports.

13754 ■ Cornell University - Cornell Waste Management Institute (CWMI)
817 Bradfield Hall, Cornell University
  Ithaca, NY 14853
Ph: (607)255-1187
Co. E-mail: cwmi@cornell.edu
URL: http://cwmi.css.cornell.edu
Contact: Jean Bonhotal, Director

Description: Integral unit of Cornell University. Offers technical assistance to communities, including a series of audio-visual and print resources addressing waste disposal, land use, and water contamination problems. **Scope:** Solid waste management, including composting, collaborative decision making, risk communication, assessing benefits and impacts of land application of sewage sludges, waste prevention, managing agricultural solid wastes. **Founded:** 1987. **Publications:** *CWMI Fact sheets; CWMI Training manuals; Videos.*

13755 ■ Earthworm Inc.
65 Inner Belt Rd.
  Somerville, MA 02143
Ph: (617)628-1844
Fax: (617)628-2773
Co. E-mail: info@earthwormrecycling.org

URL: http://www.earthwormrecycling.org
Contact: Jeff Coyne, Executive Director
Facebook: www.facebook.com/earthwormrecycling
Instagram: www.instagram.com/earthworm_recycling

Description: A nonprofit organization that provides recycling programs for paper, bottles and cans, and office electronics. **Scope:** Recycling, resource recovery, solid waste management, environmental quality, hazardous waste, and earthworms. **Founded:** 1970. **Publications:** *Earthworm Recycling Guide.*

13756 ■ Ecology Action Centre (EAC) - Library [Centre d'Action Écologique]
2705 Fern Ln.
  Halifax, NS, Canada B3K 4L3
Ph: (902)429-2202
Fax: (902)405-3716
Co. E-mail: info@ecologyaction.ca
URL: http://www.ecologyaction.ca
Facebook: www.facebook.com/EcologyActionCentre
Linkedin: www.linkedin.com/company/ecology-action
  -centre
X (Twitter): x.com/ecologyaction

Description: Works to develop solutions to ecological problems. Fosters communication between members. **Scope:** Environmental issues, including acid rain, deforestation, hazardous wastes, recycling, nuclear power, ecosystem stability, species extinction, global warming, pesticides, and waste management. **Founded:** 1971. **Holdings:** Figures not available. **Publications:** *Between the Issues Newsletter* (3/year). **Geographic Preference:** Multinational.

EARLY STAGE FINANCING

13757 ■ "*Abt Electronics and Appliances Announces the Second Annual Earth Day Recycle Drive***" in Ecology, Environment & Conservation Business (May 3, 2014, pp. 3)**
NewsRX LLC.
  PO Box 724823
  Atlanta, GA 31139
Ph: (770)507-7777
Co. E-mail: info@newsrx.com
URL: http://www.newsrx.com/NewsRxWebsite
Contact: Kalani Rosell, Contact

Description: Abt Electronics and Appliances is the largest independent, single-store appliance and electronics retailer in the U.S. In honor of Earth Day, Abt has partnered with the City of Chicago to help local residents recycle e-waste, such as electronics and appliances, in an environmentally friendly way for the second year in a row. **Availability:** Online.

Rental Service

START-UP INFORMATION

13758 ■ *"First-Time Landlord: Your Guide to Renting Out a Single-Family Home"*
Pub: Nolo
Contact: Chris Braun, President
Released: 6th Edition. **Price:** $17.49, e-book (downloadable); $19.99, book and e-book. **Description:** The basics for becoming an landlord for anyone wishing to start an entrepreneurial pursuit in home rentals are outlined. Concise information for renting out a single-family home includes, how to determine whether the property will turn a profit, landlord business basics, finding the right tenants, preparing and signing a lead, handling repairs, complying with state rental laws, dealing with problem tenants, and preparing for the sale of the property. **Availability:** E-book.

13759 ■ *"Younger, Permenter Build New Real Estate Firm in Dallas" in Dallas Business Journal (Vol. 35, May 18, 2012, No. 36, pp. 1)*
Pub: Baltimore Business Journal
Contact: Rhonda Pringle, President
E-mail: rpringle@bizjournals.com
Ed: Candace Carlisle. **Description:** Former Grubb and Ellis brokers Moody Younger and Kathy Permenter have started Younger Partners Commercial LLC, a new commercial real estate firm based in Dallas. The idea for Younger Partners came about after Grubb and Ellis was acquired by BGC Partners Inc. The firm plans to concentrate on office leasing and corporate service. **Availability:** Print; Online.

ASSOCIATIONS AND OTHER ORGANIZATIONS

13760 ■ **American Rental Association (ARA)**
1900 19th St.
Moline, IL 61265
Free: 800-334-2177
Fax: (309)764-1533
Co. E-mail: marketing@ararental.org
URL: http://www.ararental.org
Facebook: www.facebook.com/ARAHeadquarters
Linkedin: www.linkedin.com/company/american-rental-association
X (Twitter): x.com/ararentalshow
Description: Firms engaged in the rental of event and party equipment, tools, machinery, and other products; includes independent, franchised, and chain store operators. Associates are suppliers of equipment and merchandise. Seeks to foster better business methods; promote study of economic trends in the rental industry. **Founded:** 1956. **Publications:** *ARA Rental Management* (Monthly); *Cost of Doing Business Report (CODB)*; *Who's Who in the Party Equipment Rental Industry*; *Rental Management: Official Magazine of the American Rental Association* (Monthly); *Rental Management--Who's Who in the Rental Industry* (Annual); *RM's Management Source Book* (Annual). **Educational Activities:** American Rental Association Annual Convention and Rental Trade Show (Annual). **Awards:** ARA Distinguished Service Award (Annual); ARA Meritorious Service Award (Annual); ARA Outstanding Leadership Award (Annual); Regional Person of the Year (Annual); ARA Rental Hall of Fame (Annual). **Geographic Preference:** National.

13761 ■ **Association of Progressive Rental Organizations (APRO)**
8200 N Mopac Expy., Ste. 185
Austin, TX 78759-8866
Ph: (512)794-0095
Co. E-mail: info@rtohq.org
URL: http://www.rtohq.org/board-staff
Contact: Louis Garcia, President
Facebook: www.facebook.com//RTOHQ
Linkedin: www.linkedin.com/company/apro
X (Twitter): x.com/rtohq
YouTube: www.youtube.com/user/RTOHQ
Description: Represents dealer and industry suppliers. Serves rental dealers in the home appliance, furniture, and consumer electronics industry who market their products with a rental-purchase plan. Purposes are to: foster trade and commerce; collect and disseminate information; represent members before legislative committees, government bureaus, and other bodies in matters affecting the industry. **Founded:** 1980. **Publications:** *RTO Almanac* (Annual); *APRO Rental Viewpoint Online* (Biweekly); *RTO Today* (Weekly); *RTOHQ: The Magazine* (Semiannual); *RTO Almanac* (Annual). **Educational Activities:** RTO World The National Rent-to-Own Convention and Trade Show (Annual). **Awards:** APRO Buddy Awards (Annual).

13762 ■ **Equipment Leasing and Finance Association (ELFA)**
1625 Eye St. NW, Ste. 850
Washington, DC 20006
Ph: (202)238-3400
Co. E-mail: avogt@elfaonline.org
URL: http://www.elfaonline.org
Contact: Ralph Petta, President
E-mail: rpetta@elfaonline.org
Facebook: www.facebook.com/ELFApage
Linkedin: www.linkedin.com/company/equipment-leasing-and-finance-association
X (Twitter): x.com/ELFAOnline
Instagram: www.instagram.com/elfaonline
Description: Aims to provide member companies a platform to promote and advocate for the equipment leasing and finance industry. Provides a forum for professional development and training; develops information about, and for, the industry. **Founded:** 1961. **Publications:** *Who's Who in Equipment Leasing*; *Survey of Equipment Finance Activity* (Annual); *Equipment Leasing and Finance*. **Geographic Preference:** Multinational.

13763 ■ **International Furniture Rental Association (IFRA)**
c/o Alston & Bird LLP
950 F St. NW, 10th Fl.
Washington, DC 20004
URL: http://www.ifra.org
Description: Companies whose major business is the leasing and rental of home furnishings and accessories; suppliers of products and services to these companies are associate members. Dedicated to upholding ethical standards of the furniture rental industry and providing quality products and service. Conducts industry exposition and statistical surveys. Promotes industry through nationwide consumer education program. Works to safeguard against adverse legislation and regulation. **Founded:** 1967. **Publications:** *IFRA Membership/Referral Directory* (Annual); *Furniture Rental Association of America-- Newsletter* (Quarterly). **Educational Activities:** International Furniture Rental Association Conference (Annual). **Geographic Preference:** National.

REFERENCE WORKS

13764 ■ *"$550 Cash Rent on 330 Acres in Iowa" in Farm Industry News (November 30, 2011)*
Pub: Informa Business Media, Inc.
Contact: Charlie McCurdy, President
Ed: Karen McMahon. **Description:** A farmer in Iowa accepted a bid for $550/acre for his 330-acre farm for one year. The next closest bid was $350/acre. This rent will amount to more than the farmer paid for all of his land in the 1960s and 1970s. High rents are not alarming because of the high profitability farmers are currently receiving from crops. **Availability:** Online.

13765 ■ *"The 2011 Rental Readers' Choice Award Winners" in Rental Product News (Vol. 33, October 2011)*
Description: Rental Product News conducted a survey asking readers what they considered to be the best product in their rental industry. A listing of winners is provided. **Availability:** Online.

13766 ■ *"2015 Marketing Calendar for Real Estate Pros: Own It"*
Pub: CreateSpace
Released: October 14, 2014. **Price:** $9.56, paperback. **Description:** Real estate agents, mortgage loan agents, and new home builders and site and listing agents are shown how to use low-cost, high yield, proven marketing techniques to create digital real estate listings, find more customers, and sell more homes. Advice for building a brand and public relations; attracting renters and buyers; developing a good Website; and a digital marketing plan are explained. **Availability:** Print.

13767 ■ *Airbnb for Dummies*
Pub: John Wiley & Sons, Inc.
Contact: Christina Van Tassell, Executive Vice President Chief Financial Officer
URL(s): www.wiley.com/en-us/Airbnb+For+Dummies%2C+2nd+Edition-p-9781394154630

Ed: Symon He, James Svetec. **Released:** 2nd edition. **Description:** This guide explains how to turn your rentable property into an Airbnb in order to earn an income. Tips on using the Airbnb website, navigating their policies, and even setting up your property to rent out are all included. **Availability:** paperback; Print.

13768 ■ *"Apartment Tower in River North Fetches More Than $90 Million"* in *Crain's Chicago Business (Vol. 34, October 24, 2011, No. 42, pp. 17)*
Pub: Crain Communications Inc.
Contact: Barry Asin, President

Ed: Alby Gallun. **Description:** Apartment tower in River North was sold for over $90 million to a Texas pension fund adviser. Details are included. **Availability:** Online.

13769 ■ *"Apartments Head to Schilling Farms; $48 Million Investment Includes Office, Retail Space"* in *Memphis Business Journal (Vol. 34, August 17, 2012, No. 18, pp. 1)*
Pub: Baltimore Business Journal
Contact: Rhonda Pringle, President
E-mail: rpringle@bizjournals.com

Description: Boyle Investment Company is planning to launch three new projects at its Schiling Farms development in Memphis, Tennessee. The construction plans include multifamily units and rental space. **Availability:** Print; Online.

13770 ■ *"Beware of E15 Gasoline"* in *Rental Product News (Vol. 33, October 2011)*
Ed: Curt Bennink. **Description:** Environmental Protection Agency (EPA) set a new regulation that grants partial waivers to allow gasoline containing up to 15 percent ethanol (E15) to be introduced into commerce for use in model year 2001 and newer light-duty motor vehicles, subject to certain conditions. **Availability:** Online.

13771 ■ *"Bob's Discount Furniture Moving into Harford County, Region"* in *Baltimore Business Journal (Vol. 27, January 22, 2010, No. 38, pp. 1)*
Pub: Baltimore Business Journal
Contact: Rhonda Pringle, President
E-mail: rpringle@bizjournals.com

Ed: Daniel J. Sernovitz. **Description:** Manchester, Connecticut-based Bob's Discount Furniture signed a lease for 672,000 square feet of space in Harford County, Maryland. The site will become the discount furniture retailer's distribution center in mid-Atlantic US. As many as 200 jobs could be generated when the center opens. **Availability:** Print; Online.

13772 ■ *"BRIEF: Montana Street Pawn Shop Closing Doors"* in *Montana Standard (November 6, 2010)*
Pub: Montana Standard

Ed: John Grant Emeigh. **Description:** First National Pawn located in Butte, Montana will close its doors after losing its lease. Co-owner Pat Evenson reported the lease situation coupled with the economy prompted the decision to close. **Availability:** Online.

13773 ■ *"Brown's Goal: 1,300 New Apartments and Condos"* in *Business First of Buffalo (Vol. 30, February 28, 2014, No. 24, pp. 6)*
Pub: American City Business Journals, Inc.
Contact: Mike Olivieri, Executive Vice President

Released: February 28, 2014. **Price:** $140, Digital & Print; $115, Digital only. **Description:** Buffalo, New York Mayor Bryan Brown is planning for at least 1,300 new, market-rate residential units in the city's central business district over the next four years. The additional residential units are incorporated in Brown's larger strategy for creating a 24/7 downtown Buffalo. The impact of the residential development plan on the area's periphery is examined. **Availability:** Print; Online.

13774 ■ *"Buildings to Flank Broken Spoke: Legendary Country Dance Hall To Be Surrounded But Won't Be Touched"* in *Austin Business Journal (Vol. 32, April 13, 2012, No. 6, pp. 1)*
Pub: American City Business Journals, Inc.
Contact: Mike Olivieri, Executive Vice President

Ed: Vicky Garza. **Description:** A $60 million mixed use development tentatively called 704 at the Spoke is being planned along South Lamar Boulevard in Austin, Texas. The plan includes 378 apartments and 20,000 square feet of restaurant and retail space. The project will have the historic Broken Spoke Dance Hall as its hub. **Availability:** Online.

13775 ■ *"Cash Rents Reach Sky-High Levels"* in *Farm Industry News (November 23, 2011)*
Pub: Informa Business Media, Inc.
Contact: Charlie McCurdy, President

Ed: Karen McMahon. **Description:** Strong commodity prices are driving land values creating a hot rental market for farm land. Highest rents occur when farmers compete head-to-head for land. **Availability:** Online.

13776 ■ *"Customer Preferences Control Skid Steer Choices"* in *Rental Product News (Vol. 33, June 2011)*
Released: January 06, 2011. **Description:** Understanding the types of controls available on skid steer equipment is essential. The article provides a comprehensive guide to using and maintaining skid steers for rental agencies. **Availability:** Print; Online.

13777 ■ *"Dealers Leasing Changes Name, Hopes to Stoke National Growth"* in *Wichita Business Journal (Vol. 27, January 27, 2012, No. 4, pp. 1)*
Pub: Baltimore Business Journal
Contact: Rhonda Pringle, President
E-mail: rpringle@bizjournals.com

Description: Wichita, Kansas-based Dealers Financing has changed its name to Lease Finance Partners as part of its plans to expand the market it serves. The name change was designed to better reflect the kind of business the company does, which is financing the leasing of fleet vehicles and heavy equipment.

13778 ■ *"Developers Poised to Pull Trigers"* in *Boston Business Journal (Vol. 30, November 12, 2010, No. 42, pp. 1)*
Description: Large residential projects are expected to break ground in Boston, Massachusetts in 2011, as real estate developers expect growth for the industry. Real estate experts expect more than 2,000 rental units to be available by 2011. Information on key real estate projects in Boston is presented. **Availability:** Print; Online.

13779 ■ *Dictionary of Real Estate Terms*
Pub: Barron's Educational Series Inc.
Contact: Manuel H. Barron, Contact

Ed: Jack P. Friedman, Jack C. Harris, J. Bruce Lindeman. **Released:** 9th edition. **Price:** $16.99, paperback, plus shipping charges $5.99. **Description:** More than 2,500 real estate terms relating to mortgages and financing, brokerage law, architecture, rentals and leases, property insurance, and more. **Availability:** E-book; Print.

13780 ■ *"Ditch the Rental Car: A New Way to Arrive in Style"* in *Inc. (Vol. 33, September 2011, No. 7, pp. 54)*
Pub: Inc. Magazine

Ed: Matt Rist. **Description:** EagleRider is a franchise offering various two-wheeled rentals, including BMWs and Harley-Davidsons at more than 100 locations worldwide. **Availability:** Online.

13781 ■ *"Do You Need to Reinvent Your Managers?"* in *Rental Product News (Vol. 33, June 2011)*
Description: Rental business owners need to assess their management and be sure they perform as true leaders of the organization. **Availability:** Online.

13782 ■ *"Docs Might Hold Cure for Baltimore-Area Real Estate, Banks"* in *Baltimore Business Journal (Vol. 28, November 5, 2010, No. 26, pp. 1)*
Pub: Baltimore Business Journal
Contact: Rhonda Pringle, President
E-mail: rpringle@bizjournals.com

Ed: Gary Haber. **Description:** Health care providers, including physicians are purchasing their office space instead of renting it as banks lower interest rates to 6 percent on mortgages for medical offices. The rise in demand offers relief to the commercial real estate market. It has also resulted in a boom in building new medical offices. **Availability:** Print; Online.

13783 ■ *"Dollar Thrifty Adds Franchises"* in *Journal Record (December 7, 2010)*
Pub: Dolan Media Newswires

Ed: D. Ray Tuttle. **Description:** Dollar Thrifty Automotive Group Inc. opened 31 franchise locations in 2010 as part of its expansion plan in the U.S. **Availability:** Print; Online.

13784 ■ *"Eastern Market's New Bite?"* in *Washington Business Journal (Vol. 33, August 8, 2014, No. 16, pp. 6)*
Pub: American City Business Journals, Inc.
Contact: Mike Olivieri, Executive Vice President

Price: $4, Introductory 4-Week Offer(Digital & Print). **Description:** Eastern Market continues to operate despite allegations of financial mismanagement on the part of Washington DC auditors. Many of the market's vendors have been operating their stands with expired leases for more than five years. However, the Department of General Services has vowed to draw a new standard contract for renting and renegotiate new leases. **Availability:** Print; Online.

13785 ■ *"Empty Office Blues"* in *Business Journal Portland (Vol. 26, December 4, 2009, No. 39, pp. 1)*
Pub: Portland Business Journal
Contact: Andy Giegerich, Managing Editor
E-mail: agiegerich@bizjournals.com

Ed: Wendy Culverwell. **Description:** Portland's office vacancy rates could reach almost 15 percent by the end of 2010 due to job reductions and mergers. **Availability:** Print; Online.

13786 ■ *"Enterprise Holdings Hires More Than 4,000 Military Veterans Since Joining 100,000 Jobs Mission Coalition"* in *Defense & Aerospace Business (September 3, 2014, pp. 9)*
Pub: NewsRX LLC.
Contact: Kalani Rosell, Contact

Description: Enterprise Holdings, which owns and operates the Enterprise Rent-A-Car, Alamo Rent A Car and National Car Rental brands has hired more than 4,000 military veterans since joining the 100,000 Jobs Mission coalition in 2012. The company is named after the USS Enterprise, an aircraft carrier, and its commitment to the military goes back almost sixty years. Their Website includes employment opportunities for transitioning military personnel, veterans, members of the National Guard and Reserve and their families. Enterprise Holdings has been designated a Top Veteran-Friendly Company by US Veterans Magazine. **Availability:** Online.

13787 ■ *Every Airbnb Host's Tax Guide*
Ed: Stephen Fishman. **Released:** January 26, 2021. **Description:** A guide for tracking and paying taxes for those who own Airbnb rentals.

13788 ■ *"Extra Rehab Time Boosts M-B's Off-Lease Profits"* in *Automotive News (Vol. 86, October 31, 2011, No. 6488, pp. 22)*
Pub: Crain Communications Inc.
Contact: Barry Asin, President

Ed: Arlena Sawyers. **Description:** Mercedes-Benz Financial Services USA is holding on to off-lease vehicles in order to recondition them and the move is boosting profits for the company. **Availability:** Print; Online.

13789 ■ *"Extreme Amenities" in Puget Sound Business Journal (Vol. 35, May 9, 2014, No. 3, pp. 4)*

Released: Weekly. **Price:** $4, introductory 4-week offer(Digital & Print). **Description:** Reports show that some developers are designing apartment buildings with themes. Alison Jeffries of Red Propeller believes that these buildings will rent faster if they have their own stories. This construction trend of such buildings is expected to appeal to the Millennial generation. **Availability:** Print; Online.

13790 ■ *"Firms Sue Doracon to Recoup More Than $1M in Unpaid Bills" in Baltimore Business Journal (Vol. 28, July 9, 2010, No. 9, pp. 1)*

Pub: Baltimore Business Journal
Contact: Rhonda Pringle, President
E-mail: rpringle@bizjournals.com

Ed: Scott Dance. **Description:** Concrete supplier Paul J. Rach Inc., Selective Insurance Company, and equipment leasing firm Colonial Pacific Leasing Corporation intend to sue Baltimore, Maryland-based Doracon Contracting Inc. for $1 million in unpaid bills. Doracon owed Colonial Pacific $794,000 and the equipment is still in Doracon's possession. Selective Insurance and Paul J. Rach respectively seek $132,000 and $88,000. **Availability:** Print.

13791 ■ *"General Electric Touts Going Green for Business Fleet Services" in America's Intelligence Wire (June 1, 2012)*

Description: General Capital Fleet Services if featuring alternative-fuel vehicles in Eden Prairie for its corporate customers. GE Capital is the world's largest fleet management service and is offering its customers the first of its kind service that allows corporate lease customers to test drive alternative fuel cars from 20 different manufacturers. **Availability:** Print; Online.

13792 ■ *"Generation Y Driving Portland Multifamily" in Daily Journal of Commerce, Portland (October 29, 2010)*

Ed: Nick Bjork. **Description:** Generation Y, young adults between the ages of 18-30, are interested in multifamily residents in the Portland, Oregon area. Developers in the area, particularly North Portland, have recognized this trend and are looking into multifamily investments.

13793 ■ *"Go Back to Basics to Maximize Skid Steer ROI" in Rental Product News (Vol. 33, October 2011)*

Description: There are two types of rental customers in the market for skid steers: the small contractor or weekend warrior who rents for a day or a week and the longer-term rental going to large contractor firms. **Availability:** Print; Online.

13794 ■ *"Hot Real Estate Market Means Hard Work for Investors" in Business Journal Portland (Vol. 31, March 21, 2014, No. 3, pp. 14)*

Pub: American City Business Journals, Inc.
Contact: Mike Olivieri, Executive Vice President

Description: Real estate investors are finding it difficult to improve the residential real estate market due to higher prices. Investors who purchase properties to use as rentals are struggling with the high home values in Portland, Oregon. **Availability:** Print; Online.

13795 ■ *"Housing Stats Contradicting" in Memphis Business Journal (Vol. 34, July 20, 2012, No. 14, pp. 1)*

Pub: Baltimore Business Journal
Contact: Rhonda Pringle, President
E-mail: rpringle@bizjournals.com

Ed: Cole Epley. **Description:** Home mortgage foreclosures in Memphis, Tennessee have increased despite the decrease in the number of homeowners missing out on payments, Reis Inc. has reported. Rental vacancies have also decreased. **Availability:** Print; Online.

13796 ■ *"Houston Doctors Buy In to Medical Timeshares" in Houston Business Journal (Vol. 40, December 11, 2009, No. 31, pp. 1)*

Pub: Houston Business Journal
Contact: Bob Charlet, President
E-mail: bcharlet@bizjournals.com

Ed: Mary Ann Azevedo. **Description:** Memorial Hermann Hospital System has leased to doctors three examination rooms and medical office space in the Memorial Hermann Medical Plaza in line with its new timeshare concept. The concept was designed to bring primary care physicians to its Texas Medical Center campus. **Availability:** Print; Online.

13797 ■ *"Houston (Texas) Computer Repair Adds U-Haul Rentals" in Benzinga.com (March 29, 2012)*

Pub: PR Newswire Association LLC.

Description: Houston Computer Repair has added U-Haul truck and trailer rentals in order to diversify the company. The firm also offers moving equipment and supplies for household furnishings, which includes moving vans, open trailers, closed trailers, furniture pads, appliance dollies, furniture dollies, tow dollies and auto transports. The company also continues to provide computer repair service along with shipping and packaging services. **Availability:** Online.

13798 ■ *"If We Build Them, Will They Rent Them?" in Birmingham Business Journal (Vol. 31, August 1, 2014, No. 31, pp. 4)*

Pub: American City Business Journals, Inc.
Contact: Mike Olivieri, Executive Vice President

Released: August 1, 2014. **Description:** Developers and experts opine that the current demand for multifamily homes in Birmingham, Alabama will continue to grow, despite doubts by Housing and Urban Development over the city center's ability to sustain such growth. The key factors in the city's multi-family market as well as the risks and challenges facing developers are examined.

13799 ■ *"Investment Market Heats Up on the Eastside" in Puget Sound Business Journal (Vol. 35, August 1, 2014, No. 15, pp. 4)*

Pub: American City Business Journals, Inc.
Contact: Mike Olivieri, Executive Vice President

Released: Weekly. **Price:** $4, Introductory 4-week offer(Digital & Print). **Description:** The real estate investment sales market in Puget Sound, Washington is experiencing growth along with construction activity. Office sales reached $787 million in the first half of the year, while the shortage of office space is driving up rents for office tenants and making the market attractive to investors. **Availability:** Print; Online.

13800 ■ *"Investors Eye Old Buildings" in Business Journal-Portland (Vol. 24, October 19, 2007, No. 34, pp. 1)*

Pub: Portland Business Journal
Contact: Andy Giegerich, Managing Editor
E-mail: agiegerich@bizjournals.com

Ed: Wendy Culverwell. **Description:** Office vacancy rates in downtown Portland has dipped to around five percent, causing brokers and investors to search for older buildings in the Class B and Class C categories where the rent is also cheaper. Some notable older and cheaper buildings will be renovated for use. **Availability:** Print; Online.

13801 ■ *"Is B2B a New Growth Area for Car Rental?" in AutoRental News (November 6, 2019)*

URL(s): www.autorentalnews.com/344115/is-b2b-a -new-growth-area-for-car-rental
Ed: Chris Brown. **Released:** November 06, 2019. **Description:** After car rental agencies started to rent cares to Transportation Network Company drivers, they developed another business to business — last mile deliveries. **Availability:** Online.

13802 ■ *"Largest North Texas Tenant Rep Firms" in Dallas Business Journal (Vol. 37, March 14, 2014, No. 27, pp. 6)*

Pub: American City Business Journals, Inc.
Contact: Mike Olivieri, Executive Vice President

Released: Weekly. **Price:** $22, all 22 records. **Description:** The largest tenant representative companies in North Texas as of March 14, 2014, ranked by number of tenant representative contracts are listed. CBRE got the top spot. Meanwhile, Jones Lang LaSalle ranked second. **Availability:** Print; Online.

13803 ■ *"Leaning Tower" in Business Courier (Vol. 27, June 4, 2010, No. 5, pp. 1)*

Pub: Business Courier

Ed: Jon Newberry. **Description:** New York-based developer Armand Lasky, owner of Tower Place Mall in downtown Cincinnati, Ohio has sued Birmingham, Alabama-based Regions Bank to prevent the bank's foreclosure on the property. Regions Bank claims Lasky was in default on an $18 million loan agreement. Details on the mall's leasing plan are also discussed. **Availability:** Online.

13804 ■ *"Making Money on Foreclosures" in Memphis Business Journal (Vol. 33, March 9, 2012, No. 48, pp. 1)*

Pub: Baltimore Business Journal
Contact: Rhonda Pringle, President
E-mail: rpringle@bizjournals.com

Ed: Cole Epley. **Description:** Investors and residential rental property buyers have benefited from home foreclosures in the US. Mortgage foreclosures have resulted in decreased home prices. **Availability:** Print; Online.

13805 ■ *"Multifamily Banks on Fannie, Freddie" in Memphis Business Journal (Vol. 33, February 24, 2012, No. 46, pp. 1)*

Pub: Baltimore Business Journal
Contact: Rhonda Pringle, President
E-mail: rpringle@bizjournals.com

Ed: Andy Ashby. **Description:** The possible demise of Fannie Mae and Freddie Mac is seen to adversely impact the multifamily apartment market of Memphis, Tennessee. The apartment market relies on federal loans for funding. **Availability:** Print; Online.

13806 ■ *"Nothing But Green Skies" in Inc. (November 2007, pp. 115-120)*

Ed: Alison Stein Wellner. **Description:** Profile of Enterprise Rent-A-Car, one of the largest family-owned businesses in the U.S. Andy Taylor, CEO, discusses the company's talks about the idea of offering carbon off-sets for a few years. **Availability:** Print; Online.

13807 ■ *"Old Ford Plant to Sign New Tenants" in Business Courier (Vol. 27, August 13, 2010, No. 15, pp. 1)*

Pub: Business Courier

Ed: Dan Monk. **Description:** Ohio Realty Advisors LLC, a company handling the marketing of the 1.9 million-square-foot former Ford Batavia plant is on the brink of landing one distribution and three manufacturing firms as tenants. These tenants are slated to occupy about 20 percent of the facility and generate as many as 250 jobs in Ohio. **Availability:** Print; Online.

13808 ■ *"Owners Consider Remodeling Westlake Center" in Puget Sound Business Journal (Vol. 33, September 28, 2012, No. 23, pp. 1)*

Pub: Baltimore Business Journal
Contact: Rhonda Pringle, President
E-mail: rpringle@bizjournals.com

Ed: Jeanne Lang Jones. **Description:** General Growth Properties Inc. is considering a major remodel of the Westlake Center shopping mall in Seattle, Washington and international fashion chain Zara is negotiating for space at Westlake. Such activities benefit the city's retailers and landlords along with providing a broader civic benefit to the town square. **Availability:** Print; Online.

13809 ■ *"Pegasus Logistics Expanding in Coppell" in Dallas Business Journal (Vol. 35, July 6, 2012, No. 43, pp. 1)*

Pub: Baltimore Business Journal
Contact: Rhonda Pringle, President

E-mail: rpringle@bizjournals.com

Ed: Candace Carlisle. **Description:** Coppell, Texas-based Pegasus Logistic Group has signed a lease with Teachers Insurance and Annuity Association - College Retirement Equities Fund for 255,000-square-foot office and industrial space at 301 Airport Drive. Pegasus plans to consolidate its corporate headquarters with its distribution to keep up with its growth. Details are included. **Availability:** Print; Online.

13810 ■ *"The Perks of Going Public"* in *Austin Business Journal (Vol. 31, July 15, 2011, No. 19, pp. A17)*

Pub: Austin Business Journal

Contact: Rachel McGrath, Director

E-mail: rmcgrath@bizjournals.com

Ed: Christopher Calnan. **Description:** HomeAway Inc. launched a $216 million initial public offering. Austin Ventures has generated more than $32 million from the IPO. **Availability:** Print; Online.

13811 ■ *"Plans for $160M Condo Resort in Wisconsin Dells Moves Forward"* in *Commercial Property News (March 18, 2008)*

Description: Plans for the Grand Cambrian Resort in the Wisconsin Dells is discussed. The luxury condominium resort will include condos, townhomes, and condo-hotel style residences, two water parts, meeting space and indoor entertainment space, as well as a spa, four restaurants and retail offerings. **Availability:** Online.

13812 ■ *"Play It Safe At Home, Or Take a Risk Abroad? A US Lease-To-Own Chain Considers Whether To Test Its Business In Mexico"* in *Harvard Business Review (Vol. 90, January-February 2012, No.1-2, pp. 145)*

Pub: Harvard Business Review Press

Contact: Moderna V. Pfizer, Contact

Ed: Michael Chu. **Price:** $8.95, hardcopy black and white. **Description:** A fictitious foreign-market entry scenario is presented, with contributors providing advice. Recommendations include ensuring that expansion will not compromise the firm's core business, and that expansion, while necessary to growth, must be done carefully. **Availability:** Print; Online; PDF.

13813 ■ *"Pop a Cork: Lofts' Sale Bodes Well for Urban Living"* in *Pittsburgh Business Times (Vol. 33, May 30, 2014, No. 46, pp. 3)*

Pub: American City Business Journals, Inc.

Contact: Mike Olivieri, Executive Vice President

Released: May 30, 2014. **Price:** $4, introductory 4-week offer(Digital only). **Description:** Institutional apartment investor, GMH Capital Partners, has acquired the Cork Factory Lofts in the Strip District of Pittsburgh, Pennsylvania in an $8 billion deal with McCaffery Interests and local partners. The deal is anticipated to inspire more apartment rental development in the Pittsburg area. **Availability:** Print; Online.

13814 ■ *"The Promise of the Promised Land"* in *San Francisco Business Times (Vol. 28, January 3, 2014, No. 24, pp. 4)*

Pub: American City Business Journals, Inc.

Contact: Mike Olivieri, Executive Vice President

Released: September 15, 2016. **Price:** $4, print. **Description:** San Francisco Bay Area in California has become the site selection for investment, technology and talent. The financing finding its way to the Bay Area has led to robust job creation, drawing people and increasing the population by 2.6 percent to 805,000. The impact of the Bay Area's technology boon in rents and home prices are also presented. **Availability:** Print; Online.

13815 ■ *"Proposed Accounting Changes Could Complicate Tenants' Leases"* in *Baltimore Business Journal (Vol. 28, July 2, 2010, No. 8, pp. 1)*

Pub: Baltimore Business Journal

Contact: Rhonda Pringle, President

E-mail: rpringle@bizjournals.com

Ed: Daniel J. Sernovitz. **Description:** The Financial Accounting Standards Board has proposed that companies must indicate the value of real estate leases as assets and liabilities on balance sheets instead of expenses. The proposals could cause some companies to document millions of dollars in charges on their books or find difficulty in getting loans. **Availability:** Print.

13816 ■ *"Questions to Ask Your Customers Before They Rent a Generator"* in *Rental Product News (Vol. 33, October 2011)*

Ed: Jenny Lescohier. **Description:** According to a national strategic account manager at Kohler Rental Power, the most important factors when choosing a generator include volts, amps and phase. Understanding the relationship between these three electrical values will help rent the power equipment to customers. **Availability:** Online.

13817 ■ *"Realtors Irate Over Tax Plan"* in *Providence Business News (Vol. 26, March 26, 2012, No. 51, pp. 1)*

Pub: American City Business Journals, Inc.

Contact: Mike Olivieri, Executive Vice President

URL(s): pbn.com/realtors-irate-over-tax-plan66344

Ed: Kelly L. Anderson. **Description:** Rhode Island realtors are criticizing Governor Lincoln D. Chafee's plan to tax vacation rentals and bed and breakfast operations. The plan is in line with the state's efforts to balance the 2013 budget. Comments from executives are included.

13818 ■ *"Reduce, Reuse, Recycle, Reupholster, Is Motto of Willmar, Minn., Upholstery Hobbyist Turned Pro"* in *West Central Tribune (August 14, 2012)*

Ed: David Little. **Description:** American craftsmanship in furniture is foremost to Mr. Rousseau, owner of PrairieUpholstery of Willmar, Minnesota. He learned to reupholster furniture from an expert and opened his own shop in the historic downtown district. Rousseau will reupholster new and used furniture, car and truck seats, as well as boat seats and he can repair canvas. He also will rent upholstery cleaning and carpet shampoo machines, as well as refinishing wood furniture. **Availability:** Online.

13819 ■ *"Rent Check: New Lease on Life for Tenants"* in *Boston Business Journal (Vol. 31, July 29, 2011, No. 27, pp. 1)*

Pub: Boston Business Journal

Contact: Carolyn M. Jones, President

E-mail: cmjones@bizjournals.com

Ed: Lisa Van der Pool. **Description:** Merchants at Newbury Street in Boston, Massachusetts are concerned with the annual increase of already inflated rents that prevent many small businesses from expanding. **Availability:** Print; Online.

13820 ■ *"Rent Hikes in South Florida Apartments Among Highest In Nation"* in *South Florida Business Journal (Vol. 34, July 4, 2014, No. 50, pp. 8)*

Pub: American City Business Journals, Inc.

Contact: Mike Olivieri, Executive Vice President

Released: Weekly. **Description:** Apartments in South Florida are one of the fastest growing in the U.S. in terms of rental rate growth, according to a report by Axiometrics. The average rent rose 6.9 percent to $1,485 in Miami-Dade County, while Palm Beach County and Broward County registered growth rates of 6.03 percent and 5.51 percent respectively. **Availability:** Print; Online.

13821 ■ *Rental Management--Who's Who in the Rental Industry*

Pub: American Rental Association

URL(s): news.ararental.org

Ed: Brian Alm. **Released:** Annual **Description:** Publication includes lists of about 8,500 member rental companies, branch locations, services, and suppliers to the rental industry in the United States, limited international coverage; also lists association officers, other associations in the industry, and ARA state and local groups. **Entries include:** For rental firms--Company name, address, phone, key person-

nel and kind of rental service provided (construction, general tool, health, party). For suppliers--Company name, address, phone, products or service. For associations--Organization name, contact name, address, phone. For officers--Name, company, address, phone; listings for present officers include first name of spouse; listings for past presidents show the year(s) of tenure. **Arrangement:** Rental firms are listed geographically; associations are by country or state; current officers are hierarchical, past officers are listed alphabetically, past presidents are chronological; suppliers are alphabetical. **Indexes:** Personal name. **Availability:** Print.

13822 ■ *"Renters' Review ? Secret Shoppers Strike Again"* in *Rental Product News (Vol. 33, June 2011)*

Description: Staff of Rental Product News set out to rent various items from three different rental sources in order to evaluate the rental experience from the eyes of the average customer. **Availability:** Online.

13823 ■ *"Restaurateurs Follow High-End Apartments Into Kendall Square"* in *Boston Business Journal (Vol. 31, July 22, 2011, No. 26, pp. 3)*

Pub: Boston Business Journal

Contact: Carolyn M. Jones, President

E-mail: cmjones@bizjournals.com

Ed: Lisa Van der Pool. **Description:** Kendall Square in Cambridge, Massachusetts is attracting restaurants, 16 of which have opened since 2009. The influx of restaurants is being driven by lower commercial rents.

13824 ■ *"Retail Remains Hot as More Stores Browse Around Houston"* in *Houston Business Journal (Vol. 44, January 17, 2014, No. 37, pp. 9A)*

Pub: American City Business Journals, Inc.

Contact: Mike Olivieri, Executive Vice President

Released: Weekly. **Price:** $4, Introductory 4-week offer(Digital & Print). **Description:** Houston, Texas-based Evergreen Commercial Realty president, Lilly Golden, has revealed that the city has 15 new retail projects under construction and about 30 other projects in the pipeline. Golden believes Houston's low vacancy rate and high rent growth in Class A assets cause high demand from investors nationally. The boom in the retail sector is also examined. **Availability:** Print; Online.

13825 ■ *"Revive To Sell Women's Apparel in Downtown Space"* in *Memphis Business Journal (Vol. 33, February 3, 2012, No. 43, pp. 1)*

Pub: Baltimore Business Journal

Contact: Rhonda Pringle, President

E-mail: rpringle@bizjournals.com

Ed: Andy Ashby. **Description:** Revive has signed a rental agreement with Memphis Commerce Square Partners LLC for the vacant space at One Commerce Square in Memphis, Tennessee. Revive plans to sell women's clothing, shoes and accessories in the downtown space. **Availability:** Print; Online.

13826 ■ *"A Rise in Rental Units"* in *Philadelphia Business Journal (Vol. 30, October 7, 2011, No. 34, pp. 1)*

Pub: Philadelphia Business Journal

Contact: Sierra Quinn, Director

E-mail: squinn@bizjournals.com

Ed: Natalie Kostelni. **Description:** Housing developers have been stepping up the construction of new apartment complexes throughout the suburbs of Pennsylvania in order to capture growing demand for rental properties. BPG Properties Ltd. has nearly 1,000 new apartments under construction. **Availability:** Online.

13827 ■ *"Scoring Boost Should be Coming for Renters' Credit"* in *Providence Business News (Vol. 29, July 14, 2014, No. 15, pp. 7)*

Pub: American City Business Journals, Inc.

Contact: Mike Olivieri, Executive Vice President

Released: July 12, 2014. **Description:** National credit bureaus, Experian and TransUnion, are working with online rental payment service RentTrack to include verified rental payment data into credit files so that it may be included in calculating consumer scores during mortgage applications. In addition, a study by TransUnion finds that consumer scores increase when their rental data is included in bureau records and when they move from renter status to homeowner. **Availability:** Print; Online.

13828 ■ "S.F. Leasing Off to Hottest Start Since 2000" in San Francisco Business Times (Vol. 28, January 17, No. 26, pp. 8)
Pub: American City Business Journals, Inc.
Contact: Mike Olivieri, Executive Vice President
Description: Figures show that the demand for commercial space in San Francisco, California continues to increase. Companies such as LinkedIn, Trulia, DropBox, and Pinterest are expected to lease around 700,000 square feet of space. Colin Yasukochi, research director at CBRE Group, believes that commercial space is not being constructed fast enough to accommodate demand. **Availability:** Print; Online.

13829 ■ "Shedding Light on Innovation" in Rental Product News (Vol. 33, June 2011)
Description: Light tower manufacturers have introduced numerous new products that feature alternative power sources, LED lighting and a second generation of performance and value. **Availability:** Online.

13830 ■ "Signs Point To Improving CRE Market" in Birmingham Business Journal (Vol. 31, May 2, 2014, No. 18, pp. 7)
Pub: American City Business Journals, Inc.
Contact: Mike Olivieri, Executive Vice President
Released: Weekly. **Price:** $4, introductory 4-week offer(Digital only). **Description:** Xceligent real estate research firm's data shows collective improvement in Birmingham, Alabama's retail, office and industrial markets over the first three months of 2014. The office market has a less than 10 percent vacancy rate for Class A office space. Vacancy rates for both retail and industrial markets are also provided. **Availability:** Print; Online.

13831 ■ "State Center Lease Deal High for Md." in Baltimore Business Journal (Vol. 28, August 6, 2010, No. 13, pp. 1)
Pub: Baltimore Business Journal
Contact: Rhonda Pringle, President
E-mail: rpringle@bizjournals.com
Ed: Daniel J. Sernovitz. **Description:** The proposed $1.5 billion State Center development project in Midtown Baltimore might cause the State of Maryland to pay the most expensive rental rates in the city. The state will have to pay an effective rental rate of $34 per square foot, including expenses, on the leasing. Other details of the redevelopment project are discussed. **Availability:** Print; Online.

13832 ■ "State Wants to Add Escape Clause to Leases" in Sacramento Business Journal (Vol. 28, October 14, 2011, No. 33, pp. 1)
Pub: Sacramento Business Journal
Contact: Stephanie Fretwell, Director
E-mail: sfretwell@bizjournals.com
Ed: Michael Shaw. **Description:** California Governor Jerry Brown's administration has decided to add escape clauses to new lease agreements, which created new worry for building owners and brokers in Sacramento, California. Real estate brokers believe the appropriation of funds clauses have been making the lenders nervous and would result in less competition. **Availability:** Online.

13833 ■ "Survey Says Commercial Real Estate Headed for Turbulence" in Commercial Property News (March 17, 2008)
Description: Commercial real estate sector is declining due to the sluggish U.S. economy. According to a recent survey, national office, retail and hospitality markets are also on the decline. **Availability:** Online.

13834 ■ "Take the Right Approach to Concrete Polishing Rentals" in Rental Product News (Vol. 33, June 2011)
Description: A recent trend in flooring is concrete polishing for a practical, beautiful and sustainable way to decorate homes and businesses. Things to keep in mind when assessing the value of adding concrete polishing equipment to an existing rental store are evaluated. **Availability:** Online.

13835 ■ "Tattooed Bellwethers of Economic Development" in Austin Business Journal (Vol. 34, May 2, 2014, No. 11, pp. A4)
Pub: American City Business Journals, Inc.
Contact: Mike Olivieri, Executive Vice President
Released: Weekly. **Price:** $4, Introductory 4-week offer(Digital & Print). **Description:** The creative community's art-centered business have helped Austin, Texas' growth by moving into transitional areas with low rents. Their kind of pioneering spirit primes the area for later commercial and residential development. The city's assistance programs for creative enterprises are also presented. **Availability:** Print; Online.

13836 ■ "They See It. They Like It. They Want It. They Rent It" in The New York Times (June 8, 2019)
URL(s): www.nytimes.com/2019/06/08/style/ren t-subscription-clothing-furniture.html
Ed: Sapna Maheshwari. **Released:** June 08, 2019. **Description:** Many young Americans have turned to renting almost everything from clothes, to furniture, to appliances. Many people find that they can't afford to purchase items but yet may still need them for their daily lives, so they turn to renting. With various apps and websites, it's easy to locate what is needed and shipping isn't as much as a hassle as it used to be. People often enjoy the flexibility of renting, since home ownership for people in their 20s and 30s is still low after the Great Recession. **Availability:** Online.

13837 ■ "Top Commercial Real Estate Developers" in South Florida Business Journal (Vol. 34, July 25, 2014, No. 53, pp. 14)
Pub: American City Business Journals, Inc.
Contact: Mike Olivieri, Executive Vice President
Released: Weekly. **Description:** Rankings of the commercial real estate developers in South Florida are presented. Rankings are based on the total new rentable square feet developed and square feet sold in the region in 2013. **Availability:** Print; Online.

13838 ■ "Top Statewide Commercial Real Estate Brokerages" in South Florida Business Journal (Vol. 34, April 4, 2014, No. 37, pp. 14)
Pub: American City Business Journals, Inc.
Contact: Mike Olivieri, Executive Vice President
Description: Rankings of commercial real estate brokerages in South Florida area are presented. Rankings were based on total volume sales and leasing statewide in Florida. The top five real estate executives in the region are also listed. **Availability:** Print; Online.

13839 ■ "Trammell Crow Facility in Houston is a Late Bloomer" in Houston Business Journal (Vol. 40, August 28, 2009, No. 16, pp. 1A)
Pub: Houston Business Journal
Contact: Bob Charlet, President
E-mail: bcharlet@bizjournals.com
Ed: Jennifer Dawson. **Released:** Weekly. **Description:** Trammell Crow Company leased half of the 61,000 square foot IAH International Air Cargo Centre II to Tradewinds Cargo Handling. The facility, located at George Bush Intercontinental Airport, is intended to be a destination of fresh flowers and food from Latin America. **Availability:** Print; Online.

13840 ■ "University Place Building Gets an Anchor Tenant: Groundbreaking 2.0" in Philadelphia Business Journal (Vol. 30, September 23, 2011, No. 32, pp. 1)
Pub: Philadelphia Business Journal
Contact: Sierra Quinn, Director

E-mail: squinn@bizjournals.com
Ed: Natalie Kostelni. **Description:** University Place Associates, the developer of 2.0 University Place in West Philadelphia, Pennsylvania, will break ground on a five-story, 97,000-square-foot office building in December 2011. The decision follows the Citizenship and Immigration Services signing of a 15-year lease as anchor tenant. **Availability:** Online.

13841 ■ "Walnut Hill Sheds Its Past, Name" in Philadelphia Business Journal (Vol. 33, April 4, 2014, No. 8, pp. 8)
Pub: American City Business Journals, Inc.
Contact: Mike Olivieri, Executive Vice President
Released: Weekly. **Price:** $4, introductory 4-week offer(Digital & Print). **Description:** Walnut Hill Plaza was bought by a fund comprised of Miller Investment Management and Hayden Real Estate at an auction in 2012 for $11 million and they spent $2 million in construction renovations. The property was also re-branded as 150 Walnut Warner and the once forlorn building is up to 100% leased space. The tenants renting space in the building are also highlighted. **Availability:** Print; Online.

13842 ■ "Your Career: Is It Time for a Change?" in Rental Product News (Vol. 33, October 2011)
Description: Management software for running a rental business is examined. **Availability:** Online.

STATISTICAL SOURCES

13843 ■ Consumer Electronics & Appliances Rental Industry in the US - Market Research Report
URL(s): www.ibisworld.com/united-states/market-research-reports/consumer-electronics-appliances-rental-industry/
Price: $925. **Description:** Downloadable report analyzing the current and future trends in the consumer electronics and appliance rental industries. **Availability:** Download.

13844 ■ Formal Wear & Costume Rental Industry in the US - Market Research Report
URL(s): www.ibisworld.com/united-states/market-research-reports/formal-wear-costume-rental-industry/
Price: $925. **Description:** Downloadable report analyzing the current and future trends in the formal wear and costume rental industries. **Availability:** Download.

13845 ■ RMA Annual Statement Studies
Pub: Risk Management Association
Contact: Nancy Foster, President
Released: Annual. **Description:** Contains composite balance sheets and income statements for more than 360 industries, including the accounting, auditing, and bookkeeping industries. Also contains five years of comparative historical data for discerning trends. Includes 16 commonly used ratios, computed for most of the size groupings for nearly every industry.

TRADE PERIODICALS

13846 ■ Heavy Equipment Guide
Pub: Baum Publications Ltd.
Contact: Engelbert Baum, Co-President
URL(s): www.heavyequipmentguide.ca
Facebook: www.facebook.com/HeavyEquipmentGuide
X (Twitter): x.com/HeavyEquipGuide
YouTube: www.youtube.com/channel/UCK4eU7B8jVIMa-8ZR1u-Zzw
Released: 8/year; January/February, March, April, May/June, July/August, September, October, and November/December. **Price:** C$91, for price; $149, for price outside Canada. **Description:** Trade publication for the construction, mining, truck, and municipal industries. **Availability:** Print; Online.

13847 ■ Rental Management: Official Magazine of the American Rental Association
Pub: American Rental Association

URL(s): news.ararental.org

Ed: Wayne Walley, Erin Jorgensen, Ashleigh Petersen. **Released:** Monthly **Description:** Magazine for business owners who rent equipment to consumers, industries, institutions and commercial firms. **Availability:** Print; Online.

VIDEO/AUDIO MEDIA

13848 ■ *Start an RV Rental Business Using Other People RVs with Garr Russell*
URL(s): www.eofire.com/podcast/garrrussell
Ed: John Lee Dumas. **Released:** September 21, 2023.

TRADE SHOWS AND CONVENTIONS

13849 ■ **American Rental Association Annual Convention and Rental Trade Show**
American Rental Association (ARA)
  1900 19th St.
  Moline, IL 61265
Free: 800-334-2177
Fax: (309)764-1533
Co. E-mail: marketing@ararental.org
URL: http://www.ararental.org
URL(s): arashow.org
Frequency: Annual. **Audience:** Owners and managers of rental equipment stores and industry professionals. Dates and Locations: 2025 Jan 29-Feb 01 Las Vegas Convention Center, Las Vegas, NV. **Telecommunication Services:** bridget.otten@ararental.org.

13850 ■ **RTO World The National Rent-to-Own Convention and Trade Show**
Serta
URL(s): www.rtohq.org/rtoworld
Frequency: Annual. **Description:** Products of interest to rent-to-own dealers, such as audio products, computers, home appliances, home furniture, video products, jewelry, advertising, electronics, fabric protection, marketing, promotional services, and related equipment, supplies, and services. **Audience:** Industry professionals. **Principal Exhibits:** Products of interest to rent-to-own dealers, such as audio products, computers, home appliances, home furniture, video products, jewelry, advertising, electronics, fabric protection, marketing, promotional services, and related equipment, supplies, and services. **Telecommunication Services:** expo@rtoworld.org.

FRANCHISES AND BUSINESS OPPORTUNITIES

13851 ■ **Abrakadoodle Remarkable Art Education**
Abrakadoodle Inc.
  100 Carpenter Dr., Ste. 100
  Sterling, VA 20166

Ph: (703)860-6570
Co. E-mail: info@abrakadoodle.com
URL: http://www.abrakadoodle.com
Contact: Rosemarie Hartnett, President
Facebook: www.facebook.com/Abrakadoodle
X (Twitter): x.com/Abrakadoodle
YouTube: www.youtube.com/abrakadoodleart
Pinterest: www.pinterest.com/abrakadoodle
Description: Arts education program. **No. of Franchise Units:** 70. **No. of Company-Owned Units:** 2. **Founded:** 2002. **Franchised:** 2004. **Equity Capital Needed:** $100,000 net worth. **Franchise Fee:** $29,900-$36,900. **Training:** Provides 5 days at headquarters with ongoing support.

13852 ■ **Affiliated Car Rental L.C.**
Eatontown, NJ
Free: 800-367-5159
Fax: (732)380-0404
URL: http://www.affiliatedcarrental.com
Facebook: www.facebook.com/affordable.sensible
Description: Retailer of automotive and also provides rental and repair services. **Founded:** 1987. **Financial Assistance:** Yes **Training:** Provides 2 days at headquarters, 2 days onsite with ongoing support.

13853 ■ **Cool Daddy's**
Atlanta, GA
Ph: (678)394-8009
Co. E-mail: info@cooldaddys.com
URL: http://www.cooldaddys.com
Description: Producer and retailer of frozen drinks for private parties, festivals and events. **Training:** Provides 2 weeks at headquarters. 1 week at franchisee's location, with ongoing support.

13854 ■ **Dollar Thrifty Automotive Group Canada Inc.**
The Hertz Corporation
  1369 Dundas St. E
  Mississauga, ON, Canada L4Y 2C7
Ph: (239)390-8380
Free: 800-654-4173
Co. E-mail: hertzracap@hertz.com
URL: http://www.hertz.com/rentacar/reservation
Founded: 1985. **Training:** Yes.

13855 ■ **Priceless Car Rental**
13900 Laurel Lakes Ave., Ste. 100
  Laurel, MD 20707
Free: 877-877-1400
Co. E-mail: info@rentawreck.com
URL: http://www.pricelesscarrental.com
Description: Provider of car rental services. **Founded:** 1998. **Franchise Fee:** $18,000 - $75,000. **Training:** Yes.

13856 ■ **Rent-A-Center Franchising International, Inc. (RACFI)**
Upbound Group, Inc.
  5501 Headquarters Dr.
  Plano, TX 75024-5845
Ph: (972)801-1100

Free: 800-422-8186
URL: http://upbound.com
Contact: Catherine Skula, President
Description: Distributor of furniture, electronics, appliances and computers. **Founded:** 1970.

13857 ■ **Rent A Wreck**
909 17th Ave. SW., Ste. 400
  Calgary, AB, Canada T2T 0A4
Free: 800-327-0116
Fax: (403)259-6776
Co. E-mail: info@practicar.ca
URL: http://www.practicar.ca
Description: Provider of car and truck rental services. **Founded:** 1976. **Training:** Full classroom and ongoing training provided.

13858 ■ **Triangle Building Supplies and Services Inc. [Grand Rental Station; Triangle Construction]**
1076 E Bishop St.
  Bellefonte, PA 16823
Ph: (814)355-5885
Free: 800-377-5881
Fax: (814)355-8811
URL: http://trianglebuilding.com
Contact: J. Allen Witherite, Owner
Facebook: www.facebook.com/trianglebuildingsupplies
Description: Lumber and other building materials. **Founded:** 1979.

13859 ■ **U-Save Auto Rental of America, Inc. [U-Save Car & Truck Rental]**
Green Motion Ltd.
  219 Industrial Dr.
  Ridgeland, MS 39157
Ph: 44 207 186 4000
Free: 44 0333 888 4000
URL: http://greenmotion.com
Contact: Tom McDonnell, III, Chief Executive Officer
X (Twitter): x.com/usaverental
Description: Discount car and truck rental operating in nearly 190 locations in the United States. **Founded:** 1979.

13860 ■ **Wheel Fun Rentals (WFR)**
4526 Telephone Rd., Ste. 202
  Ventura, CA 93003
Ph: (805)650-7770
Fax: (805)650-7771
Co. E-mail: info@wheelfunrentals.com
URL: http://wheelfunrentals.com
Facebook: www.facebook.com/wheelfunrentalsofficial
X (Twitter): x.com/wheelfunrentals
Instagram: www.instagram.com/wheelfunrentalsofficial
YouTube: www.youtube.com/user/WheelFunRentalsCorp
Description: Firm provides recreational rental services in leisure, tourist, park and recreational resort areas. **Founded:** 1987. **Equity Capital Needed:** $65,000-$320,000. **Financial Assistance:** Yes **Training:** Offers 7 days training headquarters, at franchisee's location and ongoing as needed.

Restaurant

START-UP INFORMATION

13861 ■ *"Blaze Pizza Adds Nine Franchise Groups" in FastCasual.com (September 2, 2014)*
Pub: Networld Media Group
Contact: Kathy Doyle, President
E-mail: publisher@networldmediagroup.com
Description: Blaze Fast Fire'd Pizza has signed nine new San Diego area development agreements that will add 67 franchise restaurants to its firm. The company will also open 315 company-owned and franchised pizza restaurants in 33 states by the end of 2015. **Availability:** Online.

13862 ■ *"'Crazy' Or Not, Baltimore-Area Restaurateurs Are Finding Ways to Open New Eateries" in Baltimore Business Journal (Vol. 28, October 8, 2010)*
Pub: Baltimore Business Journal
Contact: Rhonda Pringle, President
E-mail: rpringle@bizjournals.com
Ed: Joanna Sullivan. **Description:** New restaurants have been opening in Maryland. However, 515 restaurants have closed down due to the economic crisis. Comments from restaurateurs are also provided.

13863 ■ *Culinary Careers: How to Get Your Dream Job in Food with Advice from Top Culinary Professionals*
Pub: Clarkson Potter
Ed: Rick Smilow, Anne E. McBride. **Released:** May 04, 2010. **Price:** $23.99, paperback. **Description:** Top culinary experts offer advice for working in or owning a food service firm. **Availability:** E-book; Print.

13864 ■ *"Faces: Q&A with Kevin Huyck, Chef/Owner of R.A. MacSammy's Food Truck Specializing in Mac and Cheese" in Saint Paul Pioneer Press (March 28, 2012)*
Ed: Kathie Jenkins. **Description:** Profile of 48 year old Kevin Huyck, chef and owner of his R.A. MacSammy food truck. Huyck specializes in serving a variety of macaroni and cheese dishes. He wanted to own his own restaurant but did not have the capital for such an investment at the time and hopes to expand with either another food truck or possibly a restaurant that features mac and cheese dishes. **Availability:** Online.

13865 ■ *"Franchisee to Smash Way Into Orlando's Better Burger Race" in Orlando Business Journal (Vol. 30, January 31, 2014, No. 32, pp. 3)*
Pub: American City Business Journals, Inc.
Contact: Mike Olivieri, Executive Vice President
Released: Weekly. **Price:** $8, introductory 4-week offer(Digital & Print). **Description:** Palm Coast, Florida-based Two Spurs LLC, the new franchisee for Smashburger, has announced plans to put its first of 12 restaurants in Orlando in 2014. Two Spurs executives, Wellesley Broomfield and Ray Ruiz, have been touring potential sites in the area. Detailed requirements for owning a Smash Burger franchise are provided. **Availability:** Print; Online.

13866 ■ *"Franchises with an Eye on Chicago" in Crain's Chicago Business (Vol. 34, March 14, 2011, No. 11, pp. 20)*
Pub: Crain Communications Inc.
Contact: Barry Asin, President
Ed: Kevin McKeough. **Description:** Profiles of franchise companies seeking franchisees for the Chicago area include: Extreme Pita, a sandwich shop; Hand and Stone, offering massage, facial and waxing services; Molly Maid, home-cleaning service; Primrose Schools, private accredited schools for children 6 months to 6 hears and after-school programs; Protect Painters, residential and light-commercial painting contractor; and Wingstop, a restaurant offering chicken wings in nine flavors, fries and side dishes. **Availability:** Online.

13867 ■ *"In a Twist, Pretzel Vendors Will Be Selling Pizza: Wetzels to Launch Blaze Fast-Fire'd Concept with Two SoCal Locations" in Los Angeles Business Journal (Vol. 34, June 4, 2012, No. 23, pp. 12)*
Pub: CBJ L.P.
Contact: Terri Cunningham, Contact
Ed: Bethany Firnhaber. **Description:** Rick and Elise Wetzel, cofounders of Wetzel's Pretzels is launching its new restaurants featuring fast-casual pizza. The concept is of an assembly line process where customers can make 11-inch personalized pizzas with toppings like artichokes, gorgonzola cheese, roasted red peppers and arugula. The pizzas bake in two minutes. **Availability:** Online.

13868 ■ *"Incubator, Apartment Mix Eyed" in Providence Business News (Vol. 29, April 14, 2014, No. 2, pp. 1)*
Pub: American City Business Journals, Inc.
Contact: Mike Olivieri, Executive Vice President
URL(s): pbn.com/incubator-apartment-mix-eyed9 6427
Description: New York City-based developer, Frank Manaigo, has been working on plans to develop a culinary incubator in a vacant mill complex in the West End at the Armory District in Providence, Rhode Island. The "Rooms and Works" is a $6.5 million residential and commercial project that would feature the "Armory Kitchen". The apartment component of the project is also discussed. **Telecommunication Services:** Daddona@pbn.com.

13869 ■ *"Kitchen Aid: D.C. Food Incubator Turns Growth Tactics Inward" in Washington Business Journal (Vol. 32, February 28, 2014, No. 46, pp. 6)*
Pub: American City Business Journals, Inc.
Contact: Mike Olivieri, Executive Vice President
Released: Weekly. **Price:** $4, introductory 4-week offer(Digital only). **Description:** The founders of the 14-month-old food business incubator, Union Kitchen, are considering their own growth strategies as they open up a second space for small business owners. The incubator has 55 members that pay monthly fees from $800 to $1,000, focusing on bar services and fine dining opportunities. **Availability:** Print; Online.

13870 ■ *"Longmont's Comida Food Truck Now a Brick-and-Mortar Restaurant, Too" in Las Cruces Sun-News (February 17, 2012)*
Pub: Tribune News Service
Contact: Jack Barry, Vice President, Operations
E-mail: jbarry@tribpub.com
Ed: Tony Kindelspire. **Description:** Rayme Rosello discusses her plans to open her new Mexican-style restaurant, Comida Cantina, which grew from her pink food truck. Rosello started her food truck in 2010 and has frequented neighborhood parties as well as office parks to build her business. Details of the new restaurant are provided. **Availability:** Print; Online.

13871 ■ *"The Melting Pot Targets Calgary, Canada For Franchise Expansion" in CNW Group (September 9, 2014)*
Pub: Comtex News Network Inc.
Contact: Kan Devnani, President
Description: The Melting Pot, a premier fondue restaurant, is seeking franchisees in the Calgary, Canada region. The restaurants offer posh, casual interactive dining to their guests. The franchise is also offering franchise opportunities in the Vancouver and Greater Toronto areas. Details covering Melting Pot restaurants are included. **Availability:** Print; Online.

13872 ■ *"Mercyhurst Rolls Out Culinary Cab Food Truck" in Erie Times-News (June 19, 2012)*
Ed: Erica Erwin. **Description:** Mercyhurst University's food service company launched a Culinary Cab, or food truck, offering a variety of food choices to the campus community. Details of Parkhurst Dining Services plan for the mobile restaurant are outlined.

13873 ■ *"A Messy Job" in Washington Business Journal (Vol. 33, May 30, 2014, No. 6, pp. 6)*
Pub: American City Business Journals, Inc.
Contact: Mike Olivieri, Executive Vice President
Description: Mess Hall founder, Al Goldberg, shares his views on business incubators for culinary entrepreneurs in District of Columbia. Goldberg says he expects to accommodate up to 100 members in the space of the former warehouse turned culinary center for entrepreneurs wishing to start restaurants, bakeries or bars. **Availability:** Print; Online.

13874 ■ *"Old Town Just the First Stop for Carluccio's" in Washington Business Journal (Vol. 33, May 30, 2014, No. 6, pp. 7)*
Pub: American City Business Journals, Inc.
Contact: Mike Olivieri, Executive Vice President
Description: United Kingdom-based Carluccio's announced the opening of its first U.S. location in Old Town Alexandria, Virginia. The Italian restaurant chain reveals plans to open two more restaurants in the

region to test out the various styles of their concept. Insights into the selection of the DC are as their first market is examined. **Availability:** Print; Online.

13875 ■ *Start and Run a Delicatessen: Small Business Starters Series*

Description: Information for starting and running a successful delicatessen is provided. Insight is offered into selecting a location, researching the market, writing a business plan and more.

13876 ■ *Start Small, Finish Big*

Released: December 15, 2012. **Description:** Fred DeLuca is profiled; after founding the multi-billion dollar chain of Subway sandwich restaurants, DeLuca is committed to helping microentrepreneurs, people who start successful small businesses with less than $1,000. **Availability:** Print; Online.

13877 ■ *"Thirsty Lion Cooks Up Big Expansion Plan" in Business Journal Portland (Vol. 27, November 5, 2010, No. 36, pp. 1)*

Pub: Portland Business Journal
Contact: Andy Giegerich, Managing Editor
E-mail: agiegerich@bizjournals.com

Ed: Wendy Culverwell. **Description:** Concept Entertainment Inc.'s impending launch of the Thirsty Lion Pub and Grill at the Washington Square in downtown Portland, Oregon is part of its West Coast expansion plan. A discussion of the planning involved in realizing Thirsty Lion is discussed, along with pub offerings that are expected to be enjoyed by customers. **Availability:** Print; Online.

ASSOCIATIONS AND OTHER ORGANIZATIONS

13878 ■ Association of Food Industries (AFI)

3301 Rte. 66, Ste. 205, Bldg. C
Neptune, NJ 07753
Ph: (732)922-3008
Co. E-mail: info@afius.org
URL: http://afius.org
Contact: John Sessler, Contact
Facebook: www.facebook.com/people/Association-of
-Food-Industries/100083025566380
Linkedin: www.linkedin.com/company/association-of
-food-industries
X (Twitter): x.com/afius_org
Instagram: www.instagram.com/afius_org
YouTube: www.youtube.com/channel/
UCrvIWEKCGCxsY4HZwBxzooA

Description: Food processors, importers, and import agents nationally; food brokers in the New York metropolitan market and overseas food exporters. Maintains arbitration tribunal, government relations, and information services. **Founded:** 1906. **Publications:** *Standard Import Contract.* **Geographic Preference:** National.

13879 ■ Commercial Food Equipment Service Association (CFESA)

3605 Centre Cir.
Fort Mill, SC 29715
Ph: (336)346-4700
URL: http://www.cfesa.com
Contact: Nick Cribb, President
Facebook: www.facebook.com/CFESA
Linkedin: www.linkedin.com/company/cfesa
X (Twitter): x.com/CFESAteam
Instagram: www.instagram.com/cfesa
YouTube: www.youtube.com/channel/UC4vROZmE
tRbfiWwi6rZrCUg

Description: Represents firms that repair food preparation equipment used by restaurants, hotels, and institutions. Provides training and education for members and their employees. **Founded:** 1963. **Publications:** *On Target* (Bimonthly); *Commercial Food Equipment Service Association Directory.* **Educational Activities:** CFESA Conference (Annual). **Geographic Preference:** National.

13880 ■ Foodservice Equipment Distributors Association (FEDA)

5600 N River Rd., Ste. 740
Rosemont, IL 60018
Ph: (224)293-6500
Fax: (224)293-6505
Co. E-mail: info@feda.com
URL: http://feda.com
Contact: Cary Amundsen, President

Description: Distributors of foodservice equipment, such as ovens, ranges, dish washing machines, china, utensils, and cutlery for hotels, restaurants, and institutions. Conducts specialized education programs. **Founded:** 1933. **Publications:** *FEDA News and Views* (Bimonthly). **Educational Activities:** University of Innovative Distribution (Annual). **Awards:** Sam Anoff Lifetime Achievement Award; Sam Anoff President's Award; FEDA President Dealer-Based Distribution Award. **Geographic Preference:** National.

13881 ■ International Foodservice Manufacturers Association (IFMA)

Two Prudential Plz.
180 N, Ste.tson Ave., Ste. 850
Chicago, IL 60601
Ph: (312)540-4400
Co. E-mail: ifma@ifmaworld.com
URL: http://www.ifmaworld.com
Contact: Phil Kafarakis, President
E-mail: phil@ifmaworld.com
Facebook: www.facebook.com/ifmaworldcom
Linkedin: www.linkedin.com/company/international
-foodservice-manufacturers-association
X (Twitter): x.com/IFMAWORLD
Instagram: www.instagram.com/ifmaworld

Description: Aims to shape the future of food service by creating an environment for positive change and actionable solutions benefiting manufacturers and their food service channel partners. **Founded:** 1952. **Publications:** *Encyclopedia of the Foodservice Industry* (Irregular); *International Foodservice Manufacturers Association: Membership Directory; International Foodservice Manufacturers Association--Membership Directory* (Annual); *IFMA World* (9/year). **Educational Activities:** Chain Operators Exchange (COEX) (Annual). **Awards:** IFMA Gold Plate Award (Annual); IFMA Silver Plate Award (Annual). **Geographic Preference:** Multinational.

13882 ■ Michigan Restaurant & Lodging Association (MRLA)

225 W Washtenaw St.
Lansing, MI 48933
Free: 800-968-9668
URL: http://www.mrla.org
Contact: Justin Winslow, President
Facebook: www.facebook.com/TheOfficialMRLA
Linkedin: www.linkedin.com/company/michigan-res
taurant-association
X (Twitter): x.com/THEOFFICIALMRLA
Instagram: www.instagram.com/theofficialmrla
YouTube: www.youtube.com/user/MichiganRes
taurant

Description: Non-profit dedicated to providing services to Michigan's hospitality industry. **Founded:** 1921. **Educational Activities:** Michigan Restaurant Show (Annual). **Geographic Preference:** State.

13883 ■ National Association of Pizzeria Operators (NAPO)

c/o Pizza Today
908 S 8th St., Ste. 200
Louisville, KY 40203
Ph: (502)736-9500
Fax: (330)693-0117
URL: http://pizzatoday.com

Description: Independent and franchised pizza operators; manufacturers and suppliers of pizza equipment; research organizations; schools with hotel and restaurant management programs; similar establishments in foreign countries. Promotes the advancement of marketing and product technology in the pizza industry. Provides educational references and seminars; conducts product research and development programs. Compiles statistics. **Founded:**

1983. **Publications:** *Pizza Today--Distributor Directory.* **Educational Activities:** NAPO International Pizza Expo (Annual). **Geographic Preference:** National.

13884 ■ National Barbecue & Grilling Association (NBBQA)

500 NE 23rd St.
Fort Worth, TX 76135
Co. E-mail: admin@nbbqa.org
URL: http://www.nbbqa.org
Contact: Barbara Latimer, President
Facebook: www.facebook.com/NBBQA
Linkedin: www.linkedin.com/company/nbbqa
X (Twitter): x.com/NBBQA
Instagram: www.instagram.com/nbbqa

Description: Industry professionals and barbecue enthusiasts including restaurants, caterers, specialty equipment retailers, grill manufacturers and distributors, smoker manufacturers and distributors, food product suppliers and distributors, sauces and spice distributors, backyard hobbyists. **Founded:** 1991. **Publications:** *National Barbecue News* (Bimonthly); *NBBQA Barbecue Buyers' Guide* (Annual). **Awards:** NBBQA Award of Excellence (Annual). **Geographic Preference:** National.

13885 ■ National Black McDonald's Operators Association (NBMOA)

401 N Michigan Ave., Ste. 1200
Chicago, IL 60611
Ph: (312)822-3363
URL: http://nbmoa.org
Contact: Larry Tripplett, Chief Executive Officer
Facebook: www.facebook.com/NBMOA

Description: Black owners of McDonald's restaurants. Provides a forum for the exchange of ideas on the improvement of community relations and on the operation and management of restaurants. Seeks to build and improve the McDonald's restaurant image throughout the community. Sponsors training seminars on marketing, better sales practices, labor relations and profit sharing. **Founded:** 1972. **Geographic Preference:** National.

13886 ■ National Council of Chain Restaurants (NCCR)

c/o National Retail Federation
1101 New York Ave. NW, Ste. 1200
Washington, DC 20005
Ph: (202)783-7971
Free: 800-673-4692
Co. E-mail: contact@nrf.com
URL: http://nrf.com/about-us/national-council-chain
-restaurants
Contact: Matthew R. Shay, President

Description: Represents chain restaurant companies. Works to advance sound public policy that best serves the interests of restaurant businesses and the millions of people they employ. Major multiunit, multistate foodservice, restaurant and lodging companies in the United States. **Founded:** 1965. **Educational Activities:** Membership, Tax Forum and Food Safety. **Geographic Preference:** National.

13887 ■ National Food Truck Association (NFTA)

5792 W Jefferson Blvd.
Los Angeles, CA 90016
Ph: (202)644-8830
Co. E-mail: info@nationalfoodtrucks.org
URL: http://nationalfoodtrucks.org
Contact: Matt Geller, Chief Executive Officer
Facebook: www.facebook.com/nationalfoodtrucks
X (Twitter): x.com/natlfoodtrucks

Description: Provides access to resources and information for food truck owners. Offers location and management services.

13888 ■ National Restaurant Association Educational Foundation (NRAEF)

2055 L St. NW
Washington, DC 20036
Free: 800-424-5156
Co. E-mail: comms@nraef.org
URL: http://chooserestaurants.org
Contact: Michelle Korsmo, Chief Executive Officer

Facebook: www.facebook.com/nraefoundation
Linkedin: www.linkedin.com/company/nraef
X (Twitter): x.com/nraef
Instagram: www.instagram.com/nraefoundation
YouTube: www.youtube.com/c/NRAEF

Description: Serves as an educational foundation supported by the National Restaurant Association and all segments of the foodservice industry including restaurateurs, foodservice companies, food and equipment manufacturers, distributors and trade associations. Advances the professional standards of the industry through education and research. Offers video training programs, management courses and careers information. Conducts research and maintains hall of fame. **Founded:** 1987. **Publications:** *Directory of Computer Hardware and Software for the Food Service Industry*; *Foodservice/Hospitality College Directory* (Irregular). **Educational Activities:** NSPA Conference. **Awards:** NRAEF Scholarships (Annual); Thad and Alice Eure Ambassador of Hospitality Award (Annual); Al Schuman/Ecolab Undergraduate Entrepreneurial Scholarship (Annual). **Geographic Preference:** National.

13889 ■ North American Association of Food Equipment Manufacturers (NAFEM)

161 N Clark St., Ste. 2020
　Chicago, IL 60601
Ph: (312)821-0201
Fax: (312)821-0202
Co. E-mail: info@nafem.org
URL: http://www.nafem.org
Contact: Richard K. Packer, President
Facebook: www.facebook.com/nafem
Linkedin: www.linkedin.com/company/north-american
　-association-of-food-equipment-manufacturers
X (Twitter): x.com/nafemhq
YouTube: www.youtube.com/channel/UC9
　6REzJYEWoLIfaYvz_tgTw

Description: Firm represents and manufacturers commercial food service equipment and supplies for restaurants, hotels, and institutional purposes, conducts certification program. **Founded:** 1948. **Publications:** *NAFEM for Operators* (Quarterly); *NAFEM in Print* (Quarterly). **Educational Activities:** NAFEM Educational Exhibition: North American Association of Food Equipment Manufacturers (Biennial); The NAFEM Show (Biennial). **Awards:** NAFEM Louise O'Sullivan Award of Excellence (Biennial); William W. Carpenter's Award (Biennial); NAFEM Doctorate of Foodservice (DFS) (Annual). **Geographic Preference:** National.

13890 ■ Restaurants Canada - Library

1155 Queen St. W
　Toronto, ON, Canada M6J 1J4
Ph: (416)923-8416
Free: 800-387-5649
Fax: (416)923-1450
Co. E-mail: info@restaurantscanada.org
URL: http://www.restaurantscanada.org
Contact: Christian Buhagiar, Co-Chief Executive
　Officer Co-President
Facebook: www.facebook.com/RestaurantsCanada
Linkedin: www.linkedin.com/company/restaurants
　-canada
X (Twitter): x.com/RestaurantsCA
Instagram: www.instagram.com/RestaurantsCanada
YouTube: www.youtube.com/channel/
　UCxVckfCBIlSIl9LOufINX8w

Description: Restaurant and food service corporations, hotels, caterers, and food service suppliers and educators, seeks to create a favorable business environment for members. **Scope:** Food service; quantity cooking; legislation; administration; management; statistics; training; customer attitude surveys. **Services:** Copying; open to the public on fee basis. **Founded:** 1944. **Publications:** *CRFA National Hospitality News*; *Canadian Foodservice Industry Operations Report* (Biennial); *Foodservice Facts* (Annual); *Legislation Guide* (Quarterly). **Educational Activities:** Restaurants Canada Show (Annual); ApEx. **Geographic Preference:** National.

13891 ■ Society for Hospitality and Foodservice Management (SHFM)

326 E Main St.
　Louisville, KY 40202
Ph: (502)574-9931
Fax: (502)589-3602
Co. E-mail: shfm@hqtrs.com
URL: http://www.shfm-online.org
Contact: Damian Monticello, President
Facebook: www.facebook.com/foo
　dservicemanagement
Linkedin: www.linkedin.com/company/society-for
　-hospitality-&-foodservice-management
X (Twitter): x.com/FoodserviceMgmt
Instagram: www.Instagram.com/shfmgmt
YouTube: www.youtube.com/user/FoodserviceMgmt

Description: Operates or maintains food service and vending facilities in businesses and industrial plants, or supply food products, equipment, or other essential industry services. Serves the needs and interests of onsite employee food service executives and management. **Founded:** 1979. **Publications:** *Journal of Foodservice Systems* (Quarterly); *Society for Foodservice Management--Member Directory*. **Geographic Preference:** National.

13892 ■ Women Chefs and Restaurateurs (WCR)

115 S Patrick St., Ste. 101
　Alexandria, VA 22314
URL: http://www.womenchefs.org
Contact: Barbara Tropp, Founder

Description: Seeks to educate and advance women in the restaurant industry. **Founded:** 1992. **Geographic Preference:** National.

INCUBATORS/RESEARCH AND TECHNOLOGY PARKS

13893 ■ Plug and Play - Travel and Hospitality

440 N Wolfe Rd.
　Sunnyvale, CA 94085
URL: http://www.plugandplaytechcenter.com/indus
　tries/travel-and-hospitality

Description: An accelerator for startups in the travel and hospitality industry. Provides support with venture and angel partners, mentorship, a data center, office space, and networking opportunities. This program has a focus on the following: sustainability, operational efficiency, customer engagement and loyalty, ancillary revenues, seamless journey, and fintech and new payment solutions.

REFERENCE WORKS

13894 ■ "4 Rivers Smokehouse Eyes Four New Locations in Florida" in Orlando Business Journal (Vol. 29, August 10, 2012, No. 8, pp. 1)

Pub: Baltimore Business Journal
Contact: Rhonda Pringle, President
E-mail: rpringle@bizjournals.com

Ed: Anjali Fluker. **Description:** Four new 4 River Smokehouse locations are being planned in Florida. The restaurant opened a branch in Winter Park. **Availability:** Print; Online.

13895 ■ "50 Years of Wings Big Business for Anchor Bar" in Business First of Buffalo (Vol. 30, March 7, 2014, No. 25, pp. 4)

Pub: American City Business Journals, Inc.
Contact: Mike Olivieri, Executive Vice President

Released: Weekly. **Price:** $140, Digital & Print; $115, Digital only. **Description:** The Anchor Bar and restaurant in Buffalo, New York has celebrated its 50th anniversary. The restaurant is known for its Buffalo-style chicken wings. A brief history of the restaurant is presented. **Availability:** Print; Online.

13896 ■ "$100M Complex To Be Built on Purple People Bridge" in Business Courier (Vol. 27, November 12, 2010, No. 28, pp. 1)

Pub: Business Courier

Ed: Lucy May. **Description:** A development firm closed a deal with the Newport Southbank Bridge Company for a $100M entertainment complex that will be built on top of the Purple People Bridge. The proposed project will cover 150,000 square feet with attractions such as restaurants, a boutique hotel, and pubs. **Availability:** Print; Online.

13897 ■ "2010 Book of Lists" in Business Courier (Vol. 26, December 26, 2009, No. 36, pp. 1)

Price: $49.95. **Description:** Rankings of companies and organizations within the business services, education, finance, health care, hospitality and tourism, real estate, and technology industries in the Cincinnati, Ohio-Northern Kentucky area are presented. Rankings are based on sales, business size, or other statistics. **Availability:** PDF; Online.

13898 ■ "Airmall Mulls I-95 Travel Plazas Bid" in Baltimore Business Journal (Vol. 29, September 2, 2011, No. 17, pp. 3)

Pub: Boston Business Journal
Contact: Carolyn M. Jones, President
E-mail: cmjones@bizjournals.com

Ed: Alexander Jackson. **Description:** Airmall USA is planning to move its food courts from the Baltimore/Washington International Thurgood Marshall Airport to the new travel plazas on Interstate 95. The plazas are up for bid. **Availability:** Online.

13899 ■ "All Fired Up!" in Small Business Opportunities (November 2008)

Description: Profile of Brixx Wood Fired Pizza, which has launched a franchising program due to the amount of interest the company's founders received over the years; franchisees do not need experience in the food industry or pizza restaurant service business in order to open a franchise of their own because all franchisees receive comprehensive training in which they are educated on all of the necessary tools to effectively run the business. **Availability:** Print; Online.

13900 ■ "Although a Chain, Claim Jumper is a Good Addition to Downtown" in Sacramento Business Journal (Vol. 30, January 10, 2014, No. 46, pp. 4)

Pub: American City Business Journals, Inc.
Contact: Mike Olivieri, Executive Vice President

Released: January 08, 2014. **Description:** Claim Jumper, which opened in downtown Sacramento, California in January 2014, serves comforting and reasonably priced food. The chain restaurant is a good addition to the area because of its ability to do business in an expensive location. **Availability:** Print; Mailing list; Online.

13901 ■ "American Express Provides $1 Million in Grants to Restaurants across the U.S." in Small Business Trends (March 4, 2023)

URL(s): smallbiztrends.com/2023/03/american-express-restaurants-grants.html

Ed: Annie Pilon. **Released:** March 04, 2023. **Description:** Historic restaurants around the U.S. are getting a boost from a grant program funded by American Express. **Availability:** Online.

13902 ■ "Aramark Rolls Out Ballpark Food Truck" in Nation's Restaurant News (Vol. 45, August 8, 2011, No. 16, pp. 4)

Description: Aramark installed its first ballpark food truck serving Asian-inspired noodle bowls at the outfield concourse at Coors Field in Colorado. **Availability:** Print.

13903 ■ "As the Supply Chain Slows, Demand for Aftermarket Equipment Takes Off" in Restaurant Business (November 17, 2021)

URL(s): www.restaurantbusinessonline.com/financing/supply-chain-slows-demand-aftermarket-equipment-takes

Ed: Jonathan Maze. **Released:** November 18, 2021. **Description:** Since Covid put in a dent in the global supply chain, restaurants have taken a second look at used equipment in order to stock their kitchens. **Availability:** Online.

13904 ■ "Baltimore Restaurants Banking on Andretti Name" in Baltimore Business Journal (Vol. 30, May 18, 2012, No. 2, pp. 1)
Pub: American City Business Journals, Inc.
Contact: Mike Olivieri, Executive Vice President
Ed: Jack Lambert. **Description:** Former race car driver Michael Andretti is leading the Andretti Sports Marketing to organize the Grand Prix in Baltimore, Maryland for the next five years. Restaurant and hotel owners are banking on Andretti to drive race fans to these establishments. Details of the 2011 event as well as forecasts on the next are discussed. **Availability:** Print; Online.

13905 ■ "Baltimore's Burger Market Sizzling with Newcomers" in Boston Business Journal (Vol. 29, June 10, 2011, No. 5, pp. 1)
Pub: Boston Business Journal
Contact: Carolyn M. Jones, President
E-mail: cmjones@bizjournals.com
Ed: Ryan Sharrow. **Description:** The burger trend in Maryland is on the rise with burger joints either opening up or expanding into several branches. Startup costs for this kind of business range between $250,000 to $400,000. With a growth rate of roughly 17 percent in 2009, this so-called better burger segment of the burger categories is expected to dominate the market for quite some time. **Availability:** Print; Online.

13906 ■ "Baltimore's Steamed Crab Prices Reach New Highs: Paying the Price" in Baltimore Business Journal (Vol. 28, July 9, 2010, No. 9, pp. 1)
Pub: Baltimore Business Journal
Contact: Rhonda Pringle, President
E-mail: rpringle@bizjournals.com
Ed: Emily Mullin. **Description:** Crab prices have never been higher in Baltimore, Maryland and businesses have been led to count on strengthening demand for seafood. For instance, the average price for a dozen large crabs has increased by 5 percent to $58.90. How restaurants have responded to the increase in prices is discussed, along with factors that might have caused the harvest of smaller crabs. **Availability:** Print.

13907 ■ "Bars, Restaurants to Change Game for Baltimore Grand Prix Patrons" in Baltimore Business Journal (Vol. 29, July 22, 2011, No. 11, pp. 1)
Pub: Boston Business Journal
Contact: Carolyn M. Jones, President
E-mail: cmjones@bizjournals.com
Ed: Alexander Jackson. **Description:** Restaurants and bar owners in Baltimore, Maryland have changed the way they do business as the Baltimore Grand Prix approaches. Owners have gone so far as to offering new services or renting out their entire restaurants to companies for the three-day event in September. **Availability:** Print; Online.

13908 ■ "Baskin-Robbins Tests New Upscale Concept" in Ice Cream Reporter (Vol. 21, September 20, 2008, No. 10, pp. 1)
Description: Baskin-Robbins is opening its new upscale store, Cafe 31 in an effort to invigorate its brand. The shop will serve fondues, cakes and other treats prepared by an in-store chef. **Availability:** Print; Online.

13909 ■ "Beyond Grits: The Many Varieties of Southern Cuisine" in Women In Business (Vol. 62, June 2010, No. 2, pp. 14)
Pub: American Business Women's Association
Contact: Rene Street, Executive Director
Ed: Debbie Gold. **Released:** June 01, 2010. **Description:** Southern cuisine is believed to be associated with grits, but the cuisine is not always with grits and offers varieties from Europe, Native American and

African cooking. Southern cuisine varieties include soul food, Creole food, Cajun food and Low Country food. Examples are provided. **Availability:** Online.

13910 ■ "Bienvenido, Mercadito" in Washington Business Journal (Vol. 33, September 12, 2014, No. 21, pp. 8)
Pub: American City Business Journals, Inc.
Contact: Mike Olivieri, Executive Vice President
Released: Weekly. **Price:** $4, introductory 4-week offer(Digital & Print). **Description:** Restaurateur, Alfredo Sandoval, partnered with brothers Felipe and Patricio to open Mercadito, an upscale casual Mexican restaurant at the Marriott Marquis Hotel in Washington DC. The restaurant is geared to attract customers between 25 and 40 years of age. **Availability:** Print; Online.

13911 ■ "BK Menu Gives Casual Dining Reason to Worry" in Advertising Age (Vol. 79, November 17, 2008, No. 43, pp. 12)
Pub: Crain Communications, Inc.
Contact: Jessica Botos, Manager, Marketing
E-mail: jessica.botos@crainsnewyork.com
Ed: Emily Bryson York. **Description:** Burger King is beginning to compete with such casual dining restaurants as Applebees and the Cheesecake Factory with new premium menu items, including thicker burgers and ribs; statistical data regarding the casual dining segment which continues to fall and Burger King, whose sales continue to rise is included. **Availability:** Online.

13912 ■ "Black-Owned Company Signed $334 Million Deal with Houston's William P. Hobby Airport" in Black Enterprise(February 10, 2023)
Ed: Darryl Robertson. **Released:** February 10, 2023. **Description:** Black-owned Latrelle's Management signed a deal to operate over 17,000 square feet of the Hobby Airport's dining areas. **Availability:** Online.

13913 ■ "Bonefish Grill Debuts New Cocktail to Benefit Conservation Foundation" in Ecology, Environment & Conservation Business (May 17, 2014, pp. 5)
Pub: NewsRX LLC.
Contact: Kalani Rosell, Contact
Description: Bonefish Grill has introduced the Ocean Trust Tropic Heat Martini to support the Ocean Trust, an ocean conservation foundation. The new drink contains house-made infused pineapple Absolut vodka, with fresh mango and a thin slice of jalapeno and served at their restaurants nationwide. **Availability:** Online.

13914 ■ "Brought To You By the Letter 'W'" in Washington Business Journal (Vol. 33, August 29, 2014, No. 19, pp. 6)
Pub: American City Business Journals, Inc.
Contact: Mike Olivieri, Executive Vice President
Released: Weekly. **Price:** $4, introductory 4-week offer(Digital & Print). **Description:** W Hotel, Washington DC's food and beverage spaces are undergoing renovations. Hotel guests will see a new roof and a more stylish, upscale restaurant. W Hotel's plan to offer a luxury experience is discussed. **Availability:** Print; Online.

13915 ■ "Buildings to Flank Broken Spoke: Legendary Country Dance Hall To Be Surrounded But Won't Be Touched" in Austin Business Journal (Vol. 32, April 13, 2012, No. 6, pp. 1)
Pub: American City Business Journals, Inc.
Contact: Mike Olivieri, Executive Vice President
Ed: Vicky Garza. **Description:** A $60 million mixed use development tentatively called 704 at the Spoke is being planned along South Lamar Boulevard in Austin, Texas. The plan includes 378 apartments and 20,000 square feet of restaurant and retail space. The project will have the historic Broken Spoke Dance Hall as its hub. **Availability:** Online.

13916 ■ "Burger King Moves Forward on Commitment to Electric Vehicles" in Bizwomen (March 27, 2023)
URL(s): www.bizjournals.com/bizwomen/news/lates t-news/2023/03/burger-king.html
Ed: Jasmine Floyd. **Released:** March 27, 2023. **Description:** Burger King parent company, Restaurant Brands International Inc., set goals on reducing greenhouse gas emissions from their businesses. To help achieve that, 31% of it's Burger King fleet has transitioned to electric vehicles. **Availability:** Online.

13917 ■ "California Restaurant Association Sues to Block Berkeley, Calif., Natural Gas Ban" in Nation's Restaurant News (November 22, 2019)
URL(s): www.nrn.com/operations/california-restauran t-association-sues-block-berkeley-calif-natural-gas -ban
Ed: Lisa Jennings. **Released:** November 22, 2019. **Description:** After Berkeley became the first U.S. city to approve an ordinance to phase out natural gas pipes in new construction in an effort to go all-electric, the California Restaurant Association sued the city due to chefs needing to cook over a fire. In the complaint, the CRA argues that the ordinance in unenforceable due to conflicts with federal and state laws. **Availability:** Online.

13918 ■ "Chipotle Mexican Grill Adds Alexa for Reorders of Favorite Meals" in Nation's Restaurant News (November 21, 2019)
URL(s): www.nrn.com/fast-casual/chipotle-mexican -grill-adds-alexa-reorders-favorite-meals
Ed: Nancy Luna. **Released:** November 21, 2019. **Description:** Chipotle has added Amazon's voice ordering assistant, Alexa, to its list of ways consumers can order. However, there are limitations since it's only set up to reorder meals for delivery once a Chipotle loyalty member links their profile to the Alexa app. **Availability:** Online.

13919 ■ "Chuy's Ready to Serve New Markets" in Austin Business Journal (Vol. 31, June 17, 2011, No. 15, pp. 1)
Pub: Austin Business Journal
Contact: Rachel McGrath, Director
E-mail: rmcgrath@bizjournals.com
Ed: Cody Lyon. **Description:** Chuy's Holdings Inc. plans to expand into the Southeastern United States, particularly in Atlanta, Georgia. The restaurant, which secured $67.5 million in debt financing in May 2011, added 20 stores in five years and plans to open eight locations in 2011. **Availability:** Print; Online.

13920 ■ "City Board Tweaks Internet Cafe Ordinance" in Ocala Star-Banner (July 19, 2011)
Pub: Ocala Star-Banner
Contact: Austin L. Miller, Officer
E-mail: austin.miller@starbanner.com
Ed: Susan Latham Carr. **Description:** Ocala Planning and Zoning Commission revised the proposed draft of the Internet Cafe ordinance by eliminating the cap on the number of locations allowed, but keeping fees and number of devices the same. **Availability:** Online.

13921 ■ "Click Your Chicken" in Canadian Business (Vol. 87, October 2014, No. 10, pp. 11)
Released: October 2014. **Description:** A number of business ideas, products and strategies are ranked from the ingenious to the extremely bizarre. A mobile Web startup called FarmLogs helps farmers track everything from soil conditions to weather to profit forecasts. Kentucky Fried Chicken restaurants awards top Twitter fans in Japan with USB drive, a mouse and a keyboard designed with chicken parts.

13922 ■ "Convention Ctr. Rehab To Impact Hotels, Eateries" in Silicon Valley/San Jose Business Journal (Vol. 30, May 18, 2012, No. 8, pp. 1)
Pub: Baltimore Business Journal
Contact: Rhonda Pringle, President
E-mail: rpringle@bizjournals.com

Description: The renovation of the San Jose McEnery Convention Center is seen to adversely impact businesses in the area. Contractors have already demolished the former Martin Luther King Jr. Main Library. Business sales in the area are expected to decline owing to the renovation.

13923 ■ *"Cooking With Celeb Chef Jet Tila" in Dallas Business Journal (Vol. 37, June 6, 2014, No. 39, pp. 6)*
Pub: American City Business Journals, Inc.
Contact: Mike Olivieri, Executive Vice President
Released: June 06, 2014. **Price:** $4, Introductory 4-Week Offer(Digital & Print). **Description:** Celebrity chef, Jet Tila, discloses his plans for the Pakpao restaurant which he co-owns at Dallas Design District in Texas. He hopes to leverage the authentic Thai cuisine offered by the restaurant and bring the concept to airports or hotels. **Availability:** Print; Online.

13924 ■ *"Corrales Site of New Senior Living/ Care Complex" in America's Intelligence Wire (August 13, 2012)*
Description: David Dronet, developer of Corrales Senior Living LLC, has chosen Corrales, New Mexico as its newest site to construct a continuum of care for senior citizens. The project entails a $60 million complex of private homes and health care units with amenities like a restaurant, fitness areas, and gardens. **Availability:** Print; Online.

13925 ■ *"Counting Crabs: Supply Dips, Putting Crimp on Memorial Day Feast" in Boston Business Journal (Vol. 29, June 3, 2011, No. 4, pp. 1)*
Pub: Boston Business Journal
Contact: Carolyn M. Jones, President
E-mail: cmjones@bizjournals.com
Ed: Scott Dance. **Price:** $4, Introductory 4-Week Offer(Digital Only). **Description:** Restaurateurs in Baltimore City experienced low supply of crabs this Memorial Day 2011 owing to the early season and the fact that many small crabbers took time off during the weekend. Sales were cut in half compared with previous Memorial Day weekends and prices rose to as much as $185 to $200 per box of crabs. Normal supply is expected, though, as summer pushes on. **Availability:** Print; Online.

13926 ■ *"Couple Hopes to Lead Schlotzsky's Twin Cities Revival" in Business Journal (Vol. 31, January 17, 2014, No. 34, pp. 4)*
Pub: American City Business Journals, Inc.
Contact: Mike Olivieri, Executive Vice President
Description: Austin, Texas-based Schlotzsky's announced plans to open six Minnesota locations as it tries to regain its national prominence. The bankruptcy in 2004 and the reduction of its restaurant count had wiped out eight Minnesota restaurants and left only the Edina location. Schlotzsky's six-restaurant deal with the local franchisees is examined. **Availability:** Print; Online.

13927 ■ *"Crescent to Add Two Restaurants" in Memphis Business Journal (Vol. 33, April 6, 2012, No. 52, pp. 1)*
Pub: Baltimore Business Journal
Contact: Rhonda Pringle, President
E-mail: rpringle@bizjournals.com
Description: Highwoods Properties Inc. is planning to open two restaurants at its Crescent Center in Memphis, Tennessee. The new establishment are both upscale concepts from Darden Restaurants Inc. **Availability:** Print; Online.

13928 ■ *"Crucible: Losing the Top Job - And Winning It Back" in Harvard Business Review (Vol. 88, October 2010, No. 10, pp. 136)*
Pub: Harvard Business Publishing
Contact: Diane Belcher, Managing Director
Ed: Alison Beard. **Price:** $8.95, PDF. **Description:** Michael Mack chronicles the changes in perspectives that occurred when he was fired from Garden Fresh, a restaurant firm he co-owned. Once again at the

company helm, he is now more receptive to outside input and acknowledges the importance of work-life balance. **Availability:** Online; PDF.

13929 ■ *"Drought Takes Toll on Farmers, Restaurants" in Saint Louis Business Journal (Vol. 31, August 12, 2011, No. 51, pp. 1)*
Pub: Saint Louis Business Journal
Contact: Robert Bobroff, President
E-mail: rbobroff@bizjournals.com
Ed: E.B. Solomont. **Description:** The drought in St. Louis, Missouri has adversely impacted farmers and restaurants in the areas. Diners can expect to lose some ingredients from their menus. **Availability:** Online.

13930 ■ *"Dunnellon Welcomes Internet Cafe Jobs" in Ocala Star-Banner (August 18, 2011)*
Pub: Ocala Star-Banner
Contact: Austin L. Miller, Officer
E-mail: austin.miller@starbanner.com
Ed: Fred Hiers. **Description:** Despite the fact that a few Internet cafes offering patrons to win cash and are facing legal challenges, the city's planning commission would welcome the cafes in order to provide more jobs for its residents. **Availability:** Online.

13931 ■ *"Estate Planning Tips for Food and Beverage Entrepreneurs" in Nutter Uncommon Law (March 9, 2020)*
Released: March 09, 2020. **Description:** Discuss what an estate plan is and why food and beverage entrepreneurs should set up an estate plan. Also provides information on core estate planning documents, tax information, and family protections for your small business. **Availability:** Online.

13932 ■ *"Exporting Portlandia: Unconventional Brands Carry a Taste of Portland Across U.S." in Business Journal Portland (Vol. 30, January 17, 2014, No. 46, pp. 4)*
Pub: American City Business Journals, Inc.
Contact: Mike Olivieri, Executive Vice President
Description: Some Portland, Oregon-based food companies have been bringing the area's reputation across the U.S. Voodoo Doughnut has opened a branch in Denver, Colorado. Meanwhile, Laughing Planet is opening several West Coast cafes. **Availability:** Print; Online.

13933 ■ *"A Failed Promise: A Dream Job Gone..or Just Delayed?" in Restaurant Business (Vol. 107, September 2008, No. 9, pp. 34)*
Description: Profile of Jeremy Lycan, executive chef who taught at the California Culinary Academy. Lycan tells of accepting a position as executive chef from his mentor, and later started his own restaurant. **Availability:** Online.

13934 ■ *"Farm to Table Distribution Getting Boost" in Philadelphia Business Journal (Vol. 28, May 11, 2012, No. 13, pp. 1)*
Pub: Baltimore Business Journal
Contact: Rhonda Pringle, President
E-mail: rpringle@bizjournals.com
Price: $4, Introductory 4-Week Offer(Digital & Print). **Description:** The farm-to-table movement has changed the distribution network of food and the offerings on many restaurants in Philadelphia. A new range of companies has emerged due to the demand for local food. Green Meadow Farms and Lancaster Farm Fresh are two of the businesses that found the niche in supplying restaurants with local produce. **Availability:** Print; Online.

13935 ■ *"Fear of the Unknown Muted Impact of Baltimore Grand Prix" in Baltimore Business Journal (Vol. 29, September 9, 2011, No. 18, pp. 3)*
Pub: Boston Business Journal
Contact: Carolyn M. Jones, President
E-mail: cmjones@bizjournals.com
Ed: Alexander Jackson. **Description:** Baltimore Grand Prix caught restaurateurs, hoteliers and street vendors in Baltimore, Maryland unprepared for the

thousands of race fans who attended the inaugural event over Labor Day weekend. The race popularity is relatively unknown to them and some felt they were not able to make as much money as they had hoped. **Availability:** Online.

13936 ■ *"Fines Can't Snuff Out Hookah Sales" in Providence Business News (Vol. 28, March 3, 2014, No. 48, pp. 1)*
Pub: American City Business Journals, Inc.
Contact: Mike Olivieri, Executive Vice President
Released: March 01, 2014. **Description:** The City of Providence, Rhode Island initiated a crackdown on bars and restaurants serving Middle Eastern-style water pipes, known as hookahs in violation of state anti-smoking laws. Gianfranco Marrocco, owner of several Federal Hill nightspots, believes that many bar owners will just pay the fine because hookah lounges are a good revenue source. **Availability:** Print; Online.

13937 ■ *"Florida Fast 100: D&D Construction Services" in South Florida Business Journal (Vol. 35, September 19, 2014, No. 8, pp. 16)*
Pub: American City Business Journals, Inc.
Contact: Mike Olivieri, Executive Vice President
Description: Profile of D and D Construction, who reports increased earnings in 2013 totaling $26.5 million. The increase has been attributed to the commercial real estate market's recovery from the economic recession. The company is focusing on offering hospitality (restaurant, hotel) projects. **Availability:** Online.

13938 ■ *"Flurry of Activity from Restaurant Groups as Industry Strengthens" in Wichita Business Journal (Vol. 27, February 17, 2012, No. 7, pp. 1)*
Pub: Baltimore Business Journal
Contact: Rhonda Pringle, President
E-mail: rpringle@bizjournals.com
Description: Atlanta, Georgia-based Chick-fil-A chain is set to open two restaurants in Wichita, Kansas and those additions were highly anticipated. However, there were other local management groups and franchisees that are investing on new buildings and refurbishing stores. Insights on the increasing restaurant constructions are also given. **Availability:** Print; Online.

13939 ■ *"Food-Truck Learnings Travel Indoors" in Nation's Restaurant News (Vol. 45, June 27, 2011, No. 13, pp. 3)*
Description: Challenges faced by owners of food truck businesses are discussed. Ways a food truck can be used to promote a restaurant's menu are covered. **Availability:** Print; Online.

13940 ■ *"The Foodie Generation Grows Up" in Business Review Albany (Vol. 41, August 8, 2014, No. 20, pp. 4)*
Description: Members of Albany, New York's restaurant sector have been meeting the demands of millennials, who have become the catalyst for many of the sector's trends. Some restaurants are serving smaller plates to attract young customers. **Availability:** Print; Online.

13941 ■ *"Former NFL Player Tackles a New Restaurant Concept" in Inc. (Vol. 33, September 2011, No. 7, pp. 32)*
Pub: Inc. Magazine
Ed: Nadine Heintz. **Description:** Matt Chatham, former NFL player, launched SkyCrepers, a chain of fast-serve crepe shops with his wife Erin. Chatham entered Babson College's MBA program after retiring from football. **Availability:** Online.

13942 ■ *"Franchisee to Add 10 New Applebee's" in Memphis Business Journal (Vol. 34, June 8, 2012, No. 8, pp. 1)*
Pub: Baltimore Business Journal
Contact: Rhonda Pringle, President
E-mail: rpringle@bizjournals.com
Ed: Andy Ashby. **Description:** Apple Investor Group LLC seeks to open 10 more Applebee's restaurants in Memphis over the next two years. The franchisee

purchased the 70-county market from DineEquity for $23 million in early 2012. The group is upgrading 17 Mid-South Applbee's units. **Availability:** Print; Online.

13943 ■ *"Game On at Jordan's New Spot" in Crain's Chicago Business (Vol. 34, October 24, 2011, No. 42, pp. 34)*
Pub: Crain Communications Inc.
Contact: Barry Asin, President
Ed: Laura Bianchi. **Description:** Michael Jordan partnered with Cornerstone Restaurant Group to launch Michael Jordan's Steakhouse in Chicago. Details are included. **Availability:** Online.

13944 ■ *"Garden Bargains: Restaurant Cut Costs With Homegrown Foods" in Washington Business Journal (Vol. 33, August 22, 2014, No. 18, pp. 6)*
Pub: American City Business Journals, Inc.
Contact: Mike Olivieri, Executive Vice President
Released: Weekly. **Price:** $4, introductory 4-week offer(Digital & Print). **Description:** A number of chefs and restaurants in Washington DC are seeing the benefits of growing their own healthy kitchen gardens. The Urbana restaurant is saving $250 monthly in herbs since it started planting them in 2014 and chef, Ethan McKee expects to increase that savings to $75 monthly in 2015. **Availability:** Print; Online.

13945 ■ *"Hasslochers Welcome Home a San Antonio Tradition" in San Antonio Business Journal (Vol. 28, July 25, 2014, No. 24, pp. 8)*
Pub: American City Business Journals, Inc.
Contact: Mike Olivieri, Executive Vice President
Released: Weekly. **Price:** $4, introductory 4-week offer(Digital & Print). **Description:** Hasslocher Enterprises Inc. acquired the rights to the shuttered Texan-Mexican restaurant La Fonda Alamo Heights and brought it back to life with a grand reopening in North Central San Antonio, Texas. Restaurant general manager, Bill Sheridan, says the customers and the employees are like family to each other. **Availability:** Print; Online.

13946 ■ *"Healthful, Organic Food Is the Name of the Game at Renee's" in AZ Daily Star (May 10, 2012)*
Pub: McClatchy Tribune Information Services
Contact: Patrick J. Talamantes, President
Ed: Kristen Cook. **Description:** Profile of Renee's Organic Oven offer organic and locally grown foods at their restaurant. The eatery is owned by husband and wife team, Steve and Renee Kreager. **Availability:** Online.

13947 ■ *"Homes, Not Bars, Stay Well Tended" in Advertising Age (Vol. 79, January 28, 2008, No. 4, pp. 8)*
Pub: Crain Communications, Inc.
Contact: Jessica Botos, Manager, Marketing
E-mail: jessica.botos@crainsnewyork.com
Ed: Jeremy Mullman. **Description:** Due to the downturn in the economy, consumers are drinking less at bars and restaurants; however, according to the Distilled Spirits Council of the United States, they are still purchasing expensive liquor to keep in their homes. **Availability:** Online.

13948 ■ *"How BBQ Can Be Birmingham's Secret Sauce" in Birmingham Business Journal (Vol. 31, May 9, 2014, No. 19, pp. 4)*
Pub: American City Business Journals, Inc.
Contact: Mike Olivieri, Executive Vice President
Released: Weekly. **Price:** $4, introductory 4-week offer(Digital only). **Description:** Local barbecue joints in Birmingham, Alabama are branching out to new markets and extending distinct barbecue brand of the city through franchises and corporate expansions across the U.S. Experts say this trend is contributing to more brand awareness and tourists for Birmingham. **Availability:** Print; Online.

13949 ■ *"How South Florida Can Revive a Flagging Sector" in South Florida Business Journal (Vol. 34, April 4, 2014, No. 37, pp. 10)*
Pub: American City Business Journals, Inc.
Contact: Mike Olivieri, Executive Vice President

Released: Weekly. **Price:** $8, Introductory 4-week offer(Digital & Print). **Description:** South Florida convention centers are trying to address the sluggish demand for conventions to the area by upgrading its facilities and adding hotels. The ancillary revenue generate by the attendees at hotels, restaurants, and other establishments makes a convention as key economic drivers. The efforts to boost the region's position as convention destinations are also addressed. **Availability:** Print; Online.

13950 ■ *"How Tender Green Turns Top Chefs Into Fast-Food Cooks: a Quick-Serve Chain Lures Kitchen Starts by Treating Them Like Entrepreneurs" in Inc. (Vol. 36, March 2014, No. 2, pp. 28)*
Pub: Mansueto Ventures L.L.C.
Contact: Stephanie Mehta, Chief Executive Officer
Released: March 2014. **Description:** Chefs Erik Oberholtzer, David Dressier and Matt Lyman launched Tender Greens, a series of quick-service restaurants serving fresh organic dishes made from local produce, cheeses and meats. The three partners set out to hire fine-dining chefs to run each location. The used their entrepreneurial skills to inspire great chefs into entrepreneur type control by allowing them to run their restaurant individually, including operations, culture and menu items. Tender Greens has grown to 12 locations with an estimated $40 million annual revenue. Their business vision and strategy is examined. **Availability:** Print; Online.

13951 ■ *"How to... Harness Green Power" in The Caterer (July 20, 2012, No. 325)*
Pub: LNRS Data Services Limited
Contact: Mark Vickers Kelsey, Director
Description: Roger and Emma Stevens discuss their success as at winning the Considerate Hoteliers Association's award for Best Green Marketing Initiative. The couple discusses their restaurant and its partnership with tow nearby guesthouses. **Availability:** Online.

13952 ■ *"If They Build It, Will Customers Come?" in Business Journal Portland (Vol. 30, February 7, 2014, No. 49, pp. 7)*
Pub: American City Business Journals, Inc.
Contact: Mike Olivieri, Executive Vice President
Price: $4, Introductory 4-week offer(Digital & Print). **Description:** The Portland Trail Blazers partnered with Levy Restaurants to open a 10,000-square-foot restaurant at Moda Center in Oregon in spring 2014. GBD Architects and Lorentz Brunn Construction were enlisted for the project. **Availability:** Print; Online.

13953 ■ *In-N-Out Burger: A Behind-the-Counter Look at the Fast-Food Chain That Breaks All the Rules*
Pub: HarperCollins Publishers L.L.C.
Contact: Brian Murray, President
Ed: Stacy Perman. **Released:** December 10, 2010. **Price:** $14.99, paperback; $8.24, e-book. **Description:** Business analysis of the factors that helped In-N-Out Burgers, a family owned burger chain in California, along with a history of its founding family, the Synders. **Availability:** E-book; Print.

13954 ■ *"In the Raw: Karyn Calabrese Brings Healthy Dining to a New Sophisticated Level" in Black Enterprise (Vol. 41, September 2010)*
Pub: Earl G. Graves Ltd.
Contact: Earl Graves, Jr., President
Ed: Sonia Alleyne. **Description:** Profile of Karyn Calabrese whose businesses are based in Chicago, Illinois. Calabrese has launched a complete line of products (vitamins and beauty items), services (spa, chiropractic, and acupuncture treatments), and restaurants to bring health dining and lifestyles to a better level. **Availability:** Online.

13955 ■ *"Internet Cafe Logging in to Chardon Plaza?" in News-Herald (July 16, 2011)*
Ed: Betsy Scott. **Description:** Pearl's High Rollers Inc. applied for an Internet sweepstakes cafe license that would reside in a vacant space in Chardon Plaza.

City officials have created regulations for such businesses and Pearl's applied for a license and is awaiting approval. **Availability:** Online.

13956 ■ *"It's 4:30 p.m. Do You Know Where Your Staff Is?" in Canadian Business (Vol. 85, August 13, 2012, No. 13, pp. 62)*
Ed: Chris Johns, Courtney Shea. **Description:** Some of the best business patios in Canada are recommended. They include the Terrase Place D'Armes in Montreal, Quebec; West Restaurant and Bar in Calgary, Alberta; and Earl's Kitchen and Bar in Toronto, Ontario. **Availability:** Online.

13957 ■ *"It's Good To Be King" in South Florida Business Journal (Vol. 35, August 29, 2014, No. 5, pp. 12)*
Released: December 01, 2013. **Description:** The $11.4 billion deal that will create a new holding company for Burger King Worldwide and Tim Hortons will be based in Oakville, Ontario, Canada and was met with public outrage. Burger King declares that the merger with the Canadian coffee and doughnut franchise chain was about global growth, not a strategy to avoid millions of dollars in corporate income tax payments to the U.S. government. **Availability:** Print; Online.

13958 ■ *"La Cantera Resort Expects to Benefit from Big Transformation" in San Antonio Business Journal (Vol. 28, July 18, 2014, No. 23, pp. 8)*
Pub: American City Business Journals, Inc.
Contact: Mike Olivieri, Executive Vice President
Released: Weekly. **Price:** $4, Introductory 4-week offer(Digital & Print). **Description:** La Cantera Hill County Resort in San Antonio, Texas is planning a multimillion dollar major renovation of the property and the addition of a spa. The resort announced the suspension of overnight accommodations and restaurant operations during the major phase of the construction from November 3, 2014 until early April 2015. **Availability:** Print; Online.

13959 ■ *"Learn New Ideas from Experienced Menu Makers" in Nation's Restaurant News (Vol. 45, June 27, 2011, No. 13, pp. 82)*
Pub: Informa USA, Inc.
Contact: Stephen A. Carter, Chief Executive Officer
Ed: Nancy Kruse. **Released:** June 27, 2011. **Description:** National Restaurant Association Restaurant, Hotel-Motel Show featured the Food Truck Spot, a firm committed to all aspects of mobile catering, foodtruck manufacturers, leasers of fully equipped truck and a food-truck franchising group.

13960 ■ *"Looking To Hire Young? Be Careful" in Boston Business Journal (Vol. 30, November 19, 2010, No. 43, pp. 1)*
Pub: Boston Business Journal
Contact: Carolyn M. Jones, President
E-mail: cmjones@bizjournals.com
Ed: Lisa van der Pool. **Released:** Weekly. **Description:** The Massachusetts Commission Against Discrimination (MCAD) has been using undercover job applicants to expose discrimination. Cabot's Ice Cream and Restaurant has been accused of denying older workers equal employment opportunities. MCAD has discovered unfair hiring practices such as hiring high school and college students. **Availability:** Print; Online.

13961 ■ *"Lux Coffees, Breads Push Chains to React" in Advertising Age (Vol. 77, June 26, 2006, No. 26, pp. S14)*
Pub: Crain Communications, Inc.
Contact: Jessica Botos, Manager, Marketing
E-mail: jessica.botos@crainsnewyork.com
Ed: Kate MacArthur. **Description:** Fast-food giants such as McDonald's, Burger King, Dunkin' Donuts and Subway have adjusted their menus in order to become more competitive with gourmet coffee shops and bakeries like Panera Bread and Starbucks which have taken a large share in the market. Statistical data included. **Availability:** Online.

13962 ■ *"A Master Chef's Recipe for Business Success" in Business Strategy Review (Vol. 23, Spring 2012, No. 1, pp. 65)*

Description: Often called the world's greatest chef, Ferran Adria, longtime owner of El Built, Spain's three-star Michelin rated revolutionary restaurant, is now embarking on a new venture: the El Built Foundation, a place where chefs can create, interact, and discuss their ideas with researchers from other disciplines. He recently spoke at London Business School as part of his tour of a number of select universities to invite students to enter a competition to design an innovative business model for the new Foundation. **Availability:** Print; Online.

13963 ■ *"McDonald's Finds a Flaw in Ordering Kiosks: No Cash Accepted" in Bloomberg (November 13, 2019)*

URL(s): www.bloomberg.com/news/articles/2019 -11-13/mcdonald-s-finds-a-flaw-in-its-ordering-ki osks-no-cash-accepted

Ed: Leslie Patton. **Released:** November 13, 2019. **Description:** Since touchscreen ordering is increasing worldwide, McDonald's has been investing in kiosks as part of their effort to attract more on-the-go customers. However, the kiosks they invested in have a major flaw: they do not accept cash. Many households do not have access to debit or credit cards making these kiosks unusable to them. Adding to the frustration is that many franchises have invested their own money into the cost of the renovations featuring these kiosks. **Availability:** Online.

13964 ■ *"McDonald's Loses Its Sizzle" in Barron's (Vol. 88, March 17, 2008, No. 11, pp. 47)*

Description: McDonald's has promised to return $15 billion to $17 billion to shareholders in 2007-2009 but headwinds are rising for the company. December, 2007 same-store sales were flat and the company's traffic growth in the U.S. is slowing. Its shares are likely to trade in tandem with the market until recession fears recede. **Availability:** Online.

13965 ■ *"Meet Two of Universal CityWalk's New Restaurateurs" in Orlando Business Journal (Vol. 30, January 10, 2014, No. 29, pp. 3)*

Pub: American City Business Journals, Inc.

Contact: Mike Olivieri, Executive Vice President

Released: Weekly. **Price:** $8, introductory 4-week offer(Digital & Print). **Description:** Cowfish cofounder, Marcus Hall and Hot Dog Hall of Fame chief financial officer, Jeff Bornmann, share their plan for their restaurants at CityWalk in Orlando, Florida. Hall says his restaurant will have 5675 seats and will offer various burgers and sushi choices. Bornmann will recreate the baseball stadium setting and offer more than 13 varieties of hot dogs. **Availability:** Print; Online.

13966 ■ *"Meeting and Banquet Venues" in Business Review Albany (Vol. 41, August 8, 2014, No. 20, pp. 6)*

Released: Weekly. **Price:** $25, download. **Description:** The top 25 meeting and banquet venues in Albany, New York in 2013 are ranked by number of banquets hosted. The Desmond Hotel and Conference Center hold the top spot. The Otesega Resort Hotel ranked second. **Availability:** Print; Online.

13967 ■ *"Memphis BBQ: It's Just About the Pork" in Women in Business (Vol. 64, Summer 2012, No. 2, pp. 14)*

Ed: Debbie Gold. **Description:** Several barbeque joints located in Memphis, Tennessee are recommended. Tops BBQ is a barbeque institution with 14 locations across Memphis, Payne's Bar-B-Q is known for its pig sandwich and Central BBQ Memphis serves a pork plate with a dark, heavily smoked crust. **Availability:** Print; PDF; Online.

13968 ■ *"Menchie's Tops Restaurant Business' Future 50 List" in Ice Cream Reporter (Vol. 23, August 20, 2010, No. 9, pp. 4)*

Description: Menchie's, frozen yogurt shop, announced it placed first in the Restaurant Business

Magazine's Future 50, ranking the franchise the fastest-growing in the food industry. **Availability:** Print; Online.

13969 ■ *"More SouthPark Shopping for Charlotte" in Charlotte Business Journal (Vol. 25, July 16, 2010, No. 17, pp. 1)*

Pub: Charlotte Business Journal

Contact: Robert Morris, Editor

E-mail: rmorris@bizjournals.com

Ed: Will Boye. **Description:** Charlotte, North Carolina-based Bissel Companies has announced plans to expand its retail presence at the Siskey and Sharon properties in SouthPark. Bissel Companies has requested a rezoning to a mixed-use development classification so that it can utilize the entire ground floor of the Siskey building for restaurant and retail uses. **Availability:** Print; Online.

13970 ■ *My Life From Scratch: A Sweet Journey of Starting Over, One Cake at a Time*

Pub: Broadway Business

Ed: Gesine Bullock-Prado. **Released:** June 08, 2010. **Price:** $15, paperback; $10.99, e-book. **Description:** Lively account of Old World recipes, Bullock-Prado, a former Hollywood film developer and sister to actress Sandra Bullock, recounts the joys and heartbreak of running her own patisserie in Montpelier, Vermont. Having fled Los Angeles with her husband, Ray for the simpler pleasures of a small town near the Green Mountains, she opened her own bake shop, Gesine Confectionary in 2004, mostly on the fame of the macaroons she refashioned from her German mother's favorite almond treat, mandelhoernchen (and the casual mention of her sister in an interview). Her memoir follows one day in a busy baker's life, from waking at 3 a.m. to prepare the batter and bake her croissants, scones, and sticky buns, before opening her shop at 7 a.m., through the hectic lunch, and 3 p.m. tea time. **Availability:** E-book; Print.

13971 ■ *"New Brewpub Includes a Manapua Shop" in Pacific Business News (Vol. 52, March 14, 2014, No. 3, pp. 6)*

Pub: American City Business Journals, Inc.

Contact: Mike Olivieri, Executive Vice President

Released: March 14, 2014. **Price:** $4, Introductory 4-Week Offer(Digital & Print). **Description:** Hoku Brewing Company is set to open a brewery restaurant in Hawaii. The new restaurant will be built on the site of the former Aloha Beer Company restaurant. The project is a joint venture between Hoku and restaurateur Dave Campbell. **Availability:** Print; Online.

13972 ■ *"A New Flavor for Second Street: Lamberts Chef Backs New Restaurant" in Austin Business JournalInc. (Vol. 28, January 2, 2009)*

Description: Chef Larry McGuire has teamed up with the Icon Group to develop the La Condesa restaurant and the Malverde lounge in the Second Street district. The La Condesa restaurant will be a Mexico City-inspired restaurant, while the Malverde lounge atop the La Condesa will host DJs and live music. **Availability:** Print; Online.

13973 ■ *"A New Mix of Tenants Settles In Downtown" in Crain's New York Business (Vol. 24, January 13, 2008, No. 2, pp. 26)*

Pub: Crain Communications, Inc.

Contact: Jessica Botos, Manager, Marketing

E-mail: jessica.botos@crainsnewyork.com

Ed: Andrew Marks. **Description:** More and more nonfinancial firms are relocating downtown due to the new retailers and restaurants that are reshaping the look and feel of lower Manhattan.

13974 ■ *"New Owners Take Over at Leather District Restaurants" in Boston Business Journal (Vol. 33, January 31, 2014, No. 53, pp. 4)*

Pub: American City Business Journals, Inc.

Contact: Mike Olivieri, Executive Vice President

Released: Weekly. **Description:** Restaurateur Anthony Botta of Boston, Massachusetts partnered with Mark Tosi of Pastene Companies to acquire Les Zygomates and Sorriso restaurants at the Leather

District owned by Ian Just. Robert Fathman was hired as the executive chef of both restaurants. **Availability:** Print; Online.

13975 ■ *"Nighttime Shuttle to Connect Detroit, Ferndale, Royal Oak" in Crain's Detroit Business (Vol. 24, October 6, 2008, No. 40, pp. 24)*

Pub: Crain Communications Inc.

Contact: Barry Asin, President

Ed: Nancy Kaffer. **Description:** With hopes of bridging the social gap between the cities and suburbs, Chris Ramos has launched The Night Move, a new shuttle service that will ferry passengers between Royal Oak, Ferndale and downtown Detroit. The cost for a round trip ticket is $12. **Availability:** Online.

13976 ■ *"Noodles Founder Becomes Colorado's Chief Marketing Officer" in Denver Business Journal (Vol. 64, August 24, 2012, No. 14, pp. 1)*

Pub: Baltimore Business Journal

Contact: Rhonda Pringle, President

E-mail: rpringle@bizjournals.com

Description: Governor John Hickenlooper has hired Aaron Kennedy to become the first chief marketing officer of the state of Colorado. The founder of restaurant, Noodles & Company will begin his job on August 6, 2012 of creating a state brand to attract more entrepreneurs and businesses entreprises to invest in Colorado. **Availability:** Print; Online.

13977 ■ *"Nurturing Talent for Tomorrow" in Restaurants and Institutions (Vol. 118, September 15, 2008, No. 14, pp. 90)*

Description: Hormel Foods Corporation and The Culinary Institute of America (CIA) have teamed to develop The Culinary Enrichment and Innovation Program that supports future culinary leaders by providing creative and competitive staff development. Sixteen students attend four three-day sessions at the CIA's campus in Hyde Park, New York; sessions include classroom teaching, one-on-one interaction with leading culinarians, and hands-on kitchen time.

13978 ■ *"Ohio Franchisee Buys 21 Jacksonville-Area Papa John's" in Florida Times-Union (December 20, 2010)*

Pub: Florida Times-Union

Ed: Mark Basch. **Description:** Ohio-based Papa John's pizza franchise acquired 21 of the restaurants in Duval, Clay and St. Johns counties in Jacksonville, Florida. **Availability:** Online.

13979 ■ *"Old Friends Make Old Buildings Successful Restaurants" in Crain's Detroit Business (Vol. 24, February 4, 2008, No. 5, pp. 14)*

Pub: Crain Communications Inc.

Contact: Barry Asin, President

Ed: Brent Snavely. **Description:** Profiles of Jon Carlson and Gregory Lobdell, founders of ten new restaurants in Ann Arbor, Royal Oak, and Traverse City, Michigan, and their plans to add four more in the near future. **Availability:** Online.

13980 ■ *"On the Green: Sheila Johnson Adds $35 Million Golf Resort To Her Expanding Portfolio" in Black Enterprise (January 2008)*

Pub: Earl G. Graves Ltd.

Contact: Earl Graves, Jr., President

Ed: Donna M. Owens. **Description:** Profile of Sheila Johnson, CEO of Salamander Hospitality LLC, made history when she purchased the Innisbrook Resort and Golf Club, making her the first African American woman to own this type of property. The resort includes four championship golf courses, six swimming pools, four restaurants, eleven tennis courts, three conference halls, and a nature preserve. **Availability:** Online.

13981 ■ *"Once Derided As Rabbit Food, Humble Salad Now Fuels Business Plans" in Dallas Business Journal (Vol. 35, August 17, 2012, No. 49, pp. 1)*

Pub: Baltimore Business Journal

Contact: Rhonda Pringle, President

E-mail: rpringle@bizjournals.com

Description: Establishments offering salad concepts are on the rise in Dallas, Texas. The Salad Stop, Greenz, Salata are only some of the restaurants that have ventured into meeting the demand for health food, particularly salads. The market is only getting bigger, urging the restaurants to expand in services and facilities. The beginnings, food choices, and business plans of these restaurants are discussed.

13982 ■ "Once Is Not Enough for These Restaurateurs" in Baltimore Business Journal (Vol. 31, April 25, 2014, No. 52, pp. 16)
Pub: American City Business Journals, Inc.
Contact: Mike Olivieri, Executive Vice President
Released: Weekly. **Description:** Five Baltimore restaurateurs explain why they are looking to expand their businesses by opening multiple eateries, despite the potential risks. Among these is Spike Gjerde, owner of Woodberry Kitchen who opened a new butcher shop and restaurant in Remington, called Parts and Labor; Jason Ambrose, who owns Salt and a second unnamed restaurant in Locust Point; and Sarah Simington of Blue Moon Café at Fells Point and Federal Hill. **Availability:** Print; Online.

13983 ■ "Opening a Restaurant? Here's Your Equipment Checklist" in Business News Daily (February 21, 2023)
URL(s): www.businessnewsdaily.com/11346-res taurant-equipment-checklist.html
Ed: Kiely Kuligowski. **Released:** February 21, 2023. **Description:** Many pieces of equipment are needed before you can even think of opening the doors to your new restaurant. Included here is a comprehensive checklist of items you absolutely must have. **Availability:** Online.

13984 ■ "Outlook In Other Industries" in Crain's Detroit Business (Vol. 30, January 6, 2014, No. 1, pp. 3)
Pub: Crain Communications Inc.
Contact: Barry Asin, President
Released: January 6, 2014. **Description:** Outlook for industries in the Detroit area are listed, including small business growth, restaurants, defense contracts, nonprofits, transportation, auto suppliers, healthcare, bankruptcy, and government. **Availability:** Print; PDF; Online.

13985 ■ "Pizza or Beer? Why Kalil Made Right Call" in Business Journal (Vol. 31, January 31, 2014, No. 36, pp. 6)
Pub: American City Business Journals, Inc.
Contact: Mike Olivieri, Executive Vice President
Released: January 31, 2014. **Price:** $4, Introductory 4-week offer(Digital & Print). **Description:** Businessman, Matt Kalil, purchased the Pieology franchise rights for Minnesota. Kalil will open his first locations in Maple Grove and Saint Paul's Highland Park. The restaurant franchise is expected to have six locations by the end of 2014. **Availability:** Print; Online.

13986 ■ "Pizza Chain Enters Boston" in Boston Business Journal (Vol. 34, April 25, 2014, No. 12, pp. 3)
Pub: American City Business Journals, Inc.
Contact: Mike Olivieri, Executive Vice President
Released: April 25, 2014. **Description:** Mitch Roberts and David Peterman have decided to sign a franchise agreement with Blaze Pizza. The two restaurateurs will bring the California-based restaurant chain to Boston, Massachusetts.

13987 ■ "Plan B Saloon Opens New Year's Eve" in Bellingham Business Journal (Vol. February 2010, pp. 7)
Pub: Sound Publishing Inc.
Contact: Josh O'Connor, President
Ed: Isaac Bonnell. **Description:** Plan B Saloon, located in Bellingham, Washington, opened New Year's Eve 2010. The bar/restaurant will feature classic American food consisting of sandwiches and burgers and will host local musicians on Friday and Saturday nights.

13988 ■ "Plans for $160M Condo Resort in Wisconsin Dells Moves Forward" in Commercial Property News (March 18, 2008)
Description: Plans for the Grand Cambrian Resort in the Wisconsin Dells is discussed. The luxury condominium resort will include condos, townhomes, and condo-hotel style residences, two water parts, meeting space and indoor entertainment space, as well as a spa, four restaurants and retail offerings. **Availability:** Online.

13989 ■ "Potato Prices Rising Affecting Restaurant Owners" in Small Business Trends (October 4, 2022)
URL(s): smallbiztrends.com/2022/08/potato-prices -rising.html
Ed: Samson Haileyesus. **Released:** October 04, 2022. **Description:** Higher costs for supplies are causing restaurant owners to pass these prices along to their customers. The latest to rise are potatoes, which are often a staple in many restaurants across the U.S. **Availability:** Online.

13990 ■ "The Profit Recipe: Top Restaurant Trends and How to Use Them to Boost Your Profits"
Pub: CreateSpace
Released: September 26, 2014. **Price:** $17.50, paperback; $8.08, kindle; $10.74, paperback. **Description:** Restaurant entrepreneur shares information about food industry trends that will help make a food business more profitable. **Availability:** Print.

13991 ■ "Proposed Triangle Redo in Motion" in Crain's Cleveland Business (Vol. 28, October 15, 2007, No. 41, pp. 1)
Pub: Crain Communications Inc.
Contact: K. C. Crain, President
Ed: Stan Bullard. **Description:** Zaremba Homes and MRN Ltd. are partnering to redevelop the so-called Triangle section of University Circle. The proposed project will include a total of 434 new rental and for-sale residential suites and as much as 227,000 square feet of retail and restaurant space. **Availability:** Online.

13992 ■ "Q&A: Chuck Hughes, Celebrity Chef" in Canadian Business (Vol. 85, July 16, 2012, No. 11-12, pp. 65)
Ed: Nancy Won. **Description:** Celebrity chef Chuck Hughes feels blessed for the opportunity to work on a new cookbook based on the 'Chuck's Day Off' series and to start filming for a new U.S. show called 'Chuck Eats the Street'. For Hughes, cooking at the restaurant is the most rewarding and fulfilling job of all the things he does. **Availability:** Print; Online.

13993 ■ "Q&A: PSU's Tom Gillpatrick on How Quirkiness Gives Portland Its Edge" in Business Journal Portland (Vol. 30, January 17, 2014, No. 46, pp. 6)
Pub: American City Business Journals, Inc.
Contact: Mike Olivieri, Executive Vice President
Released: Weekly. **Price:** $4, introductory 4-week offer(Digital only). **Description:** Portland State University Food Industry Leadership Center executive director, Tom Gillpatrick, says consumers now prefer healthier food brands. He also stated the Portland, Oregon's food sector has grown owing to that trend. Gillpatrick added that the state's reputation for being different has also helped the sector. **Availability:** Print; Online.

13994 ■ "Ready, Aim, (Cool) Fire" in Saint Louis Business Journal (Vol. 32, September 2, 2011, No. 1, pp. 1)
Pub: Saint Louis Business Journal
Contact: Robert Bobroff, President
E-mail: rbobroff@bizjournals.com
Ed: E.B. Solomont. **Description:** Coolfire Originals' CEO Jeff Keane is co-producing 'Welcome Sweetie Pie's' with Los Angeles, California-based Pilgrims Films and Television Films for the Oprah Winfrey Network. The reality show focuses on restaurant owner Robbie Montgomery of Sweetie Pie's in St. Louis, Missouri. **Availability:** Print; Online.

13995 ■ "Real Estate Reinventions: Blue Tractor Barbeque and Brewery, Cafe Havana" in Crain's Detroit Business (Vol. 23, October 1, 2007, No. 40, pp. 15)
Pub: Crain Communications Inc.
Contact: Barry Asin, President
Ed: Daniel Duggan. **Description:** Two restaurants are converted from a Buddhist Temple to become the most unique spaces in Ann Arbor, Michigan.

13996 ■ "Recipe for Disaster?" in Sacramento Business Journal (Vol. 25, July 4, 2008, No. 18, pp. 1)
Pub: American City Business Journals, Inc.
Contact: Mike Olivieri, Executive Vice President
Ed: Mark Anderson. **Description:** Restaurateurs are challenged with balancing rising operating costs and what customers are willing to pay for their services. Flour prices in 2008 have increased by 46 percent from April 2007. Other views on the situation, as well as trends, forecasts and statistics on sales, outlook on economic conditions, consumer price index, and the typical split of restaurant revenue, are presented. **Availability:** Online.

13997 ■ "A Recipe for Food-Industry Growth?" in Providence Business News (Vol. 29, April 21, 2014, No. 3, pp. 1)
Pub: American City Business Journals, Inc.
Contact: Mike Olivieri, Executive Vice President
Released: April 19, 2014. **Description:** Industry experts believe that Rhode Island could become the 'Silicon Valley of Food'. The state is already known for its restaurants, chefs and ethnic cuisine, will host a Foods Innovation Summit in 2014. Ways that Rhode Island can take advantage of the economic benefits generated by the food industry are also examined. **Availability:** Print; Online.

13998 ■ "Recovery on Tap for 2010?" in Orlando Business Journal (Vol. 26, January 1, 2010, No. 31, pp. 1)
Pub: Orlando Business Journal
Contact: Julie Swyers, Director
E-mail: jswyers@bizjournals.com
Ed: Melanie Stawicki Azam, Richard Bilbao, Christopher Boyd, Anjali Fluker. **Description:** Economic forecasts for Central Florida's leading business sectors in 2010 are presented. These sectors include housing, film and TV, sports business, law, restaurants, aviation, tourism and hospitality, banking and finance, commercial real estate, retail, health care, insurance, higher education, and manufacturing. According to some local executives, Central Florida's economy will slowly recover in 2010. **Availability:** Online.

13999 ■ "Red Light's Green Light" in Washington Business Journal (Vol. 32, April 11, 2014, No. 52, pp. 6)
Pub: American City Business Journals, Inc.
Contact: Mike Olivieri, Executive Vice President
Released: Weekly. **Price:** $4, introductory 4-week offer(Digital & Print). **Description:** Restaurateur, Aaron Gordon, is opening his dessert and cocktail bar called Red Light in Washington DC on April 10, 2014. Gorden envisions Red Light as a destination and a before- or after-dinner stop for patrons wanting drinks and dessert along the hottest dining corridor of the city. Specialty drinks and baked goods are described. **Availability:** Print; Online.

14000 ■ "A Refresher Course: California Tortilla Unveils New Logo, Colors, Store Design" in Washington Business Journal (Vol. 31, June 8, 2012, No. 7, pp. 1)
Pub: Baltimore Business Journal
Contact: Rhonda Pringle, President
E-mail: rpringle@bizjournals.com
Description: California Tortilla restaurants have updated its brand with a new logo, color scheme and store design. The company has spent $250,000 on the new marketing effort. **Availability:** Print.

14001 ■ *"Reinventing the Cheeseburger"* in *Inc. (November 2007, pp. 124-125)*
Ed: Chris Lydgate. **Description:** Profile of Burgerville's Tom Mears, who turned his drive-through burger restaurant green. **Availability:** Online.

14002 ■ *"Report: McD's Pepsi Score Best With Young Hispanics"* in *Brandweek (Vol. 49, April 21, 2008, No. 16, pp. 8)*
Description: According to a new report, in order to reach Hispanic Gen Yers, marketing strategists need to understand this demographic's "bi-dentity," something which has proved an elusive task to many marketers. Another trend is the emergence of Latinas who have careers, as opposed to just jobs. There is an opportunity to tap this new, young and empowered female market with innovative messaging. Statistical data included. **Availability:** Online.

14003 ■ *"Restaurant Customers React to First Encounters with a Robot Server"* in *Small Business Trends(February 8, 2023)*
URL(s): smallbiztrends.com/2023/02/restaurant-customers-react-robot-waiter.html
Ed: Joshua Sophy. **Released:** February 08, 2023. **Description:** Robot waiters are starting to pop up around the country and customers are posting on social media about their encounters and giving feedback. **Availability:** Online.

14004 ■ *Restaurant Strong: The First Principles of Restaurant Outperformance and How to Make Them Yours*
URL(s): www.barnesandnoble.com/w/restaurant-strong-peter-lesar/1140013404?ean=2940162405825
Ed: Peter LeSar. **Released:** September 07, 2021. **Price:** $9.99, e-book. **Description:** Discusses the restaurant business and how outperformers operate and outshine their competitors. **Availability:** E-book.

14005 ■ *"Restaurants Dish Up Meal Deals To Attract Customers"* in *Crain's Detroit Business (Vol. 24, October 6, 2008, No. 40, pp. 1)*
Pub: Crain Communications Inc.
Contact: Barry Asin, President
Ed: Nathan Skid. **Description:** Restaurateurs are devising many creative and rewarding incentives to get customers to frequent their establishments during this economic crisis. Innovative ways in which even higher-end establishments are drawing in business are discussed. **Availability:** Online.

14006 ■ *"Restaurateurs Follow High-End Apartments Into Kendall Square"* in *Boston Business Journal (Vol. 31, July 22, 2011, No. 26, pp. 3)*
Pub: Boston Business Journal
Contact: Carolyn M. Jones, President
E-mail: cmjones@bizjournals.com
Ed: Lisa Van der Pool. **Description:** Kendall Square in Cambridge, Massachusetts is attracting restaurants, 16 of which have opened since 2009. The influx of restaurants is being driven by lower commercial rents.

14007 ■ *"Return to Wild for R.I. Oysters?"* in *Providence Business News (Vol. 29, August 25, 2014, No. 21, pp. 1)*
Pub: American City Business Journals, Inc.
Contact: Mike Olivieri, Executive Vice President
Released: August 23, 2014. **Description:** The Nature Conservancy is working to return wild oyster populations that have almost disappeared from Rhode Island waters and to restore the region's nearly extinct oyster reefs. The group's Oysters Gone Wild project collects hundreds of tons of oyster shells from participating Rhode Island restaurants and returns them into protected waters to build new oyster reefs. **Availability:** Mailing list; Online.

14008 ■ *"Ritz Kapalua Sells 93 Suites for $176M to Fund Renovation"* in *Commercial Property News (March 17, 2008)*
Description: Ritz-Carlton, Kapalua in Lahaina, Hawaii sold ninety-three of its units in order to fund renovations of 463 rooms and suites along with construction of a new spa and fitness center, new and expanded restaurants and pools and an environmental education center for children. **Availability:** Online.

14009 ■ *"Sacramento Businesses Must Cut Water Use 20 Percent"* in *Sacramento Business Journal (Vol. 30, January 17, 2014, No. 47, pp. 5)*
Pub: American City Business Journals, Inc.
Contact: Mike Olivieri, Executive Vice President
Released: Weekly. **Price:** $4, introductory 4-week offer(Digital & Print). **Description:** The Sacramento, California City, California Council's decision to reduce water use by 20 percent could have a big impact on businesses. Hotels and restaurants are among the biggest commercial users of water, while golf courses generally use well water. The need for businesses to purchase more efficient fixtures is also discussed. **Availability:** Print; Online.

14010 ■ *"St. Louis Restaurants Rewrite Menu to Get Financing"* in *Saint Louis Business Journal (Vol. 31, August 19, 2011, No. 52, pp. 1)*
Pub: Saint Louis Business Journal
Contact: Robert Bobroff, President
E-mail: rbobroff@bizjournals.com
Ed: E.B. Solomont. **Description:** St. Louis, Missouri-based restaurants are finding new ways to secure financing. The weak economy has made it difficult for restaurants to secure bank financing. **Availability:** Print; Online.

14011 ■ *"Salad Creations To Open 2nd Location"* in *Crain's Detroit Business (Vol. 24, March 3, 2008, No. 9, pp. 26)*
Description: Salad Creations, a franchise restaurant that allows customers to create their own salads and also offers soups and sandwiches; Salad Creations plans to open a total of five locations by the end of 2008. **Availability:** Online.

14012 ■ *"Sawatdee Rethinks Express Eatery Model"* in *Business Journal (Vol. 31, January 10, 2014, No. 33, pp. 4)*
Pub: American City Business Journals, Inc.
Contact: Mike Olivieri, Executive Vice President
Released: Weekly. **Price:** $4, Introductory 4-week offer(Digital & Print). **Description:** The two Sawatdee Express restaurants owned by Supenn Harrison closed their uptown and downtown locations in Minneapolis, Minnesota in December 2013. Harrison and her family own six other traditional, sit-down models of the Sawatdee restaurants. **Availability:** Print; Online.

14013 ■ *"Seahawks' Win? A Seattle Windfall"* in *Puget Sound Business Journal (Vol. 34, January 10, 2014, No. 39, pp. 3)*
Pub: American City Business Journals, Inc.
Contact: Mike Olivieri, Executive Vice President
Released: Weekly. **Price:** $4, introductory 4-week offer(Digital & Print). **Description:** Seattle, Washington is anticipating a windfall from the Seattle Seahawks' ninth game of the season. The sold-out CenturyLink Field can hold 67,000 spectators, who are potential customers outside the stadium at restaurants, bars, hotels and attractions. The economic benefits of hosting a high-profile sports event are explored. **Availability:** Print; Online.

14014 ■ *"Seasonal Franchises: Strategies to Advance"* in *Franchising World (Vol. 42, August 2010, No. 8, pp. 50)*
Pub: International Franchise Association
Contact: Matthew Haller, President
E-mail: mhaller@franchise.org
Ed: Jennifery Lemcke. **Price:** $5.99. **Description:** Seasonal franchises, such as tax businesses can be slow during the summer months. Restaurants are slow during the months of January and February. The various challenges faced by seasonal franchises are examined. **Availability:** Online.

14015 ■ *"Self-Order Kiosks Are Finally Having a Moment in the Fast Food Space"* in *Forbes (July 30, 2019)*
URL(s): www.forbes.com/sites/aliciakelso/2019/07/30/self-order-kiosks-are-finally-having-a-moment-in-the-fast-food-space/#730429f24275
Ed: Alicia Kelso. **Released:** July 30, 2019. **Description:** Self-ordering kiosks are becoming more popular in the fast food industry. Not only do they promote speed and convenience for the consumer, but with add-ons, it also provides more revenue for the company. **Availability:** Online.

14016 ■ *"Serious Growth Ahead for Tokyo Joe's"* in *Denver Business Journal (Vol. 65, April 4, 2014, No. 47, pp. A9)*
Pub: American City Business Journals, Inc.
Contact: Mike Olivieri, Executive Vice President
Released: Weekly. **Price:** $4, introductory 4-week offer(Digital only). **Description:** Tokyo Joe's founder and chief innovation officer, Larry Leith, shares his perspective on the franchising and expansion of the Colorado-based Asian fast food chain. Leith describes the fast-casual chain market in Denver and considers the possibility of going public in the future. **Availability:** Print; Online.

14017 ■ *"Seven Things Great Employers Do (That Others Don't); Unusual, Innovative, and Proven Tactics To Create Productive and Profitable Working Environments"* in *Gallup Business Journal (April 15, 2014)*
Pub: Gallup, Inc.
Contact: Jon Clifton, Chief Executive Officer
Price: $8.95. **Description:** Seven unusual, innovative, and proven tactics that create productive and profitable working environments are examined through researching 32 companies. These firms represented many industries, including healthcare, financial services, hospitality, manufacturing, and retail throughout the world. **Availability:** Print; PDF; Online.

14018 ■ *"Seward Restaurant Garners Accolades"* in *Alaska Business Monthly (Vol. 27, October 2011, No. 10, pp. 9)*
Pub: Alaska Business Publishing Company Inc.
Contact: Charles Bell, Vice President, Sales and Marketing
E-mail: cbell@akbizmag.com
Ed: Nancy Pounds. **Description:** Resurrection Road House of Seward, Alaska won the Wine Spectator's Aware of Excellence in 2011. The award honors restaurants that handle at least 100 gourmet wines that are skillfully paired with the cuisine. **Availability:** Print; Online.

14019 ■ *"Stirring Again: Bart Vandaele's New Venture"* in *Washington Business Journal (Vol. 31, August 24, 2012, No. 18, pp. 1)*
Pub: Baltimore Business Journal
Contact: Rhonda Pringle, President
E-mail: rpringle@bizjournals.com
Description: A profile of Washington-based restaurateur Bart Bandaele is presented. Vandaele opened Belga Cafe on Barracks Row in 2004. He is planning to open a second restaurant by December 2012. **Availability:** Print; Online.

14020 ■ *"Street Bistro Brings Food Truck Treats to Bangor"* in *Bangor Daily News (June 26, 2012)*
Ed: Emily Burnham. **Description:** Chef Kim Smith launched her food truck, Street Bistro in Bangor, Maine. Smith took a year off after closing her two restaurants called Unbridled Bistro and Bennett's Market. Smith and her husband purchased a Snap-On truck and redesigned it into a kitchen. Menu items range from French to Tex-Mex to Thai to American. **Availability:** Video; Online.

14021 ■ *"Study: Restaurants Should Use Compostable Dinnerware to Reduce Food Waste"* in *PMQ Pizza Magazine (November 2019)*
URL(s): www.pmq.com/reducing-food-waste/

Ed: Brett Jordan. **Released:** November 2019. **Description:** A new study conducted by Eco-Cycle says that restaurants can reduce food waste in landfills by offering compostable plates, cups, and utensils. The study also found that to succeed in composting, restaurants should use either all compostable serviceware or all durable serviceware, in order to cut down on confusion of how to sort the materials after use. **Availability:** Online.

14022 ■ *"Subway Launches Expanded Cafes, Drive-Thru Window Locations" in South Florida Business Journal (Vol. 33, August 10, 2012, No. 2, pp. 1)*

Pub: Baltimore Business Journal

Contact: Rhonda Pringle, President

E-mail: rpringle@bizjournals.com

Description: Subway launched its larger cafe concept at Florida Atlantic University and plans to open more drive-thru restaurants in South Florida. This could change preferred leasing locations to Subway franchisees, which are also moving into nontraditional locations. Site selection issues are covered. **Availability:** Print; Online.

14023 ■ *"Sweet Tea From McDonald's: A Marketing 50 Case Study" in Advertising Age (Vol. 79, November 17, 2008, No. 43, pp. 4)*

Pub: Crain Communications, Inc.

Contact: Jessica Botos, Manager, Marketing

E-mail: jessica.botos@crainsnewyork.com

Ed: Emily Bryson York. **Description:** McDonald's launch of iced coffee and sweat tea, which were promoted via price cuts over the summer, helped to boost sales at the fast-food chain. **Availability:** Online.

14024 ■ *"Tap Into Food Truck Trend to Rev Up Sales, Build Buzz" in Nation's Restaurant News (Vol. 45, February 7, 2011, No. 3, pp. 18)*

Ed: Brian Sacks. **Description:** Food truck trend is growing, particularly in New York City, Philadelphia, Washington DC, and Los Angeles, California. Man entrepreneurs are using a mobile food component to market their food before opening a restaurant. **Availability:** Print; Online.

14025 ■ *"Temp Job, Permanent Fulfillment: How the Desire To Earn a Bit of Extra Cash Opened the Door to a Long-Term Career" in Black Enterprise (Vol. 44, June 2014, No. 10, pp. 41)*

Pub: Earl G. Graves Ltd.

Contact: Earl Graves, Jr., President

Description: Profile of Kay Francis who started a temporary job with Darden Restaurants to earn money during her final year of college. After graduation, Francis took a permanent position with the firm and today is the Director, Concept Support and Purchasing for the company.

14026 ■ *"Then and Now" in Washington Business Journal (Vol. 32, February 21, 2014, No. 45, pp. 6)*

Pub: Conde Nast Publications

Contact: Agnes Chu, President

Released: January 05, 2016. **Description:** The new restaurants and bars at Marriott Marquis Hotel in Washington DC are offering retro lunch-counter items alongside modern offerings. The conference/convention center hotel will open across from the Walter E. Washington Convention Center on May 1, 2014. **Availability:** Print; Online.

14027 ■ *"This Week: McD's Eyes Ad Plan, Shifts Breakfast Biz" in Crain's Chicago Business (Vol. 30, February 2007, No. 6, pp. 1)*

Description: McDonald's is moving its national breakfast ad account from DDB Chicago to Arnold Worldwide of Boston and Moroch of Dallas in an attempt to change its marketing strategy. It is also doing a study to keep abreast of consumer trends. **Availability:** Print; Online.

14028 ■ *"TiVo, Domino's Team to Offer Pizza Ordering by DVR" in Advertising Age (Vol. 79, November 17, 2008, No. 43, pp. 48)*

Pub: Crain Communications, Inc.

Contact: Jessica Botos, Manager, Marketing

E-mail: jessica.botos@crainsnewyork.com

Ed: Brian Steinberg. **Description:** Domino's Pizza and TiVo are teaming up to make it possible for customers to order from the restaurant straight from their DVR. The companies see that this kind of interactive television and consumer experience will only serve to generate more sales as the customer can be exposed to a fuller range of menu selections and will not have to interrupt their viewing, while workers can spend more time making the product. **Availability:** Online.

14029 ■ *"To-Go Packaging, Streamlined Menus Remain Big in 2022" in Restaurant Business (November 16, 2021)*

URL(s): www.restaurantbusinessonline.com/food/go -packaging-streamlined-menus-remain-big-2022

Ed: Patricia Cobe. **Released:** November 16, 2021. **Description:** The National Restaurant Association's "What's Hot" report lists the number one trend in the industry is packaging for food. More people are still ordering to-go and getting the right type of packaging to keep the food hot and tasty is a priority for at least the next year. **Availability:** Online.

14030 ■ *"To Live and Thrive in L.A." in Canadian Business (Vol. 81, October 13, 2008, No. 17, pp. 78)*

Description: Toronto entrepreneur Shereen Arazm thrived in Los Angeles, California as the queen of nightlife. Arazm holds or has held ownership stakes in bars, nightspots and restaurants that include the Geisha House, Concorde, Shag, Parc and Central, and Terroni L.A. **Availability:** Online.

14031 ■ *"Transparency Tops Tate & Lyle's List of Trends" in Food Business News (November 18,2021)*

URL(s): www.foodbusinessnews.net/articles/2007 5-transparency-tops-tate-and-lyles-list-of-trends

Ed: Jeff Gelski. **Released:** November 18, 2021. **Description:** Six trends in the food and beverage industry are driving the needs of consumers. The top one, transparency, is based on customers wanting to know what the products they are eating and drinking are made of. **Availability:** Online.

14032 ■ *"Travel Tears" in Crain's Chicago Business (Vol. 31, November 17, 2008, No. 46, pp. 3)*

Pub: Crain Communications Inc.

Contact: Barry Asin, President

Ed: Bob Tita. **Description:** Hotels, restaurants and conventions are seeing a decline in profits due to corporate travel cutbacks and the sagging economy. City and state revenues derived from taxes on tourism-related industries are also suffering. **Availability:** Online.

14033 ■ *"Uneven But Imaginative, Union Sushi & Barbecue Bar Works" in Crain's Chicago Business (Vol. 34, September 12, 2011, No. 37, pp. 30)*

Pub: Crain Communications Inc.

Contact: Barry Asin, President

Ed: Alison Neumer Lara. **Description:** Japanese restaurant, Union Sushi & Barbecue Bar opened in Chicago this year. Union is a hip and urban place for business and leisure diners. **Availability:** Online.

14034 ■ *"Vino Volo Debuts at the Airmall at Boston Logan" in Travel & Leisure Close-Up (October 8, 2012)*

Description: Concessions developer, Airmall USA, presents Vino Volo, the company offering travelers a place to unwind with a glass of wine in a comfortable setting. The restaurant will offer tapas and wine or will create a themed tasting flights of two or three glasses of wine. **Availability:** Print; Online.

14035 ■ *"Want to Start Your Own Food Truck? Read This First" in Eater (November 21, 2019)*

URL(s): www.eater.com/young-guns-rising-stars/20 19/11/21/20970846/how-to-run-food-truck-business

Ed: Annie Burdick. **Released:** November 21, 2019. **Description:** More and more chefs are taking the plunge of opening up food trucks instead of a brick and mortar restaurant thinking it will be easier. Three food truck owners discuss their own experiences and successes in this industry. **Availability:** Online.

14036 ■ *"What Marketers Misunderstand about Online Reviews: Managers Must Analyze What's Really Driving Buying Decisions - and Adjust Their Strategies Accordingly" in Harvard Business Review (Vol. 92, January-February 2014, No. 1-2, pp. 23)*

Pub: Harvard Business Press

Contact: Gabriela Allmi, Regional Manager

E-mail: gabriela.allmi@hbsp.harvard.edu

Price: $6, hardcopy black and white. **Description:** Companies may overestimate the influence of online reviews, as consumers do not turn to reviews for certain products and services (for example, habitual low-involvement purchases such as groceries). Others' opinions matter more for purchases such as independent restaurants and electronics. **Availability:** Print; PDF; Online.

14037 ■ *"Why Restaurateur Mike Hoque Took a Chance on Downtown" in Dallas Business Journal (Vol. 35, July 6, 2012, No. 43, pp. 1)*

Pub: Baltimore Business Journal

Contact: Rhonda Pringle, President

E-mail: rpringle@bizjournals.com

Description: DRG Concepts owner Mike Hoque has built a small but impactful restaurant empire on Main Street in downtown Dallas, Texas. Hoque believes optimism has fueled his success and allowed him to see the downtown's potential when others didn't. **Availability:** Print; Online.

SOURCES OF SUPPLY

14038 ■ *Wholesale Grocer & Foodservice Distributor Leads*

Chain Store Guide

Contact: Kaitlyn Toner, Account Manager

URL(s): www.chainstoreguide.com/c-88-wholesale -grocer-foodservice-distributor-leads-plus.aspx

Description: Covers about 4,700 companies in the United States and Canada with at least $500,000 in sales to foodservice companies. Included companies must distribute more than one product line and obtain no more than 95% of its total sales volume from self-manufactured merchandise. **Entries include:** Company name, address, phone and fax numbers, e-mail and web addresses; Internet order processing indicator and sales percentage; total sales; foodservice and wholesale sales; product lines; total units served; foodservice accounts served; trading areas; distribution center locations; markets served; buying/marketing group name and location; subsidiaries names and locations; divisional, regional and branch office locations; year founded; public company indicator; key personnel with titles; 21,700 foodservice distribution contacts; 9,642 Name, address, phone, fax. **Arrangement:** Geographical. **Indexes:** Product lines, alphabetical, exclusions. **Availability:** Download; Online.

STATISTICAL SOURCES

14039 ■ *Restaurant Takeout and Delivery - US - May 2021*

URL(s): store.mintel.com/report/us-restaurant-takeou t-and-delivery-market-report

Price: $4,366.35. **Description:** Downloadable report discussing the impact the Covid-19 pandemic has had on the restaurant and takeout business and how these industries have adapted. Report includes an executive summary, interactive databook, PowerPoint presentation, infographic overview, report PDF, and previous years data. **Availability:** PDF.

14040 ■ *RMA Annual Statement Studies*
Pub: Risk Management Association
Contact: Nancy Foster, President
Released: Annual. **Description:** Contains composite balance sheets and income statements for more than 360 industries, including the accounting, auditing, and bookkeeping industries. Also contains five years of comparative historical data for discerning trends. Includes 16 commonly used ratios, computed for most of the size groupings for nearly every industry.

14041 ■ *Standard & Poor's Industry Surveys*
Pub: Standard And Poor's Financial Services LLC.
Contact: Douglas L. Peterson, President
Description: Two-volume book that examines the prospects for specific industries, including trucking. Also provides analyses of trends and problems, statistical tables and charts, and comparative company analyses.

TRADE PERIODICALS

14042 ■ *Cooking for Profit*
Released: Monthly **Description:** Food service trade publication for owners/operators of food service businesses. Profiles successful operations, offers management tips, recipes with photos and step-by-step instructions, new and improved uses and maintenance of gas equipment. **Availability:** Print; Online.

14043 ■ *Cornell Hospitality Quarterly (CHQ)*
Pub: SAGE Publications
Contact: Tracey Ozmina, President
URL(s): us.sagepub.com/en-us/nam/cornell-hospitality-quarterly/journal201681sha.cornell.edu/about/news-and-publications/publications/quarterly; journals.sagepub.com/home/cqx
Ed: Michael Lynn, J. Bruce Tracey. **Released:** Quarterly; February, May, August, November. **Price:** https://us.sagepub.com/en-us/nam/cornell-hospitality-quarterly/journal201681. **Description:** Peer-reviewed, scholarly journal focusing on critical research, practical applied theories, and useful case studies regarding important industry trends and timely topics in lodging, restaurant, and tourism management. Published in association between SAGE and the Cornell University School of Hotel Administration. **Availability:** Print; PDF; Download; Online.

14044 ■ *Hospitality Design*
Contact: Alissa Ponchione, Managing Editor
E-mail: alissa.ponchione@emeraldexpo.com
URL(s): www.hospitalitydesign.com/hospitalitydesign/index.shtml
Facebook: www.facebook.com/HospitalityDesignMagazine
Linkedin: www.linkedin.com/company/hospitality-design
X (Twitter): twitter.com/hdmag
Released: 10/yrs. **Description:** Magazine covering design of restaurants, hotels, facilities, clubs, cruise ships, etc. **Availability:** Print; PDF; Online.

14045 ■ *HOTELS*
Pub: Marketing & Technology Group Inc.
Contact: Mark Lefens, President
URL(s): hotelsmag.commtgmediagroup.com/hotels
Facebook: www.facebook.com/HOTELSmag
Linkedin: www.linkedin.com/company/hotels-magazine
X (Twitter): x.com/HOTELSmagazine
Released: 7/year **Description:** Magazine covering management and operations as well as foodservice and design in the hospitality industry. **Availability:** Print; Download; PDF; Online.

14046 ■ *Journal of Foodservice Business Research*
Pub: Taylor And Francis Group
Contact: Annie Callanan, Chief Executive Officer
URL(s): www.tandfonline.com/journals/wfbr20

Ed: Robin DiPietro. **Released:** 6/year; vol.27, 2024. **Price:** $1,016, Institutions for print and online; $276, Individuals for print & online; $241, Individuals for online only; $833, Institutions for online only. **Description:** Journal on restaurant and foodservice management. **Availability:** Print; PDF; Download; Online.

14047 ■ *The National Culinary Review (NCR)*
Pub: American Culinary Federation
Contact: Kimberly Brock Brown, President
E-mail: chefkbb@acfchefs.org
URL(s): www.acfchefs.org/ACF/About/Media/Publications/ACF/About/Media/Publications
Ed: Kay Orde. **Released:** 6/year **Price:** $140, for online; $40, for domestic; $200, for international; $140, for online and print. **Description:** Trade magazine covering food and cooking. Includes articles on food, drink, and menu trends; recipes; personal and professional development; and management. **Availability:** Print; PDF; Online.

14048 ■ *Restaurant Hospitality*
Pub: Informa USA Inc.
Contact: Gareth Wright, Director
URL(s): www.restaurant-hospitality.com
Facebook: www.facebook.com/RestaurantHospitality
X (Twitter): x.com/RH_restaurant
Released: Monthly **Description:** Dedicated to the success of full service restaurants and edited for chefs and other commercial foodservice professionals. Includes new food and equipment products and trends, menu and recipe ideas, industry news, new technology, food safety, emerging new concepts, consumer attitudes and trends, labor and training, and profiles of successful operations. **Availability:** Online.

VIDEO/AUDIO MEDIA

14049 ■ *Anthony Valletta on How to Gain Loyalty Instead of Frequency at Your Restaurant*
URL(s): restaurantunstoppable.com/anthony-valletta-bartaco
Ed: Eric Cacciatore. **Released:** March 21, 2023. **Description:** Podcast discusses how to gain loyalty instead of frequency with a limited marketing budget.

14050 ■ *Carrie Morey Founder and CE O of Callie's Hot Little Biscuit*
URL(s): restaurantunstoppable.libsyn.com/994-carrie-morey-founder-and-ceo-of-callies-hot-little-biscuit
Ed: Eric Cacciatore. **Released:** May 25, 2023. **Description:** Podcast offers a conversation with the owner of Callie's Hot Little Biscuit, who began by baking biscuits to take to sales meetings, and has now been featured on Unwrapped, started a popular food blog, and operates two locations.

14051 ■ *Chef David Viana Chef/Partner of Heirloom Kitchen*
URL(s): restaurantunstoppable.libsyn.com/997-chef-david-viana-chefpartner-of-heirloom-kitchen
Ed: Eric Cacciatore. **Released:** June 05, 2023. **Description:** Podcast offers discussion with someone who dropped out of law school to become a chef and now owns a restaurant and cooking school.

14052 ■ *Chef Yia Vang Chef/Owner of Hilltribe Restaurant Group*
URL(s): restaurantunstoppable.libsyn.com/1001-chef-yia-vang-chefowner-of-hilltribe-restaurant-group
Ed: Eric Cacciatore. **Released:** June 19, 2023. **Description:** Podcast follows a chef's journey from pop-ups, food trailers, and food halls to four restaurant locations.

14053 ■ *David Foulquier Chef/Owner We All Gotta Eat!*
URL(s): restaurantunstoppable.com/david-foulquier-we-all-gotta-eat
Ed: Eric Cacciatore. **Released:** February 24, 2023. **Description:** Podcast discusses customer retention, privilege, partnerships, and pop-ups in the restaurant industry.

14054 ■ *Derrick Hayes Founder & CEO of Big Dave's Cheesesteaks*
URL(s): restaurantunstoppable.com/derrick-hayes-big-daves-cheesesteaks
Ed: Eric Cacciatore. **Released:** March 29, 2023. **Description:** Podcast offers a conversation with the founder of Big Dave's, who opened his first place in a gas station.

14055 ■ *Ellen Yin Founder and Co-Owner of High Street Hospitality Group*
URL(s): restaurantunstoppable.libsyn.com/991-ellen-yin-founder-and-co-owner-of-high-street-hospitality-group
Ed: Eric Cacciatore. **Released:** May 15, 2023. **Description:** Podcast follows the journey of cook-turned-business-student who owns five restaurant concepts.

14056 ■ *Side Hustle to Small Business: Finding Your Balance as an Entrepreneur*
URL(s): www.hiscox.com/side-hustle-to-small-business/nadia-liu-spellman-dumpling-daughter-podcast-season-4
Ed: Sanjay Parekh. **Released:** March 20, 2024. **Description:** Podcast features the owner of Dumpling Daughter.

14057 ■ *Gavin Kaysen Chef and Founder of Soigné Hospitality Group*
URL(s): restaurantunstoppable.libsyn.com/998-gavin-kaysen-chef-and-founder-of-soign-hospitality-group
Ed: Eric Cacciatore. **Released:** June 08, 2023. **Description:** Podcast offers a discussion with chef/owner of a variety of restaurants.

14058 ■ *Greg Root Partner at Defined Hospitality*
URL(s): restaurantunstoppable.com/greg-root-defined-hospitality
Ed: Eric Cacciatore. **Released:** May 03, 2023. **Description:** Podcast offers a conversation with restauranteur Greg Root.

14059 ■ *HBR Ideacast: Fast Casual Food Pioneer Ron Shaich Explains How to Find a Niche - and then Scale*
URL(s): hbr.org/podcast/2023/11/fast-casual-food-pioneer-ron-shaich-explains-how-to-find-a-niche-and-then-scale
Ed: Alison Beard. **Released:** November 29, 2022. **Description:** Podcast, in a conversation with the founder of Panera Bread, offers suggestions for finding a niche: listen to customers, create a differentiated offering, execute with excellence, and find the right opportunities. .

14060 ■ *The How of Business: Roger Beaudoin - Growing Restaurant Profits*
URL(s): www.thehowofbusiness.com/episode-171-roger-beaudoin
Ed: Henry Lopez. **Released:** January 08, 2018. **Description:** Podcast offers tips to increase restaurant profits. Includes optimizing menu pricing, reducing food waste, upselling, streamlining operations, offering special promotions, diversifying revenue streams, and improving customer experience.

14061 ■ *The How of Business: Stratis Morfogen - Culinary Entrepreneurship*
URL(s): www.thehowofbusiness.com/425-stratis-morfogen-culinary-entrepreneurship
Ed: Henry Lopez. **Released:** June 06, 2022. **Description:** Podcast discusses developing, launching, and operating profitable restaurants.

14062 ■ *How I Built My Small Business: Naomi Crawford - Discover Lunchette's Hidden Secrets to a Thriving Sustainable Food Business*
URL(s): www.annemcginty.com/transcripts/naomicrawford
Released: August 20, 2024. **Description:** Podcast features the founder of an eco-friendly restaurant with socially responsible practices.

14063 ■ *How I Built This: Dave's Hot Chicken: Arman Oganesyan*
URL(s): wondery.com/shows/how-i-built-this/episode/10386-daves-hot-chicken-arman-oganesyan
Ed: Guy Raz. **Released:** June 10, 2024. **Description:** Podcast explains how Dave's Hot Chicken went from a pop-up to chain of 200 stores with franchises across the country.

14064 ■ *How I Built This: MOD Pizza & Seattle Coffee Company: Scott and Ally Svenson*
URL(s): wondery.com/shows/how-i-built-this/episode/10386-mod-pizza-amp-seattle-coffee-company-scott-and-ally-svenson
Ed: Guy Raz. **Released:** July 24, 2023. **Description:** Podcast explains how a hunt for their favorite food and drinks led Ally and Scott Svenson to launching two multi-million-dollar businesses.

14065 ■ *Jack McGarry Founder & Managing Partner at The Dead Rabbit*
URL(s): restaurantunstoppable.libsyn.com/1022-jack-mcgarry-founder-managing-partner-at-the-dead-rabbit
Ed: Eric Cacciatore. **Released:** August 31, 2023. **Description:** Podcast offers a conversation with the founder of The Dead Rabbit in Manhattan.

14066 ■ *James Bonanno CEO of Upstream Hospitality Group*
URL(s): restaurantunstoppable.libsyn.com/1017-james-bonanno-ceo-of-upstream-hospitality-group
Ed: Eric Cacciatore. **Released:** August 14, 2023. **Description:** Podcast offers a discussion with James Bonanno, who explains how one taproom evolved in a hospitality group.

14067 ■ *James and Johanna Windon Founders of Buena Papa Fry Bar*
URL(s): restaurantunstoppable.libsyn.com/1014-james-and-johanna-windon-founders-of-buena-papa-fry-bar
Ed: Eric Cacciatore. **Released:** August 03, 2023. **Description:** Podcast offers a conversation with James and Johanna Windon, who founded Buena Papa after COVID forced them to temporarily close their cleaning business.

14068 ■ *Joanna Kelley Founder of Cup of Joe*
URL(s): restaurantunstoppable.com/joanna-kelley-cup-of-joe
Ed: Eric Cacciatore. **Released:** January 18, 2023. **Description:** Podcast discusses marketing, investors, partnerships, seasonal restaurants, and employee benefits in the restaurant industry,.

14069 ■ *John Kunkel CEO at 50 Eggs Hospitality*
URL(s): restaurantunstoppable.com/john-kunkel-ceo-50-eggs
Ed: Eric Cacciatore. **Released:** March 04, 2023. **Description:** Podcast discusses expansion, growth, and the future of the hospitality industry.

14070 ■ *Jon Seelbinder Founder of Local Icon Hospitality*
URL(s): restaurantunstoppable.libsyn.com/1013-jon-seelbinder-founder-of-local-icon-hospitality
Ed: Eric Cacciatore. **Released:** July 31, 2023. **Description:** Podcast offers a conversation with a former bartender who now owns/operates six concepts.

14071 ■ *Joseph & Lucille Cacciatore Owners of Joe's Depot Diner*
URL(s): restaurantunstoppable.libsyn.com/1000-joseph-lucille-cacciatore-owners-of-joes-depot-diner
Ed: Eric Cacciatore. **Released:** June 25, 2023. **Description:** Podcast offers a conversation with the host's parents and former diner owners.

14072 ■ *Katie Dixon Head Chef/Owner Birdhouse Cafe*
URL(s): restaurantunstoppable.libsyn.com/928-katie-dixon-head-chefowner-birdhouse-cafe

Released: October 06, 2022. **Description:** Podcast offers a conversation with the owner of Birdhouse Cafe in Hattiesburg, Mississippi, who competed on The Next Food Network Star, taught cooking classes, and wrote a cookbook. .

14073 ■ *The Knowledge Project: Award Winning Chef Dan Kluger: Taking Time to Get It Right*
URL(s): fs.blog/knowldege-project-podcast/dan-kluger
Ed: Shane Parrish. **Released:** November 13, 2018. **Description:** Podcast discusses the restaurant industry and the benefits of paying your dues.

14074 ■ *The Knowledge Project: Danny Meyer: Hospitality and Humanity*
URL(s): fs.blog/knowldege-project-podcast/danny-meyer
Ed: Shane Parrish. **Released:** July 13, 2021. **Description:** Podcast discusses the intersection between hospitality and humanity, the power of hiring great people, and why restaurants can fail despite making it past the first year.

14075 ■ *Kyle and Maggie Gordon CEO and President of Dillas Quesadillas*
URL(s): restaurantunstoppable.com/kyle-and-maggie-gordon-dillas-quesadillas
Ed: Eric Cacciatore. **Released:** January 29, 2023. **Description:** Podcast discusses PR, marketing, delegating, branding, training, and letting go of the perfectionism mentality.

14076 ■ *Main Street Business Insights: Kristin Smith, The Wrigley Appalachian Eatery*
URL(s): mainstreet.org/resources/knowledge-hub/podcast/kristin-smith-the-wrigley-eatery-taproom
Ed: Matt Wagner. **Released:** July 31, 2024. **Description:** Podcast discusses how to stay rooted during growth with a restaurant proprietor.

14077 ■ *Memphis Garrett Founder & CEO Garett Hospitality Group*
URL(s): restaurantunstoppable.libsyn.com/1006-memphis-garrett-founder-ceo-garrett-hospitality-group
Ed: Eric Cacciatore. **Released:** July 06, 2023. **Description:** Podcast offers a conversation with Big Brother finalist and restauranteur.

14078 ■ *Michelle Politano Chef/Owner of Pianta*
URL(s): restaurantunstoppable.libsyn.com/1019-michelle-politano-chefowner-of-pianta
Ed: Eric Cacciatore. **Released:** August 21, 2023. **Description:** Podcast offers a discussion with the owner of Pianta, which began as a ghost kitchen post-COVID then opened a brick-and-mortar vegan restaurant.

14079 ■ *Pinky Cole CEO and Founder of Slutty Vegan*
URL(s): restaurantunstoppable.libsyn.com/1005-pinky-cole-ceo-and-founder-of-slutty-vegan
Ed: Eric Cacciatore. **Released:** July 03, 2023. **Description:** Podcast discusses the journey of Pinky Cole, who started with a vegan food truck and now has 11 locations.

14080 ■ *Profit First Nation: Transform Your Restaurant into a Profitable Venture*
URL(s): www.profitfirstnation.com/episodes/bonus-episode-transform-your-restaurant-into-a-profitable-venture-insights-from-kasey-anton-author-of-profit-first-for-restaurants
Ed: Danielle Mulvey. **Released:** June 29, 2023. **Description:** Podcast explains why restaurants fail, including the costs of menu items and labor.

14081 ■ *Robert Guarino Owner and Head Coach of 5 Napkin Burger*
URL(s): restaurantunstoppable.com/robert-guarino-5-napkin-burger

Ed: Eric Cacciatore. **Released:** February 12, 2023. **Description:** Podcast discuses opening and closing restaurants, how to create a great casual dining experience, systems, training, and scaling forward/back.

14082 ■ *Ryan Thorman CEO and Co-Founder of Bango Bowls*
URL(s): restaurantunstoppable.libsyn.com/1018-ryan-thormann-ceo-and-co-founder-of-bango-bowls
Ed: Eric Cacciatore. **Released:** August 17, 2023. **Description:** Podcast offers a conversation with Ryan Thorman, who founded Bango Bowls with a childhood friend.

14083 ■ *Sam Hart Chef and Owner of Counter*
URL(s): restaurantunstoppable.libsyn.com/996-sam-hart-chef-and-owner-of-counter
Ed: Eric Cacciatore. **Released:** June 01, 2023. **Description:** Podcast offers a conversation with someone who ditched advertising for culinary school and now owns two restaurants.

14084 ■ *Sean Finter CEO and Head Coach at Finter Group*
URL(s): restaurantunstoppable.libsyn.com/1027-sean-finter-ceo-and-head-coach-at-finter-group
Ed: Eric Cacciatore. **Released:** September 18, 2023. **Description:** Podcast offers a discussion with a restaurant coach.

14085 ■ *Side Hustle to Small Business: How a Craigslist Ad Changed Sarah Flores' Life*
URL(s): www.hiscox.com/side-hustle-to-small-business/sarah-flores-lolis-streatery-podcast-season-3
Ed: Sanjay Parekh. **Released:** October 25, 2023. **Description:** Podcast explains how a Craigslist ad led to owning a food truck.

14086 ■ *Starting a Franchise Restaurant Business*
URL(s): www.thehowofbusiness.com/episode-254-lauren-dowdus
Ed: Henry Lopez. **Released:** June 10, 2019. **Description:** Podcast explores selecting a restaurant franchise, facing a variety of challenges, planning for growth, and hiring/retaining employees.

14087 ■ *Steven Salm Founder & CEO of PLANTA*
URL(s): restaurantunstoppable.libsyn.com/1033-steven-salm-founder-ceo-of-planta
Ed: Eric Cacciatore. **Released:** October 09, 2023. **Description:** Podcast offers a conversation with the founder of PLANTA, a chain of vegan restaurants.

TRADE SHOWS AND CONVENTIONS

14088 ■ **ApEx**
Restaurants Canada
1155 Queen St. W
Toronto, ON, Canada M6J 1J4
Ph: (416)923-8416
Free: 800-387-5649
Fax: (416)923-1450
Co. E-mail: info@restaurantscanada.org
URL: http://www.restaurantscanada.org
Contact: Christian Buhagiar, Co-Chief Executive Officer Co-President
URL(s): www.apextradeshow.ca

Description: Products and services for the restaurant and hospitality industry, as well as institutions, convenience stores, delis and bakeries. **Audience:** Industry professionals. **Principal Exhibits:** Products and services for the restaurant and hospitality industry, as well as institutions, convenience stores, delis and bakeries. **Telecommunication Services:** chuckn@mediaedge.ca.

14089 ■ **Bar Convent Brooklyn**
URL(s): www.barconventbrooklyn.com
Facebook: www.facebook.com/barconventbrooklyn
Linkedin: www.linkedin.com/company/barconventbrooklyn

X (Twitter): twitter.com/bcbrooklyn
Instagram: www.instagram.com/barconventbrooklyn
YouTube: www.youtube.com/channel/UCgdehC
_nQiZyXAgS6yfObtw
Frequency: Annual. **Description:** Provides demonstrations, keynote talks, and panel discussions about the latest trends in the bar and beverage industry. **Principal Exhibits:** Provides demonstrations, keynote talks, and panel discussions about the latest trends in the bar and beverage industry. **Telecommunication Services:** inquiry@barconventbrooklyn.com.

14090 ■ Food Northwest Process & Packaging Expo
Food Northwest (NWFPA)
  8338 NE Alderwood Rd., Ste. 160
  Portland, OR 97220
Ph: (503)327-2200
URL: http://www.foodnorthwest.org
Contact: Pam Barrow, Vice President
E-mail: pbarrow@foodnw.org
URL(s): web.cvent.com/event/fc3d7c2a-f7e6-4126-8
  3f1-4481b8457646/websitePage:b5ff82bf-4966-47
  df-9b1b-681d20f18c44?previewToken=323b2a4e
  424bbb153f91b4518ddc3b62
Frequency: Annual. **Description:** Food processing industry equipment, supplies, and services. **Audience:** Industry professionals. **Principal Exhibits:** Food processing industry equipment, supplies, and services. Dates and Locations: Oregon Convention Center, Portland, OR. **Telecommunication Services:** kurt@foodnw.org.

14091 ■ The Hotel Experience (HX)
Guest Supply Inc.
  300 Davidson Ave.
  Somerset, NJ 08873
Ph: (732)868-2200
Free: 800-772-7676
Fax: (800)480-7878
Co. E-mail: info@guestworldwide.com
URL: http://guestsupply.com
URL(s): thehotelexperience.com/show/about-hx/
Frequency: Annual. **Description:** Products and services for lodging and food serving properties, including: technology, uniforms, linens and bedding, tabletop accessories, guest amenities and services, food and beverages, cleaning maintenance, food service equipment and supplies, franchising information, finance and management furnishings and fixtures, fitness equipment, and leisure and entertainment services. **Audience:** Hotel and restaurant professionals. **Principal Exhibits:** Products and services for lodging and food serving properties, including: technology, uniforms, linens and bedding, tabletop accessories, guest amenities and services, food and beverages, cleaning maintenance, food service equipment and supplies, franchising information, finance and management furnishings and fixtures, fitness equipment, and leisure and entertainment services. **Telecommunication Services:** kevin.gaffney@emeraldx.com.

14092 ■ Michigan Restaurant Show
Michigan Restaurant & Lodging Association (MRLA)
  225 W Washtenaw St.
  Lansing, MI 48933
Free: 800-968-9668
URL: http://www.mrla.org
Contact: Justin Winslow, President
URL(s): www.mrlashow.org
Frequency: Annual. **Description:** Equipment, supplies, and services for the food service industry. **Audience:** Industry professionals and public. **Principal Exhibits:** Equipment, supplies, and services for the food service industry.

14093 ■ Multi-Unit Foodservice Operators Conference (MUFSO)
Thomas Foods International (TFI)
  Level 2, 162 Fullarton Rd.
  Rose Park, SA 5067, Australia
Ph: 61 8 8165 5100
Co. E-mail: corporate@thomasfoods.com
URL: http://thomasfoods.com
Contact: Chris Thomas, Contact

URL(s): www.mufso.com/2019/Public/Enter.aspx
Facebook: www.facebook.com/MUFSO
Linkedin: www.linkedin.com/showcase/mufso
X (Twitter): twitter.com/mufso
Frequency: Annual. **Description:** Exhibits related to foodservice equipment, supplies, and services. **Audience:** Foodservice leaders, innovators, experts and change makers. **Principal Exhibits:** Exhibits related to foodservice equipment, supplies, and services.

14094 ■ Multi-Unit Restaurant Technology Conference
URL(s): www.murtec.com
Frequency: Annual. **Description:** Provides seminars about new technology restaurants are now using. **Principal Exhibits:** Provides seminars about new technology restaurants are now using.

14095 ■ National Fiery Foods and Barbeque Show
URL(s): www.fieryfoodsshow.com
Facebook: www.facebook.com/FieryFoodsShow
X (Twitter): twitter.com/fieryfoodsshow
Instagram: www.instagram.com/fieryfoodsshow
Frequency: Annual. **Description:** Tradeshow featuring hot and spicy foods and condiments. Live demonstrations and networking. **Principal Exhibits:** Tradeshow featuring hot and spicy foods and condiments. Live demonstrations and networking.

14096 ■ Ocean City Trade Expo
URL(s): oceancitytradeexpo.com
Frequency: Annual. **Description:** Features new products for the hotel, motel, and restaurant industries. **Principal Exhibits:** Features new products for the hotel, motel, and restaurant industries.

14097 ■ Restaurant Loss Prevention & Security Association
URL(s): www.rlpsa.com/annualconference
Frequency: Annual. **Description:** Presents industry best practices regarding loss prevention and security for restaurants. **Principal Exhibits:** Presents industry best practices regarding loss prevention and security for restaurants.

14098 ■ RestaurantPoint East
URL(s): cpmgevents.com/restaurantpointeast
Frequency: Annual. **Description:** Networking event that connects restaurant chain executives east of the Mississippi with suppliers. **Principal Exhibits:** Networking event that connects restaurant chain executives east of the Mississippi with suppliers.

14099 ■ RestaurantPoint West
URL(s): cpmgevents.com/restaurantpointwest
Frequency: Annual. **Description:** Networking event that connects restaurant chain executives based on the westside of the Mississippi with suppliers. **Principal Exhibits:** Networking event that connects restaurant chain executives based on the westside of the Mississippi with suppliers.

14100 ■ Texas Restaurant Association Marketplace
Texas Restaurant Association (TRA)
  512 East Riverside Dr., Ste. 250
  Austin, TX 78704
Ph: (512)457-4100
Co. E-mail: communications@txrestaurant.org
URL: http://txrestaurant.org
Contact: Emily Williams Knight, President
E-mail: communications@txrestaurant.org
URL(s): www.txrestaurantshow.com
Frequency: Annual. **Description:** Exhibits relating to the food service industry. **Audience:** Professionals in the restaurant and hospitality industry, single and multi-unit independent operators, franchisees, franchisors, corporate executives, chefs, unit managers, institutional food service providers, hotels, and caterers. **Principal Exhibits:** Exhibits relating to the food service industry. **Telecommunication Services:** membership@txrestaurant.org.

14101 ■ United Fresh Convention
Fresh Produce and Floral Council (FPFC)
  PO Box 3627
  Lake Arrowhead, CA 92352
Ph: (714)739-0177
Fax: (714)739-0226
Co. E-mail: info@fpfc.org
URL: http://www.fpfc.org
Contact: Don Gann, President
E-mail: don@fpfc.org
URL(s): www.fpfc.org/fpfc-2021-calendar-of-events
Frequency: Annual. **Description:** It's the place where leaders are ready to forge new connections, make purchases and see cutting-edge products and services for the fresh produce industry. **Audience:** General public. **Principal Exhibits:** It's the place where leaders are ready to forge new connections, make purchases and see cutting-edge products and services for the fresh produce industry.

14102 ■ Western Association of Food Chains Annual Convention
URL(s): www.wafc.com/convention
Description: Provides education and networking for the food industry. **Principal Exhibits:** Provides education and networking for the food industry.

14103 ■ WestEx - Colorado Foodservice & Restaurant Conference
Sapporo
  1-1, Odori Nishi, Chuo-ku
  Sapporo, Hokkaido 060-8703, Japan
URL: http://www.nhk.or.jp
URL(s): www.coloradorestaurant.com/education-even
  ts/calendar/61_2015-WestEx:-Colorado-Restauran
  t-&-Foodservice-Conference
Description: Food service and lodging products, equipment, and services. **Audience:** Food service and restaurant industry personnel. **Principal Exhibits:** Food service and lodging products, equipment, and services.

CONSULTANTS

14104 ■ Beer Associates, L.L.C.
1274 50th St.
  Brooklyn, NY 11219
Description: Provider of management and planning services serves banking and financial organizations, general business and industry groups and municipal and government agencies. **Scope:** Provider of management and planning services serves banking and financial organizations, general business and industry groups and municipal and government agencies. **Training:** Integrating Food Service Facilities Plans into Engineering Documents; Specifications: Key to a Successful Project.

14105 ■ Cini-Little International Inc.
20251 Century Blvd., Ste. 375
  Germantown, MD 20874
Ph: (301)528-9700
Co. E-mail: kheld@cinilittle.com
URL: http://cinilittle.com
Contact: Kathleen M. Held, Chief Executive Officer
E-mail: kheld@cinilittle.com
Facebook: www.facebook.com/CiniLittle
Linkedin: www.linkedin.com/company/cini-little-in
  ternational
X (Twitter): x.com/cinilittle
Pinterest: www.pinterest.com/cinilittle
Description: Firm provides planning, operational consulting and designing service. **Founded:** 1968.

14106 ■ Clevenger Associates (CA)
PO Box 811
  Elma, WA 98541
Ph: (253)841-7811
Co. E-mail: info@clevengerassoc.com
URL: http://clevengerassoc.com
Contact: Brent Hall, President
E-mail: brent@clevengerassoc.com
Facebook: www.facebook.com/ClevengerAssociates
Linkedin: www.linkedin.com/company/clevenger
  -associates
X (Twitter): x.com/ClevengerAssoc

Description: Firm provides consulting and design services such as equipment design, facility master planning, and much more. **Founded:** 1970.

14107 ■ Cornell SC Johnson College of Business - Nestle Library
Cornell SC Johnson College of Business
Ithaca, NY 14853-6201
URL: http://business.cornell.edu
Linkedin: www.linkedin.com/company/cornell
-business
YouTube: www.youtube.com/channel/UC4uNGYE
6aV8zzLlOlqL9sdg

Description: Provides hospitality such as food and beverage to real estate and finance, entrepreneurship, labor and employment relations. **Scope:** Provider of reference service for the hospitality industry in the areas such as hotel management, franchising and management contracts, tourism and travel, and food and beverage management. **Services:** Interlibrary loan. **Founded:** 1922. **Subscriptions:** journals newspapers Articles; books; research reports; catalogs; guides. **Publications:** *School of Hotel Administration.*

14108 ■ The Hysen Group
820 Watershed Dr.
Ann Arbor, MI 48105
Contact: Paul P. Hysen, President

Description: Firm engages in design, engineering and management consulting activities to all types of food service facilities. **Scope:** Firm engages in design, engineering and management consulting activities to all types of food service facilities. **Founded:** 1972. **Publications:** "Hot or Cold, Sizzling Salads Sell-Food Management," 2011; "University of Utah Hospital Turns to a POD Squad Strategy - Food Management," 2010; "How to Tap Your Inner Hardhat-Food Management," 2008; "Tear Down the Walls-Food Management," 2007.

14109 ■ Neumeier Consulting Inc.
601 Academy Ave.
Owings Mills, MD 21117
URL: http://www.gameplanforretirement.net
Contact: Michael A. Numerier, Contact

Description: Provider of consulting services on financial aspects such as retirement, social security, and much more. **Founded:** 1983. **Training:** Retirement Planning Today.

14110 ■ Progressive Sales & Service
1163 Ave. Roosevelt
San Juan, PR 00920
Ph: (787)782-7474
URL: http://progressivesales.net
Contact: Carlos Berdeguer, President
E-mail: berdeguer@progressivesales.net

Description: Retailer of commercial equipment and utensils for hotels, restaurants, cafes, and institutions. **Scope:** Retailer of commercial equipment and utensils for hotels, restaurants, cafes, and institutions. **Founded:** 1958. **Training:** Designing Food Service Facilities.

14111 ■ Riedel Marketing Group (RMG)
5327 E Pinchot Ave.
Phoenix, AZ 85018
Contact: Ann Riedel, Member
E-mail: ajr@4rmg.com

Description: The house wares and food service industry strategic marketing planning experts. Help manufacturers of house wares and food products solve marketing problems and identify and exploit marketing opportunities. Provides a full-range of strategic marketing planning services including development of marketing strategy, development of fact-based sales presentations, category management, definition of market opportunities and new product development exclusively to the house wares and food service industries. **Scope:** The house wares and food service industry strategic marketing planning experts. Help manufacturers of house wares and food products solve marketing problems and identify and exploit marketing opportunities. Provides a full-range of strategic marketing planning services including development of marketing strategy, develop-

ment of fact-based sales presentations, category management, definition of market opportunities and new product development exclusively to the house wares and food service industries. **Founded:** 1991. **Publications:** "Your Key Consumer: Her Take on the International Home & Housewares Show," Mar, 2008; "What's Hot, What's Not: The Consumer Speaks," Mar, 2006; "HIPsters SPEAK: What We Love to Buy and Why," Apr, 2005; "Influentials: Who They Are and Why You Should Care," Jun, 2004; "The Seven Secrets to Selling More Housewares," Jan, 2003. **Training:** Consumers Speak: What We Love to Buy and Why, What Do Those Consumers Think; The Seven Secrets to Selling More House wares. **Special Services:** Home Trend Influentials Panel.

14112 ■ Synergy Restaurant Consultants
Newport Beach, CA
Free: 888-861-9212
Co. E-mail: info@synergyconsultants.com
URL: http://www.synergyconsultants.com
Contact: Dean Small, Founder Managing Partner
Facebook: www.facebook.com/synergyrestauran
tconsultants
Linkedin: www.linkedin.com/company/synergy-res
taurant-consultants
X (Twitter): x.com/synergy20
Instagram: www.instagram.com/synergyconsultants
YouTube: www.youtube.com/channel/UCpgkawY
5UzSdPOPJnB9VkmQ

Description: Consultancy for restaurants at a variety of stages, from development to turnaround. Deals with menu development, restaurant branding, and marketing services. . **Founded:** 1988.

FRANCHISES AND BUSINESS OPPORTUNITIES

14113 ■ A&W Food Services of Canada Inc.
300 - 171 W Esplanade
North Vancouver, BC, Canada V7M 3K9
URL: http://web.aw.ca
X (Twitter): twitter.com/AWCanada
Instagram: www.instagram.com/awcanada
YouTube: www.youtube.com/channel/UCIE8FsYCwp
_JPcDhsAuU3Dw

Description: Chain of restaurants. **Founded:** 1919. **Training:** Provides 4-6 weeks of in-store training and ongoing support.

14114 ■ A&W Restaurants Inc.
2251 War Admiral Way, Ste. 110
Lexington, KY 40509
Ph: (859)543-1625
URL: http://awrestaurants.com
Contact: Dale Mulder, Chairman
URL(s): awfranchising.com
Facebook: www.facebook.com/awlexingtonky
X (Twitter): x.com/awlexingtonky
Instagram: www.instagram.com/awrestaurants
YouTube: www.youtube.com/user/awmugclub

Description: Retailer of fast-food restaurants. **Founded:** 1919.

14115 ■ ABC Country Restaurants Inc.
401-1901 Rosser Ave.
Burnaby, BC, Canada V5C 6S3
Ph: (604)637-7272
Fax: (604)637-8874
Co. E-mail: info@abccountry.ca
URL: http://www.abccountry.ca
Facebook: www.facebook.com/abccountryres
taurants

Description: Operator of restaurant. **Training:** Provides 4-6 weeks before and ongoing support.

14116 ■ Amato's
312 St. John St. 2nd Fl.
Portland, ME 04102
Ph: (207)828-5981
Fax: (207)761-0977
Co. E-mail: customerservice@amatos.com
URL: http://www.amatos.com
Contact: Dominic Reali, President
Facebook: www.facebook.com/amatos
X (Twitter): x.com/amatosinc

Instagram: www.instagram.com/amatos_official

Description: Chain of Italian restaurants. **Founded:** 1902. **Training:** Yes.

14117 ■ Applebee's Restaurants LLC
Dine Brands Global, Inc.
3404 Rainbow Blvd.
Kansas City, KS 66103
Ph: (818)240-6055
Free: 866-995-3463
Co. E-mail: askdine@dinebrands.com
URL: http://www.dinebrands.com/en
Contact: Johnny Mosquera, Director

Description: Chain of restaurants. **Founded:** 1980. **Financial Assistance:** No

14118 ■ Asian Chao/Maki of Japan/Chao Cajun
750 Florida Central Pky.
Longwood, FL 32750
Ph: (407)830-5338
Fax: (407)830-4443
URL: http://www.foodsystemsunlimited.com
Contact: Biagio Schiano, Founder

Description: Chain of fast-food restaurants. **Founded:** 1991. **Franchised:** 2001. **Training:** Provides 2 weeks training at headquarters, 2 weeks onsite and ongoing support.

14119 ■ Austin Grill (AG)
Thompson Hospitality Corporation, Inc.
1741 Business Ctr. Dr., Ste. 200.
Reston, VA 20190
Ph: (703)757-5500
URL: http://www.thompsonhospitality.com

Description: Tex-Mex inspired restaurant. **Founded:** 1988. **Training:** Available for 10 days at headquarters, 10 days at franchisee's location, at opening, at an existing location and ongoing support.

14120 ■ Avis Budget Group, Inc. (ABG)
Avis Budget Group, Inc. (ABG)
379 Interpace Pkwy.
Parsippany, NJ 07054
Ph: (973)496-4700
Free: 800-352-7900
URL: http://www.avisbudgetgroup.com
Contact: Joe Ferraro, President
Linkedin: www.linkedin.com/company/avis-budge
t-group

Description: Provides value-conscious vehicle rental and car sharing services through its domestic brand locations and global licensing arrangements. **Founded:** 1946. **Financial Assistance:** Yes **Managerial Assistance:** To help franchisees develop their skills in getting and retaining customers. Trainers will thoroughly teach how to train staff so your preparers will be up-to-date on the latest tax laws. **Training:** Safety training. **Educational Activities:** Annual Airport Business Diversity Conference (Annual).

14121 ■ Bandana's Bar-B-Q
16141 Swingley Ridge Rd., Ste. 205
Chesterfield, MO 63017
Ph: (636)537-8200
Free: 877-729-0022
Fax: (636)537-8444
Co. E-mail: info@bandanasbbq.com
URL: http://www.bandanasbbq.com
Facebook: www.facebook.com/bandanasbbq
X (Twitter): x.com/BandanasBBQ
Instagram: www.instagram.com/bandanasbbq

Description: Chain of restaurants cooking food with wood pit smokers and the firm operates and serves food online. **Founded:** 1996. **Training:** Wood pit smokers restaurant.

14122 ■ Bar-B-Cutie SmokeHouse
1 Terminal Dr.
Nashville, TN 37211
Co. E-mail: inquiry@bar-b-cutie.com
URL: http://www.bar-b-cutie.com
Facebook: www.facebook.com/barbcutie
X (Twitter): x.com/barbcutie
Instagram: www.instagram.com/barbcutie

Description: Restaurant offering dining and other services. **Founded:** 1950. **Franchise Fee:** $35,000. **Royalty Fee:** 5%. **Financial Assistance:** Yes **Training:** Provides 3 weeks at headquarters, 1 week onsite with ongoing support.

14123 ■ Beef O'Bradys Family Sports Pubs
5660 W Cypress St., Ste. A
  Tampa, FL 33607
Ph: (813)226-2333
Free: 800-728-8878
Fax: (813)226-0030
Co. E-mail: marketing@fscfranchiseco.com
URL: http://www.beefobradysfranchise.com
Facebook: www.facebook.com/BeefsHomeOffice
X (Twitter): x.com/beefobrady
Instagram: www.instagram.com/beefobradys1985
Description: Operator of family sports restaurant. **Founded:** 1985. **Equity Capital Needed:** $ 250,000 in liquid assets ; net worth of $ 450,000. **Franchise Fee:** $35,000. **Royalty Fee:** 4%. **Financial Assistance:** Yes **Training:** 8 week training at headquarters included with 2 weeks onsite and ongoing support.

14124 ■ Big Apple Bagels (BAB)
500 Lake Cook Rd., Ste. 475
  Deerfield, IL 60015
Free: 800-251-6101
Fax: (847)405-8140
Co. E-mail: info@babcorp.com
URL: http://www.babcorp.com
Contact: Michael W. Evans, President
Description: Operator of restaurant. **Founded:** 1993. **Franchised:** 1993. **Equity Capital Needed:** $294,700 - $398,100. **Franchise Fee:** $25,000. **Royalty Fee:** 5% of gross revenues – weekly. **Training:** Extensive training covers all aspects of operations and management, combines hands-on experience at our corporate store training facility with classroom presentations by management and key note vendors.

14125 ■ Blaze Pizza, LLC
35 N Lake Ave., Ste. 810
  Pasadena, CA 91101
Ph: (626)585-5880
Fax: (844)270-1480
URL: http://www.blazepizza.com
Contact: Beto Guajardo, Chief Executive Officer
Description: Operates the Blaze Pizza chain of more than 150 mostly franchised fast-casual pizza restaurants. **Founded:** 2011.

14126 ■ Blenz Coffee
220-21320 Gordon Way
  Richmond, BC, Canada V6W 1J8
Ph: (604)682-2995
Co. E-mail: concerns@blenz.com
URL: http://blenz.com
Facebook: www.facebook.com/BlenzCoffee
X (Twitter): x.com/BlenzCoffee
Instagram: www.instagram.com/BlenzCoffee
Description: Chain of coffee shop. **Founded:** 1992. **Training:** Yes.

14127 ■ Blimpie Subs & Salads
Description: National quick-service restaurant, serving fresh-sliced submarine sandwiches and salads. **No. of Franchise Units:** 733. **No. of Company-Owned Units:** 6. **Founded:** 1964. **Franchised:** 1970. **Equity Capital Needed:** $136,150-$385,050. **Franchise Fee:** $18,000. **Royalty Fee:** 6%. **Financial Assistance:** Yes **Training:** Training includes 1 week at headquarters, 2 weeks onsite and ongoing support.

14128 ■ Bojangles', Inc. [Bojangles' Famous Chicken 'n Biscuits]
9432 S Pine Blvd.
  Charlotte, NC 28273
Ph: (704)527-2675
Co. E-mail: copyright@bojangles.com
URL: http://www.bojangles.com
Contact: Brian Unger, Chief Operating Officer
Facebook: www.facebook.com/Bojangles
X (Twitter): x.com/Bojangles

Instagram: www.instagram.com/bojangles
YouTube: www.youtube.com/ItsBoTime
Description: Chain of fast food restaurants serving chicken and biscuits. **Founded:** 1977. **Franchise Fee:** $25,000. **Managerial Assistance:** Ongoing training, marketing and Operations is part of the franchise support. **Training:** Offers an 5 week training program at as well as a one week training program at Bojangles University.

14129 ■ Boston Pizza International Inc.
100-10760 Shellbridge Way
  Richmond, BC, Canada V6X 3H1
Ph: (604)270-1108
Free: 833-303-6398
Fax: (604)270-4168
Co. E-mail: bpffutureprospects@bostonpizza.com
URL: http://bostonpizza.com
Contact: Jim Treliving, Chairman Owner
Facebook: www.facebook.com/bostonpizza
X (Twitter): twitter.com/bostonpizza
Instagram: www.instagram.com/bostonpizzacanada
YouTube: www.youtbue.com/user/BostonPizzaCanada
Description: Operator of pizza restaurant. **Founded:** 1964. **Franchised:** 1968. **Equity Capital Needed:** Net worth of $1.5M to $2M. **Franchise Fee:** $60,000. **Royalty Fee:** 0.07. **Training:** Offers 7 weeks training.

14130 ■ Boston's The Gourmet Pizza
14850 Quorum Dr., Ste. 201
  Dallas, TX 75254
Ph: (972)484-9022
Free: 866-277-8721
Fax: (972)484-7630
Co. E-mail: contact@bostons.com
URL: http://www.bostons.com
Facebook: www.facebook.com/BostonsPizzaUSA
Linkedin: www.linkedin.com/company/boston's-restaurant-&-sports-bar
X (Twitter): x.com/bostonspizzausa
Instagram: www.instagram.com/bostonspizzausa
YouTube: www.youtube.com/c/BostonsPizzaUSA
Description: Operator of casual restaurant specializes in pizza. **No. of Operating Units:** 400. **Franchised:** 1968. **Equity Capital Needed:** $1,500,000 net worth, $500,000 liquid assets. **Franchise Fee:** $50,000. **Royalty Fee:** 5% of gross sales. **Training:** Yes.

14131 ■ Buffalo Philly's - Wings, Cheesesteaks N' More
2072 Daniel Stuart Sq.
  Woodbridge, VA 22191
Ph: (703)491-9464
Co. E-mail: info@buffalophilly.com
URL: http://www.buffalophilly.com
Facebook: www.facebook.com/buffalophillys
Description: A fast casual concept wings and cheesesteaks. **No. of Franchise Units:** 5. **No. of Company-Owned Units:** 1. **Founded:** 2000. **Franchised:** 2004. **Equity Capital Needed:** $200,000-$300,000. **Franchise Fee:** $18,000. **Training:** Yes.

14132 ■ Buffalo Wild Wings Inc. [BW-3]
Buffalo Wild Wings Inc.
  3 Glenlake Pkwy.
  Atlanta, GA 30328-3584
Free: 866-704-0777
Co. E-mail: publicrelations@buffalowildwings.com
URL: http://www.buffalowildwings.com
Contact: Sally Smith, President
Facebook: www.facebook.com/BuffaloWildWings
X (Twitter): x.com/bwwings
Instagram: www.instagram.com/bwwings
YouTube: www.youtube.com/user/buffalowildwings
Description: American casual dining restaurant and sports bar. **No. of Franchise Units:** 504. **No. of Company-Owned Units:** 325. **Founded:** 1982. **Franchised:** 1991. **Equity Capital Needed:** $1,371,700-$3,150,700 total investment. **Franchise Fee:** $40,000. **Royalty Fee:** 5%. **Training:** Offers 7 weeks training at certified training restaurant. **Educational Activities:** Great American Beer Festival (GABF) (Annual).

14133 ■ Buffalo Wings & Rings L.L.C.
8377 Winton Rd.
  Cincinnati, OH 45231
Ph: (513)521-9464
Free: 866-946-4787
Co. E-mail: contact@buffalo-wing.com
URL: http://www.wingsandrings.com
Contact: Nader Masadeh, President
Facebook: www.facebook.com/wingsandrings
X (Twitter): x.com/wingsandrings
Instagram: www.instagram.com/wingsandrings
Description: Operator of restaurant that serves burgers, sandwich, quesadillas, salads and soups. **No. of Franchise Units:** 43. **No. of Company-Owned Units:** 2. **Founded:** 1984. **Franchised:** 1988. **Equity Capital Needed:** $998,500-$2,722,500. **Franchise Fee:** $35,000. **Royalty Fee:** 5%. **Training:** Yes.

14134 ■ Burger King Corporation (BKC)
Burger King Corporation (BKC)
  5505 Blue Lagoon Dr.
  Miami, FL 33126
Ph: (305)378-3000
Free: 866-394-2493
Co. E-mail: app@bk.com
URL: http://www.bk.com
Contact: Tom Curtis, President
Facebook: www.facebook.com/burgerking
X (Twitter): x.com/BurgerKing
Instagram: www.instagram.com/burgerking
YouTube: www.youtube.com/channel/UC23ZqC
2LTzl7dfOi6EmwJhg
Description: Chain of hamburger fast food restaurants. **Founded:** 1954. **Training:** Yes.

14135 ■ Carl's Jr. Restaurants LLC
CKE Restaurants Holdings, Inc.
  6700 Tower Cir., Ste. 1000
  Franklin, TN 37067
Ph: (615)538-9400
URL: http://www.ckr.com
Contact: Mike Woida, President
Facebook: www.facebook.com/carlsjr
X (Twitter): x.com/CarlsJr
Instagram: www.instagram.com/carlsjr
YouTube: www.youtube.com/user/Carlsjr
Description: Chain of fast food restaurant. **Founded:** 1941. **Training:** Yes.

14136 ■ Charo Chicken Systems Inc.
1170 Baker St., No G1.
  Costa Mesa, CA 92626
URL: http://charochicken.com/delivery
X (Twitter): x.com/charochicken
Instagram: www.instagram.com/charochicken
Description: Chain of fast-food restaurants. **Founded:** 1984. **Financial Assistance:** Yes **Training:** Yes.

14137 ■ Checkers - Rally's
2820 W Dr. Martin Luther King Jr. Blvd.
  Tampa, FL 33607
Ph: (813)872-0780
Free: 800-800-8072
URL: http://www.checkers.com
Facebook: www.facebook.com/checkersrallys
X (Twitter): x.com/checkersrallys
Instagram: www.instagram.com/checkersrallys
YouTube: www.youtube.com/channel/UC5ChdadDb
5D8IwAH3eREx7Q
Description: Operator of restaurant offers burgers, fish and chicken sandwiches, hot dogs, fries and soft drinks. **No. of Franchise Units:** 505. **No. of Company-Owned Units:** 324. **No. of Operating Units:** 829. **Founded:** 1985. **Franchise Fee:** $30,000 per location. **Royalty Fee:** 4% of net sales. **Training:** 4-6 weeks initial training and ongoing support.

14138 ■ Cheeburger Cheeburger Restaurants, Inc.
11595 Kelly Rd., Ste. 316
  Fort Myers, FL 33908
URL: http://cheeburger.com/locations
Facebook: www.facebook.com/CheeburgerOfficial
Linkedin: www.linkedin.com/company/cheeburger-cheeburger
X (Twitter): x.com/CheeburgerBrand

Instagram: www.instagram.com/cheeburgerofficial
Description: Chain of fast-food restaurants. **Founded:** 1986. **Franchised:** 1986. **Equity Capital Needed:** $328,500-$585,000 . **Franchise Fee:** $22,500-$27,500. **Royalty Fee:** 0.05. **Training:** Yes.

14139 ■ Chesters International, LLC
2020 Cahaba Rd.
 Birmingham, AL 35223
Contact: Ted W. Giles, Member
Description: Chain of licensed and franchised restaurants. **Founded:** 1952. **Training:** Offers turn-key supply, marketing support and ongoing operations support. Franchisee's benefit from Chester's University, where employees participate in a hands-on, 5 day training program in a high-tech classroom and in-store settings, plus onsite training and grand opening support.

14140 ■ Chicken Connection Franchise Corp.
4531 Ponce de Leon Blvd., Ste. 300
 Coral Gables, FL 33146
URL: http://www.irmgusa.com
Description: Firm that provides restaurant services. **Founded:** 1997. **Franchised:** 1998. **Financial Assistance:** Yes **Training:** Yes.

14141 ■ Chicken Delight
395 Berry St.
 Winnipeg, MB, Canada R3J 1N6
Ph: (204)885-7570
Fax: (204)831-6176
URL: http://www.chickendelight.com
Facebook: www.facebook.com/ChickenDelightInternational
YouTube: www.youtube.com/user/ChickenDelightDotCom
Description: Chain of restaurant. **Founded:** 1952. **Franchised:** 1952. **Equity Capital Needed:** $273,000-$306,000. **Franchise Fee:** $20,000. **Royalty Fee:** 5%. **Training:** Offers an intensive 4 week, in-field training program at our corporate stores.

14142 ■ Church's Fried Chicken Inc.
980 Hammond Dr., Ste. 1100
 Atlanta, GA 30328
Free: 866-345-6788
URL: http://www.churchs.com
Contact: Joe Christina, President
Facebook: www.facebook.com/churchschicken
X (Twitter): x.com/churchschicken
Instagram: www.instagram.com/churchschicken
Description: Chain of fast-food restaurants. **Founded:** 1952.

14143 ■ CiCi Enterprises, LP
SSCP Management
 120 S Denton Tap Rd.
 Coppell, TX 75019
URL: http://sscpmanagement.com
Facebook: www.facebook.com/Cicis
X (Twitter): x.com/MyCiCis
Instagram: www.instagram.com/officialcicis
YouTube: www.youtube.com/user/cicispizza1985
Description: Operates a chain of pizza restaurants. **Founded:** 1985.

14144 ■ City Wok
Description: Authentic Chinese cuisine. **No. of Franchise Units:** 1. **No. of Company-Owned Units:** 4. **Founded:** 1990. **Franchised:** 2004. **Equity Capital Needed:** $243,400-$568,500. **Franchise Fee:** $30,000. **Royalty Fee:** 5%. **Training:** Yes.

14145 ■ Cora Breakfast and Lunch
16 Sicard St., Local 50
 Sainte Therese, QC, Canada J7E 3W7
Ph: (450)435-2426
Fax: (450)435-2428
Co. E-mail: info@chezcora.com
URL: http://www.chezcora.com/en
Contact: Cora Mussely, Contact
Instagram: www.instagram.com/corarestaurants
Pinterest: www.pinterest.fr/corarestaurants
Description: Chain of casual restaurants for break-fast and lunch. It offers menu sandwich, burger, salmon, crepe, salad and more. **No. of Franchise**

Units: 130. **Founded:** 1987. **Franchised:** 1993. **Equity Capital Needed:** $550,000-$900,000. **Franchise Fee:** $45,000. **Royalty Fee:** 0.06. **Financial Assistance:** No **Training:** Provides 4-6 week training program consisting of theoretical and practical training.

14146 ■ Cousins Subs
N83 W13400 Leon Rd.
 Menomonee Falls, WI 53051
Ph: (262)253-7700
URL: http://www.cousinssubs.com
Facebook: www.facebook.com/cousinssubs
X (Twitter): x.com/cousinssubs
Instagram: www.instagram.com/cousinssubs
Description: Submarine sandwich operation, with over 20 years of expertise. Volume-oriented, fast-service concept in an upscale, in-line, strip or free-standing location, some with drive-up windows. Franchising opportunities available for single, multi-unit and area developer franchisees, seminars and training classes. A corporate area representative meets with each franchise location management 3 times per month to maintain communications and assist in problem solving. **No. of Franchise Units:** 141. **No. of Company-Owned Units:** 16. **Founded:** 1972. **Franchised:** 1985. **Equity Capital Needed:** $80,000 cash, $106,700-$288,300 total investment. **Franchise Fee:** $25,000. **Training:** Includes a store building seminar for site selection, lease negotiation and construction 30 days of hands-on training, plus 10 days of opening assistance and training. National and local store marketing support.

14147 ■ Crepemaker
5749-A SW 40 St.
 Miami, FL 33155
Ph: (305)233-1113
Co. E-mail: catering@crepemaker.com
URL: http://www.crepemaker.com
Contact: Maria Suñé Lopez, Owner
Facebook: www.facebook.com/crepemakercatering
X (Twitter): x.com/crepemaker
Instagram: www.instagram.com/crepemaker
Pinterest: www.pinterest.com/ccrepemaker
Description: Producer of fast food products. **Founded:** 1992. **Franchised:** 2001. **Equity Capital Needed:** CrepeMaker Kiosk or Cafe-$141,800.00 – $300,250.00; The CrepeMaker Kiosk and Cafe-$131,800.00 – $290,250.00. **Franchise Fee:** $25,000. **Royalty Fee:** 5% of gross sales. **Financial Assistance:** Yes **Training:** Yes.

14148 ■ Dairy Queen Canada (DQ)
International Dairy Queen, Inc. (DQ)
 1111 International Blvd.
 Burlington, ON, Canada L7R 3Y3
Free: 866-793-7582
Co. E-mail: internationaldevelopment2@idq.com
URL: http://www.dairyqueen.com/en-us
Instagram: www.instagram.com/dqcanada
Description: Chain of soft serve ice cream and fast-food restaurants. **Founded:** 1953. **Training:** Yes.

14149 ■ D'Angelo Grilled Sandwiches
600 Providence Hwy.
 Dedham, MA 02026
Ph: (781)329-1946
Free: 800-727-2446
Co. E-mail: digitalmarketing@papaginos.com
URL: http://dangelos.com
Facebook: www.facebook.com/DangeloSandwiches
Description: Operator of the sandwich restaurant. **Founded:** 1967. **Training:** Yes.

14150 ■ De Dutch Pannekoek House Restaurants
No. 108-8484 162nd St.
 Surrey, BC, Canada V4N 1B4
Ph: (604)543-3101
Fax: (604)543-3107
Co. E-mail: dedutch@dedutch.com
URL: http://dedutch.com
Contact: Bill Waring, President
Facebook: www.facebook.com/dedutch
X (Twitter): x.com/dedutch
Instagram: www.instagram.com/dedutch

Description: Chain of food restaurant for breakfast and lunch. **Founded:** 1975. **Franchised:** 1979. **Equity Capital Needed:** Net worth of $1.5M to $2M. **Franchise Fee:** $42,500, includes training fee. **Training:** Provides 7 weeks at corporate training unit in Vancouver and an additional 2-3 weeks at new location.

14151 ■ Denny's Corporation
Denny's Corporation
 203 E Main St.
 Spartanburg, SC 29319
Ph: (864)597-8000
Free: 800-733-6697
Fax: (864)597-8780
URL: http://www.dennys.com
Contact: Kelli F. Valade, President
Facebook: www.facebook.com/dennys
Linkedin: www.linkedin.com/company/denny's
X (Twitter): twitter.com/dennysdiner
Instagram: www.instagram.com/dennysdiner/
YouTube: www.youtube.com/user/dennys
Description: Family-style restaurant chain offering breakfast items, appetizers, salads, sandwiches, burgers, dinner entrees, and desserts. **Founded:** 1953.

14152 ■ Dickey's Barbecue Pit
Dickey's Barbecue Restaurants Inc.
 4514 Cole Ave., Ste. 1015
 Plano, TX 75025
Ph: (214)370-4550
URL: http://www.dickeys.com
Contact: Ed Herman, Senior Vice President, Operations
Facebook: www.facebook.com/dickeysbarbecuepit
Linkedin: www.linkedin.com/company/dickey's-barbe-cue-pit
X (Twitter): x.com/dickeys
Instagram: www.instagram.com/dickeysbarbecuepit
YouTube: www.youtube.com/user/dickeysbarbecue
Description: Provide online and franchise catering services. **No. of Operating Units:** 530.0. **Founded:** 1941. **Franchised:** 1994. **Equity Capital Needed:** Net Worth $300,000 ; Liquidity $100,000. **Franchise Fee:** $15,000. **Training:** Barbecue catering service providers.

14153 ■ Dine Brands Global, Inc.
Dine Brands Global, Inc.
 10 W Walnut St., 5th Fl.
 Pasadena, CA 91103
Ph: (818)240-6055
Free: 866-995-3463
Co. E-mail: askdine@dinebrands.com
URL: http://www.dinebrands.com/en
Contact: John Peyton, Chief Executive Officer
Facebook: www.facebook.com/DineBrandsCareers/
Linkedin: www.linkedin.com/company/dinebran dsglobal/
X (Twitter): twitter.com/dinecareers
Instagram: www.instagram.com/dinebrandsglobal/
Description: Owns, franchises, and operates casual dining bar and grill concept restaurants and family dining concept restaurants, each concept restaurant chain provides different menu items, which include breakfast, lunch and dinner entrees, appetizers, desserts, and beverage alcohol offerings, respectfully. **No. of Operating Units:** 1650. **Founded:** 1958. **Equity Capital Needed:** Net worth of $1.5 million; $500,000 in liquid assets . **Franchise Fee:** single restaurant domestic development is $50,000, international franchise development is $40,000 . **Royalty Fee:** domestic restaurants is 4.5% of gross sales, international restaurants is 5.5% of gross sales. **Financial Assistance:** No **Training:** Yes.

14154 ■ East Side Mario's
5855 Rodeo Dr.
 Mississauga, ON, Canada L5R 3Z2
Ph: (905)502-6600
Free: 844-332-1022
URL: http://www.eastsidemarios.com
Description: Chain of casual restaurants. **Training:** Yes.

14155 ■ Edo Japan
310-6807 Railway St. SE
  Calgary, AB, Canada T2H 2V6
Ph: (403)215-8800
Free: 877-974-7234
Co. E-mail: contactus@edojapan.com
URL: http://www.edojapan.com
Contact: Dave Minnett, President
Facebook: www.facebook.com/edojapanofficial
X (Twitter): x.com/edo_japan
YouTube: www.youtube.com/edojapaninc
Description: Operator of Japanese restaurant. **No. of Franchise Units:** 100. **Founded:** 1979. **Equity Capital Needed:** $306,000-$525,000. **Franchise Fee:** $30,000-$35,000. **Training:** Provides 5 weeks of training.

14156 ■ El Pollo Loco, Inc.
El Pollo Loco Holdings, Inc.
  3535 Harbor Blvd., Ste. 100
  Costa Mesa, CA 92626
Ph: (714)599-5000
Free: 877-375-4968
Co. E-mail: giftcards@elpolloloco.com
URL: http://www.elpolloloco.com
Contact: Larry Roberts, Chief Executive Officer
Facebook: www.facebook.com/ElPolloLoco
X (Twitter): x.com/ElPolloLoco
Description: Restaurants specializing in Mexican-style broiled chicken. **Founded:** 1980. **Franchise Fee:** $40,000. **Financial Assistance:** No **Training:** Available at headquarters 6 weeks, 2 weeks onsite with ongoing support.

14157 ■ Empress Chili
7934 Alexandria Pke.
  Alexandria, KY 41001
Ph: (859)635-5900
Co. E-mail: info@empresschilialexandria.com
URL: http://empresschilialexandria.com
Contact: John Kiradjieff, Co-Founder
Facebook: www.facebook.com/EmpressChili
Instagram: www.instagram.com/empresschilialexandria
Description: Producer and distributor of food products. **Founded:** 1922. **Training:** Yes.

14158 ■ Escape Enterprises Ltd.
1099 Sullivant Ave.
  Columbus, OH 43223
Ph: (614)224-0300
URL: http://steakescape.com
Contact: Ken Smith, Contact
Facebook: www.facebook.com/steakescape
X (Twitter): x.com/steakescape
Instagram: www.instagram.com/steakescape
Description: Operates and franchises a quick-service restaurant chain in the United States, Mexico, and Bahrain, the company specializes in cheesesteak sandwiches, and its menu also features sub-style sandwiches, wraps, salads, side dishes, beverages, desserts and offers buffet catering services for office meetings and private parties. **Founded:** 1982. **Financial Assistance:** No **Training:** Yes.

14159 ■ The Extreme Pita
841 Commerce Dr.
  Aurora, ON, Canada L4G 0H5
URL: http://extremepita.com
Facebook: www.facebook.com/extremepitahq
X (Twitter): x.com/extremepitahq
Instagram: www.instagram.com/extremepitahq
Description: Chain of food restaurant. It offers menu pita wraps, baked sandwich, salads, sides and drinks. **Founded:** 1997. **Equity Capital Needed:** $100,000 in encumbered cash or liquid assets; net worth of $200,000. **Training:** At least 6 weeks of training.

14160 ■ Farmer Boys Food, Inc.
3452 University Ave.
  Riverside, CA 92501
Ph: (951)275-9900
Free: 888-930-3276
URL: http://www.farmerboys.com
Contact: Mark Lobb, Contact
Facebook: www.facebook.com/FarmerBoysFood
X (Twitter): x.com/FarmerBoys
Instagram: www.instagram.com/farmerboysfood
YouTube: www.youtube.com/user/FarmerBoysFood
Description: Aim is to protect and serve farm fresh food. **Founded:** 1981. **Royalty Fee:** 5%. **Financial Assistance:** Yes **Training:** Yes.

14161 ■ Fazoli's System Management
2470 Palumbo Dr.
  Lexington, KY 40509
Ph: (859)275-1955
URL: http://fazolis.com
Contact: Carl Howard, Chief Executive Officer
Facebook: www.facebook.com/Fazolis
X (Twitter): x.com/fazolis
Instagram: www.instagram.com/fazolisitalian
Description: Producer and retailer of pizzas, salads, sandwiches, samplers, flat bread piazzas, bread sticks and sauces. **Founded:** 1988.

14162 ■ Firkin Group of Pubs
20 Steelcase Rd. W, Unit 1C
  Markham, ON, Canada L3R 1B2
Ph: (905)305-9792
Co. E-mail: comments@firkinpubs.com
URL: http://www.firkinpubs.com
Facebook: www.facebook.com/firkinpubs
X (Twitter): x.com/FirkinPubs
Instagram: www.instagram.com/firkinpubs
Description: Chain of pubs. **Founded:** 1987. **Training:** Training provided at headquarters and ongoing support.

14163 ■ First Watch Restaurants, Inc.
Freeman Spogli & Co. (FS)
  8027 Cooper Creek Blvd., Ste. 103
  University Park, FL 34201
Ph: (212)758-2555
URL: http://www.freemanspogli.com
Facebook: www.facebook.com/FirstWatch
Description: Chain of fast food restaurants. **Founded:** 1983.

14164 ■ Five Guys Enterprises, LLC [Five Guys Burgers and Fries]
1940 Duke St., 5th Fl.
  Alexandria, VA 22314
Ph: (703)339-9500
Free: 866-345-4897
URL: http://www.fiveguys.com
Contact: Jerry Murrell, Founder
Facebook: www.facebook.com/fiveguys
Linkedin: www.linkedin.com/company/five-guys-enterprises
X (Twitter): x.com/fiveguys
Instagram: www.instagram.com/fiveguys
Description: Chain of fast food restaurants. **Founded:** 1986. **Training:** Yes.

14165 ■ The Flame Broiler Inc.
1175 E Baker St.
  Costa Mesa, CA 92626
Ph: (714)540-5850
Co. E-mail: comments@flamebroilerusa.com
URL: http://flamebroilerusa.com
Contact: Young Lee, Founder
Facebook: www.facebook.com/TheFlameBroiler
Instagram: www.instagram.com/theflamebroiler
Description: Operator of restaurants. **Founded:** 1995. **Franchised:** 1999. **Training:** Yes.

14166 ■ Flamers Grill-Charbroiled Hamburgers and Chicken
1515 International Pky., Ste. 2013
  Heathrow, FL 32746
Ph: (407)574-8363
Free: 866-749-4889
URL: http://flamersgrille.com
Description: Chain of fast food restaurant. **Founded:** 1987. **Equity Capital Needed:** $4,000-$6,000. **Franchise Fee:** $30,000. **Financial Assistance:** Yes **Training:** Yes.

14167 ■ Flying Biscuit
1001 Piedmont Ave.
  Atlanta, GA 30309
Ph: (404)874-8887
URL: http://www.flyingbiscuit.com
Facebook: www.facebook.com/FlyingBiscuitMidtown
X (Twitter): x.com/FBCafe
Instagram: www.instagram.com/flyingbiscuitcafe
Description: Producer and retailer of food products. **Founded:** 1993. **Training:** Raving Brands University classroom and onsite training provided.

14168 ■ Fox and Fiddle Corp.
35 Bay St.
  Toronto, ON, Canada
Ph: (416)869-3535
Co. E-mail: info@foxandfiddle.com
URL: http://www.foxandfiddle.com/locations
Facebook: www.facebook.com/FoxandFiddleCorporate
X (Twitter): x.com/FoxandFiddle
Instagram: www.instagram.com/foxandfiddle
Description: Chain of food restaurant. It offers menu wraps, sandwich, salads, drinks and more. **Founded:** 1989. **Training:** Yes.

14169 ■ Fuddruckers Inc. [Luby's Fuddruckers Restaurants, LLC]
415 W Slaughter Ln.
  Austin, TX 78748
Ph: (512)590-7540
Co. E-mail: comments@fuddruckers.com
URL: http://www.fuddruckers.com
Facebook: www.facebook.com/fuddruckers
X (Twitter): x.com/fuddruckers
Instagram: www.instagram.com/fuddruckers
Description: A franchised restaurant chain specializing in hamburgers. **Founded:** 1980. **Financial Assistance:** Yes

14170 ■ Genghis Grill - The Mongolian Stir Fry
5500 Greenville Ave.
  Dallas, TX 75206
Ph: (214)987-3330
URL: http://www.genghisgrill.com
Description: Chain of restaurants. **Founded:** 1998. **Franchised:** 2004. **Franchise Fee:** $346,600-$973,500. **Financial Assistance:** Yes **Training:** Yes.

14171 ■ Golden Corral Corporation
5400 Trinity Rd., Ste. 309
  Raleigh, NC 27607
Ph: (919)781-9310
Co. E-mail: goodasgoldclubsupport@fishbowl.com
URL: http://www.goldencorral.com
Contact: Lance Trenary, President
Facebook: www.facebook.com/goldencorral
X (Twitter): x.com/goldencorral
Instagram: www.instagram.com/goldencorral
Description: Operator of fast food restaurant. **Founded:** 1973.

14172 ■ Golden Franchising Corporation [Golden Chick]
1131 Rockingham Dr., Ste. 250
  Richardson, TX 75080
Ph: (972)831-0911
Fax: (972)831-0401
Co. E-mail: gfcinfo@goldenchick.com
URL: http://goldenchick.com
Contact: Kelly Creighton, President
Facebook: www.facebook.com/GoldenChick
X (Twitter): x.com/GoldenChick
Instagram: www.instagram.com/goldenchickofficial
Description: Franchiser of fast food restaurants. **Founded:** 1967. **Training:** Yes.

14173 ■ Golden Griddle Family Restaurants
1119 Fennell Ave. E
  Hamilton, ON, Canada L8T 1S2
URL: http://goldengriddlehamilton.com
Description: Operator of restaurant that serves home style meals everyday. **Founded:** 1997. **Training:** 4-6 weeks training and ongoing support included.

14174 ■ Grandy's L.L.C.
624 Grassmere Pk. Dr., Ste. 30
  Nashville, TN 37211
URL: http://www.grandys.com
Contact: Scott Wilson, Director, Operations
E-mail: scott_wilson@grandys.com

Facebook: www.facebook.com/grandys

X (Twitter): x.com/grandys

Description: Quick service restaurant. **Founded:** 1972. **Training:** Yes.

14175 ■ The Great Canadian Bagel Ltd.
RPO Mavis Rd.
 Mississauga, ON, Canada L5B 4A7
Ph: (905)566-1903
Co. E-mail: info@greatcanadianbagel.com
URL: http://www.greatcanadianbagel.com
Facebook: www.facebook.com/TheGreatCana
 dianBagel

Description: Retailer of cream cheese spread, sandwiches, soups, salads and beverages. **Founded:** 1993. **Training:** 3 weeks and ongoing support provided.

14176 ■ Great Steak
9311 E Via De Ventura
 Scottsdale, AZ 85258
Ph: (480)362-4800
Free: 866-452-4252
Fax: (480)362-4812
Co. E-mail: customerservice@kahalamgmt.com
URL: http://www.thegreatsteak.com
Contact: Kari Combs, Contact
URL(s): greatsteakfranchise.com
Facebook: www.facebook.com/GreatSteak
X (Twitter): x.com/GreatSteak
Instagram: www.instagram.com/greatsteakofficial

Description: Chain of fast food restaurants. **Founded:** 1982. **Franchised:** 1982. **Equity Capital Needed:** $146,600-$511,050. **Franchise Fee:** $30,000. **Royalty Fee:** 6%. **Financial Assistance:** Yes **Training:** Offers 2 week training program at headquarters, onsite training the first 2 weeks, and ongoing support at existing locations as needed.

14177 ■ Great Wraps! (GW)
6000 N Terminal Pky.
 Atlanta, GA 30320
Ph: (404)344-7905
URL: http://www.greatwraps.com
Contact: Bob Solomon, President
Instagram: www.instagram.com/GreatWraps
YouTube: www.youtube.com/user/GreatWraps
Pinterest: www.pinterest.com/GreatWraps

Description: Operator of fast food restaurant provides wrapped sandwiches, cheese steaks, rice bowls and frozen smoothies. **Founded:** 1989. **Training:** Yes.

14178 ■ Hamburger Mary's Bar & Grille
8288 Santa Monica Blvd.
 West Hollywood, CA 90046
Ph: (323)654-3800
Fax: (323)654-3808
Co. E-mail: weho@hamburgermarys.com
URL: http://www.hamburgermarys.com
Contact: Diana Dunlap, Owner
Facebook: www.facebook.com/MarysWeHo
X (Twitter): x.com/marysweho
Instagram: www.instagram.com/
 hamburgermaryoweho

Description: Full service bar and restaurants. **Founded:** 1972. **Equity Capital Needed:** $250,000. **Training:** Yes.

14179 ■ Hardee's Restaurants L.L.C.
CKE Restaurants Holdings, Inc.
 6700 Tower Cir., Ste. 1000
 Franklin, TN 37067
Ph: (615)538-9400
URL: http://www.ckr.com
Contact: Mike Woida, President
Facebook: www.facebook.com/Hardees
X (Twitter): x.com/Hardees
Instagram: www.instagram.com/hardees
YouTube: www.youtube.com/user/Hardees

Description: Chain of restaurants. **No. of Franchise Units:** 1,926. **Founded:** 1960. **Franchised:** 1961. **Equity Capital Needed:** $300,000-$1,000,000. **Franchise Fee:** $15,000-$25,000. **Royalty Fee:** 4%. **Financial Assistance:** No **Training:** Provides training at franchisee's location, 8 weeks management training and at grand opening with ongoing support.

14180 ■ Harvey's
199 Four Valley Dr.
 Vaughan, ON, Canada L4K 0B8
Ph: (905)760-2244
Free: 844-729-7828
URL: http://www.harveys.ca
Facebook: www.facebook.com/HarveysCanada
X (Twitter): x.com/harveyscanada
Instagram: www.instagram.com/harveys

Description: Chain of restaurants. **No. of Operating Units:** 800. **Founded:** 1959. **Equity Capital Needed:** $650,000 - $950,000. **Franchise Fee:** $25,000. **Royalty Fee:** 5% of sales. **Training:** Provides 10 weeks of training.

14181 ■ Hero Certified Burgers
78 Signet Dr., Ste. No.201
 Toronto, ON, Canada M9L 1T2
Ph: (416)740-2304
Fax: (416)740-5398
Co. E-mail: info@heroburgers.com
URL: http://heroburgers.com
Facebook: www.facebook.com/HeroBurgers
Instagram: www.instagram.com/heroburgersca

Description: Chain of food restaurants that serves burgers, beef, onion ring pro burger, bacon pro burger. **Founded:** 2003. **Equity Capital Needed:** $300,000-$325,000. **Franchise Fee:** No Franchise Fee. **Royalty Fee:** 0.06. **Training:** Provides 4 weeks training.

14182 ■ The Honey Baked Ham Company L.L.C. (HBH)
3875 Mansell Rd.
 Alpharetta, GA 30022
Free: 800-367-7720
URL: http://www.honeybaked.com/home
Contact: Harry J. Hoenselaar, Founder
Facebook: www.facebook.com/HoneyBake
 dHamOfficial
X (Twitter): x.com/honeybakedham
Instagram: www.instagram.com/honeybaked_ham
YouTube: www.youtube.com/channel/UCCG-6tQN0T
 dL20TECiHyGWQ
Pinterest: www.pinterest.com/honeybaked_ham

Description: Producer and retailer of ham and turkey products. **Founded:** 1957. **Training:** Comprehensive 14 day program at corporate training store.

14183 ■ Huddle House, Inc. (HHI)
Huddle House, Inc. (HHI)
 5901 Peachtree Dunwoody Rd., Ste. B450
 Atlanta, GA 30328
Ph: (770)325-1300
Co. E-mail: digital@huddlehouse.com
URL: http://www.huddlehouse.com
Contact: Michael Abt, Chief Executive Officer
Facebook: www.facebook.com/HuddleHouse
X (Twitter): x.com/huddlehouse
Instagram: www.instagram.com/huddlehouse

Description: Twenty-four-hour fast-food restaurants featuring breakfast items, steaks, sandwiches, and seafood. **No. of Franchise Units:** 400. **Founded:** 1964. **Franchised:** 1966. **Equity Capital Needed:** Liquid Capital $200,000; Net Worth Required $600,000. **Franchise Fee:** $25,000. **Financial Assistance:** No **Training:** 7-week performance-based program covering all aspects of operations. Ongoing support in operations and field support.

14184 ■ HuHot Mongolian Grills, LLC
223 E Main St.
 Missoula, MT 59802
Ph: (406)251-4303
Fax: (406)327-1232
Co. E-mail: missoula1@huhot.com
URL: http://www.huhot.com
Facebook: www.facebook.com/huhot
X (Twitter): x.com/huhot
Instagram: www.instagram.com/huhot
YouTube: www.youtube.com/user/HuHo
 tMongolianGrill

Description: Operator of restaurant. **Founded:** 1999. **Franchised:** 2002. **Financial Assistance:** Yes **Training:** Provides 3 weeks training at headquarters and ongoing support.

14185 ■ Humpty's Restaurants International Inc.
401-1901 Rosser Ave.
 Burnaby, BC, Canada V5C 6R6
Ph: (403)269-4675
Fax: (403)266-1973
URL: http://www.humptys.com
Contact: Don Koenig, Founder
Facebook: www.facebook.com/HumptysOfficial
X (Twitter): x.com/humptysofficial
Instagram: www.instagram.com/humptysbigplate

Description: Chain of food restaurants. **No. of Operating Units:** 49. **Founded:** 1977. **Franchised:** 1986. **Equity Capital Needed:** 690000. **Franchise Fee:** $30,000. **Royalty Fee:** 5% . **Training:** Provides 7 weeks of training.

14186 ■ Inspire Brands, Inc.
Inspire Brands, Inc.
 3 Glenlake Pkwy. NE
 Atlanta, GA 30328
Ph: (678)514-4100
Co. E-mail: franchising@inspirebrands.com
URL: http://inspirebrands.com
Contact: Paul J. Brown, Chief Executive Officer
Facebook: www.facebook.com/InspireBrandsInc
Linkedin: www.linkedin.com/company/27156989
X (Twitter): x.com/InspireBrands

Description: Chain of restaurant. **No. of Company-Owned Units:** 2000. **Founded:** 2018. **Equity Capital Needed:** $500,000 in liquidity and $1,000,000 net worth. **Franchise Fee:** $332,700 – $856,500 or $904,700 – $1,647,000. **Financial Assistance:** Yes **Training:** Provides 5 days at certified training restaurant and ongoing onsite support.

14187 ■ Izzo's Illegal Burrito
4250 Burbank Dr.
 Baton Rouge, LA 70808
Ph: (225)214-0870
URL: http://www.izzos.com
Facebook: www.facebook.com/izzosillegalburrito
X (Twitter): x.com/izzos
Instagram: www.instagram.com/izzosillegalburrito

Description: Fast-casual Mexican food providers. **No. of Franchise Units:** 2. **No. of Company-Owned Units:** 4. **Founded:** 2001. **Franchised:** 2006. **Equity Capital Needed:** $544,500-$859,100. **Franchise Fee:** $40,000. **Royalty Fee:** 5%. **Training:** Includes 12 days training at headquarters, 7 days onsite and ongoing support.

14188 ■ Jerry's Subs and Pizza
Jerry's Systems, Inc.
 16260 S Frederick Rd.
 Gaithersburg, MD 20877
Free: 800-990-9176
Fax: (301)948-3508
X (Twitter): x.com/jerrysusa

Description: Fresh-dough pizza and stuffed submarine sandwiches, served in upscale retail outlets, featuring take-out service and self-service dining. **No. of Franchise Units:** 135. **No. of Company-Owned Units:** 3. **Founded:** 1954. **Franchised:** 1981. **Equity Capital Needed:** $250,000-$350,000. **Franchise Fee:** $25,000. **Royalty Fee:** 6%. **Financial Assistance:** Yes **Training:** Available 5 weeks at headquarters.

14189 ■ Jersey Mike's Franchise Systems Inc.
2251 Landmark Pl.
 Manasquan, NJ 08736
Free: 800-321-7676
Co. E-mail: marketing@jerseymikes.com
URL: http://www.jerseymikes.com
Contact: Peter Cancro, Chief Executive Officer
Facebook: www.facebook.com/jerseymikes
X (Twitter): x.com/jerseymikes
YouTube: www.youtube.com/user/jerseymikestv

Description: Chain of restaurants that serve sandwiches and related items.. **No. of Franchise Units:** 195. **Founded:** 1956. **Franchised:** 1987. **Equity**

Capital Needed: $201,357 – $471,164.50. **Franchise Fee:** $18,500. **Financial Assistance:** No **Training:** Offers 9 week training program with ongoing support.

14190 ■ Joey's Only Seafood Restaurant
3048 9th St. SE
 Calgary, AB, Canada T2G 3B9
Ph: (403)243-4584
Free: 800-661-2123
Co. E-mail: marketing@joeys.ca
URL: http://joeys.ca
Contact: Max Gagnon, Vice President
Facebook: www.facebook.com/JoeysRestaurants
Instagram: www.instagram.com/joeyscanada

Description: Chain of seafood restaurants that serves salads, soups, fish chips, sandwiches. **Founded:** 1985. **Training:** Offers 5 week training program.

14191 ■ Johnny Rockets Licensing Corp.
25550 Commercentre Dr., STE. 200
 Lake Forest, CA 92630
Contact: Becky Degeorge, Contact

Description: Hamburger malt shop. **No. of Franchise Units:** 330.0. **Founded:** 1986. **Equity Capital Needed:** $524,000 - $1,088,000. **Franchise Fee:** $60,000. **Royalty Fee:** 6% . **Training:** Offers 4 weeks at certified training store with ongoing support.

14192 ■ Jugo Juice
4825 Mt Royal Gate SW,Rec Centre, Office J212
 Calgary, AB, Canada T3E 6K6
Free: 877-377-5846
Co. E-mail: contact@jugojuice.com
URL: http://jugojuice.com
Facebook: www.facebook.com/jugojuice
Instagram: www.instagram.com/jugojuice

Description: Retailer of foods and beverages such as smoothies, juices, wrap, grab, flatbreads and breakfast. **No. of Franchise Units:** 135. **Founded:** 1998. **Equity Capital Needed:** $185,000-$300,000. **Franchise Fee:** 25000. **Royalty Fee:** 0.06. **Financial Assistance:** No **Training:** Yes.

14193 ■ Keg Restaurants Ltd. [Keg Steakhouse & Bar]
10100 Shellbridge Way
 Richmond, BC, Canada V6X 2W7
Ph: (604)276-0242
Co. E-mail: thekeg@kegrestaurants.com
URL: http://kegsteakhouse.com
Contact: Nick Dean, President
Facebook: www.facebook.com/thekegsteakhousean
 dbar
Linkedin: www.linkedin.com/company/the-keg-s
 teakhouse-and-bar
X (Twitter): twitter.com/TheKeg
Instagram: www.instagram.com/thekegsteakhouse

Description: Retailer of prepared foods and drinks such as soup, salads, steak, ribs, baked garlic shrimp, calamari, chicken, seafood and desserts. **Founded:** 1971. **Training:** Provides 2 weeks training.

14194 ■ Kelly's Cajun Grill Franchise Corp.
4531 Ponce de Leon Blvd., Ste. 300
 Coral Gables, FL 33146
URL: http://www.irmgusa.com
Contact: Hoi Sang Yeung, President

Description: Chain of restaurant. **Founded:** 1996. **Training:** Yes.

14195 ■ Kentucky Fried Chicken Canada Company (KFC) [KFC Canada]
Yum! Brands, Inc.
 191 Creditview Rd
 Vaughan, ON, Canada L4L 9T1
Ph: (502)874-8300
URL: http://www.yum.com
Linkedin: www.linkedin.com/company/kfc-canada
X (Twitter): x.com/kfc_canada
Instagram: www.instagram.com/kfc_canada
YouTube: www.youtube.com/user/KFCCanadaTV

Description: Chain of the fast-food restaurant. It offers menus crispy strips, large popcorn chicken, fries, dips and gravy, chicken buckets, chicken meal, bowels, and more. **Founded:** 1953. **Training:** Yes.

14196 ■ Krystal Restaurants LLC
1455 Lincoln Pky., Ste. 600
 Dunwoody, GA 30346
Ph: (770)351-4500
URL: http://www.krystal.com
Contact: Thomas Stager, President
Facebook: www.facebook.com/Krystal
X (Twitter): x.com/krystal
Instagram: www.instagram.com/krystal
YouTube: www.youtube.com/channel/
 UCZjRsWApNR1zxvoA6Hdu7wA

Description: Fast food hamburger concept, offering proven, destination-oriented products. Restaurants are open 24 hours. **Founded:** 1932. **Training:** Provide in the restaurant training, computer training at the home office. Also, it provides area directors in the field to assist with the business. **Awards:** The Square Up Scholarship Program.

14197 ■ La Salsa
320 Commerce, Ste. 100
 Irvine, CA 92602
URL: http://www.lasalsa.com
Facebook: www.facebook.com/lasalsa
X (Twitter): twitter.com/Viva_LaSalsa
Instagram: www.instagram.com/
 lasalsafreshmexicangrill
Pinterest: www.pinterest.com/lasalsafresh

Description: Operator of Mexican food restaurant. **Founded:** 1979. **Equity Capital Needed:** $200,000 liquid cash per restaurant, $500,000 net worth per restaurant. **Franchise Fee:** 50000. **Royalty Fee:** 0.05. **Training:** Yes.

14198 ■ Lazy Dog Restaurants, LLC (LDR)
8800 Apollo Way
 Downey, CA 90242
Ph: (714)596-9960
URL: http://www.lazydogrestaurants.com
Contact: Chris Simms, Chief Executive Officer
Facebook: www.facebook.com/LazyDogRestaurants
Instagram: www.instagram.com/lazydogrestaurants

Description: Chain of casual dining restaurants. **Founded:** 2003.

14199 ■ Le Muffin Plus
3200 Boul. Laframboise, Les Galeries St-Hyacinthe,
 No1451 Saint-Hyacinthe
 Quebec, QC, Canada J2S 4Z5
Ph: (514)336-8885
Co. E-mail: info@muffinplus.ca
URL: http://muffinplus.ca
Facebook: www.facebook.com/muffinplus.ca

Description: Operator of fast food restaurant. It offers menus sandwiches, panini, salads, muffins and hot meals. **Founded:** 1982. **Training:** Yes.

14200 ■ Long John Silver's LLC
10350 Ormsby Park Pl., Ste. 300
 Louisville, KY 40223
Ph: (502)815-6100
Co. E-mail: ljsfeedback@ljsilvers.com
URL: http://www.ljsilvers.com
Contact: Christopher Caudill, Senior Vice President
Facebook: www.facebook.com/LongJohnSilvers
Instagram: www.instagram.com/longjohnsilvers

Description: Seafood chain in the fish and seafood segment. Offers a menu of fish, seafood and chicken. Eat-in, take-out and drive-thru. **Founded:** 1969. **Training:** Yes.

14201 ■ Mama Fu's Asian House
3355 Bee Caves Rd., Ste. 609
 Austin, TX 78746
Contact: Mark Adams, Director

Description: Operator of restaurant. **Founded:** 2002. **Training:** Yes.

14202 ■ Manchu Wok Inc.
1100 Boul. Maloney, Quest No. 911 Les
 Promenades
 Gatineau, QC, Canada J8T 6G3

Ph: (819)243-5888
URL: http://manchuwok.com
Facebook: www.facebook.com/people/Manchu-Wok/
 100090219246097

Description: Operator of Chinese food restaurant. **No. of Franchise Units:** 130. **Founded:** 1980. **Equity Capital Needed:** $395,000-$590,000. **Franchise Fee:** $30,000 for a food-court location; $50,000 for a street-front location. **Royalty Fee:** 7% of gross sales for a "food-court" location and 5% for a "street-front" location. **Training:** 3 weeks real estate, marketing, field support, and product development included.

14203 ■ Mancino's, Samuel Italian Eatery
401b N Clippert St.
 Lansing, MI 48912
Co. E-mail: info@samuelmancinos.com
URL: http://www.samuelmancinos.com

Description: Firm is a franchise of restaurants and provides food delivery services. **Franchised:** 1994. **Training:** Yes.

14204 ■ Mandarin Restaurant Franchise Corp.
8 Clipper Ct.
 Brampton, ON, Canada L6W 4T9
Ph: (905)451-4100
Fax: (905)456-3411
Co. E-mail: info@mandarinrestaurant.com
URL: http://www.mandarinrestaurant.com
Contact: Diana Chiu, Co-Founder
Facebook: www.facebook.com/mandarinrestaurants
X (Twitter): x.com/eatmandarin
Instagram: www.instagram.com/themandarinres
 taurants

Description: Chain of food restaurant. It offers menu soup and salad bars, grill table, prime rib counter, sushi corner, desserts. **Founded:** 1979. **Training:** 1-3 years and ongoing support provided.

14205 ■ Mary Browns Inc. (MB)
Woodbine & Hwy. 7
 8600 Woodbine Ave., Unit C-3
 Markham, ON, Canada L3R 4X8
Ph: (905)513-0044
URL: http://marybrowns.com
Facebook: www.facebook.com/MaryBrowns
X (Twitter): x.com/MaryBrowns
Instagram: www.instagram.com/marybrownsofficial
YouTube: www.youtube.com/user/
 MaryBrownsCanada

Description: Chain of fast food restaurant. **Founded:** 1969. **Training:** Offers 3 weeks initial training and ongoing support.

14206 ■ McDonald's Corporation
McDonald's Corporation
 110 N Carpenter St.
 Chicago, IL 60607
Ph: (630)623-3000
Free: 800-244-6227
URL: http://www.mcdonalds.com
Contact: Chris Kempczinski, President
URL(s): corporate.mcdonalds.com
Facebook: www.facebook.com/McDonalds
Linkedin: www.linkedin.com/company/mcdonald's
 -corporation
X (Twitter): twitter.com/McDonalds
Instagram: www.instagram.com/McDonalds
YouTube: www.youtube.com/McDonalds

Description: Operates and franchises fast-food restaurants. **Founded:** 1940. **Training:** Franchisees required to participate in a training and evaluation program which may, on a part-time basis, take 2 years or longer to complete.

14207 ■ McDonald's Restaurants of Canada Ltd.
McDonald's Corporation
 2 McDonald's Pl.
 Toronto, ON, Canada M3C 3L4
Ph: (630)623-3000
Free: 800-244-6227
URL: http://www.mcdonalds.com
Contact: Michele Boudria, President
Facebook: www.facebook.com/McDonaldsCanada
Instagram: www.instagram.com/mcdocanada

YouTube: www.youtube.com/user/McDonaldsCanada
Pinterest: www.pinterest.com/mcdonaldscanada
Description: Chain of fast-food restaurant. It offers menu beef, chicken, eggs, dairy products, salads, snacks, sides. **No. of Franchise Units:** 1400. **Founded:** 1981. **Franchised:** 1968. **Equity Capital Needed:** 800000. **Financial Assistance:** No Training: Offers 1-2 years training.

14208 ■ McGhin's Southern Pit Bar-B-Que
2964 N Expy.
  Griffin, GA 30223
Ph: (770)229-5887
Fax: (770)229-5838
Co. E-mail: info@southernpitbbq.com
URL: http://www.southernpitbbq.com
Contact: Deanna Gregory, Manager
E-mail: deanna@southernpitbbq.com
Facebook: www.facebook.com/mcghinssouthernpit
Description: Operator of restaurant. **Founded:** 1984. **Training:** Provides 3 weeks training at headquarters, 1 week at franchisee's location and ongoing support.

14209 ■ Melting Pot Restaurants Inc.
7886 Woodland Ctr. Blvd.
  Tampa, FL 33614
Ph: (813)881-0055
Free: 800-783-0867
URL: http://www.meltingpot.com
Contact: Bob Johnston, Chief Executive Officer
Facebook: www.facebook.com/themeltingpotres
  taurants
X (Twitter): x.com/TheMeltingPot
Instagram: www.instagram.com/themeltingpotres
  taurants
YouTube: www.youtube.com/user/TheMeltingPotTV
Description: Offers a unique opportunity to stand apart from the competition. Select the franchise system that offers a unique concept, coupled with training, education and outstanding support. **Founded:** 1975. **Training:** Franchisees and their managers pay their own costs of lodging, meals and transportation during training.

14210 ■ Mexicali Rosa's
683 Main St.
  Moncton, NB, Canada E1C 1E3
Ph: (506)855-7672
Co. E-mail: info@mexicalirosas.com
URL: http://www.mexicalirosas.com
Description: Chain of food restaurants. **Founded:** 1979. **Training:** Assistance with site selection, restaurant design and construction with ongoing operational, advertising, and central purchasing support.

14211 ■ MOD Super Fast Pizza Holdings L.L.C. [MOD Pizza]
2035 158th Ct. NE, Ste. 200
  Bellevue, WA 98008
Free: 877-212-0465
Co. E-mail: feedback@modpizza.com
URL: http://www.modpizza.com
Contact: Scott Svenson, Chief Executive Officer
Facebook: www.facebook.com/MODPizza
X (Twitter): x.com/modpizza
Instagram: www.instagram.com/modpizza
Description: Chain of fast casual pizza restaurants. **Founded:** 2008.

14212 ■ Moe's Southwest Grill
GOTO Foods
  5620 Glenridge Dr. NE
  Atlanta, GA 30342
Ph: (404)255-3250
Free: 800-227-8353
URL: http://www.gotofoods.com
Contact: Paul Damico, President
Facebook: www.facebook.com/MoesSouthwestGrill
X (Twitter): x.com/moes_hq
Instagram: www.instagram.com/moessouthwestgrill
YouTube: www.youtube.com/user/moessouthwes
  tgrill1
Description: Operator of restaurant. **Founded:** 2006. **Training:** Includes 2 weeks initial training at headquarters, 1 week at franchisee's location and ongoing support.

14213 ■ Mr. Goodcents Subs & Pastas
8997 Commerce Dr.
  De Soto, KS 66018
URL: http://goodcentssubs.com
Contact: Joseph Bisogno, Founder
Description: Chain of fast food restaurants. **Founded:** 1989. **Franchised:** 1990. **Training:** 30 days of comprehensive in-house training.

14214 ■ Mr. Greek Mediterranean Grill
44 Upjohn Rd.
  Toronto, ON, Canada M3B 2W1
Ph: (416)444-3266
Co. E-mail: franchising@mrgreek.com
URL: http://www.mrgreek.com
Contact: Peter Rakovalis, Contact
Facebook: www.facebook.com/mrgreek
X (Twitter): x.com/mrgreek
Instagram: www.instagram.com/mrgreek
Description: Operator of restaurant. **Founded:** 1988. **Training:** Offers 10 weeks training with ongoing support.

14215 ■ Mr. Greek Rxpress
44 Upjohn Rd.
  Toronto, ON, Canada M3B 2W1
Ph: (416)444-3266
Co. E-mail: feedback@mrgreek.com
URL: http://www.mrgreek.com
Description: Mr. Greek Express is a quick-service restaurant concept with a limited menu of the most popular specialty dishes of the Mr. Greek Mediterranean Grill franchise, as well as some dishes available only at the Mr. Greek Express locations. The Express units are counter-service restaurants offering seating and take-out and, where possible, drive-through facilities. Great Food, Served Fast. The Mr. Greek Express is an outstanding business opportunity for highly motivated, customer-oriented individuals who have the desire to succeed. **No. of Franchise Units:** 18. **No. of Company-Owned Units:** 2. **Founded:** 1988. **Franchised:** 1993. **Equity Capital Needed:** $160,000 start-up capital required; $350,000-$500,000 capital required. **Franchise Fee:** $35,000. **Training:** Offers 10 weeks training and ongoing support.

14216 ■ Mr. Hero Restaurants
Restaurant Developers Corp.
  7002 Engle Rd., Ste. 100
  Middleburg Heights, OH 44130
Ph: (440)625-3080
Co. E-mail: tfreeman@mrhero.com
URL: http://www.mrhero.com
Facebook: www.facebook.com/mrhero
X (Twitter): x.com/mrhero
Instagram: www.instagram.com/mrhero_restaurants
Description: Specialty sandwiches & fast food. **No. of Franchise Units:** 103. **No. of Company-Owned Units:** 7. **Founded:** 1965. **Franchised:** 1970. **Equity Capital Needed:** $113,000-$305,000. **Franchise Fee:** $18,000. **Royalty Fee:** 5.5%. **Training:** Offers 4 weeks at headquarters, 1 week at franchisees location with ongoing support.

14217 ■ Mr. SUB
2 E Beaver Creek Rd., Bldg., 1
  Richmond Hill, ON, Canada L4B 2N3
Ph: (905)764-7066
Co. E-mail: info@mrsub.com
URL: http://mrsub.ca
Facebook: www.facebook.com/mrsub
X (Twitter): x.com/mrsub1968
Instagram: www.instagram.com/mrsubofficial
Description: Chain of food restaurant. It offers menus sandwiches, salads, sides, wraps. **Founded:** 1968. **Franchised:** 1972. **Training:** Yes.

14218 ■ Mucho Burrito
2 E Beaver Creek Rd., Bldg. 1
  Richmond Hill, ON, Canada L4B 2N3
Ph: (416)346-5506
Free: 800-563-6688
Fax: (905)764-0476
Co. E-mail: info@muchoburrito.com
URL: http://muchoburrito.com
Facebook: www.facebook.com/MuchoBurritoHQ

X (Twitter): x.com/MuchoBurritoHQ
YouTube: www.youtube.com/channel/UCHcEoaX
  tsozuHTLUm4KYmZA
Description: Chain of Mexican restaurants. **Founded:** 2006. **Training:** At least 4 (four) to 5 1/2 weeks training.

14219 ■ Nando's
4711 McClellan Rd.
  Richmond, BC, Canada V6X 0M5
Ph: (604)244-8004
Co. E-mail: marketing@nandosindia.com
URL: http://www.nandos.ca
Facebook: www.facebook.com/NandosCanada
X (Twitter): x.com/nandosperiperi
Instagram: www.instagram.com/nandoscanada
Description: Operator of food restaurant offers sandwiches, pitas, wraps, wings, sides. **Founded:** 1987. **Training:** Provides full training.

14220 ■ Nathan's
1 Jericho Plz.
  Jericho, NY 11753
Ph: (516)338-8500
Co. E-mail: fl@nathansfamous.com
URL: http://www.nathansfamous.com
Facebook: www.facebook.com/nathansfamous
X (Twitter): x.com/OriginalNathans
Instagram: www.instagram.com/originalnathans
Description: Chain of fast-food restaurants. **Founded:** 1916. **Franchised:** 1989. **Franchise Fee:** $30,000. **Royalty Fee:** 5.5%. **Training:** Famous hot dog restaurant.

14221 ■ Noodle Time Inc.
21500 Biscayne Blvd., Ste. 900
  Aventura, FL 33180
URL: http://www.benihana.com
Contact: Thomas Baldwin, President
Facebook: www.facebook.com/Benihana
X (Twitter): x.com/Benihana
Instagram: www.instagram.com/benihana
YouTube: www.youtube.com/user/benihana
Pinterest: www.pinterest.com/benihanaus
Description: Prepared foods, wines, sake, and dipping sauces. **Founded:** 1964.

14222 ■ Nothing But Noodles
7950 E Redfield Rd., Ste. 130
  Scottsdale, AZ 85260
Ph: (602)881-0388
URL: http://nothingbutnoodles.com
Contact: Chad Everts, Founder
E-mail: chad.everts@nothingbutnoodles.com
Description: Noodles, pasta and salads. **Founded:** 2002.

14223 ■ O'Charley's Restaurants
3038 Sidco Dr.
  Nashville, TN 37204
Ph: (615)256-8500
URL: http://www.ocharleys.com
Contact: Craig Barber, Chief Executive Officer
Facebook: www.facebook.com/ocharleysfans
X (Twitter): x.com/OCharleys
Instagram: www.instagram.com/ocharleys
YouTube: www.youtube.com/user/ocharleysUS
Description: Chain of casual dining restaurants. **Founded:** 1971. **Equity Capital Needed:** $1,000,000 of Liquidity - $3,000,000 of Net Worth. **Royalty Fee:** 0.04. **Training:** Yes.

14224 ■ The Pantry Restaurants
2309 Guildford Town Ctr.
  Surrey, BC, Canada V4A 4N5
Ph: (604)584-1090
Fax: (604)584-0866
Co. E-mail: info@thepantry.ca
URL: http://www.thepantry.ca
Facebook: www.facebook.com/ThePantryRes
  taurants
X (Twitter): x.com/ThePantryOnline
YouTube: www.youtube.com/user/ThePantryRes
  taurants

Description: Chain of food restaurants. **Founded:** 1975. **Training:** 6 weeks and ongoing support provided.

14225 ■ Pepe's Mexican Restaurants
1325 W 15th St.
  Chicago, IL 60608
Ph: (312)733-2500
URL: http://pepes.com
Contact: Robert Ptak, President
Description: Full-service Mexican restaurant franchise, featuring a full range of Mexican items, including beer, wine and liquor. **Founded:** 1967. **Financial Assistance:** No **Training:** Operator of restaurants.

14226 ■ The Perfect Pita L.L.C.
2200 Clarendon Blvd.
  Arlington, VA 22206
Ph: (703)527-1511
Co. E-mail: info@theperfectpita.com
URL: http://www.theperfectpita.com
Contact: Erica Dodd, President
Facebook: www.facebook.com/theofficialperfectpita
X (Twitter): x.com/theperfectpita
Instagram: www.instagram.com/theperfectpita_official
Description: Operator of restaurants. **Founded:** 1994. **Financial Assistance:** Yes **Training:** Yes.

14227 ■ PH Canada Company
Yum! Brands, Inc.
  191 Creditview Rd., Ste. 100
  Vaughan, ON, Canada L4L 9T1
Ph: (502)874-8300
URL: http://www.yum.com
Facebook: www.facebook.com/pizzahutcanada
X (Twitter): x.com/PizzaHutCanada
YouTube: www.youtube.com/channel/UCyw
  _PoEkfj0kA_2t_gOjtOQ
Description: Operator of fast food restaurant. It offer menu pizza, chicken and Mexican-style foods. **Founded:** 1958. **Training:** Yes.

14228 ■ The Philly Connection
2980 Cobb Pky. S, Ste. 200
  Atlanta, GA 30339
Ph: (770)955-0086
Co. E-mail: info@phillyconnection.com
URL: http://www.phillyconnection.com
Facebook: www.facebook.com/phillyconnectionfoo
  dtrucks
X (Twitter): x.com/pcfoodtrucks
Instagram: www.instagram.com/pcfoodtrucks
Description: Producer and distributor of food products such as philly cheese steaks, hoagies, salads. **Founded:** 1984. **Franchised:** 1988. **Equity Capital Needed:** $160,000 - $249,000. **Franchise Fee:** $18,500. **Financial Assistance:** Yes **Training:** Provides 80 hours at training facility and ongoing support.

14229 ■ Pizza Delight
264 Botsford St., Ste. 201
  Moncton, NB, Canada E1C 4X7
Ph: (506)853-0990
URL: http://www.pizzadelight.com
Facebook: www.facebook.com/mypizzadelight
Instagram: www.instagram.com/pizzadelight
Description: Operator of fast food restaurant. **Founded:** 1968. **Training:** Offers 3-4 weeks of training.

14230 ■ Pizza Factory Inc.
40120 Hwy. 41
  Oakhurst, CA 93644
Ph: (559)683-2700
Free: 800-654-4840
Co. E-mail: info@pizzafactoryinc.com
URL: http://www.pizzafactory.com
Contact: Mary Jane Riva, Chief Executive Officer
Facebook: www.facebook.com/pizzafactoryinc
X (Twitter): x.com/PizzaFactoryInc
Instagram: www.instagram.com/pizzafactoryinc
Description: Family-oriented pizza restaurant, serving pizza, pasta, sandwiches and salad bar. Specializing in communities of 15,000 or less. **No. of Franchise Units:** 100. **Founded:** 1979. **Franchised:** 1985. **Financial Assistance:** No **Training:** Offers 325 hours training.

14231 ■ Pizza Ranch Inc.
204 19th St. SE
  Orange City, IA 51041
Ph: (712)707-8800
Free: 800-321-3401
URL: http://pizzaranch.com
Contact: Adrie Groeneweg, Founder
Facebook: www.facebook.com/PizzaRanchRes
  taurants
X (Twitter): x.com/pizzaranch
Instagram: www.instagram.com/pizzaranchres
  taurants
YouTube: www.youtube.com/c/pizzaranchrestaurants
Description: Chain of restaurants. **Founded:** 1981. **Training:** Yes.

14232 ■ Popeyes Louisiana Kitchen, Inc.
Restaurant Brands International Inc.
  5707 Blue Lagoon Dr.
  Miami, FL 33126
URL: http://www.rbi.com
Contact: Sami Siddiqui, Chief Executive Officer
Description: Develops, operates and franchises quick-service restaurants. The company is distinguished through its Louisiana-style menu that features spicy chicken, fried shrimp and other seafood, red beans, rice and other regional cuisine items. **No. of Company-Owned Units:** 2000. **Founded:** 1976. **Franchised:** 2008. **Equity Capital Needed:** $1,000,000 and $500,000 in liquid assets. **Franchise Fee:** $35000. **Royalty Fee:** 5%. **Financial Assistance:** Yes **Training:** Popeyes Operations Management Training (OMT) Program must be attended by up to four management employees prior to the opening of a restaurant. The OMT Program covers an extensive range of subjects related to the operation of a restaurant. This 6 week program indoctrinates employee of job station areas and restaurant administration management, application of job skills and techniques, and classroom materials needed in the management of a restaurant.

14233 ■ Port of Subs, Inc.
5365 Mae Anne Ave., Ste. A-29
  Reno, NV 89523
Free: 800-245-0245
Co. E-mail: feedback@portofsubs.com
URL: http://www.portofsubs.com
Contact: John Larsen, Contact
Description: Submarine sandwich franchise, featuring unique front-line method of preparing specialty sandwiches, soups, salads and party platters. Bread is baked fresh daily on premises. **No. of Operating Units:** 140.0. **Founded:** 1972. **Franchised:** 1985. **Equity Capital Needed:** $197,100 - $358,000. **Franchise Fee:** $18,500. **Royalty Fee:** 5.5%. **Financial Assistance:** No **Managerial Assistance:** operations assistance. **Training:** Offers 2 weeks of training, plus 2 weeks in the franchisee's unit during initial opening.

14234 ■ Qdoba Restaurant Corp.
7611 W Colfax Ave.
  Lakewood, CO 80214
Ph: (303)237-1062
Free: 888-736-2224
URL: http://www.qdoba.com
Contact: Prashant Budhale, Chief Technology Officer
Description: Chain of fast casual restaurants in the United States and Canada. **Founded:** 2003. **Training:** Yes.

14235 ■ The Quizno's Master L.L.C.
PO Box 6340
  Denver, CO 80206
Description: Chain of restaurants that provides toasted sandwiches, soups, and salads for lunch or dinner. **Founded:** 1981. **Training:** Twenty two day training program includes classroom and in-store training. Grand opening and initial onsite assistance.

14236 ■ Raising Cane's USA L.L.C. [Raising Cane's Chicken Fingers]
100 North St., Ste. 802
  Baton Rouge, LA 70802
Free: 866-552-2637
Co. E-mail: info@raisingcanes.com

URL: http://www.raisingcanes.com
Contact: Todd Graves, Chief Executive Officer
Facebook: www.facebook.com/
  RaisingCanesChickenFingers
X (Twitter): twitter.com/Raising_Canes
Instagram: www.instagram.com/raisingcanes/
YouTube: www.youtube.com/user/
  RaisingCanesOneLove
Description: Chain of restaurant that serve chicken fingers and assorted side dishes. **Founded:** 1996.

14237 ■ Ranch 1 Grilled Chicken
9311 E Via De Ventura
  Scottsdale, AZ 85258
Ph: (480)362-4800
Free: 866-452-4252
Fax: (480)362-4812
Co. E-mail: customerservice@kahalamgmt.com
URL: http://www.ranchone.com
Facebook: www.facebook.com/ranchone
X (Twitter): x.com/ranchone
Description: Chain of fast-food restaurants. **Founded:** 1990. **Franchised:** 1990. **Equity Capital Needed:** $175,400-$544,750. **Franchise Fee:** $30,000. **Royalty Fee:** 6%. **Financial Assistance:** Yes **Training:** Provides 1 week training at headquarters, 2 weeks at franchisee's location, and ongoing support.

14238 ■ Rice King
8369 Vickers St., Ste. 205
  San Diego, CA 92111
Free: 800-418-4421
Fax: (858)505-8668
Co. E-mail: info@riceking.com
URL: http://www.riceking.com
Description: Operator of restaurant. **Financial Assistance:** Yes **Training:** Yes.

14239 ■ Ricky's All Day Grill
401-1901 Rosser Ave.
  Burnaby, BC, Canada V5C 6S3
Ph: (604)637-7272
Free: 888-597-7272
Fax: (604)637-8874
Co. E-mail: info@rickysr.com
URL: http://rickysrestaurants.ca
Contact: Stacey Hansson, Contact
E-mail: stacey@rickysr.com
Facebook: www.facebook.com/rickysfamilyres
  taurants
X (Twitter): x.com/Rickys_Grill
Instagram: www.instagram.com/rickysfamilyres
  taurants
Description: Chain of food restaurant. **Founded:** 1962. **Training:** Complete hands-on-training and strong support.

14240 ■ Rockin'Baja Lobster
Rockin'Baja Lobster, LLC
  258 Harbor Dr.
  Oceanside, CA 92054
Ph: (949)719-3800
Free: 877-762-2252
Fax: (949)721-4053
Contact: Rick DiRienzo, Founder
Description: Baja cantina and grill. **No. of Company-Owned Units:** 40. **Founded:** 1992. **Franchised:** 2003. **Equity Capital Needed:** $240,400-$1,200,000. **Franchise Fee:** $30,000. **Royalty Fee:** 5%. **Training:** Provides 2 weeks training at headquarters and ongoing support.

14241 ■ Rockwell's Grill & Bar
33048-1583 Marine Dr.
  West Vancouver, BC, Canada V7V 4W7
Ph: (604)281-1380
Fax: (604)281-1381
URL: http://www.rockwells.ca
Facebook: www.facebook.com/RockwellsGrillBar
X (Twitter): x.com/RockwellsGB
Description: Chain of food restaurant and pub. It offers menus chicken wings, chili chicken, pasta, sandwiches. **Founded:** 2001. **Training:** Provides 6 weeks training and ongoing support.

14242 ■ Rollerz
9311 E Via de Ventura
Scottsdale, AZ 85258
URL: http://www.kahalamgmt.com/index.html
Description: Firm is a restaurant operator and franchiser. **Founded:** 2000.

14243 ■ Ronzio Pizza
490 Lincoln St.
Worcester, MA 01605
URL: http://ronziopizza.com
Description: Producer of pizza in Rhode Island. **No. of Operating Units:** 20.0. **Founded:** 1986. **Franchised:** 1992. **Equity Capital Needed:** $136,500 - $207,500. **Franchise Fee:** $12,000* - $15,000. **Royalty Fee:** 5% of the total gross. **Financial Assistance:** No **Training:** Yes.

14244 ■ Roy Rogers Restaurants (RR)
4991 New Design Rd., Ste. 109
Frederick, MD 21703
Co. E-mail: customerrelations@royrogersrestaurants .com
URL: http://www.royrogersrestaurants.com
Facebook: www.facebook.com/RoyRogersRes taurants
Linkedin: www.linkedin.com/company/roy-rogers-res taurants-plamondon-enterprises-inc
X (Twitter): x.com/RoysRestaurants
YouTube: www.youtube.com/user/RoyRogersRes taurants
Description: Chain of fast-food restaurants. **No. of Franchise Units:** 27. **No. of Company-Owned Units:** 23. **No. of Operating Units:** 46. **Founded:** 1980. **Equity Capital Needed:** $753,250 to $1,410,450; Liquid Assets: $500,000; Net Worth: $1,000,000. **Franchise Fee:** $30,000. **Royalty Fee:** 5% of gross sales. **Training:** Yes.

14245 ■ St. Louis Bar & Grill
2050 Yonge St., Ste. 200B
Toronto, ON, Canada M4S 1Z9
Ph: (416)480-0202
URL: http://www.stlouiswings.com
Description: Operator of food restaurant and bar. **No. of Franchise Units:** 50. **Founded:** 1992. **Franchised:** 2002. **Equity Capital Needed:** $600,000-$750,000; $350,000. **Franchise Fee:** $40,000. **Royalty Fee:** 6% of Weekly Gross Sales. **Training:** Yes.

14246 ■ Salsarita's Fresh Cantina [Salsarita's Fresh Mexican Grill]
1530 Overland Pk. Ln., Ste. 1 100
Charlotte, NC 28262
Ph: (704)971-7230
Co. E-mail: marketing@salsaritas.com
URL: http://salsaritas.com
Facebook: www.facebook.com/salsaritas
Linkedin: www.linkedin.com/company/salsarita's -franchising
X (Twitter): x.com/salsaritas
Instagram: www.instagram.com/salsaritas
Pinterest: www.pinterest.com/salsari tasfreshmexicangrill
Description: Fresh Mexican in a cantina atmosphere. **Founded:** 2000. **Training:** Yes.

14247 ■ Sammy J's Grill & Bar
15770 Croydon Dr.
South Surrey, BC, Canada V3S 2L6
Ph: (604)385-2577
URL: http://www.sammyjs.ca
Description: Operator of restaurant. **Founded:** 1996. **Training:** Offers 4-6 weeks training in Vancouver, BC.

14248 ■ Sawmill Prime Rib & Steak House
4810 Calgary Trl. NW
Edmonton, AB, Canada T6H 5H5
Ph: (780)437-5616
URL: http://sawmillrestaurant.com/edmonton-south
Contact: Calgary Trail, Contact
E-mail: calgarytrail@sawmillrestaurant.com
Facebook: www.facebook.com/SawmillRestaurants
X (Twitter): x.com/sawmillprimerib
Instagram: www.instagram.com/sawmillrestaurant

Description: Chain of food and beverage restaurant. **Founded:** 1976. **Training:** Yes.

14249 ■ Sbarro The Italian Eatery
131 Colonie Ctr.
Albany, NY 12205
Ph: (518)482-2499
URL: http://sbarro.com
Facebook: www.facebook.com/Sbarro
X (Twitter): x.com/Sbarro
Instagram: www.instagram.com/sbarroofficial
Description: Italian eateries through Internet database. **Founded:** 1959. **Training:** Yes.

14250 ■ Scores Rotisserie & Ribs
200, 8150 Rte Transcanadienne
Saint-Laurent, QC, Canada H4S 1M5
Ph: (514)336-8885
Fax: (514)341-6236
Co. E-mail: info@scores.ca
URL: http://www.scores.ca
Facebook: www.facebook.com/RestaurantScores
Linkedin: www.linkedin.com/company/rotisserie -scores
Instagram: www.instagram.com/restoscores
YouTube: www.youtube.com/channel/UCXnWyP0 _IXx7SKwSuEeAgGA/featured
Description: Operator of chicken and ribs restaurant. **Founded:** 1995. **Training:** Provides 8 weeks training.

14251 ■ Seattle Sutton's Franchise Corp.
611 E Stevenson Rd.
Ottawa, IL 61350
Free: 800-442-3438
Co. E-mail: corp@sshe.com
URL: http://www.seattlesutton.com
Contact: Rene Ficek, President
Description: Firm engages in manufacturing freshly prepared healthy meals. **Founded:** 1985. **Training:** Yes.

14252 ■ Select Sandwich Co.
155 Gordon Baker Rd., Unit 214
Toronto, ON, Canada M2H 3N5
Ph: (416)391-1244
Free: 866-567-5648
Co. E-mail: fresh@selectsandwich.com
URL: http://www.selectsandwich.com
Contact: Brian Kahn, President
Facebook: www.facebook.com/selectsandwichgta
Linkedin: www.linkedin.com/company/select-san dwich
X (Twitter): x.com/select_sandwich
Pinterest: www.pinterest.com/selectsandwich
Description: An established brand leader operating quick-service gourmet sandwich restaurants. Now expanding nationally. **No. of Franchise Units:** 23. **Founded:** 1979. **Franchised:** 1980. **Equity Capital Needed:** $125,000-$150,000 start-up capital required; $250,000-$300,000 investment required. **Franchise Fee:** $25,000. **Training:** Offers 6 weeks training.

14253 ■ Shake Shack Inc.
225 Varick St., Ste. 301
New York, NY 10014
Ph: (646)747-7200
URL: http://shakeshack.com
Contact: Randy Garutti, Chief Executive Officer
Facebook: www.facebook.com/shakeshack
Linkedin: www.linkedin.com/company/shakeshack
X (Twitter): twitter.com/shakeshack
Instagram: www.instagram.com/shakeshack
YouTube: www.youtube.com/shakeshack
Pinterest: www.pinterest.com/shakeshack
Description: Restaurant chain specializing in classic American foods, including burgers, fries, and hot dogs. **Founded:** 2004.

14254 ■ Shakey's Pizza & Buffet
2200 W Valley Blvd.
Alhambra, CA 91803
Ph: (626)576-0616
Free: 888-444-6686
Co. E-mail: contactus@shakeys.com
URL: http://www.shakeys.com

Facebook: www.facebook.com/ shakeyspizzaparlorusa
X (Twitter): x.com/ShakeysUSA
Instagram: www.instagram.com/shakeysusa
YouTube: www.youtube.com/user/shakeyspizzaparlor
Description: Chain of pizza restaurants. **Founded:** 1954. **Equity Capital Needed:** $584,000-$2,035,000. **Franchise Fee:** $35,000. **Royalty Fee:** 5%. **Training:** Yes.

14255 ■ Shane's Rib Shack
3155 Cobb Pky.
Atlanta, GA 30339
Ph: (770)951-7211
Co. E-mail: appsupport@shanesribshack.com
URL: http://www.shanesribshack.com
Contact: Shane Thompson, Contact
Facebook: www.facebook.com/shanesribshack
Instagram: www.instagram.com/shanesribshack
YouTube: www.youtube.com/shanesribshack
Description: Chain of restaurants. **Founded:** 2002. **Training:** Raving Brands University classroom and onsite training provided. From register operation to food preparation, from hiring staff to accounting procedures, you'll improve your management skills, setup your back office and develop airtight sales and marketing plan.

14256 ■ Silver Mine Subs (SMS)
4619 S Mason St., No. C3
Fort Collins, CO 80525
Co. E-mail: feedback@silverminesubs.com
URL: http://silverminesubs.com
Contact: John Langreck, Co-Founder
Facebook: www.facebook.com/silverminesubs
X (Twitter): x.com/SilverMineSubs
Instagram: www.instagram.com/SilverMineSubs
Description: Operator of fast food restaurant provides wrapped sandwiches, salads, soups. **Founded:** 1996. **Training:** Yes.

14257 ■ Sizzler Inc.
23352 Madero Rd., Ste. B
Mission Viejo, CA 92691
Ph: (949)273-4497
Co. E-mail: info@sizzlerusa.com
URL: http://www.sizzler.com
Contact: Dwight D. Eisenhower, President
Facebook: www.facebook.com/sizzler
X (Twitter): x.com/sizzler_usa
Instagram: www.instagram.com/sizzlerusa
Description: Chain of restaurants. **Founded:** 1958. **Training:** Yes.

14258 ■ Skyline Chili, Inc.
4180 Thunderbird Ln.
Fairfield, OH 45014
Free: 800-443-4371
Co. E-mail: customer_relations@skylinechili.com
URL: http://www.skylinechili.com
Contact: Kevin R. McDonnell, President
Facebook: www.facebook.com/SkylineChili
Instagram: www.instagram.com/officialskylinechili
YouTube: www.youtube.com/c/SkylineChiliChannel/ featured
Description: Restaurant franchise is engaged in offering unique Greek-inspired chili spaghetti and coney menu items, the company also provides catering services and additionally, its products are packaged and distributed to grocery stores and through online channels. **Founded:** 1949. **Equity Capital Needed:** $200,000 - $400,000 liquid capital; $500,000 net worth. **Franchise Fee:** $20,000. **Royalty Fee:** 4% . **Training:** Yes.

14259 ■ Smitty's
No. 500-501 18th Ave. SW
Calgary, AB, Canada T2S 0C7
Ph: (403)229-3838
Free: 800-927-0366
Fax: (844)274-4056
Co. E-mail: info@smittys.ca
URL: http://www.smittys.ca
Contact: Jim Weidinger, President
Facebook: www.facebook.com/SmittysRestaurants
Instagram: www.instagram.com/smittysrestaurants

Description: Operator of restaurant. **Founded:** 1960. **Franchised:** 1960. **Franchise Fee:** $35,000 plus GST. **Royalty Fee:** 5% of gross sales . **Training:** Yes.

14260 ■ SNS Investment Co.
10701 E Washington St.
 Indianapolis, IN 46229
URL: http://www.steaknshake.com
Contact: Gus Belt, Founder
Facebook: www.facebook.com/steaknshake
X (Twitter): x.com/steaknshake
Instagram: www.instagram.com/steaknshake
YouTube: www.youtube.com/steaknshake
Pinterest: www.pinterest.com/steaknshake

Description: A restaurant offering quick-seared steak burgers, thin French fries, genuine chili, and hand-dipped milkshakes. Offers drive-thru and take-out service, in an environment reminiscent of the '50s. **Founded:** 1934. **Franchised:** 1939. **Financial Assistance:** No **Training:** Provides on-the-job training program, utilizing personal instructions, training videos and workbooks.

14261 ■ Sonic Drive-In Restaurants [Sonic, America's Drive-In]
Inspire Brands, Inc.
 Oklahoma City, OK 73104
Ph: (678)514-4100
Co. E-mail: franchising@inspirebrands.com
URL: http://inspirebrands.com
Contact: Claudia San Pedro, President
Facebook: www.facebook.com/sonicdrivein
X (Twitter): x.com/sonicdrivein
Instagram: www.instagram.com/sonicdrivein
YouTube: www.youtube.com/user/sonicdrivein

Description: Drive-in fast-food restaurant offering hamburgers, hot dogs, French fries, and onion rings, and frozen drinks. **No. of Franchise Units:** 3,005. **No. of Company-Owned Units:** 438. **Founded:** 1953. **Franchised:** 1959. **Equity Capital Needed:** $1,112,300-$3,002,700. **Franchise Fee:** $45,000. **Royalty Fee:** 2-5%. **Financial Assistance:** Yes **Training:** Provides 1 week training at headquarters, 11 weeks onsite, 1 day to 1 week additional training with ongoing support.

14262 ■ Steak-Out Charbroiled Delivery
2300 Holcomb Bridge Rd., Ste. 103-363
 Roswell, GA 30076
Free: 877-878-3257
Co. E-mail: info@steakout.com
URL: http://steakout.com
Facebook: www.facebook.com/savorthesizzle
X (Twitter): x.com/SteakOutUSA

Description: Full meal delivery chain featuring charbroiled steaks, chicken, seafood, burgers, chef salads and deserts. **Founded:** 1986. **Financial Assistance:** Yes **Training:** Training is 4 weeks in the store and at headquarters for 3 to 4 management employees. Complete support in site finding, store opening, marketing and ongoing.

14263 ■ Suki Hana & Chicken Connection
4531 Ponce de Leon Blvd., Ste. 300
 Coral Gables, FL 33146
Ph: (305)476-1611
Fax: (305)476-9622
URL: http://www.irmgusa.com
Contact: Michel Smith, General Manager
Facebook: www.facebook.com/irmgusa

Description: Operator of Japanese restaurant. **Founded:** 1989. **Franchised:** 1998. **Training:** Yes.

14264 ■ Sunset Grill
5100 Erin Mills Town Ctr.
 Mississauga, ON, Canada L5M 5A7
Ph: (905)286-5833
Fax: (905)829-1142
Co. E-mail: info@sunsetgrill.ca
URL: http://sunsetgrill.ca
Contact: Vanessa Diver, Director, Marketing Director, Communications
Facebook: www.facebook.com/SunsetGrillBreakfast
Linkedin: www.linkedin.com/company/sunset-grill-res
 taurants-ltd
X (Twitter): x.com/SunsetGrillCA

Instagram: www.instagram.com/sunsetgrill
Description: Operator of food restaurant and bar. **Founded:** 1985. **Franchised:** 2003. **Equity Capital Needed:** 573000. **Franchise Fee:** 55000. **Royalty Fee:** 0.05. **Training:** Offers training before and after opening.

14265 ■ SW Liquidation, LLC
161 Washington St.
 Conshohocken, PA 19428

Description: Restaurant franchise, meeting the drive-in, carryout and delivery requirements of the customers. **Founded:** 1986. **Training:** Yes.

14266 ■ Sweet Peppers Deli (SPD)
Jackson Sq., 2017 Hwy. 45 N
 Columbus, MS 39701
Ph: (662)327-6982
Fax: (662)328-6889
URL: http://sweetpeppersdeli.com
Contact: John Bean, President

Description: Producer of sandwiches, salads, wraps and much more. **Founded:** 1984. **Franchised:** 2002. **Franchise Fee:** $30,000. **Royalty Fee:** 5%. **Training:** Yes.

14267 ■ Taco John's International, Inc.
808 W 20th St.
 Cheyenne, WY 82001
Free: 800-854-0819
URL: http://www.tacojohns.com
Contact: Jim Creel, President
Facebook: www.facebook.com/tacojohns
X (Twitter): x.com/tacojohns
Instagram: www.instagram.com/tacojohns
YouTube: www.youtube.com/user/tacojohnsinc

Description: A fast-food chain offering Mexican food. **Founded:** 1969. **Equity Capital Needed:** $350,000 liquid assets; net worth of $500,000 for a single unit. **Training:** Yes.

14268 ■ Taco Maker Inc.
Oriental Tower290 Ave Jesus T. PineroSuite 11B
 San Juan, PR 00918
Ph: (787)273-3160
Fax: (787)793-3160
Co. E-mail: sales@fransglobal.com
URL: http://www.tacomaker.com
Facebook: www.facebook.com/tacomaker

Description: Fresh made Mexican fast food. **Founded:** 1978. **Training:** Yes.

14269 ■ Taco Mayo
10405 Greenbriar Pl.
 Oklahoma City, OK 73159
Ph: (405)691-8226
Co. E-mail: customerservices@tacomayo.com
URL: http://www.tacomayo.com
Contact: James W. Garner, Contact
Facebook: www.facebook.com/FreshMexGrill
X (Twitter): x.com/tacomayo
Instagram: www.instagram.com/tacomayo

Description: Quick service Tex-Mex restaurant. **No. of Franchise Units:** 76. **No. of Company-Owned Units:** 16. **Founded:** 1978. **Franchised:** 1980. **Equity Capital Needed:** $100,000-$120,000, includes franchise fee. **Franchise Fee:** $15,000. **Training:** Yes.

14270 ■ Taco Time Canada Inc.
Unit A8, 416 Meridian Rd. SE
 Calgary, AB, Canada T2A 1X2
Free: 866-835-8226
Co. E-mail: letstacoboutit@tacotimecanada.com
URL: http://www.tacotimecanada.com
Facebook: www.facebook.com/tacotimecanada
Instagram: www.instagram.com/tacotimecanada

Description: Chain of fast-food restaurants. **Founded:** 1978. **Training:** Offers 2 weeks at corporate plus onsite at opening.

14271 ■ TacoTime
9311 E Via De Ventura
 Scottsdale, AZ 85258
Ph: (480)362-4800
Free: 866-452-4252
URL: http://www.tacotime.com

X (Twitter): x.com/TacoTime
Instagram: www.instagram.com/tacotimefresh
YouTube: www.youtube.com/user/TacoTimeCorp

Description: Chain of fast food restaurants. **No. of Operating Units:** 225.0. **Founded:** 1960. **Franchised:** 1961. **Equity Capital Needed:** $200,150 and $819,050. **Franchise Fee:** $30,000. **Royalty Fee:** 6%. **Financial Assistance:** Yes **Training:** Provides 2-4 weeks training at headquarters and ongoing support.

14272 ■ TB Canada Company
Yum! Brands, Inc.
 1 Bass Pro Mills Dr., FCno7
 Vaughan, ON, Canada L4K2M9
Ph: (502)874-8300
URL: http://www.yum.com
Facebook: www.facebook.com/tacobellcanada
X (Twitter): x.com/tacobellcanada
Instagram: www.instagram.com/tacobellcanada
YouTube: www.youtube.com/user/TacoBellCanadaTV

Description: Chain of fast food restaurants. **No. of Operating Units:** 170. **Founded:** 1962. **Franchise Fee:** 49100. **Royalty Fee:** 0.07. **Training:** Offers 12 weeks minimum.

14273 ■ Tony Roma's Inc.
1700 Alma Dr.
 Plano, TX 75075
URL: http://tonyromas.com
Facebook: www.facebook.com/TonyRomas
X (Twitter): twitter.com/tonyromas
Instagram: www.instagram.com/tonyromas
YouTube: www.youtube.com/user/TonyRomasVideo

Description: Chain of fast food restaurants. **Founded:** 1972. **Training:** Yes.

14274 ■ Topper's Pizza
551 Bryne Dr., Unit N
 Barrie, ON, Canada L4N 9Y3
Free: 877-558-5581
Co. E-mail: info@toppers.ca
URL: http://www.toppers.ca
Facebook: www.facebook.com/topperspizzacanada
X (Twitter): x.com/topperscanada
Instagram: www.instagram.com/topperspizzacanada

Description: Chain of pizza restaurant. **Founded:** 1982. **Franchise Fee:** $25,000. **Royalty Fee:** 0.05. **Training:** Offers 4-6 of training weeks.

14275 ■ Triple O's
200-8223 Sherbrooke St.
 Vancouver, BC, Canada V5X 4E6
Ph: (604)321-6631
Fax: (604)325-1499
URL: http://www.tripleos.com
Facebook: www.facebook.com/tripleosrestaurant
X (Twitter): x.com/TripleOs
Instagram: www.instagram.com/tripleosrestaurant
YouTube: www.youtube.com/user/TheTripleOs

Description: Chain of fast food restaurants that serves burgers, sides, milkshakes and treats. **Founded:** 1928.

14276 ■ Tropical Smoothie Cafe, LLC
1117 Perimeter Center W, Ste. W200
 Atlanta, GA 30338
Ph: (770)821-1900
URL: http://www.tropicalsmoothiecafe.com
Facebook: www.facebook.com/tropicalsmoothiecafe
Linkedin: www.linkedin.com/company/tropical-smoo
 thie-cafe
X (Twitter): x.com/TSmoothieCafe
YouTube: www.youtube.com/channel/UCf6pHZ4g6oY
 tjSy3Mjar5BQ
Pinterest: www.pinterest.com/tropicalsmoothiecafe

Description: Restaurant chain offering nutritional smoothies. **Founded:** 1997. **Training:** Comprehensive training on operations, marketing & management of your business.

14277 ■ True Food Kitchen
2502 E Camelback Rd.
 Phoenix, AZ 85016
Ph: (602)774-3488
URL: http://www.truefoodkitchen.com
Contact: Dr. Andrew Weil, Founder

Facebook: www.facebook.com/TrueFoodKitchen
Instagram: www.instagram.com/livetruefood
Description: Chain of restaurants offering healthy, seasonal food and drinks. **Founded:** 2008.

14278 ■ Tubby's Sub Shops Inc.
Tubby's Sub Shops Inc.
30551 Edison Dr.
Roseville, MI 48066
Ph: (586)293-5088
Co. E-mail: info@tubbys.com
URL: http://www.tubbys.com
Contact: Robert Paganes, Chief Executive Officer
Facebook: www.facebook.com/TubbysGrilledSubmarines
X (Twitter): x.com/TubbysSubShops
Description: Operates as a restaurant. **Founded:** 1968. **Franchised:** 1978. **Training:** Classroom sessions where very facet of your business is covered. Additional on-site assistance is given just prior to opening and during your first few weeks of operation.

14279 ■ Urban Kitchen
155 Gordon Baker Rd. Unit 214.
Toronto, ON, Canada M2H 3N5
Free: 866-567-5648
Fax: (416)499-5202
Co. E-mail: selects.sandwich@gmail.com
URL: http://www.selectsandwich.com
Contact: Brian Kahn, President
Facebook: www.facebook.com/selectsandwichgta
X (Twitter): x.com/select_sandwich
Pinterest: www.pinterest.com/selectsandwich
Description: Operator of food restaurant. It offers menu sandwiches, paninis, crust pizza, salads. **Founded:** 2007. **Franchise Fee:** 30000. **Royalty Fee:** 0.07. **Training:** Provides 6 weeks training.

14280 ■ VHooters of America LLC.
1815 The Exchange
Atlanta, GA 30339
Ph: (770)951-2040
URL: http://www.hooters.com
Contact: Claudia Levitas, Officer
Facebook: www.facebook.com/hooters
X (Twitter): x.com/hooters
YouTube: www.youtube.com/hooters
Description: Business of restaurant and food delivery services. **No. of Franchise Units:** 416. **No. of Company-Owned Units:** 190. **Founded:** 1983. **Equity Capital Needed:** Net worth of $2,500,000; Liquidity of $1,500,000. **Franchise Fee:** $75,000. **Royalty Fee:** 5%. **Publications:** *Hooters Magazine* (Quarterly). **Training:** Yes.

14281 ■ Villa Restaurant Group Inc. (VRG)
25 Washington St.
Morristown, NJ 07960
Ph: (973)285-4800
Co. E-mail: customerservice@villarestaurantgroup.com
URL: http://www.villarestaurantgroup.com
Contact: Biagio Scotto, President
Linkedin: www.linkedin.com/company/villa-restaurant-group
Description: Quick service pizza and Italian restaurant. **Founded:** 1964. **Training:** Yes.

14282 ■ Virginia Barbeque (VA BBQ)
6920 Lakeside Ave.
Richmond, VA 23228
Ph: (804)262-6660
Fax: (804)262-6669
Co. E-mail: info@virginiabbq.com
URL: http://www.virginiabbq.com
Contact: Richard Ivey, Chief Executive Officer
Description: Quick service "Genuine Southern" barbeque. **No. of Franchise Units:** 14. **No. of Company-Owned Units:** 2. **Founded:** 2000. **Franchised:** 2004. **Equity Capital Needed:** $81,500-$221,500. **Franchise Fee:** $25,000. **Royalty Fee:** 6%. **Training:** Provides 2 weeks at headquarters and 1 week at franchisee's location.

14283 ■ Wendy's Restaurants of Canada Inc.
The Wendy's Co.
240 Wyecroft Rd.
Oakville, ON, Canada L6K 2G7
Ph: (614)764-3100
Free: 888-624-8140
Co. E-mail: customercare@wendys.com
URL: http://www.wendys.com
Contact: Kirk Tanner, President
Facebook: www.facebook.com/wendys/?brand_redir=132856246727566
Linkedin: www.linkedin.com/company/wendys-international/
X (Twitter): twitter.com/WendysCanada
Instagram: www.instagram.com/wendyscanada/
YouTube: www.youtube.com/channel/UCXUT7IkngMjUSV003I8pkQw
Description: Operator of fast food restaurant. It offers menu burger, chicken and wraps, salads, sides. **Founded:** 1969. **Training:** Initial 16-26 weeks of training provided.

14284 ■ Western Sizzlin Corp.
Biglari Holdings Inc.
VA
Ph: (210)344-3400
Fax: (210)344-3411
URL: http://www.biglariholdings.com
Contact: Nick Pascarella, Founder
Description: Family style steak house, buffet and bakery. **No. of Operating Units:** 75.0. **Founded:** 1962. **Franchised:** 1966. **Equity Capital Needed:** $1,000,000 - $300,000. **Franchise Fee:** $30,000. **Royalty Fee:** 0.02. **Financial Assistance:** No **Training:** Yes.

14285 ■ Wetzel's Pretzels
Facebook: www.facebook.com/WetzelsPretzels/
Description: Pretzels. **No. of Franchise Units:** 253. **No. of Company-Owned Units:** 11. **Founded:** 1994. **Franchised:** 1996. **Equity Capital Needed:** $156,300-$369,950. **Franchise Fee:** $35,000. **Royalty Fee:** 7%. **Training:** Offers 2 weeks at headquarters, 4 days at franchisee's location and ongoing support.

14286 ■ Whata Lotta Pizza
7011 Warner Ave.
Huntington Beach, CA 92647
Ph: (714)848-6148
URL: http://www.whatalottapizza.com
Contact: Wayne Lavigne, Founder
Description: Chain of restaurants. **Founded:** 1992. **Training:** Yes.

14287 ■ White Spot Restaurants
200-8223 Sherbrooke St.
Vancouver, BC, Canada V5X 4E6
Ph: (604)321-6631
Co. E-mail: feedback@whitespot.ca
URL: http://www.whitespot.ca
Facebook: www.facebook.com/whitespot
X (Twitter): x.com/White_Spot
Instagram: www.instagram.com/whitespot_restaurants
Description: Chain of Canadian restaurants. **No. of Franchise Units:** 40. **No. of Company-Owned Units:** 24. **No. of Operating Units:** 64. **Founded:** 1928. **Equity Capital Needed:** $900,000 to a high of $2.6 million. **Franchise Fee:** $75,000. **Royalty Fee:** 0.05. **Training:** Offers 3-10 weeks of training, and assistance with staff and management.

14288 ■ Wienerschnitzel
Galardi Group Inc.
8950 Montecito Ave.
Atascadero, CA 93422
Contact: John Galardi, Founder
Facebook: www.facebook.com/Wienerschnitzel
X (Twitter): twitter.com/Wienerschnitzel
Instagram: www.instagram.com/wienerschnitzel/
YouTube: www.youtube.com/user/mostwantedwiener/videos

Description: Fast food, including soft-serve ice cream and desserts. **Founded:** 1950. **Financial Assistance:** Yes **Training:** Consists of 2 weeks at the corporate office - total operation and business training given.

14289 ■ Wimpy's Diner Inc.
3555 St Clair Ave. E
Scarborough, ON, Canada M1K 1L6
Ph: (416)261-9584
Co. E-mail: info@wimpysdiner.ca
URL: http://wimpysdiner.ca
Instagram: www.instagram.com/wimpysdiner
Description: Chain of fast food restaurants that serves sandwiches, burgers, york steak and eggs, drinks and much more. **Founded:** 1988. **Training:** Provides 4-8 weeks training.

14290 ■ Winger's Grill & Bar [Wingers Restaurant & Alehouse]
4790 S State St.
Murray, UT 84107
Ph: (801)685-8889
URL: http://wingerbros.com
Contact: Eric Slaymaker, President
Facebook: www.facebook.com/WingersRestaurants
X (Twitter): x.com/WingersRG
Description: Chain of fast-food restaurants. **No. of Franchise Units:** 35. **Founded:** 1993. **Equity Capital Needed:** $125,000-$250,000. **Training:** Operator of restaurants specializing in grilled food.

14291 ■ Wings to Go
909 Praire Trl.
Austin, TX 78758
Contact: Alchaer Fadi, Contact
Description: Operator of restaurants. **Founded:** 1985. **Training:** Yes.

14292 ■ Wingstop Inc. [Wingstop Restaurants Inc.]
5501 LBJ Fwy., 5th Fl.
Dallas, TX 75240
Ph: (972)686-6500
Fax: (214)853-9296
URL: http://www.wingstop.com
Contact: Michael Skipworth, President
Facebook: www.facebook.com/Wingstop
X (Twitter): twitter.com/wingstop
Instagram: www.instagram.com/wingstop/
Description: Non-vegetarian restaurant famous for buffalo-style chicken wings throughout southern United States. **Founded:** 1994. **Training:** Yes.

14293 ■ Woody's Bar-B-Q
4745 Sutton Pk. Ct., Ste. 301
Jacksonville, FL 32224
Ph: (904)992-0556
Fax: (904)992-0551
URL: http://woodys.com
Contact: Yolanda Mills-Mawman, President
Facebook: www.facebook.com/WoodysFranchiseSystems
Linkedin: www.linkedin.com/company/22302205
X (Twitter): x.com/woodysbbqcorp
Instagram: www.instagram.com/woodysbarbqcorp
YouTube: www.youtube.com/channel/UCQdG6-YDxwOUwdl5Z83CHtw
Description: Operator of restaurant. **No. of Franchise Units:** 26. **Founded:** 1980. **Financial Assistance:** Yes **Training:** Required to attend and successfully complete Woody's 6 week franchise training program. Store opening provided by Corporate Training Team for 6 days prior to the opening date and 4 days after and ongoing operational support through field service represent.

14294 ■ WOW Cafe & Wingery
13130 LA-1085
Covington, LA 70433
Ph: (985)276-4978
URL: http://www.wowamericaneats.com
Facebook: www.facebook.com/wowamericaneats
Instagram: www.instagram.com/wowamericaneats
Description: All American Cafe. **No. of Franchise Units:** 66. **Founded:** 2001. **Franchised:** 2002. **Equity Capital Needed:** $234,400-$754,500. **Fran-**

chise Fee: $15,000-$35,000. **Royalty Fee:** 5%. **Financial Assistance:** Yes **Training:** Provides 15 days training at headquarters, 14 days at franchisee's location and ongoing support.

14295 ■ Yaya's Flame Broiled Chicken
521 S Dort Hwy.
 Flint, MI 48503
Ph: (810)235-6550
Fax: (810)235-5210
Co. E-mail: customerservice@yayas.com
URL: http://www.yayas.com

Description: Chain of a restaurant. **Founded:** 1986. **Franchised:** 1988. **Equity Capital Needed:** $335,500-$460,000. **Franchise Fee:** $15,000. **Royalty Fee:** 6% of gross sales. **Training:** Yes.

14296 ■ Yeung's Lotus Express Franchise Corp.
4531 Ponce de Leon Blvd., Ste. 300
 Coral Gables, FL 33146
Ph: (305)476-1611
URL: http://www.irmgusa.com
Contact: Hoi-Sang Yeung, President

Description: Firm affiliated with restaurants in the world. **Founded:** 1997. **Training:** Yes.

14297 ■ ZOUP!
29177 NW Hwy.
 Southfield, MI 48034
Ph: (248)799-2800
Co. E-mail: marketing@zoup.com
URL: http://zoup.com
Facebook: www.facebook.com/ZoupEatery
Instagram: www.instagram.com/zoupeatery

Description: Quick, casual soup restaurant. **No. of Franchise Units:** 38. **No. of Company-Owned Units:** 3. **Founded:** 1997. **Franchised:** 2003. **Equity Capital Needed:** $327,500-$563,000. **Franchise Fee:** $39,000. **Royalty Fee:** 6%. **Financial Assistance:** Yes **Training:** Offers 3 weeks at headquarters, 1 week onsite and ongoing support.

14298 ■ Zyng Asian Grill
PO Box 72108- RPO Atwater
 Montreal, QC, Canada H3J 2Z6
Ph: (514)288-8800
Free: 888-328-9964
Fax: (514)939-8808
Co. E-mail: info@zyng.com
URL: http://www.zyng.com
Contact: Chris Kassab, Contact
E-mail: ckassab@zyng.com

Description: Chain of Japanese restaurants. **Founded:** 1998. **Training:** Provides 4 weeks and ongoing support.

COMPUTER SYSTEMS/ SOFTWARE

14299 ■ *Bottom Line Service System*
Bottom Line Software
 7108 E 88th Pl.
 Tulsa, OK 74133
Co. E-mail: support@blss.com
URL: http://www.blss.com
Contact: Gene C. Napier, Contact
URL(s): www.blss.com/blser.htm

Price: $1,500, for bottom line cloud system annual fee; $250, for cloud set-up fee. **Description:** The Bottom Line Service System is a Windows based service management system designed specifically to meet the needs of customer service businesses. HVAC, Refrigeration, Plumbing, Electrical and Mechanical service and installation companies use our system with great deal of success. **Availability:** Online.

LIBRARIES

14300 ■ American Beverage Association (ABA)
1275 Pennsylvania Ave. NW, Ste. 1100
 Washington, DC 20004
Ph: (202)463-6774
Fax: (202)463-8277
Co. E-mail: media@americanbeverage.org
URL: http://www.americanbeverage.org/about-us/aba -team
Contact: Katherine Lugar, President

Description: Conducts government affairs activities on the national and state levels, discussion of industry problems, and general improvement of operating procedures. Conducts research on beverage laws. **Founded:** 1919. **Publications:** *Promoting Recycling to the Public*; *Directory of Members & Buyers Guide.* **Geographic Preference:** National.

14301 ■ City College of San Francisco (CCSF) - Culinary Arts and Hospitality Studies - Alice Statler Library
50 Frida Kahlo Way
 Statler Wing, Rm. 10
 San Francisco, CA 94112
Ph: (415)239-3460
URL: http://library.ccsf.edu/locations/statler

Scope: Culinary arts and hospitality study; historical menus; notable titles; local chefs, restaurateurs, hoteliers and entrepreneurs in the industry. **Services:** Copying; Wi-Fi; library open to the public for reference use only. **Founded:** 1964. **Holdings:** Books; menus; archives; monographs; periodicals; DVDs.

14302 ■ Cornell University - The Nestlé Library
G80 Statler Hall, Cornell University
 Ithaca, NY 14850
Ph: (607)255-3673
Co. E-mail: hotellibrary@cornell.edu
URL: http://hotel.library.cornell.edu
Contact: Ken Bolton, Librarian, Public Services
E-mail: ktb4@cornell.edu

Scope: Hospitality and real estate. **Services:** Interlibrary loan; library open to the public by appointment on a fee basis. **Founded:** 1922. **Holdings:** 28,348 print volumes; 17,551 microforms.

14303 ■ Culinary Institute of America - Conrad N. Hilton Library
1946 Campus Dr.
 Hyde Park, NY 12538-1430
Ph: (845)451-1747
Co. E-mail: library@culinary.edu
URL: http://library.culinary.edu/index
Contact: Jon Grennan, Director
E-mail: j_grenna@culinary.edu

Scope: Arts materials. **Services:** Interlibrary loan; copying; library open to the public by appointment. **Founded:** 1946. **Holdings:** 86,000 volumes; 30,000 menus; 4,500 DVDs and videos. **Subscriptions:** 280 journals and other serials.

14304 ■ Food Institute (FI)
330 Changebridge Rd., Ste. 101
 Pine Brook, NJ 07058
Ph: (201)791-5570
Free: 855-791-5570
Co. E-mail: questions@foodinstitute.com
URL: http://www.foodinstitute.com
Contact: Anika Wilson, Contact
E-mail: anika.wilson@foodinstitute.com
Facebook: www.facebook.com/foodinstitutenj
Linkedin: www.linkedin.com/company/the-food-insti tute
X (Twitter): x.com/FoodInstitute
Instagram: www.instagram.com/foodinstitute
YouTube: www.youtube.com/channel/UCYAPI0TXN tJa04aQre4h4pA

Description: Strives to provide food industry-related information to its members. **Scope:** The food industry. **Services:** Center open to the public on fee basis. **Founded:** 1928. **Holdings:** Figures not available. **Publications:** *Today in Food*; *Get It Out, Get It Right, Get It Over! Avoiding Food Product Recalls*; *The Food Institute* (Weekly); *Almanac of the Canning, Freezing, Preserving Industries* (Annual); *Food Business Mergers and Acquisitions*; *OSHA Inspection Manual*; *Regulatory Directory* (Periodic); *Food Business Mergers & Acquisitions.* **Geographic Preference:** Multinational.

14305 ■ Le Cordon Bleu College of Culinary Arts Library
350 Rhode Island St.
 San Francisco, CA 94103
URL: http://www.careered.com/closedschool/loca tions

Scope: Culinary arts; nutrition; restaurant and hospitality industry. **Services:** Library open to the public by special appointment only. **Founded:** 1989. **Holdings:** 3,500 books.

14306 ■ National Restaurant Association (NRA)
2055 L St. NW, Ste. 700
 Washington, DC 20036
Ph: (202)331-5900
Free: 800-424-5156
Co. E-mail: askus@restaurant.org
URL: http://www.restaurant.org
Contact: Michelle Korsmo, President
Facebook: www.facebook.com/WeRRestaurants
Linkedin: www.linkedin.com/company/22205
X (Twitter): x.com/WeRRestaurants
Instagram: www.instagram.com/werrestaurants
YouTube: www.youtube.com/user/restaurantdotorg

Description: Restaurants, cafeterias, contract food-service management, drive-ins, caterers, institutional food services and other members of the foodservice industry; represents establishments belonging to non-affiliated state and local restaurant associations in governmental affairs. Supports foodservice education and research in several educational institutions. Affiliated with the Educational Foundation of the National Restaurant Association to provide training and education for operators, food and equipment manufacturers, distributors and educators. **Founded:** 1919. **Publications:** *Restaurants USA: The Monthly Magazine of the National Restaurant Assn* (Monthly); *Who's Who in the Foodservice Industry*; *Restaurant Information Abstracts* (Biweekly); *Foodservice/ Hospitality College Directory* (Irregular); *National Restaurant Association--Washington Report* (Semimonthly); *Restaurant Operations Report.* **Educational Activities:** National Restaurant Association Restaurant and Hotel-Motel Show (Annual). **Awards:** John L. Hennessy Award (Annual); NRA Restaurant Neighbor Award (Annual). **Geographic Preference:** National.

14307 ■ Prince Edward Island Food Technology Centre - Information Services
101 Belvedere Ave.
 Charlottetown, PE, Canada C1A 7N8
Ph: (902)368-5548
Free: 877-368-5548
Fax: (902)368-5549
Co. E-mail: biofoodtech@biofoodtech.ca
URL: http://www.biofoodtechpei.ca
Contact: Jillian Sproul, Executive Director
Facebook: www.facebook.com/concept.pilot.market
X (Twitter): twitter.com/BioFoodTech

Scope: Agriculture; food; technology; food research. **Services:** Interlibrary loan; library open to the public by permission only. **Founded:** 1987. **Holdings:** 200 books; 9 bound periodical volumes.

14308 ■ Restaurants Canada - Library
1155 Queen St. W
 Toronto, ON, Canada M6J 1J4

Ph: (416)923-8416
Free: 800-387-5649
Fax: (416)923-1450
Co. E-mail: info@restaurantscanada.org
URL: http://www.restaurantscanada.org
Contact: Christian Buhagiar, Co-Chief Executive
  Officer Co-President
Facebook: www.facebook.com/RestaurantsCanada
Linkedin: www.linkedin.com/company/restaurants
  -canada

X (Twitter): x.com/RestaurantsCA
Instagram: www.instagram.com/RestaurantsCanada
YouTube: www.youtube.com/channel/
  UCxVckfCBllSII9LOuflNX8w
Description: Restaurant and food service corporations, hotels, caterers, and food service suppliers and
educators, seeks to create a favorable business
environment for members. **Scope:** Food service;
quantity cooking; legislation; administration; management; statistics; training; customer attitude surveys.

Services: Copying; open to the public on fee basis.
Founded: 1944. **Publications:** *CRFA National
Hospitality News*; *Canadian Foodservice Industry
Operations Report* (Biennial); *Foodservice Facts* (An-
nual); *Legislation Guide* (Quarterly). **Educational
Activities:** Restaurants Canada Show (Annual);
ApEx. **Geographic Preference:** National.

START-UP INFORMATION

14309 ■ *"Etsy: Etsy Business for Beginners! Master Etsy and Build a Profitable Business In No Time"*

Released: December 23, 2014. **Price:** $6.99, regular price is $13.99. **Description:** Craft artisans take note: information is offered to start an online business through Etsy. Whether handmade home accessories, clothing, or knick-knacks, Etsy is the perfect option for artists and crafters to start a home-based, online retail operation. **Availability:** Print; Download.

ASSOCIATIONS AND OTHER ORGANIZATIONS

14310 ■ **National Resume Writers' Association (NRWA)**
2331 Rock Spring Rd.
  Forest Hill, MD 21050
Co. E-mail: info@thenrwa.org
URL: http://thenrwa.org
Contact: Sara Timm, President
E-mail: president@thenrwa.org
Facebook: www.facebook.com/NationalResumeWritersAssociation
X (Twitter): x.com/thenrwa
Instagram: www.instagram.com/the_nrwa
Pinterest: www.pinterest.com/thenrwa

Description: Promotes high standards of excellence in resume writing through mentoring, education and support services. Represents the interests of writers, recruiters, counselors and other employment and career-related professionals. **Founded:** 1997. **Geographic Preference:** National.

14311 ■ **Professional Association of Resume Writers and Career Coaches (PARW/CC)**
204 37th Ave. N, Ste. 112
  Saint Petersburg, FL 33704-1388

Ph: (727)350-2218
Co. E-mail: association@parwcc.com
URL: http://parwcc.com
Contact: Margaret Phares, Executive Director
E-mail: mphares@parwcc.com
Facebook: www.facebook.com/parwcc
Linkedin: www.linkedin.com/company/parw-cc
Instagram: www.instagram.com/parwcc
YouTube: www.youtube.com/channel/UCbGeiBOyCk
  dCVouK7MLGVMQ

Description: Provides educational programs. Offers certification for Certified Professional Resume Writers (CPRW) and for Certified Employment Interview Professionals (CEIP). **Founded:** 1990. **Awards:** PARW/CC Certified Professional Resume Writer (Annual). **Geographic Preference:** National.

REFERENCE WORKS

14312 ■ **Business and Professional Communication: A Practical Guide to Workplace Effectiveness**
Released: May 28, 2020. **Description:** Fundamentals in writing in the business industry. Includes resumes, interviews, and communications for later after landing the job.

14313 ■ *How to Write the Perfect Resume: Stand Out, Land Interviews, and Get the Job You Want*
Ed: Dan Clay. **Released:** May 28, 2018. **Price:** $11.68, Paperback; $3.99, E-book. **Description:** A guide to writing a resume that will put you in the top 1% of candidates for the job. A precise set of instructions are included along along with access to a free companion website. **Availability:** E-book; Print.

14314 ■ **Resume and Job Interview Mastery**
URL(s): amazon.com/Resume-Interview-Mastery-Digital-World/dp/B07VCVP91Z/ref=sr_1_10?keywords=resume+service+books&qid=1574542852&sr=8-10

Released: 2019. **Description:** Instructional video on how to write a good resume to secure job interviews. **Availability:** Online.

14315 ■ *"'Resume Mining' Services Can Save Time, Money" in HR Specialist (Vol. 8, September 2010, No. 9, pp. 7)*
Pub: Capitol Information Group Inc.
Contact: Allie Ash, Chief Executive Officer

Description: Low-cost resume mining services can help human resource departments save time and money by searching online resume databases for candidates matching specific job qualifications. **Availability:** PDF; Online.

14316 ■ *"Tracking Your Fleet Can Increase Bottom Line" in Contractor (Vol. 56, November 2009, No. 11, pp. 26)*
Ed: Candace Roulo. **Description:** GPS fleet management system can help boost a contractor's profits, employee productivity, and efficiency. These are available as a handheld device or a cell phone that employees carry around or as a piece of hardware installed in a vehicle. These lets managers track assets and communicate with employees about jobs. **Availability:** Online.

STATISTICAL SOURCES

14317 ■ *Document Preparation Services Industry in the US - Market Research Report*
URL(s): www.ibisworld.com/united-states/market-research-reports/document-preparation-services-industry/

Price: $925. **Description:** Downloadable report analyzing data about the document preparation industry and the competition it faces from other similar industries. **Availability:** Download.

ASSOCIATIONS AND OTHER ORGANIZATIONS

14318 ■ American Subcontractors Association (ASA)
1004 Duke St.
Alexandria, VA 22314
Ph: (703)684-3450
Co. E-mail: asaoffice@asa-hq.com
URL: http://www.asaonline.com
Contact: Richard Bright, Chief Operating Officer
E-mail: rbright@asa-hq.com
Facebook: www.facebook.com/subcontractors
X (Twitter): x.com/ASAupdate
Description: Construction subcontractors of trades and specialties such as foundations, concrete, masonry, steel, mechanical, drywall, electrical, painting, plastering, roofing and acoustical. Formed to deal with issues common to subcontractors. Works with other segments of the construction industry in promoting ethical practices, beneficial legislation and education of construction subcontractors and suppliers. Manages the Foundation of the American Subcontractors Association (FASA). **Founded:** 1966. **Publications:** *ASAtoday* (Weekly); *The Subcontractor* (Monthly); *Action ASA*; *The Contractor's Compass* (Monthly). **Geographic Preference:** National.

14319 ■ Asphalt Roofing Manufacturers Association (ARMA)
2331 Rock Spring Rd.
Forest Hill, MD 21050
Ph: (202)640-1075
Fax: (202)640-1031
URL: http://www.asphaltroofing.org
Facebook: www.facebook.com/Asphal tRoofingManufacturersAssociation
Linkedin: www.linkedin.com/company/asphalt-roofing -manufacturers-association
YouTube: www.youtube.com/user/asphaltroofingvi deo
Description: An association committed to the long-term sustainability of the asphalt roofing industry and to advocate and advance the interests of the asphalt roofing industry by leveraging the collective expertise of its members. **Founded:** 1915. **Publications:** *Publication and Audio Visual Directory* (Biennial); *ARMA eNewsletter* (Semiannual); *Guide to Preparing Build-Up Roofing Specifications* (Irregular). **Geographic Preference:** National.

14320 ■ Association Canadienne des Entrepreneurs en Couverture (ACEC) [Canadian Roofing Contractors Association (CRCA)]
2430 Don Reid Dr., Ste. 100
Ottawa, ON, Canada K1H 1E1
Ph: (613)232-6724
Free: 800-461-2722
Fax: (613)232-2893
Co. E-mail: crca@roofingcanada.com
URL: http://www.roofingcanada.com
Contact: Murray Tysowski, President

Facebook: www.facebook.com/Canadian-Roofing -Contractors-Association-113028683592871
Linkedin: www.linkedin.com/company/crcanews
X (Twitter): x.com/crcanews
Instagram: www.instagram.com/crcanews
Description: Roofing contractors. Seeks to advance the building industries. Facilitates communication and cooperation among members; represents members' interests before labor and industrial organizations, government agencies, and the public. **Founded:** 1959. **Publications:** *Roofing Canada* (Semiannual). **Awards:** Jacques Chevalier Scholarship (Annual). **Geographic Preference:** National.

14321 ■ National Roofing Contractors Association (NRCA)
National Roofing Contractors Association (NRCA)
10255 W Higgins Rd., Ste. 600
Rosemont, IL 60018-5607
Ph: (847)299-9070
Free: 866-275-6722
Fax: (847)299-1183
Co. E-mail: info@nrca.net
URL: http://www.nrca.net
Contact: Reid Ribble, Chief Executive Officer
Facebook: www.facebook.com/nrcainfo
Linkedin: www.linkedin.com/company/national-roofing -contractors-association
X (Twitter): x.com/NRCAnews
Instagram: www.instagram.com/NRCAnews
YouTube: www.youtube.com/user/nrcanews
Description: Roofing, roof deck, and waterproofing contractors and industry-related associate members. Assists members to successfully satisfy their customers through technical support, testing and research, education, marketing, government relations, and consultation. **Founded:** 1886. **Publications:** *Steep-slope Roofing Materials Guide*; *National Roofing Contractors Association--Membership Directory*; *Low-Slope Roofing Materials Guide*; *Professional Roofing* (10/year); *NRCA Buyers Guide*. **Educational Activities:** NRCA Annual Convention and International Roofing Expo (Annual). **Geographic Preference:** National.

14322 ■ Roof Coatings Manufacturers Association (RCMA)
529 14th St. NW, Ste. 1280
Washington, DC 20045
Ph: (202)591-2452
Co. E-mail: questions@roofcoatings.org
URL: http://www.roofcoatings.org
Contact: Chris Huettig, President
Description: Association of companies involved in the manufacture and distribution of cold-process protective roof coatings. **Founded:** 1982. **Publications:** *Roof Coatings Manufacturers Association Membership Directory* (Annual). **Educational Activities:** RCMA Annual Meeting (Annual). **Awards:** Martin A. Davis Industry Leadership Award (Annual). **Geographic Preference:** National.

14323 ■ *Roofing Canada*
2430 Don Reid Dr., Ste. 100
Ottawa, ON, Canada K1H 1E1
Ph: (613)232-6724
Free: 800-461-2722
Fax: (613)232-2893
Co. E-mail: crca@roofingcanada.com
URL: http://www.roofingcanada.com
Contact: Murray Tysowski, President
URL(s): roofingcanada.com/roofing-canada -magazine
Ed: Roma Ihnatowycz. **Released:** Semiannual **Price:** Free. **Description:** Contains news and background information related to industry issues and general interest topics. **Availability:** Online.

14324 ■ Tile Roofing Institute (TRI)
2150 N 107th St., Ste. 205
Seattle, WA 98133
Ph: (206)209-5300
Co. E-mail: info@tileroofing.org
URL: http://tileroofing.org
Contact: Rick Olson, President
E-mail: rolson@tileroofing.org
Facebook: www.facebook.com/TileRoofTraining
Linkedin: www.linkedin.com/company/tile-roofing-in dustry-alliance
Instagram: www.instagram.com/tileroofingindustry
YouTube: www.youtube.com/c/Tileroofingorg1
Description: Manufacturers and suppliers of clay and concrete roofing tiles; cement companies; mineral pigment producers; and others furnishing equipment and materials for manufacturing roof tiles. Promotes the use of "firesafe" roof construction, especially clay and concrete tile roofs; educates the architectural, design, and construction industries regarding the advantages of tile roofs; presents to the home-owning public the advantages and economies of tile roofs. Conducts international programs for architects, builders, building inspectors, and roofing contractors; provides sound/slide presentations, speakers, mailers, and specifications relating to tile roof construction. **Founded:** 1971. **Geographic Preference:** National.

REFERENCE WORKS

14325 ■ *"ABC Supply Company Finally Finds Idaho"* in Idaho Business Review (September 17, 2014)
Pub: BridgeTower Media
Contact: Adam Reinebach, President
Description: The nation's largest wholesale distributor, ABC Supply Company, has entered a store in Idaho. The roofing supply firm has now has stores in 48 states. Franklin Lumber Supply, a home supply chain will be ABCs its major competitor in the area.

14326 ■ *"Guide to Starting Your Own Roofing Business"* in Home Business (May 24, 2022)
URL(s): homebusinessmag.com/business-start-up/ how-to-guides/guide-starting-roofing-business/

Released: May 24, 2022. **Description:** Starting your own roofing business may be the solution you need to break away from working for someone else. Included are tips to consider while doing so. **Availability:** Online.

14327 ■ *"Hanson's to Widen Marketing Window; Company Plans Mall Kiosks, to Attend Events" in Crain's Detroit Business (Vol. 28, May 28, 2012, No. 22, pp. 3)*

Pub: Crain Communications Inc.
Contact: Barry Asin, President

Ed: Sherri Welch. **Description:** Hanson's Window and Construction Company is expanding its presence through the use of kiosks installed at malls as well as attending local events in order to increase awareness of their firm. Las year Hanson spent nearly $9.2 million on marketing their vinyl replacement windows, siding and roofing for homes. **Availability:** Print; Online.

14328 ■ *"Housing Slide Picks Up Speed" in Crain's Chicago Business (Vol. 31, April 19, 2008, No. 16, pp. 2)*

Pub: Crain Communications Inc.
Contact: Barry Asin, President

Ed: Eddie Baeb. **Description:** According to Tracy Cross & Associates Inc., a real estate consultancy, sales of new homes in the Chicago area dropped 61 percent from the year-earlier period which is more bad news for homebuilders, contractors and real estate agents who are eager for an indication that market conditions are improving. **Availability:** Online.

14329 ■ *Low-Slope Roofing Materials Guide*

Pub: National Roofing Contractors Association
Contact: Reid Ribble, Chief Executive Officer
URL(s): www.nrca.net/Technical/LibraryDetail/e-ZY7 3-IyHM%3D

Released: Last Update 2006-07. **Description:** Covers approximately 250 manufacturers and suppliers of low-slope roof membrane, metal roof panels, cements and coatings, insulation board, and roof fastener products for commercial, industrial, and institutional purposes. **Entries include:** Company name, location, phone, name and title of contact, description of products, warranty information. **Arrangement:** Alphabetical. **Indexes:** Company name, trade name, product. **Availability:** Print.

14330 ■ *"Malarkey Using Upcycled Plastics in Shingles" in Roofing Contractor (December 28, 2018)*

URL(s): www.roofingcontractor.com/articles/9 3334-malarkey-using-upcycled-plastics-in-shingles

Released: December 28, 2018. **Description:** Malarkey Roofing Products is going ot offer NEX polymer modified asphalt in all of its roofing shingles, keeping many materials out of the landfill. The company is focused on using upcycled materials to keep unnecessary waste from entering the environment. **Availability:** Online.

14331 ■ *National Roofing Contractors Association--Membership Directory*

Pub: National Roofing Contractors Association
Contact: Reid Ribble, Chief Executive Officer
URL(s): www.nrca.net/Members

Description: Covers 5,000 contractors applying all types of commercial and residential roofing; 600 associate member manufacturers, suppliers, and distributors; 300 foreign members; and 100 institutions and related industries. **Entries include:** Company name, address, phone, and names of voting representatives. **Arrangement:** Alphabetical. **Indexes:** Geographical, voting representative, Alphabetical, member product guide. **Availability:** Print.

14332 ■ *"The Roofing Industry Continues Its Upward Slope" in Forbes (June 3, 2018)*

URL(s): www.forbes.com/sites/sageworks/2018/06/0 3/the-roofing-industry-continues-its-upward-slope/# 33baed452c8c

Ed: Mary Ellen Biery. **Released:** June 03, 2018. **Description:** The roofing industry is seeing an increase in profits again after new home construction has jumped and damage repairs to storm-related events. **Availability:** Online.

STATISTICAL SOURCES

14333 ■ *RMA Annual Statement Studies*

Pub: Risk Management Association
Contact: Nancy Foster, President

Released: Annual. **Description:** Contains composite balance sheets and income statements for more than 360 industries, including the accounting, auditing, and bookkeeping industries. Also contains five years of comparative historical data for discerning trends. Includes 16 commonly used ratios, computed for most of the size groupings for nearly every industry.

TRADE PERIODICALS

14334 ■ *Professional Roofing*

Pub: National Roofing Contractors Association
Contact: Reid Ribble, Chief Executive Officer
URL(s): www.professionalroofing.net

Ed: Ambika Puniani Bailey. **Released:** 10/year; last update may 2024. **Description:** Roofing industry magazine. **Availability:** Print; Online.

TRADE SHOWS AND CONVENTIONS

14335 ■ *International Roofing Expo*

URL(s): www.theroofingexpo.com/en/home.html

Frequency: Annual. **Description:** Provides education, product sourcing, and networking for those in the roofing industry. **Audience:** Residential and commercial contractors, remodelers, builders, distributors, architects, engineers, suppliers, and manufacturers. **Principal Exhibits:** Provides education, product sourcing, and networking for those in the roofing industry.

14336 ■ **NERCA Convention and Trade Show**

Frequency: Annual. **Description:** Tradeshow featuring products and services geared towards the roofing industry. **Principal Exhibits:** Tradeshow featuring products and services geared towards the roofing industry.

14337 ■ **NRCA Annual Convention and International Roofing Expo**

National Roofing Contractors Association (NRCA)
10255 W Higgins Rd., Ste. 600
Rosemont, IL 60018-5607
Ph: (847)299-9070
Free: 866-275-6722
Fax: (847)299-1183
Co. E-mail: info@nrca.net
URL: http://www.nrca.net
Contact: Reid Ribble, Chief Executive Officer
URL(s): www.theroofingexpo.com/en/home.html

Frequency: Annual. **Description:** Provides opportunity for the roofing contractors to network and discuss about their welfare and development. **Audience:** Industry professionals. **Principal Exhibits:** Provides opportunity for the roofing contractors to network and discuss about their welfare and development. Dates and Locations: 2025 Feb 19-21 Henry B. González Convention Center, San Antonio, TX;

2026 Jan 20-22 Las Vegas Convention Center, Las Vegas, NV. **Telecommunication Services:** info@ theroofingexpo.com.

14338 ■ **Roof Consultants Institute International Convention and Trade Show**

RCI, Inc.
1500 Sunday Dr., Ste. 204
Raleigh, NC 27607
Ph: (919)859-0742
Free: 800-828-1902
Fax: (919)859-1328
Co. E-mail: rci@rci-online.org
URL: http://www.rci-online.org
Contact: Edward A. Sheridan, President
URL(s): rci-online.org/building-envelope-edu/conven tion-ts

Frequency: Annual. **Description:** Exhibits relating to roofing consultants. **Audience:** Professionals and public. **Principal Exhibits:** Exhibits relating to roofing consultants.

14339 ■ **Roofing Contractors Association of Texas Expo**

URL(s): www.roofingcontractors-texas.com/texas -roofing-conference.html
Facebook: www.facebook.com/RoofingContrac torsTexas
Linkedin: www.linkedin.com/company/roofing-contrac tors-association-of-texas
X (Twitter): twitter.com/RooferTexas
YouTube: www.youtube.com/channel/UCyAEYpK 1DoyrhmQxrH5Ryig

Frequency: Annual. **Description:** Offers educational sessions, networking, and a trade show for roofers. **Principal Exhibits:** Offers educational sessions, networking, and a trade show for roofers. **Telecommunication Services:** rcat.admin@rooftex.com.

CONSULTANTS

14340 ■ **A/R/C Associates Inc.**

601 N Fern Creek Ave., Ste. 100
Orlando, FL 32803-4899
Ph: (407)896-7875
Fax: (407)898-6043
Co. E-mail: info@arc-arc.com
URL: http://www.arc-arc.com
Contact: Joseph J. Williams, President

Description: Firm provides building survey, priority maintenance program. **Scope:** Firm provides building survey, priority maintenance program. **Founded:** 1982.

14341 ■ **Roofing Materials Science & Technology**

9037 Monte Mar Dr.
Los Angeles, CA 90035-4235
Ph: (310)559-6090
Fax: (310)559-6090
URL: http://roofsandroofing.com
Contact: Dr. Heshmat O. Laaly, President
E-mail: laaly.roofsandroofing@gmail.com

Description: Publisher and distributor of books on roofing materials science and technology. **Publications:** "The Science and Technology of Traditional and Modern Roofing Systems," 1992. **Training:** State of the Art in Roofing Technology.

LIBRARIES

14342 ■ **Construction Consultants Library (ccl)**

4600 College Blvd., Ste. 104
Overland Park, KS 66211
Contact: Michael T. Callahan, Contact

Description: Construction consultants provides advice on construction. **Scope:** Construction; design, waterproofing, facility asset management, roofing, concrete. **Services:** Library open to the public with restrictions. **Founded:** 1986. **Holdings:** 500 books.

ASSOCIATIONS AND OTHER ORGANIZATIONS

14343 ■ Electronics Technicians Association International (ETA) [ETA International]
5 Depot St.
  Greencastle, IN 46135
Ph: (765)653-8262
Free: 800-288-3824
Fax: (765)653-4287
Co. E-mail: eta@etai.org
URL: http://www.etai.org
Contact: Bryan Allen, President
Facebook: www.facebook.com/ETAInternational
X (Twitter): x.com/ETAIntl
YouTube: www.youtube.com/user/ETAINTL

Description: Represents the electronics industry, from the technician and educator to the corporate institution. **Founded:** 1978. **Publications:** *The High-Tech News* (Bimonthly); *Directory of Professional Electronics Technicians* (Irregular). **Awards:** ETA Technician of the Year (Annual); Wallace Medeiros Memorial - Educator of the Year (Annual); ETA President's Award (Annual). **Geographic Preference:** Multinational.

REFERENCE WORKS

14344 ■ "Dish Network to Buy EchoStar's Broadcast Satellite Business" in The Wall Street Journal (May 20, 2019)
URL(s): www.wsj.com/articles/dish-network-buys
  -echostar-broadcast-satellite-business-11558
  348751

Ed: Patrick Thomas. **Released:** May 20, 2019. **Description:** Dish Network has reached an agreement to purchase EschoStar Corp.'s broadcast satellite-service business for about $800 million in stock. Dish already depends on EchoStar to operate most of its satellites, and the deal also includes various real estate. **Availability:** Online.

14345 ■ "The Future of Satellite TV is Unclear" in MediaPost (March 6, 2019)
URL(s): www.mediapost.com/publications/article/
  332791/the-future-of-satellite-tv-is-unclear.html

Ed: Wayne Friedman. **Released:** March 06, 2019. **Description:** Satellite TV is finding itself with several competitors, mainly 5G technology, streaming services, and on-demand programming. Their current business model may need to be adjusted in the upcoming years in order to stay profitable as their competition takes up larger chunks of the market share. **Availability:** Online.

TRADE PERIODICALS

14346 ■ The Orbiter
Pub: Society of Satellite Professionals International
Contact: Katherine Gizinski, President
URL(s): www.sspi.org/articles/the-orbiter-the-big-view

Released: Quarterly **Description:** Covers member and chapter activities, developments in commercial satellite communications technology and applications, and activities of corporate sponsors. Recurring features include a calendar of events, reports of meetings, and columns titled Letter from the President and Corporate Corner. **Availability:** Online.

14347 ■ Wireless Satellite and Broadcasting
Pub: Information Gatekeepers Inc.
Contact: Will Ashley, Manager
E-mail: washley@igigroup.com
URL(s): www.igigroup.com/nl/pages/wiresb.html

Released: Monthly **Price:** $10,000, for 50+ users pdf email version; $745, Other countries for print one year; $4,000, for 11 - 20 users email pdf version; $7,500, for 21 -50 users pdf email version; $695, U.S. and Canada for print; $2,500, for 2 - 10 users pdf email version; $695, for pdf, email. **Description:** Covers developments in technology, business activity, and regulation for the statellite and broadcasting telecommunications industry. **Availability:** Print; Online; PDF.

CONSULTANTS

14348 ■ AMC Networks Inc.
AMC Networks Inc.
  11 Penn Plaza
  New York, NY 10001
Ph: (212)324-8500
Co. E-mail: info@amctv.com
URL: http://www.amcnetworks.com
Contact: Dan McDermott, President
Facebook: https://www.facebook.com/amc
Linkedin: www.linkedin.com/company/amc-networks
X (Twitter): https://twitter.com/AMC_Networks
Instagram: https://www.instagram.com/amc_tv

Description: American entertainment company that is active in cable television broadcasting produces programming and movie content, owns various entertainment channels, and distributes films across various media platforms. **Educational Activities:** The WICT Network Leadership Conference (Annual).

REFERENCE WORKS

14349 ■ *5 Best Screen Printing Machines for Small Business*

Released: March 26, 2020. **Description:** Screen printing can be a great and profitable option for anyone thinking about starting their own business. Good equipment is key to operating successfully. This article provides details on five of the best screen printing machines for your small business. **Availability:** Online.

14350 ■ *"Avoid These Common Pitfalls in Order to Run a Profitable Screen Printing Business" in Printa Blog (August 8, 2013)*

Released: August 08, 2013. **Description:** Starting a small screen printing business at home can be a lucrative endeavor. With a small initial investment, plenty of motivation, and a solid marketing plan, you can launch your own screen printing business and turn a profit in no time. However, many screen printers focus so much on the screen printing process that they forget about the business side of things. This article provides information on five mistakes to avoid when starting your screen printing business.

14351 ■ *The Equipment Needed for a T-shirt Business*

Released: April 16, 2019. **Description:** For those looking to start their own custom t-shirt business, commercial screen printing equipment is a necessity. This article discusses equipment you'll need to get started. **Availability:** Online.

14352 ■ *How to Start a Screen Printing Business*

Description: Provides information on startup costs and costs for everyday operation for a screen printing business as well as marketing information. **Availability:** Online.

14353 ■ *"How to Start a Shirt-Printing Business" in Chron (April 30, 2019)*

Ed: Zach Lazzari. **Released:** April 30, 2019. **Description:** The shirt printing business is a straightforward model with excellent potential. This article discusses shirt designs, screen printing and embroidery, outsourcing printing, and selling online. **Availability:** Online.

14354 ■ *"KSE Imprints Hits Mother Lode With Logos" in Denver Business Journal (Vol. 65, January 31, 2014, No. 38, pp. A9)*

Pub: American City Business Journals, Inc.
Contact: Mike Olivieri, Executive Vice President

Description: Denver, Colorado-based KSE Imprints has been designing sports and business logos for various customers. KSE, which maintains a high quality standard for their work, can produce sponsored rally towels, business names on coffee mugs, and logo shirts. The firm's recent investment in a digital printer is also discussed. **Availability:** Online.

14355 ■ *Screen Printing Equipment & Supply Startup Checklist*

Ed: Terry Combs. **Released:** January 02, 2016. **Description:** Provides a detailed list of equipment needed to start your own screen printing business. **Availability:** Online.

14356 ■ *"Screenprinting Marketing Ideas" in Chron*

Ed: Linda Ray. **Description:** Marketing your screen printing business comes in many forms ranging from straight advertising to public relations and networking. This article provides marketing ideas to explore to expand your business reach. **Availability:** Online.

14357 ■ *Step-by-Step Guide to Starting an Online T-shirt Printing Business in 2020*

Ed: Maulik Shah. **Description:** Provides a complete, step-by-step guide to help you establish your t-shirt printing business including business planning, e-commerce, software, design tools, printing methods, t-shirt supplier, printing infrastructure, logistics infrastructure, launch, and marketing. **Availability:** Online.

14358 ■ *Top 5 Marketing Tips for Your Shop*

Released: October 13, 2018. **Description:** Provides five marketing tips that you can use today to get more sales traffic to your screen printing shop. **Availability:** Online.

14359 ■ *"Why Screen Printers Should Add DTG to Their Shops" in Advertising Specialty Institute (April 16, 2019)*

URL(s): www.asicentral.com/news/web-exclusive/
april-2019/why-screen-printers-should-add-dtg-to
-their-shops/

Ed: Ed Levy. **Released:** April 16, 2019. **Description:** Five reasons screen print shops should look into direct-to-garment (DTG) printing. **Availability:** Online.

14360 ■ *Why Your Screen Printing Shop Needs a Well-Crafted Business Plan*

Released: September 07, 2018. **Description:** Whether you are in the beginning stages of exploring opening your own screen printing shop or you are a seasoned screen printer whose business has been operating for years, you need a well-crafted business plan. This article discusses the essential elements to include in your business plan. **Availability:** Online.

FRANCHISES AND BUSINESS OPPORTUNITIES

14361 ■ Bad Ass Coffee Co.
10447 Sorrento Rd., Unit 101
Pensacola, FL 32507
Ph: (850)857-8152
Free: 888-473-3959
Co. E-mail: customercare@badasscoffee.com
URL: http://badasscoffee.com
Facebook: www.facebook.com/Ba
dAssCoffeeOfHawaii
Instagram: www.instagram.com/ba
dasscoffeeofhawaii
Description: Producer and retailer of coffee and also logo wear such as hats, mugs. **Founded:** 1989. **Financial Assistance:** Yes **Training:** Provides 2 weeks at headquarters, onsite if requested with ongoing support.

14362 ■ Printwear Xpress
1819 Wazee St.
Denver, CO 80202
Contact: Brian E. Spindel, Contact
Description: Printwear Xpress (PWX) combines shopping experience, technology & customer service to deliver a highly competitive business model. PWX stores are modern, attractive & well merchandised to help customers select the right product for their needs. Production is showcased to illustrate the capabilities of the business & customer service is second to none. PWX stores are located in neighborhood strip centers & don't require an anchor tenant. **No. of Company-Owned Units:** 1. **Founded:** 2007. **Franchised:** 2007. **Equity Capital Needed:** $148,200-$169,600. **Franchise Fee:** $29,900. **Royalty Fee:** 5%. **Financial Assistance:** Yes **Training:** Offers 1 week classroom in Denver and 1 week onsite during opening, as well as vendor training.

RESEARCH CENTERS

14363 ■ Western Michigan University - Paper and Imaging
Western Michigan University
Kalamazoo, MI 49008-5200
URL: http://libguides.wmich.edu/engineering/paper
Contact: Edward Eckel, Librarian
E-mail: edward.eckel@wmich.edu
Description: Research and educational activity of Lou Calder Paper Research and Development Center at Western Michigan University. Offers industrial seminars and courses on coated paper manufacture. **Scope:** Pulping, papermaking, coating, recycling, and printing. **Founded:** 1958. **Educational Activities:** Barrier coating symposium; Flexo Day; Gravure Day; Litho Day; Paper coating course.

START-UP INFORMATION

14364 ■ *"GeoEye CEO Sees Investors In His Future: Matt O'Connell Eyeing Intel Startup Post-Sale" in Washington Business Journal (Vol. 31, September 14, 2012, No. 21, pp. 1)*
Pub: Baltimore Business Journal
Contact: Rhonda Pringle, President
E-mail: rpringle@bizjournals.com
Description: GeoEye Inc. chief executive officer, Matt O'Connell, plans to start a new technology venture in Northern Virginia like the one that supports intelligence gathering once DigitalGlobe Inc. has completed the acquisition of his company in 2013. He will work in an advisory role for DigitalGlobal following the acquisition and will not be involved in satellite imagery security for competitive reasons. **Availability:** Print; Online.

14365 ■ *"Macomb County, OU Eye Business Incubator" in Crain's Detroit Business (Vol. 24, February 11, 2008, No. 6, pp. 1)*
Pub: Crain Communications Inc.
Contact: Barry Asin, President
Ed: Chad Halcom. **Description:** Officials in Macomb County, Michigan are discussing plans to create a defense-themed business incubator in the county. Macomb County was awarded $282,000 in federal budget appropriation for the project. **Availability:** Print; Online.

14366 ■ *"Secure Future" in Small Business Opportunities (November 2010)*
Pub: Harris Publishing, Inc.
Contact: Janet Chase, Contact
Ed: Stan Roberts. **Description:** Fed up with the corporate world, this first-time business owner sells security equipment over the phone. Last year, sales hit $4 million. Profile of the founder of SmartWatch Security & Sound, Madelaine Lock is included. **Availability:** Print; Online.

14367 ■ *"Tax Credits As Good As Raised Cash for Cyber Firms" in Baltimore Business Journal (Vol. 31, March 28, 2014, No. 48, pp. 16)*
Pub: American City Business Journals, Inc.
Contact: Mike Olivieri, Executive Vice President
Price: $4, print. **Description:** The State of Maryland is offering tax incentives to its cyber security startups in order to capitalize on growing talent and to help the budding cyber security sector grow in the state. Three such tax incentives are outlined, including the cyber security investment incentive tax credit, employer security clearance costs tax credit, and research and development tax credit. Mark Vulcan, program manager of tax incentives for DBED describes this as Maryland'Es endeavor to attract a high growth and high wage industry. **Availability:** Print; Online.

ASSOCIATIONS AND OTHER ORGANIZATIONS

14368 ■ **ASIS International (ASIS) - Library**
1625 Prince St.
Alexandria, VA 22314-2882
Ph: (703)519-6200
Fax: (703)519-6299
Co. E-mail: asis@asisonline.org
URL: http://www.asisonline.org
Contact: Tim M. McCreight, President
Facebook: www.facebook.com/ASISInternational
X (Twitter): x.com/ASIS_Intl
YouTube: www.youtube.com/user/ASISInternational
Description: Dedicated to security professionals. Presents seminars and exhibits; offers educational programs on security issues in a number of fields, including communications. **Scope:** Security and asset protection. **Services:** Open to the public by appointment; access to members only. **Founded:** 1955. **Holdings:** Webinars. **Publications:** *Security Journal* (Quarterly); *ASIS International--Annual Membership Directory* (Annual); *Security Management* (Monthly); *Security Industry Buyers Guide* (Annual); *Dynamics.* **Educational Activities:** Global Security Exchange (GSX) (Annual). **Awards:** ASIS Foundation Chapter Matching Scholarship (Annual); Road to Certification Scholarships (Annual). **Geographic Preference:** Multinational.

14369 ■ **Association Canadienne D'Alarme Incendie (CFAA) [Canadian Fire Alarm Association (CFAA)]**
85 Citizen Ct., Units 3 & 4
Markham, ON, Canada L6G 1A8
Ph: (905)944-0030
Free: 800-529-0552
Fax: (905)479-3639
Co. E-mail: admin@cfaa.ca
URL: http://cfaa.ca
Contact: John MacDonald, President
E-mail: president@cfaa.ca
Description: Promotes improved fire safety through use of fire alarms. Facilitates communication and cooperation among members; represents members' commercial and regulatory interests; sponsors research and educational programs. **Founded:** 1973. **Geographic Preference:** National.

14370 ■ **Canadian Security Association (CANASA) - Library [L'Association Canadienne de la Securite]**
50 Acadia Ave., Ste. 201
Markham, ON, Canada L3R 0B3
Ph: (905)513-0622
Free: 800-538-9919
Co. E-mail: info@canasa.org
URL: http://www.canasa.org/CANASA
Contact: Ellery Demedash, President
Facebook: www.facebook.com/pages/Canadian -Security-Association-CANASA/169077016452968
Linkedin: www.linkedin.com/company/canadian -security-association
X (Twitter): x.com/CANASA_News
Description: Alarm and security equipment manufacturers, installers, monitors, and private security guard services. Seeks to advance the industry and enhance the professionalism of members. Serves as a clearinghouse on security systems and services; acts a unified voice representing the national electronic

security industry. Conducts lobbying activities; sponsors continuing professional development programs for members; sets standards of practice and ethics for the security systems and services industries. **Scope:** Alarms and security. **Founded:** 1977. **Holdings:** Figures not available. **Publications:** *English/ French EFlash* (Monthly). **Educational Activities:** Security Canada Central - International Security Conference & Exposition (Annual). **Awards:** R.A. Henderson Award (Irregular). **Geographic Preference:** National.

14371 ■ **Electronic Privacy Information Center (EPIC)**
1519 New Hampshire Ave. NW
Washington, DC 20036
Ph: (202)483-1140
Co. E-mail: info@epic.org
URL: http://epic.org
Contact: Alan Butler, President
E-mail: butler@epic.org
Facebook: www.facebook.com/epicprivacy
X (Twitter): x.com/EPICprivacy
Description: Advocates for electronic privacy, free expression, public voice. Sponsors educational and research programs; compiles statistics; conducts litigation. **Founded:** 1994. **Publications:** *The Consumer Law Sourcebook: Electronic Commerce and the Global Economy*; *EPIC Alert* (Monthly). **Geographic Preference:** National.

14372 ■ **Electronic Security Association (ESA)**
2222 S Service Rd., Ste. 230
Dallas, TX 75261
Ph: (972)807-6800
Co. E-mail: membership@esaweb.org
URL: http://esaweb.org
Contact: Merlin Guilbeau, Chief Executive Officer
E-mail: merlin.guilbeau@esaweb.org
Facebook: www.facebook.com/ESAonline
Linkedin: www.linkedin.com/company/electronic -security-association-esa
X (Twitter): x.com/ESATweet
YouTube: www.youtube.com/channel/UCkDpqx-b1-f -DQ_THIVmcZA
Description: Represents electronic safety, security and systems professionals. **Founded:** 1948. **Publications:** *National Burglar and Fire Alarm Association--Member Services Directory* (Annual); *National Burglar and Fire Alarm Association--Membership Directory* (Annual); *Security Nation* (Bimonthly). **Educational Activities:** ESA Leadership Summit (Annual). **Awards:** Sara Jackson Award (Annual); Morris F. Weinstock Memorial Award (Annual); Sara E. Jackson Award (Annual); Morris F. Weinstock Person of the Year (Annual). **Geographic Preference:** National.

14373 ■ **International Association of Professional Security Consultants (IAPSC)**
136 Everett Rd.
Albany, NY 12205
Ph: (415)536-0288
Co. E-mail: iapsc@iapsc.org

URL: http://iapsc.org
Contact: Michael Silva, President
Facebook: www.facebook.com/International-Associa
tion-of-Professional-Security-Consultants-1059688
60944868
X (Twitter): x.com/IAPSCIAPSC
Instagram: www.instagram.com/iapsc
Description: Promotes understanding and coopera-
tion among members and industries or individuals
requiring such services. Seeks to enhance members'
knowledge through seminars, training programs and
educational materials. **Founded:** 1984. **Publica-
tions:** *International Association of Professional
Security Consultants--Directory; IAPSC Consultants
Directory* (Annual); *IAPSC News* (Semimonthly).
Educational Activities: International Association of
Professional Security Consultants Convention (Annual); How to Succeed as a Professional Security
Consultant. **Awards:** The IAPSC Charles A.
Sennewald Distinguished Service Accolade (Ir-
regular). **Geographic Preference:** National.

14374 ■ International Security Management Association (ISMA)
Washington, DC
Co. E-mail: info@isma.com
URL: http://www.isma.com
Contact: Kirsten Meskill, President
Linkedin: www.linkedin.com/company/international
-security-management-association-isma
X (Twitter): x.com/isma_hq
Description: Senior security executives of multinational business firms and chief executive officers of
full service security services companies. Aims to assist senior security executives in coordinating and
exchanging information about security management
and to establish high business and professional
standards. **Founded:** 1983. **Geographic Preference:** Multinational.

14375 ■ Jewelers' Security Alliance (JSA)
6 E 45th St.
  New York, NY 10017
Free: 800-537-0067
Fax: (212)808-9168
Co. E-mail: jsa2@jewelerssecurity.org
URL: http://jewelerssecurity.org
Contact: John J. Kennedy, President
Linkedin: www.linkedin.com/in/jewelerssecuri
tyalliance
Description: Advocates for crime prevention in the
jewelry industry. Provides crime information and as-
sistance to the jewelry industry and law enforcement.
Founded: 1883. **Publications:** *Annual Report on
Crime Against the Jewelry Industry in U.S.* (Annual);
JSA Manual of Jewelry Security. **Educational Activi-
ties:** Security Seminar and Expo for Retail Jewelry
Chains (Annual). **Geographic Preference:** National.

14376 ■ National Association of Security Companies (NASCO)
444 N Capitol St. NW, Ste. 203
  Washington, DC 20001
Ph: (202)347-3257
Co. E-mail: information@nasco.org
URL: http://www.nasco.org
Contact: Steve Amitay, Executive Director
E-mail: steve@amitayconsulting.com
Description: Major security guard companies. Moni-
tors legislation affecting the industry. **Founded:** 1972.
Geographic Preference: National.

14377 ■ National Council of Investigation and Security Services Inc. (NCISS)
PO Box 200615
  Evans, CO 80620
Free: 800-445-8408
Fax: (970)480-7794
URL: http://www.nciss.org
Contact: Tina Thomas, President
E-mail: tthomas@subrosapi.com
Description: Monitors national and state legislative
and regulatory activities. Encourages the practice of
high standards of personal and professional conduct.
Acquires and disseminates information. Provides
information about state legislation and regulatory

activities that could have an impact on a particular
firm or on the industry in general; acts as spokesman
for the industry before legislative and regulatory bodies at both federal and state levels. **Founded:** 1975.
Publications: *NCISS Report* (Semiannual). **Awards:**
John J. Duffy Memorial Achievement Award (Annual);
Wayne J. Wunder Memorial Award (Annual). **Geographic Preference:** National.

14378 ■ Nine Lives Associates (NLA)
c/o Executive Protection Institute
  16 Penn Pl., Ste. 1130
  New York, NY 10001
URL: http://www.personalprotection.com/Home/NLA
Description: Provides professional recognition for
qualified individuals engaged in executive protection
assignments. **Founded:** 1978. **Educational Activities:** Nine Lives Associates Conference (Annual).
Geographic Preference: Multinational.

14379 ■ Security Industry Association (SIA)
8405 Colesville Rd., Ste. 500
  Silver Spring, MD 20910
Ph: (301)804-4700
Fax: (301)804-4701
Co. E-mail: info@securityindustry.org
URL: http://www.securityindustry.org
Contact: Don Erickson, Chief Executive Officer
E-mail: derickson@securityindustry.org
Facebook: www.facebook.com/SecurityIndus
tryAssociation
Linkedin: www.linkedin.com/company/security-indus
try-association
X (Twitter): x.com/SIAonline
YouTube: www.youtube.com/user/SIAonlineTV
Description: Security equipment manufacturers and
distributors. Seeks for the advancement of companies
in the security products industry. **Founded:** 1969.
Publications: *Security Industry Association--Buyer's
Guide & Membership Directory* (Annual). **Awards:**
George R. Lippert (Annual); George R. Lippert
Memorial Award (Annual); SIA New Products and
Solutions Awards (Annual). **Geographic Preference:**
National.

REFERENCE WORKS

14380 ■ *"3 Key Growth Elements for Small Security Integrators"* in Security Distributing & Marketing (Vol. 42, July 2012, No. 7, pp. 108)
Description: Local and regional integrators facing a
choice between expansion and annihilation by global
organizations face an uphill battle. Facing down giants requires critical use of key market principles
including niche identity, co-branding, and planning for
modest growth. **Availability:** Print; Online.

14381 ■ *"7 Trends Affecting the Security Technology Business"* in IP SecurityWatch.com (March 2012)
Ed: Geoff Kohl. **Description:** Scott Harkins, president
of Honeywell Security Products for the Americas,
outlines the seven trends affecting the security
technology business. He covers smart phones and
tablets, home automation, interctive services, integration beyond security systems, cloud services, standards, and apps. **Availability:** Online.

14382 ■ *"2012 Department of Homeland Security Small Business Achievement Award Given to Compass for Outstanding Performance"* in Information Technology Business (May 1, 2012, pp. 16)
Description: Compass Systems Consulting Inc. was
presented with the 2012 Department of Homeland
Security (DHS) Small Business Achievement Award
for outstanding work in support of the DHS mission.
Compass is a management consulting company
specializing in Performance Improvement, Program &
Project Management, Acquisition Management and
Audit, and Freedom of InformationACT (FOIA). **Avail-
ability:** Online.

14383 ■ *"Actiontec and Verizon Team Up for a Smarter Home"* in Ecology,Environment & Conservation Business (November 5, 2011, pp. 3)
Pub: Comtex News Network Inc.
Contact: Kan Devnani, President
Description: Verizon is implementing Actiontec
Electronics' SG200 Service Gateway as a basic
component of its Home Monitoring and Control
service. This new smart home service allows customers to remotely check their homes, control locks and
appliances, view home-energy use and more using a
smartphone, PC, or FiOS TV. **Availability:** Online.

14384 ■ *"Adrian Ellis Wears No Cape, But His Firm Protects Execs From Bad Guys"* in Orlando Business Journal (Vol. 30, March 14, 2014, No. 38, pp. 3)
Pub: American City Business Journals, Inc.
Contact: Mike Olivieri, Executive Vice President
Released: Weekly. **Description:** Infinity Protection
Service chief executive officer, Adrian Ellis, says his
experience in providing security details led to the
formation of the company. He added that some of the
company's clients are high-profile individuals who
may have received threats. Ellis also stated that the
company is planning to expand in the U.S. through
mergers and acquisitions. **Availability:** Print; Online.

14385 ■ *"Altegrity Acquires John D. Cohen, Inc."* in (November 19, 2009, pp. 14)
Pub: Investment Weekly News
Description: John D. Cohen, Inc., a contract provider
of national security policy guidance and counsel to
the federal government, was acquired by Altegrity,
Inc., a global screening and security solutions
provider; the company will become part of US
Investigations Services, LLC and operate under the
auspices of Altegrity's new business, Altegrity
Security Consulting. **Availability:** Print; Online.

14386 ■ *"American Chemistry Council Launches Flagship Blog"* in Ecology,Environment & Conservation Business (October 29, 2011, pp. 5)
Pub: PR Newswire Association LLC.
Description: American Chemistry Council (ACC)
launched its blog, American Chemistry Matters,
where interactive space allows bloggers to respond
to news coverage and to discuss policy issues and
their impact on innovation, competitiveness, job
creation and safety. **Availability:** Online.

14387 ■ *"App Brings Real-Time Personal Security, Company Says"* in Philadelphia Business Journal (Vol. 33, July 4, 2014, No. 21, pp. 11)
Pub: American City Business Journals, Inc.
Contact: Mike Olivieri, Executive Vice President
Released: Weekly. **Price:** $4, Introductory 4-week
offer(Digital & Print). **Description:** EmergenSee,
which is a mobile technology that transforms smartphones or tablets into personal security systems by
downloading the app. It has the ability to stream live
video and audio. **Availability:** Print; Online.

14388 ■ *"Auto Bankruptcies Could Weaken Defense"* in Crain's Detroit Business (Vol. 25, June 8, 2009, No. 23, pp. 1)
Pub: Crain Communications Inc.
Contact: Barry Asin, President
Ed: Chad Halcom. **Description:** Bankruptcy and supplier consolidation of General Motors Corporation
and Chrysler LLC could interfere with the supply
chains of some defense contractors, particularly makers of trucks and smaller vehicles. **Availability:** Print;
Online.

14389 ■ *"Aviat Networks Partners With AT&T Government Solutions for Department of Homeland Security Business"* in Entertainment Close-Up August 13, 2012)
Description: Aviat Networks Inc. will provide US
Department of Homeland Security and other federal
agencies withh the capability to acquire microwave
radio communication equipment, engineering, design,

installation and maintenace services. Aviat is a subcontractor on the AT&T Government Solutions' team. Aviat has a history of partnerships in federal technology space. **Availability:** Print; PDF; Online.

14390 ▪ "Baltimore-Area Businesses Still on the Mend 10 Years After 9/11" in Baltimore Business Journal (Vol. 29, September 9, 2011, No. 18, pp. 1)
Pub: Boston Business Journal
Contact: Carolyn M. Jones, President
E-mail: cmjones@bizjournals.com
Ed: Scott Dance. **Description:** The 9/11 terrorist attacks have caused many companies in the US to dramatically shift course in response to changes in the economy. The concern that the cost of being unprepared for future disasters could be larger has remained among many companies. **Availability:** Online.

14391 ▪ "Beware the Hotspot: How You're Vulnerable" in Philadelphia Business Journal (Vol. 33, June 13, 2014, No. 18, pp. 7)
Pub: American City Business Journals, Inc.
Contact: Mike Olivieri, Executive Vice President
Released: Weekly. **Price:** $4, introductory 4-week offer(Digital only). **Description:** Pete Hazen, technology consultant for Determinant Solutions talks about the dangers of connecting to open public WiFi. He mentions that such connection allows cyber criminals to capture the data like passwords, which then can be used to commit identity fraud, pay for merchandise, or steal money from the user's online accounts. **Availability:** Print; Online.

14392 ▪ "BlackBerry 10 Unlikely to Save RIM. RIM Has Few Options. Staying the Course Isn't One of Them" in Canadian Business (Vol. 85, July 16, 2012, No. 11-12, pp. 12)
Ed: Joe Castaldo. **Description:** Research in Motion (RIM) plans to launch a new line of Blackberry 10 Smartphones in 2012 as part of a strategy to stay in business despite expected operating loss in the first quarter and strong competition. Other options for RIM include a sale, opening its network to offer added security and data compression services, or reinventing itself as a niche handset provider. **Availability:** Print; Online.

14393 ▪ "Border Boletin: UA to Take Lie-Detector Kiosk to Poland" in Arizona Daily Star (September 14, 2010)
Pub: Arizona Daily Star
Contact: John D'Orlando, President
E-mail: jdorlando@tucson.com
Ed: Brady McCombs. **Description:** University of Arizona's National Center for Border Security and Immigration Research will send a team to Warsaw, Poland to show border guards from 27 European Union countries the center's Avatar Kiosk. The Avatar technology is designed for use at border ports and airports to assist Customs officers detect individuals who are lying. **Availability:** Print; Online.

14394 ▪ "Branding Spree" in Pet Product News (Vol. 66, September 2012, No. 9, pp. 40)
Ed: Michael Ventre. **Description:** The extent to which pet security firm PetSafe has continued to diversify into new product categories to realize growth opportunities is explored. An arm of Radio Systems Corporation, PetSafe has been known for manufacturing products such as wireless fenses and electronic pet collars. **Availability:** Print; Online.

14395 ▪ "Building Targeted for Marriott in Violation" in Business Journal-Milwaukee (Vol. 28, December 24, 2010, No. 12, pp. A1)
Pub: The Business Journal
Contact: Heather Ladage, President
E-mail: hladage@bizjournals.com
Ed: Sean Ryan. **Description:** Milwaukee, Wisconsin's Department of Neighborhood Services has ordered structural improvements and safeguards for the Pioneer Building after three violations from structural failures were found. Pioneer was among the five buildings wanted by Jackson Street Management LLC to demolish for the new Marriott Hotel. **Availability:** Print; Online.

14396 ▪ "Businesses Fret Over Crime Wave" in Philadelphia Business Journal (Vol. 31, February 10, 2012, No. 52, pp. 1)
Pub: Baltimore Business Journal
Contact: Rhonda Pringle, President
E-mail: rpringle@bizjournals.com
Description: Philadelphia, Pennsylvania-based businesses have expressed concern over the recent crime wave in the city. Businesses are raising $3 million to fund the Philadelphia Police Department's mounted patrol unit to ramp up security. **Availability:** Print; Online.

14397 ▪ "A Civilian Cybersecurity Center for D.C.?" in Washington Business Journal (Vol. 32, March 7, 2014, No. 47, pp. 5)
Pub: American City Business Journals, Inc.
Contact: Mike Olivieri, Executive Vice President
Description: The U.S. General Services Administration (GSA) is investigating the possibility for a civilian cybersecurity center in Washington DC to encourage further collaboration between government agencies. The GSA is seeking $35 million in the proposed 2015 federal budget for the project's design. **Availability:** Print; Online.

14398 ▪ "Comcast Corp. Enters Home Security Business" in Record (May 27, 2012)
Ed: Reed Fujii. **Description:** Comcast and Verizon are offering home security products to consumers. AT&T will launch their home security products soon. Details of the home security systems offered are provided. **Availability:** Online.

14399 ▪ "Comcast Launches New Home Security Service, Developed in Portland" in The Oregonian (June 7, 2011)
Pub: McClatchy-Tribune Regional News
Ed: Mike Rogoway. **Description:** Comcast introduced its new high-end home security system that provides 24-hour monitoring and control of homes and utilities, along with Web and mobile access. **Availability:** Print; Online.

14400 ▪ "Consumer Trust in E-Commerce Web Sites: a Meta-Study" in ACM Computing Surveys (Vol. 43, Fall 2011, No. 3, pp. 14)
Pub: Association for Computing Machinery
Contact: Yannis Ioannidis, President
Ed: Patricia Beatty, Ian Reay, Scott Dick, James Miller. **Released:** Volume 43 Issue 3. **Price:** $10, Members; $15, Nonmembers; $5, Students. **Description:** Trust is at once an elusive, imprecise concept, and a critical attribute that must be engineered into e-commerce systems. Engineering trust is examined. **Availability:** Download; PDF.

14401 ▪ Corporate Radar: Tracking the Forces That Are Shaping Your Business
Description: Ways for a business to assess the forces operating in the external environment that can affect the business and solutions to protect from outside threats. **Availability:** Print.

14402 ▪ "CradlePoint Is Adding Workers, Seeking More Space" in Idaho Business Review (September 3, 2014)
Pub: BridgeTower Media
Contact: Adam Reinebach, President
Price: $11.99, Print, Digital & Mobile(1 Month); 149, Print, Digital & Mobile(1 Year); 99, Digital & Mobile Only(1 Year); $99, Digital & Mobile Only(For 1 Year); $9.95, Print, Digital & Mobile (For 1 Month Intro Rate); $149, Print, Digital & Mobile(For 1 Year). **Description:** CradlePoint makes networking routers and software, focusing on security for businesses. The firm is hiring new workers at a rate higher than predicted and is seeking new office space in downtown Boise, Idaho. CradlePoint is a major player in the growing wireless service and cloud platform market and is growing faster than its competitors. **Availability:** Print; Online.

14403 ▪ "A Cyber Breach: More Likely Than a Fire" in Philadelphia Business Journal (Vol. 33, June 13, 2014, No. 18, pp. 6)
Pub: American City Business Journals, Inc.
Contact: Mike Olivieri, Executive Vice President
Released: June 13, 2014. **Price:** $4, introductory 4-week offer(Digital only). **Description:** Robert D'Ovidio, an IT, crime and criminal justice system researcher, and Norman Balchunas, director of strategic studies of Drexel Cybersecurity Institute, give their views on cyber security. According to them, the profile of a cyber thief has undergone a change and with it the role of security professionals in corporations globally. They state that a good information security plan that also addresses privacy would be good in security company data. **Availability:** Print; Mailing list; Online.

14404 ▪ "D-Link Enhances Small Business Professional Security Solutions with New Outdoor Bullet Cameras Featuring Cloud Services Support and Wide Dynamic Range Sensor" in PR Newswire September 10, 2012
Pub: PR Newswire Association LLC.
Description: D-Link IP surveillance cameras are offering a five-year warranty for this outdoor bullet cameras for small and medium-sized businesses. Details of all models offered are included.

14405 ▪ "The Danger from Within: The Biggest Threat to Your Cybersecurity May Be an Employee or a Vendor" in Harvard Business Review (Vol. 92, September 2014, No. 9, pp. 94)
Pub: Harvard Business Publishing
Contact: Diane Belcher, Managing Director
Price: $8.95. **Description:** Corporate computer crimes involving insiders are on the rise. To reduce vulnerability, firms should incorporate employees into the watchdog process, perform regular audits of distributors and suppliers, and implement security procedures involving both management and information technology personnel. **Availability:** Online; PDF.

14406 ▪ "Data Security is No. 1 Compliance Concern" in HRMagazine (Vol. 53, October 2008, No. 10, pp. 32)
Description: Electronic data protection and data privacy are the leading ethics and compliance issues faced by companies today. **Availability:** Print; Online.

14407 ▪ "Defense Budget Ax May Not Come Down So Hard on Maryland" in Baltimore Business Journal (Vol. 28, August 20, 2010, No. 15, pp. 1)
Pub: Baltimore Business Journal
Contact: Rhonda Pringle, President
E-mail: rpringle@bizjournals.com
Ed: Daniel J. Sernovitz. **Description:** U.S. Defense Secretary Robert M. Gates' planned budget cuts are having little effect on Maryland's defense industry. Gates will reduce spending on intelligence service contracts by 10 percent. **Availability:** Print; Online.

14408 ▪ "Delivering the Milk" in Barron's (Vol. 92, July 23, 2012, No. 30, pp. M7)
Pub: Dow Jones & Company Inc.
Contact: Almar Latour, Chief Executive Officer
Ed: Kopin Tan. **Description:** The stocks of China Mengniu Dairy could continue losing value in the short term but could gain value in the long term. The company's revenue growth and profit margins face downward pressure due to aggressive pricing after food safety scandals. **Availability:** Online.

14409 ▪ "Dougherty: AuthenTec Embedded Security Business Building Momentum" in Benzinga.com (March 5, 2012)
Pub: Benzinga.com
Contact: Jason Raznick, Founder
Ed: Delores Land. **Description:** According to research conducted by Dougherty & Company, Authen-Tec Inc.'s embedded security business is waiting for the fingerprint sensor businesss is completely developed. **Availability:** Online.

14410 ■ *"Eight Tips For Leaders On Protecting the Team" in Puget Sound Business Journal (Vol. 35, August 22, 2014, No. 18, pp. 13)*

Pub: American City Business Journals, Inc.

Contact: Mike Olivieri, Executive Vice President

Description: Advice on ways to protect corporate teams is given. Unnecessary information and processes should be filtered to avoid distraction of the team. Team action plans must be prioritized. **Availability:** Print; Online.

14411 ■ *Electronic Commerce*

Ed: Gary P. Schneider, Bryant Chrzan, Charles McCormick. **Released:** 12th edition. **Price:** $29.49, e-book. **Description:** E-commerce can open the door to more opportunities than ever before for small business. Packed with real-world examples and cases, the book delivers comprehensive coverage of emerging online technologies and trends and their influence on the electronic marketplace. It details how the landscape of online commerce is evolving, reflecting changes in the economy and how business and society are responding to those changes. Balancing technological issues with the strategic business aspects of successful e-commerce, the new edition includes expanded coverage of international issues, social networking, mobile commerce, Web 2.0 technologies, and updates on spam, phishing, and identity theft. **Availability:** Print.

14412 ■ *"Encouraging Study in Critical Languages" in Occupational Outlook Quarterly (Vol. 55, Summer 2011, No. 2, pp. 23)*

Description: Proficiency in particular foreign languages is vital to the defense, diplomacy, and security of the United States. Several federal programs provide scholarships and other funding to encourage high school and college students to learn languages of the Middle East, China, and Russia. **Availability:** Print; Online.

14413 ■ *"EOTech Product Improves Holographic Gun Sights" in Crain's Detroit Business (Vol. 24, February 4, 2008, No. 5, pp. 9)*

Pub: Crain Communications Inc.

Contact: Barry Asin, President

Ed: Chad Halcom. **Description:** L-3 Communications EOTech Inc. procured new business contracts to fulfill military and law enforcement's demand for improved holographic sites used on handheld weapons. **Availability:** Online.

14414 ■ *"Eye in the Sky: A Look at Security Tech from All Angles" in Bellingham Business Journal (October 2008, pp. 23)*

Ed: Lance Henderson. **Description:** High tech solutions to security issues in any company are not the only things to be considered; a low-tech evaluation of a building and its security fixtures, such as door knobs, locks, doors and windows as well as lighting are important aspects to security any office. **Availability:** Print; Online.

14415 ■ *"General Clark Stresses Ethanol's Role In National Security At AgConnect" in Farm Industry News (January 11, 2011)*

Pub: Informa Business Media, Inc.

Contact: Charlie McCurdy, President

Ed: Lynn Grooms. **Description:** General Clark stressed the role of ethanols in national security at the AgConnect. **Availability:** Online.

14416 ■ *"GM's Volt Woes Cast Shadow on E-Cars" in Wall Street Journal Eastern Edition (November 28, 2011, pp. B1)*

Pub: Dow Jones & Company Inc.

Contact: Almar Latour, Chief Executive Officer

Ed: Sharon Terlep. **Description:** The future of electric cars is darkened with the government investigation by the National Highway Traffic Safety Administration into General Motor Company's Chevy Volt after two instances of the car's battery packs catching fire during crash tests conducted by the Agency. **Availability:** Online.

14417 ■ *"Google Gets Creepy" in Canadian Business (Vol. 85, September 17, 2012, No. 14, pp. 28)*

Ed: Jeff Beer. **Description:** Google's move to integrate its more than 70 different privacy agreements into just one has simplified the privacy deal the search engine company made with its users and improved its ability to obtain information for advertising. Google is addressing concerns about online privacy and allegations of anticompetitive practices in the U.S. and Europe. **Availability:** Online.

14418 ■ *"Having a Head for Security Means Being In the Know: Security Print Explored" in Print Week (July 4, 2012)*

Ed: Jon Severs. **Description:** The security market is expanding and presenting opportunities for printers, a fundamental part of security procedures. Print is an environment where digital media is not used. Details for printers wishing to enter the print security market are presented. **Availability:** Print; Online.

14419 ■ *"Heartbleed Headache Will Pound For Years" in Puget Sound Business Journal (Vol. 34, April 18, 2014, No. 53, pp. 7)*

Pub: American City Business Journals, Inc.

Contact: Mike Olivieri, Executive Vice President

Description: Seattle, Washington-based technology experts expressed concerns about the cybersecurity implications of the Heartbleed bug for years to come. The bug affected most virtual private network (VPN) software, which is the way most encrypted communications travel. The impact of the Heartbleed bug on critical infrastructure is examined. **Availability:** Online.

14420 ■ *Hiring & Retaining Great Security Officers*

Ed: David Mathena. **Released:** December 25, 2022. **Price:** $14.95, e-book. **Description:** This guide from a former security management professional will help you not only hire the best people for security, but give you tips on retaining their services. **Availability:** E-book.

14421 ■ *"Home Security Systems That Are Fast, Easy and Totally Not Creepy" in The Wall Street Journal (August 26, 2018)*

URL(s): www.wsj.com/articles/home-security-systems -that-are-fast-easy-and-totally-not-creepy -1535288400

Ed: David Pierce. **Released:** August 26, 2018. **Description:** Reviews for four different home security kits that are easy to install and pair with an app on the phone. Each one is slightly different from the other and descriptions of what comes in the kit and how invasive they to your privacy are given. **Availability:** Online.

14422 ■ *"Hopkins' Security, Reputation Face Challenges in Wake of Slaying" in Baltimore Business Journal (Vol. 28, August 6, 2010, No. 13)*

Pub: Baltimore Business Journal

Contact: Rhonda Pringle, President

E-mail: rpringle@bizjournals.com

Ed: Gary Haber. **Description:** The slaying of Johns Hopkins University researcher Stephen Pitcairn has not tarnished the reputation of the elite school in Baltimore, Maryland among students. Maintaining Hopkins' reputation is important since it is Baltimore's largest employer with nearly 32,000 workers. Insights on the impact of the slaying among the Hopkins' community are also given.

14423 ■ *"How Business Intelligence Can Affect Bottomline" in Canadian Electronics (Vol. 23, February 2008, No. 1, pp. 6)*

Description: Business intelligence has an important role in delivering the right information in a secured manner. However, coping with data volume, cost, workload, time, availability and compliance have been a problem for business intelligence projects. Ways to avoid problems in business intelligence projects and examples of business intelligence applications are provided. **Availability:** Online.

14424 ■ *"How Foreigners Could Disrupt U.S. Markets" in Barron's (Vol. 90, September 13, 2010, No. 37, pp. 30)*

Pub: Barron's Editorial & Corporate Headquarters

Ed: Jim McTague. **Description:** An informal meeting by the House Homeland Security Panel concluded that U.S. stock exchanges and related trading routes can be the subject of attacks from rogue overseas traders. A drop in funding for the U.S. Department of Defense is discussed. **Availability:** Online.

14425 ■ *"How To Disaster-Proof Your Business" in Inc. (Vol. 33, September 2011, No. 7, pp. 38)*

Pub: Inc. Magazine

Ed: J.J. McCorvey, Dave Smith. **Description:** Twelve products to and services designed to help small businesses run smoothly in the event of a disaster are outlined. **Availability:** Online.

14426 ■ *"How To Pirate-Proof a Freighter" in Canadian Business (Vol. 85, June 28, 2012, No. 11-12, pp. 20)*

Ed: Sarah Barmak. **Description:** Security experts offer advice on how to protect cargo ships and crew from pirate attacks. Some anti-piracy measures suggested include hiring a well-trained team of armed guards, securing lage coils of razor wire along the sides of the vessel and using the Long Range Acoustic Device to help distinguish pirates. **Availability:** Print; Online.

14427 ■ *"How To Prevent Cyber Crime At Your Biz" in Birmingham Business Journal (Vol. 31, March 14, 2014, No. 11, pp. 10)*

Pub: American City Business Journals, Inc.

Contact: Mike Olivieri, Executive Vice President

Released: Weekly. **Price:** $4, introductory 4-week offer(Digital only). **Description:** Ways businesses can prevent cyber attacks are prevented. Employees should be educated to be aware of cyber crimes. Policies on confidentiality and privacy should also be established in business organizations. **Availability:** Print; Online.

14428 ■ *"Investment In Israel Is Investment in the Future of Georgia" in Atlanta Business Chronicle (May 30, 2014, pp. 22A)*

Pub: American City Business Journals, Inc.

Contact: Mike Olivieri, Executive Vice President

Description: Georgia Governor Nathan Deal will travel to Israel to lead an economic and trade mission and consolidate Georgia's trade ties with Israel. Israel and the State of Georgia are already collaborating in the fields of health information technology, agrotechnology, homeland security, defense, aerospace and cybersecurity, and microelectronics and nanotechnology. The proposed visit by the Governor will build on this particular partnership from which both parties will benefit. **Availability:** Print; Online.

14429 ■ *"iRobot Appoints Former BAE Systems Vice President, Frank Wilson to Lead Defense & Security Business Unit" in News Bites US (August 9, 2012)*

Description: Frank Wilson will serve as senior vice president and general manager of iRobot's Defense & Security business unit. He will focus on strategic business development and product development in order for the firm to meet military, civil defense, and security needs. Tim Trainer, previous acting interim general manager, will remain vice president of programs. **Availability:** Print; Online.

14430 ■ *"Kratos Announces Buy of Critical Infrastructure Security Business" in M & A Navigator (January 3, 2012)*

Description: Kratos Defense & Security Solutions Inc., a US national security firm, purchased a competitor for USD $20 million. The acquisition will help expand its critical infrastructure security business. **Availability:** Print.

14431 ■ *"Littleton Firm Chips In On Security Solution"* in *Denver Business Journal (Vol. 65, May 9, 2014, No. 52, pp. A6)*
Pub: American City Business Journals, Inc.
Contact: Mike Olivieri, Executive Vice President
Released: Weekly. **Price:** $4, introductory 4-week offer(Digital & Print). **Description:** CPI Card Group of Littleton, Colorado has been preparing for the nationwide transition to computer chip cards to secure credit and debit cards in the U.S. Banks and merchants in the country need to make the switch by October 2015 or risk being financially liable for fraud if not using the chipped cards in their retail establishments. **Availability:** Print; Online.

14432 ■ *"Local Companies Land Federal Securities Pacts"* in *Sacramento Business Journal (Vol. 31, March 7, 2014, No. 2, pp. 6)*
Pub: American City Business Journals, Inc.
Contact: Mike Olivieri, Executive Vice President
Description: Three companies in Sacramento, California have received Federal security contracts in 2014. Capitol Digital Document Solutions has a five-year contract with the U.S. Department of Homeland Security, while Hewlett-Packard signed a deal with the same government agency. Stratovan Corporation secured two contracts from the U.S. Transportation Security Board. **Availability:** Online.

14433 ■ *"Local Company Seeks Patent For Armored Trucks"* in *Crain's Detroit Business (Vol. 24, February 4, 2008, No. 5, pp. 10)*
Pub: Crain Communications Inc.
Contact: Barry Asin, President
Description: Profile of James LeBlanc Sr., mechanical engineer and defense contractor, discusses his eleven utility patents pending for a set of vehicles and subsystems that would work as countermeasures to explosively formed projectiles. **Availability:** Print; Online.

14434 ■ *"Macho Men"* in *Canadian Business (Vol. 81, November 10, 2008, No. 19, pp. 23)*
Description: Professors Robin Ely and Debra Meyerson found that oil rigs decreased accidents and increased productivity when they focused on improving safety and admitting errors rather than on a worker's individual strength. Professor Jennifer Berdahl shows there is pressure for men to be seen as masculine at work, which makes them avoid doing 'feminine' things such as parental leaves. **Availability:** Print; Online.

14435 ■ *"Melamine Analytical Methods Released"* in *Feedstuffs (Vol. 80, October 6, 2008, No. 41, pp. 2)*
Pub: Miller Publishing Company
Description: Romer Labs has released new validations for its AgraQuant Melamine enzyme-linked immunosorbent assay. The test kit screens for melamine in feed and diary products, including pet foods, milk and milk powder. Melamine by itself is nontoxic in low doses, but when combined with cyanuric acid it can cause fatal kidney stones. The Chinese dairy industry is in the midst of a huge melamine crisis; melamine-contaminated dairy and food products from China have been found in more than 20 countries. **Availability:** Print; Online.

14436 ■ *"Microsoft Partners With Good Technology to Provide Enterprise-Class Security for Business Customers on Windows Phone Devices"* in *Benzinga.com (February 27, 2012)*
Pub: PR Newswire Association LLC.
Description: Microsoft has partnered with Good Technology in order to provide its Windows Phone 7.5 Preferred Partner Solution for secured encrypted mobile mail services. Details of the strategic partnership are outlined.

14437 ■ *"Microsoft Releases Office Security Updates"* in *Mac World (Vol. 27, November 2010, No. 11, pp. 66)*
Description: Office for Mac and Mac Business Unit are Microsoft's pair of security- and stability-enhancing updates for Office 2008 and Office 2004.

The software will improve the stability and compatibility and fixes vulnerabilities that would allow attackers to overwrite Mac's memory with malicious code. **Availability:** Online.

14438 ■ *"nCircle Launches PCI DSS Compliance Package for Small Businesses"* in *Health & Beauty Close-Up (May 14, 2012)*
Description: nCircle presents the results of small business security scans from March 30 through April 28, 2012. The provider of information risk and security performance management reportes that eight of the toptne highest risk vulnerabilities detected on small business networks are connected with blank or default passwords. **Availability:** Print; Online.

14439 ■ *"NETGEAR Upgrades Small Business Security Line With Multiple Industry Firsts"* in *Benzinga.com (March 1, 2012)*
Pub: PR Newswire Association LLC.
Description: Netgear's launched its new firmware that delivers affordable application firewall and redundant connectivity as well as extending virtually unlimited logging capacity.

14440 ■ *"New Wave of Business Security Products Ushers in the Kaspersky Anti-Malware Protection System"* in *Internet Wire (October 26, 2010)*
Description: Kaspersky Anti-Malware System provides anti-malware protection that requires minimal in-house resources for small businesses. The system offers a full range of tightly integrated end-to-end protection solutions, ensuring unified protection across an entire network, from endpoint and mobile device protection to file server, mail server, network storage and gateway protection. It provides flexible centralized management, immediate threat visibility and a level of responsiveness not seen in other anti-malware approaches. **Availability:** Print; Online.

14441 ■ *"Next Generation Security Awareness"* in *Security Management (Vol. 56, September 2012, No. 9, pp. 32)*
Description: Carnegie Mellon University (CMU) has purchased Wombat Security Technologies' PhishGuru to reduce the phishing attacks. CMU also purchased Wombat's two educational games, Anti-Phishing and Anti-Phishing Phyllis, partly due to the PhishGuru's success. Insights on the software-as-a-service solution are also given.

14442 ■ *"Not In Our Backyard"* in *Canadian Business (Vol. 80, October 22, 2007, No. 21, pp. 76)*
Description: Alberta Energy and Utilities Board's proposed construction of electric transmission line has let to protests by landowners. The electric utility was also accused of spying on ordinary citizens and violating impartiality rules. Details of the case between Lavesta Area Group and the Board are discussed. **Availability:** Online.

14443 ■ *"No. 123: Protecting People, From the Bronx to the Beltway"* in *Inc. (Vol. 36, September 2014, No. 7, pp. 106)*
Pub: Mansueto Ventures L.L.C.
Contact: Stephanie Mehta, Chief Executive Officer
Released: August 20, 2014. **Description:** Profile of Michael S. Rogers, founder of Securityhunter, located in Baltimore, Maryland. The firm installs security systems for military bases and government agencies. The company developed a security system that was used to protect Colin Powell while traveling. **Availability:** Print; Online.

14444 ■ *"Online Security Crackdown"* in *Chain Store Age (Vol. 84, July 2008, No. 7, pp. 46)*
Ed: Samantha Murphy. **Description:** Online retailers are beefing up security on their Websites. Cyber thieves use retail systems in order to gain entry to consumer data. David's Bridal operates over 275 bridal showrooms in the U.S. and has a one-stop wedding resource for new brides planning weddings. **Availability:** Online.

14445 ■ *"Outside Cash Fuels 'Growth' Tech Deals"* in *Washington Business Journal (Vol. 31, September 7, 2012, No. 20, pp. 1)*
Pub: Baltimore Business Journal
Contact: Rhonda Pringle, President
E-mail: rpringle@bizjournals.com
Description: Outside investors have been contributing to technology firms' growth in Washington. Technology Crossover Ventures has invested $136 million in Alarm.com. **Availability:** Print; Online.

14446 ■ *"PC Connection Acquires Cloud Software Provider"* in *New Hampshire Business Review (Vol. 33, March 25, 2011, No. 6, pp. 8)*
Description: Merrimack-based PC Connection Inc. acquired ValCom Technology, a provider of cloud-based IT service management software. Details of the deal are included. **Availability:** Print; Online.

14447 ■ *"Pete Carroll's Winning Rule: Protect Your Team"* in *Puget Sound Business Journal (Vol. 35, July 25, 2014, No. 14, pp. 12)*
Pub: American City Business Journals, Inc.
Contact: Mike Olivieri, Executive Vice President
Released: Weekly. **Price:** $4, Introductory 4-week offer(Digital & Print). **Description:** Seattle Seahawks coach, Pete Carroll, has three simple rules for team success and the first rule is to always protect the team. The rule is also important in every workplace because it will help align the workers attention to their behavior. Seven ways to protect the team are outlined. **Availability:** Print; Online.

14448 ■ *"Prevent Identity Theft: Simple Steps To Protect Yourself Against Identity Theft"* in *Small Business Opportunities (January 2008)*
Description: Expert shares tips to help individuals and businesses protect themselves from identity theft.

14449 ■ *"The Problem With Passwords"* in *Canadian Business (Vol. 85, August 13, 2012, No. 13, pp. 61)*
Ed: Richard Warnica. **Description:** A study found that most tips for protecting passwords do nothng to protect against the most common forms of security breaches such as phishing, keystroke logging and looking over shoulders. According to researchers, it is not necessary to switch passwords or make it harder to guess because there is a chance that it will not do any good. **Availability:** Print; Online.

14450 ■ *"Protect Your Domain Name From Cybersquatters"* in *Idaho Business Review (September 1, 2014)*
Pub: BridgeTower Media
Contact: Adam Reinebach, President
Description: Cybersquatting is the practice of registering, trafficking in or using domain names with the intent to profit from the goodwill of recognizable trade names or trademarks of other companies. Companies can protect their Website domain by following these steps: register domain names, promptly renew registrations, maintain proper records, obtain additional top-level domains, and monitor your site for cybersquatters.

14451 ■ *"Research and Market Adds Report: Endpoint Security for Business"* in *Wireless News (October 26, 2009)*
Description: Summarizes Research and Markets Adds Report: Endpoint Security for Business: Desktops, Laptops & Mobile Devices 2009-2014; highlights include a detailed analysis of where the industry is at present and forecasts regarding how it will develop over the next five years.

14452 ■ *"Retailers Report 'Shrinkage' - Disappearance of Inventory - on the Rise"* in *Arkansas Business (Vol. 26, September 28, 2009, No. 39, pp. 17)*
Pub: Arkansas Business Publishing Group
Contact: Mitch Bettis, President
Ed: Mark Friedman. **Description:** According to a National Retail Security Survey report released last June, retailers across the country have lost about

$36.5 billion in shrinkage, most of it at the hands of employees and shoplifters alike. Statistical data included. **Availability:** Online.

14453 ■ *"RF Technologies Celebrates 25th Anniversary of Keeping Patients and Senior Care Residents Safe and Secure"* in PR Newswire (August 1, 2012).

Pub: PR Newswire Association LLC.

Description: RF Technologies has entered into the senior care market by offering wireless wandering managemnt systems and transmitters to help reduce the risk of resident elopements. RF is a leading provider of customized radio frequency identification (RFID) healthcare safety and security solutions for the healthcare sector.

14454 ■ *"Securing our Cyber Status"* in San Antonio Business Journal (Vol. 28, May 16, 2014, No. 14, pp. 4)

Pub: American City Business Journals, Inc.

Contact: Mike Olivieri, Executive Vice President

Released: Weekly. **Price:** $4, introductory 4-week offer(Digital & Print). **Description:** The San Antonio Chamber of Commerce commissioned Deloitte to conduct a study on the local cyber security sector of San Antonio, Texas. Industry insiders are looking forward to securing the status of San Antonio as a top tier cyber city with the results of the study research. **Availability:** Print; Online.

14455 ■ *Selling Online: Canada's Bestselling Guide to Becoming a Successful E-Commerce Merchant*

Description: Helps individuals build online retail enterprises; this updated version includes current tools, information and success strategies, how to launch an online storefront, security, marketing strategies, and mistakes to avoid. **Availability:** Online.

14456 ■ *"Senator Grills Collection Agency, Health System Executives"* in Collections & Credit Risk (May 31, 2012)

Pub: SourceMedia LLC

Contact: Gemma Postlethwaite, Chief Executive Officer

Description: Accretive Health Inc. and Fairview Health Services executives were questioned by Senator Al Franken about its debt collection practices. The suit was initiated after unencrypted private information on 23,500 patients was stolen from an Acrretive employee's vehicle. Details of the lawsuit are outlined.

14457 ■ *"Shellshocked: Dealing With Cyber Insecurity"* in Philadelphia Business Journal (Vol. 33, June 13, 2014, No. 18, pp. 4)

Pub: American City Business Journals, Inc.

Contact: Mike Olivieri, Executive Vice President

Description: The threat of cyber theft or data breach is increasing globally as technology becomes advanced and more companies start storing their important data electronically. Therefore, the importance of cyber security has increased. Although big businesses suffer more from data breaches, small companies can also take a beating if data breach happens. A survey found that small businesses were wary of spending money on security issues; good investment in IT and creating a privacy policy will help companies fight cyber threats. **Availability:** Online.

14458 ■ *"Social Media Privacy Law Impacts Employers"* in Providence Business News (Vol. 29, July 21, 2014, No. 16, pp. 14)

Pub: American City Business Journals, Inc.

Contact: Mike Olivieri, Executive Vice President

Released: July 19, 2014. **Description:** Rhode Island's new social media privacy law, which was enacted on June 30, 2014, will have an impact on all employers in the state. The implications of the new law and some best practices employers can implement with regard to the legislation are discussed. **Availability:** PDF; Online.

14459 ■ *"Social Safety, Thanks to New App"* in Providence Business News (Vol. 29, July 21, 2014, No. 16, pp. 10)

Pub: American City Business Journals, Inc.

Contact: Mike Olivieri, Executive Vice President

URL(s): pbn.com/social-safety-thanks-to-new-app98633

Description: Middletown-based Vizsafe Inc. has developed the Vizsafe application (app) for public safety and community engagement and is offering it to police departments and to citizens at no cost. Vizsafe president and CEO, Peter Mottur, asserts that the 24/7 crowdsourcing platform is available to smartphone users and can be used as an additional safety resource by individuals and emergency responders. **Telecommunication Services:** Miller@pbn.com.

14460 ■ *"Stakes Rising on Business Cyber Security"* in Denver Business Journal (Vol. 63, May 18, 2012, No. 52, pp. A1)

Pub: Baltimore Business Journal

Contact: Rhonda Pringle, President

E-mail: rpringle@bizjournals.com

Ed: Greg Avery. **Description:** Congress and federal regulators are seeking to tighten rules for companies in infrastructure industries amid a series of high profile cyber attacks. The federal legislation might give the US Department of Homeland Security a role in ensuring they are not left vulnerable to cyber warfare and foreign Internet spies. **Availability:** Print; Online.

14461 ■ *"Starting a Successful Home Security Company: Step-By-Step Guide"* in Home Business (January 30, 2023)

URL(s): homebusinessmag.com/business-start-up/how-to-guides/starting-successful-home-security-company-step-by-step-guide/

Released: January 30, 2023. **Description:** Relates tips on starting a home security company, including developing a business model and deciding on inventory. **Availability:** Online.

14462 ■ *"State Democrats Push for Changes to Plant Security Law"* in Chemical Week (Vol. 172, July 19, 2010, No. 17, pp. 8)

Description: Legislation has been introduced to revise the existing U.S. Chemical Facility Anti-Terrorism Standards (CFATS) that would include a requirement for facilities to use inherently safer technology (IST). The bill would eliminate the current law's exemption of water treatment plants and certain port facilities and preserve the states' authority to establish stronger security standards. **Availability:** PDF; Online.

14463 ■ *"Stuff that Works for You: In the Mobikey of Life"* in Canadian Business (Vol. 81, June 11, 2008, No. 11, pp. 42)

Pub: Rogers Media Inc.

Contact: Neil Spivak, Chief Executive Officer

Ed: John Gray. **Description:** Toronto-based Route1 has created a data security software system that allows employees to access files and programs stored in the head office without permanently transferring data to the actual computer being used. Mobikey technology is useful in protecting laptops of chief executive officers, which contain confidential financial and customer data. **Availability:** Online.

14464 ■ *"A Survey of DHT Security Techniques"* in ACM Computing Surveys (Vol. 43, Summer 2011, No. 2, pp. 8)

Pub: Association for Computing Machinery

Contact: Yannis Ioannidis, President

Ed: Guido Urdaneta, Guillaume Pierre, Maarten Van Steen. **Released:** Volume 43 Issue 2. **Price:** $10, Members; $15, Nonmembers; $5, Students. **Description:** Peer-to-peer networks based on distributed hash tables (DHTs) have received considerable attention since their introduction in 2001. Unfortunately, DHT-based systems have been shown to be difficult to protect against security attacks. An overview of techniques reported in literature for making DHT-based systems resistant to the three most important

attacks that can be launched by malicious nodes participating in the DHT is given: the Sybil attack, the Eclipse attack, and routing and storage attacks. **Availability:** Download; PDF.

14465 ■ *"Sutter Court Win is Part of Trend"* in Sacramento Business Journal (Vol. 31, July 25, 2014, No. 22, pp. 3)

Pub: American City Business Journals, Inc.

Contact: Mike Olivieri, Executive Vice President

Released: July 25, 2014. **Description:** The Third District Court of Appeals dismissed 13 coordinated data-breach lawsuits filed against Sutter Health of Sacramento, California. The plaintiffs claim $4 billion in damages over theft of patient data from a local Sutter Health office in October 2011.

14466 ■ *"Symantic Completes Acquisition of VeriSign's Security Business"* in Internet Wire (August 9, 2010)

Description: Symantec Corporation acquired Veri-Sign's identity and authentication business, which includes Secure Sockets Layer (SSL) and Code Signing Certificate Services, the Managed Public Key Infrastructure (MPKI) Services, the VeriSign Trust Seal, the VeriSign Identity Protection (VIP) Authentication Service and the VIP Fraud Protection Service (FDS). The agreement also included a majority stake in VeriSign Japan. **Availability:** Online.

14467 ■ *"Taking on 911 - and Making a New Tech Biz In the Process"* in Orlando Business Journal (Vol. 30, January 24, 2014, No. 31, pp. 3)

Pub: American City Business Journals, Inc.

Contact: Mike Olivieri, Executive Vice President

Released: Weekly. **Price:** $8, introductory 4-week offer(Digital & Print). **Description:** Central Florida-based TapShield LLC is on the path to growth. The firm has developed a mobile application that enables University of Florida students to coordinate with police. Meanwhile, TapShield is in negotiations with large companies for similar deals. **Availability:** Print; Online.

14468 ■ *"Tax Preparation Made Easier With Carbonite Online Backup"* in Investment Weekly News (March 10, 2012, pp. 783)

Pub: PR Newswire Association LLC.

Description: Carbonite, Inc. provides a secure backup protection service, making tax preparation easier for consumers and small- to medium-sized businesses. Details on Carbonite.com and its services are included. **Availability:** Online.

14469 ■ *"Tech Data Launches Unified Communications and Network Security Specialized Business Units"* in Wireless News (October 22,2009)

Description: Responding to the growing demand for unified communications and network security, Tech Data announced the formation of two new Specialized Business Units. **Availability:** Online.

14470 ■ *"There's Risk, Reward for Business in Baltimore's Edgier Areas: Taking a Chance"* in Baltimore Business Journal (Vol. 28, July 16, 2010, No. 10, pp. 1)

Pub: Baltimore Business Journal

Contact: Rhonda Pringle, President

E-mail: rpringle@bizjournals.com

Ed: Scott Dance. **Description:** North Avenue in Baltimore, Maryland is considered a rough neighborhood due to the dangers of prostitution and drug dealing. However, some entrepreneurs have taken the risk of building their businesses on North Avenue as revitalization efforts grow. One of the challenges for businesses in rough neighborhoods is bringing customers to their stores or offices. **Availability:** Print.

14471 ■ *"Total Defense Launches Mobile Security for Business"* in Benzinga.com (August 1, 2012)

Pub: Benzinga.com

Contact: Jason Raznick, Founder

Ed: Aaron Wise. **Description:** Total Defense Inc. launched its Total Defense Mobile Secuirty Suite, a cloud-based solution for business that secures and manages mobile devices. Total Defense is a leading provider of malware protection against cybercrime. **Availability:** Online.

14472 ■ *"Trust Management of Services in Cloud Environments: Obstacles and Solutions" in ACM Computing Surveys (Vol. 46, Spring 2014, No. 1, pp. 12)*
Pub: Association for Computing Machinery - University of Wyoming
Contact: Ed Seidel, President
E-mail: uwpres@uwyo.edu

Description: Trust management is one of the most challenging issues in the emerging cloud computing area. Over the past few years, many studies have proposed different techniques to address trust management issues. However, despite these past efforts, several trust management issues such as identification, privacy, personalization, integration, security, and scalability have been mostly neglected and need to be addressed before cloud computing can be fully embraced. An overview of the cloud service models and a survey of the main techniques and research prototypes that efficiently support trust management services in cloud environments is presented. Open research issues for trust management in cloud environments is also examined. **Availability:** PDF; Online.

14473 ■ *"Twitter Hack: Made in Japan? User Says Attack Showed Security Flaw" in Houston Chronicle (September 24, 2010, pp. 3)*
Description: Details of the attack on Twitter caused by a Japanese computer hacker are revealed. **Availability:** Print; Mailing list; Online.

14474 ■ *"Unbound ID Raises $2 Million" in Austin Business JournalInc. (Vol. 28, December 12, 2008, No. 39, pp. 1)*
Description: Austin, Texas-based Unbound ID Corporation has secured $2 million in funding from venture capital firm Silverton Partners. The company has developed identity management software for network directories. The market for identity management technology is expected to grow to more than $12.3 billion by 2014. **Availability:** Print; Online.

14475 ■ *"Utah Collection Agency Settles File-Sharing Charges" inPaymentsSource (June 11, 2012)*
Pub: SourceMedia LLC
Contact: Gemma Postlethwaite, Chief Executive Officer

Ed: Darren Waggoner. **Description:** EPN Inc., doing business as Checknet Inc., settled charges filed by the Federal Trade Commission that it exposed sensitive information on its computers and networks creating a potential security risk to the consumer information it stored. Details of the suit are provided.

14476 ■ *"UTM Appliances Protect Small Businesses/Hotspots/Branch Offices" in Product News Network (March 7, 2012)*
Pub: Thomas Publishing Company
Contact: Tony Uphoff, President
E-mail: tuphoff@thomaspublishing.com

Description: Five 1GbE ports, WatchGuard(R) XTM 25 and XTM 26 are profiled. All deliver intrusion prevention, spam-blocking, and gateway anti-virus functionality. Borth models profiled integrate VPN, HTTPS inspection and VoIP support along with options for Application Control and other WatchGuard security services already available. Details are included. **Availability:** Online.

14477 ■ *"Vandal-Resistant Mortise Locks" in Building Design and Construction (Vol. 49, September 1, 2008, No. 12, pp. 78)*
Description: Stanley Security Solutions offers mortise locks with a vandal-resistant feature that includes a clutch mechanism designed to break away when excessive force is applied either by kicking or

standing on the lever. Once the mortise lock breaks away it can be easily reset to its original position without sustaining damage. **Availability:** Print; Online.

14478 ■ *"VASCO DIGIPASS GO3 in Combination With IDENTIKEY Enhances the Security of Business Intelligence Solution Developed by CDS for General Motors Brazil" in News Bites US (March 29, 2012)*
Description: VASCO Data Security International Inc. will provide Condominio de Corporativas, a vendor and business solutions integrator, its DIGIPASS GO 3 authentication solution along with IDENTIKEY Authentacation Server to provide security to the BI Retail Program developed for General Motors Brazil. VASCO is a leading software security firm specializing in authentication products. **Availability:** Print; Online.

14479 ■ *"Veteran-owned Business: EPG Security Group" in Business Journal (Vol. 31, May 16, 2014, No. 51, pp. 10)*
Pub: American City Business Journals, Inc.
Contact: Mike Olivieri, Executive Vice President
Released: Weekly. **Price:** $4, introductory 4-week offer(Digital only). **Description:** Profile of Erik Bergling, a former Marine, and owner of EPG Security Group. The firm provides security guards for special events, music venues, and executive protection. Bergling was forced to retire early from the Marines due to a hip injury. **Availability:** Print; Online.

14480 ■ *"Video Surveillance Enters Digital Era, Makes Giant Strides" in Arkansas Business (Vol. 26, September 28, 2009, No. 39, pp. 1)*
Description: Arkansas business owners are finding that the newest technology in video surveillance is leading to swift apprehension of thieves due to the high-quality digital imagery now being captured on surveillance equipment. Motion detection software for these systems is enhancing the capabilities of these systems and providing opportunities for businesses that would normally have problems integrating these systems. **Availability:** Print; Online.

14481 ■ *"Virtually Secure" in Rough Notes (Vol. 155, February 2012, No. 2, pp. 46)*
Pub: The Rough Notes Company Inc.
Contact: Walter J. Gdowski, President
E-mail: waltg@roughnotes.com
Ed: Nabeel Sayegh. **Availability:** PDF; Online.

14482 ■ *"Watchful Eye: Entrepreneur Protects Clients and His Bottom Line" in Black Enterprise (Vol. 38, March 1, 2008, No. 8, pp. 46)*
Pub: Earl G. Graves Ltd.
Contact: Earl Graves, Jr., President
Ed: Tennille M. Robinson. **Description:** Profile of Elijah Shaw, founder of Icon Services Corporation, a full service security and investigative service; Shaw shares his plans to protect clients while growing his business. **Availability:** Online.

14483 ■ *"Wegmans Uses Database for Recall" in Supermarket News (Vol. 56, September 22, 2008, No. 38)*
Pub: Informa USA, Inc.
Contact: Stephen A. Carter, Chief Executive Officer
Ed: Carol Angrisani. **Description:** Wegmans used data obtained through its loyalty card that, in turn, sent automated telephone calls to every customer who had purchased tainted pet food when Mars Petcare recalled dog food products.

14484 ■ *"A Well-Crafted Employee Handbook Can Make Work Run More Smoothly" in Idaho Business Review (September 17, 2014)*
Pub: BridgeTower Media
Contact: Adam Reinebach, President
Description: An employee handbook will provide a complaint process, provide company management flexibility and clarity and keep a company out of legal problems. Training, compensation, benefits, security, health, performance appraisals, and safety issues

must be covered. Human resource managers and other mangers should cover basics to help communicate with workers.

14485 ■ *"What the Future Holds for Consumers" in Black Enterprise (Vol. 41, August 2010, No. 1, pp. 47)*
Pub: Earl G. Graves Ltd.
Contact: Earl Graves, Jr., President
Ed: Sheiresa Ngo. **Description:** The way people purchase goods and service has changed with technology. With an increased focus on security (as well as privacy and fairness) the U.S. Congress began regulating the credit card industry with the Fair Credit Reporting Act of 1970 and the Credit Card Accountability, Responsibility, and Disclosure (CARD) Act of 2009. **Availability:** Online.

STATISTICAL SOURCES

14486 ■ *RMA Annual Statement Studies*
Pub: Risk Management Association
Contact: Nancy Foster, President
Released: Annual. **Description:** Contains composite balance sheets and income statements for more than 360 industries, including the accounting, auditing, and bookkeeping industries. Also contains five years of comparative historical data for discerning trends. Includes 16 commonly used ratios, computed for most of the size groupings for nearly every industry.

14487 ■ *Security Alarm Services Industry in the US - Market Research Report*
URL(s): www.ibisworld.com/united-states/market-research-reports/security-alarm-services-industry/
Price: $925. **Description:** Downloadable report analyzing data about the current and future trends in the security alarm services industry. **Availability:** Download.

14488 ■ *Security Services Industry in the US - Market Research Report*
URL(s): www.ibisworld.com/united-states/market-research-reports/security-services-industry/
Price: $925. **Description:** Downloadable report analyzing current and future trends in the security services industry. **Availability:** Download.

TRADE PERIODICALS

14489 ■ *Security Management*
Pub: ASIS International
Contact: Tim M. McCreight, President
URL(s): www.asisonline.org/security-management-magazine/latest-news/sm-homepage
Facebook: www.facebook.com/SecMgmtMag
Released: Monthly **Price:** $60, for 1 year price U.S., Canada and Mexico; $162, for 3 year U.S., Canada and Mexico; $120, for International shipment One year. **Description:** Loss prevention and security magazine. **Availability:** Print; Download; Online.

14490 ■ *Security Nation*
Pub: Electronic Security Association
Contact: Merlin Guilbeau, Chief Executive Officer
E-mail: merlin.guilbeau@esaweb.org
URL(s): esaweb.org/resources/securitynation
Released: Bimonthly **Description:** Provides news on the security industry, including marketing tips for small businesses and false alarm prevention ideas. Recurring features include interviews, a calendar of events, reports of meetings, news of educational opportunities, book reviews, and notices of publications available. **Availability:** Print; PDF; Online; Download.

TRADE SHOWS AND CONVENTIONS

14491 ■ *ABA Insurance Risk Management Annual Forum*
Axis
2nd fl., Jesus is Able House, Remera
Kigali, Rwanda
URL: http://www.axis.rw

URL(s): www.aba.com/training-events/conferences/insurance-risk-management-forum

Frequency: Annual. **Description:** Exhibits that demonstrate how to design an effective and efficient security department. **Audience:** Insurance risk managers, directors of corporate insurance, brokers / underwriters, lawyers, bank counsel, CFO's / treasurers, fraud / security professionals, compliance managers, insurance consultants/managers, presidents / CEO's of community banks. **Principal Exhibits:** Exhibits that demonstrate how to design an effective and efficient security department. Dates and Locations: 2025 Jan 26-29 Manchester Grand Hyatt, San Diego, CA. **Telecommunication Services:** reghousing@aba.com.

14492 ■ Restaurant Loss Prevention & Security Association

URL(s): www.rlpsa.com/annualconference

Frequency: Annual. **Description:** Presents industry best practices regarding loss prevention and security for restaurants. **Principal Exhibits:** Presents industry best practices regarding loss prevention and security for restaurants.

FRANCHISES AND BUSINESS OPPORTUNITIES

14493 ■ Direct Link

4760 Red Bank Expy., Ste. 300
 Cincinnati, OH 45227
URL: http://www.homehelpershomecare.com/santa-rosa/services/24-hour-monitoring/home-helpers-direct-link

Description: Firm offers variety of home care assistance services and in-home emergency monitoring system for seniors. **Founded:** 1997. **Franchised:** 1997. **Financial Assistance:** Yes **Training:** Yes.

14494 ■ EYESthere

2100 N SH Hwy. 360, Ste. 1404
 Grand Prairie, TX 75050

Free: 877-393-7548
URL: http://eyesthere.com

Description: Custom designs solutions that protect and empower businesses with live and recorded video. Franchises help protect our customer's premises, property, people and transactions and empower the owners, employees and customers with EYES there unique Digital Video solutions. **Founded:** 2006. **Training:** Provides 2 weeks at headquarters, 2 weeks at franchisee's location and ongoing support.

14495 ■ MonitorClosely

3873 Schaefer Ave.
 Chino, CA 91710
Ph: (909)342-6535
Co. E-mail: sales@monitorclosely.com
URL: http://www.monitorcloselyca.com

Description: Digital surveillance systems. **No. of Franchise Units:** 117. **Founded:** 2006. **Franchised:** 2006. **Equity Capital Needed:** $45,000-$60,000. **Franchise Fee:** $39,500. **Royalty Fee:** 8%. **Training:** Provides 4 days training at headquarters and ongoing support.

14496 ■ SHIELD Security Systems

Buffalo, NY
Ph: (716)681-6677
Co. E-mail: info@getyourshield.com
URL: http://www.shield-security.com/shield-locations/buffalo
Contact: Ken Jezioro, Officer
Facebook: www.facebook.com/GetYourShield
X (Twitter): x.com/getyourshield
YouTube: www.youtube.com/channel/UCABwH4o3DXGz1rgCM-MpeOw

Description: Firm engages in distribution and installation of burglar and fire alarm systems. **Founded:** 1976. **Franchised:** 2000. **Equity Capital Needed:** net worth of $250,000 and $75,000 in liquid assets. **Franchise Fee:** $40,000. **Royalty Fee:** 5% of Gross Sales. **Financial Assistance:** No **Training:** Yes.

14497 ■ Signature Alert Security

7452 Sycamore Glen Cir.
 West Jordan, UT 84081
URL: http://signaturealert.com
Facebook: www.facebook.com/signaturealertsecurity

Description: Retailing, installing, and monitoring of security systems. **Founded:** 1999. **Financial Assistance:** Yes **Training:** Includes 5 days training at corporate headquarters, 2 days at franchisee's location and ongoing support.

14498 ■ Sonitrol Corp.

Stanley Black & Decker, Inc.
 219 E St. Joseph St.
 Indianapolis, IN 46202
Ph: (860)225-5111
Co. E-mail: corporaterequest@sbdinc.com
URL: http://www.stanleyblackanddecker.com
Contact: Chip Shiver, Contact
Facebook: www.facebook.com/SonitrolVerify
Linkedin: www.linkedin.com/company/sonitrol
X (Twitter): x.com/sonitrolverify
YouTube: www.youtube.com/channel/UCt0plGOy19MYGKueUm_SNCg

Description: Franchises auto intrusion alarm systems. **No. of Franchise Units:** 178. **No. of Company-Owned Units:** 57. **Founded:** 1964. **Franchised:** 1965. **Equity Capital Needed:** $245,000-$500,000. **Franchise Fee:** $25,000-$55,000. **Royalty Fee:** 4.5%. **Training:** Includes training at headquarters, franchisee's location and ongoing.

PUBLICATIONS

14499 ■ "The Cybersecurity Shortage Is Real, and Women May Be the Solution" in BizTech (August 4, 2021)

Released: August 04, 2021. **Description:** Discusses the opportunities businesses have to bring women on board for technical positions, especially in the cybersecurity field, to help fill these open positions. **Availability:** Online.

START-UP INFORMATION

14500 ■ *"Event-Planning Startup Extends Its Reach"* in Indianapolis Business Journal (Vol. 33, June 18, 2012, No. 16, pp. 2A)

Description: Snappening.com offers a searchable database of central Indiana event venues ad professional planners and is expanding its service to four new markets. **Availability:** Print; Online.

14501 ■ *How to Start a Home-Based Event Planning Business*

Ed: Jill Moran. **Released:** 4th edition. **Price:** $19.95, paperback; $9.99; Paperback. **Description:** Guide to starting and growing a business planning events from a home-based firm. **Availability:** E-book; Print.

ASSOCIATIONS AND OTHER ORGANIZATIONS

14502 ■ **Connected International Meeting Professionals Association (CIMPA)**
8803 Queen Elizabeth Blvd.
  Annandale, VA 22003
Co. E-mail: info@cimpa.org
URL: http://www.cimpa.org
Contact: Lida Peterson, CPPM, CDMP, CTA,
  President

Description: Meeting planners, incentive organizers, travel agents, tour operators, and seminar organizers in 42 countries. **Scope:** Works to improve the skills of professional conference and convention planners. **Founded:** 1982. **Publications:** "Mice International"; "How Meeting Planners are Using Technology In Their Jobs"; "Internet Tools for Meeting Planners and Event Organizers"; "Getting Along With Others: Gut Instincts"; "How to Sell to Meeting Planners"; "Meeting Checklists"; "How to Organize International Meetings". **Training:** How to Sell to Meeting Planners; How to Be a Convention Planner; Career Opportunities in Conference Management; MAKING CONNECTIONS. **Educational Activities:** CIMPA International Technology Meetings and Incentives Conference. **Geographic Preference:** National.

14503 ■ **International Association of Speakers Bureaus (IASB)**
1922 E Fairmont Dr.
  Tempe, AZ 85282
Ph: (480)839-1423
Co. E-mail: info@iasbweb.org
URL: http://www.iasbweb.org
Contact: Tim Mathy, President
Facebook: www.facebook.com/IASBpage
X (Twitter): x.com/IASBWEB

Description: Maintains speakers' bureau representing 15 countries. Focuses on continuing education for its members, promotes awareness among meeting planners and raises the bar on accepted practices in the speakers' bureau industry. **Founded:** 1986. **Geographic Preference:** Multinational.

14504 ■ **National Speakers Association (NSA)**
323 Washington Ave., N Ste. 200
  Minneapolis, MN 55401
Ph: (480)968-2552
Co. E-mail: memberservices@nsaspeaker.org
URL: http://nsaspeaker.org
Contact: Jaime Nolan, President
Facebook: www.facebook.com/nsaspeaker
Linkedin: www.linkedin.com/company/nsaspeaker
X (Twitter): x.com/nsaspeaker
Instagram: www.instagram.com/nsaspeaker

Description: Professional speakers. Works to increase public awareness of the speaking profession, advance the integrity and visibility of professional speakers, and provide a learning and communication vehicle to professional speakers. Sponsors workshops, conventions, and labs. **Scope:** An association for experts who speak professionally. Members include experts in a variety of industries and disciplines, who reach audiences as trainers, educators, humorists, motivators, consultants and authors. Provides resources and education designed to enhance the business skills and platform performance of professional speakers. **Founded:** 1973. **Publications:** National speakers association. **Awards:** Cavett Award (Annual); Certified Speaking Professional Certification (CSP) (Annual); CPAE Speaker Hall of Fame (Annual). **Geographic Preference:** National.

14505 ■ **Société Canadienne de Planificateurs Professionnels d'Événements (CanSPEP) [Canadian Society of Professional Event Planners (CanSPEP)]**
18 Fire Rte. 40
  Havelock, ON, Canada K0L 1Z0
Co. E-mail: info@canspep.ca
URL: http://canspep.ca
Contact: Shaina Scrimgeour, President
E-mail: president@canspep.ca
Facebook: www.facebook.com/CanSPEP
Linkedin: www.linkedin.com/company/canspep-cana
  dian-society-of-professional-event-planners
X (Twitter): x.com/CanSPEP
Instagram: www.instagram.com/canspep

Description: Provides a forum for entrepreneurs in the meetings, conferences and event planning profession to meet, share ideas, gain new and valuable information about the industry and work together to form a strong presence in the marketplace. Promotes professionalism and builds awareness of independent meeting planning industry to the target markets. **Founded:** 1996. **Publications:** *The Independent* (Quarterly). **Geographic Preference:** National.

EDUCATIONAL PROGRAMS

14506 ■ **EEI Communications Design for Presentations**
URL(s): www.eeicom.com

Description: Covers enhancing presentation design; creating more effective grids and graphs; using color and typeface effectively, and how to avoid ten design disasters. **Audience:** Writers, editors, designers, proofreaders, and publication specialists. **Principal Exhibits:** Covers enhancing presentation design; creating more effective grids and graphs; using color and typeface effectively, and how to avoid ten design disasters. **Telecommunication Services:** train@eei-com.com.

REFERENCE WORKS

14507 ■ *"The Art and Business of Motivational Speaking: Your Guide"* in Inc. (Volume 32, December 2010, No. 10, pp. 124)
Pub: Inc. Magazine

Description: Profile of Josh Shipp that discusses his career as a motivational speaker. **Availability:** Print; Online.

14508 ■ *"Calendar"* in Crain's Detroit Business (Vol. 24, March 10, 2008, No. 10, pp. 21)
Pub: Crain Communications Inc.
Contact: Barry Asin, President

Description: Listing of events in the Detroit area include conferences addressing entrepreneurialism, economic development, and women business ownership. **Availability:** Print; Online.

14509 ■ *"Calling All Creatives, Innovators, 'Expats': Detroit Is Hopping In September"* in Crain's Detroit Business (Vol. 30, September 1, 2014, No. 35, pp. 6)
Pub: Crain Communications Inc.
Contact: Barry Asin, President

Description: Wayne State University is hosting a seminar September 16, 2014 which will focus on Detroit, Michigan as a center for innovation. Six other such seminars seeking investment in the city will be held in September. **Availability:** Online.

14510 ■ *"The Center of Success: Author Explores How Confidence Can Take You Further"* in Black Enterprise (Vol. 38, March 1, 2008, No. 8)
Pub: Earl G. Graves Ltd.
Contact: Earl Graves, Jr., President

Ed: Ayana Dixon. **Description:** Motivational speaker and author, Valorie Burton, provides a 50-question confidence quotient assessment to help business owners and managers develop confidence in order to obtain goals. **Availability:** Online.

14511 ■ *The Complete Guide to Successful Event Planning*

Ed: Shannon C. Kilkenny. **Released:** July 30, 2016. **Price:** $31.22, Paperback; $23.99, E-book. **Description:** The newly-revised 3rd edition now includes sections on social media, social networking, cultural sensitivity, ethics, and diversity to help you plan special events. **Availability:** E-book; Print.

14512 ■ *"Conference Calendar" in Marketing to Women (Vol. 21, April 2008, No. 4, pp. 7)*
Description: Listing of current conferences and events concerning women, marketing and business. **Availability:** Print; PDF; Download; Online.

14513 ■ *"Conference Networking Tips" in Women In Business (Vol. 66, Summer 2014, No. 1, pp. 14)*
Ed: Diane Stafford. **Description:** American Business Women's Association will hold its National Women's Leadership Conference from October 30, 2014 to November 1, 2014 in Overland, Kansas. Attendees are advised to study the conference agenda before the event. Participants also need to become good listeners when other attendees introduce themselves. **Availability:** Online.

14514 ■ *"How To Find More Customers and Clients with Webinars, Seminars and Workshops"*
Pub: CreateSpace
Released: September 27, 2014. **Price:** $2.34, kindle. **Description:** Steps to present successful Webinars, seminars and workshops to market your products at conferences and trade shows are highlighted. A checklist is also provided. **Availability:** Print.

14515 ■ *"Learning Charisma: Transform Yourself Into the Person Others Want to Follow" in Harvard Business Review (Vol. 90, June 2012, No. 6, pp. 127)*
Pub: Harvard Business Review Press
Contact: Moderna V. Pfizer, Contact
Ed: John Antonakis, Marika Fenley, Sue Liechti. **Price:** $8.95, hardcopy black and white. **Description:** Chrismatic leadership tactics include gestures, facial expressions, and an animated voice, all of which can enhance the receptiveness of a given message. Tips include engaging listeners and distilling points, and demonstrating passion, authority, and integrity. **Availability:** Print; Online; PDF.

14516 ■ *"Not Your Father's Whiteboard" in Inc. (Vol. 33, November 2011, No. 9, pp. 50)*
Pub: Inc. Magazine
Ed: Adam Baer. **Description:** Sharp's new interactive whiteboard is really a 70-inch touch screen monitor with software for importing presentations from any Windows 7 computer. **Availability:** Online.

14517 ■ *"Pennsylvania DEP To Conduct Natural Gas Vehicle Seminar" in Travel & Leisure Close-Up (October 8, 2012)*
Description: Pennsylvania Department of Environmental Protection is holding a Natural Gas Vehicle seminar at the Bayfront Convention Center in Erie, PA, as well as other locations throughout the state. The seminars will help municipal and commercial fleet owners make better informed decisions when converting fleets from compressed natural gas and liquefied natural gas. **Availability:** Print; Online.

14518 ■ *"A Renewed Sisterhood" in Women in Business (Vol. 64, Summer 2012, No. 2, pp. 6)*
Ed: Rene Street. **Description:** The American Business Women's Association (ABWA) regional conference highlighted a new sense of enthusiasm and sisterhood as well as effective visioning exercise and

breakout sessions. The ABWA National Women's Leadership Conference in October 2012 will feature the graduates of the Kansas University MBA Essentials Program and keynote speakers Bob Eubanks and Francine Ward. **Availability:** Online.

14519 ■ *"Seminar on Crowdfunding Set for Aug. 1" in Gazette (July 25, 2012)*
URL(s): gazette.com/seminar-on-crowdfunding-set-for-aug.-1/article/142192#!
Description: Senator Michael Bennet is co-hosting a seminar with Epicentral Coworking on crowdfunding featuring two panels with local entrepreneurs and business owners, legal experts, and representatives from investment firms. The seminar will be held August 1, 2012. **Availability:** Print; Online.

14520 ■ *"Show and Tell: How Everybody Can Make Extraordinary Presentations"*
Pub: Portfolio Hardcover
Contact: Adrian Zackheim, President
Released: March 01, 2016. **Price:** $19, paperback. **Description:** Whether in a one-on-one meeting, a conference room with strangers, or a lecture hall in front of thousands, giving a presentation can be difficult. Even good speakers can learn from the tips presented. Understanding your audience, organizing your content, building a clear storyline, creating effective visual effects, and channeling fear into fun will help create effective and successful presentations. **Availability:** Print.

14521 ■ *"So You Want To Hold a Conference: Event Planning Resources" in Searcher (Vol. 20, July-August 2012, No. 6, pp. 12)*
Pub: Information Today Inc.
Contact: Thomas H. Hogan, President
Ed: Cynthia Shamel. **Description:** Tips for planning any sort of event requires organizational skills, attention to detail, and the hope that everything will go according to plan. According to the Bureau of Labor Statistics' Occupational Outlook Handbook, the event planning industry is growing. The article shares information for planning your next conference.

14522 ■ *"Talk Like Ted: The 9 Public-Speaking Secrets of the World's Top Minds"*
Released: March 04, 2014. **Price:** $15.99, paperback; $29.99, compact disc; $14.99, digital audio; $26.99, hardcover; $9.99, e-book. **Description:** TED Talks redefines the elements of a successful presentation. Entrepreneurs must be able to sell themselves and their ideas in order to succeed. Public speaking coach provides a step-by-step guide to create, design, and deliver a TED-style presentation that is engaging, persuasive, and memorable. **Availability:** CD-ROM; E-book; Print; Audio.

14523 ■ *"Tic-Tac-Show: Line Up the Opportunities at Graph Expo" in American Printer (Vol. 128, August 1, 2011, No. 8)*
Description: Graph Expo has become the US print industry's main event. There will be as many as 500 exhibitors at this year's event and the Graphic Arts Show Company lists over 30 co-located events as well as 53 new sessions in the seminar program's 28 education categories. **Availability:** PDF; Online.

14524 ■ *"Vision Statement: Tired of PowerPoint? Try This Instead" in Harvard Business Review (Vol. 88, September 2010, No. 9, pp. 30)*
Pub: Harvard Business Publishing
Contact: Diane Belcher, Managing Director
Ed: Daniel McGinn, Stephanie Crowley. **Price:** $6, PDF. **Description:** Usefulness of graphic recording, also known as storyboarding or visual facilitation, during client meetings is illustrated. **Availability:** Online; PDF.

14525 ■ *"The Weeks Ahead" in Crain's New York Business (Vol. 24, January 7, 2008, No. 1, pp. 26)*
Description: Listing of events in the Detroit area include conferences addressing entrepreneurialism, economic development, and women business ownership. **Availability:** Print; Online.

TRADE PERIODICALS

14526 ■ **Public Speaking Tips**
Pub: Toastmasters International
Contact: Aletta Rochat, Director
URL(s): www.toastmasters.org/resources/public-speaking-tips
Description: Contains leadership tips, organization, and club programming suggestions. Recurring features include a calendar of events and news of speech competitions and awards. **Availability:** Print.

14527 ■ **Toastmaster**
Pub: Toastmasters International
Contact: Aletta Rochat, Director
URL(s): www.toastmasters.org/magazine
Released: Monthly **Description:** Magazine providing information and "how-to" articles on communication and leadership. **Availability:** Print; Download; PDF; Online.

CONSULTANTS

14528 ■ **National Speakers Association (NSA)**
323 Washington Ave., N Ste. 200
 Minneapolis, MN 55401
Ph: (480)968-2552
Co. E-mail: memberservices@nsaspeaker.org
URL: http://nsaspeaker.org
Contact: Jaime Nolan, President
Facebook: www.facebook.com/nsaspeaker
Linkedin: www.linkedin.com/company/nsaspeaker
X (Twitter): x.com/nsaspeaker
Instagram: www.instagram.com/nsaspeaker
Description: Professional speakers. Works to increase public awareness of the speaking profession, advance the integrity and visibility of professional speakers, and provide a learning and communication vehicle to professional speakers. Sponsors workshops, conventions, and labs. **Scope:** An association for experts who speak professionally. Members include experts in a variety of industries and disciplines, who reach audiences as trainers, educators, humorists, motivators, consultants and authors. Provides resources and education designed to enhance the business skills and platform performance of professional speakers. **Founded:** 1973. **Publications:** National speakers association. **Awards:** Cavett Award (Annual); Certified Speaking Professional Certification (CSP) (Annual); CPAE Speaker Hall of Fame (Annual). **Geographic Preference:** National.

ASSOCIATIONS AND OTHER ORGANIZATIONS

14529 ■ Auto Care Association
7101 Wisconsin Ave., Ste. 1300
  Bethesda, MD 20814-3415
Ph: (301)654-6664
Co. E-mail: info@autocare.org
URL: http://www.autocare.org
Contact: Bill Hanvey, President
E-mail: bill.hanvey@autocare.org
Facebook: www.facebook.com/autocareorg
Linkedin: www.linkedin.com/company/autocareorg
X (Twitter): x.com/autocareorg
YouTube: www.youtube.com/user/AAIAssociation

Description: Companies that manufacture, distribute, and sell motor vehicle parts, accessories, tools, equipment, materials, and supplies, and perform vehicle service and repair. Strives to support and advocate for the auto care industry distribution channel. **Publications:** *AAPEX Show Directory* (Annual); *Automotive Parts & Accessories Association--Directory of International Visitors* (Annual); *Latin American Buyers Directory*; *Latin America-Ready Directory*; *APAA Who's Who* (Annual); *Automotive Parts & Accessories Association--Manufacturers' Representatives Roster, Aftermarket Resource Bibliography* (Annual); *Aftermarket Insider* (Bi-monthly); *Key Contact and Buyer List* (Annual); *Mexican Buyers Guide*; *Merchandising Aids Directory*; *Automotive Service Training & Job Skills Directory*. **Educational Activities:** Automotive Aftermarket Products Expo (AAPEX) (Annual). **Awards:** Florida Automotive Industry Scholarships; Tom Babcox Memorial Scholarships (Annual); Sloan Northwood University Heavy-Duty Scholarships.

14530 ■ Automotive Maintenance and Repair Association (AMRA)
3321 Hobson Rd., Ste. A
  Woodridge, IL 60517
Ph: (847)947-2650
Co. E-mail: amra@motorist.org
URL: http://amra.org
Contact: Jeffrey Cox, President
Facebook: www.facebook.com/MAP.Motoris
tAssuranceProgram
YouTube: www.youtube.com/channel/
UCTGLK9iJguv8Gb4ERuilGjQ

Description: Promotes ethical and effective practice of automotive repair and maintenance; works to improve relations between auto owners and automotive service providers. **Publications:** *Directions*; *How to Find Your Way Under the Hood and Around the Car* (Biennial); *Uniform Inspection and Communications Standards for Automotive Systems* (Biennial). **Geographic Preference:** Multinational.

14531 ■ Automotive Service Association (ASA) - Library
8209 Mid Cities Blvd., Ste. 100
  North Richland Hills, TX 76182-4712
Ph: (817)514-2900

Co. E-mail: info@asashop.org
URL: http://www.asashop.org
Contact: Ray Fisher, Executive Director
E-mail: rayf@asashop.org
Facebook: www.facebook.com/ASAshop
Linkedin: www.linkedin.com/company/automotive
-service-association
X (Twitter): x.com/asashop
Instagram: www.instagram.com/asa_national
YouTube: www.youtube.com/user/asawebops

Description: Serves the needs of mechanical, transmission, and collision shop owners through education and representation on legislation affecting the automotive service industry. **Scope:** Automobiles; repair. **Founded:** 1951. **Holdings:** Figures not available. **Publications:** *AutoInc.* (Bimonthly). **Educational Activities:** Congress of Automotive Repair and Service (CARS) (Annual); International Autobody Congress and Exposition - NACE (Annual). **Geographic Preference:** National.

14532 ■ Automotive Service Association - Midwest (MWACA)
5950 N Oak Trafficway, Ste. 201
  Gladstone, MO 64118
Ph: (816)413-9800
URL: http://www.mwaca.org
Contact: Tim Davison, President
Facebook: www.facebook.com/asamidwest
Linkedin: www.linkedin.com/company/midwest-auto
-care-alliance
Instagram: www.instagram.com/mwaca

Description: Works to promote and strive for professionalism and excellence within the independent automotive service industry through education, training, support, mentoring, and fellowship of members. **Publications:** *Driving Force* (Monthly). **Geographic Preference:** Local.

14533 ■ Gasoline and Automotive Service Dealers Association (GASDA)
94 S Washington St.
  Lake Orion, MI 48362
Ph: (203)327-4773
Fax: (203)323-6935
URL: http://gasda.org
Contact: Michael J. Fox, Executive Director
E-mail: mike@gasda.org

Description: Represents owners/operators or dealers of service stations or automotive repair facilities. Aims to educate, inform, and help increase professionalism of members and of the industry. Offers periodic technical training clinics and other educational programs, including technical training and legal services. Informs members of political and legislative action or changes affecting their industry. **Founded:** 1956. **Geographic Preference:** National.

14534 ■ Inter-Industry Conference on Auto Collision Repair (I-CAR)
5125 Trillium Blvd.
  Hoffman Estates, IL 60192
Ph: (847)590-1198
Free: 800-422-7872

Fax: (800)590-1215
URL: http://www.i-car.com
Contact: Jim Guthrie, Chairman of the Board
Linkedin: www.linkedin.com/company/i-car
X (Twitter): x.com/I_CAR_Education
Instagram: www.instagram.com/icareducation
YouTube: www.youtube.com/user/icartraining

Description: Supports education and skills related to the automobile collision repair industry, serving car manufacturers, collision repair shops, insurance companies, tool, equipment and supply manufacturers, vocational institutions and related industrial organizations such as auto dismantlers and recyclers, appraisers, and technical publishers. **Founded:** 1979. **Publications:** *I-CAR E-newsletter*. **Awards:** I-CAR Lifetime Achievement Award (Annual); I-CAR Founders Award (Annual); I-CAR Regional Instructor of the Year Award (Annual). **Geographic Preference:** National.

14535 ■ International Midas Dealers Association (IMDA)
4919 Lamar Ave.
  Mission, KS 66202
Free: 877-543-6203
Co. E-mail: imda@dci-kansascity.com
URL: http://imda.today
Contact: Chery Whelan, Contact

Description: Midas auto service shop franchisees. **Founded:** 1979. **Publications:** *IMDA today*; *Franchise Focus* (Bimonthly). **Educational Activities:** International Midas Dealers Association Annual Convention (Annual). **Geographic Preference:** Multinational.

14536 ■ NARSA - The International Heat Exchange Association
450 S Denton Tap Rd.
  Coppell, TX 75019
Ph: (724)799-8415
Co. E-mail: narsanow@gmail.com
URL: http://www.narsa-idea.org
Contact: Mark Taylor, Author
E-mail: mtaylor@narsa.org
Facebook: www.facebook.com/narsatheinterna
tionalheattransferassociation
Linkedin: www.linkedin.com/company/narsanow
X (Twitter): x.com/narsanow
Instagram: www.instagram.com/narsanow
YouTube: www.youtube.com/channel/
UCGEEvNfxkliyCYAfbm6ck4Q

Description: Represents operators of automotive radiator and air conditioning repair shops and cooling system service businesses as well as manufacturers and suppliers for the trade. Maintains hall of fame. **Founded:** 1954. **Publications:** *NARSA Service Reports* (Bimonthly); *Automotive Cooling Journal--Convention Issue* (Annual). **Educational Activities:** National Automotive Radiator Service Association National Convention (Annual).

14537 ■ National Auto Body Council (NABC)
Cornelius, NC
Free: 855-843-6222

Co. E-mail: nabcadministration@nationalautobo
dycouncil.org
URL: http://nationalautobodycouncil.org
Contact: Bill Garoutte, President
E-mail: billg@nationalautobodycouncil.org
Facebook: www.facebook.com/NationalAutoBo
dyCouncil
Linkedin: www.linkedin.com/company/nationalautobo
dycouncil
X (Twitter): x.com/NABCGivesBack
Instagram: www.instagram.com/nationalautobo
dycouncil
Description: Members from the collision repair
industry. Seeks to promote pride in professionalism
and increase consumer confidence. **Founded:** 1985.
Geographic Preference: National.

14538 ■ National Institute for Automotive Service Excellence (ASE) [Auto Service Excellence (ASE)]

1503 Edwards Ferry Rd, N E Ste. 401
Leesburg, VA 20176
Ph: (703)669-6600
Free: 877-346-9327
Fax: (703)669-6127
Co. E-mail: contactus@ase.com
URL: http://www.ase.com
Contact: Tim Zilke, Senior Vice President
Facebook: www.facebook.com/asetests
Linkedin: www.linkedin.com/company/asetests
X (Twitter): x.com/asetests
YouTube: www.youtube.com/user/asetests
Description: A public interest organization which
promotes high standards in automotive service and
repair. Encourages effective training programs for
automobile mechanics/technicians. Affiliated with
National Automotive Technicians Education Founda-
tion. **Founded:** 1972. **Publications:** The Blue Seal;
ASE Catalogs of Tests (Annual); ASE Certification
Test Registration Booklet. **Educational Activities:**
ASE Annual Meeting (Annual). **Geographic Preference:** National.

14539 ■ New York State Association of Service Stations and Repair Shops (NYSASSRS)

6 Walker Way
Albany, NY 12205
Ph: (518)452-4367
Co. E-mail: state@nysassrs.com
URL: http://www.nysassrs.com
Contact: Jim McGill, Contact
Facebook: www.facebook.com/New-York-State
-Association-of-Service-Stations-and-Repair-Shops
-459330534080401
Description: Service station dealers united for: passage of national, state, and local legislation supportive of the service station dealer; promotion of
fraternity and unity among dealers in New York State
and throughout the country; achievement of the highest standards of service and safety for the motoring
public. Conducts trade exhibits and seminars in
automotive mechanics. **Founded:** 1967. **Publications:** Service Station News (Quarterly). **Geographic
Preference:** National; State.

14540 ■ SAE International (SAE) - Library

400 Commonwealth Dr.
Warrendale, PA 15096
Ph: (724)776-4841
Free: 877-606-7323
Fax: (724)776-0790
Co. E-mail: customerservice@sae.org
URL: http://www.sae.org
Contact: David L. Schutt, Contact
Linkedin: www.linkedin.com/company/sae-interna
tional
X (Twitter): x.com/SAEIntl
Description: Produces technical publications, con-
ducts numerous meetings, seminars and educational
activities, and fosters information exchange among
the worldwide automotive and aerospace communi-
ties. **Scope:** Technical learning. **Holdings:** Figures
not available. **Publications:** SAE International
Journal of Aerospace (3/year); SAE International
Journal of Commercial Vehicles (Quarterly); SAE

International Journal of Engines (8/year); Automotive
Engineering International (Monthly); SAE International
Journal of Passenger Vehicle Systems (3/year); SAE
International Journal of Passenger Vehicle Systems
(3/year); SAE Journal (JSAE) (Semiannual); Automo-
tive Engineering (10/year); Worldwide Automotive
Supplier Directory (Annual); SAE Handbook; SAE
Online Roster (Continuous); Aerospace Engineering
& Manufacturing (10/year); Consultants Directory:
Aerospace Automotive, ISO 9000 Quality Systems/
Management; Aerospace Engineering Magazine;
SAE International Journal of Fuels and Lubricants
(3/year); SAE International Journal of Materials and
Manufacturing (Quarterly); Automotive Consultants
Directory; Aerospace Engineering (7/year); Bosch
Handbook (Annual). **Educational Activities:** SAE
Aerospace Manufacturing and Automated Fastening
Conference & Exhibition (Annual); SAE Aerospace
Manufacturing and Automated Fastening Conference
& Exhibition (Biennial); Aerospace Manufacturing
Technology Conference and Exposition (Annual);
Brake Colloquium & Exhibition (Annual); DoD Mainte-
nance Symposium (Annual); General Aviation Tech-
nology Conference and Exhibition (Biennial); Noise
and Vibration Conference and Exhibition (Biennial);
SAE International's AeroTech Congress & Exhibition
(Annual); SAE Commercial Vehicle Engineering
Congress (COMVEC); SAE International WCX World
Congress Experience (Annual); Aerospace Systems
and Technology Conference (ASTC) (Biennial); SAE/
JSAE Small Engine Technology Conference (Annual);
Thermal Management Systems Symposium (TMSS)
(Annual); SAE World Congress Experience (Annual);
Energy & Propulsion Conference & Exhibition (An-
nual); Offhighway and Powerplant Congress.
Awards: SAE Aerospace Chair Award (Annual); Gary
Dickinson Award for Teaching Excellence (Irregular);
Lloyd Reuss Award for Teaching Excellence (Peri-
odic); SAE Medal of Honor (Annual); Max Bentele
Award for Engine Technology Innovation (Annual);
Award for Research on Automotive Lubricants (Ir-
regular); Vincent Bendix Automotive Electronics
Engineering Award (Annual); L. Ray Buckendale
Lecture (Annual); Edward N. Cole Award for Automo-
tive Engineering Innovation (Irregular); Arch T. Colwell
Cooperative Engineering Medal (Annual); Henry Ford
II Distinguished Award for Excellence in Automotive
Engineering (Occasionally); Cliff Garrett Turboma-
chinery and Applications Engineering Award (Annual);
Harry L. Horning Memorial Award (Annual); Ralph H.
Isbrandt Automotive Safety Engineering Award (An-
nual); Franklin W. Kolk Air Transportation Progress
Award (Irregular); William Littlewood Memorial
Lecture (Annual); Charles M. Manly Memorial Medal
(Annual); Forest R. McFarland Award (Annual);
Engineering Meetings Board Outstanding Oral
Presentation Award (Irregular); SAE Fellow Grade of
Membership (Annual); Elmer A. Sperry Award (An-
nual); Russell S. Springer Award (Annual); James M.
Crawford Executive Standards Committee Outstand-
ing Achievement Award (Annual); Ralph R. Teetor
Educational Award (Annual); Marvin Whitlock Award
(Annual); Wright Brothers Medal (Irregular); Aero-
space Engineering Leadership Award (Periodic);
SAE/AEM Outstanding Young Engineer Award (An-
nual); Edward N. Cole Distinguished Younger Member
Award (Annual); Honeywell Outstanding Collegiate
Branch Award (Annual); Thomas H. Speller Award
(Annual); SAE International Leadership Citation (An-
nual); SAE/AEM Outstanding Young Engineer Award
(Irregular); Bill Agnew Award for Outstanding AWIM
Volunteers (Occasionally); Bruce R. Aubin Aerospace
Customer Support Award for Excellence (Annual);
SAE Max Bentele Award for Engine Technology In-
novation (Annual); J. Cordell Breed Award for Women
Leaders (Annual); John Connor Environmental Award
(Annual); Delco Electronics Intelligent Transportation
Systems Award (ITS) (Periodic); SAE Environmental
Excellence in New Methods and Tools Transportation
Award (E2T) (Annual); Excellence in Engineering
Education - Triple "E" Award (Annual); SAE Faculty
Advisors Award (Annual); Henry O. Fuchs Student
Award (Semiannual); Daniel Guggenheim Medal (An-
nual); SAE/InterRegs Standards and Regulations
Award for Young Engineers (Annual); Clarence L.
(Kelly) Johnson Aerospace Vehicle Design and
Development Award (Annual); Barry D. McNutt Award

for Excellence in Automotive Policy Analysis (Annual);
SAE/AISI Sydney H. Melbourne Award for Excellence
in the Advancement of Automotive Sheet Steel (An-
nual); Myers Award for Outstanding Student Paper
(Annual); Sid Olsen Engineering Executive of the
Year Award (Annual); Heinz C. Prechter Award for
Automotive Excellence (Annual); Rumbaugh Out-
standing Student Leader Award (Annual); Arnold W.
Siegel International Transportation Safety Award (An-
nual); SAE/Timken-Howard Simpson Automotive
Transmission and Driveline Innovation Award (Peri-
odic); Lloyd L. Withrow Distinguished Speaker Award
(Annual); Stefan Pischinger Young Industry Leader-
ship Award (Annual). **Geographic Preference:**
Multinational; National.

14541 ■ Society of Collision Repair Specialists (SCRS)

PO Box 3037
Mechanicsville, VA 23116
Free: 877-841-0660
Fax: (877)851-0660
Co. E-mail: info@scrs.com
URL: http://scrs.com
Contact: Aaron Schulenburg, Executive Director
Facebook: www.facebook.com/SCRSCollision
Linkedin: www.linkedin.com/company/5383724
X (Twitter): x.com/scrscollision
YouTube: www.youtube.com/scrscollision
Description: Businesses; associations; individual
owners and managers of auto collision repair shops,
suppliers, insurance and educational associates.
Distributes management and technical information;
maintains industry standards; works to promote
professionalism within the industry. **Founded:** 1982.
Educational Activities: Society of Collision Repair
Specialists Seminar. **Awards:** SCRS Affiliate Associa-
tion Award (Annual); SCRS Collision Industry Individual Service Award (Annual); SCRS Collision
Industry Non-Individual Service Award; SCRS Industry Achievement Award. **Geographic Preference:**
National.

14542 ■ Society of Independent Gasoline Marketers of America (SIGMA)

1330 Braddock Pl., Ste. 501
Alexandria, VA 22314
Ph: (703)709-7000
Co. E-mail: sigma@sigma.org
URL: http://www.sigma.org
Contact: Ryan McNutt, Chief Executive Officer
E-mail: rmcnutt@sigma.org
Linkedin: www.linkedin.com/company/sigma-fuel
-marketers
Description: Represents chain gasoline marketers,
wholesale and retail. Works to inform members of
current governmental and legislative activities;
represents the marketers' interests before govern-
ment and legislative and regulatory agencies; and
provides statistical data on industry. **Founded:** 1958.
Publications: Society of Independent Gasoline
Marketers Membership Directory; Society of Independent Gasoline Marketers of America--Weekly Report
(Weekly); Statistical Report (Annual). **Educational
Activities:** Winter Management Conference (Annual); Executive Leadership Conference (Annual).
Awards: SIGMA Distinguished Marketer Award (Oc-
casionally); SIGMA Distinguished Statesman Award.
Geographic Preference: National.

14543 ■ Truck-Frame and Axle Repair Association (TARA)

1040 Willis Hill Rd.
Victor, NY 14564
Ph: (585)703-4295
Co. E-mail: info@taraassociation.com
URL: http://www.taraassociation.com
Contact: Bill Hinchcliffe, Treasurer
E-mail: bill.hinchcliffe@mail.com
Description: Owners and operators of heavy-duty
truck repair facilities and mechanics; allied and as-
sociate members are manufacturers of heavy-duty
trucks and repair equipment, engineers, trade press
and insurance firms. Seeks to help members share
skills and technical knowledge and keep abreast of
new developments and technology to better serve

customers in areas of minimum downtime, cost and maximum efficiency. Conducts studies and surveys regarding safety, fuel conservation and heavy-duty truck maintenance and repairs. **Founded:** 1966. **Publications:** *Truck Frame & Axle Repair Association--Membership Directory* (Biennial; Annual). **Educational Activities:** Truck-Frame and Axle Repair Association Conference (Annual). **Geographic Preference:** National.

REFERENCE WORKS

14544 ■ *4 Reasons Why Auto Repair Shops Need Business Insurance*

Description: Every day is different when you run an auto repair shop. For this reason, business insurance for auto repair shops is a must-have. **Availability:** Online.

14545 ■ *"5 Tips for Choosing the Right Location for Your Automotive Business" in Small Business Trends (May 9, 2018)*

Ed: Annie Pilon. **Released:** May 09, 2018. **Description:** Provides information on why the location of your automotive repair shop is important. Tips include convenience for customers, best ways to use signage, choosing a spot that trucks can get to, and ensuring that the spot you choose is zoned for your business. **Availability:** Online.

14546 ■ *"Auto Repair Shop Financing" in Small Business Funding*

Description: The costs of operating an auto repair shop including equipment, inventory, and licensing and regulatory requirements. This article discusses when to consider a small business loan and the financing options that exist. **Availability:** Online.

14547 ■ *"Autonomous Vehicles and the Future of Auto Repair" in Ratchet + Wrench (October 3, 2018)*

URL(s): www.ratchetandwrench.com/articles/7092-au tonomous-vehicles-and-the-future-of-auto-repair

Ed: Anna Zeck. **Released:** October 03, 2018. **Description:** Discusses what could happen in the future with the advancement of autonomous vehicles. With car manufactures spending a lot of money developing these vehicles, at some point independent auto repair shops will have to either adapt their business model to these cars or face losing profits. **Availability:** Online.

14548 ■ *"The Average Salary of Auto Repair Owners" in Chron (June 29, 2018)*

Ed: Anne Kinsey. **Released:** June 29, 2018. **Description:** Discusses transitioning from being an auto mechanic to owning your own auto repair shop. Also discusses education requirements, median salary based on years of experience, and job growth trends. **Availability:** Online.

14549 ■ *"Collision Centers See Business Boom" in Atlanta Business Chronicle (February 7, 2014, pp. 3A)*

Pub: American City Business Journals, Inc.

Contact: Mike Olivieri, Executive Vice President

Released: February 07, 2014. **Price:** $4, Introductory 4-Week Offer(Digital & Print). **Description:** Collision repair shops in Atlanta, Georgia are benefitting from the recent snow storm. The storm resulted in $10 million insured losses to homes and automobiles. Meanwhile, collision centers have also extended business hours to accommodate more customers. **Availability:** Print; Online.

14550 ■ *"Convenience Store Owners Will Request New Zoning Once More" in Daily Republic (November 1, 2010)*

Pub: McClatchy Tribune Information Services

Contact: Patrick J. Talamantes, President

Ed: Tom Lawrence. **Description:** Zoning change has been requested for a proposed convenience store in Mitchell, South Dakota. Details are included. **Availability:** Online.

14551 ■ *"Fix-It Careers: Jobs in Repair" in Occupational Outlook Quarterly (Vol. 54, Fall 2010, No. 3, pp. 26)*

Pub: U.S. Department of Labor Bureau of Labor Statistics

Contact: Amrit Kohli, Director

E-mail: kohli.amrit@bls.gov

Ed: Elka Maria Torpey. **Description:** Auto mechanics and HVAC technician occupations require repair skills. Advantages for individuals with proper skills are outlined. **Availability:** Online; PDF.

14552 ■ *"How to Create an Auto Repair Shop Business Plan" in The Bottom Line (January 9, 2020)*

Ed: Sonya Stinson. **Released:** January 09, 2020. **Description:** Discusses the importance of a business plan and how to structure it for your auto repair business. Shows the difference between lean and traditional business plans. Also includes information on auto repair business loans. **Availability:** Online.

14553 ■ *"How to Legally Start a Business in Auto Repair" in Chron (March 4, 2019)*

Ed: Matt McKay. **Released:** March 04, 2019. **Description:** Legally starting a business in auto repair requires specific permits and licenses that differ with each state and local municipality. This article provides details using a systematic approach to ensure that your legal paperwork is efficient and organized. **Availability:** Online.

14554 ■ *"How to Start a Car Shop From the Ground Up" in Chron (April 9, 2019)*

Ed: Brenna Swanston. **Released:** April 09, 2019. **Description:** Provides details on building your own auto shop from scratch. Discusses raising capital, renting space, developing a business plan, hiring staff, and marketing. **Availability:** Online.

14555 ■ *"Neighboring Auto Body Shops Merge as Parks Royal Body Works" in Idaho Business Review (August 26, 2014)*

Pub: BridgeTower Media

Contact: Adam Reinebach, President

Description: Parks Royal Body Works and Auto Body Specialists operated next door to each other and were rivals for many years. Ted Vinson, owner of Auto Body, recently sold his business to Ted Thornton's son, Matt in order for Parks Royal to expand. Thornton discusses his company's 13 percent growth in 2013. Details of the purchase are discussed.

14556 ■ *"Opening an Auto Repair Shop: 6 Things You Should Know" in Advanced Technology Institute (April 21, 2016)*

Released: April 21, 2016. **Description:** Discusses the advantages of owning your own auto repair shop and includes information on important things to do before opening such as certification, understanding startup costs, whether to specialize or not, getting legal advice, hiring, and marketing. **Availability:** Online.

14557 ■ *"The Right Equipment and Premises to Start an Auto Repair Workshop" in AxleAddict (April 25, 2016)*

Released: April 25, 2016. **Description:** Details essential equipment needed to start your own auto shop. This article describes the tools and equipment needed to do a broad range of work so that you can serve a wide variety of customers. **Availability:** Online.

14558 ■ *"Top Body Shop Consolidators Step up Competition with Dealers" in Automotive News (June 18, 2018)*

URL(s): www.autonews.com/article/20180618/RE-TAIL05/180619883/top-body-shop-consolidators-s tep-up-competition-with-dealers

Ed: Rick Popely. **Released:** June 18, 2018. **Description:** The four largest body shop consolidators are taking back market share from dealership-owned shops. They have the capital and scale to now fix vehicles that are technologically advanced and that need to meet certain regulations. Consumers typi-

cally took these types of repairs to dealerships, which cost the smaller body shops since they didn't invest in new equipment until recently. **Availability:** Online.

14559 ■ *What to Know Before Buying a Gas Station Franchise*

Ed: Bruce Hakutizwi. **Description:** With gas stations ranking as one of the most popular and profitable franchises, purchasing a gas station franchise can eliminate some of the startup costs and headaches that come with opening a new station. This article provides key factors to keep in mind if you are exploring the idea of purchasing a franchise. **Availability:** Online.

STATISTICAL SOURCES

14560 ■ *RMA Annual Statement Studies*

Pub: Risk Management Association

Contact: Nancy Foster, President

Released: Annual. **Description:** Contains composite balance sheets and income statements for more than 360 industries, including the accounting, auditing, and bookkeeping industries. Also contains five years of comparative historical data for discerning trends. Includes 16 commonly used ratios, computed for most of the size groupings for nearly every industry.

TRADE PERIODICALS

14561 ■ *BodyShop Business*

Pub: Babcox Media Inc.

Contact: Bill Babcox, Chief Executive Officer

E-mail: bbabcox@babcox.com

URL(s): www.bodyshopbusiness.combabcox.com/ brand/bodyshop-business

Facebook: www.facebook.com/BodyShopBusiness

Linkedin: www.linkedin.com/showcase/bodyshop -business

X (Twitter): x.com/BodyShop_Biz

YouTube: www.youtube.com/channel/UCHJrm8nC dre732pse5zrlAQ

Ed: Jason Stahl. **Released:** Monthly **Description:** Magazine providing management and technical information that can be applied to run an efficient and profitable collision repair shop and business. **Availability:** Print; PDF; Download; Online.

14562 ■ *Cooling Journal*

Contact: Wayne Juchno, Executive Director

URL(s): narsa.org/publication/cooling-journal

Price: $130, Other countries; $97, Canada. **Description:** Automotive trade magazine. **Availability:** Print.

14563 ■ *Engine Builder*

Pub: Babcox Media Inc.

Contact: Bill Babcox, Chief Executive Officer

E-mail: bbabcox@babcox.com

URL(s): www.enginebuildermag.com

Facebook: www.facebook.com/EngineBuilder

X (Twitter): x.com/enginebuildmag

Instagram: www.instagram.com/enginebuildermag

YouTube: www.youtube.com/channel/UCPKREfGyH _0thm6h-TeVldQ

Ed: Greg Jones. **Released:** Bimonthly **Price:** $129, for one year airmail or foreign; $89, Canada for one year; $69, U.S. for 1 year. **Description:** Magazine for engine builders, machinists, and enthusiasts. **Availability:** Print; PDF; Download; Online.

14564 ■ *Engine Professional*

Pub: Automotive Engine Rebuilders Association

Contact: Jim Rickoff, President

E-mail: jim@aera.org

URL(s): engineprofessional.com

Released: Quarterly **Description:** Recurring features include interviews, news of research, a calendar of events, reports of meetings, news of educational opportunities, and notices of publications available. **Availability:** Print; Online.

14565 ■ *GASDA-Newsletter*

Pub: Gasoline and Automotive Service Dealers Association, Ltd.

Contact: Wayne Bombardiere, Executive Director

URL(s): www.gasda-ny.com/newsletters.html

Released: Monthly **Description:** Reports on industry news, laws, and regulations affecting service station operators in New York. Updates Association news and provides general tips on operation. Recurring features include news of research, news of educational opportunities and Association programs, reports of meetings, and a calendar of events. **Availability:** PDF; Online.

14566 ■ *Motor Magazine*
Pub: Motor Information Systems
Contact: Jeff Nosek, Executive Vice President
URL(s): www.motor.com/magazine
Ed: JOHN LYPEN, John Lypen. **Released:** Monthly **Description:** Magazine for the automotive aftermarket trade, professional technicians, and shop owners. **Availability:** Print; Online.

14567 ■ *Professional Tool & Equipment News: The Independent Tool Authority*
Contact: Sarah Shelstrom, Publisher
E-mail: sarah@vehicleservicepros.com
URL(s): www.vehicleservicepros.com/magazine
Facebook: www.facebook.com/ptenmagazine
Released: 10/year **Description:** Magazine for automotive shop owners and technicians. Reports on new tools and equipment. **Availability:** Print; Online.

14568 ■ *Truck Parts & Service*
Pub: Randall-Reilly
Contact: Matt Reilly, President
URL(s): www.truckpartsandservice.com
Facebook: www.facebook.com/TrucksPartsService
X (Twitter): twitter.com/TPSdaily
YouTube: www.youtube.com/channel/UCcBeotmXyiX
_LLp7CYcjY_Q
Ed: Lucas Deal, Derek Smith. **Released:** Monthly **Description:** Trade magazine for truck parts and service market. **Availability:** Online.

14569 ■ *Underhood Service*
Pub: Babcox Media Inc.
Contact: Bill Babcox, Chief Executive Officer
E-mail: bbabcox@babcox.com
URL(s): www.underhoodservice.com
Facebook: www.facebook.com/UnderhoodService
Linkedin: www.linkedin.com/showcase/underhoo
d-service
X (Twitter): x.com/UnderHoodServ
Instagram: www.instagram.com/babcox_underhood
YouTube: www.youtube.com/channel/UCA7Yzkz8Q
55bfKSk9SnYPTw
Ed: Doug Kaufman. **Released:** Monthly **Description:** Magazine covering service and repair shops doing 50% or more of service underhood. **Availability:** PDF; Download; Online.

VIDEO/AUDIO MEDIA

14570 ■ *Think Business: Clean Bathrooms and Competitive Edges with Dave Newell*
URL(s): thinktyler.com/podcast_episode/bathrooms
-competitive-dave-newell
Ed: Tyler Martin. **Released:** January 22, 2024. **Description:** Podcast examines the intersection of strategy and identity can shape businesses with something as simple as clean bathrooms at a gas station.

TRADE SHOWS AND CONVENTIONS

14571 ■ National Automotive Radiator Service Association National Convention
NARSA - The International Heat Exchange Association
450 S Denton Tap Rd.
Coppell, TX 75019
Ph: (724)799-8415
Co. E-mail: narsanow@gmail.com
URL: http://www.narsa-idea.org
Contact: Mark Taylor, Author
E-mail: mtaylor@narsa.org
URL(s): www.narsa.org/events.php

Frequency: Annual. **Description:** Exhibits related to heat exchange products and services. **Audience:** Business people, industry professionals, and entrepreneurs. **Principal Exhibits:** Exhibits related to heat exchange products and services.

14572 ■ NATSO Connect
URL(s): www.natso.com/events/natso-connect-2022
Frequency: Annual. **Description:** Expo and meeting to discuss new trends in the truckstop and plaza industry. **Audience:** Truckstop and travel plaza leaders. **Principal Exhibits:** Expo and meeting to discuss new trends in the truckstop and plaza industry.

FRANCHISES AND BUSINESS OPPORTUNITIES

14573 ■ AAMCO Transmissions, LLC
Icahn Enterprises L.P.
470 Easton Rd., Rear
Horsham, PA 19044
Ph: (305)422-4100
Free: 800-255-2737
URL: http://www.ielp.com
Facebook: www.facebook.com/AAMCO
X (Twitter): x.com/aamco
YouTube: www.youtube.com/aamcocarcare
Description: Chain of transmission service centers, specializing in all types of automobile transmission and related repairs. The company philosophy is to continue to increase its competitive advantage and market share through technical expertise and customer satisfaction. AAMCO provides a complete A to Z training course at its corporate headquarters. No automotive experience is needed. Operational, technical and sales support is provided on an ongoing basis. **Founded:** 1963. **Training:** Offers 3 weeks training at home office, plus in field support.

14574 ■ All Night Auto Repair
33729 Plymouth Rd.
Livonia, MI 48150
Ph: (734)427-3100
Fax: (734)427-3131
Co. E-mail: elitetireautocare@gmail.com
URL: http://www.elitetireandautocare.com
Contact: Wahid Makki, Contact
Facebook: www.facebook.com/elitetireandauto/wall
Description: Full service automotive repair shop. **Founded:** 1994. **Training:** Provides 3-4 weeks of training.

14575 ■ All Tune and Lube (ATL)
8334 Veterans Hwy.
Millersville, MD 21108
Free: 800-935-8863
URL: http://www.alltuneandlube.com
Facebook: www.facebook.com/ATL-Total-Car-Care
-Corporate-Office-239957309236
X (Twitter): x.com/alltuneandlube
Description: Provider of automotive maintenance and repair services. **Founded:** 1985. **Financial Assistance:** Yes **Training:** All Tune and Lube provides extensive training at headquarters and in the individual center locations. Provides 1 week of center management training and operational support.

14576 ■ Big O Tires Inc.
4280 Professional Ctr. Dr., Ste. 400
Palm Beach Gardens, FL 33410
Free: 866-649-8473
URL: http://www.bigotires.com
Contact: Lauren Bourrut, Manager
X (Twitter): x.com/bigotires
Instagram: www.instagram.com/bigotiresofficial
Description: Manufacturer and retailer of tires. **Founded:** 1962.

14577 ■ Brake Masters
4260 E Grant Rd.
Tucson, AZ 85712
Ph: (520)323-9000
URL: http://www.brakemasters.com
Facebook: www.facebook.com/BrakeMastersTucson
X (Twitter): x.com/brake_masters
YouTube: www.youtube.com/user/brakemasters1

Description: Provider of automotive services and repairs including oil changes, tire alignment, brake repair and much more. **Founded:** 1983. **Financial Assistance:** Yes **Training:** Training includes classroom instruction, as well as several weeks of on the job training in stores.

14578 ■ Car-X Associates Corp.
423 W Golf Rd.
Schaumburg, IL 60195
Ph: (847)882-2535
URL: http://www.carx.com
Facebook: www.facebook.com/CarxAuto
X (Twitter): x.com/CarX_Man
Description: Provider of automotive repair and maintenance services for muscle cars, sports vehicles and light trucks. **Founded:** 1971. **Franchise Fee:** $25,000. **Financial Assistance:** Yes **Training:** Initial training for 3 weeks, plus 2 weeks at new shop at opening. Ongoing support and training programs.

14579 ■ ColorAll Technologies (CA)
PO Box 10
Green Mountain, NC 28740
URL: http://www.colorall.com
Description: Onsite auto appearance and repair management. **Training:** Yes.

14580 ■ Dent Doctor
11301 W Markham St.
Little Rock, AR 72211
Ph: (501)224-0500
Co. E-mail: info@dentdoctor.com
URL: http://www.dentdoctor.com
Facebook: www.facebook.com/dentdoctor
X (Twitter): x.com/dentdoctor
Description: Paint less dent removal services for both wholesale and retail vehicle owners. **Founded:** 1986. **Franchised:** 1990. **Financial Assistance:** Yes **Training:** An intensive 8 week training program is required to learn the Dent Doctor painless dent removal system. Dent Doctor also offers ongoing refresher training.

14581 ■ Dr. Vinyl and Associates Ltd.
1350 SE Hamblen Rd.
Lees Summit, MO 64081
Ph: (816)525-6060
Free: 800-531-6600
Fax: (816)525-6333
Co. E-mail: info@drvinyl.com
URL: http://www.drvinyl.com
Contact: Richard Reinders, Chief Executive Officer
E-mail: richard@drvinyl.com
Description: Mobile repair, reconditioning and aftermarket sales and services to auto dealers and other commercial accounts, such as vinyl, leather, velour, fabric, bumper, windshield, plastic and paint less dent repair, application of striping, body moldings, deck racks, graphics, gold plating, etc. **Founded:** 1972. **Financial Assistance:** Yes **Training:** (Missouri for combined classroom and field training and 4-5 days in franchisees territory). Training also available for franchisees employees or sub-contractors.

14582 ■ The Doctors Touch
1350 SE Hamblen Rd.
Lees Summit, MO 64081
Free: 800-531-6600
URL: http://www.thedoctorstouch.com
Description: Provider of paint repairing services such as scratch removal, bumper repair and more for automotive. **Founded:** 2005. **Training:** Provides 3 weeks training at headquarters and ongoing support.

14583 ■ Econo Lube N' Tune Inc.
440 S Church St., Ste. 700
Charlotte, NC 28202
Free: 855-325-5444
URL: http://www.econolube.com
Description: Provider of automotive repair and maintenance services. **Founded:** 1973. **Franchise Fee:** $39,500. **Financial Assistance:** Yes **Training:** Yes.

14584 ■ Honest-1 Auto Care Inc.
15420 N 59th Ave.
  Glendale, AZ 85306
Ph: (602)910-2539
Co. E-mail: info@honest1glendaleaz.com
URL: http://www.honest1glendaleaz.com
Facebook: www.facebook.com/Honest1GlendaleAZ
X (Twitter): twitter.com/honest1usa
YouTube: www.youtube.com/watch?v=XiYCYn
  5Mxuw
Description: Provider of auto repair services.
Founded: 2003. **Training:** Yes.

14585 ■ Maaco Franchising Inc.
Driven Brands Inc.
  440 S Church St., Ste. 700
  Charlotte, NC 28202
Ph: (704)377-8855
URL: http://www.drivenbrands.com
Contact: John Wierman, Manager
URL(s): www.maaco.com
Facebook: www.facebook.com/MaacoFranchise
Description: Maaco Auto Painting & Bodyworks
Centers are complete production auto paint and body
repair centers. No prior automotive experience neces-
sary. **No. of Franchise Units:** 459. **Founded:** 1972.
Franchised: 1972. **Equity Capital Needed:** $90,000
minimum cash required. **Franchise Fee:** $40,000.
Financial Assistance: Yes **Training:** 4 weeks formal
training at corporate headquarters, continuing operational support thereafter. Assistance in financing, site
selection and installation of equipment.

14586 ■ The Master Mechanic
3250 Ridgeway Dr., Unit 1
  Mississauga, ON, Canada L5L 5Y6
Ph: (905)820-2552
Fax: (905)820-2558
Co. E-mail: info@mastermechanic.ca
URL: http://www.mastermechanic.ca
Contact: Wayne Cole, Contact
E-mail: wayne@mastermechanic.ca
Facebook: www.facebook.com/talktoourmechanics
X (Twitter): x.com/mastermechanic_
YouTube: www.youtube.com/user/MyMas
  terMechanic/videos
Description: Firm provides auto repair and vehicle
maintenance services. **No. of Franchise Units:** 39.
Founded: 1982. **Franchised:** 1982. **Training:**
Procedures and technical training are conducted
onsite and at existing locations and head office.
Management training courses provided by specialists
in management and automotive servicing. Business
training by franchisor accountants.

14587 ■ Meineke Car Care Centers, LLC (MCCC)
Driven Brands Inc.
  440 S Church St., Ste. 700
  Charlotte, NC 28202
Ph: (704)377-8855
URL: http://www.drivenbrands.com
Contact: Devin Hughes, Vice President, Develop-
  ment
Facebook: www.facebook.com/meinekecarcareusa
X (Twitter): x.com/meinekecarcare
Instagram: www.instagram.com/meinekecarcare
YouTube: www.youtube.com/user/MeinekeCorp
Description: Provider of automotive repairing ser-
vices. **No. of Franchise Units:** 941. **Founded:** 1972.
Franchised: 1972. **Equity Capital Needed:** $60,000-
$75,000 personal investment. **Franchise Fee:**
$30,000. **Financial Assistance:** Yes **Training:** 4
weeks training at the Meineke University Campus in
Charlotte, NC. In addition, Meineke provides Continuous field supervision and group operational meetings. is open, franchisees receive ongoing sales
analysis and operational analysis, including personnel, facility, service and sales review. Dealers also
receive customer service assistance in the form of
counseling and mediation assistance.

14588 ■ Merlin 200,000 Mile Shops
3815 E Main St., Ste. D
  Saint Charles, IL 60174
URL: http://www.merlins.com

Description: Provider of automotive repair services.
Founded: 1975. **Franchised:** 1975. **Financial Assistance:** Yes **Training:** 6 week management training program at training center and selected company-
operated shops. Each franchisee receives a minimum
of four visits/year by field personnel as well as manuals, ongoing electronic and printed communications,
ongoing training, employee recruitment programs,
etc.

14589 ■ Midas Inc.
1150 E Rand Rd.
  Arlington Heights, IL 60004
Ph: (847)481-8902
URL: http://www.midas.com
X (Twitter): x.com/midas
YouTube: www.youtube.com/mymidasguy
Description: Wholesaler of mufflers, brakes, exhaust
and suspension systems. **Founded:** 1956. **Training:**
Onsite participation with certified technicians, shop
managers and owners. 2 week training program at
Midas Institute of Technology in Palatine, IL. We want
to share with you the best of what we've learned
before you even open your bays for business.

14590 ■ Mighty Distributing System of America Inc.
650 Engineering Dr.
  Norcross, GA 30092
Free: 800-829-3900
Co. E-mail: info@mightyautoparts.com
URL: http://www.mightyautoparts.com
Contact: Josh D'Agostino, President
Facebook: www.facebook.com/MightyAutoParts
Linkedin: www.linkedin.com/company/mightyau
  toparts
X (Twitter): x.com/theMightyPros
Instagram: www.instagram.com/mightyautoparts
YouTube: www.youtube.com/MightyAutoParts
Description: Wholesale suppliers of automotive parts
for the automotive industry. **Founded:** 1963. **Royalty
Fee:** 5%. **Training:** Offers 4-5 days at headquarters,
5-10 days at franchisee's location with ongoing sup-
port.

14591 ■ Milex Complete Auto Care
11524 W 183rd Pl., Ste. 100
  Orland Park, IL 60467
Free: 888-227-8468
Co. E-mail: info@milexcompleteautocare.com
URL: http://milexcompleteautocare.com
Contact: Peter Baldine, President
Facebook: www.facebook.com/MilexCompleteAu
  toCare
Linkedin: www.linkedin.com/company/milex-complete
  -auto-care
X (Twitter): x.com/my_milex
YouTube: www.youtube.com/channel/UCZ
  36Y9rT7AoJ9Y6Z-d-K2XQ
Description: Provider of automotive repair and
maintenance services. **Founded:** 1963. **Franchised:**
1967. **Financial Assistance:** Yes **Training:** Yes.

14592 ■ Mister Transmission International Ltd.
9555 Yonge St., Ste. 204
  Richmond Hill, ON, Canada L4C 9M5
Ph: (905)884-1511
Free: 800-373-8432
Fax: (905)884-4727
Co. E-mail: info@mistertransmission.com
URL: http://www.mistertransmission.com
Contact: Tony Kuczynski, President
Facebook: www.facebook.com/MisterTransmissionIn
  ternational
Linkedin: www.linkedin.com/company/mister
  -transmission-international
X (Twitter): x.com/mistransmission
YouTube: www.youtube.com/channel/UC29Y
  6qKSMFVutyBrZAdfKVg
Description: Provider of transmission maintenance,
repair and vehicle transmission technological ser-
vices. **Founded:** 1963. **Training:** Yes.

14593 ■ Mr. Lube
2330-6900 Graybar Rd.
  Richmond, BC, Canada V6W 0A5

Ph: (604)759-4300
Co. E-mail: info@mrlube.com
URL: http://www.mrlube.com
Contact: Stuart Suls, President
X (Twitter): x.com/mrlube
Description: Provider of automotive services such
as oil changes and other scheduled maintenance
services. **Founded:** 1976. **Training:** 3 months train-
ing.

14594 ■ Mr. Transmission
1524 W 183rd Pl.
  Orland Park, IL 60467
Free: 888-227-8468
Co. E-mail: info@mrtransmission.com
URL: http://mrtransmission.com
Facebook: www.facebook.com/
  MrTransmissionProfessionals
Linkedin: www.linkedin.com/company/mr
  --transmission
X (Twitter): x.com/my_mrtrans
Instagram: www.instagram.com/mr.transmission
YouTube: www.youtube.com/channel/UCZ
  36Y9rT7AoJ9Y6Z-d-K2XQ
Description: Transmission repair and services. **No.
of Franchise Units:** 102. **No. of Company-Owned
Units:** 1. **Founded:** 1956. **Franchised:** 1976. **Equity
Capital Needed:** $165,281-$211,835. **Franchise
Fee:** $30,000. **Royalty Fee:** 7%. **Financial As-
sistance:** Yes **Training:** Offers 2 weeks at headquarters, 3 weeks at franchisee's location, 1 week operations visit at location when open with ongoing
support.

14595 ■ Precision Tune Auto Care Inc.
Icahn Enterprises L.P.
  748 Miller Dr. SE
  Leesburg, VA 20175
Ph: (703)422-4100
Free: 800-255-2737
URL: http://www.ielp.com
Description: Firm provides automotive repairs and
maintenance services. **Founded:** 1975. **Training:**
Yes.

14596 ■ Speedy Transmission Centers
330 N Congress Ave.
  Delray Beach, FL 33445
Ph: (561)404-7740
URL: http://www.speedytransmissiondelray.com
Description: Firm provides repair, replacement and
servicing of components to the automotive drive train,
including transmission repair, automatic and standard.
Founded: 1983. **Financial Assistance:** Yes **Training:** Franchisee attends a 3 week training course in
either Atlanta, GA or Boca Raton, FL. Included in this
period is 1 week of classroom operational training.
Training can vary depending on the background and
experience of the franchisee. Ongoing management
training classes are provided by the franchisor in local
areas.

14597 ■ Tilden Your Total Car Care Centers
Tilden Associates
  1025 Old Country Rd., Ste. No. 425
  Westbury, NY 11590
Ph: (516)746-7911
Free: 800-845-3367
Fax: (516)746-1288
Contact: Robert Baskind, President
Description: Offers maintenance and repair services
for automobiles. **No. of Franchise Units:** 41.
Founded: 1923. **Franchised:** 1996. **Equity Capital
Needed:** $155,433-$200,133. **Franchise Fee:**
$29,900. **Royalty Fee:** 6%. **Financial Assistance:**
Yes **Training:** Offers 2 weeks at headquarters, 1
week at franchisee's location and ongoing as needed.

14598 ■ Transmission Depot
2006 Hwy. 7, Unit 3
  Concord, ON, Canada L4K 1W6
Ph: (905)761-1616
Co. E-mail: info@transmissiondepot.ca
URL: http://transmissiondepot.ca
Facebook: www.facebook.com/people/Transmission
  -Depot/100082079637600

Description: Provider of transmission and complete automotive repair services. **Founded:** 1996. **Financial Assistance:** Yes **Training:** Yes.

14599 ■ Tuffy Tire & Auto Service Centers
7150 Granite Cir.
 Toledo, OH 43617
Ph: (419)865-6900
Free: 800-228-8339
URL: http://www.tuffy.com
Contact: Roger W. Hill, President
URL(s): tuffyfranchising.com
Facebook: www.facebook.com/Tuffy
YouTube: www.youtube.com/user/TuffyAutoService
Description: Provider of automotive repairing services. **Founded:** 1970. **Financial Assistance:** Yes **Training:** 3 weeks initial training and ongoing support.

14600 ■ Tunex, Inc.
745 S 1950 W
 Springville, UT 84663
Free: 855-998-8639
Co. E-mail: info@tunex.com
URL: http://tunex.com
Contact: Clay Liston, Owner
Description: Provider of full car services include air conditioning, brake, electrical system. **Founded:** 1974. **Financial Assistance:** Yes **Training:** 2 weeks initial training and 1 week during start-up of franchisee's business.

14601 ■ Valvoline Instant Oil Change (VIOC)
Valvoline Inc.
 100 Valvoline Way
 Lexington, KY 40509

Ph: (859)357-7777
Free: 800-832-6825
Co. E-mail: feedback@valvoline.com
URL: http://www.valvoline.com
Contact: David Fint, Contact
Facebook: www.facebook.com/viocofficial
Description: Provider of oil changes and maintenance services. **Founded:** 1986. **Training:** Yes.

14602 ■ Ziebart International Corporation
1290 E Maple Rd.
 Troy, MI 48083
Co. E-mail: info@ziebartworld.com
URL: http://www.ziebartworld.com
Contact: Thomas E. Wolfe, President
Linkedin: www.linkedin.com/company/ziebart-international
Instagram: www.instagram.com/ziebartinternational
YouTube: www.youtube.com/user/ziebartinternational
Description: Firm offers automobile detailing and automotive protection services. **No. of Franchise Units:** 400. **Founded:** 1959. **Franchised:** 1959. **Financial Assistance:** Yes **Training:** Yes.

COMPUTERIZED DATABASES

14603 ■ *Audatex Collision Estimating Database*
Availability: Print. **Type:** Software.

LIBRARIES

14604 ■ Automotive Service Association (ASA) - Library
8209 Mid Cities Blvd., Ste. 100
 North Richland Hills, TX 76182-4712

Ph: (817)514-2900
Co. E-mail: info@asashop.org
URL: http://www.asashop.org
Contact: Ray Fisher, Executive Director
E-mail: rayf@asashop.org
Facebook: www.facebook.com/ASAshop
Linkedin: www.linkedin.com/company/automotive-service-association
X (Twitter): x.com/asashop
Instagram: www.instagram.com/asa_national
YouTube: www.youtube.com/user/asawebops
Description: Serves the needs of mechanical, transmission, and collision shop owners through education and representation on legislation affecting the automotive service industry. **Scope:** Automobiles; repair. **Founded:** 1951. **Holdings:** Figures not available. **Publications:** *AutoInc.* (Bimonthly). **Educational Activities:** Congress of Automotive Repair and Service (CARS) (Annual); International Autobody Congress and Exposition - NACE (Annual). **Geographic Preference:** National.

14605 ■ Western Maryland Regional Library (WMRL)
100 S Potomac St.
 Hagerstown, MD 21740
Ph: (301)739-3250
Co. E-mail: whilbr@washcolibrary.org
URL: http://www.wmrl.info
Contact: Jenny Bakos, Executive Director
E-mail: wcfl@washcolibrary.org
Facebook: www.facebook.com/whilbr
Scope: History. **Services:** Interlibrary loan; copying; library open to the public with restrictions. **Founded:** 1967. **Holdings:** Figures not available.

ASSOCIATIONS AND OTHER ORGANIZATIONS

14606 ■ NASSCO
5285 Westview Dr., Ste. 202
Frederick, MD 21703
Ph: (301)624-2400
Co. E-mail: info@nassco.org
URL: http://nassco.org
Contact: Max Gowdy, President
Facebook: www.facebook.com/sewersavvy
Linkedin: www.linkedin.com/company/nasscoinc
YouTube: www.youtube.com/channel/UCf
   -h9NrhmosfuF6kXDbgwdQ

Description: Companies providing services including sewer evaluation, cleaning, inspection, and rehabilitation; manufacturers and suppliers of sewer service equipment; consulting engineers and municipal government officials. Serves as a forum for discussion of needs, ideas and information among members. Works to: improve standards and procedures for sewer evaluation, maintenance, rehabilitation and worker safety; promote members' services and assist in marketing sewer service of equipment, materials and supplies; educate owners, engineers and inspectors about sewer rehabilitation methods and procedures. Conducts training seminars in maintenance and rehabilitation, inspection and safety. Provides referral services. **Founded:** 1976. **Awards:** Jeffrey D. Ralston Memorial Scholarship. **Geographic Preference:** National.

14607 ■ Sump and Sewage Pump Manufacturers Association (SSPMA)
c/o Blake Jeffery, Managing Director
   PO Box 44071
   Indianapolis, IN 46244
Ph: (317)636-0278
Co. E-mail: hdqtrs@sspma.org
URL: http://www.sspma.org
Contact: Blake Jeffery, Managing Director
Facebook: www.facebook.com/pages/Sump-an
   d-Sewage-Pump-Manufacturers-Association/18
   4112338445952
YouTube: www.youtube.com/channel/UCQye8QG
   4Docsst1wt2pZlvw

Description: Manufacturers of residential sump pumps (cellar drainers) and sewage pumps. Seeks to: develop and promulgate quality standards; implement a certification and labeling program for all products conforming to these standards; investigate market size and activity; promote improved provisions in building codes on the use of sump and sewage pumps. **Founded:** 1956. **Geographic Preference:** National.

REFERENCE WORKS

14608 ■ *"Acing the Test" in Contractor (Vol. 57, January 2010, No. 1, pp. 32)*
Pub: Informa USA, Inc.
Contact: Stephen A. Carter, Chief Executive Officer

Ed: Robert P. Mader. **Released:** January 01, 2010. **Description:** A ward winning mechanical system retrofitting of a middle school in Ohio is discussed. The school now operates at 37,800 Btu/sq. ft and reduced a significant amount of pollutants from being emitted into the environment.

14609 ■ *"Be Wary of Dual-Flush Conversion Kits" in Contractor (Vol. 56, September 2009, No. 9, pp. 66)*
Ed: John Koeller, Bill Gauley. **Description:** Recommendation of untested dual-flush conversion devices for tank-type toilets in the United States has been questioned. The products are being advertised as having the ability to convert single-flush to a dual-flush toilet. No evidence of water conservation from using such devices has been recorded. **Availability:** Print; Online.

14610 ■ *"BIM and You: Know Its Benefits and Risks" in Contractor (Vol. 57, January 2010, No. 1, pp. 46)*
Ed: Susan Linden McGreevy. **Description:** Building Information Modeling is intended to be "collaborative" and this could raise legal issues if a contractor sends an electronic bid and it is filtered out. Other legal issues that mechanical contractors need to consider before using this technology are discussed. **Availability:** Print; Online.

14611 ■ *"Commercial Water Efficiency Initiatives Announced" in Contractor (Vol. 56, November 2009, No. 11, pp. 5)*
Ed: Robert P. Mader. **Description:** Plumbing engineers John Koeller and Bill Gauley are developing a testing protocol for commercial toilets. The team said commercial toilets should have a higher level of flush performance than residential toilets for certification. The Environmental Protection Agency's WaterSense program wants to expand the program into the commercial/institutional sector. **Availability:** Print; Online.

14612 ■ *"Corporate Park Retrofits for Water Savings" in Contractor (Vol. 56, October 2009, No. 10, pp. 5)*
Description: Merrit Corporate Park in Norwalk, Connecticut has been interested in improving building efficiency and one of their buildings has been retrofitted with water-efficient plumbing systems which will allow them to save as much as two million gallons of water. ADP Service Corp. helped the park upgrade their plumbing system. **Availability:** Online.

14613 ■ *"The Customer Is Always Right Even When He's Wrong" in Contractor (Vol. 57, February 2010, No. 2, pp. 12)*
Ed: Al Schwartz. **Description:** Mechanical contractors should note that customers will make a judgment based upon the impression that they form on their first meeting. Contractors can maintain a professional image by washing their trucks and having the personnel dress uniformly. Contractors have every right to demand that employees clean up and make a better impression on customers. **Availability:** Print; Online.

14614 ■ *"Ga. PMA Launches Online Education Program" in Contractor (Vol. 56, October 2009, No. 10, pp. 8)*
Description: Plumbing & Mechanical Association of Georgia launched an online program that covers technical and business management that will help contractors run their businesses. Future courses will include math for plumbers, graywater systems, and recession-proofing your business. **Availability:** Print; Online.

14615 ■ *"Got to be Smarter than the Average Bear" in Contractor (Vol. 56, September 2009, No. 9, pp. 82)*
Ed: Robert P. Mader. **Description:** International Association of Plumbing and Mechanical Officials Green Technical Committee has debated the need for contractors to have certifications in installing green plumbing. Some have argued that qualifications would discourage homeowners from improving their properties. Comments from executives are also included. **Availability:** Print; Online.

14616 ■ *"Grainger Show Highlights Building Green, Economic Recovery" in Contractor (Vol. 57, February 2010, No. 2, pp. 3)*
Ed: Candace Roulo. **Description:** Chief U.S. economist told attendees of the Grainger's 2010 Total MRO Solutions National Customer Show that the economic recovery would be subdued. Mechanical contractors who attended the event also learned about building sustainable, green products, and technologies, and economic and business challenges. **Availability:** Print; Online.

14617 ■ *"Hansen Mechanical Performs Boiler Upgrade at Zoo" in Contractor (Vol. 57, February 2010, No. 2, pp. 7)*
Description: Hansen Mechanical installed a donated boiler in the Brookfield Zoo from Weil-McLain. The boilers were installed in the zoo's 'The Swamp' and 'The Living Coast' exhibits. **Availability:** Print; Online.

14618 ■ *"Homebuilders Continue to be Our Nemesis" in Contractor (Vol. 56, July 2009, No. 7, pp. 50)*
Ed: Robert P. Mader. **Description:** Homebuilders rank high on the greed scale along with Wall Street brokers. There is this one instance when a builder gave copies of another contractor's quotes that have just been blackened out and another instance when one builder let other bidders visit a site while the current mechanical contractor is working. **Availability:** Print; Online.

14619 ■ *"How to Detect and Prevent Employee Fraud" in Contractor (Vol. 56, October 2009, No. 10, pp. 57)*
Ed: James R. Leichter. **Description:** Mechanical contractors can prevent employee fraud by handing out a detailed employment policy manual to their employees and making sure that their invoices are numbered. It is also highly advised to have bank statements reconciled by a third party. **Availability:** Print; Online.

14620 ■ *"IAPMO GTC Debates Supplement"*
in Contractor (Vol. 56, September 2009, No. 9,
pp. 3)

Ed: Robert P. Mader. **Description:** Green Technical Committee of the International Association of Plumbing and Mechanical Officials is developing a Green Plumbing and Mechanical Supplement. The supplement provides for installation of systems by licensed contractors and installers. Comments from officials are also presented. **Availability:** Print; Online.

14621 ■ *"IAPMO GTC Votes to Limit Showers*
to 2.0-GPM" in Contractor (Vol. 56, September
2009, No. 9, pp. 1)

Description: Green Technical Committee of the International Association of Plumbing and Mechanical Officials has voted to limit showers to 2.0 GPM. It is also developing a Green Plumbing and Mechanical Supplement. Comments from executives are also supplied. **Availability:** Print; Online.

14622 ■ *"IAPMO Seeks Group Participants" in*
Contractor (Vol. 56, September 2009, No. 9,
pp. 37)

Description: International Association of Plumbing and Mechanical Officials is accepting applications for task groups that will develop its Uniform Plumbing Code and Uniform Mechanical Code. The codes are developed using American National Standards Institute accredited consensus process. Task groups are assigned to address a specific topic or problem. **Availability:** Print; Online.

14623 ■ *"Keep Customers Out of the Yellow*
Pages" in Contractor (Vol. 56, November
2009, No. 11, pp. 47)

Ed: Matt Michel. **Description:** Mechanical contractors should keep customers away from the Yellow Pages where they could find their competition by putting stickers on the water heater or the front of the directory. Giving out magnets to customers and putting the company name on sink rings and invoices are other suggestions. **Availability:** Print; Online.

14624 ■ *"LA Passes HET Ordinance,*
California Greens Code" in Contractor (Vol.
56, September 2009, No. 9, pp. 1)

Ed: Candace Roulo. **Description:** Los Angeles City Council has passed a Water Efficiency Requirements ordinance. The law mandates lower low-flow plumbing requirements for plumbing fixtures installed in new buildings and retrofits. Under the ordinance, a toilet's maximum flush volume may not exceed 1.28-gpf. **Availability:** Print; Online.

14625 ■ *"The Latest on E-Verify" in*
Contractor (Vol. 56, September 2009, No. 9,
pp. 58)

Ed: Susan McGreevy. **Description:** United States government has required federal contractors to use its E-Verify program to verify the eligibility of incoming and existent employees. The use of the program is seen to eliminate Social Security mismatches. **Availability:** Print; Online.

14626 ■ *"Major Advances in Heat Pump*
Technology" in Contractor (Vol. 57, January
2010, No. 1, pp. 42)

Ed: Mark Eatherton. **Description:** Tax credits make ground-source heat pump technology more economically feasible. Suggestions on how to choose the right ground-source heat pump technology to install in a house are discussed. **Availability:** Print; Online.

14627 ■ *"Most Popular Tools? The Survey*
Says" in Contractor (Vol. 57, February 2010,
No. 2, pp. 1)

Ed: Robert P. Mader. **Description:** According to a survey of individuals in the field, mechanical contractors are purchasing more of their tools at home centers and they are also increasingly working in the service, repair, and retrofit markets. The survey also

found that the reciprocating saw is the most used corded power tool. Additional purchasing habits of mechanical contractors are listed. **Availability:** Print; Online.

14628 ■ *"A Necessary Balancing Act:*
Bookkeeping" in Contractor (Vol. 56,
November 2009, No. 11, pp. 22)

Ed: Al Schwartz. **Description:** Pros and cons of getting a bookkeeper or a certified public accountant for the subcontractor are discussed. A bookkeeper can help a subcontractor get new accounting software up and running while an accountant will more than likely keep after the books at regular intervals throughout the year. **Availability:** Print; Online.

14629 ■ *"Pre-Certified LEED Hotel Prototype*
Reduces Energy Use, Conserves Water" in
Contractor (Vol. 57, January 2010, No. 1, pp.
3)

Pub: Informa USA, Inc.

Contact: Stephen A. Carter, Chief Executive Officer

Ed: Candace Roulo. **Released:** January 01, 2010. **Description:** Marriott International Inc.'s LEED pre-certified prototype hotel will reduce a hotel's energy and water consumption by 25 percent and save owners approximately $100,000. Their Courtyard Settler's Ridge in Pittsburgh will be the first hotel built based on the prototype.

14630 ■ *"Public Bathroom Pressure Woes*
Resolved" in Contractor (Vol. 56, September
2009, No. 9, pp. 44)

Ed: Dave Yates. **Description:** Design and construction of a public bathroom's plumbing system in the United States are discussed. Installed plumbing fixtures with flush valves would not function properly. The installation of Grundfos SQE variable-speed pumps has resolved problems with the bathroom's water pressure. **Availability:** Print; Online.

14631 ■ *"Selling a Job When There's Buyer's*
Remorse" in Contractor (Vol. 56, December
2009, No. 12, pp. 37)

Ed: H. Kent Craig. **Description:** Advice on how contractors should manage low-profit jobs in the United States is presented. Efforts should be made to try and find at least one quality field foreman or superintendent. Contractors should also try to respectfully renegotiate the terms of the job. **Availability:** Online.

14632 ■ *"Sewage from RVs May Be*
Contaminating Waterways, Seattle
Businesses Warn" in King5News (October 24,
2019)

URL(s): www.king5.com/article/news/sewage-from -rvs-may-be-contaminating-waterways/281-717e50 5f-57e7-4de1-957d-349ee97946a4

Ed: Ted Land. **Released:** October 24, 2019. **Description:** Seattle Public Utilities ran tests in SODO and found elevated fecal coliform levels, which was due to incorrect private sewer connections. Locals fear that these elevated levels are due to people living in nearby RVs who have nowhere to dump their waste. **Availability:** Online.

14633 ■ *"Three Productivity Solutions" in*
Contractor (Vol. 57, February 2010, No. 2, pp.
26)

Ed: William Feldman, Patti Feldman. **Description:** Singletouch is a real-time data capture solution for mechanical and other contractors that work in jobs that require materials and workload tracking. Contractors get information on extreme weather and sudden changes in the cost of materials. The OptimumHVAC optimization software by Optimum Energy is designed to optimize energy savings in commercial buildings. **Availability:** Print; Online.

14634 ■ *"Tracking Your Fleet Can Increase*
Bottom Line" in Contractor (Vol. 56,
November 2009, No. 11, pp. 26)

Ed: Candace Roulo. **Description:** GPS fleet management system can help boost a contractor's profits, employee productivity, and efficiency. These are available as a handheld device or a cell phone that employees carry around or as a piece of hardware installed in a vehicle. These lets managers track assets and communicate with employees about jobs. **Availability:** Online.

14635 ■ *"Trade Craft: Take Pride in Your*
Trade, Demand Excellence" in Contractor
(Vol. 56, October 2009, No. 10, pp. 24)

Ed: Al Schwartz. **Description:** There is a need for teaching, developing, and encouraging trade craft. An apprentice plumber is not only versed in the mechanical aspects of the trade but he also has a working knowledge of algebra, trigonometry, chemistry, and thermal dynamics. Contractors should be demanding on their personnel regarding their trade craft and should only keep and train the very best people they can hire. **Availability:** Print; Online.

14636 ■ *"Train Now to Get the Competitive*
Edge" in Contractor (Vol. 56, October 2009,
No. 10, pp. 58)

Ed: Merry Beth Hall. **Description:** Due to the harsh economic climate, mechanical contractors would be well-served to train their employees while they have time to take them out of the field. This will help ensure that they are not behind when the economic recovery happens. Suggestions on how to choose the best type of training are presented. **Availability:** Print; Online.

14637 ■ *"Use Social Media to Enhance*
Brand, Business" in Contractor (Vol. 56,
December 2009, No. 12, pp. 14)

Ed: Elton Rivas. **Description:** Advice on how plumbing contractors should use online social networks to increase sales is presented including such issues as clearly defining goals and target audience. An additional advantage to this medium is that advertisements can easily be shared with other users.

14638 ■ *"Water Efficiency Bills Move*
Through Congress" in Contractor (Vol. 56,
July 2009, No. 7, pp. 20)

Ed: Kevin Schwalb. **Description:** National Association, a plumbing-heating-cooling contractor, was instrumental in drafting the Water Advanced Technologies for Efficient Resource Use Act of 2009 and they are also backing the Water Accountability Tax Efficiency Reinvestment Act. The first bill promotes WaterSense-labeled products while the other promotes water conservation through tax credits. **Availability:** Print; Online.

STATISTICAL SOURCES

14639 ■ *Portable Toilet Rental & Septic Tank*
Cleaning Industry in the US - Market
Research Report

URL(s): www.ibisworld.com/united-states/market-re search-reports/portable-toilet-rental-septic-tank -cleaning-industry/

Price: $925. **Description:** Downloadable report analyzing current and future trends in the portable toilet rental and septic tank cleaning industry. **Availability:** Download.

TRADE PERIODICALS

14640 ■ *Contractor Connection*

Pub: Indiana Association of Plumbing Heating Cooling Contractors

Contact: Tyler Frame, President

URL(s): www.iaphcc.com/contractor-connection

Released: Quarterly; Jan/Feb/Mar; Apr/May/June; July/Aug/Sept; and Oct/Nov/Dec. **Description:** Official publication of the Indiana Association of Plumbing, Heating, Cooling Contractors, Inc. **Availability:** Print; PDF.

FRANCHISES AND BUSINESS OPPORTUNITIES

14641 ■ Rooter-Man
North Billerica, MA
Ph: (978)667-7771

Free: 866-577-1221
Co. E-mail: info@rooterman.com
URL: http://rooterman.com
Contact: Vincent MacDonald, President
Facebook: www.facebook.com/RooterManToTheRescue
Linkedin: www.linkedin.com/company/rooter-man
X (Twitter): x.com/RooterMan
Instagram: www.instagram.com/officialrooterman
YouTube: www.youtube.com/channel/UCE 6fGXGOAs7L3Nhm0Nil9uQ
Description: A successful and proven system built around the exclusive use of the Rooter-Man Trade-mark territory. With your license you will have access to the management skills and know how of professionals who have had years of experience in the plumbing, and drain clearing industries. **No. of Franchise Units:** 445. **Founded:** 1970. **Franchised:** 1981. **Equity Capital Needed:** $25,000. **Franchise Fee:** $7,950. **Financial Assistance:** Yes **Training:** A complete 2 day training program devoted to advanced techniques in both practical and management training. Training will consist of 2 days at various locations across the country. Provides unlimited ongoing support by personal coach.

ASSOCIATIONS AND OTHER ORGANIZATIONS

14642 ■ American Needlepoint Guild (ANG)
100 E Washington
Springfield, IL 62701
Ph: (856)380-6911
Fax: (856)439-0525
Co. E-mail: ang@needlepoint.org
URL: http://www.needlepoint.org
Contact: Carley Linn, President
E-mail: president@needlepoint.org
Facebook: www.facebook.com/AmericanNeedlepoin
tGuild
Instagram: www.instagram.com/ang_needlepoint
Pinterest: www.pinterest.com/AmericanNeedlepoin
tGuild

Description: Provides educational and cultural development through participation in and encouragement of interest in needlepoint. Sponsors needlework exhibits; offers correspondence courses and teacher and judging certification programs. **Founded:** 1972. **Publications:** *Needle Pointers* (6/year). **Educational Activities:** American Needlepoint Guild Show (Annual). **Geographic Preference:** Multinational.

14643 ■ American Sewing Guild (ASG)
9660 Hillcroft, Ste. 510
Houston, TX 77096
Ph: (713)729-3000
Fax: (713)721-9230
Co. E-mail: info@asg.org
URL: http://www.asg.org
Contact: Margo Martin, Executive Director
Facebook: www.facebook.com/sewingguild
Instagram: www.instagram.com/asguildhq
YouTube: www.youtube.com/channel/
UCaNyoekwXVAJMn18tS4mUsg
Pinterest: www.pinterest.com/asghq

Description: Home sewers and people interested in sewing. Provides current sewing information and advice through lectures, demonstrations, classes, seminars, and fashion shows. Seeks to improve communication between home sewers and sewing industry. Encourages the development of neighborhood workshop groups. **Founded:** 1978. **Geographic Preference:** National.

REFERENCE WORKS

14644 ■ *4 Mistakes to Avoid When Starting a Sewing Business*
Description: Starting a sewing business can be a big step to securing your financial independence. Though much of your success will depend on your skills, you also must be a creative and skilled entrepreneur for your business to succeed. This article covers some common mistakes to avoid when getting started in the business of sewing. **Availability:** Online.

14645 ■ *"10 Ways to Make Money Sewing"* in *Sew My Place* (April 5, 2016)
Released: April 05, 2016. **Description:** This article discusses five different sewing businesses you can start right now, whether you're a newbie or a sewing master. Also includes tips on how to get your business up and running and how to turn a profit. **Availability:** Online.

14646 ■ *11 Best Embroidery Machines for Small Business*
Description: For those running their own sewing and embroidery business, having good equipment is a necessity. This article details the top 11 embroidery machines that can be used for commercial purposes. **Availability:** Online.

14647 ■ *"50 Best Home Sewing Business Ideas for 2021"* in *Profitable Venture Magazine*
Ed: Ajaero Tony Martins. **Description:** Provides fifty ways you can showcase your passion for sewing and earn money while doing it. **Availability:** Online.

14648 ■ *"50 Things to Sew and Sell"* in *Small Business Trends* (October 9, 2019)
Ed: Annie Pilon. **Released:** October 09, 2019. **Description:** If you know how to sew, you're well on your way to starting a successful business. This article lists a variety of products you can sew and sell online, at local craft fairs, and in retail boutiques. **Availability:** Online.

14649 ■ *Business Opportunities for People Who Sew at Home*
Ed: Kelly Cardenas. **Released:** January 25, 2020. **Description:** If you are a sewing enthusiast, you can start a rewarding career from your living room. This article provides ideas to consider as you decide what to specialize in. **Availability:** Online.

14650 ■ *"How I Make $10K/Month Selling Printable Sewing Patterns from My Fashion Blog"* in *Starter Story* Website (July 26, 2020)
Ed: Lisa Miller-Mecham. **Released:** July 26, 2020. **Description:** Lisa Miller-Mecham, award-winning fashion designer and DIY blogger, tells the story of her career which has brought her to making a good living selling sewing patterns online. **Availability:** Online.

14651 ■ *How to Make Money in the Sewing Business*
Ed: Miki Markovich. **Description:** Before you can make money in the sewing business, you must decide where to concentrate your efforts. This article details how to choose an appropriate specialty, how to sell and market, how to create a portfolio, and how to stand out from the competition. **Availability:** Online.

14652 ■ *"How to Start My Own Sewing Business"* in *Chron* (February 12, 2019)
Ed: Jessica Jones. **Released:** February 12, 2019. **Description:** For those who enjoy sewing, creating interesting clothing patterns or performing alterations

and tailoring, starting a sewing business may be the perfect opportunity for you. This article discusses how to create a business plan, how to take care of paperwork, where to make space for your work, what tools you'll need, how to prepare a portfolio, and how to find clients and market your business. **Availability:** Online.

14653 ■ *"How-To Workshops in St. Charles Teach Sewing, Styles"* in *St. Louis Post-Dispatch* (September 14, 2010)
Pub: St. Louis Post-Dispatch LLC.
Contact: Gilbert Bailon, Editor
E-mail: gbailon@post-dispatch.com
Ed: Kalen Ponche. **Description:** Profile of DIY Style Workshop in St. Charles, Missouri, where sewing, designing and teaching is offered. The shop is home base for DIY Style, a Website created by mother and daughter to teach younger people how to sew. **Availability:** Online.

14654 ■ *"Jo-Ann Fabric and Craft Stores Joins ArtFire.com to Offer Free Online Craft Marketplace"* in *Marketwired* (January 26, 2010)
Pub: Comtex News Network Inc.
Contact: Kan Devnani, President
Description: Jo-Ann Fabric and Craft Stores has entered into a partnership with ArtFire.com which will provide sewers and crafters all the tools they need in order to make and sell their products from an online venue. **Availability:** Print; Online.

14655 ■ *"Jo-Ann Launches Quilt Your Colors Contest to Celebrate National Sewing Month"* in *Marketwired* (September 10, 2010)
Pub: Comtex News Network Inc.
Contact: Kan Devnani, President
Description: Jo-Ann Fabric and Craft Stores featured a contest to create a quilt in order to promote National Sewing Month.

14656 ■ *"Make It Yourself: Home Sewing, Gender, and Culture, 1890-1930"* in *Business History Review* (Vol. 84, Autumn 2010, No. 3, pp. 602)
Description: Review of the publication, 'Make It Yourself: Home Sewing, Gender, and Culture, 1890-1930, a nonfiction work. **Availability:** Download; PDF; Online.

14657 ■ *"The Ode: S. M. Whitney Co. (1868 – 2010)"* in *Canadian Business* (Vol. 83, October 12, 2010, No. 17, pp. 27)
Pub: Rogers Media Inc.
Contact: Neil Spivak, Chief Executive Officer
Ed: Angelina Chapin. **Released:** October 12, 2010. **Description:** A history of S.M. Whitney Company is presented. The cotton company was opened in 1868. The cotton is sold to textile manufacturers after crops have been picked, ginned and baled. The company closed down in 2010 after chief executive officer Barry Whitney decided to sell his last bale of cotton. **Availability:** Print; Online.

14658 ■ *"Readers Share How Sewing Shaped the Fabric of Their Lives" in Virginian-Pilot (September 14, 2010)*
Pub: The Virginian-Pilot
Contact: Kevin Goyette, Director
E-mail: kgoyette@dailypress.com

Ed: Jamesetta M. Walker. **Description:** People discuss the ways sewing has help enrich their lives, from public service projects and conventions centered on sewing. **Availability:** Print; Online.

14659 ■ *"Sewing Is a Life Skill; Teaching To Sew Is An Art" in Virginia-Pilot (August 31, 2010)*
Pub: The Virginian-Pilot
Contact: Kevin Goyette, Director
E-mail: kgoyette@dailypress.com

Ed: Jamesetta M. Walker. **Description:** In conjunction with National Sewing Month, the American Sew-ing Guild is sponsoring a two-day workshop featuring Stephanie Kimura. **Availability:** Print; Online.

TRADE SHOWS AND CONVENTIONS

14660 ■ **IFAI Expo**
Tarp Association (TA)
   1801 County Rd. B W, Ste. 100
   Roseville, MN 55113-4052
URL: http://tarp.textiles.org
Contact: Amy Collins, Director, Sales and Marketing
E-mail: amy.collins@textiles.org
URL(s): advancedtextilesexpo.com
X (Twitter): twitter.com/IFAIExpo

Frequency: Annual. **Description:** Industrial and commercial fabric equipment, supplies, and services. **Audience:** Industry professionals. **Principal Exhibits:** Industrial and commercial fabric equipment, supplies, and services. Dates and Locations: 2025 Nov 05-07 Indianapolis. **Telecommunication Services:** amy.collins@textiles.org.

FRANCHISES AND BUSINESS OPPORTUNITIES

14661 ■ **Color-Glo International**
Minneapolis, MN
Ph: (952)835-1338
Co. E-mail: info@colorglo.com
URL: http://colorglo.com
Contact: Gary E. Smith, President
X (Twitter): x.com/ColorGlo
Instagram: www.instagram.com/colorglointernational
YouTube: www.youtube.com/channel/
   UCx0VuYqEDqEN7oExUISmS2A

Description: Fabric re-dyeing and restoration service franchises. **Founded:** 1976. **Financial Assistance:** No **Training:** Yes.

ASSOCIATIONS AND OTHER ORGANIZATIONS

14662 ■ Shoe Service Institute of America (SSIA)
20 Danada Sq. W, No. 234
  Wheaton, IL 60189
Ph: (410)569-3425
Fax: (410)569-8333
URL: http://www.ssia.info
Contact: Mark Dorothy, President
E-mail: markedorothy@gmail.com

Description: Finders (wholesalers) of shoe repair supplies and equipment. Supplier members are manufacturers, tanners and distributors. **Founded:** 1904. **Publications:** *Shoe Service Institute of America--Membership Directory.* **Awards:** SSIA Robert DiRinaldo Grand Silver Cup (Irregular). **Geographic Preference:** National.

REFERENCE WORKS

14663 ■ *"Cobblers Face Extinction — and Are Busier Than Ever" in U.S. News & World Report (March 23, 2019)*
URL(s): www.usnews.com/news/best-states/
  pennsylvania/articles/2019-03-23/cobblers-face-ex
  tinction-and-are-busier-than-ever
Ed: Diana Nelson Jones. **Released:** March 23, 2019. **Description:** Even though shoe repair shops have drastically dwindled over the years, there is still plenty of work. So much so, that the cobblers who remain can't keep up with the workload. Very few people enter the cobbler business, so those that remain handle the orders as best they can. **Availability:** Online.

STATISTICAL SOURCES

14664 ■ *Shoe Repair Industry in the US - Market Research Report*
URL(s): www.ibisworld.com/united-states/market-re
  search-reports/shoe-repair-industry/
Price: $925. **Description:** Downloadable report analyzing current and future trends in the shoe repair industry. **Availability:** Download.

START-UP INFORMATION

14665 ■ *"Stepping Out" in Small Business Opportunities (Get Rich At Home 2010)*
Description: Earn $1 million a year selling flip flops? A Flip Flop Shop franchise will help individuals start their own business. **Availability:** Print; Online.

14666 ■ *"Well-Heeled Startup Plots Course for a Run at Garmin" in Business Journal Portland (Vol. 27, November 12, 2010, No. 37, pp. 1)*
Pub: Portland Business Journal
Contact: Andy Giegerich, Managing Editor
E-mail: agiegerich@bizjournals.com

Description: Oh! Shoes LLC expects to receive about $1.5 million in funding from angel investors, while marketing a new line of high heel shoes that are comfortable, healthy, and attractive. The new line of shoes will use the technology of athletic footwear while having the look of an Italian designer. Oh! Shoes hopes to generate $35 million in sales by 2014. **Availability:** Print; Online.

ASSOCIATIONS AND OTHER ORGANIZATIONS

14667 ■ **Footwear Distributors and Retailers of America (FDRA)**
1319 F St. NW, Ste. 700
 Washington, DC 20004
Ph: (202)737-5660
Fax: (202)645-0789
Co. E-mail: info@fdra.org
URL: http://fdra.org
Contact: Matt Priest, President
E-mail: mpriest@fdra.org
Facebook: www.facebook.com/FDRADC
Linkedin: www.linkedin.com/company/fdra
X (Twitter): x.com/FDRA
Instagram: www.Instagram.com/fdra1944

Description: Volume shoe store chains. Conducts traffic, foreign sourcing, customs, leadership and employment relations' seminars. **Founded:** 1944. **Publications:** *Shoe Stats*; *Footwear Distributors and Retailers of America--Membership Listing Online*. **Geographic Preference:** National.

14668 ■ **National Shoe Retailers Association (NSRA)**
7386 N La Cholla Blvd.
 Tucson, AZ 85741
Ph: (520)209-1710
Co. E-mail: memberservices@nsra.org
URL: http://www.nsra.org
Contact: Mark Denkler, President
Facebook: www.facebook.com/NationalShoeRe
 tailersAssociation
Linkedin: www.linkedin.com/company/national-shoe
 -retailers-association
Instagram: www.instagram.com/nationalshoere
 tailersassoc

Description: Proprietors of independent shoe stores and stores with major shoe departments. Provides business services and professional development programs including bankcard processing, shipping, freight discounts, free website listing, employee training; conducts research; monitors legislation. **Founded:** 1912. **Publications:** *Business Performance Report (BPR)*; *Shoe Retailing Today* (Bimonthly). **Educational Activities:** NSRA Education Conference (Semiannual); NSRA Leadership Conference (Annual); The Atlanta Shoe Market (TASM) (Semiannual). **Awards:** NSRA Retailer of the Year Award (Annual). **Geographic Preference:** National.

14669 ■ **Pedorthic Footcare Association (PFA)**
8736 SE 165th Mulberry Ln., Unit 206
 The Villages, FL 32162
Ph: (229)389-3440
Co. E-mail: info@pedorthics.org
URL: http://www.pedorthics.org
Contact: Giuseppe Lombardo, President
E-mail: g.lombardo@pfabod.org
Facebook: www.facebook.com/Pedorthic-Footcare
 -Association-107051868682076
Linkedin: www.linkedin.com/in/pedorthic-footcare
 -association-66a58a53
X (Twitter): x.com/pfapedorthics
Instagram: www.instagram.com/pedorthicfoo
 tcareassociation
YouTube: www.youtube.com/channel/UC
 -w9u0npeQsTAZFs4VQh62w

Description: Professionals involved in the field of pedorthics. (Pedorthics is the design, manufacture, fit and modification of shoes and foot orthoses to alleviate foot problems caused by disease, overuse, or injury). **Founded:** 1958. **Educational Activities:** Pedorthic Footcare Association Annual Symposium and Exposition (Annual). **Awards:** PFA Vendor of the Year (Annual); PFA Seymour Lefton Award (Annual). **Geographic Preference:** Multinational.

14670 ■ **United Shoe Retailers Association (USRA)**
23890 Copperhill Dr., Ste. 444
 Valencia, CA 91354
Ph: (661)367-4816
URL: http://usraonline.org
Contact: Linda Hauss, Executive Director
E-mail: linda@usraonline.org
Facebook: www.facebook.com/UnitedShoeRe
 tailersAssn
X (Twitter): x.com/USRA_Shoes
Instagram: www.instagram.com/usrashoes
Pinterest: www.pinterest.com/unitedshoe

Description: Represents and promotes the independent shoe retailer. **Founded:** 1977. **Educational Activities:** United Shoe Retailers Association Seminar. **Geographic Preference:** National.

REFERENCE WORKS

14671 ■ *"11 Minutes That Rocked the Sneaker World" in Business Journal Portland (Vol. 30, February 14, 2014, No. 50, pp. 8)*
Pub: American City Business Journals, Inc.
Contact: Mike Olivieri, Executive Vice President

Released: Weekly. **Price:** $4, Introductory 4-week offer(Digital & Print). **Description:** The sale of the Nike Air Yeezy 2, the latest shoes from a partnership with artist Kanye West, sparked a social media debate on the importance of limited edition shoes for the Nike brand. The shoes sold out in 11 minutes and made their way to eBay for as much as $10,000. **Availability:** Print; Online.

14672 ■ *"Adidas' Brand Ambitions" in Business Journal Portland (Vol. 27, December 10, 2010, No. 41, pp. 1)*
Pub: Portland Business Journal
Contact: Andy Giegerich, Managing Editor
E-mail: agiegerich@bizjournals.com

Ed: Erik Siemers. **Description:** Adidas AG, the second-largest sporting goods brand in the world, hopes to increase global revenue by 50 percent by 2015. The German company, which reported $14.5 billion sales, plans to improve its U.S. market. The U.S. is Adidas' largest, but also the most underperforming market for the firm. **Availability:** Print; Online.

14673 ■ *"Blazing Trails Placing One Foot in Front of the Other" in Minority Business Entrepreneur (Vol. 39, Fall, 2022, No. 4, pp. 42-44)*
URL(s): digital.mbemag.com/?m=53732&i=769780
 &p=42&ver=html5

Ed: Alexa Peters. **Price:** $7.95. **Description:** Profile on Gloria and Keith Scott, a mother and son duo who formed a small business with a focus on foot thongs. **Availability:** Print; Online.

14674 ■ *"Design program in Athletic Footwear" in Occupational Outlook Quarterly (Vol. 55, Fall 2011, No. 3, pp. 21)*
Description: The Fashion Institute of Technology offers the only certificate program in performance athletic footwear design in the U.S. The program focuses on conceptualizing and sketching shoe designs and covers ergonomic, anatomical, and material considerations for athletic footwear design. **Availability:** Print; Online.

14675 ■ *"Funky Footwear: Walk This Way" in Barron's (Vol. 90, August 23, 2010, No. 34, pp. 13)*
Pub: Barron's Editorial & Corporate Headquarters

Ed: Christopher C. Williams. **Description:** Crocs and Skechers are selling very popular shoes and sales show no signs of winding down. The shares of both companies are attractively prices. **Availability:** Online.

14676 ■ *"How I Did It: Zappos's CEO on Going to Extremes for Customers" in Harvard Business Review (Vol. 88, July-August 2010, No. 7-8, pp. 41)*
Pub: Harvard Business Publishing
Contact: Diane Belcher, Managing Director

Ed: Tony Hsieh. **Price:** $8.95, PDF. **Description:** Footwear firm Zappos.com Inc. improved corporate performance through enhanced customer service. Enhancements include highly visible phone numbers, avoidance of scripts, and viewing call centers as marketing departments. **Availability:** Online; PDF.

14677 ■ "In My Shoes: A Memoir"
Pub: Portfolio Hardcover
Contact: Adrian Zackheim, President
Released: October 01, 2013. **Price:** $3.48, kindle; $32.80, hardcover; $0.25, hardcover(49 used from $0.25); $25.60, hardcover (6 new from $25.60); $8.86, paperback; $1.55, paperback(93 used from $1.55); $4.01, paperback(49 new from $4.01). **Description:** Profile of Tamara Mellon, woman entrepreneur who built Jimmy Choo into a premier name in the global fashion industry. She addresses her family life, her battles with anxiety and depression, as well as time spend in rehabilitation. She shares her entire life story from her work as a young editor at Vogue to her partnership with shoemaker, Jimmy Choo to her public relationships. She confides what it was like working with an obstinate business partner but also her ability to understand what customers want. **Availability:** E-book; Print; Audio.

14678 ■ "Jordan Still Soaring" in Business Journal Portland (Vol. 30, January 17, 2014, No. 46, pp. 7)
Pub: American City Business Journals, Inc.
Contact: Mike Olivieri, Executive Vice President
Released: Weekly. **Price:** $4, introductory 4-week offer(Digital only). **Description:** Nike Inc. is planning to open retail stores that will exclusively sell Jordan Brand merchandise. The company is seeking to grow its direct-to-consumer sales to $8 billion by 2017. Nike's capital spending is also expected to increase by 3 to 4 percent. **Availability:** Print; Online.

14679 ■ "Laced Up and Ready to Run" in Barron's (Vol. 89, July 6, 2009, No. 27, pp. 12)
Pub: Dow Jones & Company Inc.
Contact: Almar Latour, Chief Executive Officer
Ed: Christopher C. Williams. **Description:** Shares of Foot Locker could raise from $10 to about $15 a share with the improvement of the economy. The company has benefited from prudent management and merchandising as well as better cost cutting, allowing it to better survive in a recession. **Availability:** Online.

14680 ■ "Life's Work: Manolo Blahnik" in Harvard Business Review (Vol. 88, December 2010, No. 12, pp. 144)
Pub: Harvard Business Publishing
Contact: Diane Belcher, Managing Director
Ed: Alison Beard. **Price:** $8.95, PDF. **Description:** Shoe designer Manolo Blahnik recounts his beginnings in the shoe industry and the influence art has had on his work, as well as balancing art and commerce. He also discusses the importance of quality materials and craftsmanship and the benefits of managing an independent, family-owned business. **Availability:** Online; PDF.

14681 ■ "The Nation's #1 Children's Shoe Retailer, Payless ShoeSource(R), Launches Hassle-Free Back-to-School Shoe Shopping" in Benzinga.com (July 25, 2012)
Pub: PR Newswire Association LLC.
Description: Nation's largest shoe retailer, Payless ShoeSource(R), is offering a Happiness Guarantee for back-to-school shoe shopping. The firm's goal is to make shoppers happy and keep them returning to purchase shoes during the rest of the year.

14682 ■ "Nike's FlyEase Continues Smart Innovations in Growing Adaptive Fashion Market" in Footwear News (November 22, 2019)
URL(s): footwearnews.com/2019/focus/athletic-ou tdoor/nike-flyease-adaptive-shoes-hands-free-120 2877446/
Ed: Erin E. Clack. **Released:** November 22, 2019. **Description:** Nike's groundbreaking FlyEase technology continues to produce new innovations in the shoe

industry. Beginning with a shoe with a wrap-around zipper that opens in the back, it allowed people with disabilities to easily put on and take off these shoes. Nike has expanded the line with a shoe with a magnetic backing that can be slipped on and off with no hands. **Availability:** Online.

14683 ■ "Portland Wooing Under Armour to West Coast Facility" in Baltimore Business Journal (Vol. 27, January 29, 2010, No. 39, pp. 1)
Pub: Baltimore Business Journal
Contact: Rhonda Pringle, President
E-mail: rpringle@bizjournals.com
Ed: Andy Giegerich. **Description:** Baltimore, Maryland sports apparel maker, Under Armour, is planning a west coast expansion with Portland, Oregon among the sites considered to house its apparel and footwear design center. Portland officials counting on the concentration of nearly 10,000 activewear workers in the city will help lure the company to the city. **Availability:** Print; Online.

14684 ■ "Revive To Sell Women's Apparel in Downtown Space" in Memphis Business Journal (Vol. 33, February 3, 2012, No. 43, pp. 1)
Pub: Baltimore Business Journal
Contact: Rhonda Pringle, President
E-mail: rpringle@bizjournals.com
Ed: Andy Ashby. **Description:** Revive has signed a rental agreement with Memphis Commerce Square Partners LLC for the vacant space at One Commerce Square in Memphis, Tennessee. Revive plans to sell women's clothing, shoes and accessories in the downtown space. **Availability:** Print; Online.

14685 ■ "The Rise and Fall of Payless ShoeSource" in Business Insider (June 25, 2019)
URL(s): www.businessinsider.com/the-rise-and-fall-of -payless-shoesource-2019-6
Ed: Frank Olito. **Released:** June 25, 2019. **Description:** A history of Payless ShoeSource from it's beginnings as a small chain of stores in the Midwest in 1956 to it's bankruptcy in 2019. **Availability:** Online.

14686 ■ "Under Armour Hopes to Stomp on Nike with Basketball Shoe" in Baltimore Business Journal (Vol. 28, October 22, 2010, No. 24, pp. 1)
Pub: Baltimore Business Journal
Contact: Rhonda Pringle, President
E-mail: rpringle@bizjournals.com
Ed: Erik Siemers. **Description:** Uner Armour Inc. will release its Micro G line of four basketball sneakers on October 23, 2010. The company's executives mentioned that Under Armour's goal is to appeal to customers, and not to chip away at Nike Inc.'s supremacy in basketball shoes. The new sneakers will range from $80 to $110. **Availability:** Print; Online.

14687 ■ "Unpleasant Surprise - When a Stock Distribution is Taxed as Dividend Income" in Barron's (Vol. 88, March 24, 2008, No. 12, pp. 60)
Pub: Dow Jones & Company Inc.
Contact: Almar Latour, Chief Executive Officer
Ed: Shirley A. Lazo. **Description:** Discusses the $175 million that footwear company Genesco received in a settlement with Finish Line and UBS is considered as a stock distribution and is taxable as dividend income. Railroad company CSX raised its quarterly common payout from 15 cents to 18 cents. **Availability:** Online.

STATISTICAL SOURCES

14688 ■ RMA Annual Statement Studies
Pub: Risk Management Association
Contact: Nancy Foster, President
Released: Annual. **Description:** Contains composite balance sheets and income statements for more than 360 industries, including the accounting, auditing, and bookkeeping industries. Also contains five years

of comparative historical data for discerning trends. Includes 16 commonly used ratios, computed for most of the size groupings for nearly every industry.

14689 ■ US Footwear Online Retailing Market Report 2021
URL(s): store.mintel.com/report/us-footwear-online-re tailing-market-report
Price: $4,366.35. **Description:** Downloadable report providing data on the online footwear retailing market. Report includes an executive summary, interactive databook, PowerPoint presentation, infographic overview, report PDF, and previous years data. **Availability:** PDF.

TRADE PERIODICALS

14690 ■ Shoe Retailing Today
Pub: National Shoe Retailers Association
Contact: Mark Denkler, President
URL(s): www.nsra.org/page/benefits
Released: Bimonthly **Description:** Provides news of activities and developments in independent shoe retailing. Recurring features include member news, calendar of events, product reference guide and vendor profiles. **Availability:** Print; Online.

VIDEO/AUDIO MEDIA

14691 ■ Marketplace: On Tulsa's Black Wall Street, Shop Owner Finds Inspiration in Local Sports History
URL(s): www.marketplace.org/2023/06/15/on-tulsas -black-wall-street-shop-owner-finds-inspiration-in -local-sports-history
Ed: Sean McHenry. **Released:** June 15, 2023. **Description:** Podcast discusses issues affecting sales at a sneaker shop,.

TRADE SHOWS AND CONVENTIONS

14692 ■ Chicago Shoe Market
URL(s): chicagoshoemarket.com
Frequency: Annual. **Description:** Tradeshow featuring footwear and accessories for retailers. **Principal Exhibits:** Tradeshow featuring footwear and accessories for retailers.

14693 ■ Independent Retailers Buying Group Spring Trade Show
URL(s): n2b.goexposoftware.com/events/wbg22sp/ goExpo/public/login.php
Frequency: Annual. **Description:** Retailer tradeshow with a focus on shooting sports, sporting goods, and fall/winter apparel and footwear. **Principal Exhibits:** Retailer tradeshow with a focus on shooting sports, sporting goods, and fall/winter apparel and footwear.

14694 ■ Michigan Shoe Market
URL(s): www.michiganshoeshow.com
Facebook: www.facebook.com/michiganshoemarket
Frequency: Annual. **Description:** Tradeshow featuring shoes and accessories from manufacturers and retailers from Indiana, Ohio, and Michigan. **Audience:** Shoe retailers. **Principal Exhibits:** Tradeshow featuring shoes and accessories from manufacturers and retailers from Indiana, Ohio, and Michigan.

FRANCHISES AND BUSINESS OPPORTUNITIES

14695 ■ Kiddie Kobbler Ltd.
1177 St Laurent Blvd.
Ottawa, ON, Canada K1K 3B7
Ph: (613)746-6411
Free: 800-561-9762
Co. E-mail: inquiries@kiddiekobbler.ca
URL: http://www.kiddiekobblerstlaurent.ca
URL(s): kiddiekobbler.ca/locations/st-laurent
Facebook: www.facebook.com/KiddieKobblerStLau rent
Pinterest: www.pinterest.com/kiddiekobbler1

Description: Operator of children shoe store. **Founded:** 2007. **Training:** 3 weeks in an existing location.

14696 ■ Les Franchises Panda Ltee./Panda Franchises Ltd.

1060 Boul. Michèle-Bohec, No. 108
 Blainville, QC, Canada J7C 5E2
Ph: (579)637-9741
Co. E-mail: info.panda@pandashoes.com
URL: http://www.pandashoes.com/en
Facebook: www.facebook.com/Pandachaussures

Description: Chain of footwear stores for babies, kids and teenagers. **Founded:** 1972. **Training:** Yes.

14697 ■ Shoes-n-Feet

15015 Main St., No. 102
 Kelsey Creek Ctr.
 Bellevue, WA 98007
Ph: (425)653-2329
Fax: (425)653-2690
Co. E-mail: bellevue@shoesnfeet.com
URL: http://shoesnfeet.com
Contact: Chris Bentvelzen, Owner
Facebook: www.facebook.com/shoesnfeet
X (Twitter): x.com/shoesnfeet
Instagram: www.instagram.com/shoes_n_feet_walk
 _run

YouTube: www.youtube.com/user/SHOESnFEETstores

Description: Education based healthy shoe store servicing the baby-boomer generation. **No. of Franchise Units:** 8. **No. of Company-Owned Units:** 1. **Founded:** 1998. **Franchised:** 2002. **Equity Capital Needed:** $185,000-$226,500. **Franchise Fee:** $25,000. **Royalty Fee:** 5%. **Training:** Provides up to 160 hours training at headquarters and at franchisee's location as needed with ongoing support.

14698 ■ Z-Coil Pain Relief Footwear

Description: Retailing of revolutionary line of footwear specifically designed for foot, leg and back pain relief. **No. of Franchise Units:** 66. **No. of Company-Owned Units:** 1. **Founded:** 1995. **Franchised:** 2005. **Equity Capital Needed:** $88,150-$160,800. **Franchise Fee:** $15,000. **Financial Assistance:** Yes **Training:** Offers 5 day training program and ongoing support.

LIBRARIES

14699 ■ National Shoe Retailers Association (NSRA)

7386 N La Cholla Blvd.
 Tucson, AZ 85741

Ph: (520)209-1710
Co. E-mail: memberservices@nsra.org
URL: http://www.nsra.org
Contact: Mark Denkler, President
Facebook: www.facebook.com/NationalShoeRetailersAssociation
Linkedin: www.linkedin.com/company/national-shoe
 -retailers-association
Instagram: www.instagram.com/nationalshoeretailersassoc

Description: Proprietors of independent shoe stores and stores with major shoe departments. Provides business services and professional development programs including bankcard processing, shipping, freight discounts, free website listing, employee training; conducts research; monitors legislation. **Founded:** 1912. **Publications:** *Business Performance Report (BPR)*; *Shoe Retailing Today* (Bimonthly). **Educational Activities:** NSRA Education Conference (Semiannual); NSRA Leadership Conference (Annual); The Atlanta Shoe Market (TASM) (Semiannual). **Awards:** NSRA Retailer of the Year Award (Annual). **Geographic Preference:** National.

Sign Shop

ASSOCIATIONS AND OTHER ORGANIZATIONS

14700 ■ International Sign Association (ISA)
1001 N Fairfax St., Ste. 301
  Alexandria, VA 22314
Ph: (703)836-4012
Fax: (703)836-8353
Co. E-mail: info@signs.org
URL: http://www.signs.org
Contact: Lori Anderson, President
E-mail: lori.anderson@signs.org
Facebook: www.facebook.com/ISAsigns
X (Twitter): x.com/ISASigns
Instagram: www.instagram.com/isasigns
YouTube: www.youtube.com/user/IntlSignAssociation

Description: Promotes and improve the $30 billion-a-year sign industry, which sustains the nation's nearly $3 trillion-a-year retail industry. **Founded:** 1944. **Publications:** *International Sign Association--Membership Directory.* **Educational Activities:** ISA International Sign Expo (Annual). **Awards:** ISA Sign Design Competition Award (Annual); Kirk L. Brimley Distinguished Service Award (Annual). **Geographic Preference:** Multinational.

REFERENCE WORKS

14701 ■ "First, the Merger: Then, The Culture Clash. How To Fix the Little Things That Can Tear a Company Apart" in Inc. (January 2008)
Ed: Elaine Appleton Grant. **Description:** Ways three CEOs handled the culture classes that followed after company mergers; companies profiled include Fuel Outdoor, an outdoor advertising company; Nelson, an interior design and architecture firm; and Beber Silverstein, an ad agency. **Availability:** Online.

14702 ■ "Hundreds of Complaints Flood in about New York Store Signs, but from Whom?" in The New York Times (December 11, 2018)
URL(s): www.nytimes.com/2018/12/11/nyregion/311-nyc-store-sign-fines.html
Ed: Karen Zraick. **Released:** December 11, 2018. **Description:** Mysterious complaint calls were lodged in New York City's boroughs against a large number of businesses that had potential violations on their store signs. Many owners were fined and others pre-emptively took their signs down in order to avoid hefty fines, since all calls must be investigated. It's being speculated that a sign hanger may be responsible, in order to gain more work. **Availability:** Online.

14703 ■ "Is There a Future for Traditional Sign Shops in the Face of Digital Signage?" in Digital Signage Today (April 8. 2016)
URL(s): www.digitalsignagetoday.com/blogs/is-there-a-future-for-traditional-sign-shops-in-the-face-of-digital-signage/

Ed: A. Jay. **Released:** April 08, 2016. **Description:** Discusses the challenges traditional sign shops face when digital signage is starting to dominate the market. In order to compete, many shops are adapting digital strategies, which also allows them to manage the process in-house and still offer their customers a degree of flexibility. **Availability:** Online.

14704 ■ "Remember Those Great Volkswagen Ads?"
Pub: Merrell Publishers
Contact: Hugh Merrell, Publisher
E-mail: hugh.merrell@merrellpublishers.com

Price: $65; C$72. **Description:** The Volkswagen advertising campaign of the 1960s and 1970s is rated the best and most influential of the century. Also included is a section on billboards signs used to advertise. **Availability:** Print.

14705 ■ "UEDs Would Light Up Street with News, Ads" in Philadelphia Business Journal (Vol. 33, April 11, 2014, No. 9, pp. 8)
Pub: American City Business Journals, Inc.
Contact: Mike Olivieri, Executive Vice President

Description: Catalyst Outdoor head, Thaddeus Bartkowski, has been working on legislation to create a digital district that would permit urban experiential displays (UEDs) in a well-defined area in Center City. UEDs, which would communicate advertising and news, are being considered as a potential revenue stream for the city. The challenges in the installation of UEDs are also presented. **Availability:** Online.

STATISTICAL SOURCES

14706 ■ RMA Annual Statement Studies
Pub: Risk Management Association
Contact: Nancy Foster, President

Released: Annual. **Description:** Contains composite balance sheets and income statements for more than 360 industries, including the accounting, auditing, and bookkeeping industries. Also contains five years of comparative historical data for discerning trends. Includes 16 commonly used ratios, computed for most of the size groupings for nearly every industry.

TRADE PERIODICALS

14707 ■ SignCraft: The guide to profitable and creative sign production
Pub: SignCraft Publishing Co. Inc.
Contact: Thomas D. McIltrot, Director
URL(s): www.signcraft.com
Facebook: www.facebook.com/signcraftmag
X (Twitter): twitter.com/signcraftmag
Instagram: www.instagram.com/signcraftmagazine

Released: Monthly **Price:** $2.99, for monthly; $4.99, for issue. **Description:** Trade magazine. **Availability:** Print; Online.

FRANCHISES AND BUSINESS OPPORTUNITIES

14708 ■ FastSigns International Inc.
2542 Highlander Way
  Carrollton, TX 75006-2333
Co. E-mail: info.nap@fastsigns.com
URL: http://www.fastsigns.com
Contact: Catherine Monson, President
Facebook: www.facebook.com/FASTSIGNS
Linkedin: www.linkedin.com/company/fastsigns
X (Twitter): x.com/fastsigns
Instagram: www.instagram.com/fastsigns
YouTube: www.youtube.com/user/OfficialFASTSIGNS
Pinterest: www.pinterest.com/fastsigns

Description: Sign and graphics solutions provider for businesses worldwide. **Founded:** 1985. **Financial Assistance:** Yes **Training:** Provider of sign and visual communications solutions. **Educational Activities:** International Franchise Expo (IFE) (Annual).

14709 ■ Signal Graphics Inc.
26722 Plz.
  Mission Viejo, CA 92691
Ph: (949)348-5400
Free: 800-854-3321
Co. E-mail: marketing@signalgraphics.com
URL: http://www.signalgraphics.com
Contact: Richard Lowe, President
Facebook: www.facebook.com/Signal-Graphics-Corporate-291947127523649
X (Twitter): x.com/signalgraphics
Description: Firm provides printing and marketing services. **Founded:** 1974. **Financial Assistance:** Yes **Training:** Yes.

14710 ■ Signarama Inc.
2121 Vista Pky.
  West Palm Beach, FL 33411
Ph: (561)425-9989
Free: 800-286-8671
URL: http://signarama.com
Contact: A. J. Titus, President
Facebook: www.facebook.com/signarama
X (Twitter): x.com/signarama
Instagram: www.instagram.com/signarama
YouTube: www.youtube.com/c/Signarama
Pinterest: www.pinterest.com/signarama
Description: Provider of sign and graphic services. **Founded:** 1986. **Training:** Offers 5 weeks training and ongoing support.

14711 ■ Signs Now
Alliance Franchise Brands LLC
  11685 Crossroads Cir., Ste. E
  Middle River, MD 21220
Ph: (248)596-8600
Free: 800-726-9050
Fax: (248)596-8601
URL: http://alliancefranchisebrands.com
Contact: Mike Marcantonio, Chief Executive Officer
Facebook: www.facebook.com/Signs-Now-106228668583849

Linkedin: www.linkedin.com/company/signs-now
YouTube: www.youtube.com/user/SignsNowVideos
Pinterest: www.pinterest.com/signsnowusa

Description: Provides graphics and communication services such as exhibit and vehicle graphics, magnetic signs, banners, and window graphics. **No. of Franchise Units:** 225. **Founded:** 1983. **Franchised:** 1986. **Financial Assistance:** Yes **Training:** Provides 3 week program at headquarters followed by onsite training.

14712 ■ Signs by Tomorrow
11685 Crossroads Cir., Ste. E
  Middle River, MD 21220
Ph: (410)312-3600
Free: 844-957-4467
Fax: (844)957-4467
Co. E-mail: sbtusa@signsbytomorrow.com
URL: http://www.signsbytomorrow.com
Contact: Ray L. Palmer, President
Facebook: www.facebook.com/signsbytomorrow
Linkedin: www.linkedin.com/company/signs-by
  -tomorrow

X (Twitter): x.com/SignsByTomorrow
YouTube: www.youtube.com/channel/UCsqmOQiwas
  -0XYwG_pla4Hw
Pinterest: www.pinterest.com/SignsByTomorrowHQ

Description: Computerized sign shops offering signs and graphics for virtually all sizes of businesses. Franchisee's responsibility is to manage the sales and administrative areas in servicing a business-to-business clientele during regular working hours. **No. of Franchise Units:** 149. **Founded:** 1986. **Training:** Training includes 2 weeks at headquarters, 2 weeks of onsite, and assistance with the grand opening.

REFERENCE WORKS

14713 ■ *"Why Millennials Are Reviving This Once-Tacky Home Accessory" in Refinery29 (October 4, 2018)*
URL(s): www.refinery29.com/en-us/fake-artificial-plants-home-decor-trend
Ed: Cait Munro. **Released:** October 04, 2018. **Description:** Silk plants and fake flowers have made a comeback with the Millennial generation recently. Gardening has experienced a boom but not everyone is gifted with a green thumb, yet they want to enjoy some greenery in their homes. Therefore, fake plants have come back, but they are better crafted than the plants from years ago making them a nice choice for interiors. **Availability:** Online.

TRADE PERIODICALS

14714 ■ *Interior Design*
Pub: Sandow
Contact: Peter Fain, Chief Operating Officer
URL(s): interiordesign.net
Facebook: www.facebook.com/InteriorDesignMagazine
Linkedin: www.linkedin.com/company/interior-design-magazine
X (Twitter): x.com/InteriorDesign
Instagram: www.instagram.com/interiordesignmag
Pinterest: www.pinterest.com/intdesmag
Released: Last edition 2024. **Price:** $12.95, Single issue for print. **Description:** Interior designing and furnishings magazine. **Availability:** Print; Online.

14715 ■ *Paint & Decorating Retailer*
Pub: Paint and Decorating Retailers Association
Contact: Craig Bond, Chairman of the Board
E-mail: craig@pdra.org
URL(s): pdrmag.com/pdr-magazine-overview
Facebook: www.facebook.com/PaintandDecoratingRetailer
X (Twitter): x.com/PDRMagazine

Released: Monthly **Description:** Includes information on legislation and regulation affecting the industry. For paint and wallpaper, window and floor covering and paint retailers. **Availability:** Print; Online.

ASSOCIATIONS AND OTHER ORGANIZATIONS

14716 ■ Ice Sports Industry (ISI)
539 W. Commerce St., No. 7250
Dallas, TX 75208
Ph: (972)735-8800
Fax: (972)735-8815
Co. E-mail: info@skateisi.org
URL: http://www.skateisi.org
Contact: Janice Forbes, President
E-mail: jforbes@co.pierce.wa.us
Facebook: www.facebook.com/skateisi
X (Twitter): x.com/skatingisi
Instagram: www.instagram.com/skateisi
Description: Seeks to educate ice arena owners, operators, and instructors and to increase public interest in ice skating. **Founded:** 1959. **Publications:** *ISI EDGE* (Quarterly; Quarterly); *ISI Membership Directory* (Annual); *Recreational Ice Skater Team Competition Standards*; *ISI Handbook*; *Recreational Ice Skating* (Semiannual). **Educational Activities:** ISI Conference and Tradeshow (Annual). **Awards:** ISIA Education Foundation Scholarship (Annual). **Geographic Preference:** Multinational; Local.

14717 ■ Professional Skaters Association (PSA)
3006 Allegro Pk. Ln. SW
Rochester, MN 55902
Ph: (507)281-5122
Co. E-mail: office@skatepsa.com
URL: http://skatepsa.com
Contact: Alex Chang, President
E-mail: alexanderthechang@gmail.com
Facebook: www.facebook.com/ProfSk8rsAssoc
YouTube: www.youtube.com/channel/UC 6pFPnDpwAQb01ZL-U3XSJA
Description: Professional ice skaters engaged in the teaching, coaching and performing of ice skating. **Founded:** 1938. **Publications:** *Professional Skater* (Bimonthly); *Coaches Manual*; *Professional Skaters Association--Membership Directory* (Annual); *Professional Skaters Association--Rating Systems Manual* (Periodic); *Skaters Handbook*. **Educational Activities:** U.S. Open Professional Figure Skating Championship. **Awards:** F. Ritter Shumway Award (Annual); Betty Berens Award (Annual); PSA Coach of the Year (Annual). **Geographic Preference:** National.

14718 ■ Roller Skating Association International (RSA)
6905 Corporate Dr.
Indianapolis, IN 46278
Ph: (317)347-2626
Co. E-mail: rsa@rollerskating.com
URL: http://www.rollerskating.com/pages/home/1
Contact: Jim McMahon, Executive Director
Facebook: www.facebook.com/RollerSkatingAssocia tion

Linkedin: www.linkedin.com/company/roller-skating -association-international
X (Twitter): x.com/rsaintl
Instagram: www.instagram.com/mysk8moves
YouTube: www.youtube.com/channel/UCz6V9Xmjc _HO3MWVgOu7HAA
Pinterest: www.pinterest.com/rollerskatingai
Description: Independent roller skating rink operators; associate members are rink managers, teachers, and suppliers and manufacturers. Promotes the business and recreational sport of roller skating. Provides business and marketing information to skating center owners. **Founded:** 1937. **Publications:** *Roller Skating Business* (Bimonthly); *Roller Skating Manufacturer's Newsletter*. **Educational Activities:** Roller Skating Association Convention and Trade Show (Annual). **Geographic Preference:** Multinational.

REFERENCE WORKS

14719 ■ "The Best Roller Skates, According to Roller Skaters" in New York Magazine (August 9, 2019)
URL(s): nymag.com/strategist/article/best-roller-ska tes.html
Released: August 09, 2019. **Description:** Roller skating has been coming back into style, thanks to recent shows featuring skating, and there are lots of new roller-skate brands on the market. A review of several top skates are given by experts for all experience levels, along with which type of skating one wants to pursue. Rink skating, street skating, jam skating, and roller derby are all covered. **Availability:** Online.

14720 ■ "Hailey Is Getting an Indoor Ice Rink" in Idaho Business Review (August 27, 2014)
Pub: BridgeTower Media
Contact: Adam Reinebach, President
Description: Hailey Ice, a local nonprofit which built and operates outdoor rinks in the area, is donating $4 million towards the indoor ice skating rink. the money comes from various funds and foundations and collectively believe it to be a good investment in the community.

14721 ■ "San Antonio Ice Rink to Open Earlier than Expected at Travis Park with Free Skating" in My San Antonio (November 23, 2019)
URL(s): www.mysanantonio.com/news/local/article/ San-Antonio-ice-rink-scheduled-to-open-next-148 54972.php
Ed: Priscilla Aguirre. **Description:** Thanks to H-E-B's sponsorship, the San Antonio ice rink is scheduled to open early for folks to enjoy before the annual tree lighting ceremony. The rink will be open until the end of January. **Availability:** Online.

STATISTICAL SOURCES

14722 ■ RMA Annual Statement Studies
Pub: Risk Management Association
Contact: Nancy Foster, President
Released: Annual. **Description:** Contains composite balance sheets and income statements for more than 360 industries, including the accounting, auditing, and bookkeeping industries. Also contains five years of comparative historical data for discerning trends. Includes 16 commonly used ratios, computed for most of the size groupings for nearly every industry.

TRADE PERIODICALS

14723 ■ ISI EDGE
Pub: Ice Sports Industry
Contact: Janice Forbes, President
E-mail: jforbes@co.pierce.wa.us
URL(s): www.skateisi.org/resources/isi-edgewww.isie dgemagazine.org
Ed: Eileen Viglione. **Released:** Quarterly; Quarterly; fall, winter, spring, summer. **Description:** Provides information of interest to member ice rinks: promotional ideas, management tips, energy saving suggestions, and instructional information. **Availability:** Print; PDF; Online.

14724 ■ USA Hockey Magazine
Pub: Touchpoint Media, Inc.
Contact: Laura McEwen, Chief Executive Officer
URL(s): www.usahockeymagazine.com
Facebook: www.facebook.com/usahockeymagazine
X (Twitter): x.com/USAHMagazine
Instagram: www.instagram.com/usahockey
Pinterest: www.pinterest.com/usahockeymag
Released: 10/year; Five (5) issues are published in a print format (September, October, November/ December, January/February and March) and five (5) issues are published in a digital only format (April, May, June, July and August). **Price:** $4, Single issue for back issue; $15, Individuals. **Description:** U.S.A. Hockey (sports association) magazine. **Availability:** Print; Online.

TRADE SHOWS AND CONVENTIONS

14725 ■ Roller Skating Association Convention and Trade Show
PepsiCo, Inc.
700 Anderson Hill Rd.
Purchase, NY 10577
Ph: (914)253-2000
Fax: (914)249-8086
URL: http://www.pepsico.com
Contact: Ram Krishnan, Chief Executive Officer
URL(s): www.rollerskating.com/convention2025.html

Frequency: Annual. **Description:** Skate manufacturers, suppliers, novelty companies, snack bar items, sound and lighting, flooring, and arcade games. **Audience:** Industry professionals. **Principal Exhibits:** Skate manufacturers, suppliers, novelty companies, snack bar items, sound and lighting, flooring, and arcade games. Dates and Locations: 2025 May 11-15 South Point Hotel & Casino, Las Vegas, NV. **Telecommunication Services:** atanner@rollerskating.com.

LIBRARIES

14726 ■ National Museum of Roller Skating Archives
4730 S St.
  Lincoln, NE 68506
Ph: (402)483-7551
URL: http://www.learntorollerskate.org
Scope: Historical roller skates. **Services:** Open to the public. **Founded:** 1980. **Holdings:** Patents; med-

als; trophies; photographs; artworks; films; videotapes; archival materials; roller skating memorabilia; 1,500 volumes of roller skating books and periodicals; 125 titles; 10,000 photographs; personal papers.

ASSOCIATIONS AND OTHER ORGANIZATIONS

14727 ■ Cross Country Ski Areas Association (CCSAA)
PO Box 818
 Woodstock, VT 05091
Ph: (802)236-3021
Co. E-mail: reese@xcski.org
URL: http://xcski.org
Contact: Reese Brown, Contact
Facebook: www.facebook.com/people/Cross-Country
 -Ski-Areas-Association/100062329454378
X (Twitter): x.com/crosscountryski
Instagram: www.instagram.com/ccsaatoday
Description: Is a non-profit organization representing member ski service providers which aims to promote the growth and improve the quality of cross country ski operations in North America. **Founded:** 1977. **Publications:** *Cross Country Close to Home: A Ski Area Development Manual*; *Nordic Network*; *The Best of Cross Country Skiing & Snowshoeing* (Annual); *The Best of Cross Country Skiing--Membership Directory and Beginner's Guide* (Annual); *The Best of Cross Country Skiing and Snowshoeing: Membership Directory and Beginner's Guide* (Annual). **Geographic Preference:** National.

14728 ■ Eastern Winter Sports Reps Association (EWSRA)
PO Box 88
 White Haven, PA 18661
Ph: (570)443-7180
Fax: (570)300-2715
Co. E-mail: info@ewsra.org
URL: http://www.ewsra.org
Contact: Tom Harsh, President
Description: Independent company sales representatives for firms associated with the snow-ski industry. Conducts preview showings of hard and soft goods for retailers. **Founded:** 1971. **Geographic Preference:** National.

14729 ■ Midwest Winter Sports Reps Association (MWSRA)
441 Dunhill Dr.
 Verona, WI 53593
Free: 866-623-6155
Co. E-mail: mwsraholly@gmail.com
URL: http://www.midwestwinterreps.com/p.asp
Contact: Bruce Marsh, Co-President
E-mail: bruce@brmreps.com
Description: Manufacturers' representatives serving the Midwest ski industry. Coordinates buying shows. **Founded:** 1966. **Publications:** *Buyers Guide* (Annual). **Educational Activities:** Buying Show (Irregular); Midwest Winter Sports Representatives Association (Annual). **Geographic Preference:** Multinational.

14730 ■ National Brotherhood of Skiers (NBS)
10 S Riverside Pl., Ste. 875
 Chicago, IL 60606-3728
Ph: (718)744-5727
URL: http://www.nbs.org
Contact: Henri Rivers, President
Facebook: www.facebook.com/NationalBrotherhoo
 dofSkiers
X (Twitter): x.com/NBS_BlackSkiers
Instagram: www.instagram.com/nationalbrotherhoo
 dofskiers
YouTube: www.youtube.com/channel/
 UCUvOpfy9eeycjuzSxSbSrVA
Description: Promotes winter sports among minorities, with emphasis on youth. Seeks to develop talented ski racers through local, regional, and national competitions. **Founded:** 1975. **Publications:** *NBS Directory* (Annual); *Skiers Edge* (Quarterly). **Geographic Preference:** National.

14731 ■ National Ski Patrol (NSP)
133 S Van Gordon St.
 Lakewood, CO 80228
Ph: (303)988-1111
Co. E-mail: memberservices@nsp.org
URL: http://nspserves.org
Contact: Brian Rull, Chairman
X (Twitter): x.com/NatlSkiPatrol
YouTube: www.youtube.com/channel/
 UCkEvWKmqheyVXXwJVAh9eDA
Description: Promotes ski safety and handling of injuries at ski areas. Assists municipal and federal agencies in cold weather disasters and in rescue attempts involving air crashes, mountain accidents, and blizzards. **Founded:** 1938. **Publications:** *Ski Patrol Magazine* (Annual); *Winter Catalog*. **Geographic Preference:** National.

14732 ■ National Ski and Snowboard Retailers Association (NSSRA)
3041 Woodcreek Dr., Ste. 210
 Downers Grove, IL 60515
Ph: (224)220-1522
Fax: (847)391-9827
Co. E-mail: info@nssra.com
URL: http://www.nssra.com
Contact: Julie Pitts, President
Linkedin: www.linkedin.com/company/national-ski
 -snowboard-retailers-association-nssra
X (Twitter): x.com/nssraskisboards
Description: Ski & snowboard stores. Represents the interests of members and provides services beneficial to their businesses. Compiles statistics. **Founded:** 1987. **Publications:** *NSSRA Newsletter* (Irregular). **Geographic Preference:** National.

14733 ■ National Sporting Goods Association (NSGA)
3041 Woodcreek Dr., Ste. 210
 Downers Grove, IL 60515
Ph: (847)296-6742
Fax: (847)391-9827
Co. E-mail: info@nsga.org
URL: http://www.nsga.org
Contact: Matt Carlson, President
Facebook: www.facebook.com/nsgasports
Linkedin: www.linkedin.com/company/national-spor
 ting-goods-association
X (Twitter): x.com/NSGASportingGds
YouTube: www.youtube.com/user/nsgasports
Description: Provides services, advocacy, education and information for sporting goods retailers. **Founded:** 1927. **Publications:** *NSGA Buying Guide* (Annual); *Sports Participation-Series I & II* (Annual); *National Sporting Goods Association--Buying Guide* (Annual); *NSGA Now* (Bimonthly); *NSGA Sports Retailer--Store Equipment and Services Directory Issue*; *Cost of Doing Business Survey*; *Team Line-Up*. **Educational Activities:** Annual NSGA Management Conference and Team Dealer Summit (Annual). **Geographic Preference:** National.

14734 ■ The Professional Ski Instructors of America and the American Association of Snowboard Instructors (PSIA-AASI)
133 S Van Gordon St., Ste. 200
 Lakewood, CO 80228
Ph: (303)987-9390
Co. E-mail: memberservices@thesnowpros.org
URL: http://www.thesnowpros.org
Contact: Eliza Kuntz, Chairman of the Board
Facebook: www.facebook.com/TheSnowPros
Linkedin: www.linkedin.com/company/psia-aasi
X (Twitter): x.com/thesnowpros
Instagram: www.instagram.com/thesnowpros
YouTube: www.youtube.com/user/TheSnowPros
Description: Promotes ski instruction by professional teachers. Developed American Teaching Method (ATM), which has received international recognition. **Founded:** 1961. **Publications:** *Convention Proceedings* (Annual); *PSIA-AASI Accessories Catalog*; *Ski School Management* (3/year). **Geographic Preference:** National.

14735 ■ SnowSports Industries America (SIA)
1918 Prospector Ave.
 Park City, UT 84060
Ph: (435)657-5140
Co. E-mail: info@snowsports.org
URL: http://www.snowsports.org
Contact: Nick Sargent, President
E-mail: nsargent@snowsports.org
Facebook: www.facebook.com/SIAsnowsports
Linkedin: www.linkedin.com/company/siasnowsports
X (Twitter): x.com/siasnowsports
Instagram: www.instagram.com/siasnowsports
YouTube: www.youtube.com/user/siasnowsports
Pinterest: www.pinterest.com/siasnowsports
Description: Manufacturers, distributors, and suppliers of ski, snowboard, on-snow, and outdoor action sports apparel, equipment, footwear, and accessories. Monitors activities at the federal level to protect the interest of on-snow product manufacturers and distributors. Provides information on the on-snow industry to the media. Promotes snow sports through market development programs. Conducts research programs. **Founded:** 1954. **Publications:** *Retailer/Rep Advisor* (Biennial); *SIA Trade Show Directory* (Annual); *USIA Ski Area and Associate*

Membership Directory (Annual); *USIA Ski and Outdoor Sports Show Directory* (Annual); *SIA Member Update* (Quarterly; Semimonthly); *SIA Snow Sports Directory* (Annual). **Educational Activities:** Outdoor Retailer Snow Show (Annual); Outdoor Retailer Snow Show (Annual). **Geographic Preference:** National.

14736 ■ Western Winter Sports Representatives Association (WWSRA)

726 Tenacity Dr., Unit B
  Longmont, CO 80504-7397
Ph: (303)532-4002
Co. E-mail: info@wwsra.com
URL: http://wwsra.com
Contact: Morgan Turner, President
E-mail: morganturner@comcast.net

Description: Representatives in the ski industry. Sponsors buyers' shows. Membership and activities are focused in the western part of the US. **Founded:** 1949. **Publications:** *Western Winter Sports Representatives Association--Show Directory*; *Ski Show Directory-Sporting Goods Directory* (Semiannual). **Educational Activities:** Rocky Mountain Show (Annual). **Geographic Preference:** National.

REFERENCE WORKS

14737 ■ "Iconic Boise Skateboard Shop to Close" in Idaho Business Review (August 19, 2014)

Pub: BridgeTower Media
Contact: Adam Reinebach, President

Description: Lori Wright and Lori Ambur have owned Newt & Harold's for over 30 years. The partners are closing the firm that sold skateboards and snowboards. Wright focused on the marketing and inventory aspects of the retail shop, while Ambur ran the organizational and financial end. Wright and Ambur say they are leaving retail because the industry has faced so many changes since they first opened, particularly competing with online stores.

14738 ■ "The New and Improved Ski Shop" in Powder (January 11, 2017)

URL(s): www.powder.com/stories/news/the-new-and-improved-ski-shop/

Ed: Devon O'Neil. **Released:** January 11, 2017. **Description:** Traditional ski shop have found they must compete with online sales, especially since consumers bought about $1 billion worth of snow sports equipment from the internet. Big chains have closed but some smaller shops are actually thriving due to innovations and an eye for great customer service. **Availability:** Online.

14739 ■ QuickBooks for the New Bean Counter: Business Owner's Guide 2006

Description: Profile of QuickBooks software, offering insight into using the software's accounting and bookkeeping functions.

TRADE PERIODICALS

14740 ■ Cross Country Skier: The Journal of Nordic Skiing

Pub: Cross Country Skier L.L.C.
URL(s): www.crosscountryskier.com
Facebook: www.facebook.com/xcskiermag
Instagram: www.instagram.com/xcskiermag

Ed: J.D Downing. **Released:** Semiannual; Fall and Winter. **Price:** $9.95, Single issue for digital (Downloadable PDF); $14.95, Single issue for print issue; $24.95, U.S. for 2 issues; $28.95, Canada for 2 issues; $30.95, Other countries for 2 issues; $39.95, U.S. for 4 issues; $47.95, Canada for 4 issues; $51.95, Other countries for 4 issues. **Description:** Magazine emphasizing touring, destinations, and technique in cross-country skiing. **Availability:** Print; PDF; Download; Online.

14741 ■ Ski

URL(s): www.skimag.com/uncategorized/cnn-to-air-iskii-vignettes

Released: 6/year **Price:** $10, for per year. **Description:** Magazine of the ski life. **Availability:** Print; Online.

TRADE SHOWS AND CONVENTIONS

14742 ■ Outdoor Retailer Snow Show

SnowSports Industries America (SIA)
  1918 Prospector Ave.
  Park City, UT 84060
Ph: (435)657-5140
Co. E-mail: info@snowsports.org
URL: http://www.snowsports.org
Contact: Nick Sargent, President
E-mail: nsargent@snowsports.org
URL(s): www.snowsports.org/events/outdoor-retailer-snow-show

Frequency: Annual. **Description:** Ski, snowboard, outdoor sports, snowshoe companies with equipment, clothing, and accessories. **Audience:** Industry professionals. **Principal Exhibits:** Ski, snowboard, outdoor sports, snowshoe companies with equipment, clothing, and accessories. **Telecommunication Services:** bstone@snowsports.org.

LIBRARIES

14743 ■ Canadian Ski Museum Archives [Le Musee Canadien du Ski]

1984, chemin du Village
  Ville de Mont-Tremblant, QC, Canada J8E 1K4
Co. E-mail: info@skimuseum.ca
URL: http://www.skimuseum.ca
Contact: Jean Cloutier, Director, Finance

Scope: History; skiing. **Founded:** 1971. **Holdings:** Figures not available.

START-UP INFORMATION

14744 ■ *"Local Startup Hits Big Leagues"* in *Austin Business Journal*Inc. *(Vol. 28, December 19, 2008, No. 40, pp. 1)*

Description: Qcue LLC, an Austin, Texas-based company founded in 2007 is developing a software system that can be used by Major League Baseball teams to change the prices of their single-game tickets based on variables affecting demand. The company recently completed a trial with the San Francisco Giants in 2008. **Availability:** Print; Online.

14745 ■ *"The Rise of Digital Currencies and Atlanta's Key Role" in Atlanta Business Chronicle (July 4, 2014, pp. 25A)*

Pub: American City Business Journals, Inc.

Contact: Mike Olivieri, Executive Vice President

Released: Weekly. **Price:** $4, introductory 4-week offer(Digital only). **Description:** Virtual currency bitcoin, which is an Internet protocol that defines a decentralized online payment system is discussed. A description of how bitcoin and other virtual currencies are used and concerns over its future use are examined. A short profile of Atlanta-based startup BitPay, which provides software solutions to help businesses accept bitcoin payments without risking operating cash flow is included. BitPay also enables rapid currency conversion through bitcoin ATMs or kiosks. **Availability:** Print; Online.

14746 ■ *"Startup Lucena Taking On Wall Street" in Atlanta Business Chronicle (May 23, 2014, pp. 1A)*

Pub: American City Business Journals, Inc.

Contact: Mike Olivieri, Executive Vice President

Description: Lucena Research is a predictive analytics startup firm developing software for the financial investment sector. The company's software helps investment professionals identify trading strategies and investing trends to reduce risk and increase returns. **Availability:** Print; Online.

ASSOCIATIONS AND OTHER ORGANIZATIONS

14747 ■ **Business Software Alliance (BSA)**
200 Massachusetts Ave., NW
 Ste. 310
 Washington, DC 20001
Ph: (202)872-5500
Fax: (202)872-5501
Co. E-mail: info@bsa.org
URL: http://www.bsa.org
Contact: Victoria A. Espinel, President
Facebook: www.facebook.com/BSATheSof
 twareAlliance
Linkedin: www.linkedin.com/company/bsa-the-sof
 tware-alliance
X (Twitter): x.com/BSAnews
YouTube: www.youtube.com/user/BusinessSftAlli
 ance

Description: Computer software publishers. Promotes the free world trade of business software by combating international software piracy, advancing intellectual property protection, and increasing market access. **Founded:** 1988. **Publications:** *Guide to Software Management* (Annual); *Software Review* (Quarterly). **Geographic Preference:** National.

14748 ■ **Entertainment Merchants Association (EMA)**
11304 Chander Blvd.
 North Hollywood, CA 91601
Co. E-mail: info@entmerch.org
URL: http://www.entmerch.org/digitalema
Contact: Adm. (Ret.) Mark Fisher, Chief Executive Officer

Description: Retailers and distributors of videocassettes and videodiscs; associate members are major studios or independent companies that produce video programming and manufacturers of video games, accessories, and other goods and services for the video software industry. Represents and acts as spokesperson for the video software merchandising industry. Conducts statistical survey of video retailing; offers legal counsel representing member's interests in Washington, DC. Offers seminars on management and inventory control. **Founded:** 2006. **Publications:** *VSDA Video Voice* (Monthly). **Awards:** EMA Home Entertainment Awards (Annual). **Geographic Preference:** National.

14749 ■ **Entertainment Software Association (ESA)**
601 Massachusetts Ave. NW, Ste. 300 W
 Washington, DC 20001
Ph: (202)223-2400
Co. E-mail: esa@theesa.com
URL: http://www.theesa.com
Contact: Stanley Pierre-Louis, President
Facebook: www.facebook.com/TheEntertainmentSof
 twareAssociation
Linkedin: www.linkedin.com/company/entertainmen
 t-software-association
X (Twitter): x.com/theESA
Instagram: www.instagram.com/theesaofficial

Description: Represents the interactive entertainment software publishing industry. Established an autonomous rating board to rate interactive entertainment software. Established a program to combat piracy in the U.S. and around the world. Represents members on industry issues at the federal and state level. Provides market research and information. **Founded:** 1994. **Educational Activities:** Electronic Entertainment Expo (E3) (Annual). **Awards:** ESA Foundation LGBTQ+ Service Scholarship (Annual); ESA Foundation Esports Scholarship (Annual); ESA Foundation Computer and Video Game Arts and Sciences Scholarship (Annual). **Geographic Preference:** National.

14750 ■ **Free Software Foundation, Inc. (FSF)**
51 Franklin St., 5th Fl.
 Boston, MA 02110
Ph: (617)542-5942

Fax: (617)542-2652
Co. E-mail: info@fsf.org
URL: http://www.fsf.org
Contact: Geoffrey Knauth, President

Description: Promotes computer users' right to use, study, copy, modify, and redistribute computer programs; development and use of free (as in freedom) software, particularly the GNU operating system and free (as in freedom) documentation; promotes ethical and political issues of freedom in the use of software. **Founded:** 1985. **Publications:** *GNU Service Directory* (Semiannual); *GNU Project*; *GNU's Bulletin* (Annual). **Awards:** FSF Award for the Advancement of Free Software (Annual). **Geographic Preference:** Multinational.

14751 ■ **International Computer Music Association (ICMA) - Library**
1819 Polk St., Ste. 330
 San Francisco, CA 94109
Co. E-mail: icma@umich.edu
URL: http://www.computermusic.org
Contact: Kerry L. Hagan, President
E-mail: kerry.hagan@ul.ie

Description: Works to advance individuals and institutions involved in the technical, creative and performance aspects of computer music. Provides networking opportunities; sponsors research and projects; holds competitions. **Scope:** Music; technology. **Founded:** 1974. **Holdings:** Figures not available. **Awards:** ICMC Best Presentation Award (Annual); ICMA International Computer Music Commission Awards (Annual). **Geographic Preference:** Multinational.

14752 ■ **Software and Information Industry Association (SIIA)**
1620 I St., NW, Ste. 501
 Washington, DC 20005
Ph: (202)289-7442
URL: http://www.siia.net
Contact: Jeff Joseph, President
Facebook: www.facebook.com/siiadotne
Linkedin: www.linkedin.com/company/siia
X (Twitter): x.com/siia
YouTube: www.youtube.com/channel/
 UCOggBEPEyAXDIh0U_JISHyA

Description: Promotes the interest of the software and information industries. Protects intellectual property and advocate a legal and regulatory environment that benefits the industry. **Founded:** 1984. **Publications:** *Information Times*; *Press Room*; *eNewsletters* (Daily); *Information Sources: The IIA Annual Membership Directory* (Continuous); *Information Times: A Publication of the Information Industry Association* (Bimonthly). **Awards:** SIIA CODiE Awards - Best Big Data Reporting and Analytics Solution (Annual); SIIA CODiE Awards - Best Big Data Tools and Platform (Annual); SIIA CODiE Awards - Best Business Intelligence Reporting and Analytics Solution (Annual); SIIA CODiE Awards - Best Business Intelligence Tools and Platform (Annual); SIIA CODiE Awards - Best Content Analytics Solution (Annual); SIIA CODiE Awards - Best Data Integration Solution

(Annual); SIIA CODiE Awards - Best Text Analytics and Semantic Technology Solution (Annual); SIIA CODiE Awards - Best Advertising or Campaign Management Platform (Annual); SIIA CODiE Awards - Best Content Marketing Solution (Annual); SIIA CODiE Awards - Best Data Management Platform (Annual); SIIA CODiE Awards - Best Digital Marketing Solution (Annual); SIIA CODiE Awards - Best Marketing Automation Solution (Annual); SIIA CODiE Awards - Best Native Advertising Platform or Service (Annual); SIIA CODiE Awards - Best Digital Asset Management Solution (Annual); SIIA CODiE Awards - Best Real Estate or Construction Management Solution (Annual); SIIA CODiE Awards - Best Risk Management and Compliance Solution (Annual); SIIA CODiE Awards - Best Scholarly Research Information Solution (Annual); SIIA CODiE Awards - Best Science and Technology Information Solution (Annual); SIIA CODiE Awards - Best CRM Mobile Application (Annual); SIIA CODiE Awards - Best Financial Management Mobile Application (Annual); SIIA CODiE Awards - Best Customer Success Management Solution (Annual); SIIA CODiE Awards - Best Information Service Delivered as Mobile App or Platform (Annual); SIIA CODiE Awards - Best Mobile Development Solution (Annual); SIIA CODiE Awards - Best Mobile Healthcare Application (Annual); SIIA CODiE Awards - Best Project Management Mobile Application (Annual); SIIA CODiE Awards - Best Sales and Marketing Mobile Application (Annual); SIIA CODiE Awards - Best Cloud Infrastructure (Annual); SIIA CODiE Awards - Best Cloud Management Solution (Annual); SIIA CODiE Awards - Best Internet of Things Solution (Annual); SIIA CODiE Awards - Best IT Asset Management Solution (Annual); SIIA CODiE Awards - Best IT Service Management Solution (Annual); SIIA CODiE Awards - Best Platform as a Service (Annual); SIIA CODiE Awards - Best Storage and Back-up Solution (Annual); SIIA CODiE Awards - Best Endpoint Security Management Solution (Annual); SIIA CODiE Awards - Best Identity and Access Security Solution (Annual); SIIA CODiE Awards - Best Network Security Solution (Annual); SIIA CODiE Awards - Best Pre-K/Early Childhood Learning Solution (Annual); SIIA CODiE Awards - Best Classroom Management Solution (Annual); SIIA CODiE Awards - Best Content Rights and Entitlement Solution (Annual); SIIA CODiE Awards - Best Content Search and Discovery Solution (Annual); SIIA CODiE Awards - Best Multi-Channel Publishing Platform or Service (Annual); SIIA CODiE Awards - Best Service Using Aggregated Content (Annual); SIIA CODiE Awards - Best Event Management Solution (Annual); SIIA CODiE Awards - Best Collaboration Solution (Annual); SIIA CODiE Awards - Best Customer Relationship Management Solution (Annual); SIIA CODiE Awards - Best eCommerce Solution (Periodic); SIIA CODiE Awards - Best Financial Management Solution (Annual); SIIA CODiE Awards - Best Human Capital or Talent Management Solution (Annual); SIIA CODiE Awards - Best Metadata Management Solution (Annual); SIIA CODiE Awards - Best Project Management Solution (Annual); SIIA CODiE Awards - Best Social Media Management and Enablement Solution (Annual); SIIA CODiE Awards - Best Solution for Integrating Content into Workflow (Annual); SIIA CODiE Awards - Best Billing & Subscription Management Solution (Annual); SIIA CODiE Awards - Best Supply Chain Management Solution (Periodic); SIIA CODiE Awards - Best Webcast Platform (Annual); SIIA CODiE Awards - Best Big Data Cleansing Tool or Solution (Annual); SIIA CODiE Awards - Best Content Curation Platform (Annual); SIIA CODiE Awards - Best Sales and Marketing Intelligence Solution (Annual); SIIA CODiE Awards - Best Business Information Solution (Annual); SIIA CODiE Awards - Best Financial and Market Data Information Solution (Annual); SIIA CODiE Awards - Best Customer Service Solution (Annual); SIIA CODiE Awards - Best Health and Medical Information Solution (Annual); SIIA CODiE Awards - Best Healthcare Technology Solution (Annual); SIIA CODiE Awards - Best Legal Intelligence Solution (Annual); SIIA CODiE Awards - Best K-12 Course or Learning Management Solution (Annual); SIIA CODiE Awards - Best K-12 Enterprise Solution (Annual); SIIA CODiE Awards - Best Authoring/Development Tool (Annual); SIIA

CODiE Awards - Best K-20 Data Solution (Annual); SIIA CODiE Awards - Best Collaborative Social Media Solution for Educators (Annual); SIIA CODiE Awards - Best Education Cloud-Based Solution (Annual); SIIA CODiE Awards - Best Educational App for a Mobile Device (Irregular); SIIA CODiE Awards - Best Learning Capacity-Building Solution (Annual); SIIA CODiE Awards - Best Source for Reference or Education Resources (Annual); SIIA CODiE Awards - Best Formative Student Assessment Solution (Annual); SIIA CODiE Awards - Best Cross-Curricular Solution (Annual); SIIA CODiE Awards - Best ESL, ELL or World Language Acquisition Solution (Annual); SIIA CODiE Awards - Best Game-Based Curriculum Solution (Annual); SIIA CODiE Awards - Best Instructional Solution in Other Curriculum Areas (Annual); SIIA CODiE Awards - Best Mathematics Instructional Solution for Grades 9-12 & Higher Education (Annual); SIIA CODiE Awards - Best Professional Learning Solution for K-20 Faculty and Administrative Staff; SIIA CODiE Awards - Best Reading/English/Language Arts Instructional Solution (Annual); SIIA CODiE Awards - Best College and Career Readiness Solution (Annual); SIIA CODiE Awards - Best Science Instructional Solution (Annual); SIIA CODiE Awards - Best Social Sciences or Social Studies Instructional Solution (Annual); SIIA CODiE Awards - Best Solution for Special Needs Students (Irregular); SIIA CODiE Awards - Best Virtual Learning Solution (Annual); SIIA CODiE Awards - Best Postsecondary Enterprise Solution (Annual); SIIA CODiE Awards - Best Postsecondary LMS or Learning Platform (Annual); SIIA CODiE Awards - Best Postsecondary Learning Content Solution (Annual); SIIA CODiE Awards - Best Corporate/Workforce Learning Solution (Annual); SIIA CODiE Awards - Best Education Solution (Irregular). **Geographic Preference:** National.

INCUBATORS/RESEARCH AND TECHNOLOGY PARKS

14753 ■ Plug and Play - Fintech
440 N Wolfe Rd.
Sunnyvale, CA 94085
Ph: (408)524-1400
URL: http://www.plugandplaytechcenter.com/industries/fintech
Description: An accelerator for startups in the fintech industry. Provides support with venture and angel partners, mentorship, a data center, office space, and networking opportunities. **Founded:** 2014.

REFERENCE WORKS

14754 ■ "Abacast, Citadel Strike Radio Ad Deal" in Business Journal Portland (Vol. 27, December 31, 2010, No. 44, pp. 3)
Pub: Portland Business Journal
Contact: Andy Giegerich, Managing Editor
E-mail: agiegerich@bizjournals.com
Ed: Erik Siemers. **Description:** Software firm Abacast Inc. has partnered with Citadel Media to aid the latter's advertising sales. Citadel provides radio networks and syndicated programs to 4,200 affiliate stations. **Availability:** Print; Online.

14755 ■ "All Those Applications, and Phone Users Just Want to Talk" in Advertising Age (Vol. 79, August 11, 2008, No. 31, pp. 18)
Pub: Crain Communications, Inc.
Contact: Jessica Botos, Manager, Marketing
E-mail: jessica.botos@crainsnewyork.com
Ed: Mike Vorhaus. **Description:** Although consumers are slowly coming to text messaging and other data applications, a majority of those Americans surveyed stated that they simply want to use their cell phones to talk and do not care about other activities. Statistical data included. **Availability:** Online.

14756 ■ "Apps For Anybody With an Idea" in Advertising Age (Vol. 79, October 17, 2008, No. 39, pp. 29)
Pub: Crain Communications, Inc.
Contact: Jessica Botos, Manager, Marketing

E-mail: jessica.botos@crainsnewyork.com
Ed: Beth Snyder Bulik. **Description:** Apple's new online App Store is open to anyone with an idea and the ability to write code and many of these developers are not only finding a sense of community through this venue but are also making money since the sales are split with Apple, 30/70 in the developer's favor. **Availability:** Online.

14757 ■ "As Windows 8 Looms, Tech Investors Hold Their Breath" in Barron's (Vol. 92, July 23, 2012, No. 30, pp. 22)
Pub: Dow Jones & Company Inc.
Contact: Almar Latour, Chief Executive Officer
Ed: Tiernan Ray. **Description:** Launch of the Microsoft Windows 8 operating system could affect the stock prices of Microsoft and Intel. The effects of the software's introduction on the market share of personal computers remains uncertain. **Availability:** Online.

14758 ■ "Baseline Metrics CEOs Need for Online Brand Oversight" in South Florida Business Journal (Vol. 34, May 23, 2014, No. 44, pp. 16)
Pub: American City Business Journals, Inc.
Contact: Mike Olivieri, Executive Vice President
Released: Weekly. **Price:** $8, Introductory 4-week offer(Digital & Print). **Description:** Chief executive officers have the option to use metrics that will allow them to monitor their online brands. Social media engagement is an effective customer service metric because it presents a clear assessment of a business social media prowess. Reputation management software, on the other hand, ranks a firm's weekly, hourly, and daily sentiments online. **Availability:** Print; Online.

14759 ■ "BayTSP, NTT Data Corp. Enter Into Reseller Pact to Market Online IP Monitoring" in Professional Services Close-Up (Sept. 11, 2009)
Description: Due to incredible interest from distributors and content owners across Asia, NTT Data Corp. will resell BayTSP's online intellectual property monitoring, enforcement, business intelligence and monetization services in Japan.

14760 ■ "Being All a-Twitter" in Canadian Business (Vol. 81, December 8, 2008, No. 21, pp. 22)
Description: Marketing experts suggest that advertising strategies have to change along with new online social media. Companies are advised to find ways to incorporate social software because workers and customers are expected to continue its use. **Availability:** Print; Online.

14761 ■ "Beyond Microsoft and Yahoo!: Some M&A Prospects" in Barron's (Vol. 88, March 17, 2008, No. 11, pp. 39)
Pub: Dow Jones & Company Inc.
Contact: Almar Latour, Chief Executive Officer
Ed: Eric J. Savitz. **Description:** Weak quarterly earnings report for Yahoo! could pressure the company's board to cut a deal with Microsoft. Electronic Arts is expected to win its hostile $26-a-share bid for Take-Two Interactive Software. Potential targets and buyers for mergers and acquisitions are mentioned. **Availability:** Online.

14762 ■ "Bitcoin 'Killer App' Or the Currency of the Future?" in Providence Business News (Vol. 28, January 6, 2014, No. 40, pp. 1)
Pub: American City Business Journals, Inc.
Contact: Mike Olivieri, Executive Vice President
URL(s): pbn.com/bitcoin-killer-app-or-the-currency-of-the-future94158
Description: The Providence Bitcoin Meetup has gathered several technology experts to discuss Bitcoin, the popular digital currency. However, software developers, engineers and entrepreneurs see Bitcoin as the next killer app for the Internet and is changing how information and data is stored, shared and veri-

fied. The Bitcoin's impact in Rhode Island is examined. **Availability:** Online. **Telecommunication Services:** Anderson@pbn.com.

14763 ■ *"Blog Buzz Heralds Arrival of IPhone 2.0" in Advertising Age (Vol. 79, June 9, 2008, No. 40, pp. 8)*
Pub: Crain Communications, Inc.
Contact: Jessica Botos, Manager, Marketing
E-mail: jessica.botos@crainsnewyork.com
Ed: Abbey Klaassen. **Description:** Predictions concerning the next version of the iPhone include a global-positioning-system technology as well as a configuration to run on a faster, 3G network. **Availability:** Online.

14764 ■ *"Bringing Healthcare Home" in Austin Business Journal (Vol. 34, June 6, 2014, No. 16, pp. B13)*
Pub: American City Business Journals, Inc.
Contact: Mike Olivieri, Executive Vice President
Description: Chris Hester, founder and president of Kinnser Software feels that the company's growth since its inception has been both a blessing and a challenge. He states that his company's policy not to hire people until there's a strong need has increased productiveness of the company and the singular focus on customer service success has driven the company forward. **Availability:** Online.

14765 ■ *"BusinessOnLine Launches New Web-Based Search Engine Optimization Tool: First Link Checker for Google" in Marketwired (October 19, 2009)*
Pub: Comtex News Network Inc.
Contact: Kan Devnani, President
Description: First Link Checker, a complimentary new search engine optimization tool that helps site owners optimize their on-page links by understanding which of those links are actually being counted in Google's relevancy algorithm, was developed by BusinessOnLine, a rapidly growing Internet marketing agency. This tool will make it easy for the average web master to ensure that their internal link structure is optimized. **Availability:** Print.

14766 ■ *"CADD Microsystems Launches the CADD Community, Partners with Global eTraining to Provide Online, On-Demand Training for Autodesk Software" in Computer Business Week (August 28, 2014, pp. 24)*
Pub: NewsRX LLC.
Contact: Kalani Rosell, Contact
Description: A new online customer-only portal the integrates on-demand training, applications and extension, videos and additional value-added content for customers only was developed by CADD Microsystems. The Autodesk Platinum Partner calls this training program, CADD Community. **Availability:** Online.

14767 ■ *"CarBiz Inc. Speaking At NABD" in Marketwired (May 14, 2007)*
Pub: Comtex News Network Inc.
Contact: Kan Devnani, President
Description: CarBiz Inc., a leading provider of software, consulting, and training solutions to the United States' automotive industry, had two of its executive officers speak at the National Alliance of Buy Here - Pay Here Dealers (NABD), a conference that draws over 2,000 dealers, service providers, and experts from across the United States. **Availability:** Print; Online.

14768 ■ *"ClickFuel Unveils Internet Marketing Tools for Small Businesses" in Marketwired (October 19, 2009)*
Pub: Comtex News Network Inc.
Contact: Kan Devnani, President
Description: ClickFuel, a firm that manages, designs and tracks marketing campaigns has unveiled a full software suite of affordable services and technology solutions designed to empower small business owners and help them promote and grow their businesses through targeted Internet marketing campaigns. **Availability:** Online.

14769 ■ *"Cloud City: An Industry - and a Region - On the Rise" in Puget Sound Business Journal (Vol. 34, February 28, 2014, No. 46, pp. 4)*
Pub: American City Business Journals, Inc.
Contact: Mike Olivieri, Executive Vice President
Description: Seattle, Washington is experiencing an influx of the world's most innovative cloud companies. Businesses are shifting their applications from in-house servers or private data center into public cloud infrastructure, which is less expensive than buying the servers and managing the data systems. Seattle software companies are taking advantage of this trend and developing products. **Availability:** Online.

14770 ■ *"Clouds in the Forecast" in Information Today (Vol. 28, September 2011, No. 8, pp. 10)*
Pub: Information Today Inc.
Contact: Thomas H. Hogan, President
Ed: Paula J. Hane. **Description:** Cloud computing is software, applications, and data stored remotely and accessed via the Internet with output displayed on a client device. Recent developments in cloud computing are explored.

14771 ■ *"CradlePoint Is Adding Workers, Seeking More Space" in Idaho Business Review (September 3, 2014)*
Pub: BridgeTower Media
Contact: Adam Reinebach, President
Price: $11.99, Print, Digital & Mobile(1 Month); 149, Print, Digital & Mobile(1 Year); 99, Digital & Mobile Only(1 Year); $99, Digital & Mobile Only(For 1 Year); $9.95, Print, Digital & Mobile (For 1 Month Intro Rate); $149, Print, Digital & Mobile(For 1 Year).
Description: CradlePoint makes networking routers and software, focusing on security for businesses. The firm is hiring new workers at a rate higher than predicted and is seeking new office space in downtown Boise, Idaho. CradlePoint is a major player in the growing wireless service and cloud platform market and is growing faster than its competitors. **Availability:** Print; Online.

14772 ■ *"Ditch the Pet Store! MindJolt SGN and The Humane Society of the United States Unleash Fluff Friends Rescue" in Benzinga.com (January 4, 2012)*
Pub: Benzinga.com
Contact: Jason Raznick, Founder
Ed: Aaron Wise. **Description:** The Humane Society of the United States has partnered with MindJolt SGN, a multiplatform game developer and distributor, to release a mobile game called Fluff Friends Rescue. The game introduces players to the real-world challenges of rescuing pets by nursing animals back to health while running their own animal shelter.

14773 ■ *"Eagles Measure Suite Success" in Philadelphia Business Journal (Vol. 30, September 9, 2011, No. 30, pp. 1)*
Pub: Philadelphia Business Journal
Contact: Sierra Quinn, Director
E-mail: squinn@bizjournals.com
Ed: John George. **Description:** Philadelphia Eagles have a new software program that helps suite holders keep track of how their suite is being used and whether they are getting a return on their investment. The software allows suite holders to better utilize and distribute their tickets. **Availability:** Online.

14774 ■ *"Elastic Path Software Joins Canada in G20 Young Entrepreneur Summit" in Marketwire (June 14, 2010)*
Pub: Comtex News Network Inc.
Contact: Kan Devnani, President
Description: The Canadian Youth Business Foundation hosted the G20 Young Entrepreneur Summit and announced that Harry Chemko of British Columbia's Elastic Path Software will be a member of the Canadian delegation at the G20 Young Entrepreneur Summit. Details are included. **Availability:** Print; Online.

14775 ■ *"The Emergence of Governance In an Open Source Community" in Academy of Management Journal (Vol. 50, No. 5, October 1, 2007, pp. 1079)*
Pub: Academy of Management
Contact: Sharon Alvarez, President
Ed: Siobhan O'Mahony, Fabrizio Ferraro. **Description:** Study examined the method of self-governance among small communities producing collective goods, focusing on an open source software community. Results revealed that a combination of bureaucratic and democratic practices helped its governance system. **Availability:** Electronic publishing; PDF; Download; Online.

14776 ■ *"The Evolution of the Laws of Software Evolution: a Discussion Based On a Systematic Literature Review" in ACM Computing Surveys (Vol. 46, Summer 2014, No. 2, pp. 28)*
Pub: Association for Computing Machinery - Manor College Student Chapter
Contact: Mary Cecilia Jurasinski, President
Description: After more than 40 years of life, software evolution should be considered as a mature field. However, despite such a long history, many research questions still remain open, and controversial studies about the validity of the laws of software evolution are common. During the first part of these 40 years, the laws themselves evolved to adapt to the changes in both the research and the software industry environments. This process of adaption to new paradigms, standards, and practices stopped about 15 years ago, when the laws were revised for the last time. The current state of affairs about the validity of software laws, how they are perceived by the research community, and the developments and challenges likely to occur in the future are addressed. **Availability:** Print; PDF; Online.

14777 ■ *"Firms Bet On Games To Hike Wellness" in Business Journal (Vol. 30, June 1, 2012, No. 1, pp. 1)*
Pub: American City Business Journals, Inc.
Contact: Mike Olivieri, Executive Vice President
Ed: Katharine Grayson. **Released:** Weekly. **Price:** $4, introductory 4-week offer(Digital only). **Description:** Twin Cities-based firms providing corporate wellness services are integrating games into these programs. These games include friendly competitions between work teams or high-tech smartphone applications. **Availability:** Print; Online.

14778 ■ *"Five Easy Ways to Fail: Nothing Like a Weak Team Or An Unrealistic Schedule To Start a Project Off Right" in Inc. (November 2007, pp. 85-87)*
Ed: Joel Spolsky. **Description:** Five easy ways to fail meeting a project deadline are discussed by the owner of a software development company: start with second-rate team of developers, set weekly milestones, negotiate a deadline, divide tasks equitably, and work until midnight. **Availability:** Online.

14779 ■ *"Game On: When Work Becomes Play" in Canadian Business (Vol. 80, February 12, 2007, No. 4, pp. 15)*
Description: The plan of president of TransGaming Vikas Gupta to create innovative software programs for games that can be played in different operating systems is discussed. **Availability:** Online.

14780 ■ *"Game Plan: The Business of Bingo" in Canadian Business (Vol. 79, September 11, 2006, No. 18, pp. 50)*
Ed: Joe Castaldo. **Released:** September 08, 2016. **Description:** Strategies adopted by gaming companies to revitalize their business and give a stimulus to their falling resources are presented. **Availability:** Print; Online.

14781 ■ *"German Win Through Sharing" in Canadian Business (Vol. 83, September 14, 2010, No. 15, pp. 16)*
Pub: Rogers Media Inc.
Contact: Neil Spivak, Chief Executive Officer

Ed: Jordan Timm. **Released:** September 14, 2010. **Description:** German economic historian Eckhard Hoffner has a two-volume work showing how German's relaxed attitude toward copyright and intellectual property helped it catch up to industrialized United Kingdom. Hoffner's research was in response to his interest in the usefulness of software patents. Information on the debate regarding Canada's copyright laws is given. **Availability:** Print; Online.

14782 ■ *"Getting Rid of Global Glitches: Choosing Software For Trade Compliance" in Black Enterprise (Vol. 41, September 2010, No. 2, pp. 48)*
Pub: Earl G. Graves Ltd.
Contact: Earl Graves, Jr., President
Ed: Marcia Wade Talbert. **Description:** Compliance software for trading with foreign companies must be compatible with the U.S. Census Bureau's Automated Export System (www.aesdirect.gov). It has to be current with regulatory requirements for any country in the world. Whether owners handle their own compliance or hire a logistics company, they need to be familiar with this software in order to access reports and improve transparency and efficiency of theft supply chain. **Availability:** Online.

14783 ■ *"Google Places a Call to Bargain Hunters" in Advertising Age (Vol. 79, September 29, 2008, No. 36, pp. 13)*
Pub: Crain Communications, Inc.
Contact: Jessica Botos, Manager, Marketing
E-mail: jessica.botos@crainsnewyork.com
Ed: Abbey Klaassen. **Description:** Google highlighted application developers who have created tools for its Android mobile phone in the device's unveiling; applications such as ShopSavvy and CompareEverywhere help shoppers to find bargains by allowing them to compare prices in their local areas and across the web. **Availability:** Online.

14784 ■ *"Growing Encryptics Trades Frisco for Austin" in Austin Business Journal (Vol. 34, April 25, 2014, No. 10, pp. A8)*
Pub: American City Business Journals, Inc.
Contact: Mike Olivieri, Executive Vice President
Released: Weekly. **Price:** $4, Introductory 4-week offer(Digital & Print). **Description:** Frisco, Texas-based Encryptics Inc. has announced plans to relocate its headquarters with its 21 employees and negotiating for office space in West Austin's Loop 360 area. Encryptics also plans to increase the number of its employees to about 80 next year. Insights into Encryptics' email security softward area also given. **Availability:** Print; Online.

14785 ■ *"A Heart for Software; Led by Its Upbeat CEO, Menlo Spreads Joy of Technology" in Crain's Detroit Business (Vol. 30, October 13, 2014, No. 41, pp. 1)*
Pub: Crain Communications Inc.
Contact: Barry Asin, President
Description: Profile of Rich Sheridan, one of the most prominent names in IT in Ann Arbor, Michigan. Sheridan believes in common-sense solutions and manages his workers to be empowered employees to come up with their own solutions to software coding issues, and he is a consummate salesman and marketer. He runs his company so it goes beyond understanding what the user needs, and managing a great team, to being the front man selling his goods and services. **Availability:** Print; Online.

14786 ■ *"Heartbleed Headache Will Pound For Years" in Puget Sound Business Journal (Vol. 34, April 18, 2014, No. 53, pp. 7)*
Pub: American City Business Journals, Inc.
Contact: Mike Olivieri, Executive Vice President
Description: Seattle, Washington-based technology experts expressed concerns about the cybersecurity implications of the Heartbleed bug for years to come. The bug affected most virtual private network (VPN) software, which is the way most encrypted communications travel. The impact of the Heartbleed bug on critical infrastructure is examined. **Availability:** Online.

14787 ■ *"Holiday Sales Look Uncertain for Microsoft and PC Sellers" in Puget Sound Business Journal (Vol. 29, November 28, 2008, No. 32)*
Ed: Todd Bishop. **Description:** Personal computer makers face uncertain holiday sales for 2008 as a result of the weak U.S. economy and a shift toward low-cost computers. Personal computer shipments for the fourth quarter 2008 are forecast to drop 1 percent compared to the same quarter 2007. **Availability:** Online.

14788 ■ *"Horse Race: Putting the App in Apple" in Inc. (Vol. 30, November 2008, No. 11)*
Pub: Mansueto Ventures L.L.C.
Contact: Stephanie Mehta, Chief Executive Officer
Ed: Nitasha Tiku. **Description:** Aftermarket companies are scrambling to develop games and widgets for Apple's iPhone. Apple launched a kit for developers interested in creating iPhone-specific software along with the App Store, and an iTunes spinoff. Profiles of various software programs that may be used on the iPhone are given. **Availability:** Online.

14789 ■ *"Ingrian and Channel Management International Sign Distribution Agreement" in Canadian Corporate News (May 16, 2007)*
Description: Channel Management International (CMI), a Canadian channel management and distribution company, and Ingrian Networks, Inc., the leading provider of data privacy solutions, announced a Canadian distribution agreement to resell Ingrian encryption solutions to the Canadian market. **Availability:** Online.

14790 ■ *"Innovation Central: Tech, Tweets, and Trolls" in Inc. (Vol. 36, September 2014, No. 7, pp. 102)*
Pub: Mansueto Ventures L.L.C.
Contact: Stephanie Mehta, Chief Executive Officer
Description: Results of a survey regarding the ways small business is using technology to grow their businesses is presented. Information covers social media applications, government software patents, trends impacting small business, and the most innovative technology companies. **Availability:** Print; Online.

14791 ■ *"Inside Intel's Effectiveness System for Web Marketing" in Advertising Age (Vol. 81, January 25, 2010, No. 4, pp. 4)*
Pub: Crain Communications, Inc.
Contact: Jessica Botos, Manager, Marketing
E-mail: jessica.botos@crainsnewyork.com
Ed: Beth Snyder Bulik. **Description:** Overview of Intel's internally developed program called Value Point System in which the company is using in order to evaluate and measure online marketing effectiveness. **Availability:** Online.

14792 ■ *"Inside Waterloo's Quiet Tech Titan" in Canadian Business (Vol. 87, July 2014, No. 7, pp. 39)*
Description: OpenText chief executive officer Mark Barrenechea feels confident about the financial health of the Waterloo, Ontario-based software company. He adds that the company is exploring opportunities by the big data phenomenon. **Availability:** Online.

14793 ■ *"Kinnser: Sales In Overdrive" in Austin Business Journal (Vol. 32, March 30, 2012, No. 4, pp. 1)*
Pub: American City Business Journals, Inc.
Contact: Mike Olivieri, Executive Vice President
Ed: Christopher Calnan. **Description:** Kinnser Software Inc.'s receipt of fresh capitalization is seen to enable the company to pursue its acquisition strategy. The company is planning to grow organically. It is also planning to double the number of its employees. **Availability:** Online.

14794 ■ *"Largest North Texas Software Developers" in Dallas Business Journal (Vol. 37, January 31, 2014, No. 21, pp. 8)*
Pub: American City Business Journals, Inc.
Contact: Mike Olivieri, Executive Vice President

Released: September 29, 2017. **Description:** The largest software development companies in North Texas as of February 6, 2014, ranked by full time local staff are listed. Sabre got the top spot. Meanwhile, Crossmark ranked second. **Availability:** Print; Online.

14795 ■ *"Lights, Camera, Action: Tools for Creating Video Blogs" in Inc. (Volume 32, December 2010, No. 10, pp. 57)*
Pub: Mansueto Ventures L.L.C.
Contact: Stephanie Mehta, Chief Executive Officer
Ed: John Brandon. **Description:** A video blog is a good way to spread company news, talk about products, and stand out among traditional company blogs. New editing software can create two- to four-minute blogs using a webcam and either Windows Live Essentials, Apple iLife 2011, Powerdirector 9 Ultra, or Adobe Visual Communicator 3. **Availability:** Online.

14796 ■ *"Longwood's FamilLab More Than Just a Hackerspace: It's a Free Form Research and Development Lab" in Orlando Business Journal (Vol. 30, January 17, 2014, No. 30, pp. 4)*
Pub: American City Business Journals, Inc.
Contact: Mike Olivieri, Executive Vice President
Description: FamilLab is a nonprofit hackerspace in Longwood, Florida that has turned into a free-form research and development outfit. The group has at least 70 members who share the same passion for technology and push the limits and boundaries of computer hardware and software, and sometimes start their own business. **Availability:** Print; Online.

14797 ■ *"Microsoft Goes Macrosoft" in Barron's (Vol. 89, July 27, 2009, No. 30, pp. 25)*
Pub: Dow Jones & Company Inc.
Contact: Almar Latour, Chief Executive Officer
Ed: Mark Veverka. **Description:** Microsoft reported a weak quarter on the heels of a tech rally which suggests the economy has not turned around. Marc Andreesen describes his new venture-capital fund as focused on "classic tech" and that historical reference places him in the annals of the last millennium. **Availability:** Online.

14798 ■ *"Microsoft Releases Office Security Updates" in Mac World (Vol. 27, November 2010, No. 11, pp. 66)*
Description: Office for Mac and Mac Business Unit are Microsoft's pair of security- and stability-enhancing updates for Office 2008 and Office 2004. The software will improve the stability and compatibility and fixes vulnerabilities that would allow attackers to overwrite Mac's memory with malicious code. **Availability:** Online.

14799 ■ *"Microsoft's Diversity Program Clicks into High Speed" in Hispanic Business (Vol. 30, July-August 2008, No. 7-8, pp. 54)*
Ed: Derek Reveron. **Description:** Microsoft's diversity hiring and vendor diversity program to capture more Hispanic consumer and business-to-business market is described. One of the main goals of these programs is to hire more Hispanic executives and managers who will help the company develop and market products and services that will appeal and benefit Hispanic consumers.

14800 ■ *"More Leading Retailers Using Omniture Conversion Solutions to Boost Sales and Ecommerce Performance" in Marketwired (September 22, 2009)*
Pub: Comtex News Network Inc.
Contact: Kan Devnani, President
Description: Many retailers are utilizing Omniture conversion solutions to improve the performance of their ecommerce businesses; recent enhancements to Omniture Merchandising and Omniture Recommendations help clients drive increased conversion to their Internet ventures.

14801 ■ *"My Favorite Tool for Organizing Data" in Inc. (Vol. 33, November 2011, No. 9, pp. 46)*
Pub: Inc. Magazine
Ed: Abram Brown. **Description:** Intelligence software firm uses Roambi, a Web-based service that turns spreadsheet data into interactive files for iPhones and iPads. **Availability:** Online.

14802 ■ *"New IPhone Also Brings New Way of Mobile Marketing" in Advertising Age (Vol. 79, June 16, 2008, No. 24, pp. 23)*
Pub: Crain Communications, Inc.
Contact: Jessica Botos, Manager, Marketing
E-mail: jessica.botos@crainsnewyork.com
Ed: Abbey Klaassen. **Description:** Currently there are two kinds of applications for the iPhone and other mobile devices: native applications that allow for richer experiences and take advantage of features that are built into a phone and web applications, those that allow access to the web through specific platforms. Marketers are interested in creating useful experiences for customers and opening up the platforms which will allow them to do this. **Availability:** Online.

14803 ■ *"New Wave of Business Security Products Ushers in the Kaspersky Anti-Malware Protection System" in Internet Wire (October 26, 2010)*
Description: Kaspersky Anti-Malware System provides anti-malware protection that requires minimal in-house resources for small businesses. The system offers a full range of tightly integrated end-to-end protection solutions, ensuring unified protection across an entire network, from endpoint and mobile device protection to file server, mail server, network storage and gateway protection. It provides flexible centralized management, immediate threat visibility and a level of responsiveness not seen in other anti-malware approaches. **Availability:** Print; Online.

14804 ■ *"Next Generation Security Awareness" in Security Management (Vol. 56, September 2012, No. 9, pp. 32)*
Description: Carnegie Mellon University (CMU) has purchased Wombat Security Technologies' PhishGuru to reduce the phishing attacks. CMU also purchased Wombat's two educational games, Anti-Phishing and Anti-Phishing Phyllis, partly due to the PhishGuru's success. Insights on the software-as-a-service solution are also given.

14805 ■ *"Next-Level E-Commerce" in Entrepreneur (June 2014)*
Pub: Entrepreneur Media Inc.
Contact: Dan Bova, Director
E-mail: dbova@entrepreneur.com
Description: BloomReach's SNAP software enables consumers to see the products they want upon arriving at an e-commerce Website. The software does this by evaluating the users' intent and preferences based on previous site usage. The enterprise-level software, which costs retailers at least $7,500/month, aims to use big data to help consumers choose products based on their intent. The cloud-based service indexes every page on a client's site and automatically generates appropriate content for visitors. The use of machine learning reduces lag time between application and positive results. **Availability:** Print; Online.

14806 ■ *"Nonprofit NAIC Acquires Software Developer as For-Profit Arm" in Crain's Detroit Business (Vol. 25, June 22, 2009, No. 25, pp. 10)*
Pub: Crain Communications Inc.
Contact: Barry Asin, President
Ed: Sherri Begin Welch. **Description:** Details of National Association of Investors Corporation's acquisition of a Massachusetts investment software developer in order to offer more products to investment clubs and individual investors nationwide. **Availability:** Online.

14807 ■ *"Not Your Father's Whiteboard" in Inc. (Vol. 33, November 2011, No. 9, pp. 50)*
Pub: Inc. Magazine
Ed: Adam Baer. **Description:** Sharp's new interactive whiteboard is really a 70-inch touch screen monitor with software for importing presentations from any Windows 7 computer. **Availability:** Online.

14808 ■ *"Paging Dr. Phil" in Canadian Business (Vol. 79, September 25, 2006, No. 19, pp. 21)*
Description: Increasing corporate crimes in software industry is discussed by focusing on recent case of Hewlett and Packard. **Availability:** Print; Mailing list; Online.

14809 ■ *"PC Connection Acquires Cloud Software Provider" in New Hampshire Business Review (Vol. 33, March 25, 2011, No. 6, pp. 8)*
Description: Merrimack-based PC Connection Inc. acquired ValCom Technology, a provider of cloud-based IT service management software. Details of the deal are included. **Availability:** Print; Online.

14810 ■ *"PC Running Slowly? How to Rev Up Your Machine" in Inc. (Vol. 33, November 2011, No. 9, pp. 46)*
Pub: Mansueto Ventures L.L.C.
Contact: Stephanie Mehta, Chief Executive Officer
Ed: John Brandon. **Released:** November 01, 2011. **Description:** Software that keeps PCs tuned up and running smoothing are profiled: AUSLO6ICS BOOST-SPEED 5, $50; Tuneup Utilities 2011, $40; Slimware Slimcleaner 1.9, free; and IOBIT Advanced Systemcare Pro 4, $20 a year. **Availability:** Print; Online.

14811 ■ *"Platforms and Publishers: The End of an Era" in Columbia Journalism Review (November 22, 2019)*
URL(s): www.cjr.org/tow_center_reports/platforms-and-publishers-end-of-an-era.php
Ed: Nushin Rashidian, George Tsiveriotis, Pete Brown, Emily, Bell, Abigail Hartstone. **Released:** November 22, 2019. **Description:** News publishers are calling the end of an era when it comes to digital platforms in the field of journalism. This in-depth piece investigates why publishers are abandoning platforms and moving back to serving their loyal readers with their own properties. **Availability:** Online.

14812 ■ *"The Power of Negative Thinking" in Inc. (Volume 32, December 2010, No. 10, pp. 43)*
Pub: Inc. Magazine
Ed: Jason Fried. **Description:** A Website is software and most businesses have and need a good Website to generate business. Understanding for building a powerful Website is presented. **Availability:** Online.

14813 ■ *"Power Ranger" in Inc. (November 2007, pp. 131)*
Ed: Nitasha Tiku. **Description:** Surveyor software is designed to power down computers when not in use, in order to save energy. **Availability:** Online.

14814 ■ *"Powering Intelligent Commerce: eCommera Rebrands as OrderDynamics, Helping Retailers Activate Commerce from First Interaction to Fulfillment" in Computer Business Week (August 28, 2014, pp. 20)*
Pub: NewsRX LLC.
Contact: Kalani Rosell, Contact
Description: OrderDynamics, a new global brand created by eCommera, is profiled. The firm will continue to provide an integrated suite of software-as-a-service (SaaS) big data products and service that power intelligent commerce for retailers and brands around the world. Details of the integration of the new brand are included. **Availability:** Online.

14815 ■ *"Precision Crop Control with Valley Irrigation/CropMetrics Partnership" in Farm Industry News (January 6, 2011)*
Pub: Informa Business Media, Inc.
Contact: Charlie McCurdy, President

Ed: Karen McMahon. **Description:** Irrigation systems have become a precision farming tool since partnering with agronomic software systems to apply products across the field by prescription. Valley Irrigation and CropMetrics have partnered in order to variably control water, fertilizer and other crop management products through a center pivot irrigation system. **Availability:** Print; Online.

14816 ■ *"Press Release: Trimble Introduces CFX-750 Display" in Farm Industry News (January 4, 2011)*
Description: Trimble is offering a touch screen display called the CFX-750. The new 8-inch full-color display allows farmers to choose the specific guidance, steering and precision agriculture capabilities that best fit their farm's particular needs. The display can be upgraded as business needs change, including the addition of GLONASS capabilities, or the addition of section and rate control for crop inputs such as seed, chemicals and fertilizer. **Availability:** Print; Online.

14817 ■ *"Programs Provide Education and Training" in Contractor (Vol. 56, September 2009, No. 9, pp. 56)*
Ed: William Feldman, Patti Feldman. **Description:** Opportunity Interactive's Showroom v2 software provides uses computer graphics to provide education and training on HVAC equipment and systems. It can draw heat pump balance points for a specific home. Meanwhile, Simutech's HVAC Training Simulators provide trainees with 'hands-on' HVACR training. **Availability:** Print; Online.

14818 ■ *"Providers Ride First Wave of eHealth Dollars" in Boston Business Journal (Vol. 31, June 10, 2011, No. 20, pp. 1)*
Pub: Boston Business Journal
Contact: Carolyn M. Jones, President
E-mail: cmjones@bizjournals.com
Ed: Julie M. Donnelly. **Released:** Weekly. **Description:** Health care providers in Massachusetts implementing electronic medical records technology started receiving federal stimulus funds. Beth Israel Deaconess Medical Center was the first hospital to qualify for the funds. **Availability:** Print.

14819 ■ *Publishers, Distributors, and Wholesalers of the United States*
Pub: R.R. Bowker L.L.C.
URL(s): www.greyhouse.com/Publishers-Distributors-and-Wholesalers-of-the-United-States
Price: $995, Individuals. **Description:** Covers over 196,066 publishers, distributors, and wholesalers; includes associations, museums, software producers and manufacturers, and others not included in 'Books in Print'. **Entries include:** Publisher name, editorial and ordering addresses, e-mail, websites, phone, Standard Address Numbers (SANs), International Standard Book Number prefix. **Arrangement:** Alphabetical; distributors and wholesalers are listed separately. **Indexes:** ISBN prefix, abbreviation, type of business, imprint name, geographical, inactive and out of business company name, toll-free phone and fax, wholesaler and distributor. **Availability:** Print; PDF.

14820 ■ *QuickBooks 2014 on Demand*
Pub: Que Publishing
Ed: Gail Perry. **Released:** 1st edition. **Price:** $22.39, Members, e-book. **Description:** Step-by-step training for using various small business financial software programs; includes illustrated, full color explanations. **Availability:** watermarked; E-book; Print; Electronic publishing; PDF.

14821 ■ *"RES Stakes Its Claim in Area" in Philadelphia Business Journal (Vol. 28, January 29, 2010, No. 50, pp. 1)*
Pub: Philadelphia Business Journal
Contact: Sierra Quinn, Director
E-mail: squinn@bizjournals.com
Ed: Peter Key. **Description:** RES Software Company Inc. of Amsterdam, Netherlands appointed Jim Kirby as president for the Americas and Klaus Besier as chairman in an effort to boost the firm's presence in

the US. Brief career profiles of Kirby and Besier are included. RES develops software that allows management of information flow between an organization and its employees regardless of location. **Availability:** Online.

14822 ■ *"Route Optimization Impacts the Bottom Line" in Contractor (Vol. 56, November 2009, No. 11, pp. 48)*

Ed: Dave Beaudry. **Description:** Plumbing and HVAC businesses can save a significant amount of money from route optimization. The process begins with gathering information on a fleet and a routing software tool can determine the effectiveness of current route configurations and identify preferable route plans. **Availability:** Print; Online.

14823 ■ *"Search Engines: Image Conscious" in Canadian Business (Vol. 81, February 26, 2008, No. 4, pp. 36)*

Pub: Rogers Media Inc.

Contact: Neil Spivak, Chief Executive Officer

Ed: Andrew Wahl. **Description:** Idee Inc. is testing an Internet search engine for images that does not rely on tags but compares its visual data to a database of other images. The company was founded and managed by Leila Boujnane as an off-shoot of their risk-management software firm. Their software has already been used by image companies to track copyrighted images and to find images within their own archives. **Availability:** Online.

14824 ■ *"Sense of Discovery" in Business Journal Portland (Vol. 27, November 19, 2010, No. 38, pp. 1)*

Pub: Portland Business Journal

Contact: Andy Giegerich, Managing Editor

E-mail: agiegerich@bizjournals.com

Description: Tigard, Oregon-based Exterro Inc. CEO Bobby Balachandran announced plans to go public without the help of an institutional investor. Balachandran believes Exterro could grow to a $100 million legal compliance software company in the span of three years. Insights on Exterro's growth as market leader in the $1 billion legal governance software market are also given. **Availability:** Print; Online.

14825 ■ *"Siri Creator SRI International Hopes Lola Cashes In, Too" in Silicon Valley/San Jose Business Journal (Vol. 30, July 6, 2012, No. 15, pp. 1)*

Pub: Baltimore Business Journal

Contact: Rhonda Pringle, President

E-mail: rpringle@bizjournals.com

Description: Software developer and SRI and BBVA have partnered to create virtual personal assistant Lola. The program assists customers with their banking needs. Program features and dimensions are also included. **Availability:** Print; Online.

14826 ■ *"Slow but Steady into the Future" in Barron's (Vol. 88, July 7, 2008, No. 27, pp. M)*

Pub: Dow Jones & Company Inc.

Contact: Almar Latour, Chief Executive Officer

Ed: Mark Veverka. **Description:** Investors are advised to maintain their watch on the shares of business software company NetSuite. The company's chief executive officer, Zach Nelson, claims that the company has a 10-year lead on its competitors with the development of software-as-a service. **Availability:** Online.

14827 ■ *"Small Is Bountiful for Intuit" in Barron's (Vol. 90, September 13, 2010, No. 37, pp. 22)*

Pub: Barron's Editorial & Corporate Headquarters

Ed: Mark Veverka. **Description:** Finance software maker Intuit wants to tap the underserved small business market. One analyst sees Intuit's shares rising 25 percent to 55 percent in the next 12 months from September 2010. **Availability:** Online.

14828 ■ *"Social Apps, Business Style: Savvy App Makers Bring Consumer Features to the Enterprise" in Silicon Valley/San Jose Business Journal (Vol. 30, September 28, 2012, No. 27, pp. 1)*

Pub: Baltimore Business Journal

Contact: Rhonda Pringle, President

E-mail: rpringle@bizjournals.com

Description: Companies like Good Technology Inc. and Socialtext Inc. are developing mobile apps software for business enterprises with consumer features such as photo sharing and location check-ins. Consumer tendencies have influenced the growth of the enterprise mobiel apps market, which is prediced to reach $11.5 billion by 2004. **Availability:** Print; Online.

14829 ■ *"A Software Company's Whimsical Widgets Were an Instant Hit. But Its Core Product Was Getting Overshadowed" in Inc. (January 2008)*

Ed: Alex Salkever. **Description:** A widget designed as a marketing tool turned into a hit on Facebook. Should ChipIn shift its focus?. **Availability:** Online.

14830 ■ *"Software Developers" in Business Review Albany (Vol. 41, July 18, 2014, No. 17, pp. 9)*

Description: The top software development companies in Albany, New York are ranked by local software revenue in 2013. CMA Consulting Services is listed in the top spot, with GCOM Software following in second place. **Availability:** Online.

14831 ■ *"Software Publishers Industry: What's Next for the Industry?" in Via.news (June 20, 2020)*

Ed: Ruchi Gupta. **Released:** June 20, 2020. **Description:** Software publishing is a fast-growing industry worth about $474.5 billion. Discusses the short- and long-term outlooks and sectors where software publishing is more active. **Availability:** Online.

14832 ■ *"Software's Last Hurrah" in Canadian Business (Vol. 81, December 24, 2007, No. 1, pp. 27)*

Description: Canada's software industry could be facing a challenge with IBM's acquisition of Cognos, which was the country's last major independent business intelligence company and was also IBM's largest acquisition ever. Next in line to Cognos in terms of prominence is Open Text Corporation, which could also be a possible candidate for acquisition, as analysts predict. **Availability:** Print; Online.

14833 ■ *"Spinout Success: New Leadership Steps In At UW's C4C" in Puget Sound Business Journal (Vol. 35, June 27, 2014, No. 10, pp. 11)*

Pub: American City Business Journals, Inc.

Contact: Mike Olivieri, Executive Vice President

Description: University of Washington's Center for Commercialization vice provost, Vikram Jandhyala, talks about his new position with the school. Jandhyala says he plans to build more synergy between the medical school and engineering and between social sciences and computer science. He also says the medical and software industry need to grow to accommodate the volume of data crossing and stored within the Internet. **Availability:** Online.

14834 ■ *"The Story Of Diane Greene" in Barron's (Vol. 88, July 14, 2008, No. 28, pp. 31)*

Pub: Dow Jones & Company Inc.

Contact: Almar Latour, Chief Executive Officer

Ed: Mark Veverka. **Description:** Discusses the ousting of Diane Greene as a chief executive of VMWare, a developer of virtualization software, after the firm went public; in this case Greene, a brilliant engineer, should not be negatively impacted by the decision because it is common for companies to bring in new executive leadership that is more operations oriented after the company goes public. **Availability:** Online.

14835 ■ *"A Survey of Combinatorial Testing" in ACM Computing Surveys (Vol. 43, Summer 2011, No. 2, pp. 11)*

Pub: Association for Computing Machinery

Contact: Yannis Ioannidis, President

Ed: Changhai Nie, Hareton Leung. **Description:** Combinatorial Testing (CT) can detect failures triggered by interactions of parameters in the Software Under Test (SUT) with a covering array test suite generated by some sampling mechanisms. Basic concepts and notations of CT are covered. **Availability:** Download; PDF; Online.

14836 ■ *"A Survey of Comparison-Based System-Level Diagnosis" in ACM Computing Surveys (Vol. 43, Fall 2011, No. 3, pp. 22)*

Pub: Association for Computing Machinery

Contact: Yannis Ioannidis, President

Ed: Elias P. Duarte, Jr., Roverli P. Ziwich, Luiz C. P. Albini. **Released:** Volume 43 Issue 3. **Price:** $10, Members; $15, Nonmembers; $5, Students. **Description:** The growing complexity and dependability requirements of hardware, software, and networks demand efficient techniques for discovering disruptive behavior in those systems. Comparison-based diagnosis is a realistic approach to detect faulty units based on the outputs of tasks executed by system units. This survey integrates the vast amount of research efforts that have been produced in this field. **Availability:** Download; PDF.

14837 ■ *"Taking Off" in Puget Sound Business Journal (Vol. 34, January 31, 2014, No. 42, pp. 4)*

Pub: American City Business Journals, Inc.

Contact: Mike Olivieri, Executive Vice President

Description: Washington State is at the forefront of the U.S. space flight industry, as the federal government shrinks its role and entrepreneurs are filling the gap. The region is becoming a leader in the space sector because of its high-tech aerospace skills, software intellectuals, and investors willing to fund these enterprises. **Availability:** Online.

14838 ■ *"Teakwood Capital Raises $40M to Buy Tech Companies" in Dallas Business Journal (Vol. 35, March 2, 2012, No. 25, pp. 1)*

Pub: Baltimore Business Journal

Contact: Rhonda Pringle, President

E-mail: rpringle@bizjournals.com

Description: Dallas, Texas-based private equity firm Teakwood Capital LP has raised $40 million following the raising of $25 million as its initial fund in 2006. Teakwood Capital LP targets the purchase of businesses that apply technology to enhance operational efficiencies of their clients, mainly through software deals. The fund raising process of Teakwood Capital LP is also described. **Availability:** Print; Online.

14839 ■ *"Thinking Strategically About Technology" in Franchising World (Vol. 42, August 2010, No. 8, pp. 9)*

Pub: International Franchise Association

Contact: Matthew Haller, President

E-mail: mhaller@franchise.org

Ed: Bruce Franson. **Released:** 2010. **Description:** Nearly 25 percent of companies waste money from their technology budget. Most of the budget is spent on non-strategic software. Ways to spend money on technology for any franchise are examined. **Availability:** Online.

14840 ■ *"Three Productivity Solutions" in Contractor (Vol. 57, February 2010, No. 2, pp. 26)*

Ed: William Feldman, Patti Feldman. **Description:** Singletouch is a real-time data capture solution for mechanical and other contractors that work in jobs that require materials and workload tracking. Contractors get information on extreme weather and sudden changes in the cost of materials. The OptimumHVAC optimization software by Optimum Energy is designed to optimize energy savings in commercial buildings. **Availability:** Print; Online.

14841 ■ *"Two Field Service Management Solutions" in Contractor (Vol. 56, November 2009, No. 11, pp. 37)*

Ed: William Feldman, Patti Feldman. **Description:** Bella Solutions Field Service Software v. 4.2 is a web based solution for HVAC service contractors that enables scheduling of emergency, one-time, multi-visit or periodically recurring jobs with drag and drop appointments. VaZing is another web based solution that costs $99 per month for contractors. It can handle line-item discounting and invoices aside from scheduling. **Availability:** Print; Online.

14842 ■ *"Unbound ID Raises $2 Million"* in *Austin Business JournalInc. (Vol. 28, December 12, 2008, No. 39, pp. 1)*

Description: Austin, Texas-based Unbound ID Corporation has secured $2 million in funding from venture capital firm Silverton Partners. The company has developed identity management software for network directories. The market for identity management technology is expected to grow to more than $12.3 billion by 2014. **Availability:** Print; Online.

14843 ■ *"Unbreakable: Computer Software"* in *Canadian Business (Vol. 79, October 9, 2006, No. 20, pp. 111)*

Pub: Rogers Media Inc.

Contact: Neil Spivak, Chief Executive Officer

Ed: Robert Hercz. **Description:** The features and functions of Neutrino, an embedded operating system developed by QNX Software Systems are discussed. **Availability:** Online.

14844 ■ *"uTest Discusses the Evolution of Crowdsourcing Models at CrowdConf 2010"* in *Marketwired (October 1, 2010)*

Pub: Comtex News Network Inc.

Contact: Kan Devnani, President

Description: World's largest software testing marketplace, uTest, announces its first conference dedicated to the emerging field of crowdsourcing along with the future of distributed work. A panel of experts will discuss common misconceptions about crowdsourcing using real-world examples. **Availability:** Print; Mailing list; Online.

14845 ■ *"Washington Post Licenses Its Arc Software to BP"* in *Techradar.pro (September 26, 2019)*

URL(s): www.techradar.com/news/washington-post-licenses-its-arc-software-to-bp

Ed: Anthony Spadafora. **Released:** September 26, 2019. **Description:** The Washington Post licenses out its proprietary Arc publishing software and for the first time has a non-media customer, BP, which plans on using it to publish articles and videos across its internal websites. **Availability:** Online.

14846 ■ *"What Has Sergey Wrought?"* in *Barron's (Vol. 89, July 13, 2009, No. 28, pp. 8)*

Pub: Dow Jones & Company Inc.

Contact: Almar Latour, Chief Executive Officer

Ed: Alan Abelson. **Description:** Sergey Aleynikov is a computer expert that once worked for Goldman Sachs but he was arrested after he left the company and charged with theft for bringing with him the code for the company's proprietary software for high-frequency trading. The stock market has been down for four straight weeks as of July 13, 2009 which reflects the reality of how the economy is still struggling. **Availability:** Online.

14847 ■ *"Winners Dream: A Journey from Corner Store to Corner Office"*

Pub: Simon & Schuster Adult Publishing Group

Contact: Jonathan Karp, President

Released: October 14, 2014. **Price:** $28.99, hardcover, plus $2.24 shipping charges. **Description:** Bill McDermott, CEO of the world's largest business software company, SAP, profiles his career. He discusses his career moves, sales strategies, employee incentives to create high performance teams, and the competitive advantages of optimism and hard work. The entrepreneur offers a blueprint for success and the knowledge that the real dream is the journey, not the preconceived destination. **Availability:** E-book; Print; Download; Audio.

14848 ■ *"Yammer Gets Serious"* in *Inc. (Volume 32, December 2010, No. 10, pp. 58)*

Pub: Inc. Magazine

Ed: Eric Markowitz. **Description:** Yammer, an internal social network for companies, allows coworkers to share ideas and documents in real-time. Details of this service are included. **Availability:** Online.

14849 ■ *Zotero for Genealogy: Harnessing the Power of Your Research*

Ed: Donna Cox Baker. **Price:** $21.99, Paperback; $9.99, E-book. **Description:** A guide on how to use the Zotero download for genealogy research. The product eliminates bulky files, binders, papers and allows the user to keep all notes and citations on any computing device. **Availability:** E-book; Print.

STATISTICAL SOURCES

14850 ■ *RMA Annual Statement Studies*

Pub: Risk Management Association

Contact: Nancy Foster, President

Released: Annual. **Description:** Contains composite balance sheets and income statements for more than 360 industries, including the accounting, auditing, and bookkeeping industries. Also contains five years of comparative historical data for discerning trends. Includes 16 commonly used ratios, computed for most of the size groupings for nearly every industry.

14851 ■ *Software Publishing Industry in the US - Market Research Report*

URL(s): www.ibisworld.com/united-states/market-research-reports/software-publishing-industry/

Price: $925. **Description:** Downloadable report analyzing the current and future trends in the software publishing industry. **Availability:** Download.

14852 ■ *Standard & Poor's Industry Surveys*

Pub: Standard And Poor's Financial Services LLC.

Contact: Douglas L. Peterson, President

Description: Two-volume book that examines the prospects for specific industries, including trucking. Also provides analyses of trends and problems, statistical tables and charts, and comparative company analyses.

TRADE PERIODICALS

14853 ■ *Amplify*

Pub: Cutter Information Corp.

Contact: Tanaia Parker, President

URL(s): www.cutter.com/journals/amplify

Released: Monthly **Description:** Provides IT managers with practical and objective views on the latest technology and management trends. **Availability:** Print; PDF; Download; Online.

14854 ■ *DCL News*

Pub: Data Conversion Laboratory

Contact: Mark Gross, President

URL(s): www.dataconversionlaboratory.com/newsletter

Released: Monthly **Description:** E-journal providing you insider information on XML and SGML, along with the latest technology and e-publishing news. **Availability:** Online.

14855 ■ *Journal of Software: Evolution and Process*

Pub: John Wiley & Sons, Inc.

Contact: Christina Van Tassell, Executive Vice President Chief Financial Officer

URL(s): onlinelibrary.wiley.com/journal/20477481

Ed: Xin Peng, Massimiliano Di Penta, Darren Dalcher, Dr. David Raffo. **Released:** 8/year **Price:** $5,151, Institutions for online only US, India, Japan, Canada. **Description:** Journal covering state-of-the-art research and practice papers dealing with the conception, development, testing, management, quality, maintenance, and evolution of software, systems, and services, along with the continuous improvement of processes and capabilities surrounding them. Incorporates Software Process: Improvement and Practice. **Availability:** Print; PDF; Online; Download.

14856 ■ *Productivity Software*

Pub: Worldwide Videotex

URL(s): wvpubs.com/publications

Released: Annual **Price:** $200, Individuals for hard copy; $185, Individuals for hard copy; $165, Other countries for e-file (PDF or DOC). **Description:** Provides information on computer software. **Availability:** Print; Online; PDF.

14857 ■ *Software: Practice and Experience*

Pub: John Wiley & Sons Ltd.

Contact: Matthew Kissner, Chief Executive Officer

URL(s): onlinelibrary.wiley.com/journal/1097024x

Facebook: www.facebook.com/SoftwareJournal

Ed: Rami Bahsoon, Prof. Rajkumar Buyya, Prof. Agostino Poggi, Satish Srirama, Prof. Daniel Lemire. **Released:** Monthly **Price:** $9,707, Institutions for print and online; $8,644, Institutions for online only; $9,016, Institutions for print only. **Description:** Refereed journal focused on software systems and applications. **Availability:** Print; PDF; Download; Online.

VIDEO/AUDIO MEDIA

14858 ■ *Design that Drives: Software Development Requirements*

URL(s): www.startuphustlepodcast.com/design-that-drive-software-development-requirements

Released: January 30, 2024. **Description:** Podcast discusses software development, particularly software requirements.

14859 ■ *How I Built This: Audible: Don Katz*

URL(s): www.npr.org/202110/29/1050501655/audible-don-katz

Ed: Guy Raz. **Released:** November 01, 2021. **Description:** Podcast explains how the founder of Audible launched the first digital player for audiobooks with no direct experience in tech. Also discusses how it fared during the dot-com bust and how its luck changed with the release of the iPod and a partnership with Apple.

14860 ■ *How I Built This: Goodreads: Otis and Elizabeth Chandler*

URL(s): www.npr.org/2022/02/04/1078415544/goodreads-otis-and-elizabeth-chandler

Ed: Guy Raz. **Released:** February 07, 2022. **Description:** Podcast explains how Otis Chandler coded and launched Goodreads from his apartment.

14861 ■ *How I Built This: Grindr: Joel Simkhai*

URL(s): wondery.com/shows/how-i-built-this/episode/10386-grindr-joel-simkhai

Ed: Guy Raz. **Released:** July 17, 2023. **Description:** Podcast explains how someone with no coding or app design experience bootstrapped Grindr into a global phenomenon.

14862 ■ *How I Built This: Headspace: Andy Puddicombe and Rich Person*

URL(s): www.npr.org/2021/12/17/1065288259/headspace-andy-puddicombe-and-rich-pierson-2019

Ed: Guy Raz. **Released:** January 03, 2022. **Description:** Podcast offers a conversation with the founders of Headspace, a guided meditation app.

14863 ■ *How I Built This: Robert Reffkin: Compass*

URL(s): www.npr.org/2021/07/23/1019734077/robert-reffkin-compass

Ed: Guy Raz. **Released:** July 26, 2021. **Description:** Podcast explains how Reffkin went from writing a business plan for a job interview to launching it as an actual business that builds technology for real estate agents.

14864 ■ *How I Built This: The Tetris Company: Henk Rogers*

URL(s): wondery.com/shows/how-i-built-this/episode/10386-the-tetris-company-henk-rogers

Ed: Guy Raz. **Released:** July 21, 2023. **Description:** Podcast explains how a software developer acquired rights to Tetris despite a tangle of red tape from Asia to the U.S. to the Soviet Union and a bevy of legal wrangling.

14865 ■ *How I Built This: Twilio: Jeff Lawson*
URL(s): wondery.com/shows/how-i-built-this/episode/10386-twilio-jeff-lawson
Ed: Guy Raz. **Released:** April 03, 2023. **Description:** Podcast explains how previous start-ups (even the ones that fizzled) offered insights that let to building one of the most extensive communication platforms in business.

14866 ■ *Noah Glass Founder and CEO of Olo*
URL(s): restaurantunstoppable.libsyn.com/1020-noah-glass-founder-and-ceo-of-olo
Ed: Eric Cacciatore. **Released:** August 24, 2023. **Description:** Podcast offers a conversation with Noah Glass, the founder of Olo, who chose entrepreneurship instead of Harvard Business School.

14867 ■ *Side Hustle to Small Business: From Designing Video Games to Getting Funded by Mark Cuban*
Released: February 15, 2023. **Description:** Podcast discusses software-based startups.

TRADE SHOWS AND CONVENTIONS

14868 ■ **Game Developers' Conference (GDC)**
UBM L.L.C.
2 Penn Plz.
New York, NY 10121
Ph: (212)600-3000
URL: http://www.ubm.com
Contact: Tim Cobbold, Chief Executive Officer
URL(s): www.gdconf.com/about
Price: $1,599, Pre-registered all-access pass; $2,099, Onsite all-access pass. **Frequency:** Annual. **Description:** Equipment, supplies, and services for developers and producers of computer games. **Audience:** Programmers, artists, producers, game designers, audio professionals, and business leaders. **Principal Exhibits:** Equipment, supplies, and services for developers and producers of computer games.

CONSULTANTS

14869 ■ **Century Tax & Bookkeeping Services**
937 E Main St., Ste. 201
Santa Maria, CA 93454
Ph: (805)934-5370
Co. E-mail: info@cbizco.com
URL: http://www.cbizco.com
Contact: Benjamin Rodriguez, Manager
Description: Focuses on improving the profitability of growth-oriented small businesses through business planning, controlling expenses, marketing to find new customers and tax planning to minimize taxes. **Scope:** Focuses on improving the profitability of growth-oriented small businesses through business planning, controlling expenses, marketing to find new customers and tax planning to minimize taxes. **Founded:** 1959. **Training:** QuickBooks training and Budgeting for your Small Business.

14870 ■ **CheckMark Software Inc.**
323 W Drake Rd., Ste. 100
Fort Collins, CO 80526
Free: 800-444-9922
Fax: (970)225-0611
Co. E-mail: sales@checkmark.com
URL: http://www.checkmark.com
Contact: Mohammed A. Ghani, Contact
X (Twitter): x.com/CheckMark_Inc
YouTube: www.youtube.com/channel/UCpJam_8CH-fjiC4eUG--wSA
Description: Developer of accounting and payroll software. **Scope:** Developer of accounting software tools for small businesses and provides fast, easy to use, affordable accounting and payroll solutions to small and medium sized businesses. Provides payroll software and multiledger integrated accounting software. **Founded:** 1984. **Special Services:** MultiLedger; Payroll.

14871 ■ **Cloud Computing Technologies (CCT)**
4939 W Ray Rd., Ste. 4-502
Chandler, AZ 85226
Free: 800-804-9726
Co. E-mail: info@cloudcomputingtechnologies.com
URL: http://cloudcomputingtechnologies.com
Contact: Dr. Alan F. Castillo, President
Facebook: www.facebook.com/Cloud-Computing-Technologies-1443322019279020
Linkedin: www.linkedin.com/company/cloud-computing-tech
YouTube: www.youtube.com/c/CloudComputingTechnologiesChandler
Pinterest: www.pinterest.com/cloudcomputing1
Description: Provides cloud systems integration and services. Services include cloud hosting, cloud services, and cloud desktop. **Scope:** Provides cloud systems integration and services. Services include cloud hosting, cloud services, and cloud desktop.

14872 ■ **CloudBees Inc.**
16192 Coastal Hwy.
Lewes, DE 19958
Co. E-mail: info@cloudbees.com
URL: http://www.cloudbees.com
Contact: Anuj Kapur, President
Facebook: www.facebook.com/CloudBees
Linkedin: www.linkedin.com/company/cloudbees
X (Twitter): x.com/cloudbees
Instagram: www.instagram.com/cloudbeesinc
YouTube: www.youtube.com/c/CloudBeesTV
Description: Provider of continuous delivery software services. **Founded:** 2010.

14873 ■ **Cloudera, Inc.**
395 Page Mill Rd.
Palo Alto, CA 94306
Ph: (650)362-0488
Free: 888-789-1488
Co. E-mail: info@cloudera.com
URL: http://www.cloudera.com
Contact: Mick Hollison, President
Facebook: www.facebook.com/cloudera
Linkedin: www.linkedin.com/company/cloudera
X (Twitter): x.com/cloudera
Description: Developer of data management software. **Founded:** 2008.

14874 ■ **Cloudium.Net**
3005 W Lake Mary Blvd., Ste. 111-300
Lake Mary, FL 32746
Ph: (407)644-6500
Co. E-mail: info@cloudium.net
URL: http://www.cloudium.net
Description: Provider of desktop virtualization hardware and software services and much more.

14875 ■ **Cloudmark Inc.**
Proofpoint, Inc.
128 King St., 2nd Fl.
San Francisco, CA 94107
Ph: (408)517-4710
Fax: (408)517-4711
Co. E-mail: info@proofpoint.com
URL: http://www.proofpoint.com/us
Contact: Ashan Willy, Chief Executive Officer
Description: Firm provides of developer of email security software service. **Founded:** 2001. **Special Services:** Cloud mark trident, cloud mark security platform for email.

14876 ■ **Cloudnexa**
18 Campus Blvd., Ste. 100
Newtown Square, PA 19073
Ph: (484)497-9939
URL: http://www.cloudnexa.com
Contact: M. J. DiBerardino, Chief Executive Officer
Description: Services: Provider of a cloud hosting platform. **Founded:** 2008.

14877 ■ **CloudNine**
14655 NW Fwy., Ste. 135
Houston, TX 77040
Ph: (713)462-6464
Free: 877-595-6464
Co. E-mail: info@cloudnine.com

URL: http://cloudnine.com
Contact: Georges Sabongui, Chief Executive Officer
E-mail: gsabongui@cloudnine.com
Facebook: www.facebook.com/CloudNineDiscovery
Linkedin: www.linkedin.com/company/cloudnine-discovery
X (Twitter): x.com/cloud9discovery
Description: Services: Prepackaged Software: Provider of document management software and services. **Founded:** 2002.

14878 ■ **Cognetics Corp.**
PO Box 386
Princeton Junction, NJ 08550
URL: http://www.cognetics.com
Contact: Dr. Charles B. Kreitzberg, Chief Executive Officer
Description: Developer of hypertext software, technical support and computer consulting firm for large companies. **Scope:** Offers services including technical, programming, human factors, content, graphics, and writing. Designs interactive products such as website, web applications and web communities. **Founded:** 1982. **Publications:** "10 Steps to Creating the Perfect Web Site"; "The Beginning of the End or the End of the Beginning"; "Is Your Project at Risk"; "Selling Usability: Scope and Schedule Estimates," Society for Technical Communication, Dec, 2003. **Special Services:** LUCID™.

14879 ■ **Data Conversion Laboratory (DCL)**
61-18 190th St., Ste. 205
Fresh Meadows, NY 11365
Ph: (718)357-8700
URL: http://www.dataconversionlaboratory.com
Contact: Mark Gross, President
Linkedin: www.linkedin.com/company/dclab
YouTube: www.youtube.com/channel/UCrs_D323yvVDBGV8FbdWmMw
Description: Developer of data conversion software. **Scope:** Provides electronic document conversion services. Services help to refine document conversion strategies, identify content redundancy, extract metadata and transform legacy and future documents. Specialize in projects comprised of complex technical documentation typically characterized by elaborate tables, equations, cross-referencing, special characters, footnotes and specialized imaging requirements. Our proprietary software can be adapted and modified to manage any data set producing any uncompromisingly consistent end-product. Expertise in Document Conversion, Content Reuse Analysis, Digital Publishing Services, eBook Production Services, Structured Product Labeling, PubMed XML Conversion, Consulting and Management. **Founded:** 1981. **Publications:** "Discovery and Monetization: Two Important Challenges Facing eBook Publishers," Jul, 2011. **Training:** Data Conversion Panel, May, 2010. **Special Services:** Harmonizer.

14880 ■ **GitHub, Inc.**
GitHub, Inc.
88 Colin P Kelly Jr St.
San Francisco, CA 94107
Ph: (415)735-4488
Free: 877-448-4820
Co. E-mail: support@github.com
URL: http://www.github.com
X (Twitter): x.com/github
YouTube: www.youtube.com/github
Description: Provider of web-hosting service that enables software programmers to collaborate on projects. **Founded:** 2008. **Educational Activities:** SIGCSE Symposia (Annual).

14881 ■ **On-Q Software Inc.**
13764 SW 11 St.
Miami, FL 33184
URL: http://www.on-qsoftware.com
Contact: Teresita Cajigas, President
Description: Developer of computer software solutions. **Scope:** Developer of computer software solutions. **Founded:** 1987.

14882 ■ Payroll Processors
1401 Branding Ave.
Downers Grove, IL 60515
Ph: (847)288-8080
Co. E-mail: support@payprohcm.com
URL: http://www.payrollprocessors.com
Contact: Shari Gamer, Contact
Description: Developer of automated payroll software and human resources solutions. **Founded:** 1965.

14883 ■ Payroll Solution Inc.
Intuit Inc.
1215 Country Club Ln., Ste. 100
Fort Worth, TX 76112-2304
Ph: (650)944-6000
Free: 800-446-8848
Fax: (650)944-5656
URL: http://www.intuit.com
Contact: Roper W. A. Vaughan, Contact
Description: Provider of small business, tax preparation and employment software. **Founded:** 1983.

14884 ■ Profit Associates Inc.
26 Hunters Forest Dr.
Charleston, SC 29414
Free: 800-688-6304
URL: http://www.profit-associates.com
Contact: Bob Rogers, Managing Director
E-mail: bobrog@awod.com
Description: Firm offers executive coaching and on-site management consulting services for small- to medium-sized businesses and provides strategic business and production planning, funding, change management, marketing and public relations, profit and expense control, employee productivity and incentive services for clients in manufacturing, distribution, construction, software, healthcare, and transportation industries. **Training:** Essential Elements of a Good Incentive Program; Why Look at Management Re-engineering; The Profit & Expense Control Process; The Executive Coaching Alternative.

14885 ■ RC Bryan
526 S Main St., Ste. 801F
Akron, OH 44311
Free: 888-722-7926
URL: http://www.rcbryan.com
Description: Consultant offering software and application development, business coaching, mentoring, and support services. Serves non-profits, logistics and supply organizations, auto dealerships, online marketers, and investment firms.

14886 ■ Rothman Consulting Group Inc.
34 Bradley Rd.
Arlington, MA 02474
Ph: (781)641-4046
URL: http://www.jrothman.com
Contact: Johanna Rothman, President
E-mail: jr@jrothman.com
Description: Firm works with software organizations to improve product development practices, to find the leverage points that will increase their effectiveness as organizations and as managers, helping ship the night products at the right time, recruit and retain the best people. **Scope:** Firm works with software organizations to improve product development practices, to find the leverage points that will increase their effectiveness as organizations and as managers, helping ship the night products at the right time, recruit and retain the best people. **Founded:** 1994.
Publications: "Manage Your Project Portfolio: Increase Your Capacity and Finish More Projects"; "Manage It! Your Guide to Modern, Pragmatic Project Management"; "Behind Closed Doors: Secrets of Great Management"; "Hiring the Best Knowledge Workers, Techies & Nerds"; "Corrective Action for the Software Industry". **Training:** Transitioning to Agile in Stockholm, May, 2012; PSL:Problem Solving Leadership, May, 2012; Working Effectively In Geographically Distributed Agile Project Teams, Apr, 2012.

14887 ■ Software Success
1580 W El Camino Real
Mountain View, CA 94040

Ph: (650)390-6400
Free: 877-794-9511
Co. E-mail: customer.service@trademarkia.com
URL: http://www.trademarkia.com
Facebook: www.facebook.com/Trademarkia
Linkedin: www.linkedin.com/company/trademarkia
X (Twitter): twitter.com/trademarkia
Instagram: www.instagram.com/trademarkia
YouTube: www.youtube.com/channel/UC3mORyKn
10b6LRrEfr4xhhQ
Description: Publishes consulting newsletter for the software industry. Serves software start up ventures needing marketing or business consulting, ongoing software companies requiring marketing or product planning assistance, investors evaluating present or future software investments and corporations wanting to start new software businesses in the U.S. and Canada. **Scope:** Publishes consulting newsletter for the software industry. Serves software start up ventures needing marketing or business consulting, ongoing software companies requiring marketing or product planning assistance, investors evaluating present or future software investments and corporations wanting to start new software businesses in the U.S. and Canada. **Founded:** 1984. **Publications:** "Open Source: The Unauthorized"; "The Product Marketing Handbook for Software"; "In Search of Stupidity: Over 20 Years of High-Tech Marketing Disasters"; "Us Software Distribution Guide"; "The Unauthorized Whitepapers"; "MARKETING THAT'S NOT SO STUPID". **Training:** Valuing and Selling a Software Business; Launching New Software Products; Rising Stars of the Software Industry.

PUBLICATIONS

14888 ■ Flagship Technologies, Inc.
14976 Monroe Rd. 1039
Madison, MO 65263-2259
Contact: Mark Wilsdorf, Officer
Description: Company is engaged in developing software products and training materials. **Scope:** Company is engaged in developing software products and training materials. **Publications:** "The Quick-Books Farm Accounting Cookbook"; "Do I Need Quicken. QuickBooks Basic. Or QuickBooks Pro?"; "Getting Rid of Old Account and Class Names"; "Accounts, Categories & Classes Defined"; "Tracking Personal Spending with QuickBooks Equity Accounts"; "Account/Category Setup Basics"; "Classes As Enterprise Profit Centers and Cost Centers"; "Setting Up Classes That Meet Your Information Goals"; "Calculating Rolling Herd Average Milk Production with QuickBooks". **Training:** A Computer for Your Farm; Database Interface Design Techniques for Rapid Scanning by Users; QuickBooks Interfacing Techniques; Then and Now. **Special Services:** ManagePLUS™; FormCalc™.

14889 ■ Geekers Magazine
URL(s): www.geekersmagazine.com
Facebook: www.facebook.com/geekersmagazine
X (Twitter): twitter.com/geekersmag
Instagram: www.instagram.com/geekersmagazine
Description: Online magazine featuring articles about the latest technology, gaming, and business within the tech sector. **Availability:** Online. **Telecommunication Services:** Email: geekersmagazine1@gmail.com .

PUBLISHERS

14890 ■ Cloud Sherpas
Accenture plc
15 N mill St.
New York, NY 10001
Ph: 353 1 646-2000
Co. E-mail: dataprivacyofficer@accenture.com
URL: http://www.accenture.com
Description: Firm provides software as a service. **Founded:** 2007.

LIBRARIES

14891 ■ IBM Corporation - IBM Knowledge Center
11400 Burnet Rd.
Austin, TX 78758
URL: http://www.ibm.com/support/pages/what-ibm
-knowledge-center
Description: Access to information for planning, installing, and maintaining IBM Mainframes. **Scope:** Management. **Founded:** 2014. **Subscriptions:** journals Logical files, Physical files.

RESEARCH CENTERS

14892 ■ Carnegie Mellon University - Software Engineering Institute (SEI)
4720 Forbes Ave.
Pittsburgh, PA 15213-3890
Ph: (412)268-5800
Free: 888-201-4479
Fax: (412)268-5758
Co. E-mail: info@sei.cmu.edu
URL: http://www.sei.cmu.edu
Contact: Dr. Paul D. Nielsen, Chief Executive Officer
Facebook: www.facebook.com/SEICMU
Linkedin: www.linkedin.com/company/software-engineering-institute
X (Twitter): x.com/SEInews
YouTube: www.youtube.com/user/TheSEICMU
Description: Federally Funded Research and Development Center (FFRDC) operated by Carnegie Mellon University. Offers CERT Coordination Center, workshops, continuing education, and special training courses. **Scope:** Software engineering, including software process, software risk management, disciplined engineering of software-intensive systems, product lines, cyber security, survivable systems, COTS-based systems, software components, trustworthy networks, software engineering education, and technology transition. **Founded:** 1984. **Publications:** news@sei interactive; SEI Annual Report (Annual); SEI Software Engineering Education Directory. **Educational Activities:** SEI Software Engineering Process Group Conference; SEI Conferences (Annual).

14893 ■ Montana State University, Bozeman - University Information Technology (UIT)
Renne Library, 1st Fl. Ste. 115G
Bozeman, MT 59717-3240
Ph: (406)994-1777
URL: http://www.montana.edu/uit/index.html
Contact: Dr. Ryan Knutson, Vice President
E-mail: ryan.knutson2@montana.edu
Description: Integral unit of Montana State University-Bozeman. Offers computer software consultation and seminar courses. **Scope:** Computer systems (especially software development), computer and information networks, and administrative information systems.

14894 ■ University of Illinois at Chicago Department of Computer Science - Electronic Visualization Laboratory (EVL)
851 S Morgan, Rm. 1120
Chicago, IL 60607-7053
Ph: (312)996-3002
URL: http://cs.uic.edu/profiles/andrew-johnson
URL(s): www.evl.uic.edu
Facebook: www.facebook.com/UIC.EVL
X (Twitter): x.com/evl_uic
YouTube: www.youtube.com/user/evltube
Description: Integral unit of Department of Electrical Engineering and Computer Science, University of Illinois at Chicago. **Scope:** Computer graphics and interactive techniques, including virtual reality, multimedia, scientific visualization, new methodologies for informal science and engineering education, paradigms for information display, televisualization (distributed graphics over networks), algorithm optimization for scalable and parallel computing, sonification, and abstract mathematical visualization. **Founded:** 1973.

14895 ■ University of North Florida - Training and Services Institute (UNF) - Institute of Police Technology and Management (IPTM)
12000 Alumni Dr.
 Jacksonville, FL 32224
Ph: (904)620-4786
Fax: (904)620-2453
Co. E-mail: info@iptm.org

URL: http://iptm.unf.edu
Contact: Cameron Pucci, Director
E-mail: cpucci@unf.edu
Facebook: www.facebook.com/IPTMNews
Linkedin: www.linkedin.com/company/iptm1
X (Twitter): x.com/IPTMnews
Description: Publishes on police training for police and civilians. Offers video cassettes. Reaches market through direct mail, reviews and listings. **Scope:** Develops software products for police agencies, including a computer management system that collects and tracks records for a drug investigative unit or task force. This system, Drug-Trak for Windows, provides reports based on people, vehicles, businesses, aircraft, watercraft, and telephone numbers. **Founded:** 1980. **Publications:** *Traffic Accident Investigations* and *Traffic Accident Reconstruction.*

START-UP INFORMATION

14896 ■ *"Sustainable Advantage" in Inc. (Vol. 36, September 2014, No. 7, pp. 86)*
Pub: Mansueto Ventures L.L.C.
Contact: Stephanie Mehta, Chief Executive Officer
Price: $8.95, hardcopy black and white. **Description:** Four startup companies committed to providing sustainable, eco-friendly products and services while protecting the environment and bettering human health are profiled. Holganix(TM) offers organic lawn care products; Motiv Power Systems electrifies large vehicles; Clean Energy Collective Solar Power builds lareg community solar panel arrays; and Protein Bar offers healthy alternatives to fast food in its chain of restaurants. The company also works with nonprofits focused on wellness and education and has created 167 Learning Gardens nationwide. **Availability:** Print; PDF; Online.

ASSOCIATIONS AND OTHER ORGANIZATIONS

14897 ■ **Air-Conditioning, Heating, and Refrigeration Institute (AHRI)**
2311 Wilson Blvd., Ste. 400
Arlington, VA 22201
Ph: (703)524-8800
Co. E-mail: ahricommunications@ahrinet.org
URL: http://www.ahrinet.org
Contact: Stephen Yurek, President
Facebook: www.facebook.com/AHRIconnect
Linkedin: www.linkedin.com/company/the-air-condi tioning-heating-and-refrigeration-institute
X (Twitter): x.com/AHRIConnect
YouTube: www.youtube.com/user/AHRIcommunica tions

Description: Represents companies that manufacture air conditioning, heating, water heating, and commercial refrigeration units. Maintains a continuing presence within Congress and government agencies to monitor and respond to policies and regulations affecting the industry and represent the collective interests of members. **Founded:** 1959. **Publications:** *CRMA Newsbreak* (Periodic); *Recommended Guidelines for Retail Food Store Design*; *Recommended Guidelines for Retail Food Store Energy Conservation*; *Voluntary Minimum Standard for Retail Food Store Refrigerators-Health and Sanitation*; *Directory of Certified Unitary Air-Conditioners, Unitary Air-Source Heat Pumps and Sound-Rated Outdoor Unitary Equipment* (Semiannual); *Directory of Certified Air-to-Air Energy Recovery Ventilation Equipment* (Periodic); *Directory of Certified Automatic Commercial Ice-Cube Machines and Ice Storage Bins*; *Directory of Certified Direct Geoexchange Heat Pumps*; *Directory of Certified Drinking Water Coolers* (Annual); *Directory of Certified Refrigerant Recovery/ Recycling Equipment and Reclaimed Refrigerants, and Refrigerant Testing Laboratories* (Semiannual); *Directory of Certified Transport Refrigeration Units* (Annual); *AHRI Curriculum Guide*; *Minuteman*

(Monthly); *Educational Institutions Offering Courses in Air-Conditioning and Refrigeration* (Annual); *Directory of Certified Applied Air-Conditioning Products* (Semiannual). **Educational Activities:** AHR Expo Mexico (Annual). **Geographic Preference:** National.

14898 ■ **Alternative Energy Resources Organization (AERO) - Library**
32 S Ewing St., Ste. 333.
Helena, MT 59601
Ph: (406)443-7272
Co. E-mail: aero@aeromt.org
URL: http://aeromt.org
Contact: Robin Kelson, Executive Director
E-mail: rkelson@aeromt.org
Facebook: www.facebook.com/aeromt
Instagram: www.instagram.com/aeromt
YouTube: www.youtube.com/user/aeromt1974
Description: Promotes sustainable agriculture, resource conservation and transportation choices through community education and citizen representation. Provides current programs that focus on sustainable agriculture, farm improvement clubs, beginning and retiring farmers, smart growth, and a more localized food system for greater community self-reliance. **Scope:** Food; energy; education. **Founded:** 1974. **Holdings:** Figures not available. **Publications:** *Abundant Montana*; *AERO Sun-Times* (Quarterly); *Big Sky or Big Sprawl Montana at the Crossroads*; *Montana's Sustainable Agriculture Farming with Foresight*. **Educational Activities:** Alternative Energy Resources Organization Expo and Annual Meeting (Annual). **Awards:** Northern Rockies Sustainable Agriculture Award (Annual). **Geographic Preference:** National.

14899 ■ **American Solar Energy Society (ASES)**
2525 Arapahoe Ave. Ste. E4 253
Boulder, CO 80302
Ph: (303)443-3130
Co. E-mail: info@ases.org
URL: http://www.ases.org
Contact: Carly Rixham, Executive Director
E-mail: crixham@ases.org
Facebook: www.facebook.com/ americansolarenergysociety
Linkedin: www.linkedin.com/company/ases-solar
X (Twitter): x.com/ASES_Solar
Instagram: www.instagram.com/ases_solar
YouTube: www.youtube.com/channel/UCF9nN tHuTDY4NrA4ObpxVkA
Description: Promotes education by compiling and disseminating information to schools, universities, and the community. Publishes books on solar energy, engineering, architecture, physics, electro chemistry and conservation. Accepts unsolicited manuscripts. Reaches market through direct mail. **Founded:** 1954. **Publications:** *Solar Today* (Quarterly); *American Solar Energy Society--Membership Directory*. **Awards:** ASES Fellows (Annual); Rebecca Vories Award (Annual); Charles Greeley Abbot Award (Annual); Hoyt Clarke Hottel Award (Annual); John and Barbara Yellott Award (Annual); Leadership in Solar

Architecture and Design Award (Annual); ASES Women in Solar Energy Award (Annual). **Geographic Preference:** National.

14900 ■ **Renew the Earth (RTE)**
c/o Susan Caumont, President
8 Robin Ann Ln.
Westerlo, NY 12193
Ph: (518)797-3377
Co. E-mail: susancaumont@renew-the-earth.org
URL: http://www.renew-the-earth.org
Contact: Susan Caumont, President
E-mail: susancaumont@renew-the-earth.org
Description: Individuals and groups working toward a sustainable future by promoting a safe and healthy environment. Coordinates National Awards for Environmental Sustainability program to recognize positive environmental programs. Operates the Environmental Success Index, a clearinghouse of more than 1600 working environmental projects available to community groups, the media, businesses, policy makers, and individuals dedicated to implementing and promoting positive environmental change. Moving toward developing an international program. **Founded:** 1989. **Publications:** *Environmental Success Index* (Annual); *RTE Environmental Success Index* (Annual). **Geographic Preference:** Multinational.

14901 ■ **Solar Energy Industries Association (SEIA)**
1425 K St. NW, Ste. 1000
Washington, DC 20005
Ph: (202)682-0556
Co. E-mail: info@seia.org
URL: http://www.seia.org
Contact: Abigail Ross Hopper, President
E-mail: ahopper@seia.org
Facebook: www.facebook.com/TheSolarIndustry
Linkedin: www.linkedin.com/company/solarindustry
X (Twitter): x.com/SEIA
Instagram: www.instagram.com/solarindustry
YouTube: www.youtube.com/c/SeiaOrg
Description: Manufacturers, installers, distributors, contractors, and engineers of solar energy systems and components. Aims to accelerate and foster commercialization of solar energy conversion for economic purposes. Maintains Solar Energy Research and Education Foundation. Compiles statistics; offers computerized services. **Founded:** 1974. **Publications:** *Solar Industry*; *Directory of State Government Renewable Energy Contacts*; *IREC Directory*. **Educational Activities:** SOLTECH (Annual). **Geographic Preference:** National.

14902 ■ **Solar Rating and Certification Corporation (SRCC)**
3060 Saturn St., Ste. 100
Brea, CA 92821
Free: 888-422-7233
Co. E-mail: srcc@solar-rating.org
URL: http://solar-rating.org
Linkedin: www.linkedin.com/company/solar-rating

Description: Serves as a rating and certification board for domestic solar hot water and pool heating panels and systems. **Founded:** 1980. **Publications:** *Directory of SRCC Certified Solar Collector and System Ratings* (Annual); *Directory of SRCC Certified Collectors and Solar Water Heating Systems Ratings*; *SRCC Certification & Listing Directories*. **Geographic Preference:** National.

REFERENCE WORKS

14903 ■ *"Acing the Test" in Contractor (Vol. 57, January 2010, No. 1, pp. 32)*
Pub: Informa USA, Inc.
Contact: Stephen A. Carter, Chief Executive Officer
Ed: Robert P. Mader. **Released:** January 01, 2010. **Description:** A ward winning mechanical system retrofitting of a middle school in Ohio is discussed. The school now operates at 37,800 Btu/sq. ft and reduced a significant amount of pollutants from being emitted into the environment.

14904 ■ *"Advanced Energy Showcases Industry Leading Inverters and Energy Management Solutions at Solar Power International 2012" in Benzinga.com (September 11, 2012)*
Pub: PR Newswire Association LLC.
Description: Advanced Energy Industries Inc. is presenting its energy management solutions suite at the Solar Power International (SPI) conference to be held in Orlando, Florida in September 2012. Details of the conference and this exhibit are included.

14905 ■ *"Adventures at Hydronicahh" in Contractor (Vol. 56, September 2009, No. 9, pp. 52)*
Ed: Mark Eatherton. **Released:** Part 6. **Description:** Installations of the heating system of a lakeview room are described. The room's radiant windows are powered by electricity from a solar PV array and a propane-powered hydrogen fuel cell. The system will be programmed to use the most energy available. **Availability:** Print; Online.

14906 ■ *"Alternative Energy Calls for Alternative Marketing" in Indoor Comfort Marketing (Vol. 70, June 2011, No. 6, pp. 8)*
Pub: Spray Technology & Marketing
Contact: Ava Caridad, Director, Editorial
E-mail: acaridad@spraytm.com
Ed: Richard Rutigliano. **Released:** June 01, 2011. **Description:** Advice for marketing solar energy products and services is given. **Availability:** Print; Online.

14907 ■ *"Analysis of the U.S. Residential Solar Power Market" in PR Newswire (September 19, 2012)*
Pub: PR Newswire Association LLC.
Description: Analysis of the residential solar power market in the United States is presented. Solar PV is the fastest growing technology in the energy sector for the nation during the last three years due to rising energy prices, volatile fuel costs, and government incentives for renewable energy.

14908 ■ *"Arden Fair Stops Using Parking Lot Solar Panels" in Sacramento Business Journal (Vol. 31, April 18, 2014, No. 8)*
Pub: American City Business Journals, Inc.
Contact: Mike Olivieri, Executive Vice President
Released: Weekly. **Description:** Arden Fair, a shopping center in Sacramento, California will remove solar panels in its parking lot. the panels were initially installed in 2002 by the Sacramento Municipal Utility District. Citing high repair cost and damages from vehicles, mall officials have decided to remove the panels. Rooftop solar panels will still be used at the site. **Availability:** Print; Online.

14909 ■ *"Breaking from Tradition Techstyle" in Providence Business News (Vol. 28, March 17, 2014, No. 50, pp. 1)*
Pub: American City Business Journals, Inc.
Contact: Mike Olivieri, Executive Vice President

Released: March 15, 2014. **Description:** Providence, Rhode Island's Techstyle Haus is being constructed by a group of students from Brown University. The textile house features a flexible exterior that uses high-performance materials and solar cells. Techstyle Haus is one of two entries from the U.S. competing in the Solar Decathlon Europe 2014. **Availability:** Print; Online.

14910 ■ *"California Water Treatment Facility Turns to Solar Power" in Chemical Business Newsbase (September 11, 2012)*
Description: Ramona, California municipal water district providing water, sewer, recycled water, fire protection, emergency medical services, and park services to the community has commissioned a 530KWp solar energy installation. Enfinity America Corporation developed and financed the solar panels and EPC services were provided by manufacturer Siliken. **Availability:** Print; Online.

14911 ■ *"Canadian Solar Expands Into Puerto Rico With Planned 26MW Solar Power Plant Installation" in Benzinga.com (October 2, 2012)*
Pub: Benzinga.com
Contact: Jason Raznick, Founder
Description: Canadian Solar Inc. is expanding into Puerto Rico with the delivery of 26mg of CS6P-P solar power modules for the San Fermin solar power plant. Canadian Solar is one of the world's largest solar firms. The solar power system is expected to be completed and connected to the national grid by December 2012.

14912 ■ *"The CEO Poll: Fuel for Thought II Canadian Business Leaders on Energy Policy" in Canadian Business (Vol. 81, September 15, 2008, No. 14-15, pp. 12)*
Pub: Rogers Media Inc.
Contact: Neil Spivak, Chief Executive Officer
Ed: Joe Castaldo. **Description:** Most Canadian business leaders worry about the unreliability of the oil supply but feel that Canada is in a better position to benefit from the energy supply crisis than other countries. Many respondents also highlighted the need to invest in renewable energy sources. **Availability:** Online.

14913 ■ *"Check Out the Top 20 Commercial Users of Solar Power" in Electrical Wholesaling (Vol. 93, October 1, 2012, No. 10)*
Description: Report issued by the Solar Energy Industries Association and the Vote Solar Initiative names companies using solar on their facilities in the United States. The companies are ranked by cumulative solar energy capacity. **Availability:** Print; Online.

14914 ■ *"China's Transition to Green Energy Systems: The Economics of Home Solar Water Heaters and Their Popularization in Dezhou City" in Energy Policy (Vol. 39, October 2011, No. 10, pp. 5909-5919)*
Ed: Wei Li, Guojun Song, Melanie Beresford, Ben Ma. **Released:** 2011. **Description:** The economics of home solar water heaters and their growing popularity in Dezhous City, China is discussed. **Availability:** PDF; Online.

14915 ■ *"City-Owned Buildings Get an Injection of Solar Power" in America's Intelligence Wire (September 11, 2012)*
Description: City of Toronto, Ontario, Canada and Toronto Hydro-Electric System Ltd. have launched the first phase of a program that will outfit city-owned buildings with over 8,800 solar photovoltaic (PV) panels. Construction begins at MimicoArena, York Mills Arena, and Goulding Park Community Centre/Arena. Details of the project are included. **Availability:** Online.

14916 ■ *"Cover Story: Minnesota Firms Plug Into Solar" in Business Journal (Vol. 31, April 25, 2014, No. 48, pp. 10)*
Pub: American City Business Journals, Inc.
Contact: Mike Olivieri, Executive Vice President

Released: April 25, 2014. **Price:** $4, Introductory 4-week offer(Digital & Print). **Description:** Minneapolis, Minnesota-based companies have been benefiting from the increase in solar energy projects. Xcel Energy Inc.'s demand for more power is expected to lure national solar companies to the city. Meanwhile, Geronimo Energy is planning a $250 million solar project in the state. **Availability:** Print; Online.

14917 ■ *"East Coast Solar" in Contractor (Vol. 57, February 2010, No. 2, pp. 17)*
Ed: Dave Yates. **Description:** U.S. Department of Energy's Solar Decathlon lets 20 college student-led teams from around the world compete to design and build a solar-powered home. A mechanical contractor discusses his work as an advisor during the competition. **Availability:** Print; Online.

14918 ■ *"Eco Smart Home Will Showcase Green Technology" in Contractor (Vol. 56, September 2009, No. 9, pp. 3)*
Ed: Steve Spaulding. **Description:** Eco Smart World Wide is building the Eco Smart Demonstration House to promote the latest in sustainable, renewable and high-efficiency practices and products. The company will use insulated concrete forms in the construction of the building. Features and dimensions of the structure are also presented. **Availability:** Print; Online.

14919 ■ *"Elon Musk's Solar Firm Is Nearly Doubling Its Massachusetts Workforce" in Boston Business Journal (Vol. 34, May 30, 2014, No. 17, pp. 3)*
Pub: American City Business Journals, Inc.
Contact: Mike Olivieri, Executive Vice President
Released: Weekly. **Description:** SolarCity is planning to add 100 jobs to its Massachusetts operations. The solar panel firm opened a second operations center in the state. State business incentives have enabled the company to expand presence in the area. **Availability:** Print; Online.

14920 ■ *"ENERGY: Georgia Power to Buy More Solar: Customer Bills Will Not Be Affected By Renewable Energy Plan, Utility Says" in Atlanta Journal-Constitution (September 27, 2012, pp. A13)*
Pub: The Atlanta Journal-Constitution
Contact: Kevin Riley, Editor
E-mail: kriley@ajc.com
Description: Georgia Power announces plans to increase the amount of solar power it distributes to consumers due to the falling prices of solar energy, making it more competitive. However, customers will not see a reduction in their rates. **Availability:** Online.

14921 ■ *"ESolar Partners With Penglai on Landmark Solar Thermal Agreement for China" in Business of Global Warming (January 25, 2010, pp. 8)*
Description: Penglai Electric, a privately-owned Chinese electrical power equipment manufacturer, and eSolar, a global provider of cost-effective and reliable solar power plants, announced a master licensing agreement in which eSolar will build at least 2 gigawatts of solar thermal power plants in China over the next 10 years. **Availability:** Print; Online.

14922 ■ *"Fast Times for the US Residential Solar Market" in Greentech Media (November 21, 2019)*
URL(s): www.greentechmedia.com/articles/read/the-latest-trends-in-residential-solar-q3
Ed: Julian Spector, Emma Foehringer Merchant. **Released:** November 21, 2019. **Description:** The latest trends in the U.S. home solar market are discussed, and surprisingly, rooftop solar installing is starting to gain momentum against utility-scale plants. Solar-and-storage saw an uptick with the California wildfires and PG&E's forced blackouts as vulnerable people invested in alternative forms of energy. **Availability:** Online.

14923 ■ *"First Solar Signs Power Purchase Agreements with Pacific Gas and Electric Company for 72 Megawatts"* in Benzinga.com (September 11, 2012)
Pub: Benzinga.com
Contact: Jason Raznick, Founder

Ed: Paul Quintaro. **Description:** First Solar has signed power purchase agreements with Pacific Gas and Electric Company for 72 megawatts of solar electricity to be generated at two photovoltaic power plants in central California. Details of the projects are included. **Availability:** PDF; Online.

14924 ■ *"For Giving Us a Way To Say Yes To Solar: Lynn Jurich and Edward Fenster"* in Inc. (Volume 32, December 2010, No. 10, pp. 110)
Pub: Mansueto Ventures L.L.C.
Contact: Stephanie Mehta, Chief Executive Officer

Ed: Leigh Buchanan. **Released:** December 01, 2010. **Description:** Profile of entrepreneurs Lynn Jurich and Edward Fenster, cofounders of SunRun. The firm installs solar panels at little or no cost and homeowners sign 20-year contracts to buy power at a fixed price. **Availability:** Online.

14925 ■ *"FSU's OGZEB Is Test Bed for Sustainable Technology"* in Contractor (Vol. 56, October 2009, No. 10, pp. 1)

Ed: Candace Roulo. **Description:** Florida State University has one of 14 off-grid zero emissions buildings (OGZEB) in the U.S.; it was built to research sustainable and alternative energy systems. The building produces electricity from 30 photovoltaic panels and it also has three AET water heating solar panels on the roof. **Availability:** Print; Online.

14926 ■ *"Germans Win Solar Decathlon Again"* in Contractor (Vol. 56, November 2009, No. 11, pp. 1)

Ed: Robert P. Mader. **Description:** Students from Technische Universtat Darmstadt won the U.S. Department of Energy's Solar Decathlon by designing and building the most attractive and efficient solar-powered home. The winner's design produced a surplus of power even during three days of rain and photovoltaic panels covered nearly every exterior surface. **Availability:** Print; Online.

14927 ■ *"GM Scores High Marks For Its Use of Solar Power"* in Blade (September 13, 2012)
Pub: McClatchy Tribune Information Services
Contact: Patrick J. Talamantes, President

Ed: Tyrel Linkhorn. **Description:** General Motors scores high among top corporate generators of solar power in the United States. The Solar Energy Industries Assocation ranked GM's on-site solar power generation capacity at number 13, making GM the first in the automotive sector. Details of GM's solar projects are outlined. **Availability:** Online.

14928 ■ *"Got to be Smarter than the Average Bear"* in Contractor (Vol. 56, September 2009, No. 9, pp. 82)

Ed: Robert P. Mader. **Description:** International Association of Plumbing and Mechanical Officials Green Technical Committee has debated the need for contractors to have certifications in installing green plumbing. Some have argued that qualifications would discourage homeowners from improving their properties. Comments from executives are also included. **Availability:** Print; Online.

14929 ■ *"Green Light"* in The Business Journal-Portland (Vol. 25, July 11, 2008, No. 18, pp. 1)

Description: Ecos Consulting, a sustainability consulting company based in Portland, Oregon, is seeing a boost in revenue as more businesses turn to sustainable practices. The company's revenue rose by 50 percent in 2007 and employees increased from 57 to 150. Other details about Ecos' growth are discussed. **Availability:** Print; Online.

14930 ■ *"Greenhouse Announces Reverse Merger With Custom Q, Inc."* in Investment Weekly (January 30, 2010, pp. 338)
Pub: Investment Weekly News

Description: In accordance with an Agreement and Plan of Share Exchange, GreenHouse Holdings, Inc., an innovative green solutions provider, has gone public via a reverse merger with Custom Q, Inc. **Availability:** Print; Online.

14931 ■ *"How Green Is The Valley?"* in Barron's (Vol. 88, July 4, 2008, No. 28, pp. 13)

Description: San Jose, California has made a good start towards becoming a leader in alternative energy technology through the establishment of United Laboratories' own lab in the city. The certification process for photovoltaic cells will be dramatically shortened with this endeavor. **Availability:** Print.

14932 ■ *"Magpower May Build Solar Panels in Pflugerville"* in Austin Business Journal (Vol. 31, May 13, 2011, No. 10, pp. A1)
Pub: Austin Business Journal
Contact: Rachel McGrath, Director
E-mail: rmcgrath@bizjournals.com

Ed: Christopher Calnan. **Description:** RRE Austin Solar LLC CEO Doven Mehta has revealed plans to partner with Portugal-based Magpower SA, only if Austin energy buys electricity from planned solar energy farm in Pflugerville. Austin Energy has received 100 bids from 35 companies to supply 200 megawatts of solar- and wind-generated electricity. **Availability:** Print; Online.

14933 ■ *"Making Solar Energy Even More Sustainable with Light-Powered Technology"* in Science Daily (November 16, 2021)
URL(s): www.sciencedaily.com/releases/2021/11/211116131736.htm

Released: November 16, 2021. **Description:** A new process is being studied for the advancement of extending the life of solar panels. **Availability:** Online.

14934 ■ *"New APS AZ Sun Launches"* in Manufacturing Close-Up (September 19, 2012)

Description: Permit process has begun to construct the Hyder II Solar Power Plant located in Hyder, Arizona. The project is a partnership between Arizona Public Service and McCarthy Building Companies. The Arizona Sun Program is adding 200 MW of solar photovoltaic power plants across Arizona by 2015. **Availability:** Print; Online.

14935 ■ *"New Ways to Finance Solar Power Projects Expected to Lower Cost of Capital, Cut Electricity Rates, Boost Profits, and Expand Investor Pool"* in PR Newswire (September 28, 2012)
Pub: PR Newswire Association LLC.

Description: Renewable energy companies are examining new ways to finance solar power projects. One such strategy includes the use of the REIT structure as a means to lowering costs of capital, lower the cost of generating solar power by nearly 20 percent. Investors would be more interested in the easy and liquid means in which to own a part of the fast growing solar market. Statistical details included.

14936 ■ *"PSC Approves $130M TECO Solar Project"* in Tampa Bay Business Journal (Vol. 30, December 18, 2009, No. 52, pp. 1)
Pub: Tampa Bay Business Journal
Contact: Ian Anderson, President
E-mail: ianderson@bizjournals.com

Ed: Michael Hinman. **Description:** Florida's Public Service Commission has endorsed Tampa Electric Company's plan to add 25 megawatts of solar energy to its portfolio. TECO's plan needed the approval by PSC to defray additional costs for the project through ratepayers. **Availability:** Print; Online.

14937 ■ *"PSC Decision Could Help Bolster a Solar Market Supernova"* in Tampa Bay Business Journal (Vol. 29, November 6, 2009, No. 46, pp. 1)
Pub: Tampa Bay Business Journal
Contact: Ian Anderson, President

E-mail: ianderson@bizjournals.com

Ed: Michael Hinman. **Description:** Florida's Public Service Commission (PSC) decision on a power purchase agreement that could add 25 megawatts of solar energy on Tampa Electric Company's offerings is presented. The decision could support the growing market for suppliers and marketers of renewable energy such as Jabil Circuit Inc., which manufactures photovoltaic modules. Details of the agreement are discussed. **Availability:** Print; Online.

14938 ■ *"PSEG Queen Creek Solar Farm in Arizona Begins Commercial Operation"* in Benzinga.com (October 4, 2012)

Description: PSEG Solar Source will launch the commercial operation of the 25.2 megawatt DC (19 megawatt AC) Queen Creek Solar Farm in Queen Creek, Arizona. The Salt River Project (SRP) has a 20-year agreement to acquire acquire all of the solar energy generated by the project. More details are included.

14939 ■ *"Research and Markets: Directory of Solar Power Facilities, United States"* in Benzinga.com (October 1, 2012)
Pub: Benzinga.com
Contact: Jason Raznick, Founder

Released: October 01, 2012. **Description:** A comprehensive directory of solar power facilities (photovoltaic and concentrated solar power) across the nation are is provided. Information is shown both nationally and by state. **Availability:** Print; Online.

14940 ■ *"R.I. Lags in Solar Incentives"* in Providence Business News (Vol. 29, May 26, 2014, No. 8, pp. 1)
Pub: American City Business Journals, Inc.
Contact: Mike Olivieri, Executive Vice President

Released: May 24, 2014. **Description:** The state of Rhode Island has offered less in government renewable energy incentives than its neighboring states and has yet to experience the growth of residential solar energy projects. The Rhode Island Renewable Energy Fund allocated $800,000 to the small scale solar program in 2014. **Availability:** Print; Online.

14941 ■ *"Saving the Planet: A Tale of Two Strategies: Thomas Malthus Advised Restraint; Robert Solow Promotes Innovation. Let's Pursue Both To Solve the Environmental Crisis"* in Harvard Business Review (Vol. 90, April 2012, No. 4, pp. 48)
Pub: Harvard Business Review Press
Contact: Moderna V. Pfizer, Contact

Ed: Roger Martin, Alison Kemper. **Price:** $8.95, hardcover. **Description:** Theories of economists Thomas Malthus and Robert Solow are merged to address specific environmental problems. Malthusian restraint includes fuel economy, refillable bottles, and recycling. Solovian innovation includes water supply chlorination, solar cooking, and geothermal energy. **Availability:** PDF; Online.

14942 ■ *"SCS Renewables Helps Hook Up Solar Deals"* in Silicon Valley/San Jose Business Journal (Vol. 30, July 13, 2012, No. 16, pp. 1)
Pub: Baltimore Business Journal
Contact: Rhonda Pringle, President
E-mail: rpringle@bizjournals.com

Description: Campbell, California-based SCS Renewables Inc. has launched a new system that will provide a standardized overview of a solar project's characteristics and match it with a bank or other interested investor. SCS executives believe their technology enables the process of funding solar projects to become simple and faster. **Availability:** Print; Online.

14943 ■ *"Sky Harvest Windpower Corp. - Operational Update"* in Investment Weekly News (March 10, 2012, pp. 744)
Pub: PR Newswire Association LLC.

Description: Sky Harvest Windpower Corporation is rebranding its focus on gas and power activities both nationally and internationally. The firm's Canadian projects are outlined as well as its commitment to purse the Green Options Partners Program in 2012. **Availability:** Online.

14944 ■ "Solar Choices" in Contractor (Vol. 56, October 2009, No. 10, pp. 32)
Ed: Tom Scheel. **Description:** Price, performance, and ease of installation of a flat plate versus an evacuated tube collector for a plumbing and heating job are compared. The better choice with regards to weight, aesthetics, efficiency in warm or cool climates, year round load, and space heating is discussed. **Availability:** Print; Online.

14945 ■ "Solar Gaining Power in Tennessee" in Memphis Business Journal (Vol. 34, June 15, 2012, No. 9, pp. 1)
Pub: Baltimore Business Journal
Contact: Rhonda Pringle, President
E-mail: rpringle@bizjournals.com
Ed: Michael Sheffield. **Description:** Tennessee's solar energy industry has grown, the Tennessee Solar Institute has reported. Solar energy use, manufacture and employment in the state have increase in the past four years. **Availability:** Print; Online.

14946 ■ "Solar Hot Water Sales Are Hot, Hot, Hot" in Contractor (Vol. 56, December 2009, No. 12, pp. 22)
Ed: Dave Yates. **Description:** Plumbing contractors in the United States can benefit from the increased sales of solar thermal water systems. Licensed plumbers have the base knowledge on the risks associated from heating and storing water. Safety issues associated with solar water heaters are also included. **Availability:** Online.

14947 ■ "Solar Integrity"
Pub: Archway Publishing
Contact: Melissa Bauer, Contact
Released: October 07, 2014. **Price:** $30.99, Hardcover. **Description:** The instability of the solar industry in American is discussed. **Availability:** E-book; Print; Online.

14948 ■ "Solectria Renewables Supplies Solar Stations for Solar Farm in New England" in Professional Close-Up (October 2, 2012)
Description: Solectria Renewables LLC reported that its Megawatt Solar Stations (MSS) will be used for the 5MW True North solar farm in Salisbury, Massachusetts. Solectria is an American PV inverter manufacturer. Details of the project are given. **Availability:** PDF; Online.

14949 ■ "'Stalking Horse' Bidder Keeping Plextronics Here" in Pittsburgh Business Times (Vol. 33, March 28, 2014, No. 37, pp. 6)
Pub: American City Business Journals, Inc.
Contact: Mike Olivieri, Executive Vice President
Released: March 28, 2014. **Price:** $4, Introductory 4-week offer(Digital & Print). **Description:** Chemical company Solvay American has acquired solar and lighting company Plextronics Inc. of Pittsburgh, Pennsylvania. Solvay's research and innovation department is seen as a better fit for Plextronics because it is developing a new technology. **Availability:** Print; Online.

14950 ■ "State Regulators Reject AEP Ohio's Plans to Build 400MW of Solar Funded by Ratepayers" in Greentech Media (November 21, 2019)
URL(s): www.greentechmedia.com/articles/read/ohio -regulators-reject-aep-ohios-solar-plans
Ed: Emma Foehringer Merchant. **Released:** November 21, 2019. **Description:** Arguing that the power isn't needed, Ohio regulators rejected plans from American Electric Power's Ohio subsidiary to charge ratepayers to build a new solar project. **Availability:** Online.

14951 ■ "Sumitomo Invests in Desert Sunlight Solar Farm, the Largest PV Project Approved for Federal Land" in PR Newswire (October 2, 2012)
Pub: PR Newswire Association LLC.
Description: The Desert Sunlight Solar Farm, 550MW solar power project being constructed in the California desert area east of Palm Springs, is the largest solar photovoltaic (PV) facility approved for US public land. Sumitomo Corporation of America is investing in the project and plans to expand its renewable energy portfolio across the US.

14952 ■ "SunEdison Sells 30MW Spectrum Solar Project To Southern Company and Turner Renewable Energy" in Benzinga.com (September 28, 2012)
Pub: Benzinga.com
Contact: Jason Raznick, Founder
Ed: Paul Quintaro. **Description:** SunEdison sold its Spectrum Solar Project, a 30 MW solar photovoltaic power plant, to Southern Company and Turner Renewable Energy. Construction of the project is planned to begin in October 2012 in Clark County, Nevada. Details are included. **Availability:** Print; Online.

14953 ■ "Sustainability Is Top Priority for GreenTown Chicago" in Contractor (Vol. 56, November 2009, No. 11, pp. 1)
Ed: Candace Roulo. **Description:** GreenTown Chicago 2009 conference tackled energy-efficient practices and technologies, green design and building, and sustainable policies. Water conservation was also a topic at the conference and one mayor who made a presentation said that reducing the water loss in the system is a priority in the city's endeavor. **Availability:** Print; Online.

14954 ■ "Tax Credits for Renewables Get Another Shot in Congress" in Greentech Media (November 19, 2019)
URL(s): www.greentechmedia.com/articles/read/ renewable-tax-credits-get-another-shot-in-congress
Ed: Emma Foehringer Merchant. **Released:** November 19, 2019. **Description:** The U.S. House Ways and Means Committee drafted legislation that will extend tax credits for renewable technologies. It also includes incentives for energy storage, electric vehicles, and environmental justice programs at colleges and universities. **Availability:** Online.

14955 ■ "Texas Lands $1 Billion Investment in Solar and Battery Projects" in Renewable Energy World (November 16, 2021)
URL(s): www.renewableenergyworld.com/storage/ texas-lands-1-billion-investment-in-solar-and-ba ttery-projects
Ed: John Engle. **Released:** November 16, 2021. **Description:** Chem-Energy is investing more than $1 billion in a solar and battery plant in Central Texas. **Availability:** Online.

14956 ■ "U.S. Court Reopens Solar-Tariff Loophole That Trump Killed" in Bloomberg (November 16, 2021)
Ed: Brian Eckhouse, Maxwell Adler, Susan Decker. **Description:** A tariff exemption on some imported solar panels has been reinstated after former president Trump eliminated a loophole but which was deemed to be outside the his authority. **Availability:** Online.

14957 ■ "Water Conservation Helps GC's Building Attain LEED Gold Status" in Contractor (Vol. 56, September 2009, No. 9, pp. 5)
Description: Green contractor Marshall Erdman has built a new office building using green design. The facility is seen to become a prime Leadership in

Energy and Environmental Design (LEED) building model. Details of the building's design and features are also provided. **Availability:** Print; Online.

14958 ■ "Yates Turns Log Home Green - Part Three" in Contractor (Vol. 57, January 2010, No. 1, pp. 5)
Released: January 12, 2010. **Description:** Dave Yates of F.W. Behler Inc. discusses remodeling a log home's HVAC system with geo-to-radiant heat and thermal-solar systems. The solar heater's installation is discussed.

14959 ■ "Yudelson Challenges San Antonio Groups" in Contractor (Vol. 56, October 2009, No. 10, pp. 6)
Description: Green building consultant and author Jerry Yudelson made a presentation for the Central Texas Green Building Council and Leadership San Antonio where he discussed the European approach to sustainability and how it can be used for designing green buildings. Yudelson also discussed how to use sustainable practices for planning 25 years into the future. **Availability:** Print; Online.

STATISTICAL SOURCES

14960 ■ Solar Power Industry in the US - Market Research Report
URL(s): www.ibisworld.com/united-states/market-re search-reports/solar-power-industry/
Price: $925. **Description:** Downloadable report analyzing current and future trends in the solar power industry. **Availability:** Download.

TRADE SHOWS AND CONVENTIONS

14961 ■ SEPA Solar Power International
Smart Electric Power Alliance (SEPA)
1800 M St., NW Front 1 No. 33159
Washington, DC 20036
Ph: (202)857-0898
Co. E-mail: communications@sepapower.org
URL: http://sepapower.org
Contact: Seth Frader-Thompson, President
URL(s): www.re-plus.com
Frequency: Annual. **Description:** Solar energy, including thermal applications, storage, climate control, heating, and new technologies. **Audience:** Distributors, installers and contractors, engineering firms, architects, builders and developers, investors and financiers, industry experts, leaders, and professionals. **Principal Exhibits:** Solar energy, including thermal applications, storage, climate control, heating, and new technologies. **Telecommunication Services:** spi@xpressreg.net.

LIBRARIES

14962 ■ Alternative Energy Resources Organization (AERO) - Library
32 S Ewing St., Ste. 333.
Helena, MT 59601
Ph: (406)443-7272
Co. E-mail: aero@aeromt.org
URL: http://aeromt.org
Contact: Robin Kelson, Executive Director
E-mail: rkelson@aeromt.org
Facebook: www.facebook.com/aeromt
Instagram: www.instagram.com/aeromt
YouTube: www.youtube.com/user/aeromt1974
Description: Promotes sustainable agriculture, resource conservation and transportation choices through community education and citizen representation. Provides current programs that focus on sustainable agriculture, farm improvement clubs, beginning and retiring farmers, smart growth, and a more localized food system for greater community self-reliance.

Scope: Food; energy; education. **Founded:** 1974. **Holdings:** Figures not available. **Publications:** *Abundant Montana*; *AERO Sun-Times* (Quarterly); *Big Sky or Big Sprawl Montana at the Crossroads*; *Montana's Sustainable Agriculture Farming with Foresight.* **Educational Activities:** Alternative Energy Resources Organization Expo and Annual Meeting (Annual). **Awards:** Northern Rockies Sustainable Agriculture Award (Annual). **Geographic Preference:** National.

14963 ■ Arizona State University Architectural and Environmental Design Library
300 E Orange Mall
  Tempe, AZ 85281
Ph: (480)965-6400
URL: http://lib.asu.edu/design/collections/caed
Contact: Debra Riley-Huff, Department Head
E-mail: debra.riley-huff@asu.edu

Scope: Architecture; landscape architecture; industrial; interior; urban and visual communication design. **Services:** Interlibrary loan; copying; printing; scanning; open to the public. **Holdings:** 50,000 books; journals; media items; textual records; project files.

14964 ■ Arizona State University Architectural and Environmental Design Library - Solar Energy Collection
PO Box 871006
  Tempe, AZ 85287-1006
URL: http://lib.asu.edu/design/collections/solarenergy

Description: Aims to encourage research on solar energy and promote its use, the Association organized conferences addressing solar issues and began building its own library of technical literature. **Scope:** Solar energy. **Services:** Interlibrary loan; copying; library open to the public. **Founded:** 1954. **Holdings:** personal papers; technical papers; reports; conference materials; manuscripts; photographs.

14965 ■ Ball State University - Center for Energy Research/Education/Service (CERES)
Architecture Bldg.
  Rm. 018
  Muncie, IN 47306
Ph: (765)285-1135
Fax: (765)285-5622
Co. E-mail: ceres@bsu.edu
URL: http://www.bsu.edu/academics/centersandinsti
  tutes/ceres
Contact: Robert J. Koester, Director
E-mail: rkoester@bsu.edu

Description: Integral unit of Ball State University. **Scope:** Carries out interrelation of disciplines in energy related methods of analysis, performance evaluation, and decision making, including studies of community planning, urban design, building design, materials technology, computer application, solar and other alternative energy sources, energy education methodologies, and economic analysis. **Services:** Copying; center open to the public with restrictions. **Founded:** 1982. **Holdings:** Books; technical reports. **Publications:** *CERES Annual Report* (Annual). **Educational Activities:** CERES workshops and energy awareness programs to the periodic public lectures.

14966 ■ Boston Architectural Center - Alfred Shaw and Edward Durell Stone Library
320 Newbury St.
  Boston, MA 02115
URL: http://the-bac.edu/info-for/campus-an
  d-community/shaw-and-stone-library
Contact: Robert Adams, Director

Scope: Educational material. **Services:** Interlibrary Loan. **Founded:** 1966. **Subscriptions:** 120 journals 600,000 titles; 52,000 physical items; 120 print periodical titles; theses; films; maps; eBooks; books.

14967 ■ Florida Solar Energy Center Research Library (FSEC)
1679 Clearlake Rd.
  Cocoa, FL 32922-5703
Ph: (321)638-1000
Fax: (321)638-1010
Co. E-mail: info@fsec.ucf.edu
URL: http://energyresearch.ucf.edu
Contact: James Fenton, Director
E-mail: jfenton@fsec.ucf.edu
Facebook: www.facebook.com/Flori
  daSolarEnergyCenter
X (Twitter): x.com/morethansolar

Scope: Solar and other alternative sources of energy; science; technology. **Services:** Interlibrary loan; copying; library open to the public with restrictions. **Founded:** 1975. **Holdings:** 13,000 books; 2,364 bound periodical volumes; 12,477 technical documents; 7,715 vertical files; 7,572 slides; 56,522 microfiche; 10 films; 213 videotapes.

14968 ■ Northeast Sustainable Energy Association (NESEA)
20 Federal Str, Ste. 8
  Greenfield, MA 01301
Ph: (413)774-6051
Co. E-mail: nesea@nesea.org
URL: http://www.nesea.org
Contact: Miriam Aylward, Executive Director
E-mail: maylward@nesea.org
Facebook: www.facebook.com/NESEA.org
Linkedin: www.linkedin.com/company/northeast-sus
  tainable-energy-association
X (Twitter): x.com/NESEA_org
YouTube: www.youtube.com/user/NESEAorg

Description: Promotes energy conservation, non-polluting and renewable energy technologies. **Founded:** 1974. **Publications:** *BuildingEnergy* (Annual); *NESEA Business Member Directory.* **Educational Activities:** Advanced Residential Construction Conference. **Awards:** NESEA Zero Net Energy Building Award (Annual); NESEA Distinguished Service Award (Annual); NESEA Professional Leadership Award (Annual). **Geographic Preference:** National; Regional.

14969 ■ U.S. Department of Energy (USE) - Library
1000 Independence Ave. SW
  Washington, DC 20585
Ph: (202)586-5000
Fax: (202)586-4403
URL: http://www.energy.gov
Contact: Jennifer M. Granholm, Secretary
Facebook: www.facebook.com/energygov
X (Twitter): x.com/energy
Instagram: www.instagram.com/energy
YouTube: www.youtube.com/user/USdepartmen
  tofenergy

Description: Miscellaneous Publishing. **Scope:** Energy resources and Technologies. **Founded:** 1947. **Publications:** *Hydrogen Energy Coordinating Committee Annual Report: Summary of Department of Energy Hydrogen Programs* (Annual); *Listing of Awardee Names: Retired Awards* (Annual); *Listing of Awardee Names: Active Awards* (Quarterly); *Petroleum Statement, Annual Energy Report.* **Awards:** Secretary of Energy's Project Management Excellence Awards (Annual).

RESEARCH CENTERS

14970 ■ Ball State University - Center for Energy Research/Education/Service (CERES)
Architecture Bldg.
  Rm. 018
  Muncie, IN 47306
Ph: (765)285-1135
Fax: (765)285-5622
Co. E-mail: ceres@bsu.edu

URL: http://www.bsu.edu/academics/centersandinsti
  tutes/ceres
Contact: Robert J. Koester, Director
E-mail: rkoester@bsu.edu

Description: Integral unit of Ball State University. **Scope:** Carries out interrelation of disciplines in energy related methods of analysis, performance evaluation, and decision making, including studies of community planning, urban design, building design, materials technology, computer application, solar and other alternative energy sources, energy education methodologies, and economic analysis. **Services:** Copying; center open to the public with restrictions. **Founded:** 1982. **Holdings:** Books; technical reports. **Publications:** *CERES Annual Report* (Annual). **Educational Activities:** CERES workshops and energy awareness programs to the periodic public lectures.

14971 ■ California State Polytechnic University, Pomona College of Environmental Design - John T. Lyle Center for Regenerative Studies
3801 W Temple Ave.
  Pomona, CA 91768
Ph: (909)869-5155
Fax: (909)869-5188
Co. E-mail: crs@cpp.edu
URL: http://www.cpp.edu/env
Contact: Dr. Kyle D. Brown, Professor
E-mail: kdbrown@cpp.edu

Description: Integral unit of California State Polytechnic University, Pomona. **Scope:** Regenerative technologies, including integrated agriculture/aquaculture systems, agroforestry, passive solar heating and cooling, waste water recycling, and small scale intensive agriculture. **Founded:** 1994.

14972 ■ U.S. Department of Energy - National Renewable Energy Laboratory (NREL)
15013 Denver W Pky.
  Golden, CO 80401
Ph: (303)275-3000
Co. E-mail: public.affairs@nrel.gov
URL: http://www.nrel.gov
Contact: Dr. Martin Keller, President
E-mail: martin.keller@nrel.gov
Facebook: www.facebook.com/na
  tionalrenewableenergylab
Linkedin: www.linkedin.com/company/national-renew-
  able-energy-laboratory
X (Twitter): x.com/nrel
Instagram: www.instagram.com/na
  tionalrenewableenergylab
YouTube: www.youtube.com/user/NRELPR

Description: Publishes reference materials, teachers' lessons, and project ideas on renewable energy and energy efficiency topics. **Scope:** Renewable energy technologies, including the fundamental nature of light and its interaction with matter, focusing on the development of cost-effective solar technologies capable of producing significant amounts of energy. Studies encompass the areas of photovoltaics, alternative fuels, wind energy, transportation technologies, and energy efficiency technologies (active and passive solar). Specific areas include production of biomass fuel, photon conversion for the production of hydrogen from water, and the development of high-efficiency semiconductor solar cells. **Founded:** 1977. **Publications:** *Solar Collector Manufacturing Activity and Applications in the Residential Sector.* **Educational Activities:** SOLTECH (Annual).

14973 ■ University of Central Florida - Florida Solar Energy Center (FSEC)
1679 Clearlake Rd.
  Cocoa, FL 32922-5703
Ph: (321)638-1000
Fax: (321)638-1010
Co. E-mail: info@fsec.ucf.edu

URL: http://energyresearch.ucf.edu
Contact: Philip Fairey, Director
E-mail: pfairey@fsec.ucf.edu
Facebook: www.facebook.com/Flori
daSolarEnergyCenter
X (Twitter): x.com/morethansolar
Description: Publishes on solar energy. **Scope:** Photovoltaics, energy-efficient building design, solar water heating, energy-efficient, industrialized housing, innovative air conditioning systems, electrical end-uses, photoelectrochemical processes, solar waste detoxification, production, storage and utilization of hydrogen, and other energy efficiency, and solar energy activities for the state of Florida.

Program objectives include research and development, testing, certification, establishment of standards, educational services, and information dissemination. Responsible for mandatory certification of all solar energy systems manufactured and/or sold in Florida. **Founded:** 1973. **Publications:** *FSEC Annual Report* (Annual); *Photocatalyst Report*; *Solar Collector Newsletter*. **Educational Activities:** FSEC Distance learning program; FSEC Short courses, For solar and energy efficiency.

14974 ■ University of Wisconsin--Madison - Solar Energy Laboratory (SEL)
1500 Engineering Dr.
  Madison, WI 53706-1687

Ph: (608)265-6626
Co. E-mail: gfnellis@engr.wisc.edu
URL: http://sel.me.wisc.edu
Contact: Gregory F. Nellis, Director
E-mail: gfnellis@engr.wisc.edu
Description: Integral unit of University of Wisconsin—Madison. **Scope:** Computer programs used in solar energy research, development, and design; solar and non-solar air conditioning and heating systems. **Founded:** 1954.

ASSOCIATIONS AND OTHER ORGANIZATIONS

14975 ■ Learning Forward
504 S Locust St.
 Oxford, OH 45056
Ph: (513)523-6029
Free: 800-727-7288
Fax: (513)523-0638
Co. E-mail: office@learningforward.org
URL: http://learningforward.org
Contact: Denise Glyn Borders, President
E-mail: denise.borders@learningforward.org
Facebook: www.facebook.com/learningforward
Linkedin: www.linkedin.com/company/learning
 -forward
X (Twitter): x.com/learningforward
YouTube: www.youtube.com/user/learningforward
Description: Sponsors regional workshops on topics such as conducting effective staff development programs. **Founded:** 1969. **Publications:** *The Learning Professional* (Bimonthly); *The Learning Principal* (8/year); *Teachers Teaching Teachers* (8/year). **Awards:** Learning Forward Best Research Award (Annual); Susan Loucks-Horsley Award (Annual). **Geographic Preference:** National.

14976 ■ OAS Staff Association (OASSA)
1889 F St. NW
 Washington, DC 20006
Ph: (202)458-3000
Co. E-mail: staffadmin@oas.org
URL: http://staff.oas.org/spanish
Contact: Ernest Cossich, President
Facebook: www.facebook.com/OasStaffAssociation
X (Twitter): x.com/oas_staff
Instagram: www.instagram.com/oasstaffassociation
YouTube: www.youtube.com/channel/UCLIm-XGPGE
 thaM87UPkEp7A
Description: Staff members of the Organization of American States General Secretariat. Serves as a union to negotiate employment conditions and labor rights with the OAS administration. **Founded:** 1928. **Publications:** *Staff News* (Irregular). **Geographic Preference:** Multinational.

REFERENCE WORKS

14977 ■ "Bankruptcies" in Crain's Detroit Business (Vol. 24, March 24, 2008, No. 12, pp. 6)
Pub: Crain Communications Inc.
Contact: Barry Asin, President
Description: Current list of business that filed for Chapter 7 or 11 protection in U.S. Bankruptcy Court in Detroit include a construction company, a medical care company, a physical therapy firm and a communications firm. **Availability:** Online.

14978 ■ *Complete Guide to Public Employment*
Pub: Development Concepts Inc.
Contact: Ronald L. Krannich, President

URL(s): www.impactpublications.com/product/comple
te-guide-to-public-employment-3rd-edition
Ed: Ron Krannich, PhD, Caryl Krannich, PhD. **Released:** Latest 3rd edition. **Price:** $19.95, Individuals. **Description:** Publication includes list of federal, state, and local government agencies and departments, trade and professional associations, contracting and consulting firms, nonprofit organizations, foundations, research organizations, political support groups, and other organizations offering public service career opportunities. **Entries include:** Organization name, address, phone, name and title of contact. Complete title is "Complete Guide to Public Employment: Opportunities and Strategies with Federal, State, and Local Government;" Trade and Professional Associations; Contracting and Consulting Firms; Foundations; Research Organizations; and Political Support Groups. **Arrangement:** Classified by type of service. **Indexes:** Subject. **Availability:** Print.

14979 ■ *Directory of Contract Staffing Firms*
Pub: C.E. Publications Inc.
Contact: Jerry A. Erickson, Publisher
URL(s): www.cjhunter.com/dcsf/index-visitors.html
Ed: Jerry A. Erickson. **Released:** Daily **Price:** $50, for one year; $25, for additional. **Description:** Covers nearly 1,300 contract firms actively engaged in the employment of engineering, IT/IS, and technical personnel for 'temporary' contract assignments throughout the world. **Entries include:** Company name, address, phone, name of contact, email, web address. **Arrangement:** Alphabetical. **Indexes:** Geographical. **Availability:** Print; Online.

14980 ■ "How to Use Flexible Staffing Models to Solve Staffing Challenges" in Forbes (November 17, 2021)
URL(s): www.forbes.com/sites/
forbesbusinesscouncil/2021/11/17/how-to-use-flex
ible-staffing-models-to-solve-staffing-challenges/
?sh=73eafc2364e6
Ed: Sumir Meghani. **Released:** November 17, 2021. **Description:** Examines the labor market during the Covid pandemic as businesses struggle to hire and find the right workers to suit their customers' needs. Also addresses the viewpoint from employees and why they are not returning to hourly positions and what their expectations are moving forward. **Availability:** Online.

14981 ■ *Insight into Diversity: The EEO Recruitment Publication*
Pub: INSIGHT Into Diversity
Contact: Lenore Pearlstein, Publisher
E-mail: lpearlstein@insightintodiversity.com
URL(s): www.insightintodiversity.com
Facebook: www.facebook.com/insightintodiversity
Linkedin: www.linkedin.com/company/insight-into
 -diversity
X (Twitter): x.com/INSIGHT_News
Ed: Alexandra Vollman. **Released:** Monthly **Description:** Journal for business, academia, non-profit organizations and the government to use in recruiting

females, Native Americans, minorities, veterans, and persons with disabilities. **Availability:** Print; PDF; Online.

14982 ■ "King of the Crib: How Good Samaritan Became Ohio's Baby HQ" in Business Courier (Vol. 27, June 18, 2010, No. 7, pp. 1)
Pub: Business Courier
Ed: James Ritchie. **Description:** Cincinnati's Good Samaritan hospital had 6,875 live births in 2009, which is more than any other hospital in Ohio. They specialize in the highest-risk pregnancies and deliveries and other hospitals are trying to grab Good Samaritan's share in this niche. **Availability:** Print; Online.

14983 ■ "The People Puzzle; Re-Training America's Workers" in The Economist (Vol. 390, January 3, 2009, No. 8612, pp. 32)
Description: With thousands of workers losing their jobs, America is now facing the task of getting them back to work. With an overall unemployment rate of 6.7 percent, the federal government has three main ways for leading workers back to employment: training them for new jobs, providing unemployment insurance in order to replace lost wages during the period of job-hunting; and matching employers who desire a skill with workers who have that skill. Specialized staffing agencies provide employers and potential employees with the help necessary to find a job in some of the more niche markets. **Availability:** Online.

14984 ■ "Q&A With Devin Ringling: Franchise's Services Go Beyond Elder Care" in Gazette (October 2, 2010)
Pub: The Gazette
Contact: Vicki Cederholm, Director, Operations
E-mail: vicki.cederholm@gazette.com
Ed: Bill Radford. **Description:** Profile of franchise, Interim HealthCare, in Colorado Springs, Colorado; the company offers home care services that include wound care and specialized feedings to shopping and light housekeeping. It also runs a medical staffing company that provides nurses, therapists and other health care workers to hospitals, prisons, schools and other facilities. **Availability:** Online.

14985 ■ "Sign of the Times: Temp-To-Perm Attorneys" in HRMagazine (Vol. 54, January 2009, No. 1, pp. 24)
Description: A growing number of law firms are hiring professional staff on a temp-to-perm basis according to the president of Professional Placement Services in Florida. Firms can save money while testing potential employees on a temporary basis. **Availability:** Print; Online.

14986 ■ "Small Business and the Staffing Shortage by Industry" in Forbes (May 27, 2021)
URL(s): www.forbes.com/sites/williamdunkelberg/20
21/05/27/small-business-and-the-staffing-shortage
-by-industry/?sh=10a95d7724a3

Ed: William Dunkelberg. **Released:** May 27, 2021. **Description:** Small businesses are struggling to find employees now that Covid shutdowns are a thing of the past. Transportation, communication, and public utilities had the biggest hits to employment. **Availability:** Online.

SOURCES OF SUPPLY

14987 ■ *Federal Career Opportunities*
URL(s): www.fedjobs.com

Released: Biweekly; Latest edition 2014. **Price:** $195, Individuals 26 issues, 1 year; $7.95, Individuals single issue; $92, Individuals 6 months, 12 issues. **Description:** Covers more than 3,000 current federal job vacancies in the United States and overseas; includes permanent, part-time, and temporary positions. **Entries include:** Position title, location, series and grade, job requirements, special forms, announcement number, closing date, application address. **Arrangement:** Classified by occupation. **Availability:** Print; Online.

14988 ■ *International Employment Hotline*
URL(s): www.internationaljobs.org/monthly.html

Released: Monthly **Price:** $69, Individuals per 1 year; $21, Individuals per 3 months; $39, Individuals per 6 months; $129, Two years. **Description:** Covers temporary and career job openings overseas and advice for international job hunters. **Entries include:** Company name, address, job title, description of job, requirements, geographic location of job. **Arrangement:** Geographical. **Availability:** Print.

TRADE PERIODICALS

14989 ■ *Graduating Engineer & Computer Careers*
URL(s): www.graduatingengineer.comwww.graduatingengineer.com/about-the-magazine
Facebook: www.facebook.com/Graduating-Engineer-Computer-Careers-77077728959

Description: Magazine focusing on employment, education, and career development for entry-level engineers and computer scientists. **Availability:** Print; Online.

14990 ■ *Insight into Diversity: The EEO Recruitment Publication*
Pub: INSIGHT Into Diversity
Contact: Lenore Pearlstein, Publisher
E-mail: lpearlstein@insightintodiversity.com
URL(s): www.insightintodiversity.com
Facebook: www.facebook.com/insightintodiversity
Linkedin: www.linkedin.com/company/insight-into-diversity
X (Twitter): x.com/INSIGHT_News

Ed: Alexandra Vollman. **Released:** Monthly **Description:** Journal for business, academia, non-profit organizations and the government to use in recruiting females, Native Americans, minorities, veterans, and persons with disabilities. **Availability:** Print; PDF; Online.

14991 ■ *Mobility: The total relocation magazine*
Pub: Employee Relocation Council
Contact: Peggy Smith, President
URL(s): www.worldwideerc.org/MOBILITY/Pages/index.aspx

Released: Monthly **Price:** $48, U.S.; $148, Other countries. **Description:** Magazine for professionals in the relocation industry. **Availability:** Print.

14992 ■ *Public Personnel Management (PPM)*
Pub: SAGE Publications
Contact: Tracey Ozmina, President
URL(s): journals.sagepub.com/home/ppm
X (Twitter): x.com/PPMgmtJournal

Ed: Heather Getha-Taylor. **Released:** Quarterly **Price:** $540, Institutions for backfile lease, combined plus backfile (current volume print & all online content); $466, Institutions for backfile lease, e-access plus backfile (all online content); $954, Institutions for backfile purchase, e-access (content through 1998); $132, Institutions for single print issue; $46, Individuals for single print issue; $141, Individuals for print and online; $491, Institutions for print and online; $417, Institutions for online only; $481, Institutions for print only. **Description:** Journal for human resource executives and managers in the public sector. Contains articles on trends, case studies, legislation, and industry research. Founded by the International Public Management Association for Human Resources (IPMA-HR). **Availability:** Print; PDF; Download; Online.

CONSULTANTS

14993 ■ Optimus | SBR
33 Yonge St., Ste. 900
Toronto, ON, Canada M5E 1G4
Ph: (416)649-6000
Co. E-mail: info@optimussbr.com
URL: http://www.optimussbr.com
Contact: Kevin Gauci, Chief Executive Officer
YouTube: www.youtube.com/channel/UCO1Dh1VZyNDpm2dQ_CTcyUA

Description: Firm provides strategy, process and project management advisory services. **Scope:** Firm provides strategy, process and project management advisory services. **Founded:** 1979. **Training:** Electronic counter measures; Strategic planning; Project management.

FRANCHISES AND BUSINESS OPPORTUNITIES

14994 ■ Lloyd Staffing
445 Broadhollow Rd., Ste. 119
Melville, NY 11747
Ph: (631)777-7600
Free: 888-292-6678
Fax: (631)777-7626
URL: http://www.lloydstaffing.com
Contact: Keith Banks, President
Facebook: www.facebook.com/LLoydstaffing
X (Twitter): x.com/lloydstaffing
Instagram: www.instagram.com/lloydstaffing
YouTube: www.youtube.com/channel/UCLuGEn-10rBQ-PDO3G3nMTg
Pinterest: www.pinterest.com/lloydstaffing

Description: Specialized staffing services. **Scope:** Firm provides staffing and recruitment services. **Founded:** 1971. **Training:** Yes. **Special Services:** e-Procurement through Ringo.

14995 ■ Luttrell Staffing Group
1040 Tidewater Ct.
Kingsport, TN 37660
Ph: (423)272-7897
Fax: (423)765-1881

URL: http://www.luttrellstaffing.com
Contact: Lana Luttrell, Chief Executive Officer
E-mail: lluttrell@lstaff.com
Linkedin: www.linkedin.com/company/luttrell-staffing-group
X (Twitter): x.com/luttrellstaff
YouTube: www.youtube.com/channel/UCRu45kl7zb9wrRl-M8HQmog

Description: Provider of staffing needs and related services such as administrative staffing, light industrial staffing, nurse staffing and much more. **Founded:** 1990. **Royalty Fee:** 6.1-1.6%. **Training:** Training includes 5 days minimum at headquarters, 3-5 days onsite, 2 days of meeting and ongoing support.

COMPUTERIZED DATABASES

14996 ■ *Library Literature & Information Science Full Text™*
EBSCO Information Services
10 Estes St.
Ipswich, MA 01938
Ph: (978)356-6500
Free: 800-653-2726
Co. E-mail: information@ebsco.com
URL: http://www.ebsco.com
Contact: Tim Collins, Chief Executive Officer
URL(s): www.ebsco.com/products/research-databases/library-literature-information-science-full-text

Availability: Online. **Type:** Bibliographic; Full-text; Image.

LIBRARIES

14997 ■ Brandeis University - Center for Youth and Communities (CYC) - Library
415 South St. 35
Waltham, MA 02453
Ph: (781)736-4835
URL: http://heller.brandeis.edu/cyc
Contact: Susan P. Curnan, Executive Director
E-mail: curnan@brandeis.edu

Description: Integral unit of the Heller School for Social Policy and Management, Brandeis University. **Scope:** Youth development policy and programs, including education, workforce, family and community connections, management and leadership in non-profit organizations. **Founded:** 1983. **Holdings:** Figures not available. **Publications:** *Anthology*; *CYD Journal* (Occasionally); *CYC Reports*.

14998 ■ New York Department of Labor - Library
Bldg. 12 WA. Harriman Campus
Albany, NY 12240
Ph: (518)457-9000
Free: 888-469-7365
Co. E-mail: pressoffice@labor.ny.gov
URL: http://dol.ny.gov
Contact: Roberta Reardon, Commissioner
Facebook: www.facebook.com/nyslabor
Linkedin: www.linkedin.com/company/new-york-state-department-of-labor
X (Twitter): x.com/nyslabor
Instagram: www.instagram.com/nyslabor
YouTube: www.youtube.com/user/NYSLabor

Scope: Unemployment benefits; jobs and careers; workforce protections; labor data. **Founded:** 1901. **Holdings:** Figures not available.

ASSOCIATIONS AND OTHER ORGANIZATIONS

14999 ▪ American Cheese Society (ACS)
PO Box 3406
Englewood, CO 80155
Ph: (720)328-2788
Fax: (303)200-7099
Co. E-mail: info@cheesesociety.org
URL: http://www.cheesesociety.org
Contact: Mike Koch, President
Facebook: www.facebook.com/
AmericanCheeseSociety
X (Twitter): x.com/cheesesociety
Instagram: www.instagram.com/american_cheese
_society
Description: Represents producers, manufacturers, retailers, distributors, and others interested in the specialty and farmstead cheese industry. **Founded:** 1983. **Publications:** *American Cheese Society-- Membership Directory.* **Geographic Preference:** National.

15000 ▪ Greek Food and Wine Institute (GFWI)
34-80 48th St.
Long Island City, NY 11101
Ph: (718)729-5277
Co. E-mail: info@gfwi.org
URL: http://www.gfwi.org
Description: Food, wine and spirits producers, importers, and distributors from Greece and the US. Educates food and wine trade and consumers about the quality, variety, uses, and healthfulness of Greek foods, wines, and spirits. Conducts educational programs. **Founded:** 1992. **Publications:** *Gastronomia; Greek Wine Manual: Guide Sommeliers & Wine Professionals.* **Geographic Preference:** National.

15001 ▪ International Dairy-Deli-Bakery Association (IDDBA)
8317 Elderberry Rd.
Madison, WI 53717-2603
Ph: (608)310-5000
Fax: (608)238-6330
Co. E-mail: iddba@iddba.org
URL: http://www.iddba.org
Contact: Mike Eardley, President
Facebook: www.facebook.com/myiddba
Linkedin: www.linkedin.com/company/iddba
X (Twitter): x.com/myiddba
Description: Companies and organizations engaged in the production, processing, packaging, marketing, promotion, and/or selling of cheese and cheese products, bakery, or delicatessen and delicatessen-related items. Aims to further the relationship between manufacturing, production, marketing and distribution channels utilized in the delivery of deli, dairy, and bakery foods to the marketplace. Develops and disseminates information concerning deli, dairy, and bakery foods. **Founded:** 1964. **Publications:** *IDBA Membership Directory (Public); WrapUp (Quarterly); IDDBA Legis-Letter; Dairy-Deli-Bake Digest*

(Monthly); *IDDBA and You* (Monthly); *Trainer's Tool Kit.* **Educational Activities:** IDDBA Show (Annual). **Awards:** Scholarship for Growing the Future (Annual). **Geographic Preference:** Multinational.

15002 ▪ Opimian Society [La Societe Opimian]
2170 Rene-Levesque Blvd. W, Ste. 300
Montreal, QC, Canada H3H 2T8
Free: 800-361-9421
Co. E-mail: memberservice@opimian.ca
URL: http://opimian.ca
Contact: Michael Lutzmann, Managing Director
Facebook: www.facebook.com/OpimianWineClub
deVin
Linkedin: www.linkedin.com/company/opimian
Instagram: www.instagram.com/OpimianWineClub
deVin
Description: Individuals interested in wine. Promotes increased public appreciation of wine. Conducts educational programs. **Founded:** 1973. **Geographic Preference:** National.

15003 ▪ Specialty Food Association Inc.
136 Madison Ave., 12th Fl.
New York, NY 10016-6788
Ph: (212)482-6440
Fax: (212)482-6459
URL: http://www.specialtyfood.com
Contact: Phil Kafarakis, President
Facebook: www.facebook.com/SpecialtyFoodAssocia
tion
Linkedin: www.linkedin.com/company/specialty-foo
d-association
X (Twitter): x.com/Specialty_Food
Instagram: www.instagram.com/specialtyfoodassocia
tion
YouTube: www.youtube.com/user/NASFT
Pinterest: www.pinterest.com/craftcarejoy
Description: Manufacturers, distributors, processors, importers, retailers, and brokers of specialty and gourmet foods. Fosters trade, commerce and interest in the specialty food industry. **Founded:** 1952. **Publications:** *Specialty Food Magazine.* **Educational Activities:** Fancy Food Show (Semiannual); Specialty Food Association Winter Fancy Food Show (Annual); Summer Fancy Food Show (Annual). **Awards:** Sofi Awards (Annual). **Geographic Preference:** National.

REFERENCE WORKS

15004 ▪ *"Airport Adds More Detroit Flavor; Local Brands Bolster Metro Dining, Retail" in Crain's Detroit Business (Vol. 30, July 28, 2014, No. 30, pp. 3)*
Pub: Crain Communications Inc.
Contact: Barry Asin, President
Description: Gayle's Chocolates, Hockeytown Café, and National Coney Island have operated at the Detroit Metropolitan Airport for years. Soon new Detroit favorites will be joining the lineup for the enjoyment of both business and leisure travelers with

a food court offering local foods and beverages, including wine and 18 craft brewery beers. There will also be a self-serve kiosk where travelers can buy items to take with them. **Availability:** Print; Online.

15005 ▪ *"Baldor Specialty Foods, Bronx Brewery Release Beer to Benefit Brownsville Community Center" in Brewbound (September 18, 2019)*
URL(s): www.brewbound.com/news/baldor-specialty
-foods-bronx-brewery-release-beer-to-benefi
t-brownsville-community-culinary-center
Released: September 18, 2019. **Description:** The Brownsville Community Culinary Center is set to benefit from sales of a new beer from the joint efforts of Baldor Specialty Foods, The Bronx Brewery, and Union Beer Distributors. B-Note will be sold in the Bronx Brewery Taproom and in select stores. **Availability:** Online.

15006 ▪ *"Bodovino Is a World Leader in Self-Service Wine Tasting" in Idaho Business Review (September 8, 2014)*
Pub: BridgeTower Media
Contact: Adam Reinebach, President
Description: Bodovino's wine bar and retail shop offers self-service wine tasting for its customers. It is the largest outlet globally for the Italian wine dispenser manufacturer WineEmotion. Visitors to the shop can choose from 144 wines set up in the dispensing machines.

15007 ▪ *"Business Briefs: Alcoholic Beverage Manufacturing Is Big Business In Idaho" in Idaho Business Review (August 19, 2014)*
Pub: BridgeTower Media
Contact: Adam Reinebach, President
Description: Idaho's alcoholic beverage manufacturing industry is growing at a steady pace, reporting an $8.7 million payroll in 2013. Breweries, as well as wineries and distilleries are also strong. Statistical data included.

15008 ▪ *"California Wines Nab 64 Percent of U.S. Sales" in Sacramento Business Journal (Vol. 31, April 25, 2014, No. 9)*
Pub: American City Business Journals, Inc.
Contact: Mike Olivieri, Executive Vice President
Released: Weekly. **Description:** California wine sales represented 64 percent of all wine sales in the U.S. in 2013. This totaled $23.1 billion in sales at the retail level. California has held this level of market share in the U.S. wine market for some time. In 2003, the state shipped 65 percent of all wine in the country. **Availability:** Print; Online.

15009 ▪ *"Closures Pop Cork on Wine Bar Sector Consolidation" in Houston Business Journal (Vol. 40, January 22, 2010, No. 37, pp. A2)*
Pub: Houston Business Journal
Contact: Bob Charlet, President
E-mail: bcharlet@bizjournals.com

Ed: Allison Wollam. **Description:** Wine bar market in Houston, Texas is in the midst of a major shift and heads toward further consolidation due to the closure of pioneering wine bars that opened in the past decade. The Corkscrew owner, Andrew Adams, has blamed the creation of competitive establishments to the closure which helped wear out his concept. **Availability:** Print; Online.

15010 ■ *"Colorado's Oldest Craft Brewery is Downsizing, Ending Distribution and Laying Off 21 Employees" in The Denver Post (October 10, 2019)*
URL(s): www.denverpost.com/2019/10/10/boulder -beer-co-downsizing/
Ed: Josie Sexton. **Released:** October 10, 2019. **Description:** Boulder Beer Company, Colorado's first craft brewery is downsizing by shrinking its operations and laying off 21 employees. It's brew will only be available in its taproom, Wilderness Place, which is located outside of Boulder. Too much competition in the local brew industry is causing these changes, but the company hopes that by cutting back it can still survive. **Availability:** Online.

15011 ■ *"Event Will Highlight Underappreciated Rose Wines" in Sacramento Business Journal (Vol. 31, July 18, 2014, No. 21, pp. 4)*
Pub: American City Business Journals, Inc.
Contact: Mike Olivieri, Executive Vice President
Released: July 18, 2014. **Description:** The Pink Party is a rose wine tasting event that will be hosted by WineCentric founder and sommelier, Matthew Lewis, in Sacramento, California on July 25, 2014. Lewis hopes that the event will provide a comprehensive understanding of the range of possibilities among difference varieties of these wines.

15012 ■ *"Fine Wine, Poor Returns" in Barron's (Vol. 92, September 17, 2012, No. 38, pp. 11)*
Description: Investing in wines in not considered a good idea due to irrationally high wine prices. Wine collectors buying wines at very high prices are not expected to make money and are charged with a 28 percent 'collectibles' tax. **Availability:** Online.

15013 ■ *"Heat Brings Out Flavor, Not Visitors to Missouri Wineries" in Saint Louis Business Journal (Vol. 31, August 12, 2011, No. 51, pp. 1)*
Pub: Saint Louis Business Journal
Contact: Robert Bobroff, President
E-mail: rbobroff@bizjournals.com
Ed: Rick Desloge. **Description:** St. Louis, Missouri's wine industry seems to benefit from the heat wave. The hot weather is expected to give grapes more flavor. **Availability:** Print; Online.

15014 ■ *"Homes, Not Bars, Stay Well Tended" in Advertising Age (Vol. 79, January 28, 2008, No. 4, pp. 8)*
Pub: Crain Communications, Inc.
Contact: Jessica Botos, Manager, Marketing
E-mail: jessica.botos@crainsnewyork.com
Ed: Jeremy Mullman. **Description:** Due to the downturn in the economy, consumers are drinking less at bars and restaurants; however, according to the Distilled Spirits Council of the United States, they are still purchasing expensive liquor to keep in their homes. **Availability:** Online.

15015 ■ *"Law Firms Cash In On Alcohol" in Business Journal Portland (Vol. 27, November 19, 2010, No. 38, pp. 1)*
Pub: Portland Business Journal
Contact: Andy Giegerich, Managing Editor
E-mail: agiegerich@bizjournals.com
Ed: Andy Giegerich. **Description:** Oregon-based law firms have continued to corner big business on the state's growing alcohol industry as demand for their services increased. Lawyers, who represent wine, beer and liquor distillery interests, have seen their workload increased by 20 to 30 percent in 2009. **Availability:** Print; Online.

15016 ■ *"LCB Puts a Cork in Kiosk Wine Sales" in Times Leader (December 22, 2010)*
Ed: Andrew M. Seder. **Description:** The Pennsylvania Liquor Control Board closed down thirty Pronto Wine Kiosks located in supermarkets throughout the state. The Board cited mechanical and technological issues such as products not dispensing. **Availability:** Online.

15017 ■ *"Little Cheer in Holiday Forecast for Champagne" in Advertising Age (Vol. 88, November 17, 2008, No. 43, pp. 6)*
Pub: Crain Communications, Inc.
Contact: Jessica Botos, Manager, Marketing
E-mail: jessica.botos@crainsnewyork.com
Ed: Jeremy Mullman. **Description:** Due to a weak economy that has forced consumers to trade down from the most expensive alcoholic beverages as well as a weak U.S. dollar that has driven already lofty Champagne prices higher, makers of the French sparkling wine are anticipating a brutally slow holiday season. **Availability:** Online.

15018 ■ *"Mazel Tov: L'Chaim Gets a Deal to Expand with Southern Wine" in South Florida Business Journal (Vol. 33, September 7, 2012, No. 6, pp. 1)*
Pub: Baltimore Business Journal
Contact: Rhonda Pringle, President
E-mail: rpringle@bizjournals.com
Description: L'Chaim Kosher Vodka could triple its sales in 2012. The company won a deal to expand with Southern Wine and Spirits, which is the largest distributor of wine and spirits in the United States. The Distilled Spirits Council of the United States reported that vodka drives 31 percent of all spirit sales.

15019 ■ *"Millennials: The Great White Hope for Wine Industry" in Advertising Age (Vol. 81, December 6, 2010, No. 43, pp. 2)*
Pub: Crain Communications, Inc.
Contact: Jessica Botos, Manager, Marketing
E-mail: jessica.botos@crainsnewyork.com
Ed: E.J. Schultz. **Description:** Generation offers category of most growth potential in 30 years and 7-Eleven and vintner are taking notice. **Availability:** Online.

15020 ■ *"New Biz Mixes Paint, Wine; Will It Yield Green?" in Crain's Detroit Business (Vol. 30, September 8, 2014, No. 36, pp. 6)*
Pub: Crain Communications Inc.
Contact: Barry Asin, President
Description: Profile of Leanna Haun, owner of Picasso's Grapevine in downtown Clarkston, Michigan. Haun describes her business as one part wine, one part paint, and one part entertainment. Sessions include as many as ten people who are given instruction to paint a picture while enjoying wine and conversation with others. **Availability:** Print; Online.

15021 ■ *"New Recipes Added to IAMS Naturals Pet Food Line" in MMR (Vol. 28, August 1, 2011, No. 11, pp. 17)*
Description: Procter & Gamble Company's IAMS brand has created a new pet food line called IAMS Naturals for pet owners wishing to feed their pets natural, wholesome food. IAMS Sensitive Naturals has ocean fish and its first ingredient for dogs with sensitivities. IAMS Simple & Natural features chicken with no fillers. **Availability:** Print; Online.

15022 ■ *"Olive Oil Store and Tap Room To Open In Downtown Boise" in Idaho Business Review (May 15, 2014)*
Pub: BridgeTower Media
Contact: Adam Reinebach, President
Description: Profile of the new olive oil store and tap room called Olivin, which is opening a retail store in Boise, Idaho. The shop will offer various premium olive oils and specialty vinegars. The woman-owned store plans to employ one worker in the startup phase.

15023 ■ *"Russian Renaissance" in Chicago Tribune (September 22, 2008)*
Pub: Tribune News Service
Contact: Jack Barry, Vice President, Operations
E-mail: jbarry@tribpub.com
Ed: Alex Rodriguez. **Description:** Winemakers from Russia are returning to the craft and quality of winemaking now that they are free from Soviet restraints. **Availability:** Print; Online.

15024 ■ *"Santa Clara Wineries at Odds with County Over Regulations" in Silicon Valley/ San Jose Business Journal (Vol. 30, September 7, 2012, No. 24, pp. 1)*
Pub: Baltimore Business Journal
Contact: Rhonda Pringle, President
E-mail: rpringle@bizjournals.com
Description: A proposed ordinance in Santa Clara County, California will change existing winery regulations and implement a sliding fee system for event permits. Officials believe that the government ordinance will improve agricultural tourism, but winery owners claim that it would force them to choose between canceling events and footing the bill for certain costs. **Availability:** Print; Online.

15025 ■ *"Secaucus-Based Freshpet is Barking Up the Right Tree" in Record (September 8, 2011)*
Pub: North Jersey Media Group
Contact: Scott Muller, Director
E-mail: muller@northjersey.com
Ed: Rebecca Ollales. **Description:** Freshpet produces a variety of nutritious, refrigerated pet foods and treats for cats and dogs. The firm introduced five new recipes and treats to its grain-free line called Vital line. The Vital line mimics the ancestral diets of dogs and cats. **Availability:** Online.

15026 ■ *"Seward Restaurant Garners Accolades" in Alaska Business Monthly (Vol. 27, October 2011, No. 10, pp. 9)*
Pub: Alaska Business Publishing Company Inc.
Contact: Charles Bell, Vice President, Sales and Marketing
E-mail: cbell@akbizmag.com
Ed: Nancy Pounds. **Description:** Resurrection Road House of Seward, Alaska won the Wine Spectator's Aware of Excellence in 2011. The award honors restaurants that handle at least 100 gourmet wines that are skillfully paired with the cuisine. **Availability:** Print; Online.

15027 ■ *"Silver Springs Creamery Opens Retail Store" in Bellingham Business Journal (Vol. March 2010, pp. 3)*
Pub: Sound Publishing Inc.
Contact: Josh O'Connor, President
Ed: Isaac Bonnell. **Description:** Eric Sundstrom, owner of Silver Springs Creamery, announced the opening of its on-site retail store that will sell the farm's goat and cow cheese, yogurt, ice cream and flesh milk.

15028 ■ *"Social Networking: Growing Pains" in Canadian Business (Vol. 81, July 22, 2008, No. 12-13, pp. 35)*
Pub: Rogers Media Inc.
Contact: Neil Spivak, Chief Executive Officer
Ed: Alex Mlynek. **Description:** Laughing Stock Vineyards' Cynthia Enns and David Enns plan to target young buyers by using social media. The Enns however, are concerned that targeting younger buyers may affect Laughing Stock's image as a premium brand. Additional information regarding the company's future plans is presented. **Availability:** Print; Online.

15029 ■ *"A Soggy Harvest" in Business Journal-Portland (Vol. 24, October 5, 2007, No. 32, pp. 1)*
Pub: Portland Business Journal
Contact: Andy Giegerich, Managing Editor
E-mail: agiegerich@bizjournals.com
Ed: Robin J. Moody. **Description:** Vintners in Willamette Valley are facing a tough challenge with a rainy wine harvest season and a delay in the ripening

of grapes due to a cool spring and August. Rain decreased the sugar content of grapes and poses a danger with molds. The economic impact of the rainy harvest season in wine making is discussed. **Availability:** Print; Online.

15030 ■ "Specialty Food Sales Hit Hight of $170.4 Billion in 2020" in Supermarket News (June 10, 2021)
Ed: Michael Browne. **Released:** June 10, 2021. **Description:** An annual report published by the Specialty Foods Association concluded that the specialty foods industry saw a 13% increase in sales. Much of the increase can be traced back to the COVID-19 pandemic and people having to stay home and cook, due to restaurants closing.

15031 ■ "Strange Brew" in Canadian Business (Vol. 85, June 11, 2012, No. 10, pp. 52)
Ed: Paul Brent. **Description:** Molson Coors is launching the Coors Light Iced T beer in summer 2012 as part of its effort to improve weak sales in North America. The new product is aimed at female drinkers and is part of an effort to win back sales from wine and spirits. **Availability:** Print; Online.

15032 ■ "Trends at the 2019 Summer Fancy Food Show" in Food Business News (June 25, 2019)
URL(s): www.foodbusinessnews.net/articles/13969 -trends-at-the-2019-summer-fancy-food-show
Ed: Monica Watrous. **Released:** June 25, 2019. **Description:** The Summer Fancy Food Show in New York was held and featured over 2,400 exhibitors. Specialty food sales have increased with refrigerated and frozen plant-based meat alternatives, rice cakes, ready-to-drink beverages, and frozen desserts leading the way. Alternatives to meat and dairy are also gaining a strong foothold in the industry. **Availability:** Online.

15033 ■ "The Trouble With $150,000 Wine" in Barron's (Vol. 88, July 7, 2008, No. 27, pp. 33)
Pub: Dow Jones & Company Inc.
Contact: Almar Latour, Chief Executive Officer
Ed: Jay Palmer. **Description:** Review of the book, "The Billionaire's Vinegar: The Mystery of the World's Most Expensive Bottle of Wine," which discusses vintners along with the marketing and distribution of wine as well as the winemaking industry as a whole. **Availability:** Online.

15034 ■ "United Natural Foods Establishes Charitable Foundation to Support Healthy, Sustainable and Organic Food Systems" in United Natural Foods, Inc. (May 14, 2012)
Pub: The Financial Times Ltd.
Contact: John Ridding, Chief Executive Officer
E-mail: john.ridding@ft.com
Description: United Natural Foods Inc. (UNFI) has established a foundation committed to supporting healthy, sustainable and organic food systems. UNFI distributes natural, organic and specialty foods and related products. **Availability:** PDF; Online.

15035 ■ "Uptown Goes Local To Fill Final Entertainment District Vacancy" in Birmingham Business Journal (Vol. 31, May 9, 2014, No. 19, pp. 8)
Pub: American City Business Journals, Inc.
Contact: Mike Olivieri, Executive Vice President
Released: Weekly. **Price:** $4, introductory 4-week offer(Digital & Print). **Description:** A new butcher, beer and wine shop called Bottle & Bone will become the final tenant for the new Uptown entertainment district in Birmingham, Alabama, slated to open by fall 2014. The shop is owned by Freshfully founder Jen Barnett and will focus on local offerings, particularly fresh meats, wine and beer. **Availability:** Print; Online.

15036 ■ "Vino Volo Debuts at the Airmall at Boston Logan" in Travel & Leisure Close-Up (October 8, 2012)
Description: Concessions developer, Airmall USA, presents Vino Volo, the company offering travelers a place to unwind with a glass of wine in a comfortable setting. The restaurant will offer tapas and wine or will create a themed tasting flights of two or three glasses of wine. **Availability:** Print; Online.

15037 ■ "Yao Ming Courts China's Wine Boom" in Wall Street Journal Eastern Edition (November 28, 2011, pp. B4)
Pub: Dow Jones & Company Inc.
Contact: Almar Latour, Chief Executive Officer
Ed: Jason Chow. **Description:** Yao Ming, the former NBA 7-foot 6-inch Chinese basketball star, is set to cash in on the market potential for wine in China. He has created his own winery in California, Yao Family Wines, which will produce wines solely for the Chinese market. **Availability:** Online.

STATISTICAL SOURCES

15038 ■ Specialty Food Stores Industry in the US - Market Research Report
URL(s): www.ibisworld.com/united-states/market-re-search-reports/specialty-food-stores-industry/
Price: $925, Single report. **Description:** Provides data on the specialty food stores industry in the US. Report includes industry financial ratios, revenue forecasts, historical and forecast growth, industry market size, industry major players, profitability analysis, SWOT analysis, industry trends, industry operating conditions, and Porter's 5 Forces analysis. **Availability:** Online; Download.

TRADE PERIODICALS

15039 ■ The Cheese Reporter
Pub: Cheese Reporter Publishing Co.
Contact: Dick Groves, Publisher Editor
E-mail: dgroves@cheesereporter.com
Ed: Dick Groves. **Released:** Weekly **Price:** $140, By mail for 1 year price (periodical mail); $205, By mail for 2 year price (periodical mail); $195, By mail for 1 year price (first class mail); $320, By mail for 2 year price (first class mail); $195, By mail for 1 year price for Canada or Mexico; $320, By mail for 2 year price for Canada or Mexico; $260, By mail for 1 year price for foreign (airmail); $390, By mail for 2 year price for foreign (airmail); $10, By mail for 1 week price; $50, By mail for 4 weeks price; $70, By mail for 12 weeks price; $85, By mail for 26 weeks price; $5, By mail for week; $30, By mail for 4 weeks; $85, By mail for 26 weeks periodical; $140, By mail for 1 year; $205, By mail for 2 year; $70, By mail for 12 weeks. **Description:** Newspaper (tabloid) serving the cheese and dairy industry. **Availability:** Print; Online.

15040 ■ The Food & Beverage International
Contact: Ellen Walsh, Editor
E-mail: ewalsh@fbworld.com
URL(s): www.fandbi.com
Ed: Ellen Walsh. **Description:** Trade magazine covering the food and beverage industry. **Availability:** Print.

15041 ■ Gourmet News
Pub: Oser Communications Group Inc.
Contact: Kimberly Oser, President
URL(s): www.gourmetnews.com
Released: Monthly **Price:** $65, for annually US and Canada; $150, for annually cover air delivery. **Description:** Business newspaper for the specialty food industry. **Availability:** Print; Online.

15042 ■ The National Culinary Review (NCR)
Pub: American Culinary Federation
Contact: Kimberly Brock Brown, President
E-mail: chefkbb@acfchefs.org
URL(s): www.acfchefs.org/ACF/About/Media/Publica tions/ACF/About/Media/Publications
Ed: Kay Orde. **Released:** 6/year **Price:** $140, for online; $40, for domestic; $200, for international; $140, for online and print. **Description:** Trade magazine covering food and cooking. Includes articles on food, drink, and menu trends; recipes; personal and professional development; and management. **Availability:** Print; PDF; Online.

15043 ■ the Art of Eating
Pub: The Art of Eating LLC.
Contact: Kimberly Behr, Publisher
URL(s): www.theartofeatingllc.com
Facebook: www.facebook.com/theartofeatingllc
X (Twitter): x.com/ArtOfEatingLLC
Instagram: www.instagram.com/theartofeatingllc
Ed: Edward Behr. **Released:** Quarterly **Description:** Consumer publication featuring essays on food and wine. **Availability:** Print; Online.

15044 ■ Wine & Spirits Magazine
Pub: Wine & Spirits Magazine Inc.
Contact: Joshua Greene, President
URL(s): www.wineandspiritsmagazine.com/about-ws
Facebook: www.facebook.com/WineSpiritsMag
X (Twitter): x.com/wineandspirits
Released: Quarterly **Price:** $4.99, for per month online; $24.95, for one year online only; $36.95, for 2 year online only; $44.95, for 3 year online only. **Description:** Magazine containing consumer buying information on wine and spirits with in-depth articles on regions and trends in food and wine. **Availability:** Print; Online.

15045 ■ Wines & Vines
Pub: Wines and Vines
URL(s): winebusinessanalytics.com/digitaledition
Facebook: www.facebook.com/people/Wines-Vines/ 100035392436400
Instagram: www.instagram.com/wines_and_vines_
Ed: Andrew Adams, Jim Gordon. **Released:** Monthly **Price:** $175, for print Nno-US; $80, for print additional copy; $495, for monthly online. **Description:** Periodical on wine industry. **Availability:** Print; Online.

VIDEO/AUDIO MEDIA

15046 ■ How I Built This: Dang Foods: Vincent and Andrew Kitirattragam
URL(s): www.npr.org/2022/01/21/1074911897/dang -foods-vincent-and-andrew-kitirattragam
Released: January 24, 2022. **Description:** Podcast explains how a home-cooking experiment let to the founding of an Asian-inspired snack food brand.

15047 ■ How I Built This: Halo Top Ice Cream: Justin Woolverton
URL(s): wondery.com/shows/how-i-built-this/episode/ 10386-halo-top-ice-cream-justin-woolverton
Ed: Guy Raz. **Released:** April 17, 2023. **Description:** Podcast explains how a frustrated lawyer developed the Halo Top ice cream recipe in his Cuisinart.

15048 ■ How I Built This: Mary's Gone Crackers: Mary Waldner
URL(s): wondery.com/shows/how-i-built-this/episode/ 10386-marys-gone-crackers-may-waldner
Ed: Guy Raz. **Released:** July 20, 2023. **Description:** Podcast explains how someone turned making gluten-free crackers that she could eat at restaurants into a multi-million-dollar business.

15049 ■ How I Built This: Orgain: Andrew Abraham
URL(s): wondery.com/shows/how-i-built-this/episode/ 10386-orgain-andrew-abraham
Ed: Guy Raz. **Released:** August 07, 2023. **Description:** Podcast explains how a medical student used his experience with a life-threatening diagnosis to make nutritional organic shakes.

15050 ■ How I Built This: Stacy's Pita Chips: Stacy Madison
URL(s): www.npr.org/2021/08/04/1024913084/stacys -pita-chips-stacy-madison-2019
Released: August 09, 2021. **Description:** Podcast explains how Stacy Madison went from selling sandwiched from a converted hog dog cart to making chips with the leftover pita to launching Stacy's Pita Chips.

15051 ■ How I Built This: Yasso: Amanda Klane and Drew Harrington
URL(s): wondery.com/shows/how-i-built-this/episode/ 10386-yasso-amanda-klane-and-drew-harrington

Ed: Guy Raz. **Released:** September 25, 2023. **Description:** Podcast explains how childhood friends founded Yasso, a company that offers high-protein, low-calorie yogurt bars, despite initial rejections from prospective manufacturers.

TRADE SHOWS AND CONVENTIONS

15052 ■ IDDBA Show

International Dairy-Deli-Bakery Association (IDDBA)
  8317 Elderberry Rd.
  Madison, WI 53717-2603
Ph: (608)310-5000
Fax: (608)238-6330
Co. E-mail: iddba@iddba.org
URL: http://www.iddba.org
Contact: Mike Eardley, President
URL(s): www.iddba.org/iddba-show/about/iddba-2025
Frequency: Annual. **Description:** Topics include those related to the food industry. Event contains speakers, exhibitions, workshops, and entertainment. **Audience:** Buyers, bakers, merchandisers, and executives who have a shared passion for food and the industry. **Principal Exhibits:** Topics include those related to the food industry. Event contains speakers, exhibitions, workshops, and entertainment. Dates and Locations: 2025 Jun 01-3 Ernest N. Morial Convention Center, New Orleans, LA. **Telecommunication Services:** wisl@iddba.org.

15053 ■ SNAXPO: Annual Snack Food Association Convention

SNAC International
  1560 Wilson Blvd., No550
  Arlington, VA 22209
Co. E-mail: eavery@snacintl.org
URL: http://www.snacintl.org
Contact: Elizabeth Avery, President
E-mail: eavery@snacintl.org
URL(s): snaxpo.com
Frequency: Annual. **Description:** Snack food suppliers and related products and services. **Audience:** Snack food manufacturers, suppliers, owners, executives, and buyers. **Principal Exhibits:** Snack food suppliers and related products and services. Dates and Locations: 2025 Mar 30-Apr 01 Orange County Convention Center, Orlando, FL. **Telecommunication Services:** avalentino@snacintl.org.

15054 ■ Specialty Food Association Winter Fancy Food Show

Specialty Food Association Inc.
  136 Madison Ave., 12th Fl.
  New York, NY 10016-6788
Ph: (212)482-6440
Fax: (212)482-6459
URL: http://www.specialtyfood.com
Contact: Phil Kafarakis, President
URL(s): www.specialtyfood.com/fancy-food-shows/winter
Price: $60, Onsite. **Frequency:** Annual. **Description:** Exhibits relating to international specialty food and dessert. **Audience:** Retailers, the educational sector, buyers from various food businesses, manufacturers, the press, and other industry professionals. **Principal Exhibits:** Exhibits relating to international specialty food and dessert. Dates and Locations: 2025 Jan 19-21 Las Vegas Convention Center, Las Vegas, NV. **Telecommunication Services:** mboulefrakh@specialtyfood.com.

FRANCHISES AND BUSINESS OPPORTUNITIES

15055 ■ Auntie Anne's LLC

Auntie Anne's Franchisor SPV LLC
  5620 Glenridge Dr. NE
  Atlanta, GA 30342
Co. E-mail: franchising@auntieannes.com
URL: http://auntieannesfranchising.com
Facebook: www.facebook.com/auntieannespretzels
X (Twitter): x.com/auntieannes

Description: Serves fresh, hot hand-rolled soft pretzels. **Founded:** 1988. **Training:** 2 week training program is provided for owners, including onsite training at time of store opening.

15056 ■ Blenz Coffee

220-21320 Gordon Way
  Richmond, BC, Canada V6W 1J8
Ph: (604)682-2995
Co. E-mail: concerns@blenz.com
URL: http://blenz.com
Facebook: www.facebook.com/BlenzCoffee
X (Twitter): x.com/BlenzCoffee
Instagram: www.instagram.com/BlenzCoffee
Description: Chain of coffee shop. **Founded:** 1992. **Training:** Yes.

15057 ■ Bulk Barn Foods Ltd.

320 Don Hillock Dr.
  Aurora, ON, Canada L4G 0G9
Ph: (905)726-5000
Fax: (905)726-5011
Co. E-mail: customerservicew@bulkbarn.ca
URL: http://www.bulkbarn.ca
Facebook: www.facebook.com/BulkBarnFoods
Instagram: www.instagram.com/bulkbarnfoods
Pinterest: www.pinterest.com/bulkbarn
Description: Retailer of food products such as nuts, candy, snacks, baking ingredients, health and natural food products and much more. **Founded:** 1982. **Training:** Start-up and onsite.

15058 ■ Crescent Wines

No.108-2255 King George Hwy
  South Surrey, BC, Canada V4A 5A4
Ph: (604)542-0211
Co. E-mail: info@crescentwines.com
URL: http://www.crescentwines.com
Contact: Kathy Lawler, Owner
Facebook: www.facebook.com/crescentwines
Description: Production and distributor of wines. **Founded:** 2007. **Training:** Offers full-training and ongoing support.

15059 ■ The Honey Baked Ham Company L.L.C. (HBH)

3875 Mansell Rd.
  Alpharetta, GA 30022
Free: 800-367-7720
URL: http://www.honeybaked.com/home
Contact: Harry J. Hoenselaar, Founder
Facebook: www.facebook.com/HoneyBakedHamOfficial
X (Twitter): x.com/honeybakedham
Instagram: www.instagram.com/honeybaked_ham
YouTube: www.youtube.com/channel/UCCG-6tQN0TdL20TECiHyGWQ
Pinterest: www.pinterest.com/honeybaked_ham
Description: Producer and retailer of ham and turkey products. **Founded:** 1957. **Training:** Comprehensive 14 day program at corporate training store.

15060 ■ Pretzels Plus, Inc.

225 Penn St.
  Hanover, PA 17331
Description: Soft pretzels. **Founded:** 1991. **Equity Capital Needed:** $25,000-$150,000. **Franchise Fee:** 10000. **Royalty Fee:** 6%. **Training:** Yes.

15061 ■ Rosevine Winery, LLC

1375 Gateway Blvd.
  Boynton Beach, FL 33426
Contact: DeRossett Thomas, Contact
Description: Retailer of wine. **Founded:** 2003. **Training:** Offers 3-5 days training at franchisees location, 10 days at 1810 Winery and ongoing support.

15062 ■ Sushi Shop

643 rue Wellington
  Montreal, QC, Canada H3C 1T2
Ph: (514)336-8885
Co. E-mail: info@sushishop.com
URL: http://www.sushishop.com
Facebook: www.facebook.com/sushishopboutique
Description: Producer and retailer of sushi, sashimi and other Japanese specialties. **Founded:** 2000. **Training:** Yes.

15063 ■ We're Rolling Pretzel Co.

2500 W State St.
  Alliance, OH 44601
Ph: (330)823-0575
Co. E-mail: corporate@wererolling.com
URL: http://www.wererolling.com
Contact: Kevin Krabill, President
E-mail: kkrabill@wererolling.com
Facebook: www.facebook.com/people/Were-Rolling-Pretzel-Company/100063675634560
Description: Operator of restaurant offers hand rolled pretzels and beverages. **No. of Operating Units:** 32.0. **Founded:** 1996. **Franchised:** 2000. **Franchise Fee:** $15,000 ; $10,000 for subsequent locations. **Royalty Fee:** 5%. **Financial Assistance:** No **Training:** Sells cookies and ice cream.

15064 ■ Wetzel's Pretzels

Facebook: www.facebook.com/WetzelsPretzels/
Description: Pretzels. **No. of Franchise Units:** 253. **No. of Company-Owned Units:** 11. **Founded:** 1994. **Franchised:** 1996. **Equity Capital Needed:** $156,300-$369,950. **Franchise Fee:** $35,000. **Royalty Fee:** 7%. **Training:** Offers 2 weeks at headquarters, 4 days at franchisee's location and ongoing support.

15065 ■ Wine Lovers Agency

5407 Eglinton Ave. W, Ste. 203
  Etobicoke, ON, Canada M9C 5K6
Ph: (416)551-6898
Co. E-mail: shop@wineloversagency.com
URL: http://www.wineloversagency.com
X (Twitter): x.com/wineloversca
Description: Distributor and retailer of wine. **Founded:** 1985.

PUBLICATIONS

15066 ■ *Cheese Market News: The Weekly Newspaper of the Nation's Cheese and Dairy-Deli Business*

5315 Wall St., Ste. 100
  Middleton, WI 53562
Ph: (608)831-6002
URL: http://www.cheesemarketnews.com
Contact: Susan Quarne, Publisher
E-mail: squarne@cheesemarketnews.com
URL(s): www.cheesemarketnews.com
Facebook: www.facebook.com/cheesemarketnews
X (Twitter): x.com/CMN_CheeseNews
Released: Weekly **Price:** $210, for 1 year price for Email with 2nd Class Mail Service (digital); $315, for 2 year price for Email with 2nd Class Mail Service; $145, By mail for 1 year price for 2nd Class (USA only); $200, By mail for 1 year price for 1st Class/Canada/Mexico - Airmail; $330, By mail for 1 year price for International (Airmail); $205, By mail for 2 years price for 2nd Class (USA only); $325, By mail for 2 years price for 1st Class/Canada/Mexico - Airmail; $8.50, Single issue for price for print or digital; $525, for 2 years price for International (Airmail); $145, for 1 year price for email only, without mail service (digital); $205, for 2 year price for email only, without mail service (digital). **Description:** Newspaper (tabloid) covering the cheese manufacturing and marketing business. **Availability:** Print; Online.

15067 ■ *Market Watch: Market Intelligence on the Wine, Spirits, and Beer Business*

825 8th Ave., 33rd Fl.
  New York, NY 10019-7475
Co. E-mail: ssenatore@mshanken.com
URL: http://www.mshanken.com
Contact: Barry Abrams, Vice President Associate Publisher
E-mail: babrams@mshanken.com
URL(s): www.mshanken.com/marketwatch
Facebook: www.facebook.com/shankenmwmag
X (Twitter): x.com/marketwatchmag
Ed: Marvin R. Shanken. **Released:** 11/year; January/February, March, April, May, June, July/August, September, October, November, December. **Price:** $60, for annual. **Description:** Magazine for the alcohol industry. **Availability:** Print; Online.

15068 ■ *Wine Business Monthly: The Industry's Leading Publication for Wineries and Growers*
584 First St. E
  Sonoma, CA 95476
Free: 800-895-9463
Fax: (707)940-3930
Co. E-mail: info@winebusiness.com
URL: http://www.winebusiness.com
Contact: Alan Talbot, Director
E-mail: alan@winesvinesanalytics.com
URL(s): www.winebusiness.com/wbm
Ed: Cyril Penn. **Released:** Monthly **Price:** $29, for per year use. **Description:** Trade magazine for the wine industry. **Availability:** Print; Online.

LIBRARIES

15069 ■ **Food Institute (FI)**
330 Changebridge Rd., Ste. 101
  Pine Brook, NJ 07058
Ph: (201)791-5570
Free: 855-791-5570
Co. E-mail: questions@foodinstitute.com
URL: http://www.foodinstitute.com
Contact: Anika Wilson, Contact
E-mail: anika.wilson@foodinstitute.com
Facebook: www.facebook.com/foodinstitutenj
Linkedin: www.linkedin.com/company/the-food-insti
  tute
X (Twitter): x.com/FoodInstitute
Instagram: www.instagram.com/foodinstitute
YouTube: www.youtube.com/channel/UCYAPI0TXN
  tJa04aQre4h4pA
Description: Strives to provide food industry-related information to its members. **Scope:** The food industry. **Services:** Center open to the public on fee basis. **Founded:** 1928. **Holdings:** Figures not available. **Publications:** *Today in Food*; *Get It Out, Get It Right, Get It Over! Avoiding Food Product Recalls*; *The Food Institute* (Weekly); *Almanac of the Canning, Freezing, Preserving Industries* (Annual); *Food Business Mergers and Acquisitions*; *OSHA Inspection Manual*; *Regulatory Directory* (Periodic); *Food Business Mergers & Acquisitions*. **Geographic Preference:** Multinational.

15070 ■ **Napa Valley Wine Library Association Library (NVWLA)**
PO Box 328
  Saint Helena, CA 94574
Ph: (707)963-5145
Co. E-mail: info@napawinelibrary.com
URL: http://www.napawinelibrary.com
Contact: Diana H. Stockton, Manager
E-mail: editor@napawinelibrary.com
Facebook: www.facebook.com/napawinelibrary
X (Twitter): x.com/napawinelibrary
Instagram: www.instagram.com/napawinelibrary
Scope: Viticulture; neology; wine lore; winegrowing; winemaking. **Services:** copying; library open to the public. **Founded:** 1962. **Holdings:** Books.

15071 ■ **St. Joseph's University - Academy of Food Marketing - Campbell Library**
Saint Joseph's University, 5600 City Ave.
  387 Mandeville Hall
  Philadelphia, PA 19131
URL: http://www.sju.edu/haub-school-business/afm/
  campbell-collection
Scope: Food marketing. **Services:** Interlibrary loan. **Founded:** 1965. **Holdings:** 100+ food-related research guides; 500+ topical print files.

15072 ■ **University of California, Davis - Archives and Special Collections**
Shields Library, 100 NW Quad
  Davis, CA 95616
Ph: (530)752-1621
Co. E-mail: speccoll@ucdavis.edu
URL: http://library.ucdavis.edu/archives-and-special
  -collections
Contact: William Garrity, Head Librarian
E-mail: wfgarrity@ucdavis.edu
Scope: Agriculture; American; British literature; apiculture; botany; British history; entomology; religion; viticulture; enology and zoology. **Services:** Copying; collections open to the public for reference use only. **Founded:** 1966. **Holdings:** 183,000 volumes; 17,000 lin.ft. of archives and manuscripts; books; rare books; pamphlets; articles; journals.

RESEARCH CENTERS

15073 ■ **Texas Tech University - Texas Wine Marketing Research Institute (TWMRI)**
2500 Broadway
  Lubbock, TX 79409
Ph: (806)742-3077
Co. E-mail: texaswine@ttu.edu
URL: http://www.depts.ttu.edu/hs/texaswine
Contact: Dr. Tim H. Dodd, Director
E-mail: tim.dodd@ttu.edu
Facebook: www.facebook.com/texaswinemarketing
X (Twitter): x.com/txwinemarketing
Description: Integral unit of Texas Tech University. **Scope:** Wine marketing, including supermarkets, wine tourism, restaurants and winery sales. Also studies the Texas wine and wine grape industry. **Founded:** 1988. **Publications:** *Profile of the Texas Wine Industry* (Annual); *TWMRI Research articles*; *TWMRI Research reports*.

15074 ■ **University of British Columbia Faculty of Land and Food Systems - Wine Research Centre (WRC)**
EME4145 - 1137 Alumni Ave.
  Kelowna, BC, Canada V1V 1V7
Co. E-mail: wine.research@ubc.ca
URL: http://www.ubc.ca
Contact: Dr. Hennie J. J. van Vuuren, Director
E-mail: hjjvv@mail.ubc.ca
URL(s): www.landfood.ubc.ca/research/lfs-research
  -centres-groups/food-science-group
X (Twitter): x.com/ubcwine
Description: Integral unit of Faculty of Land and Food Systems, University of British Columbia. **Scope:** Enology and viticulture. **Founded:** 1999.

ASSOCIATIONS AND OTHER ORGANIZATIONS

15075 ■ Association of Golf Merchandisers (AGM)
2351 Sunset Blvd., Ste. 170 No. 331
Rocklin, CA 95765
Ph: (602)604-8250
Co. E-mail: info@agmgolf.org
URL: http://agmgolf.org
Contact: Desane Blaney, Executive Director
Facebook: www.facebook.com/Associa
tionGolfMerchandisers
Linkedin: www.linkedin.com/company/association-of
-golf-merchandisers
Description: Dedicated to maximizing members' learning and earning capabilities. Conducts continuing educational programs; provides networking opportunities, scholarships and a forum for communication; compiles statistics. **Founded:** 1989. **Publications:** *AGM Merchandise Manual.* **Geographic Preference:** National.

15076 ■ Athletic Equipment Managers Association (AEMA)
c/o Sam Trusner, Office Manager
207 E Bodman
Bement, IL 61813
Ph: (217)678-1004
Co. E-mail: samtrusner@gmail.com
URL: http://equipmentmanagers.com
Contact: Sam Trusner, Office Manager
E-mail: samtrusner@gmail.com
Facebook: www.facebook.com/AthleticEquipmen
tManagersAssociation
X (Twitter): x.com/aema_74
Description: Athletic equipment managers and others who handle sports equipment for junior high and high schools, colleges, recreation centers, and professional sports; individuals involved in athletic management and coaching or the handling or purchasing of athletic, physical education, or recreational equipment. Aims to improve the profession of equipment management and promote a better working relationship among those interested in problems of management. Works collectively to facilitate equipment improvement for greater safety among participants in all sports. **Founded:** 1974. **Publications:** *The Scoreboard* (3/year). **Educational Activities:** AEMA Convention (Annual). **Awards:** Jimmy Callaway Scholarships (Annual); Glenn Sharp Award (Annual); Russell Athletics Scholarship (Annual). **Geographic Preference:** National.

15077 ■ Canadian Sporting Goods Association (CSGA) [Association Canadienne d'Articles de Sport]
Nobleton, ON, Canada L7B 0N9
Co. E-mail: info@csga.ca
URL: http://www.csga.ca
Contact: Bryan Loucks, President
Linkedin: www.linkedin.com/company/canadian-spor
ting-goods-association

Instagram: www.instagram.com/csgahub
Description: Covers the sporting goods industry in Canada. Represents members' interests in international trade matters and functions as liaison between members and government agencies involved in the manufacture and trade of sporting goods. **Publications:** *CSGA Newsletter* (Periodic); *CSGA Sport-Trade Directory.* **Geographic Preference:** Multinational.

15078 ■ National Association of Sporting Goods Wholesalers (NASGW)
1255 SW Prairie Trl., Pky.
Ankeny, IA 50023-7068
Ph: (515)334-1484
Fax: (515)334-1174
Co. E-mail: info@nasgw.org
URL: http://nasgw.org
Contact: Kenyon Gleason, President
E-mail: kgleason@nasgw.org
X (Twitter): x.com/NASGW_Pros
Description: Represents wholesalers and manufacturers of primarily fishing tackle and shooting equipment. **Founded:** 1953. **Publications:** *InSight: The Latest in NASGW and Industry News* (Semimonthly). **Geographic Preference:** National.

15079 ■ National Ski and Snowboard Retailers Association (NSSRA)
3041 Woodcreek Dr., Ste. 210
Downers Grove, IL 60515
Ph: (224)220-1522
Fax: (847)391-9827
Co. E-mail: info@nssra.com
URL: http://www.nssra.com
Contact: Julie Pitts, President
Linkedin: www.linkedin.com/company/national-ski
-snowboard-retailers-association-nssra
X (Twitter): x.com/nssraskisboards
Description: Ski & snowboard stores. Represents the interests of members and provides services beneficial to their businesses. Compiles statistics. **Founded:** 1987. **Publications:** *NSSRA Newsletter* (Irregular). **Geographic Preference:** National.

15080 ■ National Sporting Goods Association (NSGA)
3041 Woodcreek Dr., Ste. 210
Downers Grove, IL 60515
Ph: (847)296-6742
Fax: (847)391-9827
Co. E-mail: info@nsga.org
URL: http://www.nsga.org
Contact: Matt Carlson, President
Facebook: www.facebook.com/nsgasports
Linkedin: www.linkedin.com/company/national-spor
ting-goods-association
X (Twitter): x.com/NSGASportingGds
YouTube: www.youtube.com/user/nsgasports
Description: Provides services, advocacy, education and information for sporting goods retailers. **Founded:** 1927. **Publications:** *NSGA Buying Guide* (Annual); *Sports Participation-Series I & II* (Annual); *National Sporting Goods Association--Buying Guide*

(Annual); *NSGA Now* (Bimonthly); *NSGA Sports Retailer--Store Equipment and Services Directory Issue*; *Cost of Doing Business Survey*; *Team Line-Up.* **Educational Activities:** Annual NSGA Management Conference and Team Dealer Summit (Annual). **Geographic Preference:** National.

15081 ■ Soccer Industry Council of America (SICA)
962 Wayne Ave.
Silver Spring, MD 20910
Ph: (301)495-6321
Co. E-mail: info@sfia.org
URL: http://sfia.org/about/committees/soccer-industry
-council-of-america
Description: Supports grassroots programs that offer playing opportunities to economically-disadvantaged youth, as well as the physically and mentally handicapped. Publishes statistical abstract and overview of the American soccer marketplace. **Founded:** 1985. **Publications:** *National Soccer Participation Survey* (Annual); *Retail Soccer USA*; *Soccer in the USA.* **Educational Activities:** Leadership Conference (Annual); Soccer Industry Council of America Seminar (Annual). **Geographic Preference:** National.

15082 ■ Sports and Fitness Industry Association (SFIA)
962 Wayne Ave., Ste. 300
Silver Spring, MD 20910
Ph: (301)495-6321
Co. E-mail: info@sfia.org
URL: http://sfia.org
Contact: Tom Cove, President
E-mail: tcove@sfia.org
Facebook: www.facebook.com/TheSFIA
X (Twitter): x.com/thesfia
Instagram: www.instagram.com/thesfia
Description: Manufacturers of athletic clothing, footwear, and sporting goods. Seeks to increase sports participation and create growth in the sporting goods industry. Owns and operates the largest sports products trade show in the world. **Founded:** 1906. **Publications:** *American Sports Data Analysis Participation Summary Report*; *SGMA Recreation Market Report* (Periodic); *Sports Edge NewsWire* (Semiweekly). **Educational Activities:** Retail Summit (Annual); The Super Show. **Geographic Preference:** National.

15083 ■ Water Sports Industry Association (WSIA)
PO Box 568512
Orlando, FL 32856-8512
Ph: (407)835-1363
Fax: (407)835-1363
Co. E-mail: info@wsia.net
URL: http://www.wsia.net
Contact: Roswell Marine, President
Facebook: www.facebook.com/watersportsIA
X (Twitter): x.com/wsiahq
Instagram: www.instagram.com/wsiahq

Description: Represents manufacturers and distributors of water sports equipment including skis, boats, wetsuits, and towlines. Monitors legislation affecting the water sports industry. Promotes the sports of water skiing, wakeboarding, kneeboarding, tubing, and riding personal watercraft. **Founded:** 1986. **Geographic Preference:** National.

REFERENCE WORKS

15084 ■ *"Adidas' Brand Ambitions" in Business Journal Portland (Vol. 27, December 10, 2010, No. 41, pp. 1)*
Pub: Portland Business Journal
Contact: Andy Giegerich, Managing Editor
E-mail: agiegerich@bizjournals.com

Ed: Erik Siemers. **Description:** Adidas AG, the second-largest sporting goods brand in the world, hopes to increase global revenue by 50 percent by 2015. The German company, which reported $14.5 billion sales, plans to improve its U.S. market. The U.S. is Adidas' largest, but also the most underperforming market for the firm. **Availability:** Print; Online.

15085 ■ *"Anderson Pitches Liberty Towne Place" in Business Courier (Vol. 27, June 18, 2010, No. 7, pp. 1)*
Pub: Business Courier

Ed: Dan Monk. **Description:** Jeffrey R. Anderson Real Estate Inc.'s plan for a retail center in Butler County, Ohio could have three department stores in the 1.1 million-square-foot property. An outdoor sports retailer is also part of the plans. **Availability:** Print; Online.

15086 ■ *"Bass Pro Shops Plans Megastore for Rocklin" in Sacramento Business Journal (Vol. 51, February 14, 2014, No. 51, pp. 4)*
Pub: American City Business Journals, Inc.
Contact: Mike Olivieri, Executive Vice President

Description: Bass Pro Shops is set to open its 120,000-square-foot Outdoor World store in Rocklin, California in 2015. The move will allow the Missouri-based outdoor retailer to bring its low prices and friendly, expert service to the sportsmen and women of the area. **Availability:** Online.

15087 ■ *"Cabela's Plans Outpost Strategy for Smaller Markets" in Pet Product News (Vol. 66, April 2012, No. 4, pp. 21)*
Description: Sidney, Nebraska-based outdoor gear retailer Cabela's Inc. plans to launch its first Cabelas Outpost Store, a retail initiative aimed at markets with fewer than 250,000 people. The initial 40,000-square-foot Cabela's Outpost Store is scheduled for a fall 2012 opening in Union Gap, Washington. Online order kiosks are among the features of the new store. **Availability:** Print; Online.

15088 ■ *"Consignment Shop Blends Business With a Giving Spirit" in Gazette (January 17, 2012)*
Ed: Bill Radford. **Description:** Mountain Equipment Recyclers, located in Colorado Springs, Colorado, sells outdoor gear. Mike Mazzola, owner, has expanded his consignment shop to include a nonprofit entity to raise money for our veterans and their families. So far, he has exceeded his goal by giving five percent of sales of consigned gear and 50 percent of donated gear to three nonprofit organizations: AspenPoint, which helps veterans and their families; The Home Front Cares, supporting families of deployed soliders; and LifeQuest Transitions, which helps soldiers and veterans relearn life skills through cognitive exercises and adventure sports. The funds are split equally to the three agencies. **Availability:** Online.

15089 ■ *"Design program in Athletic Footwear" in Occupational Outlook Quarterly (Vol. 55, Fall 2011, No. 3, pp. 21)*
Description: The Fashion Institute of Technology offers the only certificate program in performance athletic footwear design in the U.S. The program focuses on conceptualizing and sketching shoe designs and covers ergonomic, anatomical, and material considerations for athletic footwear design. **Availability:** Print; Online.

15090 ■ *"Dick's Sporting Goods Distances Itself further from Firearms" in USA Today (October 6, 2019)*
URL(s): www.usatoday.com/story/money/2019/10/06/dicks-sporting-goods-distances-itself-further-from-firearms/40243337/
Ed: Rich Duprey. **Released:** October 06, 2019. **Description:** After implementing new policies to restrict access to firearms in its stores and lobbying for more gun control laws Dick's Sporting Goods is poised to exit the hunting and firearms market. It already agreed to sell several of its Field & Stream stores. **Availability:** Online.

15091 ■ *"Fledgling Brands May Take the Fall With Steve & Barry's" in Advertising Age (Vol. 79, July 7, 2008, No. 26, pp. 6)*
Pub: Crain Communications, Inc.
Contact: Jessica Botos, Manager, Marketing
E-mail: jessica.botos@crainsnewyork.com

Ed: Natalie Zmuda. **Description:** Steve & Barry's, a retailer that holds licensing deals with a number of designers and celebrities, may have to declare bankruptcy; this leaves the fate of the retailer's hundreds of licensing deals and exclusive celebrity lines in question. **Availability:** Online.

15092 ■ *"Global Retail Chains' Revenues Inched Up 1% Last Year" in Sporting Goods Intelligence (November, 2021)*
Released: November 2021. **Description:** Discusses the small increase in sales for the sporting goods industry during the COVID-19 shutdowns. **Availability:** Online.

15093 ■ *"Hitting the Green" in Canadian Business (Vol. 81, July 22, 2008, No. 12-13, pp. 34)*
Description: RBC is sponsoring the Canadian Open golf tournament, which is the second-oldest event in the PGA Tour. RBC is expected to receive television exposure on CBS and the Golf Channel. Additional information relating to the sponsorship is presented. **Availability:** Print; Online.

15094 ■ *"Hoop Culture Opens Showroom, Expands Reach Globally" in Orlando Business Journal (Vol. 30, February 28, 2014, No. 36, pp. 3)*
Pub: American City Business Journals, Inc.
Contact: Mike Olivieri, Executive Vice President

Released: Weekly. **Description:** Hoop Culture Inc. president, Mike Brown, shares how the online basketball apparel retailer/wholesaler online store has expanded globally. He mentions that Orlando, Florida is one of their biggest markets. **Availability:** Print; Online.

15095 ■ *"An Ice Boost in Revenue; Wings Score With Expanded Corporate Sales" in Crain's Detroit Business (Vol. 25, June 1, 2009, No. 22)*
Pub: Crain Communications Inc.
Contact: Barry Asin, President

Ed: Bill Shea. **Description:** Stanley Cup finals always boost business for the Detroit area, even during a recession. The Red Wings corporate office reported corporate sponsorship revenue luxury suite rentals, Legends Club seats and advertising were up 40 percent this year over 2008. **Availability:** Print; Online.

15096 ■ *"Jordan Still Soaring" in Business Journal Portland (Vol. 30, January 17, 2014, No. 46, pp. 7)*
Pub: American City Business Journals, Inc.
Contact: Mike Olivieri, Executive Vice President

Released: Weekly. **Price:** $4, introductory 4-week offer(Digital only). **Description:** Nike Inc. is planning to open retail stores that will exclusively sell Jordan Brand merchandise. The company is seeking to grow its direct-to-consumer sales to $8 billion by 2017. Nike's capital spending is also expected to increase by 3 to 4 percent. **Availability:** Print; Online.

15097 ■ *"Lawyers Sued Over Lapsed Lacrosse Patent" in Crain's Detroit Business (Vol. 25, June 8, 2009, No. 23, pp. 5)*
Pub: Crain Communications Inc.
Contact: Barry Asin, President

Ed: Chad Halcom. **Description:** Warrior Sports Inc., a manufacturer of lacrosse equipment located in Warren, Michigan is suing the law firm Dickinson Wright PLLC and two of its intellectual property lawyers over patent rights to lacrosse equipment. **Availability:** Print; Online.

15098 ■ *"Portland Wooing Under Armour to West Coast Facility" in Baltimore Business Journal (Vol. 27, January 29, 2010, No. 39, pp. 1)*
Pub: Baltimore Business Journal
Contact: Rhonda Pringle, President
E-mail: rpringle@bizjournals.com

Ed: Andy Giegerich. **Description:** Baltimore, Maryland sports apparel maker, Under Armour, is planning a west coast expansion with Portland, Oregon among the sites considered to house its apparel and footwear design center. Portland officials counting on the concentration of nearly 10,000 activewear workers in the city will help lure the company to the city. **Availability:** Print; Online.

15099 ■ *"Recovery on Tap for 2010?" in Orlando Business Journal (Vol. 26, January 1, 2010, No. 31, pp. 1)*
Pub: Orlando Business Journal
Contact: Julie Swyers, Director
E-mail: jswyers@bizjournals.com

Ed: Melanie Stawicki Azam, Richard Bilbao, Christopher Boyd, Anjali Fluker. **Description:** Economic forecasts for Central Florida's leading business sectors in 2010 are presented. These sectors include housing, film and TV, sports business, law, restaurants, aviation, tourism and hospitality, banking and finance, commercial real estate, retail, health care, insurance, higher education, and manufacturing. According to some local executives, Central Florida's economy will slowly recover in 2010. **Availability:** Online.

15100 ■ *"Showalter Has Orioles Rising, But is Business Following?: Buck-ing the Trend?" in Baltimore Business Journal (Vol. 28, August 13, 2010, No. 14, pp. 1)*
Pub: Baltimore Business Journal
Contact: Rhonda Pringle, President
E-mail: rpringle@bizjournals.com

Ed: Gary Haber. **Description:** Baltimore Orioles' new manager Buck Showalter has managed to win games for fans. However, not all businesses around Camden Yards were boosted by the Orioles' surge as street vendors complained of worsening business. **Availability:** Print.

15101 ■ *"Three Ways Columbia's Stock Can Keep Rising" in Business Journal Portland (Vol. 30, February 21, 2014, No. 51, pp. 8)*
Pub: American City Business Journals, Inc.
Contact: Mike Olivieri, Executive Vice President

Released: Weekly. **Price:** $4, Introductory 4-week offer(Digital & Print). **Description:** The shares of Columbia Sportswear Company reached a record high of $88.25 in February 2014. The company's cold-weather gear, its TurboDown technology and its new joint venture with China are expected to contribute significantly in keeping stock prices high. **Availability:** Print; Online.

15102 ■ *"Tigers Put to Test: Can Team Win Back Fans, Advertisers?" in Crain's Detroit Business (Vol. 24, October 6, 2008, No. 40, pp. 1)*
Pub: Crain Communications Inc.
Contact: Barry Asin, President

Ed: Bill Shea. **Description:** Despite the enormous amount of money the Detroit Tigers' owner Mike Illitch spent on player salaries, a record $137.6 million this season, the team finished in last-place; ticket sales and advertising dollars for next season are expected to fall dramatically. Additional speculation regarding the future of the ball team is included. **Availability:** Online.

15103 ■ *"Tony Armand, Shock Doctor CEO"* *in Business Journal (Vol. 31, March 21, 2014, No. 43, pp. 6)*
Pub: American City Business Journals, Inc.
Contact: Mike Olivieri, Executive Vice President
Released: March 21, 2014. **Price:** $4, print. **Description:** Tony Armand, CEO of Shock Doctor Inc., discusses the company's acquisition by private equity firm Bregal Partners. Armand believes the deal will give the sports protective equipment manufacturer a strong financial partner that will help with the executive strategy. **Availability:** Print; Online.

15104 ■ *"Under Armour Wants to Equip Athletes, Too" in Boston Business Journal (Vol. 29, July 8, 2011, No. 9, pp. 1)*
Pub: Boston Business Journal
Contact: Carolyn M. Jones, President
E-mail: cmjones@bizjournals.com
Ed: Ryan Sharrow. **Description:** Baltimore sportswear maker Under Armour advances plans to enter into the equipment field, aiming to strengthen its hold on football, basketball and lacrosse markets where it already has a strong market share. The company is now cooking up licensing deals to bolster the firm's presence among athletes. **Availability:** Print; Online.

15105 ■ *"Under Armour's Founder On Learning to Leverage Celebrity Endorsements" in Harvard Business Review (Vol. 90, May 2012, No. 5, pp. 45)*
Pub: Harvard Business Review Press
Contact: Moderna V. Pfizer, Contact
Ed: Kevin Plank. **Description:** Using his athletic apparel company Under Armour as an illustration, the author identifies two key points in effective utilization of endorsement advertising: balancing freebies with fair-price contracts, and offering stock opportunities so that celebrities can be personally engaged with growth.

15106 ■ *"Wave of Resale, Consignment Shops Pop Up In Springs" in Gazette (March 19, 2012)*
Ed: Bill Radford. **Description:** The depressed economy has spurred the growth of consignment shops across the nation. Colorado Springs, Colorado area urges people to shop at these resale locations because they promote green initiatives by recycling goods. WeeCycle, Knit Wits, Once Upon a Child and Re-Generation, Moutain Equipment Recyclers, and Gearonimo, are among the established consignment stores in the area. **Availability:** Print.

15107 ■ *"Why the Gap is Stalking Lululemon" in Canadian Business (Vol. 85, August 22, 2012, No. 14, pp. 7)*
Ed: Jim Sutherland. **Description:** Lululemon Athletica is facing competition against Gap Inc.'s Athleta as the retail giant plans to have about 50 new shops across Canada by the end of 2012. Athleta is also carrying lines of yoga- and activewear similar to that of Lululemon's and are even located near their stores. **Availability:** Online.

15108 ■ *"World Cup Kicks G-Form Into High Gear for Protection" in Providence Business News (Vol. 29, August 4, 2014, No. 18, pp. 4)*
Pub: American City Business Journals, Inc.
Contact: Mike Olivieri, Executive Vice President
URL(s): pbn.com/world-cup-kicks-g-form-into-high -gear-for-protection98984
Description: Thomas Cafaro, Vice President of Innovations at G-Form LLC, discusses the growing popularity of the company's shin guard following its use by soccer teams at the 2014 World Cup. Cafaro asserts that G-Form is primarily an athletics gear company, despite its focus on electronic protection gear. **Telecommunication Services:** Anderson@ pbn.com.

15109 ■ *"Zacks Industry Outlook Highlights: Starbucks, Nike, Big Lots, Deckers Outdoor and Family Dollar Stores" in PR Newswire (August 8, 2012)*
Pub: PR Newswire Association LLC.
Description: Zacks takes a look at the retail industry and covers the outlook for this highly competitive sector. Retailers discussed include: Starbucks Corporation, Nike Inc., Big Lots Inc., Deckers Outdoor Corporation, and Family Dollar Stores Inc. **Availability:** Online.

15110 ■ *"Zacks Industry Outlook Highlights: Target, Cabela's and Family Dollar Stores" in Marketing Weekly News (April 28, 2012, pp. 351)*
Description: Zacks Industry Outlook focuses on retailers such as Target, Cabela's and Family Dollar Stores. An examination of ways retailers are working to improve sales and profits and productivity is given, including supply-chain management, cost containment, inventory management, and merchandise initiatives. **Availability:** Print; Online.

STATISTICAL SOURCES

15111 ■ *RMA Annual Statement Studies*
Pub: Risk Management Association
Contact: Nancy Foster, President
Released: Annual. **Description:** Contains composite balance sheets and income statements for more than 360 industries, including the accounting, auditing, and bookkeeping industries. Also contains five years of comparative historical data for discerning trends. Includes 16 commonly used ratios, computed for most of the size groupings for nearly every industry.

15112 ■ *Sporting Goods Retail - US - 2021*
URL(s): store.mintel.com/report/sporting-goods-retail -us-2021
Price: $4,366.35. **Description:** Before the Covid-19 pandemic, the sporting goods industry was in a decline, but with people home and looking for recreation, this industry is bouncing back. This report includes how Covid affected consumer behavior, strategies from industry leaders, creating enhanced consumer experiences, and perceptions of various types of retailers. **Availability:** PDF.

15113 ■ *Sporting Goods Stores Industry in the US - Market Research Report*
URL(s): www.ibisworld.com/united-states/market-re search-reports/sporting-goods-stores-industry/
Price: $925. **Description:** Downloadable report analyzing the current and future trends in the sporting goods industry. **Availability:** Online.

TRADE PERIODICALS

15114 ■ *NSSRA Newsletter*
Pub: National Ski and Snowboard Retailers Association
Contact: Julie Pitts, President
URL(s): www.nssra.com/newsletters
Released: Irregular **Description:** Informs ski and snowboard retail stores on critical industry issues such as guidelines and litigation exposure and marketing. **Availability:** Electronic publishing.

15115 ■ *Out Your Backdoor (OYB)*
Pub: Out Your Backdoor
Contact: Jeff Potter, Contact
E-mail: jeff@outyourbackdoor.com
URL(s): www.outyourbackdoor.com/about
Facebook: www.facebook.com/outyourbackdoor
YouTube: www.youtube.com/channel/UCTCegrAm3X -THTkSNEJ0k0A
Description: Magazine focusing on bicycling, adventure, culture, the outdoors, hobbies, and sports. **Availability:** Print.

VIDEO/AUDIO MEDIA

15116 ■ *How I Built This: Osprey Packs: Mike Pfotenhauer*
URL(s): wondery.com/shows/how-i-built-this/episode/ 10386/osprey-packs-mike-pfotenhauer
Ed: Guy Raz. **Released:** February 20, 2023. **Description:** Podcast explains how Osprey grew from a little shop with no advertising except for a sign out front.

TRADE SHOWS AND CONVENTIONS

15117 ■ **Detroit Boat Show**
Michigan Boating Industries Association (MBIA)
8625 Richardson Rd.
Commerce Township, MI 48390
Ph: (734)261-0123
Fax: (734)261-0880
Co. E-mail: boatmichigan@mbia.org
URL: http://www.mbia.org
Contact: Nicki Polan, Executive Director
E-mail: npolan@mbia.org
URL(s): boatmichigan.org/detroit-boat-show/#detroi t-exhibitor-list
Facebook: www.facebook.com/DetroitBoatShow
Price: $12, adults. **Frequency:** Annual. **Description:** Boats, fishing equipment, boat-related accessories, charter rentals, nautical attire, trailer and outboard motors, and personal watercraft. **Audience:** Boat enthusiasts and manufacturers. **Principal Exhibits:** Boats, fishing equipment, boat-related accessories, charter rentals, nautical attire, trailer and outboard motors, and personal watercraft. Dates and Locations: 2025 Jan Huntington Place, Detroit, MI. **Telecommunication Services:** boatmichigan@mbia. org.

15118 ■ **Highpointers Annual Convention**
Highpointers Club
PO Box 1496
Golden, CO 80402-1496
Co. E-mail: newsletter@highpointers.org
URL: http://highpointers.org
Contact: Alan Ritter, President
E-mail: president@highpointers.org
URL(s): highpointers.org/tag/conventions
Frequency: Annual. **Description:** Climbing and hiking gear. **Audience:** Industry professionals. **Principal Exhibits:** Climbing and hiking gear. Dates and Locations: 2025 SD.

15119 ■ **Independent Retailers Buying Group Spring Trade Show**
URL(s): n2b.goexposoftware.com/events/wbg22sp/ goExpo/public/login.php
Frequency: Annual. **Description:** Retailer tradeshow with a focus on shooting sports, sporting goods, and fall/winter apparel and footwear. **Principal Exhibits:** Retailer tradeshow with a focus on shooting sports, sporting goods, and fall/winter apparel and footwear.

15120 ■ **Kansas City Boat Sportshow**
Japan Management Association (JMA)
3-1-22 Shibakoen
Minato, Tokyo 105-8522, Japan
Ph: 81 3 3434-1601
Fax: 81 3 3434-8076
URL: http://www.jma.or.jp
Contact: Masami Nakamura, Chairman
URL(s): www.kansascitysportshow.com
X (Twitter): twitter.com/KCBoatSportshow
Frequency: Annual. **Description:** Exhibits related to boat, equipment, supplies, and services. **Audience:** Industry professionals and general public. **Principal Exhibits:** Exhibits related to boat, equipment, supplies, and services. **Telecommunication Services:** tod@sportshows.com.

15121 ■ **Midwest Winter Sports Representatives Association**
Midwest Winter Sports Reps Association (MWSRA)
441 Dunhill Dr.
Verona, WI 53593

Free: 866-623-6155
Co. E-mail: mwsraholly@gmail.com
URL: http://www.midwestwinterreps.com/p.asp
Contact: Bruce Marsh, Co-President
E-mail: bruce@brmreps.com
URL(s): www.midwestwinterreps.com/p.asp?pgi
   d=2005009
Frequency: Annual. **Description:** Exhibits related to winter sports equipment, supplies, and services. **Audience:** Buyers of winter sports products and trade professionals. **Principal Exhibits:** Exhibits related to winter sports equipment, supplies, and services.

15122 ■ Northwest Sportshow
Berkley
   4007 Paramount Blvd.
   Lakewood, CA 90712
URL: http://www.goberkley.com
Contact: Jeff Berkley, Co-Founder Chairman
URL(s): www.northwestsportshow.com
Price: $12, adults; $9, senior; free for children 15 & younger. **Frequency:** Annual. **Description:** Boating, fishing, hunting, camping, RVing. **Audience:** Sporting enthusiasts, sporting goods professionals. **Principal Exhibits:** Boating, fishing, hunting, camping, RVing. Dates and Locations: 2025 Mar 13-16 Minneapolis Convention Center, Minneapolis, MN. **Telecommunication Services:** info@northwestsportshow.com.

15123 ■ SHAPE America National Convention & Expo
Society of Health and Physical Educators (SHAPE)
   PO Box 225
   Annapolis Junction, MD 20701

Ph: (703)476-3400
Free: 800-213-7193
Fax: (703)476-9527
Co. E-mail: education@shapeamerica.org
URL: http://www.shapeamerica.org
Contact: Terri Drain, President
URL(s): convention.shapeamerica.org/Convention/
   past-future-dates.aspx
Frequency: Annual. **Audience:** K-12 educators, PETE/HETE professionals, school/district administrators, and related professionals and students. Dates and Locations: 2025 Apr 01-05 Baltimore, MD. **Telecommunication Services:** education@shapeamerica.org.

15124 ■ United States Professional Tennis Association Convention
United States Professional Tennis Association (US-PTA)
   11961 Performance Dr.
   Orlando, FL 32827
Ph: (407)634-3050
Free: 800-877-8248
Co. E-mail: uspta@uspta.org
URL: http://www.uspta.com
Contact: Richard Slivocka, President
E-mail: usptaboard@uspta.org
URL(s): www.uspta.com/uspta/Events/Event_Display
   .aspx?EventKey=DCONFFL24A
Frequency: Irregular. **Description:** Tennis equipment, supplies, and services. **Audience:** Tennis professionals, industry leaders and representatives, manufacturers, wholesalers, and media. **Principal Exhibits:** Tennis equipment, supplies, and services. **Telecommunication Services:** mike.baugh@uspta.org.

FRANCHISES AND BUSINESS OPPORTUNITIES

15125 ■ Golf Etc.
2461 E Hwy. 377
   Granbury, TX 76049
Ph: (817)579-5400
URL: http://golfetcgranbury.com
Facebook: www.facebook.com/people/Golf-Etc-of
   -Granbury/100045062997085
Description: Retailer of golf products such as bags, footwear, balls, gloves, golf related giftware. **Founded:** 2008. **Training:** Provides 5 days training at corporate office in Granbury, TX, 3-4 days at franchisees location, 5 days plus optional advanced training and ongoing support.

15126 ■ Play it Again Sports (PIAS)
Winmark Corporation
   605 Hwy. 169 N, Ste. 400
   Minneapolis, MN 55441
Ph: (763)520-8500
Fax: (763)520-8410
Co. E-mail: winmark.information@winmarkcorpora
   tion.com
URL: http://www.winmarkcorporation.com
Contact: Tamara L. Harmon, Contact
Facebook: www.facebook.com/playitagainsports
Instagram: www.instagram.com/playitagainsports
Description: Retailer of new and used sports equipment and clothing's. **Founded:** 1983. **Training:** Training includes product acquisition, inventory management, staff hiring and training, customer service, advertising and marketing, and merchandising. Ongoing regional meetings and national training conferences held annually.

ASSOCIATIONS AND OTHER ORGANIZATIONS

15127 ■ **International Gay Rodeo Association (IGRA)**
PO Box 460504
  Aurora, CO 80046-0504
URL: http://www.igra.com
Contact: Candy Pratt, President
E-mail: igracpratt@rrra-tx.com
Facebook: www.facebook.com/IGRARodeo

Description: Gay rodeo associations in the United States and Canada. Promotes public interest in rodeo events and seeks to increase participation in rodeo by gay people. Facilitates communication and cooperation among members; sponsors competitions. **Founded:** 1985. **Geographic Preference:** National.

REFERENCE WORKS

15128 ■ *"6 Powerful Sports Marketing Promotions That Are Better Than Google" in Forbes (February 6, 2014)*
URL(s): www.forbes.com/sites/markfidelman/2014/0
2/19/6-powerful-sports-marketing-promotions-tha
t-are-better-than-google/#43d1b6116603

Ed: Mark Fidelman. **Released:** February 19, 2014. **Description:** Discusses new social media strategies to help sports companies gain a competitive edge in promoting and advertising. **Availability:** Online.

15129 ■ *"Arena Football League Sees S.A. as Crucial Market" in San Antonio Business Journal (Vol. 28, August 1, 2014, No. 25, pp. 6)*
Pub: American City Business Journals, Inc.
Contact: Mike Olivieri, Executive Vice President

Released: Weekly. **Price:** $4, introductory 4-week offer(Digital only). **Description:** The Arena Football League, which took control of the San Antonio Talons, believes that San Antonio, Texas is a key market. Reports show that football fans continue to support the Talons despite the ownership changes. The league's ability to attract high-profile investors is also examined. **Availability:** Print; Online.

15130 ■ *Athletic Business--Professional Directory Section*
Pub: Athletic Business Publications Inc.
Contact: Jason Scott, Managing Editor
E-mail: jason@athleticbusiness.com
URL(s): www.athleticbusiness.com/directory

Ed: Andrew Cohen. **Description:** Publication includes list of architects, engineers, contractors, and consultants in athletic facility planning and construction; all listings are paid. **Entries include:** Company name, address, phone, fax and short description of company. **Arrangement:** Alphabetical. **Availability:** Print; Online.

15131 ■ *"Ballpark Sales Tax Extension Could Fund New Arena" in Milwaukee Business Journal (Vol. 27, January 29, 2010, No. 18, pp. A1)*
Pub: The Business Journal
Contact: Heather Ladage, President
E-mail: hladage@bizjournals.com

Ed: Mark Kass. **Description:** Milwaukee, Wisconsin-area business executives believe the extension of the Miller Park 0.1 percent sales tax could help fund a new basketball arena to replace the 21-year-old Bradley Center in downtown Milwaukee. However, any sales tax expansion that includes the new basketball arena would need approval by Wisconsin's legislature. **Availability:** Print; Online.

15132 ■ *"Baltimore Eyeing Tax Breaks for New Arena" in Boston Business Journal (Vol. 29, June 3, 2011, No. 4, pp. 1)*
Pub: Boston Business Journal
Contact: Carolyn M. Jones, President
E-mail: cmjones@bizjournals.com

Ed: Daniel J. Sernovitz. **Description:** Baltimore City is opting to give millions of dollars in tax breaks and construction loans to a group of private investors led by William Hackerman who is proposing to build a new arena and hotel at the Baltimore Convention Center. The project will cost $500 million with the state putting up another $400 million for the center's expansion.

15133 ■ *"Baltimore Grand Prix Didn't Fill Up City Hotels" in Baltimore Business Journal (Vol. 29, September 16, 2011, No. 19, pp. 1)*
Pub: Boston Business Journal
Contact: Carolyn M. Jones, President
E-mail: cmjones@bizjournals.com

Ed: Alexander Jackson. **Description:** Baltimore Grand Prix inaugural race failed to fill the hotels in Baltimore, Maryland as hoteliers reported rooms to spare during the three-day event. City officials expected downtown hotels to nearly sell out Labor Day weekend. **Availability:** Online.

15134 ■ *"Baltimore Grand Prix Week Schedule Filling Up With Galas, Nonprofit Fundraisers" in Baltimore Business Journal (Vol. 29, July 22, 2011, No. 11, pp. 1)*
Pub: Boston Business Journal
Contact: Carolyn M. Jones, President
E-mail: cmjones@bizjournals.com

Ed: Alexander Jackson. **Description:** Baltimore, Maryland-based businesses and nonprofit groups have been planning their own events to coincide with the Baltimore Grand Prix during the Labor Day weekend. They also plan to partner with others in hopes of drumming up new business, raising money or to peddle their brands.

15135 ■ *"Baltimore Ravens Back to Business as NFL Lockout Ends" in Baltimore Business Journal (Vol. 29, July 29, 2011, No. 12, pp. 1)*
Pub: Boston Business Journal
Contact: Carolyn M. Jones, President

E-mail: cmjones@bizjournals.com

Ed: Scott Dance. **Description:** The Baltimore Ravens football team has been marketing open sponsorship packages following the end of the National Football League lockout. Team officials are working to get corporate logos and slogans on radio and television commercials and online advertisements. **Availability:** Print; Online.

15136 ■ *"Baltimore Restaurants Banking on Andretti Name" in Baltimore Business Journal (Vol. 30, May 18, 2012, No. 2, pp. 1)*
Pub: American City Business Journals, Inc.
Contact: Mike Olivieri, Executive Vice President

Ed: Jack Lambert. **Description:** Former race car driver Michael Andretti is leading the Andretti Sports Marketing to organize the Grand Prix in Baltimore, Maryland for the next five years. Restaurant and hotel owners are banking on Andretti to drive race fans to these establishments. Details of the 2011 event as well as forecasts on the next are discussed. **Availability:** Print; Online.

15137 ■ *"Bars, Restaurants to Change Game for Baltimore Grand Prix Patrons" in Baltimore Business Journal (Vol. 29, July 22, 2011, No. 11, pp. 1)*
Pub: Boston Business Journal
Contact: Carolyn M. Jones, President
E-mail: cmjones@bizjournals.com

Ed: Alexander Jackson. **Description:** Restaurants and bar owners in Baltimore, Maryland have changed the way they do business as the Baltimore Grand Prix approaches. Owners have gone so far as to offering new services or renting out their entire restaurants to companies for the three-day event in September. **Availability:** Print; Online.

15138 ■ *"Ben Hulse" in Canadian Business (Vol. 85, August 13, 2012, No. 13, pp. 55)*
Ed: Graham F. Scott. **Description:** Graphic designer Ben Hulse explains the reason for rebranding Canada's Olympic team and how it differs from rebranding a private corporate logo. Hulse discusses his background in music and how he shifted to design. **Availability:** Print; Online.

15139 ■ *"The Blazers' Money Maker" in Business Journal Portland (Vol. 31, April 18, 2014, No. 7, pp. 4)*
Pub: American City Business Journals, Inc.
Contact: Mike Olivieri, Executive Vice President

Released: April 18, 2014. **Price:** $4, Introductory 4-Week Offer(Digital & Print). **Description:** The turnaround strategy used by CEO, Chris McGowan, to make the Portland Trail Blazers basketball team profitable by July 2016 is discussed. His personal restructuring effort was aimed at combining the Blazers' operations with day-to-day management of the Moda Center. The team also returned to selling tickets and sponsorship deals. **Availability:** Print; Online.

15140 ■ *"Braves' Parking Pitch Fails to Connect With Property Owners" in Atlanta Business Chronicle (June 27, 2014, pp. 1)*
Pub: American City Business Journals, Inc.
Contact: Mike Olivieri, Executive Vice President
Released: June 27, 2014. **Price:** $4, introductory 4-week offer(Digital only). **Description:** A new $672 million ballpark plan of the Atlanta Braves was given the green light by Cobb County Commissioners recently. However, the Braves are facing a new hurdle for securing parking spaces in the office complexes around the proposed ballpark site. The stadium itself will have more than 6,000 parking spots, but the Braves also want an additional 4,000 to 5,000 spaces, and although the Braves are said to be offering building owners around the stadium up to $100 per space, the owners have not been swayed to give access to their parking. **Availability:** Print; Mailing list; Online.

15141 ■ *"The Carpenter: A Story About the Greatest Success Strategies of All"*
Pub: John Wiley & Sons, Inc.
Contact: Christina Van Tassell, Executive Vice President Chief Financial Officer
Released: May 23, 2014. **Price:** $23, hardcover; $14.99, e-book. **Description:** John Gordon draws upon his work with business leaders, sales people, professional and college sports teams, nonprofit organizations and schools to share a story that will inspire people to build a better life, career and team with successful business strategies. **Availability:** E-book; Print.

15142 ■ *"Chew On This: Soul Fans to 'Chews' Games' First Play" in Philadelphia Business Journal (Vol. 30, September 30, 2011, No. 33, pp. 3)*
Pub: Philadelphia Business Journal
Contact: Sierra Quinn, Director
E-mail: squinn@bizjournals.com
Ed: John George. **Description:** Arena football team Philadelphia Soul extended its marketing partnership with Just Born Inc. The team's fans will enter a contest where the winner will be allowed to select the team's first play during a home game. **Availability:** Online.

15143 ■ *"Cincinnati Reds Hit Ratings Homer" in Business Courier (Vol. 27, July 30, 2010, No. 13, pp. 1)*
Pub: Business Courier
Ed: Steve Watkins, John Ourand. **Description:** Cincinnati Reds fans have tuned in to their TVs and radios as their team made a hottest start to a season. The Reds TV ratings have increased 49 percent during the first six months of 2010 and continued to rise while the Reds' games broadcast on WLW-AM reported the highest average audience share per game of any Major League Baseball team. **Availability:** Print; Online.

15144 ■ *"Citrus Bowl Construction Bids Going Out This Year" in Orlando Business Journal (Vol. 29, June 29, 2012, No. 2, pp. 1)*
Pub: Baltimore Business Journal
Contact: Rhonda Pringle, President
E-mail: rpringle@bizjournals.com
Description: The city of Orlando, Florida is expected to seek construction bids for the Florida Citrus Bowl's renovation in 2012. The project is estimated to cost $175 million. **Availability:** Print; Online.

15145 ■ *"The Colt Effect" in Hawaii Business (Vol. 53, January 2008, No. 7, pp. 30)*
Pub: PacificBasin Communications
Contact: Chuck Tindle, Director
E-mail: chuckt@pacificbasin.net
Ed: David K. Choo. **Description:** Participation at the Bowl Championship Games can help the University of Hawaii financially. Playing at a prominent sports event could provoke donations from alumni and increase enrollment at the university. Examples of universities that earned generous income by becoming a part of prestigious sporting events are presented. **Availability:** Online.

15146 ■ *"DHR Hires Carr for Sports Group" in Crain's Detroit Business (Vol. 25, June 8, 2009, No. 23, pp. 5)*
Pub: Crain Communications Inc.
Contact: Barry Asin, President
Ed: Sherri Begin Welch. **Description:** Lloyd Carr, former head football coach for University of Michigan, has taken a position with DHR International in order to expand its searches for collegiate and professional sports organizations, recruit athletic directors, head coaches and other executives. **Availability:** Print; Online.

15147 ■ *"Eagles Add Sponsors to Nest" in Orlando Business Journal (Vol. 28, August 24, 2012, No. 28, pp. 1)*
Pub: Baltimore Business Journal
Contact: Rhonda Pringle, President
E-mail: rpringle@bizjournals.com
Description: New and for-renewal sponsorship deals are being secured by the Philadelphia Eagles football team with marketing partners are described. Compared with some National Football League teams having more than 100 deals, the Eagles restrict their corporate sponsors to 46 in an attempt to generate more value for limited supply. **Availability:** Print; Online.

15148 ■ *"Eagles Measure Suite Success" in Philadelphia Business Journal (Vol. 30, September 9, 2011, No. 30, pp. 1)*
Pub: Philadelphia Business Journal
Contact: Sierra Quinn, Director
E-mail: squinn@bizjournals.com
Ed: John George. **Description:** Philadelphia Eagles have a new software program that helps suite holders keep track of how their suite is being used and whether they are getting a return on their investment. The software allows suite holders to better utilize and distribute their tickets. **Availability:** Online.

15149 ■ *"Energy Exec Bankrolls Big-Budget UT Film" in Austin Business Journal (Vol. 34, June 6, 2014, No. 16, pp. A8)*
Pub: American City Business Journals, Inc.
Contact: Mike Olivieri, Executive Vice President
Released: Weekly. **Price:** $4, introductory 4-week offer(Digital only). **Description:** Bud Brigham, CEO of the energy firm Brigham Resources is bankrolling the film, "My All American" that focuses on University of Texas football coach Darrell K. Royal. The film is about his bond with star player Freddie Steinmark during the 1969 national championship season. Through this film, Brigham hopes to establish himself in Hollywood and dreams of being as big as Disney. **Availability:** Print; Online.

15150 ■ *"Ex-NFL Players' Game Plan: 2 New Nissan Dealerships" in Crain's Detroit Business (Vol. 30, July 28, 2014, No. 30, pp. 1)*
Pub: Crain Communications Inc.
Contact: Barry Asin, President
Description: All Pro Motors LLC, a New Jersey automobile dealership management company, is bringing National Football League star power to both Dearborn and Clinton Township, Michigan opening new Nissan dealerships. Detail of the new retail stores is revealed. **Availability:** Print; Online.

15151 ■ *"Fair or Foul? Ballparks and their Impact on Urban Revitalization" in Real Estate Review (Vol. 41, Spring 2012, No. 1, pp. 15)*
Description: The influence of ballparks on urban renewal in the United States is examined. Cities have been using ballparks as a way to revitalize downtowns and redevelop/restore neighborhoods. **Availability:** Online.

15152 ■ *"Fantasy in the Workplace" in Orlando Business Journal (Vol. 28, September 7, 2012, No. 30, pp. 1)*
Pub: Baltimore Business Journal
Contact: Rhonda Pringle, President
E-mail: rpringle@bizjournals.com
Description: A 2011 research report from the Fantasy Sports Trade Association shows that participation in fantasy sports increased by 60 percent over the past four years to more than 32 million people over the age of 12. Implications of the increase on employees' workplace productivity and time management as well as employers' monitoring of computer usage are discussed. **Availability:** Print; Online.

15153 ■ *"Fear of the Unknown Muted Impact of Baltimore Grand Prix" in Baltimore Business Journal (Vol. 29, September 9, 2011, No. 18, pp. 3)*
Pub: Boston Business Journal
Contact: Carolyn M. Jones, President
E-mail: cmjones@bizjournals.com
Ed: Alexander Jackson. **Description:** Baltimore Grand Prix caught restaurateurs, hoteliers and street vendors in Baltimore, Maryland unprepared for the thousands of race fans who attended the inaugural event over Labor Day weekend. The race popularity is relatively unknown to them and some felt they were not able to make as much money as they had hoped. **Availability:** Online.

15154 ■ *"Game Changing" in Business Strategy Review (Vol. 23, Spring 2012, No. 1, pp. 26)*
Released: Spring 2012. **Description:** Barney Francis is Managing Director of Sky Sports. In a television career spanning 18 years, he has worked in the multichannel terrestrial and independent sectors. At Sky, he was executive producer for cricket, leading his team through two ICC World Cups, two Ashes Tours, England tours to nine nations, and the first Twenty20 Cup. In 2007, he became executive producer for Sky's Premier league football and in 2008 executive producer for the UEFA Champions League.

15155 ■ *"Game On at Jordan's New Spot" in Crain's Chicago Business (Vol. 34, October 24, 2011, No. 42, pp. 34)*
Pub: Crain Communications Inc.
Contact: Barry Asin, President
Ed: Laura Bianchi. **Description:** Michael Jordan partnered with Cornerstone Restaurant Group to launch Michael Jordan's Steakhouse in Chicago. Details are included. **Availability:** Online.

15156 ■ *"Goodyear Extends Exclusive Deal to Supply NASCAR's Tires" in Charlotte Observer (February 4, 2007)*
Description: Goodyear tires will continue to be the exclusive tire provider at NASCAR's Nextel Cup, Busch and Truck series through the year 2012. **Availability:** Print; Online.

15157 ■ *"Health Giants Throw Support Behind Sports Centers" in Pittsburgh Business Times (Vol. 34, July 25, 2014, No. 1, pp. 8)*
Pub: American City Business Journals, Inc.
Contact: Mike Olivieri, Executive Vice President
Released: Weekly. **Price:** $4, introductory 4-week offer(Digital & Print). **Description:** Allegheny Health Network will provide health services for the $19 million Cool Springs Sports Complex being constructed in two phases in Bethel Park. Meanwhile, UPMC is developing the $70 UPMC Lemieux Sports Complex in Cranberry Township, which will include a center for sports medicine together with two ice rinks that will be used as a practice facility for the Pittsburgh Penguins as well as by high school teams and figure skaters. **Availability:** Print; Online.

15158 ■ *"Healthy Start for Medical Kiosks; Lions Kick in $20K" in Crain's Detroit Business" (Vol. 28, June 11, 2012, No. 24, pp. 18)*
Pub: Crain Communications Inc.
Contact: Barry Asin, President
Ed: Jay Greene. **Description:** Detroit Lions Charities has given Henry Ford Health System's school-based and community health program money to purchase nine interactive health kiosks. These kiosks will be provided by Medical Imagineering LLC, a spinoff of

Henry Ford's Innovation Institute and installed in elementary and middle schools in Detroit. **Availability:** Print; Online.

15159 ■ *"Hitting the Green" in Canadian Business (Vol. 81, July 22, 2008, No. 12-13, pp. 34)*
Description: RBC is sponsoring the Canadian Open golf tournament, which is the second-oldest event in the PGA Tour. RBC is expected to receive television exposure on CBS and the Golf Channel. Additional information relating to the sponsorship is presented. **Availability:** Print; Online.

15160 ■ *"Hoop Culture Opens Showroom, Expands Reach Globally" in Orlando Business Journal (Vol. 30, February 28, 2014, No. 36, pp. 3)*
Pub: American City Business Journals, Inc.
Contact: Mike Olivieri, Executive Vice President
Released: Weekly. **Description:** Hoop Culture Inc. president, Mike Brown, shares how the online basketball apparel retailer/wholesaler online store has expanded globally. He mentions that Orlando, Florida is one of their biggest markets. **Availability:** Print; Online.

15161 ■ *"How to Brand-Crash the Olympics" in Canadian Business (Vol. 85, August 13, 2012, No. 13, pp. 18)*
Ed: Jeff Beer. **Description:** Several ways of taking advantage of the marketing opportunities in the 2012 London Olympics without having to spend millions in sponsorship fees are recommended. A few suggestions include securing advertising placements just outside of the brand exclusion zones, establishing presence on the Web and sponsoring an individual athlete.

15162 ■ *"An Ice Boost in Revenue; Wings Score With Expanded Corporate Sales" in Crain's Detroit Business (Vol. 25, June 1, 2009, No. 22)*
Pub: Crain Communications Inc.
Contact: Barry Asin, President
Ed: Bill Shea. **Description:** Stanley Cup finals always boost business for the Detroit area, even during a recession. The Red Wings corporate office reported corporate sponsorship revenue luxury suite rentals, Legends Club seats and advertising were up 40 percent this year over 2008. **Availability:** Print; Online.

15163 ■ *"If They Build It, Will Customers Come?" in Business Journal Portland (Vol. 30, February 7, 2014, No. 49, pp. 7)*
Pub: American City Business Journals, Inc.
Contact: Mike Olivieri, Executive Vice President
Price: $4, Introductory 4-week offer(Digital & Print). **Description:** The Portland Trail Blazers partnered with Levy Restaurants to open a 10,000-square-foot restaurant at Moda Center in Oregon in spring 2014. GBD Architects and Lorentz Brunn Construction were enlisted for the project. **Availability:** Print; Online.

15164 ■ *"KSE Imprints Hits Mother Lode With Logos" in Denver Business Journal (Vol. 65, January 31, 2014, No. 38, pp. A9)*
Pub: American City Business Journals, Inc.
Contact: Mike Olivieri, Executive Vice President
Description: Denver, Colorado-based KSE Imprints has been designing sports and business logos for various customers. KSE, which maintains a high quality standard for their work, can produce sponsored rally towels, business names on coffee mugs, and logo shirts. The firm's recent investment in a digital printer is also discussed. **Availability:** Online.

15165 ■ *"Life's Work: Interview With Kareem Abdul-Jabbar" in Harvard Business Review (Vol. 90, January-February 2012, No.1-2, pp. 156)*
Pub: Harvard Business Review Press
Contact: Moderna V. Pfizer, Contact
Ed: Alison Beard. **Description:** Former basketball player Kareem Abdul-Jabbar believes that a solid work ethic and practice always wins over lazy,

undeveloped talent. Although he was known as a strictly-focused athlete, he now feels he relates to others on a more personal level than before. His interests in history and writing have made him a multidimensional individual.

15166 ■ *"Local Startup Hits Big Leagues" in Austin Business JournalInc. (Vol. 28, December 19, 2008, No. 40, pp. 1)*
Description: Qcue LLC, an Austin, Texas-based company founded in 2007 is developing a software system that can be used by Major League Baseball teams to change the prices of their single-game tickets based on variables affecting demand. The company recently completed a trial with the San Francisco Giants in 2008. **Availability:** Print; Online.

15167 ■ *"Marketing at the Olympics is No Longer Worth It: An Exercise in Olympic Vanity" in Canadian Business (Vol. 85, August 13, 2012, No. 13, pp. 15)*
Ed: Bruce Philp. **Description:** The cost and return on investment of sponsoring the 2012 London Olympics is examined. Given the high price of official sponsorship in the Olympics, marketers should realize the value of the television advertising audience. **Availability:** Online.

15168 ■ *Marketing Outrageously Redux: How to Increase Your Revenue by Staggering Amounts*
Pub: Bard Press
Contact: Ray Bard, Founder
Ed: Jon Spoelstra, Mark Cuban. **Released:** February 16, 2011. **Description:** Creative marketing strategies are defined. The book shows how considering marketing problems as outrageously but consistently can benefit any small business. The author talks about his own experience when there were not adequate funds for marketing and advertising and the outrageous approach he created to promote sports teams. **Availability:** Print; Electronic publishing.

15169 ■ *"Minor-League Baseball's Sliders Plan Stock Offering" in Crain's Detroit Business (Vol. 25, June 15, 2009, No. 24, pp. 3)*
Pub: Crain Communications Inc.
Contact: Barry Asin, President
Ed: Bill Shea. **Description:** New minor-league baseball team is raising funds to build a new stadium in Waterford Township, Michigan because banks are unwilling to provide loans for the project. Owners of the Midwest Sliders in Ypsilanti, Michigan are waiting for the federal Securities and Exchange Commission to approve a Regulation A public offering. **Availability:** Print; Online.

15170 ■ *"New Giants CEO Goes to Bat for Sponsorships" in Silicon Valley/San Jose Business Journal (Vol. 29, February 3, 2012, No. 45, pp. 1)*
Pub: Baltimore Business Journal
Contact: Rhonda Pringle, President
E-mail: rpringle@bizjournals.com
Description: New San Jose Giants baseball team, chief executive Dan Orum, is planning to increase the team's sponsorship, advertising, and ticket revenue. Orum will target technology companies and other firms as prospective sponsors. Orum's career background and achievements are outlined. **Availability:** Print; Online.

15171 ■ *"Olympic Challenge: The Skinny on Sponsors" in Barron's (Vol. 92, July 23, 2012, No. 30, pp. 13)*
Pub: Dow Jones & Company Inc.
Contact: Almar Latour, Chief Executive Officer
Ed: Jacqueline Doherty. **Description:** Sponsorship of the Olympics by Coca-Cola and McDonald's has been criticized due to the nature of their products. Representatives of the two companies, however, claim that their products are also enjoyed by athletes and can still remain part of a healthy lifestyle. **Availability:** Online.

15172 ■ *"On Comcast, Sarge, Wheels and the Big Price" in Philadelphia Business Journal (Vol. 32, February 7, 2014, No. 52, pp. 4)*
Pub: American City Business Journals, Inc.
Contact: Mike Olivieri, Executive Vice President
Released: Weekly. **Price:** $4, introductory 4-week offer(Digital & Print). **Description:** In an interview with David Montgomery, president and CEO of the Philadelphia Phillies team, he shares his views on the upcoming baseball season, the tremendous fan support the team is receiving, and the marketability of the team, with a special focus on their association with Comcast SportsNet as a broadcast provider. He also disclosed the league's plans for spending the new incoming TV money and said they will try to deliver the best product using the available resources. **Availability:** Print; Online.

15173 ■ *"Orlando City Lions May Score MLS Dream With Stadium" in Orlando Business Journal (Vol. 29, August 31, 2012, No. 11, pp. 1)*
Pub: Baltimore Business Journal
Contact: Rhonda Pringle, President
E-mail: rpringle@bizjournals.com
Description: The Orlando City Lions soccer team may play Major League Soccer as early as 2014 or 2015 if it gets its own stadium. Although the MLS did not assign a stadium as a requirement for joining the league, it did ask the team if it could build a 22,000-seater stadium. The team has plans to find land and create a design for the facility, with construction costs estimated at around $200 million. **Availability:** Print; Online.

15174 ■ *"Peter Bynoe Trades Up" in Black Enterprise (Vol. 38, July 2008, No. 12, pp. 30)*
Pub: Earl G. Graves Ltd.
Contact: Earl Graves, Jr., President
Description: Chicago-based Loop Capital Markets L.L.C. has named Peter Bynoe managing director of corporate finance. Bynoe was previously a senior partner at the law firm DLA Piper U.S. L.L.P., where he worked on stadium deals.

15175 ■ *"Politics & Pros: D.C. Considering Sports-Based Marketing Campaign" in Washington Business Journal (Vol. 31, July 13, 2012, No. 12, pp. 1)*
Description: Events D.C. is mulling over a targeted marketing campaign at boosting the sports reputation of Washington, D.C. Aside from making presentations to city stakeholders, Events D.C. has organized a growing number of sport-related events. Other actions that have been done by Events D.C. to further its goal of pushing a sports-based marketing campaign are discussed. **Availability:** Print; Online.

15176 ■ *"Pricing To Create Shared Value: Rethinking the Way Prices Are Set Can Expand the Pie for Everyone" in Harvard Business Review (Vol. 90, June 2012, No. 6, pp. 96)*
Pub: Harvard Business Review Press
Contact: Moderna V. Pfizer, Contact
Ed: John T. Gourville, Marco Bertini. **Description:** Five pricing strategies to create shared value are: focusing on relationships rather than transactions; being proactive; placing a premium on flexibility; promoting transparency; and managing market standards for fairness. Pricing practices for the 2012 Olympic Games in London, England are used as an illustration.

15177 ■ *"Race Benefits: Changes Afoot for Ironman" in Business Journal Serving Greater Tampa Bay (Vol. 30, October 29, 2010, No. 45, pp. 1)*
Pub: Tampa Bay Business Journal
Contact: Ian Anderson, President
E-mail: ianderson@bizjournals.com
Ed: Margaret Cashill. **Description:** World Triatholon Corporation, organizer of the Ironman World Championship 70.3, will move the sports event from Florida to Nevada in 2011. A replacement event, the 5150 Triathlon Series, will be held in 2011 and the series

finale will be staged in Florida's Clearwater Beach. How hotels and motels in the area will benefit from the 5150 Triathlon Series is discussed. **Availability:** Online.

15178 ■ *"Raising the Game"* in Birmingham Business Journal (Vol. 31, May 2, 2014, No. 18, pp. 4)

Pub: American City Business Journals, Inc.
Contact: Mike Olivieri, Executive Vice President

Description: Birmingham, Alabama has grown its reputation in the sports world in recent years by hosting global events that draw tourists and overage from around the world. However, the Metro needs a facilities upgrade to further elevate its game. The long-debated project to replace the Birmingham-Jefferson Convention Complex and Legion Field is also examined. **Availability:** Online.

15179 ■ *"Raptor Opens Austin Office"* in Austin Business Journal (Vol. 31, July 8, 2011, No. 18, pp. 1)

Pub: Austin Business Journal
Contact: Rachel McGrath, Director
E-mail: rmcgrath@bizjournals.com

Ed: Christopher Calnan. **Description:** Boston hedge fund operator Raptor Group launched Raptor Accelerator, a consulting business providing sales and advisory services to early-stage companies in Central Texas. Aside from getting involved with the startups in which the Raptor Group invests, Raptor Accelerator will target firms operating in the sports, media, entertainment, and content technology sectors. **Availability:** Print; Online.

15180 ■ *"Recovery on Tap for 2010?"* in Orlando Business Journal (Vol. 26, January 1, 2010, No. 31, pp. 1)

Pub: Orlando Business Journal
Contact: Julie Swyers, Director
E-mail: jswyers@bizjournals.com

Ed: Melanie Stawicki Azam, Richard Bilbao, Christopher Boyd, Anjali Fluker. **Description:** Economic forecasts for Central Florida's leading business sectors in 2010 are presented. These sectors include housing, film and TV, sports business, law, restaurants, aviation, tourism and hospitality, banking and finance, commercial real estate, retail, health care, insurance, higher education, and manufacturing. According to some local executives, Central Florida's economy will slowly recover in 2010. **Availability:** Online.

15181 ■ *"Reinventing the Rings"* in Business Strategy Review (Vol. 23, Spring 2012, No. 1, pp. 75)

Released: March 06, 2012. **Description:** Over the last three decades, the Olympic Games has undergone a dramatic reversal of fortune. And yet, until now, the story has remained largely untold. Michael Payne provided the inside story in this article originally published in Spring 2005. Payne worked for the Olympic Movement for over 21 years and was involved in 15 Winter and Summer Olympic Games. In 1989 he became the IOC's first marketing director and in 2003 the first director of global broadcast and media rights. He authored 'Olympic Turnaround' and now acts as an adviser to the Olympic host cities and potential host cities. **Availability:** Print; PDF; Online.

15182 ■ *"St. Louis Blues Asking Price Out of Their League"* in Saint Louis Business Journal (Vol. 32, September 23, 2011, No. 4, pp. 1)

Pub: Saint Louis Business Journal
Contact: Robert Bobroff, President
E-mail: rbobroff@bizjournals.com

Ed: Armir Kurtovic. **Description:** St. Louis Blues owner Dave Checketts wanted the hockey team sold before the start of the season and he believed the team could fetch $200 million or more. However, Hockey insiders believe the price was too high when considering the team's high debt ratio and several other National Hockey League teams on the market. **Availability:** Online.

15183 ■ *Scorecasting: The Hidden Influences Behind How Sports Are Played and Games Are Won*

Released: January 25, 2011. **Price:** $1.25, hardcover; $12.75, Paperback. **Description:** Behavioral economist and veteran writer partner to write about research and studies revealing the hidden forces that shape how basketball, baseball, football and hockey games are played, won and lost. **Availability:** audiobook; E-book; Print.

15184 ■ *"Seahawks' Win? A Seattle Windfall"* in Puget Sound Business Journal (Vol. 34, January 10, 2014, No. 39, pp. 3)

Pub: American City Business Journals, Inc.
Contact: Mike Olivieri, Executive Vice President

Released: Weekly. **Price:** $4, introductory 4-week offer(Digital & Print). **Description:** Seattle, Washington is anticipating a windfall from the Seattle Seahawks' ninth game of the season. The sold-out CenturyLink Field can hold 67,000 spectators, who are potential customers outside the stadium at restaurants, bars, hotels and attractions. The economic benefits of hosting a high-profile sports event are explored. **Availability:** Print; Online.

15185 ■ *"Showalter Has Orioles Rising, But is Business Following?: Buck-ing the Trend?"* in Baltimore Business Journal (Vol. 28, August 13, 2010, No. 14, pp. 1)

Pub: Baltimore Business Journal
Contact: Rhonda Pringle, President
E-mail: rpringle@bizjournals.com

Ed: Gary Haber. **Description:** Baltimore Orioles' new manager Buck Showalter has managed to win games for fans. However, not all businesses around Camden Yards were boosted by the Orioles' surge as street vendors complained of worsening business. **Availability:** Print.

15186 ■ *"Sounders Kicking Ball to Fans"* in Puget Sound Business Journal (Vol. 29, November 28, 2008, No. 32, pp. 1)

Ed: Greg Lamm. **Description:** Major League Soccer expansion team, Seattle Sounders FC, hopes to build fan support leading to its inaugural season 2009-2010 by tapping online social networks. The club launched fan clubs with actual powers over its decision making and Websites similar to Facebook. **Availability:** Print; Online.

15187 ■ *"Sport: The Peformance Business: Special Report"* in Business Strategy Review (Vol. 23, Spring 2012, No. 1, pp. 17)

Ed: Stuart Crainer. **Description:** Sport is universal. From Australia rules football in Tromso, Norway, to golf at the Scott Base Country Club just 13 degrees above the South Pole, sport fascinates, thrills and exhilarates. It is also now a huge global business. At its heart is the art and science of performance. **Availability:** PDF; Online.

15188 ■ *"Stadium Developers Seek a Win With the State"* in The Business Journal-Serving Metropolitan Kansas City (Vol. 26, August 22, 2008)

Description: Three Trails Redevelopment LLC is hoping to win $30 million in state tax credits from the Missouri Development Finance Board for the construction of an 18,500-seat Wizards stadium. The project is contingent on state tax incentives and the company remains optimistic about their goal.

15189 ■ *"Still No Arena Financing Plan"* in Sacramento Business Journal (Vol. 28, May 27, 2011, No. 13, pp. 1)

Pub: Sacramento Business Journal
Contact: Stephanie Fretwell, Director
E-mail: sfretwell@bizjournals.com

Ed: Kelly Johnson. **Description:** The government of Sacramento, California has yet to devise a plan to finance the construction of a proposed stadium. The arena is estimated to cost $387 million. A brief description of the facility is also included. **Availability:** Online.

15190 ■ *"StubHub Launches in the UK"* in Entertainment Close-Up (March 25, 2012)

Description: StubHub, an eBay company, is expanding to the United Kingdom. The firm sells tickets, third party, to music, sport, and entertainment events by connecting buyers and sellers. Details of the service and expansion are explored. **Availability:** Online.

15191 ■ *"Supersized: Delaware North Ready to Feed 80,000 NFL Fans"* in Business First of Buffalo (Vol. 30, January 31, 2014, No. 20, pp. 3)

Pub: American City Business Journals, Inc.
Contact: Mike Olivieri, Executive Vice President

Released: January 31, 2014. **Description:** Delaware North is set to cater the food, retailing and beverage needs of 80,000 football fans at the Super Bowl games in New York. The company will bring 80 top venue managers and 30 high-level executive sous chefs to the event. Menu for the event is presented.

15192 ■ *"Ticketmaster Unveils Pink Tickets to Support Breast Cancer Awareness Month"* in Travel & Leisure Close-Up (October 8, 2012)

Description: National Football League is helping to raise awareness for the National Breast Cancer Awareness Month by issuing all tickets purchased through Ticketmaster be pink. A portion of every NFL ticket sold on Ticketmaster and on NFL Ticket Exchange will go toward the American Cancer Society's fight against breast cancer. **Availability:** Print; Online.

15193 ■ *"Tigers Put to Test: Can Team Win Back Fans, Advertisers?"* in Crain's Detroit Business (Vol. 24, October 6, 2008, No. 40, pp. 1)

Pub: Crain Communications Inc.
Contact: Barry Asin, President

Ed: Bill Shea. **Description:** Despite the enormous amount of money the Detroit Tigers' owner Mike Illitch spent on player salaries, a record $137.6 million this season, the team finished in last-place; ticket sales and advertising dollars for next season are expected to fall dramatically. Additional speculation regarding the future of the ball team is included. **Availability:** Online.

15194 ■ *"Tim Tebow Foundation to Hold Pink 'Cleats for a Cure' Auction"* in Travel & Leisure Close-Up (October 20, 2011)

Pub: Close-Up Media Inc.
Contact: Caroline S. Moore, President
E-mail: cms@closeupmedia.com

Description: Tim Tebow Foundation partnered with XV Enterprises to hold the 'Cleats for a Cure' auction on eBay. Tebow is auctioning off a pair of pink cleans he wore during the Denver Broncos vs. Tennessee Titans game October 3, 2010. All funds will go toward finding a cure for breast cancer. **Availability:** Print; Online.

15195 ■ *"Top Stadium Builders Likely To Vie For Vikings Project"* in Business Journal (Vol. 29, May 18, 2012, No. 51, pp. 1)

Ed: John Vomhof Jr. **Description:** The $975 million Minnesota Vikings stadium project has been approved and is expected to attract big construction firms to bid for the project. A new Minnesota Sports Facility Authority will need to be appointed first, however, before actual selection of design-build team. Architecture firm Populous and contractor Mortenson Construction are among the frontrunners for the project. **Availability:** Print; Online.

15196 ■ *"UFC: Money and the Mayhem"* in Canadian Business (Vol. 83, September 14, 2010, No. 15, pp. 52)

Pub: Rogers Media Inc.
Contact: Neil Spivak, Chief Executive Officer

Ed: Greg Hudson. **Description:** Ultimate Fighting Championship (UFC) has hired Tom Wright as director of operations for Canada, who finally managed to get mixed martial arts sanctioned in Ontario. Canada is UFC's largest market after the US and accounting for about 15-20 percent in annual revenue. **Availability:** Print; Online.

15197 ■ *"Under Armour Wants to Equip Athletes, Too"* in Boston Business Journal (Vol. 29, July 8, 2011, No. 9, pp. 1)
Pub: Boston Business Journal
Contact: Carolyn M. Jones, President
E-mail: cmjones@bizjournals.com

Ed: Ryan Sharrow. **Description:** Baltimore sportswear maker Under Armour advances plans to enter into the equipment field, aiming to strengthen its hold on football, basketball and lacrosse markets where it already has a strong market share. The company is now cooking up licensing deals to bolster the firm's presence among athletes. **Availability:** Print; Online.

15198 ■ *"Under Armour's Founder On Learning to Leverage Celebrity Endorsements"* in Harvard Business Review (Vol. 90, May 2012, No. 5, pp. 45)
Pub: Harvard Business Review Press
Contact: Moderna V. Pfizer, Contact

Ed: Kevin Plank. **Description:** Using his athletic apparel company Under Armour as an illustration, the author identifies two key points in effective utilization of endorsement advertising: balancing freebies with fair-price contracts, and offering stock opportunities so that celebrities can be personally engaged with growth.

15199 ■ *"Up Close With: Learfield Sports CEO Greg Brown"* in San Antonio Business Journal (Vol. 28, February 28, 2014, No. 3, pp. 7)
Pub: American City Business Journals, Inc.
Contact: Mike Olivieri, Executive Vice President

Released: Weekly. **Price:** $4, Introductory 4-week offer(Digital only). **Description:** Learfield Sports chief executive officer, Greg Brown, says the sports marketing company stands to benefit from having a college program in San Antonio, Texas. He also said that the company has been developing relationships with the University of Texas San Antonio. Brown added that Learfield will aggressively market the University. **Availability:** Print; Online.

15200 ■ *"USF Plans $30M Sports Complex"* in Tampa Bay Business Journal (Vol. 29, October 23, 2009, No. 44, pp. 1)
Pub: Tampa Bay Business Journal
Contact: Ian Anderson, President
E-mail: ianderson@bizjournals.com

Ed: Jane Meinhardt. **Description:** University of South Florida (USF) is going to build a new sports complex with the aid of a $30 million loan from BB&T. The project, which is also comprised of new and renovated athletic facilities on USF's Tampa campus, is projected to create more than $37 million in revenue in its first year. Revenues from the said facilities are expected to achieve an annual growth of at least four percent. **Availability:** Print; Online.

15201 ■ *"The View From the Front Row"* in Philadelphia Business Journal (Vol. 32, January 31, 2014, No. 51, pp. 6)
Pub: American City Business Journals, Inc.
Contact: Mike Olivieri, Executive Vice President

Released: Weekly. **Price:** $4, introductory 4-week offer(Digital & Print). **Description:** Eric Smallwood, senior vice president of Front Row Analytics, reveals that the company conducts full-season sponsorship marketing analysis for the Seattle Seahawks. He mentions that a 30-second Super Bowl commercial could cost $4 million. Information about his favorite Super Bowl commercials is revealed. **Availability:** Print; Online.

15202 ■ *"Wells' Is Title Sponsor for Volleyball Championship"* in Ice Cream Reporter (Vol. 22, August 20, 2008, No. 9, pp. 4)

Description: Wells' Dairy was chosen to sponsor the 29th Annual National Association of Intercollegiate Athletics (NAIA) Volleyball National Championship to be held in Sioux City, Iowa. Blue Bunny will sponsor the 2008 NAIA Women's Volleyball National Championship, also a Wells' brand. **Availability:** Print; Online.

15203 ■ *"Winter Puts Golf Industry Off Course"* in Baltimore Business Journal (Vol. 31, April 4, 2014, No. 49, pp. 17)
Pub: American City Business Journals, Inc.
Contact: Mike Olivieri, Executive Vice President

Released: Weekly. **Price:** $4, introductory 4-week offer(Digital & Print). **Description:** Due to extreme cold and heavy snow in Maryland and the rest of the country, playing golf has become so impossible that the golf industry is struggling to stay on budget. Golf courses are closing down due to lack of revenue generation. Country clubs are working to be more creative with various winter events to supplement income. For example, one country club hosted a winter fest, indoor putting contests, a karaoke night, a comedy night, and a kids' activity day; while Waverly Woods Golf Club is offering members temperature pricing throughout the winter. **Availability:** Print; Online.

15204 ■ *"With Traffic Jam in Super Bowl, Can Any Auto Brand Really Win?"* in Advertising Age (Vol. 81, December 6, 2010, No. 43, pp. 1)
Pub: Crain Communications, Inc.
Contact: Jessica Botos, Manager, Marketing
E-mail: jessica.botos@crainsnewyork.com

Ed: Rupal Parekh. **Description:** Car marketers are doubling down for Super Bowl XLV in Arlington, Texas and asking their ad agencies to craft commercials unique enough to break through the clutter and to capture viewers' attention. **Availability:** Online.

TRADE PERIODICALS

15205 ■ *The American Quarter Horse Journal*
Pub: American Quarter Horse Association
Contact: Craig Huffhines, Executive Vice President
URL(s): www.aqha.com/news-and-publications/ magazines/the-american-quarter-horse-journal

Released: 6/year; January / February , March / April , May / June, July / August , September / October and November / December. **Description:** Magazine promoting advancement and improvement of the breeding and performance of the American Quarter Horse. **Availability:** Print; Online.

15206 ■ *Cutting Horse Chatter*
Pub: National Cutting Horse Association
Contact: Jay Winborn, Executive Director
E-mail: jwinborn@nchacutting.com
URL(s): www.nchacutting.com/cutting-horse-chatter -magazine

Released: Quarterly; last edition: Summer 2024. **Price:** $6, for price. **Description:** Magazine promoting the cutting horse industry. **Availability:** Print; PDF; Online; Download.

15207 ■ *Open Season Sportsman's Expo*
Pub: Bonnier LLC
Contact: David Ritchie, Co-Chief Executive Officer
URL(s): www.openseasonsportsmansexpo.com
Facebook: www.facebook.com/OpenSeasonSpor tsmansExpo
Instagram: www.instagram.com/Open_Season_Spor tsmans_Expo

Description: Five magazines on 5 deer and turkey hunting shows. **Availability:** Print; Online.

15208 ■ *The Quarter Racing Journal*
Pub: American Quarter Horse Association
Contact: Craig Huffhines, Executive Vice President
URL(s): www.aqha.com/news-and-publications/ magazines/quarter-racing-journal

Ed: Andrea Caudill. **Released:** Semiannual; Spring, Winter. **Description:** Magazine promoting breeding and performance of the racing Quarter Horse. **Availability:** Print; Online.

15209 ■ *South Carolina Wildlife*
Pub: South Carolina Department of Natural Resources
Contact: Robert H. Boyles, Jr., Director
URL(s): www.scwildlife.com

Ed: Joey Frazier. **Released:** Irregular; last issue 2022. **Price:** $18, for per year; $24, Canada for foreign. **Description:** Magazine promoting resource management, wildlife, and better understanding of South Carolina's environment. Official publication of the state department of natural resources. **Availability:** Print; Online.

VIDEO/AUDIO MEDIA

15210 ■ *Side Hustle to Small Business: Pitch Pefect: How Rob Friedman Became the Pitching Ninja*
URL(s): www.hiscox.com/side-hustle-to-small-business/rob-friedman-pitching-ninja-podcast-season-3

Ed: Sanjay Parekh. **Released:** January 04, 2023. **Description:** Podcast offers a conversation with a lawyer-turned-baseball analyst.

TRADE SHOWS AND CONVENTIONS

15211 ■ *Michigan Interscholastic Athletic Administrators Mid-Winter Conference*
Michigan Interscholastic Athletic Administrators Association (MIAAA)
c/o Karen Leinaar, Executive Director
PO Box 1708
Frankfort, MI 49635
Ph: (231)218-6983
Co. E-mail: karenleinaar@gmail.com
URL: http://www.miaaa.com
Contact: Karen Leinaar, Executive Director
E-mail: karenleinaar@gmail.com
URL(s): www.miaaa.com/conferences

Frequency: Annual. **Description:** To bring together athletic directors from all parts of Michigan to discuss new ideas and solutions to problems common to all. **Audience:** Athletic directors and administrators. **Principal Exhibits:** To bring together athletic directors from all parts of Michigan to discuss new ideas and solutions to problems common to all. Dates and Locations: 2025 Mar 13-16; 2026 Mar 19-22; 2027 Mar 18-21. Grand Traverse Resort Hotel, Traverse City, MI. **Telecommunication Services:** tjohnston1977@gmail.com.

FRANCHISES AND BUSINESS OPPORTUNITIES

15212 ■ *i9 Sports*
9410 Camden Field Pky.
Riverview, FL 33578
Ph: (813)324-2000
Co. E-mail: customerservice@i9sports.com
URL: http://www.i9sports.com
Facebook: www.facebook.com/i9sports
Linkedin: www.linkedin.com/company/i9-sports
X (Twitter): x.com/i9Sports
Instagram: www.instagram.com/i9_Sports
YouTube: www.youtube.com/user/i9SportsFranchise
Pinterest: www.pinterest.com/i9sports

Description: Operator of sports leagues. **Founded:** 2003. **Financial Assistance:** Yes **Training:** 1 week provided at headquarters, 2 days of on-site and optional refresher training available.

15213 ■ Puckmasters International
Port Coquitlam, ON, Canada V3C 6K5
Co. E-mail: detroit@puckmasters.com
URL: http://www.puckmasters.com
Contact: Stephen Schaeffler, Manager
URL(s): www.franchising.com/puckmastershockeytra

Description: Center provides hockey training, silk, goalie training, team training and much more. **Founded:** 1993. **Royalty Fee:** 6%. **Training:** 14 days at headquarters, 9 days at franchisees location and ongoing support.

15214 ■ Skyhawks Sports & Supertots Sports Academy
1826 E Sprague Ave.
  Spokane, WA 99202
Free: 800-804-3509
Co. E-mail: skyhawks@skyhawks.com
URL: http://www.skyhawks.com
Contact: Jason Frazier, President
E-mail: jfrazier@skyhawks.com
Facebook: www.facebook.com/SkyhawksSports
X (Twitter): x.com/skyhawkssports
Instagram: www.instagram.com/skyhawkssports
YouTube: www.youtube.com/channel/UCI4gX9Gq
  3BkTxBalLgaXlSg

Description: Teaches life skills through sports. **Founded:** 1979. **Training:** Yes.

COMPUTERIZED DATABASES

15215 ■ *CustomWire*
Comtex News Network Inc.
  295 Madison Ave., 12th Fl.
  New York, NY 10017
Ph: (212)688-6240
Fax: (212)688-6241
Co. E-mail: cs@comtex.com
URL: http://www.comtex.com
Contact: Kan Devnani, President
URL(s): www.comtex.com/customwires
Availability: Download; PDF; Online. **Type:** Full-text.

ASSOCIATIONS AND OTHER ORGANIZATIONS

15216 ■ **National Society of Professional Surveyors (NSPS)**
21 Byte Ct., Ste. H
Frederick, MD 21704
Ph: (240)439-4615
Fax: (240)439-4952
Co. E-mail: info@nsps.us.com
URL: http://www.nsps.us.com
Contact: Bob Akins, President
E-mail: twogunpete@reagan.com
Facebook: www.facebook.com/nspsinc
Linkedin: www.linkedin.com/company/national-socie ty-of-professional-surveyors
X (Twitter): x.com/NSPSINC
Instagram: www.instagram.com/nsps.us
YouTube: www.youtube.com/channel/UCSWFUr 5kRwt1FhRHxi6gLDw
Description: Consists of professional surveyors, pre-professionals, technicians, and students. Encourages members to adopt and adhere to standards of ethical and professional behavior and to provide a professional service to the public. Maintains liaison with other professional societies; promotes public confidence in services rendered by members; monitors laws and regulations affecting the profession; helps to develop curricula for teaching surveying. **Founded:** 1941. **Publications:** *ACSM Bulletin: Promoting Advancement in the Collection, Analysis and Graphic Representation of Geo-Spatial Data* (Bimonthly). **Awards:** NSPS Map Plat Competition (Annual); Walter Robillard Scholarship in Surveying (Annual); Cady McDonnell Memorial Scholarship (Annual); Slovoj (Dr. Ing Desider E.) Scholarship (Annual); Geographic and Land Information Society Scholarship (Annual); West Virginia Society of Professional Surveyors Scholarship (Annual); NSPS Berntsen International Scholarship in Surveying Technology (Annual); NSPS Excellence in Professional Journalism Awards (Annual); NSPS Surveying Excellence Award (Annual); NSPS Scholarship (Annual); New Jersey Society of Prof. Land Surveyors Scholarship for Land Surveying Education (Annual); Public Land Survey System Foundation Scholarship - 2 Year (Annual); Public Land Survey System Foundation Scholarship - 4 Year (Annual). **Geographic Preference:** National.

15217 ■ **Professional Surveyors Canada (PSC) [Geometres professionnels du Canada]**
900 Dynes Rd., Ste. 101B
Ottawa, ON, Canada K2C 3L6
Ph: (613)695-8333
Free: 800-241-7200
Co. E-mail: info@psc-gpc.ca
URL: http://psc-gpc.ca
Contact: Bill Roberton, Executive Director
E-mail: bill@psc-gpc.ca
Description: Represents the interests of professional surveyor in Canada. Aims to build and enable a strong multi-faced community of surveying profes-

sionals. Works on behalf of its members to encourage and enable an environment where their work is valued as underpinning the fabric of society for the safety and economic well being of Canadians. **Founded:** 1976. **Awards:** Champlain Award (Irregular). **Geographic Preference:** National.

15218 ■ **Surveyors Historical Society (SHS)**
150 E Wilson Bridge Rd., Ste. 300
Worthington, OH 43085
Ph: (614)798-5257
Co. E-mail: info@surveyorshistoricalsociety.com
URL: http://www.surveyorshistoricalsociety.com/aws/ SHS/pt/sp/home_page
Contact: Paula Hammer, Executive Director
Description: Persons interested in the history of surveying. Dedicated to the preservation of surveying instruments, records, memorabilia, and relics. Seeks to educate the public about the history of surveying. Organizes displays of surveying memorabilia and instruments. Conducts research projects. Operates speakers' bureau and museum; compiles statistics. **Founded:** 1977. **Publications:** *Backsights* (Annual). **Geographic Preference:** National.

15219 ■ **U.S. Surveyors Association (USSA)**
13430 McGregor Blvd.
Fort Myers, FL 33919
Ph: (239)481-5150
Free: 800-245-4425
Co. E-mail: navsurvey@aol.com
URL: http://www.navsurvey.com
Contact: Harold Roebuck, Member
YouTube: www.youtube.com/channel/UCg3O 5VSJfVgQqMdl79w5-UA
Description: Maintains high training and ethical standards and provide inspection of vessels according to U.S. Coast Guard requirements. Conducts educational and research programs. **Founded:** 1987. **Geographic Preference:** National.

REFERENCE WORKS

15220 ■ *"Crime and Punishment" in Canadian Business* (Vol. 81, December 24, 2007, No. 1, pp. 21)
Description: Cmpass Inc.'s survey of 137 Canadian chief executive officers showed that they want tougher imposition of sentences on white-collar criminals, as they believe that the weak enforcement of securities laws gives an impression that Canada is a country where it is easy to get away with fraud. **Availability:** Online.

15221 ■ *"DMW Gets MBE Certification" in Wireless News* (July 29, 2012)
Description: Towson, Maryland's Daft McCune Walker (DMW) received the Minority Business Enterprise (MBE) Certification from the State of Maryland for Engineering, Surveying, Environmental and CAD services. The firm is a multidisciplinary consulting organization and is woman-owned. **Availability:** Print; Online.

15222 ■ *"The Duty of Wealth: Canadian Business Leaders on Nepotism and Philanthropy" in Canadian Business* (Vol. 80, Winter 2007, No. 24)
Description: Fifty-one percent of the respondents in a survey of business leaders say that the decision to allow adult children to join a family firm should be based on the circumstances at the time. He CEOs that were surveyed also believed that billionaires should donate an average of forty percent of their estates and keep the rest for their family.

15223 ■ *"ForeSee Finds Satisfaction On Web Sites, Bottom Line" in Crain's Detroit Business* (Vol. 24, February 25, 2008, No. 8, pp. 3)
Pub: Crain Communications Inc.
Contact: Barry Asin, President
Ed: Tom Henderson. **Description:** Ann Arbor-based ForeSee Results Inc. evaluates user satisfaction on Web sites. The company expects to see an increase of 40 percent in revenue for 2008 with plans to expand to London, Germany, Italy and France by the end of 2009.

15224 ■ *"Reading the Public Mind" in Harvard Business Review* (Vol. 88, October 2010, No. 10, pp. 27)
Pub: Harvard Business Publishing
Contact: Diane Belcher, Managing Director
Ed: Andrew O'Connell. **Price:** $6, PDF. **Description:** Examination of the various methods for obtaining public opinion and consumer preferences is provided; an outline of the disadvantages and benefits of both are also given. **Availability:** Online; PDF.

15225 ■ *"Survey Says Commercial Real Estate Headed for Turbulence" in Commercial Property News* (March 17, 2008)
Description: Commercial real estate sector is declining due to the sluggish U.S. economy. According to a recent survey, national office, retail and hospitality markets are also on the decline. **Availability:** Online.

STATISTICAL SOURCES

15226 ■ **Credit Counselors, Surveyors & Appraisers Industry in the US - Market Research Report**
URL(s): ibisworld.com/united-states/market-research -reports/credit-counselors-surveyors-appraisers-in dustry/
Price: $925. **Description:** Downloadable report analyzing the current and future trends in various industries that include credit counselors, surveyors, and appraisers. **Availability:** Download.

TRADE PERIODICALS

15227 ■ **Civil + Structural Engineer**
Contact: Bob Drake, Editor
E-mail: bdrake@zweiggroup.com
URL(s): www.cenews.com

Facebook: www.facebook.com/
csENGINEERmagazine
X (Twitter): twitter.com/csENGINEERmag

Ed: Bob Drake. **Released:** Monthly **Description:** Trade magazine serving civil engineers and land surveyors engaged in land development, highways, bridges, structural, environmental, geotechnical, water resources, and industrial engineering projects including surveying. **Availability:** Print; PDF; Online.

15228 ■ *Geomatica*
Pub: Canadian Institute of Geomatics
Contact: Mir Abolfazl Mostafavi, President
URL(s): cdnsciencepub.com/journal/geomat

Ed: Izaak de Rijcke. **Released:** Quarterly **Description:** Surveying and mapping journal. **Availability:** Print; PDF; Online.

15229 ■ *The Ontario Professional Surveyor (OPS)*
Pub: Association of Ontario Land Surveyors
Contact: Andy Shelp, President
URL(s): www.aols.org/about/media

Ed: Maureen Mountjoy. **Released:** Quarterly; Winter, Spring, Summer, Fall. **Price:** $40, Nonmembers for annual. **Description:** Surveying magazine. **Availability:** Print; PDF; Online.

TRADE SHOWS AND CONVENTIONS

15230 ■ California Land Surveyors Association Conference
California Land Surveyors Association (CLSA)
2520 Venture Oaks Way, Ste. 150
Sacramento, CA 95833
Ph: (916)239-4083
Fax: (916)924-7323
Co. E-mail: clsa@californiasurveyors.org
URL: http://www.californiasurveyors.org
Contact: Warren Smith, President
E-mail: wdsmith@co.tuolumne.ca.us
URL(s): www.californiasurveyors.org/conference
.aspx

Frequency: Annual. **Description:** Land surveying equipment, computers, vehicles, software, and two-way communication systems. **Audience:** Land surveyors and civil engineers. **Principal Exhibits:** Land surveying equipment, computers, vehicles, software, and two-way communication systems. **Telecommunication Services:** kim@californiasurveyors.org.

15231 ■ Michigan Society of Professional Surveyors Annual Meeting
Michigan Society of Professional Surveyors (MSPS)
2123 University Pk., Dr., Ste. 100
Okemos, MI 48864
Ph: (517)484-2413
Fax: (734)677-2407
Co. E-mail: centraloffice@misps.org
URL: http://www.misps.org
Contact: Michelle Batora, Executive Director
E-mail: mbatora@misps.org

Frequency: Annual. **Description:** Surveying equipment, publications, and computers. **Audience:** Licensed professional surveyors. **Principal Exhibits:** Surveying equipment, publications, and computers.

COMPUTER SYSTEMS/ SOFTWARE

15232 ■ *Land Survey Calculator*
Price: $19.95. **Description:** Available for PC computers. Program for performing land survey calculations.

LIBRARIES

15233 ■ British Columbia Land Surveyors Foundation - Anna Papove Memorial Library
No. 301-2400 Bevan Ave.
Sidney, BC, Canada V8L 1W1
URL: http://www.abcls.ca/page/programs-and-initia
tives

Description: Contains reference materials, journals, books, online materials, and video and audio materials, and historical documents or records. **Scope:** Land surveying. **Services:** Copying; library open to the public. **Founded:** 2002. **Holdings:** 900 books;

100 serials; 100 reports; 100 VF drawers; 5 videotapes; 50 other cataloged items; archival records. **Subscriptions:** 10 journals and other serials.

15234 ■ Washington State Department of Natural Resources Public Land Survey Office Library (PLSO)
801 88th Ave. SE, MS 47019
Tumwater, WA 98501-7019
Ph: (360)902-1230
Free: 888-902-1190
Fax: (360)902-1785
Co. E-mail: plso@dnr.wa.gov
URL: http://www.dnr.wa.gov/public-land-survey-office
Contact: Stephanie Earls, Librarian
E-mail: stephanie.earls@dnr.wa.gov
Facebook: www.facebook.com/WashDNR
X (Twitter): x.com/waDNR
Instagram: www.instagram.com/washdnr
YouTube: www.youtube.com/user/WAstateDNR

Scope: Geology. **Services:** Copying; office open to the public for a fee (appointment preferred). **Founded:** 1951. **Holdings:** 300,000 aperture cards of survey maps; 300 reels of microfilm of original government survey notes; 3,500 field books from private surveyors; 500,000 scanned images of survey maps and historic survey documents.

RESEARCH CENTERS

15235 ■ Frost Research Center for Data and Research
100 E 8th St., Ste. 260
Holland, MI 49423
Ph: (616)395-7556
Co. E-mail: frostcenter@hope.edu
URL: http://hope.edu/offices/frost-research-center
Contact: Dr. Kathy Kremer, Senior Director
E-mail: kremerk@hope.edu

Description: Integral unit of Hope College. **Scope:** Social science research in conjunction with corporate, educational, governmental, and nonprofit organizations. Research includes mail, telephone and web surveys, questionnaire design, data management and analysis, focus group discussions, etc. **Founded:** 1990. **Publications:** *Carl Frost Center for Social Science Research Reports.* **Awards:** Carl Frost Center for Social Science Research Student Internship; Frost Center Research Student-Faculty Research Grants (Annual).

ASSOCIATIONS AND OTHER ORGANIZATIONS

15236 ■ Diving Equipment and Marketing Association (DEMA)
6050 Santo Rd., Ste. 220
San Diego, CA 92124
Ph: (858)616-6408
Free: 800-862-3483
Fax: (858)616-6495
Co. E-mail: info@dema.org
URL: http://www.dema.org
Contact: Tom Ingram, President
E-mail: tom@dema.org
Facebook: www.facebook.com/DEMAorg
Linkedin: www.linkedin.com/company/dema-org
X (Twitter): x.com/DEMAorg
Instagram: www.instagram.com/demaorg
YouTube: www.youtube.com/user/demaassn
Description: International recreational scuba diving and snorkeling organizations and associations promoting or reporting diving activities, individuals or organizations providing educational, retail, travel, media or other services in the field. Aims to promote advancement within the diving equipment industry, encourage the growth of diving activities, and enhance public enjoyment of recreational diving. Cooperates with domestic governmental and private agencies that develop standards or are involved in regulating activities affecting the diving industry and related products. Seeks to establish continuing education programs to instruct and assist industry members in business, quality control and the marketing of diving products. Organizes conferences dealing with topics such as governmental regulations, product standards, quality control, and standardized bookkeeping methods. **Founded:** 1975. **Publications:** *DEMA News & Industry Report* (Monthly). **Educational Activities:** DEMA Show (Annual). **Geographic Preference:** National.

15237 ■ International Association of Plumbing and Mechanical Officials (IAPMO) [IAPMO Research and Testing Inc.]
4755 E Philadelphia St.
Ontario, CA 91761
Ph: (909)472-4100
Fax: (909)472-4150
Co. E-mail: iapmo@iapmo.org
URL: http://www.iapmo.org
Contact: D. J. Nunez, President
Facebook: www.facebook.com/IAPMO
X (Twitter): x.com/IAPMO
Instagram: www.instagram.com/iapmo
YouTube: www.youtube.com/user/IAPMOGroup
Description: Government agencies, administrative officials, sales representatives, manufacturers, associations, and members of associations related to the plumbing field. Sponsors and writes Uniform Plumbing Codes; also sponsors Uniform Mechanical Code. **Publications:** *Directory of Listed Plumbing Products for Mobile Homes and Recreational Vehicles* (Bimonthly); *Official Magazine* (Quarterly); *Backflow*

Prevention Journal (Bimonthly); *2009 Idaho State Plumbing Code CD-ROM*; *Directory of Listed Plumbing Products*; *Directory of Manufactured Housing/RV Research Recommendations* (Bimonthly); *Uniform Mechanical Code Illustrated Training Manual*; *Uniform Plumbing Code Illustrated Training Manual*; *2010 Green Plumbing & Mechanical Code Supplement CD-ROM*; *2012 Uniform Plumbing Code CD-ROM*; *2012 Uniform Mechanical Code CD-ROM*; *2013 California Plumbing Code CD-ROM*; *2013 California Mechanical Code on CD-ROM*; *2011 Oregon Plumbing Specialty Code on CD-ROM*. **Educational Activities:** Annual Education and Business Conference (Annual). **Awards:** IAPMO Government Person of the Year (Annual); IAPMO Industry Person of the Year (Annual); Joseph Kneidinger Green Professional of the Year Award (Annual); IAPMO American Flag Award (Annual); George Kauffman Lifetime Achievement Award (Annual). **Geographic Preference:** National; Multinational.

REFERENCE WORKS

15238 ■ "5 Things You Need to Know About Water Parks, But Probably Don't' in healthychildren.org (June 6, 2019)
URL(s): www.healthychildren.org/English/safety-prevention/at-play/Pages/Water-Park-Safety.aspx
Released: June 04, 2019. **Description:** Over 85 million people visit the 1,300 water parks in the US each year. Before spending the day in the water park, five important factors are discussed which should help keep you and family safe and allow you to have an enjoyable experience. **Availability:** Online.

15239 ■ "Everyone Out of the Pool' in Barron's (Vol. 89, July 20, 2009, No. 29, pp. 18)
Pub: Dow Jones & Company Inc.
Contact: Almar Latour, Chief Executive Officer
Ed: Sandra Ward. **Description:** Shares of Pool Corp. could drop as continued weakness in the housing market weakens the market for swimming pool equipment. The company's shares are trading at $18.29, about 20 times projected 2009 earnings of $0.91 a share. **Availability:** Online.

15240 ■ "Survey Reveals Shifting Preferences in Pool Chemicals and Sanitation Systems" in Pool and Spa News (November 20, 2017)
URL(s): www.poolspanews.com/how-to/maintenance/survey-reveals-shifting-preferences-in-pool-chemicals-and-sanitation-systems_o
Ed: Nate Traylor. **Released:** November 20, 2017. **Description:** Pool and Spa News conducted a survey to see which type of pool system consumers prefer to use and how loyal they are to their brands and local stores. **Availability:** Online.

SOURCES OF SUPPLY

15241 ■ AQUA--Buyers' Guide Issue
Athletic Business Publications Inc.
Contact: Jason Scott, Managing Editor

E-mail: jason@athleticbusiness.com
URL(s): www.aquamagazine.com/directory
Ed: Scott Webb. **Description:** Covers swimming pool and spa product manufacturers, distributors, representatives, and trade shows. **Entries include:** Company name, address, phone, fax, E-mail, toll-free phone, website, name and title of contact, number of employees, geographical area served for distributors and representatives only, year established, products manufactured (or sold in the case of the distributors & representatives). **Arrangement:** Alphabetical; distributors and representatives also listed geographical by state. **Indexes:** Brand name; product manufactured; state covered (distributors & representatives). **Availability:** Print; Online.

STATISTICAL SOURCES

15242 ■ RMA Annual Statement Studies
Pub: Risk Management Association
Contact: Nancy Foster, President
Released: Annual. **Description:** Contains composite balance sheets and income statements for more than 360 industries, including the accounting, auditing, and bookkeeping industries. Also contains five years of comparative historical data for discerning trends. Includes 16 commonly used ratios, computed for most of the size groupings for nearly every industry.

TRADE PERIODICALS

15243 ■ AQUA Magazine: The Business Magazine for Spa and Pool Professionals
Pub: Athletic Business Publications Inc.
Contact: Jason Scott, Managing Editor
E-mail: jason@athleticbusiness.com
URL(s): www.aquamagazine.com
Facebook: www.facebook.com/AQUAMagazine
Linkedin: www.linkedin.com/company/aqua-magazine
X (Twitter): x.com/aquamagazine
Pinterest: www.pinterest.com/aquamagazine
Released: Monthly **Description:** Trade magazine for spa and pool professionals. **Availability:** Online.

15244 ■ Pool & Spa Marketing
Pub: Kenilworth Media Inc.
Contact: Erik Tolles, Chief Executive Officer
URL(s): www.poolspamarketing.comkenilworth.com/pool-spa-marketing
Facebook: www.facebook.com/PoolSpaMarketing
X (Twitter): x.com/PoolSpaMktg
Instagram: www.instagram.com/poolspamarketing
Released: 7/year **Price:** $77, U.S. for 1 year; $98, for 1 year foreign; $49, U.S. for 1 year; $59, for online international. **Description:** Magazine covering the pool and spa industry. **Availability:** Print; Online.

TRADE SHOWS AND CONVENTIONS

15245 ■ Education Conference
Ball Horticultural Company
622 Town Rd.
West Chicago, IL 60185

Ph: (630)231-3600
Fax: (630)231-1383
URL: http://www.ballhort.com
Contact: Al Davidson, President
URL(s): www.thepoolspashow.com/nespa2023/Public/Content.aspx?ID=3273
Frequency: Annual. **Description:** Platform for manufacturers of pool and spa products to showcase their products. **Audience:** Pool & spa professionals. **Principal Exhibits:** Platform for manufacturers of pool and spa products to showcase their products.

CONSULTANTS

15246 ■ Short Elliott Hendrickson Inc. (SEH)
3535 Vadnais Center Dr.
  Saint Paul, MN 55110-3507
Ph: (651)490-2150
Free: 800-325-2055
Fax: (888)908-8166
Co. E-mail: info@sehinc.com
URL: http://www.sehinc.com
Contact: David Ott, President
Facebook: www.facebook.com/sehinc
Linkedin: www.linkedin.com/company/seh
X (Twitter): x.com/sehinc

Description: Firm provides airport planning and design, architectural design, electrical or mechanical engineering, environmental, municipal, wastewater and water engineering, heavy civil, transportation, and urban design. **Scope:** Firm provides airport planning and design, architectural design, electrical or mechanical engineering, environmental, municipal, wastewater and water engineering, heavy civil, transportation, and urban design. **Founded:** 1927. **Publications:** "Sending the Right Signals: Project Management for Telecommunication Sites on Water Tanks," Journal of Protective Coatings & Linings, May, 2008; "The Transportation Aspect of Disaster Planning," 2008; "Performance Or Preference? a Look at Selected Systems for Water Tank Interiors," Journal of Protective Coatings & Linings, May, 2007; "Old Tanks, Tight Budgets: How Does the Job Get Done," Journal of Protective Coatings & Linings, May, 2005; "Painting for Antenna Installations on Water Storage Facilities," Today Magazine, Feb, 2003; "Bioterrorism, Cyberterrorism and Water Supplies," Wisconsin Water Well Association Journal, Jan, 2003; "They're Water Storage Tanks," Today Magazine, Jul, 2002. **Special Services:** SEH®.

15247 ■ Veenstra & Kimm Inc.
3000 Westown Pky.
  West Des Moines, IA 50266
Ph: (515)225-8000
Free: 800-241-8000
Fax: (515)225-7848
URL: http://www.v-k.net
Facebook: www.facebook.com/VeenstraAndKimm
X (Twitter): x.com/VeenstraKimmInc

Description: Firm provides comprehensive engineering solutions for civil, environmental, and transportation such as wastewater management, storm water design, structural, municipal and much more. **Scope:** Firm provides comprehensive engineering solutions for civil, environmental, and transportation such as wastewater management, storm water design, structural, municipal and much more. **Founded:** 1961.

FRANCHISES AND BUSINESS OPPORTUNITIES

15248 ■ ASP-America's Swimming Pool Co. [America's Swimming Pool Co.]
3986 Lake St.
  Macon, GA 31204
Ph: (478)242-2343
Free: 866-277-7665
Co. E-mail: info@asppoolco.com
URL: http://www.asppoolco.com
Facebook: www.facebook.com/ASPpoolco
Linkedin: www.linkedin.com/company/asp---america's-swimming-pool-company
X (Twitter): x.com/americaspoolco
YouTube: www.youtube.com/user/ASPFranchise
Pinterest: www.pinterest.com/ASPfranchising

Description: Firm provides swimming pool maintenance and repairing services. **Founded:** 2001. **Financial Assistance:** Yes **Training:** Provides 12 days training at headquarters, 2 days onsite and ongoing support.

LIBRARIES

15249 ■ International Swimming Hall of Fame (ISHOF) - The Henning Library and Archive
1 Hall of Fame Dr.
  Fort Lauderdale, FL 33316
Ph: (954)462-6536
URL: http://www.ishof.org
Contact: Dr. Bill Kent, Chairman of the Board
Facebook: www.facebook.com/ISHOF
Linkedin: www.linkedin.com/company/international-swimming-hall-of-fame-inc
X (Twitter): x.com/ishof
Instagram: www.instagram.com/ishof_museum
YouTube: www.youtube.com/user/swimminghalloffame

Description: Promotes aquatic education. Honors and supports swimming, diving, water polo, synchronized swimming, water safety, and aquatic art. **Scope:** Swimming history and instruction; sports medicine and psychology; pool care and management; diving and water polo; swim officiating; synchronized swimming. **Services:** Copying; research services; photo duplication; Library open to the public by appointment. **Founded:** 1965. **Subscriptions:** 114 magazines 31,000 discreet aquatic sports items; 1,000 monographs; 424 periodical titles; 700 interview cassettes; 5,000 vertical file items; 400 pre-1900 vintage volumes; 310 scrapbooks. **Publications:** International Swimming Hall of Fame--News (Monthly). **Awards:** ISHOF Gold Medallion Award (Annual); International Swimming Hall of Fame (Annual); John K. Williams Jr. International Adaptive Aquatics Award (Annual); ISHOF Presidential Honor Award (Irregular); G. Harold Martin Award (Irregular); Al Schoenfield Media Award (Irregular); International Marathon Swimming Hall of Fame (IMSHOF) (Annual); ISHOF Aquatic Awards (Annual). **Geographic Preference:** National.

Tailor Shop

REFERENCE WORKS

15250 ■ *"A Family's Fortune" in Canadian Business (Vol. 80, Winter 2007, No. 24, pp. 103)*

Price: $23. **Description:** James Richardson started as a tailor before moving into the grain business because his clients paid him in sacks of wheat and barley. The James Richardson and Sons Ltd. entered the radio business in 1927 but later sold it off in 1951. **Availability:** Print; Online.

15251 ■ *How to Start Your Own Tailoring Ship Business: A Beginner's Guide*

Description: There are endless opportunities in tailoring from generalized sewing, focusing on all kinds of clothes or specialized sewing, centering on bridal attire. This article details nine important steps to take to start your tailoring business from scratch. **Availability:** Online.

15252 ■ *"New Tailor Shop in Uptown Dallas Is a Great Fit for the Neighborhood's Renewed Energy" in Dallas News (July 26, 2019)*

URL(s): www.dallasnews.com/arts-entertainment/20 19/07/26/new-tailor-shop-in-uptown-dallas-is-a-grea t-fit-for-the-neighborhood-s-renewed-energy/
Ed: Kimber Westphall. **Released:** July 26, 2019. **Description:** Edit Alternations has joined the crowd in Uptown Dallas and hopes to fill a quality void in the tailoring industry. The business caters to both men and women and will even make house calls, which is something the competition doesn't offer. **Availability:** Online.

15253 ■ *"Quintessential Gentleman: Going Old-School on Calvert" in Baltimore Business Journal (Vol. 31, February 7, 2014, No. 41, pp. 6)*

Pub: American City Business Journals, Inc.
Contact: Mike Olivieri, Executive Vice President
Description: Quintessential Gentleman owner, Craig Martin shares his vintage idea in the expansion of his men's barbershop, spa, and tailor business in the Jewelers Building at South Calvert Street in downtown Baltimore, Maryland. Martin says his idea is to bring back tradition combined with modern amenities. He also shares his plan to model the business on a department store. **Availability:** Print; Online.

15254 ■ *"Tailoring Is the Secret of Well-Dressed Women" in The Wall Street Journal (December 11, 2013)*

URL(s): www.wsj.com/articles/tailoring-is-the-secre t-of-welldressed-women-1386810054
Ed: Christina Binkley. **Released:** December 11, 2013. **Description:** With cheap clothing being bought, many people do not care if their clothes fit them well. Tailoring is slowly fading away across the nation as more men bypass the industry, but women have been requiring more tailoring to achieve a professional work look. Once a piece has been fixed, consumers often go back because the clothes fit better and it can often save money in the long run. **Availability:** Online.

ASSOCIATIONS AND OTHER ORGANIZATIONS

15255 ■ Association of Talent Agents (ATA)
3019 Ocean Pk. Blvd., Ste. 344
Santa Monica, CA 90405
Ph: (310)274-0628
URL: http://www.agentassociation.com
Contact: Rita Vennari, President
Description: Employs legal counsel to prepare opinions upon request and to file briefs in arbitrations and labor commission hearings. Maintains liaison with labor commission representatives in San Francisco and Los Angeles, CA, and intervenes on behalf of individual members having special problems. Conducts seminars and symposia. **Founded:** 1937. **Publications:** *Employment Law.* **Geographic Preference:** National.

15256 ■ International Entertainment Buyers Association (IEBA)
412 E Iris Dr.
Nashville, TN 37204
Ph: (615)679-9601
Co. E-mail: info@ieba.org
URL: http://www.ieba.org
Contact: Becky Colwell, President
Facebook: www.facebook.com/iebaconference
Linkedin: www.linkedin.com/company/international-en
   tertainment-buyers-association-ieba
Instagram: www.instagram.com/iebaconf
Description: Talent buyers and sellers, artists, managers, agents, venue operators and managers, and entertainment organizations; others with an interest in the entertainment industry, including advertisers, promoters, lighting, sound, and film technicians, and staging, production, and music businesses. Promotes professional advancement of members; seeks to ensure provision of high-quality entertainment purchasing services to customers. Serves as a clearinghouse on talent agencies and upcoming performances; facilitates exchange among members; represents members' commercial and professional interests. **Founded:** 1970. **Geographic Preference:** Multinational.

REFERENCE WORKS

15257 ■ "Fire Your Agent? Not Yet. Hollywood Writers and Talent Agencies Extend Talks" in The New York Times (April 7, 2019)
URL(s): www.nytimes.com/2019/04/07/business/me
   dia/writers-guild-talent-agencies.html
Ed: John Koblin. **Released:** April 07, 2019. **Description:** Writers and agents in Hollywood have been operating under an old agreement from 1976 which is set to expire. The crux of the issue is that the Writers Guild of America is claiming that talent agencies have been enriching themselves at the expensive of the writers. Both sides are meeting to hash out their differences and to come to a new agreement. **Availability:** Online.

TRADE SHOWS AND CONVENTIONS

15258 ■ IAFE Trade Show
International Association of Fairs and Expositions
   (IAFE)
3043 E Cairo St.
Springfield, MO 65802
Ph: (417)862-5771
Free: 800-516-0313
Co. E-mail: iafe@fairsandexpos.com
URL: http://www.fairsandexpos.com
Contact: Marla Calico, President
URL(s): www.iafeconvention.com
Frequency: Annual. **Description:** Talent agencies, concessionaires, novelties, amusement devices, insurance, ribbons, plaques, attractions, and equipment. Products and services for the fair industry. **Audience:** IAFE members, special event producers, entertainment buyers, carnival executives, concessionaires, facility managers, Fair industry professionals. **Principal Exhibits:** Talent agencies, concessionaires, novelties, amusement devices, insurance, ribbons, plaques, attractions, and equipment. Products and services for the fair industry. **Telecommunication Services:** registration@fairsandexpos.com.

REFERENCE WORKS

15259 ■ *"Does Spray Tanning Have Side Effects?"* in U.S. News & World Report (July 8, 2019)
URL(s): health.usnews.com/conditions/cancer/skin
-cancer/articles/spray-tanning-side-effects
Ed: Elaine K. Howley. **Released:** July 08, 2019.
Description: People who pay for spray tans often ask if it's safe and if there are any side effects. While the process seems to be a healthier option than tanning beds or sitting directly in the sun for hours, the truth is, is that no one really knows for sure. Spray tans acts as a stain on the skin, but there hasn't been many studies done on the process or if there is any risk to the exposure of eyes, lips, mucus membranes, or internal organs. The only assumption is that since these products have been around for years, there hasn't been significant reports of adverse effects.
Availability: Online.

15260 ■ *"Environmental Working Group Names Whole Foods Market (R) Leading National Retailer for 'Green' Sunscreen"* in Ecology, Environment & Conservation Business (June 14, 2014, pp. 5)
Pub: NewsRX LLC.
Contact: Kalani Rosell, Contact
Description: Whole Foods Market has been named as the leading retailer selling the largest selection of 'green' rated sunscreen to shoppers. **Availability:** Online.

15261 ■ *"Image Consultants"* in Entrepreneur (June 2014)
Pub: Entrepreneur Media Inc.
Contact: Dan Bova, Director
E-mail: dbova@entrepreneur.com
Description: The ASAP54 mobile application, created by a company of the same name, uses visual recognition technology to help users determine the name of the designer or retailer of a clothing item using photographs. The company has compiled a database consisting of more than 1 million products from its retail partners. It claims an average of 5 percent commission on purchases completed through the application. Other useful wearable gadgets include Nymi, which authenticates identities based on cardiac rhythms, and Netatmo, a bracelet that measures daily sun exposure. **Availability:** Online.

15262 ■ *"Indoor Tanning Business Is Drying Up, Says National Group"* in Idaho Business Review (August 20, 2014)
Pub: BridgeTower Media
Contact: Adam Reinebach, President
Description: According to the Indoor Tanning Association in Washington DC, the recession, a new tax under the Affordable Care Act on indoor tanning businesses, and legislation by states to ban minors using tanning booths, have all contributed to their slow decline. Idaho has lost one-third of the tanning firms that once operated in the state. Statistical data included.

15263 ■ *"Indoor Tanning and the Myth of a Healthy Tan"* in U.S. News and World Report (September 1, 2015)
URL(s): health.usnews.com/health-news/patient-a
dvice/articles/2015/09/01/indoor-tanning-and-the
-myth-of-a-healthy-tan
Ed: Sophie Balk, M.D. **Released:** September 01, 2015. **Description:** Indoor tanning is still a common practice even though pediatricians, dermatologists, and other health care workers try to spread awareness of the dangers. **Availability:** Online.

15264 ■ *"Tanning Bed Use Declining Among U.S. Adults"* in Reuters (June 8, 2017)
URL(s): www.reuters.com/article/us-health-tanning
-usa/tanning-bed-use-declining-among-u-s-adults-i
dUSKBN18Z278
Ed: Carolyn Crist. **Released:** June 08, 2017. **Description:** It seems as if the word is out that tanning beds are causing cancer, due to the decline of popularity of indoor tanning. Studies of adults and adolescents have found that both sets have dropped numbers when it comes to tanning. **Availability:** Online.

STATISTICAL SOURCES

15265 ■ *Tanning Salons Industry in the US - Market Research Report*
URL(s): www.ibisworld.com/united-states/market-re
search-reports/tanning-salons-industry/
Price: $925. **Description:** Downloadable report analyzing current and future trends in the tanning salon industry. **Availability:** Download.

FRANCHISES AND BUSINESS OPPORTUNITIES

15266 ■ **Aruba Tanning Franchise**
3456 Emmorton Rd.
Abingdon, MD 21009
Description: Tanning salon. **Founded:** 2005. **Training:** Yes.

15267 ■ **The Grand Palms Tanning Resort**
8577 E Arapahoe Rd., Ste. A
Greenwood Village, CO 80112
Ph: (720)488-6890
Co. E-mail: info@thegrandpalmstanningresort.com
URL: http://thepalmstanningresort.com
Contact: Keith Rodenberger, Contact
Facebook: www.facebook.com/tanning.denver
X (Twitter): twitter.com/palmstanning
Instagram: www.instagram.com/thepalms
tanningresort
Description: Provider of sunless, cocktail, sunbed tanning, red light therapy and much more. **Founded:** 2003. **Royalty Fee:** 6%. **Financial Assistance:** Yes **Training:** Offers 1 week training at headquarters, 1 week onsite and ongoing support.

15268 ■ **Image Sun Tanning Centers**
111 Cass Ave.
Mount Clemens, MI 48043
Free: 800-837-1388
URL: http://www.imagesun.com

X (Twitter): twitter.com/ImageSunTanning
Description: Retailer of watches, sunglasses and accessories for men and women. **Financial Assistance:** Yes **Training:** Up to 1 week and 5 days onsite with ongoing support.

15269 ■ **Palm Beach Mega Tan**
300 Taunton Rd., E
Oshawa, ON, Canada L1G 7T4
Ph: (905)434-6342
URL: http://www.palmbeachmegatan.com
Facebook: www.facebook.com/palmbeachmegatan
X (Twitter): x.com/palmbeachmega1
Description: Upscale and professional tanning salon franchise. Extensive in-house training with ongoing support. State of the art equipment, looks better and gets fast effective tanning results. Secure and successful operating system comes with extensive manuals. President nominated for Canadian Woman Entrepreneur of the Year 2003, Business Excellence Award 2002, Canadian Salon of the Year Award 1995 and 1997. **No. of Franchise Units:** 25. **No. of Company-Owned Units:** 3. **Founded:** 1992. **Franchised:** 2001. **Equity Capital Needed:** $50,000 start-up capital; $270,000 total investment. **Franchise Fee:** $20,000. **Training:** Full salon and classroom training provided.

15270 ■ **Planet Beach Franchising Corporation**
5145 & 5161 Taravella Rd.
Marrero, LA 70072
Ph: (504)361-5550
URL: http://planetbeach.com
Contact: Stephen Smith, Contact
Facebook: www.facebook.com/PlanetBeach
Instagram: www.instagram.com/planetbeachofficial
Description: Tanning spa franchise. **No. of Franchise Units:** 228. **No. of Operating Units:** 151. **Founded:** 1996. **Equity Capital Needed:** $60,000 in cash/liquid assets + Net worth of $300,000 or higher . **Franchise Fee:** Single-Unit: $39,950; Multi-Unit: $69,950; Master Franchise fee and investment to be discussed on intro call. **Financial Assistance:** Yes **Training:** Yes.

15271 ■ **Sunbanque Island Tanning**
2533A Yonge St.
Toronto, ON, Canada M4P 2H9
Ph: (416)488-5838
URL: http://sunbanque.ca
Description: Operator of tanning saloons for Torontonians. **Financial Assistance:** Yes **Training:** Yes.

15272 ■ **Tropi Tan**
5152 Commerce Rd.
Flint, MI 48507
URL: http://www.tropitan.biz
Contact: Vince Lorraine, Founder
E-mail: vince@tropitan.biz
Description: Chain of tanning salons. **Founded:** 1979. **Franchise Fee:** $25,000. **Royalty Fee:** $400. **Training:** Yes.

START-UP INFORMATION

15273 ■ *How Much Does It Cost to Start a Tattoo Parlor Business?*
URL(s): www.starterstory.com/ideas/tattoo-parlor -business/startup-costs
Ed: Pat Walls. **Released:** October 21, 2022. **Description:** Details tattoo parlor business startup costs across a number of categories. **Availability:** Online.

15274 ■ *"How Much Does It Cost to Start a Tattoo Parlor?" in Chron*
URL(s): smallbusiness.chron.com/need-start-bathtub -reglazing-business-30622.html
Ed: Nicholas Pell. **Description:** After working as an apprentice and a journeyman tattoo artist, you may wish to open your own studio. This article presents information on startup costs to consider. **Availability:** Online.

15275 ■ *"How to Start a Tattoo Business – Equipment You Need" in Tycoon Story (Oct. 16, 2020)*
URL(s): www.tycoonstory.com/starting-a-business/ how-to-start-a-tattoo-business-equipment-you -need/
Released: October 16, 2020. **Description:** Discusses all aspects of what it takes to become a tattoo artist as well as information on the type of equipment needed for your tattoo shop. **Availability:** Online.

15276 ■ *"How to Start a Tattoo Business and Make Money" in TattooPro Blog (Apr. 8, 2021)*
URL(s): www.tattoopro.io/blog/how-to-start-a-tattoo -business-and-make-money/
Released: April 08, 2021. **Description:** Presents steps on how to start a tattoo business including business plan, location, marketing and advertising, pricing, licensing, and FAQs. **Availability:** Online.

15277 ■ *How to Start a Tattoo Parlor*
URL(s): howtostartanllc.com/business-ideas/tattoo -parlor
Released: October 08, 2022. **Description:** Provides a 10-step process to follow when starting a tattoo parlor from business planning to legalities and taxes and on to insurance and accounting. **Availability:** Online.

15278 ■ *How to Start a Tattoo Studio*
URL(s): startingyourbusiness.com/how-to-start-a-ta ttoo-studio/
Released: May 19, 2022. **Description:** Provides information for entrepreneurial tattoo artists who are interested in opening their own tattoo studio. Includes an industry summary and industry trends as well as a step-by-step checklist to get you started. **Availability:** Online.

15279 ■ *Opening a Tattoo Shop: Everything You Need To Know*
URL(s): www.daysmartbodyart.com/news/opening-a -tattoo-shop/

Ed: Steve Martin. **Released:** August 16, 2021. **Description:** A guide to how to open a tattoo shop. Includes info on the art side, the business side, the location, and marketing. **Availability:** Online.

ASSOCIATIONS AND OTHER ORGANIZATIONS

15280 ■ **Alliance of Professional Tattooists, Inc. (APT)**
7770 Regents Rd., Ste. 113 No. 635
San Diego, CA 92122
Ph: (816)979-1300
Co. E-mail: info@safe-tattoos.com
URL: http://safe-tattoos.com
Contact: Shahn Anderson, President
Facebook: www.facebook.com/safe.tattoo
Linkedin: www.linkedin.com/company/alliance-of -professional-tattooists-inc
X (Twitter): x.com/apt_1992
Instagram: www.instagram.com/aptinc
YouTube: www.youtube.com/channel/UCEPiO7U tmyZooobP1ODxTnw
Description: Seeks to address the health and safety issues facing the tattoo industry. Strives to educate lawmakers, dispel myths and counter misinformation with researched facts about tattooing. **Founded:** 1992. **Publications:** *Basic Guidelines for Getting a Tattoo*; *Skin Scribe* (Bimonthly). **Geographic Preference:** National.

15281 ■ **Coalition for Tattoo Safety**
Ph: (708)852-2277
Co. E-mail: info@coalitionfortattoosafety.org
URL: http://coalitionfortattoosafety.org
Facebook: www.facebook.com/CoalitionForTa ttooSafety/
Instagram: www.instagram.com/coalitionforta ttoosafety/
Description: Non-profit made up of tattoo artists, tattoo enthusiasts, and industry leaders unified under one organization. Works to be a voice for tattooing rights and regulations worldwide.

15282 ■ **National Tattoo Association, Inc. (NTA) - Library**
2565 Broadview Dr.
Kissimmee, FL 34744
Ph: (407)319-0018
Co. E-mail: ntacruisers@gmail.com
URL: http://ntanewsletter.com
Contact: Pat Sinatra, Editor-in-Chief
Facebook: www.facebook.com/NationalTa ttooAssociation
Instagram: www.instagram.com/nationaltattooassocia tion
Description: Promotes tattooing as a viable contemporary art form; seeks to upgrade standards and practices of tattooing. Offers advice on selecting a tattoo artist and studio. **Scope:** Tattoos. **Holdings:** Figures not available. **Educational Activities:** NTA Convention (Annual). **Awards:** Best Sleeve; Best Tattooist; NTA Best Large Tattoo (Annual); NTA Best

Traditional Style Tattoo (Annual); NTA Nicest Tattoo Studio; NTA Best Black and Gray Design Sheet (Irregular); Best Black/White Design Sheet (Annual); Best Cover-Up Tattoo; Best Portrait Tattoo; Best Tattooed Female; Best Tattooed Male; Best Traditional Tattoo (Annual); Best Unique Tattoo; Bob Shaw Golden Age Award (Annual); Elizabeth Weinzirl Award (Annual); Fine Art Award; Best Realistic Tattoo; Nicest Studio Award. **Geographic Preference:** Multinational.

15283 ■ **Tattoo Artists' Guild**
URL: http://www.tattooartistsguild.com
X (Twitter): twitter.com/TattooGuild
Description: An international association of dedicated and responsible members working to elevate and advance the art of tattooing.

15284 ■ **TrueArtists**
2995 Woodside Rd., No. 400
Woodside, CA 94062
Co. E-mail: info@trueartists.com
URL: http://trueartists.com
Contact: W. James, Officer
Description: Association of certified tattoo artists whose membership is restricted to tattoo artists who exhibit not only artistic ability, but a good command of the craft of tattooing, from quality workmanship to clean, safe work environments. **Founded:** 2011.

EDUCATIONAL PROGRAMS

15285 ■ **Tattooing 101 LLC**
30N Gould St., Ste. R
Sheridan, WY 82801
Contact: Gordon Tan, Contact
Description: Online school and training for today's tattoo artists. Provides free, instant access to tools and resources that take you behind the curtain of all things tattooing. Teaches foundations, techniques, and placement.

REFERENCE WORKS

15286 ■ *"3 Tattoo Studio Marketing Strategies That Are Extremely Easy to Execute" in TattooPro blog (Sept. 6, 2020)*
URL(s): www.tattoopro.io/blog/tattoo-studio-marke ting-strategies/
Released: September 06, 2020. **Description:** Whether you have been running an established tattoo studio for decades or are about to jump into the business for the first time, marketing, advertisements, and promotions are something to continually master. This article provides the best tattoo studio marketing strategies and tips for your business. **Availability:** Online.

15287 ■ *6 Great Marketing Strategies Your Tattoo Studio Needs to Try*
URL(s): salonist.io/blog/marketing-strategies-your-ta ttoo-studio-needs-to-try/

Ed: Sophie Jobs. **Released:** July 02, 2021. **Description:** Making your tattoo studio visible to your target audience is essential. This article reveals effective marketing strategies to build your tattoo studio and bring in more clients. **Availability:** Online.

15288 ■ *"7 Reasons to Use Cloud Based Applications for Your Tattoo Shop" in DaySmart Body Art blog (April 15, 2022)*

URL(s): www.daysmartbodyart.com/news/7-reasons-to-use-cloud-based-applications-for-your-tattoo-shop/

Ed: Jenna Brookner. **Released:** April 15, 2022. **Description:** Provides seven advantages to using cloud-based technology to help manage your tattoo business. **Availability:** Online.

15289 ■ *"7 Tattoo Artist Tips for Taking Your Business Digital" in DaySmart Body Art blog (Feb. 15, 2022)*

URL(s): www.daysmartbodyart.com/news/tattoo-artist-tip/

Ed: Brock Wackerle. **Released:** February 15, 2022. **Description:** Provides 7 tips about taking your tattoo shop management to a digital space. Digital management can help streamline your bookings, provide appointment reminders, utilize image boards, take deposits, and help manage supplies and inventory. **Availability:** Online.

15290 ■ *"8 Best Tattoo Shop Marketing Strategies to Grow Your Business" in Appointy blog (Apr. 1, 2022)*

URL(s): blog.appointy.com/2022/04/01/tattoo-shop-marketing-strategies/

Released: April 01, 2022. **Description:** Lists tattoo shop marketing strategies to appeal to consumer needs. **Availability:** Online.

15291 ■ *11 Best Tattoo Shop Marketing Ideas in 2022*

URL(s): www.appointfix.com/blog/best-tattoo-shop-marketing-ideas.html

Ed: Aimee L. **Released:** April 20, 2022. **Description:** Lists 11 effective tattoo shop marketing ideas. **Availability:** Online.

15292 ■ *14 Viral Tattoo Marketing Content Ideas for Insta & TikTok*

URL(s): nextlevelbros.com/blog/tattoo-marketing-ideas/

Released: January 03, 2022. **Description:** Details 19 areas of compiled information on proven viral tattoo marketing and content examples that can drive and inspire your content posting strategy. **Availability:** Online.

15293 ■ *15 Steps to Growing Your Tattooing Business*

URL(s): tattooing101.com/learn/business/marketing-your-tattoo-business/

Ed: Nathan Molenaar. **Description:** Allowing your tattoo business to grow passively through word of mouth is slow and leaves success to chance. This article provides tactics to employ to get more clients through your door via essential marketing channels. **Availability:** Online.

15294 ■ *"20 Lessons Learnt from Owning a Tattoo Shop" in Painful Pleasures Blog (October 2, 2018)*

Released: October 02, 2018. **Description:** Provides a list of twenty important lessons, business and personal, from a tattoo shop owner to future tattoo shop owners. **Availability:** Online.

15295 ■ *"The Best Tattoo Machines for Beginners" in DaySmart Body Art blog (Oct. 4, 2022)*

URL(s): www.daysmartbodyart.com/news/the-best-tattoo-machines-for-beginners/

Ed: Andrea Miller. **Released:** October 04, 2022. **Description:** As a new tattoo artist, one of the most important things you have to consider is the equipment you need. There are plenty of tattoo machines on the market, so it can be difficult to figure out the

right gear to get. This article gives a rundown of some of the best tattoo machines for beginners. **Availability:** Online.

15296 ■ *Business Insurance for Tattoo Parlors*

URL(s): howtostartanllc.com/business-insurance/business-insurance-for-tattoo-parlors

Description: Insurance is an essential investment for a tattoo parlor business. This article covers the main insurance coverage for your tattoo parlor, general liability insurance, and suggests additional policies that are suitable for your business. **Availability:** Online.

15297 ■ *"Friday the 13th, a 'Tattoo Holiday'" in The New York Times (July 13, 2018)*

URL(s): www.nytimes.com/2018/07/13/nyregion/friday-the-13th-tattoo.html

Ed: Zoe Greenberg. **Released:** July 13, 2018. **Description:** Tattoo shops have developed a new tradition of Friday the 13th tattoos. Shops often release a sheet of pre-designed tats, many of which are only $13 with a suggested lucky $7 tip. The promotions have worked as people line up to get their first tattoo or to add on to their collection. The tradition started in 1996 with "Ink Master" Oliver Peck holding this promotion, and then it escalated when he tattooed the most people in a 24-hour period by tattooing the number 13 on 415 participants on Friday June 13, 2008. **Availability:** Online.

15298 ■ *Good Locations for a Tattoo Business*

Ed: Sherrie Scott. **Description:** Choosing a good location for a tattoo business depends on several factors, including how many artists will be employed and the vicinity of the shop to the targeted customers. This article discusses different location options and why they may or may not work for your tattoo business. **Availability:** Online.

15299 ■ *How Do Tattoo Artists Get Paid?*

Ed: Erica Salvalaggio. **Released:** March 24, 2019. **Description:** Discusses what goes into pricing of tattoos and how tattoo artist compensation works. **Availability:** Online.

15300 ■ *"How to Go from Tattoo Artist to Boss" in DaySmart Body Art blog (Sept. 2, 2022)*

URL(s): www.daysmartbodyart.com/news/employee-to-boss/

Ed: Andrea Miller. **Released:** September 02, 2022. **Description:** This article is for experienced tattoo artists with an entrepreneurial spirit and are interested in moving from being a tattoo artist to opening their own shop. Provides information on how to create your own business plan. **Availability:** Online.

15301 ■ *How Much Do Tattoo Parlors Make? (And the Most Popular Tattoo Days of the Year)*

Description: Discusses how much tattoo parlors make on a typical day, which days of the week are biggest for tattoo parlors, what time of year tattoo parlors are busiest, what the biggest days of the year are for tattoo parlors, and how to get the most out of the busy season. **Availability:** Online.

15302 ■ *"How to Start a Tattoo Shop" in Chron (March 8, 2019)*

Ed: Michelle Renee. **Released:** March 08, 2019. **Description:** Discusses the average cost of opening a tattoo parlor and how to recoup your investment in a short amount of time. **Availability:** Online.

15303 ■ *How Women Are Rethinking the Tattoo Parlor*

URL(s): www.nytimes.com/2018/02/28/style/women-tattoo-artists.html

Released: February 28, 2018. **Description:** Nice Tattoo Parlor in Brooklyn is looking to change how people view tattoo parlors by using chic decor and a staff of friendly female artists. Women have been

interested in tattoos and are making a bigger impact in the industry, either through getting a tattoo or by becoming an artist. **Availability:** Online.

15304 ■ *"Inking the Deal" in Slate (October 1, 2014)*

URL(s): slate.com/business/2014/10/tattoo-parlors-a-surprisingly-great-small-business-bet.html

Ed: Jesse Dorris. **Released:** October 01, 2014. **Description:** Discusses how tattoo parlors are often a good bet when it comes to opening a small business. Tattoos have been gaining in popularity with the Instagram crowd and their reputations are much higher than they used to be because so many people have tattoos that they have gone mainstream. Local governments are also surprisingly friendly to the industry, making it easier on owners. **Availability:** Online.

15305 ■ *"Inking the Deal - Why Tattoo Parlors Are a Great Small-Business Bet" in Slate (October 1, 2014)*

Ed: Jesse Dorris. **Released:** October 01, 2014. **Description:** Discusses the diversity of the tattoo industry clientele as well as the types of tattoos and how to run a profitable business. **Availability:** Online.

15306 ■ *Is Starting an LLC for a Tattoo Parlor Good Idea?*

URL(s): www.moneyaisle.com/starting-an-llc-for-a-tattoo-parlor/

Ed: Alfie Wilson. **Description:** There are a number of things to think about when starting your own tattoo parlor. This article discusses the legal structures that are available to you and presents legal information why an LLC is a great choice. **Availability:** Online.

15307 ■ *"King Ink" in Inc. (November 2007, pp. 98-102, 104, 106, 108)*

Ed: Max Chafkin. **Description:** Profile of Mario Barth, whose goal is to build the Starbucks of tattoo parlors; the tattoo industry is worth $2.3 billion in the U.S.

15308 ■ *"Managing Your Tattoo Shop" in Painful Pleasures Blog (March 1, 2015)*

Released: March 01, 2015. **Description:** Discusses the basics of managing your tattoo shop from shop safety and managing day-to-day operations to marketing your business. **Availability:** Online.

15309 ■ *"Marketing Guide to Promote Tattoo and Piercing Studios" in EDIT.org blog*

URL(s): edit.org/blog/templates-marketing-guide-tattoo-studios

Description: A guide to promoting your tattoo studio. This guide also provides access to editable templates in which you can add your logo, images, font, and colors to create unique and customized promotional designs. **Availability:** Online.

15310 ■ *"Pandemic Woes and a 'YOLO Mentality' Have Ignited a Boom Time for Tattoo Artists" in Time (Aug. 25, 2021)*

Ed: Megan McCluskey. **Released:** August 25, 2021. **Description:** Presents information on the pandemic's effect and a "You Only Live Once" mentality have contributed to a boom for tattoo artists. **Availability:** Online.

15311 ■ *"A Tattoo Artist's Guide to Instagram: How To Promote Your Tattoo Business" in PainfulPleasures blog (Nov. 3, 2021)*

URL(s): www.painfulpleasures.com/community/blog/tattoo/a-tattoo-artists-guide-to-instagram-how-to-promote-your-tattoo-business/

Released: November 03, 2021. **Description:** Social media has become the most powerful platform available to tattoo artists. This guide details how to utilize Instagram to promote your tattoo business. **Availability:** Online.

15312 ■ *"Tattoo Forms and Waivers Required for Clients" in DaySmart Body Art blog (Aug. 3, 2022)*

URL(s): www.daysmartbodyart.com/news/tattoo-forms-required-for-new-clients/

Ed: Andrea Miller. **Released:** August 03, 2022. **Description:** Provides information on necessary legal tattoo releases and waivers that your customers need to fill out so that you are legally compliant. **Availability:** Online.

15313 ■ *"Tattoo School: The Educational Path for Tattoo Artists" in DaySmart Body Art blog (May 11, 2021)*
URL(s): www.daysmartbodyart.com/news/tattoo -school/

Ed: Brock Wackerle. **Released:** May 11, 2021. **Description:** Offers information on how to become a tattoo artist, including needed courses, apprenticeship information, pre-license training and certification, licensing, and equipment. **Availability:** Online.

15314 ■ *Tattoo Shop Business Plan Template*
URL(s): www.growthink.com/businessplan/help-cen ter/tattoo-shop-business-plan

Ed: Dave Lavinsky. **Description:** Presents information on why create a business plan for your tattoo business is important and shows how to write a business plan step-by-step so that you can create your plan today. **Availability:** Online.

15315 ■ *Tattoo Shop Insurance: For Businesses and Individuals*
URL(s): www.xinsurance.com/risk-class/tattoo-shop -insurance/

Description: Discusses customized insurance solutions for your tattoo parlor or for you as a tattoo artist. Includes FAQ about tattoo shop insurance. **Availability:** Online.

15316 ■ *"Tattooed Bellwethers of Economic Development" in Austin Business Journal (Vol. 34, May 2, 2014, No. 11, pp. A4)*
Pub: American City Business Journals, Inc.
Contact: Mike Olivieri, Executive Vice President

Released: Weekly. **Price:** $4, Introductory 4-week offer(Digital & Print). **Description:** The creative community's art-centered business have helped Austin, Texas' growth by moving into transitional areas with low rents. Their kind of pioneering spirit primes the area for later commercial and residential development. The city's assistance programs for creative enterprises are also presented. **Availability:** Print; Online.

15317 ■ *"Tattoos Now Have an Exit Strategy" in The Atlantic (October 29, 2019)*
URL(s): www.theatlantic.com/health/archive/2019/10/ semi-permanent-tattoos/601012/

Ed: Amanda Mull. **Released:** October 29, 2019. **Description:** Tattoos are one of the favorite trends of Millennials with nearly half of adults between 18 and 35 having at least one. The boom can possibly be attributed to social media platforms such as Instagram, where it's popular to display your ink. However, many people are still wary of making a design permanent so they have been getting semipermanent tattoos. These last about 10 days and have a wide appeal to many people. **Availability:** Online.

15318 ■ *The Ultimate Guide to Growing Your Tattoo Business*

Description: A detailed guide on how to get your tattoo business off the ground. **Availability:** Online.

15319 ■ *"What You Need to Know Before Opening a Tattoo Shop Franchise" in Black Hat Tattoo blog*
URL(s): www.theblackhattattoo.com/blog/what-you -need-to-know-before-opening-a-tattoo-franchise

Description: Discusses the risks and challenges of operating a franchise, specifically why opening a tattoo franchise may be a good option. Includes information on how franchises work, why to choose a tattoo franchise over other types of franchises, how tattoo studios operate, how to manage tattoo artists and customers, and what type of returns you can expect from a tattoo shop franchise. **Availability:** Online.

SOURCES OF SUPPLY

15320 ■ Alliance Tattoo Supply
Facebook: www.facebook.com/alliancetattoosupply
X (Twitter): x.com/tattoo_alliance
YouTube: www.youtube.com/channel/UC4b_GA5m _20EXAga7LNiYCA

Description: Tattooer-owned and operated supply company focused on providing equipment and supplies made by tattooers.

15321 ■ Cam Supply Inc.
Description: Global tattoo supplier, manufacturer, distributor, and wholesaler. **Founded:** 1993.

15322 ■ Diversified Product Supplier (DPS) [Rockstar Ready Tattoo Supplies]
Description: Created by artists for artists and shop owners. Provides a full line of tattoo supplies, machines, disposables, needles, pigments and inks, sterilization, cleaning products, and many other shop accessories. **Founded:** 1993.

15323 ■ Element Tattoo Supply
Facebook: www.facebook.com/elementtattoosupply
YouTube: www.youtube.com/eddietana

Description: A professional tattoo supply company serving professional tattoo artists and enthusiasts. Manufactures and distributes exclusive brand of Element Tattoo ink, traditional tattoo needles, needle cartridges, tattoo tubes, custom tattoo kits, tattoo machines, and a wide range of tattoo shop supplies.

15324 ■ Eternal Tattoo Supply (ETS)
Facebook: www.facebook.com/eternaltattoosupply
Instagram: www.instagram.com/eternalink

Description: Tattoo supply store for professional artists and tattoo studios.

15325 ■ Hildebrandt Tattoo Equipment
X (Twitter): x.com/hildbrandt

Description: Provider of tattoo supplies for professionals including tattoo machines, ink, needles, medical supplies, and power supply.

15326 ■ Intenze Products Inc. [INTENZE Advanced Tattoo Ink]
Facebook: www.facebook.com/intenzeink
X (Twitter): x.com/intenzeink
Instagram: www.instagram.com/intenzetattooink
YouTube: www.youtube.com/channel/UCNPPHf 5eWDEDNAzyuMqZUJA

Description: Offers tattoo inks, ink sets, and cartridges as well as tattoo supplies and power supplies.

15327 ■ Joker Tattoo
X (Twitter): x.com/JokerTattoo
YouTube: www.youtube.com/JokerTattooInk

Description: Supports professional tattoo artists by providing tattoo supplies, equipment, and piercing supplies.

15328 ■ Kingpin Tattoo Supply
Facebook: www.facebook.com/kingpintattoosupply
Instagram: www.instagram.com/kingpintattoosupply
YouTube: www.youtube.com/channel/UC2Sj9xUTKm dyW0pGnGJqNgQ

Description: Committed to providing the highest quality tools and supplies for professional tattoo artists across the U.S.

15329 ■ National Tattoo Supply Inc.
Description: Supplier of tattoo equipment and supplies to professional tattoo artists. **Founded:** 1974.

15330 ■ Needlejig Tattoo Supply
Facebook: www.facebook.com/needlejig
X (Twitter): x.com/needlejig
YouTube: www.youtube.com/channel/UCv9 tznOvBUpk8kxLabJhrKQ

Description: Provides tattoo needles, tattoo ink, tattoo machines, tattoo tubes, power supplies, medical supplies, apparel, and studio supplies to professional tattoo shops.

15331 ■ Obsidian Tattoo Supply
Facebook: www.facebook.com/obsidianta ttoosupplypdx

Instagram: www.instagram.com/obsidiantattoosupply

Description: Artist-owned tattoo supplier specializing in eco-friendly professional tattoo supplies.

15332 ■ Painful Pleasures, Inc.
Facebook: www.facebook.com/painfulpleasures
X (Twitter): x.com/painfulpleasure
Instagram: www.instagram.com/painfulpleasures
YouTube: www.youtube.com/channel/UC0tL46bP -o0x0E3Q7N1njXw
Pinterest: www.pinterest.com/painfulpleasure

Description: Distributor of tattoo and piercing supplies and body jewelry. **Founded:** 2002.

15333 ■ Saltwater Tattoo Supply
Description: Supplier of hand-made tattoo machines and creator of the Original Tattoo Pen. Also sells everything from premium tattoo needles, cartridge tubes, tattoo machine hardware, and exclusive sketchbooks.

15334 ■ TATSoul
YouTube: www.youtube.com/channel/UC 1CoNDhysaSht7A2Ta_bCIA

Description: Tattoo supply company working to pair top quality tattoo equipment with exceptional customer service. **Founded:** 2006.

15335 ■ Tommy's Supplies
Facebook: www.facebook.com/tommyssupplies
YouTube: www.youtube.com/channel/UCP0rzmKV teX-JxPhBiRuaGg

Description: Provider of tattoo products, professional knowledge of the industry, and same-day shipping of tattoo shop supplies.

15336 ■ Ultimate Tattoo Supply
Description: Provider of tattoo supplies including inks, machines, shop supplies, and permanent makeup.

15337 ■ WorldWide Tattoo Supply
Description: Manufacturer of tattoo equipment, specializing in tattoo needles and disposable tubes. Also offers an extensive range of shop equipment, medical, and piercing supplies. **Founded:** 1993.

STATISTICAL SOURCES

15338 ■ *Global Color Tattoo Ink Market Growth 2022-2028*
URL(s): www.marketresearch.com/LP-Information-Inc -v4134/Global-Color-Tattoo-Ink-Growth-31984776/

Price: $3,660. **Description:** Presents a comprehensive overview, market shares, and growth opportunities of the color tattoo ink market by product type, application, key manufacturers and key regions and countries. **Availability:** PDF.

TRADE SHOWS AND CONVENTIONS

15339 ■ Boston Tattoo Convention
URL(s): bostontattooconvention.com

Price: $25, Onsite. **Frequency:** Annual. **Description:** Networking, vendor booths, and tattooing. **Principal Exhibits:** Networking, vendor booths, and tattooing. **Telecommunication Services:** info@bos tontattooconvention.com.

15340 ■ NTA Convention
National Tattoo Association, Inc. (NTA)
2565 Broadview Dr.
Kissimmee, FL 34744
Ph: (407)319-0018
Co. E-mail: ntacruisers@gmail.com
URL: http://ntanewsletter.com
Contact: Pat Sinatra, Editor-in-Chief
URL(s): nationaltattooassociation.com/wp/convention

Frequency: Annual. **Description:** Tattooing, jewelry, books, t-shirts, and other tattoo related items. **Audience:** Tattooists and enthusiasts. **Principal Exhibits:** Tattooing, jewelry, books, t-shirts, and other tattoo related items. **Telecommunication Services:** red@ nationaltattoo.com.

CONSULTANTS

15341 ■ MD Tattoo Consulting
9545 Reseda Blvd., Unit 2
  Northridge, CA 91324
Ph: (818)700-2818
Co. E-mail: info@mdtattoostudio.com
URL: http://mdtattoostudio.com
Contact: Mike Devries, Owner
Facebook: www.facebook.com/mdtattoostudio
Instagram: www.instagram.com/mdtattoostudio

Description: Provides one-on-one tattoo education for all skill levels. Specializes in offering new thought processes and the best ways to execute amazing tattoos from concept to final photo. **Founded:** 2008.

FRANCHISES AND BUSINESS OPPORTUNITIES

15342 ■ Aliens Art Private Limited
Gala No. K2, Old Sonal Industrial Premises,
  Ramchandra Ln.
  Kanchpada, Malad Link Rd., Malad W
  Mumbai 400064, Maharashtra, India
Ph: 91 22 98330 65209
Co. E-mail: ink@alienstattoo.com
URL: http://www.alienstattoo.com
Facebook: www.facebook.com/alienstattoomalad
Instagram: www.instagram.com/alienstattooindia

Description: Worldwide chain of tattoo studios.

15343 ■ Fine Ink Studios Corp.
11681 S Orange Blossom Trl., Ste.2
  Orlando, FL 32837
Ph: (407)361-3434
Co. E-mail: booking@fineinkstudios.com
URL: http://www.fineinkstudios.com
Contact: Richard Barnett, President
Description: Tattoo studio offering franchise opportunities. **Founded:** 2018.

PUBLICATIONS

15344 ■ *Animal Ink*
URL(s): www.tattoomachineequipment.com/product/mike-devries-animal-ink-tattoo-book
Ed: Mike Devries. **Price:** $59.99. **Description:** Contains full-color tattoo work from 160 artists as well as 62 stories about specific animal tattoos with details, meanings, and inspiration from the collectors who wear the ink and the artists who inked them. **Availability:** Print.

15345 ■ *Basic Fundamentals of Modern Tattoo*
Ed: Charles Jordan. **Price:** $19.99. **Description:** Textbook that teaches readers how to get into the tattoo trade. Covers essential topics including machine building, sourcing of supplies, proper hygiene, machine setups, and techniques. **Availability:** Print.

15346 ■ *Blood Sweat & Script*
URL(s): www.tattoomachineequipment.com/product/blood-sweat-script-tattoo-flash-design-book
Ed: Sir Twice. **Price:** $59.99. **Description:** Flash/design art book with 65 pages of original script designs, instructional thought, and insight on creating flow in your script. Includes 10 pages of alphabets, flourishes, and numbers. **Availability:** Print.

15347 ■ *Reinvent Yourself*
URL(s): www.tattoomachineequipment.com/product/reinvent-yourself-volume-1
Ed: Halo Jankowski. **Price:** $99.99. **Description:** Covers Adobe Photoshop techniques and processes that tattoo artist Halo Jankowski uses to fuel his creative vision. Provides detailed examples to benefit artists of all experience levels. **Availability:** Print.

15348 ■ *Tattoo Extremeties*
URL(s): www.tattoomachineequipment.com/product/mike-devries-tattoo-extremities
Ed: Mike Devries. **Price:** $49.99. **Description:** Full-color book featuring over 800 photos of art by 170 tattoo artists. Describes placement of tattoo art on extremities (hands, heads, and feet). **Availability:** Print.

INFORMATION SERVICES

15349 ■ *Tattoo.com*
URL(s): www.tattoo.com

Description: One-stop shop for exploring all aspects of the tattoo industry, music industry, and sub-genres that tie into tattoo culture. **Availability:** Online.

ASSOCIATIONS AND OTHER ORGANIZATIONS

15350 ■ American Taxation Association (ATA)
c/o LeAnn Luna, Representative
University of Tennessee-Knoxville
711 Stokely Management Ctr.
Knoxville, TN 37996
URL: http://aaahq.org/ATA
Contact: Jenny Brown, President
Facebook: www.facebook.com/aaahqata

Description: Membership comprises primarily university professors teaching federal income tax, federal estate, and/or gift tax courses; other members are practitioners, including certified public accountants. Seeks to further taxation education. Researches the impact of the tax process, particularly tax code sections, on the social and economic structure of the US. Maintains speakers' bureau. **Founded:** 1974. **Awards:** Ray M. Sommerfeld Outstanding Tax Educator Award (Annual); ATA Tax Manuscript Award (Annual); ATA Deloitte Teaching Innovation Award (Annual). **Geographic Preference:** National.

15351 ■ Canadian Tax Foundation (CTF) - Douglas J. Sherbaniuk Research Centre [L'Association Canadienne d'Études Fiscales (ACEF)]
145 Wellington St. W Ste. 1400
Toronto, ON, Canada M5J 1H8
Ph: (416)599-0283
Free: 877-733-0283
Fax: (416)599-9283
Co. E-mail: ctfmembership@ctf.ca
URL: http://www.ctf.ca
Contact: Heather L. Evans, Chief Executive Officer
E-mail: hevans@ctf.ca
X (Twitter): x.com/cdntaxfdn

Description: Promotes increased awareness of the Canadian Tax Code and the social ramifications of taxation. Serves as a clearinghouse on taxation; sponsors research and educational programs. **Scope:** sponsors or directly carries out expert research in the fields of taxation and public finance, publishes the results of that research. **Services:** Interlibrary loan; copying; open to the public. **Founded:** 1945. **Holdings:** Periodicals; documents; books. **Publications:** *Annual Conference Report* (Annual); *CTF Annual Report* (Monthly); *Canadian Tax Highlights* (Monthly); *Canadian Tax Journal* (Quarterly); *Canadian Tax Papers Series*; *Finances of the Nation* (Annual); *Tax Memos*; *Tax for the Owner Manager* (Quarterly); *Taxation of Private Corporations and Their Shareholders* (Occasionally). **Geographic Preference:** National.

15352 ■ Canadian Tax Journal
145 Wellington St. W Ste. 1400
Toronto, ON, Canada M5J 1H8
Ph: (416)599-0283
Free: 877-733-0283
Fax: (416)599-9283
Co. E-mail: ctfmembership@ctf.ca
URL: http://www.ctf.ca
Contact: Heather L. Evans, Chief Executive Officer
E-mail: hevans@ctf.ca
URL(s): www.ctf.ca/EN/EN/Publications/CTJ.aspx

Ed: Brian Carr, Kevin Milligan, Alan MacNaughton, Alan Macnaughton. **Released:** Quarterly **Price:** C$360, Nonmembers for CTJ-four hardcopy issues per year; C$460, Nonmembers for CTJ Plus-four hardcopy issues per year plus electronic access; $75, for per copy; $75, Members; C$100, for outside Canada. **Description:** Journal for professional tax practitioners, government officials, and public finance economists and university students. **Availability:** Print; PDF; Online.

15353 ■ Chartered Professional Accountants of Canada (CPA CANADA) - Library
277 Wellington St., W
Toronto, ON, Canada M5V 3H2
Ph: (416)977-3222
Free: 800-268-3793
Fax: (416)977-8585
Co. E-mail: member.services@cpacanada.ca
URL: http://www.cpacanada.ca
Contact: Pamela Steer, President
Facebook: www.facebook.com/CPACanada
Linkedin: www.linkedin.com/company/cpa-canada
X (Twitter): x.com/CPAcanada
Instagram: www.instagram.com/cpa.canada
YouTube: www.youtube.com/cpacanada

Description: Aims to represent professional accountants in Canada by providing the highest standards of accounting, ethics, and best business practices. **Scope:** Accounting. **Founded:** 2013. **Holdings:** Figures not available. **Publications:** *CA Magazine: For Canada's Chartered Accountants*; *Directory of Canadian Chartered Accountants* (Periodic; Biennial); *CMA Magazine* (6/year). **Geographic Preference:** National.

15354 ■ National Association of Tax Professionals (NATP)
3517 N McCarthy Rd.
Appleton, WI 54913
Free: 800-558-3402
Fax: (800)747-0001
Co. E-mail: natp@natptax.com
URL: http://www.natptax.com/Pages/default.aspx
Contact: Gerard Cannito, President
Facebook: www.facebook.com/natptax
X (Twitter): x.com/NATPTAX
Instagram: www.instagram.com/natptax

Description: Serves professionals who work in all areas of tax practice, including individual practitioners, enrolled agents, certified public accountants, accountants, attorneys and certified financial planners. **Founded:** 1979. **Publications:** *TAXPRO Journal* (Quarterly); *TAXPRO Weekly* (Weekly); *TAXPRO Monthly* (Monthly). **Educational Activities:** NATP National Conference & Expo. **Awards:** NATP Tax Professional of the Year (Annual). **Geographic Preference:** National.

15355 ■ National Society of Accountants (NSA)
1330 Braddock Pl., Ste. 540
Alexandria, VA 22314
Free: 800-966-6679
Fax: (703)549-2984
URL: http://www.nsacct.org/nsamain/nsa-homepage
Contact: Marchelle Foshee, President
E-mail: marchelle.foshee@gmail.com
Facebook: www.facebook.com/nsacct
Linkedin: www.linkedin.com/company/national-socie
ty-of-accountants
X (Twitter): x.com/NSAtax

Description: Professional organization and its affiliates represent 30,000 members who provide auditing, accounting, tax preparation, financial and estate planning, and management services to approximately 19 million individuals and business clients. Most members are sole practitioners or partners in small to mid-size accounting firms. **Founded:** 1969. **Publications:** *NSAlert* (Biweekly); *NSA Practice Advisor* (8/year); *NSPA Washington Reporter*; *National Society of Public Accountants--Yearbook*; *National Society of Public Accountants - Yearbook*; *Main Street Practitioner*; *Income and Fees of Accountants in Public Practice*. **Educational Activities:** NSA Annual Convention (Annual). **Awards:** NSA Scholarship Foundation (Annual); The Stanley H. Stearman Awards (Annual); NSA Accountant of the Year (Annual); NSA ASO of the Year (Annual). **Geographic Preference:** National.

15356 ■ National Tax Association (NTA)
1100 Vermont Ave. NW Ste. 650
Washington, DC 20005
Ph: (202)737-3325
Co. E-mail: nta@ntanet.org
URL: http://ntanet.org
Contact: Jennifer Blouin, President
X (Twitter): x.com/NatlTax

Description: Government and corporate tax officials, accountants, consultants, economists, attorneys, and others interested in the field of taxation. Promotes nonpartisan academics, study of taxation; encourages better understanding of the common interests of national, state, and local governments in matters of taxation and public finance; and disseminates higher quality research through publications and conferences. **Founded:** 1907. **Publications:** *National Tax Association Conference Proceedings* (Annual); *National Tax Journal (NTJ)* (Quarterly). **Awards:** Daniel M. Holland Medal (Annual); NTA Outstanding Doctoral Dissertation in Government Finance and Taxation (Annual); Steven D. Gold Award (Annual). **Geographic Preference:** National.

15357 ■ Pennsylvania Society of Tax and Accounting Professionals - Buxmont Chapter
c/o Tamatha Polichetti, President
82 Annawanda Rd.
Ottsville, PA 18942
Ph: (215)795-0212
Fax: (215)795-0445
URL: http://www.pstap.org/about-us/chapters

Contact: Aaron Perriello, Co-President

Description: Represents certified public accountants (CPAs), public accountants, enrolled agents, and tax practitioners. Protects the interests of public accountants and small accounting firms to become visible and establish integrity of public accounting profession. **Geographic Preference:** Local.

15358 ■ Pennsylvania Society of Tax and Accounting Professionals - Lehigh Valley Chapter
c/o Deborah Mininger Lahneman, President
528 W Broad St.
Quakertown, PA 18951-1216
Ph: (215)536-6829
Fax: (215)536-8781
URL: http://pstap.org/about-us/chapters
Contact: Aaron Perriello, Co-President

Description: Represents certified public accountants (CPAs), public accountants, enrolled agents, and tax practitioners. Protects the interests of public accountants and small accounting firms to become visible and establish integrity of public accounting profession. **Geographic Preference:** Local.

15359 ■ Pennsylvania Society of Tax and Accounting Professionals - Northeast Chapter
c/o Philip Reid, President
1130 Twin Stacks Dr.
Dallas, PA 18612
Ph: (570)991-0551
URL: http://pstap.org/about-us/chapters
Contact: Philip Reid, President

Description: Represents certified public accountants (CPAs), public accountants, enrolled agents, and tax practitioners. Protects the interests of public accountants and small accounting firms to become visible and establish integrity of public accounting profession. **Geographic Preference:** Local.

15360 ■ Pennsylvania Society of Tax and Accounting Professionals - Philadelphia Tri-County Chapter
c/o Margaret Rovinski, President
139 Scenic Rd.
Springfield, PA 19064
Ph: (610)256-3416
Fax: (610)543-8295
Co. E-mail: info@pstap.org
URL: http://pstap.org/about-us/chapters/?fsubpg
=chapterdetails&chapterid=6
Contact: Margaret Rovinski, President

Description: Represents certified public accountants (CPAs), public accountants, enrolled agents, and tax practitioners. Protects the interests of public accountants and small accounting firms to become visible and establish integrity of public accounting profession. **Geographic Preference:** Local.

15361 ■ Pennsylvania Society of Tax and Accounting Professionals - South Central Chapter
c/o Celestine Henderson, President
2032 Green St.
Harrisburg, PA 17102
Ph: (717)238-3332
Fax: (717)238-8153
URL: http://pstap.org/about-us/chapters
Contact: Aaron Perriello, Co-President

Description: Represents Certified Public Accountants (CPAs), public accountants, enrolled agents, and tax practitioners. Protects the interests of public accountants and small accounting firms to become visible and establish integrity of public accounting profession. **Geographic Preference:** Local.

15362 ■ Society of Professional Accountants of Canada (SPAC) [La societe des comptables professionnels du Canada; RPA Canada]
48 Village Ctr. Pl., Ste., 100
Mississauga, ON, Canada L4Z 1V9
Ph: (416)350-8145
Free: 877-515-4447
Co. E-mail: info@rpacanada.org
URL: http://rpacanada.org

Contact: Zubair Choudhry, President
Facebook: www.facebook.com/Registere
dProfessionalAccountants
Linkedin: www.linkedin.com/in/registered-professional
-accountant-555378190
X (Twitter): x.com/rpcanada
YouTube: www.youtube.com/channel/UCqo7eFpci_fk
tegT5vwjB8A

Description: Professional accountants and individuals working to pass qualifying accountancy examinations. Promotes ongoing professional education among accountants; encourages students to enter the accounting field; works to advance the profession of accounting. Gathers and disseminates information on accounting; sponsors educational programs; conducts professional accountancy qualifying examinations. **Founded:** 1978. **Publications:** *Professional Accountant* (Quarterly). **Geographic Preference:** National.

15363 ■ Tax Executives Institute (TEI)
1200 G St. NW, Ste. 300
Washington, DC 20005
Ph: (202)638-5601
Fax: (202)638-5607
Co. E-mail: asktei@tei.org
URL: http://www.tei.org
Contact: Mitchell Trager, President
Facebook: www.facebook.com/TaxExecutivesInsti
tute
Linkedin: www.linkedin.com/company/tax-executives
-institute
X (Twitter): x.com/tei_updates
YouTube: www.youtube.com/channel/UCJJVYpl
1TASAnZbQN5WUfrg

Description: Professional society of executives administering and directing tax affairs for corporations and businesses. Maintains TEI Education Fund. **Founded:** 1944. **Publications:** *The Tax Executive* (Bimonthly). **Awards:** TEI Distinguished Service Award (Annual). **Geographic Preference:** Multinational.

REFERENCE WORKS

15364 ■ "2011 Tax Information of Interest" in Business Owner (Vol. 35, November-December 2011, No. 6, pp. 10)

Description: Compilation of 2011 tax information to help small business take advantage of all tax incentives. **Availability:** Print; Online.

15365 ■ "Accrual vs. Cash Accounting, Explained" in Business Owner (Vol. 35, July-August 2011, No. 4, pp. 13)

Description: Cash method versus accrual accounting methods are examined, using hypothetical situations.

15366 ■ "At-Home Tax Prep Trend Likely to Grow After Pandemic's Boost" in Bloomberg Tax (July 10, 2020)

Released: July 10, 2020. **Description:** With many businesses closed or people wanting to avoid closed-spaces in an accountant's office during the COVID-19 pandemic, the do-it-yourself tax industry grew. Many people also took advantage of the extra three months given by the government to file taxes and learned how to do so.

15367 ■ "A Better Way to Tax U.S. Businesses" In (Vol. 90, July-August 2012, No. 7-8, pp. 134)
Pub: Harvard Business Review Press
Contact: Moderna V. Pfizer, Contact

Ed: Mihir A. Desai. **Price:** $8.95, PDF and hardcover black and white. **Description:** Correcting the US corporate tax code will require ending the disconnect between earnings stated to investors and taxable income, implementing rate reductions, eliminating the taxing of overseas income, and securing an agreement by business leaders to acknowledge taxes as a responsibility. **Availability:** Print; PDF; Online.

15368 ■ "Campaign Launches to Educate Hispanics on Tax Preparation" in Economics Week (February 3, 2012, pp. 35)
Pub: NewsRX LLC.
Contact: Kalani Rosell, Contact

Description: Hispanic Access Foundation has partnered with H&R Block to offer a program to help Hispanics file their taxes while avoiding fraud and misinformation. The campaign is called, 'Preparate Para Un Futuro Mejor' (Prepare Yourself for a Better Future) and will help fill the void for tax preparation education for Hispanics. **Availability:** Online.

15369 ■ "Catholic Charities USA Releases 4th Quarter Snapshot Survey Showing Agencies Save Americans in Need More Than $7 Million per Year through Tax Preparation Assistance" in Investment Weekly News (March 31, 2012, pp. 231)
Pub: PR Newswire Association LLC.

Description: Human services organization, Catholic Charities USA (CCUSA) reports saving low income Americans approximately $7.4 million annually with their free tax preparation assitance program. CCUSA, one of the country's largest human services organizations, believes these numbers reinforce the need for a holistic approach to providing programs and services to those in need.

15370 ■ "Changing the Rules of the Accounting Game" in Canadian Business (Vol. 81, December 8, 2008, No. 21, pp. 19)

Description: Interference from world politicians in developing accounting standards is believed to have resulted in untested rules that are inferior to current standards. European lawmakers have recently asked to change International Financial Reporting Standards. **Availability:** Online.

15371 ■ "Column: It's Time to Take Full Responsibility" in Harvard Business Review (Vol. 88, October 2010, No. 10, pp. 42)
Pub: Harvard Business Publishing
Contact: Diane Belcher, Managing Director

Ed: Rosabeth Moss Kanter. **Price:** $6, PDF. **Description:** A case for corporate responsibility is cited, focusing on long-term impact and the effects of public accountability. **Availability:** Online; PDF.

15372 ■ "Convergence Collaboration: Revising Revenue Recognition" in Management Accounting Quarterly (Vol. 12, Spring 2011, No. 3, pp. 18)
Pub: Management Accounting Quarterly
Contact: Mike DePrisco, President

Ed: Jack T. Ciesielski, Thomas R. Weirich. **Description:** While revenue recognition is critical, regulations have been developed on an ad hoc basis until now. The joint FASB/IASB proposed accounting standard on revenue recognition is a meaningful convergence of standards that will require a major adjustment for financial statement preparers. The proposal is a radical departure from the way revenue has been recognized by the U.S. GAAP. For industries such as consulting, engineering, construction, and technology, it could dramatically change revenue recognition, impacting the top line. The new proposed standard, its potential impact, and the critical role that contracts play is examined thoroughly. **Availability:** PDF; Online.

15373 ■ Deduct It! Lower Your Small Business Taxes
Pub: Nolo
Contact: Chris Braun, President

Ed: Stephen Fishman. **Released:** 19th edition. **Price:** $17.99, e-book; $19.99, book and e-book; $17.99, E-Book; $19.99, book and e-book; $17.99, e-book. **Description:** Information is provided to help small companies maximize taxable deductions. **Availability:** Handheld; E-book; Print; Electronic publishing; PDF.

15374 ■ "Defer Tax with Installment Sale Election" in Business Owner (Vol. 35, September-October 2011, No. 5, pp. 12)

Description: It is critical to consult with a tax professional before selling any high-value asset in order to minimize taxes. **Availability:** Print; Online.

15375 ■ *"Do Fair Value Adjustments Influence Dividend Policy?" in Accounting and Business Research (Vol. 41, Spring 2011, No. 2, pp. 51)*

Ed: Igor Goncharov, Sander van Triest. **Description:** The impact of positive fair value adjustments on corporate distributions is examined using a Russian setting that requires disclosure of unrealized fair value adjustments in income. It was found that there is no rise in dividends due to positive fair value adjustments and that on the contrary, a negative relationship exists between adjustments and dividend changes.

15376 ■ *"Ducking the New Health-Care Taxes" in Barron's (Vol. 92, September 15, 2012, No. 38, pp. 34)*

Pub: Dow Jones & Company Inc.

Contact: Almar Latour, Chief Executive Officer

Ed: Elizabeth Ody. **Description:** Strategies that investors can use to avoid paying higher taxes starting January 2013 are discussed. These include selling assets by December 2012, distributing dividends, purchasing private-placement life insurance and converting individual retirement accounts. **Availability:** Online.

15377 ■ *EBay Income: How ANYONE of Any Age, Location, and/or Background Can Build a Highly Profitable Online Business with eBay*

Pub: Atlantic Publishing Co.

Contact: Dr. Heather L. Johnson, Contact

Description: A complete overview of eBay is given and guides any small company through the entire process of creating the auction and auction strategies, photography, writing copy, text and formatting, multiple sales, programming tricks, PayPal, accounting, creating marketing, merchandising, managing email lists, advertising plans, taxes and sales tax, best time to list items and for how long, sniping programs, international customers, opening a storefront, electronic commerce, buy-it now pricing, keywords, Google marketing and eBay secrets.

15378 ■ *"Economic Crisis and Accounting Evolution" in Accounting and Business Research (Vol. 41, Summer 2011, No. 3, pp. 2159)*

Pub: Routledge, Taylor & Francis Group

Ed: Gregory Waymire, Sudipta Basu. **Description:** Financial reporting changes at the face of economic crises are studied using a punctuated equilibrium evolution. Findings show that financial reporting has a minor impact but may amplify economic crises. Attempts to enhance accounting and economic crises may not be as beneficial as planned. **Availability:** PDF; Online; Download.

15379 ■ *Employer Legal Forms Simplified*

Released: First edition. **Description:** Business reference containing the following forms needed to handle employees in any small business environment: application, notice, confidentiality, absence, federal employer forms and notices, and many payroll forms. All forms are included on a CD that comes in both PDF and text formats. Adobe Acrobat Reader software is also included on the CD. The forms are valid in all fifty states and Washington, DC. **Availability:** Print.

15380 ■ *"Family Child Care Record-Keeping Guide, Ninth Edition (Redleaf Business Series)"*

Pub: Redleaf Press

Contact: Barbara Yates, President

Released: 9th edition. **Price:** $21.95, soft bound. **Description:** Writer, trainer, lawyer, and consultant provides concise information for home-based family child care (day care) providers. The book covers tracking expenses, being profitable, filing taxes, and meeting government regulations. This resources covers the process of accurate bookkeeping and record-keeping to take advantage of all allowable tax deductions. Changes in depreciation rules, adjustments to

food and mileage rates, and clarifications on how to calculate the Time-Space percentage are defined. **Availability:** Print.

15381 ■ *"Feds Finalize I-9 Form Rules Allowing Electronic Storage" in HR Specialist (Vol. 8, September 2010, No. 9, pp. 5)*

Pub: Capitol Information Group Inc.

Contact: Allie Ash, Chief Executive Officer

Description: U.S. Department of Homeland Security issued regulations that give employers more flexibility to electronically sing and store I-9 employee verification forms. **Availability:** Print; PDF; Online.

15382 ■ *"For Tax Preparation Agencies, Inbound Consumer Calls Trend Higher in January than April" in Marketing Weekly News (May 5, 2012)*

Pub: NewsRX LLC.

Contact: Kalani Rosell, Contact

Description: According to Marchex Institute, caller activity is highest in January, no April when tax deadlines loom. Online advertising campaigns for tax preparers should be optimized at the beginning of the year when peak calls occurred during the week of January 9, 2012. **Availability:** Online.

15383 ■ *"Former Owner of Spartanburg Tax Preparation Business Pleads Guilty to Fraud in Multi-Million Dollar Scheme" in Internet Wire (January 26, 2012)*

Description: TaxACT tax preparation software includes all e-fileable forms necesary for both simple and complex returns. A full list of forms, that include 1040, 1040A and 1040EZ, Schedules A and B for itemized deductions and interest and dividends, as well as Schedules C, D, E, and F for business owners and investors, can be found at their Website: www.taxact.com. The software also includes free guidance. **Availability:** Online.

15384 ■ *"Free File Alliance & IRS Launch 10th Year of Free Online Tax Preparation Services for Millions of Americans" in Economics Week (February 3, 2012, pp. 82)*

Pub: PR Newswire Association LLC.

Description: A coalition of tax software companies have partnered with the Internal Revenue Service to offer the 212 IRS Free File progam. The Free File Alliance offers low-to-moderate income taxpayers free access to online commercial tax preparation software. Details of the program are included. **Availability:** Online.

15385 ■ *"Getting More Out of Retirement" in Agency Sales Magazine (Vol. 39, November 2009, No. 10, pp. 48)*

Description: Overview of the Tax Increase Prevention and Reconciliation Act, which lets employees convert to a Roth IRA in 2010. The benefits of conversion depend on age and wealth and it is best to consult a tax advisor to determine the best strategy for retirement planners. **Availability:** Print; Online.

15386 ■ *"H&R Block Launches One-of-a-Kind Tax Preparation Solution: Block Live" in Investment Weekly News (February 4, 2012, pp. 384)*

Pub: Comtex News Network Inc.

Contact: Kan Devnani, President

Description: Block Live, H&R Blocks latest offering, allows taxpayers to have their tax return prepared by an H&R Block tax professional in real time usng an online video conferencing or chat venue. H&R Block is offering a $100 discount for those using virtual tax preparation service. Details of the new program are provided. **Availability:** Online.

15387 ■ *Home Business Tax Deductions: Keep What You Earn*

Pub: Nolo

Contact: Chris Braun, President

Ed: Stephen Fishman. **Released:** November 2020. **Price:** $27.99, book and e-book; $24.99, e-book (downloadable). **Description:** Home business tax

deductions are outlined. Basic information on the ways various business structures are taxed and how deductions work is included. **Availability:** E-book; Print.

15388 ■ *"How Accountants Break the Bad News about Tax Refunds: with Chocolate and Tissues" in The Wall Street Journal (March 4, 2019)*

URL(s): www.wsj.com/articles/tax-preparers-stock-up-on-tissues-to-deliver-bad-news-about-your-refund-11551715931

Ed: Laura Saunders. **Released:** March 04, 2019. **Description:** Changes in the Treasury Department rules have made it a difficult tax season because many Americans are either getting a lower tax refund, none at all, or are having to pay the IRS. Accountants are preparing to break the bad news as gently as possible and have found ways to soften the blow by offering treats or even just a kind and sympathetic ear. **Availability:** Online.

15389 ■ *How to Pay Zero Taxes: Your Guide to Every Tax Break the IRS Allows*

Released: 2020-2021 edition. **Price:** $12.96, e-book; $24, paperback. **Description:** Simple strategies to save your small business money in taxes, while following the government's tax regulations are covered, for this year and years beyond. The guide covers deductions organized into six categories: exclusions, general deductions, below the line deductions, traditional tax shelters, and super tax shelters. **Availability:** E-book; Print.

15390 ■ *"How to Start a Home-Based Tax Preparation Business" in Home Business (June 3, 2022)*

URL(s): homebusinessmag.com/business-start-up/how-to-guides/how-to-start-home-based-tax-preparation-business/

Released: June 03, 2022. **Availability:** Online.

15391 ■ *"How To: Manage Your Cash Better" in Inc. (Volume 32, December 2010, No. 10, pp. 69)*

Pub: Mansueto Ventures L.L.C.

Contact: Stephanie Mehta, Chief Executive Officer

Released: December 01, 2010. **Description:** A monthly guide to policies, procedures and practices for managing cash for a small business. **Availability:** Online.

15392 ■ *"Independent Contractor, Sole Proprietor, and LLC Taxes Explained in 100 Pages or Less"*

Description: A small business tax primer which includes information of home office deduction, estimated tax payments, self-employment tax, business retirement plans, numerous business deductions, and audit protection. **Availability:** Print; Online.

15393 ■ *"Internal Auditor Wants Ethics Review of City's Billy Casper Golf Contract" in Business Courier (Vol. 27, September 10, 2010, No. 19, pp. 1)*

Pub: Business Courier

Ed: Dan Monk. **Description:** Mark Ashworth, an internal auditor for Cincinnati, Ohio is pushing for an ethics review of management contract for seven city-owned golf courses. Ashworth wants the Ohio Ethics Commission to investigate family ties between a superintendent for the Cincinnati Recreation Commission and Billy Casper Golf. **Availability:** Print; Online.

15394 ■ *"IRS Announces New Standards for Tax Preparers" in Bellingham Business Journal (Vol. February 2010, pp. 9)*

Pub: Sound Publishing Inc.

Contact: Josh O'Connor, President

Ed: Isaac Bonnell. **Description:** A new oversight plan was announced by the Internal Revenue Services (IRS) that will require tax professionals to pass a competency test and register with the government in order to ensure greater accountability in the industry.

15395 ■ "Is Your Tax Pro Worth the Money?" in U.S. News & World Report (February 15, 2018)

URL(s): money.usnews.com/money/personal-finance/taxes/articles/2018-02-15/is-your-tax-pro-worth-the-money

Ed: Maryalene LaPonsie. **Released:** February 15, 2018. **Description:** Although it may be easier to pay someone to do your taxes, how do you know you are not being taken advantage of? Experts advise doing some research to see what kind of tax professional you need and to meet in person. Set expectations and learn what kind of services will be provided and what price. It's also advisable to look up industry standards for pricing and compare. **Availability:** Online.

15396 ■ J.K. Lasser's 1001 Deductions and Tax Breaks 2023: Your Complete Guide to Everything Deductible

Pub: John Wiley & Sons, Inc.

Contact: Christina Van Tassell, Executive Vice President Chief Financial Officer

URL(s): www.wiley.com/en-us/J+K+Lasser%27s+1001+Deductions+and+Tax+Breaks+2023%3A+Your+Complete+Guide+to+Everything+Deductible-p-9781119931201

Ed: Barbara Weltman. **Released:** November 2022. **Price:** $15, E-book; $25, paperback. **Description:** Recent legislation, the latest tax court rulings, and IRS guidance are all given in this guide for ordinary Americans to help them navigate deductions and tax breaks for their personal tax filings. **Availability:** E-book; Print.

15397 ■ "Kaboom!" in Canadian Business (Vol. 81, November 10, 2008, No. 19, pp. 18)

Description: International Financial Reporting Standards (IFRS) is a good idea in theory but was implemented in a hurry and had poor quality standards from the beginning. **Availability:** Print; Online.

15398 ■ "Liberty Tax Service is Registering Students for Fall Tax Preparation Courses" in Economics Week (August 3, 2012)

Description: Liberty Tax Service is enrolling for fall income tax preparation classes across the nation. The ten-week school teaches students strategies and advantages for personal tax savings. Liberty Tax Service offers a three-tier skill certification examination for its preparers. **Availability:** Online.

15399 ■ "Lifesavers" in Black Enterprise (Vol. 41, December 2010, No. 5, pp. 38)

Pub: Earl G. Graves Ltd.

Contact: Earl Graves, Jr., President

Ed: Tamara E. Holmes. **Description:** Profile of Interventional Nephrology Specialists Access Center and founders Dr. Omar Davis and Dr. Natarsha Grant; the center generated $5.5 million in revenue for 2009. Details on how they run their successful center are included. **Availability:** Online.

15400 ■ "Living in a 'Goldfish Bowl'" in WorkingUSA (Vol. 11, June 2008, No. 2, pp. 277)

Description: Recent changes in laws, regulations and even the reporting format of labor organization annual financial reports in both the U.S. and Australia have received surprisingly little attention, yet they have significantly increased the amount of information available both to union members and the public in general, as reports in both countries are available via government Websites. While such financial reporting laws are extremely rare in European countries, with the exception of the UK and Ireland, the U.S. and Australian reporting systems have become among the most detailed in the world. After reviewing these changes in financial reporting and the availability of these reports, as well as comparing and contrasting the specific reporting requirements of each country, this paper then examines the cost-benefit impact of more detailed financial reporting. **Availability:** Print; Online.

15401 ■ Make Sure It's Deductible

Released: Fourth edition. **Description:** Tax planning, strategies are provided to help small businesses maximize deductions. **Availability:** Print; Online.

15402 ■ "My Favorite Tool for Managing Expenses" in Inc. (Volume 32, December 2010, No. 10, pp. 60)

Pub: Inc. Magazine

Ed: J.J. McCorvey. **Description:** Web-based service called Expensify is outlined. The service allows companies to log expenses while away from the office using the service's iPhone application. **Availability:** Online.

15403 ■ "National Award Goes to eSmartTax.com for Having 'Best Tax Preparation Software' Available to Online Tax Filers" in Investment Weekly News (February 18, 2012, pp. 706)

Pub: PR Newswire Association LLC.

Description: eSmartTax.com was voted the best tax preparation software in About.com's Reader's Choice Awards 2011. Over 10,000 online tax filers voted for their favorite finance and tax software. eSmartTax.com provides a live online chat where tax professionals can answer specific questions.

15404 ■ "New Institutional Accounting and IFRS" in Accounting and Business Research (Vol. 41, Summer 2011, No. 3, pp. 309)

Pub: Routledge, Taylor & Francis Group

Ed: Peter Wysocki. **Description:** A new framework for institutional accounting research is presented. It has five fundamental components: efficient versus inefficient results, interdependencies, causation, level of analysis, and institutional structure. The use of the framework for evaluation accounting institutions such as the international financial reports standards (IFRS) is discussed. **Availability:** PDF; Online; Download.

15405 ■ "Olympus is Urged to Revise Board" in Wall Street Journal Eastern Edition (November 28, 2011, pp. B3)

Pub: Dow Jones & Company Inc.

Contact: Almar Latour, Chief Executive Officer

Ed: Phred Dvorak. **Description:** Koji Miyata, once a director on the board of troubled Japanese photographic equipment company, is urging the company to reorganize its board, saying the present group should resign their board seats but keep their management positions. The company has come under scrutiny for its accounting practices and costly acquisitions. **Availability:** Online.

15406 ■ "Privacy Concern: Are 'Group' Time Sheets Legal?" in HR Specialist (Vol. 8, September 2010, No. 9, pp. 4)

Pub: Capitol Information Group Inc.

Contact: Allie Ash, Chief Executive Officer

Description: Under the Fair Labor Standards Act (FLSA) employers are required to maintain and preserve payroll or other records, including the number of hours worked, but it does not prescribe a particular order or form in which these records must be kept. **Availability:** PDF; Online.

15407 ■ "Proposed Accounting Changes Could Complicate Tenants' Leases" in Baltimore Business Journal (Vol. 28, July 2, 2010, No. 8, pp. 1)

Pub: Baltimore Business Journal

Contact: Rhonda Pringle, President

E-mail: rpringle@bizjournals.com

Ed: Daniel J. Sernovitz. **Description:** The Financial Accounting Standards Board has proposed that companies must indicate the value of real estate leases as assets and liabilities on balance sheets instead of expenses. The proposals could cause some companies to document millions of dollars in charges on their books or find difficulty in getting loans. **Availability:** Print.

15408 ■ "PwC to Add 400 Workers in North Texas" in Dallas Business Journal (Vol. 35, April 6, 2012, No. 30, pp. 1)

Pub: Baltimore Business Journal

Contact: Rhonda Pringle, President

E-mail: rpringle@bizjournals.com

Description: London, England-headquartered PwC, formerly known as PricewaterhouseCoopers LLP, announced plans to hire 400 employees for its North Texas operations during the next 12 months. The firm provides auditing, consulting, and tax services to public, private and government clients. **Availability:** Print; Online.

15409 ■ "Quicken Starter Edition 2008" in Black Enterprise (Vol. 38, March 1, 2008, No. 8, pp. 54)

Pub: Earl G. Graves Ltd.

Contact: Earl Graves, Jr., President

Ed: Dale Coachman. **Description:** Profile of Quicken Starter Edition 2008 offering programs that track spending; it will also categorize tax deductible expenses. **Availability:** Online.

15410 ■ Reading Financial Reports for Dummies

Pub: John Wiley & Sons, Inc.

Contact: Christina Van Tassell, Executive Vice President Chief Financial Officer

URL(s): www.amazon.com/gp/product/1119871360/ref=as_li_tl?ie=UTF8&tag=wiley01-20

Ed: Lita Epstein. **Released:** 4th Edition. **Price:** $27.18, paperback; $18, e-book. **Description:** The fourth edition contains more new and updated information. This book is meant as a guide to help the reader interpret and understand financial reports, annual reports, balance sheets, income statements, statements of cash flow and consolidated statements. Real-world examples are given. . **Availability:** E-book; Print.

15411 ■ Schaum's Outline of Financial Management

Pub: McGraw-Hill Professional

Ed: Jae K. Shim, Joel G. Siegel. **Released:** Third edition. **Description:** Rules and regulations governing corporate finance, including the Sarbanes-Oxley Act are discussed. **Availability:** E-book; Print; Download.

15412 ■ "Sears and H&R Block Offer New Tax Preparation Options and Savings Through Tax Season" in Benzinga.com (January 30, 2012)

Description: Individuals preparing their own tax forms can file using www.sears.com/hrblock and receive a 15 percent discount on the purchase of Basic, Deluxe, and Premium H&R Block online editions. H&R Block at Sears also offers free 1040EZ filing online and in Sears stores. Customers filing on the site can also import previous year's tax data from TurboTax and TaxAct Online.

15413 ■ "SECU's Tax Preparation Services Net Members More Than $86 Million in Refunds" in Economics Week (May 11, 2012)

Description: State Employees' Credit Union (SECU) helped nearly 65,000 North Carolina members file their income taxes in 2012. SECU reports $86 million in refunds and saving members more than $8 million in preparation fees. The credit union promotes its tax preparation services so members can avoid the high fees paid to tax preparers. **Availability:** Print; Online.

15414 ■ Self-Employed Tax Solutions: Quick, Simple, Money-Saving, Audit-Proof Tax and Recordkeeping Basics

Released: Second edition. **Description:** A simple system for maintaining tax records and filing tax forms for any small business is explored.

15415 ■ "Smart Year-End Tax Moves" in Business Owner (Vol. 35, November-December 2011, No. 6, pp. 8)

Description: Managing small business and individual taxes is more important in a bad economy. It is imperative to seek all tax incentives that apply to your business.

15416 ■ *"Surviving an IRS Audit: Tips for Small Businesses"* in *Agency Sales Magazine (Vol. 39, July 2009, No. 7, pp. 52)*

Description: It is a good idea to enlist the services of a tax professional even if an audit is expected to go smoothly since the IRS is likely to scrutinize the unreported income and personal as well as business expenses of a small business during an audit. **Availability:** Online.

15417 ■ *"Tax Preparation Made Easier With Carbonite Online Backup"* in *Investment Weekly News (March 10, 2012, pp. 783)*

Pub: PR Newswire Association LLC.

Description: Carbonite, Inc. provides a secure backup protection service, making tax preparation easier for consumers and small- to medium-sized businesses. Details on Carbonite.com and its services are included. **Availability:** Online.

15418 ■ *Tax Savvy for Small Business*

Pub: Nolo

Contact: Chris Braun, President

Ed: Frederick W. Daily, Jeffrey A. Quinn. **Released:** 22nd edition. **Price:** $31.99, book & e-book; $20.99, E-Book; $23.99; $22.99, E-book. **Description:** Tax strategies for small business. Includes the latest tax numbers and laws as well as current Internal Revenue Service forms and publications. **Availability:** E-book; Print; Electronic publishing; PDF.

15419 ■ *"Tax Services Firm Ryan Prepares for Growth"* in *Dallas Business Journal (Vol. 35, June 29, 2012, No. 42, pp. 1)*

Pub: Baltimore Business Journal

Contact: Rhonda Pringle, President

E-mail: rpringle@bizjournals.com

Ed: Candace Carlisle. **Description:** Ryan LLC is seen to grow with three pending acquisitions. The tax services firm has opened offices in Australia and Singapore. **Availability:** Print; Online.

15420 ■ *"Tax Tip: Streamlining Sales Tax Collections"* in *Pet Product News (Vol. 66, September 2012, No. 9, pp. 38)*

Ed: Mark E. Battersby. **Description:** Pointers on how pet supplies retailers and managers can streamline sales taxes are presented. Businesses are being challenge by the pressure to collect taxes on goods sold to local customers and competititon from Internet merchants that are not required to collect sales taxes. **Availability:** Online.

15421 ■ *"Throughput Metrics Meet Six Sigma"* in *Management Accounting Quarterly (Vol. 12, Spring 2011, No. 3, pp. 12)*

Pub: Management Accounting Quarterly

Contact: Mike DePrisco, President

Ed: Shaun Aghili. **Description:** Throughput accounting (TA) metrics can be combined with six sigma's DMAIC methodology and various time-tested analysis and measurement tools for added effectiveness in resolving resource constraint issues. The goal is to optimize not only the output of a specific department but that of the entire system, by implementing a cost accounting system that is conducive to system optimization while increasing product quality, process integrity, or ideally, both. **Availability:** Print; PDF; Online.

15422 ■ *Top Tax Savings Ideas: How to Survive in Today's Tough Tax Environment*

Released: Second edition. **Price:** $16.11. **Description:** Tax deductions, fringe benefits, and tax deferrals for small businesses.

15423 ■ *"UB Program Offers Free Tax Preparation"* in *Buffalo News (January 29, 2012)*

Ed: Jonathan D. Epstein. **Description:** University of Buffalo's Schhol of Management in New York is offering free tax preparation for low-income individuals and families. The program is available on North and South campuses and is designed to help these people save money and collect all refunds in which they are eligible. **Availability:** Online.

15424 ■ *"United Way Offers Free Tax Assistance for Local Low-Income Families"* in *The Blade (January 6, 2012)*

Pub: Block Communications Inc.

URL(s): www.toledoblade.com

Ed: Kate Giammarise. **Description:** United Way of Greater Toledo, Ohio is offering free income tax preparation for households earning under $50,000 in 2011. United Way has partnered with the Lucas County Commissioner, Tina Skeldon Wozniak; Lucas County Treasurer, Wade Kapszukiewicz; and other social service agencies to help low-income workers in their region. **Availability:** Online.

15425 ■ *"Waiting for the Sunset on Taxes"* in *Memphis Business Journal (Vol. 34, September 28, 2012, No. 24, pp. 1)*

Pub: Baltimore Business Journal

Contact: Rhonda Pringle, President

E-mail: rpringle@bizjournals.com

Description: The implementation of the Tax Relief, Unemployment Reauthorization and Job Creation Act of 2010 will end on December 31, 2012. The exemption threshold will fall to $1 million, and the tax rate on transfers above that limit will be at 55 percent. The effect of political uncertainty on tax planning is also discussed. **Availability:** Print; Online.

15426 ■ *"Wal-Mart Offering In-Store Tax Return Preparation Services"* in *Tax Notes (Vol. 134, January 16, 2012, No. 3, pp. 301)*

Ed: Eric Kroh. **Description:** Wal-Mart is offering tax preparation services to customers in their retail stores. Details of the program included. **Availability:** Online.

15427 ■ *"Walk-Ins Being Accepted for Free Tax-Preparation Service"* in *Akron Beacon Journal (January 26, 2012)*

Ed: Betty Lin-Fisher. **Description:** Akron Summit Earned Income Tax Program, despite technical issues, is offering free service to walk in wishing free tax preparation. Details of the program are included. **Availability:** Print.

15428 ■ *"The Walmart Foundation and Leading Nonprofits Launch the MyFreeTaxes Program, Offering Eligible Taxpayers Free Tax Preparation in 2012"* in *Economics Week (February 10, 2012, pp. 274)*

Pub: PR Newswire Association LLC.

Description: United Way Worldwide, One Economy, and the National Disability Institute's Real Economic Impact Tour received funding in the amount of $4.35 million from Walmart Foundation to provide free tax filing services to eligible U.S. citizens. Earned Income Tax Credit (EITC), SNAP, and WIC elgibility education are also included in the program. The program will not only file income taxes for eligible individuals and families, it will also educate them about rights and options. **Availability:** Online.

15429 ■ *"Who Writes the Best Tax Code?"* in *Barron's (Vol. 92, February 20, 2012, No. 8, pp. 30)*

Pub: Dow Jones & Company Inc.

Contact: Almar Latour, Chief Executive Officer

Ed: Mike Hogan. **Description:** Tax preparation sites such as Turbo Tax, H&R Block and TaxACT assist investors in the preparation of their tax returns. These sites enhance tax preparation through state-specific questions and can transfer federal information onto state forms. **Availability:** Online.

STATISTICAL SOURCES

15430 ■ *Tax Preparation Services Industry in the US - Market Research Report*

URL(s): www.ibisworld.com/united-states/market-research-reports/tax-preparation-services-industry/

Price: $925. **Description:** Downloadable report analyzing the current and future trends in the tax preparation services industry. **Availability:** Download.

TRADE PERIODICALS

15431 ■ *Canadian MoneySaver*

Pub: Canadian Money Saver Inc.

Contact: Ken Kivenko, President

URL(s): www.canadianmoneysaver.ca

Released: 9/year **Price:** $24.95, Individuals print only; $19.99, Individuals online only; $34.95, Individuals print and online. **Description:** Examines taxes, investment, and financial planning in Canada. Recurring features include interviews, book reviews, and notices of publications available. **Availability:** Print; Online.

15432 ■ *The Exempt Organization Tax Review (EOTR)*

Pub: Tax Analysts

Contact: Thomas L. Evans, Chairman

URL(s): www.taxnotes.com/document-list/tax-topics/exempt-organizations-and-financing/exempt-organizations

Description: Journal covering tax exemption laws and policies, including summaries of court opinions, IRS rulings, related regulations and administrative pronouncements, and analysis of current issues. Contains federal, state, and international nonprofit tax news, commentary, and analysis. **Availability:** Print.

15433 ■ *International Tax and Public Finance*

Pub: Springer US

Contact: Derk Haank, Chief Executive Officer

URL(s): link.springer.com/journal/10797

Released: 6/year; February, April, June, August, October and December. **Description:** Journal covering tax and public finance worldwide. **Availability:** Print; PDF; Download; Online.

15434 ■ *Intertax*

URL(s): www.kluwerlawonline.com/toc.php?pubcode=taxi

Released: Monthly **Description:** Journal covering tax information worldwide. **Availability:** Print; Online.

15435 ■ *Journal of the American Taxation Association (JATA)*

Pub: American Accounting Association

Contact: Terry J. Shevlin, Vice President

E-mail: tshevlin@uci.edu

URL(s): aaahq.org/Research/Journals/The-Journal-of-the-American-Taxation-Association

Ed: Connie D. Weaver. **Released:** Semiannual; Spring and Fall. **Price:** $168, for print only; $25, Members for hard copy. **Description:** Academic journal covering accounting and taxation. **Availability:** Print; PDF; Online.

15436 ■ *The Journal of Taxation*

Contact: Michael J. Miller, Editor

URL(s): store.tax.thomsonreuters.com/accounting/Tax/Journal-of-Taxation/p/100200787

Ed: Michael J. Miller, Herbert H. Alpert, Lorence L. Bravenec, Joseph I. Graf. **Released:** Monthly **Price:** $720, For bundle.; $570, For online only.; $525, For print only.; $445, For e-book. **Description:** Journal for sophisticated tax practitioners. **Availability:** Print; Online.

15437 ■ *The Practical Tax Lawyer*

Pub: American Law Institute Continuing Legal Education

URL(s): www.ali-cle.org/legal-journals/PTL

Released: Quarterly **Price:** $35, Single issue for digital issue. **Description:** Professional legal magazine that contains concise, practice-oriented articles to assist lawyers with all aspects of tax law. Produced in cooperation with the Section of Taxation of the American Bar Association. **Availability:** Online.

15438 ■ *Tax Notes*

Pub: Tax Analysts

Contact: Thomas L. Evans, Chairman

URL(s): www.taxnotes.com

Facebook: www.facebook.com/TaxNotes

Linkedin: www.linkedin.com/company/taxnotes

X (Twitter): x.com/TaxNotes

Instagram: www.instagram.com/taxnotes

Ed: Ariel S. Greenblum. **Released:** Weekly **Description:** Trade magazine covering Federal tax news and reports. **Availability:** Print; Online.

15439 ■ The TaxLetter
Pub: MPL Communications Inc.
Contact: Ragaey Nassif, Contact
E-mail: rnassif@mplcomm.com
URL(s): www.adviceforinvestors.com/the-taxletter
Released: Monthly **Price:** $37, Individuals for six months. **Description:** Acts as a consumer newsletter that specializes in personal tax-planning, offering timely advice, information, and recommendations on personal and business tax-planning strategies. Features columns titled ShelterWatch, RRSP Watch, Looking Out for No. 1, Managing Your Money, and Tax-Wise Investor. **Availability:** Print; Online.

15440 ■ TAXPRO Monthly
Pub: National Association of Tax Professionals
Contact: Gerard Cannito, President
URL(s): www.natptax.com/Publications/TaxProMon thly/Pages/default.aspx
Released: Monthly **Description:** Helps to communicate the purposes of the Association, which are to foster high standards in the tax preparation profession and to promote and protect the interests of tax practitioners. Includes tax law and regulations, statistics, and news of members. **Availability:** Print.

TRADE SHOWS AND CONVENTIONS

15441 ■ Institute of Internal Auditors - International Conference
KPMG LLP
345 Pk. Ave.
New York, NY 10154
Ph: (212)758-9700
Fax: (212)758-9819
Co. E-mail: us-optout@kpmg.com
URL: http://kpmg.com/us/en.html
Contact: Erik Lange, Leader Partner
URL(s): iiaic.org
Facebook: www.facebook.com/iiaintlconf
X (Twitter): twitter.com/iiaic
Frequency: Annual. **Description:** Internal auditing equipment, supplies, and services, software, and computer related equipment. Hybrid event experiences. **Audience:** All levels of internal auditors from every industry. **Principal Exhibits:** Internal auditing equipment, supplies, and services, software, and computer related equipment. Hybrid event experiences. **Telecommunication Services:** sponsorships@theiia.org.

15442 ■ New Jersey Accounting, Business & Technology Show & Conference
New Jersey Society of Certified Public Accountants (NJCPA)
105 Eisenhower Pky., Ste. 300
Roseland, NJ 07068
Ph: (973)226-4494
Co. E-mail: njcpa@njcpa.org
URL: http://njcpa.org
Contact: Kathleen F. Powers, President
URL(s): www.flaggmgmt.com/nj
Description: Information and technology, financial and business services, computer accounting systems, software, tax preparation, accounting, audit, practice management software - windows, and computer and business systems. Banking, insurance, financial and business software. Internet, online systems and middle market software and investment services. **Audience:** CPAs, accounting professionals, business and financial executives of New Jersey, Fortune 1000 corporations, business owners and managers, and IT managers. **Principal Exhibits:** Information and technology, financial and business services, computer accounting systems, software, tax preparation, accounting, audit, practice management software - windows, and computer and business systems. Banking, insurance, financial and business software. Internet, online systems and middle market software and investment services.

CONSULTANTS

15443 ■ Hollingsworth & Associates
395 Wellington Rd. S, Ste. 101
London, ON, Canada N6C 5Z6
Ph: (519)649-2001
URL: http://www.appointmentquest.com/scheduler/2140113024
Description: Firm offers consulting services include software selection and financial information systems, accounting and tax preparation. **Scope:** Firm offers consulting services include software selection and financial information systems, accounting and tax preparation. **Founded:** 1993.

15444 ■ John Alan Cohan
16133 Ventura Blvd., NO.700
Encino, CA 91436
Ph: (310)278-0203
Co. E-mail: johnalancohan@aol.com
URL: http://cohanlawoffice.com
Contact: John Alan Cohan, Contact
E-mail: johnalancohan@aol.com
Description: Specializes in tax law, probate, and conservatorships. The company handles complex tax audits, prepares tax compliance and regulatory opinion letters for trade associations, tax-exempt organizations and individual clients. It also offers in-depth knowledge regarding livestock, horse, and agricultural matters. **Founded:** 1981.

15445 ■ Mitchell and Titus L.L.P.
80 Pine St., 32th Fl.
New York, NY 10005
Ph: (212)709-4500
Fax: (212)709-4680
Co. E-mail: info@mitchelltitus.com
URL: http://www.mitchelltitus.com
Contact: Anthony S. Kendall, Chief Executive Officer
Facebook: www.facebook.com/mitchelltitusllp
Linkedin: www.linkedin.com/company/mitchell-&-titus-llp
X (Twitter): x.com/Mitchell_Titus
Description: Firm provides public accounting, auditing, tax preparation and management consulting. **Scope:** Firm provides assurance, advisory business services, transaction support and tax services. Specializes in auditing and accounting services, tax planning and preparation services management and business advisory services. **Founded:** 1974. **Publications:** "ITEM Club Budget preview report," 2010; "Year end personal planning," 2010; "Steering towards the future using the Pre Budget Report to help the UK rebound," 2009; "Be careful what you wish for," 2009; "Year end personal planning," 2009. **Training:** Budget Seminar 2010, Mar, 2010.

FRANCHISES AND BUSINESS OPPORTUNITIES

15446 ■ Cash Plus Inc. (CP)
PO Box 2185
Anaheim, CA 92814
Ph: (714)731-2274
Free: 877-227-4758
Fax: (714)731-2099
Co. E-mail: cpcorp@cashplusinc.com
URL: http://cashplusinc.com
Contact: Craig Wells, President
Description: Provider of financial services. **Founded:** 1984. **Training:** Provides training including easy-to-run computerized operating system, promotions and check verification and payday advance process.

15447 ■ Colbert/Ball Tax Service
2616 S Loop W, Ste. 400
Houston, TX 77054
Ph: (713)592-5555
Free: 888-288-8675
Co. E-mail: franchise@colbertballtax.com
URL: http://www.colbertballtax.com
Contact: A. L. Colbert, Contact

Description: Firm provides tax and related services. **No. of Operating Units:** 350. **Founded:** 1995. **Franchised:** 2002. **Equity Capital Needed:** $30,000-$50,000. **Franchise Fee:** $15,000. **Financial Assistance:** Yes **Training:** Yes.

15448 ■ Jackson Hewitt Inc. (JH)
10 Exchange Pl., 27th Fl.
Jersey City, NJ 07302
Free: 800-234-1040
URL: http://www.jacksonhewitt.com
Contact: Jo Willetts, Director
Facebook: www.facebook.com/jacksonhewitt
X (Twitter): x.com/jacksonhewitt
YouTube: www.youtube.com/channel/UCQ9t-fuwMkK dZO0sx5p7tXQ
Description: Firm provides tax return preparation and electronic fillings service. **Founded:** 1982. **Financial Assistance:** Yes **Training:** 5 day training program designed to teach business partners the skills necessary to launch a new franchise operation. This also includes workshops, seminars and group discussions. Extensive 2 days of training for electronic filing system.

15449 ■ LedgerPlus
4643 Clyde Morris Blvd., Ste. 308
Port Orange, FL 32129
Ph: (386)767-3006
Fax: (386)767-7005
Co. E-mail: office@ledgerplusaccountants.com
URL: http://www.ledgerplusaccountants.com
Contact: Melvin Zerrusen, Owner
E-mail: mel@ledgerplusaccountants.com
Description: Firm provides tax management, assurance, advisory services, accounting, audit and payroll services. **Financial Assistance:** Yes **Training:** Yes.

15450 ■ Ledgers Professional Services
26 Wilstead Dr.
Newmarket, ON, Canada L3Y 4T9
Free: 855-LED-GERS
Co. E-mail: clientcare@ledgers.com
URL: http://ledgers.com
Contact: Savio Goveas, Contact
Facebook: www.facebook.com/LedgersCanada
X (Twitter): x.com/ledgerscanada
Description: Provider of accounting, bookkeeping and financial statement preparation services for small businesses. **Founded:** 1994. **Training:** Provides 5 days training.

15451 ■ Liberty Tax, Inc.
Franchise Group, Inc. (FRG)
1615 General Booth Blvd., Ste. 111
Virginia Beach, VA 23454
Ph: (740)363-2222
Free: 800-790-3863
Fax: (800)880-6432
URL: http://www.franchisegrp.com
Contact: Scott Terrell, Chief Executive Officer
Description: Income tax preparation and electronic filing loan service. **Founded:** 1997. **Training:** 1 week operations training followed by 2 day update training and annual advanced trainings; Year-round tax, technical, operational and marketing support.

15452 ■ Liberty Tax Service, Inc.
Franchise Group, Inc. (FRG)
110 Riviera Dr., Unit 16
Markham, ON, Canada L3R 5M1
Ph: (740)363-2222
Free: 800-790-3863
Fax: (800)880-6432
URL: http://www.franchisegrp.com
Facebook: www.facebook.com/libertytaxCA
X (Twitter): x.com/libtaxcanada
Description: Provider of tax preparation, tax returns and tax filling services, tax courses, small business accounting. **Founded:** 1997. **Training:** Provides 5 days training.

15453 ■ Padgett Business Services (PBS)
555 High St., Ste. 102
Westwood, MA 02090
Ph: (781)219-0395
URL: http://www.padgettadvisors.com

Contact: John Barucci, Contact
Facebook: www.facebook.com/PadgettBusiness
X (Twitter): x.com/PadgettBusSvcs

Description: Padgett provides an array of services to small businesses, such as consulting, financial reporting, government compliance, payroll and tax preparation services. Padgett also offers credit card processing, pension and 125 plan administration, equipment financing and workers' compensation payment service. **Founded:** 1993. **Training:** Initial training 12 days field visits, covering marketing, operations, and software. Ongoing training and support is provided through regular seminars in marketing, operations, tax, etc. Support is delivered through toll-free telephone and a wide range of information and material is provided via the company's web site.

15454 ■ The St. Simons Corporation (ETF)
1600 Kilarney Dr.
 Cary, NC 27511-5503
Contact: Rachel Wishon, President

Description: E-filing and refund loans. **No. of Franchise Units:** 44. **No. of Company-Owned Units:** 2. **Founded:** 1990. **Franchised:** 1990. **Equity Capital Needed:** $25,000. **Franchise Fee:** $10,500. **Financial Assistance:** Yes **Training:** Yes.

15455 ■ Tax Centers of America (TCOA)
1611 E Main St.
 Russellville, AR 72801
Ph: (479)968-4796
Fax: (479)968-8012
Co. E-mail: moreinfo@tcoa.net
URL: http://www.tcoa.net
Contact: Tonia S. Ouzts, President

Description: Operator of tax centers. **Founded:** 1992. **Training:** Offers 4 days of training and ongoing support.

COMPUTERIZED DATABASES

15456 ■ *Federal Income Taxation of Corporations and Shareholders*
Thomson Reuters (Tax And Accounting) Inc.
2395 Midway Rd.
Carrollton, TX 75006
Free: 888-885-0206
URL: http://tax.thomsonreuters.com/en
Contact: Brian Peccarelli, President
URL(s): store.tax.thomsonreuters.com/accounting/Tax/Federal-Income-Taxation-of-Corporations-and-Shareholders/p/100200943

Released: 3/year **Price:** $1,390, for book, latest updates(One-year subscription,). **Availability:** Print; Online. **Type:** Full-text.

15457 ■ *Federal Taxes Weekly Alert*
Thomson Reuters (Tax And Accounting) Inc.
2395 Midway Rd.
Carrollton, TX 75006
Free: 888-885-0206
URL: http://tax.thomsonreuters.com/en
Contact: Brian Peccarelli, President
URL(s): store.tax.thomsonreuters.com/accounting/Tax/US-Tax-Reporter-Estate-and-Gift/p/100200366

Released: Daily **Availability:** Online; PDF. **Type:** Full-text.

15458 ■ *IRS Practice and Procedure*
Thomson Reuters (Tax And Accounting) Inc.
2395 Midway Rd.
Carrollton, TX 75006
Free: 888-885-0206
URL: http://tax.thomsonreuters.com/en
Contact: Brian Peccarelli, President
URL(s): store.tax.thomsonreuters.com/accounting/Tax/IRS-Practice-and-Procedure/p/100200942

Price: $1,245, Individuals. **Availability:** Print; Online. **Type:** Full-text.

15459 ■ *ProQuest Accounting, Tax and Banking Collection™*
ProQuest LLC
789 E Eisenhower Pky.
Ann Arbor, MI 48108
Ph: (734)761-4700

Free: 800-521-0600
URL: http://www.proquest.com
Contact: Matti Shem Tov, Chief Executive Officer
URL(s): about.proquest.com/en/products-services/pq_accounting

Availability: Online. **Type:** Bibliographic.

15460 ■ *Tax Notes® Today*
Tax Analysts
400 S Maple Ave., Ste. 400
Falls Church, VA 22046
Free: 800-955-2444
Co. E-mail: communications@taxanalysts.org
URL: http://www.taxnotes.com
Contact: Thomas L. Evans, Chairman
URL(s): www.taxnotes.com/tax-notes-today-federal

Availability: Print. **Type:** Full-text.

COMPUTER SYSTEMS/ SOFTWARE

15461 ■ *BNA Income Tax Planner*
BNA Software
1801 S Bell St.
Arlington, VA 22202
Free: 800-424-2938
Fax: (800)253-0322
Co. E-mail: help@bloombergtax.com
URL: http://pro.bloombergtax.com
Contact: Lisa Fitzpatrick, President
URL(s): pro.bloombergtax.com/income-tax-planner

Description: Available for IBM computers and compatibles. Calculates federal and state individual income taxes. **Availability:** Online.

15462 ■ *Tax Preparer*
HowardSoft
PO Box 8432
La Jolla, CA 92038-8432
Ph: (858)454-0121
Co. E-mail: support@howardsoft.com
URL: http://www.howardsoft.com
URL(s): www.howardsoft.com/proddesc.htm

Price: $99, for annual. **Description:** Available for IBM and Apple II computers and compatibles. System automating the preparation of tax returns. Handles IRS worksheets, recordkeeping, stocks, bonds, rental, accounts, and depreciated assets. **Availability:** Online.

15463 ■ *Tax Preparer: California Supplement*
HowardSoft
PO Box 8432
La Jolla, CA 92038-8432
Ph: (858)454-0121
Co. E-mail: support@howardsoft.com
URL: http://www.howardsoft.com
URL(s): www.howardsoft.com/taxbro2.htm

Description: Available for IBM and Apple II computers and compatibles. System providing automated tax preparation for California state income taxes. **Availability:** Online.

15464 ■ *Website Relief*
AccountantsWorld L.L.C.
1412 Broadway, Ste.1200
New York, NY 10018
Ph: (631)232-1040
Free: 888-999-1366
Fax: (631)232-3160
Co. E-mail: marketing@accountantsworld.com
URL: http://www.accountantsworld.com
Contact: Chandra Bhansali, Chief Executive Officer
E-mail: cbhansali@accountantsworld.com
URL(s): www.accountantsworld.com/website-relief

Description: Available for IBM computers and compatibles. System prepares 53 tax forms and schedules and calculates various personal and business taxes. **Availability:** Online.

LIBRARIES

15465 ■ Baker & McKenzie - Library
181 Bay St., Ste. 2100
 Toronto, ON, Canada M5J 2T3

URL: http://www.bakermckenzie.com
Description: Law firm and advisors. **Scope:** Law - corporate, commercial, labor, tax. **Services:** Interlibrary loan; library not open to the public. **Founded:** 1949. **Holdings:** Figures not available.

15466 ■ Brooklyn Public Library Business & Career Center
10 Grand Army Plz.
 Brooklyn, NY 11201
Ph: (718)230-2100
URL: http://www.bklynlibrary.org/business
Contact: Linda E. Johnson, President
Description: Offers library services for business and career. **Scope:** Business & career services. **Founded:** 1943. **Holdings:** Figures not available.

15467 ■ Deloitte & Touche - Library
555 W 5th St., Ste. 2700
 Los Angeles, CA 90013-1010
URL: http://www.deloitte.com/global/en/services/tax/collections/tax-library---deloitte.html
Scope: Auditing, taxation, management consultation, actuarial services, employee benefits, valuation consultation. **Services:** Library not open to the public. **Founded:** 1845. **Holdings:** Figures not available.

15468 ■ Epstein Becker and Green, P.C. (EBG) - Library
875 Third Ave.
New York, NY 10022
Ph: (212)351-4500
Fax: (212)878-8600
URL: http://www.ebglaw.com
Contact: Robert Guilbert, Chief Information Officer
E-mail: rguilbert@ebglaw.com
Facebook: www.facebook.com/Epstein-Becker-Green-140779175933414
Linkedin: www.linkedin.com/company/epstein-becker-&-green-p-c-
X (Twitter): x.com/ebglaw
Instagram: www.instagram.com/ebglaw
YouTube: www.youtube.com/user/ebglaw

Description: Law firm provides legal services. **Scope:** Employment; labor; workforce. **Founded:** 1973. **Holdings:** Figures not available.

15469 ■ Ernst & Young Center for Business Knowledge
155 N Wacker Dr.
 Chicago, IL 60606
Ph: (312)879-2000
Fax: (312)879-4000
URL: http://www.ey.com
Contact: Joon Ko, Vice President

Scope: Accounting; taxation; consulting; healthcare. **Services:** Interlibrary loan; library not open to the public. **Holdings:** 3,000 books.

15470 ■ Ernst & Young Library
833 E Michigan St.
 Milwaukee, WI 53202
Ph: (414)273-5900
Fax: (414)223-7200
URL: http://www.ey.com
Contact: Carmine di Sibio, Chief Executive Officer
Facebook: www.facebook.com/EY
Linkedin: www.linkedin.com/company/ernstandyoung
X (Twitter): x.com/EYnews
YouTube: www.youtube.com/ernstandyoungglobal

Scope: Taxation; tax law; accounting; auditing. **Services:** Performs searches on fee basis for clients only. **Holdings:** 1,200 books.

15471 ■ Ernst & Young L.L.P., Center for Business Knowledge
One Manhattan W 401 9th Ave.
 New York, NY 10001
Co. E-mail: general@gu.ey.com
URL: http://www.ey.com
Facebook: www.facebook.com/EY
Linkedin: www.linkedin.com/company/ernstandyoung
X (Twitter): x.com/EYnews
YouTube: www.youtube.com/c/ernstyoung

Description: Helps build trust and confidence in the capital markets and in economies the world over. **Scope:** Accounting and auditing; taxation; finance.

Services: Interlibrary loan; copying; library open to clients and SLA members. **Founded:** 1953. **Holdings:** 3,500 books.

15472 ■ Fenwick & West LLP Law Library
801 California St.
  Mountain View, CA 94041
Ph: (650)988-8500
URL: http://www.fenwick.com
X (Twitter): x.com/FenwickWest

Description: Practices of law through substantial investments in proprietary technology tools and processes. **Founded:** 1973.

15473 ■ KPMG - Research Centre
777 Dunsmuir St., 11 Fl.
  Vancouver, BC, Canada V7Y 1K3
Ph: (604)691-3000
Fax: (604)691-3031
URL: http://home.kpmg/ca/en/home.html

Scope: Tax; general business; stocks. **Founded:** 1982. **Subscriptions:** journals Figures not available.

15474 ■ Polsinelli PC - Library
900 W 48th Pl., Ste. 900
  Kansas City, MO 64112
Ph: (816)753-1000
Fax: (816)753-1536
URL: http://www.polsinelli.com
Contact: Cara E. Stark, Director
E-mail: cstark@polsinelli.com
Linkedin: www.linkedin.com/company/polsinelli

Description: A full-service law firm serving clients in health care, financial services, intellectual property, middle-market corporate, labor and employment, real estate, and business litigation. **Scope:** Law - tax, bankruptcy, real estate; litigation; product liability. **Services:** Interlibrary loan; copying; library open to clients only. **Founded:** 1972. **Holdings:** 15,000 books. **Subscriptions:** 1,500 journals and other serials; 10 newspapers. **Educational Activities:** Winter Leadership Conference (Annual); ABI Annual Spring Meeting (Annual); International Car Rental Show (Annual).

15475 ■ PwC Research Centre
1250 Rene Levesque Blvd. Ouest Bureau 2500
  Montreal, QC, Canada H3B 4Y1
Ph: (514)205-5000
URL: http://www.pwc.com/gx/en/industries/
  government-public-services/public-sector-research
  -centre.html
Contact: Nicolas Marcoux, Contact
Linkedin: www.linkedin.com/company/pwc
X (Twitter): x.com/pwc
YouTube: www.youtube.com/user/PwC

Description: Public sector research center. **Scope:** Accounting, tax, management, business, finance. **Founded:** 1993. **Holdings:** Figures not available.

15476 ■ Tax Executives Institute (TEI)
1200 G St. NW, Ste. 300
  Washington, DC 20005
Ph: (202)638-5601
Fax: (202)638-5607
Co. E-mail: asktei@tei.org
URL: http://www.tei.org
Contact: Mitchell Trager, President
Facebook: www.facebook.com/TaxExecutivesInsti
  tute
Linkedin: www.linkedin.com/company/tax-executives
  -institute
X (Twitter): x.com/tei_updates
YouTube: www.youtube.com/channel/UCJJVYpl
  1TASAnZbQN5WUfrg

Description: Professional society of executives administering and directing tax affairs for corporations and businesses. Maintains TEI Education Fund. **Founded:** 1944. **Publications:** *The Tax Executive* (Bimonthly). **Awards:** TEI Distinguished Service Award (Annual). **Geographic Preference:** Multinational.

15477 ■ Trumbull County Carnegie Law Library
120 High St. NW
  Warren, OH 44481

Ph: (330)675-2525
Fax: (330)675-2527
URL: http://lawlibrary.co.trumbull.oh.us/ll_history.html
Contact: Randil J. Rudloff, President

Description: Trumball county looks after the cities Cortland, Girard, Hubbard, Newton Falls, Niles, Warren, Youngstown. **Scope:** Federal; state; tax; family; probate; real estate and labor law. **Services:** Open to the public. **Founded:** 1899. **Holdings:** 32,000 hardbound books; 50,000 microfiche; ultra fiche.

15478 ■ U.S. Department of the Treasury - Library
Freedman's Bank Bldg., Rm. 1020, 720 Madison Pl.
  Washington, DC 20220
Ph: (202)622-2000
URL: http://home.treasury.gov/services/tours-and-li
  brary/library

Scope: Local history. **Services:** Library open to the public by appointment. **Founded:** 1789. **Holdings:** Figures not available. **Publications:** *Department of the Treasury, Departmental Offices Telephone Directory* (Annual); *Roster of Minority Financial Institutions*.

15479 ■ United States Tax Court
400 2nd St. NW
  Washington, DC 20217
Ph: (202)521-0700
URL: http://www.ustaxcourt.gov
Contact: Maurice B. Foley, Chief Judge

Scope: Federal tax law - income, estate, and gift. **Services:** Interlibrary loan; library not open to the public. **Founded:** 1924. **Holdings:** 60,000 books; 9,000 bound periodical volumes; Congressional Record, Federal Register, and federal tax legislation.

15480 ■ Willamette Management Associates Library
8600 W Bryn Mawr Ave., Ste. 950 N
  Chicago, IL 60631
Ph: (773)399-4300
Fax: (773)399-4310
URL: http://www.willamette.com
Contact: Robert F. Reilly, Managing Director
E-mail: rfreilly@willamette.com
Linkedin: www.linkedin.com/company/willamette
  -management-associates

Description: Business valuation, forensic analysis, and transaction financial advisory services. **Scope:** Business valuation; tax; estate; finance. **Services:** Interlibrary loan; copying; library not open to the public. **Founded:** 1969.

RESEARCH CENTERS

15481 ■ American Institute for Economic Research (AIER) - E. C. Harwood Library
250 Division St.
  Great Barrington, MA 01230-1000
Free: 888-528-1216
Fax: (413)528-0103
Co. E-mail: press@aier.org
URL: http://www.aier.org
Contact: William J. Luther, Director
E-mail: will.luther@gmail.com
Facebook: www.facebook.com/aierdotorg
Linkedin: www.linkedin.com/company/aierdotorg
X (Twitter): x.com/aier
YouTube: www.youtube.com/user/AIERvideo
Pinterest: www.pinterest.com/aierdotorg

Description: Provides "information on economic and financial subjects that is useful and completely independent of special interests". Sponsors a fellowship program for graduate study of economics at the institute and in absentia. **Scope:** Economic and financial problems as applicable to individuals as well as private and public organizations, including all aspects of personal, community, and governmental economic and financial problems, money and banking, governmental fiscal policies, industrial development and production, domestic and foreign aid, taxation, life insurance, retirement, and investments. **Services:** Open to the public with restrictions. **Founded:** 1933. **Holdings:** Books. **Publications:** *The AIER Chart Book*; *Economic Bulletin* (Annual);

Research Reports (Semimonthly); *Economic Education Bulletin* (Monthly); *AIER Research reports* (Semimonthly); *American Institute for Economic Research--Research Reports*; *Research Reports*. **Awards:** American Institute for Economic Research Student Summer Fellowship. **Geographic Preference:** National.

15482 ■ American Law Institute (ALI) - Library
4025 Chestnut St.
  Philadelphia, PA 19104
Ph: (215)243-1600
Free: 800-253-6397
Fax: (215)243-1636
Co. E-mail: ali@ali.org
URL: http://www.ali.org
Contact: David F. Levi, President
Facebook: www.facebook.com/AmericanLawInstitute
Linkedin: www.linkedin.com/company/the-american
  -law-institute
X (Twitter): x.com/amlawinst
YouTube: www.youtube.com/channel/UCJx
  1fzQwDA7qg0GTZKl2FzA

Description: Judges, law teachers, and lawyers. Promotes the clarification and of the law and its better adaptation to social needs by continuing work on the Restatement of the Law, model and uniform codes, and model statutes. Conducts a program of continuing legal education. **Scope:** Tax law, property law, commercial law, tort law, international law, family law, and law of trusts. **Founded:** 1923. **Holdings:** Figures not available. **Publications:** *ALI Reporter* (Quarterly); *Restatements of the Law* (Periodic); *ALI Annual Report* (Annual); *Principles of the Law; Uniform Commercial Code (UCC)* (Periodic); *ALI Proceedings of Annual Meetings*; *Model Penal Code* (Occasionally). **Educational Activities:** ALI Annual Meeting (Annual), For research and development. **Awards:** John Minor Wisdom Award (Irregular); Henry J. Friendly Medal (Periodic). **Geographic Preference:** National.

15483 ■ Auburn University - Government and Economic Development Institute (GEDI) - Library
213 Extension Hall
  Auburn University, AL 36849
Co. E-mail: gedi@auburn.edu
URL: http://www.auburn.edu/outreach/gedi/index.htm
Contact: Jeremy Arthur, Director
E-mail: jarthur@auburn.edu
Facebook: www.facebook.com/GEDIAuburn
X (Twitter): x.com/gediau

Description: Governmental liaison center for Auburn University. **Scope:** Conducts research in government policy and management, civic engagement, economic prosperity, and improving quality of life for Alabama communities. **Founded:** 1976. **Holdings:** Figures not available.

15484 ■ Canadian Tax Foundation (CTF) - Douglas J. Sherbaniuk Research Centre [L'Association Canadienne d'Études Fiscales (ACEF)]
145 Wellington St. W Ste. 1400
  Toronto, ON, Canada M5J 1H8
Ph: (416)599-0283
Free: 877-733-0283
Fax: (416)599-9283
Co. E-mail: ctfmembership@ctf.ca
URL: http://www.ctf.ca
Contact: Heather L. Evans, Chief Executive Officer
E-mail: hevans@ctf.ca
X (Twitter): x.com/cdntaxfdn

Description: Promotes increased awareness of the Canadian Tax Code and the social ramifications of taxation. Serves as a clearinghouse on taxation; sponsors research and educational programs. **Scope:** sponsors or directly carries out expert research in the fields of taxation and public finance, publishes the results of that research. **Services:** Interlibrary loan; copying; open to the public. **Founded:** 1945. **Holdings:** Periodicals; documents; books. **Publications:** *Annual Conference Report* (Annual); *CTF Annual Report* (Monthly); *Canadian Tax Highlights* (Monthly); *Canadian Tax Journal* (Quarterly); *Canadian Tax Papers Series*; *Finances of the Nation* (Annual); *Tax Memos*; *Tax for the Owner Manager* (Quarterly); *Taxation of Private Corporations and Their Shareholders* (Occasionally). **Geographic Preference:** National.

15485 ■ Cascade Policy Institute

4850 SW Scholls Ferry Rd., Ste. No.103
  Portland, OR 97225
Ph: (503)242-0900
Co. E-mail: info@cascadepolicy.org
URL: http://www.cascadepolicy.org
Contact: John A. Charles, President
Facebook: www.facebook.com/CascadePolicy
Linkedin: www.linkedin.com/company/cascade-policy
  -institute
X (Twitter): x.com/CascadePolicy
Instagram: www.instagram.com/cascadepolicy
YouTube: www.youtube.com/c/cascadepolicy
Description: A nonprofit, nonpartisan public policy research and educational organization that focuses on state and local issues in Oregon. **Scope:** Explores voluntary market-oriented answers to national, regional, and state public policy issues. Areas of research include environment, education, transportation, healthcare and taxation. **Founded:** 1991. **Publications:** *Cascade Commentaries* (Weekly); *Cascade Quickpoints* (Weekly); *Cascade Update* (Semiannual).

15486 ■ Citizens for Tax Justice (CTJ)

1200 18th St. NW Ste. 675
  Washington, DC 20036
Ph: (202)299-1066
Fax: (202)299-1065
Co. E-mail: info@ctj.org
URL: http://ctj.org
Facebook: www.facebook.com/taxjustice
X (Twitter): x.com/taxjustice
YouTube: www.youtube.com/user/Citizens4TaxJus
  tice/videos
Description: Opposes measures shifting tax burdens from upper income groups and large corporations onto average taxpayers. Provides technical assistance and other services. **Scope:** Federal, state and local tax systems. **Founded:** 1979. **Publications:** *CTJ Update* (9/year; Quarterly); *Studies and analyses.* **Geographic Preference:** Local; National.

15487 ■ Competitive Enterprise Institute (CEI)

1310 L St. NW 7th Fl.
  Washington, DC 20005
Ph: (202)331-1010
Co. E-mail: info@cei.org
URL: http://cei.org
Contact: Kent Lassman, President
Facebook: www.facebook.com/CompetitiveEn
  terpriseInstitute
X (Twitter): x.com/ceidotorg
YouTube: www.youtube.com/user/CEIdotorg
Description: Independent, nonprofit public policy group. **Scope:** Domestic economic policy issues, including deregulation of industry, deficit reduction, privatization, antitrust, free trade, free-market environmentalism, intellectual property, technology and innovation, transportation deregulation, global warming, entrepreneurship and risk and insurance. **Founded:** 1984. **Publications:** *CEI Planet* (Quarterly). **Educational Activities:** CEI Warren Brooks Memorial Dinner. **Awards:** Julian L. Simon Award (Annual); Warren T. Brookes Journalism Fellowship (Annual).

15488 ■ Employee Benefit Research Institute (EBRI) - Library

901 D St., SW Ste. 802
  Washington, DC 20024
Ph: (202)659-0670
Fax: (202)775-6360
Co. E-mail: info@ebri.org
URL: http://www.ebri.org
Contact: Lori Lucas, Chief Executive Officer
Description: Corporations, consulting firms, banks, insurance companies, unions, and others with an interest in the future of employee benefit programs. Seeks to contribute to the development of effective

and responsible public policy in the field of employee benefits through research, publications, educational programs, seminars, and direct communication. Sponsors studies on retirement income, health, disability, and other benefit programs; disseminates study results. **Scope:** A public policy research organization serving as an employee benefits information source on health, welfare and retirement issues. Services include: basic benefit program descriptions, legislation analysis, media coverage and interpretation and long-range planning. Specializes in research on pensions, social security, health care, Medicare, long-term care and flexible benefits. Serves government, academic consumers, consultants, banks, insurance companies, investment managers, law and accounting firms, corporations and individuals. **Founded:** 1978. **Holdings:** Figures not available. **Publications:** Dedicated to providing unbiased, fact-based research on employee benefits. **Training:** Policy Forums, Congressional Briefings. **Awards:** EBRI Lillywhite Award (Annual). **Geographic Preference:** National.

15489 ■ First Liberty Institute (FLI)

2001 West Plano Pky., Ste. 1600
  Plano, TX 75075
Ph: (972)941-4444
Co. E-mail: info@firstliberty.org
URL: http://www.firstliberty.org
Contact: Kelly Shackelford, President
Facebook: www.facebook.com/firstlibertyinstitute
Linkedin: www.linkedin.com/company/firstliberty
X (Twitter): x.com/1stLiberty
YouTube: www.youtube.com/c/FirstLibertyInstitute
Description: Independent, nonprofit public policy organization. Provides public service announcements for radio stations. **Scope:** Public policy, focusing on limited government, free enterprise, limited taxation, and traditional family values. Sponsors briefings on issues affecting Texas. **Founded:** 1972. **Publications:** *Legislative Bulletins*; *Lone Star Report*; *Voter's Guide.*

15490 ■ Florida TaxWatch (FTW)

106 N Bronough St.
  Tallahassee, FL 32301
Ph: (850)222-5052
Co. E-mail: info@floridataxwatch.org
URL: http://floridataxwatch.org
Facebook: www.facebook.com/floridataxwatch
Linkedin: www.linkedin.com/company/florida-taxwa
  tch
X (Twitter): x.com/floridataxwatch
YouTube: www.youtube.com/user/fltaxwatch/videos
Description: Independent, nonprofit research organization. **Scope:** State government productivity and cost savings, state budgeting and taxation, internal auditing, program analysis, and taxpayer education. **Founded:** 1979. **Holdings:** Periodicals; videos; pamphlets. **Publications:** *Budget Watch Series*; *Report and Recommendations of the Government Cost Savings Task Force*; *Florida TaxWatch Research reports* (Annual). **Educational Activities:** Ideas in Action Forum, Offer exemplary teaching programs. **Awards:** Florida TaxWatch Prudential-Davis Productivity Awards (Annual).

15491 ■ Fraser Institute (FI) - Library

1770 Burrard St., 4th Fl.
  Vancouver, BC, Canada V6J 3G7
Ph: (604)688-0221
Free: 800-665-3558
Fax: (604)688-8539
Co. E-mail: info@fraserinstitute.org
URL: http://www.fraserinstitute.org
Contact: Niels Veldhuis, President
E-mail: niels.veldhuis@fraserinstitute.org
Facebook: www.facebook.com/FraserInstitute
Linkedin: www.linkedin.com/company/the-fraser-insti
  tute
X (Twitter): x.com/FraserInstitute
Instagram: www.instagram.com/fraser_institute
YouTube: www.youtube.com/user/FraserInstitute
Description: Publishes on economic, social and public policy. Reaches market through direct mail, trade sales and wholesalers, including Baker and

Taylor Books and Blackwell North America. Does not accept unsolicited manuscripts. **Scope:** Studies industrial organization, economics of discrimination, housing, marketing boards, taxation, labor markets, energy markets, the environment and other general economic issues through economic analysis. The Institute's objective is to provide a base of well-supported information about the functions of the competitive market system. **Founded:** 1974. **Holdings:** Figures not available. **Publications:** *The Fraser Institute Annual Report* (Annual); *Fraser Forum*; *Public Policy Sources and Economic Freedom of the World* (Annual).

15492 ■ Hoover Institution on War, Revolution and Peace - Library [Hoover Institution]

434 Galvez Mall
  Stanford University
  Stanford, CA 94305-6003
URL: http://www.hoover.org/library-archives
Description: Devoted to interdisciplinary scholarship and advanced research in the social sciences and public policy on domestic and international affairs. Maintains archives and library on political, economic, and social change in the 20th century. **Scope:** Analyzing social, political, and economic change and formulating a diverse range of ideas and proposals on public policy and central aspects of the research mission of the Hoover Institution. **Services:** Interlibrary loan (limited); some materials are non-circulating. **Founded:** 1919. **Holdings:** 1,000,000 volumes; 6,000 archivals. **Publications:** *Essays in Public Policy*; *Hoover Institution on War, Revolution and Peace Quarterly Newsletter* (Quarterly); *Syndicated newspaper column*; *Viewpoints*; *Hoover Archival Documentaries* (Annual); *Hoover Digest* (Quarterly); *Hoover Institution Annual Report* (Annual); *Hoover Institution E-Newsletter* (Monthly); *Hoover Press Bibliographical Series*; *Studies of Nationalities in the Former USSR.* **Educational Activities:** Hoover Institution on War, Revolution and Peace Conferences (Annual). **Awards:** W. Glenn Campbell and Rita Ricardo-Campbell National Fellows (Annual). **Geographic Preference:** National.

15493 ■ International Association of Assessing Officers - Research and Technical Services Department

314 West 10th St.
  Kansas City, MO 64105
Co. E-mail: info@iaao.org
URL: http://www.iaao.org/wcm/About/Press_and_Me
  dia/wcm/About_Us_Content/World_Bank_Programs
  16.aspx
Description: Research and service arm of International Association of Assessing Officers (IAAO), a nonprofit organization of state and local government officials responsible for administering property taxes. Offers workshops and one-day courses. **Scope:** Conducts research and surveys for U.S., state, and local government agencies and organizations in areas of assessment administration, computer-assisted appraisal techniques, mapping in assessment, property taxation, economic development, salaries, assessment office resources, and assessment practices. **Founded:** 1934. **Educational Activities:** Research and Technical Services Department Conference, Offer exemplary teaching and training programs. **Geographic Preference:** Local.

15494 ■ League of California Cities (LCC)

1400 K St., Ste. 400
  Sacramento, CA 95814
Ph: (916)658-8200
Fax: (916)658-8240
Co. E-mail: communications@calcities.org
URL: http://www.cacities.org
Contact: Carolyn Coleman, Chief Executive Officer
E-mail: ccoleman@calcities.org
Facebook: www.facebook.com/CalCities
Linkedin: www.linkedin.com/company/calcities
X (Twitter): twitter.com/CalCities
Instagram: www.instagram.com/calcities
YouTube: www.youtube.com/channel/UCu-qrC
  4LTfogjCaN-3v01yQ

Description: Incorporated cities. Aims to represent California cities before state and federal legislatures. Offers training program; conducts research; disseminates information. **Scope:** An association of California city officials who work together to enhance their knowledge and skills, exchange information, and combine resources so that they may influence policy decisions that affect cities. **Founded:** 1898. **Publications:** *Western City* (Monthly); *CA Cities Advocate* (Weekly (Wed.)); *Special reports*; *Special interest newsletters*. **Educational Activities:** League of California Cities Annual Exposition (Annual). **Geographic Preference:** Local.

15495 ■ National Bureau of Economic Research (NBER)

1050 Massachusetts Ave.
Cambridge, MA 02138
Ph: (617)868-3900
Co. E-mail: info@nber.org
URL: http://www.nber.org
Contact: James Poterba, President
E-mail: op@nber.org
Facebook: www.facebook.com/National-Bureau-of
-Economic-Research-115165771829285
Linkedin: www.linkedin.com/company/national
-bureau-of-economic-research
X (Twitter): x.com/nberpubs
YouTube: www.youtube.com/nbervideos

Description: Conducts analyses of economic issues, including economic growth and fluctuations, productivity, financial institutions, money, international economic problems, taxation, government spending, labor studies, health, and American economic history. **Scope:** Quantitative analysis of American economy, including productivity, capital formation, taxation, pensions and social insurance, business cycles, financial institutions and processes, labor economics, international economic relations, health economics, and the economics of aging. **Founded:** 1920. **Publications:** *Macroeconomics Annual* (Annual); *NBER Digest* (Monthly); *NBER Reporter* (Quarterly); *Tax Policy and the Economy* (Annual). **Educational Activities:** Summer Institute (Annual). **Geographic Preference:** National.

15496 ■ National Community Pharmacists Association (NCPA)

100 Daingerfield Rd.
Alexandria, VA 22314
Ph: (703)683-8200
Free: 800-544-7447
Fax: (703)683-3619
Co. E-mail: kathy.doucette@ncpa.org
URL: http://ncpa.org
Contact: Hashim Zaibak, Vice President
Facebook: www.facebook.com/commpharmacy
Linkedin: www.linkedin.com/company/ncpa
X (Twitter): x.com/commpharmacy
Instagram: www.instagram.com/commpharmacy
YouTube: www.youtube.com/user/NCPAvids

Description: Owners and managers of independent drugstores and pharmacists employed in community pharmacies offering pharmacy service. Provides support for undergraduate pharmacy education through National Community Pharmacists Association Foundation. **Scope:** Public policy issues, including but not limited to, taxation, health care, social security and Medicare, pensions and retirement, security, energy and the environment. **Founded:** 1898. **Publications:** *America's Pharmacist: The Voice of the Community Pharmacists* (Monthly); *NCPAA Newsletter* (Quarterly); *Daily Policy Digest* (Daily); *Health Policy Digest* (Weekly); *NCPA Alert* (Bimonthly); *Today at the NCPA* (Daily); *What's New at the NCPA* (Weekly); *NCPA Newsletter* (Semimonthly). **Educational Activities:** Hatton Sumners Distinguished Lecture Series, Offer exemplary teaching programs.; NCPA Public policy forums, Offer exemplary teaching programs.; NCPA Annual Convention (Annual). **Awards:** General NCPA Internships (3/year); J.C. and Rheba Cobb Memorial Scholarships (Annual); NCPA Foundation Presidential Scholarships (Annual); NCPA Summer Internship Program; Neil Pruitt Sr. Memorial Scholarship (Annual); Willard B. Simmons Sr. Memorial Scholarships (Annual). **Geographic Preference:** National.

15497 ■ New York Public Interest Research Group - Albany (NYPIRG)

107 Washington Ave.
Albany, NY 12210
Ph: (518)436-0876
Fax: (518)432-6178
URL: http://www.nypirg.org
Contact: Blair Horner, Executive Director
E-mail: bhorner@nypirg.org

Description: Independent, nonprofit research and public advocacy organization. **Scope:** Advocates the rights of consumers and conducts studies to protect consumer interests in such areas as toxic waste, tax policies, environmental resources, drinking water, incineration, recycling, utility rate reform, nuclear power, government and political reform, standardized testing, higher education, and mass transit. **Founded:** 1976. **Publications:** *NYPIRG AGENDA* (Quarterly); *Council Watch*. **Educational Activities:** NYPIRG Conferences, Offer exemplary teaching and training programs. **Geographic Preference:** State.

15498 ■ Peter G. Peterson Institute for International Economics (PIIE)

1750 Massachusetts Ave. NW
Washington, DC 20036-1903
Ph: (202)328-9000
Co. E-mail: comments@piie.com
URL: http://www.piie.com
Contact: Adam S. Posen, President
E-mail: posena@piie.com
Facebook: www.facebook.com/PIIEonline
Linkedin: www.linkedin.com/company/piie
X (Twitter): x.com/piie

Description: Publishes on international economic policy. Studies are geared to the needs of government officials, businesspeople, financiers, teachers and others. Reaches market through direct mail, trade sales and wholesalers. Does not accept unsolicited manuscripts. **Scope:** Principal research areas are finance, trade and investment, globalization, and regional and country studies. Understand the international economic issues confronting policymakers and to devise practical policy responses. Consult with government officials and nongovernment observers of international economic affairs. **Founded:** 1981. **Publications:** *Peter G. Peterson Institute for International Economics Books*; *Policy analyses* (Monthly); *Policy briefs* (Annual); *Peter G. Peterson Institute for International Economics Working papers* (Monthly).

15499 ■ Taxpayers' Federation of Illinois (TFI)

430 East Vine, Ste. A
Springfield, IL 62703
Ph: (217)522-6818
Co. E-mail: tfi@illinoistax.org
URL: http://www.illinoistax.org
Contact: Carol Portman, President
E-mail: carol@illinoistax.org
Facebook: www.facebook.com/taxpayersfederation
X (Twitter): x.com/TFIllinois

Description: Individual taxpayers, small businesses, and large corporations. Monitors Illinois government financial activities. Conducts lobbying efforts and research. **Scope:** Illinois tax issues, including income, property, and sales taxes; general public policy issues, especially spending and performance analysis in areas such as education, health care, and government administration. **Founded:** 1940. **Publications:** *TFI Annual report* (Annual); *Illinois Tax Facts Newsletter* (Monthly); *Legislative Directory & Fiscal Facts* (Biennial). **Geographic Preference:** State.

15500 ■ Texas Public Policy Foundation (TPPF)

901 Congress Ave.
Austin, TX 78701
Ph: (512)472-2700
Fax: (512)472-2728
Co. E-mail: info@texaspolicy.com
URL: http://www.texaspolicy.com
Contact: Kyle Stallings, Chairman
Facebook: www.facebook.com/TexasPolicy

Linkedin: www.linkedin.com/company/texas-public
-policy-foundation
X (Twitter): x.com/TPPF
YouTube: www.youtube.com/user/TexasPPF

Description: Promotes and defends liberty, personal responsibility and free enterprise in Texas through educating and affecting policymakers and the Texas public policy debate with academically sound research and outreach. **Scope:** State public policy issues, focusing on free enterprise, limited government, individual responsibility and freedom, tax policy, honesty in government, private initiative, economic growth, and open and responsive government. Specific areas of research include Texas fiscal policy, education, health care, transportation, insurance, telecommunications, water and natural resources, tort reform, and the role of government. **Founded:** 1989. **Publications:** *TPPF Newsletters*; *TPPF Reports*; *Videos*. **Educational Activities:** TPPF Policy Orientation for the Texas Legislature; TPPF Policy Primer Series. **Geographic Preference:** State.

15501 ■ University of Michigan - Stephen M. Ross School of Business - Office of Tax Policy Research (OTPR)

701 Tappan St., Rm. R5380
Ann Arbor, MI 48109-1234
Ph: (734)763-3068
Co. E-mail: otprfamily@umich.edu
URL: http://rossweb.bus.umich.edu/otpr
Contact: Prof. Joel Slemrod, PhD, Director
E-mail: jslemrod@umich.edu

Description: Integral unit of Stephen M. Ross School of Business at the University of Michigan. **Scope:** Research focuses on the tax system, and serving as a liaison on tax issues among academic institutions, businesses and policy makers in the community. Topics include tax policy, compliance, capital gains, reform, international taxation, and income dynamics. **Founded:** 1987. **Publications:** *Tax Research News* (Semiannual). **Educational Activities:** OTPR Conference on relevant tax issues.

15502 ■ University of Toronto - Joseph L. Rotman School of Management - Institute for International Business

105 St. George St.
Toronto, ON, Canada M5S 3E6
Ph: (416)978-5654
Fax: (416)978-7030
Co. E-mail: dobson@rotman.utoronto.ca
URL: http://www.rotman.utoronto.ca/FacultyAndRe-
search/ResearchCentres/InstituteForInterna
tionalBusiness
Contact: Bernardo Blum, Director
E-mail: bernardo.blum@rotman.utoronto.ca
Facebook: www.facebook.com/Ro
tmanSchoolOfManagement
Linkedin: www.linkedin.com/school/rotman-school-of
-management-university-of-toronto¿pathWildcar
d=3663
X (Twitter): twitter.com/Rotman_Intl_Biz

Description: Integral unit of Joseph L. Rotman School of Management at University of Toronto, operating under an executive committee. Offers advisory services to decision makers within government and industry; research training, both in quantitative analysis and social sciences. **Scope:** Analyses of social and economic policy, including studies on fiscal policy and taxation, applied econometrics, urban and regional economics, public expenditures, non-market decision making, economics of higher education, industry studies, and macro-econometric models. **Founded:** 1967. **Publications:** *IPA Annual Report*; *Rotman Working Papers*.

15503 ■ Utah Foundation

PO Box 387
Salt Lake City, UT 84110
Ph: (801)355-1400
Co. E-mail: outreach@utahfoundation.org
URL: http://www.utahfoundation.org
Contact: Shawn Teigen, President
E-mail: shawn@utahfoundation.org
Facebook: www.facebook.com/Utah.Foundation
X (Twitter): x.com/utahfoundation

Description: Aims to produce objective, thorough and well-reasoned research and analysis that promotes the effective use of public resources, a thriving economy, a well-prepared workforce and a high quality of life for Utahns. **Scope:** Research center focuses on public education, higher education, tax and fiscal policy, state economy, environment, health and welfare, etc. in Utah. **Founded:** 1945. **Publications:** *Utah Foundation Research Reports* (Irregular); *Special report* (Periodic); *Statistical Review of Government in Utah* (Biennial).

15504 ■ Washington Research Council (WRC)
520 Pike St., Ste. 1212
Seattle, WA 98101
Ph: (206)467-7088
Co. E-mail: wrc@researchcouncil.org
URL: http://researchcouncil.org
Contact: Dr. Kriss Sjoblom, Director, Research
E-mail: ksjoblom@researchcouncil.org
Facebook: www.facebook.com/WRCresearch
Linkedin: www.linkedin.com/company/washington-research-council
X (Twitter): x.com/WRCresearch
Description: Provides timely, credible economic research and policy analysis supporting economic vitality and private sector job creation. **Publications:** *How Washington Compares*; *Special Reports*; *State Budget Trends*; *WRC Notebook* (Monthly). **Educational Activities:** WRC Annual meeting (Annual), In the spring for members and guests. **Geographic Preference:** State.

ASSOCIATIONS AND OTHER ORGANIZATIONS

15505 ■ **American Public Transportation Association (APTA) - Library**
1300 I St. NW Ste. 1200 E
  Washington, DC 20005
Ph: (202)496-4800
Fax: (202)496-4324
Co. E-mail: info@apta.com
URL: http://www.apta.com
Contact: Linda Ford, General Counsel
Facebook: www.facebook.com/
  AmericanPublicTransportationAssociation
Linkedin: www.linkedin.com/company/american-pub-
  lic-transportation-association
X (Twitter): x.com/APTA_info
Instagram: www.instagram.com/apta_transit
YouTube: www.youtube.com/user/APTAtv

Description: Seeks to: collect information relative to public transit; assist in the training, education and professional development of all persons involved in public transit; and engage in activities which promote public transit. Provides a medium for exchange of experiences, discussion, and a comparative study of public transit affairs; Promotes research. **Scope:** Transportation. **Founded:** 1974. **Holdings:** Figures not available. **Publications:** *Rural Transit Fact Book* (Annual); *American Public Transportation Association--Member Directory*; *Transit Training Resources Directory*; *Passenger Transport: The Weekly Newspaper of the Public Transportation Industry* (Biweekly). **Awards:** Outstanding Public Transportation System Achievement Award (Triennial). **Geographic Preference:** Multinational.

15506 ■ **Chartered Institute of Logistics and Transport in North America (CILTNA) [Institut agree de la logistique et des transports Amerique du Nord]**
PO Box 45539
  Chapman Mills
  Ottawa, ON, Canada K2J 5N1
Ph: (613)209-9992
Fax: (888)636-9493
Co. E-mail: admin@ciltna.com
URL: http://ciltna.com
Contact: Bob Armstrong, President
E-mail: armstrong@ciltna.com
Facebook: www.facebook.com/CILTNA

Description: Professionals in the transportation industries. Promotes high standards of ethics and practice among members; encourages study and interest in transportation and related fields. Makes available continuing professional education opportunities to members. **Founded:** 1919. **Publications:** *Pegasus* (Quarterly). **Educational Activities:** CILTNA Fall Outlook Conference (Annual). **Awards:** CILTNA CSL Gold Medal (Annual). **Geographic Preference:** Multinational.

15507 ■ **National Bus Traffic Association (NBTA)**
111 K St. NE, 9th Fl.
  Washington, DC 20002-8110
Ph: (202)898-2700
Fax: (202)842-0850
URL: http://www.bustraffic.org
Contact: L. G. Markel, Contact

Description: Establishes by the intercity regular route bus carriers. Serves as tariff publisher for its industry. **Founded:** 1933. **Geographic Preference:** National.

15508 ■ **The Transportation Alliance (TLPA)**
10340 Democracy Ln., Ste. 300
  Fairfax, VA 22030
Ph: (301)984-5700
Co. E-mail: info@thetransportationalliance.org
URL: http://www.tlpa.org
Contact: Bill Yuhnke, President

Description: To provide members with a network of programs, services and support that will enhance their ability to effectively and profitably serve local public transportation needs. **Founded:** 1917. **Publications:** *The Transportation Leader--Buyer's Guide Issue*; *Transportation Leader* (Quarterly); *Taxi and Livery Management*. **Educational Activities:** TLPA Spring Conference & Expo (Annual). **Awards:** TLPA Driver of the Year (Annual); TLPA Operator of the Year (Annual). **Geographic Preference:** Multinational.

15509 ■ **Transportation Association of Canada (TAC) - Library [Association des Transports du Canada]**
401-1111 Prince of Wales Dr.
  Ottawa, ON, Canada K2C 3T2
Ph: (613)736-1350
Fax: (613)736-1395
URL: http://www.tac-atc.ca
Contact: Sarah Wells, Secretary
E-mail: swells@tac-atc.ca
Linkedin: www.linkedin.com/company/transportation
  -association-of-canada
X (Twitter): x.com/TAC_TranspAssn

Description: Government agencies and private organizations involved in transportation. Maintains technical information service; compiles statistics. **Scope:** Transportation. **Services:** Interlibrary loan; copying. **Founded:** 1914. **Holdings:** 17,000 volumes of documents; books; manuals; reports. **Awards:** TAC Foundation-exp Scholarships; TAC Foundation-Parsons Scholarships; TAC Foundation-407 ETR Scholarships; TAC Foundation-Canadian Council of Independent Laboratories Graduate Student Scholarships (CCIL) (Annual); TAC Foundation CCMTA Road Safety Scholarships; TAC Foundation-Amec Foster Wheeler Scholarships; TAC Foundation-SNC Lavalin Scholarships (Annual); TAC Foundation-Tetra Tech EBA Inc. Scholarships; TAC Foundation Golder Associates Ltd. Scholarships; TAC Foundation-ISL Engineering Scholarships; TAC Foundation-LEA Consulting Ltd. Scholarships (Annual); TAC Foundation – 3M Canada "Bob Margison Memorial" Scholar-

ship (Annual); TAC Foundation-Cement Association of Canada Scholarships; TAC Foundation-Dillon Consulting Scholarships; TAC Foundation-IBI Group Scholarships (Annual); TAC Foundation-MMM Group Limited Scholarships; TAC Foundation-Municipalities Scholarships; TAC Foundation-Provinces and Territories Scholarships; TAC Foundation-Stantec Consulting Dr. Ralph Haas Scholarships; TAC Foundation Scholarships (Annual); TAC Foundation-Dr. Ralph Haas Graduate Student Scholarships; TAC Foundation-HDR Corporation Graduate Student Scholarships (Annual); TAC Foundation-EllisDon Corporation Scholarships (Annual); TAC Foundation-Peto MacCallum Undergraduate & College Scholarships; TAC Foundation-ATS Traffic Scholarships. **Geographic Preference:** National.

15510 ■ **United Motorcoach Association (UMA)**
113 S W St., 4th Fl.
  Alexandria, VA 22314
Ph: (703)838-2929
Fax: (703)838-2950
Co. E-mail: info@uma.org
URL: http://uma.org
Contact: Scott Michael, President
Facebook: www.facebook.com/unitedmo
  torcoachassociation
Linkedin: www.linkedin.com/company/united-mo
  torcoach-association
X (Twitter): x.com/UMADrives
YouTube: www.youtube.com/user/UMADrives

Description: Represents bus and motor coach companies. Concerns itself with issues related to buses such as safety standards and regulations. **Founded:** 1971. **Publications:** *Operating Ratio Study*. **Educational Activities:** Motorcoach Expo (Annual). **Geographic Preference:** National.

REFERENCE WORKS

15511 ■ **"All Aboard!" Austin Business Journal (Vol. 32, April 27, 2012, No. 8, pp. A1)**
Ed: Sandra Zaragoza. **Description:** The MLK transit-oriented development in east Austin, Texas is attracting interest from real estate developers. About $22 million in real estate development projects are due to break ground in the vicinity of the station within 18 months. **Availability:** Online.

15512 ■ **"All Hail: How Taxi Companies Stay Competitive in an Evolving Marketplace" in SmartcitiesDive (March 28, 2019)**
URL(s): www.smartcitiesdive.com/news/taxi-compa-nies-ride-hailing-competitition/551449/

Ed: Katie Pyzyk. **Released:** March 28, 2019. **Description:** It's no surprise that Uber an Lyft have taken a good deal of market share from the traditional taxi business, so how do taxis still make a living? By adapting the same business model as Uber and Lyft, several taxi cab companies are still profitable and gaining back that market share. **Availability:** Online.

15513 ■ *"Boston Cab Association Gets 2012 Green Business Award" in Professional Close-Up (April 28, 2012)*

Description: Boston Cab Association was awarded the 2012 Green Business Award for its conversion to all hybrid vehicles in its fleet. The company was the first to commit to the purchase of hybrids in 2006 as part of the City of Boston's Clean Air Cab program. **Availability:** Online.

15514 ■ *"Full Speed Ahead?" in San Antonio Business Journal (Vol. 28, May 9, 2014, No. 13, pp. 4)*

Pub: American City Business Journals, Inc.

Contact: Mike Olivieri, Executive Vice President

Released: May 09, 2014. **Price:** $4, Introductory 4-Week Offer(Digital & Print). **Description:** Lyft and Uber Technologies Inc. have launched ride-sharing services in San Antonio, Texas without the city's permission and the objections of taxi and limousine industries. The ride-sharing service issues were brought into court and to the City Council, while the San Antonio Police Department issued a cease-and-desist order to the ride-sharing companies. The complaints against Lyft and Uber are outlined. **Availability:** Print; Online.

15515 ■ *How to Start a Home-Based Senior Care Business*

Ed: James L. Ferry. **Released:** 2nd edition. **Price:** Paperback,softback; Electronic Book. **Description:** Information is provided to start a home-based senior care business. **Availability:** E-book; Print.

15516 ■ *"Insurers Enter Ridesharing Dispute" in Sacramento Business Journal (Vol. 31, June 6, 2014, No. 15, pp. 8)*

Pub: American City Business Journals, Inc.

Contact: Mike Olivieri, Executive Vice President

Released: Weekly. **Price:** $4, Introductory 4-week offer(Digital & Print). **Description:** Insurance companies have been lobbying the California Assembly to pass legislation requiring ridesharing drivers to carry commercial liability insurance. Ridesharing companies provide drivers with liability coverage as a backup when an accident is not covered by personal insurance. The passage of such a bill would boost ridesharing companies' revenues. **Availability:** Print; Online.

15517 ■ *"People; E-Commerce, Online Games, Mobile Apps" in Advertising Age (Vol. 80, October 19, 2009, No. 35, pp. 14)*

Pub: Crain Communications, Inc.

Contact: Jessica Botos, Manager, Marketing

E-mail: jessica.botos@crainsnewyork.com

Ed: Nat Ives. **Description:** Profile of People Magazine and the ways in which the publisher is moving its magazine forward by exploring new concepts in a time of declining newsstand sales and advertising pages; among the strategies are e-commerce such as the brand People Style Watch in which consumers are able highlight clothing and jewelry and then connect to retailers' sites and a channel on Taxi TV, the network of video-touch screens in New Your City taxis. **Availability:** Online.

15518 ■ *"Ride Apps Uber, Lyft, Sidecar Hit Speed Bumps" in San Francisco Business Times (Vol. 28, January 24, 2014, No. 27, pp. 4)*

Pub: American City Business Journals, Inc.

Contact: Mike Olivieri, Executive Vice President

Released: Weekly. **Price:** $4, Introductory 4-week offer(Digital & Print). **Description:** California's Public Utilities Commission (PUC) has reversed its earlier prohibition and allowed mobile app ride services, while imposing insurance and safety regulations on these alternatives to taxicabs and limousine services. However, the PUC did not take action when the issue of liability and insurance were raised due to the death of Sofia Liu, who was hit by an Uber driver. The lawsuits against Uber are discussed. **Availability:** Print; Online.

15519 ■ *"Ride-Share Field Has New Player" in Providence Business News (Vol. 29, April 21, 2014, No. 3, pp. 1)*

Pub: American City Business Journals, Inc.

Contact: Mike Olivieri, Executive Vice President

URL(s): pbn.com/ride-share-field-has-new-player9 6580

Description: Lyft is Providence, Rhode Island's newest ride-sharing service. State officials continue to look for ways to regulate Internet vehicle services, taxis and limousines. Nearly all of Lyft's drivers are part-time employees using their own personal vehicles.

15520 ■ *"Ride-Share Programs Seem to Fit San Antonio's Future" in San Antonio Business Journal (Vol. 28, May 9, 2014, No. 13, pp. 6)*

Pub: American City Business Journals, Inc.

Contact: Mike Olivieri, Executive Vice President

Price: $4, Introductory 4-Week Offer(Digital & Print). **Description:** San Antonio, Texas Mayor Julian Castro has been promoting the SA2020 plan that calls for an increase in downtown living and expanded public transit options. Castro made positive comments regarding the ride sharing services, even if they include a few disqualifications. The potential benefits of the ride sharing services into the city's plan are examined. **Availability:** Print; Online.

15521 ■ *"Ride Sharing Market Size Worth Around US$344.4 Bn by 2030" in GlobeNewswire (September 28, 2021)*

Released: September 28, 2021. **Description:** The global value in ride sharing was valued at US$73.5 billion for 2020 but is expected to rise dramatically within the next ten years. Discusses the factors that are driving market growth in this industry. **Availability:** Online.

15522 ■ *"A Taxi Service for the Homeless" in Forest Park Review (April 16, 2019)*

URL(s): www.forestparkreview.com/News/Articles/ 4-16-2019/A-taxi-service-for-the-homeless-/

Ed: Tom Holmes. **Released:** April 16, 2019. **Description:** Forest Park resident John Netherly has been using his own car to transport homeless people to shelters or to receive treatment or help for the last two years. Creating a taxicab for the homeless, this social worker is willing to fill the gap that government agencies do not address. **Availability:** Online.

15523 ■ *"Taxis Are Set to Go Hybrid" in Philadelphia Business Journal (Vol. 30, September 16, 2011, No. 31, pp. 1)*

Pub: Philadelphia Business Journal

Contact: Sierra Quinn, Director

E-mail: squinn@bizjournals.com

Ed: Natalie Kostelni. **Description:** Taxis are going hybrid in several major states such as New York, California and Maryland where it is mandated, but it is yet to happen in Philadelphia, Pennsylvania with the exception of one taxi company. Freedom Taxi is awaiting Philadelphia Parking Authority's sign off. **Availability:** Online.

15524 ■ *"Uber, Lyft and the Hard Economics of Taxi Cab Medallions" in The Washington Post (May 24, 2019)*

URL(s): washingtonpost.com/business/economy/uber -lyft-and-the-hard-economics-of-taxi-cab-me dallions/2019/05/24/cf1b56f4-7cda-11e9-a5b3-34f 3edf1351e_story.html

Ed: Roger Lowenstein. **Released:** May 24, 2019. **Description:** Ride-hailing companies Uber and Lyft have greatly upset the New York taxi cab business model, which has been operating in the same way for decades. Based on a medallion model, where the city issues out these permits to drivers, the industry saw the prices of medallions jump to over a million dollars at one point. Uber and Lyft changed that dynamic and the value of the medallion has fallen. **Availability:** Online.

STATISTICAL SOURCES

15525 ■ *RMA Annual Statement Studies*

Pub: Risk Management Association

Contact: Nancy Foster, President

Released: Annual. **Description:** Contains composite balance sheets and income statements for more than 360 industries, including the accounting, auditing, and bookkeeping industries. Also contains five years of comparative historical data for discerning trends. Includes 16 commonly used ratios, computed for most of the size groupings for nearly every industry.

15526 ■ *Taxi & Limousine Services Industry in the US - Market Research Report*

URL(s): www.ibisworld.com/united-states/market-re search-reports/taxi-limousine-services-industry/

Price: $925. **Description:** Downloadable report analyzing current and future trends in the taxi and limousine services industry. **Availability:** Download.

TRADE PERIODICALS

15527 ■ *Commercial Carrier Journal*

Pub: Randall-Reilly

Contact: Matt Reilly, President

URL(s): www.ccjdigital.com

Facebook: www.facebook.com/ CommercialCarrierJournal

Linkedin: www.linkedin.com/company/commercial -carrier-journal

X (Twitter): twitter.com/CCJnow

YouTube: www.youtube.com/user/CCJDigital

Description: Magazine containing management, maintenance, and operations information for truck and bus fleets. **Availability:** Print; Online.

LIBRARIES

15528 ■ **Alabama Department of Transportation (ALDOT)**

PO Box 303050

Montgomery, AL 36130-3050

Ph: (334)353-6554

Co. E-mail: aldotinfo@dot.state.al.us

URL: http://www.dot.state.al.us

Contact: John Cooper, Director

E-mail: cooperjr@dot.state.al.us

Scope: Transportation. **Services:** Interlibrary loan; library not open to the public. **Founded:** 1953. **Holdings:** 1,000 books; 5,000 reports.

15529 ■ **California State Department of Motor Vehicles - Licensing Operations Division - Research and Development Branch - Traffic Safety Research Library**

1120 N St., Rm. 1430

Sacramento, CA 95814

Ph: (914)654-4601

Co. E-mail: library@dot.ca.gov

URL: http://dot.ca.gov/programs/transportation-library

Scope: Automobile transportation. **Services:** Copying; library not open to the public. **Holdings:** 500 books; 10,000 bound periodical volumes; reports; manuscripts. **Subscriptions:** 20 journals and other serials.

15530 ■ **Kansas Department of Transportation (KDOT) - Library**

Dwight D. Eisenhower State Office Building 700 SW Harrison St.

Topeka, KS 66603-3745

Ph: (785)296-3566

Fax: (785)368-7415

Co. E-mail: kdot#publicinfo@ks.gov

URL: http://www.ksdot.gov

Contact: Bob Brock, Director

Facebook: www.facebook.com/KSDOTHQ

X (Twitter): x.com/KDOTHQ

YouTube: www.youtube.com/user/kansastransporta tion

Pinterest: www.pinterest.com/kdothq

Description: Transportation: Local and suburban transit. **Scope:** Transportation. **Founded:** 1868. **Holdings:** Figures not available.

15531 ■ Missouri Department of Transportation-Division of Materials Library
Rm. 200 600 W Main St.
  Jefferson City, MO 65101
URL: http://www.modot.org

Scope: Transportation. **Services:** Library not open to the public. **Holdings:** Figures not available.

15532 ■ Montana Department of Transportation (MDT)
2701 Prospect Ave.
  Helena, MT 59601
Ph: (406)444-6200
Co. E-mail: mdtcommteam@mt.gov
Facebook: www.facebook.com/montanadot
Linkedin: www.linkedin.com/company/montana-depar tment-of-transportation
Instagram: www.instagram.com/mtdot
YouTube: www.youtube.com/user/MontanaDOT

Description: Mission is to serve the public by providing a transportation system and services that emphasize quality, safety, cost effectiveness, economic vitality, and sensitivity to the environment. **Scope:** Transportation. **Services:** Interlibrary loan; copying. **Founded:** 1913. **Holdings:** 20,000 titles.

15533 ■ New Jersey Department of Transportation Research Library (NJDOT)
c/o David J. Goldberg Transportation Complex
  1035 Pky., Ave.
  Trenton, NJ 08625
Ph: (609)963-1982
URL: http://www.nj.gov/transportation/business/re search/library
Contact: David J. Goldberg, Contact

Scope: Transportation. **Services:** Interlibrary loan; copying; library open to the public by appointment. **Founded:** 1962. **Holdings:** 300 books; 11,000 reports.

15534 ■ North Dakota Department of Transportation - Materials and Research Division - Library
608 East Blvd. Ave.
  Bismarck, ND 58505-0700
URL: http://www.dot.nd.gov/divisions/materials/ma terials.htm
Facebook: www.facebook.com/nddot
X (Twitter): x.com/NorthDakotaDOT
YouTube: www.youtube.com/user/NDDOTOnline

Description: Integral unit of North Dakota Department of Transportation. **Scope:** Transportation. **Services:** Library not open to the public. **Founded:** 1970. **Holdings:** 6,600 reports.

15535 ■ South Carolina Department of Transportation (SCDOT) - Library
955 Pk. St.
  Columbia, SC 29201-3959
Ph: (803)737-1200
Free: 855-467-2368
URL: http://www.scdot.org
Facebook: www.facebook.com/SCDOT
X (Twitter): x.com/SCDOTPress
YouTube: www.youtube.com/user/SCDOTconnec toronline

Scope: Transportation. **Founded:** 1998. **Holdings:** Figures not available.

15536 ■ University of Kentucky College of Engineering - Kentucky Transportation Center (KTC) - Library
176 Oliver H Raymond Bldg.
  Lexington, KY 40506
Ph: (859)257-4513
URL: http://ktc.uky.edu
URL(s): www.engr.uky.edu/research-faculty/depar tments/civil-engineering/kentucky-transportation -center
Facebook: www.facebook.com/ KYTRANSPORTATION

Linkedin: www.linkedin.com/company/ktc-uky
X (Twitter): x.com/kytransport
YouTube: www.youtube.com/channel/UCCkzZxbfj -2ZzMKYgH6Jn5Q

Description: Integral unit of College of Engineering, University of Kentucky, operating under its own board of control. Offers technology transfer program, including transportation workshops, audiovisual and library materials, mail lists, and technical assistance. **Scope:** Highways; bridges; the environment; geotechnology; Intelligent Transportation Systems (ITS); pavements; traffic and safety; structures; construction management; transportation policy, planning, and finance. **Services:** Interlibrary loan; copying; library open to the public. **Founded:** 1981. **Holdings:** Books; Reports; Videotapes. **Subscriptions:** 300 journals and other serials. **Publications:** *The Link Technology Transfer Newsletter.* **Educational Activities:** Annual Transportation Forum, Cosponsored with the Advanced Institute for Transportation Systems Science.

RESEARCH CENTERS

15537 ■ Southwest Region University Transportation Center (SWUTC)
Texas A&M Transportation Institute
  Texas A&M University System
  3135 TAMU
  College Station, TX 77843-3135
Ph: (979)845-5815
Fax: (979)862-1225
Co. E-mail: swutc@tamu.edu
URL: http://swutc.tamu.edu
Contact: Dr. Melissa Tooley, Director
E-mail: m-tooley@tamu.edu

Description: Research and training consortium of Texas Southern University, University of Texas at Austin, and Texas A&M University, headquartered at Texas A&M University at Austin. **Scope:** Transportation of passengers and property. **Founded:** 1988. **Educational Activities:** SWUTC Graduate Instruction, Offer exemplary teaching and training programs.

REFERENCE WORKS

15538 ■ *"Get Stuffed: Which Animals Challenge Taxidermists the Most?" in LiveScience (April 27, 2019)*
URL(s): www.livescience.com/65340-animals-hardest-to-taxidermy.html
Ed: Mindy Weisberger. **Released:** April 27, 2019. **Description:** Describes the processes taxidermists go through to create life-like displays for museums. Some animals are easy to prepare, but others can be a challenge. These include rabbits and other animals with thin skin, and large mammals like elephants simply because of the logistics of dealing with something that size. Ultimately, the hardest animals to work with are ones that the taxidermist is not familiar with, causing a lot of guesswork that may be incorrect. **Availability:** Online.

15539 ■ *"Students' Mounting Interest in Taxidermy" in Sanilac County News (November 24, 2019)*
URL(s): sanilaccountynews.mihomepaper.com/articles/students-mounting-interest-in-taxidermy/
Ed: Steven Kovac. **Released:** November 24, 2019. **Description:** Sanilac County offers an unusual class for high school students — taxidermy. Here, students learn the art of preparing, stuffing, and mounting the skins of animals. Often, the students themselves hunted the animals and in class they diligently work on preserving the carcasses with a hands-on approach to the topic. **Availability:** Online.

REFERENCE WORKS

15540 ■ *"Elkhart Education Foundation to Open Supply Store for Teachers" in The Elkart Truth (June 5, 2019)*
URL(s): www.elkharttruth.com/news/elkhart-educa tion-foundation-to-open-supply-store-for-teachers/ar ticle_828c0fea-d97f-5e41-b31e-806d82ec034c.html
Released: June 05, 2019. **Description:** The Elkhart Education Foundation has recognized that teachers often spend hundreds of their own dollars buying classroom supplies. To help alleviate that spending, the foundation is creating a teacher store where teachers can get any supplies and items they need for their classes. **Availability:** Online.

15541 ■ *"Risk and Reward" in Canadian Business (Vol. 81, October 13, 2008, No. 17, pp. 21)*
Description: Macro-economist and currency analyst Mark Venezia believes that stable financial institutions, free-market reforms, and the role of central banks in keeping inflation and exchange rates stable could make emerging-market bonds strong performers for better future returns. Venezia's other views on emerging-market bonds are discussed. **Availability:** Print; Online.

15542 ■ *"School Supply Store Has Had to Learn How to Roll with the COVID-19 Tide" in Pilot Online (September 18, 2020)*
Ed: Sandra P. Pennecke. **Released:** September 18, 2020. **Description:** When schools went virtual during the COVID-19 school shutdowns, many parents turned to their local teacher and school supply shop to pick up supplies for home learning. Stores have responded to the need by also setting up online shopping to make things easier for parents. **Availability:** Online.

15543 ■ *"The Secret to Keeping a School Supplies Store Open in the Amazon Era" in The New York Times (September 13, 2018)*
URL(s): www.nytimes.com/2018/09/13/nyregion/the -secret-to-keeping-a-school-supplies-store-open-in -the-amazon-era.html

Ed: Fabrice Robinet. **Released:** September 13, 2018. **Description:** Amazon has once again helped cause the demise of a once-booming business — the teacher supply store. Thousands used to be open around the country, but nowadays there are only a few hundred. Still, those that are still around do well because of the customer service they provide, plus it's once stop shopping for teachers and they can see all of the merchandise in one setting. **Availability:** Online.

15544 ■ *"Small Business Economic Trends: Moderate Improvement but No Clear Direction" in Small Business Economic Trends (March 2008, pp. 3)*
Pub: National Federation of Independent Business
Contact: Brad Close, President
Ed: William C. Dunkelberg, Holly Wade. **Description:** Commentary on the economic trends for small businesses in the U.S. is presented. Analysis of the labor market and low interest rates is given. The effect of the Federal Reserve's policy announcement on small business owner optimism is also discussed. **Availability:** Print; Online.

TRADE PERIODICALS

15545 ■ *Educational Dealer: The Magazine for the School Supply Industry*
Pub: Fahy-Williams Publishing Inc.
URL(s): educationaldealermagazine.com
Facebook: www.facebook.com/Educa tionalDealerMagazine
Linkedin: www.linkedin.com/company/educational dealermagazine
X (Twitter): x.com/EdDealerMag
Instagram: www.instagram.com/educationaldealer
Released: 5/year **Description:** Trade magazine for school supply dealers, distributors, and retailers. Includes articles on retailing, cataloging, marketing, management, product lines, trends, and industry news. **Availability:** Print; Online.

VIDEO/AUDIO MEDIA

15546 ■ *Main Street Business Insights: Jamie & Jerry Baker, Trendy Teachers*
URL(s): mainstreet.org/resources/knowledge-hub/po dcast/jamie-jerry-baker-trendy-teachers

Ed: Matt Wagner. **Released:** October 18, 2023. **Description:** Podcast discusses the use of social media and pivoting strategies with the owners of a teaching boutique and educational toy store.

TRADE SHOWS AND CONVENTIONS

15547 ■ EDexpo
Education Market Association (EDmarket)
9841 Washington Blvd., Ste. 200-1041
Gaithersburg, MD 20878
Free: 800-395-5550
Fax: (301)495-3330
Co. E-mail: membership@edmarket.org
URL: http://www.edmarket.org
Contact: Jim McGarry, President
E-mail: jmcgarry@edmarket.org
URL(s): www.edexpo.com
Frequency: Annual. **Description:** Educational supplies and instructional materials. **Audience:** Industry professionals. **Principal Exhibits:** Educational supplies and instructional materials.

15548 ■ EDspaces
Education Market Association (EDmarket)
9841 Washington Blvd., Ste. 200-1041
Gaithersburg, MD 20878
Free: 800-395-5550
Fax: (301)495-3330
Co. E-mail: membership@edmarket.org
URL: http://www.edmarket.org
Contact: Jim McGarry, President
E-mail: jmcgarry@edmarket.org
URL(s): ed-spaces.com
Frequency: Annual. **Description:** Conference features professional development sessions, and sharing of ideas, hands-on sessions, and keynote speakers. **Audience:** Industry professionals. **Principal Exhibits:** Conference features professional development sessions, and sharing of ideas, hands-on sessions, and keynote speakers. **Telecommunication Services:** joe.tucker@emeraldx.com.

REFERENCE WORKS

15549 ■ *"The FCC Has Fined Robocallers $208 Million. It's Collected $6,790" in The Wall Street Journal (March 28, 2019)*
URL(s): www.wsj.com/articles/the-fcc-has-fine
d-robocallers-208-million-its-collected-6-790
-11553770803

Ed: Sarah Krouse. **Released:** March 28, 2019. **Description:** Since 2015 the FCC has ordered violators of the Telephone Consumer Protection Act to pay $208.4 million, but has only managed to collect $6,790 of that amount. Collecting these fines is difficult because illegal operations close up shop quickly and change their names. Others are based overseas making it almost impossible to seize assets. **Availability:** Online.

15550 ■ *"In the Era of Endless Robocalls, Why Telemarketers Persist" in NBC News (December 9, 2018)*
URL(s): www.nbcnews.com/news/us-news/era-en
dless-robocalls-why-telemarketers-persist-n943831

Ed: Corky Siemaszko. **Released:** December 09, 2018. **Description:** With most people receiving daily unwanted calls from telemarketers, spammers, scammers, and spoofers, why do telemarketers still persist in calling? The answer is that it is still making money. Most people hang up but there is a small percentage of people out there who say yes, giving telemarketers the smallest incentive to keep going. **Availability:** Online.

15551 ■ *"State Accuses Eight Companies of Making Sales Calls to People Who Signed up to Stop Them" in WTVA.com (September 4, 2019)*
URL(s): www.wtva.com/content/news/State-accuses
-eight-companies-of-violating-the-law-concerning
-telemarketing-calls-559422281.html

Ed: Craig Ford. **Released:** September 04, 2019. **Description:** The Mississippi Pubic Service Commission is charging eight companies with breaking the law by making telemarketing calls to people who specifically signed up to not receive such calls. They face $5,000 per illegal call. **Availability:** Online.

CONSULTANTS

15552 ■ **Business by Phone Inc.**
10410 S 144th St., No. 3
Omaha, NE 68138
Contact: Art Sobczak, President
Description: Publishes books, tapes and manuals regarding how-to ideas and techniques that help salespeople use the phone more effectively. Also publishes newsletters. **Scope:** Telemarketing specialists providing consulting resources that help people be more effective in sales, service and negotiation situations by phone. Provide customized on-site training, public seminars, products such as newsletters, audiotapes, videos and special reports and manuals. **Publications:** "Tel-E Sales Tip of the Week," Apr, 2010; "How to Place the Successful Sale and Prospecting Call"; "How to Sell More, in Less Time, With No Rejection, Using Common Sense Telephone Techniques, Volumes 1 & 2," Dec, 1998; "Telephone Tips That Sell: 501 How-To Ideas and Affirmations to Help You Get More Business by Phone," 1996; "The Tele-Sales Hot Tips of the Week"; "Telephone Prospecting and Selling Report"; "How to Place the Successful Sales and Prospecting Call- Exactly What to Say and AVOID to Get Agreement and Eliminate Resistance". **Training:** The Telesales Rep College; Prospecting for Profits; Telephone Selling Skills for Outside Salespeople; How to Sell More, In Less Time, With No Rejection, Using Common Sense Telephone Techniques; The Top 10 Mistakes Made By Sales Reps When Using the Phone, and What You Can Do to Avoid These Errors; 30 Telephone Sales Tips You Can Use Right Now.

COMPUTERIZED DATABASES

15553 ■ *FONE*Data*
Melissa Data Corp.
22382 Avenida Empresa
Rancho Santa Margarita, CA 92688
Free: 800-635-4772
Co. E-mail: info@melissa.com
URL: http://www.melissa.com
Contact: Ray Melissa, President
E-mail: ray@melissadata.com
URL(s): www.melissa.com/fonedata-reference-data
-sets
Price: $175, for single update; $450, for per year. **Availability:** PDF; Download. **Type:** Directory; Statistical.

RESEARCH CENTERS

15554 ■ **Columbia University - Columbia Business School - Columbia Institute for Tele-Information (CITI)**
3022 Broadway, Uris Hall 603
New York, NY 10027
URL: http://business.columbia.edu/citi
Contact: Jason Adam Buckweitz, Executive Director
Description: Integral unit of Columbia Business School, Columbia University focused on policy, management and strategy issues in computing, electronic mass media and telecommunications. **Scope:** Economic, management, and policy issues of telecommunications, electronic mass-media, and computer systems. Research has focused on the continuing transformation of the information industry, specifically relating to integration and decentralization. Other areas of research include private and public networking, the economics of networks, studies of telecommunications in the U.S., Europe, the Pacific Basin, Latin America, Africa, and Western Asia, visions of the communications future, globalization of communications media, the future of local communication, video software, free speech and new electronic media, pricing of access in network industries, economics of technology adoption in the public network, American competitiveness in global information markets, specialization and performance in the personal computer industry, economics of electronic stock exchanges, marketing in the motion picture industry, quality choices in network industries, and cryptology. **Founded:** 1983. **Publications:** *CITI Working Paper Series*; *Information Exchange Newsletter* (Semiannual).

ASSOCIATIONS AND OTHER ORGANIZATIONS

15555 ■ *Advisor*
22 Spiral Dr.
 Florence, KY 41042
Ph: (859)283-1885
Fax: (859)283-8178
Co. E-mail: info@nkadd.org
URL: http://nkadd.org
URL(s): us7.campaign-archive.com/home/?u=bb379
 4330c2da62b5d8595091&id=78ba71998a
Released: Monthly; last update, April 2023. **Availability:** Print.

15556 ■ Association of TeleServices International (ATSI)
1000 Westgate Dr., Ste. 252
 Saint Paul, MN 55114
Free: 866-896-2874
Co. E-mail: admin@atsi.org
URL: http://atsi.org
Contact: Jim Reandeau, President

E-mail: jim@focustele.com
Facebook: www.facebook.com/ATSIorg
X (Twitter): x.com/atsiorg
Description: Seeks to foster growth and development in the industry. Represents the industry before Congress and regulatory agencies; negotiates with telephone companies. **Founded:** 1942. **Publications:** *Association of Telemessaging Services International--Membership Directory* (Annual); *Connections* (Bimonthly); *TeleCommunicator* (Bimonthly). **Educational Activities:** ATSI Annual Conference (Annual). **Geographic Preference:** National.

15557 ■ Canadian Call Management Association (CAM-X)
24 Olive St., Unit No 10
 Grimsby, ON, Canada L3M 2B6
Ph: (905)309-0224
Free: 800-896-1054
Fax: (905)309-0225
Co. E-mail: info@camx.ca
URL: http://www.camx.ca
Contact: Linda Osip, Executive Director
E-mail: linda@camx.ca

Facebook: www.facebook.com/people/CAM-X/1000
 57082765650
Linkedin: www.linkedin.com/company/cam-x-cana
 dian-call-management-association
Description: Facilitates technical advancement in the field of telecommunications. **Founded:** 1964. **Publications:** *Advisor* (Monthly). **Awards:** CAM-X Award of Excellence (Annual); CAM-X Call Centre Award of Distinction (Annual). **Geographic Preference:** National.

REFERENCE WORKS

15558 ■ *"5 Surprising Things an Answering Service Can Do for Your Business" in Small Business Trends (March 20, 2018)*
URL(s): smallbiztrends.com/2018/03/benefits-of
 -telephone-answering-services.html
Released: March 20, 2018. **Description:** Telephone answering services have evolved over the years to offer more to their customers. Collecting leads, scheduling appointments, and using scripts, and other services can help your business and save you time and money. **Availability:** Online.

ASSOCIATIONS AND OTHER ORGANIZATIONS

15559 ■ **Electronics Technicians Association International (ETA) [ETA International]**
5 Depot St.
  Greencastle, IN 46135
Ph: (765)653-8262
Free: 800-288-3824
Fax: (765)653-4287
Co. E-mail: eta@etai.org
URL: http://www.etai.org
Contact: Bryan Allen, President
Facebook: www.facebook.com/ETAInternational
X (Twitter): x.com/ETAIntl
YouTube: www.youtube.com/user/ETAINTL
Description: Represents the electronics industry, from the technician and educator to the corporate institution. **Founded:** 1978. **Publications:** *The High-Tech News* (Bimonthly); *Directory of Professional Electronics Technicians* (Irregular). **Awards:** ETA Technician of the Year (Annual); Wallace Medeiros Memorial - Educator of the Year (Annual); ETA President's Award (Annual). **Geographic Preference:** Multinational.

15560 ■ **International Society of Certified Electronics Technicians (ISCET) - Library**
PO Box 378
  Hillsboro, TX 76645
Ph: (817)921-9101
Free: 800-946-0201
Fax: (817)921-3741
Co. E-mail: info@iscet.org
URL: http://www.iscet.org
Contact: Steve Gelman, President
E-mail: steve@nationalservicealliance.com

Description: Seeks to provide a fraternal bond among certified electronics technicians, raise their public image and improve the effectiveness of industry education programs for technicians. Offers training programs in new electronics information. **Scope:** Electronics; technicians. **Founded:** 1965. **Holdings:** Figures not available. **Publications:** *ISCET Update* (Quarterly); *ProService Directory and Yearbook* (Annual). **Educational Activities:** National Professional Service Convention (NPSC) (Annual). **Awards:** Technician of the Year (Annual). **Geographic Preference:** National.

REFERENCE WORKS

15561 ■ *"Don't' Hate the Cable Guy" in Saint Louis Business Journal (Vol. 31, August 5, 2011, No. 50, pp. 1)*
Pub: Saint Louis Business Journal
Contact: Robert Bobroff, President
E-mail: rbobroff@bizjournals.com
Ed: Angela Mueller. **Description:** Charter Communications named John Birrer as senior vice president of customer experience. The company experienced problems with its customer services. **Availability:** Print; Online.

15562 ■ *"For Apple, It's Showtime Again" in Barron's (Vol. 90, August 30, 2010, No. 35, pp. 29)*
Pub: Barron's Editorial & Corporate Headquarters
Ed: Eric J. Savitz. **Description:** Speculations on what Apple Inc. will unveil at its product launch event are presented. These products include a possible new iPhone Nano, a new update to its Apple TV, and possibly a deal with the Beatles to distribute their songs over iTunes. **Availability:** Online.

TRADE PERIODICALS

15563 ■ *The High-Tech News*
Pub: Electronics Technicians Association International
Contact: Bryan Allen, President

URL(s): www.etai.org/high_tech_news.html
Released: Bimonthly **Price:** $25, Nonmembers for print. **Description:** Serves member technicians with news of the Association and the electronics industry, including items on service, education, employment, management, and events. Contains information on membership, management, telecommunications, and business and technical training programs. Recurring features include editorials, news of research, letters to the editor, book reviews, and a calendar of events. **Availability:** Print; PDF; Online.

LIBRARIES

15564 ■ **Antique Wireless Association - Library**
6925 NY-5
  Bloomfield, NY 14469
Ph: (585)257-5119
URL: http://www.antiquewireless.org
Contact: Robert Hobday, President
E-mail: director@antiquewireless.org
Facebook: www.facebook.com/antiquewirelessmuseum
X (Twitter): x.com/antiquewireless
Instagram: www.instagram.com/antiquewirelessmuseum

Description: Maintains museum of 25,000 historical items. Develops and presents historical radio and radio film programs. Sponsors several historical radio meets annually. Has compiled list of members' private museums and collections. **Scope:** History of the technology. **Services:** Open to educators and historians by appointment. **Founded:** 1952. **Holdings:** Monographs. **Publications:** *Telegraph Anthology*; *The AWA Review*; *The AWA Review* (Annual); *AWA Journal* (Quarterly); *The AWA Journal on CD-ROM*. **Awards:** Houck Award for Preservation (Annual); Houck Award for Documentation (Periodic). **Geographic Preference:** Multinational.

Television Station

START-UP INFORMATION

15565 ■ *"Former WCVB Anchor Bianca De la Garza Discusses the Launch of Her New Media Venture" in Boston Business Journal (Vol. 34, June 6, 2014, No. 18, pp. 4)*
Pub: American City Business Journals, Inc.
Contact: Mike Olivieri, Executive Vice President
Released: June 02, 2014. **Description:** News anchor, Bianca de la Garza says career advancement prompted her to form Lucky Gal Productions LLC. She said her entrepreneurial pursuit will develop a television show focusing on lifestyle and entertainment. De la Garza admits she will miss her co-anchor job at WCVB-TV's morning show, 'EyeOpener'. **Availability:** Print; Online.

ASSOCIATIONS AND OTHER ORGANIZATIONS

15566 ■ **Alliance of Canadian Cinema Television and Radio Artists (ACTRA)**
625 Church St., Ste. 300
Toronto, ON, Canada M4Y 2G1
Ph: (416)489-1311
Free: 800-387-3516
Co. E-mail: actraonline@actra.ca
URL: http://www.actra.ca
Contact: Eleanor Noble, President
Facebook: www.facebook.com/ACTRANational
X (Twitter): twitter.com/ACTRAnational
Instagram: www.instagram.com/actranational
YouTube: www.youtube.com/ACTRANational
Description: Seeks to obtain equitable compensation and safe working conditions for members. **Founded:** 1943. **Publications:** *InterACTRA News* (Quarterly); *ACTRASCOPE* (Quarterly). **Geographic Preference:** National.

15567 ■ **America's Public Television Stations (APTS)**
1225 S Clark St., 410
Arlington, VA 22202
Ph: (202)654-4200
Fax: (202)654-4236
Co. E-mail: jobs@apts.org
URL: http://apts.org
Contact: Patrick Butler, President
Facebook: www.facebook.com/AmericasPublicTelevisionStations
X (Twitter): x.com/aptstweet
Description: Public television licensees. Organizes efforts of public television stations in areas of planning and research and in representation before the government. Maintains current information on the public television system including such areas as licensee characteristics, financing and industry trends; makes projections on system growth and income. Monitors social, economic and demographic trends that have an impact on public television services. Disseminates information about public television to policymaking agencies, the press, and

the public. **Founded:** 1979. **Publications:** *Transitions* (Quarterly); *MPRA Newsletter* (Monthly). **Awards:** David J. Brugger Grassroots Advocacy Award (Annual). **Geographic Preference:** National.

15568 ■ **Associated Press Broadcast Services (AP)**
200 Liberty St.
New York, NY 10281
Ph: (212)621-1500
Co. E-mail: info@ap.org
URL: http://www.ap.org/en
Contact: Daisy Veerasingham, President
Facebook: www.facebook.com/APNews
Linkedin: www.linkedin.com/company/associated-press
X (Twitter): x.com/AP
YouTube: www.youtube.com/ap
Description: Broadcast stations in the United States that are members of the Associated Press. Advances journalism through radio and television. Cooperates with the AP in order to make available accurate and impartial news. Serves as a liaison between radio and television stations that are members of the AP and representatives of those stations. **Founded:** 1946. **Geographic Preference:** National; Middle Atlantic States.

15569 ■ **Association Canadienne des Radiodiffuseurs (ACR) [Canadian Association of Broadcasters (CAB)]**
770-45 O' Connor St.
Ottawa, ON, Canada K1P 1A4
Ph: (613)233-4035
URL: http://cab-acr.ca
Contact: Kevin Desjardins, President
Linkedin: www.linkedin.com/company/canadian-association-of-broadcasters
X (Twitter): x.com/CAB_ACR
Description: Collective voice of the majority of Canada's private radio and television stations, networks, and specialty services. Develops industry-wide strategic plans, works to improve the financial health of the industry, and promotes private broadcasting's role as Canada's leading programmer and local service provider. **Founded:** 1926. **Geographic Preference:** National.

15570 ■ **Broadcast Cable Credit Association (BCCA)**
550 W Frontage Rd. Ste. 3600
Northfield, IL 60093
Ph: (847)881-8757
Fax: (847)784-8059
Co. E-mail: info@bccacredit.com
URL: http://www.bccacredit.com/webroot/index.asp
Contact: Mary Collins, President
E-mail: mary.collins@mediafinance.org
Description: Enables members to efficiently manage credit risk and increase profitability. Provides industry specific credit reports on individual agencies, advertisers, or buying services (local or national). **Founded:** 1972. **Publications:** *BCCA Credit Handbook* (Annual); *Credit and Collection Survey*; *The Financial*

Manager (Bimonthly); *Update* (Monthly). **Educational Activities:** Broadcast Cable Credit Association Annual Conference (Annual). **Geographic Preference:** National.

15571 ■ **Broadcast Education Association (BEA)**
1 M St. SE
Washington, DC 20003
Co. E-mail: help@beaweb.org
URL: http://www.beaweb.org/wp
Contact: Kim Fox, President
Description: Universities and colleges; faculty and students. Promotes research, improvement of curriculum and teaching methods, and overall excellence in media production. **Founded:** 1955. **Publications:** *Journal of Radio & Audio Media* (Semiannual); *Journal of Broadcasting & Electronic Media (JoBEM)* (Quarterly); *Feedback* (6/year). **Awards:** Abe Voron Award (Annual); Vincent T. Wasilewski Award (Annual). **Geographic Preference:** Multinational.

15572 ■ **CTAM: Cable and Telecommunications Association for Marketing (CTAM)**
120 Waterfront St., Ste. 200
National Harbor, MD 20745
Ph: (301)485-8900
Fax: (304)485-8898
Co. E-mail: info@ctam.com
URL: http://www.ctam.com
Contact: Vicki Lins, President
Linkedin: www.linkedin.com/company/ctam
X (Twitter): x.com/ctam
Description: Network of cable and telecommunications professionals dedicated to the pursuit of marketing excellence. Provides its members with competitive marketing resources including education, research, networking and leadership opportunities. **Founded:** 1982. **Publications:** *CTAM Quarterly Journal* (Quarterly). **Awards:** CTAM TAMI Awards (Irregular). **Geographic Preference:** National.

15573 ■ **International Radio and Television Society Foundation (IRTS)**
1697 Broadway, Ste. 404
New York, NY 10019
Ph: (212)867-6650
Co. E-mail: info@irts.org
URL: http://irtsfoundation.org
Contact: Joyce Tudryn, President
Facebook: www.facebook.com/TheIRTS
Linkedin: www.linkedin.com/company/the-irts-foundation
Instagram: www.instagram.com/irts.foundation
Description: Individuals interested in management, sales, or executive production in the radio, television, and cable industries and their allied fields. Seeks to educate members through seminars. Conducts summer internships for college students majoring in communications. **Founded:** 1939. **Publications:** *International Radio and Television Society Foundation-- Roster Yearbook* (Annual); *International Radio* (Annual). **Educational Activities:** International Radio

and Television Society Foundation Luncheon. **Awards:** IRTS Gold Medal Award (Annual); International Radio and Television Society Foundation Summer Fellowships Program (Annual). **Geographic Preference:** National.

15574 ■ Jones NCTI
6855 S Havana St., Ste. 300
 Centennial, CO 80112
Free: 866-575-7206
Co. E-mail: customercare@ncti.com
URL: http://ncti.com
Contact: Stacey Slaughter, Chief Executive Officer
Facebook: www.facebook.com/NCTITraining
Linkedin: www.linkedin.com/company/jonesncti/
 mycompany
X (Twitter): x.com/NCTItraining
YouTube: www.youtube.com/channel/UCIDTzvLtv7
 5BxeqZBGke9iw

Description: Firm provides learning solutions to nurture committed employees, supporting their education and career goals. **Founded:** 1968. **Geographic Preference:** National.

15575 ■ National Association of Broadcasters (NAB)
1 M St. SE
 Washington, DC 20003
Ph: (202)429-5300
Co. E-mail: nab@nab.org
URL: http://www.nab.org
Contact: Gordon H. Smith, President
Facebook: www.facebook.com/Broadcasters
Linkedin: www.linkedin.com/company/national
 -association-of-broadcasters
X (Twitter): x.com/nabtweets
Instagram: www.instagram.com/wearebroadcasters
YouTube: www.youtube.com/user/nabroadcasters

Description: Serves as the voice for the nation's radio and television broadcasters. Advances the interests of members in federal government, industry and public affairs; improves the quality and profitability of broadcasting; encourages content and technology innovation; and spotlights the important and unique ways stations serve their communities. Delivers value to its members through advocacy, education and innovation. Relies on the grassroots strength of its television and radio members and state broadcast associations. Helps broadcasters seize opportunities in the digital age. Offers broadcasters a variety of programs to help them grow in their careers, promote diversity in the workplace and strengthen their businesses. **Founded:** 1922. **Educational Activities:** NAB Show. **Awards:** NAB Crystal Radio Awards (Annual); NAB Distinguished Service Award (Annual); NAB Engineering Achievement in Radio Award (Annual); NAB Engineering Achievement in Television Award (Annual); NAB National Radio Award (Annual); NAB Celebration of Service to America Awards (Annual); Marconi Radio Awards (Annual); NAB Spirit of Broadcasting Award (Periodic); NAB International Broadcasting Excellence Award (Annual); Wally Jorgenson Award. **Geographic Preference:** National.

15576 ■ National Association of Television Program Executives (NATPE)
3940 Laurel Canyon Blvd., Ste. 324
 Studio City, CA 91604
Contact: Jean-Pierre Bommel, Contact
E-mail: jpbommel@natpe.org

Description: Seeks to contribute to the improvement of television programming by providing a forum for discussion of ideas and exchange of information concerning programming, production and related fields. Maintains NATPE Educational Foundation. Sponsors faculty development program, seminars and international exchange program. Sponsors six faculty internships. **Founded:** 1978. **Publications:** *Pocket Station Listing Guide* (Quarterly); *The NATPE Guide to North American Media* (Biennial); *NATPE International--Media Content Directory* (Annual). **Educational Activities:** Annual NATPE Miami Market

& Conference (Annual). **Awards:** NATPE Faculty Development Grant (Annual); Brandon Tartikoff Legacy Awards (Annual). **Geographic Preference:** Multinational.

15577 ■ National Cable and Telecommunications Association (NCTA)
25 Massachusetts Ave. NW, Ste. 100
 Washington, DC 20001
Ph: (202)222-2300
Co. E-mail: info@ncta.com
URL: http://www.ncta.com
Contact: Michael Powell, President
Facebook: www.facebook.com/NCTAitv
Linkedin: www.linkedin.com/company/ncta
X (Twitter): x.com/NCTAitv

Description: A trade association of the cable industry in the United States whose mission is to provide its members with a strong national presence by providing a single, unified voice on issues affecting the cable and telecommunications industry. Publishes cable television-related directories. **Founded:** 1952. **Publications:** *Cable Industry Overview* (Semiannual). **Awards:** NCTA Distinguished Vanguard Awards for Leadership (Annual); NCTA Vanguard Award for Cable Operations Management (Annual). **Geographic Preference:** National.

15578 ■ North American Broadcasters Association (NABA)
NABA c/o Canadian Broadcasting Centre (CBC)
 205 Wellington St. W, Ste. 9C200
 Toronto, ON, Canada M5V 3G7
Ph: (416)205-3363
Fax: (416)205-2901
Co. E-mail: contact@nabanet.com
URL: http://nabanet.com
Contact: Richard Friedel, President
Facebook: www.facebook.com/North-American-Broa
 dcasters-Association-NABA-2705058279524102
Linkedin: www.linkedin.com/company/north-american
 -broadcasters-association
X (Twitter): x.com/NABA_ORG

Description: Network broadcasters in North America concerned with international matters that affect broadcasting. Seeks to identify, study and provide solutions to international questions concerning broadcasting. Creates opportunities for North American broadcasters to share information, identify common interests and reach on issues of an international nature. Works with other international broadcasters' associations and unions toward gaining an effective voice in international circles on matters that affect broadcasting. Organizes international conferences in conjunction with other broadcasting associations. **Founded:** 1972. **Educational Activities:** North American Broadcasters Association Meeting (Annual). **Awards:** NABA International Achievement Award (Annual). **Geographic Preference:** Multinational.

15579 ■ Public Media Business Association (PMBA)
1300 Piccard Dr., Ste. LL 14
 Rockville, MD 20850
Ph: (240)844-3600
Co. E-mail: info@pmbaonline.org
URL: http://www.pmbaonline.org
Contact: Sara L. Wood, Executive Director
E-mail: swood@pmbaonline.org
Facebook: www.facebook.com/PMBAonline/wall
Linkedin: www.linkedin.com/company/public-media
 -business-association
X (Twitter): x.com/pmbaonline

Description: Represents finance, human resources, information systems, and administrative managers in public broadcasting. **Founded:** 1982. **Geographic Preference:** National.

15580 ■ Radio Television Digital News Association - Canada (RTDNA)
Toronto, ON, Canada V6E 2V2
Co. E-mail: admin@rtdnacanada.com
URL: http://rtdnacanada.com
Contact: Lis Travers, President
Linkedin: www.linkedin.com/company/rtdna-canada

YouTube: www.youtube.com/channel/UCjfaGm
 3YaUnOIsnKHFFXxZw

Description: Radio and television news executives and personnel. Promotes the professional development of broadcast journalists in Canada. Sponsors national scholarship program. **Founded:** 1962. **Awards:** RTDNA National Awards (Annual); RTDNA Lifetime Achievement Award (Annual); RTDNA President's Award (Annual). **Geographic Preference:** National.

15581 ■ Television Bureau of Advertising (TVB)
120 Wall St., 15th Fl.
 New York, NY 10005-3908
URL: http://www.tvb.org
Contact: Steve Lanzano, President
Linkedin: www.linkedin.com/company/tvb_2
X (Twitter): x.com/TVBTweets

Description: Television stations, station sales representatives, and program producers/syndicates. Strives to increase advertiser dollars to U.S. spot television. Represents television stations to the advertising community. **Founded:** 1954. **Educational Activities:** Television Bureau of Advertising Annual Conference (Annual). **Geographic Preference:** National.

REFERENCE WORKS

15582 ■ "The Best Five-Month Run Since 1938" in Barron's (Vol. 89, August 3, 2009, No. 31, pp. M3)
Pub: Dow Jones & Company Inc.
Contact: Almar Latour, Chief Executive Officer

Ed: Kopin Tan, Andrew Bary. **Description:** US stock markets ended July 2009 registering the highest five-month rise since 1938. The shares of Cablevision could rise as the company simplifies its structure and spins off its Madison Square Garden unit. The shares of Potash Corp. could fall as the company faces lower earnings due to falling potash purchases. **Availability:** Online.

15583 ■ "Betting on a Happy Ending" in Barron's (Vol. 88, July 7, 2008, No. 27, pp. 14)
Pub: Dow Jones & Company Inc.
Contact: Almar Latour, Chief Executive Officer

Ed: Dimitra DeFotis. **Description:** Shares of Time Warner, priced at $14.69 each, appear under-priced as financial analysts discount the value of the company. The company should be worth more than $20 a share as the company is spinning off Time Warner Cable. **Availability:** Online.

15584 ■ "'Biggest Loser' Adds Bit of Muscle to Local Economy" in Crain's Detroit Business (Vol. 26, January 4, 2010, No. 1, pp. 1)
Pub: Crain Communications Inc.
Contact: Barry Asin, President

Ed: Chad Halcom. **Description:** NBC's weight-loss reality show, "The Biggest Loser" has helped the local economy and generated a new crop of local startup businesses due to past contestants that were from the Detroit area. **Availability:** Print; Online.

15585 ■ "Branded Entertainment: Dealmaking Strategies & Techniques for Industry Professionals"
Pub: J. Ross Publishing Inc.
Contact: Stephen Buda, President

Released: October 01, 2014. **Price:** $39.95, hardcover, plus shipping charge extra. FL sale tax $3.36. **Description:** Branded entertainment, also known as branded content or advertisement, is an entertainment-based method that is funded by and complementary to a brand's marketing strategy. These projects are usually a partnership between brands, television or radio producers, and broadcasters. **Availability:** E-book; Print; Download.

15586 ■ *"Campaign Ads Lucrative for Denver's TV Stations" in Denver Business Journal (Vol. 64, September 7, 2012, No. 16, pp. 1)*

Pub: Baltimore Business Journal

Contact: Rhonda Pringle, President

E-mail: rpringle@bizjournals.com

Description: US presidential election campaign advertising is seen to boost the earnings of Denver, Colorado's television broadcasting sector. Presidential candidate Mitt Romney and US president Barrack Obama have spent $2.6 million on advertising in Denver.

15587 ■ *"CBC Eyes Partners for TV Downloads" in Globe & Mail (February 9, 2006, pp. B1)*

Description: The details on Canadian Broadcasting Corp.'s distribution agreement with Google Inc. and Apple Computer Inc. are presented. **Availability:** Online.

15588 ■ *"Cincinnati Reds Hit Ratings Homer" in Business Courier (Vol. 27, July 30, 2010, No. 13, pp. 1)*

Pub: Business Courier

Ed: Steve Watkins, John Ourand. **Description:** Cincinnati Reds fans have tuned in to their TVs and radios as their team made a hottest start to a season. The Reds TV ratings have increased 49 percent during the first six months of 2010 and continued to rise while the Reds' games broadcast on WLW-AM reported the highest average audience share per game of any Major League Baseball team. **Availability:** Print; Online.

15589 ■ *"CRTC Signals CHUM Deal Will Get Nod" in Globe & Mail (May 2, 2007, pp. B3)*

Ed: Grant Robertson. **Description:** The likely approval of Canadian Radio-Television and Telecommunications Commission to the proposed acquisition of CHUM Ltd. by CTVglobemedia Inc. is discussed. **Availability:** Print; Online.

15590 ■ *"CTV's CHUM Proposal Gets Chilly Reception" in Globe & Mail (May 1, 2007, pp. B1)*

Ed: Grant Robertson. **Description:** The possible violation of broadcast regulations in case of acquisition of CHUM Ltd. by CTV Inc. for $1.4 billion is discussed. **Availability:** Online.

15591 ■ *"Defend Your Research: Commercials Make Us Like TV More" in Harvard Business Review (Vol. 88, October 2010, No. 10, pp. 36)*

Pub: Harvard Business Publishing

Contact: Diane Belcher, Managing Director

Ed: Leif Nelson. **Price:** $6, PDF. **Description:** Research indicates that people prefer commercial interruption over uninterrupted shows due to the break creating a reactivation of the initial pleasure when beginning a desirable activity. **Availability:** Online; PDF.

15592 ■ *"Discovery Networks" in Brandweek (Vol. 49, April 21, 2008, No. 16, pp. SR9)*

Description: Provides contact information for sales and marketing personnel for the Discovery networks as well as a listing of the station's top programming and an analysis of the current season and the target audience for those programs running in the current season. The networks flagship station returned to the top 10 in 2007, averaging 1.28 million viewers.

15593 ■ *"Don't' Hate the Cable Guy" in Saint Louis Business Journal (Vol. 31, August 5, 2011, No. 50, pp. 1)*

Pub: Saint Louis Business Journal

Contact: Robert Bobroff, President

E-mail: rbobroff@bizjournals.com

Ed: Angela Mueller. **Description:** Charter Communications named John Birrer as senior vice president of customer experience. The company experienced problems with its customer services. **Availability:** Print; Online.

15594 ■ *"Game Changing" in Business Strategy Review (Vol. 23, Spring 2012, No. 1, pp. 26)*

Released: Spring 2012. **Description:** Barney Francis is Managing Director of Sky Sports. In a television career spanning 18 years, he has worked in the multichannel terrestrial and independent sectors. At Sky, he was executive producer for cricket, leading his team through two ICC World Cups, two Ashes Tours, England tours to nine nations, and the first Twenty20 Cup. In 2007, he became executive producer for Sky's Premier league football and in 2008 executive producer for the UEFA Champions League.

15595 ■ *"Hitting the Green" in Canadian Business (Vol. 81, July 22, 2008, No. 12-13, pp. 34)*

Description: RBC is sponsoring the Canadian Open golf tournament, which is the second-oldest event in the PGA Tour. RBC is expected to receive television exposure on CBS and the Golf Channel. Additional information relating to the sponsorship is presented. **Availability:** Print; Online.

15596 ■ *"It Could Be Worse" in Barron's (Vol. 89, July 27, 2009, No. 30, pp. 5)*

Pub: Dow Jones & Company Inc.

Contact: Almar Latour, Chief Executive Officer

Ed: Alan Abelson. **Description:** Media sources are being fooled by corporate America who is peddling an economic recovery rather than reality as shown by the report of a rise in existing home sales which boosted the stock market even if it was a seasonal phenomenon. The phrase "things could be worse" sums up the reigning investment philosophy in the U.S. and this has been stirring up the market. **Availability:** Online.

15597 ■ *"KCET Takes On Elder-Care With Robust Your Turn To Care Website" in PR Newswire (July 31, 2012)*

Pub: PR Newswire Association LLC.

Description: Your Turn To Care is a new Website created by KCET, the nation's largest independent public television station. The network, serving southern and central California, offers the Website to serve as a resource for families, caregivers and seniors in te US facing the challenges of caring for an ailing or aging loved one. The Website also covers issues involved in aging.

15598 ■ *"KXAN Seeks Larger Studio, Office Space in Austin" in Austin Business Journal (Vol. 31, May 27, 2011, No. 12, pp. A1)*

Pub: Austin Business Journal

Contact: Rachel McGrath, Director

E-mail: rmcgrath@bizjournals.com

Ed: Cody Lyon. **Description:** Austin NBC affiliate KXAN Television is opting to sell its property north of downtown and relocate to another site. The station is now inspecting possible sites to house its broadcasting facility and employees totaling as many as 200 people. Estimated cost of the construction of the studios and offices is $13 million plus another million in moving the equipment. **Availability:** Print; Online.

15599 ■ *"Local Film Industry Stands To Lose Jobs, Millions of Dollars Unless Florida Expands" in Orlando Business Journal (Vol. 30, March 14, 2014, No. 38, pp. 4)*

Pub: American City Business Journals, Inc.

Contact: Mike Olivieri, Executive Vice President

Released: Weekly. **Price:** $8, introductory 4-week offer(Digital & Print). **Description:** Central Florida's motion picture and TV production industries are in need of more government incentives. Many TV programs have been cancelled due to lack of this funding. Meanwhile, members of the sectors are set to lobby legislature to pass a $1.2 billion incentive package. **Availability:** Print; Online.

15600 ■ *"Local TV Hits Media Radar Screen" in Business Courier (Vol. 27, July 2, 2010, No. 9, pp. 1)*

Pub: Business Courier

Ed: Dan Monk. **Description:** Fort Wright, Kentucky-based broadcasting company Local TV LLC has acquired 18 television stations since its founding in 2007, potentially boosting its chances of becoming a media empire. In the last twelve months that ended in March 2010, Local TV LLC has posted total revenues of $415 million. How Local TV LLC has entered into cost-sharing deals with other stations is also discussed. **Availability:** Print; Online.

15601 ■ *"Marketing at the Olympics is No Longer Worth It: An Exercise in Olympic Vanity" in Canadian Business (Vol. 85, August 13, 2012, No. 13, pp. 15)*

Ed: Bruce Philp. **Description:** The cost and return on investment of sponsoring the 2012 London Olympics is examined. Given the high price of official sponsorship in the Olympics, marketers should realize the value of the television advertising audience. **Availability:** Online.

15602 ■ *"Marketing: You Are On the Air: Radio and TV Producers Are Looking For Shows Starring Smart CEOs" in Inc. (December 2007, pp. 67-69)*

Ed: Sarah Goldstein. **Description:** Many successful entrepreneurs are being hired to host television and radio shows in order to share business expertise. **Availability:** Print; Online.

15603 ■ *"Md.'s Film Industry Professionals have to Leave the State to Find Work: Exiting Stage Left" in Baltimore Business Journal (Vol. 28, June 18, 2010, No. 6, pp. 1)*

Pub: Baltimore Business Journal

Contact: Rhonda Pringle, President

E-mail: rpringle@bizjournals.com

Ed: Scott Dance. **Released:** Weekly. **Description:** Film professionals including crew members and actors have been leaving Maryland to find work in other states such as Michigan, Louisiana, and Georgia where bigger budgets and film production incentives are given. Other consequences of this trend in local TV and film production are discussed. **Availability:** Print.

15604 ■ *"Media Measurement Uncertainty - Tracking TV, Social and Digital" in AdAge (March 23, 2023)*

URL(s): adage.com/live-blog/media-measuremen t-uncertainty-tracking-tv-social-and-digital?adobe _mc=MCMID%3D124867048736473001820 36321386782796270%7CMCORGID%3D138FFF 2554E6E7220A4C98C6%2540AdobeOrg%7CTS% 3D1679594240&CSAuthResp=1679594300335% 3A0%3A5711370%3A0%3A24%3Asuccess%3A 1EFF88D004EE577C93CBE051A81BB0E 5#liveblogpost-4116

Released: March 23, 2023. **Description:** Discusses Nielsen ratings as it relates to streaming services. **Availability:** Online.

15605 ■ *Media, Organizations and Identity*

Pub: Palgrave Macmillan

Released: First edition. **Description:** The mass media, press, and television are essential in the formation of corporate identity and the promotion of business image and reputation. This book offers a new perspective into the interrelationships between media and organizations over three dimensions: media as business, media in business and business in the media.

15606 ■ *"Merger Expected to Bring New Player to TV Market" in Providence Business News (Vol. 28, March 31, 2014, No. 52, pp. 1)*

Pub: American City Business Journals, Inc.

Contact: Mike Olivieri, Executive Vice President

URL(s): pbn.com/merger-expected-to-bring-new -player-to-tv-market96073

Description: The proposed merger of Media General and Providence, Rhode Island-based LIN Media LLC has the potential to change the TV landscape in the state. The two media companies' TV stations overlap in five markets and ownership at one of the stations is expected to change due to federal regulations regarding TV station ownership. The two TV stations are outlined.

15607 ■ *"New Sony HD Ads Tout Digital" in Brandweek (Vol. 49, April 21, 2008, No. 16, pp. 5)*

Description: Looking to promote Sony Electronics' digital imaging products, the company has launched another campaign effort known as HDNA, a play on the words high-definition and DNA; originally Sony focused the HDNA campaign on their televisions, the new ads will include still and video cameras as well and marketing efforts will consist of advertising in print, Online, television spots and publicity at various venues across the country. **Availability:** Online.

15608 ■ *"Nortel Makes Customers Stars in New Campaign" in Brandweek (Vol. 49, April 21, 2008, No. 16, pp. 8)*

Description: Nortel has launched a new television advertising campaign in which the business-to-business communications technology provider cast senior executives in 30-second TV case studies that show how Nortel's technology helped their businesses innovate. **Availability:** Online.

15609 ■ *"No. 82: a Few Good Apps" in Inc. (Vol. 36, September 2014, No. 7, p. 103)*

Pub: Mansueto Ventures L.L.C.

Contact: Stephanie Mehta, Chief Executive Officer

Description: Alan S. Knitowski, former U.S. Army Captain, and his Austin, Texas-based mobile-focused development company is profiled. Phunware, creates apps for clients like ESPN, Cisco, Noscar, WWE, and NBC Sports. The firm won awards for its MythBusters app. **Availability:** Online.

15610 ■ *"On Comcast, Sarge, Wheels and the Big Price" in Philadelphia Business Journal (Vol. 32, February 7, 2014, No. 52, pp. 4)*

Pub: American City Business Journals, Inc.

Contact: Mike Olivieri, Executive Vice President

Released: Weekly. **Price:** $4, introductory 4-week offer(Digital & Print). **Description:** In an interview with David Montgomery, president and CEO of the Philadelphia Phillies team, he shares his views on the upcoming baseball season, the tremendous fan support the team is receiving, and the marketability of the team, with a special focus on their association with Comcast SportsNet as a broadcast producer. He also disclosed the league's plans for spending the new incoming TV money and said they will try to deliver the best product using the available resources. **Availability:** Print; Online.

15611 ■ *"OTA Broadcaster Adding Telemundo, Other Channels" in Idaho Business Review (September 12, 2014)*

Pub: BridgeTower Media

Contact: Adam Reinebach, President

Description: Cocola Broadcasting Company, based in Fresno, California, is adding the Spanish language network Telemundo to its channel lineup. Cocola's stations are broadcast digitally and anyone with an antenna can watch their programming for free. Cocola offers Telemundo, shopping channel QVC along with two nostalgia networks that rerun older TV sitcoms and dramas.

15612 ■ *"Private TV Industry's Profit Climbs 4 Per Cent" in Globe & Mail (March 29, 2006, pp. B6)*

Ed: Simon Tuck. **Description:** The private television industry in Canada is experiencing 4 percent increase in its profits, i.e. $242.2 millions. The revenues of CTV contributed more to this increase in profits. **Availability:** Online.

15613 ■ *"Recovery on Tap for 2010?" in Orlando Business Journal (Vol. 26, January 1, 2010, No. 31, pp. 1)*

Pub: Orlando Business Journal

Contact: Julie Swyers, Director

E-mail: jswyers@bizjournals.com

Ed: Melanie Stawicki Azam, Richard Bilbao, Christopher Boyd, Anjali Fluker. **Description:** Economic forecasts for Central Florida's leading business sectors in 2010 are presented. These sectors include housing, film and TV, sports business, law, restaurants, aviation, tourism and hospitality, banking and finance, commercial real estate, retail, health care, insurance, higher education, and manufacturing. According to some local executives, Central Florida's economy will slowly recover in 2010. **Availability:** Online.

15614 ■ *"Revenge of the Scorned Protege" in Canadian Business (Vol. 85, September 17, 2012, No. 14, pp. 48)*

Ed: Joanna Pachner. **Released:** September 17, 2012. **Description:** The prospect of a merger between Canadian distributor Alliance Films and international television and independent films distributor Entertainment One Group is expected to control the Canadian market and could rationalize competition in Great Britain. Entertainment One's offerings to broadcasters and other partners will be added with Alliance's 11,000 movie titles.

15615 ■ *"Study: New Moms Build A Lot of Brand Buzz" in Brandweek (Vol. 49, April 21, 2008, No. 16, pp. 7)*

Description: According to a new survey which sampled 1,721 pregnant women and new moms, this demographic is having 109 word-of-mouth conversations per week concerning products, services and brands. Two-thirds of these conversations directly involve brand recommendations. The Internet is driving these word-of-mouth, or W-O-M, conversations among this segment, beating out magazines, television and other forms of media. **Availability:** Online.

15616 ■ *"What We Know - And What We Don't - About Apple TV" in Barron's (Vol. 92, August 25, 2012, No. 38, pp. 27)*

Pub: Dow Jones & Company Inc.

Contact: Almar Latour, Chief Executive Officer

Ed: Alexander Eule. **Description:** Apple Inc.'s entry into the television market is not likely to involve an introduction of disruptive technologies. Cable companies are the most likely partners of Apple as it seeks to enter the televisiion broadcasting market. **Availability:** Online.

TRADE PERIODICALS

15617 ■ *Broadcaster*

Contact: James A. Cook, Sr., Publisher

E-mail: jcook@broadcastermagazine.com

URL(s): www.broadcastermagazine.com

X (Twitter): twitter.com/broadcastermag?lang=en

Released: Monthly **Price:** Free for qualified, industry professionals. **Description:** Magazine covering communications industry. **Availability:** Print; Online.

TRADE SHOWS AND CONVENTIONS

15618 ■ NAB Show

Nikon Inc.

1300 Walt Whitman Rd.

Melville, NY 11747-3064

Free: 800-645-6687

URL: http://www.nikonusa.com

Contact: Naoki Onozato, Chief Executive Officer

URL(s): nabshow.com/2024/about

Facebook: www.facebook.com/officialnabshow

X (Twitter): twitter.com/nabshow

Description: Radio and television broadcasting equipment, supplies, and services; supplies and services for production, post-production, computing, multimedia, telecommunications and corporate communications. **Audience:** Media, entertainment & technology professionals. **Principal Exhibits:** Radio and television broadcasting equipment, supplies, and services; supplies and services for production, post-production, computing, multimedia, telecommunications and corporate communications. Dates and

Locations: Las Vegas Convention Center, Las Vegas, NV; 2025 Apr 06-09; 2026 Apr 19-22. **Telecommunication Services:** nabshow@maritz.com.

15619 ■ RTNDA International Conference & Exhibition/Radio-Television News Directors Association

Radio Television Digital News Association (RTDNA)

The National Press Bldg., 529 14th St. NW, Ste. 1240

Washington, DC 20045

Ph: (202)221-4282

Co. E-mail: membership@rtdna.org

URL: http://www.rtdna.org

Contact: Dan Shelley, Executive Director

E-mail: dans@rtdna.org

URL(s): www.rtdna.org/events/rtdna25-new-orleans

Frequency: Annual. **Description:** Offer exemplary teaching programs. **Audience:** Actors, directors, producers, reporters, correspondents, and radio and television announcers and newscasters. **Principal Exhibits:** Offer exemplary teaching programs. Dates and Locations: 2025 Jun 11-13 Hotel Monteleone, New Orleans, LA. **Telecommunication Services:** events@rtdna.org.

CONSULTANTS

15620 ■ Baker Scott & Co.

34 North Lenhome Dr., Ste. 107

Cranford, NJ 07016

Ph: (973)263-3355

Co. E-mail: exec.search@bakerscott.com

URL: http://www.bakerscott.com

Description: Firm provides consulting services for executive search process such as telecommunications industry, residential and commercial, assisting executives, and much more. **Scope:** Firm provides consulting services for executive search process such as telecommunications industry, residential and commercial, assisting executives, and much more. **Founded:** 1979. **Training:** Offers seminar programs on interview techniques, management skills, and customer service.

15621 ■ The Benchmark Co.

200-C Parker Dr., Ste. 100

Austin, TX 78728

Ph: (512)310-4000

Free: 833-246-2400

URL: http://www.bench.com

Contact: Mark Ogburn, General Manager

Description: Firm provides advertising, health care, financial, e-commerce, broadcasting and other related services. **Scope:** Firm provides advertising, health care, financial, e-commerce, broadcasting and other related services. **Publications:** "Radio in the 90S; Audience, Promotion and Marketing Strategies". **Training:** The Rules of the Ratings Game Seminar.

15622 ■ Bentley Miller Lights Inc. (BML)

Toronto, ON, Canada

URL: http://www.bentleymiller.com

Contact: Bently Miller, Director

E-mail: bentley@bentleymiller.com

Description: Lighting design and consulting company provides lighting design and photography services for private and government television production groups. **Scope:** Lighting design and consulting company provides lighting design and photography services for private and government television production groups. **Founded:** 1993. **Publications:** "Ace lightning and the carnival of the doom". **Training:** Sony Professional Workshops; Ryerson Summer Workshops; Lightsource Creativity Clinics.

15623 ■ D.E.M. Allen & Associates Ltd. (DEMA)

Winnipeg, MB, Canada

Ph: (204)889-9202

Co. E-mail: info@dema.ca

URL: http://www.dema.ca

Description: Firm provides planning, design, supervision and adjustment of broadcast transmitting facilities. **Scope:** Telecommunications consultants, experienced in AM, FM and television broadcasting, CATV systems, LF/HF, VHF/UHF and microwave systems and satellite earth stations, RF measurements and evaluations related to SCADA, LMCS in the millimeters portion of the spectrum as well as the 2.5Ghz MDS/MMDS field, electromagnetic compatibility and electromagnetic immunity including non-ionizing radiation evaluation and measurement. Services include planning, design, supervision and adjustment of broadcast transmitting facilities, including specifications, tender evaluation, preparation of reports, technical briefs for Federal Regulatory bodies, evaluation and measurements associated with RF propagation and electromagnetic energy throughout the radio frequency spectrum. **Founded:** 1965.

15624 ■ DeMers Programming Media Consultants
617 Newcomen Rd.
Exton, PA 19341
Ph: (610)363-2626
URL: http://www.demersprogramming.com
Contact: Peter Smith, Consultant
E-mail: peter@demersprogramming.com
Description: Firm is engaged in advisory services to radio broadcasters and provides market visits, competitive analysis, product maintenance, informatics, stationality, creative benchmarks, promotional tactics, marketing strategies, personality management, managerial development, research strategies and much more. **Founded:** 1986. **Publications:** "12 Steps To A One Share - Uncovering The Clutter," Feb, 2005; "Get Your Mind Out Of The Clutter - DeMers Dispatch Winter '05"; "See Spot Run...Over The Golden Goose"; "Radio's Attention Deficit Disorder"; "Program The Seller"; "At Issue: Staying Creative"; "Take A Hard Look At Your Special Programming"; "A Fresh Coat Of Paint"; "Guerrilla Radio". **Training:** Diary Keepers Plus Research; Marketing, Merchandising and Money.

15625 ■ Financial Solutions Inc.
309 W Jefferson St.
La Grange, KY 40031
Ph: (502)225-9900
URL: http://www.oldhamfinancial.com
Contact: Robin Lawson, President
E-mail: robin@oldhamfinancialsolutions.com
Facebook: www.facebook.com/financial.solutions.inc
Linkedin: www.linkedin.com/company/ol
dhamfinancialsolutions
Description: Firm is engaged in developing, implementing, and monitoring financial strategy and provides services such as financial and insurance planning, and investment management. **Scope:** Firm is engaged in developing, implementing, and monitoring financial strategy and provides services such as financial and insurance planning, and investment management. **Publications:** "Eighty percent of Americans agree they would benefit from having basic financial education and information," 2009; "Finra Investor Education Survey, 2007"; "How Are Mutual Funds Taxed". **Training:** Long Term Care, Estate Planning, Retirement, Financial Management.

15626 ■ Victory Studios
2247 15th Ave. W
Seattle, WA 98119
Ph: (206)282-1776
Co. E-mail: info@victorystudios.com
URL: http://www.victorystudios.com
Contact: Laura Denke, Founder
Facebook: www.facebook.com/victorystudios
X (Twitter): x.com/victorystudios
Instagram: www.instagram.com/victorystudios
YouTube: www.youtube.com/victorystudios
Description: Provider of video production services such as editing, creative services, post-production, duplication, archiving for television, corporate customers and the web. **Scope:** Offers marketing, distribution, and syndication consultation regarding television programming for program producers. **Founded:** 1973.

COMPUTERIZED DATABASES

15627 ■ *Baseline Intelligence*
URL(s): www.baselineintel.com
Type: Full-text; Numeric.

LIBRARIES

15628 ■ CBC/Radio Canada Maritimes - Halifax Broadcast Centre
Halifax, NS, Canada
URL: http://www.cbc.ca/productionfacilities/halifax
Contact: Shawn Cole, Contact
E-mail: shawn.cole@cbc.ca
Scope: Television news; children's television; television comedy; agriculture and resources television; performance; programming television. **Services:** Library open to the public by appointment. **Founded:** 1955. **Holdings:** 100,000 television archival items.

15629 ■ The National Press Club (NPC) - The Eric Freidheim Library
529 14th St. NW, 13th Fl.
Washington, DC 20045
Ph: (202)662-7500
Co. E-mail: members@press.org
URL: http://www.press.org
Contact: Jen Judson, President
Facebook: www.facebook.com/PressClubDC
X (Twitter): x.com/pressclubdc
Instagram: www.instagram.com/pressclubdc
YouTube: www.youtube.com/c/Na
tionalPressClubLive
Description: Reporters, writers and news people employed by newspapers, wire services, magazines, radio and television stations and other forms of news media. Sponsors sports, travel events, rap sessions with news figures and authors and newsmaker breakfasts and luncheons. **Scope:** Journalism. **Services:** Interlibrary loan available upon request. **Founded:** 1908. **Holdings:** Figures not available. **Subscriptions:** newspapers magazines Books. **Publications:** *National Press Club Directory.* **Educational Activities:** National Press Club Seminar. **Awards:** Online Journalism Award (Annual); Washington Regional Reporting Award (Periodic); NPC Consumer Journalism Award (Annual); Edwin M. Hood Award for Diplomatic Correspondence (Annual); NPC Newsletter Journalism Award (Annual); NPC Washington Regional Reporting Award (Annual); Sandy Hume Memorial Award for Excellence in Political Journalism (Annual); Arthur Rowse Award for Press Criticism (Annual); Joseph D. Ryle Award for Excellence in Writing on the Problems of Geriatrics (Annual); Joan M. Friedenberg Online Journalism Award (Annual); Angele Gingras Humor Award (Annual); Ann Cottrell Free Animal Reporting Award (Annual); Michael A. Dornheim Award (Annual). **Geographic Preference:** National.

15630 ■ Right Management Inc. - Library
Right Management Inc.
100 Manpower Pl.
Milwaukee, WI 53212
Free: 800-237-4448
Co. E-mail: contactus@right.com
URL: http://www.right.com
Contact: Caroline Pfeiffer, Senior Vice President
Facebook: www.facebook.com/rightmanagement
Linkedin: www.linkedin.com/company/righ
t-management
X (Twitter): twitter.com/rightmanagement
Description: Provides consulting in career transition and human resources management. **Scope:** Workforce. **Founded:** 1980. **Holdings:** Figures not available. **Publications:** "Seven Days to Online Networking: Make Connections to Advance Your Career and Business Quickly"; "Networking for Job Search and Career Success," Jist Publishing, Jun, 2004; "The Unofficial Guide to Landing a Job"; "Re Inventing Hr

Changing Roles to Create the High Performance Organization"; "Corporate Mvps Managing Your Companys Most Valuable Performers"; "Help Wanted: A Complete Guide to Human Resources for Canadian Entrepreneurs"; "Flexible Leadership Creating Value By Balancing Multiple Challenges and Choices," Pfeiffer, May, 2004; "On the Fly Executing Strategy in a Changing World," John Wiley and Sons, Jan, 2004; "Global Leaders: Why they succeed and fail," Leadership Excellence, Aug, 2011; "Navigating Change Together," Talent Management, Feb, 2011; "Coaching: Navigating the Emerging Trends in Financial Services," The International Journal of Coaching in Organizations, 2009.

15631 ■ University of California, Los Angeles - UCLA Film and Television Archive - Research and Study Center
Powell Library, Rm. 46
Los Angeles, CA 90095-1517
Ph: (310)206-5388
Co. E-mail: arsc@cinema.ucla.edu
URL: http://www.cinema.ucla.edu/archive-research-s
tudy-center
Contact: May Hong HaDuong, Director
Scope: Film collection; television program collection. **Services:** Library open to the research for appointment use only. **Founded:** 1965. **Holdings:** 350,000 films and television programs; 100,000 News and Public Affairs (NAPA) programs; 2,000 radio programs.

15632 ■ Youth Media Alliance (YMA) - Library [L'Alliance Medias Jeunesse]
5165 Sherbrooke St., W Ste. 407
Montreal, QC, Canada H4A 1T6
Co. E-mail: alliance@ymamj.org
URL: http://www.ymamj.org/en
Contact: Chantal Bowen, Executive Director
E-mail: cbowen@ymamj.org
Facebook: www.facebook.com/ymamj
X (Twitter): x.com/YMAMJ
Instagram: www.instagram.com/ymamj
Description: Promotes quality television programming for children. Works with broadcasters to develop quality children's programs. **Scope:** Television and children, media, broadcasting. **Services:** Library open with permission only. **Founded:** 1974. **Holdings:** Figures not available. **Publications:** *Alliance Info* (Quarterly). **Educational Activities:** Media-Jeunes Conference (Annual). **Awards:** Awards of Excellence (Annual); YMA Best Program (Annual); Outstanding Achievement Award (Annual); Special Jury Award (Annual); YMA Emerging Talent Award (Annual); YMA Awards of Excellence (Annual); Outstanding Achievement Award (Annual). **Geographic Preference:** National.

RESEARCH CENTERS

15633 ■ Massachusetts Institute of Technology School of Architecture and Planning - Media Lab
Bldg. E14, 75 Amherst St., Wiesner Bldg. E15, 20 Ames St.
Cambridge, MA 02139-4307
Ph: (617)253-9783
Co. E-mail: member-info@media.mit.edu
URL: http://www.media.mit.edu
Contact: Hiroshi Ishii, Associate Director
E-mail: ishii@media.mit.edu
Facebook: www.facebook.com/mitmedialab
Linkedin: www.linkedin.com/company/mit-media-lab
X (Twitter): twitter.com/medialab
Instagram: www.instagram.com/mitmedialab/
Description: Interdepartmental laboratory of the Massachusetts Institute of Technology School of Architecture and Planning. **Scope:** Conducts processing, engineering, and research in the areas of biomechatronics, neuroengineering, machines with common sense, viral communications, advanced sen-

sor networks, innovative interface design, and sociable robots. Projects range from wearable sensors for monitoring health, to new programming tools for children. **Founded:** 1985. **Subscriptions:** items.

15634 ■ Texas Tech University - College of Media & Communication - Center for Communications Research (CCR)
2500 Broadway
  Lubbock, TX 79409

URL: http://www.depts.ttu.edu/comc/research/ccr
Description: Integral unit of College of Mass Communications at Texas Tech University. **Scope:** Center for communications research deals with public opinion and consumer surveys, communication experiments, economic and policy studies, and television/radio production and testing, including studies on communication immunization and functions, and television personality and viewers' preference.

Founded: 1972. **Publications:** *Journal of Broadcasting and Electronic Media*; *Journal of Media Economics*; *Journalism Educator*; *Journalism Quarterly*; *Public Opinion Quarterly* (Quarterly).

Temporary Employment Agency

ASSOCIATIONS AND OTHER ORGANIZATIONS

15635 ■ American Staffing Association (ASA)
277 S Washington St., Ste. 200
Alexandria, VA 22314
Ph: (703)253-2020
Fax: (703)253-2053
URL: http://americanstaffing.net
Contact: Richard Wahlquist, President
Facebook: www.facebook.com/AmericanS
taffingAssociation
Linkedin: www.linkedin.com/company/american-s
taffing-association
X (Twitter): x.com/StaffingTweets
Instagram: www.instagram.com/americans
taffingassociation
YouTube: www.youtube.com/user/ASAStaffingTube
Description: Promotes and represents the staffing industry through legal and legislative advocacy, public relations, education, and the establishment of high standards of ethical conduct. **Founded:** 1966. **Publications:** *Staffing Success* (Bimonthly); *Co-Employment: Employer Liability Issues in Third-Party Staffing Arrangements*; *ASA Member Directory*. **Educational Activities:** ASA Staffing World (Annual). **Awards:** ASA Care Award (Biennial); ASA Staffing VOICE Awards (Annual); ASA Chapter Merit Awards (Annual); ASA Leadership Hall of Fame Award (Annual); ASA National Staffing Employee of the Year (Annual). **Geographic Preference:** National.

15636 ■ Association of Manpower Franchise Owners (AMFO)
1219 N Jackson St., Unit 107
Milwaukee, WI 53202
Contact: Jane Svinicki, Contact
Description: Serves as a forum for exchange of ideas and information among members; acts as liaison between members and the parent company. Studies and critiques procedures and policies of Manpower International; solicits suggestions from members regarding smooth operation of a temporary employee service. Provides formalized procedure for resolution of grievances among members and between members and the parent company. **Founded:** 1971. **Geographic Preference:** National.

15637 ■ National Association of Personnel Services (NAPS)
800 Dailans Way
Uniontown, PA 15401
Free: 844-NAP-S360
URL: http://www.naps360.org
Contact: Trinette R. Cunningham, President
Facebook: www.facebook.com/NAPS360
Linkedin: www.linkedin.com/company/national
-association-of-personnel-services
X (Twitter): x.com/naps360
Description: Private employment and temporary service firms. Compiles statistics on professional agency growth and development; conducts certification program and educational programs. Association

is distinct from former name of National Association of Personnel Consultants. **Founded:** 1961. **Publications:** *National Directory of Personnel Service Firms* (Annual); *Inside NAPS* (Monthly). **Geographic Preference:** National.

15638 ■ National Association of Professional Employer Organizations (NAPEO)
707 N St. Asaph St.
Alexandria, VA 22314
Ph: (703)836-0466
Fax: (703)836-0976
Co. E-mail: info@napeo.org
URL: http://www.napeo.org
Contact: Pat Cleary, President
E-mail: pcleary@napeo.org
Facebook: www.facebook.com/napeo
Linkedin: www.linkedin.com/company/national
-association-of-professional-employer-organizations
-napeo
X (Twitter): x.com/napeo
YouTube: www.youtube.com/channel/UC_Zz
2DaAyuocuP3fXq03h9A
Description: Professional employer organizations. Seeks to enhance professionalism in the professional employer industry. Sponsors educational and public information programs. Maintains speakers' bureau; compiles statistics. **Founded:** 1984. **Educational Activities:** NAPEO Annual Conference & Marketplace (Annual); NAPEO Annual Conference & Marketplace (Annual). **Geographic Preference:** National.

15639 ■ TempNet Staffing Association
6919 Vista Dr.
West Des Moines, IA 50266
Ph: (515)282-8192
Co. E-mail: tempnetadmin@assoc-mgmt.com
URL: http://www.tempnetstaffingassociation.org
Contact: Jeana Schultz, Executive Director
Facebook: www.facebook.com/tempnets
taffingassociation
Linkedin: www.linkedin.com/company/tempnet-s
taffing-association
Description: Independent staffing service association.

REFERENCE WORKS

15640 ■ *"Florida Hospital Planning $104.1M in Expansions"* in Orlando Business Journal (Vol. 29, June 8, 2012, No. 53, pp. 1)
Pub: Baltimore Business Journal
Contact: Rhonda Pringle, President
E-mail: rpringle@bizjournals.com
Description: Florida Hospital is planning $104.1 million in expansion projects that will create about 140 new permanent health care jobs and 576 temporary contruction jobs. The projects include an emergency department and medical office space in Winter Garden, an expanded emergency department at Florida Hospital East Orlando and additional floors in Ginsburg Tower at Florida Hospital Orlando. **Availability:** Print; Online.

15641 ■ *"MBAs for Hire, By the Hour"* in Entrepreneur (August 2014)
Pub: Entrepreneur Media Inc.
Contact: Dan Bova, Director
E-mail: dbova@entrepreneur.com
Description: HourlyNerd started from a classroom project by Pat Petitti and Rob Biederman at Harvard Business School in Boston, Massachusetts in 2003. the temporary-staffing firm recruits business students to act as consultants to small businesses that hire them. Consultants must come from one of the top 40 Master of Business Administration Programs in the U.S. in order to bid on a project. The firm receives 15 percent of the project fee from the hiring company while the business consultants pay 5 percent to the company. **Availability:** Online.

15642 ■ *"NIOSH Teams with Staffing Association to Promote Temp Worker Safety and Health"* in Safety+Health (August 30, 2021)
URL(s): www.safetyandhealthmagazine.com/articles/
21653-niosh-teams-with-staffing-association-to
-promote-temp-worker-safety-and-health
Released: August 30, 2021. **Description:** Key safety issues are being promoted between a multi-year partnership between the National Institute for Occupational Safety & Health, and temp agencies in order to better protect all workers. **Availability:** Online.

15643 ■ *"Overseas Overtures"* in Business Journal-Portland (Vol. 24, October 26, 2007, No. 35, pp. 1)
Pub: Portland Business Journal
Contact: Andy Giegerich, Managing Editor
E-mail: agiegerich@bizjournals.com
Ed: Robin J. Mood. **Description:** Oregon has a workforce shortage, specifically for the health care industry. Recruiting agencies, such as the International Recruiting Network Inc., answers the high demand for workforce by recruiting foreign employees. The difficulties recruiting companies experience with regards to foreign labor laws are investigated. **Availability:** Print; Online.

15644 ■ *"Q&A With Devin Ringling: Franchise's Services Go Beyond Elder Care"* in Gazette (October 2, 2010)
Pub: The Gazette
Contact: Vicki Cederholm, Director, Operations
E-mail: vicki.cederholm@gazette.com
Ed: Bill Radford. **Description:** Profile of franchise, Interim HealthCare, in Colorado Springs, Colorado; the company offers home care services that include wound care and specialized feedings to shopping and light housekeeping. It also runs a medical staffing company that provides nurses, therapists and other health care workers to hospitals, prisons, schools and other facilities. **Availability:** Online.

15645 ■ *"The Rise of the Supertemp: The Best Executive and Professional Jobs May No Longer Be Full-Time Gigs"* in Harvard Business Review (Vol. 90, May 2012, No. 5, pp. 50)
Pub: Harvard Business Review Press
Contact: Moderna V. Pfizer, Contact

Ed: Jody Grenstone Miller, Matt Miller. **Price:** $8.95, hardcopy and PDF. **Description:** Supertemps are independent contractors who perform mission-critical work on a project basis. Supertemps enjoy a high degree of flexibility and freedom, and offer companies new opportunities for innovation and growth. **Availability:** Print; Online; PDF.

15646 ▪ *"Sign of the Times: Temp-To-Perm Attorneys" in HRMagazine (Vol. 54, January 2009, No. 1, pp. 24)*
Description: A growing number of law firms are hiring professional staff on a temp-to-perm basis according to the president of Professional Placement Services in Florida. Firms can save money while testing potential employees on a temporary basis. **Availability:** Print; Online.

15647 ▪ *"Temp Job, Permanent Fulfillment: How the Desire To Earn a Bit of Extra Cash Opened the Door to a Long-Term Career" in Black Enterprise (Vol. 44, June 2014, No. 10, pp. 41)*
Pub: Earl G. Graves Ltd.
Contact: Earl Graves, Jr., President
Description: Profile of Kay Francis who started a temporary job with Darden Restaurants to earn money during her final year of college. After graduation, Francis took a permanent position with the firm and today is the Director, Concept Support and Purchasing for the company.

STATISTICAL SOURCES

15648 ▪ *Employment & Recruiting Agencies Industry in the US - Market Report*
URL(s): www.ibisworld.com/united-states/market-research-reports/employment-recruiting-agencies-industry/
Price: $925. **Description:** Downloadable report analyzing data about the current and future trends of the employment and recruiting industries. **Availability:** Download.

15649 ▪ *Office Staffing & Temp Agencies Industry in the US - Market Research Report*
URL(s): www.ibisworld.com/united-states/market-research-reports/office-staffing-temp-agencies-industry/
Price: $925. **Description:** Downloadable report analyzing current and future trends in the office staffing and temp agencies industries. **Availability:** Download.

15650 ▪ *RMA Annual Statement Studies*
Pub: Risk Management Association
Contact: Nancy Foster, President
Released: Annual. **Description:** Contains composite balance sheets and income statements for more than 360 industries, including the accounting, auditing, and bookkeeping industries. Also contains five years of comparative historical data for discerning trends. Includes 16 commonly used ratios, computed for most of the size groupings for nearly every industry.

CONSULTANTS

15651 ▪ **Business Control Systems L.P. (BCS)**
16415 Addison Rd., Ste. 150
Addison, TX 75001
Ph: (972)241-8392
Fax: (972)241-6893
URL: http://www.bcsmis.com
Contact: Bernie Francis, Chief Executive Officer
Facebook: www.facebook.com/BusinessControlSystemsLP
Linkedin: www.linkedin.com/company/businesscontrolsystems
X (Twitter): x.com/BCS_MIS

Description: Provides workforce and staffing solutions for IT and engineering professionals. **Founded:** 1981.

15652 ▪ **Business Control Systems L.P. (BCS)**
No. 102
Charlotte, NC 28202
Linkedin: www.linkedin.com/company/businesscontrolsystems
X (Twitter): x.com/BCS_MIS
Description: Firm provides professional staffing solutions. **Founded:** 1981.

15653 ▪ **Business Control Systems L.P. (BCS)**
Greensboro, NC
URL: http://www.bcsmis.com
Contact: Bernie Francis, X, Chief Executive Officer
Description: Firm provides IT and engineering staffing augmentation services including term-specific, indefinite term, contract to permanent and permanent placement services, payroll services and many more.

FRANCHISES AND BUSINESS OPPORTUNITIES

15654 ▪ **AHEAD Human Resources Inc.**
2209 Heather Ln.
Louisville, KY 40218
Free: 888-749-1000
Co. E-mail: ahr@aheadhr.com
URL: http://www.aheadhr.com
Contact: Kristi Hagan-Mullins, President
Facebook: www.facebook.com/AheadHumanResources
Instagram: www.instagram.com/aheadhumanresourceslouky
Description: Provider of human resources and staffing services. **Founded:** 1995. **Financial Assistance:** No **Training:** Yes.

15655 ▪ **AtWork Group**
6700 Baum Dr., Ste. 25
Knoxville, TN 37919
Ph: (865)444-3530
Co. E-mail: atwork@atwork.com
URL: http://www.atwork.com
Contact: Jason Leverant, President
E-mail: jleverant@atwork.com
Facebook: www.facebook.com/atworkpersonnel
Linkedin: www.linkedin.com/company/atworkpersonnel
X (Twitter): x.com/atworkgroup
Description: Provider of health care recruitment and health staffing services for hospital and health care sector. **Founded:** 1990. **Training:** Provides 5 days at headquarters, 2-5 days onsite and ongoing support.

15656 ▪ **Careers USA, Inc.**
6501 Congress Ave., Ste. 200
Boca Raton, FL 33487
Ph: (561)995-7000
Free: 888-227-3377
URL: http://www.careersusa.com
Contact: Marilyn J. Ounjian, Founder
Facebook: www.facebook.com/CareersUSA
Linkedin: www.linkedin.com/company/careersusa
X (Twitter): x.com/CareersUSA
Description: Provider of staffing services including temporary, temp-to-hire and direct hire personnel. **Founded:** 1981. **Financial Assistance:** Yes **Training:** Yes.

15657 ▪ **Express Services, Inc.**
Express Services, Inc.
9701 Boardwalk Blvd.
Oklahoma City, OK 73162
Ph: (405)840-5000
URL: http://www.expresspros.com

Facebook: www.facebook.com/ExpressEmploymentInternational
Linkedin: www.linkedin.com/company/expressemploymentinternational
X (Twitter): x.com/expresspros
Instagram: www.instagram.com/expressemploymentinternational
YouTube: www.youtube.com/user/expressep
Description: Firm provides staffing and recruitment services. **Founded:** 1983. **Financial Assistance:** Yes **Training:** 2 week initial training at headquarters, 1 week in certified training office and ongoing field training and support. Followed by additional time in new office with assigned field representative. **Educational Activities:** IFA Annual Convention (Annual).

15658 ▪ **Link Staffing Services**
Personnel Concepts
1800 Bering Dr., Ste. 800
Houston, TX 77057
Ph: (713)784-4400
Free: 800-848-5465
URL: http://www.linkstaffing.com
Contact: Bill Pitts, Co-Founder
Facebook: www.facebook.com/linkstaffing
Linkedin: www.linkedin.com/company/35145
X (Twitter): x.com/LinkStaffing
Instagram: www.instagram.com/linkstaffing
Description: Supplies light industrial and industrial personnel to a variety of retail, commercial and manufacturing businesses. **Founded:** 1980. **Financial Assistance:** Yes **Training:** Support center classes include operations, management, sales and computer applications and an ongoing program of advanced curriculum including field training.

15659 ▪ **PrideStaff**
7535 N Palm Ave., Ste. 101
Fresno, CA 93711
Free: 800-774-3316
Fax: (559)432-4371
Co. E-mail: info@pridestaff.com
URL: http://www.pridestaff.com
Contact: Rob Hale, Chief Information Officer
Facebook: www.facebook.com/PrideStaff
Linkedin: www.linkedin.com/company/pridestaff
X (Twitter): x.com/PrideStaff
Instagram: www.instagram.com/pridestaff
YouTube: www.youtube.com/channel/UCjjuj-VBhlwYBDK6gSPU9cQ
Description: Recruiting Agency. **No. of Franchise Units:** 36. **No. of Company-Owned Units:** 3. **Founded:** 1978. **Franchised:** 1995. **Equity Capital Needed:** $162,000-$237,000. **Franchise Fee:** $32,000. **Training:** Yes.

15660 ▪ **Protingent Staffing**
Lincoln Plz., Bldg. A, 11235 SE 6th St., Ste. 220
Bellevue, WA 98004
Ph: (425)284-7777
Free: 866-244-4396
Fax: (425)642-8001
Co. E-mail: info@protingent.com
URL: http://www.protingent.com
Contact: Tim Bruce, President
Facebook: www.facebook.com/Protingent
Linkedin: www.linkedin.com/company/protingent
X (Twitter): x.com/Protingent
Description: Firm provides staffing and recruitment services. **Founded:** 2001. **Training:** Offers 2 weeks training at Seattle headquarters covering account management, recruiting, back office and client/candidate tracking system training.

15661 ▪ **Remedy Intelligent Staffing**
25W. Anapuma St., Ste. C
Santa Barbara, CA 93101
Description: Provider of human resource services such as staffing, management. **Founded:** 1965.

15662 ■ Spherion Staffing, LLC
Randstad N.V.
  3626 Cumberland Blvd., Ste. 600
  Atlanta, GA 30339
Ph: 31 20 569-5911
Co. E-mail: contactus@randstad.com
URL: http://www.randstad.com
Description: Offers temporary staffing, light industrial staffing, clerical staffing, and temporary-to-hire employment opportunities. **Founded:** 1946.

15663 ■ TRC Staffing Services Inc.
5909 Peachtree Dunwoody Rd. Bldg. D, 11th Fl.
  Atlanta, GA 30328
Ph: (404)261-0012
URL: http://trctalent.com
Contact: C. Emmanuel, Contact
Linkedin: www.linkedin.com/company/trcs
  taffingservices
X (Twitter): x.com/TRC_Staffing
Instagram: www.instagram.com/trc_staffing
Pinterest: www.pinterest.com/trcstaffing
Description: Provides office support, clerical, word processing, data processing, marketing and light industrial personnel to businesses. **Scope:** Provider of staffing, contract labor, outsourcing, and other related services. **Founded:** 1980. **Training:** Yes. **Special Services:** TRC®.

ASSOCIATIONS AND OTHER ORGANIZATIONS

15664 ■ American Sports Builders Association (ASBA)
2331 Rock Spring Rd.
  Forest Hill, MD 21050
Ph: (443)640-1042
Free: 866-501-2722
Co. E-mail: info@sportsbuilders.org
URL: http://sportsbuilders.org
Contact: Fred Stringfellow, Executive Director
Facebook: www.facebook.com/sportsbuilders
Linkedin: www.linkedin.com/company/sportsbuilders
X (Twitter): x.com/sportsbuilders
Description: Contractors who install running tracks, synthetic turf fields, tennis courts and indoor sports surfaces; manufacturers who supply basic materials for construction; accessory suppliers, designers, architects, and consultants of facilities. Provides guidelines for tennis court construction, running track construction, fencing, synthetic turf field construction and lighting. Offers certification and awards programs. **Founded:** 1965. **Publications:** *American Sports Builders Association--Membership Directory* (Annual); *Buyers Guide for Tennis Court Construction; Running Tracks: A Construction & Maintenance Manual; Tennis and Track Construction Guidelines* (Periodic); *U.S. Tennis Court and Track Builders Association Membership Directory* (Annual). **Educational Activities:** ASBA Technical Meeting (Annual); ASBA Winter Meeting (Annual). **Geographic Preference:** National.

15665 ■ American Tennis Association (ATA)
9701 Apollo Dr., Ste. 100
  Largo, MD 20774
Ph: (240)487-5953
Co. E-mail: igutierrez@yourata.org
URL: http://www.yourata.org
Contact: Adm. (Ret.) Roxanne Aaron, President
E-mail: raaron@yourata.org
Facebook: www.facebook.com/OfficialATA1916
X (Twitter): x.com/OfficialATA1916
Instagram: www.instagram.com/american
  tennisassociation
Description: Promotes and develops tennis regardless of race. Supports training programs to develop teaching professionals. Sponsors training programs for young players. Conducts 60 state and local tournaments. **Founded:** 1916. **Publications:** *ATA Advantage.* **Geographic Preference:** National.

15666 ■ International Health, Racquet and Sportsclub Association (IHRSA) - Library
70 Fargo St.
  Boston, MA 02210
Ph: (617)951-0055
Free: 800-228-4772
Co. E-mail: info@ihrsa.org
URL: http://www.ihrsa.org
Contact: Chris Craytor, Chairman of the Board
Facebook: www.facebook.com/IHRSA
Linkedin: www.linkedin.com/company/ihrsa

X (Twitter): x.com/IHRSA
Instagram: www.instagram.com/ihrsa
YouTube: www.youtube.com/user/IHRSALive
Description: Promotes the continued growth of the health, racket, and sports club industry in 70 countries. Aids member clubs in making educated business decisions. Sets standards for club management; offers group purchasing program. **Scope:** Fitness industry. **Founded:** 1980. **Holdings:** Figures not available. **Publications:** *Club Business International (CBI)* (Monthly); *Profiles of Success* (Annual). **Educational Activities:** IHRSA International Convention & Trade Show (Annual).

15667 ■ International Tennis Hall of Fame (ITHOF) - The Information Research Center Library
194 Bellevue Ave.
  Newport, RI 02840
Ph: (401)849-3990
Co. E-mail: newport@tennisfame.com
URL: http://www.tennisfame.com
Contact: Todd Martin, Chief Executive Officer
E-mail: aahlborg@tennisfame.com
Facebook: www.facebook.com/TennisHallofFame
X (Twitter): x.com/tennishallofame
Instagram: www.instagram.com/tennishallofame
YouTube: www.youtube.com/user/tennisfamer
Description: Seeks to foster interest in tennis, its history, and its athletic heroes. Supports junior tennis training programs; conducts amateur and professional grass-court competitions; maintains a museum. Produces video programs. Inducts new Hall of Fame members annually, including administrators, coaches, players, and writers. **Scope:** History; Sports. **Services:** Open to the public by appointment. **Founded:** 1986. **Holdings:** 30,000 photographs and slides; 5,000 prints; 3,500 film; yearbooks; guides; magazines; periodicals; documents; videotape; audiotape; audiovisuals. **Publications:** *Hall of Fame News* (Quarterly). **Awards:** Eugene L. Scott Awards (Annual); Joseph F. Cullman 3rd Awards (Annual); Fed Cup Award of Excellence (Annual); International Tennis Hall of Fame Chairman's Award (Annual); Samuel Hardy Award (Annual); Tennis Educational Merit Award for Men (Annual); Davis Cup Award of Excellence (Annual); International Tennis Hall of Fame Golden Achievement Award (Annual); Tennis Educational Merit Award for Women (Annual). **Geographic Preference:** National.

15668 ■ Professional Tennis Registry (PTR)
4 Office Way, Ste. 200
  Hilton Head Island, SC 29928
Ph: (843)785-7244
Free: 800-421-6289
Fax: (843)686-2033
Co. E-mail: ptr@ptrtennis.org
URL: http://ptrtennis.org
Contact: Julie Jilly, Vice President
E-mail: julie@ptrtennis.org
Facebook: www.facebook.com/ptrtennis
Linkedin: www.linkedin.com/company/ptrtennis
X (Twitter): x.com/ptrtennis

Description: Tests, certifies, and registers international tennis teaching professionals; Certification requires successful completion of a written and on-court examinations. Sponsors workshops, tennis clinics, and charitable program. Holds competitions; compiles statistics; maintains placement service. **Founded:** 1976. **Publications:** *TennisPro* (Bimonthly); *USPTR Membership Directory* (Annual). **Geographic Preference:** National.

15669 ■ Sony Ericsson WTA Tour
100 2nd Ave. S, Ste. 1100-S
  Saint Petersburg, FL 33701
URL: http://www.wtatennis.com/tournament/808/wta
  -finals/2005/overview
Description: Works to increase and strengthen the global popularity and stature of the women's professional tennis tour, and to further advance the game as the preeminent sport for women worldwide. **Founded:** 1973. **Awards:** WTA Jerry Diamond ACES Award (Annual); WTA Most Improved Player of the Year (Annual). **Geographic Preference:** Multinational.

15670 ■ Tennis Industry Association (TIA)
35 E Wacker Dr., Ste. 850
  Chicago, IL 60601-2106
Ph: (312)596-5281
Co. E-mail: info@tennisindustry.org
URL: http://www.tennisindustry.org
Contact: Kurt Kamperman, Chief Executive Officer
Facebook: www.facebook.com/TennisIndustry
Linkedin: www.linkedin.com/company/tennis-industry
  -association
X (Twitter): x.com/tennisindustry
Description: Aims to promote and encourage participation in recreational tennis and to work for the betterment of the game. Represents members' interests in Washington, DC; supports implementation of recreational tennis programs. Compiles statistics. **Founded:** 1974. **Publications:** *Tennis Industry* (10/year). **Educational Activities:** The Super Show. **Geographic Preference:** National.

15671 ■ United States Professional Tennis Association (USPTA)
11961 Performance Dr.
  Orlando, FL 32827
Ph: (407)634-3050
Free: 800-877-8248
Co. E-mail: uspta@uspta.org
URL: http://www.uspta.com
Contact: Richard Slivocka, President
E-mail: usptaboard@uspta.org
Facebook: www.facebook.com/USPTA.Official
Linkedin: www.linkedin.com/company/united-states
  -professional-tennis-association
X (Twitter): x.com/USPTA_Tennis
Instagram: www.instagram.com/uspta
YouTube: www.youtube.com/channel/
  UC7WIJTsecebbmTBObiM9RkA
Description: Seeks to improve tennis instruction in the United States; maintains placement bureau and library. **Founded:** 1927. **Publications:** *ADDvantage.*

Educational Activities: United States Professional Tennis Association Convention (Irregular). **Awards:** USPTA Large Division of the Year (Annual); USPTA Newsletter of the Year (Annual); USPTA Players of the Year (Annual); Alex Gordon Award for Professional of the Year (Annual). **Geographic Preference:** Multinational.

15672 ■ United States Racquet Stringers Association (USRSA)

1000 Peachtree Industrial Blvd., Ste. 6-492
 Suwanee, GA 30024-6777
Ph: (760)536-1177
Fax: (760)536-1171
Co. E-mail: usrsa@racquettech.com
URL: http://www.racquettech.com
Contact: Bob Patterson, Executive Director
E-mail: bob@racquettech.com

Description: Conducts experiments with new racquets and patterns. Provides free stringing business consulting service. Offers Certification Program. Offers instruction-workshops and video instruction. **Founded:** 1975. **Publications:** *Tennis Industry* (10/year); *RacquetTECH.com* (Monthly); *The Stringer's Digest* (Semiannual). **Geographic Preference:** National.

15673 ■ United States Tennis Association (USTA)

2500 Westchester Ave.
 Purchase, NY 10577
Ph: (914)696-7000
Free: 800-990-8782
URL: http://www.usta.com/en/home.html
Contact: Dr. Brian Hainline, President
Facebook: www.facebook.com/USTA
Linkedin: www.linkedin.com/company/usta
X (Twitter): x.com/usta
Instagram: www.instagram.com/usta

Description: Federation of local tennis clubs, educational institutions, recreation departments, and other groups and individuals interested in the promotion of tennis. **Founded:** 1881. **Publications:** *USTA Adult and Senior National Championships Booklet* (Irregular); *USTA Magazine* (Quarterly); *Tennis USTA* (Annual). **Educational Activities:** SHAPE America National Convention and Expo (Annual). **Awards:** Maureen Connolly Brinker Award (Annual); Bobby Kaplan Sportsmanship Award (Annual); John T. McGovern Umpires Award (Annual); USTA Member Organization of the Year Award (Annual); USTA Seniors' Service Award (Annual); USTA Service Bowl Award (Annual); Jack Stahr Award (Annual); USTA Outstanding Facility Awards (Annual); United States Open Tennis Championships (Annual); Dr. Allen B. Stowe Sportsmanship Award (Annual); Ralph W. Westcott UTSA Family of the Year Award (Annual); Bill Talbert Junior Sportsmanship Awards (Annual); Eve Kraft Community Service Award (Annual); USTA Volunteer Service Award (Annual); USTA Girls' 18

National Championships Sportsmanship Award (Annual); NJTL Chapter of the Year Award (Annual). **Geographic Preference:** National.

15674 ■ US Squash

25 N 33rd St.
 Philadelphia, PA 19104
Ph: (212)268-4090
Fax: (212)268-4091
Co. E-mail: media@ussquash.org
URL: http://ussquash.org
Contact: Kevin Klipstein, President
E-mail: kevin.klipstein@ussquash.org
Facebook: www.facebook.com/ussquash
Linkedin: www.linkedin.com/company/u.s.-squash
X (Twitter): x.com/ussquash
Instagram: www.instagram.com/ussquash
YouTube: www.youtube.com/channel/UCApmg7J
 -jrjcZF9P7p55TNw

Description: Member of United States Olympic Committee. Aims to establish and enforce uniformity in the rules of the game, standardize court specifications and schedules, and conduct tournaments. **Founded:** 1904. **Publications:** *Squash Magazine* (10/year); *National Court Survey* (Triennial). **Geographic Preference:** National.

15675 ■ USA Racquetball (USAR)

1661 Mesa Ave.
 Colorado Springs, CO 80906-2917
Ph: (719)635-5396
Fax: (719)635-0685
Co. E-mail: communications@usaracquetball.com
URL: http://www.usaracquetball.com
Contact: Mike Grisz, Executive Director
E-mail: ed@usaracquetball.com
Facebook: www.facebook.com/USARacquetball
X (Twitter): x.com/usaracquetball
Instagram: www.instagram.com/usaracquetball
YouTube: www.youtube.com/user/usaracquetball

Description: Represents racquetball players and enthusiasts. Promotes racquetball as a sport; organizes racquetball to be a self-governing sport of, by, and for the players; encourages building of facilities for the sport; conducts racquetball events including annual national and international tournaments. Maintains hall of fame, junior player programs, and charitable programs. **Founded:** 1969. **Publications:** *Racquetball Magazine* (Quarterly). **Educational Activities:** United States Racquetball Association Competition; High Performance Camp. **Awards:** Hall of Fame (Annual); Racquetball Hall of Fame (Irregular); Joe Sobek Outstanding Contribution Award (Annual); John Halverson Fair Play Award (Annual). **Geographic Preference:** National.

REFERENCE WORKS

15676 ■ "Architect's Designs for Proposed Underwater Tennis Court Look Unreal" in Bleacher Report (May 16, 2015)

URL(s): bleacherreport.com/articles/2466785-archi tect-wants-to-build-an-underwater-tennis-court-the -designs-look-unreal

Released: May 16, 2015. **Description:** Incredible underwater tennis court designs were unveiled by Polish architect Krysztof Kotala and his design firm, 8+8 Concept Studio. **Availability:** Online.

TRADE PERIODICALS

15677 ■ *Black Tennis Magazine: Tennis*

Pub: Black Tennis Magazine Inc.
Contact: Marcus Freeman, Jr., Contact
URL(s): blacktennismagazine.com
Instagram: www.instagram.com/blacktennismagazine

Released: Quarterly **Description:** Sports magazine featuring black tennis players, clubs, and parks. **Availability:** Print; Online.

TRADE SHOWS AND CONVENTIONS

15678 ■ United States Professional Tennis Association Convention

United States Professional Tennis Association (USPTA)
 11961 Performance Dr.
 Orlando, FL 32827
Ph: (407)634-3050
Free: 800-877-8248
Co. E-mail: uspta@uspta.org
URL: http://www.uspta.com
Contact: Richard Slivocka, President
E-mail: usptaboard@uspta.org
URL(s): www.uspta.com/uspta/Events/Event_Display .aspx?EventKey=DCONFFL24A

Frequency: Irregular. **Description:** Tennis equipment, supplies, and services. **Audience:** Tennis professionals, industry leaders and representatives, manufacturers, wholesalers, and media. **Principal Exhibits:** Tennis equipment, supplies, and services. **Telecommunication Services:** mike.baugh@uspta. org.

LIBRARIES

15679 ■ International Tennis Hall of Fame and Museum Library

194 Bellevue Ave.
 Newport, RI 02840
URL: http://www.tennisfame.com/museum-and-groun ds/information-research-center/library-collection
Contact: Nicole Markham, Curator, Collections
E-mail: nmarkham@tennisfame.com

Scope: History; tennis and racquet sports. **Services:** Open to the members; non-circulating. **Founded:** 1954. **Holdings:** 5,000 items - books, yearbooks, media guides, magazines, periodicals.

ASSOCIATIONS AND OTHER ORGANIZATIONS

15680 ■ Tire Industry Association (TIA)
1532 Pointer Ridge Pl., Ste. G
Bowie, MD 20716-1883
Ph: (301)430-7280
Free: 800-876-8372
Fax: (301)430-7283
Co. E-mail: info@tireindustry.org
URL: http://www.tireindustry.org
Contact: Roy Littlefield, Chief Executive Officer
Facebook: www.facebook.com/tireindustry
Linkedin: www.linkedin.com/company/tire-industry
-association
X (Twitter): x.com/thetireindustry
Instagram: www.instagram.com/tireindustryassocia
tion

Description: Corporations engaged in all sectors of the replacement tire industry. Seeks to advance members' interests. Serves as a clearinghouse on economic and regulatory issues affecting the replacement tire industry; conducts educational programs; sponsors lobbying activities. **Founded:** 1921. **Publications:** *Tire Retreading/Repair Journal* (Monthly). **Educational Activities:** Global Tire Expo/SEMA Show (Annual). **Geographic Preference:** National.

15681 ■ Tire Retread & Repair Information Bureau (TRIB)
2202 18th St. NW
Washington, DC 20009
Ph: (703)533-7677
Co. E-mail: info@retread.org
URL: http://www.retread.org
Contact: Doug Conley, Jr., President
Facebook: www.facebook.com/voiceofretreading
Linkedin: www.linkedin.com/company/tire-retread-re-
pair-information-bureau-trib
X (Twitter): x.com/voiceofretreads
YouTube: www.youtube.com/user/RetreadInfo

Description: Retreaders, tire repair information, suppliers to the retread industry. Serves as information resource for the retread industry. Receives logistical support from industry associations, suppliers and retreaders. Operates speakers' bureau. **Founded:** 1974. **Geographic Preference:** Multinational.

REFERENCE WORKS

15682 ■ "CEO Putting Rubber to Road at Lanxess Corporation" in Pittsburgh Business Times (Vol. 33, May 2, 2014, No. 42, pp. 4)
Pub: American City Business Journals, Inc.
Contact: Mike Olivieri, Executive Vice President

Released: May 02, 2014. **Price:** $4, introductory 4-week offer(Digital only). **Description:** Flemming Bjoernslev, CEO for the North American operations of Germany-based Lanxess Corporation, discusses their recovery efforts following their first financial loss

in 2013. He is confident that the U.S. tire manufacturing industry will help their business further in North America. **Availability:** Print; Online.

15683 ■ "Goodyear Extends Exclusive Deal to Supply NASCAR's Tires" in Charlotte Observer (February 4, 2007)
Description: Goodyear tires will continue to be the exclusive tire provider at NASCAR's Nextel Cup, Busch and Truck series through the year 2012. **Availability:** Print; Online.

15684 ■ "Tire CEOs Focus on Sustainability" in Modern Tire Dealer (November 22, 2019)
URL(s): www.moderntiredealer.com/news/736494/tire
-ceos-focus-on-sustainability
Released: November 22, 2019. **Description:** The Global Platform for Sustainable Natural Rubber (GPSNR) is being supported by the CEOs of 11 global tire manufacturers, with the goal of improving the socioeconomic and environmental performance of the natural rubber value chain. **Availability:** Online.

TRADE PERIODICALS

15685 ■ Tire Business: Your Number One information resource
Contact: Sigmund J. Mikolajczyk, Managing Editor
E-mail: smikolajczyk@crain.com
URL(s): www.tirebusiness.com
Facebook: www.facebook.com/crainstirebusiness
X (Twitter): twitter.com/tirebusiness

Ed: Dave Zielasko, Don Detore. **Released:** Semi-weekly **Price:** $35, for one year Online; $74, for one year Print; $79, for one year Print plus Online. **Description:** Newspaper (tabloid) serving independent tire dealers, retreaders, tire wholesalers and others allied to the tire industry. **Availability:** Print; Online.

15686 ■ Tire Review
Pub: Babcox Media Inc.
Contact: Bill Babcox, Chief Executive Officer
E-mail: bbabcox@babcox.com
URL(s): www.tirereview.com
Facebook: www.facebook.com/TireReview
Linkedin: www.linkedin.com/showcase/tirereview
X (Twitter): x.com/tire_review
Instagram: www.instagram.com/tire_review
YouTube: www.youtube.com/channel/UCUswYJsDNu
5h8U6wSk29U4A

Ed: Madeleine Winer. **Released:** Monthly **Description:** Magazine containing news and business information about the tire, custom wheel, automotive service, and retreading industries. **Availability:** PDF; Download; Online.

TRADE SHOWS AND CONVENTIONS

15687 ■ Global Tire Expo/SEMA Show
Tire Industry Association (TIA)
1532 Pointer Ridge Pl., Ste. G
Bowie, MD 20716-1883

Ph: (301)430-7280
Free: 800-876-8372
Fax: (301)430-7283
Co. E-mail: info@tireindustry.org
URL: http://www.tireindustry.org
Contact: Roy Littlefield, Chief Executive Officer
URL(s): www.tireindustry.org/events/gte-2024
Frequency: Annual. **Description:** Exhibits related to tire re-treading and repairing equipment, tires, reduction and removal, computer systems, waste to energy systems, allied services, including: brake equipment, wheel alignment, tire balancers, tire drangers, and service trucks, rubber recycling technologies, recycled rubber products. **Audience:** Tire dealers, trucking industry personnel, government personnel, environmentalists and recyclers. **Principal Exhibits:** Exhibits related to tire re-treading and repairing equipment, tires, reduction and removal, computer systems, waste to energy systems, allied services, including: brake equipment, wheel alignment, tire balancers, tire drangers, and service trucks, rubber recycling technologies, recycled rubber products. **Telecommunication Services:** lpindell@tireindustry.org.

FRANCHISES AND BUSINESS OPPORTUNITIES

15688 ■ Big O Tires Inc.
4280 Professional Ctr. Dr., Ste. 400
Palm Beach Gardens, FL 33410
Free: 866-649-8473
URL: http://www.bigotires.com
Contact: Lauren Bourrut, Manager
X (Twitter): x.com/bigotires
Instagram: www.instagram.com/bigotiresofficial
Description: Manufacturer and retailer of tires. **Founded:** 1962.

15689 ■ Canadian Tire Corporation, Limited
Canadian Tire Corporation, Limited
2180 Yonge St., Station K
Toronto, ON, Canada M4P 2V8
Ph: (416)480-3000
Free: 800-387-8803
URL: http://www.canadiantire.ca
Contact: Greg Hicks, President
Facebook: www.facebook.com/Canadiantire
X (Twitter): twitter.com/CanadianTire
Instagram: www.instagram.com/canadiantire/?hl=en
YouTube: www.youtube.com/canadiantire
Pinterest: www.pinterest.ca/canadiantire/

Description: Owns and operates retail stores and gas stations, offers products such as general merchandise and apparel, automotive parts, accessories, and services, sports and leisure products, and home, sports, and hardware products. In addition, the company offers personal loans, insurance, and warranty products, manages a credit card franchise, provides roadside assistance program, and offers other financial products. **Founded:** 1922. **Training:** 6 month Retail Leadership Development Program.

15690 ■ RNR Tire Express
13922 Monroes Business Pk.
  Tampa, FL 33635
Ph: (813)977-9800
Free: 888-466-7655
Co. E-mail: marketing@rnrwheels.com
URL: http://rnrtires.com
Contact: Larry Sutton, Founder
Facebook: www.facebook.com/RNRtires
X (Twitter): x.com/RNRtires
Instagram: www.instagram.com/rnrtires
YouTube: www.youtube.com/user/rnrwheels

Description: Manufacturer and distributor of wheels and tires. **Founded:** 2000. **Franchise Fee:** $35,000. **Royalty Fee:** 4%. **Financial Assistance:** Yes **Training:** Available 2 weeks at headquarters, 2 weeks at franchisee's location and ongoing support.

PUBLICATIONS

15691 ■ *Tire Business*
1155 Gratiot Ave.
  Detroit, MI 48207-2732
Ph: (313)446-6000

Co. E-mail: info@crain.com
URL: http://www.crain.com
Contact: Barry Asin, President
URL(s): www.tirebusiness.com
Facebook: www.facebook.com/TireBusinessCrain
Linkedin: www.linkedin.com/company/tire-business
X (Twitter): x.com/tirebusiness
Instagram: www.instagram.com/tirebusinesscrain
Released: Latest issue July 15, 2024. **Price:** $99, for digital only annual; $225, Other countries for Print + Digital; $119, for print+ digital. **Description:** Edited for independent tire retailers and wholesalers. **Availability:** Print; PDF; Download; Online. **Type:** Full-text; Numeric.

ASSOCIATIONS AND OTHER ORGANIZATIONS

15692 ■ Convenience Distribution Association (CDA)
11250 Roger Bacon Dr. 8
Reston, VA 20190
Ph: (703)208-3358
Free: 800-482-2962
Fax: (703)573-5738
Co. E-mail: info@cdaweb.net
URL: http://www.cdaweb.net
Contact: Kimberly Bolin, President
E-mail: kimberlyb@cdaweb.net
Facebook: www.facebook.com/conveniencedistribu
tion
X (Twitter): x.com/CDA_01

Description: Represents the interests of distributors of convenience-related products. Its members include wholesalers, retailers, manufacturers, brokers and allied organizations from across the US. and abroad. Programs include strong legislative representation in Washington and a broad spectrum of targeted education, business and information services. Sponsors the country's largest show for candy and convenience related products in conjunction with its semi-annual convention. **Founded:** 1945. **Publications:** *Convenience Distribution: AWMA's Magazine for Candy, Tobacco, Grocery, Foodservice and General Merchandiser Marketers* (Monthly); *Quick Topics Newsletter*, *Convenience Distribution* (Bimonthly); *Buying Guide and AWMA Directory* (Annual); *Buying Guide and Membership Directory*. **Educational Activities:** University of Innovative Distribution (Annual); Convenience Distribution Marketplace (Annual); Convenience Distribution Business Exchange (CDBX) (Annual); Summit and Business Exchange (Annual). **Awards:** CDA's Hall of Fame Award (Annual). **Geographic Preference:** National.

15693 ■ Premium Cigar Association (PCA)
513 Capital Ct. NE, Ste. 300
Washington, DC 20002
Ph: (202)621-8064
Co. E-mail: info@premiumcigars.org
URL: http://premiumcigars.org
Contact: Greg Zimmerman, President
E-mail: greg@tobaccocompany.com
Facebook: www.facebook.com/PCA1933
Linkedin: www.linkedin.com/company/pca1933
X (Twitter): x.com/PCA1933
Instagram: www.instagram.com/pca1933
YouTube: www.youtube.com/channel/
UCwnclYHOhKj1i2-XnRhGZsg

Description: Retailers of legal tobacco products and related items. Conducts marketing and merchandising programs. **Founded:** 1933. **Publications:** *Tobacco Retailers Almanac* (Annual). **Educational Activities:** IPCPR Annual Convention & International Trade Show (Annual). **Geographic Preference:** National.

15694 ■ Tobacco Merchants Association (TMA)
1121 Situs Ct., Ste. 370
Raleigh, NC 27606
Ph: (609)275-4900
Co. E-mail: tma@tma.org
URL: http://www.tma.org
X (Twitter): x.com/tma_org

Description: Manufacturers of tobacco products, leaf dealers, suppliers, distributors, and others related to the tobacco industry. Maintains records of trademarks. **Scope:** Tobacco industry and products. **Services:** Copying; Library open to the public for reference use only by appointment only. **Founded:** 1915. **Holdings:** 2,000 books; 296 bound periodical volumes; 150 VF drawers of pamphlets, archives, and clippings; 18 shelves of government reports; 135 drawers of trademark file cards; 25 drawers of brand file cards. **Publications:** *Executive Summary* (Weekly); *Issues Monitor* (Bimonthly); *Tobacco Weekly* (Weekly (Thurs.)); *World Alert* (Weekly); *DeskTop TMA*; *Tobacco Import-Export Database*; *Tobacco Barometer: Cigarettes, Cigars, Smoking Tobacco, Chewing Tobacco and Snuff* (Monthly); *US Tobacco Trade Barometer: Exports* (Monthly); *Tobacco Trade Barometer* (Monthly); *TMA Tobacco Tax Guide: Summaries of Key Provisions of Tobacco Tax Laws, All Tobacco Products, All States* (Quarterly); *TMA Legislative Bulletin*; *TMA Issues Monitor*, *Legislative Bulletin* (Weekly); *US Tobacco Barometer* (Monthly); *Tobacco Trade Barometer* (Monthly); *TMA Tobacco Weekly* (Semiweekly (Mon. and Thurs.)); *TMA Monthly Trademark Report* (Monthly); *TMA World Alert* (Weekly). **Educational Activities:** TMA Annual Meeting (Annual). **Geographic Preference:** National.

15695 ■ Tobacconists' Association of America (TAA)
PO Box 81152
Conyers, GA 30013
Ph: (770)597-6264
Co. E-mail: info@thetaa.org
URL: http://thetaa.org
Contact: Jennifer Groh, President
Facebook: www.facebook.com/TAACigars

Description: Provides tools and relationship building opportunities that will optimize their success in the Brick and Mortar business. **Founded:** 1968. **Geographic Preference:** National.

REFERENCE WORKS

15696 ■ "Clarence Firm Gets OK To Make Tobacco Products" in Business First of Buffalo (Vol. 30, March 14, 2014, No. 26, pp. 3)
Pub: American City Business Journals, Inc.
Contact: Mike Olivieri, Executive Vice President

Released: March 14, 2014. **Price:** $4, Introductory 4-Week Offer(Digital & Print). **Description:** Clarence, New York-based 22nd Century Group Inc.'s subsidiary Goodrich Tobacco Company, has received ap-proval from the Alcohol and Tobacco Tax Trade Bureau to produce tobacco products. The approval came after 22nd Century purchased the assets of North Carolina-based Nasco Products LLC, which holds a similar permit. Details of the deal are included. **Availability:** Print; Online.

15697 ■ "Fines Can't Snuff Out Hookah Sales" in Providence Business News (Vol. 28, March 3, 2014, No. 48, pp. 1)
Pub: American City Business Journals, Inc.
Contact: Mike Olivieri, Executive Vice President

Released: March 01, 2014. **Description:** The City of Providence, Rhode Island initiated a crackdown on bars and restaurants serving Middle Eastern-style water pipes, known as hookahs in violation of state anti-smoking laws. Gianfranco Marrocco, owner of several Federal Hill nightspots, believes that many bar owners will just pay the fine because hookah lounges are a good revenue source. **Availability:** Print; Online.

15698 ■ "How Quitting Tobacco Reshaped CVS: Q&A with CEO Larry Merlo" in USA Today (September 14, 2019)
URL(s): www.usatoday.com/story/money/2019/09/03/
cvs-pharmacy-tobacco-sales-ceo-larry-merlo/
2151148001/

Description: In September 2014, CVS quit selling tobacco products. CEO Larry Merlo discusses the impact that decision has made on its stores and the health of the American people. **Availability:** Online.

15699 ■ "Loss of Tobacco Revenue Is Unlikely To Cost CVS" in Providence Business News (Vol. 28, February 17, 2014, No. 46, pp. 1)
Pub: American City Business Journals, Inc.
Contact: Mike Olivieri, Executive Vice President
URL(s): pbn.com/loss-of-tobacco-revenue-is-unlikely
-to-cost-cvs95149

Description: CVS Caremark Corporation will stop selling tobacco products beginning October 1, 2014. CEO, Larry J. Merlo believes the sale of tobacco products is inconsistent with the drug retailer's purpose. The company's role in providing care through its nurse practitioners and pharmacists is also examined. **Availability:** Online. **Telecommunication Services:** Anderson@pbn.com.

15700 ■ "Non-Users Still Inhale Nicotine From E-Cigarettes" in Business First of Buffalo (Vol. 30, February 7, 2014, No. 21, pp. 6)
Pub: American City Business Journals, Inc.
Contact: Mike Olivieri, Executive Vice President

Released: Weekly. **Price:** $140, Digital & Print; $115, Digital only. **Description:** A group of researchers at Roswell Park Cancer Institute's Department of Health Behavior, led by Maciej Goniewicz, found traces of some potentially dangerous chemical in the vapor of electronic cigarettes. Although smoking e-cigarettes is less harmful than regular cigarettes, non-users are still exposed to nicotine in the same way as second-hand smoke. **Availability:** Print; Online.

15701 ■ "Professor: More Will Follow CVS Ban on Tobacco" in Philadelphia Business Journal (Vol. 33, February 14, 2014, No. 1, pp. 6)
Pub: American City Business Journals, Inc.
Contact: Mike Olivieri, Executive Vice President

Released: Weekly. **Price:** $4, introductory 4-week offer(Digital & Print). **Description:** Professor Daniel A. Hussar believes that CVS Caremark's decision to discontinue the sale of tobacco products reflects the company's concern for the health of consumers. He thinks that other drugstores will follow suit. The need for CVS Caremark to emphasize the importance of pharmacists' services is also examined. **Availability:** Print; Online.

15702 ■ "Roll Your Own" in Business North Carolina (Vol. 28, March 2008, No. 3, pp. 66)
Description: Profile of U.S. Flue-Cured Tobacco Growers who process tobacco and make cigarettes. Details of the program are outlined. **Availability:** Online.

15703 ■ "San Marcos May Ban Smoking" in Austin Business Journal (Vol. 31, June 17, 2011, No. 15, pp. 1)
Pub: Austin Business Journal
Contact: Rachel McGrath, Director
E-mail: rmcgrath@bizjournals.com

Ed: Vicky Garza. **Description:** The City Council of San Marcos, Texas will hold a public hearing regarding a proposed citywide smoking ban. The city is moving towards the smoking ban because it appears a statewide ban may be enacted. **Availability:** Print; Online.

15704 ■ "Vape, Smoke Shops on Edge as Santa Maria Mulls Ban of Flavored Tobacco Products" in Santa Maria Times (November 17, 2019)
URL(s): santamariatimes.com/news/local/govt-an d-politics/vape-smoke-shops-on-edge-as-santa-ma ria-mulls-ban/article_60b3d1ca-ba4a-5580-b851-f9 d51ff2c940.html

Ed: Razi Syed. **Released:** November 17, 2019. **Description:** After dozens of municipalities across California have moved to ban the sale of flavored tobacco and vaping products, the city of Santa Maria is considering it as well. If passed, the ordinance would also require that tobacco retailers become licensed with the city. **Availability:** Online.

15705 ■ "Vaping: From 'Safer Than Cigarettes' to Public Health Crisis" in U.S. News & World Report (September 30, 2019)
URL(s): www.usnews.com/news/healthiest-communi ties/articles/2019-09-30/vaping-from-safer-than -cigarettes-to-public-health-crisis

Ed: Joseph P. Williams. **Released:** September 30, 2019. **Description:** Originally intended as a way to wean off of regular cigarettes, vaping instead gained popularity not only with adults, but with teens as well. As more people vape and the effects are becoming known, the CDC has urged people to stop vaping. **Availability:** Online.

15706 ■ "What's Working Now: In Providing Jobs for North Carolinians" in Business North Carolina (Vol. 28, February 2008, No. 2, pp. 16)
Pub: Business North Carolina
Contact: Peggy Knaack, Manager
E-mail: pknaack@businessnc.com

Ed: Edward Martin, Frank Maley. **Description:** Individuals previously employed in the furniture, tobacco, or textile manufacturing sectors have gone back to school to be trained in new sectors in the area such as life sciences, finances and other emerging sectors. **Availability:** Online.

15707 ■ "Why CVS May Not Get Burned By Its Tobacco Decision (Part 2); Looking at CVS' Decision To Discontinue Selling Tobacco Products In Purely Dollar Terms Misses the Bigger Picture" in Gallup Business Journal (March 20, 2014)
Pub: Gallup, Inc.
Contact: Jon Clifton, Chief Executive Officer

Description: Drug retailer, CVS, made a strategic play in organizational identity, mission, and purpose when it decided to quit selling cigarettes at its retail stores. The decision to discontinue sales of tobacco products could, long term, strengthen the company's identity in the U.S. marketplace, thus increasing sales. **Availability:** Print; Online.

TRADE PERIODICALS

15708 ■ Cigar Aficionado
Pub: M. Shanken Communications Inc.
Contact: Barry Abrams, Vice President Associate Publisher
E-mail: babrams@mshanken.com
URL(s): www.cigaraficionado.comwww.mshanken .com/cigaraficionado
Facebook: www.facebook.com/CigarAficionado
X (Twitter): twitter.com/CigarAficMag
Instagram: www.instagram.com/cigaraficmag
YouTube: www.youtube.com/user/cigaraficionadovi deo

Ed: Marvin R. Shanken, Gordon Mott. **Released:** 6/year **Price:** $29.95, Individuals for 1 Year; $54.90, for combined. **Description:** Men's lifestyle magazine directed toward those who wish to expand their knowledge of premium cigars. **Availability:** Print; Online.

15709 ■ Convenience Distribution: AWMA's Magazine for Candy, Tobacco, Grocery, Foodservice and General Merchandiser Marketers
Pub: Convenience Distribution Association
Contact: Kimberly Bolin, President
E-mail: kimberlyb@cdaweb.net
URL(s): www.cdaweb.net/Resources/Magazine

Ed: Lisa White, Bob Gatty. **Released:** Monthly; latest edition Sprint 2024. **Description:** For service based distributors marketing to the retail trade. **Availability:** Online.

15710 ■ Tobacco Barometer: Cigarettes, Cigars, Smoking Tobacco, Chewing Tobacco and Snuff
Pub: Tobacco Merchants Association
URL(s): www.tma.org/basic-page/products-services -tma-publications
Released: Monthly **Description:** Lists statistics on quarterly and cumulative production and sales of smoking tobacco, chewing tobacco, and snuff. Makes comparisons with the same period of the previous year, and has an analysis of current developments and trends. Recurring features include legislative and labor activities which affect the prices of these products. **Availability:** Print.

15711 ■ US Tobacco Trade Barometer: Exports
Pub: Tobacco Merchants Association
URL(s): www.tma.org/tma-publications/us-tobacco-tra de-barometer
Released: Monthly **Description:** Carries statistics on exports of tobacco and tobacco products. Gives listings by country of destination, with quantities and values exported in the current month, in the year to date, and in comparison with previous periods. **Availability:** Print.

TRADE SHOWS AND CONVENTIONS

15712 ■ Tobacco Plus Expo Trade Show
National Association of Tobacco Outlets (NATO)
Lakeville, MN
Ph: (952)683-9270
Co. E-mail: info@natocentral.org

URL: http://www.natocentral.org
Contact: David Spross, Executive Director
E-mail: david.spross@natocentral.org
URL(s): www.natocentral.org/seminars
Description: Brings together the top tobacco retailers, manufacturers and wholesalers, and provides the perfect environment to learn, conduct business and network. **Audience:** Tobacco retailers, manufacturers and wholesalers. **Principal Exhibits:** Brings together the top tobacco retailers, manufacturers and wholesalers, and provides the perfect environment to learn, conduct business and network.

FRANCHISES AND BUSINESS OPPORTUNITIES

15713 ■ Shefield Gourmet Cup Beverage Station
2265 W Railway St.
Abbotsford, BC, Canada V2S 2E3
URL: http://shefield.com
Description: Operator of coffee shop. **Training:** Yes.

LIBRARIES

15714 ■ Imperial Tobacco Ltd. - Corporate Information Center
3711 St. Antoine St.
Montreal, QC, Canada H4C 3P6
Ph: (514)932-6161
URL: http://www.imperialtobaccocanada.com
X (Twitter): x.com/BATCanadaNews
YouTube: www.youtube.com/user/WelcomeToBAT
Scope: Tobacco; management; science. **Services:** Interlibrary loan. **Founded:** 1938. **Holdings:** 6,000 books; 10,000 pamphlets; 20 VF drawers of photographs and patents.

15715 ■ New York Public Library Rare Books Division - Arents Tobacco Collection
Brooke Russell Astor Reading Rm., 3rd Fl., Rm. 328
5th Ave. and 42nd St.
New York, NY 10018-2788
Ph: (212)642-0110
Fax: (212)302-4815
Co. E-mail: rarebook@nypl.org
URL: http://nypl.org/about/divisions/rare-books -division/arents-collection
Scope: History; literature and lore of tobacco. **Services:** Open to qualified researchers by card of admission secured in Special Collections Office. **Founded:** 1944. **Holdings:** 1,200 items; books and manuscripts; cards and pieces of ephemera.

15716 ■ Philip Morris USA Inc. (PM USA) - Library
Altria Group, Inc.
6601 W Broad St.
Richmond, VA 23230
Ph: (804)274-2200
URL: http://www.altria.com
Contact: Jon Moore, President
Description: Manufacturer and distributor of tobacco products such as cigarettes. **Scope:** Tobacco. **Founded:** 1933. **Holdings:** Figures not available.

15717 ■ Tobacco Merchants Association (TMA)
1121 Situs Ct., Ste. 370
Raleigh, NC 27606
Ph: (609)275-4900
Co. E-mail: tma@tma.org
URL: http://www.tma.org
X (Twitter): x.com/tma_org

Description: Manufacturers of tobacco products, leaf dealers, suppliers, distributors, and others related to the tobacco industry. Maintains records of trademarks. **Scope:** Tobacco industry and products. **Services:** Copying; Library open to the public for reference use only by appointment only. **Founded:** 1915. **Holdings:** 2,000 books; 296 bound periodical volumes; 150 VF drawers of pamphlets, archives, and clippings; 18 shelves of government reports; 135 drawers of trademark file cards; 25 drawers of brand file cards. **Publications:** *Executive Summary*

(Weekly); *Issues Monitor* (Bimonthly); *Tobacco Weekly* (Weekly (Thurs.)); *World Alert* (Weekly); *DeskTop TMA*; *Tobacco Import-Export Database*; *Tobacco Barometer: Cigarettes, Cigars, Smoking Tobacco, Chewing Tobacco and Snuff* (Monthly); *US Tobacco Trade Barometer: Exports* (Monthly); *Tobacco Trade Barometer* (Monthly); *TMA Tobacco Tax Guide: Summaries of Key Provisions of Tobacco Tax Laws, All Tobacco Products, All States* (Quarterly); *TMA Legislative Bulletin*; *TMA Issues Monitor*; *Legislative Bulletin* (Weekly); *US Tobacco Barometer* (Monthly); *Tobacco Trade Barometer* (Monthly); *TMA Tobacco Weekly* (Semiweekly (Mon. and Thurs.)); *TMA Monthly Trademark Report* (Monthly); *TMA World Alert* (Weekly). **Educational Activities:** TMA Annual Meeting (Annual). **Geographic Preference:** National.

15718 ■ U.S. Bureau of Alcohol, Tobacco, Firearms and Explosives Reference Library (ATF)
99 New York Ave. NE
  Washington, DC 20226
Ph: (202)648-7080
Free: 800-800-3855
Co. E-mail: atfmail@atf.gov
URL: http://www.atf.gov
Contact: Steven Dettelbach, Director
Facebook: www.facebook.com/HQATF
X (Twitter): x.com/atfhq
Instagram: www.instagram.com/atfhq
YouTube: www.youtube.com/user/ATFHQ
Scope: Alcohol; tobacco; firearms; explosives. **Services:** Interlibrary loan; copying; SDI; reading room open to the public by appointment; archives

open to the public with written permission. **Founded:** 1979. **Holdings:** 750 books; 100 bound periodical volumes; 1000 lin.ft. of indexed hearings, projects, tasks, and correspondence; 25 drawers of microfiche of historical documents; CD-ROMs.

15719 ■ U.S. Bureau of Alcohol, Tobacco and Firearms - National Laboratory Center Library (NLC)
Ammendale, MD
URL: http://www.atf.gov/laboratories
Contact: Marvin G. Richardson, Deputy Director
Scope: Alcohol; analytical techniques; forensic sciences; firearms; tobacco; explosives. **Services:** Library not open to the public. **Holdings:** 5,700 books; 4,000 bound periodical volumes; 200 total journal titles; government documents; archives.

ASSOCIATIONS AND OTHER ORGANIZATIONS

15720 ■ Adventure Travel Trade Association (ATTA)
14751 N Kelsey St., Ste. 105
Monroe, WA 98272
Ph: (360)805-3131
Fax: (360)805-0649
Co. E-mail: info@adventuretravel.biz
URL: http://www.adventuretravel.biz
Contact: Kim Hogle, Manager, Production Manager, Operations
Facebook: www.facebook.com/adventuretraveltra deassociation
Linkedin: www.linkedin.com/company/adventure -travel-trade-association
X (Twitter): x.com/adventuretweets
Instagram: www.instagram.com/adventure travelassociation
YouTube: www.youtube.com/user/AdvTravTrade

Description: Serves the adventure travel industry. Aims to grow the adventure travel industry overall and to help build up its member organizations. Provides exposure, marketing expertise, education, research, and discount to its members. **Founded:** 1990. **Educational Activities:** The New York Times Travel Show (Annual); Adventure Travel World Summit (ATWS) (Annual). **Geographic Preference:** Multinational.

15721 ■ Association of Canadian Travel Agencies (ACTA)
Martinway Plz.
Etobicoke, ON, Canada M9R 4C7
Ph: (905)282-9294
Free: 888-257-2282
Fax: (905)282-9826
Co. E-mail: memberservices@acta.ca
URL: http://www.acta.ca
Contact: Wendy Paradis, President
E-mail: wparadis@acta.ca
Facebook: www.facebook.com/ACTACanada
X (Twitter): x.com/ACTACanada
Instagram: www.instagram.com/actacanada_

Description: Represents individual travel professionals in Canada; promotes professional development through seminars, home study courses, conferences and workshops; offers professional certification programs leading to the Certified Travel Counsellor (CTC) and Certified Travel Manager (CTM) designations, and consumer awareness. **Founded:** 1977. **Publications:** *The Buzz* (Monthly). **Educational Activities:** ACTA Atlantic Regional Council Annual Meeting (Annual). **Geographic Preference:** National.

15722 ■ Canadian Tourism Research Institute (CTRI)
135 Laurier Ave., W
Ottawa, ON, Canada K1P 5J2
URL: http://www.conferenceboard.ca

Description: Seeks to increase understanding of the needs and interests of tourists. Serves as a clearing-house on tourism in Canada. Sponsors commercial tourism research. **Geographic Preference:** National.

15723 ■ International Galapagos Tour Operators Association (IGTOA)
MA
URL: http://www.igtoa.org
Contact: Jim Lutz, President
Facebook: www.facebook.com/interna tionalgalapagostouroperatorsassociation
YouTube: www.youtube.com/user/igtoagalapagos
Pinterest: www.pinterest.com/igtoapins

Description: Individuals and corporations conducting tours to the Galapagos Islands; educational and scientific institutions with an interest in the Islands and their ecosystems. Promotes tourism with the lowest possible environmental impact; seeks to preserve the unique ecosystems and species indigenous to the Galapagos Islands. Raises funds to support environmental protection initiatives; serves as a clearinghouse on low-impact nature tourism. **Founded:** 1997. **Geographic Preference:** Multinational.

15724 ■ National Federation of Tourist Guide Associations USA (NFTGA-USA)
c/o Michael Dillinger, President
516 E 79th St. 2M
New York, NY 10075
URL: http://www.nftga.com
Contact: Michael Dillinger, President
E-mail: president@nftga.com

Description: Represents and promotes tourist guide associations in the U.S. **Founded:** 1998. **Geographic Preference:** National.

15725 ■ National Tour Association (NTA)
101 Prosperous Pl., Ste. 350
Lexington, KY 40591
Ph: (859)264-6540
Free: 800-682-8886
Fax: (859)264-6570
Co. E-mail: headquarters@ntastaff.com
URL: http://www.ntaonline.com
Contact: Catherine Prather, President
E-mail: catherine.prather@ntastaff.com
Facebook: www.facebook.com/NTAnow
X (Twitter): x.com/NTAnews
YouTube: www.youtube.com/user/ntaonline

Description: Operators of group tours and packaged travel; travel industry-related companies providing services/facilities to tour operators (hotels, attractions, restaurants); and destination marketing organizations such as convention and visitor bureaus, and state tourism departments. Seeks to: maintain a code of ethical standards within the tour industry; develop and increase public interest in packaged travel. Represents members before governmental bodies and agencies. Conducts research and educational programs. **Founded:** 1951. **Publications:** *NTA Tuesday* (Weekly (Tues.)); *Tuesday* (Weekly).

Awards: Bob Everidge Lifetime Achievement Award (Irregular); NTA Volunteer of the Year (Annual). **Geographic Preference:** Multinational.

15726 ■ *TIAC Talk*
1300-180 rue Elgin St.
Ottawa, ON, Canada K2P 2K3
Ph: (613)238-7887
Co. E-mail: contact@tiac-aitc.ca
URL: http://tiac-aitc.ca
Contact: Nina Kressler, Chairman of the Board
URL(s): tiac-aitc.ca/cgi/page.cgi/TIAC_Talk.html

Description: Contains updates about the association's activities and government policies affecting the tourism industry. **Availability:** Online.

15727 ■ Tourism Industry Association of Canada (TIAC)
1300-180 rue Elgin St.
Ottawa, ON, Canada K2P 2K3
Ph: (613)238-7887
Co. E-mail: contact@tiac-aitc.ca
URL: http://tiac-aitc.ca
Contact: Nina Kressler, Chairman of the Board
Facebook: www.facebook.com/TIACAITC
Linkedin: www.linkedin.com/company/tourism-indus try-association-of-canada
X (Twitter): x.com/tiac_aitc
YouTube: www.youtube.com/user/TIACchannel

Description: Promotes viability of Canada's tourism industries. Represents industry at a national level and advocates for policies that will benefit the growth of tourism-related businesses. **Founded:** 1930. **Publications:** *RVC Directory* (Annual); *TIAC Talk*; *TIAC Talk Issue Focus* (Periodic). **Educational Activities:** Canada's Tourism Leadership Summit. **Awards:** TIAC/Canada Sustainable Tourism Award (Annual). **Geographic Preference:** National.

15728 ■ United States Tour Operators Association (USTOA)
345 7th Ave., Ste. 1801
New York, NY 10001
Ph: (212)599-6599
Fax: (212)599-6744
Co. E-mail: information@ustoa.com
URL: http://www.ustoa.com
Contact: Terry Dale, President
Facebook: www.facebook.com/USTourOpera torsAssoc
X (Twitter): x.com/ustoa
Instagram: www.instagram.com/ustoanyc
YouTube: www.youtube.com/user/ustoanyc
Pinterest: www.pinterest.com/ustoa

Description: Wholesale tour operators, common carriers, associations, government agencies, suppliers, purveyors of travel services, trade press, communications media, and public relations and advertising representatives. **Founded:** 1972. **Educational Activities:** The New York Times Travel Show (Annual); USTOA Annual Conference & Marketplace (Annual). **Geographic Preference:** National.

REFERENCE WORKS

15729 ■ *"The 7 Wonders of Tourism" in Business Journal Portland (Vol. 31, May 9, 2014, No. 10, pp. 10)*
Pub: American City Business Journals, Inc.
Contact: Mike Olivieri, Executive Vice President
Description: Travel Oregon's new travel campaign called '7 Wonders of Oregon' is expected to generate the area's economy. Reports show that the travel industry contributed $9.6 billion to the state's economy in 2013. The sector also employed a total of 93,900 Oregonians during the same year. Statistical data included. **Availability:** Online.

15730 ■ *"2010 Book of Lists" in Business Courier (Vol. 26, December 26, 2009, No. 36, pp. 1)*
Price: $49.95. **Description:** Rankings of companies and organizations within the business services, education, finance, health care, hospitality and tourism, real estate, and technology industries in the Cincinnati, Ohio-Northern Kentucky area are presented. Rankings are based on sales, business size, or other statistics. **Availability:** PDF; Online.

15731 ■ *"B&B Hopes to Appeal to Fiat Execs" in Crain's Detroit Business (Vol. 25, June 15, 2009, No. 24, pp. 21)*
Pub: Crain Communications Inc.
Contact: Barry Asin, President
Ed: Daniel Duggan. **Description:** Cobblestone Manor, a ten-room bed and breakfast in Auburn Hills, Michigan is hoping to provide rooms for Fiat executives. The owners have been working with travel organizations to promote the castle-like bed and breakfast which appeals to European visitors. **Availability:** Online.

15732 ■ *"Black Travelers, an Untapped Market with Tremendous Buying Power" in Host Agency Reviews(February 18, 2022)*
URL(s): hostagencyreviews.com/blog/cruiseplanners -02-2022
Released: February 18, 2022. **Description:** Discusses travel advisors tapping into the African American market, which is growing each year.

15733 ■ *"Chafee Eyes Tax On Travel Sites" in Providence Business News (Vol. 28, March 24, 2014, No. 51, pp. 1)*
Pub: American City Business Journals, Inc.
Contact: Mike Olivieri, Executive Vice President
URL(s): pbn.com/chafee-eyes-tax-on-travel-sites9 5903
Description: Rhode Island Governor, Lincoln D. Chafee's 2015 budget will include new tax rules for travel Websites. State officials claim the new regulations will deal with a loophole that has allowed travel Websites to pay less in taxes. Many hotels enter into partnerships with travel Websites in order to sell rooms in bulk. **Availability:** Online. **Telecommunication Services:** Anderson@pbn.com.

15734 ■ *"Cradle of Commerce" in San Antonio Business Journal (Vol. 28, August 29, 2014, No. 29, pp. 4)*
Pub: American City Business Journals, Inc.
Contact: Mike Olivieri, Executive Vice President
Description: Renewed interest in the Alamo is seen to boost tourism in San Antonio, Texas. The Alamo has been lagging behind other sites in terms of visitors. However, efforts to preserve and improve the grounds and visitor experience have heightened. **Availability:** Print; Online.

15735 ■ *Cruise Travel--Cruise Calendar Section: The Worldwide Cruise Vacation Magazine*
Contact: Charles Doherty, Editor
URL(s): www.cruisetravelmag.com
Ed: Charles Doherty. **Released:** Bimonthly; Three times yearly; April, August, and December. **Price:** $19.97, Individuals per year. **Description:** Publication includes listing of cruises by major cruise lines worldwide. **Entries include:** Cruise line company name, name of cruise ship, length of cruise, departure dates, destinations and ports-of-call, price range. **Arrangement:** Classified by cruising area, then port of departure. **Availability:** Print.

15736 ■ *Driving With No Brakes: How a Bunch of Hooligans Built the Best Travel Company in the World*
Pub: Grand Circle Corp.
Ed: Alan Lewis, Harriet Lewis. **Released:** 2010. **Description:** Inspirational book about how two courageous leaders built a remarkable company that can thrive in change and succeed in an unpredictable world. Important lessons for any business leader trying to create value in the 21st Century are included. **Availability:** Print.

15737 ■ *"Eco-Preneuring" in Small Business Opportunities (Feb. 6, 2012)*
Pub: Harris Publishing, Inc.
Contact: Janet Chase, Contact
Description: Iceland Naturally is a joint marketing effort among tourism and business interests hoping to increase demand for Icelandic products including frozen seafood, bottled water, agriculture, and tourism in North America.

15738 ■ *"Family-Owned Train Service Offers a Ride for Your Raft" in Idaho Business Review (June 11, 2014)*
Pub: BridgeTower Media
Contact: Adam Reinebach, President
Description: Payette River Flyer's run between Smith's Ferry and Cascade is part of Thunder Mountain's Line new rail service that allows rafters to leave their vehicles at Smith's Ferry and load whitewater gear onto the train. The train provides a scenic ride along the Payette River. Details of this family-operated tourist train service is profiled.

15739 ■ *"Faux Down Below" in Entrepreneur (May 2014)*
Pub: Entrepreneur Media Inc.
Contact: Dan Bova, Director
E-mail: dbova@entrepreneur.com
Description: Walter Marine of Orange Beach, Alabama has installed over 35,000 artificial reefs in waters in the U.S. and other countries to help prevent erosion and boost the tourism business. David Walter started his business in 1986 by sinking junk cars and items such as helicopters and kitchen sinks. Walter Marine is now focusing on custom-designed artificial reefs that are made of limestone and concrete. The company is hoping to increase its business by means of privately commissioned reefs. **Availability:** Print.

15740 ■ *"Fighting for Civil Rights Tourism" in Memphis Business Journal (Vol. 33, March 2, 2012, No. 47, pp. 1)*
Pub: Baltimore Business Journal
Contact: Rhonda Pringle, President
E-mail: rpringle@bizjournals.com
Ed: Michael Sheffield. **Description:** Memphis, Tennessee-based National Civil Rights Museum will complete its $27 million renovation in late 2013. It faces competition from Smithsonian Institution's National Museum of African-American History and Culture in Washington DC and the National Center for Civil and Human Rights in Atlanta, Georgia. **Availability:** Print; Online.

15741 ■ *"Galveston Invests In Future as Major Cruise Destination" in Houston Business Journal (Vol. 44, February 28, 2014, No. 43, pp. 4)*
Pub: American City Business Journals, Inc.
Contact: Mike Olivieri, Executive Vice President
Released: Weekly. **Price:** $4, introductory 4-week offer(Digital only). **Description:** The Port of Galveston in Texas is planning to build a third cruise terminal to capitalize on the growing cruise industry as it faces new competition with the Bayport Cruise terminal of the Port of Houston Authority. Architecture firm McTigue of Los Angeles, California was commissioned to design the new terminal. **Availability:** Print; Online.

15742 ■ *"Goldbelt Inc.: Targeting Shareholder Development" in Alaska Business Monthly (Vol. 27, October 2011, No. 10, pp. 108)*
Pub: Alaska Business Publishing Company Inc.
Contact: Charles Bell, Vice President, Sales and Marketing
E-mail: cbell@akbizmag.com
Ed: Tracy Kalytiak. **Description:** Profile of Goldbelt Inc., the company that has changed its original focus of timber to real estate to tourism and then to government contracting opportunities. **Availability:** Print; Online.

15743 ■ *A Guide to College Programs in Hospitality, Tourism, & Culinary Arts*
Pub: International Council on Hotel, Restaurant, and Institutional Education
Contact: Chrystel Masdupuy, President
E-mail: chrystel.masdupuy@institutpaulbocuse.com
URL(s): www.chrie.org/guide-to-college-programs
Released: Latest issue 2021. **Description:** Covers about 500 secondary and technical institutes, colleges, and universities; international coverage. **Entries include:** School name, address, areas of study, degrees offered, name and title of contact, program description, financial aid information, tuition and fees, admission and graduation requirements. **Arrangement:** Alphabetical, geographical, specialization. **Availability:** PDF; Download; Online.

15744 ■ *"Happy Trails: RV Franchiser Gives Road Traveling Enthusiasts a Lift" in Black Enterprise (Vol. 38, July 2008, No. 12, pp. 47)*
Pub: Earl G. Graves Ltd.
Contact: Earl Graves, Jr., President
Ed: Tamara E. Holmes. **Description:** Overview of Bates International Motor Home Rental Systems Inc., a growing franchise that gives RV owners the chance to rent out their big-ticket purchases to others when they are not using them; Sandra Williams Bate launched the company as a franchise in July 1997 and now has a fleet of 30 franchises across the country. She expects the company to reach 2.2 million for 2008 due to a marketing initiative that will expand the company's presence.

15745 ■ *"History Partners with Tour Guide Associations to Promote Members" in Breaking Travel News (November 8, 2019)*
URL(s): www.breakingtravelnews.com/news/article/ history-partners-with-tour-guide-associations-to -promote-members/
Released: November 08, 2019. **Description:** The entertainment channel, History, has partnered with the World Federation of Tourist Guide Association and the European Federation of Tourist Guide Associations in an effort to promote their tourist guide members around the world. The partnership will also make sure that tourist guides are promoted and protected. **Availability:** Online.

15746 ■ *"Hotels Get a Fill-Up: Fee Helps Bring Back Hot Rod Tour, Replace Biz Travel" in Crain's Detroit Business (Vol. 25, June 1, 2009, No. 22, pp. 1)*
Pub: Crain Communications Inc.
Contact: Barry Asin, President
Ed: Daniel Duggan. **Description:** Hot Rod Power Tour will have a $1 million economic impact on the area when it arrives in June 2009; the tour will bring 3,500 out-of-state custom vehicles to the event, whose owners will be needing hotel rooms. **Availability:** Print; Online.

15747 ■ *"Hottest Culinary School Vacations" in TravelChannel.com*
URL(s): www.travelchannel.com/interests/food-an d-drink/articles/hottest-culinary-school-vacations
Ed: Meghann Foye. **Description:** Culinary tourism is on the rise and is something that everyone can participate in because it's not a huge time commitment and it can be a fun adventure when on vacation. These classes are held throughout the world, so where ever you are on vacation, you can find a class or two to help increase your skill knowledge and help you take in the local culture. **Availability:** Online.

15748 ■ "III Winds; Cuba's Economy" in The Economist (Vol. 390, January 3, 2009, No. 8612, pp. 20)
Description: Cuba's long-term economic prospects remain poor with the economy forecasted to grow only 4.3 percent for the year, about half of the original forecast, due in part to Hurricane Gustav which caused $10 billion in damage and disrupted the food-supply network and devastated farms across the region; President Raul Castro made raising agricultural production a national priority and the rise in global commodity prices hit the country hard. The only bright spot has been the rise in tourism which is up 9.3 percent over 2007. **Availability:** Online.

15749 ■ "Indigenous Tourism Operators: The Vanguard of Economic Recovery in the Chatham Islands" in International Journal of Entrepreneurship and Small Business (Vol. 10, July 6, 2010, No. 4)
Ed: Andrew Cardow, Peter Wiltshier. **Description:** Emergent enthusiasm for tourism as a savior for economic development in the Chatham Islands of New Zealand is highlighted. **Availability:** Online.

15750 ■ "Las Vegas Convention and Visitors Authority Kicks Off Halloween Promotion" in Travel & Leisure Close-Up (October 8, 2012)
Description: Las Vegas Convention and Visitors Authority (LVCVA) is promoting the city as the premier destination for Halloween celebrations. LVCVA sites the holiday as a favorite for events and experiences for visitors. **Availability:** Print; Online.

15751 ■ "London's Gold-Medal Hotels" in Canadian Business (Vol. 85, August 13, 2012, No. 13, pp. 65)
Ed: Chris Johns. **Description:** Several new hotels in London, England, including Me by Melia, Apex Temple Court Hotel, and Bulgari Hotel London are presented. Prices and tips on how to best maximize the service are provided. **Availability:** Print; Online.

15752 ■ "The Next Wave" in Hawaii Business (Vol. 53, January 2008, No. 7, pp. 27)
Pub: PacificBasin Communications
Contact: Chuck Tindle, Director
E-mail: chuckt@pacificbasin.net
Ed: Cathy S. Cruz-George. **Description:** Only 40,000 Koreans took a visit to Hawaii in 2007, a decline from the pre-September averages of 123,000 visits. The number of Korean visitors in Hawaii could increase if the visa waiver proposal is passed. Efforts to improve Hawaiian tourism are presented. **Availability:** Print; Online.

15753 ■ "Norwegian Cruise Line Adds to Fleet with $3B Prestige Deal" in South Florida Business Journal (Vol. 35, September 5, 2014, No. 6, pp. 6)
Pub: American City Business Journals, Inc.
Contact: Mike Olivieri, Executive Vice President
Released: Weekly. **Price:** $8, introductory 4-week offer(Digital only). **Description:** Norwegian Cruise Line Holdings has agreed to purchase Prestige Cruises International for $3 billion. Norwegian will finance the acquisition with debt and by selling 20.3 million shares of its common stock. The deal will add five ships to Norwegian's 13-ship fleet. **Availability:** Print; Online.

15754 ■ "Philadelphia Tourism Push Rising in Fall" in Philadelphia Business Journal (Vol. 30, August 26, 2011, No. 28, pp. 1)
Pub: Philadelphia Business Journal
Contact: Sierra Quinn, Director
E-mail: squinn@bizjournals.com
Ed: Peter Van Allen. **Description:** Philadelphia is offering events for tourists this fall despite massive cuts for tourism promotion. Governor Tim Corbet slashed $5.5 million in funding for the state's tourism-promotion agencies which received $32 million in 2009. The agencies were forced to cooperate and fend for themselves using the hotel taxes that sustain them. **Availability:** Online.

15755 ■ "Plans for $160M Condo Resort in Wisconsin Dells Moves Forward" in Commercial Property News (March 18, 2008)
Description: Plans for the Grand Cambrian Resort in the Wisconsin Dells is discussed. The luxury condominium resort will include condos, townhomes, and condo-hotel style residences, two water parts, meeting space and indoor entertainment space, as well as a spa, four restaurants and retail offerings. **Availability:** Online.

15756 ■ "Port Canaveral Plans to Make Big Waves of Business in C. Fla." in Orlando Business Journal (Vol. 30, June 6, 2014, No. 50, pp. 4)
Pub: American City Business Journals, Inc.
Contact: Mike Olivieri, Executive Vice President
Released: Weekly. **Price:** $8, Introductory 4-week offer(Digital & Print). **Description:** Port Canaveral CEO, John Walsh, has big plans for the expansion of the Port, which include a $500 million cargo and cruise expansion that could net billions of dollars in new economic impact and create more than 15,000 new jobs. Walsh plans to expand cargo capacity, dig deeper harbors for large cruise ships and build a rail transport cargo and, eventually, passengers in and out of the 380-acre Port Canaveral. The Port is the fifth-largest cargo port in Central Florida. **Availability:** Print; Online.

15757 ■ "Salmon's Gem Air Wants Grant For Year-round Boise Flight" in Idaho Business Review (September 3, 2014)
Pub: BridgeTower Media
Contact: Adam Reinebach, President
Description: Gem Air offers four flights between Salmon and Boise, for both tourists and business-people including doctors and architects. The airline is requesting a $250,000 federal grant in order to compete with larger airlines and hopes to attract more business travelers with a direct flight between Boise and Atlanta.

15758 ■ Selling the Invisible: A Field Guide to Modern Marketing
Ed: Harry Beckwith. **Released:** March 20, 2012. **Price:** $16, paperback, ($21.00 in canada); $13.98, audiobook abridged library($16.99 in canada); $16.98, audiobook abridged($19.75 in canada); $9.98, audiobook abridged($12.98 in canada); $9.99, electronic book($9.99 in canada). **Description:** Tips for marketing and selling intangibles such as health care, entertainment, tourism, legal services, and more are provided. **Availability:** audiobook; E-book; Print.

15759 ■ "S.F. Tourism Soars to Giddy Heights" in San Francisco Business Times (Vol. 28, January 10, 2014, No. 25, pp. 11)
Pub: American City Business Journals, Inc.
Contact: Mike Olivieri, Executive Vice President
Released: Weekly. **Price:** $4, Introductory 4-week offer(Digital & Print). **Description:** Taylor Safford, CEO of Pier 39, believes that San Francisco, California's tourism industry is very robust. He reveals that the industry is now focusing on inbound visitors. He also thinks that transportation and housing are major issues for the sector. **Availability:** Print; Online.

15760 ■ "Small Dutch Islands Saba, Statia Content With Low-Key Niche" in Travel Weekly (Vol. 69, August 16, 2010, No. 33, pp. 22)
Pub: NorthStar Travel Media
Ed: Gay Nagle Myers. **Description:** Small Caribbean islands market and promote their region for tourism by never competing with the bigger destinations. Saba and Statia are the two smallest islands in the Caribbean and rely on repeat guests, word-of-mouth recommendations and travel agents willing to promote them. **Availability:** Print; Online.

15761 ■ "Tiki Boats Could Be Start of Untapped Business Opportunity on Detroit River" in Detroit Free Press(August 22, 2019)
Pub: Detroit Free Press Inc.
Contact: Peter Bhatia, Vice President Editor
E-mail: pbhatia@freepress.com

URL(s): https://www.freep.com/story/money/business/john-gallagher/2019/08/22/tiki-boats-detroit-river/2061155001/
Ed: John Gallagher. **Description:** A new venture called Aloha Tiki Tours offers sightseeing to partyers on the Detroit River. **Availability:** Online.

15762 ■ Tourism and Entrepreneurship: International Perspectives
Price: $69.95, Individuals, Paperback. **Description:** Trends in tourism development are explored, focusing on the impact of entrepreneurship in the context of regional and local tourism development. **Availability:** Print; Online.

15763 ■ The Travel Agent's Complete Desk Reference, 5th Edition
Released: Fifth edition. **Description:** Reference book that provides essential information to the home-based travel agent.

15764 ■ "Travel Tears" in Crain's Chicago Business (Vol. 31, November 17, 2008, No. 46, pp. 3)
Pub: Crain Communications Inc.
Contact: Barry Asin, President
Ed: Bob Tita. **Description:** Hotels, restaurants and conventions are seeing a decline in profits due to corporate travel cutbacks and the sagging economy. City and state revenues derived from taxes on tourism-related industries are also suffering. **Availability:** Online.

15765 ■ "Turbulent Times and Golden Opportunities" in Business Strategy Review (Vol. 21, Spring 2010, No. 1, pp. 34)
Ed: Don Sull. **Released:** February 09, 2010. **Description:** For those feeling storm-tossed by today's economy, the author believes there's much to learn from Carnival Cruise Lines, a company that discovered that turbulence often has an upside. **Availability:** Print; PDF; Online.

15766 ■ "TW Trade Shows to Offer Seminars On Niche Selling, Social Media" in Travel Weekly (Vol. 69, October 4, 2010, No. 40, pp. 9)
Pub: NorthStar Travel Media
Description: Travel Weekly's Leisure World 2010 and Fall Home Based Travel Agent Show focused on niche selling, with emphasis on all-inclusives, young consumers, groups, incentives, culinary vacations, and honeymoon or romance travel. **Availability:** Print; Online.

15767 ■ "Up in the Air" in The Business Journal-Serving Greater Tampa Bay (Vol. 28, July 18, 2008, No. 30, pp. 1)
Description: Views and information on Busch Gardens and on its future, are presented. The park's 3,769 employees worry for their future, after tourism industry experts have expressed concerns on possible tax cuts and other cost reductions. The future of the park, which ranks number 19 as the most visited park in the world, is expected to have a major impact on the tourism industry. **Availability:** Online.

15768 ■ "Watch Hill Gaining Traction as Luxury Destination" in Providence Business News (Vol. 28, March 24, 2014, No. 51, pp. 1)
Pub: American City Business Journals, Inc.
Contact: Mike Olivieri, Executive Vice President
Released: March 22, 2014. **Description:** Rhode Island's tourism leaders believe that the increase in the number of leisure tourists visiting Watch Hill can help improve the village's marketability. Mark Brodeur of the Rhode Island Commerce Corporation and Lisa Konicki of the Westerly-Pawcatuck Chamber of Commerce claim that the reopening of the Ocean House Hotel in 2010 led to the village's revival. **Availability:** Print; Online.

TRADE PERIODICALS

15769 ■ National Bus Trader
Pub: National Bus Trader Inc.
Contact: Lawrence J. Plachno, President

URL(s): busmag.com

Facebook: www.facebook.com/NBTBusMag

Ed: Larry Plachno. **Released:** Monthly **Price:** $30, U.S. for 1 year; $35, for Canada and International. **Description:** Magazine for bus tour planners. **Availability:** Print; Online; PDF.

15770 ■ *Travel Weekly's Hotel Search*

Pub: Travel Weekly

Contact: Bob Sullivan, President

E-mail: rsullivan@travelweekly.com

URL(s): www.travelweekly.com/Hotels

Released: Weekly **Description:** International hotel directory. **Availability:** Print.

15771 ■ *Travelweek*

Pub: Concepts Travel Media Ltd.

Contact: Annie Cicvaric, Director, Business Development

URL(s): www.travelweek.ca/about

Facebook: www.facebook.com/travelweek.ca

Linkedin: www.linkedin.com/company/travelweek

X (Twitter): x.com/TravelweekGroup

Instagram: www.instagram.com/travelweek

YouTube: www.youtube.com/user/travelweek

Released: Weekly **Description:** Trade publication covering the travel industry. **Availability:** Print; Online.

15772 ■ *Tuesday*

Pub: National Tour Association

Contact: Catherine Prather, President

E-mail: catherine.prather@ntastaff.com

URL(s): ntaonline.com/tuesday-newsletter

Released: Weekly **Description:** Promotes high standards in the tour industry and public interest in North American escorted tours. Provides information for group tour operators and suppliers in the U.S. and Canada. Carries legislative updates. Recurring features include Association and member news. **Availability:** Online.

VIDEO/AUDIO MEDIA

15773 ■ *Tia Clark Founder of Casual Crabbing with Tia*

URL(s): restaurantunstoppable.libsyn.com/983-tia -clark-founder-of-casual-crabbing-with-tia

Ed: Eric Cacciatore. **Released:** April 17, 2023. **Description:** Podcast offers a conversation with someone who teaches crabbing.

TRADE SHOWS AND CONVENTIONS

15774 ■ Colorado RV Adventure Travel Show

Colorado Recreation Vehicle Association

PO Box 480084

Denver, CO 80248-0084

URL: http://www.rvda.org/RVDA/About/State_/RVDA/ About1/Nationaal__State_and_Regional_Associa tions.aspx?hkey=655b202a-c8bc-47da-a54a-d4fa 35be9668

Contact: Jeff Haughton, Contact

URL(s): www.rvda.org/convention

Frequency: Annual. **Description:** Exhibits related to recreational vehicles, accessories and travel. **Audience:** Social studies educators, school administrators, professional development providers, and publishers. **Principal Exhibits:** Exhibits related to recreational vehicles, accessories and travel. Dates and Locations: 2025 Nov 10-14 Paris Las Vegas, Las Vegas, NV. **Telecommunication Services:** jnewhouse@rvda.org.

15775 ■ Heartland Travel Showcase

URL(s): www.heartlandtravelshowcase.com

Frequency: Annual. **Description:** Features exhibits from tour operators in Midwest states. **Principal Exhibits:** Features exhibits from tour operators in Midwest states.

15776 ■ Travel Media Showcase (TMS)

DeKalb Convention & Visitors Bureau (DCVB)

1990 Lakeside Pky., Ste. 170

Tucker, GA 30084

Free: 866-633-5252

URL: http://discoverdekalb.com

Contact: James Tsismanakis, Director

E-mail: james@discoverdekalb.com

URL(s): www.travelmediashowcase

Facebook: www.facebook.com/Travel-Media-Show-case-184526638300239

X (Twitter): twitter.com/TMShowcase

Description: Tourism industry and travel media convention. **Audience:** Editors, staff & freelance travel writers, Magazine and newspaper, travel writers, broadcast travel journalists, internet travel journalists and bloggers. **Principal Exhibits:** Tourism industry and travel media convention. **Telecommunication Services:** joanne@jveroassociates.com.

FRANCHISES AND BUSINESS OPPORTUNITIES

15777 ■ Lantis Fireworks & Lasers

PO Box 491

Draper, UT 84020

Ph: (801)768-2255

Free: 800-443-3040

Co. E-mail: info@lantisfireworks.com

URL: http://www.lantisfireworks.com

Contact: Catherine Lantis, President

E-mail: catherine@lantisfireworks.com

Facebook: www.facebook.com/lantisfireworksandla-sers

Description: Provider of event organizing, custom design solutions and more. **Founded:** 1945. **Training:** Available at headquarters 4-6 weeks.

LIBRARIES

15778 ■ Davenport University - Thomas F. Reed, Jr. Memorial Library

6767 W O Ave.

Kalamazoo, MI 49003

Ph: (269)552-3328

Fax: (269)353-2723

Co. E-mail: info@davenport.edu

URL: http://www.davenport.edu

Contact: Richard J. Pappas, President

Facebook: www.facebook.com/DavenportU

X (Twitter): x.com/davenportu

Instagram: www.instagram.com/davenportuniversity

YouTube: www.youtube.com/channel/ UCaxSQhSboBlHxBkPJOpCvTQ

Description: A quiet corner for studying and fast access to a wealth of information, the Library Information Commons is home to many students looking to study or down time between classes. **Scope:** Education. **Services:** Interlibrary loan; copying; faxing. **Founded:** 1981. **Holdings:** Figures not available.

15779 ■ U.S. Travel Association - Library

1100 New York Ave. NW Ste. 450

Washington, DC 20005

Ph: (202)408-8422

Co. E-mail: feedback@ustravel.org

URL: http://www.ustravel.org

Contact: Roger Dow, President

Facebook: www.facebook.com/U.S.TravelAssociation

Linkedin: www.linkedin.com/company/us travelassociation

X (Twitter): twitter.com/USTravel

Instagram: www.instagram.com/ustravel_association

Description: Facilitates communication and cooperation among members. **Scope:** Travel. **Founded:** 1941. **Holdings:** Figures not available. **Publications:** *Survey of State Travel Offices* (Annual); *Travel Industry Association of America--Travel Media Directory* (Annual); *Survey of State Tourism Offices* (Annual); *Outlook for Travel and Tourism*; *Survey of Business Travelers*. **Educational Activities:** IPW (Annual); Sports Travel Forum. **Awards:** Travel Hall of Leaders (Annual); Ronald H. Brown Memorial Scholarship; Hall of Leaders (Annual); U.S. Travel Association Mercury Awards (Annual). **Geographic Preference:** National.

15780 ■ University of Wisconsin - Stout (UW-STOUT) - Robert S. Swanson Library and Learning Center

315 Tenth Ave. E

Menomonie, WI 54751

Ph: (715)232-1215

Co. E-mail: reference@uwstout.edu

URL: http://www.uwstout.edu/directory/reference

Scope: Education. **Services:** Interlibrary loan; Copying; document delivery. **Founded:** 1908.

RESEARCH CENTERS

15781 ■ State University of New York at Buffalo School of Management - Center for Executive Development

160 Jacobs Management Ctr.

Buffalo, NY 14260-4000

URL: http://management.buffalo.edu/en trepreneurship/center-for-entrepreneurial-leadership -cel/advisory-board.html

Contact: Courtney J. Walsh, Assistant Dean

E-mail: cjwalsh@buffalo.edu

Description: Integral unit of Center for Management Development, School of Management, State University of New York at Buffalo. **Scope:** Administrates and coordinates market, tourism, and public policy research conducted by School of Management faculty, bringing faculty and student research expertise to bear upon specific business and economic issues. As a State Data Center Affiliate designate, the Center collects, analyzes, and distributes data for business and community planning purposes. **Founded:** 1978. **Educational Activities:** Seminars and training programs for industry, Including a continuing education program in accounting.

15782 ■ University of Central Florida - Rosen College of Hospitality Management - Dick Pope Sr. Institute for Tourism Studies (DPI)

9907 Universal Blvd.

Orlando, FL 32819

URL: http://hospitality.ucf.edu/faculty-and-staff/re-search/dick-pope-sr-institute-for-tourism-studies

Contact: Dr. Abraham Pizam, Professor

E-mail: abraham.pizam@ucf.edu

Description: Integral unit of Rosen College of Hospitality Management, University of Central Florida. **Scope:** Tourism and travel industry in Florida, U.S., and other countries, including development of tourism forecasts and investigations of characteristics and motivations of travelers. Identifies and analyzes problems in the tourism industry. Provides primary data sources to aid in management decision making. Sponsorship opportunities. **Founded:** 1979. **Publications:** *Proprietary Research Reports*. **Educational Activities:** Dick Pope Sr. Institute for Tourism Studies Conferences, Offer exemplary teaching and training programs.; Dick Pope, Sr. Institute for Tourism Studies Faculty workshops, Offer exemplary teaching and training programs.; Dick Pope, Sr. Institute for Tourism Studies Industry seminars, Offer exemplary teaching and training programs.; Public and private research consultation opportunities, Offer exemplary teaching and training programs.; Dick Pope Sr. Institute for Tourism Studies Research colloquiums (Monthly), Offer exemplary teaching and training programs.

15783 ■ **University of Colorado at Boulder - Leeds School of Business - Business Research Division (BRD)**
995 Regent Dr., 419 UCB
 Boulder, CO 80309
Ph: (303)492-3307

Co. E-mail: brdinfo@colorado.edu
URL: http://www.colorado.edu/business/business
 -research-division#overview
Contact: Brian Lewandowski, Executive Director
E-mail: brian.lewandowski@colorado.edu
Description: Publishes directories. **Scope:** Regional and local economic impact studies, and forecasting. **Founded:** 1915. **Publications:** *Environmental Concerns: The 1999-2000 Directory of the Environmental Industry in Colorado*; *Directory of Colorado*

Manufacturers--Information, Science, & Technology; *Colorado Biomedical Directory*; *Colorado Photonics Industry Directory*; *Colorado Ski Industry* (Annual); *Directory of Colorado Manufacturers with International Sales*; *Colorado Manufacturers Directory* (Annual); *Directory of Colorado High Tech Manufacturers*. **Educational Activities:** Annual Colorado Business Economic Outlook Forum (Annual), Offer exemplary teaching and training programs.

ASSOCIATIONS AND OTHER ORGANIZATIONS

15784 ■ The Toy Association Inc.
1375 Broadway 10th Fl.
New York, NY 10018
Ph: (212)675-1141
Co. E-mail: info@toyassociation.org
URL: http://www.toyassociation.org
Contact: Steve Pasierb, President
Facebook: www.facebook.com/TheToyAssociation
Linkedin: www.linkedin.com/company/thetoyassociation
X (Twitter): x.com/TheToyAssoc
YouTube: www.youtube.com/TheToyAssociation

Description: Provides business services to US. manufacturers and importers of toys. Manages American International Toy Fair; represents the industry before Federal, State and Local government on issues of importance; provides legal and legislative counsel; conducts educational programs; compiles industry statistics. **Founded:** 1916. **Publications:** *American International Toy Fair Official Directory* (Annual); *Toy Challenges and Opportunities* (Annual); *The Official American International Toy Fair Directory* (Annual). **Educational Activities:** Toy Fair (Annual). **Awards:** TIA Toy of the Year Award (Annual). **Geographic Preference:** National.

15785 ■ USA Toy Library Association (USA-TLA)
2719 Broadway Ave.
Evanston, IL 60201
Ph: (847)612-6966
Fax: (847)864-8473
Co. E-mail: usatla.org@gmail.com
URL: http://usatla.org
Contact: Judith Iacuzzi, Executive Director
Facebook: www.facebook.com/USA-Toy-Library-Association-118012331559912

Description: Child care professionals, parents, and others interested in the role of toys and play in child development. Promotes the importance of play and the development of toy libraries in public and school libraries, hospitals, day care centers, and mobile collections. Seeks to broaden understanding of how toys can educate, increase parent-child interaction, and aid in development and therapy of disabled children. **Founded:** 1984. **Geographic Preference:** National.

REFERENCE WORKS

15786 ■ "Bakugan Battle Brawlers From Spin Master: A Marketing 50 Case Study" in Advertising Age (Vol. 79, November 17, 2008, No. 43, pp. S2)
Pub: Crain Communications, Inc.
Contact: Jessica Botos, Manager, Marketing
E-mail: jessica.botos@crainsnewyork.com

Ed: Kate Fitzgerald. **Description:** Spin Master toys has a new hit, Bakugan Battle Brawlers, an interactive game board with 106 characters that battle with one another in tournaments. Bakugan tournaments are being held at Toys "R" Us stores. **Availability:** Online.

15787 ■ "Consignment Shop Offers Children's Clothes, Products" in Frederick News-Post (August 19, 2010)
Pub: Federick News-Post
Contact: Connie Hastings, Director
E-mail: chastings@newspost.com

Ed: Ed Waters, Jr. **Description:** Sweet Pea Consignments for Children offers used items for newborns to pre-teens. The shop carries name brand clothing as well as toys, books and baby products. **Availability:** Print; Online.

15788 ■ "Counting on Cornhole: Popular Bean Bag Game Brings Crowds to Bars" in Baltimore Business Journal (Vol. 29, July 15, 2011, No. 10, pp. 1)
Pub: Boston Business Journal
Contact: Carolyn M. Jones, President
E-mail: cmjones@bizjournals.com

Ed: Alexander Jackson. **Description:** Cornhole game is being used by bars to spur business as the games hikes beer and food sales on slow weekdays. The game is played with two cornhole boards facing each other and is played with one or two people on one team who try to place a bag on the board. **Availability:** Print; Online.

15789 ■ "Disney's High Hopes for Duffy" in Canadian Business (Vol. 83, October 12, 2010, No. 17, pp. 14)
Pub: Rogers Media Inc.
Contact: Neil Spivak, Chief Executive Officer

Ed: James Cowan. **Description:** The reintroduction of Duffy is expected to create a new, exclusive product line that distinguishes Disney's parks and stores from competitors. Duffy, a teddy bear, was first introduced at a Disney World store in Florida in 2002. The character was incorporated into the Disney mythology when its popularity grew in Japan. **Availability:** Online.

15790 ■ "Down on the Boardwalk" in Retail Merchandiser (Vol. 51, September-October 2011, No. 5, pp. 56)

Description: Classic board game, Monopoly, continues to be the most recognized game brand while staying fresh by entering new markets and gaming platforms for all walks of life. Monopoly is available in over 100 countries, translated into 43 languages and played by more than 1 billion people since its introduction, and the game is tailored to each geographic market it enters. **Availability:** Online.

15791 ■ "Inside Out" in Playthings (Vol. 107, January 1, 2009, No. 1, pp. 3)

Description: Mattel signed on as the global master toy licensee for Cartoon Network's The Secret

Saturdays while Toy Island signed a deal for wooden toys based on several leading Nick Jr. properties. **Availability:** Print; Online.

15792 ■ "Look Out, Barbie, Bratz are Back" in Canadian Business (Vol. 83, August 17, 2010, No. 13-14, pp. 18)
Pub: Rogers Media Inc.
Contact: Neil Spivak, Chief Executive Officer

Ed: Joe Castaldo. **Description:** California-based MGA Entertainment has wrestled back control over Bratz from Mattel after a six-year legal battle. However, MGA owner Isaac Larian could still face legal hurdles if Mattel pursues a retrial. He now has to revive the brand which virtually disappeared from stores when Mattel won the rights for Bratz. **Availability:** Online.

15793 ■ "Target to Power New Toys 'R' Us Online Business" in Reuters (October 8, 2019)
URL(s): www.reuters.com/article/us-target-toys-r-us/target-to-power-new-toys-r-us-online-business-idUSKBN1WN1GG

Released: October 08, 2019. **Description:** Target announced a partnership with Tru Kids, which is the parent of the Toys 'R' Us brand, in order to run their toy website, ToysRUs.com. Consumers have the option to complete their purchase at Target.com. **Availability:** Online.

15794 ■ "Toys R Us Is Coming Back But with a Different Approach" in NPR (July 18, 2019)
URL(s): www.npr.org/2019/07/18/743157480/toys-r-us-is-coming-back-but-with-a-different-approach

Ed: Dani Matias. **Released:** July 18, 2019. **Description:** The iconic chain of stores, Toys R Us, is coming back and relaunched in the US, but with a different twist from its old business model. Tru Kids Brand, the parent company, announced that Toys R Us will come back with smaller stores that will feature toy demonstrations and open play areas. This is in partnership with b8ta, which owns similar stores. **Availability:** Online.

15795 ■ "Toys R Us Tries for a Comeback a Year After Going Out of Business" in CNBC (February 11, 2019)
URL(s): www.cnbc.com/2019/02/11/toys-r-us-executives-plot-retailers-comeback-with-tru-kids.html

Ed: Lauren Hirsch. **Released:** February 11, 2019. **Description:** The brand new company, Tru Kid, is a new concept developed to help bring back the Toys R Us brand, along with the Baby's R Us and Geoffrey brands. **Availability:** Online.

15796 ■ "Weathering the Economic Storm" in Playthings (Vol. 107, January 1, 2009, No. 1, pp. 10)

Ed: J. Tol Broome, Jr. **Description:** Six steps for toy companies to survive the economic turndown are outlined: Outline your business model; seek professional input; meet with your banker; cut your costs; manage your inventory; and use your trade credit. **Availability:** Print; Online.

15797 ■ *"Work for Play: Careers in Video Game Development" in Occupational Outlook Quarterly (Vol. 55, Fall 2011, No. 3, pp. 2)*
Pub: U.S. Department of Labor Bureau of Labor Statistics
Contact: Amrit Kohli, Director
E-mail: kohli.amrit@bls.gov

Ed: Drew Liming, Dennis Vilorio. **Description:** Game developers make a living creating the games the public enjoys playing. The video gaming industry reported sales over $10 billion in 2009 and employed 32,000 people in 34 states. Career options in video game development are featured. **Availability:** PDF; Online.

15798 ■ *"Xbox 360 Excels As a Media Hub" in Hispanic Business (October 2009, pp. 40)*
Ed: Jeremy Nisen. **Description:** Xbox 360 video game console from Microsoft offers games, amazing graphics and state-of-the-art accessories. The trend towards purchase of the Xbox includes more than teenagers.

STATISTICAL SOURCES

15799 ■ *RMA Annual Statement Studies*
Pub: Risk Management Association
Contact: Nancy Foster, President

Released: Annual. **Description:** Contains composite balance sheets and income statements for more than 360 industries, including the accounting, auditing, and bookkeeping industries. Also contains five years of comparative historical data for discerning trends. Includes 16 commonly used ratios, computed for most of the size groupings for nearly every industry.

15800 ■ *Standard & Poor's Industry Surveys*
Pub: Standard And Poor's Financial Services LLC.
Contact: Douglas L. Peterson, President

Description: Two-volume book that examines the prospects for specific industries, including trucking. Also provides analyses of trends and problems, statistical tables and charts, and comparative company analyses.

15801 ■ *US Traditional Toys and Games Market Report 2020*
URL(s): store.mintel.com/report/us-traditional-toys-and-games-market-report

Price: $4,366.35. **Description:** Downloadable report discussing the toys and games market in the US plus the impact COVID-19 has had on the industry. Report includes an executive summary, interactive databook, PowerPoint presentation, infographic overview, report PDF, and previous years data. **Availability:** PDF.

TRADE PERIODICALS

15802 ■ *The Toy Book*
Pub: Adventure Publishing Group Inc.
Contact: Laurie Schacht, President
E-mail: laurieschacht@aol.com
URL(s): toybook.comwww.adventurepublishinggroup.com/ap-toy-book.html
Facebook: www.facebook.com/TheToyBook
X (Twitter): x.com/toybook
Instagram: www.instagram.com/thetoybook
Released: Annual **Price:** $200, for 1 year foreign; $48, for print 6 issue; $56, Canada for per year. **Description:** Tabloid for buyers in the toy and hobby industries. **Availability:** Print; PDF; Download; Online.

15803 ■ *Toys & Games: Canada's Toy Industry Magazine*
Pub: Playtonic Communications

Released: Bimonthly **Description:** Toys and games magazine. **Availability:** Print; Online.

VIDEO/AUDIO MEDIA

15804 ■ *How I Built This: Spin Master/PAW Patrol: Ronnen Harary*
URL(s): www.npr.org/2021/12/17/1065352806/spin-master-paw-patrol-ronnen-harary

Ed: Guy Raz. **Released:** December 20, 2021. **Description:** Podcast explains how two guys went from selling chi-pet-like novelty gifts to building a $4 billion toy company without relying on market research or focus groups.

15805 ■ *Marketplace: Summertime Is Stocking Season for This Toy Store Owner*
URL(s): www.marketplace.org/2023/07/03/summertime-is-stocking-season-for-this-toy-store-owner

Ed: Livi Burdette. **Released:** July 03, 2023. **Description:** Podcast discusses the seasons of a toy store.

15806 ■ *Side Hustle to Small Business: Launching a Business to Make a Lasting Impact on the World*
URL(s): www.hiscox.com/side-hustle-to-small-business/tim-holmes-kingdom-quest-podcast-season-4

Ed: Sanjay Parekh. **Released:** September 04, 2024. **Description:** Podcast features the founder of Kingdom Quest, a toy company in Columbus, Ohio.

TRADE SHOWS AND CONVENTIONS

15807 ■ *CHA Create and Connect Conference and Trade Show*
Association For Creative Industries (AFCI)
330 N Wabash Ave., Ste. 2000
Chicago, IL 60611
Ph: (312)321-6811
Co. E-mail: info@creativeindustries.org
URL: http://creativeindustries.org
Contact: Peter Finn, Executive Director
E-mail: pfinn@creativeindustries.org
URL(s): www.craftandhobby.org/eweb/DynamicPage.aspx?WebKey=E94EE351-A89C-492E-888F-A45138487AA6

Frequency: Annual. **Description:** Crafts, ceramics, floral accessories, dollhouse miniatures, aromatics, art materials and frames, jewelry findings, fabrics, needlework and quilting supplies, home decor, rubber stamps, stencils and scrapbooking supplies. **Audience:** Owners, corporate officers and buyers from craft, general merchandise stores, wholesalers, professional crafters and CHA professionals. **Principal Exhibits:** Crafts, ceramics, floral accessories, dollhouse miniatures, aromatics, art materials and frames, jewelry findings, fabrics, needlework and quilting supplies, home decor, rubber stamps, stencils and scrapbooking supplies.

15808 ■ *GAMA Trade Show*
Game Manufacturers Association (GAMA)
258 E Campus View Blvd.
Columbus, OH 43235
Ph: (614)255-4500
Fax: (614)255-4499
Co. E-mail: admin@gama.org
URL: http://www.gama.org
Contact: Eric Price, President
E-mail: eric.price@gama.org
URL(s): www.gama.org/page/gama-expo

Frequency: Annual. **Description:** Exhibits relating to gaming hobby market. **Audience:** Manufacturers, retail stores, game designers and other industry professionals. **Principal Exhibits:** Exhibits relating to gaming hobby market. Dates and Locations: 2025 Feb 23-27 The Galt House Hotel & KICC, Louisville, KY; 2026 Mar 01-05 The Galt House Hotel & KICC, Louisville, KY. **Telecommunication Services:** julie.yeager@gama.org.

15809 ■ Toy Fair
The Toy Association Inc.
1375 Broadway 10th Fl.
New York, NY 10018
Ph: (212)675-1141
Co. E-mail: info@toyassociation.org
URL: http://www.toyassociation.org
Contact: Steve Pasierb, President
URL(s): www.toyfairny.com/
Facebook: www.facebook.com/toyfairny
X (Twitter): twitter.com/toyfairny
Frequency: Annual. **Audience:** Industry professionals. Dates and Locations: 2025 Mar 01-04 Jacob K. Javits Center, New York, NY; 2026 Feb 14-17 New York, NY; 2027 Feb 20-23 New York, NY. **Telecommunication Services:** toyfair@xpressreg.net.

FRANCHISES AND BUSINESS OPPORTUNITIES

15810 ■ Compuchild
Compuchild Services of America
3736 Fallon Rd., Ste. 125
Dublin, CA 94568
Ph: (317)817-9817
Free: 800-619-5437
Fax: (317)818-8184
Contact: Shubhra Kant, President
Facebook: www.facebook.com/CompuChild
Linkedin: www.linkedin.com/company/compuchild/about
X (Twitter): x.com/CompuChild
Instagram: www.instagram.com/compuchild_franchise
YouTube: www.youtube.com/channel/UCEHzHydnaCoZKj_Ut5piemg
Pinterest: www.pinterest.com/compuchild

Description: Computer education to children. **No. of Franchise Units:** 69. **No. of Company-Owned Units:** 1. **Founded:** 1994. **Franchised:** 1995. **Equity Capital Needed:** $15,000. **Franchise Fee:** $12,500 or $17,500. **Financial Assistance:** Yes **Training:** Yes.

15811 ■ Once Upon a Child
605 Hwy. 169 N, Ste. 400
Minneapolis, MN 55441
Ph: (763)520-8500
Co. E-mail: ouac-corporate-operations@ouac.com
URL: http://www.onceuponachild.com
Contact: Tamara L. Harmon, Contact
Facebook: www.facebook.com/onceuponachild
X (Twitter): x.com/OnceUponAChild
Instagram: www.instagram.com/onceuponachild
YouTube: www.youtube.com/user/OnceUponAchildTV

Description: Franchises consignment shops featuring children products including toys, books, furniture and apparel. **Founded:** 1985. **Equity Capital Needed:** $250,000 ; $75,000 – Cash or liquid assets. **Training:** Yes.

PUBLICATIONS

15812 ■ *iGaming Business Directory*
33 Needham St.
Newton, MA 02461
Ph: (617)332-2850
Free: 800-490-1715
Co. E-mail: sales@casinocitypress.com
URL: http://www.casinocitypress.com
Contact: Lisa Pasquarosa, Director, Sales
E-mail: lisa@casinocity.com
URL(s): www.casinocitypress.com/onlinegaming/onlinegamingdirectory

Released: Annual **Price:** $899.95, for Book and Multi-User Online; $874.95, for Multi-User Online; $599.95, Single issue for standard license book and online; $574.95, Single issue for online; $350, for printed book. **Description:** Covers 3,000 iGaming sites, 1,100 site owners, 5,700 iGaming portal sites, site rankings, software manufacturers, and 1,000 affiliate programs. **Availability:** Print; Online.

COMPUTERIZED DATABASES

15813 ■ *Gifts & Decorative Accessories*
Sandow
 3651 NW 8th Ave.
 Boca Raton, FL 33431

Ph: (561)961-7600
Co. E-mail: hello@sandow.com
URL: http://www.sandow.com
Contact: Peter Fain, Chief Operating Officer
URL(s): www.giftsanddec.com
Facebook: www.facebook.com/giftsanddecmag
Linkedin: www.linkedin.com/company/gifts-&-decorative-accessories-magazine
X (Twitter): x.com/Gifts_and_Dec

Instagram: www.instagram.com/gifts_and_dec
Released: Monthly **Price:** $55.97, for online 1 Year (11 issues); $68.97, for print and online 1 year (11 issues). **Description:** International magazine for retailers of gifts, greeting cards, decorative accessories, and stationery-related merchandise. **Availability:** Print; Online. **Type:** Full-text; Directory.

START-UP INFORMATION

15814 ■ *"Event-Planning Startup Extends Its Reach"* in Indianapolis Business Journal (Vol. 33, June 18, 2012, No. 16, pp. 2A)

Description: Snappening.com offers a searchable database of central Indiana event venues ad professional planners and is expanding its service to four new markets. **Availability:** Print; Online.

15815 ■ *How to Start a Home-Based Event Planning Business*

Ed: Jill Moran. **Released:** 4th edition. **Price:** $19.95, paperback; $9.99; Paperback. **Description:** Guide to starting and growing a business planning events from a home-based firm. **Availability:** E-book; Print.

ASSOCIATIONS AND OTHER ORGANIZATIONS

15816 ■ **Canadian National Exhibition (CNE) [Exposition Nationale Canadienne]**
210 Princes' Blvd.
  Toronto, ON, Canada M6K 3C3
Ph: (416)263-3330
Free: 844-398-3278
Co. E-mail: info@theex.com
URL: http://www.theex.com
Contact: Suzan Hall, President
Facebook: www.facebook.com/TheEx
X (Twitter): x.com/letsgototheex
Instagram: www.instagram.com/letsgototheex
YouTube: www.youtube.com/user/CNEToronto

Description: Organizations sponsoring and participating in the Canadian National Exhibition. Promotes efficient and profitable operation of the exhibition. Facilitates cooperation among members; conducts promotional activities. **Founded:** 1879. **Educational Activities:** Canadian National Exhibition (Annual). **Geographic Preference:** National.

15817 ■ **Center for Exhibition Industry Research (CEIR)**
12700 Pk. Central Dr., Ste. 308
  Dallas, TX 75251
Ph: (972)687-9242
Fax: (972)692-6020
Co. E-mail: info@ceir.org
URL: http://www.ceir.org
Contact: Cathy Breden, CMP, CAE, Chief Executive Officer
Facebook: www.facebook.com/CEIRHQ
X (Twitter): x.com/ceir_hq
YouTube: www.youtube.com/user/CEIRHQ

Description: Promotes the growth and value of exhibitions and other face-to-face marketing events by delivering research-based knowledge tools. Consists of exhibition organizers, service providers, exhibitors, CVBs, and facilities. **Founded:** 1978. **Geographic Preference:** National.

15818 ■ **Council of Protocol Executives (COPE)**
1133 Ave. Americas
  New York, NY 10036-6799
Contact: Peter R. Porcino, Contact

Description: Persons who coordinate executive level meetings and special events for governments, corporations, and professional and nonprofit organizations; dedicated to increasing the level of professionalism in the field. Works to develop new ideas in all areas of meeting planning and identify trends in the industry. Reviews and recommends new and existing facilities and suppliers; conducts educational programs covering topics such as invitations, sports marketing, wines, entertainment of foreign guests, and speakers and entertainers; facilitates networking among members. **Founded:** 1988. **Publications:** *COPE & PROTOCOL*. **Geographic Preference:** National.

15819 ■ **Event Service Professionals Association (ESPA)**
191 Clarksville Rd.
  Princeton Junction, NJ 08550
Ph: (609)799-3712
Fax: (609)799-7032
Co. E-mail: info@espaonline.org
URL: http://espaonline.org
Contact: Denise Reid, President
Facebook: www.facebook.com/ESPAOnline
Linkedin: www.linkedin.com/company/event-service
  -professionals-association-espa-
X (Twitter): x.com/ESPATweets

Description: Represents professionals in the hospitality industry, including those who work for hotels and convention centers. Works to establish high ethical standards, improve professional management techniques, and increase awareness of client, employer, and provider needs. Holds summer conference. Maintains speakers' bureau, resource center, and placement services; compiles statistics. Conducts research and educational programs. **Founded:** 1988. **Awards:** ESPA Inspiration in Service Award (Annual); ESPA Executive Excellence Award (Annual); ESPA Meeting Professional of the Year Award (Annual); ESPA Member of the Year Award (Annual). **Geographic Preference:** Multinational.

15820 ■ **Exhibit Designers and Producers Association (EDPA)**
239 E Michigan Ave., Ste. 212
  Paw Paw, MI 49079
Free: 866-806-3372
Co. E-mail: info@edpa.com
URL: http://www.edpa.com
Contact: Dan Serebin, President
Facebook: www.facebook.com/edpassociation
X (Twitter): x.com/EDPAAssociation
YouTube: www.youtube.com/user/EDPAssociation

Description: Firms designing and building exhibits for trade shows and museums. Conducts educational and research programs. **Founded:** 1954. **Publications:** *EDP Action News* (Bimonthly); *EDPA.COMmunications* (Monthly); *EDPA Today* (Quarterly).

Awards: EDPA Chapter of the Year (Annual); Hazel Hayes Award (Annual); EDPA Ambassador Award (Annual); EDDIE Award (Annual); Michael R. Westcott Designer of the Year Award (Annual). **Geographic Preference:** Multinational.

15821 ■ **Exposition Services & Contractors Association (ESCA)**
2245 Keller Way, Ste. 310
  Carrollton, TX 75006
Ph: (972)777-9282
Co. E-mail: info@esca.org
URL: http://www.esca.org
Contact: Bob Ryley, President
Facebook: www.facebook.com/esca.org
Linkedin: www.linkedin.com/company/exhibition-ser-
  vices-&-contractors-association
Instagram: www.instagram.com/esca_org_

Description: Engages in the provision of material and/or services normally furnished for trade shows, conventions, exhibitions and corporate meetings. Serves as a clearinghouse for the exchange of information among members and all other entities of the trade show and convention field. Seeks to promote and maintain progressive business and professional standards; advances better show techniques; improves the efficiency of material handling and on-site organization; enhances the use of manpower. **Founded:** 1970. **Publications:** *Guide to Exposition Service* (Annual); *Annual Guide to Exposition Service* (Annual). **Geographic Preference:** National.

15822 ■ **International Association of Conference Center Administrators (IACCA)**
575 Burton Rd.
  Greenwich, NY 12834
URL: http://www.iacca.org
Contact: Carla Odell, Treasurer

Description: Provides support to conference center administrators and furthers their professional development. **Founded:** 1976. **Publications:** *IACCA Journal* (Periodic). **Educational Activities:** IACCA Annual Conference (Annual); Journey of Leadership. **Geographic Preference:** National.

15823 ■ **International Association of Conference Centres (IACC)**
35 E Wacker Dr., Ste. 850
  Chicago, IL 60601
Ph: (312)224-2580
Fax: (312)644-8557
Co. E-mail: info@iacconline.org
URL: http://www.iacconline.org
Contact: Sean Anderson, President
E-mail: sean.anderson@sodexo.com
Facebook: www.facebook.com/IACCmeetings
X (Twitter): x.com/IACCmeetings
Instagram: www.instagram.com/iaccmeetings
YouTube: www.youtube.com/channel/
  UCArjlcSgqRDBrPC93m0iYBg

Description: To bring together the brightest industry minds to promote the best meeting venues, which deliver exceptional meeting experiences. **Founded:**

1981. **Publications:** *Conference Center Concept; International Association of Conference Centers-- Global Membership Directory* (Annual). **Educational Activities:** IACC-Australia Asia Pacific Annual Conference (Annual). **Awards:** IACC Future Leaders Award (Annual). **Geographic Preference:** Multinational.

15824 ■ International Association of Exhibitions and Events (IAEE) - Library

12700 Pk. Central Dr., Ste. 308
Dallas, TX 75251
Ph: (972)458-8002
Fax: (972)458-8119
Co. E-mail: info@iaee.com
URL: http://www.iaee.com
Contact: David Dubois, President
Facebook: www.facebook.com/iaeehq
Linkedin: www.linkedin.com/company/international
 -association-of-exhibits-and-events
X (Twitter): x.com/IAEE_HQ
Instagram: www.instagram.com/iaee_hq
YouTube: www.youtube.com/user/IAEEHeadquarters

Description: Works to promote the exhibition industry throughout the world and to provide for the education and professional growth of its members. **Scope:** Events; exhibitions. **Founded:** 1928. **Holdings:** Figures not available. **Publications:** *E2: Exhibitions and Events* (Monthly); *IAEM Membership Directory and Buyer's Guide* (Annual). **Educational Activities:** Expo! Expo! IAEEs Annual Meeting and Exhibition (Annual). **Awards:** IAEE Distinguished Service Award (Annual). **Geographic Preference:** National.

15825 ■ Professional Convention Management Association (PCMA)

35 E Wacker Dr., Ste. 500
Chicago, IL 60601
Ph: (312)423-7262
Free: 877-827-7262
Fax: (312)423-7222
Co. E-mail: membership@pcma.org
URL: http://www.pcma.org
Contact: Sherrif Karamat, President
Facebook: www.facebook.com/PCMAHQ
Linkedin: www.linkedin.com/company/pcma_2
X (Twitter): x.com/pcmahq
Instagram: www.instagram.com/pcmahq
YouTube: www.youtube.com/user/PCMAHQ

Description: Represents the interests of meeting management executives from associations, non-profit organizations, corporations, independent meeting planning companies, and multi-management firms who recognize the importance of meetings to their organization. Provides education, research and advocacy to advance the meetings and hospitality industry. **Founded:** 1957. **Publications:** *Professional Convention Management Association--Membership Directory; Convene* (Monthly). **Educational Activities:** PCMA Convening Leaders Annual Meeting (Annual). **Awards:** PCMA Distinguished Meeting Professional of the Year Award (Annual); PCMA Distinguished Service Professional of the Year Award (Annual); Distinguished Member of the Year Award (Annual); PCMA Distinguished Educator of the Year Award (Annual); PCMA Outstanding Service to a Chapter Award (Annual); PCMA Achievement Award (Annual). **Geographic Preference:** Multinational.

REFERENCE WORKS

15826 ■ *"$3 Million in Repairs Prep Cobo for Auto Show"* in *Crain's Detroit Business (Vol. 26, January 4, 2010, No. 1, pp. 1)*
Pub: Crain Communications Inc.
Contact: Barry Asin, President

Ed: Nancy Kaffer. **Description:** Overview of the six projects priced roughly at $3 million which were needed in order to host the North American International Auto Show; show organizers stated that the work was absolutely necessary to keep the show in the city of Detroit. **Availability:** Print; Online.

15827 ■ *"3rd Annual 'OneMedForum NY 2012', July 11th-12th, to Spotlight JOBS Act, Crowdfunding, and Promising Areas for Healthcare Investment"* in *Investment Weekly (June 23, 2012)*
Description: Third annual forum presented by OneMed provided sessions for understanding the changes in regulation due to the new JOBS Act, which will create opportunities for investors and entrepreneurs. Experts in healthcare and life science investments will be featured. Details of the event are covered. **Availability:** Online.

15828 ■ *"2011 Report on the $9 Billion US Trade Show & Event Planning Services Industry"* in *Investment Weekly (January 21, 2012, pp. 47)*
Description: The US trade show and event planning industry is made up of meeting planners and suppliers. These professionals organize, design, promote, and manage business and consumer trade shows, conferences, and meetings. The US trade show industry represents nearly 4,000 compaines and reports a $9 billion annual revenue. **Availability:** Online.

15829 ■ *"2012 Outlook: ROI Still Piles on the Pressure"* in *Conference & Incentive Travel (March 1, 2012, pp. 14)*
Description: According to a recnt poll, more than one-third of 500 event planners preict lower budgets for 2012 than last year. Event planners for EDF Energy, Deloitte, Allianz Insurance, Sanofi Pasteur MSD, and Fico discuss their predictions for the industry for 2012. **Availability:** Online.

15830 ■ *"Advice at Entrepreneurs Event: Make Fast Decisions, See Trends"* in *Crain's Detroit Business (Vol. 30, July 28, 2014, No. 30, pp. 4)*
Pub: Crain Communications Inc.
Contact: Barry Asin, President

Description: Crain's entrepreneurial event was held a The Henry Ford in Dearborn, Michigan. Panelists at the event advised entrepreneurs to make fast decisions and to be aware of small business trends in order to be successful. George Matick Chevrolet was honored. Details of the event are covered. **Availability:** PDF; Online.

15831 ■ *"ALA: Hot Topics for Librarianship"* in *Information Today (Vol. 28, September 2011, No. 8, pp. 17)*
Pub: Information Today Inc.
Contact: Thomas H. Hogan, President

Ed: Barbara Brynko. **Description:** Highlights from the American Library Association Annual Conference and Exhibition are listed. Thousands of attendees sought out services, displays, demos, new product rollouts, and freebies. Emerging technology for librarians, staff development, gray literature, interlibrary loans, and next-generation interfaces were among the topics discussed.

15832 ■ *"Alternative Fuels Take Center Stage at Houston Auto Show"* in *Houston Business Journal (Vol. 44, January 31, 2014, No. 39, pp. 8)*
Pub: American City Business Journals, Inc.
Contact: Mike Olivieri, Executive Vice President

Released: January 31, 2014. **Price:** $4, Introductory 4-Week Offer(Digital & Print). **Description:** An energy summit was held at the Houston Auto Show in Texas on January 22, 2014, where energy executives discussed new technology and initiatives. They considered the market for electric and natural gas-fueled vehicles as well as other options including hydrogen, fuel cells, and biofuels. **Availability:** Print; Online.

15833 ■ *"Attorney Panel Tackles Contract Questions"* in *Agency Sales Magazine (Vol. 39, September-October 2009, No. 9, pp. 8)*
Description: MANAfest conference tackled issues regarding a sales representative's contract. One attorney from the panel advised reps to go through

proposed agreements with attorneys who are knowledgeable concerning rep laws. Another attorney advised reps to communicate with a company to ask about their responsibilities if that company is facing financial difficulty. **Availability:** Online.

15834 ■ *"Auto Show Aims to Electrify"* in *Crain's Detroit Business (Vol. 26, January 11, 2010, No. 2, pp. 1)*
Pub: Crain Communications Inc.
Contact: Barry Asin, President

Ed: Ryan Beene. **Description:** Overview of the North American International Auto show include sixteen production and concept vehicles including eight from the Detroit 3. High-tech battery suppliers as well as hybrid and electric vehicles will highlight the show. **Availability:** Print; Online.

15835 ■ *"Avanti Hosts 19th Annual User's Conference in Washington, DC"* in *American Printer (Vol. 128, July 1, 2011, No. 7)*
Description: Avanti Computer Systems Ltd. hosted its 19th annual users conference in Washington DC. In-plant and commercial printers were in attendance. **Availability:** Online.

15836 ■ *"The Booth and Beyond: Art Fair Design and the Viewing Experience"* in *Entrepreneur (September 2014)*
Pub: Entrepreneur Media Inc.
Contact: Dan Bova, Director
E-mail: dbova@entrepreneur.com

Description: Entrepreneurs need advance planning before joining trade shows in order to capitalize on the opportunity to present their organization. Steps to ensure a successful trade show event are highlighted. **Availability:** Online.

15837 ■ *"Bottom-Fishing and Speed-Dating in India-How Investors Feel About the Indian Market"* in *Barron's (Vol. 88, March 24, 2008, No. 12, pp. M12)*
Pub: Dow Jones & Company Inc.
Contact: Almar Latour, Chief Executive Officer

Ed: Elliot Wilson. **Description:** Indian stocks have fallen hard in 2008, with Mumbai's Sensex 30 down 30 percent from its January 2008 peak of 21,000 to 14,995 in March. The India Private Equity Fair 2008 attracted 140 of the world's largest private equity firms and about 24 of India's fastest-growing corporations. Statistical data included. **Availability:** Online.

15838 ■ *"Business Builders: Tradeshow Attendance Incentives Add Up"* in *Pet Product News (Vol. 64, December 2010, No. 12, pp. 14)*
Ed: Mark E. Battersby. **Description:** Pointers on how pet specialty retailers can claim business travel tax and income tax deductions for expenses paid or incurred in participation at tradeshows, conventions, and meetings are presented. Incentives in form of these deductions could allow pet specialty retailers to gain business benefits, aside from the education and enjoyment involved with the travel. **Availability:** Online.

15839 ■ *"Businesses Encouraged to Imagine the Possibilities With Meeting Planner Package"* in *Internet Wire (May 23, 2012)*
Pub: Comtex News Network Inc.
Contact: Kan Devnani, President

Description: Courtyard Orlando Lake Buena Vista, Florida is featuring an inclusive room rate and Double Event Planning Rewards Points for business planners using the hotel's professional event managers for their future meetings and events. Details of the program are included. **Availability:** Print; Online.

15840 ■ *"Calendar"* in *Crain's Detroit Business (Vol. 24, March 10, 2008, No. 10, pp. 21)*
Pub: Crain Communications Inc.
Contact: Barry Asin, President

Description: Listing of events in the Detroit area include conferences addressing entrepreneurialism, economic development, and women business ownership. **Availability:** Print; Online.

15841 ■ "CarBiz Inc. Speaking At NABD" in Marketwired (May 14, 2007)
Pub: Comtex News Network Inc.
Contact: Kan Devnani, President
Description: CarBiz Inc., a leading provider of software, consulting, and training solutions to the United States' automotive industry, had two of its executive officers speak at the National Alliance of Buy Here - Pay Here Dealers (NABD), a conference that draws over 2,000 dealers, service providers, and experts from across the United States. **Availability:** Print; Online.

15842 ■ "Celebrate Success. Embrace Innovation" in Black Enterprise (Vol. 37, February 2007, No. 7, pp. 145)
Description: 2007 Women of Power Summit provides networking opportunities, empowerment sessions, and nightly entertainment. More than 500 executive women of color are expected to attend this inspiring summit in Phoenix, February 7-10. **Availability:** Print; Online.

15843 ■ "Certain Predicts 2012 as Breakthrough Year for Events" in Internet Wire (January 5, 2012)
Pub: Comtex News Network Inc.
Contact: Kan Devnani, President
Description: Certain Inc. discusses its threetop predictions for 2012 on technology trends that will promote increased business value in the events industry. Certain Inc. is a leading provider of cloud-based event management software that is used for global meetings and events. **Availability:** Print; Online.

15844 ■ "Change Is in the Air" in Agency Sales Magazine (Vol. 39, August 2009, No. 8, pp. 30)
Description: Highlights of the Power-Motion Technology Representatives Association (PTRA) 37th Annual Conference, which projected an economic upturn, are presented. Allan Bealulieu of the Institute for Trend Research gave the positive news while Manufacturer's Agents National Association (MANA) president Brain Shirley emphasized the need to take advantage of a turnaround. **Availability:** Print; Online.

15845 ■ "Clusters Last Stand?" in Canadian Electronics (Vol. 23, February 2008, No. 1, pp. 6)
Description: Survival of technology clusters was the focus of Strategic Microelectronics Council's conference entitled, "The Power of Community: Building Technology Clusters in Canada". Clusters can help foster growth in the microelectronics sector, and it was recognized that government intervention is needed to maintain these clusters. **Availability:** Download; PDF; Online.

15846 ■ "Conference Calendar" in Marketing to Women (Vol. 21, April 2008, No. 4, pp. 7)
Description: Listing of current conferences and events concerning women, marketing and business. **Availability:** Print; PDF; Download; Online.

15847 ■ "Conference Networking Tips" in Women In Business (Vol. 66, Summer 2014, No. 1, pp. 14)
Ed: Diane Stafford. **Description:** American Business Women's Association will hold its National Women's Leadership Conference from October 30, 2014 to November 1, 2014 in Overland, Kansas. Attendees are advised to study the conference agenda before the event. Participants also need to become good listeners when other attendees introduce themselves. **Availability:** Online.

15848 ■ "Conference To Aid Minority Business Ties" in Tulsa World (July 24, 2012)
Description: Preview of the 34th Annual Oklahoma Minority Supplier Development Council Business Conference and Opportunity Fair is presented. The event will be hold in downtown Tulsa, OK and brings

together corporate, government and minority representatives. Business opportunities for minority suppliers will also be presented. **Availability:** Online.

15849 ■ "Convention Budgeting Best Practices" in Franchising World (Vol. 42, November 2010, No. 11, pp. 11)
Pub: International Franchise Association
Contact: Matthew Haller, President
E-mail: mhaller@franchise.org
Ed: Steve Friedman. **Description:** Franchise conventions can offer benefits to both franchisor and franchisee in terms of culture-building, professional education and networking. However, these conventions can be costly. Tips for planning a successful franchising convention on a budget are outlined. **Availability:** Online.

15850 ■ "Convention Ctr. Rehab To Impact Hotels, Eateries" in Silicon Valley/San Jose Business Journal (Vol. 30, May 18, 2012, No. 8, pp. 1)
Pub: Baltimore Business Journal
Contact: Rhonda Pringle, President
E-mail: rpringle@bizjournals.com
Description: The renovation of the San Jose McEnery Convention Center is seen to adversely impact businesses in the area. Contractors have already demolished the former Martin Luther King Jr. Main Library. Business sales in the area are expected to decline owing to the renovation.

15851 ■ "Detroit Hosts Conferences on Green Building, IT, Finance" in Crain's Detroit Business (Vol. 25, June 1, 2009, No. 22, pp. 9)
Pub: Crain Communications Inc.
Contact: Barry Asin, President
Ed: Tom Henderson. **Description:** Detroit will host three conferences in June 2009, one features green technology, one information technology and the third will gather black bankers and financial experts from across the nation. **Availability:** Online.

15852 ■ "Dow Champions Innovative Energy Solutions for Auto Industry at NAIAS" in Business of Global Warming (January 25, 2010, pp. 7)
Description: This year's North American International Auto Show in Detroit will host the "Electric Avenue" exhibit sponsored by the Dow Chemical Company. The display will showcase the latest in innovative energy solutions from Dow as well as electric vehicles and the technology supporting them. This marks the first time a non-automotive manufacturer is part of the main floor of the show. **Availability:** Print; PDF; Online.

15853 ■ "Downtowns Must Court Young, CEOs for Cities President Says" in Crain's Detroit Business (Vol. 24, October 6, 2008, No. 40, pp. 18)
Description: It is important to produce more college graduates, and keep them in Michigan, according to CEOs for Cities President Carol Coletta when she spoke to a session at the West Michigan Regional Policy Conference which was held in September in Grand Rapids. Ways in which city leaders can connect students to communities, resulting in employees who have vested interest in the region, are also discussed.

15854 ■ "East-Side Real Estate Forum Detours To Grand Rapids" in Crain's Detroit Business (Vol. 24, October 6, 2008, No. 40, pp. 17)
Pub: Crain Communications Inc.
Contact: Barry Asin, President
Ed: Daniel Duggan. **Description:** Tom Wackerman was elected chairman of the University of Michigan-Urban Land Institute Real Estate Forum and proposed that the annual conference be held in Grand Rapids due to the brisk economic activity he was finding there; although the idea was initially met with resistance, the plan to introduce East-siders to the West side began receiving more enthusiasm due to the revitalization of the area, which was once considered to have a bleak outlook. Many are hoping

to learn the lessons of those who were able to change a negative economic climate into a positive one in which the cooperation of private business and government can work together to accomplish goals. **Availability:** Print; Online.

15855 ■ "Effective Networking" in Women in Business (Vol. 64, Summer 2012, No. 2, pp. 50)
Ed: Diane Stafford. **Description:** Tips on effective networking at the 2012 American Business Women's Association National Women's Leadership Conference are suggested. The purpose of networking is to make contacts and build relationships so asking for too much free advice or selling personal services are not advisable. **Availability:** Online.

15856 ■ "Entrepreneurs Conference Recap: the Business Revolution: Start Focusing On a Growth Strategy For Your Company" in Black Enterprise (Vol. 45, July-August, 2014, No. 1, pp. 17)
Pub: Earl G. Graves Ltd.
Contact: Earl Graves, Jr., President
Released: 2014. **Description:** Small business owners must concentrate on growth in order to survive using a vision and strategic focus. The 2014 Black Enterprise Entrepreneurs Conference and Expo, sponsored by Nationwide, drew about 1,000 entrepreneurs and professionals.

15857 ■ "Events, Improved Economy Mean Full Hotels in Silicon Valley" in Silicon Valley/San Jose Business Journal (Vol. 30, September 28, 2012, No. 27, pp. 1)
Pub: Baltimore Business Journal
Contact: Rhonda Pringle, President
E-mail: rpringle@bizjournals.com
Description: The increase in hotel occupancy rates in Silicon Valley was attributed to the improving economy and a wide range of local trade shows and events. The city of Santa Clara, California reached an 82 percent occupancy rate in August 2012, while in downtown San Jose, hotels said they started experiencing increased demand since late 2011. **Availability:** Print; Online.

15858 ■ "Ex-Medical Student Stages Career In Event Planning: Barcelona Owner Makes Inroads with Luxury Car Dealerships" in Los Angeles Business Journal (Vol. 34, June 18, 2012, No. 25, pp. 10)
Pub: CBJ L.P.
Contact: Terri Cunningham, Contact
Description: Barcelona Enterprises started as a company designing menus for restaurants, organizing food shows, to planning receptions for luxury car dealers. The fim will be launching the first Las Vegas Chocolate Festival & Pastry Show in July 2012. Presently, the company runs 24 wine and food festivals, organizes events for an upscale dog shampoo maker, and sports car dealerships. **Availability:** Print; Online.

15859 ■ "Four Exhibition Considerations" in American Printer (Vol. 128, August 1, 2011, No. 8)
Description: Four questions to ask at the Graph Expo will help printers improve their own business. **Availability:** Print; Download; PDF.

15860 ■ "Future of Convention and Visitors Bureau In Question" in Houston Business Journal (Vol. 44, April 4, 2014, No. 48, pp. 10)
Pub: American City Business Journals, Inc.
Contact: Mike Olivieri, Executive Vice President
Released: Weekly. **Price:** $4, introductory 4-week offer(Digital & Print). **Description:** Greater Houston Convention and Visitors Bureau (GHCVB) chairwoman Sonia Garza-Monarchi shares her views about the merger talks with Houston First Corporation. Garza-Monarchi says the current proposal is for the continuing existence of the GHCVB board, which approves its own budget and business plan. She also says the members and the board just want an open and fair merger process. **Availability:** Print; Online.

15861 ■ *"Grainger Show Highlights Building Green, Economic Recovery"* in Contractor (Vol. 57, February 2010, No. 2, pp. 3)

Ed: Candace Roulo. **Description:** Chief U.S. economist told attendees of the Grainger's 2010 Total MRO Solutions National Customer Show that the economic recovery would be subdued. Mechanical contractors who attended the event also learned about building sustainable, green products, and technologies, and economic and business challenges. **Availability:** Print; Online.

15862 ■ *"Grand Action Makes Grand Changes in Grand Rapids"* in Crain's Detroit Business (Vol. 25, June 1, 2009, No. 22, pp. M012)

Pub: Crain Communications Inc.

Contact: Barry Asin, President

Ed: Amy Lane. **Description:** Businessman Dick De-Vos believes that governments are not always the best to lead certain initiatives. That's why, in 1991, he gathered 50 west Michigan community leaders and volunteers to look consider the construction of an arena and expanding or renovating local convention operations. Grand Action has undertaken four major projects in the city. **Availability:** Online.

15863 ■ *"Half a World Away"* in Tampa Bay Business Journal (Vol. 30, December 4, 2009, No. 50, pp. 1)

Description: Enterprise Florida has offered four trade grants for Florida's marine industry businesses to give them a chance to tap into the Middle East market at the Dubai International Boat Show on March 9 to 13, 2010. The grants pay for 50 percent of the exhibition costs for the qualifying business. **Availability:** Online.

15864 ■ *"Hotels Up the Ante in Bid to Lure Visitors"* in Sacramento Business Journal (Vol. 29, June 1, 2012, No. 14, pp. 1)

Pub: Baltimore Business Journal

Contact: Rhonda Pringle, President

E-mail: rpringle@bizjournals.com

Description: Hotel owners in Sacramento, California will spend more on marketing the region to convention planners and tourists. The Sacramento Tourism Marketing District is set to replace a 10-year-old marketing business improvement district on July 1, 2012. It is believed that convention and travel business is an economic driver in the city. **Availability:** Print; Online.

15865 ■ *"How Detroit Built Its Marquee Auto Show"* in Crain's Detroit Business (Vol. 30, January 6, 2014, No. 1, pp. 17)

Pub: Crain Communications Inc.

Contact: Barry Asin, President

Description: Detroit-area automobile dealers and business leaders, along with staff from the Detroit Auto Dealers Association, promoted Detroit as the premier North American International Auto Show event, upstaging New York. Few would have considered cold and snowy Detroit as a January destination, but they succeeded in their marketing campaign and the show has continued to grow since. **Availability:** Online.

15866 ■ *"How South Florida Can Revive a Flagging Sector"* in South Florida Business Journal (Vol. 34, April 4, 2014, No. 37, pp. 10)

Pub: American City Business Journals, Inc.

Contact: Mike Olivieri, Executive Vice President

Released: Weekly. **Price:** $8, Introductory 4-week offer(Digital & Print). **Description:** South Florida convention centers are trying to address the sluggish demand for conventions to the area by upgrading its facilities and adding hotels. The ancillary revenue generate by the attendees at hotels, restaurants, and other establishments makes a convention as key economic drivers. The efforts to boost the region's position as convention destinations are also addressed. **Availability:** Print; Online.

15867 ■ *"How To Find More Customers and Clients with Webinars, Seminars and Workshops"*

Pub: CreateSpace

Released: September 27, 2014. **Price:** $2.34, kindle. **Description:** Steps to present successful Webinars, seminars and workshops to market your products at conferences and trade shows are highlighted. A checklist is also provided. **Availability:** Print.

15868 ■ *"Javo Beverage to Feature On-Demand Coffee System and Introduce New Specialty Dispensed Beverages at the National Convenience Store Show"* in GlobeNewswire (October 20, 2009)

Pub: Comtex News Network Inc.

Contact: Kan Devnani, President

Description: During the National Association of Convenience Store Show (NACS) at the Las Vegas Convention Center, Javo Beverage Company, Inc., a leading provider of premium dispensable coffee and tea-based beverages to the foodservice industry, will introduce its on-demand hot coffee system as well as a new line of products for the convenience store industry. **Availability:** Online.

15869 ■ *"Kuno Creative to Present the Three Steps of a Successful B2B Social Media Campaign"* in Business Tech & Wireless (August 25, 2011)

Pub: Close-Up Media Inc.

Contact: Caroline S. Moore, President

E-mail: cms@closeupmedia.com

Released: August 24, 2011. **Description:** Kuno Creative, an inbound marketing agency, will host Three Steps of a Successful B2B Social Media Campaign. The firm is a provider of Website development, branding, marketing strategy, public relations, Internet marketing, and inbound marketing. **Availability:** Print; Online.

15870 ■ *"Let's Put On a Show"* in Inc. (November 2007, pp. 127)

Ed: Elaine Appleton Grant. **Description:** Profile of Jeff Baker, CEO of Image 4, designer of trade show exhibits. Baker shares details of the firm's commitment to being green. **Availability:** Online.

15871 ■ *"Major Golf Retail Show in the Rough for 2010"* in Orlando Business Journal (Vol. 26, January 15, 2010, No. 33, pp. 1)

Pub: Orlando Business Journal

Contact: Julie Swyers, Director

E-mail: jswyers@bizjournals.com

Ed: Anjali Fluker. **Description:** The 57th Annual PGA Merchandise Show in Orlando, Florida is projected to attract 39,000 attendees in 2010, compared with 41,000 in 2009. According to the Orange County Convention Center, economic benefits that could be obtained from the 2010 edition of the golf retail show might reach only $77 million, compared with $78 million generated last year. **Availability:** Print; Online.

15872 ■ *"Meeting and Banquet Venues"* in Business Review Albany (Vol. 41, August 8, 2014, No. 20, pp. 6)

Released: Weekly. **Price:** $25, download. **Description:** The top 25 meeting and banquet venues in Albany, New York in 2013 are ranked by number of banquets hosted. The Desmond Hotel and Conference Center hold the top spot. The Otesega Resort Hotel ranked second. **Availability:** Print; Online.

15873 ■ *"Minnesota ABC Event Looks at Government Contracting"* in Finance and Commerce Daily Newspaper (November 23, 2010)

Ed: Brian Johnson. **Description:** Minnesota Associated Builders and Contractors hosted an event focusing on doing business with government agencies. Topics included bidding work, awarding jobs, paperwork, guidelines, certifications and upcoming projects. **Availability:** Online.

15874 ■ *"The Missing Piece"* in Washington Business Journal (Vol. 33, April 25, 2014, No. 1, pp. 6)

Pub: American City Business Journals, Inc.

Contact: Mike Olivieri, Executive Vice President

Description: The hospitality industry is looking forward to the additional business that the opening of the $520 million, 1,175-room Marriott Marquis Hotel in Washington DC will bring. The hotel has signed up a number of first time DC corporate events and 15 citywide conventions for 2016. **Availability:** Online.

15875 ■ *"'Nobody Knows What To Do' To Make Money on the Web"* in Barron's (Vol. 88, March 17, 2008, No. 11, pp. 40)

Pub: Dow Jones & Company Inc.

Contact: Almar Latour, Chief Executive Officer

Ed: Mark Veverka. **Description:** Attendees of the South by Southwest Interactive conference failed to get an insight on how to make money on the Web from former Walt Disney CEO Michael Eisner when Eisner said there's no proven business model for financing projects. Eisner said he finances his projects with the help of his connections to get product-placement deals. **Availability:** Online.

15876 ■ *"Norvax University Health Insurance Sales Training and Online Marketing Conference"* in Marketwired (January 27, 2010)

Pub: Comtex News Network Inc.

Contact: Kan Devnani, President

Description: Overview of the Norvax University Marketing and Sales Success Conference Tour which includes insurance sales training seminars, proven and innovative online marketing techniques and a host of additional information and networking opportunities. **Availability:** Print; Online.

15877 ■ *"Nowspeed and OneSource to Conduct Webinar: How to Develop Social Media Content That Gets Results"* in Marketwired (December 14, 2009)

Pub: Comtex News Network Inc.

Contact: Kan Devnani, President

Description: OneSource, a leading provider of global business information, and Nowspeed, an Internet marketing agency, will conduct a webinar titled "How to Develop Social Media Content That Gets Results" in order to provide marketers insight into how to develop and optimize effective social media content to get consumer results that translate into purchases and lead generation. **Availability:** Print; Mailing list; Online.

15878 ■ *"O'Loughlin Cuts $6 Million Deal for Chesterfield Doubletree"* in Saint Louis Business Journal (Vol. 32, September 2, 2011, No. 1, pp. 1)

Pub: Saint Louis Business Journal

Contact: Robert Bobroff, President

E-mail: rbobroff@bizjournals.com

Ed: Angela Mueller. **Description:** Lodging Hospitality Management (LHM) acquired the Doubletree Hotel and Conference Center in Chesterfield, Missouri and added it as the 18th hotel in its portfolio. LHM chairman and CEO Bob O'Loughlin plans to invest nearly $15 million in the hotel, including $9 for renovation. **Availability:** Print; Online.

15879 ■ *"One World"* in American Printer (Vol. 128, August 1, 2011, No. 8)

Description: Graph Expo will highlight entrepreneurs focused on the connection between content, technology and business models. **Availability:** Print; Online.

15880 ■ *"The Open Mobile Summit Opens in San Francisco Today: John Donahoe CEO eBay to Keynote"* in Benzinga.com (November 2, 2011)

Pub: Benzinga.com

Contact: Jason Raznick, Founder

Description: eBay's CEO, John Donahoe was keynote speaker at the 4th Annual Open Mobile Summit held in San Francisco, California. eBay is one of the 130 companies participating as speakers at the event.

15881 ■ "PHCC Convention, Show Get High Marks" in Contractor (Vol. 56, December 2009, No. 12, pp. 1)

Ed: Robert P. Mader. **Description:** Plumbing-Heating-Cooling Contractors National Association has held its first convention and trade show in New Orleans, Louisiana. Attendees were treated to a variety of seminars and exhibitors during the event. Comments from event organizers are also given. **Availability:** Print; Online.

15882 ■ "Phoenix Hospitality Plans to Develop Hotel in Live Oak" in San Antonio Business Journal (Vol. 28, May 2, 2014, No. 12, pp. 8)

Pub: American City Business Journals, Inc.

Contact: Mike Olivieri, Executive Vice President

Released: Weekly. **Price:** $4, introductory 4-week offer(Digital only). **Description:** Phoenix Hospitality Group is developing the Hilton Garden Inn and Live Oak Conference Center in San Antonio, Texas. The hotel will feature 139 guest rooms, along with 14,000-square-feet of meeting, banquet and convention space. **Availability:** Print; Online.

15883 ■ "Plan Your Next Event at Newport News Marriott at City Center" in Benzinga.com (July 29, 2011)

Pub: PR Newswire Association LLC.

Description: Newport News Marriott at City Center is promoting itself as the premier venue for business meetings, conventions and weddings.

15884 ■ "Planned Convention Center Expansion Already Boosting Business" in San Antonio Business Journal (Vol. 27, January 3, 2014, No. 48, pp. 6)

Pub: American City Business Journals, Inc.

Contact: Mike Olivieri, Executive Vice President

Released: Weekly. **Price:** $4, Introductory 4-week offer(Digital only). **Description:** The expansion of Henry B. Gonzalez Convention Center in San Antonio, Texas will be completed in 2016, but the San Antonio Convention and Visitors Bureau has already booked eight businesses as of January 2014 for the facility. The expansion is expected to generate 515,000 square feet of prime contiguous exhibit space. **Availability:** Print; Online.

15885 ■ "Plumbing, Heating Products Shine at Greenbuild Expo" in Contractor (Vol. 56, December 2009, No. 12, pp. 1)

Ed: Robert P. Mader. **Description:** Greenbuild Show held in Phoenix, Arizona has showcased the latest in plumbing and heating products. Zurn displayed its EcoVantage line of fixtures and valves during the event. Meanwhile, Sloan Valve offered its washdown 1-pint/flush Alphine urinal. **Availability:** Online.

15886 ■ "Raising the Game" in Birmingham Business Journal (Vol. 31, May 2, 2014, No. 18, pp. 4)

Pub: American City Business Journals, Inc.

Contact: Mike Olivieri, Executive Vice President

Description: Birmingham, Alabama has grown its reputation in the sports world in recent years by hosting global events that draw tourists and overage from around the world. However, the Metro needs a facilities upgrade to further elevate its game. The long-debated project to replace the Birmingham-Jefferson Convention Complex and Legion Field is also examined. **Availability:** Online.

15887 ■ "Real-Life Coursework for Real-Life Business People" in Women In Business (Vol. 63, Summer 2011, No. 2, pp. 22)

Pub: American Business Women's Association

Contact: Rene Street, Executive Director

Ed: Leigh Elmore. **Released:** June 22, 2011. **Description:** American Business Women's Association National Women's Leadership Conference provides members with academic business training courses. Members can take a variety of MBA-level courses that are taught by University of Kansas School of Business professors. Courses include marketing, management, leadership and communication and decision making. **Availability:** Print; Online.

15888 ■ "A Renewed Sisterhood" in Women in Business (Vol. 64, Summer 2012, No. 2, pp. 6)

Ed: Rene Street. **Description:** The American Business Women's Association (ABWA) regional conference highlighted a new sense of enthusiasm and sisterhood as well as effective visioning exercise and breakout sessions. The ABWA National Women's Leadership Conference in October 2012 will feature the graduates of the Kansas University MBA Essentials Program and keynote speakers Bob Eubanks and Francine Ward. **Availability:** Online.

15889 ■ "Renren Partners With Recruit to Launch Social Wedding Services" in Benzinga.com (June 7, 2011)

Pub: PR Newswire Association LLC.

Description: Renren Inc., the leading real name social networking Internet platform in China has partnered with Recruit Company Limited, Japan's largest human resource and classified media group to form a joint venture to build a wedding social media catering to the needs of engaged couples and newlyweds in China.

15890 ■ "RPA Preps for Building Radiant Conference, Show" in Contractor (Vol. 57, January 2010, No. 1, pp. 5)

Description: Radiant Panel Association is accepting registrations for its Building Radiant 2010 Conference and Trade Show. The conference will discuss radiant heating as well as insurance and other legal matters for mechanical contractors. **Availability:** Print; Online.

15891 ■ "St. Louis Convention Business 'Fully Recovered" in St. Louis Business Journal (Vol. 32, July 13, 2012, No. 47, pp. 1)

Pub: Baltimore Business Journal

Contact: Rhonda Pringle, President

E-mail: rpringle@bizjournals.com

Description: Saint Louis Convention and Visitor Commission (CVC) sales team has booked 479,991 room nights at the America's Center in its fiscal 2012, a 28 percent increased compared with 2011. The CVC also was able to book a major convention with Herbalife for the week when the Saint Loui Rams will travel to London, United Kingdom. **Availability:** Print; Online.

15892 ■ "Santa Clara Wineries at Odds with County Over Regulations" in Silicon Valley/San Jose Business Journal (Vol. 30, September 7, 2012, No. 24, pp. 1)

Pub: Baltimore Business Journal

Contact: Rhonda Pringle, President

E-mail: rpringle@bizjournals.com

Description: A proposed ordinance in Santa Clara County, California will change existing winery regulations and implement a sliding fee system for event permits. Officials believe that the government ordinance will improve agricultural tourism, but winery owners claim that it would force them to choose between canceling events and footing the bill for certain costs. **Availability:** Print; Online.

15893 ■ "Secrets To Trade Show Success" in Women Entrepreneur (September 12, 2008)

Description: Trade shows require an enormous amount of work, but they are an investment that can pay off handsomely because they allow a business to get their product or service in front of their target market. Advice regarding trade shows is given including selecting the correct venue, researching the affair and following up on leads obtained at the event. **Availability:** Online.

15894 ■ "Sherwin-Williams Workers Forgo Travel for Virtual Trade Show" in Crain's Cleveland Business (Vol. 28, October 15, 2007, No. 41, pp. 4)

Pub: Crain Communications Inc.

Contact: K. C. Crain, President

Ed: John Booth. **Description:** Overview of Cyber-Coating 2007, a cutting-edge virtual three-dimensional trade show that exhibitors such as Sherwin-Williams Co.'s Chemical Coatings Division will take part in by chatting verbally or via text messages in order to exchange information and listen to pitches just like they would on an actual trade show floor. **Availability:** Online.

15895 ■ "Show and Tell: How Everybody Can Make Extraordinary Presentations"

Pub: Portfolio Hardcover

Contact: Adrian Zackheim, President

Released: March 01, 2016. **Price:** $19, paperback. **Description:** Whether in a one-on-one meeting, a conference room with strangers, or a lecture hall in front of thousands, giving a presentation can be difficult. Even good speakers can learn from the tips presented. Understanding your audience, organizing your content, building a clear storyline, creating effective visual effects, and channeling fear into fun will help create effective and successful presentations. **Availability:** Print.

15896 ■ "So You Want To Hold a Conference: Event Planning Resources" in Searcher (Vol. 20, July-August 2012, No. 6, pp. 12)

Pub: Information Today Inc.

Contact: Thomas H. Hogan, President

Ed: Cynthia Shamel. **Description:** Tips for planning any sort of event requires organizational skills, attention to detail, and the hope that everything will go according to plan. According to the Bureau of Labor Statistics' Occupational Outlook Handbook, the event planning industry is growing. The article shares information for planning your next conference.

15897 ■ "Social Media Conference NW 2010" in Bellingham Business Journal (Vol. February 2010, pp. 3)

Pub: Sound Publishing Inc.

Contact: Josh O'Connor, President

Ed: Lance Henderson. **Description:** Center for Economic Vitality (CEV) and the Technology Alliance Group (TAG) will host the 2010 Social Media Conference at the McIntyre Hall Performing Arts & Conference Center in Mt. Vernon, Washington. The event will provide networking opportunities for attendees.

15898 ■ "Special Events Pro Mary Tribble Reveals Secrets of Winning Bids for Political Convention Business" in Special Events Magazine (May 30, 2012)

Ed: Lisa Hurley. **Description:** Mary Tribble, successful event planner, offers tips for winning bids for political conventions. Tribble serves as chief of event planning for the "Charlotte in 2012" convention for the Democratic National Convention.

15899 ■ "Sponsorships, Booths Available for Business Showcase" in Bellingham Business Journal (February 2010, pp. 3)

Pub: Sound Publishing Inc.

Contact: Josh O'Connor, President

Ed: Lance Henderson. **Description:** Third Annual Spring Business Showcase still have space available for vendors and sponsors. The event gives local businesses the opportunity to increase their visibility and provides a means to increase sales and build relationships.

15900 ■ "State Fairgrounds Adding Year-Round Attractions" in Crain's Detroit Business (Vol. 24, February 18, 2008, No. 7, pp. 17)

Pub: Crain Communications Inc.

Contact: Barry Asin, President

Ed: Robert Ankeny. **Description:** Michigan State Fairgrounds and Exposition Center shares its plans to become a year-round recreation, entertainment and education center. **Availability:** Print; Online.

15901 ■ *"Tax-Free Zones Need Shows: Out-of-State Shoppers Are Key To Success" in Crain's Detroit Business (Vol. 24, January 28, 2008, No. 4)*
Pub: Crain Communications Inc.
Contact: Barry Asin, President
Ed: Daniel Duggan. **Description:** Sales tax-free zones are being considered by Michigan's legislators in order to promote the state as a conference destination. **Availability:** Online.

15902 ■ *"Teachable Moments: Worth Every Penny" in Pet Product News (Vol. 64, December 2010, No. 12, pp. 34)*
Ed: Cheryl Reeves. **Description:** Pet bird retailers can attain both outreach to customers and enhanced profitability by staging educational events such as the annual Parrot Palooza event of Burlington, New Jersey-based Bird Paradise. Aside from attracting a global audience, Parrot Palooza features seminars, workshops, classes, and bird-related contests. **Availability:** Print; Online.

15903 ■ *"Then and Now" in Washington Business Journal (Vol. 32, February 21, 2014, No. 45, pp. 6)*
Pub: Conde Nast Publications
Contact: Agnes Chu, President
Released: January 05, 2016. **Description:** The new restaurants and bars at Marriott Marquis Hotel in Washington DC are offering retro lunch-counter items alongside modern offerings. The conference/convention center hotel will open across from the Walter E. Washington Convention Center on May 1, 2014. **Availability:** Print; Online.

15904 ■ *"Tic-Tac-Show: Line Up the Opportunities at Graph Expo" in American Printer (Vol. 128, August 1, 2011, No. 8)*
Description: Graph Expo has become the US print industry's main event. There will be as many as 500 exhibitors at this year's event and the Graphic Arts Show Company lists over 30 co-located events as well as 53 new sessions in the seminar program's 28 education categories. **Availability:** PDF; Online.

15905 ■ *"TopGolf Plans Three-Level Entertainment Center in S.A." in San Antonio Business Journal (Vol. 27, January 10, 2014, No. 49, pp. 6)*
Pub: American City Business Journals, Inc.
Contact: Mike Olivieri, Executive Vice President
Released: Weekly. **Price:** $4, Introductory 4-week offer(Digital & Print). **Description:** TopGolf plans to construct a golf entertainment complex in San Antonio, Texas. The proposed facility is expected to house about 2,900 square feet of private event space. The entertainment center could also attract around 400,000 visitors in the facility's first year of operation. **Availability:** Print; Online.

15906 ■ *Trade Show Calendar*
URL(s): www.expomarketing.com/trade-show-calendar/
Released: 2019. **Description:** Hundreds of trade shows are presented in an online website, complete with links directly to the events' webpages. **Availability:** Online.

15907 ■ *"Travel Tears" in Crain's Chicago Business (Vol. 31, November 17, 2008, No. 46, pp. 3)*
Pub: Crain Communications Inc.
Contact: Barry Asin, President
Ed: Bob Tita. **Description:** Hotels, restaurants and conventions are seeing a decline in profits due to corporate travel cutbacks and the sagging economy.

City and state revenues derived from taxes on tourism-related industries are also suffering. **Availability:** Online.

15908 ■ *"Trends at the 2019 Summer Fancy Food Show" in Food Business News (June 25, 2019)*
URL(s): www.foodbusinessnews.net/articles/13969-trends-at-the-2019-summer-fancy-food-show
Ed: Monica Watrous. **Released:** June 25, 2019. **Description:** The Summer Fancy Food Show in New York was held and featured over 2,400 exhibitors. Specialty food sales have increased with refrigerated and frozen plant-based meat alternatives, rice cakes, ready-to-drink beverages, and frozen desserts leading the way. Alternatives to meat and dairy are also gaining a strong foothold in the industry. **Availability:** Online.

15909 ■ *"The Weeks Ahead" in Crain's New York Business (Vol. 24, January 7, 2008, No. 1, pp. 26)*
Description: Listing of events in the Detroit area include conferences addressing entrepreneurialism, economic development, and women business ownership. **Availability:** Print; Online.

15910 ■ *"Welcome to Babesland" in Women In Business (Vol. 62, June 2010, No. 2, pp. 33)*
Description: Music group, Four Bitchin' Babes will be performing at the 2010 American Business Women's Association's National Women's Leadership Conference. The group has been in the industry for 20 years and has released nine albums. The Four Bitchin' Babes consist of Sally Fingerett, Nancy Moran, Deirdre Flint, and Debi Smith. **Availability:** Online.

15911 ■ *"Where a Dozen Bagels Will Cost You 45 Bucks" in Philadelphia Business Journal (Vol. 28, July 6, 2012, No. 21, pp. 1)*
Pub: Baltimore Business Journal
Contact: Rhonda Pringle, President
E-mail: rpringle@bizjournals.com
Description: The Pennsylvania Convention Center is seen as an expensive place to hold a trade show. The center is known for its high labor costs. **Availability:** Print; Online.

15912 ■ *"Women of Power Summit" in Black Enterprise (Vol. 38, February 2008, No. 7, pp. 163)*
Description: Third annual Women of Power Summit, hosted by State Farm, will host over 700 executive women of color offering empowerment sessions, tips for networking, along with entertainment. **Availability:** Online.

15913 ■ *"Worry No. 1 at Auto Show: Recession" in Crain's Detroit Business (Vol. 24, January 21, 2008, No. 3, pp. 1)*
Pub: Crain Communications Inc.
Contact: Barry Asin, President
Ed: Brent Snavely. **Description:** Recession fears clouded activity at the 2008 Annual North American International Auto Show. Automakers are expecting to see a drop in sales due to slow holiday retail spending as well as fallout from the subprime lending crisis. **Availability:** Online.

15914 ■ *"WQA's Leadership Conference Tackles Industry Issues" in Contractor (Vol. 56, October 2009, No. 10, pp. 3)*
Ed: Candace Roulo. **Description:** Water Quality Association's Mid-Year Leadership Conference held in Bloomingdale, Illinois in September 2009 tackled lead regulation, water softeners, and product efficiency. The possibility of a WQA green seal was discussed by the Water Sciences Committee and the Government Relations Committee meeting. **Availability:** Online.

STATISTICAL SOURCES

15915 ■ *Trade Show and Conference Planning Industry in the US - Market Research Report*
URL(s): www.ibisworld.com/united-states/market-research-reports/trade-show-conference-planning-industry/
Price: $925. **Description:** Downloadable report analyzing current and future trends in the trade show and conference planning industries. **Availability:** Download.

TRADE PERIODICALS

15916 ■ *Corporate & Incentive Travel (C&IT)*
Pub: Coastal Communications Corp.
Contact: Harvey Grotsky, President
E-mail: harvey.grotsky@themeetingmagazines.com
URL(s): www.themeetingmagazines.com/corporate-incentive-travel
Facebook: www.facebook.com/corpinctravel
Linkedin: www.linkedin.com/company/corpinctravel
X (Twitter): x.com/CorpIncTravel
Instagram: www.instagram.com/corpinctravel
Released: Monthly **Description:** Magazine for corporate executives with the responsibility for site selection, staging and planning meetings, incentive travel programs, conferences, and conventions. **Availability:** Print; Online.

15917 ■ *Meetings & Conventions*
Pub: Northstar Travel Media
Contact: Robert G. Sullivan, President
URL(s): www.meetings-conventions.com
Released: Monthly **Description:** Magazine focusing on meetings, conferences and trade show. **Availability:** Print; Online.

TRADE SHOWS AND CONVENTIONS

15918 ■ **HSMAI's National MEET**
Alabama Dietetic Association (ALDA)
  1045 Ambassador Ct.
  Montgomery, AL 36117
Ph: (334)260-7970
Fax: (334)272-7128
Co. E-mail: alda@gmsal.com
URL: http://www.eatrightalabama.org
Contact: Julie Dzrewiecki, President
URL(s): www.hsmai.org/events
Frequency: Annual. **Description:** Expand their networks, learn the latest trends and technologies, and enhance their careers. **Audience:** Planning professionals. **Principal Exhibits:** Expand their networks, learn the latest trends and technologies, and enhance their careers.

15919 ■ **IAFE Trade Show**
International Association of Fairs and Expositions (IAFE)
  3043 E Cairo St.
  Springfield, MO 65802
Ph: (417)862-5771
Free: 800-516-0313
Co. E-mail: iafe@fairsandexpos.com
URL: http://www.fairsandexpos.com
Contact: Marla Calico, President
URL(s): www.iafeconvention.com
Frequency: Annual. **Description:** Talent agencies, concessionaires, novelties, amusement devices, insurance, ribbons, plaques, attractions, and equipment. Products and services for the fair industry. **Audience:** IAFE members, special event producers, entertainment buyers, carnival executives, concessionaires, facility managers, Fair industry professionals. **Principal Exhibits:** Talent agencies, concessionaires, novelties, amusement devices, insurance, ribbons, plaques, attractions, and equipment. Products and services for the fair industry. **Telecommunication Services:** registration@fairsandexpos.com.

START-UP INFORMATION

15920 ■ *"Can You Say $1 Million? A Language-Learning Start-Up Is Hoping That Investors Can"* in Inc. (Vol. 33, November 2011, No. 9, pp. 116)
Pub: Inc. Magazine

Ed: April Joyner. **Description:** Startup, Verbling is a video platform that links language learners and native speakers around the world. The firm is working to raise money to hire engineers in order to build the product and redesign their Website. **Availability:** Online.

15921 ■ *"Open English Touted as Startup Worth Emulating"* in South Florida Business Journal (Vol. 34, January 24, 2014, No. 27, pp. 30)
Pub: American City Business Journals, Inc.
Contact: Mike Olivieri, Executive Vice President

Released: Weekly. **Price:** $8, Introductory 4-week offer(Digital & Print). **Description:** Open English, a language education company, received more than $150 million in investments from venture capitalists. The firm's cloud-based platform is still in its infancy, but the startup's success has shown that entrepreneurs can generate money and grow their businesses in Florida. Open English is the only online English school that offers live classes with native English-speaking teachers. **Availability:** Print; Online.

ASSOCIATIONS AND OTHER ORGANIZATIONS

15922 ■ The American Association of Language Specialists (TAALS)
3051 Idaho Ave. NW, Ste. 425
Washington, DC 20016
Ph: (650)619-7625
Co. E-mail: info@taals.net
URL: http://www.taals.net
Contact: Pascale Ledeur Kraus, President
Facebook: www.facebook.com/taalsnet

Description: Professional association of conference interpreters, translators, revisers and precis-writers. **Founded:** 1957. **Geographic Preference:** National.

15923 ■ American Translators Association (ATA)
225 Reinekers Ln., Ste. 590
Alexandria, VA 22314
Ph: (703)683-6100
Fax: (703)683-6122
Co. E-mail: ata@atanet.org
URL: http://www.atanet.org
Contact: Ted R. Wozniak, President
E-mail: president@atanet.org
Facebook: www.facebook.com/AmericanTranslatorsAssociation
Linkedin: www.linkedin.com/company/american-translators-association
X (Twitter): x.com/atanet

Instagram: www.instagram.com/americantranslatorsassn
YouTube: www.youtube.com/c/AmericanTranslatorsAssociationATA
Description: Fosters the professional development of translators and interpreters and promotes the translation and interpretation professions. **Founded:** 1959. **Publications:** *Directory of Translators and Interpreters*; *Directory of Language Companies*; *ATA Chronicle* (Bimonthly); *American Translators Association--Membership Directory*; *The ATA Compensation Survey*; *Translator and Interpreter Programs in North America*; *ATA Directory of Translators and Interpreters*. **Educational Activities:** American Translators Association Annual Conference (Annual). **Awards:** Lewis Galantière Award (Biennial); The Alexander Gode Medal (Annual); ATA Ungar German Translation Award (Biennial); ATA Student Translation Award (Annual). **Geographic Preference:** National.

15924 ■ Association des Traducteurs et Interpretes Judiciaires (ATIJ)
438 St. Antoine E
Montreal, QC, Canada H2Y 1A5
Ph: (514)845-3113
Fax: (514)845-3006
Co. E-mail: admin@atij.ca
URL: http://www.atij.ca/en/home

Description: Interpreters and translators working in courts of law. Promotes professional advancement of members; seeks to insure high standards of practice in the field of court translation. Conducts continuing professional education programs; facilitates exchange of information among members. **Geographic Preference:** National.

15925 ■ Association des Traducteurs et Traductrices Littéraires du Canada (ATTLC) [Literary Translators' Association of Canada (LTAC)]
1400, de Maisonneuve Boulevard W Office
LB-631.03
Montreal, QC, Canada H3G 1M8
URL: http://www.attlc-ltac.org
Facebook: www.facebook.com/ATTLC.LTAC
X (Twitter): x.com/attlc_ltac

Description: Literary translators. Promotes literary translation and the interests of literary translators in Canada. Networks with cultural associations and agencies worldwide; lobbies government and cultural agencies regarding funding and copyright. **Founded:** 1975. **Publications:** *Literary Translators Association of Canada--Directory of Members' Works* (Periodic); *Transmission* (Quarterly). **Educational Activities:** Literary Translators' Association of Canada Congress. **Geographic Preference:** National.

15926 ■ Association of Visual Language Interpreters of Canada (AVLIC)
Town Ctr.
Pickering, ON, Canada L1V 6P7
Ph: (437)370-8127
Co. E-mail: casli@casli.ca
URL: http://www.avlic.ca

Contact: Jessica Siegers, President
E-mail: president@casli.ca
Facebook: www.facebook.com/canadacasli

Description: Promotes standardization of sign language; seeks to insure excellence in the practice of visual language interpretation. **Founded:** 1979. **Publications:** *AVLIC News* (3/year). **Awards:** David Still Memorial IEP Graduating Student Award (Annual); Edward C. Bealer Award of Merit (Biennial); Phyllis Joynt Mentorship Award (Biennial). **Geographic Preference:** National.

15927 ■ Canadian Translators Terminologists and Interpreters Council (CTTIC)
1 Nicholas St., Ste. 1202
Ottawa, ON, Canada K1N 7B7
Ph: (613)562-0379
Fax: (613)241-4098
Co. E-mail: info@cttic.org
URL: http://www.cttic.org
Contact: Claudine Belhomme, President

Description: Promotes advancement of the professions of translation and interpretation. **Founded:** 1970. **Publications:** *Meta* (Quarterly); *Action CTIC Action* (Periodic). **Geographic Preference:** National.

15928 ■ National Translator Association (NTA)
c/o John Terrill., President
453 Simoron Dr.
Ogden, UT 84404
Ph: (801)399-0012
Co. E-mail: j.terrill@att.net
URL: http://www.nationaltranslatorassociation.org
Contact: John Terrill, President
E-mail: j.terrill@att.net

Description: Operators of translator television and FM stations; manufacturers and suppliers of equipment, as well as licensure applicants. Promotes and preserves the transmission of television and FM signals to all parts of the U.S., with emphasis upon service to unserved and underserved communities. Sponsors seminars conducted by professional leaders of industry and government on topics such as engineering and technical requirements, issues of channel allocation, ownership policies, legal concerns, operating procedures and programming options. **Founded:** 1967. **Geographic Preference:** National.

REFERENCE WORKS

15929 ■ *5 Things You Should Know About the Highest Paying Translation Services*
Released: April 10, 2019. **Description:** Income in translation can vary depending on many things including the language pair, the type of translation services requested (medical, legal, juridical, technical, financial, business, or literary), translation speed, the translator's geographical location, and the type of documents involved. Each of these types garner different payment. This article details the variables and

provides details about how to get the highest paying translation services and how much a translator can earn. **Availability:** Online.

15930 ■ American Translators Association--Membership Directory
Pub: American Translators Association
Contact: Ted R. Wozniak, President
E-mail: president@atanet.org
URL(s): www.atanet.org/certification-program/ata -board-delays-decoupling-certification-exam
Description: Includes more than 11,000 member translators, interpreters, and linguists in the United States and over 60 countries. **Entries include:** Name, address, phone, languages in which member has ATA certification. **Arrangement:** Alphabetical. **Availability:** Print.

15931 ■ "The Americans Are Coming" in The Economist (Vol. 390, January 3, 2009, No. 8612, pp. 44)
Description: Student recruitment consultancies, which help place international students at universities in other countries and offer services such as interpreting or translating guidelines, are discussed; American universities who have shunned these agencies in the past; the result has been that America underperforms in relation to its size with a mere 3.5 percent of students on its campuses that are from abroad. **Availability:** Print; Online.

15932 ■ ATA Directory of Translators and Interpreters (Online)
Pub: American Translators Association
Contact: Ted R. Wozniak, President
E-mail: president@atanet.org
URL(s): www.atanet.org/directory
Description: Covers over 6,509 member translators and interpreters. **Entries include:** Name, address, languages in which proficient, subject competencies, professional background. **Arrangement:** Alphabetical, area of specialization, language. **Indexes:** Language-subject competency (with state). **Availability:** Print.

15933 ■ "The Best Business Translation Services" in Business News Daily (January 23, 2019)
Ed: Chad Brooks. **Released:** January 23, 2019. **Description:** With more and more businesses expanding their operations globally, ensuring that businesses are communicating effectively with their foreign counterparts is of the utmost importance. To help bridge the language barrier, many small business owners are employing the use of business translation services. This article provides recommended services. **Availability:** Online.

15934 ■ "A Crash Course in Global Relations" in Canadian Business (Vol. 87, July 2014, No. 7, pp. 77)
Description: Teach Away Inc. is a global education firm based in Toronto, Ontario that recruits English-speaking teachers to work abroad. The firm's revenues have grown by 1,621 percent from 2008 to 2013, placing it in the 37th spot on the 2014 Profit ranking of fastest growing companies in Canada. **Availability:** Online.

15935 ■ "DT Interpreting VideoHub Service Expanding" in Internet Wire (March 26, 2012)
Pub: Comtex News Network Inc.
Contact: Kan Devnani, President
Description: Profile of the Deaf-Talk Inc. has launched its new DTViedoHub, to improve and expand its interpreting services to healthcare facilities. Details of the new program are included. **Availability:** Online.

15936 ■ "Encouraging Study in Critical Languages" in Occupational Outlook Quarterly (Vol. 55, Summer 2011, No. 2, pp. 23)
Description: Proficiency in particular foreign languages is vital to the defense, diplomacy, and security of the United States. Several federal programs provide scholarships and other funding to encourage high school and college students to learn languages of the Middle East, China, and Russia. **Availability:** Print; Online.

15937 ■ "From the Business of Language to the Language of Business: The Future of Translation Worldwide" in D!gitalist Magazine (May 17, 2018)
Ed: VR Ferose, Barney Pell, Lorien Pratt. **Released:** May 17, 2018. **Description:** Even the smallest businesses today are potentially serving a global client base making the need to communicate across languages and cultures imperative. This article discusses the importance of reliable translation services and trends in the industry. **Availability:** Online.

15938 ■ "The Future Is Another Country; Higher Education" in The Economist (Vol. 390, January 3, 2009, No. 8612, pp. 43)
Description: Due to the growth of the global corporation, more ambitious students are studying at universities abroad; the impact of this trend is discussed. **Availability:** Print; Online.

15939 ■ "GeneTree.com Unveils New Family Consultation Service in Interpreting Genealogical DNA Data" in Benzinga.com (February 2, 2012)
Description: Family Consultation Services has been launched by GeneTree.com. The service will provide an in-depth examination of genealogical and DNA information to help genealogist help families identify ancestors in specific family lines. The new DNA test called Y-19 will be used by the service. **Availability:** Print; Online.

15940 ■ "Husband-Wife Team Opens Somali Interpreting Business in Willmar, Minn." in West Central Tribune (May 22, 2012)
Ed: Linda Vanderwerf. **Description:** Profile of husband and wife team who launched an interpreting service in Somali. Details of the business are included. **Availability:** Online.

15941 ■ "International Business Law: Interpreting the Term 'Like Products'" in Business Recorder (June 7, 2012)
Ed: Zafar Azeem. **Description:** The term 'like products' needs to be defined for international trade. The battle between the United States and Indonesia regarding this issue is discussed. A technical barrier clause being used by foreign countries is prohibiting imports and hurting competitiveness. **Availability:** Online.

15942 ■ "Kentucky Counties Rely on 911 Translation Services as Diversity Increases" in EMS1.com (November 25, 2019)
URL(s): www.ems1.com/communications-dispatch/ar ticles/ky-counties-rely-on-911-translation-services -as-diversity-increases-JZIPLmQC1LrbUhtn/
Ed: James Mayse. **Released:** November 25, 2019. **Description:** With the rise in diversity in the Kentucky population, 911 dispatch centers have had to adapt in order to serve callers with emergencies. To solve the issue and bridge any language gaps, the dispatch center has two translation services they employ, which can translate 150 different languages. **Availability:** Online.

15943 ■ The Language That Will Get You The Most Profitable Translation Jobs
Ed: Michael Bastin. **Released:** July 16, 2017. **Description:** Discusses what languages will net you the most when in comes to translation jobs and working with translation agencies. **Availability:** Online.

15944 ■ "Linguists Wanted! 10 Language Jobs Big Tech is Hiring For Right Now" in Slator (November 24, 2021)
URL(s): slator.com/10-language-jobs-big-tech-is -hiring-for-right-now
Released: November 24, 2021. **Description:** Ten of the biggest companies in the nation are hiring linguists for particular roles, especially in the customer support and QA departments. However, these roles often cross over to to machine translation (MT). Discussed are the companies hiring the jobs being offered. **Availability:** Online.

15945 ■ "Machine Transliteration Survey" in ACM Computing Surveys (Vol. 43, Fall 2011, No. 3, pp. 17)
Pub: Association for Computing Machinery
Contact: Yannis Ioannidis, President
Ed: Sarvnaz Karimi, Falk Scholer, Andrew Turpin. **Released:** Volume 43 Issue 3. **Price:** $10, Members; $15, Nonmembers; $5, Students. **Description:** Machine transliteration is the process of automatically transforming the script of a word from a source language to a target language, while preserving pronunciation. The development of algorithms specifically for machine transliteration began over a decade ago based on the phonetics of source and target languages, followed by approaches using statistical and language-specific methods. In this survey, the key methodologies introduced in transliteration literature are reviewed. The approaches are categorized based on the resources and algorithms used, and the effectiveness is compared. **Availability:** Download; PDF.

15946 ■ "Online Translation Service Aids Battlefield Troops" in Product News Network (August 30, 2011)
Pub: Thomas Publishing Company
Contact: Tony Uphoff, President
E-mail: tuphoff@thomaspublishing.com
Description: Linquist online service, LinGo Link provides real-time interpreter support to military troops overseas. Interpreters skilled in multiple languages and dialects are used in various areas and in multiple instances without requiring physical presence. The service is available through commercial cellular or WiFi services or tactical communications network. The system accommodates exchange of audio, video, photos, and text during conversations via smartphones and mobile peripheral devices. **Availability:** Online.

15947 ■ "The Pros and Cons of Starting a Translation Services Business" in The Balance Small Business (January 2, 2020)
Ed: Alyssa Gregory. **Released:** January 02, 2020. **Description:** If you are fluent in more than one language and can translate from one language to another, a small business providing translation services could be the perfect small business for you. This article provides information on what you need to know before you decide if this business idea is the right fit for you. **Availability:** Online.

15948 ■ "Speaking In Tongues: Rosetta Stone's TOTALE Adds 'Social' To Language Learning" in Black Enterprise (Vol. 41, September 2010, No. 2)
Pub: Earl G. Graves Ltd.
Contact: Earl Graves, Jr., President
Ed: Sonya A. Donaldson. **Description:** As small businesses become more globalized, it is necessary to learn new languages in order to compete. Rosetta Stone's TOTALe is profiled. **Availability:** Online.

15949 ■ "Start a Translating Business" in Business Know-How (November 20, 2019)
Ed: Tim Parker. **Released:** November 20, 2019. **Description:** Although some translation services are now handled by technology, human translators are still needed for high quality, accurate translation. This article details how to start a translation business. **Availability:** Online.

15950 ■ Translation for Startups and Small Businesses - Top Tips for Getting the Best from Your Language Services
Ed: Ofer Tirosh. **Released:** July 24, 2019. **Description:** Provides tips to startups and small business owners to help you find the right professional translation service and ensure that you're getting the most from it. **Availability:** Online.

15951 ■ "Web Translation Made Simple" in Inc. (Vol. 33, October 2011, No. 8, pp. 44)
Pub: Inc. Magazine
Ed: Adam Baer. **Description:** Smartling is a Web-based service that translates sites into more than 50 foreign languages. The software will begin translation right after setting up the account. **Availability:** Online.

STATISTICAL SOURCES

15952 ■ Translation Services Industry in the US - Market Research Report
URL(s): www.ibisworld.com/united-states/market-research-reports/translation-services-industry/
Price: $925. **Description:** Downloadable report analyzing the current and future trends of the translation services industry. **Availability:** Online.

TRADE PERIODICALS

15953 ■ Views
Pub: R I D Publications
Contact: Ritchie Bryant, President
URL(s): rid.org/programs/membership/publications
Released: Quarterly **Description:** Newsletter for interpreters for the deaf. **Availability:** Online.

TRADE SHOWS AND CONVENTIONS

15954 ■ American Translators Association Annual Conference
American Translators Association (ATA)
  225 Reinekers Ln., Ste. 590
  Alexandria, VA 22314
Ph: (703)683-6100
Fax: (703)683-6122
Co. E-mail: ata@atanet.org
URL: http://www.atanet.org
Contact: Ted R. Wozniak, President
E-mail: president@atanet.org
URL(s): www.atanet.org/ata65
Frequency: Annual. **Audience:** Translators, interpreters, and company owners. Dates and Locations: 2025 Oct 22-25 Boston, MA. **Telecommunication Services:** ata@atanet.org.

CONSULTANTS

15955 ■ Argos Multilingual (USA)
1680 38th St., Ste. 120
  Boulder, CO 80301
URL: http://www.argosmultilingual.com
Contact: Kimon Fountoukidis, Chairman Founder
Facebook: www.facebook.com/ArgosMultilingual
Linkedin: www.linkedin.com/company/argos-multilingual
X (Twitter): x.com/ArgosMultiling
YouTube: www.youtube.com/c/ArgosMultilingual
Description: Provider of enterprise language solutions. **Founded:** 1968. **Publications:** "Cross-Cultural Training and Localization," Feb, 2008; "Using Symbols and Icons in Localization"; "Marketing Communications, Culture, and Localization"; "Culture: Overlooked Web Globalization Ingredient"; "Documentation Localization Process Tune-Up"; "Multilin-

gual Flash Production"; "How to Economize When Localizing Graphics"; "Xml Internationalization and Localization," Sams, Jun, 2001. **Training:** A growing market: Non-English speakers in the US. **Special Services:** Rainbow™; Album™; Horizon™; Lexikon™.

15956 ■ DTS Language Services Inc.
65 TW Alexander Dr.
  800 Pk. Offices Dr., Ste. 400
  Durham, NC 27709
Ph: (919)719-1406
Free: 800-524-0722
Co. E-mail: services@dtstranslates.com
URL: http://www.dtstranslates.com
Contact: Duncan R. Shaw, President
Facebook: www.facebook.com/dtstranslates
Linkedin: www.linkedin.com/company/dts-language-services-inc
X (Twitter): x.com/dtstranslates
Instagram: www.instagram.com/dtslanguageservices
YouTube: www.youtube.com/channel/UCNc_y89l3mP0w63cNZp07Hg
Description: Provider of language translation services such as web-based translation, medical editing and technical translation services, desktop publishing, localization, and much more. **Founded:** 1972.

15957 ■ Rosetta Stone Associates
34 Franklin St., Ste. 200A
  Nashua, NH 03064
Description: Firm provides technical and scientific translation and localization services. **Scope:** Firm provides technical and scientific translation and localization services. **Publications:** "Rosetta Stone Bought By Eurotext Translations," Oct, 2002. "Partnership with Eurotext," Ireland, Jun, 2000.

15958 ■ Suzuki, Myers & Associates Ltd.
46320 10 Mile Rd.
  Novi, MI 48374
Ph: (248)344-0909
Fax: (248)344-0092
Co. E-mail: office@suzukimyers.com
URL: http://www.suzukimyers.com
Contact: Izumi Suzuki, President
E-mail: izumi.suzuki@suzukimyers.com
Description: Firm provides bilingual communication and interpreting services for small meetings and large conferences, negotiations, and courtroom proceedings and also offers language courses in English as a second language and Japanese language classes. **Founded:** 1984. **Training:** Selling Goods and Services to the Japanese; Hosting Japanese; Education in Japan; Single in Japan; PR: The US/Japan Interface; Lawyers and the Japanese Client; A Japan Cultural Sampler.

15959 ■ Transimpex Translations Inc.
2300 Main St., 9th Fl.
  Kansas City, MO 64108
Ph: (816)561-3777
Fax: (816)561-5515
Co. E-mail: translations@transimpex.com
URL: http://www.transimpex.com
Contact: Doris Ganser, President
Description: Firm provides language translation services. **Scope:** Firm provides language translation services. **Founded:** 1974. **Training:** Legal and Technical Translation Workshop; Starting and Operat-

ing a Translation Business; Translator Ethics; Language Identification; Translation and Localization for International Trade; Culture Training; T and I Training.

LIBRARIES

15960 ■ New Brunswick Translation Bureau Library
Marysville Pl.
  Fredericton, NB, Canada E3B 5H6
Ph: (506)457-6485
Fax: (506)444-5086
Co. E-mail: reception.marysville@gnb.ca
URL: http://www.gnb.ca
Description: New Brunswick translation bureau library. **Scope:** Communications; terminology; lexicography; interpretation; language arts. **Services:** Interlibrary loan; copying. **Founded:** 1967. **Holdings:** 6,500 books.

15961 ■ University of Texas at Dallas - Center for Translation Studies
800 West Campbell Rd.
  Richardson, TX 75080-3021
Ph: (972)883-2092
Co. E-mail: translationcenter@utdallas.edu
URL: http://translation.utdallas.edu
Contact: Dr. Rainer Schulte, Director
E-mail: schulte@utdallas.edu
Facebook: www.facebook.com/utdtranslationcenter
Instagram: www.instagram.com/utdtranslationcenter
YouTube: www.youtube.com/channel/UCsJIUf7Z8LMXdZ1K23wfLZw
Description: Publishes international poetry, fiction, prose and drama in translation. Does not accept unsolicited manuscripts. **Scope:** Literary translations, translation methodologies in the humanities, and cross-cultural communications. **Services:** Library open to the public. **Founded:** 1980. **Holdings:** Literary works in translation; original source language texts. **Publications:** Translation Review (3/year). **Educational Activities:** Center for Translation Studies Translation Workshops.

RESEARCH CENTERS

15962 ■ University of Texas at Dallas - Center for Translation Studies
800 West Campbell Rd.
  Richardson, TX 75080-3021
Ph: (972)883-2092
Co. E-mail: translationcenter@utdallas.edu
URL: http://translation.utdallas.edu
Contact: Dr. Rainer Schulte, Director
E-mail: schulte@utdallas.edu
Facebook: www.facebook.com/utdtranslationcenter
Instagram: www.instagram.com/utdtranslationcenter
YouTube: www.youtube.com/channel/UCsJIUf7Z8LMXdZ1K23wfLZw
Description: Publishes international poetry, fiction, prose and drama in translation. Does not accept unsolicited manuscripts. **Scope:** Literary translations, translation methodologies in the humanities, and cross-cultural communications. **Services:** Library open to the public. **Founded:** 1980. **Holdings:** Literary works in translation; original source language texts. **Publications:** Translation Review (3/year). **Educational Activities:** Center for Translation Studies Translation Workshops.

START-UP INFORMATION

15963 ■ *"Former Dell Exec Turns Entrepreneur, Buys Travel Agency" in Austin Business Journal (Vol. 34, May 9, 2014, No. 12, pp. 9)*
Pub: American City Business Journals, Inc.
Contact: Mike Olivieri, Executive Vice President
Released: Weekly. **Price:** $4, Introductory 4-week offer(Digital & Print). **Description:** Robin Goad, former sales executive for Dell Inc., is buying Tramex Travel of Austin, Texas. She hopes to reinvent the travel agency into a corporate powerhouse it once was when she worked there in the 1990s before working for Dell. **Availability:** Print; Online.

ASSOCIATIONS AND OTHER ORGANIZATIONS

15964 ■ **Adventure Travel Trade Association (ATTA)**
14751 N Kelsey St., Ste. 105
Monroe, WA 98272
Ph: (360)805-3131
Fax: (360)805-0649
Co. E-mail: info@adventuretravel.biz
URL: http://www.adventuretravel.biz
Contact: Kim Hogle, Manager, Production Manager, Operations
Facebook: www.facebook.com/adventuretraveltra
deassociation
Linkedin: www.linkedin.com/company/adventure
-travel-trade-association
X (Twitter): x.com/adventuretweets
Instagram: www.instagram.com/adventure
travelassociation
YouTube: www.youtube.com/user/AdvTravTrade
Description: Serves the adventure travel industry. Aims to grow the adventure travel industry overall and to help build up its member organizations. Provides exposure, marketing expertise, education, research, and discount to its members. **Founded:** 1990. **Educational Activities:** The New York Times Travel Show (Annual); Adventure Travel World Summit (ATWS) (Annual). **Geographic Preference:** Multinational.

15965 ■ **American Society of Travel Agents (ASTA)**
675 N Washington St., Ste. 490
Alexandria, VA 22314
Free: 800-275-2782
Fax: (703)684-8319
Co. E-mail: askasta@asta.org
URL: http://www.asta.org
Contact: Zane Kerby, President
E-mail: zkerby@asta.org
Facebook: www.facebook.com/ASTATravelAdvisors
Linkedin: www.linkedin.com/company/american-socie
ty-of-travel-advisors
X (Twitter): x.com/ASTAAdvisors
Instagram: www.instagram.com/astatraveladvisors

YouTube: www.youtube.com/user/ASTAsVideos
Description: Travel agents; allied members are representatives of carriers, hotels, resorts, sightseeing and car rental companies, official tourist organizations, and other travel interests. Aims to: promote and encourage travel among people of all nations and the use of professional travel agents worldwide; serve as an information resource for the travel industry worldwide; promote and represent the views and interests of travel agents to all levels of government and industry; promote professional and ethical conduct in the travel agency industry worldwide; facilitate consumer protection and safety for the traveling public. Maintains biographical archives and travel hall of fame. Conducts research and education programs. **Founded:** 1931. **Publications:** *ASTA Officials Directory*; *Dateline ASTA* (Weekly); *American Society of Travel Advisors--Membership Directory*. **Educational Activities:** The New York Times Travel Show (Annual); ASTA Global Convention (AGC) (Annual). **Awards:** Allied Member Award (Annual); ASTA Alaska Airlines Scholarships (Annual); America Express Travel Scholarships (Annual); Avis Budget Group Scholarships (Annual); David J. Hallissey Memorial Internships (Annual); ASTA Rigby, Healy, Simmons Scholarships (Annual); George Reinke Scholarships (Annual); Allegheny Branch of Mid-America Chapter - Nancy Stewart Professional Development Scholarships (Annual); ASTA Travel Journalist of the Year Award (Annual); ASTA Extra Mile Award (Annual); ASTA Travel Hall of Fame (Annual); ASTA Holland America Line Graduate Research Scholarships (Annual); ASTA Lifetime Achievement Award (Periodic); ASTA Young Professional Award (Annual). **Geographic Preference:** Multinational.

15966 ■ **Association of Canadian Travel Agencies (ACTA)**
Martinway Plz.
Etobicoke, ON, Canada M9R 4C7
Ph: (905)282-9294
Free: 888-257-2282
Fax: (905)282-9826
Co. E-mail: memberservices@acta.ca
URL: http://www.acta.ca
Contact: Wendy Paradis, President
E-mail: wparadis@acta.ca
Facebook: www.facebook.com/ACTACanada
X (Twitter): x.com/ACTACanada
Instagram: www.instagram.com/actacanada_
Description: Represents individual travel professionals in Canada; promotes professional development through seminars, home study courses, conferences and workshops; offers professional certification programs leading to the Certified Travel Counsellor (CTC) and Certified Travel Manager (CTM) designations, and consumer awareness. **Founded:** 1977. **Publications:** *The Buzz* (Monthly). **Educational Activities:** ACTA Atlantic Regional Council Annual Meeting (Annual). **Geographic Preference:** National.

15967 ■ **Association of Destination Management Executives International (ADMEI)**
PO Box 2464
Wimberley, TX 78676

Ph: (512)345-8833
Fax: (512)893-7558
Co. E-mail: info@admei.org
URL: http://www.admei.org
Contact: Jeff Nelke, President
Facebook: www.facebook.com/ADMEInternational
Linkedin: www.linkedin.com/groups/1842734/profile
X (Twitter): x.com/ADMEIntl
Instagram: www.instagram.com/admeintl

Description: Works to increase the professionalism of owners, CEOs and employees of destination management companies. **Founded:** 1995. **Publications:** *ADME Xpressions* (Quarterly). **Educational Activities:** ADMEI Annual Conference (Annual). **Awards:** ADMEI Achievement Awards - Best Innovative Event (Annual); ADMEI Best Overall Program (Annual); ADMEI Destination Management Rising Star (DMRS) (Annual); ADMEI Achievement Awards - Best Logistics (Annual); ADMEI Destination Management Professional of the Year (DMPY) (Annual). **Geographic Preference:** Multinational.

15968 ■ **Association of Retail Travel Agents (ARTA)**
PO Box 45260
Phoenix, AZ 85064
Ph: (602)834-4411
Co. E-mail: artasocal@gmail.com
URL: http://www.artatravel.org/home
Contact: Adj. Gordon Macaw, President

Description: Represents retail travel agents and agencies in North America. Promotes the interests of retail travel agents through representation on industry councils, testimony before Congress and participation government proceedings. Conducts joint marketing and educational programs; sponsors work-study program. **Founded:** 1963. **Publications:** *ARTAFAX*. **Geographic Preference:** National.

15969 ■ *The Buzz*
19 Dewhirst St.
Goulburn, NSW 2580, Australia
Ph: 61 4 90 346 195
Co. E-mail: administration@awia.org.au
URL: http://www.awia.org.au
Contact: Natalie Sommerville, President
URL(s): navyhistory.au/members-area-content/the
-buzz

Released: Monthly **Description:** Contains details of coming events and items of topical historical interest. **Availability:** Online.

15970 ■ **Canadian Tourism Research Institute (CTRI)**
135 Laurier Ave., W
Ottawa, ON, Canada K1P 5J2
URL: http://www.conferenceboard.ca

Description: Seeks to increase understanding of the needs and interests of tourists. Serves as a clearinghouse on tourism in Canada. Sponsors commercial tourism research. **Geographic Preference:** National.

15971 ■ European Travel Commission (ETC) [Commission Europeenne du Tourisme (CET)]

Rue de Marche aux Herbes 61
1000 Brussels, Belgium
Ph: 32 2 5489000
Co. E-mail: info@visiteurope.com
URL: http://www.etc-corporate.org
Contact: Luís Araújo, President
Linkedin: www.linkedin.com/company/european
-travel-commission
X (Twitter): x.com/etc_corporate
YouTube: www.youtube.com/channel/
UCkPU8vpoOkC-9M0fw5lm0ow

Description: National tourist organizations from 33 countries working to promote Europe as a tourist destination overseas. Conducts research and New Media activities. **Founded:** 1948. **Publications:** VisitEurope. **Educational Activities:** Trans-Atlantic Travel Marketing Conference (Annual). **Geographic Preference:** Multinational.

15972 ■ International Galapagos Tour Operators Association (IGTOA)

MA
URL: http://www.igtoa.org
Contact: Jim Lutz, President
Facebook: www.facebook.com/interna
tionalgalapagostouroperatorsassociation
YouTube: www.youtube.com/user/igtoagalapagos
Pinterest: www.pinterest.com/igtoapins

Description: Individuals and corporations conducting tours to the Galapagos Islands; educational and scientific institutions with an interest in the Islands and their ecosystems. Promotes tourism with the lowest possible environmental impact; seeks to preserve the unique ecosystems and species indigenous to the Galapagos Islands. Raises funds to support environmental protection initiatives; serves as a clearinghouse on low-impact nature tourism. **Founded:** 1997. **Geographic Preference:** Multinational.

15973 ■ The International LGBTQ+ Travel Association

5079 N Dixie Hwy., No. 367Fort
Fort Lauderdale, FL 33334
Ph: (954)630-1637
Co. E-mail: iglta@iglta.org
URL: http://www.iglta.org
Contact: John Tanzella, President
E-mail: john.tanzella@iglta.org
Facebook: www.facebook.com/IGLTA
Linkedin: www.linkedin.com/company/iglta
X (Twitter): x.com/iglta
Instagram: www.instagram.com/iglta
Pinterest: www.pinterest.com/iglta83

Description: Travel agents, tour operators, hoteliers, guesthouse and resort owners, travel clubs, and allied businesses interested in promoting travel services to the gay community. Works to: enhance member businesses; inform travel agents and consumers about properties, businesses, and destinations welcoming gay clientele; provide a networking opportunity for members. Offers familiarization trips to promote member businesses in locations of special appeal to gay travelers. Operates public awareness campaign. **Founded:** 1983. **Publications:** IGLTA Connections (Annual). **Educational Activities:** International Gay and Lesbian Travel Association Conference. **Geographic Preference:** Multinational.

15974 ■ National Tour Association (NTA)

101 Prosperous Pl., Ste. 350
Lexington, KY 40591
Ph: (859)264-6540
Free: 800-682-8886
Fax: (859)264-6570
Co. E-mail: headquarters@ntastaff.com
URL: http://www.ntaonline.com
Contact: Catherine Prather, President
E-mail: catherine.prather@ntastaff.com
Facebook: www.facebook.com/NTAnow
X (Twitter): x.com/NTAnews
YouTube: www.youtube.com/user/ntaonline

Description: Operators of group tours and packaged travel; travel industry-related companies providing services/facilities to tour operators (hotels, attractions, restaurants); and destination marketing organizations such as convention and visitor bureaus, and state tourism departments. Seeks to: maintain a code of ethical standards within the tour industry; develop and increase public interest in packaged travel. Represents members before governmental bodies and agencies. Conducts research and educational programs. **Founded:** 1951. **Publications:** NTA Tuesday (Weekly (Tues.)); Tuesday (Weekly). **Awards:** Bob Everidge Lifetime Achievement Award (Irregular); NTA Volunteer of the Year (Annual). **Geographic Preference:** Multinational.

15975 ■ Opening Door

8049 Ormesby Ln.
Woodford, VA 22580
URL: http://www.travelguides.org

Description: Acts as clearinghouse and consultant to the travel and lodging industry for disabled travelers. Sponsors seminars on disability etiquette and the effect of the Americans with Disabilities Act on public accommodations. Maintains speakers' bureau. Conducts activities internationally. Publishes travel and access guides. **Founded:** 1987. **Publications:** The Virginia Travel Guide for Persons with Disabilities. **Geographic Preference:** National.

15976 ■ Pacific Asia Travel Association (PATA) - Library

Level 26, Gaysorn Tower, 127 Ratchadamri Rd.,
Lumpini, Pathumwan
Bangkok 10330, Thailand
Ph: 66 2 017-5757
Co. E-mail: membership@pata.org
URL: http://www.pata.org
Contact: Dr. Mario Hardy, Chief Executive Officer
Facebook: www.facebook.com/pata.hq
X (Twitter): x.com/pata_hq

Description: Conducts marketing program to promote travel to the countries and islands of the Greater Pacific region; works to facilitate and unify entry and exit procedures in members' countries. **Scope:** Travel. **Founded:** 1951. **Holdings:** Figures not available. **Publications:** Pacific Asia Travel Association--Annual Report (Annual); PATA Quarterly Statistical Report (Quarterly); PATA Worldwide Chapter Directory. **Educational Activities:** The New York Times Travel Show (Annual). **Awards:** PATA Chapter Awards (Annual); PATA Honorary Membership Award; PATA Face of the Future Award (Annual); PATA Award of Merit (Annual); PATA Gold Awards (Annual). **Geographic Preference:** Multinational.

15977 ■ TIAC Talk

1300-180 rue Elgin St.
Ottawa, ON, Canada K2P 2K3
Ph: (613)238-7887
Co. E-mail: contact@tiac-aitc.ca
URL: http://tiac-aitc.ca
Contact: Nina Kressler, Chairman of the Board
URL(s): tiac-aitc.ca/cgi/page.cgi/TIAC_Talk.html

Description: Contains updates about the association's activities and government policies affecting the tourism industry. **Availability:** Online.

15978 ■ Tourism Industry Association of Canada (TIAC)

1300-180 rue Elgin St.
Ottawa, ON, Canada K2P 2K3
Ph: (613)238-7887
Co. E-mail: contact@tiac-aitc.ca
URL: http://tiac-aitc.ca
Contact: Nina Kressler, Chairman of the Board
Facebook: www.facebook.com/TIACAITC
Linkedin: www.linkedin.com/company/tourism-indus
try-association-of-canada
X (Twitter): x.com/tiac_aitc
YouTube: www.youtube.com/user/TIACchannel

Description: Promotes viability of Canada's tourism industries. Represents industry at a national level and advocates for policies that will benefit the growth of tourism-related businesses. **Founded:** 1930. **Publications:** RVC Directory (Annual); TIAC Talk; TIAC Talk Issue Focus (Periodic). **Educational**

Activities: Canada's Tourism Leadership Summit. **Awards:** TIAC/Canada Sustainable Tourism Award (Annual). **Geographic Preference:** National.

15979 ■ The Travel Institute

945 Concord St.
Framingham, MA 01701
Ph: (781)237-0280
Free: 800-542-4282
Fax: (781)237-3860
Co. E-mail: info@thetravelinstitute.com
URL: http://www.thetravelinstitute.com
Contact: Diane Petras, President
E-mail: dpetras@thetravelinstitute.com
Facebook: www.facebook.com/thetravelinstitute
Linkedin: www.linkedin.com/company/the-travel-insti
tute
X (Twitter): x.com/TRAVELinstitute
Instagram: www.instagram.com/thetravelinstitute

Description: Individuals who have been accredited as Certified Travel Counselors (CTC) or Certified Travel Associates (CTA) must meet the institute's testing and experience requirements. Seeks to increase the level of competence in the travel industry. Provides continuing education and examination and certification programs; conducts workshops and professional management seminars. Operates Travel Career Development Program to increase professional skills and Destination Specialist Programs to enhance the geographical knowledge of sales agents. Organizes study groups of instruction with enrolled student bodies in most major cities. **Founded:** 1964. **Publications:** Travel Counselor (Bimonthly); Institute of Certified Travel Agents--Directory (Annual); ICTA Travel Management Text Series. **Geographic Preference:** National.

15980 ■ United States Tour Operators Association (USTOA)

345 7th Ave., Ste. 1801
New York, NY 10001
Ph: (212)599-6599
Fax: (212)599-6744
Co. E-mail: information@ustoa.com
URL: http://www.ustoa.com
Contact: Terry Dale, President
Facebook: www.facebook.com/USTourOpera
torsAssoc
X (Twitter): x.com/ustoa
Instagram: www.instagram.com/ustoanyc
YouTube: www.youtube.com/user/ustoanyc
Pinterest: www.pinterest.com/ustoa

Description: Wholesale tour operators, common carriers, associations, government agencies, suppliers, purveyors of travel services, trade press, communications media, and public relations and advertising representatives. **Founded:** 1972. **Educational Activities:** The New York Times Travel Show (Annual); USTOA Annual Conference & Marketplace (Annual). **Geographic Preference:** National.

15981 ■ U.S. Travel Association - Library

1100 New York Ave. NW Ste. 450
Washington, DC 20005
Ph: (202)408-8422
Co. E-mail: feedback@ustravel.org
URL: http://www.ustravel.org
Contact: Roger Dow, President
Facebook: www.facebook.com/U.S.TravelAssociation
Linkedin: www.linkedin.com/company/us
travelassociation
X (Twitter): twitter.com/USTravel
Instagram: www.instagram.com/ustravel_association

Description: Facilitates communication and cooperation among members. **Scope:** Travel. **Founded:** 1941. **Holdings:** Figures not available. **Publications:** Survey of State Travel Offices (Annual); Travel Industry Association of America--Travel Media Directory (Annual); Survey of State Tourism Offices (Annual); Outlook for Travel and Tourism; Survey of Business Travelers. **Educational Activities:** IPW (Annual); Sports Travel Forum. **Awards:** Travel Hall of Leaders (Annual); Ronald H. Brown Memorial Scholarship; Hall of Leaders (Annual); U.S. Travel Association Mercury Awards (Annual). **Geographic Preference:** National.

REFERENCE WORKS

15982 ■ *"The 7 Wonders of Tourism" in Business Journal Portland (Vol. 31, May 9, 2014, No. 10, pp. 10)*
Pub: American City Business Journals, Inc.
Contact: Mike Olivieri, Executive Vice President
Description: Travel Oregon's new travel campaign called '7 Wonders of Oregon' is expected to generate the area's economy. Reports show that the travel industry contributed $9.6 billion to the state's economy in 2013. The sector also employed a total of 93,900 Oregonians during the same year. Statistical data included. **Availability:** Online.

15983 ■ *"2010 Book of Lists" in Business Courier (Vol. 26, December 26, 2009, No. 36, pp. 1)*
Price: $49.95. **Description:** Rankings of companies and organizations within the business services, education, finance, health care, hospitality and tourism, real estate, and technology industries in the Cincinnati, Ohio-Northern Kentucky area are presented. Rankings are based on sales, business size, or other statistics. **Availability:** PDF; Online.

15984 ■ *"B&B Hopes to Appeal to Fiat Execs" in Crain's Detroit Business (Vol. 25, June 15, 2009, No. 24, pp. 21)*
Pub: Crain Communications Inc.
Contact: Barry Asin, President
Ed: Daniel Duggan. **Description:** Cobblestone Manor, a ten-room bed and breakfast in Auburn Hills, Michigan is hoping to provide rooms for Fiat executives. The owners have been working with travel organizations to promote the castle-like bed and breakfast which appeals to European visitors. **Availability:** Online.

15985 ■ *"The Best in Business Travel" in Entrepreneur (May 2014)*
Pub: Entrepreneur Media Inc.
Contact: Dan Bova, Director
E-mail: dbova@entrepreneur.com
Description: A number of companies have been recognized for making business travel more efficient, comfortable and enjoyable. Kayak CEO Steve Hafner's goal to create the world's best travel Website with the fewest people has made the travel search engine profitable. The subscription model of Surf Air, starting at $1,599 per month for unlimited flights, provides more efficient travel experience for executives. The Club Lounge at the Langham Hotel in Chicago, Illinois combines the efficiency of a working office with a private ambiance.

15986 ■ *"Black Travelers, an Untapped Market with Tremendous Buying Power" in Host Agency Reviews(February 18, 2022)*
URL(s): hostagencyreviews.com/blog/cruiseplanners-02-2022
Released: February 18, 2022. **Description:** Discusses travel advisors tapping into the African American market, which is growing each year.

15987 ■ *"Chafee Eyes Tax On Travel Sites" in Providence Business News (Vol. 28, March 24, 2014, No. 51, pp. 1)*
Pub: American City Business Journals, Inc.
Contact: Mike Olivieri, Executive Vice President
URL(s): pbn.com/chafee-eyes-tax-on-travel-sites95903
Description: Rhode Island Governor, Lincoln D. Chafee's 2015 budget will include new tax rules for travel Websites. State officials claim the new regulations will deal with a loophole that has allowed travel Websites to pay less in taxes. Many hotels enter into partnerships with travel Websites in order to sell rooms in bulk. **Availability:** Online. **Telecommunication Services:** Anderson@pbn.com.

15988 ■ *"Corporate Travel Planners is Geared Up for More Growth" in San Antonio Business Journal (Vol. 26, September 7, 2012, No. 32, pp. 1)*
Pub: Baltimore Business Journal
Contact: Rhonda Pringle, President

E-mail: rpringle@bizjournals.com
Description: San Antonio, Texas-based Corporate Travel Planners (CTP) registered an 11.6 percent increase in revenues through July compared to the same period in 2011 and it is expected to reach $135 million by the end of 2012. CTP is one of the companies that helped lead the travel industry out of the deep hole. **Availability:** Print; Online.

15989 ■ *Driving With No Brakes: How a Bunch of Hooligans Built the Best Travel Company in the World*
Pub: Grand Circle Corp.
Ed: Alan Lewis, Harriet Lewis. **Released:** 2010. **Description:** Inspirational book about how two courageous leaders built a remarkable company that can thrive in change and succeed in an unpredictable world. Important lessons for any business leader trying to create value in the 21st Century are included. **Availability:** Print.

15990 ■ *"Eco-Preneuring" in Small Business Opportunities (Feb. 6, 2012)*
Pub: Harris Publishing, Inc.
Contact: Janet Chase, Contact
Description: Iceland Naturally is a joint marketing effort among tourism and business interests hoping to increase demand for Icelandic products including frozen seafood, bottled water, agriculture, and tourism in North America.

15991 ■ *"Fighting for Civil Rights Tourism" in Memphis Business Journal (Vol. 33, March 2, 2012, No. 47, pp. 1)*
Pub: Baltimore Business Journal
Contact: Rhonda Pringle, President
E-mail: rpringle@bizjournals.com
Ed: Michael Sheffield. **Description:** Memphis, Tennessee-based National Civil Rights Museum will complete its $27 million renovation in late 2013. It faces competition from Smithosonian Institution's National Museum of African-American History and Culture in Washington DC and the National Center for Civil and Human Rights in Atlanta, Georgia. **Availability:** Print; Online.

15992 ■ *"Formula One Makes Room(s) for Aspiring Entrepreneur in Austin" in Austin Business Journal (Vol. 31, July 1, 2011, No. 17, pp. 1)*
Pub: Austin Business Journal
Contact: Rachel McGrath, Director
E-mail: rmcgrath@bizjournals.com
Ed: Vicky Garza. **Description:** Formula One fan and graphic designer Danielle Crespo cashes in on the June 17, 2012 racing event in Austin, Texas via hosting a Website that allows users to book hotel rooms. She invested less than $100 and long hours on this enterprise which now has 74,000-plus visitors. **Availability:** Print; Online.

15993 ■ *"Galveston Invests In Future as Major Cruise Destination" in Houston Business Journal (Vol. 44, February 28, 2014, No. 43, pp. 4)*
Pub: American City Business Journals, Inc.
Contact: Mike Olivieri, Executive Vice President
Released: Weekly. **Price:** $4, introductory 4-week offer(Digital only). **Description:** The Port of Galveston in Texas is planning to build a third cruise terminal to capitalize on the growing cruise industry as it faces new competition with the Bayport Cruise terminal of the Port of Houston Authority. Architecture firm McTigue of Los Angeles, California was commissioned to design the new terminal. **Availability:** Print; Online.

15994 ■ *"Goldbelt Inc.: Targeting Shareholder Development" in Alaska Business Monthly (Vol. 27, October 2011, No. 10, pp. 108)*
Pub: Alaska Business Publishing Company Inc.
Contact: Charles Bell, Vice President, Sales and Marketing
E-mail: cbell@akbizmag.com

Ed: Tracy Kalytiak. **Description:** Profile of Goldbelt Inc., the company that has changed its original focus of timber to real estate to tourism and then to government contracting opportunities. **Availability:** Print; Online.

15995 ■ *"Happy Trails: RV Franchiser Gives Road Traveling Enthusiasts a Lift" in Black Enterprise (Vol. 38, July 2008, No. 12, pp. 47)*
Pub: Earl G. Graves Ltd.
Contact: Earl Graves, Jr., President
Ed: Tamara E. Holmes. **Description:** Overview of Bates International Motor Home Rental Systems Inc., a growing franchise that gives RV owners the chance to rent out their big-ticket purchases to others when they are not using them; Sandra Williams Bate launched the company as a franchise in July 1997 and now has a fleet of 30 franchises across the country. She expects the company to reach 2.2 million for 2008 due to a marketing initiative that will expand the company's presence.

15996 ■ *"Hotel Industry: Getting Better All the Time" in Orlando Business Journal (Vol. 28, May 18, 2012, No. 50, pp. 1)*
Pub: Baltimore Business Journal
Contact: Rhonda Pringle, President
E-mail: rpringle@bizjournals.com
Description: Smith Travel Research report has shown Central Florida's hotel industry's average occupancy rate reached 74.5 percent for 2012's first quarter, while daily room rates are up 3.5 percent to reach $105.51. Revenue per room is also up 6.8 percent to hit $75.58, indicating the increasing health of the industry. Insights on Orlando's tourism industry are examined. **Availability:** Print; Online.

15997 ■ *"Hotels Up the Ante in Bid to Lure Visitors" in Sacramento Business Journal (Vol. 29, June 1, 2012, No. 14, pp. 1)*
Pub: Baltimore Business Journal
Contact: Rhonda Pringle, President
E-mail: rpringle@bizjournals.com
Description: Hotel owners in Sacramento, California will spend more on marketing the region to convention planners and tourists. The Sacramento Tourism Marketing District is set to replace a 10-year-old marketing business improvement district on July 1, 2012. It is believed that convention and travel business is an economic driver in the city. **Availability:** Print; Online.

15998 ■ *"How BBQ Can Be Birmingham's Secret Sauce" in Birmingham Business Journal (Vol. 31, May 9, 2014, No. 19, pp. 4)*
Pub: American City Business Journals, Inc.
Contact: Mike Olivieri, Executive Vice President
Released: Weekly. **Price:** $4, introductory 4-week offer(Digital only). **Description:** Local barbecue joints in Birmingham, Alabama are branching out to new markets and extending distinct barbecue brand of the city through franchises and corporate expansions across the U.S. Experts say this trend is contributing to more brand awareness and tourists for Birmingham. **Availability:** Print; Online.

15999 ■ *"Ill Winds; Cuba's Economy" in The Economist (Vol. 390, January 3, 2009, No. 8612, pp. 20)*
Description: Cuba's long-term economic prospects remain poor with the economy forecasted to grow only 4.3 percent for the year, about half of the original forecast, due in part to Hurricane Gustav which caused $10 billion in damage and disrupted the food-supply network and devastated farms across the region; President Raul Castro made raising agricultural production a national priority and the rise in global commodity prices hit the country hard. The only bright spot has been the rise in tourism which is up 9.3 percent over 2007. **Availability:** Online.

16000 ■ *"Indigenous Tourism Operators: The Vanguard of Economic Recovery in the Chatham Islands" in International Journal of Entrepreneurship and Small Business (Vol. 10, July 6, 2010, No. 4)*
Ed: Andrew Cardow, Peter Wiltshier. **Description:** Emergent enthusiasm for tourism as a savior for

economic development in the Chatham Islands of New Zealand is highlighted. **Availability:** Online.

16001 ■ *The Itty Bitty Guide to Business Travel*

Description: Advice on all aspects of business travel, including low-price airfare, packing and coping with stress.

16002 ■ *"Las Vegas Convention and Visitors Authority Kicks Off Halloween Promotion" in Travel & Leisure Close-Up (October 8, 2012)*

Description: Las Vegas Convention and Visitors Authority (LVCVA) is promoting the city as the premier destination for Halloween celebrations. LVCVA sites the holiday as a favorite for events and experiences for visitors. **Availability:** Print; Online.

16003 ■ *"London's Gold-Medal Hotels" in Canadian Business (Vol. 85, August 13, 2012, No. 13, pp. 65)*

Ed: Chris Johns. **Description:** Several new hotels in London, England, including Me by Melia, Apex Temple Court Hotel, and Bulgari Hotel London are presented. Prices and tips on how to best maximize the service are provided. **Availability:** Print; Online.

16004 ■ *"Marriott Readies for Uptick in Leisure Travel" in Dallas Business Journal (Vol. 35, April 13, 2012, No. 31, pp. 1)*

Pub: Baltimore Business Journal
Contact: Rhonda Pringle, President
E-mail: rpringle@bizjournals.com

Description: Dallas Marriott City Center hotel has conducted a $16 million renovation that it hopes will attract leisure travelers visiting the upcoming improvements along Woodall Rodgers Freeway in Dallas. The Dallas Marriott's general manager, Nour Laasri, expects leisure travel and events to gro for the 416-room hotel. **Availability:** Print; Online.

16005 ■ *"The Next Wave" in Hawaii Business (Vol. 53, January 2008, No. 7, pp. 27)*

Pub: PacificBasin Communications
Contact: Chuck Tindle, Director
E-mail: chuckt@pacificbasin.net

Ed: Cathy S. Cruz-George. **Description:** Only 40,000 Koreans took a visit to Hawaii in 2007, a decline from the pre-September averages of 123,000 visits. The number of Korean visitors in Hawaii could increase if the visa waiver proposal is passed. Efforts to improve Hawaiian tourism are presented. **Availability:** Print; Online.

16006 ■ *"Philadelphia Tourism Push Rising in Fall" in Philadelphia Business Journal (Vol. 30, August 26, 2011, No. 28, pp. 1)*

Pub: Philadelphia Business Journal
Contact: Sierra Quinn, Director
E-mail: squinn@bizjournals.com

Ed: Peter Van Allen. **Description:** Philadelphia is offering events for tourists this fall despite massive cuts for tourism promotion. Governor Tim Corbet slashed $5.5 million in funding for the state's tourism-promotion agencies which received $32 million in 2009. The agencies were forced to cooperate and fend for themselves using the hotel taxes that sustain them. **Availability:** Online.

16007 ■ *"Plans for $160M Condo Resort in Wisconsin Dells Moves Forward" in Commercial Property News (March 18, 2008)*

Description: Plans for the Grand Cambrian Resort in the Wisconsin Dells is discussed. The luxury condominium resort will include condos, townhomes, and condo-hotel style residences, two water parts, meeting space and indoor entertainment space, as well as a spa, four restaurants and retail offerings. **Availability:** Online.

16008 ■ *"Recovery on Tap for 2010?" in Orlando Business Journal (Vol. 26, January 1, 2010, No. 31, pp. 1)*

Pub: Orlando Business Journal
Contact: Julie Swyers, Director
E-mail: jswyers@bizjournals.com

Ed: Melanie Stawicki Azam, Richard Bilbao, Christopher Boyd, Anjali Fluker. **Description:** Economic forecasts for Central Florida's leading business sectors in 2010 are presented. These sectors include housing, film and TV, sports business, law, restaurants, aviation, tourism and hospitality, banking and finance, commercial real estate, retail, health care, insurance, higher education, and manufacturing. According to some local executives, Central Florida's economy will slowly recover in 2010. **Availability:** Online.

16009 ■ *Selling the Invisible: A Field Guide to Modern Marketing*

Ed: Harry Beckwith. **Released:** March 20, 2012. **Price:** $16, paperback, ($21.00 in canada); $13.98, audiobook abridged library($16.99 in canada); $16.98, audiobook abridged($19.75 in canada); $9.98, audiobook abridged($12.98 in canada); $9.99, electronic book($9.99 in canada). **Description:** Tips for marketing and selling intangibles such as health care, entertainment, tourism, legal services, and more are provided. **Availability:** audiobook; E-book; Print.

16010 ■ *"S.F. Tourism Soars to Giddy Heights" in San Francisco Business Times (Vol. 28, January 10, 2014, No. 25, pp. 11)*

Pub: American City Business Journals, Inc.
Contact: Mike Olivieri, Executive Vice President

Released: Weekly. **Price:** $4, Introductory 4-week offer(Digital & Print). **Description:** Taylor Safford, CEO of Pier 39, believes that San Francisco, California's tourism industry is very robust. He reveals that the industry is now focusing on inbound visitors. He also thinks that transportation and housing are major issues for the sector. **Availability:** Print; Online.

16011 ■ *"Small Dutch Islands Saba, Statia Content With Low-Key Niche" in Travel Weekly (Vol. 69, August 16, 2010, No. 33, pp. 22)*

Pub: NorthStar Travel Media

Ed: Gay Nagle Myers. **Description:** Small Caribbean islands market and promote their region for tourism by never competing with the bigger destinations. Saba and Statia are the two smallest islands in the Caribbean and rely on repeat guests, word-of-mouth recommendations and travel agents willing to promote them. **Availability:** Print; Online.

16012 ■ *Tourism and Entrepreneurship: International Perspectives*

Price: $69.95, Individuals, Paperback. **Description:** Trends in tourism development are explored, focusing on the impact of entrepreneurship in the context of regional and local tourism development. **Availability:** Print; Online.

16013 ■ *"Travel Agencies Still Make 7 Times More in Commissions Than Fees" in Skift (October 7, 2019)*

URL(s): skift.com/2019/10/07/travel-agencies-still-make-7-times-more-in-commissions-than-fees/
Ed: Dennis Schaal. **Released:** October 07, 2019. **Description:** A Travel Agent Commission Report recently discovered from a survey that travel advisors belonging to host agencies earned seven times as much commission revenue than they did from service fees. **Availability:** Online.

16014 ■ *The Travel Agent's Complete Desk Reference, 5th Edition*

Released: Fifth edition. **Description:** Reference book that provides essential information to the home-based travel agent.

16015 ■ *"Travel Tears" in Crain's Chicago Business (Vol. 31, November 17, 2008, No. 46, pp. 3)*

Pub: Crain Communications Inc.
Contact: Barry Asin, President

Ed: Bob Tita. **Description:** Hotels, restaurants and conventions are seeing a decline in profits due to corporate travel cutbacks and the sagging economy. City and state revenues derived from taxes on tourism-related industries are also suffering. **Availability:** Online.

16016 ■ *"Turbulent Times and Golden Opportunities" in Business Strategy Review (Vol. 21, Spring 2010, No. 1, pp. 34)*

Ed: Don Sull. **Released:** February 09, 2010. **Description:** For those feeling storm-tossed by today's economy, the author believes there's much to learn from Carnival Cruise Lines, a company that discovered that turbulence often has an upside. **Availability:** Print; PDF; Online.

16017 ■ *"TW Trade Shows to Offer Seminars On Niche Selling, Social Media" in Travel Weekly (Vol. 69, October 4, 2010, No. 40, pp. 9)*

Pub: NorthStar Travel Media

Description: Travel Weekly's Leisure World 2010 and Fall Home Based Travel Agent Show focused on niche selling, with emphasis on all-inclusives, young consumers, groups, incentives, culinary vacations, and honeymoon or romance travel. **Availability:** Print; Online.

16018 ■ *"Up In the Air" in The Business Journal-Serving Greater Tampa Bay (Vol. 28, July 18, 2008, No. 30, pp. 1)*

Description: Views and information on Busch Gardens and on its future, are presented. The park's 3,769 employees worry for their future, after tourism industry experts have expressed concerns on possible tax cuts and other cost reductions. The future of the park, which ranks number 19 as the most visited park in the world, is expected to have a major impact on the tourism industry. **Availability:** Online.

16019 ■ *"Watch Hill Gaining Traction as Luxury Destination" in Providence Business News (Vol. 28, March 24, 2014, No. 51, pp. 1)*

Pub: American City Business Journals, Inc.
Contact: Mike Olivieri, Executive Vice President

Released: March 22, 2014. **Description:** Rhode Island's tourism leaders believe that the increase in the number of leisure tourists visiting Watch Hill can help improve the village's marketability. Mark Brodeur of the Rhode Island Commerce Corporation and Lisa Konicki of the Westerly-Pawcatuck Chamber of Commerce claim that the reopening of the Ocean House Hotel in 2010 led to the village's revival. **Availability:** Print; Online.

STATISTICAL SOURCES

16020 ■ *RMA Annual Statement Studies*

Pub: Risk Management Association
Contact: Nancy Foster, President

Released: Annual. **Description:** Contains composite balance sheets and income statements for more than 360 industries, including the accounting, auditing, and bookkeeping industries. Also contains five years of comparative historical data for discerning trends. Includes 16 commonly used ratios, computed for most of the size groupings for nearly every industry.

16021 ■ *Travel Agencies Industry in the US - Market Research Report*

URL(s): www.ibisworld.com/united-states/market-research-reports/travel-agencies-industry/
Price: $925. **Description:** Downloadable report analyzing current and future trends in the travel agency industry. **Availability:** Download.

16022 ■ *Travel Tours and Activities: Incl Impact of COVID-19 - US - April 2020*

URL(s): store.mintel.com/report/travel-tours-and-activities-incl-impact-of-covid-19-us-april-2020
Price: $4,366.35. **Description:** Downloadable reporting detailing data about the travel and tourism industries and how COVID-19 has impacted them. Report includes an executive summary, interactive databook, PowerPoint presentation, infographic overview, report PDF, and previous years data. **Availability:** PDF.

TRADE PERIODICALS

16023 ■ *Business Traveller Middle East*

Pub: Motivate Publishing

URL(s): motivatemedia.com/brands/business
-traveller
Facebook: www.facebook.com/BusinessTravellerME
Instagram: www.instagram.com/businesstravellerme
Released: 10/year **Description:** Magazine covering business travel. **Availability:** Print; Online.

16024 ■ *Corporate & Incentive Travel (C&IT)*
Pub: Coastal Communications Corp.
Contact: Harvey Grotsky, President
E-mail: harvey.grotsky@themeetingmagazines.com
URL(s): www.themeetingmagazines.com/corporate
-incentive-travel
Facebook: www.facebook.com/corpinctravel
Linkedin: www.linkedin.com/company/corpinctravel
X (Twitter): x.com/CorpIncTravel
Instagram: www.instagram.com/corpinctravel
Released: Monthly **Description:** Magazine for corporate executives with the responsibility for site selection, staging and planning meetings, incentive travel programs, conferences, and conventions. **Availability:** Print; Online.

16025 ■ *Entree*
Pub: Entree Travel
Contact: William Tomicki, Contact
E-mail: wtomicki@gmail.com
URL(s): www.entreenews.com/pages/About.html
Released: Monthly **Price:** $75, for online annual; $100, for print per year. **Description:** Features an insider's look at luxury hotels, cruises, tours, spas, restaurants, and travel around the world. Contains advice and tips on luxury travel, bargains, and services. Recurring features include book/wine reviews. **Availability:** Print; Online.

16026 ■ *International Journal of Tourism Research*
Pub: John Wiley & Sons, Inc.
Contact: Christina Van Tassell, Executive Vice President Chief Financial Officer
URL(s): www.wiley.com/en-in/International+Journal
+of+Tourism+Research-p-15221970onlinelibrary
.wiley.com/journal/15221970
Ed: John Fletcher. **Released:** Bimonthly **Price:** $1,847, Institutions for online, US, Canada, India; $802, Individuals for online only US, Canada, India. **Description:** International journal concerned with promoting the tourism and hospitality industries by keeping professionals abreast of current research and debate topics. **Availability:** Print; PDF; Download; Online.

16027 ■ *Travel Weekly: The National Newspaper of the Travel Industry*
Pub: Northstar Travel Media
Contact: Robert G. Sullivan, President
URL(s): www.travelweekly.com
Facebook: www.facebook.com/travelweeklyus
Linkedin: www.linkedin.com/company/travel-weekly
X (Twitter): x.com/TravelWeeklyUS
Instagram: www.instagram.com/travelweeklyus
Pinterest: www.pinterest.com/travelweekly
Released: Weekly **Description:** Travel industry magazine. **Availability:** Print; Online.

16028 ■ *Travel World News Magazine: The Magazine for Destination Travel Specialists*
Contact: Charles Gatt, Publisher
E-mail: charlie@travelworldnews.com
URL(s): www.travelworldnews.com
Ed: Carol A. Petro. **Released:** Monthly **Description:** Magazine for the travel industry professional. **Availability:** Print; Online.

16029 ■ *TravelAge West*
Pub: Northstar Travel Media
Contact: Robert G. Sullivan, President
URL(s): www.travelagewest.com
Facebook: www.facebook.com/TravelAgeWest
Linkedin: www.linkedin.com/company/travelage-west
Instagram: www.instagram.com/travelagewest
Pinterest: www.pinterest.com/travelagewest
Released: Biweekly **Description:** Magazine for retail travel agents in western U.S. and western Canada. **Availability:** Print; Online.

16030 ■ *Travelweek*
Pub: Concepts Travel Media Ltd.
Contact: Annie Cicvaric, Director, Business Development
URL(s): www.travelweek.ca/about
Facebook: www.facebook.com/travelweek.ca
Linkedin: www.linkedin.com/company/travelweek
X (Twitter): x.com/TravelweekGroup
Instagram: www.instagram.com/travelweek
YouTube: www.youtube.com/user/travelweek
Released: Weekly **Description:** Trade publication covering the travel industry. **Availability:** Print; Online.

VIDEO/AUDIO MEDIA

16031 ■ *The How of Business: Pam Lopez - Travel Consulting Business*
URL(s): www.thehowofbusiness.com/533-pam-lopez
-travel-consulting
Ed: Henry Lopez. **Released:** August 12, 2024. **Description:** Podcast discusses opening a travel consulting business.

TRADE SHOWS AND CONVENTIONS

16032 ■ IPW
U.S. Travel Association
1100 New York Ave. NW Ste. 450
Washington, DC 20005
Ph: (202)408-8422
Co. E-mail: feedback@ustravel.org
URL: http://www.ustravel.org
Contact: Roger Dow, President
URL(s): www.ipw.com
Frequency: Annual. **Description:** Exhibits relating to the travel industry. **Audience:** Travel professionals. **Principal Exhibits:** Exhibits relating to the travel industry. Dates and Locations: 2025 Jun 14-18 Chicago, IL; 2026 May 17-21 Greater Fort Lauderdale, FL; 2027 May 03-07 New Orleans, LA; 2028 Jun 10-14 Detroit, MI; 2029 May 19-23 Denver, CO; 2030 Jun 01-05 Anaheim, CA.

16033 ■ Travel Media Showcase (TMS)
DeKalb Convention & Visitors Bureau (DCVB)
1990 Lakeside Pky., Ste. 170
Tucker, GA 30084
Free: 866-633-5252
URL: http://discoverdekalb.com
Contact: James Tsismanakis, Director
E-mail: james@discoverdekalb.com
URL(s): www.travelmediashowcase
Facebook: www.facebook.com/Travel-Media-Show-
case-184526638300239
X (Twitter): twitter.com/TMShowcase
Description: Tourism industry and travel media convention. **Audience:** Editors, staff & freelance travel writers, Magazine and newspaper, travel writers, broadcast travel journalists, internet travel journalists and bloggers. **Principal Exhibits:** Tourism industry and travel media convention. **Telecommunication Services:** joanne@jveroassociates.com.

FRANCHISES AND BUSINESS OPPORTUNITIES

16034 ■ All About Honeymoons
5690 DTC Blvd., 350W
Greenwood Village, CO 80111
Contact: Greg Strobach, Contact
Description: Firm provides romance travel agency services for couples. **Founded:** 1994. **Financial Assistance:** Yes **Training:** Initial 3-day training program at corporate headquarters, optional training at franchisee's location with onging support.

16035 ■ CP Franchising L.L.C. (CP)
3111 N University Dr., Ste. 800
Coral Springs, FL 33065
Ph: (954)344-8060
Free: 888-582-2150
Co. E-mail: digitalmarketing@cruiseplanners.com

URL: http://www.cruiseplanners.com
Contact: Michelle Fee, Chief Executive Officer
Facebook: www.facebook.com/CruisePlannersHea
dquarters
Linkedin: www.linkedin.com/company/cruise
-planners-hq
X (Twitter): x.com/cruisitude
Instagram: www.instagram.com/cruiseplanners
YouTube: www.youtube.com/user/CruisePlanners123
Description: Firm is a travel agency. **Founded:** 1994. **Financial Assistance:** Yes **Training:** Pre-training commencement materials, 5 day training seminar (includes airfare, hotel, ground transportation, all meals, ship inspections, classroom seminars, materials). Advanced training seminars available.

16036 ■ Cruise Holidays
3033 Campus Dr., Ste. W320
Plymouth, MN 55441
Free: 800-335-TRIP
URL: http://cruiseholidays.com
Description: Largest cruise-travel franchise in North America. Headquartered in Minneapolis with over 200 locations throughout North America. **No. of Franchise Units:** 134. **No. of Company-Owned Units:** 4. **No. of Operating Units:** 178. **Founded:** 1984. **Franchised:** 1984. **Equity Capital Needed:** $10,350-$160,350. **Franchise Fee:** $9,500-$30,000. **Royalty Fee:** to 3%. **Financial Assistance:** Yes **Training:** Provides 1 week at headquarters, at franchisee's location that varies, conference calls, 2 day annual mid-year meeting, 6-7 day annual convention, and 7 day annual group training seminar.

16037 ■ CruiseOne
World Travel Holdings (WTH)
1201 W Cypress Creek Rd., Ste. 100
Fort Lauderdale, FL 33309
Ph: (954)958-3700
Fax: (954)958-3703
Co. E-mail: desaissetmuseum@scu.edu
URL: http://worldtravelholdings.com
Contact: Bradley J. Tolkin, Chief Executive Officer
Facebook: www.facebook.com/CruiseOne
YouTube: www.youtube.com/channel/UCDnzV
-tN0AryWV-ucH9Ceug
Description: Operator of cruise ships, provides vacation packages. **Founded:** 1992. **Franchise Fee:** $9,800 plus discounts for veterans and minorities. **Training:** Comprehensive 6 day training program at corporate headquarters in Ft. Lauderdale and ongoing support.

16038 ■ Expedia CruiseShip Centers
Expedia Group, Inc.
131-555 West 12th Ave.
Vancouver, BC, Canada V5Z 3X7
Ph: (206)481-7200
URL: http://www.expediainc.com
Description: Firm provides retail travel agency services. **No. of Franchise Units:** 220. **Founded:** 1987. **Franchised:** 1987. **Equity Capital Needed:** $99,430-$183,900. **Training:** Initial week long training and ongoing support.

16039 ■ Tix Travel and Ticket Agency Inc.
PO Box 1595
Oldsmar, FL 34677
Co. E-mail: exec@tixtravel.com
URL: http://tixtravel.com
Contact: Richard Klein, President
Facebook: www.facebook.com/tixticket
Description: Travel agency and concert and sporting event tickets outlet. **Founded:** 1982. **Training:** Yes.

16040 ■ TPI Travel Services
Travel Pros Inc.
2901 W Busch Blvd., Ste. 205
Tampa, FL 33618
Ph: (813)281-5670
Free: 800-393-7767
Co. E-mail: support@tpitravel.com
URL: http://www.tpitravel.com
Description: Full service travel agency. **No. of Franchise Units:** 460. **No. of Company-Owned Units:** 1. **Founded:** 1987. **Equity Capital Needed:** $10,000. **Franchise Fee:** $4,995. **Training:** Yes.

16041 ■ Travel Lines Express Franchise Group
9858 Glades Rd., No. 208
 Boca Raton, FL 33434
Ph: (561)482-9557
Co. E-mail: tley2k@aol.com
URL: http://www.travellinesexpress.com
Contact: Bernard Korn, President
Description: Full service home based travel agency.
No. of Franchise Units: 150. **Founded:** 1980.
Franchise Fee: $500. **Royalty Fee:** $75/Month.
Financial Assistance: No **Training:** Yes.

16042 ■ Uniglobe Travel International L.P.
1285 W Pender St., Ste. 500
 Vancouver, BC, Canada V6E 4B1
Ph: (604)718-2600
Co. E-mail: info@uniglobe.com
URL: http://www.uniglobe.com
Contact: Martin Charlwood, President
Facebook: www.facebook.com/uniglobetravelinterna
tional
Linkedin: www.linkedin.com/company/uniglobe-travel
-international-lp
X (Twitter): x.com/uniglobetravel
YouTube: www.youtube.com/user/UniglobeTravel
Description: Charity organization that helps to
provide clean water, disaster relief, shelter and
education. **Founded:** 1981.

16043 ■ UNIGLOBE Travel (USA) LLC
4540 Campus Dr., Ste. 127
 Newport Beach, CA 92660
Free: 800-863-1606
Co. E-mail: utcinfo@uniglobetravel.com
URL: http://uniglobetravelcenter.com
Contact: Crystal Smith, Manager
Facebook: www.facebook.com/UniglobeTravelCenter
Linkedin: www.linkedin.com/company/unglobe-travel
-center
Instagram: www.instagram.com/uniglobetravelcenter
Description: Firm provides travel management for
SME, multinational enterprise, business and leisure
travel. **Founded:** 1996. **Training:** Provider of travel
agency services.

LIBRARIES

16044 ■ American Hotel and Lodging Association (AHLA) - Information Center
1250 Eye St. NW, Ste. 1100
 Washington, DC 20005
Ph: (202)289-3100
Co. E-mail: membership@ahla.com
URL: http://www.ahla.com
Contact: Chip Roggers, President
Facebook: www.facebook.com/hotelassociation
Linkedin: www.linkedin.com/company/american-hotel
-&-lodging-association
X (Twitter): x.com/ahla
Description: Represents state lodging associations
throughout the U.S. with 13,000 property members
worldwide, representing more than 1.7 million guest
rooms. Provides members with assistance in opera-
tions, education and communications and lobbies on

Capitol Hill to provide a business climate in which the
industry can continue to prosper. Individual state as-
sociations provide representation at the state level
and offer many additional cost-saving benefits.
Scope: Lodging; hospitality; travel; tourism.
Founded: 1910. **Holdings:** Facts, report, annual
survey. **Publications:** *Construction & Modernization
Report* (Monthly); *LODGING* (9/year; Monthly); *Who's
Who in the Lodging Industry*; *AH&LA Register*; *Green
Lodging News* (Weekly (Mon.)). **Educational Activities:** The Hotel Experience (HX) (Annual). **Awards:**
AHLA Stars of the Industry Awards (Annual). **Geo-
graphic Preference:** National.

16045 ■ Davenport University - Thomas F. Reed, Jr. Memorial Library
6767 W O Ave.
 Kalamazoo, MI 49003
Ph: (269)552-3328
Fax: (269)353-2723
Co. E-mail: info@davenport.edu
URL: http://www.davenport.edu
Contact: Richard J. Pappas, President
Facebook: www.facebook.com/DavenportU
X (Twitter): x.com/davenportu
Instagram: www.instagram.com/davenportuniversity
YouTube: www.youtube.com/channel/
UCaxSQhSboBlHxBkPJOpCvTQ
Description: A quiet corner for studying and fast ac-
cess to a wealth of information, the Library Informa-
tion Commons is home to many students looking to
study or down time between classes. **Scope:** Educa-
tion. **Services:** Interlibrary loan; copying; faxing.
Founded: 1981. **Holdings:** Figures not available.

16046 ■ Nádasdy Ferenc Múzeum Könyvtár
Varkerulet 1
 H-9600 Sarvar, Hungary
Ph: 36 95 320-158
Co. E-mail: muzeum.sarvar@mail.globonet.hu
URL: http://www.museum.hu/muzeum/669/Nadasdy
_Ferenc_Muzeum
Description: Nádasdy Ferenc Museum. **Scope:**
Regional history. **Founded:** 1951. **Holdings:** Figures
not available.

16047 ■ Society for Accessible Travel and Hospitality (SATH) - Library
2175 Hudson St.
 New York, NY 10016-5010
Ph: (212)447-7284
Fax: (212)447-1928
Co. E-mail: info@sath.org
URL: http://sath.org
Contact: Jani Nayar, Coordinator Executive
E-mail: jnayar@sath.org
Facebook: www.facebook.com/SATHTRAVEL
X (Twitter): x.com/SATHtweets
Description: Helps create training programs and
materials, improve customer service and develop bet-
ter outreach and marketing. Performs access audits
of hotels, restaurants and attractions; serves as
clearinghouse for access information. **Scope:** Travel;
hospitality; customer service; travelers with disabilities. **Holdings:** Figures not available. **Publications:** *Open World for Disability and Mature Travel*;

Open World; *SATH Newsletter* (Bimonthly). **Educational Activities:** World Travel Congress for Travel-
lers with Disabilities and the Mature (Annual).
Geographic Preference: National.

16048 ■ U.S. Travel Association - Library
1100 New York Ave. NW Ste. 450
 Washington, DC 20005
Ph: (202)408-8422
Co. E-mail: feedback@ustravel.org
URL: http://www.ustravel.org
Contact: Roger Dow, President
Facebook: www.facebook.com/U.S.TravelAssociation
Linkedin: www.linkedin.com/company/us
travelassociation
X (Twitter): twitter.com/USTravel
Instagram: www.instagram.com/ustravel_association
Description: Facilitates communication and coopera-
tion among members. **Scope:** Travel. **Founded:**
1941. **Holdings:** Figures not available. **Publications:**
Survey of State Travel Offices (Annual); *Travel
Industry Association of America--Travel Media Directory* (Annual); *Survey of State Tourism Offices* (Annual); *Outlook for Travel and Tourism*; *Survey of Business Travelers*. **Educational Activities:** IPW (Annual); Sports Travel Forum. **Awards:** Travel Hall of
Leaders (Annual); Ronald H. Brown Memorial Scholarship; Hall of Leaders (Annual); U.S. Travel Association Mercury Awards (Annual). **Geographic Preference:** National.

RESEARCH CENTERS

16049 ■ Travel and Tourism Research Association (TTRA)
2206 Village West Dr. S
 Lapeer, MI 48446
Ph: (248)708-8872
Fax: (248)814-7150
Co. E-mail: info@ttra.com
URL: http://ttra.com
Contact: Jeffrey Eslinger, President
E-mail: jeslinger@dksa.com
Facebook: www.facebook.com/travel
tourismresearchassn
Linkedin: www.linkedin.com/company/travel-an
d-tourism-research-association
X (Twitter): x.com/TTRATweets
YouTube: www.youtube.com/channel/
UCDHpW8orWYo7M3UgalDEPkw
Description: Advocates standards and promotes the
application of quality travel and tourism research and
marketing information. **Scope:** Professional providers
and users of travel and tourism research. **Founded:**
1970. **Publications:** *TTRA Connects*; *Travel and
Tourism Research Association--Membership Direc-
tory* (Annual); *Annual conference proceedings* (Annual); *Journal of Travel Research (JTR)* (8/year);
TTRA Newsletter (Quarterly). **Educational Activities:** TTRA Annual International Conference (Annual).
Awards: Keeling Dissertation Award (Biennial);
Charles R. Goeldner Article of Excellence Award (Annual); J. Desmond Slattery Professional Marketing
Award (Annual); Boeing Masters Student Research
Award (Biennial); TTRA Travel Research Grant (Biennial). **Geographic Preference:** Multinational.

START-UP INFORMATION

16050 ■ *"Road Map to Riches" in Small Business Opportunities (September 2010)*
Pub: Harris Publishing, Inc.
Contact: Janet Chase, Contact
Description: Profile of Philip Nenadov who launched The Transportation Network Group during the recession. This franchise is low cost and can earn six figures while working from home by becoming a trucking agent. **Availability:** Online.

ASSOCIATIONS AND OTHER ORGANIZATIONS

16051 ■ **American Trucking Associations (ATA)**
950 N Glebe Rd., Ste. 210
Arlington, VA 22203-4181
Ph: (703)838-1700
Free: 800-333-1759
Co. E-mail: atamembership@trucking.org
URL: http://www.trucking.org
Contact: Chris Spear, President
Facebook: www.facebook.com/
AmericanTruckingAssociations
X (Twitter): x.com/TRUCKINGdotORG
YouTube: www.youtube.com/user/atamedia
Description: Motor carriers, suppliers, state trucking associations, and national conferences of trucking companies. Works to influence the decisions of federal, state, and local government bodies; promotes increased efficiency, productivity, and competitiveness in the trucking industries; sponsors American Trucking Associations Foundation. Provides quarterly financial and operating statistics service. Offers comprehensive accounting service for all sizes of carriers. Promotes highway and driver safety; supports highway research projects; and studies technical and regulatory problems of the trucking industry. Sponsors competitions; compiles statistics. Maintains numerous programs and services including: Management Information Systems Directory; Compensation Survey; Electronic Data Interchange Standards. **Founded:** 1933. **Publications:** *Transport Topics* (Weekly); *Transport Topics Education Directory*; *Trucksource: Sources of Trucking Industry Information* (Annual); *Motor Carrier Professional Services Directory* (Annual); *North American Truck Fleet Directory* (Annual); *Fleet Advisor* (Monthly); *Fleet Maintenance and Technology* (Weekly); *Trailblazer* (Annual); *Utility Fleet Management: The Transport Topics Publishing Group Magazine for Utility and Public Works Fleet Professionals* (Monthly); *Executive and Ownership Report*; *Transport Topics* (Weekly); *How and Where to Check Driving Records and Report Accidents*; *Truck Fleet Directory* (Annual); *Standard Trucking and Transportation Statistics*; *Motor Carrier Technology Directory* (Annual). **Educational Activities:** Management Conference & Exhibition (MCE) (Annual); American Trucking Association Management Conference & Exhibition (ACE MCE) (Annual);

ATA Safety Management Council (SMC) and Transportation Security Council (TSC) Safety, Security & Human Resources National Conference & Exhibition (Annual); TMC Fall Meeting (Annual). **Awards:** ATA National Truck Driving Championships (ATA NTDC) (Annual); ATA National Truck Safety Contest; ATA Industrial Safety Contest; ATA President's Trophy (Annual); ATA National Director Safety Award (Annual). **Geographic Preference:** National.

16052 ■ **Canadian Trucking Alliance (CTA)**
555 Dixon Rd.
Toronto, ON, Canada M9W 1H8
Ph: (416)249-7401
Fax: (866)713-4188
URL: http://cantruck.ca
X (Twitter): x.com/CanTruck
Description: Seeks to advance the road transportation industries. Serves as a forum for the exchange of information among members; represents members' interests before labor and industrial organizations, government agencies, and the public. **Publications:** *Crossing International Borders: A Trucker's Guide.* **Geographic Preference:** National.

16053 ■ **Freight Carriers Association of Canada (FCA)**
1270 Central Pky. W, Ste. 301
Mississauga, ON, Canada L5C 4P4
Ph: (905)276-3835
Co. E-mail: info@fcafuel.org
URL: http://fcafuel.org
Contact: Bill Kimmel, President
E-mail: wkimmel@fcafuel.org
Description: Canadian motor carriers involved in domestic transportation. Creates and provides statistical and operational information to all parties involved in motor carrier transportation. Offers statistical information. **Founded:** 1991. **Publications:** *News* (Bimonthly); *Fuel Calculation Bulletin* (Weekly). **Geographic Preference:** National.

16054 ■ **International Truck Parts Association (ITPA)**
1720 10th Ave. S, Ste. 4.
Great Falls, MT 59405
Free: 866-346-5692
Fax: (800)895-4654
Co. E-mail: info@itpa.com
URL: http://itpa.com
Contact: Rudy Niswanger, Chairman
E-mail: rudy@joegearco.com
Description: Represents companies specializing in the purchase and sale of used and rebuilt heavy-duty truck components. **Founded:** 1974. **Geographic Preference:** Multinational.

16055 ■ **Michigan Produce Haulers Inc. (MPH)**
1340 Locust St.
Fremont, MI 49412
Ph: (231)924-4600
Free: 800-545-6189
Fax: (231)924-3010
Co. E-mail: info@mphtruck.com

URL: http://repackaging.us
Contact: Todd Gilliland, President
E-mail: mphtruck@comcast.net
Facebook: www.facebook.com/MPHTransportation
Description: Provider of Long distance trucking. **Founded:** 1945.

16056 ■ **Michigan Trucking Association (MTA)**
1131 Centennial Way
Lansing, MI 48917
Ph: (517)321-1951
Fax: (517)321-0884
Co. E-mail: info@mitrucking.org
URL: http://www.mitrucking.org
Contact: Brian Hitchcock, Chairman
Linkedin: www.linkedin.com/company/michigan
-trucking-association
YouTube: www.youtube.com/channel/UCoXuUzq
_J8c_BiyhLfE6Lvg
Description: Carrier companies and trucking-related businesses. Serves as a voice for members and represents the trucking industry before state government. **Founded:** 1934. **Publications:** *Legislative Report* (Periodic); *Michigan Trucking Today* (Monthly). **Geographic Preference:** State.

16057 ■ **Mid-West Truckers Association Inc. (MTA)**
2727 N Dirksen Pky.
Springfield, IL 62702
Ph: (217)525-0310
Co. E-mail: info@mid-westtruckers.com
URL: http://www.mid-westtruckers.com
Contact: Don Schaefer, Executive Vice President
E-mail: dons@midwesttruckers.com
Description: Owners and operators of trucking companies. Serves as a unified voice for truckers nationwide; conducts lobbying. Sponsors services to members including: mass purchasing program, whereby members may purchase parts at wholesale rates; drug and alcohol testing program; assistance with international registration; license plate procurement; group insurance programs self-funded worker's Compensation Program. Conducts seminars and educational programs; maintains speakers' bureau. **Founded:** 1961. **Publications:** *Keep on Truckin News* (Monthly); *Cost Summary Booklet.* **Educational Activities:** Illinois History Symposium (Annual); Mid-West Truck & Trailer Show (Annual). **Geographic Preference:** National.

16058 ■ **National Private Truck Council (NPTC)**
2300 Wilson Blvd., Ste. 700
Arlington, VA 22201
Ph: (703)683-1300
Co. E-mail: info@nptc.org
URL: http://www.nptc.org
Contact: Gary F. Petty, President
E-mail: gpetty@nptc.org
Facebook: www.facebook.com/NPTC1939
Linkedin: www.linkedin.com/company/national-private
-truck-council

X (Twitter): x.com/NPTC1939

YouTube: www.youtube.com/user/NPTC1939

Description: Represents private motor carrier truck fleets and their suppliers. **Founded:** 1939. **Publications:** *Business Trucking* (Monthly); *National Private Truck Council--Membership Directory & Buyer's Guide* (Annual); *Fleet Owner* (Monthly); *Private Fleet Directory/FleetSeek* (Monthly); *Weekly Update* (Weekly). **Educational Activities:** Education Management & Exhibition (Annual). **Awards:** CTP Scholarship Program (Annual); Dodi Reagan Humanitarian Award (Annual); NPTC Driver Hall of Fame (Annual); NPTC Private Fleet Executive of the Year (Annual); NPTC Fleet Safety Awards (Annual). **Geographic Preference:** Multinational.

16059 ■ National Tank Truck Carriers (NTTC)

950 N Glebe Rd., Ste. 520

Arlington, VA 22203-4183

Ph: (703)838-1960

Co. E-mail: nttcstaff@tanktruck.org

URL: http://www.tanktruck.org

Contact: Ryan Streblow, President

E-mail: rstreblow@tanktruck.org

Facebook: www.facebook.com/NationalTankTruck

Linkedin: www.linkedin.com/company/national-tank-truck-carriers

X (Twitter): x.com/TankTruckAssoc

Description: Common or contract "for-hire" tank truck carriers transporting liquid and dry bulk commodities, chemicals, food processing commodities, petroleum, and related products; allied industry suppliers. Promotes federal standards of construction, design, operation and use of tank trucks and equipment. Coordinates truck transportation system for shippers of bulk commodities. Secures improvements in tank specifications. Sponsors annual schools; conducts research. **Founded:** 1945. **Publications:** *National Tank Truck Directory* (Annual); *Washington Newsletter*; *National Tank Truck Carrier Membership Directory*. **Educational Activities:** Cargo Tank Maintenance Seminar (Annual). **Geographic Preference:** National.

16060 ■ National Truck Equipment Association (NTEA)

37400 Hills Tech Dr.

Farmington Hills, MI 48331-3414

Ph: (248)489-7090

Free: 800-441-6832

Fax: (248)489-8590

Co. E-mail: info@ntea.com

URL: http://www.ntea.com

Contact: Steve Carey, President

E-mail: steve@ntea.com

Facebook: www.facebook.com/NTEA.TheAssociationForTheWorkTruckIndustry

Linkedin: www.linkedin.com/company/239823

X (Twitter): x.com/nteanews

Instagram: www.instagram.com/the.ntea

YouTube: www.youtube.com/channel/UCQbxEMWDReFSIupUhoVLJsg

Description: Serves as a trade group for commercial truck, truck body, truck equipment, trailer and accessory manufacturers and distributors. Advises members of current federal regulations affecting the manufacturing and installation of truck bodies and equipment; works to enhance the professionalism of management and improve profitability in the truck equipment business. **Founded:** 1964. **Publications:** *National Truck Equipment Association--Market Resource Guide* (Annual); *Excise Tax Bulletin* (Periodic); *Truck Equipment Handbook*; *NTEA Technical Report* (Monthly); *NTEA News ezine* (Monthly). **Educational Activities:** The Work Truck Show (Annual). **Geographic Preference:** National.

16061 ■ National Truckers Association (NTA)

305 N Stuart Pl., Rd.

Harlingen, TX 78552

Contact: Jeffrey Stineman, President

Description: Aims to develop membership programs and products for industries, independent contractors, owner operators and motor carriers. Protects the interests of independent truck drivers. **Publications:** *National Truckers' Headlines* (Quarterly). **Geographic Preference:** National.

16062 ■ Newsbriefs

225 Main St. E, Ste. 5

Milton, ON, Canada L9T 1N9

Ph: (905)827-0587

Free: 877-501-7682

Fax: (905)827-8212

Co. E-mail: info@pmtc.ca

URL: http://www.pmtc.ca

Contact: Mike Millian, President

E-mail: trucks@pmtc.ca

URL(s): www.pmtc.ca/content.asp?contentid=176

Released: Monthly **Description:** Covers current events in the North American trucking community and activities. **Availability:** Print; Online.

16063 ■ Owner-Operator Independent Drivers Association (OOIDA)

1 NW OOIDA Dr.

Grain Valley, MO 64029

Ph: (816)229-5791

Free: 800-444-5791

Fax: (816)427-4467

URL: http://www.ooida.com

Contact: Todd Spencer, President

Facebook: www.facebook.com/OOIDA

X (Twitter): x.com/OOIDA

Instagram: www.instagram.com/ooida_truckers

YouTube: www.youtube.com/user/TruckersOOIDA

Description: Truck owner-operators, small fleet operators, and drivers. Lobbying association seeking to improve owner-operator working conditions. Provides national recognition and a channel for members to voice interests and concerns on changes that affect the trucking business. Addresses issues including: freight rates commensurate with costs; rules guaranteeing prompt payment for owner-operators; flexible hours of operation; taxes; safety initiatives. Offers medical, truck, dental, and accident programs. Sponsors research programs; compiles statistics; maintains speakers' bureau. **Founded:** 1973. **Publications:** *Owner-Operator News* (Quarterly); *Land Line* (Monthly). **Awards:** OOIDA Mary Johnston Scholarship Program (Annual); OOIDA Scholarship (Annual); OOIDA Safe Driving Award Program (Annual). **Geographic Preference:** National.

16064 ■ Private Motor Truck Council of Canada (PMTC)

225 Main St. E, Ste. 5

Milton, ON, Canada L9T 1N9

Ph: (905)827-0587

Free: 877-501-7682

Fax: (905)827-8212

Co. E-mail: info@pmtc.ca

URL: http://www.pmtc.ca

Contact: Mike Millian, President

E-mail: trucks@pmtc.ca

Facebook: www.facebook.com/Private-Motor-Truck-Council-of-Canada-1561523780752504

Linkedin: www.linkedin.com/company/private-motor-truck-council-of-canada

X (Twitter): x.com/privatefleets

Instagram: www.instagram.com/pmtcylg

YouTube: www.youtube.com/user/PMTCvideos

Description: Private truck fleet operators and others with an interest in the trucking industry. Represents members' interests before government and international regulatory bodies and the public. **Founded:** 1977. **Publications:** *The Counsellor* (Quarterly); *Newsbriefs* (Monthly). **Educational Activities:** PMTC Conference (Annual). **Geographic Preference:** National.

16065 ■ Professional Truck Driver Institute (PTDI)

44 Canal Center Plz., Ste. 120

Alexandria, VA 22314

Ph: (703)642-9444

URL: http://www.ptdi.org

Description: Stakeholders include carriers, schools, trade associations, manufacturers, insurance companies, regulatory bodies, funding organizations, and suppliers to the trucking industry. **Founded:** 1986. **Publications:** *Certification Standards and Requirements for Entry-Level Tractor-Trailer Driver Courses*; *Certification Standards and Requirements for Tractor-Trailer Driver Finishing Programs*; *Curriculum Standard Guidelines for Entry-Level Tractor-Trailer Driver Courses*; *Skill Standards for Entry-Level Tractor-Trailer Drivers*; *Skill Standards for Professional Solo Tractor-Trailer Drivers*. **Awards:** Lee J. Crittenden Memorial Award (Annual). **Geographic Preference:** National.

16066 ■ Regional and Distribution Carriers Conference (RDCC)

80 M St. SE, Ste. 800

Washington, DC 20003

URL: http://www.trucking.org/regional-and-distribution-carriers-conference

Description: Represents for-hire motor common carriers of general freight who specialize in less-than-truckload shipments throughout the U.S. Provides government relations, networking, business development programs, and publications. **Founded:** 1938. **Publications:** *Transportation Executive Update: A Publication of the Regular Common Carrier Conference* (Quarterly). **Geographic Preference:** National.

16067 ■ Specialized Carriers and Rigging Association (SC&RA)

5870 Trinity Pky., Ste. 200

Centreville, VA 20120

Ph: (703)698-0291

Co. E-mail: info@scranet.org

URL: http://www.scranet.org

Contact: Ed Bernard, President

Facebook: www.facebook.com/scranet

X (Twitter): x.com/scranet

YouTube: www.youtube.com/user/scranetorg

Description: Operates Heavy and Specialized Carriers Tariff Bureau. Conducts Fleet Safety and Outstanding Hauling, Rigging, and Millwright Job of the Year contests. Compiles statistics. **Founded:** 1948. **Publications:** *Directory of Truck Escort Services*; *Specialized Carriers and Rigging Association-Newsletter* (Weekly); *SC & RA News* (Weekly); *Specialized Carriers & Rigging Association--Membership Directory*. **Educational Activities:** Specialized Carriers and Rigging Association Annual Conference (Annual); Specialized Transportation Symposium (Annual). **Awards:** SC&R Foundation Grant Program (Annual); SC&RF Collegiate Scholarship (Annual); Hauling Job of the Year Award (Annual); SC&RA Job of the Year Competition (Annual); SC&RA Transportation Group Driver Safety Award (Annual); SCRA Golden Achievement Award (Annual); SCR&A Million Miler Safety Award (Annual); SCRA Longevity Awards (Annual); Crane & Rigging Safety/Safety Improvement Awards (Annual); Transportation Fleet Safety/Safety Improvement Awards (Annual); Crane and Rigging Zero Accidents Award (Annual); SC&RA Crane and Rigging Group Safety Awards (Annual); SC&RA Driver of the Year (Annual); Million Miler Award for Safety Excellence (Annual); SC&RA President's Award (Annual); SC&RA Hauling Job of the Year Awards (Annual). **Geographic Preference:** Multinational.

16068 ■ Trucking Management, Inc. (TMI)

PO Box 860725

Shawnee, KS 66286

Description: Less-Than-Truckload (LTL) motor carriers. Promotes economic interests of unionized LTL motor carriers. Represents members' interests in public policy and economic issues. Works as the primary multi-employer bargaining arm of the unionized general freight trucking industry. **Founded:** 1963. **Geographic Preference:** National.

16069 ■ Truckload Carriers Association (TCA)

555 E Braddock Rd.

Alexandria, VA 22314

Ph: (703)838-1950

Fax: (202)217-3877

Co. E-mail: tca@truckload.org

URL: http://www.truckload.org

Contact: Jim Ward, President

E-mail: jward@truckload.org
Facebook: www.facebook.com/Truckload-Carriers
-Association-208489819183351
Linkedin: www.linkedin.com/company/668155
X (Twitter): x.com/TCANews
Instagram: www.instagram.com/truckloa
dcarriersassociation
YouTube: www.youtube.com/tcanews

Description: Engages in the truckload segment of the motor carrier industry. Represents dry van, refrigerated, flatbed and intermodel container carriers operating in the 48 contiguous states as well as Alaska, Mexico and Canada. Represents operators of over 200,000 trucks. **Founded:** 1938. **Educational Activities:** TCA Annual Convention (Annual). **Awards:** TCA Scholarships (Annual); TCA Scholarship Fund (Annual); TCA Driver of the Year (Annual). **Geographic Preference:** National.

16070 ■ Wine and Spirits Shippers Association (WSSA)
111 Commercial St., Ste. 202
Portland, ME 04101
Ph: (207)805-1664
Free: 800-368-3167
Co. E-mail: info@wssa.com
URL: http://www.wssa.com
Contact: Louis Healey, President
Linkedin: www.linkedin.com/company/wine-and-spiri
ts-shippers-association-inc.
X (Twitter): x.com/Wssalnc

Description: Importers, exporters, and distributors of beverages and allied products. Provides members with services, either directly or through agents, that allow for the efficient and economical transportation of products between foreign sources to destinations within the U.S., and from sources within the U.S.; offers members reduced ocean freight rates. **Founded:** 1976. **Geographic Preference:** Multinational.

INCUBATORS/RESEARCH AND TECHNOLOGY PARKS

16071 ■ Plug and Play - Supply Chain
440 N Wolfe Rd.
Sunnyvale, CA 94085
URL: http://www.plugandplaytechcenter.com/indus
tries/supply-chain

Description: An accelerator for startups in the supply chain tech industry. Provides support with venture and angel partners, mentorship, a data center, office space, and networking opportunities.

REFERENCE WORKS

16072 ■ "10 Ways to Reduce Your Fuel Costs" in Business News Daily (March 8, 2023)
URL(s): www.businessnewsdaily.com/16101-reduce
-fuel-costs.html

Ed: David Gargaro. **Released:** March 08, 2023. **Description:** This article gives tips for those running a small business with a fleet of vehicles can save money when it comes to fuel costs. **Availability:** Online.

16073 ■ "Book Industry Supply Chain Delays to Impact Holiday Season" in American Booksellers Association (August 19, 2021)
Ed: Emily Behnke. **Released:** August 19, 2021. **Description:** It takes many steps and adjacent industries to get books on shelves, such as trucking and warehousing. Expect delays in the book supply chain as the COVID-19 pandemic rages on and disruptions are common. **Availability:** Online.

16074 ■ "Central Freight Lines Relocates Irving Terminal" in Dallas Business Journal (Vol. 35, March 2, 2012, No. 25, pp. 1)
Pub: Baltimore Business Journal
Contact: Rhonda Pringle, President
E-mail: rpringle@bizjournals.com

Description: Waco, Texas-based trucking firm Central Freight Lines Inc. is relocating its operational headquarters to Fort Worth from Irving. The relocation is the result of the changing vision for the old Texas stadium area, along with safety concerns related to highway and light rail construction. **Availability:** Print; Online.

16075 ■ "Compelling Opportunities for Investors in Emerging Markets" in Barron's (Vol. 88, March 10, 2008, No. 10, pp. 39)
Pub: Dow Jones & Company Inc.
Contact: Almar Latour, Chief Executive Officer

Ed: Neil A. Martin. **Description:** Michael L. Reynal, portfolio manager of Principal International Emerging Markets Fund, is bullish on the growth prospects of stocks in emerging markets. He is investing big on energy, steel, and transportation companies. **Availability:** Online.

16076 ■ "Con-Way Development Back in High Gear" in Business Journal Portland (Vol. 27, November 5, 2010, No. 36, pp. 1)
Pub: Portland Business Journal
Contact: Andy Giegerich, Managing Editor
E-mail: agiegerich@bizjournals.com

Ed: Wendy Culverwell. **Description:** Trucking firm Con-Way Inc. intends to sell parcels of land from a property comprising 16 blocks and 20 prime acres west of the Pearl District in Portland, Oregon. In 2009, Con-Way abandoned plans to sell the property. As Con-Way reclaims control over design and usage of the property, it also expressed willingness to cooperate with a master developer on a related real estate project. **Availability:** Print; Online.

16077 ■ "Dealer Gets a Lift with Acquisitions at Year's End" in Crain's Detroit Business (Vol. 26, January 11, 2010, No. 2, pp. 3)
Pub: Crain Communications Inc.
Contact: Barry Asin, President

Ed: Ryan Beene. **Description:** Alta Equipment Co., a forklift dealer, closed 2009 with a string of acquisitions expecting to double the firm's employee headcount and triple its annual revenue. Alta Lift Truck Services, Inc., as the company was known before the acquisitions, was founded in 1984 as Michigan's dealer for forklift manufacturer Yale Materials Handling Corp. **Availability:** Print; Online.

16078 ■ "Mileage Reimbursement: What You Need to Know" in Business News Daily (March 8, 2023)
URL(s): www.businessnewsdaily.com/15891-mileage
-reimbursement-laws-policies.html

Ed: Adam Uzialko. **Released:** March 08, 2023. **Description:** There are various state for federal regulations when it comes to mileage reimbursement. Small business owners should become familiar with these laws, especially fleet owners. **Availability:** Online.

16079 ■ National Tank Truck Carrier Membership Directory
Pub: National Tank Truck Carriers
Contact: Ryan Streblow, President
E-mail: rstreblow@tanktruck.org
URL(s): www.tanktruck.org/Public/Public/Engage/
Member-Directory.aspx

Description: Covers for-hire tank truck carriers serving petroleum, chemical, and other industries in the United States, Canada, Australia, England, Europe, Japan, Mexico, and South Africa. Also lists major shippers who use tank trucks, intermodal bulk facilities, industry suppliers, and state related associations affiliated with the American Trucking Associations. Includes names and addresses of the Department of Transportation field personnel. **Entries include:** Company name, address, phone, names of executives, list of products or services. **Arrangement:** Separate geographical sections for carriers and associations; shippers and industry suppliers are alphabetical. **Indexes:** Personal name, company name. **Availability:** Print.

16080 ■ "Presidential Address: Innovation in Retrospect and Prospect" in Canadian Journal of Electronics (Vol. 43, November 2010, No. 4)
Pub: Journal of the Canadian Economics Association

Ed: James A. Brander. **Description:** Has innovation slowed in recent decades? While there has been progress in information and communications technology, the recent record of innovation in agriculture, energy, transportation and healthcare sectors is cause for concern. **Availability:** PDF; Online.

16081 ■ "Ryder's Shock Absorbers Are In Place" in Barron's (Vol. 88, March 24, 2008, No. 12, pp. 19)
Pub: Dow Jones & Company Inc.
Contact: Almar Latour, Chief Executive Officer

Ed: Christopher C. Williams. **Description:** Shares of Ryder System Inc. are expected to continue rising on the back of rising earnings, forecast at $5.20 a share for 2009. The shares of the truck freight company hit a 52-week high of $62.27 each and may reach $70 a share. **Availability:** Online.

16082 ■ "Sedo Keeps Trucking in Good Times and Bad" in Crain's Chicago Business (Vol. 31, April 28, 2008, No. 17, pp. 35)
Description: Discusses Seko Worldwide Inc., an Itasca-based freight forwarder, and its complicated road to growth and expansion on a global scale. **Availability:** Print; Online.

16083 ■ "Staffing Firms are Picking Up the Pieces, Seeing Signs of Life" in Milwaukee Business Journal (Vol. 27, February 5, 2010, No. 19)
Pub: The Business Journal
Contact: Heather Ladage, President
E-mail: hladage@bizjournals.com

Ed: Rich Rovito. **Description:** Milwaukee, Wisconsin-based staffing firms are seeing signs of economic rebound as many businesses turned to temporary employees to fill the demands for goods and services. Economic observers believe the growth in temporary staffing is one of the early indicators of economic recovery. **Availability:** Print; Online.

16084 ■ "Teens Could Become Long-Haul Truckers Under New Bill" in The Drive (September 22, 2021)
Ed: Rob Stumpf. **Released:** September 22, 2021. **Description:** With a shortage in people willing to take on long-haul truck routes, a new bipartisan bill is being introduced that would allow 18-year-old individuals to obtain licenses and jobs in the field. **Availability:** Online.

16085 ■ "Trucker Jobs Are Plentiful and Safe . . . but for How Long?" in American Trucker (November 15, 2019)
URL(s): www.trucker.com/equipment/trucker-jobs-are
-plentiful-and-safe-how-long

Ed: Josh Fisher. **Released:** November 15, 2019. **Description:** Automation has been making its way across several industries, but is it going to impact the trucking industry? Technology development is increasing, but it doesn't look like fully automated trucks will be taking over the roads any time soon, and if that does happen, truckers will still be needed in the vehicle. **Availability:** Online.

16086 ■ "Yes, You're Paying About 15% More to Move This Year. Here's Why." in Forbes (August 3, 2021)
Ed: Samantha Allen. **Released:** August 03, 2021. **Description:** Discusses the labor shortage throughout the US and how it's impacting the moving industry, which is driving up costs for those moving house. **Availability:** Online.

STATISTICAL SOURCES

16087 ■ Local Freight Trucking Industry in the US - Market Research Report
URL(s): www.ibisworld.com/united-states/market-re
search-reports/local-freight-trucking-industry/

Price: $925. **Description:** Downloadable report analyzing the local freight trucking industry. **Availability:** Download.

16088 ■ *Local Specialized Freight Trucking Industry in the US - Market Research Report*
URL(s): www.ibisworld.com/united-states/market-research-reports/local-specialized-freight-trucking-industry

Price: $925. **Description:** Downloadable report analyzing current and future trends in the local specialized freight trucking industry. **Availability:** Download.

16089 ■ *Long-Distance Freight Trucking Industry in the US - Market Research Report*
URL(s): www.ibisworld.com/united-states/market-research-reports/long-distance-freight-trucking-industry/

Price: $925. **Description:** Downloadable report analyzing current and future trends in the long-distance freight trucking industry. **Availability:** Download.

16090 ■ *RMA Annual Statement Studies*
Pub: Risk Management Association
Contact: Nancy Foster, President

Released: Annual. **Description:** Contains composite balance sheets and income statements for more than 360 industries, including the accounting, auditing, and bookkeeping industries. Also contains five years of comparative historical data for discerning trends. Includes 16 commonly used ratios, computed for most of the size groupings for nearly every industry.

16091 ■ *Standard & Poor's Industry Surveys*
Pub: Standard And Poor's Financial Services LLC.
Contact: Douglas L. Peterson, President

Description: Two-volume book that examines the prospects for specific industries, including trucking. Also provides analyses of trends and problems, statistical tables and charts, and comparative company analyses.

16092 ■ *Transportation and Warehousing Industry in the US - Market Research Report*
URL(s): www.ibisworld.com/united-states/market-research-reports/transportation-warehousing-industry/

Price: $925. **Description:** Downloadable report analyzing current and future trends in the transportation and warehousing industries. **Availability:** Download.

TRADE PERIODICALS

16093 ■ *CALTRUX*
Pub: California Trucking Association
Contact: Dana Brooks, Director
E-mail: dbrooks@caltrux.org
URL(s): www.caltrux.org/member-benefits

Released: Quarterly **Description:** Provides news, commentary, announcements, and advertising of interest to California truck fleet owners and managers. Carries legislative updates, news of developments in the state regulatory agencies, and a calendar of events. **Availability:** Print; Online.

16094 ■ *Commercial Carrier Journal*
Pub: Randall-Reilly
Contact: Matt Reilly, President
URL(s): www.ccjdigital.com
Facebook: www.facebook.com/CommercialCarrierJournal
Linkedin: www.linkedin.com/company/commercial-carrier-journal
X (Twitter): twitter.com/CCJnow
YouTube: www.youtube.com/user/CCJDigital

Description: Magazine containing management, maintenance, and operations information for truck and bus fleets. **Availability:** Print; Online.

16095 ■ *Fleet Equipment*
Pub: Babcox Media Inc.
Contact: Bill Babcox, Chief Executive Officer
E-mail: bbabcox@babcox.com
URL(s): www.fleetequipmentmag.com
Facebook: www.facebook.com/FleetEquipmentMag

Linkedin: www.linkedin.com/showcase/fleet-equipment-magazine
X (Twitter): x.com/Fleet_Equipment
YouTube: www.youtube.com/user/FleetEquipment
Ed: Jason Morgan. **Released:** Monthly **Description:** Magazine for equipment managers of truck, trailer, and bus fleets. **Availability:** Print; Online.

16096 ■ *Fruit and Vegetable Truck Rate Report*
Pub: United States Department of Agriculture
URL(s): www.marketnews.usda.gov/mnp/fv-help-04

Released: Weekly **Description:** Lists truck rates per load to selected markets throughout the U.S. Also reports on trucks available in relation to shippers' needs. Recurring features include statistics on the total reported domestic and import truck shipments of fresh fruit and vegetables. **Availability:** Print.

16097 ■ *Heavy Duty Trucking (HDT)*
Pub: Bobit Business Media
Contact: Derrick Beasley, Manager, Technical Services
URL(s): www.truckinginfo.com
Facebook: www.facebook.com/heavydutytrucking
Linkedin: www.linkedin.com/company/heavy-duty-trucking-magazine
X (Twitter): x.com/HDTrucking

Released: 7/year **Description:** Magazine serving large, medium and small fleet managers whose firms operate class 6, 7 and 8 trucks in the U.S. **Availability:** Print; PDF; Online.

16098 ■ *Keep on Truckin News*
Pub: Mid-West Truckers Association Inc.
Contact: Don Schaefer, Executive Vice President
E-mail: dons@midwesttruckers.com
URL(s): www.mid-westtruckers.com/member-services

Released: Monthly **Description:** Offers owners and operators of trucks information relating to the Association and the industry in general. Contains information on services available to members, including mass purchasing, international registration assistance, license plate procurement, drug testing, self-funded workers compensation, EPA Storm Water Permits, and group insurance plans. Reports on legislative and regulatory changes that affect the industry. Recurring features include news of members, news of research, and notices of Association activities. **Availability:** Print.

16099 ■ *Land Line*
Pub: Owner-Operator Independent Drivers Association
Contact: Todd Spencer, President
URL(s): landline.media
Facebook: www.facebook.com/LandLineMag
X (Twitter): x.com/Land_Line_Mag
Instagram: www.instagram.com/landlinemedia
Released: Monthly **Description:** Business magazine for professional truckers. **Availability:** Print; PDF; Download; Online.

16100 ■ *SC & RA News*
Pub: Specialized Carriers and Rigging Association
Contact: Ed Bernard, President
URL(s): www.scranet.org/SCRA/News/Association_News/SCRA/Content/news/Association-News.aspx?hkey=70292fec-42d8-4494-a8a9-128071ea7d31

Released: Weekly **Description:** Reports on current regulatory, safety, and industrial relations developments. Offers news of business opportunities. Recurring features include news of research, news of members, book reviews, and a calendar of events. **Availability:** Online.

16101 ■ *Trucker's Connection*
Contact: Megan Cullingford, Editor
E-mail: meganc@targetmediapartners.com
URL(s): truckdrivermags.com/digital/?pub=tc
Facebook: www.facebook.com/TruckersConnectionMagazine

Ed: Megan Cullingford. **Description:** Trade magazine for over-the-road, long haul truck operators.

TRADE SHOWS AND CONVENTIONS

16102 ■ American Trucking Association Management Conference & Exhibition (ACE MCE)
FedEx
25 Agmashenebeli ave
0102 Tbilisi, Republic of Georgia
Ph: 995 32 291-0220
Co. E-mail: customerservice@icsgeorgia.ge
URL: http://www.fedex.com/en-ge/home.html
Contact: Raj Subramaniam, President
URL(s): mce.trucking.org

Frequency: Annual. **Description:** Equipment, supplies, and services related to the trucking industry. Includes education sessions, meetings, and networking. **Audience:** Chief executive officers and upper-level management of motor carrier companies, as well as executives from suppliers to the trucking industry. **Principal Exhibits:** Equipment, supplies, and services related to the trucking industry. Includes education sessions, meetings, and networking. **Telecommunication Services:** ataexhibits@trucking.org

16103 ■ ATD Convention & Expo
National Automobile Dealers Association (NADA)
8484 Westpark Dr., Ste. 500
Tysons, VA 22102
Free: 800-557-6232
Co. E-mail: customerservice@nada.org
URL: http://www.nada.org
Contact: Mike Stanton, President
URL(s): www.nada.org/nada-show-attend
Facebook: www.facebook.com/NADAexpo

Frequency: Annual. **Audience:** Industry professionals. **Dates and Locations:** 2025 Jan 23-26 New Orleans Ernest N. Morial Convention Center, New Orleans, LA; 2026 Feb 03-06 Las Vegas, NV; 2027 Feb 17-20 Orlando, FL; 2028 Mar 07-10 Las Vegas, NV. **Telecommunication Services:** nada@maritz.com.

16104 ■ Food Marketing Institute Annual Business Conference
URL(s): www.fmi.org/annual-business-conference

Frequency: Annual. **Description:** Offers networking and educational opportunities for those involved in the food supply chain shipping. **Audience:** Food Marketing Institute Retail/Wholesale members and CPG Associate members. **Principal Exhibits:** Offers networking and educational opportunities for those involved in the food supply chain shipping.

16105 ■ Food Shippers of America Annual Logistics Conference
URL(s): www.foodshippersofamerica.org

Frequency: Annual. **Description:** Networking and talks discussing shipping logistics for the food industry. **Principal Exhibits:** Networking and talks discussing shipping logistics for the food industry.

16106 ■ Jump Start
URL(s): www.smc3jumpstart.com

Frequency: Annual. **Description:** Annual conference focused on the supply chain industry. Networking opportunities, presentations, and speakers take place throughout the event. **Audience:** Carriers, shippers, logistics service providers, and technology providers. **Principal Exhibits:** Annual conference focused on the supply chain industry. Networking opportunities, presentations, and speakers take place throughout the event.

16107 ■ Mid-West Truck & Trailer Show
Mid-West Truckers Association Inc. (MTA)
2727 N Dirksen Pky.
Springfield, IL 62702
Ph: (217)525-0310
Co. E-mail: info@mid-westtruckers.com
URL: http://www.mid-westtruckers.com
Contact: Don Schaefer, Executive Vice President
E-mail: dons@midwesttruckers.com
URL(s): midwesttruckshow.com/explore-the-show

Frequency: Annual. **Description:** Trucks, trailers, financing information, computers, communication and satellite equipment insurance information, and related equipment, supplies, and services. **Audience:** Trucking and transportation professionals. **Principal Exhibits:** Trucks, trailers, financing information, computers, communication and satellite equipment insurance information, and related equipment, supplies, and services. **Telecommunication Services:** mattw@midwesttruckers.com.

16108 ■ SSA Convention

Service Specialists Association (SSA)
1531 Springside Pl.
Downers Grove, IL 60516
Ph: (224)990-1005
Co. E-mail: servicespecialists@outlook.com
URL: http://www.servicespecialistsassociation.com
Contact: Adm. (Ret.) Warren Wild, President
URL(s): www.servicespecialistsassociation.com/ssaconvention2024

Frequency: Annual. **Description:** Exhibits related to truck repair operations, equipment, supplies, and services. **Audience:** Members and industry professionals. **Principal Exhibits:** Exhibits related to truck repair operations, equipment, supplies, and services.

16109 ■ TCA Annual Convention

Truckload Carriers Association (TCA)
555 E Braddock Rd.
Alexandria, VA 22314
Ph: (703)838-1950
Fax: (202)217-3877
Co. E-mail: tca@truckload.org
URL: http://www.truckload.org
Contact: Jim Ward, President
E-mail: jward@truckload.org
URL(s): www.tcaconvention.com

Frequency: Annual; Every March. **Description:** Focuses on promoting truckload segment in the motor carrier industry. **Audience:** Industry professionals. **Principal Exhibits:** Focuses on promoting truckload segment in the motor carrier industry. Dates and Locations: 2025 Mar 15-18 Phoenix Convention Center, Phoenix, AZ; 2026 Feb 28-Mar 03 Gaylord Palms Resort & Convention Center, Kissimmee, FL; 2027 Feb 27-Mar 02 Caesar's Forum, Las Vegas, NV. **Telecommunication Services:** zgambill@truckload.org.

16110 ■ The Work Truck Show

National Truck Equipment Association (NTEA)
37400 Hills Tech Dr.
Farmington Hills, MI 48331-3414
Ph: (248)489-7090
Free: 800-441-6832
Fax: (248)489-8590
Co. E-mail: info@ntea.com
URL: http://www.ntea.com
Contact: Steve Carey, President
E-mail: steve@ntea.com
URL(s): www.worktruckweek.com/WTS/About/WTS/
 AbouttheWorkTruckShow2.aspx?hkey=406dc008
 -1095-422e-a58b-ffeba796423f

Frequency: Annual; held every March. **Description:** Chassis, commercial truck, bodies, mounted equipment, accessories, and supplies. **Audience:** Fleet managers, truck dealers and equipment distributors. **Principal Exhibits:** Chassis, commercial truck, bodies, mounted equipment, accessories, and supplies. Dates and Locations: 2025 Mar 04-07; 2026 Mar 10-13; 2027 Mar 09-12; 2028 Mar 07-10; 2029 Mar 06-09; 2030 Mar 05-08. Indiana Convention Center, Indianapolis, IN. **Telecommunication Services:** sarah@ntea.com.

LIBRARIES

16111 ■ American Truck Historical Society (ATHS) - Zoe James Memorial Library

10380 N Ambassador Dr., Ste. 101
Kansas City, MO 64153
Ph: (816)891-9900
Co. E-mail: info@aths.org
URL: http://www.aths.org
Contact: Mark Schroyer, President
E-mail: dmtransport4@gmail.com
Facebook: www.facebook.com/ATHSHeadquarters
X (Twitter): x.com/HistoricalTruck
Instagram: www.instagram.com/americantruckhis
 toricalsociety
YouTube: www.youtube.com/channel/UCOT
 20xsSaGL-YX7-uhhDdhw

Description: Promotes the dynamic history of trucks, the trucking industry, and its pioneers. **Scope:** History of the motor truck industry. **Services:** Copying; library open to the public. **Founded:** 1971. **Holdings:** 50,000 photographs; 45,000 books and periodicals; 35,000 pieces of sales literature; manuals. **Publica-**

tions: *Wheels of Time* (Bimonthly). **Educational Activities:** ATHS Convention & Truck Show (Annual). **Awards:** ATHS Golden Achievement Award (Annual); ATHS Founder Award (Annual); Harris Saunders Sr. Award (Annual). **Geographic Preference:** National.

RESEARCH CENTERS

16112 ■ American Transportation Research Institute (ATRI)

80 M St SE Ste. 800
Washington, DC 20003
Ph: (770)432-0628
Fax: (770)432-0638
Co. E-mail: atri@trucking.org
URL: http://truckingresearch.org
Contact: Rebecca M. Brewster, President
Linkedin: www.linkedin.com/company/american
 -transportation-research-institute
X (Twitter): x.com/Truck_Research

Description: Research arm of the American Trucking Association Foundation. **Scope:** Truck-related research including driver fatigue, truck crashworthiness, and the commercial drivers license; productivity, including economics of highway transportation, regulation of weights on pavements and bridges, alternative fuels, and incident management; taxes, including measurement of pavement damage for cost allocation and rationalization of cost allocation procedures; and human resources, including the truck driver shortage, worker's compensation, and the factors affecting truck driver job satisfaction. **Founded:** 1954. **Publications:** *Inventory of Truck Related Research* (Annual).

16113 ■ University of New Brunswick (UNB TG) - Transportation Group

Sir Howard Douglas Hall
Fredericton, NB, Canada E3B 5A3
URL: http://www.unb.ca/research/transportation
 -group

Description: Integral unit of University of New Brunswick. **Scope:** Traffic and transportation systems planning and design, environmental impacts of transport facilities, economics of transport systems; aviation, highway and marine transport systems; policy and management of transport systems, road and motor vehicle safety. **Founded:** 1968. **Educational Activities:** Transportation Seminar (Weekly).

START-UP INFORMATION

16114 ■ *"Advantage Tutoring Center Helps Students of All Levels"* in Bellingham Business Journal (Vol. February 2010, pp. 16)
Pub: Sound Publishing Inc.
Contact: Josh O'Connor, President
Ed: Ashley Mitchell. **Description:** Profile of the newly opened Advantage Tutoring, owned by Mary and Peter Morrison. The center offers programs ranging from basic homework help to subject-specific enrichment.

16115 ■ *Do You Need a License to Start a Tutoring Business?*
URL(s): tutorcruncher.com/starting-tutor-business/do-you-need-a-license-to-start-a-tutoring-business/
Ed: Paula Antalffy. **Released:** April 30, 2021. **Description:** Presents answers to those interested in starting their own private tutoring business. Includes information on tax and licensing, qualifications, costs, and marketing. **Availability:** Online.

16116 ■ *"How Much Does It Cost to Start a Tutoring Business?"* in Starter Story (Oct. 20, 2022)
URL(s): www.starterstory.com/ideas/tutoring-business/startup-costs
Ed: Pat Walls. **Released:** October 20, 2022. **Description:** Provides a detailed list of tutoring business service startup costs. **Availability:** Online.

16117 ■ *"How to Start a Private Tutoring Business"* in Chron (March 11, 2019)
URL(s): smallbusiness.chron.com/start-private-tutoring-business-4428.html
Ed: Jordan Meyers. **Released:** March 11, 2019. **Description:** Tutors for all subjects and students of all ages are in demand. This article provides an eight-step process to get your private tutoring business up and running. **Availability:** Online.

16118 ■ *"How to Start a Profitable Home Tutoring Business"* in Zen Business
URL(s): www.zenbusiness.com/start-a-home-tutoring-business/
Description: Tutoring as a home business is among the most flexible types of business ideas. This article provides information you'll need to start a profitable home tutoring business. **Availability:** Online.

16119 ■ *"How to Start a Tutoring Business"* in NerdWallet (Sept. 10, 2020)
URL(s): www.nerdwallet.com/article/small-business/how-to-start-a-tutoring-business
Ed: Sally Lauckner. **Released:** September 10, 2020. **Description:** Presents nine steps to follow when starting your own tutoring business. **Availability:** Online.

16120 ■ *"How to Start a Tutoring Business"* in Care.com (July 26, 2021)
URL(s): www.care.com/c/how-to-start-a-tutoring-business/

Ed: Maressa Brown. **Released:** July 26, 2021. **Description:** Discusses the growing tutoring industry and presents things to consider if you'd like to start your own tutoring business. **Availability:** Online.

16121 ■ *Is Starting a Tutoring Business a Good Idea?*
URL(s): elearningindustry.com/is-starting-tutoring-business-good-idea
Ed: Kathy Alameda. **Released:** January 14, 2021. **Description:** The online education market has become a booming industry. This guide provides detailed information on all that is needed to create your own tutoring business. **Availability:** Online.

ASSOCIATIONS AND OTHER ORGANIZATIONS

16122 ■ Association for the Coaching and Tutoring Profession
URL: http://www.myactp.com
Contact: Jack Truschel, Chairman
Facebook: www.facebook.com/actprofession/
Instagram: www.instagram.com/my_actp/
Founded: 2003.

16123 ■ Independent Educational Consultants Association (IECA)
3251 Old Lee Hwy., Ste. 510
Fairfax, VA 22030-1504
Ph: (703)591-4850
Fax: (703)591-4860
Co. E-mail: info@iecaonline.com
URL: http://www.iecaonline.com
Contact: Ibrahim Firat, President
Facebook: www.facebook.com/IECA.IndependentEducationalConsultantsAssn
Linkedin: www.linkedin.com/company/ieca-independent-educational-consultants-association
X (Twitter): x.com/IECA
Instagram: www.instagram.com/iecaheadquarters
Description: Represents the interests of established educational consultants. Advises students with special circumstances such as learning or physical disabilities, emotional or behavioral issues. Helps members update knowledge and maintain skills through meetings, workshops, training programs, and information exchanges with colleges, schools, programs, and other consultants. Members are required to maintain the highest standards of ethical practice. **Founded:** 1976. **Educational Activities:** IECA's Fall Conference (Annual); Independent Educational Consultants Association Seminars & Workshops. **Geographic Preference:** Multinational.

16124 ■ National Tutoring Association (NTA)
PO Box 6840
Lakeland, FL 33807
Ph: (863)838-3558
Co. E-mail: ntatutor@ntatutor.com
URL: http://www.ntatutor.com
Contact: Ishmael Brown, President

Facebook: www.facebook.com/NationalTutoringAssociation
X (Twitter): x.com/ntatutor
Description: Represents elementary school, middle school, high school, college/university, private practice, faith based and community tutor. Sponsors tutoring programs. **Founded:** 1992. **Publications:** *Teaching Learning Center Handbook.* **Educational Activities:** National Tutoring Association Meeting (Annual). **Awards:** NTA Professional Development Award (Annual); NTA Tutor of the Year Award (Annual). **Geographic Preference:** Multinational.

16125 ■ Tutoring America (TA)
1325 6th Ave., 28th Fl.
New York, NY 10019
Co. E-mail: tutoring@tutoringamerica.org
URL: http://www.tutoringamerica.org
Contact: Jay D. Hatfield, Founder
Description: Works to help close the education gap that prevents many low-income youth from achieving their full potential as students.

REFERENCE WORKS

16126 ■ *"5 Tutor Marketing Strategies"* in TutorCruncher (Nov. 30, 2021)
URL(s): tutorcruncher.com/business-growth/tutor-marketing
Ed: Tom Hamilton Stubber. **Released:** November 30, 2021. **Description:** Provides top strategies to consider when marketing your tutoring business. **Availability:** Online.

16127 ■ *"9 Sales Promotion Ideas for Your Tutoring Business"* in Smith.ai blog
URL(s): smith.ai/blog/9-sales-promotion-ideas-for-your-tutoring-business
Ed: Sean Lund-Brown. **Description:** Tutoring is a lucrative way to make extra money. This article provides information on how to promote your tutoring business and attract new clients. **Availability:** Online.

16128 ■ *"Advertising Your Tutor Business - How to Land More Students?"* in Superprof blog (Oct. 10, 2020)
URL(s): www.superprof.com/blog/promoting-your-lessons-as-a-private-teacher/
Released: October 10, 2020. **Description:** Discusses effective methods for publicizing your tutoring business to get new students. **Availability:** Online.

16129 ■ *"The Best Marketing Strategy for Private Tutors and Tutoring Centers"* in Bookshelf PH blog (March 30, 2022)
URL(s): bookshelf.com.ph/blogs/connect-with-content-marketing/the-best-content-marketing-strategy-for-private-tutors-and-tutoring-centers
Ed: Jack Cordero. **Released:** March 30, 2022. **Description:** Discusses the state of the tutoring industry and provides things to consider when it comes to marketing your tutoring services. **Availability:** Online.

16130 ■ "Do Private Tutors Require Insurance?" in Superprof blog (Oct. 10, 2020)
URL(s): www.superprof.com/blog/secure-yourself-as-a-home-tutor/
Released: October 10, 2020. **Description:** Explains why it is a good idea to get insurance if you plan to become a private tutor to reflect your needs as a business-of-one and to cover any risks you may face in the course of your tutoring job. **Availability:** Online.

16131 ■ "An Educated Play on China" in Barron's (Vol. 88, June 30, 2008, No. 26, pp. M6)
Pub: Dow Jones & Company Inc.
Contact: Almar Latour, Chief Executive Officer
Ed: Mohammed Hadi. **Description:** New Oriental Education & Technology Group sells English-language courses to an increasingly competitive Chinese workforce that values education. The shares in this company have been weighed down by worries on the impact of the Beijing Olympics on enrollment and the Sichuan earthquake. These shares could be a great way to get exposure to the long-term growth in China. **Availability:** Online.

16132 ■ "The Future Is Another Country; Higher Education" in The Economist (Vol. 390, January 3, 2009, No. 8612, pp. 43)
Description: Due to the growth of the global corporation, more ambitious students are studying at universities abroad; the impact of this trend is discussed. **Availability:** Print; Online.

16133 ■ "How to Advertise a Tutoring Business" in Chron
URL(s): smallbusiness.chron.com/advertise-tutoring-business-3609.html
Ed: Louise Balle. **Description:** The key to maintaining a continual flow of tutor clients is to advertise your services in places where you know students and their parents may frequent.This article provides seven tips on how to advertise your tutoring business. **Availability:** Online.

16134 ■ "How to Advertise Your Tutoring Services: The Complete Guide to Tutor Advertising" in Appointy blog (Jan. 22, 2021)
URL(s): blog.appointy.com/2021/01/22/how-to-advertise-tutoring-services/
Released: January 22, 2021. **Description:** Discusses low-cost and organic marketing and delves deeper into incorporating paid advertising into the marketing efforts for your tutoring business. **Availability:** Online.

16135 ■ "How to Get More Students for Your Online Tutoring Business" in ClassIn blog (Jan. 17, 2022)
URL(s): www.blog.classin.com/post/how-to-get-more-students-for-your-online-tutoring-business
Released: January 17, 2022. **Description:** Provides six effective ways to promote your online tutoring services and attract more students. **Availability:** Online.

16136 ■ "How a Tutoring Service Helps Students With Learning Deficits" in AZEDNEWS (May 3, 2022)
URL(s): azednews.com/how-a-tutoring-service-helps-students-with-learning-deficits/
Ed: Mingson Lau. **Released:** May 03, 2022. **Description:** Discusses the benefits of utilizing a tutor or tutoring service to guide students to connect to their lessons. **Availability:** Online.

16137 ■ "Low Cost Methods for Marketing Your Tutoring Business" in Teachworks Blog (Dec. 28, 2021)
URL(s): blog.teachworks.com/2021/12/low-cost-methods-for-marketing-your-tutoring-business/
Released: December 28, 2021. **Description:** Looks at a variety of cost-effective methods you may use to grow your tutoring business early on. **Availability:** Online.

16138 ■ "Marketing 101: How to Advertise Tutoring Services" in Constant Contact Blog (Jan. 21, 2022)
URL(s): www.constantcontact.com/blog/how-to-advertise-tutoring/
Ed: Jennifer Lyons. **Released:** January 21, 2022. **Description:** Covers nine important tips to help you connect with new clients, build a loyal customer base, and grow your tutoring business. **Availability:** Online.

16139 ■ Marketing Do's and Don'ts for Managing a Tutoring Business
URL(s): www.bizstim.com/news/article/marketing-dos-and-donts-for-managing-a-tutoring-business
Released: September 20, 2019. **Description:** Lists do's and don'ts related to marketing your tutoring business. **Availability:** Online.

16140 ■ "Marketing Tips for Online Tutoring Business" in SmartyAds blog (Sept. 22, 2020)
URL(s): smartyads.com/blog/marketing-tips-for-online-tutoring-business/
Ed: Kathy Alameda. **Released:** September 22, 2020. **Description:** The primary requirement for building an online tutoring business is creating a platform and then attracting students with value-based learning services. This article provides information on how to initiate a marketing strategy and build a better online presence. **Availability:** Online.

16141 ■ "The Ultimate Tutoring Marketing Plan: 7 Steps to Boost Your Student Roster" in PostcardMania blog (July 15, 2021)
URL(s): www.postcardmania.com/blog/tutoring-marketing-ideas/
Ed: Joy Gendusa. **Released:** July 15, 2021. **Description:** Presents seven ways to grow your tutoring business. **Availability:** Online.

STATISTICAL SOURCES

16142 ■ Private Tutoring
URL(s): www.marketresearch.com/Global-Industry-Analysts-v1039/Private-Tutoring-32280866/
Price: $5,600. **Description:** Overview of the global private tutoring market, which is expected to reach $218.1 billion by 2027. **Availability:** PDF.

16143 ■ Private Tutoring Market in US 2022-2026
URL(s): www.marketresearch.com/Infiniti-Research-Limited-v2680/Private-Tutoring-31502516/
Price: $2,500. **Description:** Report on the private tutoring market in the United States. Provides a holistic analysis, market size and forecast, trends, growth drivers and challenges, and vendor analysis. **Availability:** Download.

16144 ■ United States K-12 Tutoring Market Research Report 2022
URL(s): www.marketresearch.com/QYResearch-Group-v3531/United-States-Tutoring-Research-31907559/
Price: $2,900. **Description:** Presents market analysis and insight into the K-12 tutoring market, segmented by type and by application. **Availability:** Download.

TRADE PERIODICALS

16145 ■ Exceptional Children (EC)
Pub: SAGE Publications
Contact: Tracey Ozmina, President
URL(s): exceptionalchildren.org/improving-your-practice/cec-publications/exceptional-childrenjournals.sagepub.com/home/ecx
Released: Quarterly; Jan, April, July, Oct. **Price:** $651, Institutions for backfile lease, combined plus backfile (current volume print & all online content); $562, Institutions for backfile lease, e-access plus backfile (all online content); $2,779, Institutions for backfile purchase, e-access (content through 1998); $149, Individuals for combined (print & e-access); $592, Institutions for combined (print & e-access); $160, Institutions for single print issue; $48, Individu-
als for single print issue; $503, Institutions for online; $580, Institutions for print. **Description:** Peer-reviewed journal publishing research, reviews, methodological reviews of literature, data-based position papers and policy analyses, and registered reports on the education and development of children and youth with exceptionalities. Published in association between SAGE and the Council for Exceptional Children. **Availability:** Print; Download; PDF; Online. **Type:** Bibliographic.

16146 ■ TEACHING Exceptional Children (TEC)
Pub: SAGE Publications
Contact: Tracey Ozmina, President
URL(s): exceptionalchildren.org/improving-your-practice/cec-publications/teaching-exceptional-childrenjournals.sagepub.com/home/TCX
Ed: Dawn A. Rowe. **Released:** 6/year; January/February, March/April, May/June, July/August, September/October, November/December. **Price:** $612, Institutions for subscription & backfile lease, combined plus backfile (current volume print & all online content); $529, Institutions for institutional subscription & back file lease , e-access plus back file (all online content; $1,246, Institutions for backfile purchase, e-access; $100, Institutions for single issue print; $34, Individuals for single issue print; $155, Individuals for print & online; $556, Institutions for print + online; $545, Institutions for print only; $473, Institutions for online. **Description:** Peer-reviewed journal exploring practical methods for teaching students who have exceptionalities and those who are gifted and talented. Published in association between SAGE and the Council for Exceptional Children. **Availability:** Print; PDF; Online.

CONSULTANTS

16147 ■ ArborBridge
110 Main St., Ste. 102
Port Washington, NY 11050
Ph: (917)525-2548
Co. E-mail: info@arborbridge.com
URL: http://www.arborbridge.com
Contact: Dr. Megan Stubbendeck, Chief Executive Officer
E-mail: megan@arborbridge.com
Instagram: www.instagram.com/arborbridgeprep
Description: Provides personalized, online tutoring. Gives students and families flexibility to fit tutoring into their busy schedules.

16148 ■ Central Park Tutors
980 5th Ave.
New York, NY 10075
Ph: (917)502-9108
Co. E-mail: tutors@centralpakrtutors.com
URL: http://centralparktutors.com
Facebook: www.facebook.com/profile.php?id=100068201391225
Description: A premier tutoring company offering private tutoring from Master's Degree-level subject experts.

16149 ■ INC Education
2770 Main St., Ste. 120
Frisco, TX 75034
Ph: (682)305-3720
Co. E-mail: info@inceducationllc.com
URL: http://www.inceducationllc.com
Description: Private, prescriptive tutoring company focused on STEM and standardized test preparation. Assists students in reaching their highest potential and mentors them to succeed in a supportive environment.

16150 ■ Professional Tutors of America Inc.
3350 E Birch St., Ste. 201
Brea, CA 92821
Free: 800-832-2487
Co. E-mail: info@professionaltutors.com
URL: http://www.professionaltutors.com
Contact: Robert Harraka, Director
Facebook: www.facebook.com/ProfessionalTutors
X (Twitter): x.com/ProTutorsUSA

YouTube: www.youtube.com/ProfessionalTutors

Description: Provides educational tutoring services, including one-on-one tutoring, small group instruction, and online tutoring.

16151 ■ SEO Design Chicago
2068 N W Ave., 1F Front
  Chicago, IL 60647
Ph: (773)677-5747
Co. E-mail: info@seodesignchicago.com
URL: http://seodesignchicago.com
Contact: Sandy M. Stelzer, Contact
Facebook: www.facebook.com/seodesignchicago
Linkedin: www.linkedin.com/company/seo-design
 -chicago
X (Twitter): x.com/SeoDesignChi
Instagram: www.instagram.com/seodesignchicago

Description: A professional tutoring marketing agency that has worked with individual tutors and tutoring companies in the U.S. and abroad to find new students. **Founded:** 2015.

16152 ■ Straight North L.L.C.
1001 W 31st St., Ste. 100
  Downers Grove, IL 60515
Ph: (630)282-6911
Free: 855-883-0011
Co. E-mail: info@straightnorth.com
URL: http://www.straightnorth.com
Contact: Frank Fornaris, President

Description: A professional tutoring marketing agency that helps tutoring companies gain clients. **Scope:** Provider of internet marketing and web development services. **Founded:** 1997.

16153 ■ Varsity Tutors LLC
1201 Alaskan Way, Ste. 200
  Seattle, WA 98101
URL: http://www.varsitytutors.com
Contact: Chuck Cohn, Chief Executive Officer
Facebook: www.facebook.com/varsitytutors
Linkedin: www.linkedin.com/company/varsity-tutors

Description: A live learning platform that connects students and professionals with personalized instruction. **Founded:** 2007.

FRANCHISES AND BUSINESS OPPORTUNITIES

16154 ■ ABC In-home Tutoring
6731 W 121st St., Ste. 223
  Overland Park, KS 66209
Free: 888-222-3935
Fax: (913)685-0533
Co. E-mail: contactus@abctutors.com
URL: http://abctutors.com
Facebook: www.facebook.com/ABC_Tutorsinc
X (Twitter): x.com/ABC_Tutors

Description: Provides private in-home tutoring and academic coaching for students of all types. Offers free consultations.

16155 ■ ABC Tutors In Home Tutoring
6731 W 121st St., Ste. 223
  Overland Park, KS 66209
Ph: (913)961-7800
Free: 888-222-3935
Fax: (913)685-0533
Co. E-mail: contactus@abctutors.com
URL: http://abctutors.com
Facebook: www.facebook.com/abctutorsinc
X (Twitter): x.com/ABC_Tutors

Founded: 2004. **Royalty Fee:** 4-6%. **Training:** Provides 3 days of onsite training with ongoing support.

16156 ■ Academy for Mathematics and English
c/o Hillcrest Mall
  9350 Yonge St., Ste. 209
  Richmond Hill, ON, Canada L4C 5G2

Description: Math tutoring system. Tutoring is also offered for English, Physics and Chemistry. **No. of Franchise Units:** 35. **No. of Company-Owned**

Units: 1. **Founded:** 1993. **Franchised:** 1993. **Equity Capital Needed:** $120,000-$150,000. **Franchise Fee:** $35,000. **Training:** Maths and English tutoring center.

16157 ■ Aloha USA
Free: 877-256-4203
Co. E-mail: inquiry@aloha-usa.com
URL: http://alohamindmath.com
Facebook: www.facebook.com/ALOHA.usa

Description: Offers math tutoring services to help children meet their fullest potential.

16158 ■ Chyten Educational Services
1723 Massachusetts Ave.
  Lexington, MA 02420
Ph: (508)371-4202
Free: 800-428-8378
Co. E-mail: info@chyten.com
URL: http://www.chyten.com
Facebook: www.facebook.com/ChytenTutoring
X (Twitter): twitter.com/chyteneducation

Description: Firm provides education management services such as tutoring, test preparation, study skills, college admission counseling, subject tutoring and project-based learning. **Founded:** 1984. **Financial Assistance:** Yes **Training:** Offers training up to 10 days at corporate headquarters, up to 3 days at franchisee's location and ongoing support provided.

16159 ■ Class 101
2039 Regency Rd., Ste. 8
  Lexington, KY 40503
Ph: (859)687-9629
Co. E-mail: info@class101.com
URL: http://www.class101.com
Contact: Tom Pabin, Owner
URL(s): class101franchise.com
Facebook: www.facebook.com/my.class101
X (Twitter): x.com/my_class101
Instagram: www.instagram.com/class101lexington

Description: Offers guidance in the college search, admissions, and financial aid process. **Founded:** 1997.

16160 ■ Club SciKidz
106 Hartwood Dr.
  Woodstock, GA 30189
Ph: (678)493-5651
URL: http://www.clubscikidz.com
Contact: Bob Hagan, Owner
X (Twitter): x.com/clubscikidzcamp
YouTube: www.youtube.com/channel/UCTuagVkqbW
 6JOSEAtJVQXNg

Description: Offers after-school enrichment, STEM technology programming, in-school field trips as well as summer camps offering STEM programming. **Founded:** 1997.

16161 ■ Club Z! In-Home Tutoring
Club Z! In-Home Tutoring Services
  17425 Bridge Hill Ct., Ste. 200
  Tampa, FL 33647
Free: 800-434-2582
Co. E-mail: info@clubztutoring.com
URL: http://clubztutoring.com

Description: In-home tutoring services. **No. of Franchise Units:** 412. **No. of Company-Owned Units:** 1. **Founded:** 1995. **Franchised:** 1997. **Equity Capital Needed:** $32,500. **Franchise Fee:** $24,500. **Training:** Yes.

16162 ■ Club Z! Tutoring Services
17425 Bridge Hill Ct., Ste. 200
  Tampa, FL 33647
Free: 800-434-2582
Co. E-mail: corporate@clubztutoring.com
URL: http://clubztutoring.com
Contact: Cari E. Diaz, President
Facebook: www.facebook.com/ClubZ.Corp
Linkedin: www.linkedin.com/company/club-z-in-home
 -tutoring
Instagram: www.instagram.com/clubztutoring

Founded: 1995.

16163 ■ GradePower Learning
747 Hyde Park Rd., Ste. 230
  London, ON, Canada N6H 3S3
Free: 844-475-7323
Co. E-mail: info@gradepowerlearning.com
URL: http://gradepowerlearning.com
Facebook: www.facebook.com/GradePowerLearning
YouTube: www.youtube.com/channel/UCo9zGuJ
 5QiDgD2ZLNKc1iaA

Description: Offers tutoring and supplemental education to children from preschool to university. **Founded:** 1984.

16164 ■ Huntington Learning Centers Inc.
496 Kinderkamack Rd.
  Oradell, NJ 07649
Free: 866-821-6744
URL: http://huntingtonfranchise.com
URL(s): www.huntingtonhelps.com
X (Twitter): x.com/tutorhuntington

Description: Provides individualized instruction to school-aged children and adults in remedial and speed reading, study skills, spelling, phonics, mathematics, and Scholastic Aptitude Test (SAT) preparation. **No. of Franchise Units:** 300.0. **No. of Operating Units:** 300. **Founded:** 1977. **Franchised:** 1985. **Equity Capital Needed:** $99,245- $204,210. **Franchise Fee:** $22,000. **Financial Assistance:** Yes **Training:** Training program, provides detailed demographic data for desired location, site selection and start-up assistance.

16165 ■ JEI Learning Centers, LLC
4465 Wilshire Blvd., Ste. 302
  Los Angeles, CA 90010
Ph: (323)803-7152
Co. E-mail: info@jeilearning.com
URL: http://jeilearning.com
Contact: Sung Hoon Park, Founder
Facebook: www.facebook.com/jeilearningcenter
Linkedin: www.linkedin.com/company/jei-learning-cen
 ters-llc
X (Twitter): x.com/jeiglobal
Instagram: www.instagram.com/jeilearningcenter

Description: Offers a self-learning method that helps students develop confidence with individually paced, step-by-step learning programs. **Founded:** 1977.

16166 ■ Kumon Math and Reading Centres (KUMON)
6240 Highway 7, Ste. 300
  Woodbridge, ON, Canada L4K 4B4
Ph: (416)490-1434
Co. E-mail: franchisecanada@kumon.com
URL: http://www.kumonfranchise.com/ca-en

Description: Provides an individualized after school math and reading program for students. **No. of Franchise Units:** 330. **No. of Company-Owned Units:** 4. **Founded:** 1988. **Franchised:** 1958. **Equity Capital Needed:** $61,000-$152,000. **Franchise Fee:** $1,000. **Training:** Education franchise provider.

16167 ■ The Learning Experience Academy of Early Education (TLE)
210 Hillsboro Technology Dri.
  Boca Raton, FL 33431
Free: 888-865-7775
Fax: (561)886-6433
Co. E-mail: marketing@tlecorp.com
URL: http://thelearningexperience.com
Contact: Richard Weissman, Chief Executive Officer
Facebook: www.facebook.com/TLEChildCareCenters
Linkedin: www.linkedin.com/company/the-learning
 -experience
X (Twitter): x.com/TheLearningExp
Instagram: www.instagram.com/
 thelearningexperience
Pinterest: www.pinterest.com/tlechildcare

Description: Provides childcare services. **No. of Franchise Units:** 96. **No. of Company-Owned Units:** 19. **Founded:** 1980. **Franchised:** 2001. **Equity Capital Needed:** $150,000. **Franchise Fee:** $60,000. **Financial Assistance:** Yes **Training:** Provides an in-depth orientation on every aspect of the business, including a sophisticated but user-friendly computer system. Offers reinforcement and support systems throughout tenure as a franchisee.

16168 ■ Mathnasium Learning Centers
5120 W Goldleaf Cir., Ste. 400
  Los Angeles, CA 90056-1661
Free: 877-601-6284
Co. E-mail: marketing@mathnasium.com
URL: http://www.mathnasium.com
Contact: Henry Moore, Director
Facebook: www.facebook.com/mathnasium
X (Twitter): x.com/mathnasium
YouTube: www.youtube.com/c/mathnasium
Description: Mathnasium provides the most effective mathematics in education available to grade school children after school, in an attractive neighborhood learning center environment. The Mathnasium Method, developed over 30 years of hands-on experience, is engaging for students and builds confidence as it builds real understanding. Created to address a real need in the market by a team with unparalleled success in the industry, the business model is strong and the opportunity is now. **No. of Franchise Units:** 389. **No. of Company-Owned Units:** 2. **Founded:** 2002. **Franchised:** 2003. **Equity Capital Needed:** $82,250-$136,000 initial investment range. **Franchise Fee:** $37,000. **Training:** Initial training 1 week online followed by 1 week in person at corporate headquarters. Support continues with ongoing training, in-the-field regional managers and monthly conference calls.

16169 ■ S.A.M. Singapore Math
10450 Medlock Bridge Rd., Ste. 112
  Johns Creek, GA 30097
Ph: (770)274-4545
Co. E-mail: johnscreek@seriouslyaddictivemath.com
URL: http://www.samsingaporemath.com
Facebook: www.facebook.com/SeriouslyAddictiveMa
  thematicsOfGeorgia
Description: A math enrichment program modeled after Singapore Math Pedagogy for children ages 4-12. This program helps not only in conceptual mastery of curriculum but also in areas of lifelong learning skills and attitude development.

16170 ■ Scholars Education Centre
18 Cundles Rd. E, Unit 3
  Barrie, ON, Canada L4M 2Z5
Ph: (705)413-2609
Free: 888-901-7323
Co. E-mail: barrie@scholarsed.com
URL: http://www.scholarsed.com
Contact: Ted Kalnins, President
Facebook: www.facebook.com/ScholarsBarrie
Linkedin: www.linkedin.com/company/scholars-educa
  tion-centre
X (Twitter): x.com/scholarsec
Instagram: www.instagram.com/scholars_ed
Description: Offers Personalized Programs targeting the individual needs of students and their families. Credible, standardized Canadian assessments are used to obtain the information needed to personalize the student's program. **No. of Franchise Units:** 8. **No. of Company-Owned Units:** 3. **Founded:** 1999. **Franchised:** 2000. **Equity Capital Needed:** $50,000-$80,000 plus applicable taxes. **Franchise Fee:** $25,000 plus applicable taxes. **Training:** Online tutoring center.

16171 ■ School is Easy Tutoring
100 York Blvd., Ste. 400
  Richmond Hill, ON, Canada L4B 1J8
Free: 855-996-9977
Co. E-mail: info@schooliseasy.com
URL: http://www.schooliseasy.com

Facebook: www.facebook.com/schooliseasy
Linkedin: www.linkedin.com/company/school-is-easy
  -tutoring-academic-advantage-tutoring
X (Twitter): x.com/SIEtutoring
Instagram: www.instagram.com/schooliseasy.tutoring
Description: Offers tailor-made tutoring services to address each student's needs, goals, and capacity. **Founded:** 2002.

16172 ■ Stemtree
Vienna, VA
Ph: (703)281-7836
Co. E-mail: stem@stemtree.com
URL: http://stemtree.com
Contact: Abdelghani Bellaachia, Chief Executive Officer
Facebook: www.facebook.com/k12stemtree
X (Twitter): x.com/k12stemtree

16173 ■ Sylvan Learning Center
4 N Park Dr.Ste.500
  Hunt Valley, MD 21030
Free: 888-338-2283
URL: http://www.sylvanlearning.com/Locations/cen
  ters-by-state?state=Texas&stateabbr=TX
Contact: Emily Levitt, Vice President
Facebook: www.facebook.com/SylvanLearning
X (Twitter): twitter.com/SylvanLearning
Instagram: www.instagram.com/sylvanlearningcen
  ters
YouTube: www.youtube.com/user/sylvanlearninginc
Description: Offers services that supplements education programs in reading, mathematics, and other subjects for both children and adults. **No. of Franchise Units:** 890. **No. of Company-Owned Units:** 40. **Founded:** 1979. **Franchised:** 1980. **Equity Capital Needed:** $188,000-$305,000. **Franchise Fee:** $42,000-$48,000. **Training:** Training at corporate headquarters and locally. Basic training, regional training, regional meetings, and annual conferences.

16174 ■ Tutor Doctor
830 Dixon Rd.
  Toronto, ON, Canada M9W 5Z5
Ph: (647)490-3089
Free: 888-718-8832
Co. E-mail: info@tutordoctor.com
URL: http://www.tutordoctor.com
Contact: Kristine DeWolf, Chief Executive Officer
Description: Provides one-to-one in-home and online tutoring for all ages and all subjects. **Founded:** 2000.

16175 ■ The Tutoring Center Franchise Corp.
4300 Long Beach Blvd., Ste. 510
  Long Beach, CA 90807
Ph: (562)653-4380
URL: http://www.tutoringcenter.com
Contact: Edward Thalheimer, Contact
Linkedin: www.linkedin.com/company/the-tutoring
  -center-franchise-corp
X (Twitter): x.com/TutoringCorp
Description: Offers customized tutoring services for children. **Founded:** 1994.

16176 ■ Tutoring Club L.L.C. (TC)
11241 S E Ave.
  Henderson, NV 89052
Ph: (702)588-5280
Co. E-mail: hendersonnv@tutoringclub.com
URL: http://www.tutoringclub.com
Contact: Margot Gandy, Director
Facebook: www.facebook.com/therealtutoringclub
X (Twitter): x.com/TutorUp
Instagram: www.instagram.com/TutoringClubLV

Description: Center providing individualized after-school instruction. **Founded:** 1991. **Equity Capital Needed:** $114,900 - $190,300. **Franchise Fee:** $34,500. **Royalty Fee:** 10% of Gross Monthly Revenue. **Financial Assistance:** Yes **Training:** Offers 2 weeks at headquarters, 1 day onsite with ongoing support.

LIBRARIES

16177 ■ American Federation of Teachers (AFT) - Library
555 New Jersey Ave. NW
  Washington, DC 20001
Ph: (202)879-4400
Free: 800-238-1133
Co. E-mail: servicedesk@aft.org
URL: http://www.aft.org
Contact: Randi Weingarten, President
Facebook: www.facebook.com/AFTunion
X (Twitter): x.com/AFTunion
YouTube: www.youtube.com/user/afthq
Description: Affiliated with the AFL-CIO. Works with teachers and other educational employees at the state and local level in organizing, collective bargaining, research, educational issues, and public relations. **Scope:** Unions; education; teachers. **Founded:** 1916. **Holdings:** Figures not available. **Publications:** *American Educator* (Quarterly; Semiannual); *American Academic*; *Healthwire* (Quarterly); *On Campus* (Quarterly); *PSRP Reporter* (Quarterly); *American Teacher* (Monthly); *Zephyrhills News* (Weekly (Thurs.)). **Educational Activities:** AFT TEACH Conference (Biennial). **Awards:** AFT Robert G. Porter Scholars Program for High School Students (Quadrennial). **Geographic Preference:** National.

16178 ■ Oakland University-School of Education and Human Services-Educational Resources Laboratory - Library
Pawley Hall, Rm. 350
  456 Pioneer Dr.
  Rochester, MI 48309-4482
Ph: (248)370-2485
Fax: (248)370-4226
Co. E-mail: erl@oakland.edu
URL: http://oakland.edu/erl
Contact: Melissa Kempski, Coordinator
Facebook: www.facebook.com/ERLatOU
X (Twitter): x.com/ouERL

Scope: Children's and young adult literature. **Services:** Wireless computer lab; presentation equipment; laminator; book binder; poster maker; guest memberships with borrowing privileges available for purchase. **Founded:** 1962. **Holdings:** 30,000 books, journals, videotapes, DVDs, digital cameras and camcorders, and desktop and laptop computers.

16179 ■ Traverse City Regional Educational Media Center - REMC 2 Central - Library
1101 Red Dr.
  Traverse City, MI 49684
URL: http://www.northwested.org/services/remc
Contact: Danielle Humphrey, Contact
E-mail: dhumphrey@northwested.org
Scope: Education. **Services:** Copying (with fee); open to the public with restrictions. **Founded:** 1968. **Holdings:** 15,000 videocassettes; books.

Typesetting Business

ASSOCIATIONS AND OTHER ORGANIZATIONS

16180 ■ **Printing Brokerage/Buyers Association International (PB/BA) - Library**
1530 Locust St., Mezzanine 124
Philadelphia, PA 19102
Ph: (215)821-6581
URL: http://pbba.org
Description: Promotes understanding, cooperation, and interaction among members while obtaining the highest standard of professionalism in the graphic arts industry. **Scope:** Printing and publishing marketing and corporate development specialists, whose services include start ups, joint ventures, acquisitions, mergers, contract negotiation, international trade, seminars, workshops, facilities planning, and cost reduction programs. Serves private industries as well as government agencies. **Founded:** 1985. **Holdings:** Figures not available. **Publications:** "Hot Markets for 2007-2008," Jan, 2005. **Training:** How to Sell Printing Effectively; Sales Compensation and Management; How to Buy Printing Effectively; Hot Markets; International Priority Commerce. **Awards:** PBBA Printing Broker Reseller of the Year (Annual). **Geographic Preference:** Multinational. **Special Services:** Findprint®; Salesort®.

16181 ■ **Type Directors Club (TDC)**
450 W 31 St., 6th Fl.
New York, NY 10001
Ph: (917)509-2291
Co. E-mail: tdc@oneclub.org
URL: http://www.tdc.org
Contact: Carol Wahler, Executive Director
Facebook: www.facebook.com/TypeDirectorsClub
Linkedin: www.linkedin.com/company/type-directors
-club
X (Twitter): x.com/typedirectors
Instagram: www.instagram.com/typedirectorsclub
YouTube: www.youtube.com/channel/UCjKXDLrb
6mrftD1NW-r4l5w
Pinterest: www.pinterest.com/typedirectors
Description: Serves as a professional society of typographic designers, type directors, and teachers of typography; sustaining members are individuals with interests in typographic education. Seeks to stimulate research and disseminate information. Provides speakers, classes and offers presentations on history and new developments in typography. **Founded:** 1946. **Awards:** TDC Student Award; TDC Scholarship (Annual); Type Directors Club Medal (Periodic). **Geographic Preference:** Multinational.

REFERENCE WORKS

16182 ■ *"Agfa To Debut New: M-Press Leopard" in American Printer (Vol. 128, June 1, 2011, No. 6)*
Description: M-Press Leopard is a new version of the machine that offers advanced ink jet technology at a lower price point. Agfa Graphics introduced the new version that allows for new applications that require more manual handling. **Availability:** Print; Online.

16183 ■ *"Avanti Hosts 19th Annual User's Conference in Washington, DC" in American Printer (Vol. 128, July 1, 2011, No. 7)*
Description: Avanti Computer Systems Ltd. hosted its 19th annual users conference in Washington DC. In-plant and commercial printers were in attendance. **Availability:** Online.

16184 ■ *"Avoid a Tablet Generation Gap" in American Printer (Vol. 128, July 1, 2011, No. 7)*
Description: Individuals between the ages of 18-34 are the only generation that is more likely to own a laptop computer or netbook insead of a desktop computer. Statistical data included. **Availability:** Online.

16185 ■ *"ContiTech Celebrates 100 Years" in American Printer (Vol. 128, July 1, 2011, No. 7)*
Description: ContiTech celebrated 100 years in business. The firm started in 1911 after developing the first elastic printing blanket. Other milestones for the firm include its manufacturing process for compressible printing blankets, the Conti-Air brand and climate-neutral printing blankets. **Availability:** Print; Online.

16186 ■ *"Crouser Releases Offline UV Coating Price Report" in American Printer (Vol. 128, June 1, 2011, No. 6)*
Description: Crouser and Associates will offer the 'Pricing Off-Line UV Coating' report that provides background information on all three types of protective printing coatings and price guidance. The report will also offer comparisons of four popular types of offline equipment.

16187 ■ *"Design Center Shows Quality of Digital Paper" in American Printer (Vol. 128, June 1, 2011, No. 6)*
Description: Digital Design Centers allows printers to customize marketing tools in order to promote their own digital printing capabilities. **Availability:** Online.

16188 ■ *"Digital Printing Walks the Plank" in American Printer (Vol. 128, August 1, 2011, No. 8)*
Description: Digital print manufacturing is discussed. **Availability:** Online.

16189 ■ *"Feeding the Elephants While Searching for Greener Pastures" in American Printer (Vol. 128, July 1, 2011, No. 7)*
Ed: Bob Rosen. **Description:** Three steps to help printers to build a new business while facing the challenges to the existing business are outlined. **Availability:** Print.

16190 ■ *"Flint Group Raises Prices of Offset Inks in EMEA" in American Printer (Vol. 128, August 1, 2011, No. 8)*
Description: Due to the rising cost for raw materials, Flint Group is raising their prices for inks and coatings in North American. **Availability:** Online.

16191 ■ *"Four Exhibition Considerations" in American Printer (Vol. 128, August 1, 2011, No. 8)*
Description: Four questions to ask at the Graph Expo will help printers improve their own business. **Availability:** Print; Download; PDF.

16192 ■ *"Fujifilm Invites Printers to Take the 'Onset Challenge" in American Printer (Vol. 128, August 1, 2011, No. 8)*
Description: Fujifilm North American Corporation's Graphic Systems Division offers a new five-step product selection and return-on-investment calculator for the Onset family of wide-format printers. **Availability:** Online.

16193 ■ *"Graphic Tech Acquires First U.S. :M-Press Tiger with Inline Screen Printing" in American Printer (Vol. 128, June 1, 2011, No. 6)*
Description: Graphic Tech located in California bought M-Press Tiger, the first in North America with an inline screen printing unit. **Availability:** Online.

16194 ■ *"Interchangeable or Irreplaceable?" in American Printer (Vol. 128, August 1, 2011, No. 8)*
Description: Creating and maintaining customers is important for all graphic design and printing companies. Tips are shared to help maintain good customer satisfaction and repeat business. **Availability:** Online.

16195 ■ *"KBA, Graphic Art System Partner on Cold Foil" in American Printer (Vol. 128, June 1, 2011, No. 6)*
Description: KBA North America has partnered with Graphic Art System to retrofit and equip presses with cold foil machines. **Availability:** Online.

16196 ■ *"Kodak Offers Cloud-Based Operating Option" in American Printer (Vol. 128, June 1, 2011, No. 6)*
Description: Kodak partnered with VMware to offer its first Virtual Operating Environment option for Kodak Unified Workflow Solutions. The new feature enables cost savings, increased efficiency and failover protection. **Availability:** Online.

16197 ■ *Literary Market Place: The Directory of the American Book Publishing Industry*
Pub: Information Today Inc.
Contact: Thomas H. Hogan, President
URL(s): store.infotoday.com/product/literary-marke
t-place
Released: Latest edition 84th Edition 2024. **Price:** $539.50, for outside North America; $529.50, for Canada or Mexico; $507.50, Individuals. **Description:** Covers over 12,500 firms or organizations offering services related to the publishing industry, including book publishers in the United States and Canada who issued three or more books during the preceding year, plus a small press section of publishers who publish less than three titles per year or those who

are self-published. Also included: book printers and binders; book clubs; book trade and literary associations; selected syndicates, newspapers, periodicals, and radio and TV programs that use book reviews or book publishing news; translators and literary agents. **Entries include:** For publishers--Company name, address, phone, address for orders, principal executives, editorial directors, and managers, date founded, number of titles in previous year, number of backlist titles in print, types of books published, ISBN prefixes, representatives, imprints, and affiliations. For suppliers, etc.--Listings usually show firm name, address, phone, executives, services, etc. **Arrangement:** Classified by line of business. **Indexes:** Principal index is 35,000-item combined index of publishers, publications, and personnel; several sections have geographical and/or subject indexes; translators are indexed by source and target language. **Availability:** Print; Online.

16198 ■ "New Approach to Mechanical Binding" in American Printer (Vol. 128, July 1, 2011, No. 7)
Description: EcoBinder coil binding system from Kugler-Womako eliminates traditional plastic combs or wire spiral with the use of 22-mm wide printable paper rings. **Availability:** Online.

16199 ■ "New Typesetting Technology from Scholastica Propels Freer Future for Academic Journals" in EurekAlert! (February 8, 2018)
URL(s): www.eurekalert.org/pub_releases/2018-02/s-ntt020718.php
Released: February 08, 2018. **Description:** A new typesetting service for open access journals has been launched by Scholastica. Article formatting will be automatic making it much easier on users to created PDF and HTML articles. **Availability:** Online.

16200 ■ "One World" in American Printer (Vol. 128, August 1, 2011, No. 8)
Description: Graph Expo will highlight entrepreneurs focused on the connection between content, technology and business models. **Availability:** Print; Online.

16201 ■ "Paper Replaces PVC for Gift Cards" in American Printer (Vol. 128, June 1, 2011, No. 6)
Description: Monadnock Envi Card Stock replaces paper for gift cards, loyalty cards, membership cards, hotel keys and durable signage. This renewable wood fiber alternative to PVC card materials comes from Monadnock Paper Mills. **Availability:** Online.

16202 ■ "PrintCity Shares Guide for Carbon Footprinting" in American Printer (Vol. 128, June 1, 2011, No. 6)
Description: PrintCity Alliance published its new report, 'Carbon Footprint & Energy Reduction for Graphic Industry Value Chain.' The report aims to help improve the environmental performance of printers, converters, publishers, brand owners and their suppliers. **Availability:** Online.

16203 ■ "Printers to the Trade" in American Printer (Vol. 128, July 1, 2011, No. 7)
Description: Wholesale printing is discussed. Two wholesale printers share insight into their success, from business philosophies in general to practices that build strong relationships. **Availability:** Online.

16204 ■ "Reducing the Book's Carbon Footprint" in American Printer (Vol. 128, July 1, 2011, No. 7)
Description: Green Press Initiative's Book Industry Environmental Council is working to achieve a 20 percent reduction in the book industry's carbon footprint by 2020. The Council is made up of publishers, printers, paper suppliers, and non-governmental organizations. **Availability:** Online.

16205 ■ "Sappi Announces North American 'Printers of the Year' Gold Winners" in American Printer (Vol. 128, July 1, 2011, No. 7)
Description: Sappi Fine Paper North America honored ten gold winners of its 14th North American

Printers of the Year awards. Each gold winning printer will receive $20,000 to support marketing and brand initiatives. **Availability:** Print; Online.

16206 ■ "Seeing the Light" in American Printer (Vol. 128, July 1, 2011, No. 7)
Description: Four printing demos on sheetfed, digital, label and pad printing equipment were highlighted at the Fifth UV Days held in Stuttgart, Germany in May 2011. **Availability:** Online.

16207 ■ "Seven Tips for Continuous Improvement" in American Printer (Vol. 128, July 1, 2011, No. 7)
Description: Seven tips are given to help any graphic arts or printing company improve by integrating lean manufacturing into operations. **Availability:** Online.

16208 ■ "Successful First Year for Twin Rivers" in American Printer (Vol. 128, June 1, 2011, No. 6)
Description: Profile of Twin Rivers located in Maine. The firm manufactured 380,000 tons of free sheet and hybrid-groundwood papers in its first year. **Availability:** Online.

16209 ■ "Tic-Tac-Show: Line Up the Opportunities at Graph Expo" in American Printer (Vol. 128, August 1, 2011, No. 8)
Description: Graph Expo has become the US print industry's main event. There will be as many as 500 exhibitors at this year's event and the Graphic Arts Show Company lists over 30 co-located events as well as 53 new sessions in the seminar program's 28 education categories. **Availability:** PDF; Online.

16210 ■ "Transcontinental to Exchange Assets with Quad/Graphics" in American Printer (Vol. 128, August 1, 2011, No. 8)
Description: Transcontinental Inc. and Quad/Graphics Inc. entered into an agreement where Transcontinental will indirectly acquire all shares of Quad Graphics Canada Inc. **Availability:** Print; Online.

16211 ■ "Try a Little Social Media" in American Printer (Vol. 128, June 1, 2011, No. 6)
Description: Social media helps keep Ussery Printing on customers radar. Jim David, VP of marketing for the firm, states that 350 people following them on Facebook are from the local area. **Availability:** Print; Mailing list; Online.

16212 ■ "Web to Print" in American Printer (Vol. 128, August 1, 2011, No. 8)
Description: Jerry Kennelly, CEO and founder of Tweak.com believes that Web-to-Design is middleware with no content. His firm offers an easy to use interface that flows right into the printer's workflow with no additional costs. **Availability:** Online.

STATISTICAL SOURCES

16213 ■ RMA Annual Statement Studies
Pub: Risk Management Association
Contact: Nancy Foster, President
Released: Annual. **Description:** Contains composite balance sheets and income statements for more than 360 industries, including the accounting, auditing, and bookkeeping industries. Also contains five years of comparative historical data for discerning trends. Includes 16 commonly used ratios, computed for most of the size groupings for nearly every industry.

TRADE SHOWS AND CONVENTIONS

16214 ■ Graphics of the Americas
Florida Graphics Alliance (FGA)
10524 Moss Pk. Rd., Ste. 204
Orlando, FL 32822
Ph: (407)240-8009
Co. E-mail: gabe@floridagraphics.org
URL: http://www.floridagraphics.org
Contact: Art Abbott, Contact

E-mail: art@abbottcg.com
URL(s): www.floridagraphics.org/member-news
X (Twitter): twitter.com/goaexpo
Description: Graphic arts and specialty printing equipment, supplies, and services. **Audience:** Commercial printers, digital printers, label printers, wide format printers, graphic designers, screen printers, packaging printers, specialty printers, sign printers, book printers, publishers, binders, converting professionals, print and media buyers. **Principal Exhibits:** Graphic arts and specialty printing equipment, supplies, and services.

LIBRARIES

16215 ■ Carnegie Mellon University-Special Collections
5000 Forbes Ave.
Pittsburgh, PA 15213-3890
Ph: (412)268-2444
URL: http://www.library.cmu.edu/distinctive-collections/special-collections
Contact: Samuel Lemley, Curator
Description: Contains many of Carnegie Mellon University's rare and unique materials and the rare book collection. **Scope:** History of science; cryptology; computing; early Shakespeare editions; graphic arts. **Services:** Library open to the public. **Founded:** 1964. **Holdings:** Books.

16216 ■ Cleveland Public Library Literature Department
Main Bldg., 2nd Fl.
325 Superior Ave.
Cleveland, OH 44114
Ph: (216)623-2881
Co. E-mail: literature@cpl.org
URL: http://cpl.org/aboutthelibrary/subjectscollections/literature
Contact: Donald Boozer, Manager
Scope: World Literature and Criticism; Fiction; Poetry; Drama and Theater; Film; Television and Radio and much more. **Services:** Department open to the public; Interlibrary loan. **Founded:** 1869. **Holdings:** 500,000 volumes.

16217 ■ Free Library of Philadelphia-Social Science & History Department
1901 Vine St., Rm 201
Philadelphia, PA 19103
Ph: (215)686-5396
URL: http://libwww.freelibrary.org/locations/departments/social-science-and-history-department
Scope: History; biography; social sciences; law; travels and geography; archaeology; anthropology; sports; criminology. **Services:** Interlibrary loan. **Founded:** 1953. **Holdings:** Books; pamphlets; newspapers; government documents; ephemera; 414,000 biographies.

16218 ■ Grolier Club of New York Library
47 E 60th St.
New York, NY 10022
Ph: (212)838-6690
Fax: (212)838-2445
Co. E-mail: assistantlibrarian@grolierclub.org
URL: http://www.grolierclub.org/Default.aspx?p=DynamicModule&pageid=384831&ssid=322452&vnf=1
Contact: Meghan Constantinou, Librarian
E-mail: mconstantinou@grolierclub.org
Facebook: www.facebook.com/grolierclub
X (Twitter): x.com/GrolierClub
Instagram: www.instagram.com/grolierclub
Scope: Art and history; literature. **Services:** Library open to the public with restrictions. **Founded:** 1884. **Holdings:** 100,000 volumes; 5,000 prints and portraits; bookplates. **Subscriptions:** 100 journals and other serials.

16219 ■ Rochester Institute of Technology - Melbert B. Cary, Jr. Graphic Arts Collection
90 Lomb Memorial Dr.
Rochester, NY 14623
URL: http://archivesspace.rit.edu/repositories/2/resources/235

Scope: Graphic art. **Holdings:** 45,000 volumes.

16220 ■ Yale University - Robert B. Haas Family Arts Library Special Collections
190 York St.
  New Haven, CT 06520
Ph: (203)432-2645
Co. E-mail: artds.library@yale.edu

URL: http://web.library.yale.edu/arts/special-collec
  tions
Facebook: www.facebook.com/YaleHaasArtsLib
X (Twitter): twitter.com/YaleHaasArtsLib
Instagram: www.instagram.com/YaleHaasArtsLib/

Description: The collection includes contemporary catalogue raisonnes, 18th- and 19th-century works on artists and architecture, a wide selection of fine press and artists' books, rare research stuff in support of these subject areas, and the Faber Birren collection on color. **Scope:** Art history; drama. **Services:** Collection open to the public. **Founded:** 1967. **Holdings:** 125,000 volumes; prints and broadsides; type specimens; archive of student printing, including masters' theses from School of Graphic Design and School of Photography at Yale; 1 million bookplates; Japanese prints; stage and costume designs.

ASSOCIATIONS AND OTHER ORGANIZATIONS

16221 ■ NALS The Association for Legal Professionals (NALS)
3502 Woodview Trace, Ste. 300
Indianapolis, IN 46268
Ph: (918)582-5188
Fax: (918)582-5907
Co. E-mail: info@nals.org
URL: http://www.nals.org
Contact: Amylyn Riedling, President
Facebook: www.facebook.com/NALSpage
Linkedin: www.linkedin.com/company/nalsinc
X (Twitter): x.com/NALStweet

Description: Provides continuing legal education and resource materials, networking opportunities, and professional certification programs and designations for legal support professionals. Consists of members who represent every area of the industry from paralegals and legal assistants to legal administrators and office managers. Aims to enhance the careers of legal secretaries. Offers professional development by providing continuing legal education, certifications, information, and training. **Founded:** 1929. **Educational Activities:** National Association of Legal Secretaries International Forum and Education Conference (Annual); NALS Annual Education & Networking Conference (Annual). **Geographic Preference:** National.

16222 ■ National Court Reporters Association (NCRA)
12030 Sunrise Valley Dr., Ste. 400
Reston, VA 20191
Ph: (703)556-6272
Free: 800-272-6272
Fax: (703)391-0629
Co. E-mail: membership@ncra.org
URL: http://www.ncra.org
Contact: Debra A. Dibble, President
Facebook: www.facebook.com/NCRAfb
Linkedin: www.linkedin.com/company/nationalcour
treportersassociation
X (Twitter): x.com/NCRA
YouTube: www.youtube.com/user/NCRAonline

Description: Represents independent state, regional, and local associations. Verbatim court reporters who work as official reporters for courts and government agencies, as freelance reporters for independent contractors, and as captioners for television programming; retired reporters, teachers of court reporting, and school officials; student court reporters. **Founded:** 1899. **Publications:** *National Court Reporters Association--The Court Reporters Sourcebook* (Annual). **Educational Activities:** NCRA Convention & Expo (Annual). **Awards:** Distinguished Service Award (Annual); NCRA Fellow of the Academy of Professional Reporters (FAPR) (Annual); CASE Award of Excellence (Annual); National Court Reporters Association Student Intern Scholarship (Annual); NCRF New Professional Reporter Grant (Annual); NCRA Endorsers of the Year (Annual). **Geographic Preference:** National.

16223 ■ SEIU - District 925
1914 N 34th St.
Seattle, WA 98103
Ph: (206)322-3010
Free: 877-734-8673
Co. E-mail: action@seiu925.org
URL: http://www.seiu925.org
Contact: Tricia Schroeder, President
Facebook: www.facebook.com/seiu925
X (Twitter): x.com/SEIU925
Instagram: www.instagram.com/seiu925

Description: National union of secretaries, stenographers, typists, clerks, and other office, technical, and professional workers in the U.S. Promotes collective bargaining for office workers and sponsors research and educational programs on pay equality, automation, and career advancement. Seeks to organize the nearly 20 million office workers in the U.S.; compiles statistics. **Founded:** 1981. **Geographic Preference:** Local.

16224 ■ Society for Corporate Governance
52 Vanderbilt Ave., Ste. 903
New York, NY 10017
Ph: (212)681-2000
Fax: (212)681-2005
URL: http://www.societycorpgov.org/home
Contact: Darla C. Stuckey, President
E-mail: dstuckey@societycorpgov.org
Facebook: www.facebook.com/societycorpgov
Linkedin: www.linkedin.com/company/socie
tyforcorporategovernance
X (Twitter): x.com/search
YouTube: www.youtube.com/user/SocietyCorpSec

Description: Members are corporate secretaries, assistant secretaries, officers and executives of corporations and others interested in corporate practices and procedures. Promotes responsible corporate governance, providing news, research and "best practice" advice and providing professional development and education through seminars and conferences. **Founded:** 1946. **Publications:** *Proxy Contacts: Brokers, Banks, Depositories, Proxy Agents* (Annual); *Nominee List* (Irregular); *The Corporate Secretary.* **Educational Activities:** Society of Corporate Secretaries and Governance Professionals Annual Conference (Annual). **Geographic Preference:** National.

REFERENCE WORKS

16225 ■ *"Court Reporting: More Than Just Typing Fast" in Huseby (March 4, 2019)*
URL(s): www.huseby.com/blog/2019/court-reporting
-more-than-just-typing-fast
Ed: Brittany Clarke. **Released:** March 04, 2019. **Description:** Explains what a court reporter does and the equipment that is used. The stenograph is not the same as a regular keyboard and stenographers need to learn the phonetic steno language, which is more than just simply learning to type really fast. It's a whole system that has to be mastered before a stenographer can work in the courtroom. **Availability:** Online.

START-UP INFORMATION

16226 ■ *"Chem-Dry Carpet Cleaning Franchise on Pace for 120 New Locations In 2014" in Internet Wire (September 16, 2014)*
Pub: Comtex News Network Inc.
Contact: Kan Devnani, President

Description: Chem-Dry carpet cleaning franchise is poised to record-setting growth for 2014 with 120 new franchisees. Entrepreneur Magazine named Chem-Dry as the No. 1 carpet cleaning franchise, as well as a top home-based business opportunity with low startup-costs. **Availability:** Online.

ASSOCIATIONS AND OTHER ORGANIZATIONS

16227 ■ **Society of Cleaning and Restoration Technicians (SCRT)**
303 White Oak Dr.
Wilmington, OH 45177
Free: 800-949-4728
Co. E-mail: info@scrt.org
URL: http://www.scrt.org
Contact: Dick Wagner, President
E-mail: dick@thecrestnetwork.com
Facebook: www.facebook.com/scrt.org
Linkedin: www.linkedin.com/company/society-of
-cleaning-and-restoration-technicians-scrt
X (Twitter): x.com/SCRTorg
Instagram: www.instagram.com/scrtassociation
YouTube: www.youtube.com/channel/UCTtFqV
55o07Rv3WAixyifjw

Description: Provides a forum for the exchange of technical and procedural information, including catastrophe restoration data, updates on new chemicals and processes, and technical, management, sales, and production materials. Monitors and reports on events affecting the carpet cleaning industry. Conducts workshops. **Founded:** 1970. **Publications:** *The Monitor* (Annual); *Technical* (5/year). **Geographic Preference:** National.

REFERENCE WORKS

16228 ■ *"Crossover Skills Give Upholsterers Business Opportunities in Many Markets" in Specialty Fabrics Review (August 1, 2017)*
URL(s): specialtyfabricsreview.com/2017/08/01/
crossover-skills-give-upholsterers-business-oppor
tunities-in-many-markets/

Ed: Janice Kleinschmidt. **Released:** August 01, 2017. **Description:** Describes the pitfalls of being too specialized in the upholstery business and how branching out can boost your bottom line. There is a need for upholstery but it covers several branches, such as automotive, marine, furniture, awnings, and even wall coverings. **Availability:** Online.

16229 ■ *"Reduce, Reuse, Recycle, Reupholster, Is Motto of Willmar, Minn., Upholstery Hobbyist Turned Pro" in West Central Tribune (August 14, 2012)*
Ed: David Little. **Description:** American craftsmanship in furniture is foremost to Mr. Rousseau, owner of PrairieUpholstery of Willmar, Minnesota. He learned to reupholster furniture from an expert and opened his own shop in the historic downtown district. Rousseau will reupholster new and used furniture, car and truck seats, as well as boat seats and he can repair canvas. He also will rent upholstery cleaning and carpet shampoo machines, as well as refinishing wood furniture. **Availability:** Online.

TRADE PERIODICALS

16230 ■ *Cleaning & Restoration*
Pub: Restoration Industry Association
Contact: Ben Looper, President
URL(s): www.candrmagazine.com
Facebook: www.facebook.com/CandRMagazine
Linkedin: www.linkedin.com/company/c-r-magazine
Instagram: www.instagram.com/candrmagazine
YouTube: www.youtube.com/channel/UCTcMp
tOovWyW7re6tvfYm6g
Released: Quarterly **Description:** Journal covering drapery, rug, upholstery, and carpet cleaning; fire and water damage; and disaster restoration and mechanical systems cleaning and inspection. **Availability:** Print; Online.

16231 ■ *Floor Trends*
Pub: BNP Media
Contact: Harper Henderson, Owner Co-Chief Executive Officer
URL(s): www.floortrendsmag.com
Facebook: www.facebook.com/FloorTrendsMag
Linkedin: www.linkedin.com/company/floor-trends
-mag
X (Twitter): x.com/floortrendsmag
Instagram: www.instagram.com/floortrendsmag
YouTube: www.youtube.com/floortrendsmag
Ed: Morgan Laidlaw. **Released:** Monthly **Description:** Trade magazine covering color & design trends for both commercial & residential professionals in the floor covering industry. **Availability:** Print.

CONSULTANTS

16232 ■ **Cleaning Consultant Services Inc. (CCS)**
PO Box 98757
Seattle, WA 98198
URL: http://www.cleaningbusiness.com
Contact: Bill Griffin, Founder

Description: Firm provides engineering and consulting services and deals with claim and dispute resolution, program and material development and cleaning services and also offers business solutions and support services for cleaning professionals, and publishes books on various areas of the cleaning industry. **Scope:** Firm provides engineering and consulting services and deals with claim and dispute resolution, program and material development and cleaning services and also offers business solutions and support services for cleaning professionals, and publishes books on various areas of the cleaning industry. **Founded:** 1973. **Publications:** "Raising the Bar with Science, Training and Upward Mobility," Jan, 2010; "Technology Revolutionizes the Cleaning Process "Cleaning for Health" is the New Mantra," Distribution Sales and Management Magazine, May, 2003; "Bill Griffin's Crystal Balls-Cleaning Trends in the Usa 2001," Floor Care is Hot in 2001," Mar, 2001; "Inclean Magazine (Australia), Feb, 2001; "Maintaining Swimming Pools, Spas, Whirlpool Tubs and Saunas," Executive House keeping, Feb, 2001; "Whats New with Floor Care," 2001. **Training:** Publisher of books and magazines.

FRANCHISES AND BUSINESS OPPORTUNITIES

16233 ■ **ChemDry Canada Ltd. (CDC)**
Chilliwack, BC, Canada
Free: 888-243-6379
Co. E-mail: info@chemdry.ca
URL: http://chemdry.ca
Facebook: www.facebook.com/ChemdryCanada
X (Twitter): x.com/chemdrycanada

Description: Provider of home cleaning services such as carpet, upholstery, rugs, pet urine odor removal, tile cleaning. **Founded:** 1978. **Training:** Provides5 days training, including travel and accommodation.

16234 ■ **Coit Services Inc. [Coit Cleaning and Restoration]**
897 Hinckley Rd.
Burlingame, CA 94010
Free: 800-367-2648
Co. E-mail: info@coit.com
URL: http://www.coit.com
Facebook: www.facebook.com/COITClean
Linkedin: www.linkedin.com/company/coit-services
X (Twitter): x.com/coitclean
Instagram: www.instagram.com/coitclean

Description: Provides cleaning services in upholstery, draperies, carpeting and other flooring surfaces. **No. of Franchise Units:** 42. **No. of Company-Owned Units:** 8. **Founded:** 1950. **Franchised:** 1962. **Equity Capital Needed:** $50,000-$145,000. **Franchise Fee:** $24,000-$40,000. **Financial Assistance:** Yes **Training:** Includes 10 days in corporate office.

16235 ■ **Creative Colors International (CCI)**
19015 S Jodi Rd., Ste. E
Mokena, IL 60448
Free: 800-933-2656
Co. E-mail: comments@creativecolorsintl.com
URL: http://wecanfixthat.com
Contact: Mark J. Bollman, President
Facebook: www.facebook.com/wecanfixthatccihq
X (Twitter): x.com/wecanfixthat

Instagram: www.instagram.com/creativecolorsintl
YouTube: www.youtube.com/user/ccicomments

Description: Specializes in providing services for the repair, coloring, cleaning and restoration of leather, vinyl, cloth, velor, plastics and other upholstery surfaces and related services on a mobile basis primarily to commercial customers. These customers include auto dealerships, hotels, airports and individuals. **Founded:** 1980. **Franchised:** 1991. **Franchise Fee:** $43,500. **Financial Assistance:** Yes **Training:** An initial training course of 3 weeks is conducted at National Headquarters. In addition, a field representative will spend 1 week with franchise owner when business commences operation to establish accounts.

16236 ■ Duraclean International Inc.
180 N La Salle St., Ste. 3200
 Chicago, IL 60601-2800
Contact: Danielle Canup, President

Description: Firm provides cleaning solutions for carpet, rugs, tile, furniture and upholstery. **Founded:** 1930. **Financial Assistance:** Yes **Training:** Initial training provides training manuals, videotapes, schools, local hands-on assistance, magazines, bulletins, conventions and area meetings and ongoing support.

16237 ■ Harris Research Inc. (HRI)
Harris Research Inc. (HRI)
 1530 N 1000 W
 Logan, UT 84321
Free: 800-243-6379
URL: http://www.chemdry.com
Contact: Roabert D. Harris, Contact

Description: They offer carpet cleaning service. **No. of Franchise Units:** 3500.0. **Founded:** 1977. **Franchised:** 1978. **Equity Capital Needed:** $13,300 – 155,534. **Franchise Fee:** $21,500. **Royalty Fee:** $392.73/month. **Financial Assistance:** Yes **Training:** Provides 5 days at headquarters, video training and ongoing support.

16238 ■ Heaven's Best Carpet & Upholstery Cleaning
247 N 1st St., E
 Rexburg, ID 83440
Ph: (208)359-1106
Free: 800-359-2095
Co. E-mail: mcoinc@heavensbest.com
URL: http://www.heavensbest.com
Facebook: www.facebook.com/heavensbest.carpe
 tcleaning

Pinterest: www.pinterest.com/heavensbestfranchise

Description: Provides carpet cleaning services. **No. of Franchise Units:** 1,264. **Founded:** 1983. **Franchised:** 1983. **Equity Capital Needed:** $28,900-$65,000. **Franchise Fee:** $14,450. **Financial Assistance:** Yes **Training:** Yes.

16239 ■ Interior Magic International L.L.C.
211 Cotton Grove Rd.
 Lexington, NC 27292
Contact: Steven Raguz, Manager

Description: Provider of automotive repair services. **Founded:** 2001. **Training:** Yes.

16240 ■ Langenwalter Carpet Dyeing
1111 S Richfield Rd.
 Placentia, CA 92870-6790
Free: 800-422-4370
Co. E-mail: info@langenwalter.com
URL: http://langdye.com

Description: Complete carpet color correction, including bleach spots, sun fading, pet stains, food stains, punch and other discolorations. Also, complete color changes and full wall-to-wall carpet dyeing. **No. of Franchise Units:** 65. **No. of Company-Owned Units:** 2. **Founded:** 1978. **Franchised:** 1980. **Equity Capital Needed:** $42,000 Minimum. **Franchise Fee:** $12,500. **Training:** Yes.

16241 ■ Modernistic Cleaning LLC
1460 Rankin Dr.
 Troy, MI 48083
Free: 800-609-1000
Co. E-mail: info@modernistic.com
URL: http://www.modernistic.com
Facebook: www.facebook.com/ModernisticCleaning
X (Twitter): x.com/modernistic_mi
Instagram: www.instagram.com/modernisticcleaning
YouTube: www.youtube.com/user/modernistic123

Description: Firm is a carpet and upholstery cleaning company. **Founded:** 1972. **Financial Assistance:** Yes **Training:** Yes.

16242 ■ Professional Carpet Systems Inc. (PCS)
Raleigh, NC 27604
Ph: (919)324-6621
URL: http://pcsraleigh.com
Facebook: www.facebook.com/pcsmorrisville/book

Description: Onsite carpet re-dyeing, servicing thousands of apartment complexes, hotels and motels worldwide. Other services include carpet cleaning, rejuvenation, repair, water and flood dam-

age restoration and odor control. **Founded:** 1978. **Financial Assistance:** Yes **Training:** 2 weeks in Raleigh, NC for initial training. Eleven 2 day sessions are held every year for additional training, most with industry certification available. In addition, we have periodic workshops and an annual convention. During the training program, franchisees gain hands-on experience.

16243 ■ Servpro Industries, Inc.
801 Industrial Blvd.
 Gallatin, TN 37066
Ph: (615)451-0200
Fax: (615)675-2312
Co. E-mail: franchisesales@servpronet.com
URL: http://www.servpro.com
Contact: Rick Forster, President
Facebook: www.facebook.com/SERVPRO
Linkedin: www.linkedin.com/company/servpro-indus
 tries
X (Twitter): x.com/servpro
YouTube: www.youtube.com/user/
 SERVPROCorporate

Description: Provider of cleaning and restoration services. **Founded:** 1967. **Educational Activities:** PLRB Claims Conference & Insurance Services Expo (Annual).

16244 ■ Sparkle Carpet Cleaning

Description: Cleaners of carpet and upholstery. **No. of Franchise Units:** 2. **No. of Company-Owned Units:** 5. **Founded:** 1981. **Equity Capital Needed:** $10,000-$15,000. **Franchise Fee:** $5,000-$9,000. **Royalty Fee:** $75-150/month. **Training:** Yes.

16245 ■ Stanley Steemer International Inc.
5800 Innovation Dr.
 Dublin, OH 43016
Free: 800-783-3637
URL: http://www.stanleysteemer.com
Contact: Jack A. Bates, Founder
Facebook: www.facebook.com/stanleysteemer
Linkedin: www.linkedin.com/company/stanley-s
 teemer
X (Twitter): x.com/stanleysteemer
YouTube: www.youtube.com/user/stanleysteemer

Description: Firm provides residential and commercial cleaning services such as carpet, furniture, tiles and grout cleaning. **Founded:** 1947. **Financial Assistance:** Yes

Vending Machine Merchandising and Service Business

ASSOCIATIONS AND OTHER ORGANIZATIONS

16246 ■ Association Canadienne d'Auto Distribution (ACAD) [Canadian Automatic Merchandising Association (CAMA)]
2233 Argentia Rd., No. 304
Mississauga, ON, Canada L5N 2X7
Ph: (905)826-7695
Free: 888-849-2262
Fax: (905)826-4873
Co. E-mail: info@vending-cama.com
URL: http://www.vending-cama.com
Contact: Jim Jackson, President
X (Twitter): x.com/CAMA_Vending

Description: Corporations and individuals engaged in the vending industry. Promotes growth and development of the automatic merchandising market. Represents members' interests before industrial organizations, government agencies, and the public. **Geographic Preference:** National.

16247 ■ National Automatic Merchandising Association (NAMA)
1777 N Kent St., Ste. 1010
Arlington, VA 22209
Ph: (571)349-0149
Fax: (571)349-0138
Co. E-mail: memberinfo@namanow.org
URL: http://namanow.org
Contact: Carla Balakgie, President
E-mail: cbalakgie@vending.org
Facebook: www.facebook.com/NAMANow
Linkedin: www.linkedin.com/company/2398993
X (Twitter): x.com/namavending
Instagram: www.instagram.com/nama_now
YouTube: www.youtube.com/c/NAMANow

Description: Manufacturing and operating companies in the automatic vending machine industry; food service management firms; office coffee machine operators; suppliers of products and services. Compiles industry statistics. **Founded:** 1936. **Publications:** *National Automatic Merchandising Association-In Touch* (Quarterly); *National Automatic Merchandising Association--Directory of Members* (Annual). **Educational Activities:** The NAMA Show (Annual). **Awards:** NAMA Foundation Scholarship Program (Annual). **Geographic Preference:** National; Regional.

16248 ■ National Bulk Vendors Association (NBVA)
380 Terra Cotta Rd., Ste. F
Crystal Lake, IL 60012
Ph: (815)526-3758
Fax: (815)893-6248
Co. E-mail: admin@nbva.org
URL: http://nbva.org
Contact: David Kochan, President
Facebook: www.facebook.com/NBVA.Na
tionalBulkVendorsAssociation

Description: Manufacturers, distributors, and operators of bulk vending merchandise and equipment. **Founded:** 1950. **Educational Activities:** NBVA Conference & Tradeshow (Annual). **Geographic Preference:** National.

REFERENCE WORKS

16249 ■ Automatic Merchandiser--Blue Book Buyer's Guide Issue
Contact: Michael Martin, President
URL(s): www.vendingmarketwatch.com/directorywww
.vendingmarketwatch.com

Ed: Elliot Maras. **Released:** Annual **Description:** Publication includes suppliers of products, services, and equipment to the merchandise vending, contract foodservice, and office coffee service industries. **Entries include:** Company name, address, phone, names of executives, trade and brand names, and products or services offered. **Arrangement:** Classified by type of business. **Indexes:** Alphabetical, product. **Availability:** Print; Online.

16250 ■ "AVT Featured on TD Waterhouse Market News Website and in Vending Times Magazine" in Benzinga.com (August 17, 2011)
Pub: PR Newswire Association LLC.

Description: AVT Inc. was featured online and in an article reporting the firm's plan to install automated vending machines in high-profile areas including malls, office buildings, stadiums and arenas.

16251 ■ "AVT Launches New ExpressPay Vending Systems" in Benzinga.com (July 13, 2011)

Description: AVT Inc. has developed a new high-tech vending system that features a touch screen interface and a cashless payment system so users can find what they want easily and pay using a credit card. **Availability:** Print; Online.

16252 ■ "Baltimore Vendors Brave Heat, Red Tape to Eke Out a Living: Working the Streets" in Baltimore Business Journal (Vol. 28, July 30, 2010, No. 12, pp. 1)
Pub: Baltimore Business Journal
Contact: Rhonda Pringle, President
E-mail: rpringle@bizjournals.com

Ed: Amanda Pino. **Description:** Reports show that street vendors are popping up on new corners in Baltimore, Maryland, with city-inspected stainless steel food carts in tow. Applications for street vending licenses shot up at the end of 2009 and into this summer. It is believed that pinning down the exact number of vendors operating at any one point is difficult. **Availability:** Print.

16253 ■ "Bodovino Is a World Leader in Self-Service Wine Tasting" in Idaho Business Review (September 8, 2014)
Pub: BridgeTower Media
Contact: Adam Reinebach, President

Description: Bodovino's wine bar and retail shop offers self-service wine tasting for its customers. It is the largest outlet globally for the Italian wine dispenser manufacturer WineEmotion. Visitors to the shop can choose from 144 wines set up in the dispensing machines.

16254 ■ "Effort Is Growing to Offer Healthier Choices in Vending Machines" in Philadelphia Inquirer (July 29, 2011)
Ed: Don Sapatkin. **Description:** Since Boston's mayor announced a ban on the sale of all sugar sweetened beverages on city properties, it seems more cities, states, hospitals, businesses, and even park systems are following suit. Thus, vending machines are beginning to offer healthier snacks and drinks to consumers.

16255 ■ "The Food Truck Handbook: Start, Grow, and Succeed in the Mobile Food Business"
Pub: John Wiley & Sons, Inc.
Contact: Christina Van Tassell, Executive Vice President Chief Financial Officer

Released: March 2012. **Price:** $19.95, paperback; $12.99, e-book. **Description:** Food truck businesses have grown so much in popularity, there are actually food truck competitions and was once a television show featuring them. A practical, step-by-step handbook is offered to help an entrepreneur start a mobile food delivery service. Information includes tips on choosing vending locations, opening and closing checklists; creation of a business plan with budget and finding vendor services, daily operation issues; common operating mistakes; and insight into delivery high quality food. **Availability:** E-book; Print.

16256 ■ "H.I.G. Capital Announces Acquisition of Next Generation Vending" in Benzinga.com (October 29, 2011)
Pub: Benzinga.com
Contact: Jason Raznick, Founder

Description: H.I.G. Capital LLC, a leader in global private investments, acquired Next Generation Vending and Food Service Inc. Next Generation is a provider of vending services for corporate and institutional clients in Northeastern United States. **Availability:** Print; PDF; Online.

16257 ■ "IJ Challenges Atlanta's Vending Monopoly" in Benzinga.com (July 28, 2011)
Pub: Benzinga.com
Contact: Jason Raznick, Founder

Description: A lawsuit was filed by The Institute for Justice to challenge Atlanta's unconstitutional vending monopoly on behalf of two Atlanta street vendors. **Availability:** Print; Online.

16258 ■ "A Parisian Vending Machine for Baguettes 24/7" in Benzinga.com
Pub: Benzinga.com
Contact: Jason Raznick, Founder

Description: Jean-Louis Hecht has created a vending machine that offers fresh baguettes 24 hours a day, seven days a week. **Availability:** Online.

16259 ■ *"School Uses Book Vending Machine to Get Kids Reading" in U.S. News & World Report (November 23, 2019)*
URL(s): www.usnews.com/news/best-states/south
-dakota/articles/2019-11-23/school-uses-book-ven
ding-machine-to-get-kids-reading

Ed: Shelly Conlon. **Released:** November 23, 2019.
Description: An innovative new vending machine is a big hit with kids, not because it is dispensing candy but because it is dispensing books. Inchy, the Bookworm Vending Machine, was installed in the John Harris Elementary school and doesn't take money, but does uses special coins that kids use when they earned a good deed award at school. It's led to a higher interest in reading and the students are excited to be part of something new and unique. **Availability:** Online.

16260 ■ *"Showalter Has Orioles Rising, But is Business Following?: Buck-ing the Trend?" in Baltimore Business Journal (Vol. 28, August 13, 2010, No. 14, pp. 1)*
Pub: Baltimore Business Journal
Contact: Rhonda Pringle, President
E-mail: rpringle@bizjournals.com

Ed: Gary Haber. **Description:** Baltimore Orioles' new manager Buck Showalter has managed to win games for fans. However, not all businesses around Camden Yards were boosted by the Orioles' surge as street vendors complained of worsening business. **Availability:** Print.

16261 ■ *"Sodexo Upgrades Healthy Vending Initiative" in Entertainment Close-Up (September 25, 2011)*
Description: Sodexo launched its Your Health Your Way On-the-Go program for its vending machines across the nation. **Availability:** Online.

16262 ■ *"The Ultimate Vending Machine" in Benzinga.com (August 15, 2011)*
Pub: Benzinga.com
Contact: Jason Raznick, Founder

Ed: Louis Bedigian. **Description:** Louis Hecht, a baker from Hombourg-Haut, France is selling fresh-baked bread in vending machines. Each machine holds 90 pre-cooked loaves which are warmed before being delivered to the customer. **Availability:** Online.

16263 ■ *"Upgrade Old Vending Machines and Offer Your Customers More Options" in Vending Connection (November 1, 2021)*
Released: November 01, 2021. **Description:** Discusses replacing your cash and coin only vending machine with parts and hardware to make it possible for your customers to pay with cards, rewards, and other cashless payments. **Availability:** Online.

STATISTICAL SOURCES

16264 ■ *RMA Annual Statement Studies*
Pub: Risk Management Association
Contact: Nancy Foster, President
Released: Annual. **Description:** Contains composite balance sheets and income statements for more than 360 industries, including the accounting, auditing, and bookkeeping industries. Also contains five years of comparative historical data for discerning trends. Includes 16 commonly used ratios, computed for most of the size groupings for nearly every industry.

16265 ■ *Vending Machine Operators Industry in the US - Market Research Report*
URL(s): www.ibisworld.com/united-states/market-re-
search-reports/vending-machine-operators-industry/
Description: Downloadable report analyzing the current and future trends in the vending machine operator industry. **Availability:** Download.

TRADE PERIODICALS

16266 ■ *Automatic Merchandiser: The Monthly Management Magazine for Vending and OCS Professionals*
Contact: Denise Singsime, Manager, Sales
E-mail: denise.singsime@vendingmarketwatch.com
Released: Monthly **Price:** Free. **Description:** Vending and office coffee service industry trade magazine.
Availability: Print; Online.

TRADE SHOWS AND CONVENTIONS

16267 ■ *Atlantic Coast Exposition*
Virginia Automatic Merchandising Association
(VAMA)
PO Box 4407
Cary, NC 27519
Ph: (919)387-1221

Fax: (919)249-1394
Co. E-mail: info@virginiavend.org
URL: http://vama.wildapricot.org
Contact: Karen Harlow, President
URL(s): atlanticcoastexpo.com/About-Us
Frequency: Annual. **Description:** Vending machines, office coffee service equipment, food stuffs, and related goods and services. **Audience:** Food service industry professionals. **Principal Exhibits:** Vending machines, office coffee service equipment, food stuffs, and related goods and services. Dates and Locations: Embassy Suites/Kingston Plantation, Myrtle Beach, SC; 2025 Oct 09-11 Embassy Suites/Kingston Plantation, Myrtle Beach; 2025 Oct 09-11 Embassy Suites/Kingston Plantation, Myrtle Beach, SC; 2026 Oct 08-10 Embassy Suites/Kingston Plantation, Myrtle Beach, SC. **Telecommunication Services:** info@atlanticcoastexpo.com.

16268 ■ *The NAMA Show*
National Automatic Merchandising Association
(NAMA)
1777 N Kent St., Ste. 1010
Arlington, VA 22209
Ph: (571)349-0149
Fax: (571)349-0138
Co. E-mail: memberinfo@namanow.org
URL: http://namanow.org
Contact: Carla Balakgie, President
E-mail: cbalakgie@vending.org
URL(s): thenamashow.org
Frequency: Annual. **Description:** Features new products, technology, and solutions for the vending, micro markets, pantry, office coffee services, and foodservices industries. **Audience:** Vending and refreshment professionals. **Principal Exhibits:** Features new products, technology, and solutions for the vending, micro markets, pantry, office coffee services, and foodservices industries. Dates and Locations: 2025 May 07-09 Las Vegas, NV. **Telecommunication Services:** events@namanow.org.

FRANCHISES AND BUSINESS OPPORTUNITIES

16269 ■ *Protocol L.L.C.*
2205 Oak Ridge Rd., Ste. K PMB 161
Oak Ridge, NC 27310
Contact: Anne T. Lang, Member
Description: Distributor of vending machines.
Founded: 1987. **Financial Assistance:** Yes **Training:** 1 day at headquarters, periodically onsite, 3 day annual convention with ongoing support.

STATISTICAL SOURCES

16270 ■ *Advertising in Gaming - US - 2021*
URL(s): store.mintel.com/report/advertising-in-gaming-us-2021

Price: $4,366.35. **Description:** Downloadable report examining digital advertising in the video game industry. Discusses strategies along with player reactions and preferences. Report includes an executive summary, interactive databook, PowerPoint presentation, infographic overview, report PDF, and previous years data. **Availability:** PDF.

VIDEO/AUDIO MEDIA

16271 ■ *How I Built This: Complexly: Hank and John Green*
URL(s): wondery.com/shows/how-i-built-this/episode/10386-copmlexly-hank-and-john-green

Ed: Guy Raz. **Released:** January 16, 2023. **Description:** Podcast explains how a viral YouTube video from brothers and authors led to a collection of businesses, including a production studio.

16272 ■ *Side Hustle to Small Business: Creating a Support System as a Solopreneur*
URL(s): www.hiscox.com/side-hustle-to-small-busi

ness/ford-gunter-easy-morning-media-podcast-season-4

Ed: Sanjay Parekh. **Released:** January 17, 2024. **Description:** Podcast features a video production company in Texas.

16273 ■ *Side Hustle to Small Business: Passion to Profit: Transforming Hobbies into Side Hustles*
URL(s): www.hiscox.com/side-hustle-to-small-business/should-your-hobby-become-your-side-hustle-podcast-season-4

Ed: Sanjay Parekh. **Released:** April 17, 2024. **Description:** Podcast discusses turning hobbies into thriving businesses.

ASSOCIATIONS AND OTHER ORGANIZATIONS

16274 ■ Accreditation Council on Optometric Education (ACOE)
c/o American Optometric Association
  243 N Lindbergh Blvd., 1st Fl.
  Saint Louis, MO 63141-7881
Co. E-mail: accredit@aoa.org
URL: http://theacoe.org/?sso=y
Contact: G. Timothy Petito, Chairman

Description: Accrediting body for professional Optometric Degree (O.D.) programs (examination, diagnosis, and treatment and management of diseases and disorders of the vision system, the eyes and associated structures as well as diagnosis of related systemic conditions), paraoptometric educational programs, and optometric residency programs. Members are appointed by the president of the American Optometric Association. Works to ensure the quality of optometric education by establishing and applying valid educational standards and announces list of accredited programs. **Founded:** 1934. **Geographic Preference:** National.

16275 ■ American Academy of Optometry (AAO) - Library
925 S Semoran Blvd., Ste. 120
  Winter Park, FL 32792
Ph: (321)319-4860
Free: 877-913-4860
Fax: (321)800-3655
Co. E-mail: aaoptom@aaoptom.org
URL: http://www.aaopt.org
Contact: Susan Cotter, President
Facebook: www.facebook.com/AAOPT
Linkedin: www.linkedin.com/company/aaopt
X (Twitter): x.com/aaopt
Instagram: www.instagram.com/aaopt

Description: Represents optometrists, educators, and scientists interested in optometric education and standards of care in visual problems. Conducts continuing education for optometrists and visual scientists. **Scope:** Optometry. **Founded:** 1922. **Holdings:** Figures not available. **Publications:** *Geographic Directory of Members*; *Eye Mail Monthly* (Monthly); *Optometry and Vision Science: The Journal of the American Academy of Optometry* (Monthly); *Optometry and Vision Science-- Geographical Directory, American Academy of Optometry Issue* (Biennial). **Educational Activities:** American Academy of Optometry Conference (Annual). **Awards:** Sheldon Wechsler and George Mertz Contact Lens Residency Award (Annual); Garland W. Clay Award (Annual); Tony Adams Eminent Service Award (Annual); William Feinbloom Award (Annual); Glenn A. Fry Lecture Award (Annual); Honorary & Life Fellowship Award (Irregular); Carel C. Koch Memorial Medal Award (Annual); Julius F. Neumueller Award in Optics (Annual); AAO Founders' Award (Annual); The Charles F. Prentice Medal (Annual). **Geographic Preference:** Multinational.

16276 ■ American Academy of Optometry Foundation (AOF)
925 S Semoran Blvd., Ste. 120
  Winter Park, FL 32792
Co. E-mail: frlaaof@aaoptom.org
URL: http://aaopt.org/about-us/foundation
Contact: Stacey Coulter, President

Description: Optometrists, optometric organizations, corporations, and the public. Promotes research, education, literature, and professional advancement in the visual sciences. Supports fellowships in graduate research. **Founded:** 1947. **Publications:** *The Torch*. **Educational Activities:** American Academy of Optometry Annual Meeting (Annual). **Awards:** William C. Ezell Fellowship (Annual); Vincent Salierno Memorial Scholarship (Annual); Vincent Salierno Scholarship (Annual). **Geographic Preference:** National.

16277 ■ American Board of Opticianry (ABO)
217 N Upper St., Ste. 201
  Lexington, KY 40507
Ph: (703)719-5800
Free: 800-296-1379
Co. E-mail: mail@abo-ncle.org
URL: http://www.abo-ncle.org

Description: Provides uniform standards for dispensing opticians by administering the National Opticianry Competency Examination and by issuing the Certified Optician Certificate to those passing the exam. Administers the Master in Ophthalmic Optics Examination and issues certificates to opticians at the advanced level passing the exam. Maintains records of persons certified for competency in eyeglass dispensing. Adopts and enforces continuing education requirements; assists and encourages state licensing boards in the use of the National Opticianry Competency Examination for licensure purposes. **Founded:** 1976. **Geographic Preference:** National.

16278 ■ American Optometric Association (AOA) - The Archives and Museum of Optometry
243 N Lindbergh Blvd., 1st Fl.
  Saint Louis, MO 63141-7881
Ph: (314)991-4100
Fax: (314)991-4101
Co. E-mail: memberservices@aoa.org
URL: http://www.aoa.org
Contact: Robert C. Layman, Co-President
Facebook: www.facebook.com/American.Optometric.Association
Linkedin: www.linkedin.com/company/american-optometric-association
X (Twitter): x.com/aoaconnect
Instagram: www.instagram.com/americanoptometricassociation

Description: Optometrists, students of optometry, and paraoptometric assistants and technicians. Seeks to improve the quality and accessibility of eye and vision care; to represent the optometric profession; to help members conduct their practices; to promote the highest standards of patient care. Promotes legislation concerning the scope of optometric practice, alternate health care delivery systems, health care cost containment and Medicare. **Scope:** Optometry; public health. **Founded:** 1898. **Holdings:** Historical records; manuscripts; photographs; books; eyeglasses; contact lenses; instruments; tools; historical artifacts. **Publications:** *Astigmatism Fact Sheet* (Irregular); *Cataract Fact Sheet*; *Monovision Fact Sheet*; *Optometry: A Career with Vision*; *AOA News*; *How the Eyes Work*; *Your Eye-Q Test Fact Sheet*; *Focus on Seeing Fact Sheet*; *Healthy Eyes Checklist*; *Eyes in Action Fact Sheet*; *Visual Acuity: What Is 20/20 Vision? Fact Sheet*; *Myopia: Nearsightedness Fact Sheet*; *Hyperopia: Farsightedness Fact Sheet*; *Presbyopia Fact Sheet*; *Amblyopia--Lazy Eye Fact Sheet*; *Strabismus (Crossed Eyes), OPC Fact Sheet*; *Spots and Floaters Fact Sheet*; *Color Vision Deficiency Fact Sheet*; *Eye Coordination Fact Sheet*; *Eye Diseases Fact Sheet*; *Retinoblastoma, Optometry and InfantSEE(TM) Fact Sheet*; *Glaucoma Fact Sheet*; *Diabetic Retinopathy Fact Sheet*; *Age-Related Macular Degeneration Fact Sheet*; *Dry Eye Fact Sheet*; *Blepharitis Fact Sheet*; *Anterior Uveitis Fact Sheet*; *Conjunctivitis Fact Sheet*; *Keratoconus Fact Sheet*; *Retinitis Pigmentosa Fact Sheet*; *Ocular Hypertension Fact Sheet*; *Caring for Your Vision Fact Sheet*; *Comprehensive Eye and Vision Examination Fact Sheet*; *Nutrition Fact Sheet*; *Antioxidants and Age-Related Eye Disease Fact Sheet*; *Lutein and Zeaxanthin - Eye Friendly Nutrients Fact Sheet*; *Nutrition and Age-Related Macular Degeneration Fact Sheet*; *Nutrition and Cataracts Fact Sheet*; *U/V Protection Fact Sheet*; *Sunglasses Shopping Guide Fact Sheet*; *Protecting Your Eyes Fact Sheet*; *Computer Vision Syndrome Fact Sheet*; *Guidelines for the Use of Contact Lenses In Industrial Environments*; *Children's Vision Fact Sheet*; *Infant's Vision Fact Sheet*; *Preschool Vision Fact Sheet*; *School-Age Children Fact Sheet*; *Toys, Games, and Your Child's Vision Fact Sheet*; *Corneal Modifications Fact Sheet*; *Ortho-K Fact Sheet*; *Refractive Surgery and Corneal Modification Definitions Fact Sheet*; *Contact Lenses, OPC Fact Sheet*; *What You Need to Know About Contact Lens Hygiene and Compliance Fact Sheet*; *Facts and Stats*; *Advantages and Disadvantages of Various Types of Contact Lenses Fact Sheet*; *Do's and Don'ts Fact Sheet*; *Contact Lenses and Cosmetics Fact Sheet*; *Signs of Potential Problems Fact Sheet*; *Cost of Contact Lenses Fact Sheet*; *Warning for Consumers: Popular Halloween Eye Wear Accessory Can Permanently Damage Eyes Fact Sheet*; *Low Vision Fact Sheet*; *What Causes Low Vision? Fact Sheet*; *Common Types of Low Vision Fact Sheet*; *Low Vision Care Fact Sheet*; *Low Vision Exam Fact Sheet*; *Low Vision Devices Fact Sheet*; *Low Vision Rehabilitation Fact Sheet* (Annual); *Sports and Vision Fact Sheet*; *Important Vision Skills for Sports Fact Sheet*; *AOA Public Programs Fact Sheet*; *InfantSEE(TM) Fact Sheet*; *Vision USA Fact Sheet*; *Referral Instructions Fact Sheet*; *Vision USA Application Form Fact Sheet*; *Optometric Disaster Relief Fund Fact Sheet*; *Optometry: Journal of the American Optometric Association* (Monthly); *American Optometric Association News* (Daily); *Donate to the Optometric Disaster Relief Fund Fact Sheet*; *Request a Grant Fact Sheet*; *Additional Relief Resources Fact*

Sheet; Parents and Educators Fact Sheet; How Your Eyes Work Fact Sheet; A Look at Reading and Vision; Classroom Exercises Fact Sheet; Classroom Exercises: Day and Night Fact Sheet; Classroom Exercises: Pinhole Focusing Fact Sheet; Eye Safety Fact Sheet; Nystagmus Fact Sheet; Adult Vision: 41 to 60 Years of Age; Adult Vision: Over 60 Years of Age; Flood-Related Eye Care Precautions. **Educational Activities:** Optometry's Meeting (Annual). **Awards:** AOA Apollo Award (Annual); AOA Distinguished Service Award (Annual); AOA Optometrist of the Year Award (Annual); AOA Young Optometrist of the Year (Annual). **Geographic Preference:** National.

16279 ■ American Optometric Student Association (AOSA)
243 N Lindbergh, Blvd.
 Saint Louis, MO 63141
Ph: (315)983-4154
URL: http://www.theaosa.org
Contact: Ryan Funai, President
Facebook: www.facebook.com/American.Optometric
 .Student.Association
X (Twitter): x.com/theaosa
Instagram: www.instagram.com/theaosa

Description: Optometric students, state optometric associations, and family members of optometric students. Collects updated information on progress in the optometry field. Provides members with opportunities to work in areas of health care need such as local community health projects, school curriculum changes, and health manpower legislation. Works to improve optometric education and health care for the general population. Maintains active liaison with other optometric associations. Conducts communications program. **Founded:** 1968. **Publications:** AOSA Foresight: Optometry Looking Forward (Semiannual); Communicator (9/year). **Educational Activities:** Optometry's Meeting (Annual); Optometry's Meeting (Annual). **Geographic Preference:** National.

16280 ■ Association des Opticiens du Canada (AOC) [Opticians Association of Canada (OAC)]
St. Vital Ctr.
 Winnipeg, MB, Canada R2M 5R3
Ph: (204)982-6060
Free: 800-847-3155
Fax: (204)947-2519
Co. E-mail: canada@opticians.ca
URL: http://www.opticians.ca
Contact: Robert Dalton, Executive Director
E-mail: rdalton@opticians.ca
Facebook: www.facebook.com/OpticiansAssocia
 tionofCanada
Linkedin: www.linkedin.com/company/opticians
 -association-of-canada
X (Twitter): x.com/OACexecutiveDr
YouTube: www.youtube.com/user/opticianstv

Description: Dispensing opticians. Promotes advancement of opticianry. Works to safeguard members' economic and professional interests. Conducts educational programs. **Founded:** 1990. **Publications:** Vision (Bimonthly). **Geographic Preference:** National.

16281 ■ Association of Regulatory Boards of Optometry (ARBO)
200 S College St., Ste. 2030
 Charlotte, NC 28202
Ph: (704)970-2710
Free: 866-869-6852
Fax: (888)703-4848
Co. E-mail: arbo@arbo.org
URL: http://www.arbo.org
Contact: Coby S. Ramsey, President
Facebook: www.facebook.com/pages/Association-of
 -Regulatory-Boards-of-Optometry/127983077
 242338

Description: Represents the North American regulatory boards of optometry. Works to assist member licensing agencies in regulating the practice of optometry for the public welfare. **Founded:** 1919.

Publications: Directory of Boards of Optometry (Annual). **Educational Activities:** ARBO Southern Regional Meeting (Annual). **Geographic Preference:** Multinational.

16282 ■ Association of Schools and Colleges of Optometry (ASCO)
6110 Executive Blvd.
 Rockville, MD 20847
Ph: (301)231-5944
Fax: (301)770-1828
URL: http://www.optometriceducation.org
Contact: Kelly Nichols, President
E-mail: nicholsk@uab.edu
Facebook: www.facebook.com/OptometricEducation
Linkedin: www.linkedin.com/company/association-of
 -schools-and-colleges-of-optometry
X (Twitter): x.com/OptometricED
Instagram: www.instagram.com/optometriced
YouTube: www.youtube.com/channel/UCmws
 13yqQhOpSlR2qKjxizQ

Description: Works to achieve excellence in optometric education and to helping its member schools/colleges prepare well-qualified graduates for entrance into the profession of optometry. Aims to serve the American public through the continued advancement and promotion of all aspects of academic optometry. **Founded:** 1941. **Publications:** Faculty Directory of the Schools and Colleges of Optometry; Faculty Survey Report (Annual); Residency Directory; Student Data Report (Annual); Optometric Education (3/year). **Educational Activities:** Association of Schools and Colleges of Optometry Meeting (Annual). **Awards:** ASCO Student Award in Clinical Ethics (Annual); ALCON Guest Lecturer Program (Annual); Dr. Jack Bennett Innovation in Optometric Education Award (Periodic); Dr. Lester Janoff Award for Writing Excellence (Biennial). **Geographic Preference:** National.

16283 ■ Association of Vision Science Librarians (AVSL)
1245 Madison Ave.
 Memphis, TN 38104
URL: http://avsl.notion.site/The-Association-of-Vision
 -Science-Librarians-defc1d98038b4b07bce7dbf
 437f97d82
Contact: Adm. (Ret.) Deborah Goss, Contact

Description: Works to foster collective and individual acquisition and dissemination of vision science information. Improves services for persons seeking vision science information. Develops standards among member-affiliated libraries. **Scope:** Vision science. **Founded:** 1965. **Subscriptions:** journals and other serials magazines Books; ebooks; newsletters. **Publications:** International Directory of Members. **Educational Activities:** Association of Vision Science Librarians Meeting (Annual). **Geographic Preference:** Multinational.

16284 ■ Canadian Association of Optometrists (CAO) [L'Association Canadienne des Optometristes]
234 Argyle Ave.
 Ottawa, ON, Canada K2P 1B9
Ph: (613)235-7924
Free: 888-263-4676
Co. E-mail: info@opto.ca
URL: http://opto.ca
Contact: Harry Bohnsack, President
Facebook: www.facebook.com/CanadianOpto
X (Twitter): twitter.com/CanadianOpto

Description: Represent the profession of Optometry; to enhance the quality, availability, and accessibility of eye, vision, and related health care. **Founded:** 1941. **Publications:** Canadian Journal of Optometry (Quarterly); Canadian Journal of Optometry (CJO) (Quarterly). **Awards:** Canadian Optometric Education Trust Fund (COETF) (Annual). **Geographic Preference:** National.

16285 ■ Canadian Journal of Ophthalmology (CJO)
110-2733 Lancaster Rd.
 Ottawa, ON, Canada K1B 0A9
Ph: (613)729-6779
Free: 800-267-5763

Co. E-mail: cos@cos-sco.ca
URL: http://www.cos-sco.ca
Contact: Elisabeth Fowler, Chief Executive Officer
E-mail: efowler@cos-sco.ca
URL(s): www.canadianjournalofophthalmology.ca
X (Twitter): x.com/CanJOphth
Instagram: www.instagram.com/cjo_jco

Ed: Phil Hooper, MD. **Released:** Annual **Price:** $205, Individuals for print and online US; $177, Individuals for online US; $171, Individuals for print and online Canada; $149, Individuals for online Canada; $205, Individuals for print and online international; $177, Individuals for online international. **Description:** Journal of scientific research in ophthalmology. **Availability:** Print; PDF; Download; Online.

16286 ■ Canadian Journal of Optometry
234 Argyle Ave.
 Ottawa, ON, Canada K2P 1B9
Ph: (613)235-7924
Free: 888-263-4676
Co. E-mail: info@opto.ca
URL: http://opto.ca
Contact: Harry Bohnsack, President
URL(s): opto.ca/cjo

Released: Quarterly **Description:** Contains clinical articles, practice management advice, issues, products, and people in the news that affect your profession and your practice. **Availability:** Print; PDF; Online.

16287 ■ Canadian Ophthalmological Society (COS)
110-2733 Lancaster Rd.
 Ottawa, ON, Canada K1B 0A9
Ph: (613)729-6779
Free: 800-267-5763
Co. E-mail: cos@cos-sco.ca
URL: http://www.cos-sco.ca
Contact: Elisabeth Fowler, Chief Executive Officer
E-mail: efowler@cos-sco.ca
Facebook: www.facebook.com/CanadianOphthos
Linkedin: www.linkedin.com/company/canadian-oph
 thalmological-society
YouTube: www.youtube.com/channel/UCa92RI9LcZN
 _Xijy5cTsNXg

Description: Works to ensure the provision of optimal eye care to all Canadians by promoting excellence in ophthalmology and providing services to support its members in practice. **Founded:** 1937. **Publications:** Canadian Journal of Ophthalmology (CJO) (Annual). **Educational Activities:** Canadian Ophthalmological Society Annual Meeting and Exhibition (Annual). **Geographic Preference:** National.

16288 ■ College of Optometrists in Vision Development (COVD)
215 W Garfield Rd., Ste. 260
 Aurora, OH 44202
Ph: (330)995-0718
Fax: (330)995-0719
Co. E-mail: info@covd.org
URL: http://www.covd.org
Contact: Marie Bodack, President
E-mail: mbodack@sco.edu
Facebook: www.facebook.com/covdpage
X (Twitter): x.com/covd
Instagram: www.instagram.com/covd__connect

Description: Optometrists involved in developmental vision care and vision therapy with emphasis on visual information processing in visually related learning problems. Seeks to establish a body of practitioners who are knowledgeable in functional and developmental concepts of vision, to insure that the public will receive continually improving vision care; to enable members to maintain the highest standards of professional knowledge and competency; to educate and encourage optometrists to qualify for membership and fellowship in the college; to certify optometrists skilled in this specialty. Conducts national educational programs and public information programs. **Founded:** 1970. **Publications:** E-mail Newsletter Briefs (Weekly); Membership Directory and Desk Reference (Annual); Optometry and Vision Development Journal (Quarterly); Visions Newsletter (Quarterly); College of Optometrists in Vision

Development--Membership Directory. **Educational Activities:** COVD Annual Meeting (Annual). **Awards:** A.M. Skeffington Award (Annual); G.N. Getman Award (Annual); COVD President's Award (Annual). **Geographic Preference:** Multinational.

16289 ■ Contact Lens Manufacturers Association (CLMA)

PO Box 29398
 Lincoln, NE 68529
Ph: (402)465-4122
Free: 800-344-9060
Fax: (402)465-4187
URL: http://www.clma.net
Contact: Josh Adams, President

Description: Represents contact lens laboratories, material, solution and equipment manufacturers in the US. and abroad. Aims to increase awareness and utilization of custom-manufactured contact lenses. **Founded:** 1961. **Publications:** *Contact Lens Manufacturers Association--Member Directory.* **Educational Activities:** Contact Lens Manufacturers Association Meeting and Exhibition (Annual). **Awards:** The Dr. Josef Dallos Award (Periodic); CLMA Honorary Recognition Award (Periodic); CLMA Trailblazers Award (Irregular); The Leonardo da Vinci Award (Periodic); CLMA Creative Design and Process Award (Periodic); CLMA GPLI Practitioner of the Year (Annual); CLMA Industry Enhancement Award (Irregular). **Geographic Preference:** Multinational.

16290 ■ National Academy of Opticianry (NAO)

8401 Corporate Dr., Ste. 605
 Landover, MD 20785
Free: 800-229-4828
Fax: (301)577-3880
Co. E-mail: ctucker@nao.org
URL: http://www.nao.org
Contact: Brian Iciek, Director, Education
E-mail: brian.iciek@nao.org
Facebook: www.facebook.com/people/National-Academy-of-Opticianry/100063539501912
X (Twitter): x.com/ctucker_nao
Instagram: www.instagram.com/nationalacademyofopticianry19

Description: Offers review courses for national certification and state licensure examinations to members. Maintains speakers' bureau and Career Progression Program. **Founded:** 1963. **Publications:** *Academy Newsletter* (Quarterly). **Geographic Preference:** National.

16291 ■ National Association of Vision Professionals (NAVP)

Austin, TX
URL: http://visionpros.org
Contact: Brenda Dunn, President
E-mail: president@visionpros.org
Facebook: www.facebook.com/thenavp

Description: Individuals responsible for or connected with vision conservation and eye health programs in public or private agencies and institutions. Serves as a forum for ideas and programs, cooperates with other agencies, and promotes professional standards. Certifies vision screening personnel. **Founded:** 1978. **Publications:** *NAVP Newsletter* (Quarterly). **Geographic Preference:** National.

16292 ■ National Board of Examiners in Optometry (NBEO)

200 S College St., Ste. 2010
 Charlotte, NC 28202
Ph: (704)332-9565
Free: 800-969-EXAM
Fax: (704)332-9568
Co. E-mail: nbeo@optometry.org
URL: http://www.optometry.org
Contact: Susy Yu, President

Description: Administers entry-level criterion-referenced credentialing examinations to students and graduates of accredited schools and colleges of optometry for use by individual state licensing boards. **Founded:** 1951. **Publications:** *TestPoints* (Quarterly). **Geographic Preference:** National.

16293 ■ National Contact Lens Examiners (NCLE)

217 N Upper St., Ste. 201
 Lexington, KY 40507
Ph: (703)719-5800
Free: 800-296-1379
Co. E-mail: mail@abo-ncle.org
URL: http://www.abo-ncle.org
Facebook: www.facebook.com/opticiancertification

Description: Serves as National certifying agency promoting continued development of opticians and technicians as contact lens fitters by formulating standards and procedures for determination of entry-level competency. Assists in the continuation, development, administration, and monitoring of a national Contact Lens Registry Examination (CLRE), which verifies entry-level competency of contact lens fitters. Issues certificates. Activities include: maintaining records of those certified in contact lens fitting; encouraging state occupational licensing and credentialing agencies to use the CLRE for licensure purposes; identifying contact lens dispensing education needs as a result of findings of examination programs; disseminating information to sponsors of contact lens continuing education programs. **Founded:** 1979. **Geographic Preference:** National.

16294 ■ National Optometric Association (NOA)

5009 Beatties Ford Rd., Ste. 107, No. 278
 Charlotte, NC 28210
Free: 877-394-2020
Fax: (877)472-3492
Co. E-mail: mainoffice@natoptassoc.org
URL: http://nationaloptometricassociation.com
Contact: Dr. Edward Jones, President
Facebook: www.facebook.com/NatOptAssoc
X (Twitter): x.com/NatOptAssoc
Instagram: www.instagram.com/nationaloptometricassociation

Description: Represents optometrists dedicated to increasing awareness of the status of eye/vision health in the minority community and the national community at-large. Strives to make known the impact of the eye/vision dysfunction on the effectiveness and productivity of citizens and the academic proficiency of students. Conducts national minority recruiting programs, job placement, assistance programs for graduates, practitioners, and optometric organizations, and the promotion of delivery of care. Maintains speakers' bureau. Offers specialized education program. **Founded:** 1969. **Educational Activities:** National Optometric Association Convention (Annual). **Awards:** NOA Optometrist of the Year (Annual); NOA Cave Memorial Scholarship (Annual); John L. Howlette and C. Clayton Powell Student Founder's Award (Annual). **Geographic Preference:** National.

16295 ■ The Vision Council

225 Reinekers Ln., Ste. 700
 Alexandria, VA 22314
Ph: (703)548-4560
Free: 866-826-0290
Fax: (703)548-4580
Co. E-mail: info@thevisioncouncil.org
URL: http://thevisioncouncil.org
Contact: Ashley Mills, Chief Executive Officer
E-mail: ceo@thevisioncouncil.org
Facebook: www.facebook.com/thevisioncouncil
X (Twitter): x.com/opticalindustry
YouTube: www.youtube.com/user/thevisioncouncil

Description: Optical industry companies that sponsor exhibits at industry trade shows. Works to serve the collective interests of the ophthalmic community; encourages the public to visit eye care practitioners regularly. Seeks to produce top quality trade shows. Conducts public educational programs. **Founded:** 1940. **Publications:** *The Vision Council Annual Report* (Annual). **Educational Activities:** International Vision Expo West (Annual); International Vision Expo and Conference/East (Annual). **Geographic Preference:** National.

16296 ■ Vision Council Lab Division

225 Reinekers Ln., Ste. 700
 Alexandria, VA 22314
Ph: (703)548-4560
Free: 866-826-0290
Fax: (703)548-4580
Co. E-mail: info@thevisioncouncil.org
URL: http://www.thevisioncouncil.org
Contact: Ashley Mills, Chief Executive Officer
E-mail: ceo@thevisioncouncil.org
Facebook: www.facebook.com/thevisioncouncil
Linkedin: www.linkedin.com/company/the-vision-council
X (Twitter): x.com/opticalindustry
Instagram: www.instagram.com/thevisioncouncil
YouTube: www.youtube.com/user/thevisioncouncil

Description: Represents independent, wholesale ophthalmic laboratories and suppliers serving the ophthalmic field. **Founded:** 1894. **Educational Activities:** The OLA; The OLA. **Geographic Preference:** Multinational.

REFERENCE WORKS

16297 ■ *Contact Lens Manufacturers Association--Member Directory*

Pub: Contact Lens Manufacturers Association
Contact: Josh Adams, President
URL(s): www.clma.net/member-directory
No. of Listings: 130. **Entries include:** Company name, address, phone, name and title of contact. **Arrangement:** Alphabetical within membership categories. **Indexes:** Geographical. **Availability:** Download; PDF.

16298 ■ *"Falling Through the Cracks of Vision Care"* in U.S. News & World Report (May 15, 2018)

URL(s): www.usnews.com/news/healthiest-communities/articles/2018-05-15/falling-through-the-insurance-gaps-for-vision-care
Released: May 15, 2018. **Description:** Discusses how lack of vision insurance has created medical concerns for 16 million Americans. While not often life-threatening, having vision issues can impact learning, jobs, and just everyday life, but most medical insurance plans do not cover vision. **Availability:** Online.

16299 ■ *"Highmark-Owned Glasses Chain Eyeing Phila. Expansion"* in Philadelphia Business Journal (Vol. 28, May 18, 2012, No. 14, pp. 1)

Pub: Baltimore Business Journal
Contact: Rhonda Pringle, President
E-mail: rpringle@bizjournals.com
Description: Pittsburgh, Pennsylvania-based Highmark's subsidiary, Visionworks, has outlined its plan to open 25 stores in the Philadelphia region. The retail eyeglasses store chain has also been trying to recruit opticians to hire in the area. **Availability:** Print; Online.

16300 ■ *"HVHC's Impact on SA Could Grow as it Pursues Big Expansion"* in San Antonio Business Journal (Vol. 28, June 20, 2014, No. 19, pp. 8)

Pub: American City Business Journals, Inc.
Contact: Mike Olivieri, Executive Vice President
Released: Weekly. **Price:** $4, Introductory 4-week offer(Digital & Print). **Description:** HVHC Inc., parent company of several retail eye-care centers in the U.S., is planning to grow its Visionworks footprint by adding at least 360 new stores in the country. The company aims to grow its store count to 1,000 retail outlets across the nation. **Availability:** Print; Online.

16301 ■ *"Lincoln Firm Shows Finishing Kick"* in Providence Business News (Vol. 29, June 30, 2014, No. 13, pp. 10)

Pub: American City Business Journals, Inc.
Contact: Mike Olivieri, Executive Vice President
Released: June 28, 2014. **Description:** The advancement of the jewelry plating company, Tanury Industries, has expanded into gold-plating interiors of jets and creating durable finished for eyeglass

frames. Tanury's Physical Vapor Deposition (PVD) vacuum chamber is a unique system that applies a thin film of metal to a variety of materials. **Availability:** PDF; Online.

16302 ■ *"SCO Expanding to Meet Optometry Growth" in Memphis Business Journal (Vol. 33, March 2, 2012, No. 47, pp. 1)*
Pub: Baltimore Business Journal
Contact: Rhonda Pringle, President
E-mail: rpringle@bizjournals.com

Ed: Christopher Sheffield. **Description:** Southern College of Optometry (SCO) has begun construction of a $9.4 million expansion that will provide new classrooms, a flexible state-of-the-art lecture hall, and a glass atrium and grand hall. The project was designed to secure SCO's position among the top US optometry school as demand for its graduates grow. **Availability:** Print; Online.

16303 ■ *"SEEing an Opportunity: Golden's Eyewear Chain Has a National Vision" in Crain's Detroit Business (Vol. 24, January 7, 2008, No. 1)*
Pub: Crain Communications Inc.
Contact: Barry Asin, President

Ed: Sheena Harrison. **Description:** Richard Golden, who recently sold D.O.C. Optics Corporation is planning to build a new national eyewear chain called SEE Inc., which stands for Selective Eyewear Elements. SEE will sell expensive-looking glasses at lower prices than designer styles. **Availability:** Online.

STATISTICAL SOURCES

16304 ■ *RMA Annual Statement Studies*
Pub: Risk Management Association
Contact: Nancy Foster, President

Released: Annual. **Description:** Contains composite balance sheets and income statements for more than 360 industries, including the accounting, auditing, and bookkeeping industries. Also contains five years of comparative historical data for discerning trends. Includes 16 commonly used ratios, computed for most of the size groupings for nearly every industry.

TRADE PERIODICALS

16305 ■ *Eyecare Business: Retail Strategies for Profitable Dispensing*
Contact: Mark Durrick, Publisher
E-mail: mark.durrick@springer.com
URL(s): www.eyecarebusiness.com
Facebook: www.facebook.com/eyecarebusiness
X (Twitter): twitter.com/eyecarebusiness

Released: Monthly **Description:** Magazine for eyecare professionals. **Availability:** Print; Online.

16306 ■ *Eyewitness*
Pub: Contact Lens Society of America
Contact: Terri Klein, President
URL(s): www.clsa.info/Membership

Ed: Wendy Ford. **Released:** Quarterly **Description:** Informs members of developments in the contact lens industry. Also reports on related educational information and technical papers. Recurring features include news of research, calendar of events, reports of meetings, and associate member listing. **Availability:** Print.

16307 ■ *Gleams*
Pub: Glaucoma Research Foundation
Contact: Thomas M. Brunner, President
E-mail: tbrunner@glaucoma.org

Released: 3/year **Price:** Free. **Description:** Examines the results of clinical and basic research on glaucoma. Seeks to increase public knowledge of the eye disease and discusses prevention of blindness from the disease. Contains articles on glaucoma research, treatment updates and tips on living with glaucoma. **Availability:** Print; Download; PDF; Online.

16308 ■ *National Glaucoma Research Report*
Pub: BrightFocus Foundation
Contact: Stacy Pagos Haller, President
URL(s): www.brightfocus.org/news/newsletters

Released: 3/year; Spring, Fall, Summer. **Description:** Highlights the work of glaucoma researchers and provides tips for individuals with glaucoma. Recurring features include news of research and columns titled From the Presidents and Ask the Experts. **Availability:** Print; Download; Online; PDF.

16309 ■ *Optometric Education*
Pub: Association of Schools and Colleges of Optometry
Contact: Kelly Nichols, President
E-mail: nicholsk@uab.edu
URL(s): journal.opted.org
X (Twitter): x.com/OptometricED

Ed: Aurora Denial. **Released:** 3/year **Description:** Optometric journal. **Availability:** Print; Download; PDF.

TRADE SHOWS AND CONVENTIONS

16310 ■ Annual Meeting of the American Academy of Ophthalmology
American Academy of Ophthalmology (AAO)
655 Beach St.
San Francisco, CA 94109
Ph: (415)561-8500
Free: 866-561-8558
Fax: (415)561-8533
Co. E-mail: aaoe@aao.org
URL: http://www.aao.org
Contact: Tina McGovern, Executive Director
E-mail: tmcgovern@aao.org
URL(s): www.aao.org/annual-meeting

Frequency: Annual. **Audience:** Ophthalmologists and members. Dates and Locations: 2025 Oct 17-20 Orange County Convention Center, Orlando, FL; 2026 Oct 09-12 Ernest N. Morial Convention Center, New Orleans, LA; 2027 Nov 12-15 Venetian Expo & Hotel, Las Vegas, NV. **Telecommunication Services:** meetings@aao:org.

16311 ■ California Optometric Association OptoWest
California Optometric Association (COA)
2415 K St.
Sacramento, CA 95816
Free: 833-206-0598
Co. E-mail: contact@coavision.org
URL: http://www.coavision.org/i4a/pages/index.cfm?pageid=1
Contact: Bill Howe, Executive Director
E-mail: bhowe@coavision.org
URL(s): www.coavision.org/m/events.cfm

Frequency: Annual. **Description:** Optometric equipment, supplies, and services. **Audience:** Optometrists and professional staff. **Principal Exhibits:** Optometric equipment, supplies, and services.

16312 ■ MOA Fall Seminar
Michigan Optometric Association (MOA)
530 W Ionia St., Ste. A
Lansing, MI 48933
Ph: (517)482-0616
Fax: (517)482-1611
Co. E-mail: info@themoa.org
URL: http://www.themoa.org
Contact: James Hardie, President
URL(s): themoa.org/events/EventDetails.aspx?id=17 38651

Frequency: Annual; held every Fall. **Description:** Ophthalmic supplies and services. **Audience:** Industry professionals. **Principal Exhibits:** Ophthalmic supplies and services. **Telecommunication Services:** events@themoa.org.

FRANCHISES AND BUSINESS OPPORTUNITIES

16313 ■ Pearle Vision Inc.
24539 Cedar Rd.
Lyndhurst, OH 44124
Ph: (216)291-0120
Free: 800-937-3937
URL: http://www.pearlevision.com
Facebook: www.facebook.com/pearlevision
YouTube: www.youtube.com/channel/UCQTD9X9 _jnOC9x3CGtp5QoA

Description: Eyewear and eye-care stores. **No. of Franchise Units:** 343. **No. of Company-Owned Units:** 289. **Founded:** 1961. **Franchised:** 1980. **Equity Capital Needed:** $184,008-$528,353. **Franchise Fee:** $30,000. **Royalty Fee:** 7%. **Training:** Offers 1 week at headquarters, 1 week at franchisee's location, at company-owned location (optional) 1 week and ongoing support.

16314 ■ Sterling Optical
Emerging Vision, Inc. (EV)
392 Pearl St., Ste. 200
Buffalo, NY 14202
Ph: (646)737-1500
Free: 800-856-9664
URL: http://www.emergingvision.com
Facebook: www.facebook.com/SterlingOpticalUSA
Instagram: www.instagram.com/sterlingopticalusa

Description: Franchises optic centers. **Founded:** 1914. **Training:** Ongoing training programs with initial focus on in-store operation and business operating systems. Continuing education through on-site visits.

LIBRARIES

16315 ■ American Academy of Optometry (AAO) - Library
925 S Semoran Blvd., Ste. 120
Winter Park, FL 32792
Ph: (321)319-4860
Free: 877-913-4860
Fax: (321)800-3655
Co. E-mail: aaoptom@aaoptom.org
URL: http://www.aaopt.org
Contact: Susan Cotter, President
Facebook: www.facebook.com/AAOPT
Linkedin: www.linkedin.com/company/aaopt
X (Twitter): x.com/aaopt
Instagram: www.instagram.com/aaopt

Description: Represents optometrists, educators, and scientists interested in optometric education and standards of care in visual problems. Conducts continuing education for optometrists and visual scientists. **Scope:** Optometry. **Founded:** 1922. **Holdings:** Figures not available. **Publications:** *Geographic Directory of Members*; *Eye Mail Monthly* (Monthly); *Optometry and Vision Science: The Journal of the American Academy of Optometry* (Monthly); *Optometry and Vision Science-- Geographical Directory, American Academy of Optometry Issue* (Biennial). **Educational Activities:** American Academy of Optometry Conference (Annual). **Awards:** Sheldon Wechsler and George Mertz Contact Lens Residency Award (Annual); Garland W. Clay Award (Annual); Tony Adams Eminent Service Award (Annual); William Feinbloom Award (Annual); Glenn A. Fry Lecture Award (Annual); Honorary & Life Fellowship Award (Irregular); Carel C. Koch Memorial Medal Award (Annual); Julius F. Neumueller Award in Optics (Annual); AAO Founders' Award (Annual); The Charles F. Prentice Medal (Annual). **Geographic Preference:** Multinational.

16316 ■ American Optometric Association (AOA) - The Archives and Museum of Optometry
243 N Lindbergh Blvd., 1st Fl.
Saint Louis, MO 63141-7881
Ph: (314)991-4100
Fax: (314)991-4101
Co. E-mail: memberservices@aoa.org
URL: http://www.aoa.org
Contact: Robert C. Layman, Co-President

Facebook: www.facebook.com/American.Optometric .Association

Linkedin: www.linkedin.com/company/american-op tometric-association

X (Twitter): x.com/aoaconnect

Instagram: www.instagram.com/americanoptome tricassociation

Description: Optometrists, students of optometry, and paraoptometric assistants and technicians. Seeks to improve the quality and accessibility of eye and vision care; to represent the optometric profession; to help members conduct their practices; to promote the highest standards of patient care. Promotes legislation concerning the scope of optometric practice, alternate health care delivery systems, health care cost containment and Medicare. **Scope:** Optometry; public health. **Founded:** 1898. **Holdings:** Historical records; manuscripts; photographs; books; eyeglasses; contact lenses; instruments; tools; historical artifacts. **Publications:** *Astigmatism Fact Sheet* (Irregular); *Cataract Fact Sheet*; *Monovision Fact Sheet*; *Optometry: A Career with Vision*; *AOA News*; *How the Eyes Work*; *Your Eye-Q Test Fact Sheet*; *Focus on Seeing Fact Sheet*; *Healthy Eyes Checklist*; *Eyes in Action Fact Sheet*; *Visual Acuity: What Is 20/20 Vision? Fact Sheet*; *Myopia: Nearsightedness Fact Sheet*; *Hyperopia: Farsightedness Fact Sheet*; *Presbyopia Fact Sheet*; *Amblyopia--Lazy Eye Fact Sheet*; *Strabismus (Crossed Eyes), OPC Fact Sheet*; *Spots and Floaters Fact Sheet*; *Color Vision Deficiency Fact Sheet*; *Eye Coordination Fact Sheet*; *Eye Diseases Fact Sheet*; *Retinoblastoma, Optometry and InfantSEE(TM) Fact Sheet*; *Glaucoma Fact Sheet*; *Diabetic Retinopathy Fact Sheet*; *Age-Related Macular Degeneration Fact Sheet*; *Dry Eye Fact Sheet*; *Blepharitis Fact Sheet*; *Anterior Uveitis Fact Sheet*; *Conjunctivitis Fact Sheet*; *Keratoconus Fact Sheet*; *Retinitis Pigmentosa Fact Sheet*; *Ocular Hypertension Fact Sheet*; *Caring for Your Vision Fact Sheet*; *Comprehensive Eye and Vision Examination Fact Sheet*; *Nutrition Fact Sheet*; *Antioxidants and Age-Related Eye Disease Fact Sheet*; *Lutein and Zeaxanthin - Eye Friendly Nutrients Fact Sheet*; *Nutrition and Age-Related Macular Degeneration Fact Sheet*; *Nutrition and Cataracts Fact Sheet*; *U/V Protection Fact Sheet*; *Sunglasses Shopping Guide Fact Sheet*; *Protecting Your Eyes Fact Sheet*; *Computer Vision Syndrome Fact Sheet*; *Guidelines for the Use of Contact Lenses In Industrial Environments*; *Children's Vision Fact Sheet*; *Infant's Vision Fact Sheet*; *Preschool Vision Fact Sheet*; *School-Age Children Fact Sheet*; *Toys, Games, and Your Child's Vision Fact Sheet*; *Corneal Modifications Fact Sheet*; *Ortho-K Fact Sheet*; *Refractive Surgery and Corneal Modification Definitions Fact Sheet*; *Contact Lenses, OPC Fact Sheet*; *What You Need to Know About Contact Lens Hygiene and Compliance Fact Sheet*; *Facts and Stats*; *Advantages and Disadvantages of Various Types of Contact Lenses Fact Sheet*; *Do's and Don'ts Fact Sheet*; *Contact Lenses and Cosmetics Fact Sheet*; *Signs of Potential Problems Fact Sheet*; *Cost of Contact Lenses Fact Sheet*; *Warning for Consumers: Popular Halloween Eye Wear Accessory Can Permanently Damage Eyes Fact Sheet*; *Low Vision Fact Sheet*; *What Causes Low Vision? Fact Sheet*; *Common Types of Low Vision Fact Sheet*; *Low Vision Care Fact Sheet*; *Low Vision Exam Fact Sheet*; *Low Vision Devices Fact Sheet*; *Low Vision Rehabilitation Fact Sheet* (Annual); *Sports and Vision Fact Sheet*; *Important Vision Skills for Sports Fact Sheet*; *AOA Public Programs Fact Sheet*; *InfantSEE(TM) Fact Sheet*; *Vision USA Fact Sheet*; *Referral Instructions Fact Sheet*; *Vision USA Application Form Fact Sheet*; *Optometric Disaster Relief Fund Fact Sheet*; *Optometry: Journal of the American Optometric Association* (Monthly); *American Optometric Association News* (Daily); *Donate to the Optometric Disaster Relief Fund Fact Sheet*; *Request a Grant Fact Sheet*; *Additional Relief Resources Fact Sheet*; *Parents and Educators Fact Sheet*; *How Your Eyes Work Fact Sheet*; *A Look at Reading and Vision*; *Classroom Exercises Fact Sheet*; *Classroom Exercises: Day and Night Fact Sheet*; *Classroom Exercises: Pinhole Focusing Fact Sheet*; *Eye Safety Fact Sheet*; *Nystagmus Fact Sheet*; *Adult Vision: 41 to 60 Years of Age*; *Adult Vision: Over 60 Years of Age*; *Flood-Related Eye Care Precautions.* **Educational Activities:** Optometry's Meeting (Annual). **Awards:** AOA Apollo Award (Annual); AOA Distinguished Service Award (Annual); AOA Optometrist of the Year Award (Annual); AOA Young Optometrist of the Year (Annual). **Geographic Preference:** National.

16317 ■ Salus University - Gerard Cottet Library
8360 Old York Rd.
 Elkins Park, PA 19027
URL: http://www.salus.edu/Academics/Gerard-Cotte t-Library.aspx
Contact: Dr. Michael H. Mittelman, President
Description: Library serves students and faculties of Salus University. **Scope:** Clinical medicine; evidence-based medicine; bibliography. **Services:** Interlibrary loan; copying; library open to the public with restrictions. **Founded:** 1918. **Holdings:** 11,000 textbooks and periodicals. **Subscriptions:** 280 journals and other serials.

16318 ■ Southern California College of Optometry - M.B. Ketchum Memorial Library
2575 Yorba Linda Blvd.
 Fullerton, CA 92831
Ph: (714)449-7440
Co. E-mail: library@ketchum.edu
URL: http://ketchum.ent.sirsi.net/client/en_US/default
Contact: Whitney Sproul, Librarian
E-mail: wsproul@ketchum.edu
Facebook: www.facebook.com/mbkulibrary
Instagram: www.instagram.com/mbkulibrary
Scope: Optometry; pharmacy; physician assistant. **Founded:** 1948. **Holdings:** Books; e-books.

RESEARCH CENTERS

16319 ■ Duke University Hospital Outpatient Department - Duke Eye Center
2351 Erwin Rd.
 Durham, NC 27705-4699
Ph: (919)681-3937
URL: http://www.dukehealth.org/locations/duke-eye -center
Facebook: www.facebook.com/DukeEye
X (Twitter): twitter.com/DukeHealth
YouTube: www.youtube.com/user/Dukemedicine
Description: Integral unit of Duke University. **Scope:** Eye disorders, with special focus on retinal detachment, corneal diseases, and proliferative diabetic retinopathy. **Founded:** 1972.

16320 ■ Robert Cizik Eye Clinic
6400 Fannin St., Ste. 1980 19th Fl.
 Houston, TX 77030
Ph: (713)486-9400
URL: http://www.cizikeyedoctors.org
Facebook: www.facebook.com/CizikEyeClinic
Description: Cooperative effort between Hermann Hospital and University of Texas—Houston Health Science Center. The Hermann Eye Fund provides help for indigent patients and funds for research and teaching. **Scope:** Deals with cataracts, corneal disease, glaucoma, neuroophthalmology, ophthalmic surgery, pediatric ophthalmology, strabismus, and retinal disease. Additional studies include ocular melanoma, retinitis pigmentosa, diabetes, retinal pigment epithelial transplantation, ischemic optic neuropathy decompression, and pattern electrogram in Alzheimer's disease. **Founded:** 1977. **Educational Activities:** Cizik Eye Clinic Courses and seminars.

16321 ■ University of Calgary - Department of Psychology - Vision and Aging Laboratory (VAL)
2500 University Dr. NW
 Calgary, AB, Canada T2N 1N4
URL: http://psyc.ucalgary.ca/manageprofile/research/ publications/view/220-40336
Contact: Donald Kline, Author
E-mail: donkline@ucalgary.ca
Description: Integral unit of Department of Psychology, University of Calgary. Offers gerontological vision testing and correction. **Scope:** Aging effects on vision, optical and neural aspects of visual aging, visual aging, visual human factors and everyday tasks; visual health, refractive surgery, vision change and quality-of-life, visual testing.

16322 ■ University of California, Los Angeles (UCLA) - David Geffen School of Medicine - Jules Stein Eye Institute (JSEI)
100 Stein Plz. UCLA
 Los Angeles, CA 90095-7000
Ph: (310)825-5000
Co. E-mail: info@jsei.ucla.edu
URL: http://www.uclahealth.org/eye/stein-eye-insti tute
Contact: Johnese Spisso, Director
Description: Institute provides comprehensive programs for preservation of vision and blindness. Offers UCLA Mobile Eye Clinic. **Scope:** Specializes in the diagnosis, medical and surgical treatment of eye diseases, including glaucoma. Performs clinical research in ophthalmology. Provides the following services: Eye treatment, eye examinations, aesthetic surgery, refractive surgery and emergency eye care. Consulting services are offered for eye disorders and visual system diseases in subspecialty consultation suites, treatment centers and clinical laboratories, as well as in specially equipped ophthalmic surgical suites and a dedicated inpatient unit. Research includes cataract, external ocular and corneal disease, glaucoma, neuro-ophthalmology, ophthalmic pathology, orbital and ophthalmic plastic surgery, pediatric ophthalmology and strabismus, and retinal disease. **Founded:** 1966. **Publications:** "Clinician's view of the molecular genetics of age-related maculopathy," 2007; "Morcher iris diaphragm for treatment of light and glare sensitivity in partial or complete aniridia," 2004; "Ophtec model 311 iris reconstruction lens for the treatment of visual disturbances resulting from partial or complete aniridia," 2004; "Prospective study of extraocular muscle imaging in complex strabismus," 2003; "Phototherapeutic keratectomy versus diamond burr polishing of Bowman's membrane in the treatment of recurrent corneal erosions associated with anterior basement membrane dystrophy," Apr, 2002; "Diamond burr superficial keratectomy for recurrent corneal erosions," Mar, 2002. **Educational Activities:** JSEI Grand Rounds (Weekly (Wed.)); Jules Stein Eye Institute Seminar.

ASSOCIATIONS AND OTHER ORGANIZATIONS

16323 ■ *Advisor*
22 Spiral Dr.
 Florence, KY 41042
Ph: (859)283-1885
Fax: (859)283-8178
Co. E-mail: info@nkadd.org
URL: http://nkadd.org
URL(s): us7.campaign-archive.com/home/?u=bb379
 4330c2da62b5d8595091&id=78ba71998a
Released: Monthly; last update, April 2023. **Availability:** Print.

16324 ■ Association of TeleServices International (ATSI)
1000 Westgate Dr., Ste. 252
 Saint Paul, MN 55114
Free: 866-896-2874
Co. E-mail: admin@atsi.org
URL: http://atsi.org
Contact: Jim Reandeau, President
E-mail: jim@focustele.com
Facebook: www.facebook.com/ATSIorg
X (Twitter): x.com/atsiorg
Description: Seeks to foster growth and development in the industry. Represents the industry before Congress and regulatory agencies; negotiates with telephone companies. **Founded:** 1942. **Publications:** *Association of Telemessaging Services International--Membership Directory* (Annual); *Connections* (Bimonthly); *TeleCommunicator* (Bimonthly). **Educational Activities:** ATSI Annual Conference (Annual). **Geographic Preference:** National.

16325 ■ Canadian Call Management Association (CAM-X)
24 Olive St., Unit No 10
 Grimsby, ON, Canada L3M 2B6
Ph: (905)309-0224
Free: 800-896-1054
Fax: (905)309-0225
Co. E-mail: info@camx.ca
URL: http://www.camx.ca
Contact: Linda Osip, Executive Director
E-mail: linda@camx.ca
Facebook: www.facebook.com/people/CAM-X/1000
 57082765650
Linkedin: www.linkedin.com/company/cam-x-cana
 dian-call-management-association

Description: Facilitates technical advancement in the field of telecommunications. **Founded:** 1964. **Publications:** *Advisor* (Monthly). **Awards:** CAM-X Award of Excellence (Annual); CAM-X Call Centre Award of Distinction (Annual). **Geographic Preference:** National.

16326 ■ Telecommunications Industry Association (TIA)
1310 N Courthouse Rd., Ste. 890
 Arlington, VA 22201
Ph: (703)907-7700
Fax: (703)907-7727
URL: http://tiaonline.org
Contact: Doug Moore, President
Facebook: www.facebook.com/TIAEvents
X (Twitter): x.com/TIAonline
YouTube: www.youtube.com/c/TIANOW/featured
Description: Serves the communications and IT industry, with proven strengths in standards development, domestic and international public policy, and trade shows. Facilitates business development and opportunities and a competitive market environment; provides a forum for member companies, the manufacturers and suppliers of products and services used in global communications. **Founded:** 1988. **Publications:** *TIA Directory and Desk Reference*; *Industry Pulse*; *Channel Intelligence Report*; *Industry Beat* (Weekly); *PulseOnline* (Monthly); *TIA Network* (Weekly). **Educational Activities:** Network of the Future (Annual). **Geographic Preference:** National.

REFERENCE WORKS

16327 ■ *"How the Death of Voicemail is Changing the Way We Connect" In Phys.org (May 16, 2018)*
URL(s): phys.org/news/2018-05-death-voicemail.html
Ed: Ethan Baron. **Released:** May 16, 2018. **Description:** People are adjusting the ways they communicate with technology, and that includes phasing out voicemail. With texting and messaging on the rise, calling and leaving a voicemail is becoming obsolete. **Availability:** Online.

CONSULTANTS

16328 ■ Network Consulting & Associates Inc. (NCA)
2207 Yale Cir.
 Hoffman Estates, IL 60192
Ph: (847)551-1918
URL: http://www.nca-web.com

Description: Project management specialists with expertise in design, development, installation and ongoing operation of telecommunications systems including private networks, corporate voice networks, telephone systems, videoconferencing, voice mail systems, by-pass systems, fiber optics, microwave, facsimile and premise distribution systems. Specialty areas include requirements definitions, RFP's, proposal evaluations, feasibility studies and system cut-overs. **Scope:** Project management specialists with expertise in design, development, installation and ongoing operation of telecommunications systems including private networks, corporate voice networks, telephone systems, videoconferencing, voice mail systems, by-pass systems, fiber optics, microwave, facsimile and premise distribution systems. Specialty areas include requirements definitions, RFP's, proposal evaluations, feasibility studies and system cut-overs. **Training:** Getting Started - Your Own In-house Project; IBM Midrange AS400 Support; Network Evaluations.

16329 ■ Reston Consulting Group Inc. (RCG)
462 Herndon Pky., Ste. 203
 Herndon, VA 20170
Ph: (703)834-1155
Co. E-mail: info@rcg.com
URL: http://rcg.com
Contact: Katt Hancher, Director, Human Resources
E-mail: katt.hancher@rcg.com
Description: Provider of network designing, engineering and security services, and much more. **Scope:** Provider of network designing, engineering and security services, and much more. **Founded:** 1987.

LIBRARIES

16330 ■ Pitney Bowes Inc.
Pitney Bowes Inc.
 3001 Summer St.
 Stamford, CT 06926-0700
Ph: (203)356-5000
Free: 844-256-6444
URL: http://www.pitneybowes.com/us
Contact: Debbie Pfeiffer, Division President Executive Vice President
Facebook: www.facebook.com/PitneyBowes
Linkedin: www.linkedin.com/company/pitney-bowes
X (Twitter): twitter.com/pitneybowes
Instagram: www.instagram.com/pitneybowes
YouTube: www.youtube.com/user/PitneyBowesInc
Description: Offers solutions, services, and products in the areas of customer information management and engagement, location intelligence, shipping and mailing, and global e-commerce. **Founded:** 1920. **Publications:** *Smart Mail* (Quarterly).

ASSOCIATIONS AND OTHER ORGANIZATIONS

16331 ■ Water Quality Association (WQA)
2375 Cabot Dr.
Lisle, IL 60532-3696
Ph: (630)505-0160
Co. E-mail: wqa@wqa.org
URL: http://wqa.org
Contact: Pauli Undesser, Chief Executive Officer
E-mail: pundesser@wqa.org
Facebook: www.facebook.com/WaterQualityAssocia
tion
Linkedin: www.linkedin.com/company/water-quality
-association
X (Twitter): x.com/wqaorg
Instagram: www.instagram.com/wqa_h2o

Description: Individuals or firms engaged in the manufacture and/or assembly and distribution and/or retail selling of water treatment equipment, supplies, and services. Promotes the acceptance and use of industry equipment, products, and services. Provides activities, programs, and services designed to improve economy and efficiency within the industry. Conducts expositions and certification and equipment validation programs. Compiles statistics. **Founded:** 1974. **Publications:** *Water Professional Database*; *Validated Water Treatment Equipment Directory* (Updated continuously; printed on request); *Water Quality Association--Membership Directory* (Annual); *Directory of WQA Certified Personnel* (Annual); *Water Quality Glossary*; *WQA NewsFax*. **Educational Activities:** Water Quality Association Convention Exposition (Annual); WQA Aquatech USA. **Awards:** WQA Hall of Fame Award (Annual). **Geographic Preference:** National.

REFERENCE WORKS

16332 ■ "Blackwater Is LEED Golden for Port of Portland Building" in Contractor (Vol. 56, October 2009, No. 10, pp. 3)
Ed: Robert P. Mader. **Description:** Worrel Water Technologies' Tidal Wetlands Living Machine recycles blackwater from the toilets and sends it right back to flush the toilets. The Technology is being installed in the new headquarters of the Port of Portland which aims to get awarded a gold certificate from the Leadership in Energy and Environmental Design. **Availability:** Print; Online.

16333 ■ "Corporate Park Retrofits for Water Savings" in Contractor (Vol. 56, October 2009, No. 10, pp. 5)
Description: Merrit Corporate Park in Norwalk, Connecticut has been interested in improving building efficiency and one of their buildings has been retrofitted with water-efficient plumbing systems which will allow them to save as much as two million gallons of water. ADP Service Corp. helped the park upgrade their plumbing system. **Availability:** Online.

16334 ■ "Next Stage of Green Building will be Water Efficiency" in Contractor (Vol. 56, July 2009, No. 7, pp. 41)
Description: One market report says that water efficiency and conservation will become critical factors in green design, construction, and product selection in the next five years from 2009. The report outlines how critical it will be for the construction industry to address responsible water practices in the future. **Availability:** Print; Online.

16335 ■ Water Conditioning & Purification--Buyers Guide Issue
Pub: Publicom Inc.
Contact: Kurt C. Peterson, Director
E-mail: kcpeterson@wcponline.com
URL(s): wcponline.com/buyers-guide
Linkedin: www.linkedin.com/company/water-condi
tioning-&-purification
X (Twitter): x.com/WCPonline
Released: 10/year **Description:** Publication includes list of about 800 manufacturers and suppliers in the water treatment and purification industry. **Entries include:** Company name, address, phone, name of contact, line of business. **Arrangement:** Classified by product/service, then alphabetical. **Indexes:** Brand and trade names, product. **Availability:** Print; Online.

16336 ■ "WQA Develops Certification Program" in Contractor (Vol. 57, January 2010, No. 1, pp. 56)
Ed: Dennis Sowards. **Description:** Water Quality Association is now offering a new certification program for companies that may be affected by California's law that prohibits any products intended to convey or dispense water for human consumption that is not lead-free. All pipe or plumbing fixtures must be certified by a third party certification body. **Availability:** Print; Online.

16337 ■ "WQA's Leadership Conference Tackles Industry Issues" in Contractor (Vol. 56, October 2009, No. 10, pp. 3)
Ed: Candace Roulo. **Description:** Water Quality Association's Mid-Year Leadership Conference held in Bloomingdale, Illinois in September 2009 tackled lead regulation, water softeners, and product efficiency. The possibility of a WQA green seal was discussed by the Water Sciences Committee and the Government Relations Committee meeting. **Availability:** Online.

TRADE PERIODICALS

16338 ■ Backflow Prevention Journal
Pub: International Association of Plumbing and Mechanical Officials
Contact: D. J. Nunez, President
URL(s): backflowpreventionjournal.orgwww.iapmo
.org/bpi/publications/backflow-prevention-journal
X (Twitter): x.com/BkflowPrevInst

Released: Bimonthly **Description:** Presents articles directed toward "individuals, companies, organizations, agencies, and municipalities with an interest in drinking water protection and backflow prevention." Contains information on safety standards, water system protection, training programs, cross-connection control, and all issues related to preventing the contamination of potable drinking water supplies with backflow prevention devices. Recurring features include case studies, letters to the editor, news of research, columns titled Test Your Investigative Skills and Backflow Prevention Device Repairs, and reports of meetings. Also carries news of educational opportunities, job listings, notices of publications available, and a calendar of events. **Availability:** Online.

16339 ■ Water Desalination Report
Pub: Maria C. Smith
URL(s): www.desalination.com/publications/desalina
tion-report-wdr
Released: Weekly **Price:** $550, For Single Issue. **Description:** Concentrates on the activities of government and industry worldwide concerning the desalination of seawater and brackish water. Discusses such topics as problems with water supply and reuse, resource planning, and pollution control. Reports on federal budgets, regulation, new and future programs, opportunities in business, and research. Recurring features include book reviews and a schedule of activities. **Availability:** Print; Online; PDF.

16340 ■ Water Policy Report
Pub: Inside Washington Publishers
Contact: Robert Woolard, Contact
URL(s): iwpnews.com/index.html#products
Released: Biweekly **Price:** $730, U.S. for per year; $730, Canada for per year; $780, Elsewhere for per year. **Description:** Reports on federal water quality programs and policies. Covers topics such as drinking water, toxics, enforcement, monitoring, and state/EPA relations. **Availability:** Online.

16341 ■ Water Technology
Pub: Endeavor Business Media, LLC
Contact: Chris Ferrell, Chief Executive Officer
E-mail: cferrell@endeavorbusinessmedia.com
URL(s): www.watertechonline.com
Facebook: www.facebook.com/WaterTechnolog
Linkedin: www.linkedin.com/showcase/water
-technology-magazine
X (Twitter): x.com/WaterTechOnline
Ed: Dr. Joseph Cotruvo, Molly Rogers. **Released:** Bimonthly **Description:** Magazine focusing on point of use water treatment. **Availability:** Print; PDF; Download; Online.

TRADE SHOWS AND CONVENTIONS

16342 ■ AWRA Annual Conference
American Water Resources Association (AWRA)
PO Box 2663
Woodbridge, VA 22195

Ph: (540)687-8390
Fax: (540)687-8395
Co. E-mail: info@awra.org
URL: http://www.awra.org
Contact: Claire Bleser, President
URL(s): www.awra.org/AWRA/iCore/Events/Even
t_display.aspx?EventKey=ANNLSE2024
Frequency: Annual. **Description:** Water resources
science and technology. **Audience:** Water resource
professionals and students. **Principal Exhibits:**
Water resources science and technology. **Telecommunication Services:** membership@awra.org.

16343 ■ AWT Annual Convention & Exposition
Association of Water Technologies (AWT)
 1300 Piccard Dr., Ste. 114
 Rockville, MD 20850
Ph: (301)740-1421
Fax: (301)990-9771
Co. E-mail: awt@awt.org
URL: http://www.awt.org
Contact: Noah R. Baskin, President
URL(s): 2024.mspdev.awt.org/event/2024-annual
 -convention-and-exposition-exhibitors-sponsors
Frequency: Annual. **Description:** Provides regional
water treatment companies with technical education,
industry communication, access to information, group
purchasing discounts, legislative affairs, and sound
management techniques. **Audience:** Industry professionals. **Principal Exhibits:** Provides regional water
treatment companies with technical education,
industry communication, access to information, group
purchasing discounts, legislative affairs, and sound
management techniques. Dates and Locations: 2025
Nov 12-15 The Broadmoor Hotel, Colorado Spring,
CO; 2026 Sep 16-19 Oklahoma City Convention
Center and Omni Hotel, Oklahoma City, OK; 2027
Sep 08-11 Cleveland Convention Center, Cleveland,
OH. **Telecommunication Services:** jmartin@msp-
amc.com.

16344 ■ AWWA Annual Conference & Exposition
HDR
 10450 Holmes Rd., Ste. 600
 Kansas City, MO 64131-3471
Ph: (816)360-2700
Fax: (816)360-2777
URL: http://www.hdrinc.com
Contact: Helvi Sandvik, President
URL(s): www.awwa.org/ace
Frequency: Annual. **Description:** Wastewater treatment products and services, including distribution
systems analysis, conservation, GIS, certification,
pumps, groundwater, water supply, leak and backflow, pipes and equipment, valves, instrumentation,
chemicals, construction, modeling, software, and corrosion. **Audience:** Industry professionals, including
management, design and engineering, executives,
operations, consultants, marketing and sales, scientists, educators, and regulators. **Principal Exhibits:**
Wastewater treatment products and services, including distribution systems analysis, conservation, GIS,
certification, pumps, groundwater, water supply, leak
and backflow, pipes and equipment, valves, instrumentation, chemicals, construction, modeling, software, and corrosion. Dates and Locations: 2025 Jun
08-11 Denver, CO; 2026 Jun 21-24 Washington, DC;
2027 Jun 13-16 San Diego, CA; 2028 Jun 04-07
Atlanta, GA; 2029 Jun 10-13 Toronto, ON. **Telecommunication Services:** awwaconferences@awwa.
org.

16345 ■ FGWA Convention & Trade Show
Grundfos
 902 Koomey Rd.
 Brookshire, TX 77423
URL: http://www.grundfos.com/us
Contact: Jens Winther Moberg, Chairman of the
Board
URL(s): www.fgwa.org/annual-convention-trade-show
Frequency: Annual; held in May or early June.
Description: The protection, promotion, and develop-
ment of groundwater resources. **Audience:** Ground-
water industry professionals. **Principal Exhibits:** The

protection, promotion, and development of groundwater resources. Dates and Locations: 2025 May 27-29
Omni Orlando Resort at ChampionsGate, Orlando,
FL. **Telecommunication Services:** membership@
fgwa.org.

16346 ■ Water Quality Technology Conference and Exposition (WQTC)
URL(s): www.awwa.org/conferences-education/con-
ferences.aspx
Audience: Water professionals.

FRANCHISES AND BUSINESS OPPORTUNITIES

16347 ■ Culligan International Co.
Culligan International Co.
 9399 W Higgins Rd., Ste. No. 1100
 Rosemont, IL 60018
Ph: (847)430-2800
Fax: (847)430-1519
Co. E-mail: internationalinfo@culligan.com
URL: http://www.culligan.com
Facebook: www.facebook.com/culligan
Linkedin: www.linkedin.com/company/culligan-interna
tional-company
X (Twitter): x.com/heyculligan
YouTube: www.youtube.com/user/CulliganIntl
Description: Water treatment devices, softeners,
filters, drinking water units and bottled water. **Scope:**
A water treatment company providing water filtration
products including water softeners, water filtration
systems, drinking water systems and whole-house
filtration systems. Offers reverse osmosis and deion-
ization services, delivered bottled water, free basic
water analysis and site surveys, engineering/design
assistance, educational programs, variety of sales,
rental and leasing plans. Industries served: manufacturing, new construction, restaurants, grocery,
hospitality, education, healthcare, assisted living, car
washes, government, laundries and beauty salons/
spas. **Founded:** 1936. **Training:** Yes.

LIBRARIES

16348 ■ CDM Smith Inc. - Library
CDM Smith Inc.
 75 State St., Ste. 701
 Boston, MA 02109
Ph: (617)452-6000
Fax: (617)345-3901
URL: http://cdmsmith.com
Contact: Anthony B. Bouchard, President
Facebook: www.facebook.com/pg/CDMSmith
Linkedin: www.linkedin.com/company/cdmsmith
X (Twitter): x.com/CDMSmith
Instagram: www.instagram.com/cdmsmith
YouTube: www.youtube.com/user/CDMSmith
Description: Firm that provides environmental
engineering and consulting services. **Scope:** An
industrial engineering and management consulting
firm specializing in the operational design of distribu-
tion, fulfillment an manufacturing facilities. Focuses
on materials handling and storage system process
flow engineering including assistance in vendor
analysis and selection. **Founded:** 1947. **Holdings:**
Figures not available. **Publications:** "Arthur Kill
Storm Surge Barrier". **Training:** WateReuse Symposium, Sep, 2009; Climate Protection and Greenhouse
Gas Reduction, Feb, 2008; Cities of the Future:
Urban Sustainability and Water, Sep, 2006; Warehouse Management Systems Implementation; Materi-
als Handling System Design and Implementation;
Against the Deluge: Storm Surge Barriers to Protect
New York City; A Sustainable Southwest Florida:
Creating a Vision; Emerging Technologies and Chal-
lenges in Water Supply; Sustainable Water Supply
Challenges and Solutions; A New Vision of Sustain-
able Communities; Sustainable Energy Practices and
Technologies for Florida's Future.

16349 ■ Greeley and Hansen L.L.C. - Library
TYLin Group
 100 S Wacker Dr., Ste. 1400
 Chicago, IL 60606-4004

Contact: Matthew Cummings, President
Description: Engineering solutions provider for water
and wastewater treatment, architectural and management consulting. **Scope:** Offers sanitary and environmental engineering studies, designs and construction
services for water supply, purification, transmission,
storage and distribution; sanitary sewerage; primary,
secondary and advanced treatment of domestic and
industrial wastewater; storm water, flood control; collection, transfer and disposal of solid wastes; valuations, rate studies and financial feasibility studies.
Industries served: municipalities and other governmental authorities and private sector. Provides
architectural and management consulting services.
Founded: 1914. **Holdings:** Figures not available.

16350 ■ Massachusetts Water Resources Authority (MWRA) - Library
Charlestown Navy Yard, Bldg. 39
 100 1st Ave.
 Boston, MA 02129
Ph: (617)788-1177
Co. E-mail: ask.mwra@mwra.com
URL: http://www.mwra.com
Contact: Sean Navin, Director
X (Twitter): x.com/MWRA_update
YouTube: www.youtube.com/user/watsew1985
Description: Provides water and sewer services to
residents and industrial businesses in Massachusetts.
Scope: Water; wastewater; law. **Services:** Library
open to the public by appointment. **Founded:** 1984.
Holdings: Books; documents; reference materials;
periodicals.

16351 ■ Oklahoma State University - Ecotoxicology and Water Quality Research Laboratory Library
501 Life Sciences W
 Stillwater, OK 74078
URL: http://go.okstate.edu
Scope: Water pollution. **Holdings:** Figures not avail-
able.

16352 ■ University of Hawaii at Manoa - Water Resources Research Center (WRRC) - Library
Holmes Hall 283
 2540 Dole St.
 Honolulu, HI 96822
Ph: (808)956-7848
Fax: (808)956-5044
URL: http://www.wrrc.hawaii.edu
Contact: Daniel Aga, Director
X (Twitter): twitter.com/hawaiiwrrc
Instagram: www.instagram.com/hawaiiwrrc
Description: One of fifty-four centers of the Water
Research Institutes Program, Water Resources
Discipline, U.S. Geological Survey, located at and
affiliated with the University of Hawaii at Manoa. Of-
fers technology transfer service. **Scope:** Research
center carries out research in the following areas;
Water resources (terrestrial/coastal), including geohy-
drology, geochemistry, microbiology, environmental
engineering, public health, climatology, soil physics,
agricultural engineering, economics, agricultural
economics, law, meteorology, zoology, and ocean
engineering. Conducts water research activities in
Hawaii and the Pacific Basin area. **Services:** Library
open to the University community. **Founded:** 1964.
Holdings: Figures not available. **Publications:**
WRRC Annual report (Annual); *WRRC Bulletin*;
WRRC Project Reports; *WRRC Technical Reports*.
Educational Activities: WRRC Seminar Series (Ir-
regular); WRRC Workshops. **Awards:** L. Stephen
Lau Water Research Endowed Scholarship (Annual).

RESEARCH CENTERS

16353 ■ Central State University - International Center for Water Resources Management (ICWRM)
1400 Brush Row Rd No 142
 Wilberforce, OH 45384
URL: http://www.centralstate.edu/academics/science/
 water-resources-management
Contact: Debonne N. Wishart, Professor

E-mail: dwishart@centralstate.edu

Description: Integral unit of Central State University. Offers advisory services (occasionally). **Scope:** Water resources management, including water quality, hydrology, hydraulics, remote sensing, irrigation and drainage, socio-economic issues; agricultural water management; water resources economics, effects of water quality on the management of water resources, hydrogeology, geophysics, and geochemical modeling. **Founded:** 1987. **Publications:** *ICWRM Annual reports.*

16354 ■ Cooling Technology Institute (CTI)
3845 Cypress Creek Pky., Ste. 420
  Houston, TX 77068
Ph: (281)583-4087
Fax: (281)537-1721
URL: http://www.cti.org
Contact: Ken Mortensen, President
E-mail: ken.mortensen@spx.com
Facebook: www.facebook.com/people/Cooling-Technology-Institute/100037187895854
Linkedin: www.linkedin.com/company/cooling-technology-institute
X (Twitter): x.com/CoolingTechInst

Description: Seeks to improve the technology, design and performance of water conservation apparatus. Develops standard specifications for cooling towers; provides inspection services. Conducts research through technical subcommittees. Sponsors projects; maintains speakers' bureau. **Scope:** Investigates ways to improve technology, design, performance, and maintenance of water-cooling towers. Works to reduce water and air pollution. **Founded:** 1950. **Publications:** *CTI Journal* (Semiannual); *CTI News* (Semiannual); *CTI Manual*. **Educational Activities:** CTI Committee Workshop (Annual); Annual Conference and CTI Expo (Annual). **Geographic Preference:** National.

16355 ■ Grand Valley State University - College of Liberal Arts and Sciences - Robert B. Annis Water Resources Institute (AWRI)
740 W Shoreline Dr.
  Muskegon, MI 49441
Ph: (616)331-3749
Fax: (616)331-3864
URL: http://www.gvsu.edu/wri
Contact: Tonya Brown, Assistant
E-mail: browtony@gvsu.edu
Facebook: www.facebook.com/gvsu.awri
X (Twitter): x.com/GVSU_AWRI

Description: Integral unit of College of Liberal Arts and Sciences, Grand Valley State University. Information resource for government units and consulting engineers. **Scope:** Aquatic ecology, ecosystem restoration, education and outreach, environmental toxicology, fisheries, hydrology, limnology, microbial ecology, molecular ecology, pollution prevention, stream ecology, watershed ecology and management, wetland ecology. **Founded:** 1986. **Publications:** *Water Resources Review* (Semiannual). **Educational Activities:** Hazardous Waste Management Workshop, Designed to help meet the training standard for hazardous waste facility personnel.; Project WET. **Awards:** Dr. Ronald W. Ward Scholarship (Annual); D.J. Angus-Scientech Educational Foundation Internship (Annual); Herbert L. Vander-Mey Internship (Annual).

16356 ■ McGill University Department of Civil Engineering and Applied Mechanics - Environmental Engineering Laboratory
Macdonald Engineering Bldg., Rm. 492
  817 Sherbrooke St. W
  Montreal, QC, Canada H3A 0C3
Ph: (514)398-6860
Fax: (514)398-7361
URL: http://mcgill.ca/civil/grad/areas/environmental
Contact: Ronald Gehr, Specialist

E-mail: ronald.gehr@mcgill.ca

Description: Integral unit of Department of Civil Engineering and Applied Mechanics, McGill University. **Scope:** Water and wastewater treatment, including wastewater disinfection, bioremediation, sludge processing, odor characterization, enzyme processes, carbon dioxide sequestration, and site remediation. **Educational Activities:** Graduate research training in engineering.

16357 ■ Morehead State University Water Testing Laboratory (MSU WTL)
150 University Blvd.
  Morehead, KY 40351
Co. E-mail: admissions@moreheadstate.edu
URL: http://www.moreheadstate.edu/bwa

Description: Integral unit of Morehead State University. **Scope:** Conducts water quality testing for sewage contamination and the presence of bacteria and fungi in drinking water, recreation water, and water utilized by hemodialysis units. Also performs soil assays for Histoplama Capsulation and Cryptococcus Neoformans and performs analysis for Cryptosporidium Parvum and Giardia in raw and treated water. **Founded:** 1979.

16358 ■ Ohio State University College of Engineering - Ohio Water Resources Center (WRC)
2070 Neil Ave.
  Columbus, OH 43210
Ph: (614)292-2807
Co. E-mail: ohiowrc@osu.edu
URL: http://wrc.osu.edu
Contact: Dr. Linda Weavers, Director
E-mail: weavers.1@osu.edu
X (Twitter): twitter.com/ohio_wrc

Description: One of 54 centers of the Water Research Institutes Program, Water Resources Discipline, U.S. Geological Survey, located at and affiliated with Ohio State University. **Scope:** Administers and coordinates research in the University and within the state on water and water-related problems, including water quality, hydrology, water and wastewater treatment, industrial waste treatment, and water resource economics. Trains scientists and engineers in water management. **Founded:** 1959. **Educational Activities:** WRC Luncheon Seminar (Quarterly); WRC Symposium.

16359 ■ Oklahoma State University Department of Integrative Biology - Ecotoxicology and Water Quality Research Laboratory (EWQRL)
501 Life Sciences West.
  Stillwater, OK 74078
URL: http://integrativebiology.okstate.edu/research/ecotox-a-water-quality-lab/ecotox-and-water-quality-overview

Description: Integral unit of Oklahoma State University. **Scope:** Biological aspects of water and soil pollution, including transport, fate, and effect of water pollutants, ecotoxicology, analysis of pollutants with gas chromatography, atomic absorption, and bioassays with aquatic organisms. **Founded:** 1967.

16360 ■ South Dakota State University Department of Agricultural and Biosystems Engineering - Water Resources Institute (WRI)
1175 Medary Ave.
  Brookings, SD 57007
Co. E-mail: sdsu.wri@sdstate.edu
URL: http://www.sdstate.edu/agricultural-and-biosystems-engineering/water-resources-institute
X (Twitter): twitter.com/SD_WRI

Description: One of 54 centers of the Water Research Institutes Program, Water Resources Discipline, U.S. Geological Survey, located at and affiliated with South Dakota State University. Offers

interpretation and consultation service for use of waters analyzed through the Water Quality and Water Pesticide Lab. **Scope:** Conducts and coordinates University research in water and related resources, especially those concerned with the agricultural effect on lakes, streams, and groundwater including the plant, soil, and groundwater continuum. **Founded:** 1984. **Publications:** *Water News* (Quarterly; Quarterly). **Educational Activities:** Big Sioux Water Festival (Annual); Lake Water Quality Workshop, Offer exemplary teaching and training programs.; Lakes are Cool Festival; Northern Prairie Water Festival.

16361 ■ Tennessee Technological University - College of Engineering - Center for the Management, Utilization and Protection of Water Resources
1 William L Jones Dr.
  Cookeville, TN 38505
Ph: (931)372-3507
Co. E-mail: cmupwr@tntech.edu
URL: http://www.tntech.edu/research/centersandfacilities/wrc/center-address.php
Contact: Dr. Jeff Schaeffer, Director
E-mail: jschaeffer@tntech.edu

Description: Integral unit of College of Engineering, Tennessee Technological University. **Scope:** Water use, water availability, wastewater treatment and disposal, and toxic substance identification, focusing on management and protection of water resources to provide sustainable water supplies and habitat for fisheries, including resource management, environmental aquatic hazards, and watershed analysis.

16362 ■ Texas State University-San Marcos - College of Sciences and Engineering - Edwards Aquifer Research & Data Center (EARDC)
601 University Dr.
  248 Freeman Aquatic Bldg.
  San Marcos, TX 78666
Ph: (512)245-2329
Fax: (512)245-2669
URL: http://www.eardc.txst.edu
Contact: Dr. Benjamin Schwartz, Director
E-mail: bs37@txstate.edu

Description: Integral unit of College of Sciences and Engineering, Texas State University-San Marcos. Offers laboratory services; ten aquatic studies summer camps, aquatic studies field days, educational presentations, seminars, and workshops. **Scope:** Groundwater ecosystem studies, focusing on the Edwards Aquifer, water quality, and groundwater modeling. **Founded:** 1979. **Publications:** *Newsletter* (Annual).

16363 ■ University of Massachusetts at Amherst - Water Resources Research Center (WRRC)
250 Natural Resources Rd.
  Amherst, MA 01003-9295
Ph: (413)545-5531
Co. E-mail: wrrc@umass.edu
URL: http://wrrc.umass.edu

Description: Research center supports research, education and outreach on water resources issues of state, regional and national importance on water resources. Offers coordination of lake and river citizen monitoring. **Scope:** Research projects on lakes, streams, groundwater, and estuaries involve problems of engineering, resource planning and management, economics, geohydrology, ecology, and social sciences. Specific studies include an assessment of non-point sources dissolved of organic matter contributions to the coastal zone. **Founded:** 1965. **Publications:** *WRRC Technical reports* (Annual). **Educational Activities:** Water Resources Research Conference, In late October.; Massachusetts Water Resources Research Center Workshops, Focusing on water resources. **Awards:** USGS Water Resources Research Institute Program (Annual).

Web Site Design

START-UP INFORMATION

16364 ■ *"Brand Storytelling Becomes a Booming Business"* in *Entrepreneur* (April 2012)
Pub: Entrepreneur Media Inc.
Contact: Dan Bova, Director
E-mail: dbova@entrepreneur.com

Ed: Paula Andruss. **Description:** San Francisco-based Story House Creative engages in helping small businesses connect with their audience in communicating their brand identity. Web content, bios and tag lines are some of the marketing materials Story House Creative creates for its clients. The company also does search engine optimization, video, design, and copywriting. The Brandery, another brand-building company, helps startups promote their business. Eight to ten Brandery mentors are assigned to assist each startup client. Meanwhile, Brand Journalists is a Tennessee-based company focusing on corporate storytelling. It offers Web and blog content, human stories reporting and ghostwriting services. **Availability:** Print; Online.

16365 ■ *"Fort Lauderdale Startup Wants You To 'Join the Club"* in *South Florida Business Journal* (Vol. 35, September 19, 2014, No. 8, pp. 14)
Pub: American City Business Journals, Inc.
Contact: Mike Olivieri, Executive Vice President

Description: Profile of Florida based club is presented. The company is a top provider of Internet Websites. It also enables businesses to purchase short Website names for low prices. **Availability:** Online.

16366 ■ *How to Start a Home-Based Web Design Business*
Ed: Jim Smith. **Released:** 4th edition. **Price:** paperback/softback. **Description:** Information for starting a home-based Web design firm is given. **Availability:** Print.

16367 ■ *How to Start a Home-Based Web Design Business, 4th Edition*
Ed: Jim Smith. **Released:** Fourth edition. **Price:** Paperback. **Description:** Comprehensive guide contains all the necessary tools and strategies required to successfully launch and grow a Web design business. **Availability:** Print.

ASSOCIATIONS AND OTHER ORGANIZATIONS

16368 ■ Idealliance - Library [International Digital Enterprise Alliance]
1800 Diagonal Rd., Ste. 320
Alexandria, VA 22314-2862
Ph: (703)837-1070
Fax: (703)837-1072
Co. E-mail: membership@idealliance.org
URL: http://idealliance.org
Contact: Jordan Gorski, Executive Director

E-mail: jgorski@idealliance.org
Facebook: www.facebook.com/idealliance
Linkedin: www.linkedin.com/company/idealliance
X (Twitter): x.com/Idealliance
Instagram: www.instagram.com/idealliance
YouTube: www.youtube.com/c/idealliance

Description: Works to advance user-driven, cross-industry solutions for all publishing and content-related processes by developing standards fostering business alliances and identifying best practices. **Scope:** Training; graphics; designers. **Founded:** 1966. **Holdings:** Figures not available. **Publications:** *EDIrectory; Prepress Bulletin; Graphic Communications Association--Membership Directory* (Semiannual); *GCA Audio-Visual Listing.* **Geographic Preference:** Multinational.

EDUCATIONAL PROGRAMS

16369 ■ EEI Communications Active Server Pages I
URL(s): www.eeicom.com

Description: Covers Active Server Pages (ASP) basics and development, building an ASP dictionary object, utilizing text files, researching and installing third-party ASP components, and writing advanced database queries. **Audience:** Graphic/web designers and programmers . **Principal Exhibits:** Covers Active Server Pages (ASP) basics and development, building an ASP dictionary object, utilizing text files, researching and installing third-party ASP components, and writing advanced database queries. **Telecommunication Services:** train@eeicom.com.

16370 ■ EEI Communications Adobe ColdFusion I
URL(s): www.eeicom.com

Description: Covers creating databases and Web sites utilizing ColdFusion. **Audience:** Web designers. **Principal Exhibits:** Covers creating databases and Web sites utilizing ColdFusion. **Telecommunication Services:** train@eeicom.com.

16371 ■ EEI Communications Adobe Dreamweaver I (Onsite)
URL(s): www.eeicom.com

Description: Covers utilizing Dreamweaver's page-layout capabilities, site management tools, and support for dynamic HTML to create Web pages. **Audience:** Industry professionals. **Principal Exhibits:** Covers utilizing Dreamweaver's page-layout capabilities, site management tools, and support for dynamic HTML to create Web pages. **Telecommunication Services:** train@eeicom.com.

16372 ■ EEI Communications Adobe Dreamweaver II (Onsite)
URL(s): www.eeicom.com

Description: Covers advanced Web page development focusing on CSS Layout, advanced site building features, site management, behaviors, interactivity, and customization. **Audience:** Industry professionals. **Principal Exhibits:** Covers advanced Web page development focusing on CSS Layout, ad-

vanced site building features, site management, behaviors, interactivity, and customization. **Telecommunication Services:** train@eeicom.com.

16373 ■ EEI Communications Adobe Dreamweaver III (Onsite)
URL(s): www.eeicom.com

Description: Learn how to set up and use Dreamweaver to build server-side scripting (ASP, ColdFusion, or PHP) in order to manage database content on the Web. **Audience:** Web designers and industry professionals. **Principal Exhibits:** Learn how to set up and use Dreamweaver to build server-side scripting (ASP, ColdFusion, or PHP) in order to manage database content on the Web. **Telecommunication Services:** train@eeicom.com.

16374 ■ EEI Communications Adobe Fireworks I
URL(s): www.eeicom.com

Description: Covers utilizing Fireworks and drawing tools, photo editing tools, and optimization features to create Web graphics. **Audience:** Industry professionals. **Principal Exhibits:** Covers utilizing Fireworks and drawing tools, photo editing tools, and optimization features to create Web graphics. **Telecommunication Services:** train@eeicom.com.

16375 ■ EEI Communications Adobe GoLive
URL(s): www.eeicom.com

Description: Covers utilizing GoLive, a visual Web design program, to create complex Web pages. **Audience:** Industry professionals. **Principal Exhibits:** Covers utilizing GoLive, a visual Web design program, to create complex Web pages. **Telecommunication Services:** train@eeicom.com.

16376 ■ EEI Communications Cascading Style Sheets (CSS) I
URL(s): www.eeicom.com

Description: Covers the introduction of Document Object Module (DOM) and working with cascading style sheets. **Audience:** Industry professionals. **Principal Exhibits:** Covers the introduction of Document Object Module (DOM) and working with cascading style sheets. **Telecommunication Services:** train@eeicom.com.

16377 ■ EEI Communications JavaScript for Non-Programmers
URL(s): www.eeicom.com

Description: Covers creating and applying JavaScript to a Web site. **Audience:** IT professionals. **Principal Exhibits:** Covers creating and applying JavaScript to a Web site. **Telecommunication Services:** train@eeicom.com.

REFERENCE WORKS

16378 ■ *"2 New Tools for Safeguarding Your Website: Website Backup Made Simple"* in *Inc.* (Vol. 33, September 2011, No. 7, pp. 52)
Pub: Inc. Magazine

Ed: John Brandon. **Description:** Tools to back up content on a Website are profiled. Vaultpress works only with sites that run on the WordPress publishing platform and CodeGuard works with a variety of publishing platforms and hosting services. **Availability:** Online.

16379 ■ *"2nd Watch Rides AWS Market Maturity to 400% Growth" in Computer Business Week (August 28, 2014, pp. 21)*
Description: 2nd Watch reports record earnings for the second quarter of 2014. The firm helps companies develop and implement IT strategies that are based on Amazon Web Services (AWS). Details of the companies business strategies are outlined. **Availability:** Print; Online.

16380 ■ *"The 4 Big Reasons Apps Fail" in Engrepreneur (September 3, 2019)*
URL(s): www.entrepreneur.com/science-technology/the-4-big-reasons-apps-fail/332990
Released: September 03, 2019. **Description:** Discusses the various issues app developers do not take into consideration when creating apps for purchase and download, which keeps consumers from wanting to download them onto their phones. **Availability:** Online.

16381 ■ *"5 Reasons Why UX Design Is Important for Your Website in 2020" in Digital Agency Network (October 25, 2020)*
Ed: Gizem Tas. **Released:** October 25, 2020. **Description:** Details information on the advantages that UX design tools offer in the form of optimized usability and accessibility of your website. **Availability:** Online.

16382 ■ *"5 Tips for Designing a Logo for Your Online Store" in Digital Agency Network (October 27, 2020)*
Ed: Canberk Arinci. **Released:** October 27, 2020. **Description:** Details five tips on the importance of designing a logo for your online store. **Availability:** Online.

16383 ■ *"5 Ways to Get a Free Website for Your Small Business" in Business 2 Community (September 29, 2021)*
URL(s): www.business2community.com/small-business/5-ways-to-get-a-free-website-for-your-small-business-02433582
Ed: Emmanuel Soroba. **Released:** September 29, 2021. **Description:** Gives an overview of five popular website builders that small businesses can use for free. **Availability:** Online.

16384 ■ *"8 Web Development Trends Every CTO Should Expect in 2020" in Core dna (August 6, 2020)*
Ed: Sam Saltis. **Released:** August 06, 2020. **Description:** Details eight web development trends and technologies that make great websites. **Availability:** Online.

16385 ■ *"352 Media Group Opens New Tampa Web Design and Digital Marketing Office" in Entertainment Close-Up (May 2, 2011)*
Pub: Close-Up Media Inc.
Contact: Caroline S. Moore, President
E-mail: cms@closeupmedia.com
Description: 352 Media Group opened its newest office in Tampa, Florida in May 2011. The firm is noted for its achievements in Web design and digital marketing. **Availability:** Print; Online.

16386 ■ *"529.com Wins Outstanding Achievement in Web Development" in Investment Weekly (November 14, 2009, pp. 152)*
Pub: Investment Weekly News
Description: Web Marketing Association's 2009 WebAward for Financial Services Standard of Excellence and Investment Standard of Excellence was won by 529.com, the website from Upromise Investments, Inc., the leading administrator of 529 college savings plans. **Availability:** Online.

16387 ■ *"2015 Marketing Calendar for Real Estate Pros: Own It"*
Pub: CreateSpace
Released: October 14, 2014. **Price:** $9.56, paperback. **Description:** Real estate agents, mortgage loan agents, and new home builders and site and listing agents are shown how to use low-cost, high yield, proven marketing techniques to create digital real estate listings, find more customers, and sell more homes. Advice for building a brand and public relations; attracting renters and buyers; developing a good Website; and a digital marketing plan are explained. **Availability:** Print.

16388 ■ *"All You Need to Know About Selecting a SaaS Design Platform" in Digital Agency Network (September 11, 2020)*
Ed: Hannah Butler. **Released:** September 11, 2020. **Description:** Details on how to create astounding website designs with the help of SaaS tools. **Availability:** Online.

16389 ■ *"Auctions and Bidding: A Guide for Computer Scientists" in ACM Computing Surveys (Vol. 43, Summer 2011, No. 2, pp. 10)*
Pub: Association for Computing Machinery
Contact: Yannis Ioannidis, President
Ed: Simon Parsons, Juan A. Rodriguez-Aguilar, Mark Klein. **Released:** Volume 43 Issue 2. **Price:** $10, Members; $15, Nonmembers; $5, Students. **Description:** There are various actions: single dimensional, multi-dimensional, single-sided, double-sided, first-price, second-price, English, Dutch, Japanese, sealed-bid, and these have been extensively discussed and analyzed in economics literature. This literature is surveyed from a computer science perspective, primarily from the viewpoint of computer scientists who are interested in learning about auction theory, and to provide pointers into the economics literature for those who want a deeper technical understanding. In addition, since auctions are an increasingly important topic in computer science, the article also looks at work on auctions from the computer science literature. The aim is to identify what both bodies of work tell us about creating electronic auctions. **Availability:** Download; PDF.

16390 ■ *"avVaa World Health Care Products Rolls Out Internet Marketing Program" in Health and Beauty Close-Up (September 18, 2009)*
Description: avVaa World Health Care Products, Inc., a biotechnology company, manufacturer and distributor of nationally branded therapeutic, natural health care and skin products, has signed an agreement with Online Performance Marketing to launch of an Internet marketing campaign in order to broaden its presence online. The impact of advertising on the Internet to generate an increase in sales is explored. **Availability:** Online.

16391 ■ *"Bad Web Design Isn't Just Annoying--It Costs You" Entrepreneur NEXT (July 14, 2020)*
Ed: Mitchell Terpstra. **Released:** July 14, 2020. **Description:** Discusses how poor web design negatively affects your bottom line and offers principles of good web design. **Availability:** Online.

16392 ■ *"The Bankrate Double Play, Bankrate Is Having Its Best Quarter Yet" in Barron's (Vol. 88, March 24, 2008, No. 12, pp. 27)*
Pub: Dow Jones & Company Inc.
Contact: Almar Latour, Chief Executive Officer
Ed: Neil A. Martin. **Description:** Shares of Bankrate may rise as much as 25 percent from their level of $45.08 a share due to a strong cash flow and balance sheet. The company's Internet business remains strong despite weakness in the online advertising industry and is a potential takeover target. **Availability:** Online.

16393 ■ *"Be Wary of Legal Advice on Internet, Lawyers Warn" in Crain's Detroit Business (Vol. 24, September 22, 2008, No. 38, pp. 16)*
Pub: Crain Communications Inc.
Contact: Barry Asin, President

Ed: Harriet Tramer. **Description:** While some lawyers feel that the proliferation of legal information on the Internet can point people in the right direction, others maintain that it simply results in giving false hope, may bring about confusion or worse yet, it sometimes makes their jobs even harder. **Availability:** Online.

16394 ■ *"The Best in Business Travel" in Entrepreneur (May 2014)*
Pub: Entrepreneur Media Inc.
Contact: Dan Bova, Director
E-mail: dbova@entrepreneur.com
Description: A number of companies have been recognized for making business travel more efficient, comfortable and enjoyable. Kayak CEO Steve Hafner's goal to create the world's best travel Website with the fewest people has made the travel search engine profitable. The subscription model of Surf Air, starting at $1,599 per month for unlimited flights, provides more efficient travel experience for executives. The Club Lounge at the Langham Hotel in Chicago, Illinois combines the efficiency of a working office with a private ambiance.

16395 ■ *"Best UI & UX Design Agencies for Startups and Small Businesses in 2020" in Digital Agency Network (July 26, 2020)*
Ed: Gizem Tas. **Released:** July 26, 2020. **Description:** Lists UX design agencies who are great for startups and small businesses to help them gain an important place in the marketplace. **Availability:** Online.

16396 ■ *"Best Web Design of 2020 (So Far) - And What We Can Learn From It" in DesignRush (October 2, 2020)*
Released: October 02, 2020. **Description:** Discusses web design best practices, constantly changing trends, and highlights the need to invest in compelling UX and UI designs to improve brand credibility and increase user engagement. **Availability:** Online.

16397 ■ *"Boom has Tech Grads Mulling Their Options" in Globe & Mail (March 14, 2006, pp. B1)*
Ed: Grant Robertson. **Description:** Internet giant Google Inc. has stepped up its efforts to hire the talented people, in Canada, at Waterloo University in southern Ontario, to expand its operations. The details of the job market and increasing salaries are analyzed. **Availability:** Online.

16398 ■ *"Building a Business Website: A Small Business Guide" in Business News Daily (March 7, 2023)*
URL(s): www.businessnewsdaily.com/4661-starting-a-business-website.html
Ed: Karina Fabian. **Released:** March 07, 2023. **Description:** Even if your small business isn't an online store, having an online presence is key to targeting your audience. This article provides details on building a website and provides links for further information. **Availability:** Online.

16399 ■ *"BusinessOnLine Launches New Web-Based Search Engine Optimization Tool: First Link Checker for Google" in Marketwired (October 19, 2009)*
Pub: Comtex News Network Inc.
Contact: Kan Devnani, President
Description: First Link Checker, a complimentary new search engine optimization tool that helps site owners optimize their on-page links by understanding which of those links are actually being counted in Google's relevancy algorithm, was developed by BusinessOnLine, a rapidly growing Internet marketing agency. This tool will make it easy for the average web master to ensure that their internal link structure is optimized. **Availability:** Print.

16400 ■ *"Can You Say $1 Million? A Language-Learning Start-Up Is Hoping That Investors Can" in Inc. (Vol. 33, November 2011, No. 9, pp. 116)*
Pub: Inc. Magazine

Ed: April Joyner. **Description:** Startup, Verbling is a video platform that links language learners and native speakers around the world. The firm is working to raise money to hire engineers in order to build the product and redesign their Website. **Availability:** Online.

16401 ■ *"Citadel EFT (CDFT) Contracts With New Search Engine Optimization (SEO) and Banner Ad Web Marketing Companies" in Internet Wire (August 8, 2012)*
Pub: Comtex News Network Inc.
Contact: Kan Devnani, President
Description: Citafel EFT Inc. provides credit card terminals, online, mail order and retail credit card processing services. The firm has contracted with two Web marketing companies to increase its awareness on the Internet. **Availability:** Print; Online.

16402 ■ *Clicking Through: A Survival Guide for Bringing Your Company Online*
Released: First edition. **Description:** Summary of legal compliance issues faced by small companies doing business on the Internet, including copyright and patent laws.

16403 ■ *The Complete Guide to Google Adwords: Secrets, Techniques, and Strategies You Can Learn to Make Millions*
Pub: Atlantic Publishing Co.
Contact: Dr. Heather L. Johnson, Contact
Released: 2012. **Description:** Google AdWords, when it launched in 2002 signaled a fundamental shift in what the Internet was for so many individuals and companies. Learning and understanding how Google AdWords operates and how it can be optimized for maximum exposure, boosting click through rates, conversions, placement, and selection of the right keywords, can be the key to a successful online business. **Availability:** Print; Online.

16404 ■ *Content Rich: Writing Your Way to Wealth on the Web*
Released: 1st Edition. **Description:** A definitive search engine optimization (SEO) copywriting guide for search engine rankings and sales conversion. It includes topics not covered in other books on the subject and targets the small to medium sized business looking for ways to maximize online marketing activities as well as designers and Web developers seeking to incorporate more SEO techniques into design and content.

16405 ■ *"Conversations with Customers" in Business Journal Serving Greater Tampa Bay (Vol. 31, December 31, 2010, No. 1, pp. 1)*
Pub: Tampa Bay Business Journal
Contact: Ian Anderson, President
E-mail: ianderson@bizjournals.com
Description: Tampa Bay, Florida-based businesses have been using social media to interact with customers. Forty percent of businesses have been found to have at least one social media platform to reach customers and prospects. **Availability:** Print; Online.

16406 ■ *"Covario Recognized for Second Year in a Row as OMMA Award Finalist for Online Advertising Creativity in Both SEO and SEM' in Internet Wire (August 29, 2012)*
Pub: Comtex News Network Inc.
Contact: Kan Devnani, President
Description: Leading independent search marketing agency, Covario, providing search engine optimization (SEO) and search engine marketing (SEM) for companies was chosen as a finalist for the Media-Post Onlien Media, Marketing and Advertising award. This is Covario's second year to be recognized for this award. **Availability:** Print; Online.

16407 ■ *"Cyber Thanksgiving Online Shopping a Growing Tradition" in Marketing Weekly News (December 12, 2009, pp. 137)*
Pub: Investment Weekly News
Description: According to e-commerce analysts, Thanksgiving Day is becoming increasingly important to retailers in terms of online sales. Internet marketers are realizing that consumers are already search-ing for Black Friday sales and if they find deals on the products they are looking for, they are highly likely to make their purchase on Thanksgiving Day instead of waiting. **Availability:** Online.

16408 ■ *Designing Websites for Every Audience*
Description: Twenty-five case studies targeting six difference audiences are used to help a business design, or make over, a Website. **Availability:** E-book.

16409 ■ *"Designing Women? Apparel Apparatchic at Kmart' in Barron's (Vol. 88, March 17, 2008, No. 11, pp. 16)*
Pub: Dow Jones & Company Inc.
Contact: Almar Latour, Chief Executive Officer
Ed: Robin Goldwyn Blumenthal. **Description:** Kmart began a nationwide search for women to represent the company in a national advertising campaign. Contestants need to upload their photos to Kmart's website and winners will be chosen by a panel of celebrity judges. The contest aims to reverse preconceived negative notions about the store's quality and service. **Availability:** Online.

16410 ■ *"Do-It-Yourself Portfolio Management" in Barron's (Vol. 89, July 13, 2009, No. 28, pp. 25)*
Pub: Dow Jones & Company Inc.
Contact: Almar Latour, Chief Executive Officer
Ed: Mike Hogan. **Description:** Services of several portfolio management web sites are presented. These web sites include MarketRiders E.Adviser, TD Ameritrade and E. **Availability:** Online.

16411 ■ *"Does Your Website Violate Copyright Law? in Legal Zoom (March 27, 2023)*
URL(s): www.legalzoom.com/articles/does-your -website-violate-copyright-law
Ed: Heleigh Bostwick. **Released:** March 27, 2023. **Description:** Make sure your business website is compliant and not violating anyone's hard-earned copyright with these suggestions. **Availability:** Online.

16412 ■ *eBay Business the Smart Way*
Released: 3rd edition. **Description:** eBay commands ninety percent of all online auction business. Computer and software expert and online entrepreneur shares information to help online sellers get started and move merchandise on eBay. Tips include the best ways to build credibility, find products to sell, manage inventory, create a storefront Website, and more. **Availability:** Print; PDF.

16413 ■ *EBay Income: How ANYONE of Any Age, Location, and/or Background Can Build a Highly Profitable Online Business with eBay*
Pub: Atlantic Publishing Co.
Contact: Dr. Heather L. Johnson, Contact
Description: A complete overview of eBay is given and guides any small company through the entire process of creating the auction and auction strategies, photography, writing copy, text and formatting, multiple sales, programming tricks, PayPal, accounting, creating marketing, merchandising, managing email lists, advertising plans, taxes and sales tax, best time to list items and for how long, sniping programs, international customers, opening a storefront, electronic commerce, buy-it now pricing, keywords, Google marketing and eBay secrets.

16414 ■ *Electronic Commerce*
Ed: Gary P. Schneider, Bryant Chrzan, Charles McCormick. **Released:** 12th edition. **Price:** $29.49, e-book. **Description:** E-commerce can open the door to more opportunities than ever before for small business. Packed with real-world examples and cases, the book delivers comprehensive coverage of emerging online technologies and trends and their influence on the electronic marketplace. It details how the landscape of online commerce is evolving, reflecting changes in the economy and how business and society are responding to those changes. Balancing technological issues with the strategic business aspects of successful e-commerce, the new edition includes expanded coverage of international issues, social networking, mobile commerce, Web 2.0 technologies, and updates on spam, phishing, and identity theft. **Availability:** Print.

16415 ■ *Emerging Business Online: Global Markets and the Power of B2B Internet Marketing*
Pub: FT Press
Ed: Lara Fawzy, Lucas Dworski. **Released:** First edition. **Price:** $39.99, Members, watermarked. **Description:** An introduction into ebocube (emerging business online), a comprehensive proven business model for Internet B2B marketing in emerging markets. **Availability:** E-book; Print; Online; PDF; Electronic publishing.

16416 ■ *"Equity Crowdfunding Platform Initial Crowd Offering, Inc. Closes Equity Financing with Third-Party Investor" in GlobeNewswire (July 18, 2012)*
Description: Initial Crowd Offering Inc. closed third-party equity financing round hat provided capital to finish development of its equity crowdfunding portal to the Website. A private angel investor provided development costs to promote the firm's marketing program. Discussion on equity crowdfunding is included. **Availability:** Print; PDF; Online.

16417 ■ *The Facebook Effect: The Inside Story of the Company That Is Connecting the World*
Ed: David Kirkpatrick. **Released:** 2011. **Price:** $18, paperback; $13.99, e-book. **Description:** There's never been a Website like Facebook: more than 350 million people have accounts, and if the growth rate continues, by 2013 every Internet user worldwide will have his or her own page. No one's had more access to the inner workings of the phenomenon than Kirkpatrick, a senior tech writer at Fortune magazine. Written with the full cooperation of founder Mark Zuckerberg, the book follows the company from its genesis in a Harvard dorm room through its successes over Friendster and MySpace, the expansion of the user base, and Zuckerberg's refusal to sell. **Availability:** E-book; Print.

16418 ■ *"Five Tips for Killer Landing Pages" in Retirement Advisor (Vol. 13, October 2012, No. 10, pp. 27)*
Ed: Amy McIlwain. **Description:** The importance of Web page design is highlighted. Five tips for creating a Webpage that encourages trust and informs users about the financial products and services you offer are are given. **Availability:** Print; Online.

16419 ■ *"ForeSee Finds Satisfaction On Web Sites, Bottom Line" in Crain's Detroit Business (Vol. 24, February 25, 2008, No. 8, pp. 3)*
Pub: Crain Communications Inc.
Contact: Barry Asin, President
Ed: Tom Henderson. **Description:** Ann Arbor-based ForeSee Results Inc. evaluates user satisfaction on Web sites. The company expects to see an increase of 40 percent in revenue for 2008 with plans to expand to London, Germany, Italy and France by the end of 2009.

16420 ■ *"Get Online Quick in the Office Or in the Field" in Contractor (Vol. 56, October 2009, No. 10, pp. 47)*
Ed: William Feldman, Patti Feldman. **Description:** Contractors can set up a web site in minutes using the www.1and1.com website. Verizon's Novatel MIFI 2372 HSPA personal hotspot device lets contractors go online in the field. The StarTech scalable business management system helps contractors manage daily operations. **Availability:** Print; Online.

16421 ■ *"Google Gets Creepy" in Canadian Business (Vol. 85, September 17, 2012, No. 14, pp. 28)*
Ed: Jeff Beer. **Description:** Google's move to integrate its more than 70 different privacy agreements into just one has simplified the privacy deal

the search engine company made with its users and improved its ability to obtain information for advertising. Google is addressing concerns about online privacy and allegations of anticompetitive practices in the U.S. and Europe. **Availability:** Online.

16422 ■ "Google's Next Stop: Below 350?" in Barron's (Vol. 88, March 10, 2008, No. 10, pp. 17)
Pub: Dow Jones & Company Inc.
Contact: Almar Latour, Chief Executive Officer
Ed: Jacqueline Doherty. **Description:** Share prices of Google Inc. are expected to drop from their level of $433 each to below $350 per share. The company is expected to miss its earnings forecast for the first quarter of 2008, and its continued aggressive spending on non-core areas will eventually bring down earnings. **Availability:** Online.

16423 ■ "Grey Power: On Target" in Canadian Business (Vol. 81, July 22, 2008, No. 12-13, pp. 45)
Pub: Rogers Media Inc.
Contact: Neil Spivak, Chief Executive Officer
Ed: Calvin Leung. **Description:** Companies such as LavalifePRIME, a dating website devoted to singles 45 and older, discuss the value of marketing and services aimed at Canada's older consumers. One-third of Canada's 33 million people are 50-plus, controlling 77 percent of the countries wealth. **Availability:** Print; Online.

16424 ■ "Growth of Free Dailies Dropping" in Globe & Mail (March 24, 2007, pp. B7)
Ed: Grant Robertson. **Description:** The decrease in the readership of free newspapers in Canada, in view of growing preference for online news, is discussed. **Availability:** Online.

16425 ■ "Has Microsoft Found a Way to Get at Yahoo?" in Advertising Age (Vol. 79, July 7, 2008, No. 26, pp. 4)
Pub: Crain Communications, Inc.
Contact: Jessica Botos, Manager, Marketing
E-mail: jessica.botos@crainsnewyork.com
Ed: Abbey Klaassen. **Description:** Microsoft's attempt to acquire Yahoo's search business is discussed as is Yahoo's plans for the future at a time when the company's shares have fallen dangerously low. **Availability:** Print; Online.

16426 ■ "How to Copyright a Website" in Small Business Trends (November 16, 2021)
Ed: Rob Starr. **Released:** November 02, 2021. **Description:** Defines what it means to copyright a website, the benefits of doing so, and the steps needed to complete that task. **Availability:** Online.

16427 ■ How to Make Money with Social Media: An Insider's Guide to Using New and Emerging Media to Grow Your Business
Ed: Jamie Turner, Reshma Shah, PhD. **Released:** 2nd edition. **Description:** Marketers, executives, entrepreneurs are shown more effective ways to utilize Internet social media to make money. This guide brings together both practical strategies and proven execution techniques for driving maximum value from social media marketing. **Availability:** E-book; Print.

16428 ■ "How Marketers Can Tap the Web" in Sales and Marketing Management (November 12, 2009)
Description: Internet marketing strategies require careful planning and tools in order to track success. Businesses are utilizing this trend to attract new clients as well as keep customers they already have satisfied. Advice on website development and design is provided. **Availability:** Online.

16429 ■ How to Open and Operate a Financially Successful Bookstore on Amazon and Other Web Sites: With Companion CD-ROM
Pub: Atlantic Publishing Co.
Contact: Dr. Heather L. Johnson, Contact

Description: This book was written for every used book aficionado and bookstore owner who currently wants to take advantage of the massive collection of online resources available to start and run your own online bookstore business.

16430 ■ How to Use the Internet to Advertise, Promote, and Market Your Business or Web Site: With Little or No Money
Pub: Atlantic Publishing Co.
Contact: Dr. Heather L. Johnson, Contact
Ed: Bruce C. Brown. **Released:** Revised third edition. **Description:** Information is given to help build, promote, and make money from your Website or brick and mortar store using the Internet, with minimal costs.

16431 ■ I'm on LinkedIn - Now What?
Pub: Happy About
Contact: Ric Vatner, Chief Executive Officer
Ed: Jason Alba. **Released:** Fourth edition. **Price:** $19.95, paperback; $14.95; $9.99. **Description:** Designed to help get the most out of LinkedIn, the popular business networking site and follows the first edition and includes the latest and great approaches using LinkedIn. With over 32 million members there is a lot of potential to find and develop relationships to help in your business and personal life, but many professionals find themselves wondering what to do once they sign up. This book explains the different benefits of the system and recommends best practices (including LinkedIn Groups) so that you get the most out of LinkedIn. **Availability:** E-book; Print; PDF; DVD; Electronic publishing; Download; Online.

16432 ■ "Inside Intel's Effectiveness System for Web Marketing" in Advertising Age (Vol. 81, January 25, 2010, No. 4, pp. 4)
Pub: Crain Communications, Inc.
Contact: Jessica Botos, Manager, Marketing
E-mail: jessica.botos@crainsnewyork.com
Ed: Beth Snyder Bulik. **Description:** Overview of Intel's internally developed program called Value Point System in which the company is using in order to evaluate and measure online marketing effectiveness. **Availability:** Online.

16433 ■ "Internet Marketing 2.0: Closing the Online Chat Gap" in Agent's Sales Journal (November 2009, pp. 14)
Ed: Jeff Denenholz. **Description:** Advice regarding the implementation of an Internet marketing strategy for insurance agencies includes how and why to incorporate a chat feature in which a sales agent can communicate in real-time with potential or existing customers. It is important to understand if appropriate response mechanisms are in place to convert leads into actual sales. **Availability:** Print; Online.

16434 ■ "James Clift on How to Use AI to Create a Small Website" in Small Business Trends (November 8, 2022)
URL(s): smallbiztrends.com/2022/11/ai-website-builder.html
Ed: Holly Chavez. **Released:** November 08, 2022. **Description:** Discusses how small business owners can use AI to create websites for the business and then grow it over time. **Availability:** Online.

16435 ■ "Kuno Creative to Present the Three Steps of a Successful B2B Social Media Campaign" in Business Tech & Wireless (August 25, 2011)
Pub: Close-Up Media Inc.
Contact: Caroline S. Moore, President
E-mail: cms@closeupmedia.com
Released: August 24, 2011. **Description:** Kuno Creative, an inbound marketing agency, will host Three Steps of a Successful B2B Social Media Campaign. The firm is a provider of Website development, branding, marketing strategy, public relations, Internet marketing, and inbound marketing. **Availability:** Print; Online.

16436 ■ "Lavante, Inc. Joins Intersynthesis, Holistic Internet Marketing Company" in Marketwired (November 5, 2009)
Pub: Comtex News Network Inc.
Contact: Kan Devnani, President
Description: Lavante, Inc., the leading provider of on-demand vendor information and profit recovery audit solutions for Fortune 1000 companies has chosen Intersynthesis, a new holistic Internet marketing firm, as a provider of pay for performance services. Lavante believes that Intersynthesis' expertise and knowledge combined with their ability to develop integrated strategies, will help them fuel more growth. **Availability:** Print; Online.

16437 ■ "Legislating the Cloud" in Information Today (Vol. 28, October 2011, No. 9, pp. 1)
Pub: Information Today Inc.
Contact: Thomas H. Hogan, President
Ed: Kurt Schiller. **Description:** Internet and telecommunications industry leaders are asking for legislation to address the emerging market in cloud computing. Existing communications laws do not adequately govern the modern Internet.

16438 ■ "Lights, Camera, Action: Tools for Creating Video Blogs" in Inc. (Volume 32, December 2010, No. 10, pp. 57)
Pub: Mansueto Ventures L.L.C.
Contact: Stephanie Mehta, Chief Executive Officer
Ed: John Brandon. **Description:** A video blog is a good way to spread company news, talk about products, and stand out among traditional company blogs. New editing software can create two- to four-minute blogs using a webcam and either Windows Live Essentials, Apple iLife 2011, Powerdirector 9 Ultra, or Adobe Visual Communicator 3. **Availability:** Online.

16439 ■ "The Neighborhood Watch" in Hawaii Business (Vol. 53, March 2008, No. 9, pp. 36)
Pub: PacificBasin Communications
Contact: Chuck Tindle, Director
E-mail: chuckt@pacificbasin.net
Ed: David K. Choo. **Description:** OahuRe.com offers information on Hawaii real estate market, with spreadsheets and comparative market analysis page, which shows properties that are active, sold, or in escrow. Other details about OahuRe.com are discussed. A list of other top real estate websites in Hawaii and in the U.S. in general is provided.

16440 ■ "Nerd Alert on 3rd" in Philadelphia Business Journal (Vol. 28, August 17, 2012, No. 27, pp. 1)
Pub: Baltimore Business Journal
Contact: Rhonda Pringle, President
E-mail: rpringle@bizjournals.com
Description: The transformation of North 3rd Street in the neighborhood of Old City in Philadelphia, Pennsylvania into a cluster of technology businesses and workers, dubbed at N3rd (pronounced 'nerd'), is described. Some of the firms located in the area include the Web engineering company Jarv.us Innovations and the collaborative workspace Devnuts. Prospects of the cluster's growth are also discussed. **Availability:** Print; Online.

16441 ■ "Net Savings Link Announces SpyderShare Inc. Contract for Development of Search Engine Optimization (S.E.O.) Program" in Internet Wire (February 21, 2012)
Pub: Comtex News Network Inc.
Contact: Kan Devnani, President
Description: Net Savings Link provides electronically deliverable sales incentives for the business market along with improved Web based savings programs for consumers has partnered with SpyderShare Inc. to enhance the firm's presence on the Internet. Details of the partnership are included. **Availability:** Print; Online.

16442 ■ "Networking Web Sites: a Two-Edge Sword" in Contractor (Vol. 56, October 2009, No. 10, pp. 52)
Ed: H. Kent Craig. Description: People need to be careful about the information that they share on social networking Web sites. They should realize that future bosses, coworkers, and those that might want to hire them might read those information. Posting on these sites can cost career opportunities and respect. Availability: Print; Online.

16443 ■ "A New Globe - In Print and Online" in Marketing to Women (Vol. 22, August 2009, No. 8, pp. 3)
Description: Seventeen magazine is unifying its print and Online editions with complementary content, a strategy that seems to be working as every aspect of Seventeen drives the reader to another component. Availability: Online.

16444 ■ "New Recession-Proof Internet Marketing Package Allows Businesses to Ramp Up Web Traffic and Profits" in PR Newswire (January 25, 2010)
Pub: PR Newswire Association LLC.
Description: Profile of Reel Web Design, a leading marketing firm in New York City that caters to small to medium sized businesses with smaller budgets that need substantial return on investment; Reel Web Design offers video production and submission, web design and maintenance and press release writing among additional services. Availability: Online.

16445 ■ "New Research and Infographic: Vacation Much More Important than 'Nice to Have'" in PR Newswire (August 26, 2014)
Pub: Comtex News Network Inc.
Contact: Kan Devnani, President
Description: Search engine optimization is discussed. Tips are offered to help small companies optimize their Web presence.

16446 ■ "A New Way to Tell When to Fold 'Em" in Barron's (Vol. 88, July 7, 2008, No. 27, pp. 27)
Pub: Dow Jones & Company Inc.
Contact: Almar Latour, Chief Executive Officer
Ed: Theresa W. Carey. Description: Overview of the Online trading company SmartStops, a firm that aims to tell investors when to sell the shares of a particular company. The company's Web site categorizes stocks as moving up, down, or sideways, and calculates exit points for individual stocks based on an overall market trend. Availability: Online.

16447 ■ "Next-Level E-Commerce" in Entrepreneur (June 2014)
Pub: Entrepreneur Media Inc.
Contact: Dan Bova, Director
E-mail: dbova@entrepreneur.com
Description: BloomReach's SNAP software enables consumers to see the products they want upon arriving at an e-commerce Website. The software does this by evaluating the users' intent and preferences based on previous site usage. The enterprise-level software, which costs retailers at least $7,500/month, aims to use big data to help consumers choose products based on their intent. The cloud-based service indexes every page on a client's site and automatically generates appropriate content for visitors. The use of machine learning reduces lag time between application and positive results. Availability: Print; Online.

16448 ■ "Norvax University Health Insurance Sales Training and Online Marketing Conference" in Marketwired (January 27, 2010)
Pub: Comtex News Network Inc.
Contact: Kan Devnani, President
Description: Overview of the Norvax University Marketing and Sales Success Conference Tour which includes insurance sales training seminars, proven and innovative online marketing techniques and a host of additional information and networking opportunities. Availability: Print; Online.

16449 ■ "Online Forex Broker Tadawul FX Intros Arabic Website" in Services Close-Up (June 23, 2011)
Pub: Close-Up Media Inc.
Contact: Caroline S. Moore, President
E-mail: cms@closeupmedia.com
Description: Online forex broker, Tadawul FX, launched its Arabic language Website, noting that the Middle East is a key market for the investment firm. Availability: Online.

16450 ■ "Online Marketing and Promotion of Canadian Films via Social Media Tools: Telefilm Launches New Initiative to Foster Innovative Distribution Strategies" in CNW Group (January 27, 2010)
Pub: Comtex News Network Inc.
Contact: Kan Devnani, President
Description: Telefilm Canada announced the launch of a pilot initiative aimed at encouraging the integration of online marketing and the use of social media tools into means of distribution ahead of a films' theatrical release. During this pilot phase Web-Cine 360 will target French-language feature films. Availability: Online.

16451 ■ "Paterson Plots Comeback With Internet IPO" in Globe & Mail (February 20, 2006, pp. B1)
Ed: Grant Robertson. Description: The initial public offering plans of chief executive officer Scott Paterson of JumpTV.com are presented. Availability: Online.

16452 ■ "Play By Play: These Video Products Can Add New Life to a Stagnant Website" in Black Enterprise (Vol. 41, December 2010, No. 5)
Pub: Earl G. Graves Ltd.
Contact: Earl Graves, Jr., President
Ed: Marcia Wade Talbert. Description: Web Visible, provider of online marketing products and services, cites video capability as the fastest-growing Website feature for small business advertisers. Profiles of various devices for adding video to a Website are included. Availability: Online.

16453 ■ "The Power of Negative Thinking" in Inc. (Volume 32, December 2010, No. 10, pp. 43)
Pub: Inc. Magazine
Ed: Jason Fried. Description: A Website is software and most businesses have and need a good Website to generate business. Understanding for building a powerful Website is presented. Availability: Online.

16454 ■ "The Power of Online" in Advertising Age (Vol. 85, October 13, 2014, No. 21, pp. 4)
Pub: Crain Communications Inc.
Contact: Barry Asin, President
Description: According to Shop.org, online sales could increase by as much as 11 percent this holiday season. Retailers are not only focusing on when customers will start holiday shopping, but whether they will use online stores or shop at brick-and-mortar stores. Many retailers are expanding their online services using digital showrooms on their Websites. Availability: Online.

16455 ■ "Pro Livestock Launches Most Comprehensive Virtual Sales Barn for Livestock and Breed Stock" in Benzinga.com (October 29, 2011)
Description: Pro Livestock Marketing launched the first online sales portal for livestock and breed stock. The firm has designed a virtual sales barn allowing individuals to purchase and sell cattle, swine, sheep, goats, horses, rodeo stock, show animals, specialty animals, semen and embryos globally. It is like an eBay for livestock and will help ranchers and farmers grow. Availability: Print; PDF; Online.

16456 ■ "Promotional Marketing: How to Create, Implement & Integrate Campaigns That Really Work"
Pub: Kogan Page

Released: Sixth edition. Description: Promotional marketing helps companies stay ahead of competition to gain new customers and keep existing ones. The guide includes new developments in the field of marketing, examining the use of digital media such as mobile devices and phones, interactive television, and Web-based advertising, as well as ways to research and evaluate promotional marketing campaigns. Availability: Online; PDF.

16457 ■ "Protect Your Domain Name From Cybersquatters" in Idaho Business Review (September 1, 2014)
Pub: BridgeTower Media
Contact: Adam Reinebach, President
Description: Cybersquatting is the practice of registering, trafficking in or using domain names with the intent to profit from the goodwill of recognizable trade names or trademarks of other companies. Companies can protect their Website domain by following these steps: register domain names, promptly renew registrations, maintain proper records, obtain additional top-level domains, and monitor your site for cybersquatters.

16458 ■ "Qorvis Communications Gets Sabre Award for Search Engine Optimization" in Entertainment Close-Up (May 29, 2012)
Description: Qorvis Communications received the Gold Sabre Award by the Holmes Report for Search Engine Optimization for its work on the Marca Paid Imagen de Mexico on the MexicoToday campaign. MexicoToday.org is a next-generation Website and external branding initiative which focuses on digital and social media. The site hopes to change the world's perception of Mexico, particularly Europeans and Americans. Availability: Print; Online.

16459 ■ "Reportlinker.com Adds Report: GeoWeb and Local Internet Markets: 2008 Edition" in Entertainment Close-Up (September 11, 2009)
Description: Reportlinker.com is adding a new market research report that is available in its catalogue: GeoWeb and Local Internet Markets - 2008 Edition; highlights include the outlook for consumer mapping services and an examination of monetizing services and an analysis the development outlook for geospacial Internet market, also referred to as the Geoweb. Availability: Online.

16460 ■ "The Right Time for REITs" in Barron's (Vol. 88, July 14, 2008, No. 28, pp. 32)
Pub: Dow Jones & Company Inc.
Contact: Almar Latour, Chief Executive Officer
Ed: Mike Hogan. Description: Discusses the downturn in U.S. real estate investment trusts so these are worth considering for investment. Several Websites that are useful for learning about real estate investment trusts for investment purposes are presented. Availability: Online.

16461 ■ "Rise Interactive, Internet Marketing Agency, Now Offers Social Media Services" in Marketwired (November 4, 2009)
Pub: Comtex News Network Inc.
Contact: Kan Devnani, President
Description: Profile of Rise Interactive, a full-service Internet marketing agency which has recently added social media to its list of offerings; the agency touts that its newest service gives their clients the power to have ongoing communication with current and potential customers on the sites they are most actively visiting. Availability: Print; Online.

16462 ■ "ROIonline Announces Streaming Video Products" in Marketing Weekly News (December 5, 2009, pp. 155)
Pub: Investment Weekly News
Description: ROIonline LLC, an Internet marketing firm serving business-to-business and the industrial marketplace, has added streaming video options to the Internet solutions it offers its clients; due to the huge increase of broadband connections, videos are now commonplace on the Internet and can often convey a company's message in a must more ef-

ficient, concise and effective way that will engage a website's visitor thus delivering a high return on a company's investment. **Availability:** Print; Mailing list; Online.

16463 ■ *"St. Louis Digital Marketing Agency Publishes Free SEO Audit Tool" in Internet Wire (February 16, 2012)*
Pub: Comtex News Network Inc.
Contact: Kan Devnani, President
Description: Evolve Digital Labs has created a document to help with Search Engine Optimization. The Saint Louis digital marketing firm's 'SEO Guide for Beginners' offers comprehensive information on the topic of search engine operations, on-site component of Web pages, and strategies for improving visibility in search engine result pages (SERPs). **Availability:** Online.

16464 ■ *"Search Engine Optimization is Becoming a Must for Businesses, But Unethical Companies Can Hurt Worse than Help" in Idaho Business Review (August 3, 2012)*
Ed: Sean Olson. **Description:** Search engine optimization increases presence on the Internet for any small business wishing to market a service or product. It is critical to choose an ethical company that has experience in creating Web sites that will get noticed. **Availability:** Print; Online.

16465 ■ *"Search Engine Optimization Companies Rose From Need and Path of Least Resistance" in Idaho Business Review (August 3, 2012)*
Pub: Long Island Business News
Contact: Kathy Lombardo, Manager
E-mail: research@libn.com
Ed: Sean Olson. **Description:** Search engine optimization companies help small businesses gain presence on the Internet by higher placement during online searches. It is suggested that all small firms need to optimize their company's search engine ranking. **Availability:** Print; Online.

16466 ■ *"Search Engines: Image Conscious" in Canadian Business (Vol. 81, February 26, 2008, No. 4, pp. 36)*
Pub: Rogers Media Inc.
Contact: Neil Spivak, Chief Executive Officer
Ed: Andrew Wahl. **Description:** Idee Inc. is testing an Internet search engine for images that does not rely on tags but compares its visual data to a database of other images. The company was founded and managed by Leila Boujnane as an off-shoot of their risk-management software firm. Their software has already been used by image companies to track copyrighted images and to find images within their own archives. **Availability:** Online.

16467 ■ *"Seen & Noted: A Home's Identity in Black and White" in Crain's Chicago Business (Vol. 31, April 21, 2008, No. 16, pp. 35)*
Pub: Crain Communications Inc.
Contact: Barry Asin, President
Ed: Lisa Bertagnoli. **Description:** Real estate agents are finding that showing customers a written floor plan is a trend that is growing since many buyers feel that Online virtual tours distort a room. Although floor plans cost up to $500 to have drawn up, they clearly show potential buyers the exact dimensions of rooms and how they connect. **Availability:** Online.

16468 ■ *The SEO Manifesto: A Practical and Ethical Guide to Internet Marketing and Search Engine Optimization*
Description: Comprehensive guide for each phase of launching an online business; chapters include checklists, process descriptions, and examples.

16469 ■ *"Social Media, E-Mail Remain Challenging for Employers" in Workforce Management (Vol. 88, December 14, 2009, No. 13, pp. 4)*
Pub: Crain Communications Inc.
Contact: Barry Asin, President

Ed: Ed Frauenheim. **Description:** Examining the impact of Internet social networking and the workplace; due to the power of these new technologies, it is important that companies begin to set clear policies regarding Internet use and employee privacy. **Availability:** Online.

16470 ■ *"Stimulating Fare at the SBA" in Barron's (Vol. 89, July 20, 2009, No. 29, pp. 12)*
Pub: Dow Jones & Company Inc.
Contact: Almar Latour, Chief Executive Officer
Ed: Jim McTague. **Description:** Internet access at the Small Business Administration slowed down on 7 July 2009, apparently caused by employees streaming videos of the Michael Jackson tribute. The agency claims that the event did not disrupt its operations. **Availability:** Online.

16471 ■ *"Teksapiens, A Leading SEO Company, Offers Free SEO Consulting Services to Dallas Businesses" in Wireless News (March 29, 2012)*
Description: Dallas-based Web design firm, Teksapiens, offers free search engine optimization to Dallas businesess signing up at DallasBestSEO.com. The free service provides tips to outperform competition when marketing on the Internet. **Availability:** Print; Online.

16472 ■ *"Three Ways to Improve the Prospect's Experience" in South Florida Business Journal (Vol. 35, September 12, 2014, No. 7, pp. 12)*
Pub: American City Business Journals, Inc.
Contact: Mike Olivieri, Executive Vice President
Description: Advice on how marketers should get prospective buyers' attention by using Websites is given. Website readability on mobile devices and cell phones should be improved. Marketers should also offer a maximum of two landing pages to increase sales. **Availability:** Online.

16473 ■ *"The Top Mistakes of Social Media Marketing" in Agency Sales Magazine (Vol. 39, November 2009, No. 9, pp. 42)*
Description: One common mistake in social media marketing is having more than one image on the Internet because this ruins a business' credibility. Marketers need to put out messages that are useful to their readers and to keep messages consistent. **Availability:** Online.

16474 ■ *"Top Technologies That Will Transform Web Development in 2020" in Medium (August 20, 2020)*
Ed: Sophia Martin. **Released:** August 20, 2020. **Description:** A detailed guide including the latest web development technologies to enhance your online and app presence. **Availability:** Online.

16475 ■ *"Ultimate Guide to Google AdWords: How to Access 100 Million People in 10 Minutes"*
Pub: Entrepreneur Media Inc.
Contact: Dan Bova, Director
E-mail: dbova@entrepreneur.com
Released: 5th edition. **Price:** $24.95, paperback. **Description:** The Google AdWords experts and analytics specialist present the techniques, tools, and tricks for using Google AdWords. The experts help small businesses to write advertising and Web site copy design, work in difficult markets, advertise, increase search engine presence, bid strategies for online auctions, financial budgeting and more. **Availability:** Print.

16476 ■ *"The Ultimate Guide to Starting a Web Design Business - From Finding Your First Clients to Making a Name for Yourself" in CodeinWP (July 6, 2020)*
Ed: Maddy Osman. **Released:** July 06, 2020. **Description:** Provides detailed steps to guide a new web design business through business start up through scaling up to increase profit and value. **Availability:** Online.

16477 ■ *"Up To Code? Website Eases Compliance Burden for Entrepreneurs" in Black Enterprise (Vol. 38, March 1, 2008, No. 8, pp. 48)*
Pub: Earl G. Graves Ltd.
Contact: Earl Graves, Jr., President
Ed: Robin White-Goode. **Description:** Business.gov is a presidential E-government project created to help small businesses easily find, understand, and comply with laws and regulations pertaining to a particular industry. **Availability:** Online.

16478 ■ *"Updated LGMA Website Provides Food Safety News, Resources" in Western Farm Press (October 14, 2014)*
Description: California's Leafy Greens Marketing Agreement (LGMA) updated its Website to include easier access to news, information, and resources involving leafy greens food safety and the program developed in 2007. The site offers a blog featuring three key topic areas: Food Safety Modernization Act; LGMA's comprehensive training program, called LGMA Tech; and resources for members.

16479 ■ *"Virtus.com Wins 'Best of Industry' WebAward for Excellence in Financial Services" in Investment Weekly News (October 24, 2009, pp. 227)*
Pub: Investment Weekly News
Description: Web Marketing Association honored Virtus.com, the Website of Virtus Investment Partners, Inc., for Outstanding Achievement in Web Development and Acsys Interactive was awarded the Financial Services Standard of Excellence Award for developing the site. The site was part of a rebranding effort and is a one-stop portal for both financial advisors and their investors. **Availability:** Online.

16480 ■ *"Web-Based Solutions Streamline Operations" in Contractor (Vol. 56, December 2009, No. 12, pp. 28)*
Ed: William Feldman, Patti Feldman. **Description:** Sage Project Lifecycle Management is a Web-based service platform for plumbing and HVAC contractors. It enables effective workflow and document management. Projectmates, on the other hand, is a Web-based enterprise-wide solution for managing both commercial plumbing and HVAC projects. **Availability:** Print; Online.

16481 ■ *"Web Design and Development Companies" in Business Review Albany (Vol. 41, August 15, 2014, No. 21, pp. 6)*
Description: Rankings of Web design and development companies in the Albany, New York area are presented. Rankings are based on the 2013 Web design and development revenue. **Availability:** Print; Online.

16482 ■ *"Web Design Trends 2020: 5 Popular UI Styles" in Digital Agency Network (September 30, 2020)*
Released: September 30, 2020. **Description:** Discusses the evolution of the web design industry and discusses five web design trends in 2020 that are designed to represent your brand virtually. **Availability:** Online.

16483 ■ *"Web to Print" in American Printer (Vol. 128, August 1, 2011, No. 8)*
Description: Jerry Kennelly, CEO and founder of Tweak.com believes that Web-to-Design is middleware with no content. His firm offers an easy to use interface that flows right into the printer's workflow with no additional costs. **Availability:** Online.

16484 ■ *"Web Site Focuses on Helping People Find Jobs, Internships with Area Businesses" in Crain's Detroit Business (Vol. 26, Jan. 4, 2010)*
Pub: Crain Communications Inc.
Contact: Barry Asin, President
Ed: Dustin Walsh. **Description:** DetroitIntern.com, LLC is helping metro Detroit college students and young professionals find career-advancing internships or jobs with local businesses. **Availability:** Print; Online.

16485 ■ *"Web Translation Made Simple"* in *Inc.* (Vol. 33, October 2011, No. 8, pp. 44)
Pub: Inc. Magazine

Ed: Adam Baer. **Description:** Smartling is a Web-based service that translates sites into more than 50 foreign languages. The software will begin translation right after setting up the account. **Availability:** Online.

16486 ■ *"Website Triples Traffic in Three Weeks Using Press Releases"* in PR Newswire (January 5, 2010)
Pub: PR Newswire Association LLC.

Description: Irbtrax, an Internet marketing firm, concluded a comprehensive study revealing that online press release submission services offer measurable Website traffic-building results. **Availability:** Online.

16487 ■ *"What's In Your Toolbox"* in Women In Business (Vol. 61, August-September 2009, No. 4, pp. 7)
Pub: American Business Women's Association
Contact: Rene Street, Executive Director

Ed: Mimi Kopulos. **Description:** Business owners are increasingly turning to using social networking websites, such as Facebook, LinkedIn and Twitter, to promote their companies. The number of adult social media users has increased from 8 percent in 2005 to 35 percent in 2009. **Availability:** Online.

16488 ■ *"Why You Need to Opt for Custom Web Design?"* in DigitalAgencyNetwork (November 13, 2019)
URL(s): digitalagencynetwork.com/why-you-need-to -opt-for-custom-web-design/

Ed: Mellonie Francis. **Released:** November 13, 2019. **Description:** Discusses the pros of using a professional web design service and walks us through the process it takes to create a website and publish it. **Availability:** Online.

16489 ■ *"Wix Has a New Editor for Creating Web Pages"* in Small Business Trends (August 23, 2022)
URL(s): smallbiztrends.com/2022/08/new-wix-editor .html

Ed: Gabrielle Pickard-Whitehead. **Released:** August 23, 2022. **Description:** Wix.com released Wix Editor, which will simplify web design and allow small business owners the ability to launch the websites quickly and develop an online presence. **Availability:** Online.

16490 ■ *"Women Clicking to Earn Virtual Dollars"* in Sales and Marketing Management (November 11, 2009)

Ed: Stacy Straczynski. **Description:** According to a new report from Internet marketing firm Q Interactive, women are increasingly playing social media games where they are able to click on an ad or sign up for a promotion to earn virtual currency. Research is showing that this kind of marketing may be a potent tool, especially for e-commerce and online stores. **Availability:** Print; Online.

16491 ■ *"WordStream Announces a Pair of Firsts for SEO & PPC Keyword Research Tools"* in Marketwired (November 10, 2009)
Pub: Comtex News Network Inc.
Contact: Kan Devnani, President

Description: WordSteam, Inc., a provider of pay-per-click (PPC) and search engine optimization (SEO) solutions for continuously expanding and optimizing search marketing efforts has released two new features in their flagship Keyword Management solution; these tools will allow marketers to analyze data from paid search, organic search and estimated totals from keyword suggestion tools side-by-side. **Availability:** Print; Online.

16492 ■ *"The Yahoo Family Tree"* in Conde Nast Portfolio (Vol. 2, June 2008, No. 6, pp. 34)
Pub: Conde Nast Publications
Contact: Agnes Chu, President

Ed: Blaise Zerega. **Description:** Yahoo, founded in 1994 by Stanford students Jerry Yang and David Filo, is still an Internet powerhouse. The company's history is also outlined as well as the reasons in which Microsoft desperately wants to acquire the firm. **Availability:** Print.

16493 ■ *"Your Web Brand Counts"* in Black Enterprise (Vol. 44, June 2014, No. 10, pp. 46)
Pub: Earl G. Graves Ltd.
Contact: Earl Graves, Jr., President

Description: Forty-eight percent of employers use Google or other search engines to find information about job applicants and 25 percent of executives hired were originally identified or contacted through social media, thus the importance of a good Web presence is outlined.

TRADE PERIODICALS

16494 ■ *Online Searcher*
Pub: Information Today Inc.
Contact: Thomas H. Hogan, President
URL(s): www.infotoday.com/OnlineSearcher
Released: Bimonthly; January/February, March/April, May/June, July/August, September/October, and November/December. **Description:** Edited for librarians, Webmasters, site designers, content managers, and others concerned with knowledge/information management. Includes critical reviews of Web sites, software, search engines, and information services. (Formerly published by Online, Inc.). **Availability:** Print; Online.

VIDEO/AUDIO MEDIA

16495 ■ *How to Break into Freelance Web Design and Build Reliable Monthly Recurring Revenue with John Wooten*
URL(s): www.eofire.com/podcast/johnwooten
Ed: Jon Lee Dumas. **Released:** May 04, 2024. **Description:** Podcast explains how to start a web design business.

16496 ■ *Small Biz 101: Digital Edge: Meeting New Website Standards for Business Success*
URL(s): scatteredtostreamlined.com/digital-edge-mee ting-new-website-standards-for-business-success -sb021
Ed: Connie Whitesell. **Released:** October 04, 2023. **Description:** Podcast discusses accessibility standards for websites.

CONSULTANTS

16497 ■ *Cloudflare Inc.*
Cloudflare Inc.
101 Townsend St.
San Francisco, CA 94107
Ph: (650)319-8930
Free: 888-993-5273
Co. E-mail: support@cloudflare.com
URL: http://www.cloudflare.com
Contact: Matthew Prince, Chief Executive Officer
Facebook: www.facebook.com/Cloudflare
Linkedin: www.linkedin.com/company/cloudflare
X (Twitter): twitter.com/Cloudflare
Instagram: www.instagram.com/cloudflare
YouTube: www.youtube.com/cloudflare
Description: Firm provides website hosting services. **Founded:** 2009. **Educational Activities:** ACM Conference on Computer and Communications Security (CCS) (Annual).

16498 ■ *Creative Company Inc.*
PO Box 446
Newberg, OR 97132
Ph: (503)883-4433
Co. E-mail: optimize@creativeco.com
URL: http://www.creativeco.com
Contact: Jennifer Larsen Morrow, President
E-mail: jlmorrow@creativeco.com
Facebook: www.facebook.com/pages/McMinnville -OR/Creative-Company-Inc/58557673552

X (Twitter): x.com/optimizemybrand
YouTube: www.youtube.com/user/optimizemybrand
Pinterest: www.pinterest.com/creativecoinc
Description: Provider of marketing, brand programs, websites, marketing strategy, online branding and more. **Scope:** Provider of marketing, brand programs, websites, marketing strategy, online branding and more. **Founded:** 1978. **Publications:** "Generational Marketing"; "Apply Branding to Bring Power to Your Marketing"; "Brand Your Business".

16499 ■ *Enbede Co.*
1162 Falling Stream
Sanford, NC 27332
Ph: (603)521-0491
URL: http://www.enbede.com
Contact: Dr. Donald Job, Founder
E-mail: donjob@enbede.com
Description: Provider of business development solutions such as bio-informatics, e-commerce, web page design and network security evaluations. **Scope:** Provider of business development solutions such as bio-informatics, e-commerce, web page design and network security evaluations. **Founded:** 1979. **Publications:** "Developing a Licensing Support Activity for Inventors," Innovative Products Research & Services, 1993; "The Inventors Guide-Getting Beyond the Invention," Haley Publications, 1993; "Developing an Inventor Support Service which performs early stage Market and Manufacturing Evaluations," Oct, 1991. **Training:** Licensing Your Invention; Building a Business Around Your Invention; Enhancing Creativity; Opportunities in Biotechnology.

PUBLICATIONS

16500 ■ *"How to Choose a Professional Web Design Agency"* in Business 2 Community (October 21, 2021)
URL(s): www.business2community.com/small-busi ness/how-to-choose-a-professional-web-design -agency-02434668
Ed: Praveen Mishra. **Released:** October 21, 2021. **Description:** Practical tips for researching a web design company for your small business. **Availability:** Online.

RESEARCH CENTERS

16501 ■ *Design Management Institute (DMI)*
38 Chauncy St., Ste. 800
Boston, MA 02111
Ph: (617)338-6380
Fax: (617)338-6570
Co. E-mail: dmistaff@dmi.org
URL: http://www.dmi.org
Contact: Carole Bilson, President
E-mail: cbilson@dmi.org
Facebook: www.facebook.com/DesignManagemen tInnovation
Linkedin: www.linkedin.com/in/dmi

Description: In-house design groups and consultant design firms; individuals involved in the management of designers with in-house corporate design groups or consultant design firms. Aims to share management techniques as applied to design groups, and to facilitate better understanding by business management of the role design can play in achieving business goals. Design disciplines included are: architecture, advertising, communications, exhibit design, graphics, interior design, packaging and product design. **Scope:** Conducts field studies on the management of design in products, communications, and environments in industry, business, and public institutions, emphasizing industrial design in product development. Activities are carried out through the Center for Research and the Design Management Education and Research Forum. **Founded:** 1975. **Publications:** DMI:Review (Quarterly); Design Management Journal (DMI) (Quarterly); Design Management Institute Newsletter (Monthly); Design Management Review (DMR) (Quarterly). **Educational Activities:** DMI Conference on Design Management (Annual). **Geographic Preference:** National.

ASSOCIATIONS AND OTHER ORGANIZATIONS

16502 ■ Obesity Medicine Association (OMA)
7173 S Havana St., Ste. 600-130
Centennial, CO 80112
Ph: (303)770-2526
Fax: (303)779-4834
Co. E-mail: info@obesitymedicine.org
URL: http://obesitymedicine.org
Contact: Dr. Craig Primack, Vice President
Facebook: www.facebook.com/ObesityMe
dicineAssociation

Description: Physicians with a special interest in the study and treatment of obesity and associated conditions. Encourages excellence in the practice of bariatric medicine through exchange of information, research, and continuing education. Sponsors regional courses and clinical research programs. Offers a physician referral service. **Founded:** 1950. **Publications:** *News from ASBP* (Bimonthly); *American Society of Bariatric Physicians--Directory* (Annual); *American Journal of Bariatric Medicine: The Bariatrician* (Quarterly; Biennial). **Educational Activities:** Obesity and Associated Conditions Symposium of American Society of Bariatric Physicians; Regional Obesity Course. **Awards:** OMA Bariatrician of the Year (Annual); Dr. Raymond E. Dietz Meritorious Service Award (Annual). **Geographic Preference:** National.

16503 ■ Overeaters Anonymous World Service Office (OA WSO) [Overeaters Anonymous, Inc.]
6075 Zenith Ct. NE
Rio Rancho, NM 87174-4727
Ph: (505)891-2664
Co. E-mail: info@oa.org
URL: http://oa.org
Facebook: www.facebook.com/overea
tersanonymousofficial
Instagram: www.instagram.com/overea
tersanonymous_official

Description: Provides a twelve-step, self-help fellowship program for people who struggle with compulsive eating. (Program patterned after that of Alcoholics Anonymous.). **Founded:** 1960. **Publications:** *Lifeline* (10/year). **Educational Activities:** Overeaters Anonymous World Service Office Meeting (Annual); World Service Convention (Quinquennial). **Geographic Preference:** Multinational.

16504 ■ TOPS Club Inc.
4575 S Fifth St.
Milwaukee, WI 53207
Ph: (414)482-4620
Free: 800-932-8677
Co. E-mail: wondering@tops.org
URL: http://www.tops.org
Contact: Rick Danforth, President
Linkedin: www.linkedin.com/company/tops-club-inc
X (Twitter): x.com/TOPSWeightLoss
YouTube: www.youtube.com/user/topsclubinc

Pinterest: www.pinterest.com/TOPSweightloss
Description: Weight control self-help association using group dynamics, competition, and recognition to help members lose weight. Advocates physician-approved individual programs, and physician-set weight goals. **Founded:** 1948. **Publications:** *TOPS News* (Bimonthly). **Educational Activities:** TOPS International Recognition Days (TOPS IRD) (Annual). **Geographic Preference:** Multinational.

REFERENCE WORKS

16505 ■ *"26 Things Holding Canadians Back" in Canadian Business (Vol. 85, August 13, 2012, No. 13, pp. 27)*
Description: A list of the problems that Canada needs to address in order to succeed as an economic superpower is presented. Some of these barriers include declining fertility rate, rising percentage of overweight and obese, and obsolete copyright laws. **Availability:** Print; Online.

16506 ■ *Everything is Possible: Life and Business Lessons from a Self-Made Billionaire and the Founder of Slim-Fast*
Released: First edition. **Description:** A profile of the founder of Slim-Fast nutritional diet drink used to help people lose weight. **Availability:** E-book.

16507 ■ *"Is Medically Supervised Weight Loss Right for You?" in U.S. News and World Report (March 11, 2016)*
URL(s): health.usnews.com/health-news/patient-a
dvice/articles/2016-03-11/is-medically-supervise
d-weight-loss-right-for-you

Ed: Lisa Esposito. **Released:** March 11, 2016. **Description:** The process of medical weight loss is explored. This is not ideal for everyone who wants to lose weight so an exam is given and then a plan for weight loss is discussed. **Availability:** Online.

16508 ■ *"Where Pet Nutrition Meets Love" in Pet Product News (Vol. 66, September 2012, No. 9, pp. S14)*
Description: Michael Landa, coowner of Nulo Pet Products, discusses the role of his company in reducing pet obesity through the manufacture of high-protein foods. Aside from explaining his interest in pet obesity, Landa also describes how the company differentiates itself from competitors. **Availability:** Online.

STATISTICAL SOURCES

16509 ■ *Weight Loss Services Industry in the US - Market Research Report*
URL(s): www.ibisworld.com/united-states/market-re
search-reports/weight-loss-services-industry/

Price: $925. **Description:** Downloadable report analyzing the current and future trends in the weight loss services industry. **Availability:** Download.

TRADE PERIODICALS

16510 ■ *Shape*
Pub: Dotdash Meredith
Contact: Neil Vogel, Chief Executive Officer
URL(s): www.shape.com
Facebook: www.facebook.com/SHAPEmagazine
X (Twitter): x.com/Shape_Magazine
Instagram: www.instagram.com/shape
YouTube: www.youtube.com/c/SHAPEMagazine
Pinterest: www.pinterest.com/shapemagazine
Released: Semiannual **Description:** Magazine for women covering nutrition, weight control, physical fitness, psychology, fashion, beauty and travel. **Availability:** Print; Online.

CONSULTANTS

16511 ■ Center for Lifestyle Enhancement-Columbia Medical Center of Plano
3901 West 15th St
Plano, TX 75075
Ph: (972)596-6800
Fax: (972)519-1299
URL: http://medicalcityplano.com
Contact: Erol R. Akdamar, President
Facebook: www.facebook.com/medicalcityplano
X (Twitter): twitter.com/MedCityPlano

Description: Firm provides professional health counseling in the areas of general nutrition for weight management, eating disorders, diabetic education, cholesterol reduction and adolescent weight management. Offers work site health promotion and preventive services. Also coordinates speaker's bureau, cooking classes and physician referrals. **Scope:** Firm provides professional health counseling in the areas of general nutrition for weight management, eating disorders, diabetic education, cholesterol reduction and adolescent weight management. Offers work site health promotion and preventive services. Also coordinates speaker's bureau, cooking classes and physician referrals. **Founded:** 1975. **Training:** Rx Diet and Exercise; Smoking Cessation; Stress Management; Health Fairs; Fitness Screenings; Body Composition; Nutrition Analysis; Exercise Classes; Prenatal Nutrition; SHAPEDOWN; Successfully Managing Diabetes; Gourmet Foods for Your Heart; The Aging Heart; Heart Smart Saturday featuring Day of Dance; Weight-Loss Management Seminars; The Right Stroke for Men; Peripheral Artery Disease Screening; Menstruation: The Cycle Begins; Boot Camp for New Dads; Grand parenting 101: Caring for Kids Today; Teddy Bear C New Baby Day C Safe Sitter Babysitting Class.

FRANCHISES AND BUSINESS OPPORTUNITIES

16512 ■ Curves International, Inc.
2711 Cresthill Cir.
Waco, TX 76710

URL: http://www.curves.com
Contact: Takeshi Masumoto, President
Instagram: www.instagram.com/curvesofficial
YouTube: www.youtube.com/user/CurvesChannel
Pinterest: www.pinterest.com/CurvesStrongFitness

Description: Fitness and weight loss center for women. **No. of Operating Units:** 10000. **Training:** Yes.

16513 ■ Diet Center

395 Springside Dr.
  Akron, OH 44333
Free: 800-656-3294
Fax: (330)666-2197
URL: http://www.dietcenter.com
Contact: Charles E. Sekeres, President
Facebook: www.facebook.com/DietCenterOnline

Description: Counselors work one-on-one with clients, helping develop a personalized, low-fat eating style and a more active lifestyle. **Founded:** 1973. **Franchised:** 1973. **Franchise Fee:** $30,000. **Training:** Training is provided both at the home office and in regional. Includes nutritional training.

16514 ■ Jenny Craig Weight Loss & Management Centers

5770 Fleet St.
  Carlsbad, CA 92008-9446
Free: 866-706-4042
URL: http://www.jennycraig.com
Contact: David Pastrana, Chief Executive Officer

Description: Offers a weight loss program in the U.S. and Canada featuring personal counseling, low-calorie Jenny's Cuisine, and a supportive and motivating environment. **No. of Franchise Units:** 216. **No. of Company-Owned Units:** 431. **Founded:** 1983. **Franchised:** 1987. **Equity Capital Needed:** $165,600-$349,500. **Franchise Fee:** $25,000. **Training:** Yes.

16515 ■ L.A. Weight Loss Centers

747 Dresher Rd., Ste. 100
  Horsham, PA 19044

Description: Provider of personalized weight management services. **Founded:** 1989. **Training:** 4 weeks at headquarters, 3 weeks at franchisee's location and ongoing support.

16516 ■ Lite For Life

San Francisco Bay Area, CA
Ph: (650)535-0212
Co. E-mail: info@liteforlife.com
URL: http://liteforlife.com

Description: Weight loss and nutritional consulting. **Founded:** 1978. **Training:** Yes.

16517 ■ Lucille Roberts Fitness Express (LR)

1387 St. Nicholas Ave.
  New York, NY 10033
Co. E-mail: heretohelp@tsiclubs.com
URL: http://www.lucilleroberts.com
Facebook: www.facebook.com/lucilleroberts
X (Twitter): x.com/lucilleroberts
Instagram: www.instagram.com/lucilleroberts

Description: Women fitness and weight-loss center. **No. of Operating Units:** 50. **Founded:** 1973. **Financial Assistance:** Yes **Training:** Offers 1 week at headquarters with ongoing support.

LIBRARIES

16518 ■ Academy of Nutrition and Dietetics (AND) - Library

120 S Riverside Plz., Ste. 2190
  Chicago, IL 60606-6995
Ph: (312)899-0040
Free: 800-877-1600
URL: http://www.eatright.org
Contact: Kevin L. Sauer, President
X (Twitter): x.com/eatright
YouTube: www.youtube.com/user/EatRightTV
Pinterest: www.pinterest.com/kidseatright

Description: Represents food and nutrition professionals. Promotes nutrition, health and well-being. **Scope:** Food and nutrition. **Services:** Library not open to the public. **Founded:** 1917. **Holdings:** Figures not available. **Publications:** *Weight Loss Matters: Your Weight and Your Health Pamphlet*; *Find a Nutrition Professional Consumer Search*; *Directory of Columbus Registered Dietitians*; *Directory of Registered Dietitians*; *Directory of Dietetics Programs* (Annual); *Directory of Consulting Dietitians in Private Practice*; *Journal of the Academy of Nutrition and Dietetics* (Monthly). **Educational Activities:** Food Nutrition Conference Expo (FNCE) (Annual).

16519 ■ National Eating Disorder Information Centre (NEDIC) - Library

200 Elizabeth St., ES 7-421
  Toronto, ON, Canada M5G 2C4
Ph: (416)340-4156
Free: 866-633-4220
Co. E-mail: nedic@uhn.ca
URL: http://nedic.ca
Contact: Suzanne Phillips, Program Manager
E-mail: suzanne.phillips@uhn.ca
Facebook: www.facebook.com/thenedic
X (Twitter): x.com/theNEDIC
Instagram: www.instagram.com/the_nedic
YouTube: www.youtube.com/user/nedic85

Description: Provides information and resources on causes, symptoms of, and therapeutic and health care treatments for eating disorders and the preoccupation with food and weight. Aims to raise awareness on eating disorders through conducting lectures and workshops. **Scope:** Eating disorders. **Holdings:** Figures not available. **Educational Activities:** Eating Disorder Awareness Week (EDAW) (Annual). **Geographic Preference:** National.

RESEARCH CENTERS

16520 ■ Columbia University - College of Physicians and Surgeons - New York Nutrition and Obesity Research Center (NYNORC) [Centro de Investigacion sobre Obesidad]

1150 St. Nicholas Ave., Rm., 620
  New York, NY 10032
Ph: (212)851-5315
URL: http://www.nynorc.cuimc.columbia.edu
Contact: Dr. Rudolph Leibel, Director
E-mail: rl232@cumc.columbia.edu

Description: National Institute of Diabetes and Digestive and Kidney Diseases-funded research activity, located at College of Physicians and Surgeons, Columbia University. **Scope:** Research focuses on the causes, complications, and treatment of obesity, including molecular genetics, regulation of food intake, nutrient uptake and oxidation, body composition, stable isotope methodology, exercise physiology, diabetes, and insulin resistance. **Founded:** 1980. **Educational Activities:** DeWitt Goodman Seminar Series (Periodic); New York Obesity Research Center Symposia.

FRANCHISES AND BUSINESS OPPORTUNITIES

16521 ■ Housewarmers, LLC
519 Interstate 30, Ste. 720
  Rockwall, TX 75087-5408
Ph: (903)456-2257
URL: http://www.housewarmersusa.com
Contact: Mary Johnson, Contact

Description: Firm engages in neighborhood welcoming services. **Founded:** 1999. **Training:** Offers 3-4 days training at headquarters, 2 visits at franchisee's location and ongoing support.

REFERENCE WORKS

16522 ■ *"The Best-Dressed Windows and How to Get Them" in The New York Times (August 6, 2019)*
URL(s): www.nytimes.com/2019/08/06/realestate/the-best-dressed-windows-and-how-to-get-them.html
Ed: Michelle Higgins. **Released:** August 06, 2019.
Description: A variety of window types are mentioned with the best kind of window treatments and dressing to use. **Availability:** Online.

16523 ■ *"Celebrate Holiday Spirit With Sparkling Sales" in Pet Product News (Vol. 66, September 2012, No. 9, pp. 48)*
Ed: Cheryl Reeves. **Description:** Pet supplies retailers can increase frequency of holiday sales, from Halloween through New Year's, by integrating creative marketing strategies into merchandise and incentives that elicit customer attention. The impression of fun should also be emphasized on customers. Guidelines for presenting displays and organizing special store-related events are also provided. **Availability:** Print; Online.

TRADE PERIODICALS

16524 ■ *Creative: The Magazine of Promotion and Marketing*
Pub: Creative Magazine Inc.

URL(s): www.creativemag.com
Released: Bimonthly **Price:** $30, U.S. for annual print; $50, Other countries for 1 year; $25, for the annual illustrated guide; $5, U.S. for single copy.
Description: Magazine reporting on point of purchase displays; exhibits; premiums and incentives; audio-visual techniques; direct marketing; and sales promotion materials. **Availability:** Print; Online.

FRANCHISES AND BUSINESS OPPORTUNITIES

16525 ■ **ExSeed Marketing**
23052 Alicia Pky., No . H202
  Mission Viejo, CA 92692
Ph: (949)768-6695
URL: http://www.exseedmarketing.com
Contact: Steven Dale, Founder
E-mail: steve@exseedmarketing.com
Facebook: www.facebook.com/exseedmarketing

Description: Retailer of window coverings.
Founded: 1985. **Training:** Offers 3 days at headquarters, by phone and vendor training and ongoing support.

16526 ■ **Gotcha Covered Inc.**
303 S Broadway, Ste. 200-153
  Denver, CO 80209

Free: 888-650-6187
Co. E-mail: gccorporate@gotchacovered.com
URL: http://www.gotchacovered.com
Contact: Paul Linenberg, President
Facebook: www.facebook.com/GotchaCoveredCorporate
Linkedin: www.linkedin.com/company/gotcha-covered-franchising
YouTube: www.youtube.com/user/GotchaCoveredHQ

Description: Distributor of interior design and home decor needs such as window blinds, draperies and curtains, shutters, shades, top treatments. **Founded:** 2009.

16527 ■ **Screenmobile Corporation**
72-050A Corporate Way
  Thousand Palms, CA 92276
Free: 800-775-7795
Co. E-mail: smcorp@screenmobile.com
URL: http://www.screenmobile.com
Contact: Monty L. Walker, Contact
Facebook: www.facebook.com/screenmobile.corporation
X (Twitter): x.com/ScreenmobileUS

Description: Manufacturer and retailer of window, door, porch, patio screens and also provides mobile screening repair services. **Founded:** 1980. **Training:** American neighborhood screenstores.

ASSOCIATIONS AND OTHER ORGANIZATIONS

16528 ■ Business Technology Association (BTA)
12411 Wornall Rd., Ste. 200
Kansas City, MO 64145
Ph: (816)941-3100
Free: 800-505-2821
Co. E-mail: info@bta.org
URL: http://www.bta.org
Contact: David Polimeni, President
Facebook: www.facebook.com/BTAORG
Linkedin: www.linkedin.com/company/business
-technology-association
X (Twitter): x.com/BTA_ORG
YouTube: www.youtube.com/channel/
UCBSsarYTnpYafmHxiMDGQWw
Description: Dealers and resellers of office equipment and networking products and services. Offers 60 seminars on management, service, technology, and business systems. Conducts research, provides business-supporting services and benefits, including insurance, and legal counsel. **Founded:** 1926. **Publications:** *Business Owner* (Bimonthly); *BTA Membership Directory*. **Awards:** Channel's Choice Award (Annual); Channel's Choice Award (Annual). **Geographic Preference:** National.

REFERENCE WORKS

16529 ■ "*The Enduring Popularity of Microsoft Word*" in *TMCNet.com (November 26, 2018)*
URL(s): www.tmcnet.com/topics/articles/2018/11/26/
440392-enduring-popularity-microsoft-word.htm

Ed: Jonathan Brown. **Released:** November 26, 2018. **Description:** Explores the history of Microsoft Word and how this word processing program became so popular, which is why it is still used today. **Availability:** Online.General Topics

www.ingramcontent.com/pod-product-compliance
Lightning Source LLC
Jackson TN
JSHW060747100425
82367JS00003B/55